S0-ADC-647

TEACHER EDITION

Indiana

Biology

Stephen Nowicki

Cover Photo Credits
Sharks ©Jeffrey L. Rotman/Corbis; *beetle* ©Ocean/Corbis

Printed in the U.S.A.

ISBN 978-1-328-77339-5

1 2 3 4 5 6 7 8 9 10 0607 25 24 23 22 21 20 19 18 17 16

4500638950 A B C D E F G

Welcome to HMH Biology!

Welcome to HMH Biology!

What's New for ©2017?

- Refreshed and updated content throughout, including new and engaging feature articles
- An Engineering Design Guide that includes an overview of the engineering design process, along with activities that allow students to try engineering practices within a science context
- Bookmarks, highlighting, and notes in the eBook that are preserved when students end a session
- A correlation tool to help you match biology content to Disciplinary Core Ideas, Science and Engineering Practices, and Crosscutting Concepts of the National Academy of Sciences
- An Indiana Science Standards Guide that provides student activities for each of the Indiana Science Standards for Biology
- Google Expeditions that immerse students in entirely new virtual-reality experiences
- Four entertaining *Thing Explainer* diagrams, based on the wildly popular book in which webcomic *xkcd.com* author Randall Munroe humorously explains very complex things with very simple words

Student Edition

Your students can explore the world around them with pages of colorful photos, helpful illustrations, and activities using everyday materials. The book is built to help students succeed in biology, with content chunked into Main Ideas, relevant and motivating features, and in-depth skills support.

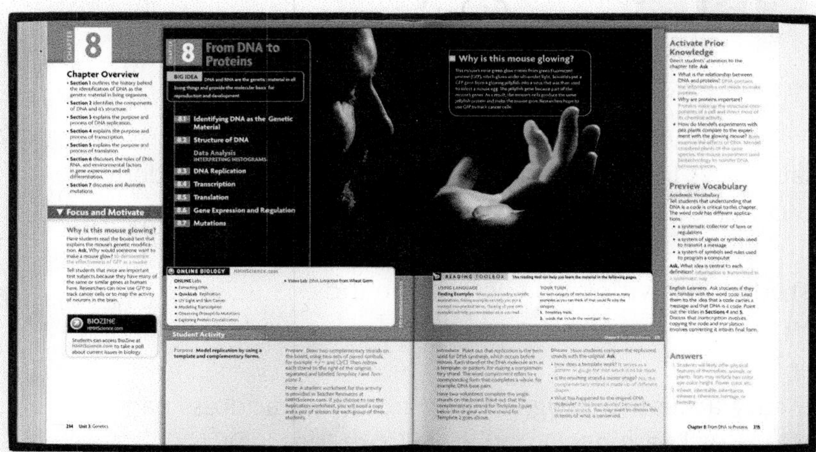

8
Chapter Overview
Focus and Motivate
Why is this mouse glowing?
8 From DNA to Proteins
8.1 Identifying DNA as the Genetic Material
8.2 Structure of DNA
Data Analysis
8.3 DNA Replication
8.4 Transcription
8.5 Translation
8.6 Gene Expression and Regulation
8.7 Mutations
Why is this mouse glowing?
Student Activity
Activate Prior Knowledge
Preview Vocabulary
Answers

Teacher Edition

The full-service TE has everything you need to enhance biology instruction, including data-analysis support, differentiated instruction, and point-of-use teaching tips.

Interactive Online Edition

Reduce your classroom's carbon footprint with the Interactive Online Edition, which provides 24/7 point-of-use access—for you and your students—to all program resources. In addition to a complete eBook version of the student textbook, the Online Edition includes alternative explanations and experiences through a wealth of multimedia activities, including animations, virtual labs, and motivating review games. An extensive array of hands-on activities is included as well.

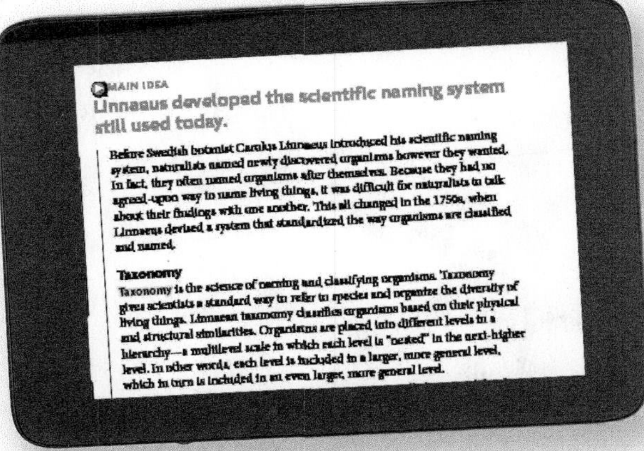

MAIN IDEA
Linnaeus developed the scientific naming system still used today.

Before Swedish botanist Carolus Linnaeus introduced his scientific naming system, naturalists named newly discovered organisms however they wanted. In fact, they often named organisms after themselves. Because they had no agreed-upon way to name living things, it was difficult for naturalists to talk about their findings with one another. This all changed in the 1750s, when Linnaeus devised a system that standardized the way organisms are classified and named.

Taxonomy

Taxonomy is the science of naming and classifying organisms. Taxonomy gives scientists a standard way to refer to species and organize the diversity of living things. Linnaean taxonomy classifies organisms based on their physical and structural similarities. Organisms are placed into different levels in a hierarchy—a multilevel scale in which each level is "nested" in the next-higher level. In other words, each level is included in a larger, more general level, which in turn is included in an even larger, more general level.

eTextbook

A digital version of the Student Edition is available for use on computers, tablet devices, and eReaders.

Fulfill the Spirit of the Indiana Standards in Your Classroom.

HMH Biology can help you plan instruction that lives up to all aspects of the Indiana Academic Standards for Science. The program includes the following useful tools:

- A correlation in the front of the Teacher Edition that shows Indiana Standards alignment to the Student Edition, Teacher Edition, and a selection of labs and other online assets. Correlations are included to ensure that students master each standard.
- An Indiana Science Standards Guide that provides student activities for each of the Indiana Science Standards for Biology. The teacher guide includes an overview of the Biology standards plus teacher tips for each activity.
- An online Correlation Tool that gives you quick and easy access to program resources that address each of the National Academy of Science's Three Dimensions of Learning: Disciplinary Core Ideas (DCIs), Cross-Cutting Concepts (CCCs), and Science and Engineering Practices (SEPs).
- An Engineering Design Guide that provides activities to connect Biology content to the engineering design process providing a full STEM experience.

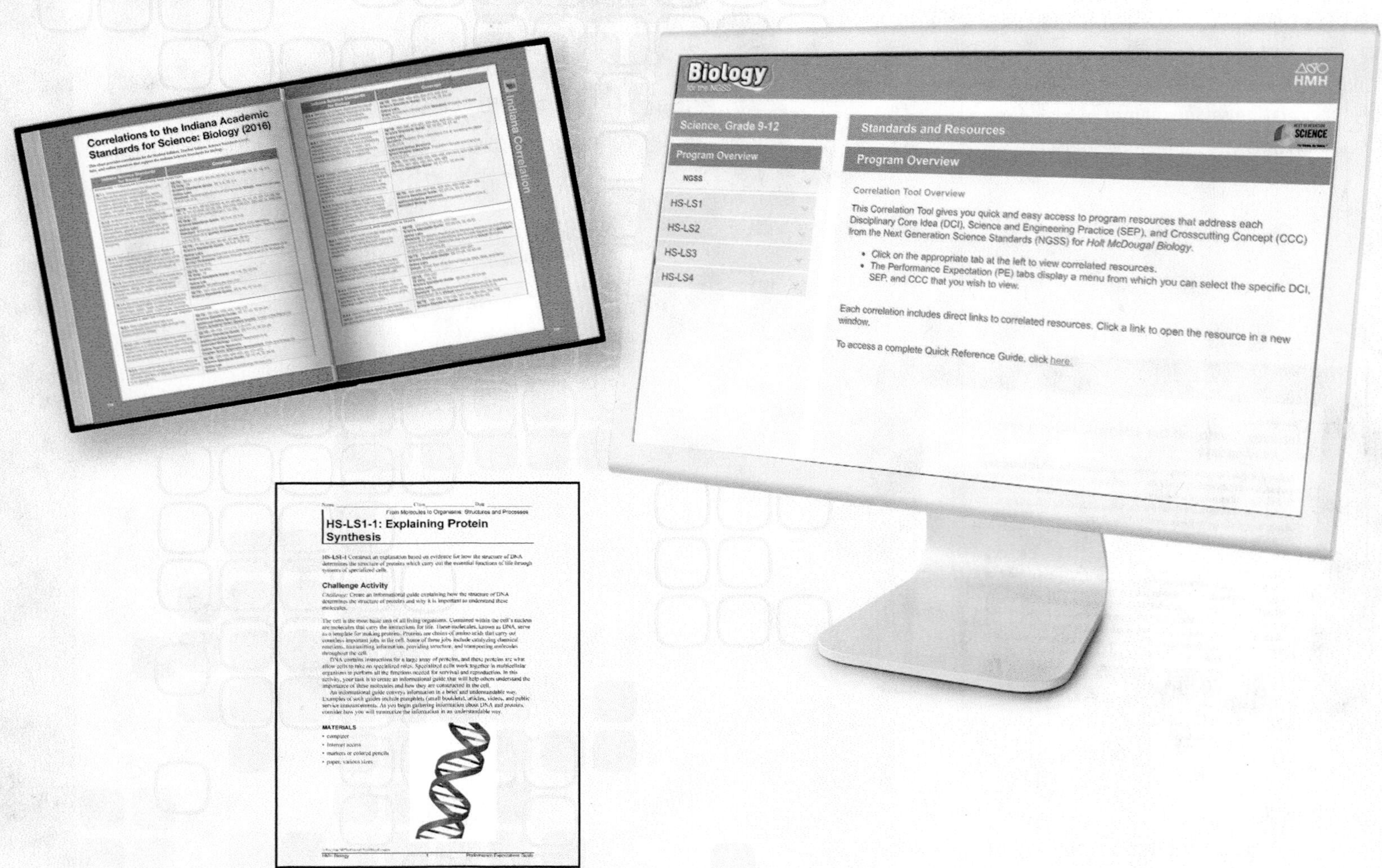

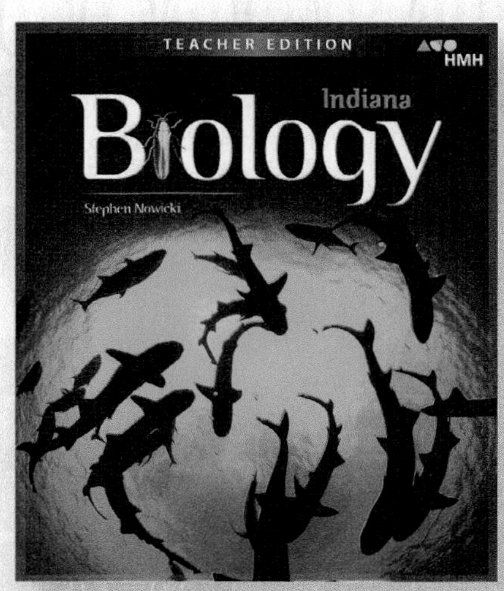

Student Edition

The student book offers a wealth of built-in tools to help students understand the content, including high-quality instructional visuals and point-of-use references to online support. Also available in Spanish.

Teacher Edition

The Teacher Edition is packed with a wide variety of strategies to help all students master biology concepts and to extend learning for advanced students.

NEW

NEW

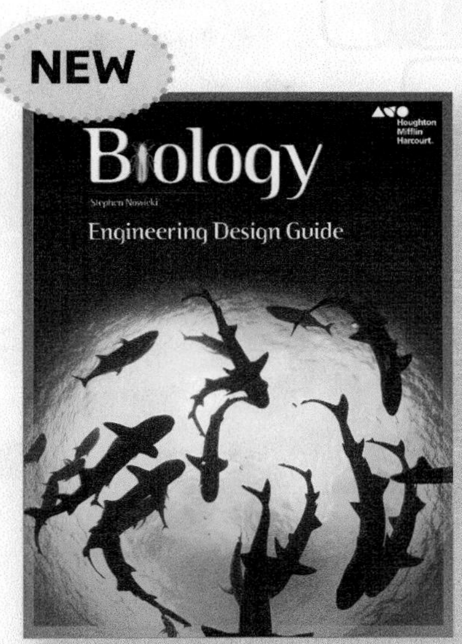

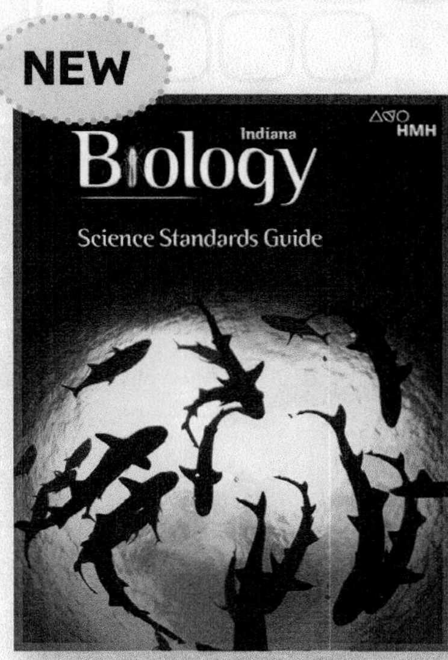

Interactive Reader

Designed for struggling students, the Interactive Reader features all essential content, written below grade level and with additional learning support.

Engineering Design Guide

The student guide presents an overview of the engineering design process, along with activities that allow students to try engineering practices within a science context. The teacher version provides strategies for integrating engineering design activities into the biology curriculum.

Indiana Science Standards Guide

This booklet provides student activities for each of the Indiana Science Standards for Biology. The teacher guide includes an overview of the Biology standards plus teacher tips for each activity.

Connect your students to the living world of biology.

HMH Biology presents a balanced and engaging approach to conceptual instruction. Many improvements have been made to the program to make the content engaging and up to date.

Inquiry

Inquiry-based learning starts with an engaging question related to the Big Idea.

Labs

All labs that reinforce the concepts in this chapter are listed here. These and all other labs in the program can be found at HMHScience.com.

Reading Support

Reading support in the Student Edition includes the Reading Toolbox feature, comprehension questions after Main Ideas, and Visual Vocab features.

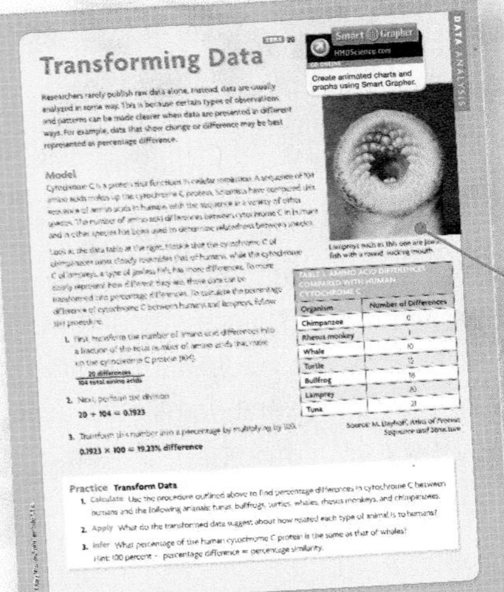

Data Analysis

These features, found in every chapter, help students hone their data analysis and graphing skills.

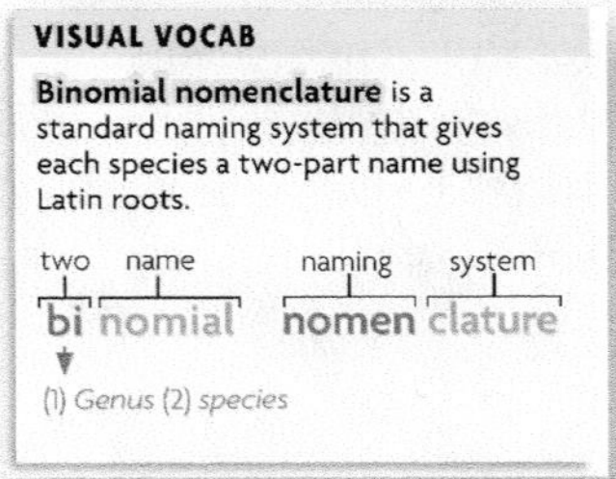

VISUAL VOCAB

Binomial nomenclature is a standard naming system that gives each species a two-part name using Latin roots.

two name — bi nomial; naming system — nomen clature

(1) *Genus* (2) *species*

NEW

STEM Interactions

These engaging feature articles cover current topics in the biological sciences, such as engineering design and "big data."

Interactive Reader

This write-in worktext provides all of the essential content and vocabulary of the Student Edition at a lower reading level. A great resource for students of all ability levels, the Interactive Reader is both a core instructional tool for struggling students and a useful study guide for others.

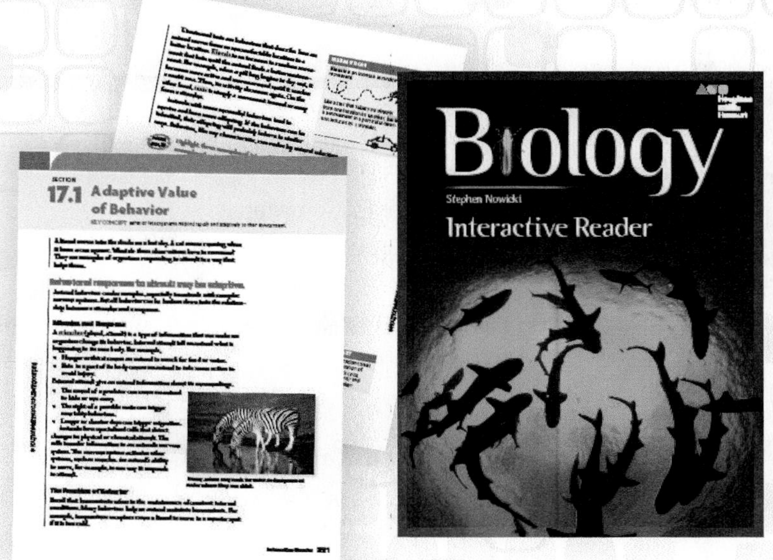

The Teacher Edition provides strong instructional support for a wide range of learners.

Activate Prior Knowledge and Preview Vocabulary

Introduce each chapter with the Activate Prior Knowledge and Preview Vocabulary features.

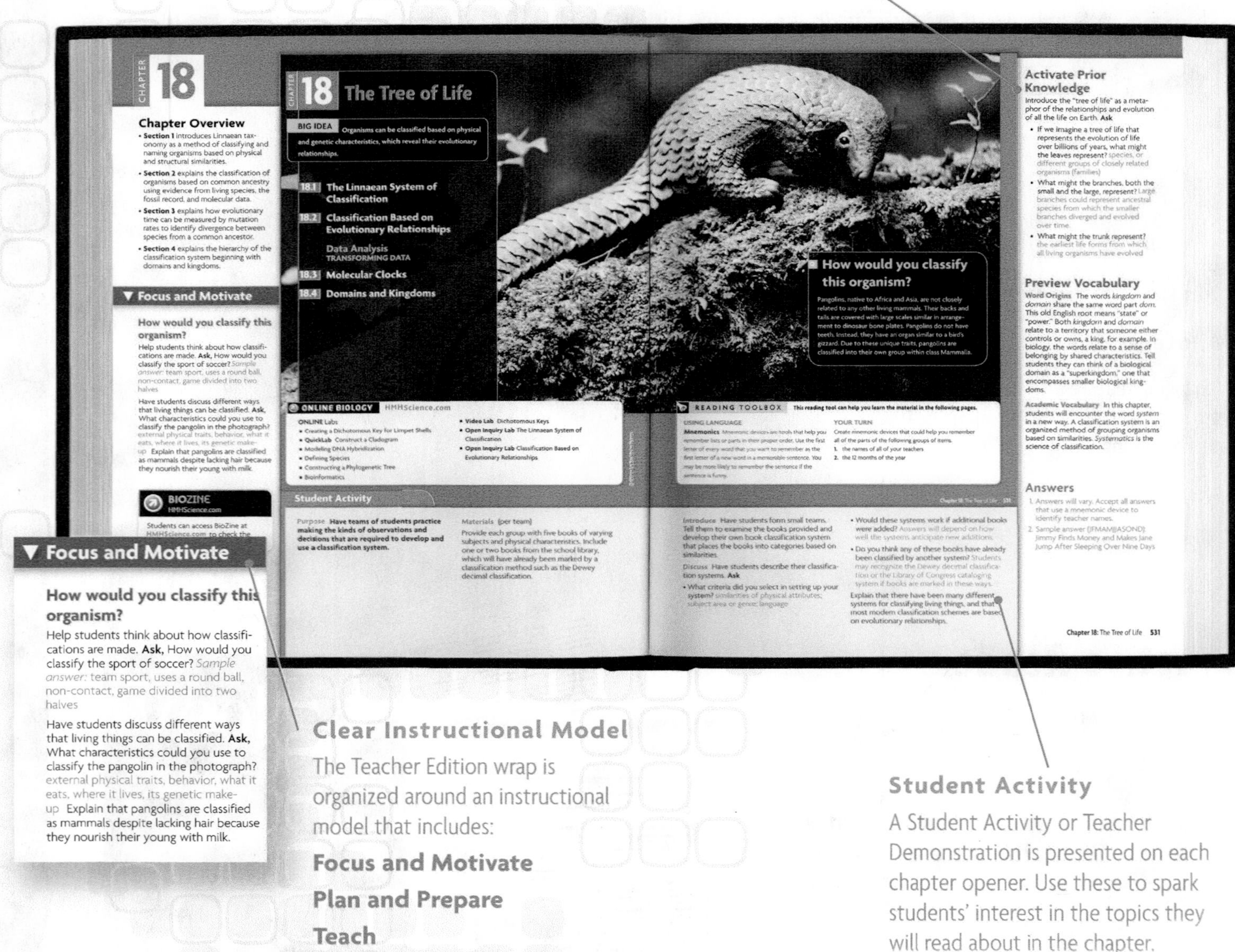

CHAPTER 18

Chapter Overview

- **Section 1** introduces Linnaean taxonomy as a method of classifying and naming organisms based on physical and structural similarities.
- **Section 2** explains the classification of organisms based on common ancestry using evidence from living species, the fossil record, and molecular data.
- **Section 3** explains how evolutionary time can be measured by mutation rates to identify divergence between species from a common ancestor.
- **Section 4** explains the hierarchy of the classification system beginning with domains and kingdoms.

▼ Focus and Motivate

How would you classify this organism?

Help students think about how classifications are made. **Ask,** How would you classify the sport of soccer? *Sample answer:* team sport, uses a round ball, non-contact, game divided into two halves

Have students discuss different ways that living things can be classified. **Ask,** What characteristics could you use to classify the pangolin in the photograph? external physical traits, behavior, what it eats, where it lives, its genetic make-up Explain that pangolins are classified as mammals despite lacking hair because they nourish their young with milk.

BIOZINE HMHScience.com

Students can access BioZine at HMHScience.com to check the

CHAPTER 18 The Tree of Life

BIG IDEA Organisms can be classified based on physical and genetic characteristics, which reveal their evolutionary relationships.

How would you classify this organism?

Pangolins, native to Africa and Asia, are not closely related to any other living mammals. Their backs and tails are covered with large scales similar in arrangement to dinosaur bone plates. Pangolins do not have teeth. Instead, they have an organ similar to a bird's gizzard. Due to these unique traits, pangolins are classified into their own group within class Mammalia.

ONLINE BIOLOGY HMHScience.com

ONLINE Labs

- Creating a Dichotomous Key for Limpet Shells
- **QuickLab** Construct a Cladogram
- Modeling DNA Hybridization
- Defining Species
- Constructing a Phylogenetic Tree
- Bioinformatics
- **Video Lab** Dichotomous Keys
- **Open Inquiry Lab** The Linnaean System of Classification
- **Open Inquiry Lab** Classification Based on Evolutionary Relationships

READING TOOLBOX This reading tool can help you learn the material in the following pages.

USING LANGUAGE

Mnemonics Mnemonic devices are tools that help you remember lists or parts in their proper order. Use the first letter of every word that you want to remember as the first letter of a new word in a memorable sentence. You may be more likely to remember the sentence if the sentence is funny.

YOUR TURN

Create mnemonic devices that could help you remember all of the parts of the following groups of items.

1. the names of all of your teachers
2. the 12 months of the year

Student Activity

Purpose **Have teams of students practice making the kinds of observations and decisions that are required to develop and use a classification system.**

Materials (per team)

Provide each group with five books of varying subjects and physical characteristics. Include one or two books from the school library, which will have already been marked by a classification method such as the Dewey decimal classification.

Introduce Have students form small teams. Tell them to examine the books provided and develop their own book classification system that places the books into categories based on similarities.

Discuss Have students describe their classification systems. **Ask**

- What criteria did you select in setting up your system? similarities of physical attributes; subject area or genre; language
- Would these systems work if additional books were added? Answers will depend on how well the systems anticipate new additions.
- Do you think any of these books have already been classified by another system? Students may recognize the Dewey decimal classification or the Library of Congress cataloging system if books are marked in these ways.

Explain that there have been many different systems for classifying living things, and that most modern classification schemes are based on evolutionary relationships.

Activate Prior Knowledge

Introduce the "tree of life" as a metaphor of the relationships and evolution of all the life on Earth. **Ask**

- If we imagine a tree of life that represents the evolution of life over billions of years, what might the leaves represent? species, or different groups of closely related organisms (families)
- What might the branches, both the small and the large, represent? Large branches could represent ancestral species from which the smaller branches diverged and evolved over time.
- What might the trunk represent? the earliest life forms from which all living organisms have evolved

Preview Vocabulary

Word Origins The words *kingdom* and *domain* share the same word part *dom.* This old English root means "state" or "power." Both *kingdom* and *domain* relate to a territory that someone either controls or owns, a king, for example. In biology, the words relate to a sense of belonging by shared characteristics. Tell students they can think of a biological domain as a "superkingdom," one that encompasses smaller biological kingdoms.

Academic Vocabulary In this chapter, students will encounter the word *system* in a new way. A classification system is an organized method of grouping organisms based on similarities. *Systematics* is the science of classification.

Answers

1. Answers will vary. Accept all answers that use a mnemonic device to identify teacher names.
2. Sample answer (JFMAMJJASOND): Jimmy Finds Money and Makes Jane Jump After Sleeping Over Nine Days

Chapter 18: The Tree of Life 531

▼ Focus and Motivate

How would you classify this organism?

Help students think about how classifications are made. **Ask,** How would you classify the sport of soccer? *Sample answer:* team sport, uses a round ball, non-contact, game divided into two halves

Have students discuss different ways that living things can be classified. **Ask,** What characteristics could you use to classify the pangolin in the photograph? external physical traits, behavior, what it eats, where it lives, its genetic make-up Explain that pangolins are classified as mammals despite lacking hair because they nourish their young with milk.

Clear Instructional Model

The Teacher Edition wrap is organized around an instructional model that includes:

Focus and Motivate

Plan and Prepare

Teach

Assess and Reteach

Student Activity

A Student Activity or Teacher Demonstration is presented on each chapter opener. Use these to spark students' interest in the topics they will read about in the chapter.

CHAPTER 18 Instruction and Intervention Support

GO ONLINE! for all your teacher resources at HMHScience.com

The Tree of Life

Core Instruction

Support and Intervention

Specialized Support

Extension and Assessment

Enrichment and Challenge

Assessment

Print Preview

Instruction and Intervention Support

Instruction and Intervention Support at the beginning of each chapter offers a full listing of the activities and classroom resources available for each section.

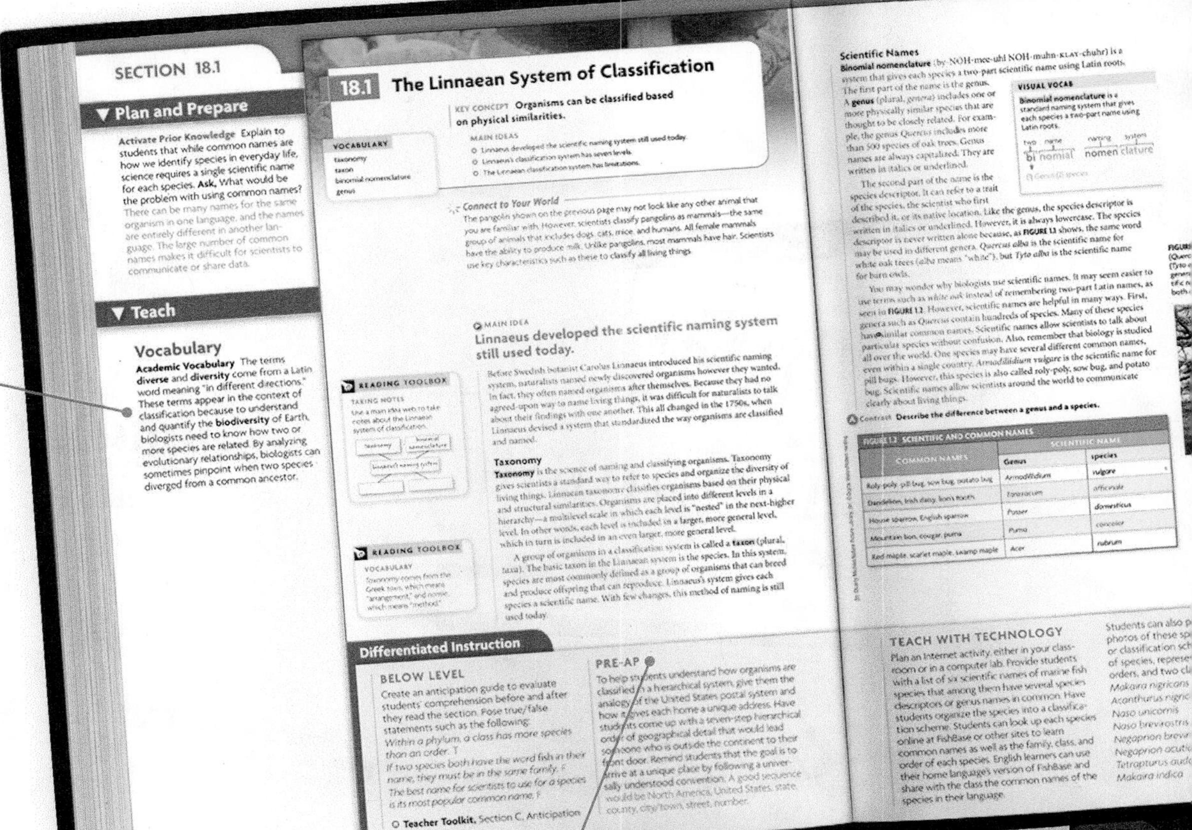

Strong Teaching Support

Point-of-use teaching support is provided throughout the chapter, including Addressing Misconceptions, Teach from Visuals, and Vocabulary support.

Differentiated Instruction

Differentiated Instruction strategies are provided for every lesson to assist you in helping students with a wide range of needs. The strategies include:

Below Level	English Learners
Hands-On Activity	Inclusion
Pre-AP	Teach with Technology

HMH Biology offers the latest technology and multimedia resources that speak directly to your students in a visual language they understand—ensuring that they will stay engaged.

THAT'S Amazing!

Video-Based Inquiry

Online video-based inquiry activities engage students by peering into the bizarre world of nature and the application of the scientific method. After being amazed by nature's wonders, students will apply the Data Analysis and Conclusion steps of the scientific method.

HMHScience.com

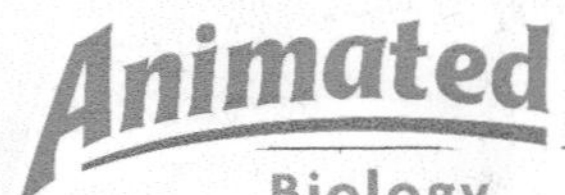

Biology

Nearly 100 animations and simulations bring biology concepts and principles to life.

WebLinks

Hand-selected resource links save you endless hours of research, bringing the BEST of the Internet to the classroom to extend and enrich each chapter's content.

WebQuests

Thirty-four inquiry-oriented biology lessons relate directly to chapter content. Each WebQuest introduces a problem, defines the tasks to be completed, provides links to key Internet resources, asks questions that probe for understanding, and assists students in reaching appropriate conclusions.

Unit Projects

Long-term projects provide opportunities for independent learning during the course of the unit and involve scientific writing, creativity, and research. Each project includes a rubric as well as teacher notes, with strategies for project management and differentiated instruction.

Interactive Review Games

Nothing encourages students to study and review more than a game! The online review games cover the key concepts and vocabulary from each chapter and will keep students engaged while they prepare for tests.

BioZine

This interactive online magazine keeps the program up to date by connecting students to current events, with features such as science news feeds, in-depth details about unit features, and updates on careers and current biology research.

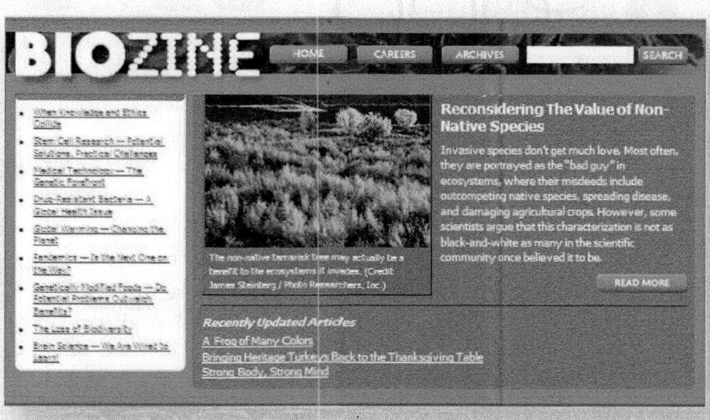

Interactive Whiteboard Resources

Key teaching visuals from each chapter have been adapted specifically for interactive whiteboard use.

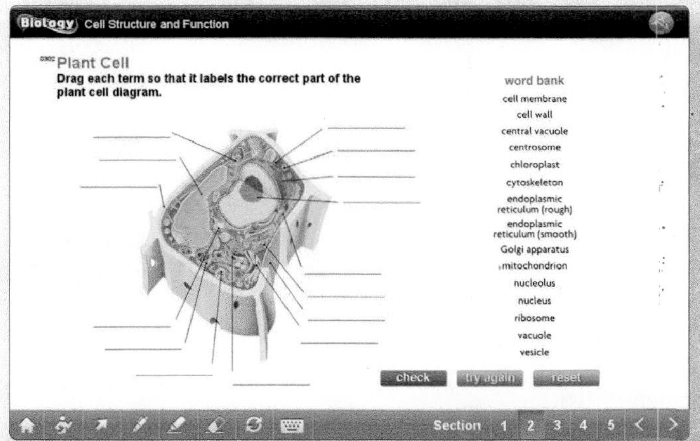

Because inquiry is the cornerstone of understanding biology, it is crucial for students to apply the concepts they are reading about. ***HMH Biology*** includes the most comprehensive lab resources with its wide variety of print and digital lab options for every classroom need.

Laboratory Experiments

Editable versions of all program labs, along with Teacher resource pages, are found at point of use online. The wide variety of bench-tested labs includes:

QuickLabs

Designed for reinforcement of key concepts using easy-to-obtain materials

Standard Labs

Focus on experimental skills and application of chapter concepts through the use of scientific methods

Core Skill Labs

Provide practice of inquiry skills and scientific methods

STEM Labs

Science, Technology, Engineering, and Mathematics problem-based labs that emphasize inquiry and the engineering design process

Open Inquiry Labs

Short project-based labs that encourage students to collaborate, strategize, and construct and evaluate a lab challenge of their own creation

Biotechnology Labs

Provide blending of technology and biological concepts

Forensics Labs

Combine the popularity of crime shows with concepts students are learning in the classroom

Challenge Labs

Two labs per unit extend concepts presented in the unit chapters for students in advanced, accelerated, or honors biology classes

Probeware Labs

Labs that use Vernier® probeware and Pasco® probeware and SPARK® technology

Virtual Investigations

These engaging presentations, interactive activities, and simulated scientific investigations reinforce students' understanding of biology and science skills as well as strengthen inquiry and lab skills.

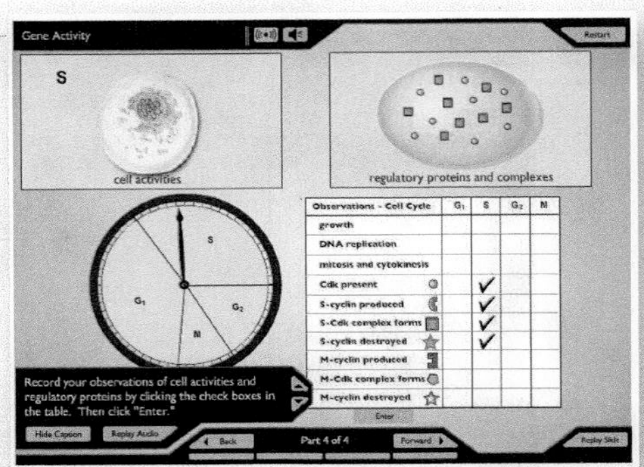

Video Labs

Forty-one professionally developed lab demonstrations are perfect for professional development, for lab pre-work, or as a lab alternative. Each lab includes an accompanying skillsheet for classroom implementation.

Virtual Labs

Fourteen virtual labs enable students to conduct meaningful experiments in a lab or field setting without the expense, time, or risk of traditional lab settings.

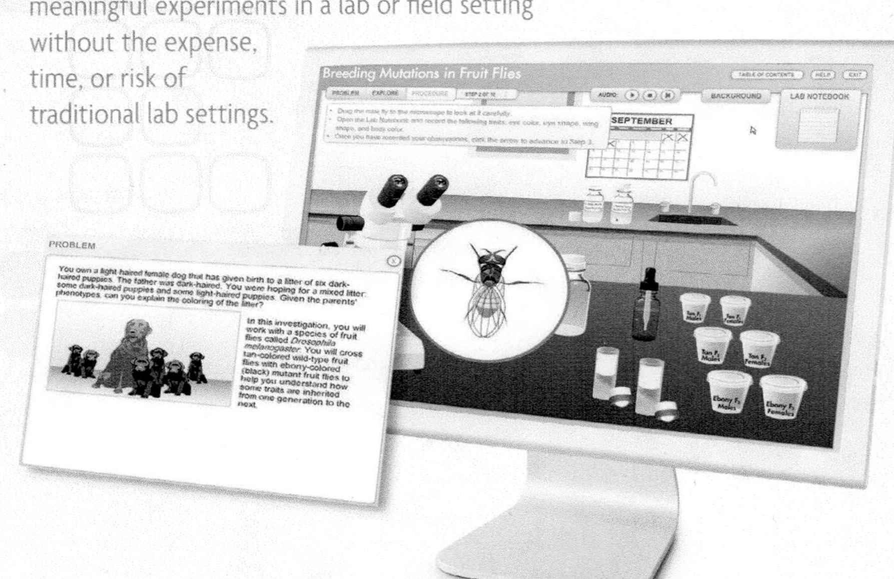

To help students develop the data analysis skills necessary to collect, graph, and analyze data like scientists, **HMHScience.com** includes resources to support the Data Analysis lesson in every chapter.

Smart Grapher

This powerful, easy-to-use online graphing tool encourages students to use their own data to create line graphs, circle graphs, and more.

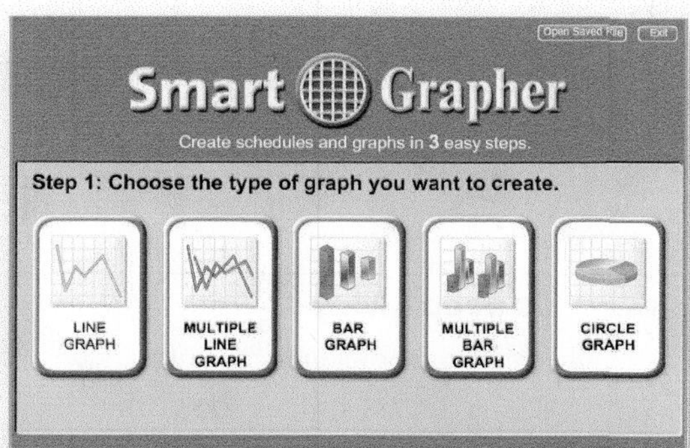

Data Analysis Activities

Connected directly to chapter content, these online data analysis activities enable students to build data analysis skills using real-world data. By applying their knowledge, students can transform raw data into meaningful graphs and charts.

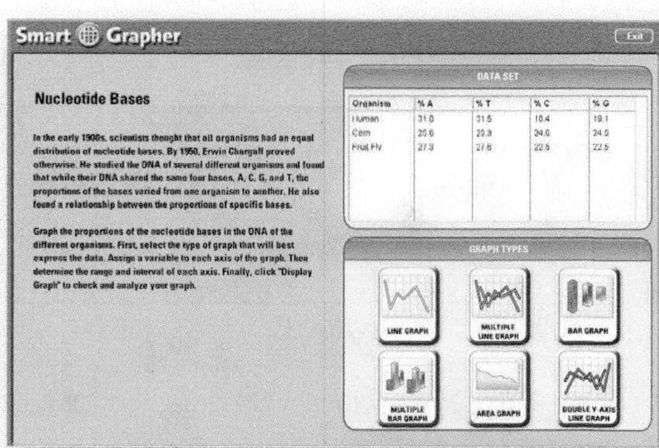

Data Analysis Practice

These chapter-based skillsheets help students build the skills necessary to understand different types of data, how to graph data, and how to analyze and interpret the meaning behind the data.

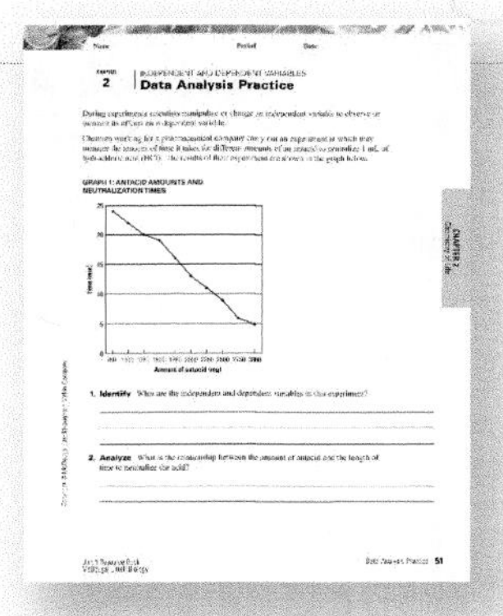

Data Analysis Practice

Online Lab Support

Lab Teacher Resources

These tools assist teachers in setting up and managing laboratory programs. Examples include a lab safety contract and quiz, an overview of common laboratory procedures, guidelines for writing lab reports, a graph paper template, and lab report evaluation rubrics.

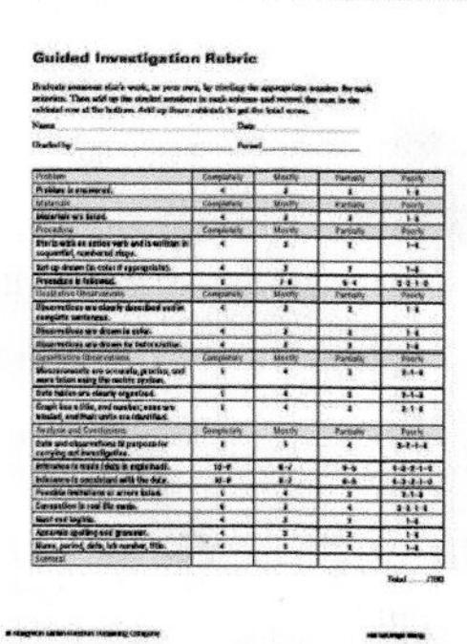

Guided Investigation Rubric

Materials List

This listing of all materials and quantities needed for the labs associated with each chapter is a useful planning resource.

Handling and Care of Organisms

This resource provides guidelines for handling and caring for the organisms used in the labs.

Scientific Reasoning Skill Builder

More than 100 exercises strengthen students' scientific reasoning skills. Topics include classifying and categorizing, cause-and-effect relationships, hypotheses, generalizations and analogies, and summarizing and reviewing.

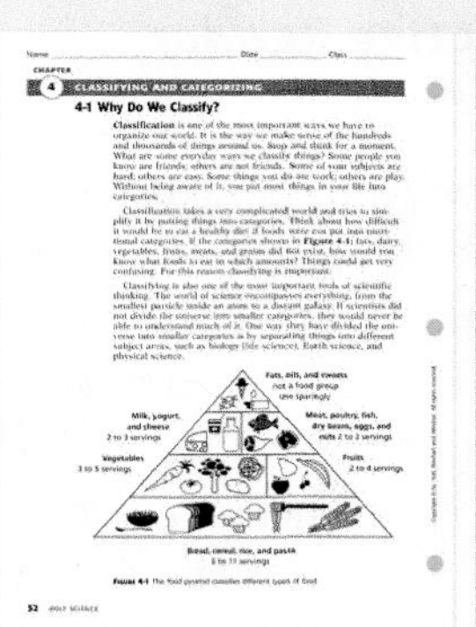

CLASSIFYING AND CATEGORIZING

4-1 Why Do We Classify?

Online Support for Reading and Vocabulary

Your students will get the most out of their reading with multimedia point-of-use resources that enable them to build understanding and retain more information on key concepts.

eBook

Just like the print version, the online Student Edition features a wealth of built-in tools to help students interact with the content, including frequent comprehension checks, support for data analysis, and high-quality instructional visuals. Features include highlighting, annotations, bookmarking, full audio, and search capabilities.

Teaching Visuals

Full-color illustrations and diagrams (many from the textbook) are ideal for whole-class instruction.

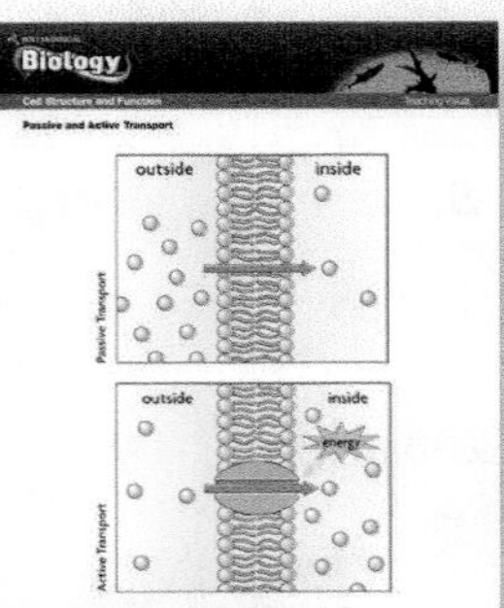

Vocabulary Practice

Vocabulary skillsheets support review and reinforcement of all vocabulary terms through a wide variety of lower-level to higher-order thinking skill strategies—vector vocabulary, word origin, word categorizing, word relationships, and crossword puzzle.

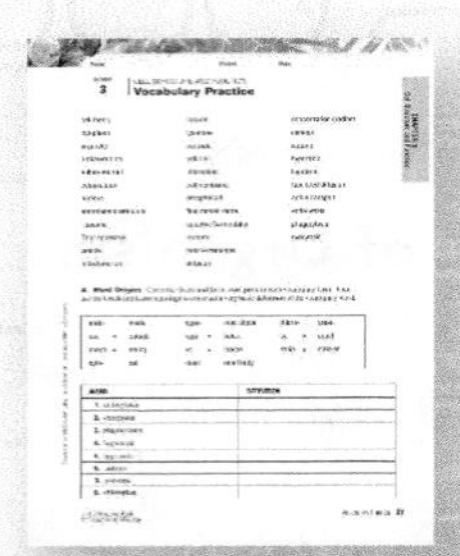

Active Reading Worksheets

Nearly 150 topical reading excerpts help boost students' science reading comprehension with questions that promote deeper thinking.

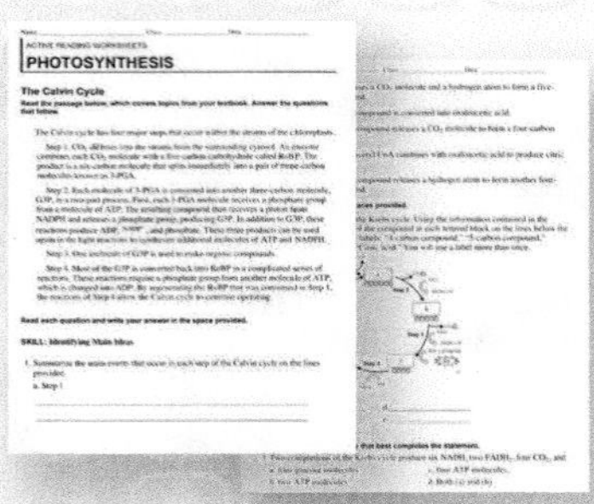

Concept Maps

Each chapter includes an interactive graphic organizer that shows the relationships among concepts covered in the chapter and helps students develop logical thinking and study skills.

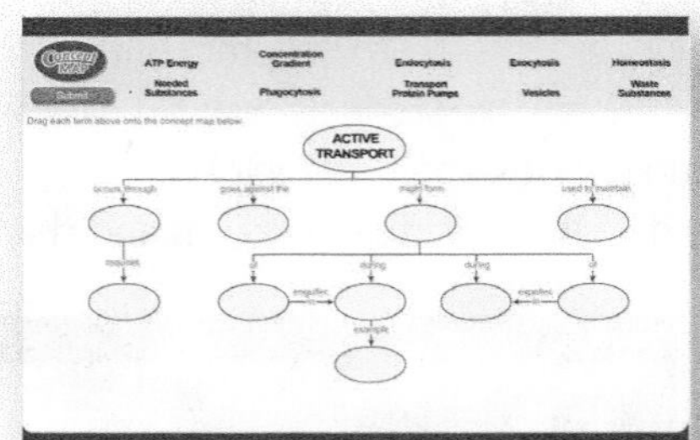

Online Resources for Differentiated Instruction

Interactive Reader

The online version of the write-in worktext presents all the vocabulary and essential content from the textbook in a lower-level, easy-to-read text, with instructional visuals and frequent comprehension checks. This unique component is a great tool for all students—the core content for struggling students and a useful study guide for others.

Reinforcement (English and Spanish)

Each one-page section-level worksheet summarizes core concepts and asks students to provide short answers to questions related to the summary.

Section Study Guides (English and Spanish)

Section Study Guides are available online. Study Guide B can be used with on-level students. Study Guide A is a lower-level version, designed for struggling students or English language learners.

Pre-AP Activity

These chapter worksheets are designed for more advanced students who need an extra challenge. They cover more advanced topics within the chapter.

Textbook Audio Files (English and Spanish)

An audio version of each section of the Student Edition is available at point of use, in English and in Spanish.

Recognizing the growing number of Spanish-speaking students in the classroom, ***HMH Biology*** provides a complete suite of time-saving, targeted resources that will engage English language learners and promote understanding of concepts needed to meet your state standards.

eBook (Spanish)

Just like the print version, the online Student Edition in Spanish features chunking of content around Key Concepts and Main Ideas with frequent comprehension checks, real-world connections, superior support for reading and vocabulary, high-quality instructional visuals, and point-of-use references to online animations, simulations, video clips, and virtual labs that bring biology to life.

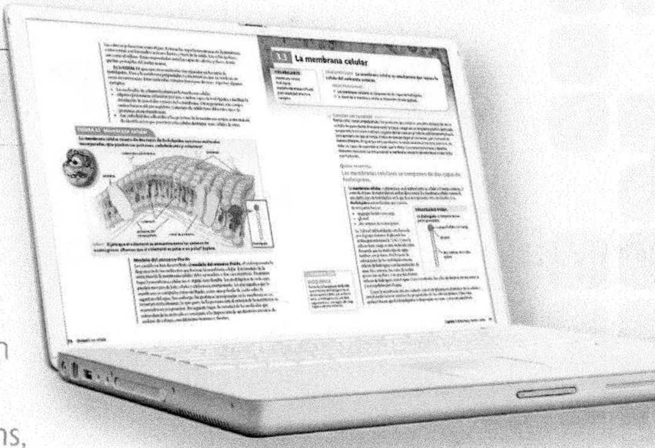

Interactive Review: Flipcards (Spanish)

Includes review of all vocabulary words in Spanish

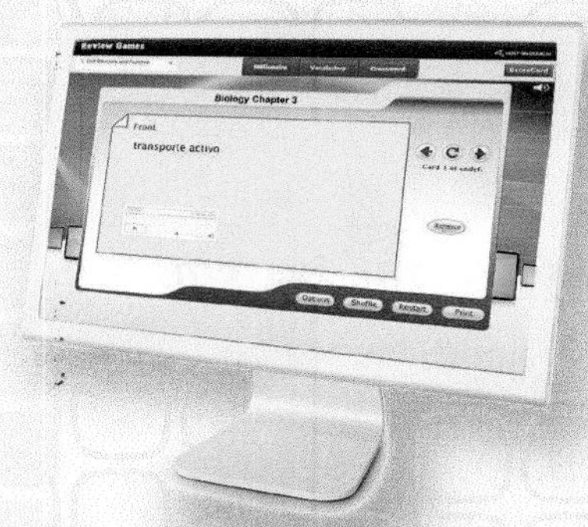

Multilanguage Glossary

This comprehensive list of biology vocabulary terms is presented in eleven different languages: English, Spanish, Chinese, Vietnamese, Khmer, Laotian, Arabic, Haitian Creole, Russian, Portuguese, and Hmong.

中文詞彙

GLOSARIO ESPAÑOL

Spanish Study Guides (2 Levels)

Two levels of section review response sheets—on-level and below-level—reinforce the vocabulary, key concepts, and main ideas covered in each section.

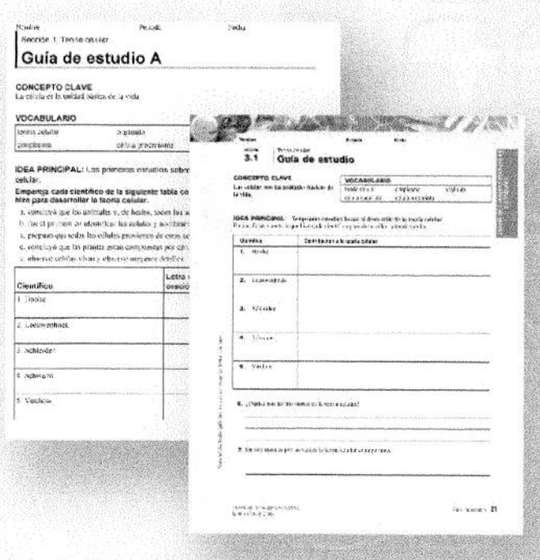
Guía de estudio A

Guía de estudio

Spanish Reinforcement

A one-page review sheet for each section summarizes main ideas and provides comprehension-check questions.

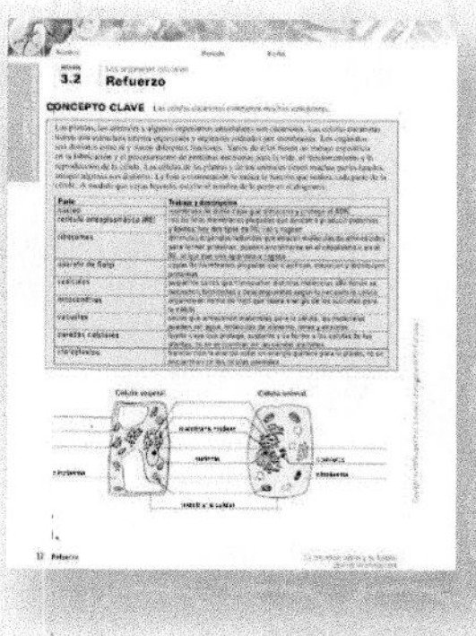
3.2 Refuerzo

Lab Datasheets (Spanish)

Many classroom labs are provided in Spanish, including QuickLabs and Chapter Investigations.

Spanish Assessments

A wide variety of tests provides you with flexible options for assessing students on your state standards. The following tests are included: Section Quizzes, Diagnostic Tests, Leveled Chapter Tests, Extended Response Tests, and Alternative Assessments with Rubrics.

Textbook Audio Files (Spanish)

A recording of the Spanish Student Edition is available at point of use.

The comprehensive assessment options located at **HMHScience.com** bring together all of ***HMH Biology*** assessment tools into one convenient place, giving you many choices for the best way to assess student learning in your classroom.

ExamView® Banks

Banks of ExamView test questions allow for easy customization of assessments to meet your needs. Included are section quizzes, chapter tests, and an extra item bank for every chapter.

EXAMVIEW® ASSESSMENT SUITE

Section Self-Check (Interactive)

There is a five-question multiple-choice online quiz for each section of the textbook. These unique online quizzes provide immediate feedback for student self-evaluation.

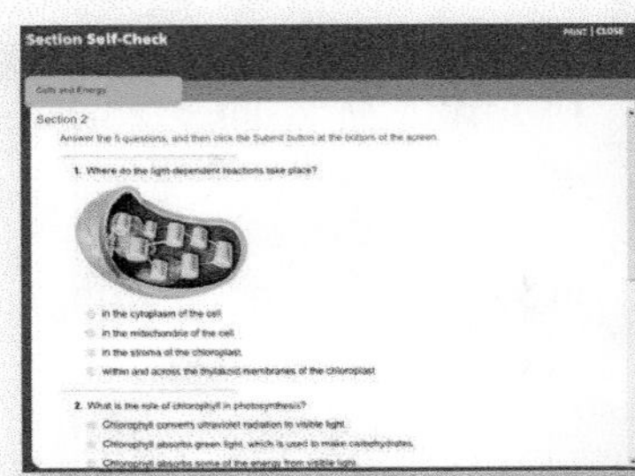

Online Assessment System

This advanced, automated assessment engine enables you to assign section quizzes to your students. The assessments are automatically graded, and remediation that uses materials from the program is prescribed. A post-test is offered to determine student mastery. Critical student performance data are recorded and made readily available to the teacher.

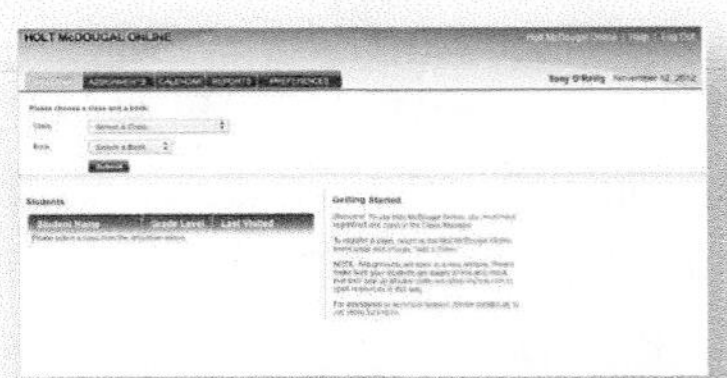

Section Quizzes (English and Spanish)

There is a five-question multiple-choice quiz for each section of the textbook. These quizzes are designed for student formative assessment to aid in remediation.

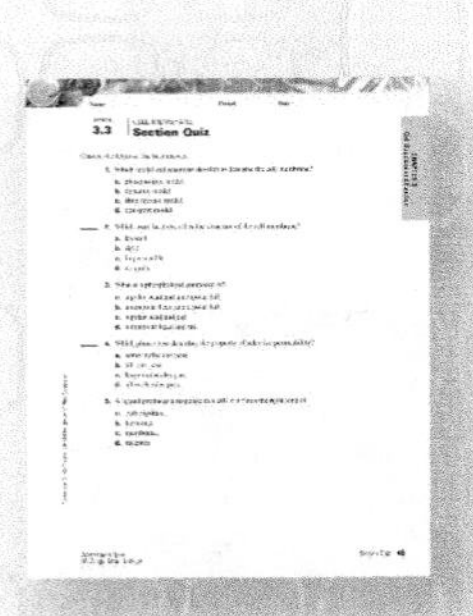

Chapter Tests A & B (English and Spanish)

Two full-length chapter tests of multiple-choice and short-answer questions are provided. Test B is an on-level test while Test A is a lower-level test of the same content.

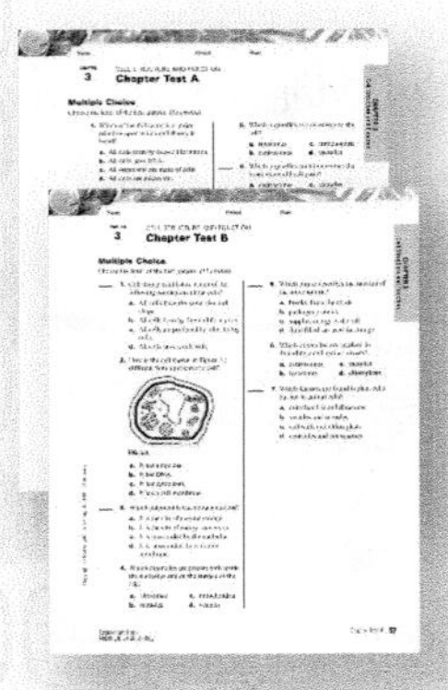

Diagnostic Tests (English and Spanish)

Diagnostic tests are designed to be given at the beginning of a topic to determine students' existing knowledge and to help you customize your lesson plan.

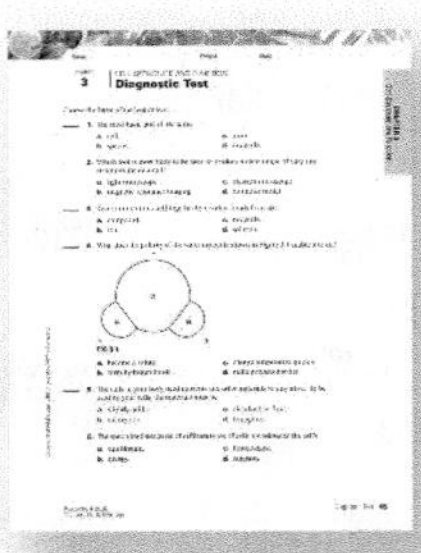

Extended Response Tests (English and Spanish)

This type of assessment strategy encourages students to think in short-essay format as they respond to chapter-specific writing prompts.

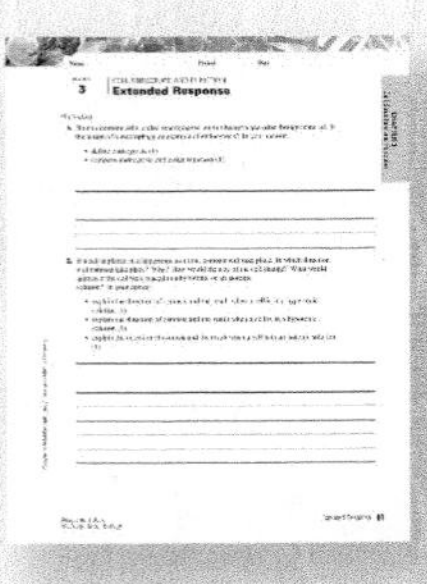

Alternative Assessment (English and Spanish)

For students who benefit from nontraditional assessments, these tests provide another way of determining their understanding of biological facts, concepts, and principles.

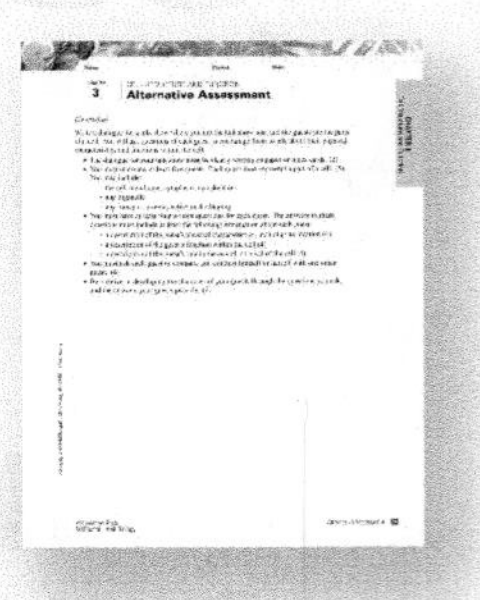

Standards-Based Assessment

The Standards-Based Assessment is also available online.

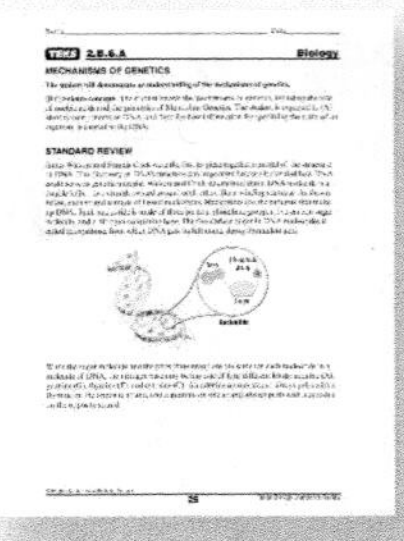

Additional Online Resources

PowerPresentations

These editable, prebuilt PowerPoint® files offer a resource of engaging multimedia presentations that present the core materials of each chapter, saving you valuable preparation time.

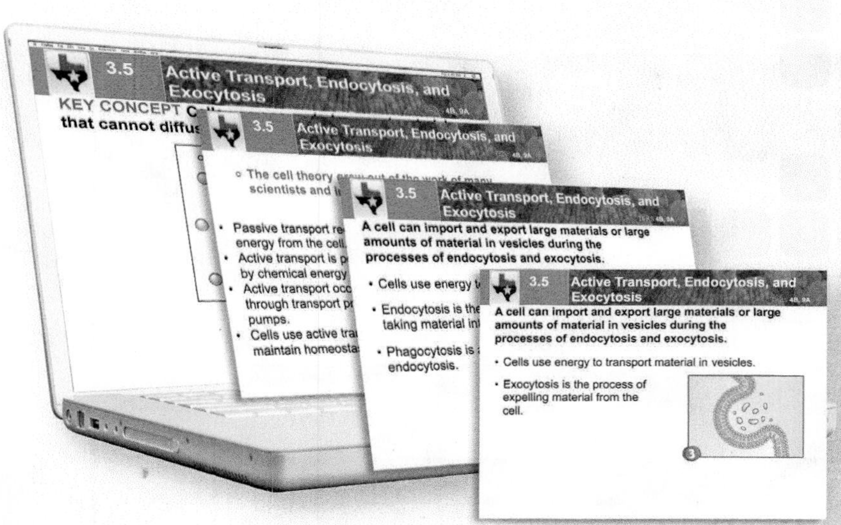

PowerNotes®

An editable student note-taking worksheet for each PowerPresentation makes organizing lecture notes a breeze.

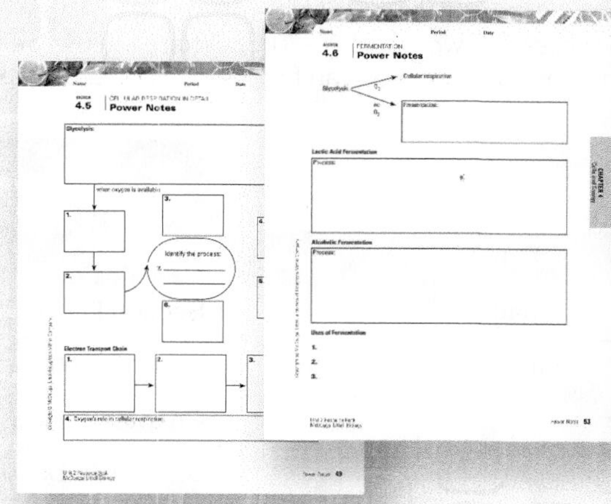

Teacher Toolkit

There are more than 200 lessons and tools to teach essential skills necessary for students to be successful in biology—with support for process and inquiry, reading, vocabulary, writing, and data analysis skills. To make your planning seamless, the Teacher Toolkit is referenced in the Differentiated Instruction strategies in the Teacher Edition.

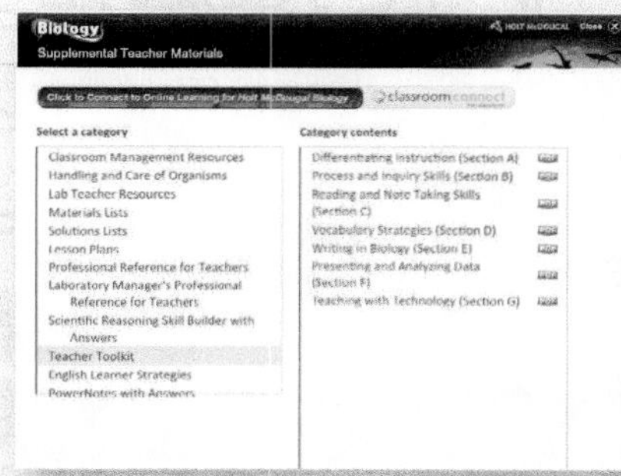

eTeacher Edition

This online version of the print Teacher Edition provides you with easy access to your teaching support.

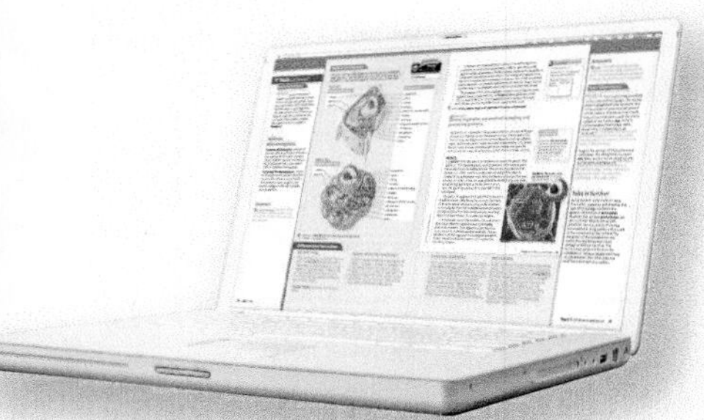

Lesson Planner

These templates, in conjunction with the Instruction and Intervention Support materials at the beginning of every chapter, can help you plan your lessons.

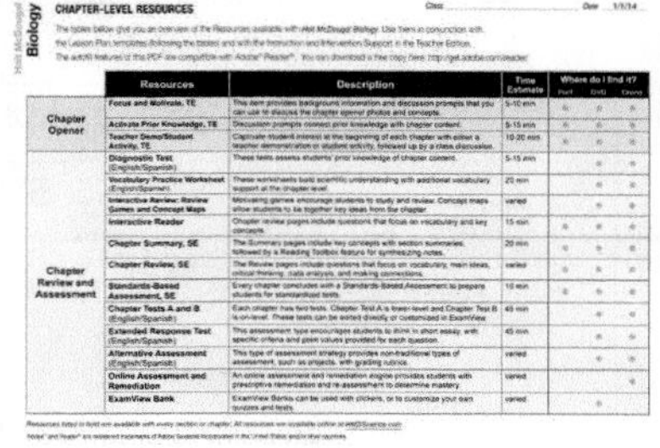

Teaching Strategies

Select strategies from the Teacher Edition have been made available online. Strategies include Activate Prior Knowledge, Differentiated Instruction, Demonstrations, and Vocabulary.

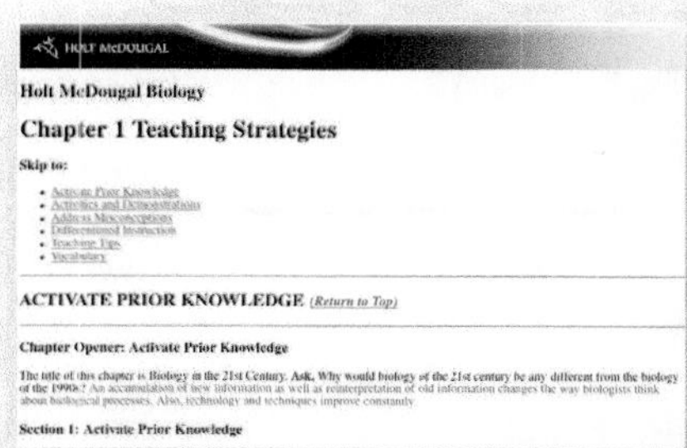

Instructional Strategies

HMH Biology provides key strategies that help teachers effectively engage students and teach the knowledge and skills of the core academic subjects. These include 21st-century skills that students must master to succeed in work and life. These strategies can be found throughout the Teacher Edition; the chart below shows where you can find samples of each.

	Look for These Heads	Find Samples on These Teacher Edition Pages
Assessment		
Formative	Section Formative Assessment	41, 475, 661
Summative	Chapter Summary	210, 494, 716
	Chapter Review	211, 415, 697
	Standards-Based Assessment	213, 497, 699
Careers		
	Careers	66, 282, 528
Cross-Curricular Connections		
	Integrating . . .	Anthropology 77 Biomechanics 37 Chemistry 197 Earth Science 299 Ecology 564 Forensic Science 25 Genetics 27 Human Biology 549 Medical Science 49 Microbiology 569 Physics 55 . . . and more
Differentiated Instruction		
Below Level	Below Level	39, 89, 472
Challenge (Enrichment)	Pre-AP	194, 473, 703
English Language Learners	English Learners	38, 192, 472
Hands-On Learning	Hands-On Activity	208, 474, 619
Inclusion	Inclusion	40, 564, 647
Technology	Teach with Technology	194, 482, 704
Labs and Activities		
	QuickLab	53, 484, 705
	Student Activity	2, 214, 444
	Unit Project	67, 385, 529

	Look for These Heads	Find Samples on These Teacher Edition Pages
Math		
Analyzing Data	Data Analysis	51, 327, 393
Graphing	Data Analysis	202, 451, 686
Misconceptions		
	Address Misconceptions	40, 208, 479
Reading and Note Taking		
Note Taking	Reading Toolbox	131, 349, 466
Vocabulary Building	Vocabulary	196, 482, 708
Real-World Connection		
	Connect to Your World	167, 316, 532
Remediation (Intervention Support)		
Reteaching	Reteach	50, 199, 678
Visual LIteracy	Teach from Visuals	40, 472, 712
Warm-Ups	Activate Prior Knowledge	37, 191, 347

21st-Century Skills and Themes

	Look for These Heads	Find Samples on These Teacher Edition Pages
Communication and Collaboration		
	Opinion Poll	156, 280, 526
Critical Thinking		
	Connect to . . .	206, 449, 501
	Take It Further	48, 131, 319
Global Awareness		
	BioZine	382, 526, 720
	Current News	65, 280, 382

Online Labs

HMH Biology includes labs to meet all of your students' needs. In addition to QuickLabs and other standard classroom labs that can be done without a great deal of preparation, the program includes specialty labs that address specific instructional goals. These include up-to-date Probeware Labs, challenging STEM Labs, motivating Forensics Labs, and realistic Virtual Labs.

All labs are fully editable and can be found online at **HMHScience.com**. QuickLabs can also be found at point of use in the textbook. Note that many of the labs are also available in Spanish. A list of the materials needed to perform the labs can be found online.

* indicates that a Spanish version is available

Unit 1	
CHAPTER 1 Biology in the 21st Century	
SECTION 1	The Study of Life *(Open Inquiry)*
	Lab Safety Review
	Field Lab Safety Review
SECTION 2	Biomimicry in Engineering *(STEM)*
SECTION 3	Fruit Preservation *(Biotechnology)*
	Manipulating Plant Growth
	Evaluating Claims About Promotional Services *(QuickLab)*
	Energy Sources for Yeast *(Probeware)*
SECTION 4	Measuring Microscopic Objects
	Life Under a Microscope *(QuickLab)* *
	Measuring with Accuracy and Precision
SECTION 5	Biotechnology and Food Products *(Biotechnology)*
	Biology in the News *
CHAPTER 2 Chemistry of Life	
SECTION 2	Testing pH *
	Acids and Bases *(Probeware)*
SECTION 3	Modeling Biochemical Compounds
SECTION 4	The Biochemistry of Compost Bins *(Challenge)*
	Chemical Reactions *(Open Inquiry)*
	Chemical Bonding *(QuickLab)*
SECTION 5	Action of Yeast *(Challenge)*
	Enzymatic Activity *
	Enzymes *
	Enzyme Action: Testing Catalase Activity *(Probeware)*
	Enzyme Action *(Probeware)*

Unit 2	
CHAPTER 3 Cell Structure and Function	
SECTION 1	Estimating a Cell Count *(Challenge)*
SECTION 2	Staining Biological Specimens *(Biotechnology)*
	Cytoplasmic Streaming in *Elodea* *(Challenge)*
	Comparing Cells *
	Modeling the Cell *
	Cell Motility and the Cytoskeleton
SECTION 3	Modeling the Cell Membrane *(QuickLab)*
	Membrane Permeability *(Probeware)*
SECTION 4	Diffusion Across a Membrane *
	Diffusion and Dialysis
	Diffusion Through Membranes *(Probeware)*
	The Effect of Alcohol on Biological Membranes *(Probeware)*
	Biological Membranes *(Probeware)*
CHAPTER 4 Cells and Energy	
SECTION 1	Energy Content of Food *(Probeware)*
SECTION 2	Rates of Photosynthesis *
SECTION 4	Cellular Respiration *
	Photosynthesis and Respiration *(Probeware)*
	Respiration of Germinating Seeds *(Probeware)*
SECTION 5	Designing an Experiment to Test a Hypothesis
SECTION 6	Investigate Fermentation in Foods *
	The Effect of Temperature on Respiration *(Probeware)*
	Fermentation *(QuickLab)* *
CHAPTER 5 Cell Growth and Division	
SECTION 1	Modeling Cell Surface Area-to-Volume Ratio *
SECTION 2	Mitosis in Onion Root Cells *
	Animating Mitosis
SECTION 3	Apoptosis *
	Cancer *(QuickLab)* *
SECTION 5	Modeling Induction in Embryos *(STEM)*

Unit 3

CHAPTER 6 Meiosis and Mendel

SECTION 2	Modeling Meiosis *
SECTION 3	Probability Practice *
SECTION 5	Allele Combinations and Punnett Squares *
	Modeling Monohybrid and Dihybrid Crosses
	Using a Test Cross to Determine Genotype *(QuickLab)* *
SECTION 6	Modeling Chromosomes in Meiosis *(STEM)*

CHAPTER 7 Extending Mendelian Genetics

SECTION 1	Sex-Linked Inheritance *(QuickLab)* *
SECTION 2	Codominance *
	Incomplete Dominance *
SECTION 3	Examining Banding Patterns in Polytene Chromosomes *(Challenge)*
SECTION 4	Pedigree Analysis *
	Human Heredity

CHAPTER 8 From DNA to Proteins

SECTION 1	Extracting DNA
SECTION 3	Replication *(QuickLab)* *
SECTION 4	Modeling Transcription *
SECTION 7	Exploring Protein Crystallization *(Challenge)*
	UV Light and Skin Cancer *
	Observing *Drosophila* Mutations

CHAPTER 9 Frontiers of Biotechnology

SECTION 1	Analysis of DNA Restriction Fragment Size *(Biotechnology)*
	Modeling Forensics *
SECTION 3	DNA Fingerprinting *(Forensics)*
SECTION 4	Modeling Genetic Engineering *
	Genetic Engineering
	Modeling Plasmids and Restriction Enzymes *(QuickLab)* *
SECTION 6	Genetic Screening *

Unit 4

CHAPTER 10 Principles of Evolution

SECTION 2	Using Patterns to Make Predictions *
SECTION 3	Adaptations in Beaks *
SECTION 4	Predator-Prey Pursuit *
	Piecing Together Evidence *(QuickLab)* *
SECTION 5	Biochemical Evidence for Evolution

CHAPTER 11 The Evolution of Populations

SECTION 2	Natural Selection in African Swallowtails *
SECTION 3	Modeling Alleles *(Challenge)*
	Genetic Drift *(QuickLab)* *
SECTION 4	Investigating an Anole Lizard Population *
	Population Genetics
	Hardy-Weinberg Equation *(STEM)*
SECTION 5	Exploring Dog Genetics and Evolution
SECTION 6	Microevolution and Antibiotic-Resistant Bacteria *(Biotechnology)*
	Investigating Plant Adaptations *(Challenge)*
	Exploring Adaptations *

CHAPTER 12 The History of Life

SECTION 1	Radioactive Decay *
	Stride Inferences *
SECTION 2	Understanding Geologic Time *
SECTION 6	Comparing Indexes Among Primates
	Geologic Clock *(QuickLab)* *

Unit 5

CHAPTER 13 Principles of Ecology

SECTION 1	Random Sampling *
	Quadrat Sampling *(QuickLab)* *
SECTION 2	Abiotic Factors and Plant Growth *
SECTION 3	Build a Terrarium *
SECTION 4	*Elodea* and the Snail *(Probeware)*
SECTION 5	Nitrogen Fixation
	Interdependence of Plants and Animals *(Probeware)*
	Plant Respiration and Photosynthesis *(Probeware)*

CHAPTER 14 Interactions in Ecosystems

SECTION 1	Making a Local Field Guide *
	Monitoring Bird Populations
SECTION 2	Modeling Predation *
SECTION 3	Survivorship Curves *(QuickLab)* *
SECTION 4	Limiting Nutrients for Algae *
	Predator-Prey Interactions
	Population Dynamics *(Probeware)*
SECTION 5	Using GPS in Ecological Surveys *(Challenge)*

CHAPTER 15 **The Biosphere**	
SECTION 2	Heating and Cooling Rates of Water and Soil *
	Microclimates *(QuickLab)* *
SECTION 3	Modeling Biomes *
SECTION 5	Winter Water Chemistry *
	Modeling the Water Cycle
	Aquatic Primary Productivity *(Open Inquiry)*
CHAPTER 16 **Human Impact on Ecosystems**	
SECTION 2	Acid Rain *
	Greenhouse Gases *(Probeware)*
SECTION 3	Investigating How Pollution Affects Plant Life *(Biotechnology)*
	Water Quality *(Open Inquiry)*
	Water Quality Testing *
	Contamination of Groundwater *
	Caffeine and Seed Germination
	Modeling Biomagnification *(QuickLab)* *
SECTION 4	Modeling the Effects of Habitat Fragmentation *(Challenge)*
	Biodiversity and Ecosystems *(Probeware)*
CHAPTER 17 **Animal Behavior**	
SECTION 1	Pill Bug Behavior *
SECTION 2	Investigating Behavior
	Human Behavior *(QuickLab)* *
SECTION 3	Using an Ethogram to Describe Animal Behavior *
SECTION 5	Animal Cognition *
Unit 6	
CHAPTER 18 **The Tree of Life**	
SECTION 1	The Linnaean System of Classification *(Open Inquiry)*
	Creating a Dichotomous Key for Limpet Shells *
SECTION 2	Classification Based on Evolutionary Relationships *(Open Inquiry)*
	Constructing a Phylogenetic Tree
	Construct a Cladogram *(QuickLab)* *
SECTION 3	Bioinformatics *(Biotechnology)*
	Modeling DNA Hybridization *
SECTION 4	Defining Species *
CHAPTER 19 **Viruses and Prokaryotes**	
SECTION 2	Modeling Viruses *
	Modeling Viral Mutations *(STEM)*
SECTION 3	Viruses and Cancer
SECTION 5	Bacteria's Role in Wastewater Treatment *(Biotechnology)*
	Leaf Print Bacteria *
	Using Bacterial to Break Down Oil *
	Examining Bacteria in Yogurt *(QuickLab)* *
CHAPTER 20 **Protists and Fungi**	
SECTION 1	Exploring Bioluminescence *(Challenge)*
SECTION 2	Investigating Motion in Protists *(QuickLab)* *
SECTION 3	Algae in Products *
SECTION 5	Chemotaxis in *Physarum* *(Challenge)*
	Exploring Mushroom Anatomy *
	Quantifying Mold Growth *
	Investigating Meiosis in *Sordaria fimicola*
CHAPTER 21 **Plant Diversity**	
SECTION 2	Habitat Clues *
	Plants and Pollinators
	Classifying Plants as Vascular or Nonvascular *(QuickLab)* *
SECTION 3	Comparing Monocots and Dicots *
SECTION 4	Phytoremediation *(Biotechnology)*
	Investigating Medicinal Plants *
CHAPTER 22 **Invertebrate Diversity**	
SECTION 3	Feeding Hydra *
SECTION 4	Cardiovascular System of Mudworms *(Challenge)*
	Anatomy of an Annelid
	Anatomy of a Clam *(QuickLab)* *
SECTION 5	Evolution of the Coelom
SECTION 6	Anatomy of a Sea Star *
CHAPTER 23 **Vertebrate Diversity**	
SECTION 1	Homologies in Vertebrate Skeletons
SECTION 3	Examining Zebrafish Development *(Challenge)*
	Fish Reproduction *
	Anatomy of a Bony Fish *
SECTION 4	Vanishing Amphibian—an Indicator Species *
	Frog Development *(QuickLab)* *
CHAPTER 24 **Human Systems and Homeostasis**	
SECTION 1	Homeostasis and Exercise *
	Examining Human Cells *
SECTION 2	Hormones and Homeostasis *
	Negative and Positive Feedback
	Negative Feedback Loop *(QuickLab)* *
	Exercise and Homeostasis *(Probeware)*
SECTION 3	Interactions Among Systems *(Open Inquiry)*

Safety in the Biology Lab

The investigations and activities in *HMH Biology* are designed to involve students in the process of science. Some of the investigations involve chemicals, glassware, and sharp tools. Some involve live animals or prepared specimens. Your insistence on everyone's adherence to safe lab practices will ensure students get the most out of their laboratory and field-work experiences.

BE PREPARED

Be sure to familiarize yourself with federal, state, and local safety regulations. It is your responsibility to provide students with a safe working environment. Post the student safety guidelines and dress code in a prominent place in the room.

Facilities Make sure all equipment is in good working order before school begins and plan a regular schedule of inspection for the school year. Inspect all safety equipment, such as the fume hood, eyewash station, and emergency shower, as well as fire equipment, such as fire extinguishers and smoke detectors. Make sure that the electrical outlets are protected with ground fault interrupters. Familiarize yourself with the location of the master shut-off valves and switches for the lab.

Storeroom and Supplies Make sure you have the supplies you need. Detailed materials lists are available in the online teacher resources. Check for shelf-life dates or dates of purchase on existing stock. Generally, chemicals should not be stored longer than two years. Organize stock so that incompatible reagents, such as acids and bases, are stored separately. It is safer to store solid reagents on upper shelves and liquid reagents on lower shelves, however, any large containers should be stored at or near floor level. Check glassware for chips and cracks.

As you review and restock your inventory, be sure that you have Material Safety Datasheets for all the chemicals in your storeroom, including household items such as bleach. Make sure you have a chemical spill kit in stock.

Biological materials, such as seeds or culture media, should be stored apart from chemical supplies. Any refrigerator intended to store laboratory materials should have a sign prohibiting personal use or food storage.

Waste Disposal Review federal, state, and local regulations for disposal and recycling of chemical and biological waste. Make sure the school has the proper containers for storage and the necessary means for removal.

Student Safety Equipment Make sure you have enough safety goggles, gloves, and aprons available for every student in class. If the same goggles will be used by students in different classes, have a plan for sanitizing the goggles after each use.

First Aid Have a first aid kit available for minor injuries, with antiseptics, bandages, ointments, tapes, and gauze pads. In the case of more serious injuries, post in the lab and place on your phone the numbers of poison control, and local police and fire departments. Be prepared to document any incident.

SAFETY ICONS

Apron

Fumes

Animal Safety

General Safety

Breakage

Gloves

Chemical Safety

Hand Washing

Disposal

Heating Safety

Electrical Safety

Hot/Glove

Safety Goggles

Poison

Fire Safety

Sharp Objects

GETTING STARTED

At the beginning of the school year, and before students conduct their first investigation, go over the safety regulations and dress code for the lab. Show students where the information is posted, point out fire exits and alarms, and discuss fire evacuation procedures. Discuss the safety equipment in the lab—how it works and when it is appropriate to use.

Discuss the safety symbols and the other material in the **Lab Handbook** at the back of the textbook (Student Resources section). The online teacher resources include a safety quiz, as well as a safety contract, which students should sign and return before their first lab. Be certain students understand that they must report any incident of student injury or report any situation or condition that could lead to injury. Tell students that a positive attitude about safety is critical—they should be not be afraid to do an investigation, but they should recognize the potential for hazards where they exist.

Make sure you are aware of any medical problems or allergies that might cause problems for a student in conducting certain labs. You might want to have parents provide a card with such information, as well as their home and work phone numbers. Also think about any accommodations you will need to make for students with special needs.

Remind students why food and drink are not allowed in the lab. Explain that edible substances used in a lab must not be eaten or placed in their mouths. Stress the importance of washing their hands with soap and water after handling lab materials of any sort, and go over the proper handling and disposal of unused materials or lab wastes.

ON LAB DAY

Have just the supplies and equipment available that you need for the lab. Make sure all chemicals and solutions are clearly labeled and that the MSDS is on hand for each. Discuss with students any special safety concerns you have and also mention any special handling needed of unused or waste materials. Go over any questions students may have on the pre-lab assignment if you gave one.

Limit the size of the groups working on an activity to a number that can productively and safely work together. Give students a timetable for the lab period and outline your expectations. Be sure to allow sufficient time for students to perform the investigation, write down data and observations, and still have enough time left over for clean up.

Make sure students keep work stations from becoming cluttered; only materials needed for an investigation should be brought to the lab station. Model the behavior you want to see in your students, wearing gloves and goggles when you expect them to do so. Encourage students to ask questions if there is any part of a procedure they are uncertain about. Remind students that it is their responsibility to make sure the lab room is clean before they leave and that all equipment has been turned off and all supplies properly stored. Be sure that the storage room and lab room are locked when you leave.

Name Period Date

Safety Contract

I, ______________________ (student's name) have read and understand all the lab safety rules and guidelines I have been given both orally and in writing. I understand and agree to follow all of these safety rules and guidelines I have been given, and all others that are stated at anytime during the school year. At all times, I will conduct myself in a responsible manner that will make sure that everyone in the lab, classroom, or anywhere else activities are conducted, including myself, my fellow students, teachers, and bystanders, is safe. I acknowledge that if I violate this safety contract, I can be instructed to leave the laboratory, complete alternative assigments, and also may fail this course and may face other disciplinary measures, including detention or suspension from school, at the discretion of my teacher and other school officials.

____
Student's signature

____
Date

I, ______________________ (parent/guardian's name), have read the safety rules detailed and understand them. I understand that my son/daughter will need to adhere to these rules whenever he/she is participating in science activities, whether in the lab, classroom, on school property, or on field trips. I agree to instruct him/her to follow all instructions from the teacher at all times. I understand my child will be subject to disciplinary action for failure to comply with any safety rules or guidelines.

____
Parent/Guardian's signature

____
Date

FIELD STUDY

If you plan to conduct any field work, be sure the activities fall within the school's guidelines for outside activities and additional supervision. Visit the site ahead of time to assess the potential for hazards and also to address any accommodations needed for special needs students.

Make sure all student permission forms are turned in the day before the trip. Go over assignments and protocols for the handling and use of equipment. Students should know what their responsibilities are and what you expect them to record in the way of data or observations. Warn students of any potential allergens at the site and tell students that they should not handle any animals or plants unless instructed to do so. Make sure to bring a first aid kit.

WORKING WITH ORGANISMS

The online teacher resources contain specific instructions for working with organisms required for a given investigation. These instructions are entitled "Handling and Care of Organisms." Also included is a reprint of the NSTA position statement, "Animals: Responsible Use of Live Animals and Dissection in the Science Classroom."

Bacteria The NSTA now recommends that bacteria not be cultured in the classroom, given the risk of inadvertently culturing resistant bacteria along with the target bacteria.

Plants Make sure any plant material is stored and kept separate from other lab materials. Use store-bought plants, seeds, and soil. Farm products may be treated with fertilizer; wild plants may contain allergens. When possible, students should wear gloves when handling plants and always wash their hands thoroughly after handling them. Dead plants may be discarded in the trash as long as they have not been treated with chemicals that require special disposal.

Animals Live animals to be used in investigations should be kept separate from other lab materials and from students. Refer to federal, state, and local laws and regulations regarding the acquisition, handling, and care of animals. Future care or disposal of animals must be considered before making an acquisition. Remind students that animals used for an investigation must be handled in a humane way, with every effort made to minimize harm. Students should wear gloves and wash their hands thoroughly after handling the animals.

Consider student attitudes when planning a dissection. Students should see a clear purpose to the activity.

With the exception of human hair suggested for a forensic lab, no human fluids, tissues, or cells are used in the investigations in the *HMH Biology* program.

TEACHER-TESTED LABS

The investigations included with the *HMH Biology* program have been tested by teachers in a classroom setting and revised based on the recommendations of those teachers. Still, it is important that you preview the labs to determine how well they will work for you in your classroom. Information about labs is available in the online teacher resources.

Correlations to the Indiana Academic Standards for Science: Biology (2016)

This chart provides correlations for the Student Edition, Teacher Edition, Science Standards Guide, labs, and online resources that support the Indiana Science Standards for Biology.

Indiana Science Standards for Biology	Coverage
STANDARD 1: CELLULAR STRUCTURE AND FUNCTION	
B.1.1 Compare and contrast the shape and function of the essential biological macromolecules (i.e. carbohydrates, lipids, proteins, and nucleic acids), as well as, how chemical elements (i.e. carbon, hydrogen, oxygen, nitrogen, phosphorus, and sulfur) can combine to form these biomolecules.	**SE/TE:** 39–41, 41 (#7), 46–50, 50 (#3, 4), 61–62 (#9, 16, 17, 18, 27) **TE Only:** 38 **Science Standards Guide:** SE 1–2, TE 1–4 **Online Labs** **Standard:** Modeling Biochemical Compounds **Virtual:** Macromolecules (2.3 of Life (2.3)
B.1.2 Analyze how the shape of a molecule determines its role in the many different types of cellular processes (e.g., metabolism, homeostasis, growth and development, and heredity) and understand that the majority of these processes involve proteins that act as enzymes.	**SE/TE:** 41 (#7), 46–50, 50 (#3, 4), 61–62 (#9, 16, 17, 18, 27), 57–58, 58 (#4, 5), 21–22 (#18, 22, 26, 30), 220–223, 226–227, 228 (#2, 3), 230–232, 232 (#4), 233–237, 249–250 (#11, 12, 26) **TE Only:** 56 **Science Standards Guide:** SE 3–4, TE 5–8 **Online Labs** **Standard:** Enzymes (2.5); Enzymatic Activity (2.5); Modeling Transcription (8.4) **Vernier Probeware:** Enzyme Action: Testing Catalase Activity (2.5)
B.1.3 Develop and use models that illustrate how a cell membrane regulates the uptake of materials essential for growth and survival while removing or preventing harmful waste materials from accumulating through the processes of active and passive transport.	**SE/TE:** 81–84, 84 (#2), 85–87, 87 (#4), 89–91 **Science Standards Guide:** SE 5–6, TE 9–12 **Online Labs** **Standard:** Modeling the Cell (3.2); Diffusion Across a Membrane (3.4) **Vernier Probeware:** Diffusion through Membranes (3.4); Biological Membranes (3.4)
B.1.4 Develop and use models to illustrate how specialized structures within cells (i.e. nuclei, ribosomes, Golgi, endoplasmic reticulum) interact to produce, modify, and transport proteins.	**SE/TE:** 94 (#32) **TE Only:** 78 **Science Standards Guide:** SE 7–8, TE 13–16 **Online Lab** **Standard:** Modeling the Cell (3.2)
B.1.5 Develop and use a model to illustrate the hierarchical organization of interacting systems (cell, tissue, organ, organ system) that provide specific functions within multicellular organisms.	**SE/TE:** 147–151, 616–620 **Science Standards Guide:** SE 9–10, TE 17–20
STANDARD 2: MATTER CYCLES AND ENERGY TRANSFER	
B.2.1 Use a model to illustrate how photosynthesis transforms light energy into stored chemical energy.	**SE/TE:** 98–100, 100–103, 106–110 **Science Standards Guide:** SE 11–12, TE 21–24 **Additional Online Resource** **That's Amazing! Video-Based Inquiry:** Lungs of the Planet (4)
B.2.2 Use a model to illustrate that cellular respiration is a chemical process whereby the bonds of food molecules and oxygen molecules are broken and the bonds in new compounds are formed resulting in a net transfer of energy.	**SE/TE:** 98–100, 111–113, 115–119 **Science Standards Guide:** SE 13–14, TE 25–28 **Additional Online Resource** **Animated Biology:** Cellular Respiration (4.4) **Online Teacher Resource** **Chapter Tests: Alternative Assessment:** Cells and Energy (4)
B.2.3 Use mathematical and/or computational representations to support claims for the cycling of matter and flow of energy among organisms in an ecosystem.	**SE/TE:** 398–399, 400–403, pp. 411–413 **Science Standards Guide:** SE 15-16, TE 29-32 **Online Lab** **Virtual:** Ecosystems and Energy Models (15)

Indiana Science Standards for Biology	Coverage
B.2.4 Develop a model to illustrate the role of photosynthesis and cellular respiration in the cycling of carbon among the biosphere, atmosphere, hydrosphere, and geosphere.	**SE/TE:** 398–399, 400–403, 404–410, 446–447 **Science Standards Guide:** SE 17–18, TE 33–36 **Online Labs** **Video:** Ecosystem Change (13.4) **Standard:** Modeling the Water Cycle (15.5)
STANDARD 3: INTERDEPENDENCE	
B.3.1 Use mathematical and/or computational representation to explain why the carrying capacity ecosystems can support is limited by the available energy, water, oxygen, and minerals and by the ability of ecosystems to recycle the remains of dead organisms.	**SE/TE:** 394–396, 420–422, 423–426, 428–431, 432–436 **Science Standards Guide:** SE 19–20, TE 37–40 **Online Labs** **Standard:** Predator–Prey Interactions (14.4); Modeling the Water Cycle (15.5) **Additional Online Resource** **Smart Grapher Interactive:** Population Growth and Carrying Capacity (14)
B.3.2 Design, evaluate, and refine a model which shows how human activities and natural phenomena can change the flow of matter and energy in an ecosystem and how those changes impact the environment and biodiversity of populations in ecosystems of different scales, as well as, how these human impacts can be reduced.	**SE/TE:** 394–396, 398–399, 400–403, 404–410, 423–426, 432–436, 458–460, 461–464, 482–484, 486–489 **Science Standards Guide:** SE 21–22, TE 41–44
B.3.3 Evaluate the claims, evidence, and reasoning that the complex interactions in ecosystems maintain relatively consistent numbers and types of organisms in stable conditions, and identify the impact of changing conditions or introducing non-native species into that ecosystem.	**SE/TE:** 394–396, 423–426, 428–431, 432–436, 437–439 **Science Standards Guide:** SE 23–24, TE 45–48 **Additional Online Resources** **Animated Biology:** What Limits Population Growth? (14.4)
STANDARD 4: INHERITANCE AND VARIATION IN TRAITS	
B.4.1 Develop and revise a model that clarifies the relationship between DNA and chromosomes in coding the instructions for characteristic traits passed from parents to offspring.	**SE/TE:** 171–173, 174–176, 177–181 **Science Standards Guide:** SE 25–26, TE 49–52 **Online Labs** **Standard:** Probability Practice (6.3); Modeling Monohybrid and Dihybrid Crosses (6.5); Allele Combinations and Punnett Squares (6.5) **QuickLab:** Using a Test Cross to Determine Genotype (6.5) **Virtual:** Breeding Mutations in Fruit Flies (6)
B.4.2 Construct an explanation for how the structure of DNA determines the structure of proteins which carry out the essential functions of life through systems of specialized cells.	**SE/TE:** 70–72, 220–223, 229–232, 233–237 **Science Standards Guide:** SE 27–28, TE 53–56 **Online Labs** **Virtual:** Virtual Tour of an Animal Cell (3); DNA, RNA, and Gene Expression (8)
B.4.3 Construct a model to explain that the unique shape and function of each protein is determined by the sequence of its amino acids, and thus is determined by the sequence of the DNA that codes for this protein.	**SE/TE:** 233–237 **TE Only:** 49, 50 **Science Standards Guide:** SE 29–30, TE 57–60 **Online Labs** **Standard:** Modeling Biochemical Compounds (2.3); Modeling Transcription (8.4) **Virtual:** Macromolecules of Life (2.3)
B.4.4 Use a model to illustrate the role of cellular division (mitosis) and differentiation in producing and maintaining complex organisms.	**SE/TE:** 130–133, 134–138, 147–151, 162–165, 702–706 **Science Standards Guide:** SE 31–32, TE 61–64

Indiana Science Standards for Biology	Coverage
B.4.5 Make and defend a claim based on evidence that inheritable genetic variations may result from: (1) new genetic combinations through meiosis, (2) viable errors occurring during replication, and (3) mutations caused by environmental factors.	**SE/TE:** 83–185, 244–247 **Science Standards Guide:** SE 33–34, TE 65–68 **Online Labs** **Standard:** Modeling Meiosis (6.2) **STEM:** Modeling Chromosomes in Meiosis (6.6) **Virtual:** Phases of Meiosis (6) **Additional Online Resource** **WebLinks:** Mutations (8)
B.4.6 Apply concepts of statistics and probability to explain the variation and distribution of expressed traits in a population.	**SE/TE:** 162–165, 167–170, 171–173, 174–176, 177–181 **Science Standards Guide:** SE 35–36, TE 69–72 **Online Labs** **Standard:** Modeling Meiosis (6.2) **STEM:** Modeling Chromosomes in Meiosis (6.6) **Virtual Investigation:** Phases of Meiosis (6)
STANDARD 5: EVOLUTION	
B.5.1 Evaluate anatomical and molecular evidence to provide an explanation of how organisms are classified and named based on their evolutionary relationships into taxonomic categories.	**SE/TE:** 538–542, 544–546, 542 (#4), 546 (#4), 552 (#19, 21) **TE Only:** 530 **Science Standards Guide:** SE 37–38, TE 73–76 **Online Labs** **Standard:** Modeling DNA Hybridization (18.3); Defining Species (18.4) **Biotechnology:** Bioinformatics (18.3)
B.5.2 Communicate scientific information that common ancestry and biological evolution are supported by multiple lines of empirical evidence including both anatomical and molecular evidence.	**SE/TE:** 298–304, 306–309 **Science Standards Guide:** SE 39–40, TE 77–79 **Online Lab** **Standard:** Biochemical Evidence for Evolution (10.5)
B.5.3 Apply concepts of statistics and probability to support a claim that organisms with an advantageous heritable trait tend to increase in proportion to organisms lacking this trait.	**SE/TE:** 286–289, 290–291, 292–297 **Science Standards Guide:** SE 41–42, TE 81–84 **Online Labs** **Virtual:** Evolution by Natural Selection (10) **PhET Simulation:** Natural Selection (10.3)
B.5.4 Evaluate evidence to explain the role of natural selection as an evolutionary mechanism that leads to the adaptation of species, and to support claims that changes in environmental conditions may result in: (1) increases in the number of individuals of some species, (2) the emergence of new species over time, and/or (3) the extinction of other species.	**SE/TE:** 292–297, 344 (#24, #36), Unit 5 BioZine: *Climate Change—Changing the Planet,* 526 **Science Standards Guide:** SE 43–44, TE 85–88 **Online Labs** **Video:** Natural Selection Simulation (10.3) **PhET Simulation:** Natural Selection (10.3) **Standard:** Adaptations in Beaks (10.4) **Additional Online Resource** **Chapter 21 Plant Diversity:** Multimedia Activity: Unit 6 BioZine: *Genetically Modified Foods—Do Potential Problems Outweigh Benefits?*
B.5.5 Construct an explanation based on evidence that the process of evolution primarily results from four factors: (1) the potential for a species to increase in number, (2) the heritable genetic variation of individuals in a species due to mutation and sexual reproduction, (3) competition for limited resources, and (4) the proliferation of those organisms that are better able to survive and reproduce in the environment.	**SE/TE:** 292–297 **Science Standards Guide:** SE 45–46, TE 89–92 **Online Labs** **Video:** Natural Selection Simulation (10.3) **PhET Simulation:** Natural Selection (10.3) **Standard:** Adaptations in Beaks (10.4)
B.5.6 Analyze and interpret data for patterns in the fossil record and molecular data that document the existence, diversity, extinction, and change of life forms throughout the history of life on Earth under the assumption that natural laws operate today as in the past.	**SE/TE:** 353–355, 355 (#1,4), 380 (#34) **TE Only:** 346 **Science Standards Guide:** SE 47–48, TE 93–96 **Online Labs** **Standard:** Radioactive Decay (12.1); Understanding Geologic Time (12.2)

Biology

Stephen Nowicki

Stephen Nowicki, Ph.D.

Stephen Nowicki grew up with a strong interest in music and at one time wanted to be a classical musician. A biology course in college sparked his excitement for biology, leading him to major in both biology and music. Nowicki obtained his bachelor's and master's degrees from Tufts University. He received his doctorate in neurobiology and behavior from Cornell University in 1985.

Nowicki is now Dean and Vice Provost for Undergraduate Education, as well as Bass Fellow and Professor in the departments of Biology, Psychology, and Neurobiology at Duke University. He has taught at Duke since 1989, where he directed a complete redesign of the introductory biology program. Nowicki's research explores animal communication and sexual selection from an integrative perspective that includes a wide range of behavioral, ecological, neuroethological, developmental, genetic, and evolutionary approaches. Birds are a common model system for his work, but he and his students also have worked with insects, spiders, shrimp, lobsters, lizards, and primates.

Nowicki's research has been published in more than 95 articles in scientific journals, including *Science, Nature,* and *Proceedings of the National Academy of Sciences.* He coauthored the book *The Evolution of Animal Communication: Reliability and Deception in Signaling Systems* and is the author of a video lecture series based on the introductory biology course he taught at Duke. In 2010, he was elected a Fellow of the American Association for the Advancement of Science.

Outside of his professional interests, Nowicki continues to enjoy music. He has played the trombone since the fourth grade, and he plays both trombone and tuba with the Duke University Pep Band at basketball games. Juggling and cooking are other hobbies that he enjoys in his free time. Nowicki is married to Susan Peters, who also studies animal communication, and they have one son, Schuyler. Nowicki and his wife live in Durham, North Carolina.

Cover Photo Credits
Sharks ©Jeffrey L. Rotman/Corbis; *beetle* ©Ocean/Corbis

Printed in the U.S.A.

ISBN 978-0-544-81798-2

1 2 3 4 5 6 7 8 9 10 0607 25 24 23 22 21 20 19 18 17 16

4500000000 A B C D E F G

HMH **BIOLOGY**

NEW

Yes, it's educational. **No,** it's not boring.

EXCLUSIVE! Webcomic *xkcd.com* author Randall Munroe's diagrams explain complex applications of biology using only 1000 simple words and a dose of humor.

Student Edition

Explore the world around you with pages of colorful photos, helpful illustrations, and activities using everyday materials. This book is built to help you succeed in biology, with content chunked into Main Ideas, relevant and motivating features, and in-depth skills support.

Interactive Online Edition

The new Interactive Online Edition provides 24/7 point-of-use access to all program resources. In addition to a complete eBook version of your textbook, the Online Edition includes alternative explanations and experiences through a wealth of multimedia activities, including videos, interactive simulations, virtual labs, exciting review games, and current news.

New Focus on Engineering

Added resources help you concentrate on STEM (Science, Technology, Engineering, and Math) skills—and introduce you to the 21st-century careers that use those skills.

ONLINE BIOLOGY
HMHScience.com

iii

Interactive

NEW

Google Expeditions

Take virtual-reality field trips into the unknown with Google Expeditions!

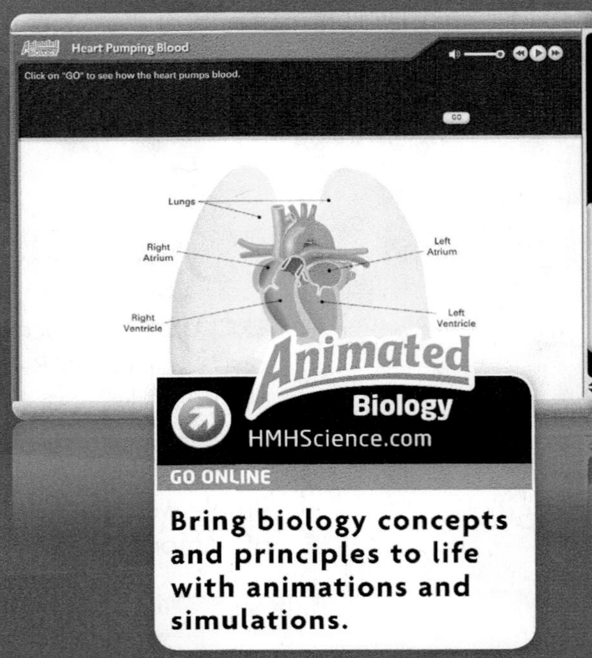

Animated Biology
HMHScience.com
GO ONLINE

Bring biology concepts and principles to life with animations and simulations.

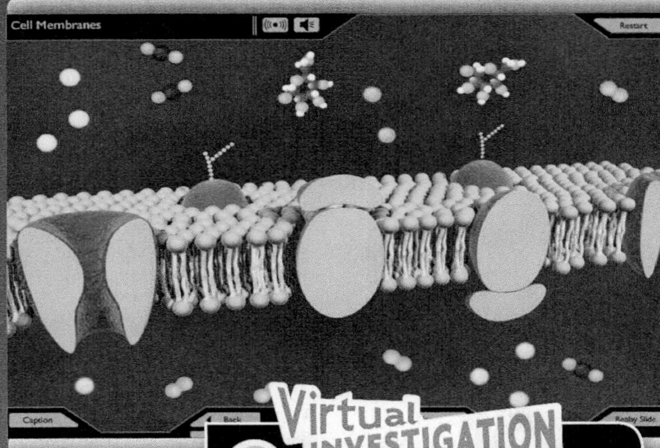

Virtual INVESTIGATION
HMHScience.com
GO ONLINE

Explore biology concepts through multimedia lessons that include engaging presentations, interactive activities, and simulated scientific investigations.

ClassZone – Biology

THAT'S Amazing! Video Inquiry
HMHScience.com
GO ONLINE

Follow Dr. Michael Heithaus and other scientists on amazing inquiry adventures.

nline Edition

HMHScience.com

SELF-CHECK Online
HMHScience.com
O ONLINE

Check your progress and
et immediate feedback.

INTERACTIVE Review
HMHScience.com
GO ONLINE

Prepare for upcoming tests in a fun format.

WEBLINKS
HMHScience.com
GO ONLINE

Extend and enrich each chapter's content with hand-selected resource links.

WebQuest
HMHScience.com
GO ONLINE

Explore the Web to answer scientific questions.

Smart Grapher
HMHScience.com
NLINE

lyze your data and
alize experimental
lts.

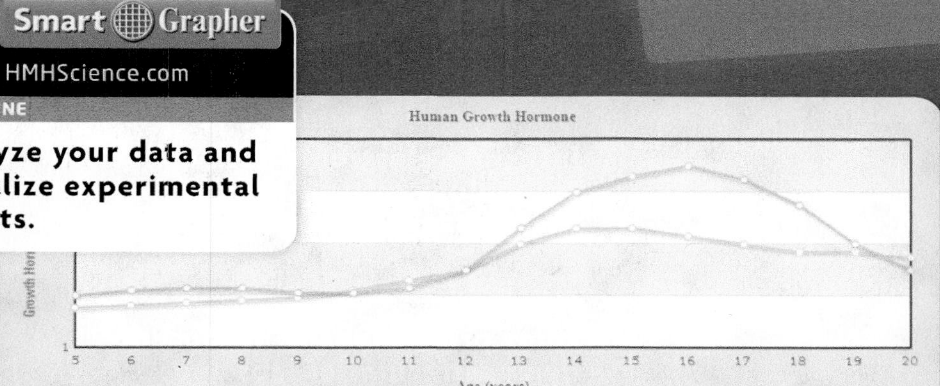

BIOZINE

Connect to current events with features such as science news feeds, updates on current biology research, careers, and in-depth detail about unit features.

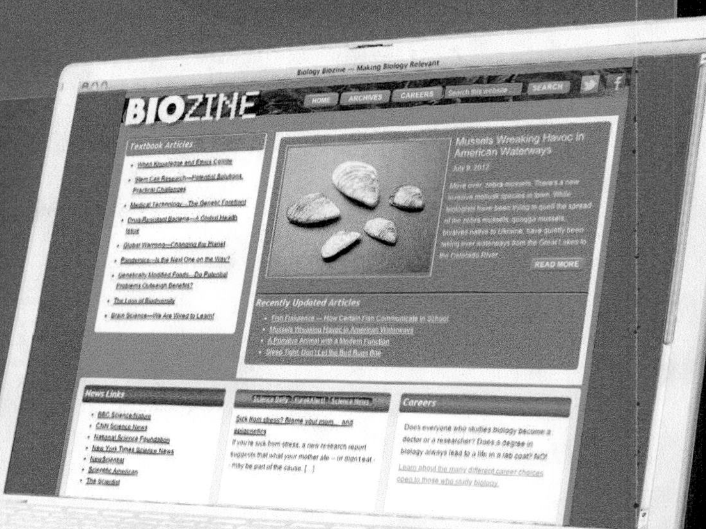

Look for Labs Online

HMHScience.com

Standard Labs

Focus on experimental skills and the application of chapter concepts through the use of scientific methods.

Open Inquiry Labs

Drive the lab activity—you make decisions about what to research and how to do it.

STEM Labs

Explore the engineering design process through hands-on inquiry projects.

QuickLabs

Encounter key concepts in your classroom with QuickLabs. They're right in your book.

Biotechnology Labs

Experience the intersection of technology and biology.

Forensics Labs

Investigate practical applications of biology, such as crime-scene analysis.

Challenge Labs

Extend your understanding and lab expertise with advanced techniques, equipment, and content.

Probeware Labs

Integrate electronic data-collection technology into exciting activities that enhance hands-on biology.

Video Labs

Enjoy professionally produced demonstrations of labs and activities.

Virtual Labs

Conduct meaningful experiments with tools, instruments, and techniques that take you beyond your classroom.

Interpreting Bird Response

VIRTUAL Lab

Content Reviewers

Mark Baustian, Ph.D.
President
West Hill Biological Resources
Spencer, NY

John Beaver, Ph.D.
Professor Emeritus
College of Education and Human Services
Western Illinois University
Macomb, IL

Elizabeth A. De Stasio, Ph.D.
Associate Professor and Raymond H. Herzog Professor of Science
Department of Biology
Lawrence University
Appleton, WI

Dan Franck, Ph.D.
Botany Education Consultant
Chatham, NY

Francine Galko, M.A.
Science Consultant
Austin, TX

Linda Graham, Ph.D.
Professor of Botany
Department of Botany
University of Wisconsin
Madison, WI

David Harbster, M.A. in Biology Education
Professor of Biology
Paradise Valley Community College
Phoenix, AZ

Anthony Ippolito, Ph.D.
Visiting Assistant Professor
Department of Biological Sciences
DePaul University
Chicago, IL

Sönke Johnsen, Ph.D.
Assistant Professor
Department of Biology
Duke University
Durham, NC

Paula Lemons, Ph.D.
Assistant Professor of the Practice
Department of Biology
Duke University
Durham, NC

Lori Marino, Ph.D.
Senior Lecturer
Neuroscience and Behavioral Biology Program
Emory University
Atlanta, GA

Louise McCullough, M.D./Ph.D.
Director of Stroke Research
Department of Neurology
University of Connecticut Health Center
Farmington, CT

Elizabeth Panter, R.D.
Dietitian
Clinical Nutrition Department
Johns Hopkins Bayview Medical Center
Baltimore, MD

Sheila Patek, Ph.D.
Assistant Professor
Department of Integrative Biology
University of California
Berkeley, CA

Adam Savage, B.S., M.F.A.
Science Consultant
Chicago, IL

F. Daniel Vogt, Ph.D.
Professor
Department of Biological Sciences
State University of New York at Plattsburgh
Plattsburgh, NY

Jerry Waldvogel, Ph.D.
Associate Professor
Department of Biological Sciences
Clemson University
Clemson, SC

Safety Reviewer

Juliana Texley, Ph.D.
Former K–12 Science Teacher and School Superintendent
Boca Raton, FL

Program Consultant

Laine Gurley, Ph.D.
Biology Teacher
Rolling Meadows High School
Rolling Meadows, IL

vii

Teacher Reviewers and Lab Evaluators

Elaine Armstrong
Battle Ground High School
Battle Ground, WA

Amy Bell
Arcadia High School
Phoenix, AZ

Jerry Bell
Desert Vista High School
Phoenix, AZ

Tracey Boyd, M.Ed.
West Brook HIgh School
Beaumont, TX

Bonnie Brenner
Niles West High School
Niles, IL

Shirley Bryant
Granada Hills Charter High School
Granada Hills, CA

Jason Campbell
Schaumburg High School
Schaumburg, IL

Christopher Dignam
Lane Tech High School
Chicago, IL

Jennifer Ellberg
Maine West High School
Des Plaines, IL

Charles Ellwood
Pebblebrook High School
Mableton, GA

Barry Feldman
Corona del Sol High School
Tempe, AZ

Gerry Foster
Desert Vista High School
Phoenix, AZ

Riley Greenwood
Valley Center High School
Valley Center, KS

Michelle Hadden
La Joya High School
Avondale, AZ

Randy Hein
Floyd Central High School
Floyds Knobs, IN

Stephen Hobbs
Seton Catholic High School
Chandler, AZ

Jason Hook
Manor ISD
Manor, TX

Janet Jones
Sullivan High School
Chicago, IL

Karen Klafeta
Morton East High School
Cicero, IL

Robert Kolenda
Neshaminy High School
Langhorne, PA

Tina Lanquist
Moorpark High School
Moorpark, CA

Michael McDowell
Napa New Technology High School
Napa, CA

Wanda Miller
Martinsburg High School
Martinsburg, WV

Birgit Musheno
Desert Vista High School
Phoenix, AZ

Kenneth Nealy
Windsor Public Schools
Windsor, CT

Lonnie Newton
Arvada West Senior High
Arvada, CO

Palak Patel
Wheaton North High School
Wheaton, IL

Heather Pereira
Amador Valley High School
Pleasanton, CA

Yvonne Perry
Douglas County High School
Douglasville, GA

Tracy Rader
Fulton Jr-Sr High School
Indianapolis, IN

Kathey Roberts
Lakeside High School
Hot Springs, AR

Tomas M. Rodriguez III
United South High School
Laredo, TX

Cassandra Ross
Redan High School
Stone Mountain, GA

Lori Ruter
Lake Norman High School
Mooresville, NC

James Rutkowski
Erie School District
Erie, PA

Sara Sagmeister
Maine South High School
Park Ridge, IL

Patricia Smith (retired)
Clear Brook HIgh School
League City, TX

Jackie Snow
Lee's Summit North High School
Lee's Summit, MO

Laura Spitznogle
Williamsville East High School
East Amherst, NY

George Wandiko
Rialto High School
Rialto, CA

Jason Wikman
Charlotte High School
Punta Gorda, FL

Contents in Brief

TABLE OF CONTENTS

UNIT 1

Introducing Biology

Unit Focus

Unit 1 gives you a general understanding of what modern biology is all about and reviews and explains the chemistry of living systems. You will explore scientific thinking, methods, equipment, and experimentation.

HMHScience.com
Go online for the full complement of labs.

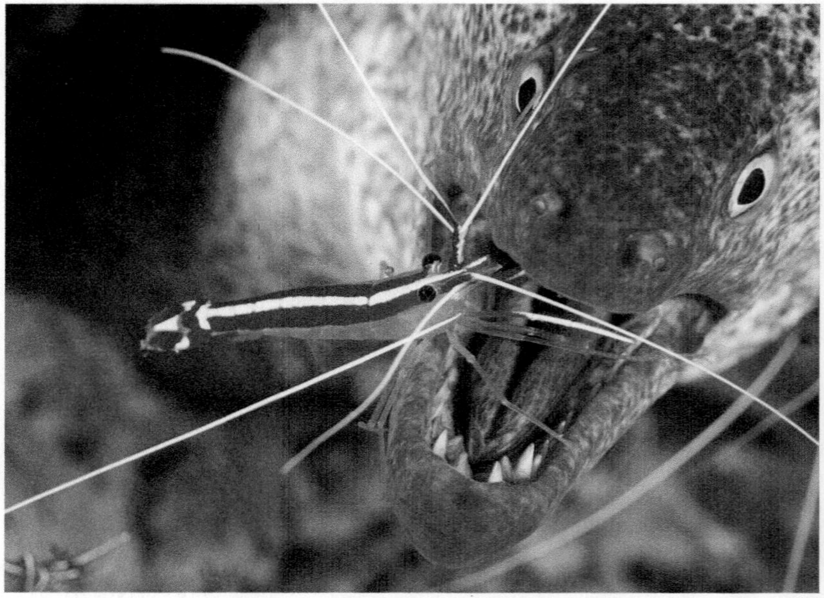

Moray eel and cleaner shrimp

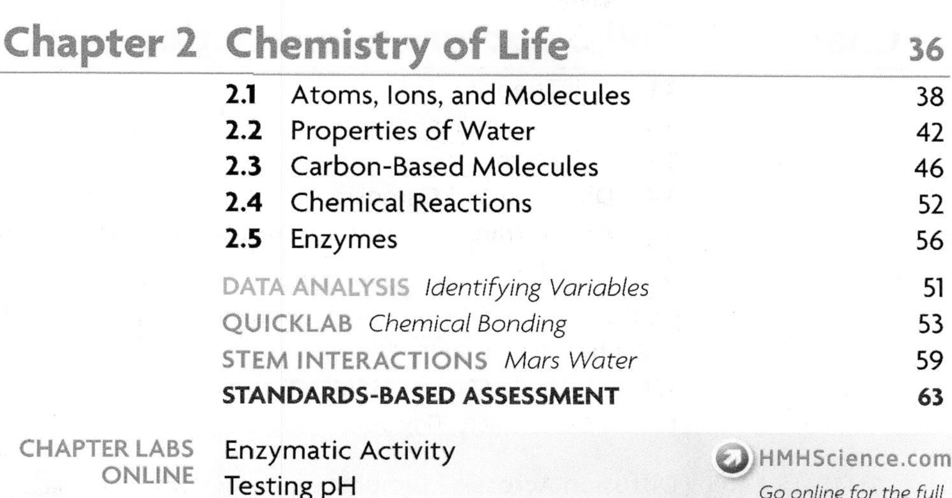

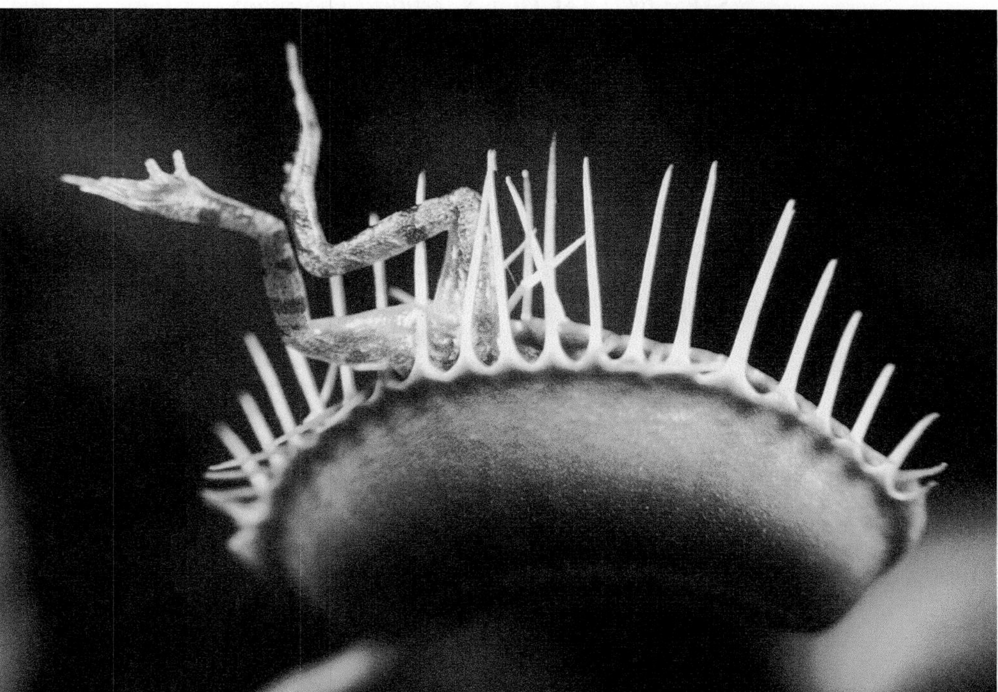

Venus flytrap and frog

ONLINE BIOLOGY
HMHScience.com

VIRTUAL Lab

Chapter 2 Calorimetry

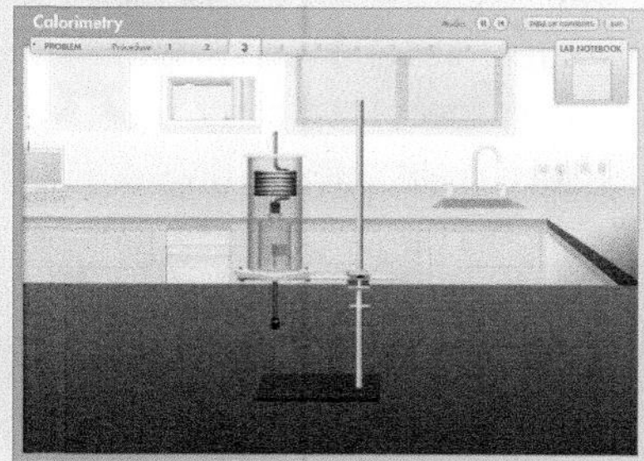

Animated **BIOLOGY**

Chapter 1 Cells Through Different Microscopes, Experimental Design

Chapter 2 Hydrogen Bonding, Energy and Chemical Reactions, Atoms and Bonding

WebQuest

Chapter 1 Bioethics

Chapter 2 Prions and Public Health

INTERACTIVE Review

Key Concepts, Vocabulary Games, Concept Maps, Animated Biology, Section Self-Checks

BIOZINE
INTERNET MAGAZINE
Continually updated articles and the latest biology news

Additional labs and a variety of online activities are available in Student Resources at

HMHScience.com.

UNIT 2

Cells

Unit Focus

In Unit 2, you will learn about different types of cells, the structures and functions of their specialized parts, energy use in cells, and cell division.

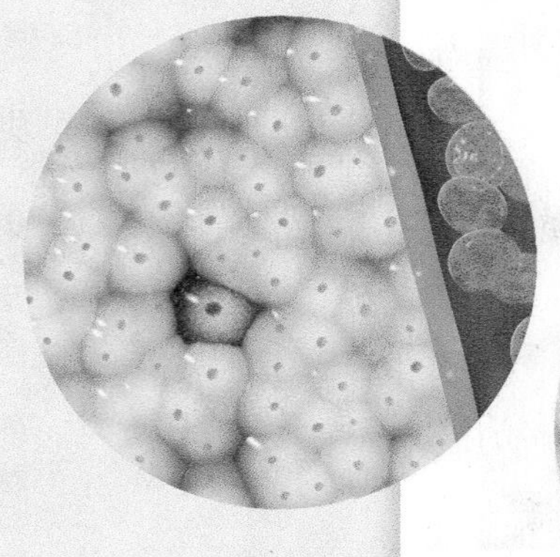

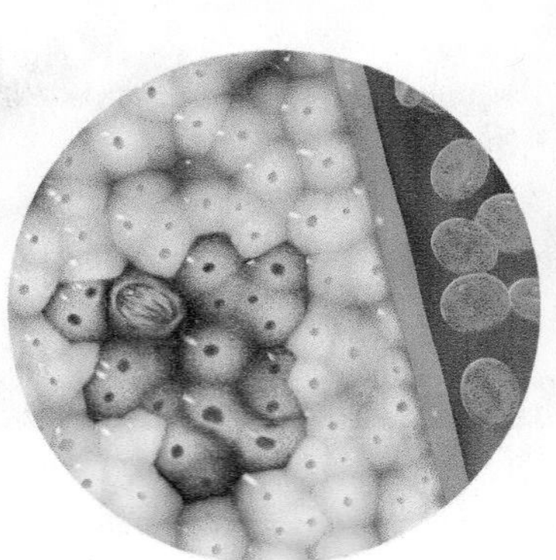

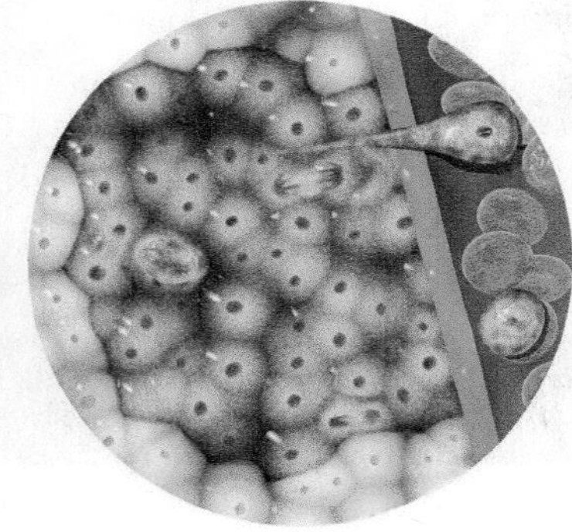

Cancer cells

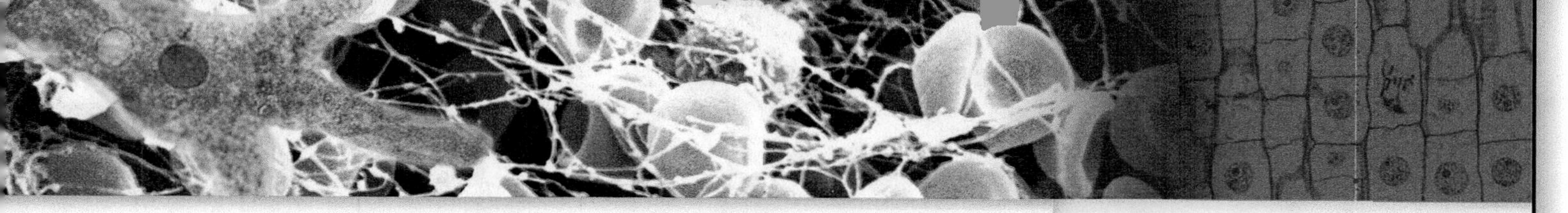

Vesicles in a cell

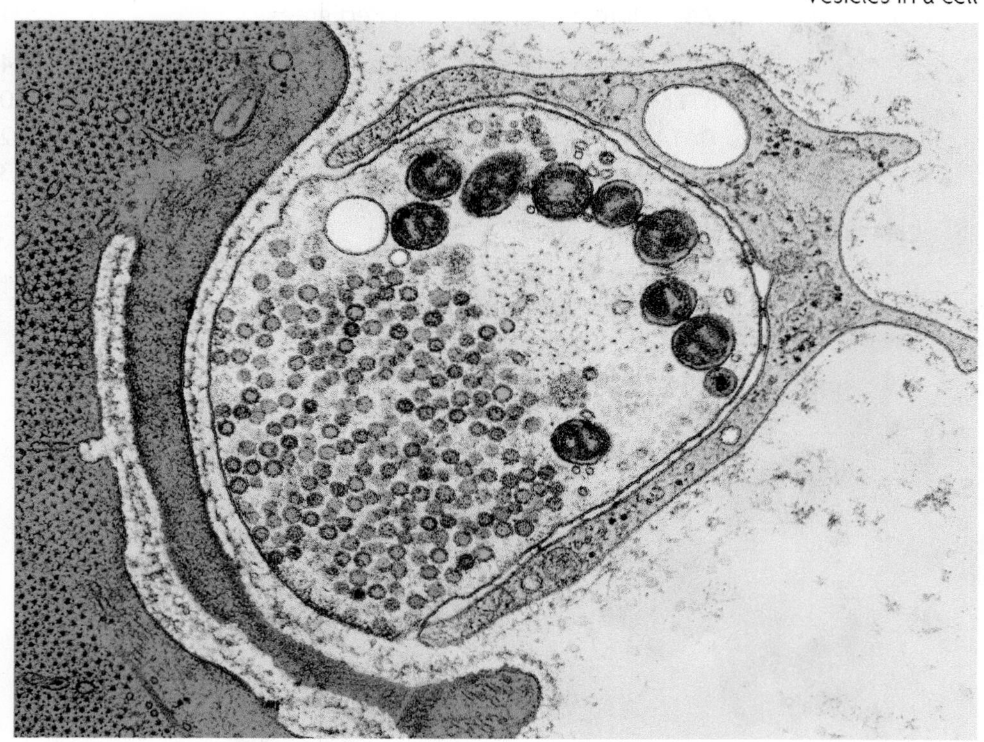

VIRTUAL Lab

Chapter 4 Carbon Dioxide Transfer Through Snails and Elodea

Chapter 5 Investigating Bacterial Growth

Animated BIOLOGY

Chapter 3 Cell Structures, Get Through a Cell Membrane

Chapter 4 Photosynthesis, Cellular Respiration, Mirror Processes

Chapter 5 Binary Fission, Mitosis Stage Matching

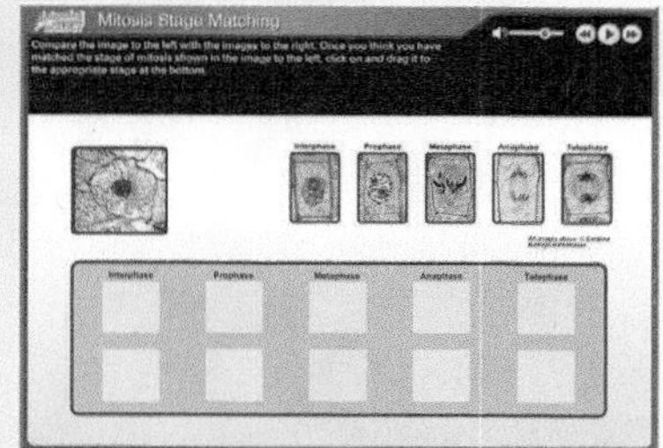

WebQuest

Chapter 3 Organelle Dysfunction

Chapter 4 Energy and Athletic Training

Chapter 5 Skin Cancer

INTERACTIVE Review

Key Concepts, Vocabulary Games, Concept Maps, Animated Biology, Section Self-Checks

BIOZINE

INTERNET MAGAZINE

Continually updated articles and the latest biology news

Additional labs and a variety of online activities are available in Student Resources at

HMHScience.com.

xiii

UNIT 3

Genetics

Unit Focus

In Unit 3, you will learn about sources of genetic variation, how the genetic makeup of an individual is determined, how the genetic code is eventually translated into proteins, and how biotechnology can change an organism's DNA.

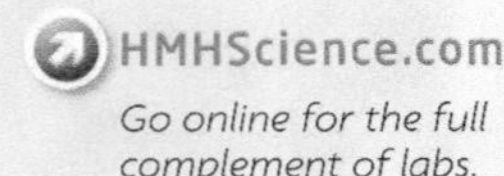

Royal blue and green betta fish

VIRTUAL Lab

Chapter 6 Breeding Mutations in Fruit Flies
Chapter 9 Gel Electrophoresis, Bacterial Transformation

Animated BIOLOGY

Chapter 6 Meiosis
Chapter 7 Human Chromosomes
Chapter 8 Replicating DNA, Build a Protein
Chapter 9 Restriction Enzymes, Polymerase Chain Reaction

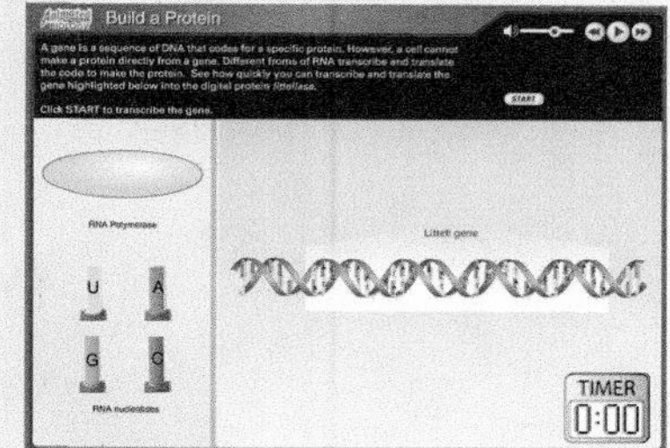

WebQuest

Chapter 6 Selective Breeding
Chapter 7 Genetic Heritage
Chapter 8 Transgenic Organisms
Chapter 9 Animal Cloning

INTERACTIVE Review

Key Concepts, Vocabulary Games, Concept Maps, Animated Biology, Section Self-Checks

BIOZINE
INTERNET MAGAZINE
Continually updated articles and the latest biology news

Additional labs and a variety of online activities are available in Student Resources at HMHScience.com.

UNIT 4

Evolution

Unit Focus

Unit 4 discusses the basic principles of evolution and natural selection, how populations evolve, and the history of life on Earth.

Chapter 10 Principles of Evolution 284

HMHScience.com
Go online for the full complement of labs.

Chapter 11 The Evolution of Populations 314

HMHScience.com
Go online for the full complement of labs.

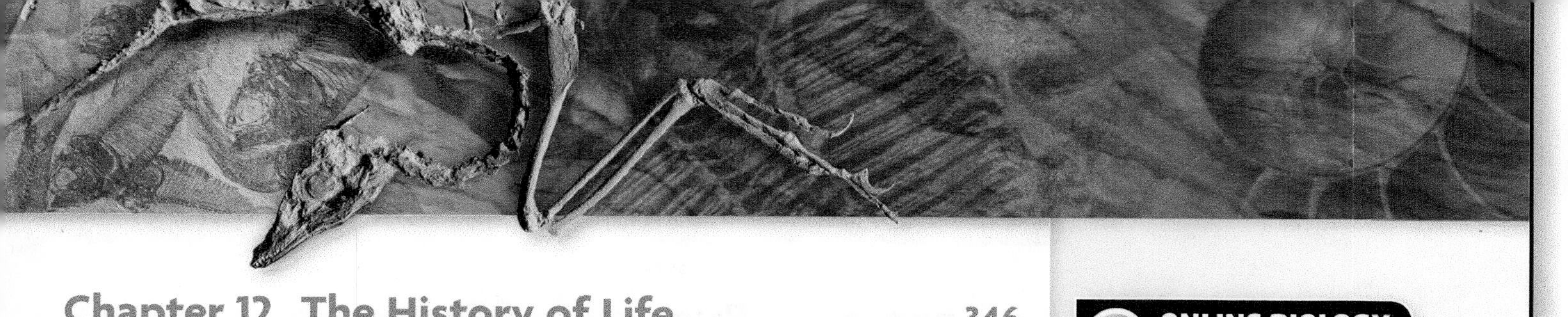

Tarsiers

ONLINE BIOLOGY
HMHScience.com

VIRTUAL Lab

Chapter 12 Comparing Hominoid Skulls

Animated BIOLOGY

Chapter 10 Principles of Natural Selection, Natural Selection

Chapter 11 Mechanisms of Evolution, Founder Effect

Chapter 12 Endosymbiosis, Geologic Time Scale

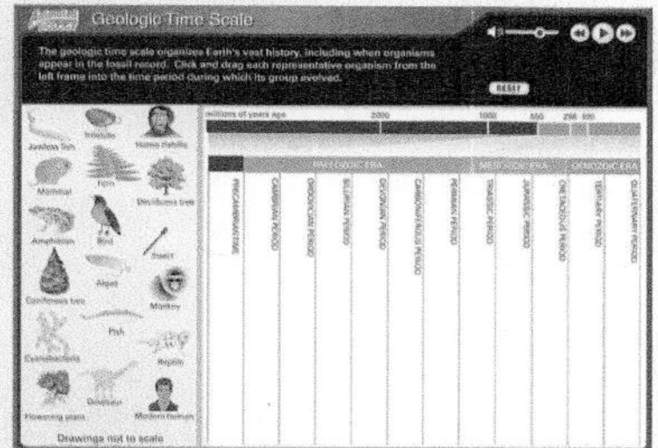

Web*Quest*

Chapter 10 Dinosaur Descendants

Chapter 11 Speciation in Action

Chapter 12 Geologic Dating

INTERACTIVE Review

Key Concepts, Vocabulary Games, Concept Maps, Animated Biology, Section Self-Checks

BIOZINE

INTERNET MAGAZINE

Continually updated articles and the latest biology news

Additional labs and a variety of online activities are available in Student Resources at HMHScience.com.

UNIT 5

Ecology

Unit Focus

In Unit 5, ecology is defined as "the study of interactions among living and nonliving things in an ecosystem." You will learn about various types of interactions and how scientists study them, how Earth is divided into biomes, and how humans can impact ecosystems within these biomes.

Chapter 16 Human Impact on Ecosystems 470

HMHScience.com
Go online for the full complement of labs.

Chapter 17 Animal Behavior 498

HMHScience.com
Go online for the full complement of labs.

ONLINE BIOLOGY
HMHScience.com

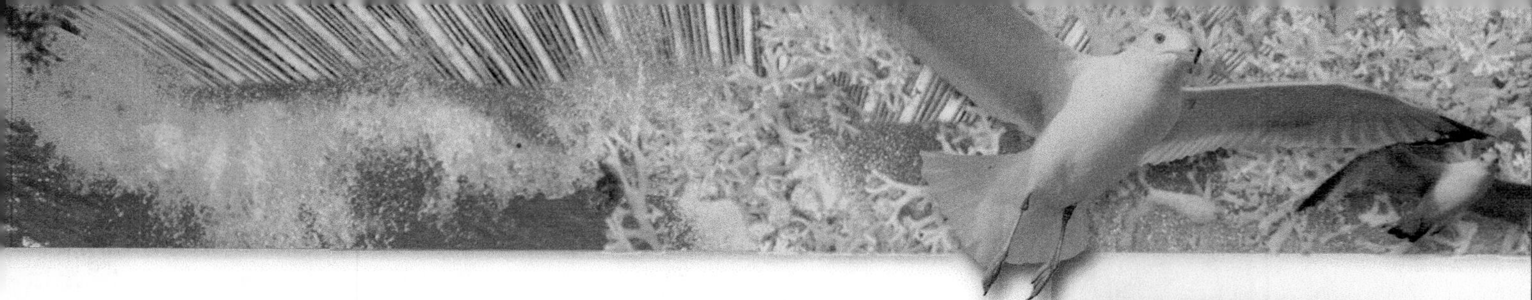

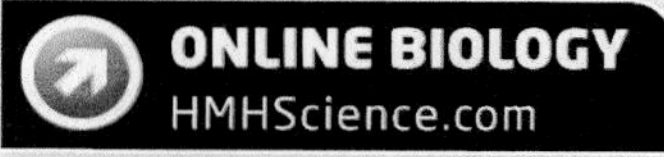

VIRTUAL Lab

Chapter 13 Estimating Population Size

Animated BIOLOGY

Chapter 13 Build a Food Web
Chapter 14 Survive Within a Niche, What Limits Population Growth?
Chapter 15 Lake Turnover, Where Do They Live?
Chapter 16 Human Effects on a Food Web
Chapter 17 Pavlov's Dog, Behavioral Costs and Benefits

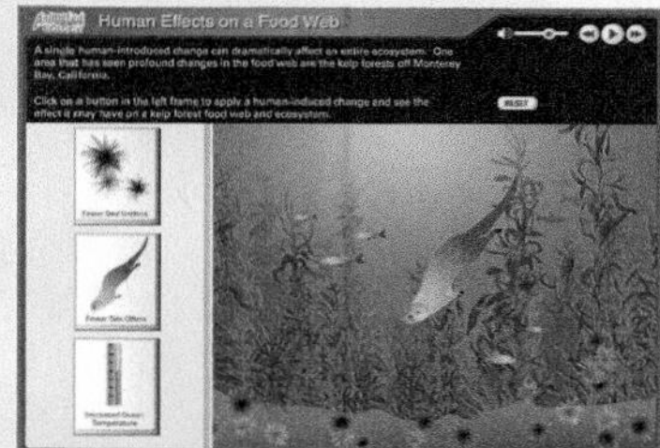

WebQuest

Chapter 13 Keystone Species
Chapter 14 Environmental Stress
Chapter 15 Explore an Ecosystem
Chapter 16 Invasive Species
Chapter 17 Animal Cognition

INTERACTIVE Review

Key Concepts, Vocabulary Games, Concept Maps, Animated Biology, Section Self-Checks

BIOZINE

INTERNET MAGAZINE

Continually updated articles and the latest biology news

Additional labs and a variety of online activities are available in Student Resources at HMHScience.com.

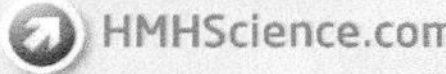

UNIT 6

Diversity of Life

Unit Focus

Unit 6 first introduces the way in which scientists classify living things. Next, it begins the exploration of diversity of living things with viruses and prokaryotes and then protists and fungi.

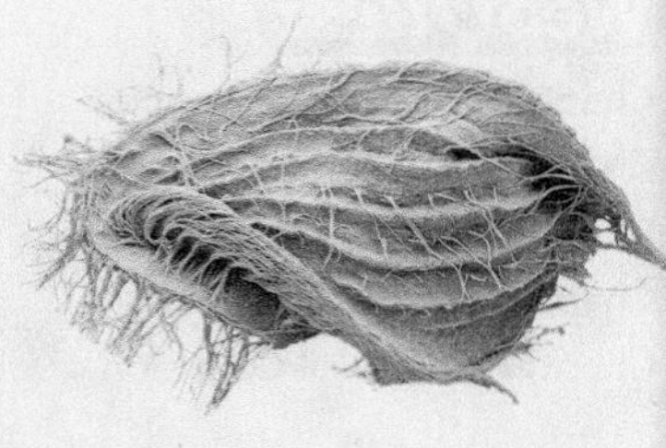

Euplotes, an animal-like protist

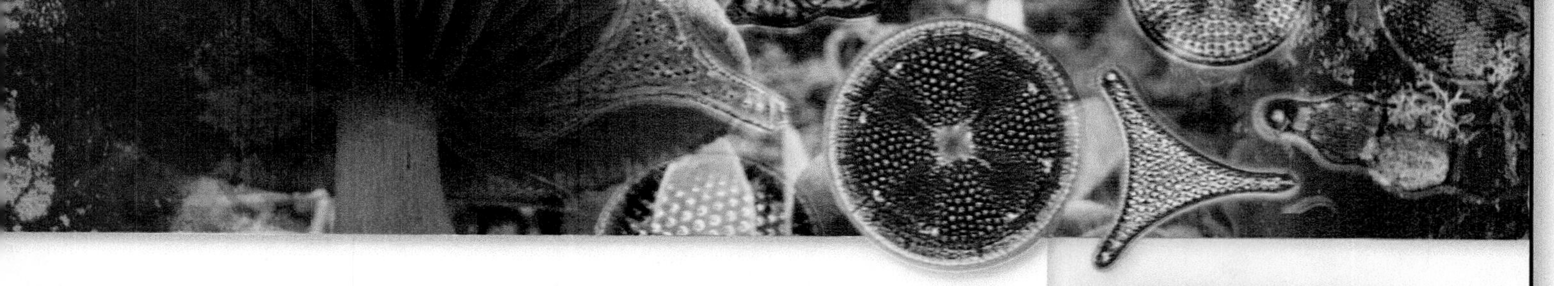

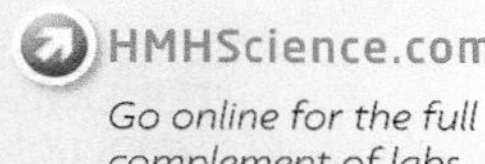

Go online for the full complement of labs.

HMHScience.com
Go online for the full complement of labs.

White oak (*Quercus alba*)

VIRTUAL Lab

Chapter 19 Testing Antibacterial Products

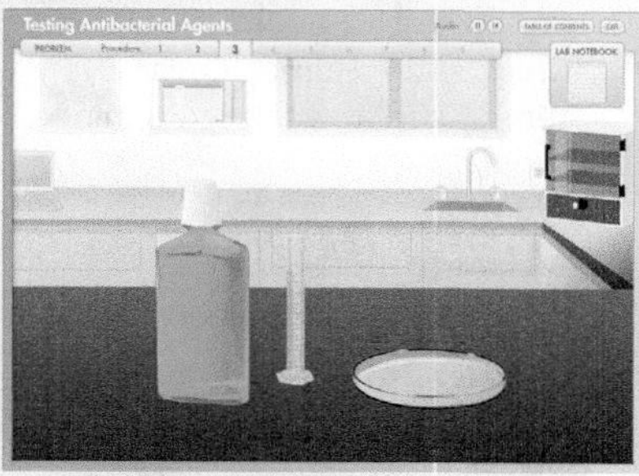

Animated BIOLOGY

Chapter 18 Molecular Clock, Build a Cladogram
Chapter 19 What Would You Prescribe?
Chapter 20 Protist and Fungus Life Cycles
Chapter 21 Plant and Pollinator Matching Game
Chapter 22 Digestive Tract Formation, Shared Body Structures

WebQuest

Chapter 18 Classify a Sea Cucumber
Chapter 19 Antibiotics in Agriculture
Chapter 20 Sickening Protists
Chapter 21 Endangered Plants
Chapter 22 Parasites

INTERACTIVE Review

Key Concepts, Vocabulary Games, Concept Maps, Animated Biology, Section Self-Checks

Additional labs and a variety of online activities are available in Student Resources at HMHScience.com.

Animated BIOLOGY

Chapter 23 Gas Exchange in Gills, Frog Metamorphosis, What Type of Fish Is It?

Chapter 24 Human Organ Systems, Keep an Athlete Running

WebQuest

Chapter 23 Fisheries on the Brink

Chapter 24 Hypothermia

INTERACTIVE Review

Key Concepts, Vocabulary Games, Concept Maps, Animated Biology, Section Self-Checks

Additional labs and a variety of online activities are available in Student Resources at HMHScience.com.

xxii

Data Analysis

Use Smart Grapher to create animated charts and graphs.

The Data Analysis activity in each chapter helps you develop skills you need to analyze data from scientific investigations.

Introducing Biology

Cells

Genetics

Evolution

Ecology

Diversity of Life

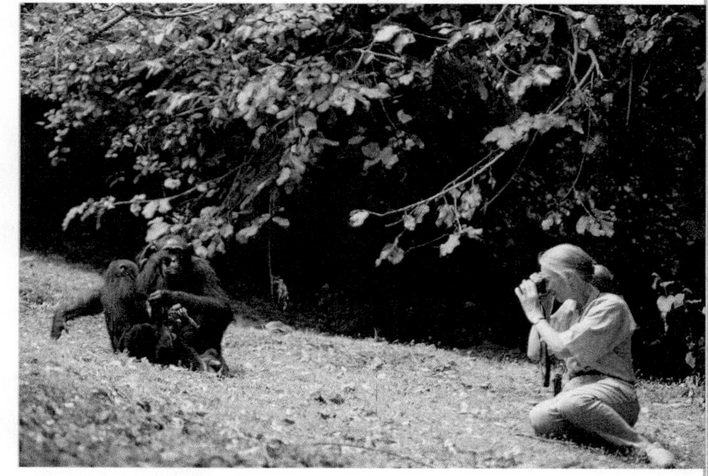

Jane Goodall and chimpanzees

QuickLabs

Explore key concepts and develop basic lab skills using these QuickLabs.

Introducing Biology

Cells

Genetics

Evolution

Ecology

Diversity of Life

STRATEGIES FOR ENGLISH LANGUAGE LEARNERS

Are you learning English? You can learn science and English at the same time. You already know a lot about science from the world around you. You can also learn English from the world around you. Your teacher will help you. Other students will be happy to help. But there are things you can do too.

Below are some ideas that will help you get ready to learn English. Other ideas will help you learn better in class and while you read. There are also some ideas to help you remember and use what you learn.

GET READY TO LEARN

You can do these things before you go to science class.

GET READY TO LEARN STRATEGIES	
Visit Your Classroom and Teacher	Go with other students if you can. Look carefully around the room. What things are there? • Ask your teacher to tell you the names of things you do not know. You can ask, "What is this?" or "Will we use this in class?" or "What does it do?" • Learn how to say and read the names of things you will use to learn science. • Are there signs on the wall? What do they say? If you do not know, ask your teacher or other students, "What does this sign say? What does it mean?" • Remember the words on signs. Signs in many places can have the same words.
Learn Some Science Words	You will learn a lot of new words in your science class. It is easier to learn them if you already know a few science words. • Ask your teacher to say and write some words you need to know. • Ask what the words mean. Then learn the words very well. • Learn how to say and read the words. Learn what they mean.
Ask Your Teacher for Help with Reading	Your teacher can help you read your science book. He or she can help you learn new words that you need to know before you read. • Your teacher might give you a list of the important words or ideas you will read or a list of questions to answer when you read. • He or she might give you a graphic organizer to help you understand what you read. A graphic organizer is a drawing that helps you learn and remember.
Read Before Class	Your teacher tells you what he or she will talk about tomorrow. If part of your book tells about the same thing, read the book today. When you are done reading, you already know some of what the teacher will say. Then it is easier for you to understand when the teacher talks.

GET READY TO LEARN STRATEGIES	
Look at Pictures Before You Read	You need to read some pages in your science book. • What should you do first? Look at the pictures. Use what you already know. • If there are words with the pictures, read the words. Try to figure out what the pictures show. • It will be easier to read the pages if you already know a little bit from looking at the pictures.
Get Ready to Ask Questions	You might have a question about what you read before class. • First, write down your question. If you are worried about how to say the question, practice it. • Bring your question to class. Listen carefully when the teacher talks about the same thing as your question. Maybe the teacher will answer the question. • If you still do not have an answer, raise your hand. Ask the question you wrote and practiced. • Listen carefully to the answer.
Start Taking Notes Before Class	Taking notes means writing something to help you remember what you read or hear. • You do not write all the words you read or hear. Write just a few important words or make drawings. • It can be hard to take notes when you listen. It is easier if you start your notes before class, when you read your book. Write down important words that you read. Write your own words or draw something to help you remember important ideas. Leave lots of space on your paper. • Then, take your notes to class. Use the same paper to take notes when you listen in class. Write more notes in the space you left.
Get Ready to Answer Questions	Science teachers ask a lot of questions. Learn these question words: *what*, *where*, *when*, *who*, *why*, *how much*, *is it*, *will it*. Learn how to answer questions that use each word. • *What:* Tell the name of a thing. • *What will happen, what happened, what happens when we:* Tell how something changes or stays the same. • *Where:* Tell a place. • *When:* Tell a time (you can also say before or after something). • *Who:* Tell a person. Your teacher might ask, "Who can tell me . . .?" That means, "Do you know the answer?" If you do, raise your hand. • *How much:* Tell an amount. • *Why:* Tell what made something happen or explain a reason. • *Is it or Will it:* Answer yes or no. You can also give a reason for your answer.

xxvi

WHILE YOU LEARN

You can do these things in your science class.

WHILE YOU LEARN STRATEGIES	
Use What You Know	When you hear or read about something new, think about what you already know. If a new word sounds like a word you already know, maybe the two words mean close to the same thing. Maybe you already know something about a new idea. Use what you know to help you understand the new word or idea.
Get Help If You Do Not Understand	If you don't understand something, get help. • Ask your teacher or another student. Raise your hand and ask in class or wait until the teacher is done talking. • If you do not understand a word, try to say the word. Then ask, "What does that word mean?" • If you do not know how to do something, you can ask, "How do I do this?" • If you do not understand an idea or picture, tell what you do know. Then ask about the part you do not understand.
Understand Instructions	Instructions tell you how to do something. They are sometimes called directions. You need to follow instructions many times in science class. Sometimes your teacher says the instructions. Sometimes you need to read the instructions. Most instructions have many parts, called steps. Sometimes the teacher or book will use numbers (1, 2, 3 . . .) to tell you when to do each step. Other times, instructions use words. Learn the words that tell you when to do things: • *first* • *then* • *next* • *before* • *after* • *while* • *last* Listen and look for these words in instructions. Use them to help you know when to do things. You can also use these words to give other people instructions. You can use them when you write or tell about something you did.

WHILE YOU LEARN STRATEGIES	
Answer Questions	When your teacher asks you a question, you need to answer. Here are some things that can help you: • Listen carefully to the question. If you do not understand the words, you can ask, "Could you repeat the question?" or "Can you say that more slowly?" • Listen for the question word. It tells you what kind of answer to give. • Look to see if the teacher is pointing at something. The question is probably about that thing. You can talk about that thing in your answer. • Remember what the teacher said before the question. The question might be about what the teacher said. Maybe you can use some of the teacher's words in your answer. • If you do not know an answer, tell the teacher you do not know. You can say, "I don't know" or "I did not understand that very well" or "I don't remember that."
Talk in Groups	In science class, you often work with other students. You need to understand what your group should do. • Read instructions if you have them. You can ask, "Can I have some more time to read?" • If you do not understand the instructions, you can ask, "Do you understand Step 4?" or "Can you help me understand this step?" • Talk about the instructions after you read. You can ask, "Who should . . .?" or "What should we do first?" • Tell what you can do. Ask the other students what they will do. • As you work, you can ask your partner for help. You can say, "Can you hold this?" or "What do we do next?" • Be sure to help your partner. You can say, "Do you need me to pour that?" • If you have an idea, you can say, "I think we should do this" or "What if we do it this way?" or "I have an idea."

REMEMBER AND USE WHAT YOU LEARN

You can do these things to help you learn important science words and ideas. Do them before class, in class, or after class.

REMEMBER AND USE WHAT YOU LEARN STRATEGIES	
Say It Again (and Again and Again)	One way to learn new words is to repeat them, or say them many times. • First, make sure that you can say the word correctly. • Be sure you know what it means too. Ask a friend or your teacher. Have the person tell you if you need to say the word differently or if you do not have the right meaning. • When you can say the word correctly and know what it means, say the word several times. This is more fun with a partner. Take turns saying the word and telling each other the meaning. • You will remember better if you say the meaning in your own words. You will remember even better if you say your own sentence that uses the word. Try to say a different sentence each time you repeat.
Use Flash Cards	Flash cards help you learn new words. • To make flash cards, use some pieces of paper that are all the same size. Get the words you need to learn. • Write one word on a piece of paper. Turn the paper over. Write the meaning of the word. • Use your own words or draw pictures to help you remember. • Write the other words on other pieces of paper. Write the meaning of each word on the back of the paper. To use flash cards, look at a word. Say what you think it means. Check the back of the paper. • If you got the meaning right, do not look at that card again. Do this with all your words. • If you get some wrong, look at them again and again. You can use flash cards alone or with a partner.
Tell Somebody	Ask a friend or a person in your family to help you learn. Have the person ask you a question. If you need to learn some science words, have him or her ask you what the words mean. If you need to remember how something in science works, have the person ask you. Then use your own words to tell what you know from your book or class. Tell the person what the words mean or how something works. Answer all the person's questions. Helping that person understand helps you understand and remember too.

REMEMBER AND USE WHAT YOU LEARN STRATEGIES	
Make a Picture	Sometimes a picture can help you remember better than words can. You can draw pictures when you take notes. Draw your own picture or use a graphic organizer. A graphic organizer is a drawing that helps you learn and remember. There are many different graphic organizers.
	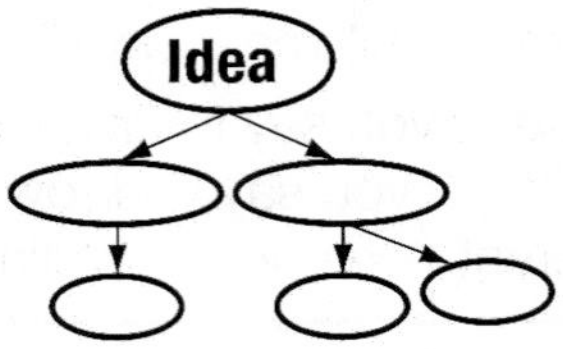 Idea A concept map shows how information is connected. Write one word or idea in the large circle. Write and draw lines to other words to show how they explain or are like the thing in the large circle.
	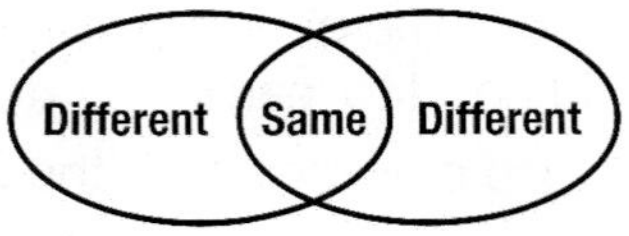 Different Same Different Use a Venn diagram to show how two things are the same and how they are different. Write how they are different in the two circles. Write how they are the same where the two circles come together.
	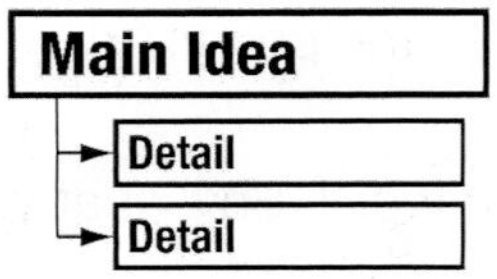 Main Idea Detail Detail Use a drawing like this to show a main idea and some important details to remember about the idea.
Summarize	When you use your own words to tell the most important parts of something, you summarize it. • You can summarize what your teacher says in class. • You can summarize what you read. Write or say in your own words what you learned in class or from your reading. Do not tell everything. Tell only the most important parts. Summarizing can help you understand and remember better.

UNIT 1

Introducing Biology

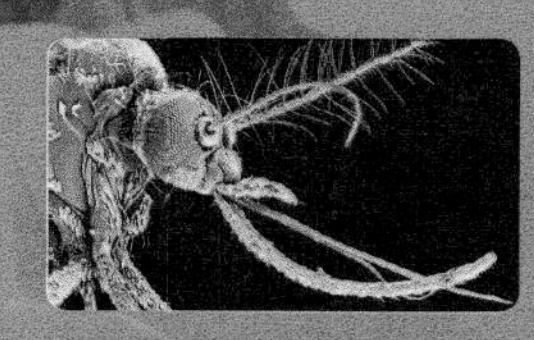

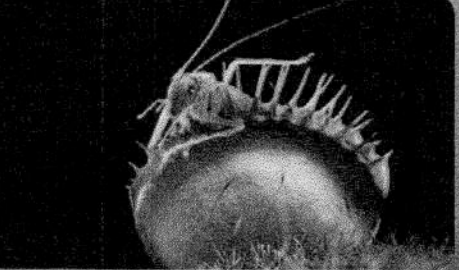

BIOZINE
HMHScience.com

When Knowledge and Ethics Collide

TECHNOLOGY Genetic Testing
CAREER Geneticist

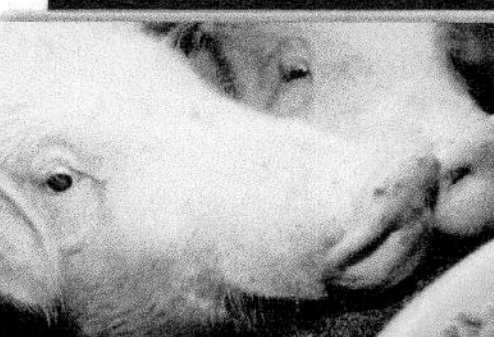

Unit Project

Purpose **Understand how to structure and write a formal laboratory report.**

Overview Students will write a formal laboratory report based on either Louis Pasteur's or Francesco Redi's experiment on spontaneous generation. Students will

- conduct a literature search to find information on the chosen experiment
- identify the problem or question each scientist was trying to answer, and then write the hypothesis, experimental procedure, data and observations, and conclusions for the experiment
- write a laboratory report based on the experiment

Preparation Make a copy of the project description and rubric for each student, and generate a timetable. A description of each experiment is included as an optional student handout.

wety concerns.

Online Student Resources Unit 1 Project

CHAPTER 1

Instruction and Intervention Support

Biology in the 21st Century

① Core Instruction

The **Core Instruction** resources below can be used for all students. Core instruction should be followed by ongoing assessment to determine which students need further help.

Available in both English and Spanish

Available Online

Section	Instruction	PRINT	ONLINE	Labs
1.1	Textbook **The Study of Life**	■	⊙	The Study of Life (Open Inquiry)
	PowerPresentation and Notes 1.1		⊙	
1.2	Textbook **Unifying Themes of Biology**	■	⊙	S.T.E.M. Lab Biomimicry in Engineering
	PowerPresentation and Notes 1.2		⊙	
1.3	Textbook **Scientific Thinking and Processes**	■	⊙	Manipulating Independent Variables Manipulating Plant Growth (Design Your Own) Fruit Preservation (Biotechnology Lab, Design Your Own)
	That's Amazing! Video Inquiry Poison Frogs		⊙	
	Animated Biology Experimental Design		⊙	
	Teaching Visuals Scientific Thinking (Fig. 3.3)		⊙	
	PowerPresentation and Notes 1.3		⊙	
1.4	Textbook **Biologists' Tools and Technology**	■	⊙	Measuring Microscopic Objects **QuickLab** Life Under a Microscope **Video Lab** SI Units **Video Lab** The Counterfeit Drug
	Animated Biology Cells Through Different Microscopes		⊙	
	PowerPresentation and Notes 1.4		⊙	
1.5	Textbook **Biology and Your Future**	■	⊙	Biology in the News Biotechnology and Food Products (Biotechnology Lab, Design Your Own) **Video Lab** Microbe Growth
	PowerPresentation and Notes 1.5		⊙	

Additional online resources available for this chapter include **Interactive Whiteboard Resources.**

GO ONLINE! for all your teacher resources at HMHScience.com

2 Support and Intervention

Support and Intervention resources are useful for students who need targeted help beyond the Core Instruction

Resources	PRINT	ONLINE
Assess and Reteach (TE wrap)	■	⊙
Concept Map		⊙
Interactive Reader	■	⊙
Interactive Review Games		⊙
Section Self-Checks		⊙
Study Guide B		⊙
Virtual Investigation The Scientific Process		⊙
Vocabulary Practice Worksheets		⊙

3 Specialized Support

Students who need more intensive personalized intervention benefit from **Specialized Support** resources.

Resources	PRINT	ONLINE
Chapter Audio Files		⊙
Differentiated Instruction Inclusion, Below Level, and English Learners (TE wrap)	■	⊙
ELL Strategies	■	⊙
Modified Lesson Plans for English Learners		⊙
Reinforcement Worksheets		⊙
Study Guide A		⊙

Extension and Assessment

Enrichment and Challenge

Resources	PRINT	ONLINE
Active Reading Worksheets		⊙
Data Analysis Practice Worksheet		⊙
Differentiated Instruction Pre-AP (TE wrap)	■	⊙
Pre-AP Activity Evolution and Natural Selection, Optics of a Microscope		⊙
Smart Grapher Activity		⊙
The Inside Story and **Take It Further** (TE wrap)	■	⊙
Unit Project		⊙
WebLinks		⊙
WebQuest Bioethics (1.5)		⊙

Assessment

Resources	PRINT	ONLINE
Alternative Assessment		⊙
Chapter Tests A and B		⊙
Diagnostic Test		⊙
ExamView Banks		⊙
Extended Response Test		⊙
Online Assessment System		⊙
Section Quizzes		⊙
Standards-Based Assessment	■	⊙

CHAPTER 1

Chapter Overview

- **Section 1** defines science and introduces biological concepts and the early history of biology.
- **Section 2** discusses the unifying themes of biology.
- **Section 3** details scientific processes including distinguishing scientific theories from scientific hypotheses, and analyzing, evaluating, and communicating scientific data.
- **Section 4** describes types of scientific data and the use and limitations of models to convey data.
- **Section 5** discusses the possible impacts of biology on society and the environment and the limitations of science.

▼ Focus and Motivate

What is biology in the 21st century?

Explain to students that even in the 21st century, biology is still the study of living things. The only things that have changed are the methods used to study living things. **Ask,** How do people benefit from scientific advancements in biology? The knowledge helps people understand the nature of life and prepares them to make informed decisions about health, medicine, genetics, and the environment.

BIOZINE
HMHScience.com

Students can access BioZine at **HMHScience.com** to learn about some of the latest research in the biological sciences.

CHAPTER 1

Biology in the 21st Century

BIG IDEA Biology is the scientific study of all aspects of living things, and it shapes our understanding of our world, from human health to biotechnology to environmental preservation.

ONLINE BIOLOGY HMHScience.com

ONLINE Labs
- Manipulating Independent Variables
- **QuickLab** Life Under a Microscope
- Manipulating Plant Growth
- Biology in the News
- Measuring Microscopic Objects
- Biotechnology and Food Products
- Fruit Preservation
- **Video Lab** SI Units
- **Video Lab** Microbe Growth
- **Video Lab** The Counterfeit Drug
- **Open Inquiry Lab** The Study of Life
- S.T.E.M. Lab Biomimicry in Engineering

Student Activity

Purpose **Have students recognize that the organization of matter and use of energy in living things is distinctly different from the interaction of energy and matter in nonliving things.**

Materials (per team)

Each team will need either pictures or physical samples of various objects, such as the following:

- crystal, rock, or mineral
- plant or insect
- apple, apple seed
- wood or shell

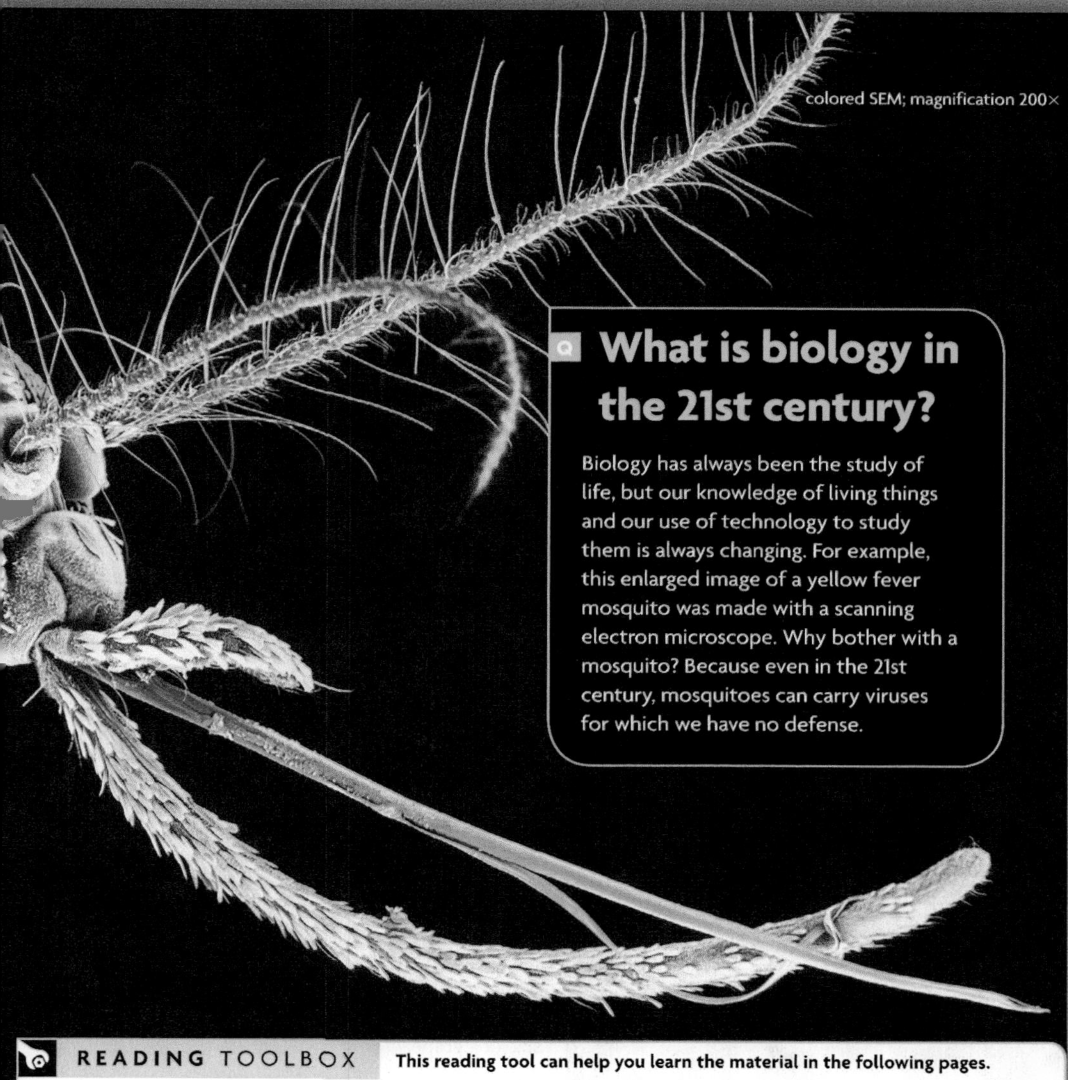

What is biology in the 21st century?

Biology has always been the study of life, but our knowledge of living things and our use of technology to study them is always changing. For example, this enlarged image of a yellow fever mosquito was made with a scanning electron microscope. Why bother with a mosquito? Because even in the 21st century, mosquitoes can carry viruses for which we have no defense.

READING TOOLBOX **This reading tool can help you learn the material in the following pages.**

USING LANGUAGE

Hypothesis or Theory? In everyday language, there is little difference between a hypothesis and a theory. But in science, the meanings of these words are more distinct. A hypothesis is a specific, testable prediction for a limited set of conditions. A theory is a general explanation for a broad range of data. A theory can include hypotheses that have been tested, and it can also be used to generate new hypotheses. The strongest scientific theories explain the broadest range of data and incorporate many well-tested hypotheses.

YOUR TURN

Use what you have learned in this paragraph to answer the following questions.

1. What is the difference between a hypothesis and a theory?
2. Propose a testable hypothesis to explain why the chicken crossed the road.

Introduce Point out that in the specimens provided, matter has been organized with an input of energy. Have students consider which of their specimens are alive or have been. Ask them to identify what is distinctive about the behavior of matter and energy in living things as opposed to nonliving things.

Discuss Have teams summarize their conclusions. Compare a crystal to a shell. **Ask,** How are these objects alike, how are they different? Neither is alive yet both "grow" as energy and matter interact in an organized way; however the living organism that produced the shell is capable of ongoing self-organizing and self-maintaining activity.

Discuss a seed. It is not living in the ordinary sense, as a plant is, but it has the potential to grow into a plant given the proper conditions. **Ask,** Why is reproduction considered a characteristic of life when not all living things reproduce? Life comes from life; reproduction is necessary for the continuity of life.

Activate Prior Knowledge

Point to the title of the chapter. **Ask,** Why would biology of the 21st century be any different from the biology of the 1990s? New information as well as reinterpretation of old information changes the way biologists think about biological processes. Also, technology and techniques improve constantly.

Preview Vocabulary

Greek and Latin Word Origins
Point out to students that the Vocabulary Handbook at the back of the book includes a selection of Greek and Latin word parts common to biology.

Academic Vocabulary Point out the list of Academic Vocabulary in the Vocabulary Handbook. Tell students that, in addition to the science vocabulary highlighted in the text, there are words they need to know when reading, writing, or speaking about any academic subject. Two such words used in this chapter are *unity* and *diversity*. Have students define these antonyms in their own words and think of other words with a similar appearance or meaning.

Related words that appear in the text include *diversity, variety, different, biodiversity, variability, variable, unity,* and *unifying*. Have students look for words they can add to each word family as they read and to note the different contexts in which the words are used.

English Learners It is important to start a conversation with the English learners in your classroom. **Ask**

- What words do you associate with science?
- Are they very different when spoken in your home language?

Answers

1. A hypothesis is a testable prediction. A theory is a general explanation for a broad range of data.
2. Accept any hypothesis that can be tested. *Sample answer:* The chicken crossed the road because there was food on the other side.

SECTION 1.1

▼ Plan and Prepare

Activate Prior Knowledge Students are probably familiar with the term *diversity* as it relates to the variation of physical traits seen in human beings. **Ask,** What do you think a biologist means by the word *biodiversity?* Students will probably mention all the different forms of life on Earth. Help students understand that diversity can exist across a species, which offers the opportunity for adaptation. It also exists as species diversity across an ecosystem.

▼ Teach

TEACH FROM VISUALS

FIGURE 1.1 Some honeypot ants in a colony gorge themselves with food, hang from the ceiling of their nest, and regurgitate food for the worker ants. **Ask,** How do honeypot ants survive in a hostile environment? Some of the ants store food and water for the rest of the colony.

1.1 The Study of Life

KEY CONCEPT **Biologists study life in all its forms.**

MAIN IDEAS
- Earth is home to an incredible diversity of life.
- Biology is the scientific study of all forms of life.
- Humans have studied living things throughout history.

VOCABULARY
biosphere
biodiversity
species
biology
science

Connect to Your World

It's a warm, summer evening. Maybe you're laughing and joking while waiting to eat at a family barbecue. As you sit down for dinner, mosquitoes flying around have the same idea. But their dinner is you, not the barbecue. Probably the most attention that you pay to mosquitoes is when you take careful aim before smacking them. Biologists have a somewhat different view of mosquitoes, unless of course they are the ones being bitten. But from a less emotional perspective, a biologist can see a mosquito as just one example of the great diversity of life found on Earth.

MAIN IDEA

Earth is home to an incredible diversity of life.

In Yellowstone National Park, there are pools of hot water as acidic as vinegar. It might be difficult to believe, but those pools are also full of life. Life is found in the darkness of the deepest ocean floors and in thousands-of-years-old ice in Antarctica. Not only are living things found just about anywhere on Earth, but they also come in a huge variety of shapes and sizes. Plants, for example, include tiny mosses and giant redwood trees on which moss can grow. There are massive animals such as the blue whale, which is the largest animal living on Earth. There are tiny animals such as the honeypot ant in **FIGURE 1.1**, which can store so much food for other ants that it swells to the size of a grape.

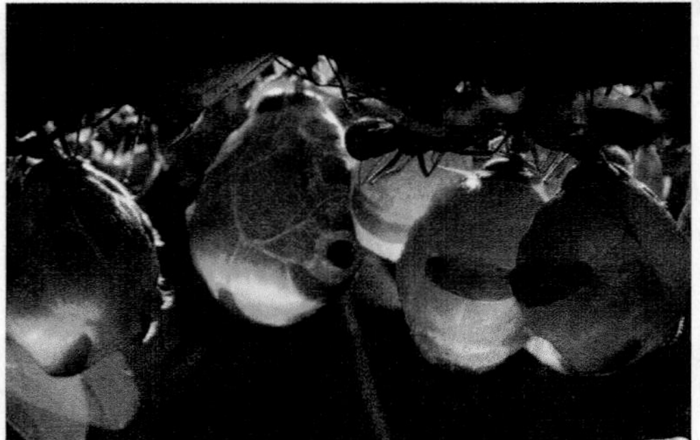

FIGURE 1.1 Honeypot ants live in deserts where food and water are scarce. Some of the ants in the colony act as storage tanks for other ants in the colony.

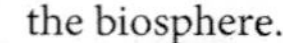

The Biosphere

All living things and all the places they are found on Earth make up the **biosphere.** Every part of the biosphere is connected, however distantly, with every other part of the biosphere. The biosphere includes land environments such as deserts, grasslands, and different types of forests. The biosphere also includes saltwater and freshwater environments, as well as portions of the atmosphere. And different types of plants, animals, and other living things are found in different areas of the biosphere. Even the inside of your nose, which is home to bacteria and fungi, is a part of the biosphere.

Differentiated Instruction

ENGLISH LEARNERS

Have students write definitions of the vocabulary terms in their notebooks in their home language and then in English. Refer them to the *Multilanguage Glossary* to check their work and, if necessary, revise their definitions. The *Multilanguage Glossary* includes all key terms in the text and their definitions in English, as well as in Spanish, Chinese, Vietnamese, Khmer, Laotian, Arabic, Haitian Creole, Russian, and Portuguese.

BELOW LEVEL

Have students survey their textbooks by completing the following tasks:

- Read the unit and chapter titles in the Contents and note how chapters are organized into units.
- Turn to several chapters and note how the subheadings are related to the main ideas listed under the Key Concepts.
- Locate a list of vocabulary words, and then find each of them within the chapter.

Teacher Toolkit, Section C, Textbook Survey

Biodiversity

The variety of organisms in a given area is called biological diversity, or **biodiversity.** Biodiversity generally increases from Earth's poles to the equator. More living things are able to survive in consistently warm temperatures than in areas that have large temperature changes during the year. Because more living things, especially plants, can survive in warm areas, those areas provide a larger, more consistent food supply for many different species.

VISUAL VOCAB

Across the **biosphere**, the variety of life is called **biodiversity.**

Biodiversity is greater closer to the equator.

biosphere = everywhere life exists

Smart Grapher HMHScience.com
GO ONLINE
Biodiversity

There are several different ways the term *species* can be defined. One definition of **species** is a group of organisms that are closely related and can produce fertile offspring. About 2 million different living species have been identified, but biologists estimate that tens of millions of species remain to be discovered. Over half of the known species are insects, but no one knows how many insect species actually exist.

Every year, biologists discover more than 10,000 new species. In contrast, some scientists estimate that over 50,000 species die out, or become extinct, every year. Occasionally, however, a species thought to be extinct is found again. For example, the ivory-billed woodpecker was thought to have become extinct in 1944, but a team of scientists reported seeing it in Arkansas in 2004.

READING TOOLBOX

TAKING NOTES

Use a two-column chart to help you summarize vocabulary terms and concepts.

term or concept	meaning

A Apply **Describe biodiversity in terms of species.**

MAIN IDEA

Biology is the scientific study of all forms of life.

The diverse organisms that live on Earth relate and interact with other organisms and their environments. **FIGURE 1.2** shows a bee collecting pollen from a flower, an interaction that benefits both the bee and the plant. When a bee collects pollen to use as food, the pollen sticks to the bee's body. Then, as the bee flies from plant to plant, the pollen from one plant is left behind on other plants. This interaction pollinates the plants and allows them to reproduce. **Biology**, or life science, is the scientific study of living things and their interactions with their environment.

The study of living things sheds new light on our understanding of humans and our world. For example, until chimpanzees were observed to use sticks and other tools to hunt insects and other organisms, high intelligence and the ability to make and use tools were considered strictly human characteristics. **Science** is the knowledge obtained by observing natural events and conditions in order to discover facts and formulate laws or principles that can be verified or tested. People who contribute to science come from all backgrounds and different fields of interest. Biology is one of three basic areas of science: life science, earth science, and physical science.

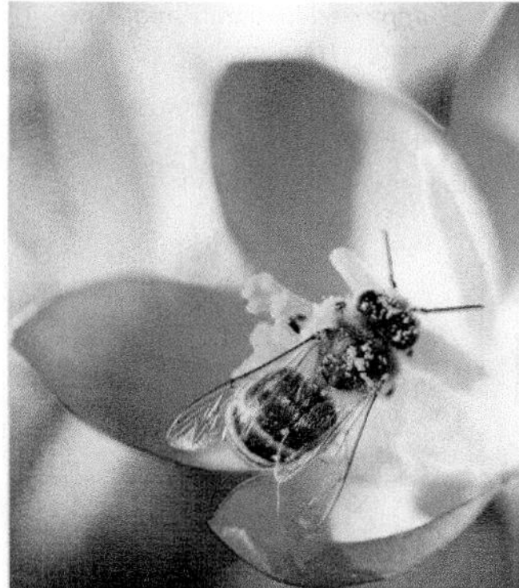

FIGURE 1.2 Life science is the study of the interaction of organisms, such as this bee and the flowering plant from which it collects pollen.

PRE-AP*

Suggest that students take notes by using the Cornell note-taking method. Have them mark a heavy line about two inches from the left side of their paper, and another across the bottom about two inches from the edge. They should take abbreviated notes in outline form in the large square on the right, and note key points in the column on the left.

As soon as after class as possible, students should use the bottom area to summarize in their own words the content of the page of notes.

*Pre-AP is a registered trademark of the College Board, which was not involved in the production of and does not endorse this product.

Teacher Toolkit, Section C, Cornell Notes

ONLINE Biology
HMHScience.com

Students can do an analysis of biodiversity of marine organisms at **HMHScience.com**.

Take It Further

The moment of extinction occurs when the last individual of a species dies. Considering the history of life on Earth, it is common for a species to go extinct within 10 million years of its first appearance, although some species have continued to exist for hundreds of millions of years. In some cases, new species, or **daughter species,** evolve from a parent species. These organisms would have most of the parent species' genetic information. Extinction of a parent species when daughter species or subspecies still exist is called **pseudo-extinction.** For example, biologists categorize dinosaurs as *pseudoextinct* because some of their descendants, birds, survive today. Students will learn about patterns of extinction in the chapter The History of Life.

Integrating Ecology

Bees, moths, and other insects are important for pollinating both wild plants and crops. However, many **bee populations** are declining, and at least one bee species has gone extinct in recent years. Studies have shown that many factors, such as habitat availability, disease, and pesticide use, contribute to bee decline. Ecologists are concerned that plant species that depend on pollination from bees and other pollinators may decline in response to pollinator decline.

Answers

A **Apply** Biodiversity is the number of different species in a given area, from a single community to Earth in its entirety.

▼ Teach *continued*

Science Trivia

- The ancient Egyptian process to embalm and wrap a body in preparation for burial took 70 days.
- Preparation for mummification involved removing all organs except the heart from the body. The body was then stuffed and covered with natron, a mixture of salts that dried out the body.
- During the 21st to the 25th dynasties, the Egyptians stored body organs in special vessels called canopic jars, which were placed in the tomb with the body.

Take It Further

Though the history of biology and other sciences in the ancient world is often focused on Greece and other European civilizations, other civilizations made significant contributions, too. Many ancient civilizations developed medical processes such as herbal remedies used by the Chinese and Ayurvedic medicine used by ancient Indians. Persian physician Abu 'Ali al-Husayn ibn 'Abd Allah ibn Sina, who lived from 980 to 1037, wrote a medical text that was translated and used throughout many cultures. His name was Latinized to Avicenna on some translated texts.

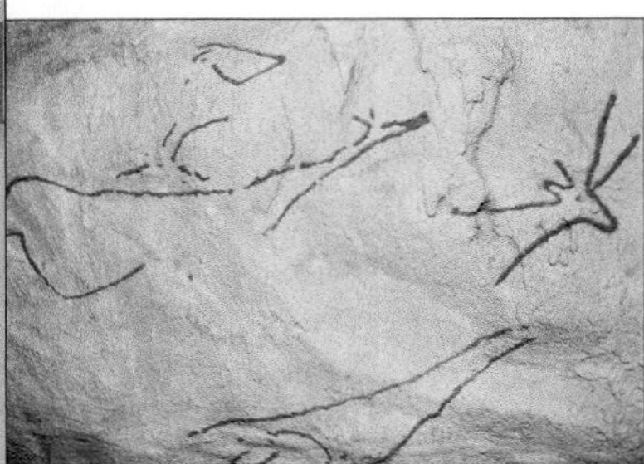

FIGURE 1.3 Prehistoric cave paintings indicate that early humans observed and studied the living things around them.

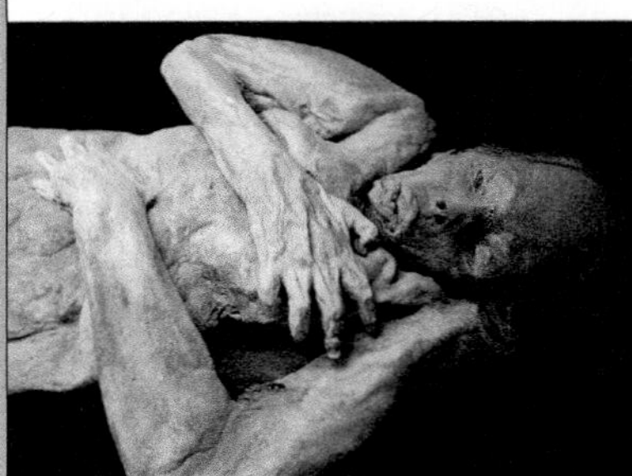

FIGURE 1.4 Mummification, a process of preserving bodies, requires precise understanding of processes and materials. Ancient Egyptian civilizations studied and improved mummification over many centuries.

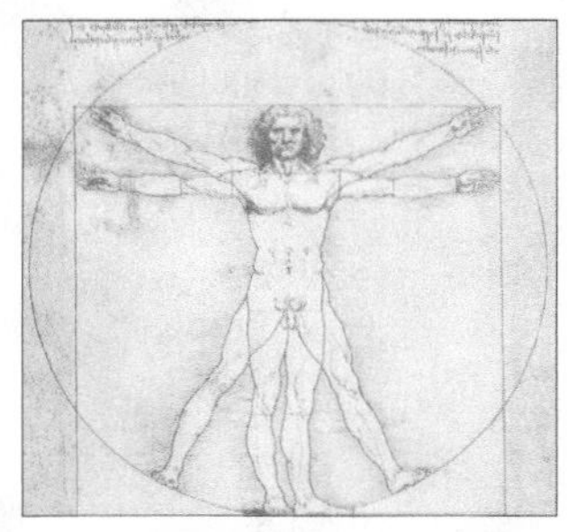

FIGURE 1.5 Leonardo da Vinci's study of many areas of science, including anatomy, were part of a renaissance of scientific learning in Europe. Leonardo's drawing *Vitruvian Man* shows a relationship of anatomy and geometry.

MAIN IDEA

Humans have studied living things throughout history.

The study of living things began long before the invention of computers, microscopes, or other scientific tools and techniques. Early records, such as the prehistoric cave painting in **FIGURE 1.3**, show that prehistoric people were interested in the animals they observed and used as food. Other art, carvings, and papyri show how early humans began to understand basic biological concepts such as anatomy, medicinal use of herbs, and embalming. Evidence shows that some human populations began domesticating animals as early as 8500 BCE. Even without knowing it, these early humans were using genetics to select for characteristics that were most valuable in the organism, such as high milk production and taste or high yield in crops.

Science in Ancient Civilizations

Many ancient civilizations studied biology. Just as we do now, they learned about natural processes and used this knowledge to address the needs of society. Asian civilizations used herbal medicines. South American civilizations developed agricultural techniques, such as crop domestication and irrigation. Ancient Egyptian civilizations practiced mummification of royalty, nobility, and the wealthy, as shown in **FIGURE 1.4.**

Greek civilization made significant contributions to the development of life science. They are credited with originating the basic principles of modern science. Around 400 BCE, Greek physician Hippocrates established a school of medicine. He taught that all living bodies were made up of four humours or fluids: blood, black bile, phlegm, and yellow bile. Imbalances in the four humours were thought to cause most illnesses.

The first classification system for living organisms is attributed to the Greek philosopher Aristotle and dates back to 330 BCE. Aristotle's system divided animals up into those with red blood, such as wolves and rabbits, and those without blood, such as mollusks and arthropods. Aristotle is also credited with developing a system of logic and a dependence on empirical evidence in science.

The Scientific Revolution

Scientists of any era are limited by the demands and rules of society. The ancient Greek and Roman societies are known for their milestones in science and philosophy, but changes in politics and governance also influenced the progress of science. The Middle Ages of European history (500s-1450s CE) are marked by little scientific development, though scientific knowledge continued to grow in other parts of the world, such as India and China.

Fifteenth century European societies gave rise to a renewal of interest in art and science and the beginning of the Scientific Revolution (1450s–1700). Early in this time period, Italian artist and scientist Leonardo da Vinci began close studies of the anatomy of both animals and humans. The drawing *Vitruvian Man,* shown in **FIGURE 1.5**, gives evidence of Leonardo's detailed

Differentiated Instruction

PRE-AP

Tell students that the study of life science has been noted throughout all of history. Ask students to select a 200–500 year range of time and conduct research to find key discoveries or individuals in that range. Students should create a timeline of the period to show important events and people.

Teacher Toolkit, Section C, Timeline

ENGLISH LEARNERS

Help students set up a table to categorize the content of this section. Suggest a table with five columns. Column 1 can include the name of scientists, Column 2 can give information on where the scientist came from, Column 3 can include dates for their writing or research, Column 4 can include their research or findings, and Column 5 can include other notes of interest. Tell students that the text may not contain information to fill all columns.

Teacher Toolkit, Section C, Content Frame

understanding of anatomy and movement. His legacy includes the introduction of systematic observation and documentation methods that are still in use today. Andreas Vesalius, a Flemish physician, published a book of anatomy in the mid-1500s. Vesalius challenged anatomical concepts made from limited observations by the ancient Greeks. Vesalius practiced dissection of corpses, so his descriptions of anatomy were based on repeated explorations of the insides of bodies, whereas the Greeks based their descriptions only on external observation and philosophy.

Scientific understanding is always limited by available technology. Many of the advances in biology and other areas of science that occurred during the Scientific Revolution were made possible by new technologies. For example, the invention of the microscope around the start of the 1600s allowed for the discovery of cells and microorganisms.

Science from the Industrial Revolution to Today

The Industrial Revolution, which began in the last half of the 18th century, brought about significant advances in science. Travel and communication allowed for the exchange of ideas, universities developed robust science programs, and technology enabled scientists to explore the natural world with greater accuracy and precision. Such explorations led to new knowledge and built upon or replaced old knowledge.

For example, the development of cell theory replaced the notion of spontaneous generation, a belief that some life forms arose from nonliving matter. Experiments by Louis Pasteur in 1859, using broth in the equipment shown in **FIGURE 1.6**, demonstrated that living things did not come from nonliving matter but were the result of reproduction by other living things. As a result of this and other studies, three German scientists, Theodor Schwann, Matthias Schleiden, and Rudolph Virchow, proposed a theory summarizing the basic properties of living organisms. These basic concepts are collectively known as the cell theory. You will read more about cell theory in the chapter Cell Structure and Function. Other important advances in biology are also discussed throughout the book.

FIGURE 1.6 The development of technology, tools, and equipment such as the swan-neck flasks used by Louis Pasteur, enable new scientific knowledge.

Ⓐ Apply **Why has scientific knowledge changed throughout history?**

1.1 Formative Assessment

SELF-CHECK Online HMHScience.com GO ONLINE

REVIEWING ➊ MAIN IDEAS

1. How are **species** related to the concept of **biodiversity**?
2. How does technology affect the advancement of **science?**
3. What societal needs were addressed by science in the ancient world?

CRITICAL THINKING

4. **Support** Explain how the history of biology demonstrates that new knowledge can change established knowledge.
5. **Synthesize** How does biodiversity depend on a species' ability to reproduce?

CONNECT TO HUMAN BIOLOGY

6. The development of the microscope requires an understanding of physics concepts such as light and reflection. How else might an understanding of physics impact biology?

1.1 FORMATIVE ASSESSMENT

1. Biodiversity is the variety and number of species in a given area.
2. Technology enables scientists to observe things in new or better ways. As technology improves, more discoveries are possible.
3. *Sample answer:* health concerns, food production, and understanding nature and human anatomy
4. The history of biology shows that new techniques of study or new technology enable discoveries that may result in established knowledge being altered or discarded altogether.
5. Without the ability to reproduce, a species would become extinct, which would lead to a decrease in biodiversity.
6. *Sample answer:* Physics includes sound, energy, mechanics, and light. An understanding of sound can explain body structures, such as ears or things that make noise. Understanding energy helps in understanding food web relationships, and mechanics can explain the relationships of structure and function in body systems.

The Inside Story

Italian **Leonardo da Vinci,** born in 1452, was an artist, inventor, and scientist. Leonardo's famous artistic works include the paintings *The Last Supper* and *Mona Lisa.* Leonardo studied anatomy and mechanics, and he built on the works of earlier thinkers. The famous sketch *Vitruvian Man,* shown in **Figure 1.5,** is Leonardo's revision of earlier models of proportions within human anatomy done first by Roman architect Vitruvius.

Vocabulary

Word Origins Explain that the word *pasteurization* comes from the last name of scientist **Louis Pasteur.** Pasteurization is the heating of a substance to a temperature below its boiling point, but high enough and for a long enough time period to kill or reduce disease and spoilage-causing microorganisms. Pasteur is credited with the discovery of this technique in wine. Modern-day pasteurization is used in many food products, but it is particularly important for dairy products, such as milk and cheeses. Other food products that are pasteurized include fruit juices, wine, and syrups.

Answers

Ⓐ **Apply** Scientific knowledge has changed as scientific exploration, often aided by improved technology, has led to new discoveries that build upon or replace old knowledge.

Assess and Reteach ▼

Assess Use the Section Self-Check or Section Quiz, both available at **HMHScience.com.**

Reteach Have pairs of students take turns quizzing each other on the main ideas and terms in this section. Each student should write a question about each main idea and term. Students should take turns asking each other questions until they have covered all the main ideas and terms.

SECTION 1.2

▼ Plan and Prepare

Activate Prior Knowledge Write on the board *How I Spent My Summer Vacation.* **Ask**

- If each person in the class wrote a paper on this subject, would all the papers be the same? no
- What are some of the things you did during your summer vacation? List responses under the title.
- How are the activities related to the title? The title is a theme and is the unifying element in a broad array of vacation activities.

Point out that similar relationships exist in biology.

▼ Teach

TEACH FROM VISUALS

FIGURE 2.1 Point out that the leaf hairs are made up of several specialized epidermal cells. Tell students that a multicellular organism's specialized cells develop through the processes of cell determination and differentiation, which are covered in the chapter Reproduction and Development.

1.2 Unifying Themes of Biology

KEY CONCEPT Unifying themes connect concepts from many fields of biology.

MAIN IDEAS

- All organisms share certain characteristics.
- All levels of life have systems of related parts.
- Structure and function are related in biology.
- Organisms must maintain homeostasis to survive in diverse environments.
- Evolution explains the unity and diversity of life.

VOCABULARY

organism
cell
metabolism
DNA
system
ecosystem
homeostasis
evolution
adaptation

Connect to Your World

What do you think about when you hear the term *theme*? Maybe you think about the music at the start of your favorite TV show or the colors and organization of a computer desktop. In both cases, that theme shows up over and over again. In biology, you will see something similar. That is, some concepts come up time after time, even in topics that might seem to be completely unrelated. Understanding these themes, or concepts, can help you to connect the different areas of biology.

MAIN IDEA

All organisms share certain characteristics.

An **organism** is any individual living thing. All organisms on Earth share certain characteristics, but an actual definition of life is not simple. Why? The categories of living and nonliving are constructed by humans, and they are not perfect. For example, viruses fall into a middle range between living and nonliving. They show some, but not all, of the characteristics of living things.

Cells All organisms are made up of one or more cells. A **cell** is the basic unit of life. In fact, microscopic, single-celled organisms are the most common forms of life on Earth. A single-celled, or unicellular, organism carries out all of the functions of life, just as you do. Larger organisms that you see every day are made of many cells and are called multicellular organisms. Different types of cells in a multicellular organism have specialized functions, as shown in **FIGURE 2.1**. Your muscle cells contract and relax, your stomach cells secrete digestive juices, and your brain cells interpret sensory information. Together, specialized cells make you a complete organism.

FIGURE 2.1 Cells can work together in specialized structures, such as these leaf hairs that protect a leaf from insects. (LM; magnification 700×)

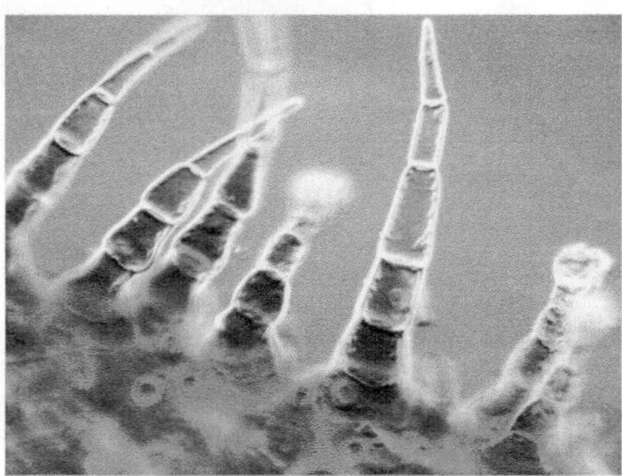

Need for energy All organisms need a source of energy to carry out life processes. Energy is the ability to cause a change or to do work. All living things, from bacteria to ferrets to ferns, use chemical energy. Some organisms use chemicals from their environment to make their own source of chemical energy. Some organisms, such as plants,

Differentiated Instruction

ENGLISH LEARNERS

Figurative language, such as "keep your eye on the ball" or "give me a hand" may be perplexing to students. Scan the text before students begin to read so you can anticipate confusion. Engage students in a discussion about the literal and figurative meanings of certain expressions. For example, **Section 2** uses "information" and "message" to describe electrochemical functions of nerve cells. Of course, the messages are not written or spoken, but rather are electrical impulses.

One way to reinforce figurative meanings is to respond visibly to such phrases. For example, respond to "give me a hand" by applauding or by offering a helping hand to demonstrate the meaning in context. Tell students they can often find context clues that will help them understand figurative meanings, such as *like, as,* and *as if,* in preceding or subsequent phrases. Make sure students can differentiate between figurative language and analogies.

Teacher Toolkit, Section D, Context Clues

algae, and some bacteria, absorb energy from sunlight and store some of it in chemicals that can be used later as a source of energy. Animals obtain energy by eating other organisms. In all organisms, energy is important for **metabolism,** or all of the chemical processes that build up or break down materials.

Response to environment All organisms must react to their environment to survive. Light, temperature, and touch are just a few of the physical factors, called stimuli, to which organisms must respond. Think about how you respond to light when you leave a dimly lit room and go into bright sunlight. One of your body's responses is to contract the pupils of your eyes. Your behavior might also change. You might put on sunglasses or raise your hand to shade your eyes. Other organisms also respond to changes in light. For example, plants grow toward light. Some fungi need light to form the structures that you know as mushrooms.

Reproduction and development Members of a species must have the ability to produce new individuals, or reproduce. When organisms reproduce, they pass their genetic material to their offspring. In all organisms, the genetic material that contains the information that determines inherited characteristics is a molecule called deoxyribonucleic acid (dee-AHK-see-RY-boh-noo-KLEE-ihk), or **DNA.**

Single-celled organisms can reproduce when one cell divides into two cells. Both new cells have genetic information that is identical to the original cell. Many multicellular organisms, such as the gold-specs jawfish in **FIGURE 2.2**, reproduce by combining the genetic information from two parents. In both cases, the instructions for growth and development of organisms, from bacteria to people, are carried by the same chemicals—DNA and ribonucleic acid (RNA). The process of development allows organisms to mature and gain the ability to reproduce.

FIGURE 2.2 Reproductive strategies differ among species. The male gold-specs jawfish protects unhatched eggs by holding them in his mouth.

A Summarize **What characteristics are shared by all living things?**

MAIN IDEA

All levels of life have systems of related parts.

Think about the separate parts of a car—tires, engine, seats, and so on. Even if you have a complete set of car parts, you might not have a functioning car. Only when all of the parts that make up a car are put together in the correct way do you have a working car. A car is a system. A **system** is an organized group of related parts that interact to form a whole. Like any other system, a car's characteristics come from the arrangement and interaction of its parts.

Systems exist on all scales in biology, from molecules that cannot be seen, to cells that can be seen only with a microscope, to the biosphere. In just one heart muscle cell, for example, chemicals and processes interact in a precise way so that the cell has energy to do its work. Moving up a level, heart muscle, valves, arteries, and veins form a system in your body—the circulatory system.

Take It Further

Tell students that the behavior of the male jaw fish shown in **FIGURE 2.2** is an example of **paternal mouth brooding.** Males may "churn" eggs by spitting them out, and then taking them back in quickly. This is done to remove debris as well as to rotate and aerate the eggs so the embryos develop properly. Behaviors such as this are referred to as **reproductive strategies,** even though the behavior may be instinctive and not learned. Students will learn more about these types of behavior in the chapter Animal Behavior.

Answers

A **Summarize** All living things are made of one or more cells, need energy, respond to the environment, and have the ability to reproduce.

PRE-AP

Have students write for ten minutes relating any two of the unifying themes of biology.

Teacher Toolkit, Section C, Quick-Write

▼ Teach *continued*

Vocabulary

Academic Vocabulary The term **system** is commonly used in science and means a group of interacting, interrelated, or interdependent elements forming a complex whole. Examples: *ecosystem, digestive system, open system, closed system, solar system, weather system.*

Integrating Systems Biology

All biologists study living systems at some level. This includes studying organisms as part of an ecosystem; studying cells, tissues, and organs as part of an organism; and studying molecules as part of a cell. Relatively new to the field of biology is **systems biology,** which extends the continuum to include the analysis of gene regulation and the effects of proteins in defining what an organism is and how it develops and functions.

A systems biologist is interested in the metabolic network and pathways that sustain life—somewhat like the underlying circuitry in a computer chip. This approach to the study of biology has been made possible by scientific advancements in molecular biology, computer technology, and genome sequencing. One obvious application of systems biology is using computer simulations of cellular models to test new drugs for effectiveness and possible side effects.

TEACH FROM VISUALS

FIGURE 2.3 Explain that this is a symbiotic relationship called mutualism, which students will learn about in the chapter Interactions in Ecosystems. Have students survey this section's Main Idea headings, which summarize some of the basic principles of biology. **Ask,** Which of these themes are related to the interaction of the moray eel and the cleaner shrimp? systems, structure and function, homeostasis, evolution

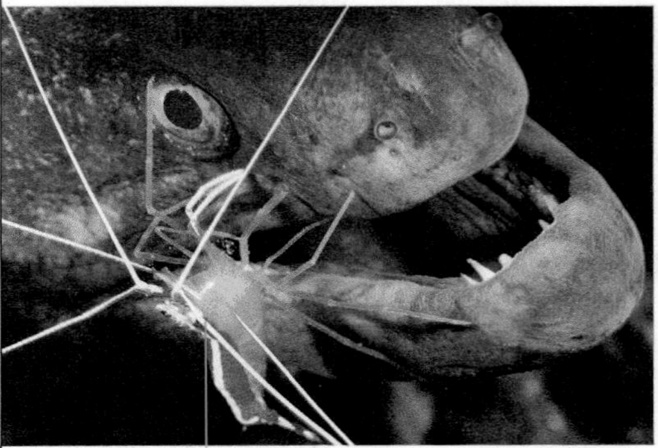

FIGURE 2.3 The moray eel and the cleaner shrimp are parts of a system in which both organisms benefit. The shrimp cleans the eel's mouth and gets food and protection in return.

Two organisms that interact can also be a system, as you can see in **FIGURE 2.3.** On a larger scale, you are a part of a biological system—an ecosystem—that has living and nonliving parts. An **ecosystem** is a community of organisms and their physical environment. When you hear the term *ecosystem,* you might think about a large region, such as a desert, a coral reef, or a forest. But an ecosystem can also be a very small area, such as an individual tree.

Often, different biologists study different systems. For example, a person studying DNA might focus on very specific chemical interactions that take place in a cell. A person studying behavior in birds might focus on predator–prey relationships in an ecosystem. However, more and more biologists are working across different system levels. For example, some scientists study how chemicals in the brain affect social interactions.

MAIN IDEA

Structure and function are related in biology.

Think about a car again. In a car, different parts have different structures. The structure of a car part gives the part a specific function. For example, a tire's function is directly related to its structure. No other part of the car can perform that function. Structure and function are also related in living things. What something does in an organism is directly related to its shape or form. For example, when you eat, you probably bite into food with your sharp front teeth. Then you probably chew it mostly with your grinding molars. All of your teeth help you eat, but different types of teeth have different functions.

Structure and function are related at the level of chemicals in cells. For example, membrane channels and enzymes are both proteins, but they have very different structures and functions. A channel is a protein molecule that extends through the membrane, or outer layer, of a cell. It has a structure like a tube that allows specific chemicals to pass into and out of a cell. Enzymes are protein molecules that make chemical processes possible in living things. These proteins have shapes that allow them to attach to only certain chemicals and then cause the chemicals to react with each other.

FIGURE 2.4 The snout beetle (below) has specialized prongs and pads on its tarsi (right) that allow it to easily walk on both smooth and rough surfaces. (colored SEMs; magnifications: beetle 20×; tarsus 100×)

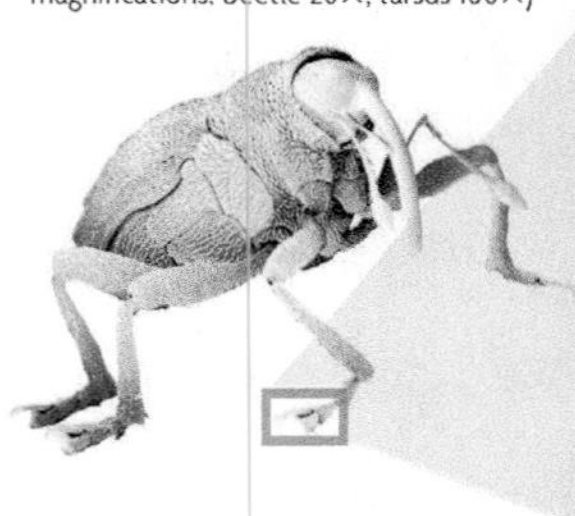

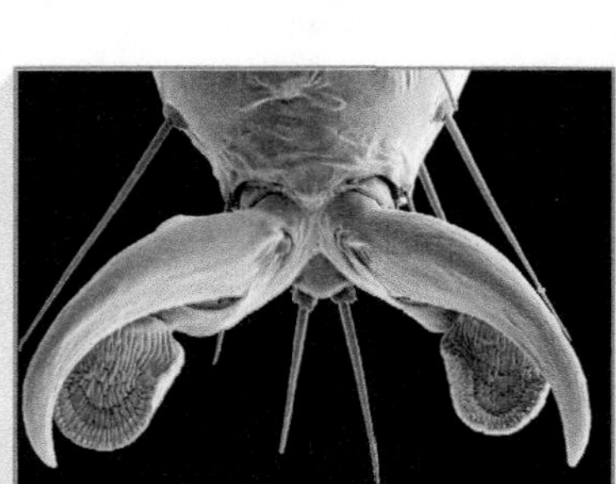

Different types of cells also have different functions that depend on their specialized structures. For example, cells in your brain process information. They have many branches that receive information from other cells. They also have long extensions that allow them to send messages to other cells. Red blood cells are very different. They are much smaller, disk shaped, and are specialized to carry oxygen. Their structure allows

Differentiated Instruction

ENGLISH LEARNERS

Remember to enunciate clearly when presenting material to students. Speak naturally, but separate words so they can be clearly understood. Because words can seem to blend together when spoken, students need plenty of cues from your mouth positions and facial expressions. To assess whether you are getting your message across, do a quick check of comprehension. Ask some simple questions as you teach, and have students write a quick response that they can hold up for you to see.

Teacher Toolkit, Section C, Slates

BELOW LEVEL

On these student pages, a car tire is given as an example of the relationship between structure and function, and then an analogy is made between the cruise control mechanism in a car and homeostasis in an animal. Point out the structure of an analogy: A is to B as C is to D. Explain that analogies are word/concept relationships. Have students form their own analogies as they read through the section.

Teacher Toolkit, Section D, Analogies

them to fit through even the smallest blood vessels to deliver oxygen throughout your body. Of course, a brain cell cannot take the place of a red blood cell.

Structure and function are also related on the level of the organism. For example, your foot structure allows you to walk easily on rough, fairly level surfaces. Walking on a surface such as ice is more difficult, and walking up a wall is impossible for you. The beetle in **FIGURE 2.4** is different. Its tarsi, or feet, have sharp prongs that can grip smooth or vertical surfaces, as well as soft pads for walking on rough surfaces. The beetle's tarsus has a different structure and function than your foot has, but both are specialized for walking.

A Infer **Do you think heart muscle has the same structure as arm muscle? Explain.**

MAIN IDEA

Organisms must maintain homeostasis to survive in diverse environments.

Temperature and other environmental conditions are always changing, but the conditions inside organisms usually stay quite stable. How does the polar bear in **FIGURE 2.5** live in the Arctic? How can people be outside when the temperature is below freezing, but still have a stable body temperature around 37°C (98.6°F)? Why do you shiver when you are cold, sweat when you are hot, and feel thirsty when you need water?

Homeostasis (HOH-mee-oh-STAY-sihs) is the maintenance of constant internal conditions in an organism. Homeostasis is important because cells function best within a limited range of conditions. Temperature, blood sugar, acidity, and other conditions must be controlled. Breakdowns in homeostasis are often life threatening.

Homeostasis is usually maintained through a process called negative feedback. In negative feedback, a change in a system causes a response that tends to return that system to its original state. For example, think about how a car's cruise control keeps a car moving at a constant set speed. A cruise control system has sensors that monitor the car's speed and then send that information to a computer. If the car begins to go faster than the set speed, the computer tells the car to slow down. If the car slows below the set speed, the computer tells the car to speed up. Similarly, if your body temperature drops below normal, systems in your body act to return your temperature to normal. Your muscles cause you to shiver, and blood vessels near your skin's surface constrict. If your body temperature rises above normal, different responses cool your body.

Behavior is also involved in homeostasis. For example, animals regulate their temperature through behavior. If you feel cold, you may put on a jacket. Reptiles sit on a warm rock in sunlight if they get too cold, and they move into shade if they get too warm.

B Summarize **What is homeostasis, and why is it important?**

FIGURE 2.5 The polar bear can maintain homeostasis in very cold climates. Its hollow hair is one adaptation that helps the bear retain its body heat. (SEM; magnification 450×)

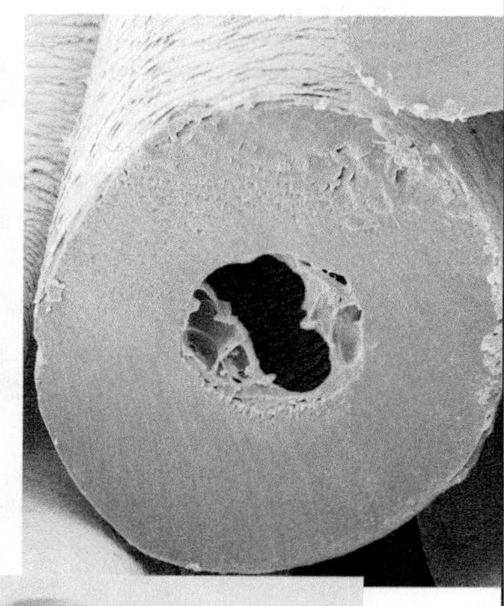

HANDS-ON ACTIVITY

To explore the unifying theme of homeostasis, have volunteers submerse one hand in a beaker of water that is 10 to 15 degrees colder than room temperature for several minutes. When students remove their hands, have them take their oral temperature with a thermometer. Then have students compare their skin temperature to their internal body temperature. Students should find that even though skin temperature decreased, internal temperature did not.

TEACH FROM VISUALS

FIGURE 2.5 Direct students' attention to the cross section of the hair of the polar bear. **Ask**

- What about the structure of the polar bear's hair relates to how it functions? Thickness offers insulation while the hollow core enables air within to be kept warm by body heat.
- What other observation can you make about the polar bear in this picture that relates structure and function and homeostasis? The bear has fat deposits that help it retain warmth.

Point out that the polar bear's skin, as evidenced by its nose, is black. Black absorbs heat and helps to keep the bear warm.

Science Trivia

- The hair of a polar bear is transparent. It appears white because it reflects visible light, in much the same way that snow and ice do.
- Polar bears at the San Diego and the Singapore zoos turned green when algae infested the hollow cores of their hairs.
- A polar bear at a zoo in Argentina turned purple in response to a medical treatment given to clear up a case of dermatitis.

Answers

A Infer Both types of tissue are made up of muscle cells. However, since the heart and arm function differently—the heart is a pump and the arm enables movement—one would expect the tissues and cells to be structured differently.

B Summarize Homeostasis is the maintenance of constant conditions within an organism. It is important because cells function best within a certain range of conditions.

▼ Teach *continued*

The Inside Story

Geneticist and evolutionary biologist **Theodosius Dobzhansky** said, "Nothing in biology makes sense except in the light of evolution." The idea of evolution by natural selection began to take shape for **Charles Darwin,** following his voyage on HMS *Beagle*. Closely associated with that trip and typically cited as a prime example of the phenomenon of natural selection are 13 species of finches known today as **Darwin's finches.**

It is often assumed that the finches Darwin observed on the Galápagos Islands played a pivotal role in the formation of his theory, but this is not the case. Darwin did not use the finches to buttress his argument for natural selection in *On the Origin of Species by Natural Selection*. In fact, some of the birds were so different in character, he didn't think they were finches at all.

It was not until much later that **Peter** and **Rosemary Grant** demonstrated conclusively that natural selection is alive and well and happening routinely in the species of finches known as Darwin's finches. Beginning in 1973, the Grants spent many years tracking thousands of individual finches across generations to show how individual finch species change in response to altered environments.

TEACH FROM VISUALS

FIGURE 2.6 Tell students that the adaptations shown in the photographs are called mimicry. They will learn more about such adaptations in the chapter Interactions in Ecosystems.

MAIN IDEA

Evolution explains the unity and diversity of life.

CONNECT TO

EVOLUTION

The processes of evolution, natural selection, and adaptation are described in more detail in the **Evolution** unit.

Evolution is the change in living things over time. More specifically, evolution is a change in the genetic makeup of a subgroup, or population, of a species. The concept of evolution links observations from all levels of biology, from cells to the biosphere. A wide range of scientific evidence, including the fossil record and genetic comparisons of species, shows that evolution is continuing today.

Adaptation

One way evolution occurs is through natural selection of adaptations. In natural selection, a genetic, or inherited, trait helps some individuals of a species survive and reproduce more successfully than other individuals in a particular environment. An inherited trait that gives an advantage to individual organisms and is passed on to future generations is an **adaptation.** Over time, the makeup of a population changes because more individuals have the adaptation. Two different populations of the same species might have different adaptations in different environments. The two populations may continue to evolve to the point at which they are different species.

Consider the orchid and the thorn bug in **FIGURE 2.6.** Both organisms have adapted in ways that make them resemble other organisms. The orchid that looks like an insect lures other insects to it. The insects that are attracted to the orchid can pollinate the flower, helping the orchid to reproduce. The thorn bug's appearance is an adaptation that makes predators less likely to see and eat it. This adaptation allows the thorn bug to survive and reproduce.

FIGURE 2.6 Through evolution, some orchids (left) have flowers that look like insects, and some insects, such as the thorn bug (right), look like parts of plants.

Differentiated Instruction

INCLUSION

To improve the teaching environment for students who are hearing impaired:

- Allow students access to your lecture notes.
- Avoid speaking when facing the board.
- Provide seating where students can hear best or lip-read.
- Allow group work during oral assignments.
- Obtain closed-captioned films.
- Provide classroom partners.
- Rephrase instructions. Some sounds may be heard or understood better than others.

In different environments, however, you would find other orchid and insect species that have different adaptations.

Adaptation in evolution is different from the common meaning of adaptation. For example, if you say that you are adapting to a new classroom or to a new town, you are not talking about evolution. Instead, you are talking about consciously getting used to something new. Evolutionary adaptations are changes in a species that occur over many generations due to environmental pressures, not through choices made by organisms. Evolution is simply a long-term response to the environment. The process does not necessarily lead to more complex organisms, and it does not have any special end point. Evolution continues today, and it will continue as long as life exists on Earth.

Unity and Diversity

Evolution is a unifying theme of biology because it accounts for both the diversity and the similarities, or the unity, of life. As you study biology, you will see time after time that organisms are related to one another. When you read about cells and genetics, you will see that all organisms have similar cell structures and chemical processes. These shared characteristics result from a common evolutionary descent.

Humans and bacteria have much more in common than you may think. Both human and bacterial genetics are based on the same molecules—DNA and RNA. Both human and bacterial cells rely upon the same sources of energy, and they have similar cell structures. Both human and bacterial cells have membranes made mostly of fats that protect the inside of the cell from the environment outside the cell.

Now think about the vast number of different types of organisms. All of the species alive now are the result of billions of years of evolution and adaptation to the environment. How? Natural selection of genetic traits can lead to the evolution of a new species. In the end, this genetic diversity is responsible for the diversity of life on Earth.

Analyze **How does evolution lead to both the diversity and the unity of life?**

1.2 Formative Assessment

REVIEWING MAIN IDEAS

1. Describe a biological **system.**
2. Why is **homeostasis** essential for living things?
3. What is the relationship between **adaptation** and natural selection?

CRITICAL THINKING

4. Analyze How are structure and function related to adaptation?
5. Apply How is the process of natural selection involved in **evolution**?
6. Apply Describe the relationship between **cells** and **organisms**.

CONNECT TO

CELLS

7. Do you think homeostasis is necessary at the level of a single cell? Explain.

1.2 FORMATIVE ASSESSMENT

1. A system is a group of interrelated, interacting parts that make up a whole. An ecosystem is a biological system of living and nonliving things interacting in an environment.
2. Homeostasis enables organisms to survive in diverse and changing environments.
3. Natural selection leads to different adaptations in different environments.
4. An adaptation is a genetic change that can affect the structure of some aspect of an organism's body and how well it functions in a given environment.
5. Natural selection of different adaptations in different environments can lead to new species.
6. Multicellular organisms are made up of tissues, organs and organ systems, which are all made up of groups of cells.
7. Stable conditions within a cell are necessary for the cell's survival, whether in a unicellular or multicellular organism. If homeostasis is not maintained within a cell, then cell functions can be disrupted. In turn, this can disrupt functions at higher levels of organization.

Take It Further

A change in an individual in response to environmental conditions is acclimation. Individuals acclimate; populations adapt. For example, climbers can take days or weeks to acclimate to oxygen levels at higher elevations. To acclimate, climbers stay a few days at base camp. They climb to the next camp where they spend a night, and then return to base camp. This process is repeated several times, extending the time spent at the higher elevation. Once a climber is used to that elevation, the process starts over at a higher camp. The golden rule for high-altitude climbers is "climb high, sleep low." This means climbers can ascend more than 300 meters (1000 ft) per day as long as they descend to a lower elevation no more than 300 meters (1000 ft) from their starting elevation to sleep.

Answers

A **Analyze** Adaptations to different environments account for diversity; similarities among all organisms suggest a common evolutionary ancestor, that which unites all living things.

Assess and Reteach

Assess Use the Section Self-Check or Section Quiz, both available at **HMHScience.com.**

Reteach Assign students to four cooperative groups and assign each group one of the following topics: systems, structure and function, homeostasis, or evolution. Ask students to collaborate in summarizing, in their own words, the unifying theme they were assigned and then to write a summary. Have each group designate a speaker to present its summary to the class. After each presentation, have group members answer questions from the class.

DATA ANALYSIS

Introduce

Every scientific investigation involves gathering and recording data. Some data are qualitative and subjective, meaning the data could be interpreted differently depending on the person gathering the data. Some data are quantitative, or objective measurements. **Ask**

- In the photograph of the jackals, how would you record data about the age of the individuals qualitatively and quantitatively? Qualitative age data could be notes that the jackals appear to be young or old. Quantitative age data could be records of their exact ages based on when each jackal was born.
- If qualitative data depend on the subjective observations, are qualitative data less valuable? No, qualitative data often describe behaviors and other qualities that cannot be easily quantified, such as color.

Discuss

Often, scientists use both types of data in their research. **Ask,** If you were studying the pod of dolphins, how could you use both qualitative and quantitative data in your research? Most research begins with observations. Qualitative data can lead to questions and hypotheses that can be tested quantitatively.

Online Student Resources, Data Analysis Practice

DATA ANALYSIS

Qualitative and Quantitative

Smart Grapher
HMHScience.com
GO ONLINE
Biodiversity

Scientists collect two different types of data: qualitative data and quantitative data.

Qualitative data Qualitative data are descriptions in words of what is being observed. They are based on some quality of an observation, such as color, odor, or texture.

Quantitative data Quantitative data are numeric measurements. The data are objective—they are the same no matter who measures them. They include measurements such as mass, volume, temperature, distance, concentration, time, or frequency.

Model

Suppose that a marine biologist observes the behavior and activities of dolphins. She identifies different dolphins within the group and observes them every day for a month. She records detailed observations about their behaviors. Some of her observations are qualitative data, and some are quantitative data.

Qualitative data examples

- Dolphin colors range from gray to white.
- Dolphins in a pod engage in play behavior.
- Dolphins have smooth skin.

Quantitative data examples

- There are nine dolphins in this pod.
- Dolphins eat the equivalent of 4–5% of their body mass each day.
- The sonar frequency most often used by the dolphins is around 100 kHz.

Notice that the qualitative data are descriptions. The quantitative data are objective, numerical measurements.

Practice Identify Data Types

Suppose that you are a biologist studying jackals in their natural habitat in Africa. You observe their behaviors and interactions and take photographs of their interactions to study later. Examine the photograph of the jackals shown to the right.

1. **Analyze** Give three examples of qualitative data that could be obtained from the photograph of the jackals.
2. **Analyze** Give three examples of quantitative data that could be obtained from the photograph of the jackals.

Answers

1. *Sample answer:* The jackals are young; the jackals are playing; the jackals appear healthy.
2. *Sample answer:* There are five jackals in the group; two jackals are engaged in play behavior; one jackal is on its back.

1.3 Scientific Thinking and Processes

KEY CONCEPT **Science is a way of thinking, questioning, and gathering evidence.**

MAIN IDEAS
- Like all science, biology is a process of inquiry.
- Biologists use experiments to test hypotheses.
- A theory explains a wide range of observations.
- Scientists communicate information in many different ways.

VOCABULARY
observation
data
hypothesis
experiment
independent variable
dependent variable
constant
theory

Connect to Your World
What does the study of fungus have in common with the study of human heart disease? How is research in a laboratory similar to research in a rain forest? Biologists, like all scientists, ask questions about the world and try to find answers through observation and experimentation. How do your daily observations help answer questions that you have about the world?

MAIN IDEA
Like all science, biology is a process of inquiry.

Science is a human process of trying to understand the world around us. There is no one method used by all scientists, but all scientific inquiry is based on the same principles. Scientific thinking is based on curiosity, skepticism, and logical thinking.

- Curiosity is what drives scientists to ask questions about the world around them.
- Skepticism is the use of critical thinking to question results and conclusions.
- Logical thinking is the use of reasoning through information to make conclusions that are supported by evidence.

One of the most important points of science is that scientific evidence may support or even overturn long-standing ideas. Scientists depend on empirical evidence as the basis for scientific knowledge. Empirical evidence is evidence that is observed directly through research and investigation. Such evidence is used to construct testable explanations and predictions of natural phenomena. The written descriptions and drawings of the gorilla in **FIGURE 3.1** are examples of observations and empirical evidence from a field investigation of gorillas. To improve our understanding of the world, scientists share their findings with each other. The open and honest exchange of data is extremely important in science.

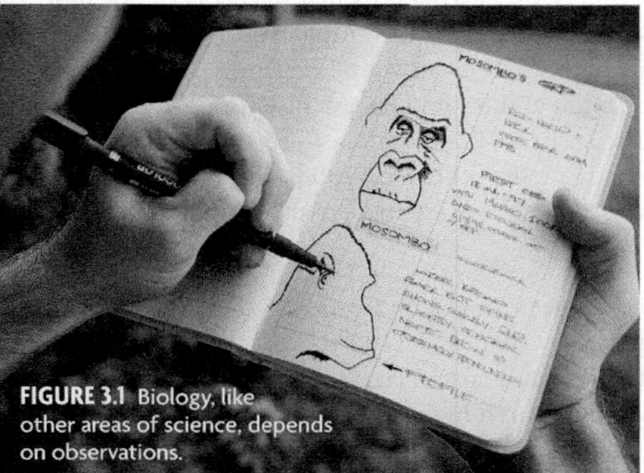

FIGURE 3.1 Biology, like other areas of science, depends on observations.

Differentiated Instruction

ENGLISH LEARNERS
Remind students that people ask questions to get information. Provide practice with clarification techniques by using phrases such as the following:

I didn't understand what you said.

Could you repeat that, please?

Does ___ mean ___?

Also, have students ask questions related to what they have read or you have explained. Review the question words *What, Who, When, Where, Why,* and *How.*

Model this technique for students by asking some questions about the nature of scientific thinking, such as the following:

What makes a scientist a scientist?

How do scientists approach their work?

Why do scientists do experiments?

Ask students to form their own questions about **Section 3** to ask one another in groups. Tell students that you consider their questions a sign of critical thinking, and emphasize that the questions are an excellent tool for making meaning clear.

SECTION 1.3

Plan and Prepare ▼

Activate Prior Knowledge Quiz students on the nature of a hypothesis. **Ask,** Is this a hypothesis: "If I keep a plant from getting any sunlight, it will die." No, it's a prediction. Remind students that a hypothesis is worded to show a relationship that can be tested. **Ask,** How can you reframe the prediction about the plant to make it a hypothesis? "If a plant needs sunlight to survive, then without sunlight, it will die."

Teach ▼

Vocabulary

Academic Vocabulary Scientists typically describe a hypothesis in terms of **validity,** rather than **truth.** *Validity* implies a proposition is logically derived. *Truth* is, more simply, the quality of being real, genuine, or factual.

▼ Teach continued

History of Science

The scientific tradition began in ancient Greece and is generally attributed to **Aristotle.** He was the first individual we know of to explain biological phenomena in terms of natural causes, as opposed to supernatural or mythical causes. He used the power of logic to find explanations for cause and effect, and form and function. Aristotle's most powerful tools consisted of his powers of observation and reasoning.

Aristotle and the natural philosophers who followed him established a set of widely held assumptions about the natural world and how it functioned. Typically, answers to specific questions had to fit within this framework of assumptions, which provided a predetermined explanation. One such assumption was that the sun and all the other stars and planets revolved around Earth.

With the **Scientific Revolution** of the 17th century, a new methodology came into being. This new scientific method started with data and observations, from which an explanation was derived, and incorporated experimentation to test assumptions. In 1620, **Francis Bacon** outlined the approach in his work *Novum Organum,* which carried the subtitle *True Suggestions for the Interpretation of Nature.* In 1637, **René Descartes** framed the principles of scientific thinking in his *Discourse on Method.* Descartes described reconstructing the accepted body of knowledge, piece by piece, trusting only that which could be seen to be beyond any doubt.

Vocabulary

Academic Vocabulary The term **significant** commonly means "important," but in statistics, the term *significant* means "not likely due to chance." Explain that a finding may be statistically significant without being important in the real world. When statisticians say that a result is **statistically significant,** they mean that a change in a dependent variable is probably due to manipulation of the independent variable. That probability is typically 95%.

CONNECT TO

DATA ANALYSIS

Biology relies on the analysis of scientific data. Use the Data Analysis activities in each chapter in this book to build your data analysis skills.

Poison Frogs

Observations, Data, and Hypotheses

All scientific inquiry begins with careful and systematic observations. Of course, **observation** includes using our senses to study the world, but it may also involve other tools. For example, scientists use computers to collect measurements or to examine past research results. Empirical evidence is gathered through observation.

Observations are often recorded as **data** that can be analyzed. Scientists collect two general types of data: qualitative data and quantitative data. Qualitative data are descriptions of a phenomenon that can include sights, sounds, and smells. This type of data is often useful to report what happens but not how it happens. In contrast, quantitative data are characteristics that can be measured or counted, such as mass, volume, and temperature. Anything that is expressed as a number is quantitative data that can be used to explore how something happens.

Scientists use observations, data, and scientific literature to form a hypothesis. A **hypothesis** (plural, *hypotheses*) is a proposed answer for a scientific question. A hypothesis must be specific and testable. You probably form and test many hypotheses every day, even though you may not be aware of it. Suppose you oversleep, for example. You needed to get up at 7 a.m., but when you wake up you observe that it is 8 a.m. What happened? Did the alarm not go off? Was it set for the wrong time? Did it go off, but you slept through it? You just made three hypotheses to explain why you overslept—the alarm did not go off, the alarm was set for the wrong time, or the alarm went off, but you did not hear it.

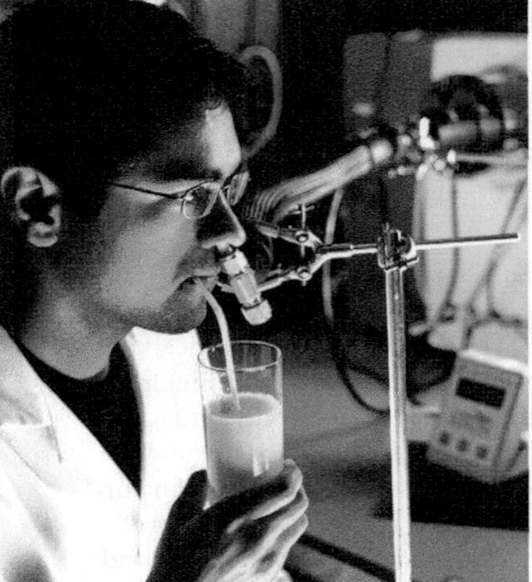

FIGURE 3.2 In this experiment, a scientist studies how chemicals are detected in the mouth and nose to produce taste.

Hypotheses, Results, and Conclusions

A hypothesis leads to testable predictions of what would happen if the hypothesis is valid. How could you use scientific thinking to test a hypothesis about oversleeping? If you slept late because the alarm was set for the wrong time, you could check the alarm to find out the time for which it was set. Suppose you check, and the alarm was actually set for 7 p.m. In this case, your hypothesis would be supported by your data.

For scientists, just one test of a hypothesis is usually not enough. Most of the time, it is only by repeating tests that scientists can be more certain that their results are not mistaken or due to chance. Why? Biological systems are highly variable. By repeating tests, scientists take this variability into account and try to decrease its effects on the experimental results. After scientists collect data, they use statistics to mathematically analyze whether a hypothesis is supported. Analyzed data are the results of the experiment. There are two possible outcomes or results.

- **Nonsignificant** The data show no effect, or an effect so small that the results could have happened by chance.
- **Statistically significant** The data show an effect that is likely not due to chance. When data do not support a hypothesis, the hypothesis is rejected. But these data are still useful because they often lead to new hypotheses.

Differentiated Instruction

BELOW LEVEL

Tell students that there are different strategies for previewing a section. Introduce students to the PLAN strategy: Predict, Locate, Add, and Note. Have students predict what the section will be about by reading the headings and locating key vocabulary. They should write down their predictions and any questions they have. As they read, they can add details and note how the material addresses their questions.

Teacher Toolkit, Section C, PLAN

FIGURE 3.3 Scientific Thinking

Science is a cycle. The steps are shown in a certain order, but the cycle does not begin or end at any one point, and the steps may take place in various orders.

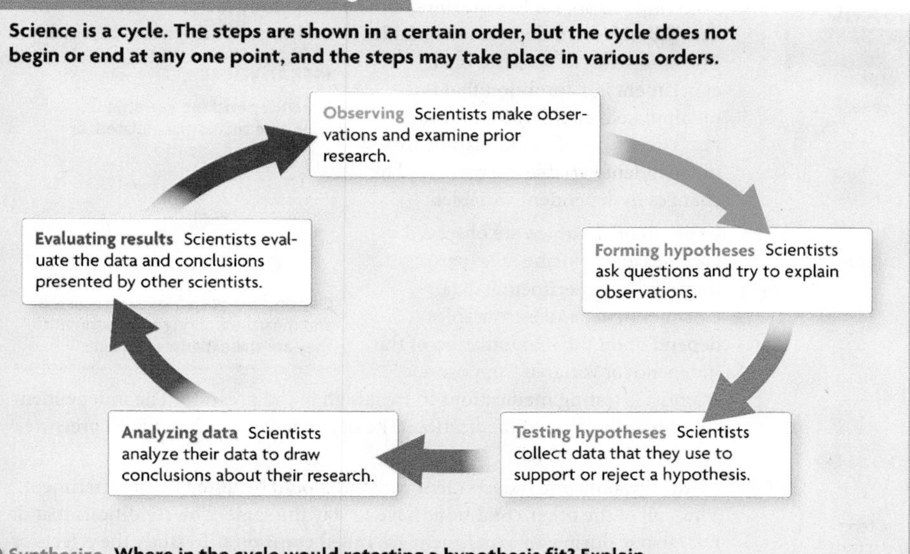

Observing Scientists make observations and examine prior research.
Forming hypotheses Scientists ask questions and try to explain observations.
Testing hypotheses Scientists collect data that they use to support or reject a hypothesis.
Analyzing data Scientists analyze their data to draw conclusions about their research.
Evaluating results Scientists evaluate the data and conclusions presented by other scientists.

A Synthesize **Where in the cycle would retesting a hypothesis fit? Explain.**

Experimental methods and results are evaluated by other scientists in a process called peer review. Only after this review process is complete are research results accepted. Whether the results support an existing theory or disagree with earlier research, they are often used as a starting point for new questions. In **FIGURE 3.3**, you see the cycle of observing, forming hypotheses, testing hypotheses, analyzing data, and evaluating results that keeps scientific inquiry going.

B Synthesize **Why is there no one correct process of scientific investigation?**

MAIN IDEA

Biologists use experiments to test hypotheses.

Observational studies help biologists describe and explain something in the world. But in observational studies, scientists try not to interfere with what happens. They try to simply observe a phenomenon. One example involves the endangered white stork. The number of white storks had decreased sharply by 1950, even becoming extinct in some countries. To help protect the storks, biologists studied the migration patterns of the birds. Observational studies can tell a biologist about changes in migration path and distance. They told scientists where the storks were breeding and how many eggs they would lay. Because of these efforts, stork populations have rebounded by 20% worldwide. Observational studies can provide much information and answer many questions. But there is one question that observations cannot answer: What causes any changes that might be observed? The only way to answer that question is through an experiment.

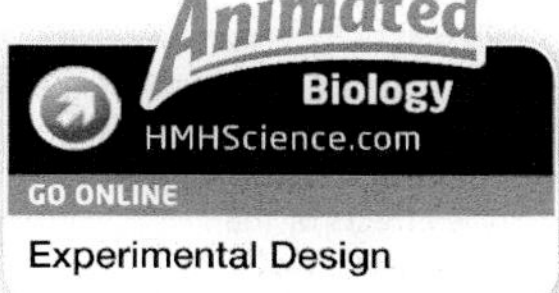

Animated
Biology
HMHScience.com
GO ONLINE
Experimental Design

INCLUSION

A science class offers a variety of students important information that will help them function in an increasingly technological society. Below is a list of ways to accommodate all students in a comfortable learning environment:

- Provide a daily, unvarying routine so your expectations are clear.
- Establish special teaching procedures that take into account a short attention span and restlessness.
- Make certain that students understand instructions before they start work.
- Seat students where classroom distractions are minimized.
- Be selective about which concepts students should master.
- Encourage repeated efforts.
- Within reasonable expectations, evaluate students' grasp of concepts, not spelling, punctuation, or sentence structure.

Take It Further

Tell students that a hypothesis cannot be proved, only tested. Applying logic, if something cannot be proved, then it cannot be disproved. Data either support or do not support a hypothesis, and the hypothesis is accepted or rejected—not proved.

Part of establishing support for a hypothesis is to subject experimental results and data to **peer review.** It is rare for one researcher to spot every mistake or flaw in a complicated investigation. The researcher may also have assumptions or expectations that can cause experimental bias. Other sources for bias include financial motivation, incomplete information, or inaccurate measuring instruments. Errors and opportunities for improvement may stand out only to another scientist with special expertise, increasing the probability that weaknesses in an experiment will be identified and fixed.

Answers

A **Synthesize** during "testing hypotheses" (to repeat the experiment) and after "analyzing data" (if the hypothesis is rejected) or "evaluating results" (if other data agree or disagree)

B **Synthesize** The steps can occur in different orders and depend on what is being investigated.

▼ Teach continued

Vocabulary

Academic Vocabulary Point out that in everyday use, an **observation** may be a comment based on something seen. In this use, an interpretation, or inference, has been made. In science, an observation must be detectable with the senses or a measurement tool. Show students an apple, and then have them identify the following statements as observations or inferences.

1. The skin is red. observation
2. The apple is edible. inference
3. There are seeds inside. inference
4. It can make you healthy. inference
5. It feels smooth. observation

Take It Further

Researchers involved in experiments that test human reactions often apply an added system of control to their investigations. This is because a test subject's expectations can affect the results. For example, in a clinical trial for a new drug, just the knowledge that a person is receiving an active drug may produce some benefit or cause a doctor to look for improvement. In such an instance, investigators use a randomized, double-blind, placebo-controlled study. This ensures that psychological factors do not affect the results.

The study employs two drugs, the active one that researchers expect to be an effective treatment and a **placebo,** a substance that has no treatment value but outwardly appears identical to the active drug. The study is made **random** by using a computer to randomly determine who receives the drug and who receives the placebo. The procedure is **double blind** because neither the participating doctors nor their test subjects know which drug (active or placebo) the subject is receiving.

Answers

A Infer A change in the independent variable is potentially the cause of a measured effect in the dependent variable.

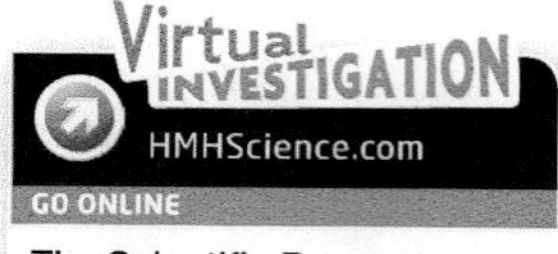

The Scientific Process

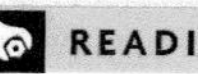

READING TOOLBOX

VOCABULARY

In common usage, the term *constant* means "unchanging." In experimental research, a constant is a condition or factor that is controlled so that it does not change.

Scientific experiments allow scientists to test hypotheses and find out how something happens. In **experiments**, scientists study factors called independent variables and dependent variables to find cause-and-effect relationships. The **independent variable** in an experiment is a condition that is manipulated, or changed, by a scientist. The effects of manipulating an independent variable are measured by changes in dependent variables. **Dependent variables** are observed and measured during an experiment; they are the experimental data. Changes in dependent variables depend upon the manipulation of the independent variable. Suppose a scientist is testing medications to treat high blood pressure. The independent variable is the dose of medication. The dependent variable is blood pressure, as shown in **FIGURE 3.4.**

VISUAL VOCAB

The **independent variable** is a condition that is manipulated, or changed, by a scientist.

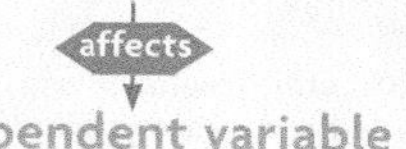

Dependent variables are observed and measured during an experiment; they are the experimental data.

Ideally, only one independent variable should be tested in an experiment. Thus, all of the other conditions have to stay the same. The conditions that do not change during an experiment are called **constants.** To study the effects of an independent variable, a scientist uses a control group or control condition. Subjects in a control group are treated exactly like experimental subjects except for the independent variable being studied. The independent variable is manipulated in experimental groups or experimental conditions.

Constants in the blood pressure medication experiment include how often the medication is given and how the medication is taken. To control the experiment, these factors must remain the same, or be held constant. For example, the medication could be tested with 0, 25, 50, or 100 milligram doses, twice a day, taken by swallowing a pill. By changing only one variable at a time—the amount of medication—a scientist can be more confident that the results are due to that variable.

A Infer How do experiments show cause-and-effect relationships?

FIGURE 3.4 COMPARING VARIABLES

This graph compares the effects of the same dosage of two different medications on blood pressure. The independent variable (dosage) stayed the same for each type of medication tested.

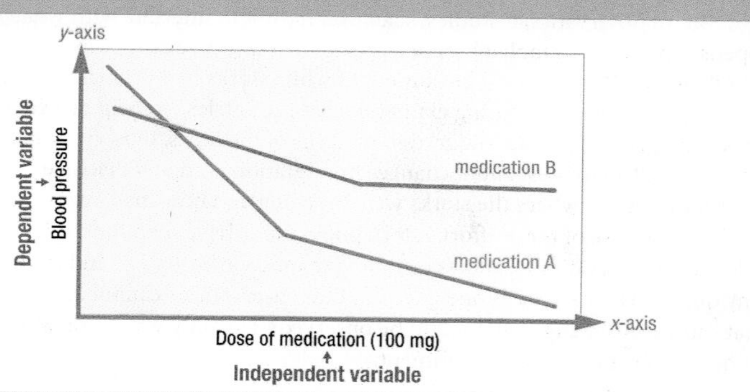

Differentiated Instruction

TEACH WITH TECHNOLOGY

To hone students' powers of observation, find a video clip that shows an interesting and complex event. It might be a magic trick or a visually arresting advertisement. Play the clip, then ask students to write down all that they saw. Play the clip again, asking them to observe the event more carefully. Then have students share what they saw, comparing their first perception of the event to their second.

MAIN IDEA

A theory explains a wide range of observations.

The meaning of a word may change depending on the context in which it is used. The word *theory* has different meanings. In everyday conversation, the word *theory* means a guess or a hunch. In science, the meaning of the word *theory* is very different. A **theory** is a proposed explanation for a wide range of observations and experimental results that is supported by a wide range of evidence. Recall that a hypothesis is a proposed answer to a scientific question. Hypotheses about natural and physical phenomena that have been tested over a wide variety of conditions are incorporated into theories. For example, natural selection is a scientific theory. It is supported by a large amount of data, and it explains how populations can evolve.

Hypotheses propose answers to scientific questions. Scientific theories provide explanations of phenomena. In contrast to hypotheses and theories, a scientific *law* defines relationships that are valid everywhere in the universe. For example, the law of conservation of energy states that energy may change form, but it cannot be created or destroyed. A law describes without providing any explanations.

Theories are not easily accepted in science, and by definition they are never proved. Eventually, a theory may be broadly accepted by the scientific community. Scientific hypotheses and theories may be supported or refuted, and they are always subject to change. New theories that better explain observations and experimental results can replace older theories. Scientists must always be willing to revise theories and conclusions as new evidence about the living world is gathered. Science is an ongoing process. New experiments and observations refine and expand scientific knowledge.

One example of how scientific understanding can change involves the cause of disease. Until the mid-1800s, illnesses were thought to be related to supernatural causes or to imbalances of the body's humours, or fluids. Then scientific research suggested that diseases were caused by microscopic organisms, such as bacteria. This is the basis of the germ theory of disease, which is still accepted today. However, the germ theory has changed over time. For example, the germ theory has been expanded due to the discoveries of viruses and prions. Viruses and prions are not living organisms, but they do cause disease. The link between prions and disease was not even suggested until the early 1980s when evidence pointed to prions as the cause of mad cow disease and, in humans, both classic and variant Creutzfeldt–Jakob disease.

Scientific inquiry is important to understanding nature, but there are limitations to the kinds of questions that scientific inquiry can answer. For example, observations must be testable and verifiable. Observations that cannot be verified or replicated cannot count as evidence in scientific inquiry. Some phenomena that are not scientifically testable now may become testable with new or better technology. Other phenomena, such as supernatural phenomena, may never be testable or scientific.

A Compare **Distinguish between a hypothesis, a theory, and a law.**

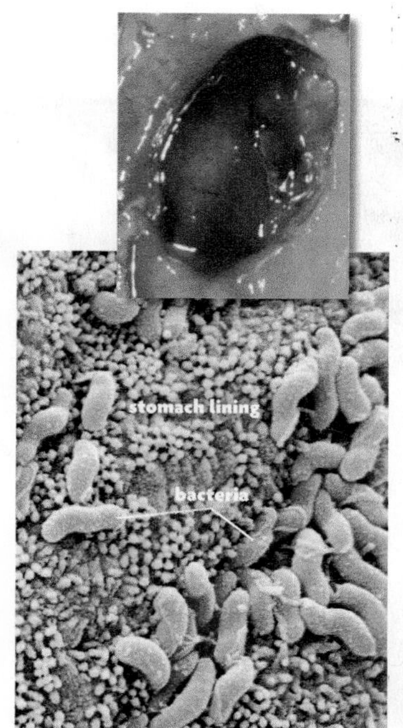

FIGURE 3.5 For many years, scientific evidence indicated that stomach ulcers (top) were caused by stress. Then new evidence showed that the ulcers are actually caused by a type of bacteria called *Helicobacter pylori* (bottom). (colored SEM; magnification 4000×)

Differentiated Instruction

PRE-AP

Working in small groups, have students consider how a theory provides a framework for the way scientific investigations are conducted. They should identify a theory that served for a time and then was supplanted by another, for example, the geocentric and heliocentric theories or spontaneous generation and the cell theory. Students should compile what they know about the theories, the effect a wrong theory has, and a theory's predictive value. Then discuss the results in class.

Teacher Toolkit, Section C, Round Table

Address Misconceptions

Common Misconception Students may think that all questions can be answered by using scientific methods.

Correcting the Misconception Explain that scientific methods apply only to the study of phenomena that can be observed and measured. Appreciation of beauty and personal tastes, for example, are outside the realm of scientific investigation.

Answers

A **Compare** A hypothesis is a proposed answer to a scientific question and is used as the basis of experiments. A theory is a proposed explanation of phenomena and often encompasses a wide range of evidence collected in the testing of many hypotheses. A law is a description of scientific phenomena under certain conditions without any explanation.

The Inside Story

Peer review is a foundation of **scientific journals.** Peer review is used to both select articles for journals and to critique the research and writing. The reviewers are experts in a field of study. Articles accepted for peer review must be accompanied by data, methods, and background information from existing research. Peer review is not without its critics. Some scientists argue that peer review is elitist and gives advantage to established researchers and ideas. Reviewers may have published conflicting works themselves and may not be open to reading and publishing new ideas. Scientific journals and the peer review process can be very time consuming and may hinder timely discoveries and reports. Many scientific journals require paid subscriptions or fees per article accessed online.

TEACH FROM VISUALS

FIGURE 3.7 The photo shows a Doppler image. **Ask,** How does including a scientific image like this one help communicate information to the audience? Doppler images provide visual reference to accompany the forecaster's explanation and prediction. Remind students that Doppler images are mathematical models based on data collected about current conditions and past trends.

Answers

A List Students' sources may include product advertisements, marketing material, magazine articles, webpages, scientific journals, news reports, textbooks, science fairs, and symposia.

FIGURE 3.6 Professional scientists present research and discuss implications at a science symposium.

FIGURE 3.7 Doppler images, like this one of Hurricane Claudette in 2003, are models of weather data. In a television report, forecasters may use a Doppler image to summarize and predict future weather patterns and advise viewers about safety.

MAIN IDEA

Scientists communicate information in many different ways.

You may have seen written sources that include scientific information, such as product advertisements, magazine articles, or webpages. Scientific information may be presented at science fairs and symposia, which are forums for professional scientists to present and discuss new research, as in **FIGURE 3.6.** Because there are so many ways to communicate scientific information, it is important to know how to evaluate different methods of communication.

Primary and Secondary Sources

Recall that new scientific research is reviewed by other scientists through the peer review process. During peer review, scientists consider many things. How was an experiment done? How were the data analyzed? Do the data support the conclusions? Is there bias in the experimental design or in the conclusions? Peer-reviewed scientific information is published in scientific journals. Scientific journals are primary sources of scientific information and include results and conclusions, along with experimental methods, data, and details that other scientists would need to recreate the investigation.

Almost all scientific knowledge presented to the public comes from secondary sources. Secondary sources summarize or report only portions of primary information. Magazine articles, news reports, textbooks, and advertisements are examples of secondary sources of information. Secondary sources may contain pieces of data that are most relevant to the source.

Evaluating Scientific Information

Not all information that is presented as scientific is reliable. Reliable sources of scientific information are based on empirical evidence, logical reasoning, and testing. When evaluating scientific information, consider the evidence that supports the scientific claim, the purpose of the source, and whether any bias is present. Use critical thinking skills to evaluate the information.

A List What are four sources that might include scientific information?

SELF-CHECK Online
HMHScience.com
GO ONLINE

1.3 Formative Assessment

REVIEWING MAIN IDEAS

1. What role do **hypotheses** play in scientific inquiry?
2. Explain why a hypothesis must be testable.
3. Why would a scientific **theory** be revised over time?

CRITICAL THINKING

4. **Compare and Contrast** How are hypotheses and theories similar? How do they differ?
5. **Criticize** What are two characteristics of a scientific information source that may indicate the information is unreliable?

CONNECT TO

SCIENTIFIC PROCESS

6. Why is the statement "All life is made of cells" an example of a theory? Explain.

1.3 FORMATIVE ASSESSMENT

1. A hypothesis provides a testable explanation for an observation.
2. A hypothesis is a proposed answer to a question. Testing the hypothesis enables scientists to evaluate the validity of the answer.
3. Scientific theories are revised because new areas of science and technology are developed and new discoveries expand or change our understanding of natural phenomena.
4. Hypotheses and theories are proposed explanations for a scientific question. Observations and data collected in testing hypotheses contribute to a theory. A theory, in turn, provides the framework for new hypotheses.
5. *Sample answer:* lack of evidence, inclusion of bias
6. The idea that all life is made of cells changed the view of an organism based on accumulated evidence and formed a framework for new investigations.

▼ Assess and Reteach

Assess Use the Section Self-Check or Section Quiz, both available at **HMHScience.com**.

Reteach Work with students to incorporate the key vocabulary of the section into either a cluster diagram or a concept map. You can print out a description of each graphic organizer, and a blank, from the *Teacher Toolkit*.

Importance of Basic Research

S.T.E.M. Interactions

In high school, students are usually required to take a variety of classes with the idea that the variety will ensure a well-rounded education. Later, students can pursue a career that allows them to focus their attention on a field where their talents and interests intersect. A foundation in basic scientific research can help set the stage for many careers. Through the collaborative nature of science, basic research contributes to a broad base of knowledge that scientists in specific research fields rely on heavily.

Basic scientific research has been compared to fishing, because it requires patience, persistence, and a bit of luck for success. It also has been compared to drilling for oil, because both money and time are required to drill many wells, but the payoff can be big once the right place is found. There is a creative element to basic research too. Scientists who pursue basic research are often simply curious about a subject and develop a method to find the answer. Sometimes the research can have very useful results.

In 1966, Indiana University professor Thomas Brock and undergraduate student Hudson Freeze were studying heat-loving microbes in the hot springs of Yellowstone National Park when they discovered a kind of bacteria that could thrive in water temperatures as warm as 50°C to 80°C. They named this bacterium *Thermus aquaticus*. Brock and Freeze did not realize at the time that their discovery would accelerate the scientific progress of everything from disease diagnosis to forensics.

Samples of *Thermus aquaticus* cultures were placed in the American Type Culture Collection in Washington D.C., where, a few years later, they were found by a biotechnology researcher who was looking for a heat-stable enzyme for polymerase chain reaction, or PCR. PCR is a technology that can make millions of copies of a DNA fragment in a short time, which is extremely useful in DNA research. The work of Brock and Freeze not only benefitted DNA research and science in general, but also indirectly benefitted society in unintended ways, such as improved healthcare. The later discovery of thermophilic, or heat-loving, microbes in deep-ocean hydrothermal vents means that other scientists now use culture methods developed by Dr. Brock.

Basic research has taught scientists so much about the bacteria *Escherichia coli*, the fruit fly *Drosophila melanogaster*, and the microscopic roundworm *Caenorhabditis elegans* that these organisms are now routinely used as model organisms for scientific studies around the world. Basic research also provides baseline data that may become important decades later when changes occur. Even when the benefits of scientific research are not immediately apparent, the sometimes-routine observations or unusual subjects of basic research can lead to a deeper understanding of current ideas and possibly even a scientific breakthrough.

Lower Geyser Basin, Yellowstone National Park, Wyoming

Introduce

Ask students to imagine a research project on any science topic of their choice. What are they most curious about? Which topic would they choose to research? Discuss some of their choices and how the research might benefit society. If there doesn't seem to be a direct benefit, is the research still useful? Might it be useful in the future?

Background Material

In 1975, a U.S. senator introduced the Golden Fleece Awards to ridicule projects he felt were examples of wasted taxpayer money. Two famous recipients of the award were a National Science Foundation study on the origins of falling in love and research to determine what conditions caused rats, monkeys, and humans to clench their jaws. NASA and the U.S. Navy were interested in the latter research, which studied how aggression occurred among people kept in close conditions for a long period of time. The Golden Fleece Awards ended in the 1980s. In 2012, scientists debuted the Golden Goose Awards for research that appeared to be obscure or trivial at the time but has provided great benefits to society. Past winners include a doctor who studied the venom of a Gila monster lizard. He ultimately found a hormone that is a useful treatment for diabetes. Another winner of the Golden Goose Award is a researcher who set out to improve the paint on Navy ships and in the process designed a way to count red blood cells that is so simple and effective it is used in laboratories worldwide.

SECTION 1.4

▼ Plan and Prepare

Activate Prior Knowledge Have students define technology. **Ask,** Does a magnifying glass represent technology? a microscope? Both do. Technology is an application or innovation that allows humans to manipulate their material environment. Point out that technology need not be scientific in nature. A sewing needle represents technology.

▼ Teach

Take It Further

Review **FIGURE 4.1** with students. Tell students that many factors affect the accuracy and precision of measurements. **Ask** students to predict whether each of the following would affect accuracy, precision, or both.

- inconsistent method for using a tool accuracy and precision
- correct use of uncalibrated equipment accuracy
- size of graduations precision

1.4 Biologists' Tools and Technology

KEY CONCEPT **Technology continually changes the way biologists work.**

VOCABULARY

measurement
accuracy
precision
microscope
gene
molecular genetics
genomics

MAIN IDEAS

- Observations include making measurements.
- Technology contributes to the progress of science.
- Complex systems are modeled on computers.
- The tools of molecular genetics give rise to new biological studies.

Connect to Your World

Can you imagine life without cars, computers, or cell phones? Technology changes the way we live and work. Technology also plays a major part in the rapid increase of biological knowledge. In the early days of biology, scientists were limited to making measurements and observations with simple tools. Today, technology allows biologists to view tiny structures within cells and activity within a human brain. Technology even allows biologists to study and change genes. What will technology allow next?

MAIN IDEA

Observations include making measurements.

A wildlife biologist records a description of the alligator mating rituals she observes in her field journal. A pharmaceutical researcher uses probes and computers to measure and calculate the pH of stomach acids. Though very different, these situations are both examples of observation and the use of tools in scientific investigations. Tools serve a variety of purposes. Some tools, such as laboratory glassware and hot plates, allow scientists to set up experiments. Tools such as microscopes and hand lenses are used to enhance senses. Rulers, balances, and timing devices enable the gathering of quantitative data. Computer software is a tool that enables scientists to analyze and report data.

FIGURE 4.1 ACCURACY AND PRECISION

Measurements can be precise, accurate, both, or neither.

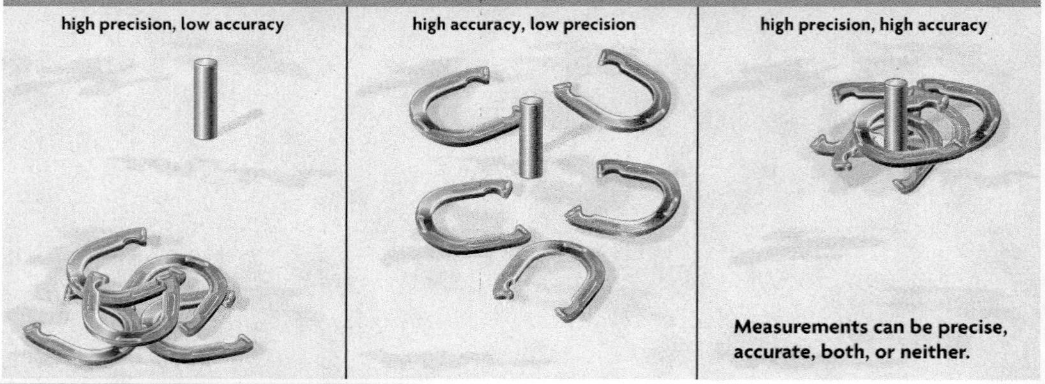

Differentiated Instruction

ENGLISH LEARNERS

Set up several common tools used in biology around the classroom, pairing similar items when possible. For example, you might pair up a hand lens and a compound microscope. Write the name of each tool on a note card in front of the tool. As you walk around the room and explain the use of each tool, invite students to write the name and function of the tool in the left column of a two-column chart. Students should sketch the tool in the right column.

Teacher Toolkit, Section C, Combination Notes

Quantitative data are gathered through **measurement,** the determination of the dimensions of something using a standard unit. The modern metric system, called the International System of Units, or SI, is the language for all scientific measurement. The quality of measurements can be described by their accuracy and precision. **Accuracy** is a description of how close a measurement is to the true value of the quantity measured. **Precision** is the exactness of a measurement. Accuracy and precision are demonstrated by the results of horseshoes tosses in **FIGURE 4.1.** When the horseshoes are close to each other, even if they are not near the goal post, the results are precise. When the horseshoes are centered around the goal post, even if they are not near each other, the results are accurate. When the horseshoes are centered around the goal post and close to each other, the results are both precise and accurate.

MAIN IDEA

Technology contributes to the progress of science.

Until the late 1600s, no one knew about cells or single-celled organisms. Then the microscope was invented. Scientists suddenly had the ability to study living things at a level they never knew existed. Thus, the microscope was the first in a long line of technologies that changed the study of biology.

Microscopes

A **microscope** provides an enlarged image of an object. Some of the most basic concepts of biology—such as the fact that cells make up all organisms—were not even imaginable before microscopes. The first microscopes magnified objects but did not produce clear images. By the 1800s, most microscopes had combinations of lenses that provided clearer images. Today's light microscopes, such as the one in **FIGURE 4.2** that you might use, are still based on the same principles. They are used to see living or preserved specimens, and they provide clear images of cells as small as bacteria. Light microscopes clearly magnify specimens up to about 1500 times their actual size, and samples are often stained with chemicals to make details stand out.

Electron microscopes, first developed in the 1930s, use beams of electrons instead of light to magnify objects. These microscopes can be used to see cells, but they produce much higher magnifications so they can also show much smaller things. Electron microscopes can clearly magnify specimens as much as 1,000,000 times their actual size. They can even be used to directly study individual protein molecules. However, electron microscopes, unlike light microscopes, cannot be used to study living organisms because the specimens being studied have to be in a vacuum.

A Explain **Describe why newer technology may not make older technology obsolete.**

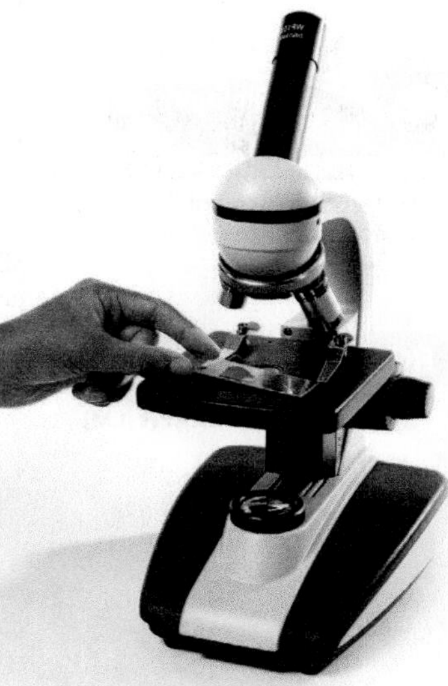

FIGURE 4.2 Biologists use microscopes to study cells which are generally too small to be seen with the naked eye.

Vocabulary

Academic Vocabulary Students may associate the term **resolution** with a course of action.

resolve, to make a firm decision about or bring to a successful conclusion

In chemistry and mathematics, the term *resolve* can mean "to separate into parts or coordinate components." In physics, the term *resolve* can refer to the capacity to make an image visible or distinct.

The *resolution* of a microscope is the minimum distance that two points can be seen as being separate. The resolution of a light microscope is limited by the shortest wavelength of visible light. Electron microscopes produce images using beams of electrons, which can have even shorter wavelengths and produce a much greater resolution.

TEACH FROM VISUALS

FIGURE 4.2 Use the photograph to review the parts of a microscope. Refer students to the Lab Handbook for more detailed information on the parts of a microscope, as well as information on magnification and specimen size.

Answers

A **Explain** New technology may add to the tools used instead of replacing existing tools. Newer technology, such as electron microscopes, may enable new details or types of observations. However, new technology may have limitations that older technology, such as light microscopes, do not have including high cost or sample limitations.

Differentiated Instruction

HANDS-ON ACTIVITY

Set up five numbered stations, each with two microscopes. Prepare slides to view ahead of time, and place a slide of a different object on each microscope. Make slides of ordinary things that students can quickly identify, such as an insect leg or wing, a fingernail clipping, a hair follicle, or a letter cut out of a newspaper. Ask students to work in pairs to focus on the objects, using the adjustment knobs. Have students view each slide under both low and high power, and then identify, sketch, and label each object.

Allow students no more than ten minutes at each station. Tell students that the slides and cover slips are delicate and can be broken if the high-power objective is pressed onto the slide with the coarse adjustment. Have alcohol swabs at each station, and tell students to wipe the eyepiece before using the microscope. When students are finished, let them compare notes to see if they identified the objects correctly.

▼ Teach *continued*

QUICKLAB

Time 20 minutes TEACHER TESTED

Purpose Observe and describe the characteristics of organisms found in a drop of pond water.

LAB MANAGEMENT

- Collect pond water less than 24 hours before the lab. To improve the chance of getting photosynthetic organisms, collect water from the surface of the pond. Keep the water aerated with a battery-powered aquarium aerator.
- Use a plankton net to obtain a more concentrated sample of organisms.
- Review with students the characteristics of protists, plants, and animals before the lab. Provide references for identifying microorganisms.
- Demonstrate how to tilt the cover slip and lower it into place on the slide to eliminate bubbles.

Safety Caution students to handle the glass slides carefully, and remind them to wipe eyepieces with alcohol wipes after using them. Make sure students wash their hands before leaving the lab.

Answers

Analyze and Conclude

1. Answers could include observations of a cell membrane, responses to stimuli, movement, endocytosis, exocytosis, and fission.
2. Answers will vary depending on the organisms observed.

TEACH FROM VISUALS

FIGURE 4.3 Have students read the captions of each image. **Ask**

- Which image has the highest magnification? the TEM
- Which image is seen in its actual color? the light micrograph
- Why don't SEMs and TEMs yield images in color? Color is part of the visible light region of the electromagnetic spectrum. SEMs and TEMs use electrons, not light.

QUICKLAB OBSERVING

Life Under a Microscope

Using a microscope properly is an important skill for many biologists. In this lab, you will review microscope skills by examining a drop of water from the surface of a local pond.

PROBLEM What types of organisms can be found in pond water?

PROCEDURE

1. Make a wet mount slide. Place a drop of pond water in the center of a microscope slide, and carefully put a cover slip over the water. Learn how to make a wet mount by reading the Lab Handbook.
2. View the pond water sample under low power on the microscope. Use the coarse focus knob to bring the sample into focus. Draw and label any organisms that you see in the sample.
3. View the slide under high power. Use the fine focus knob to bring portions of the sample into focus. Draw and label any organisms, including details of their structures, that you see in the sample.

MATERIALS

- 1 drop pond water
- eyedropper
- microscope slide
- cover slip
- microscope

ANALYZE AND CONCLUDE

1. **Connect** Describe how organisms in the sample exhibit the characteristics of living things.
2. **Compare and Contrast** Make a table to compare and contrast the characteristics of organisms in the sample of pond water.

Animated Biology HMHScience.com

GO ONLINE

Cells Through Different Microscopes

There are two main types of electron microscopes.

- A scanning electron microscope (SEM) scans the surface of a specimen with a beam of electrons. Usually, the specimen's surface is coated with a very thin layer of a metal that deflects the electrons. A computer forms a three-dimensional image from measurements of the deflected electrons.
- A transmission electron microscope (TEM) transmits electrons through a thin slice of a specimen. The TEM makes a two-dimensional image similar to that of a light microscope, but a TEM has a much higher magnification.

SEM and TEM images are artificially colorized with computers so that tiny details, such as the leaf pores, or stoma, shown in **FIGURE 4.3**, are easier to see.

FIGURE 4.3 Comparing Micrographs

LIGHT MICROGRAPH (LM)

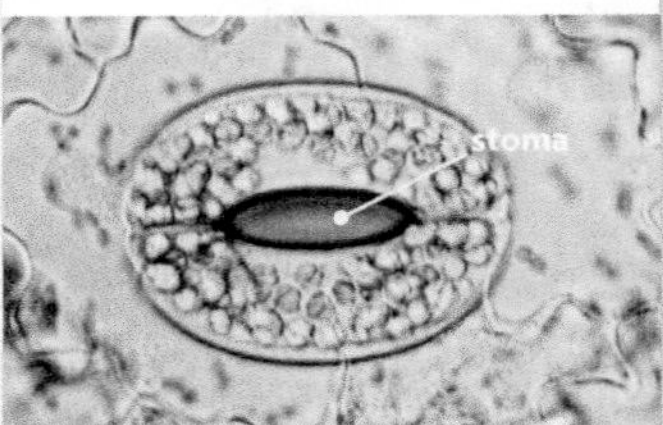

A light micrograph shows a two-dimensional image of a specimen. This light micrograph shows the actual color of the specimen.

SCANNING ELECTRON MICROGRAPH (SEM)

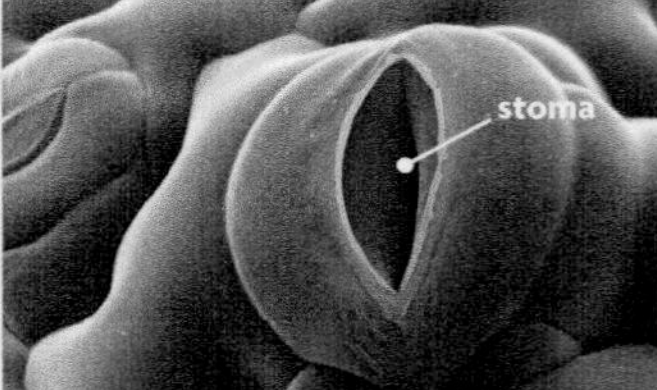

An SEM shows a three-dimensional image of a specimen's surface. (colored SEM; magnification 1500×)

TRANSMISSION ELECTRON MICROGRAPH (TEM)

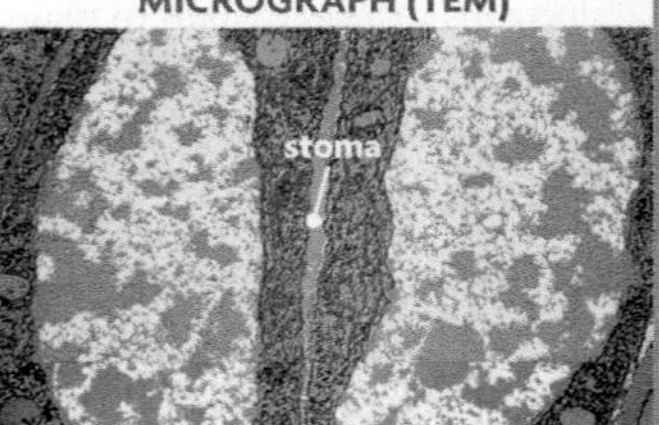

A TEM shows a two-dimensional image of a thin slice of a specimen. (colored TEM; magnification 5000×)

Differentiated Instruction

TEACH WITH TECHNOLOGY

Show students more advanced microscopy techniques. If you have microscopes with oil-immersion objective lenses, show students how to use them. Explain that because light is refracted every time it passes through a medium with a different refractive index (air to glass or vice versa), the quality of the image is reduced. Immersion oil has been formulated so that it has a refractive index identical to that of glass. Thus, there is no refraction of light when it passes from glass to oil.

To demonstrate, remove the glass dropper rod from the oil, and then replace it. **Ask,** What happens to the image of the glass rod? It vanishes. Using oil immersion will enable students to view objects at 1000×. Furnish them with prepared slides of bacteria to view and sketch.

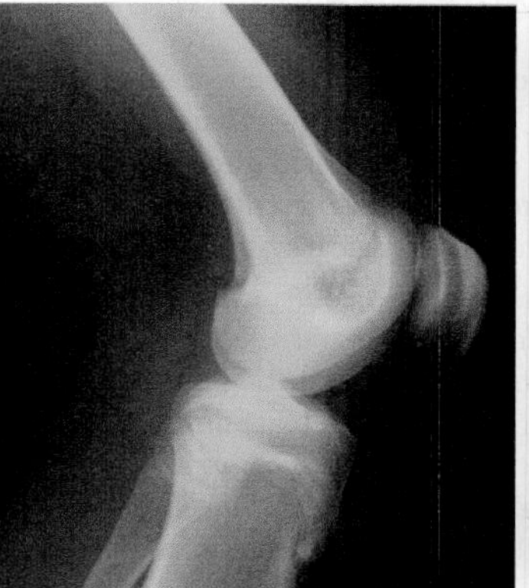
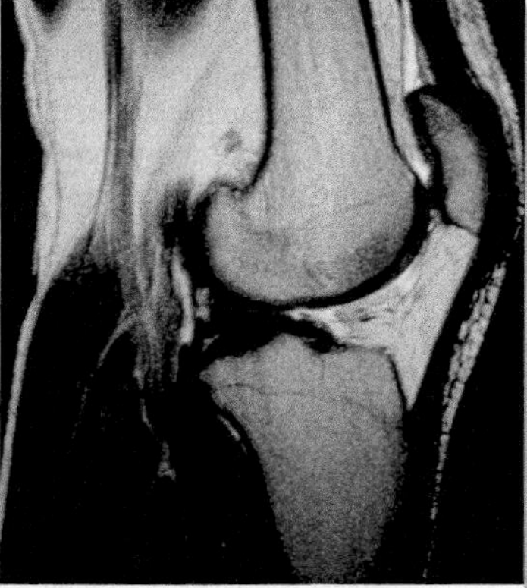

FIGURE 4.4 An x-ray of the human knee (left) shows dense tissues, such as bone, in detail. An MRI of the human knee (right) shows both soft and dense tissues in detail.

Medical Imaging

Imaging technology is not limited to microscopes. For example, doctors or dentists have probably taken x-ray images of you several times. An x-ray image is formed by x-rays, which pass through soft tissues, such as skin and muscle, but are absorbed by bones and teeth. Thus, x-ray images are very useful for looking at the skeleton but not so useful for examining soft tissues such as ligaments, cartilage, or the brain.

To image soft tissues, another imaging technology called magnetic resonance imaging (MRI) is used. MRI uses a strong magnetic field to produce a cross-section image of a part of the body. A series of MRI images can be put together to give a complete view of all of the tissues in that area, as you can see in **FIGURE 4.4.** Advances in technology have led to new uses for MRI. For example, a technique called functional MRI (fMRI) can show which areas of the brain are active while a person is doing a particular task.

Computers and Probeware

The first digital, electronic computers were invented in the 1940s. They were expensive and so large that one computer filled an entire room. As technology improved, computers, computer software, and hardware, such as probeware, have become invaluable to the practice of biology. Word processing software is used to generate reports. Spreadsheet software is used to quickly and accurately calculate, analyze, and display data in charts, graphs, and other visual representations. The use of probeware in conjunction with computers allows both data collection and analysis. Probeware are measuring tools that can take constant readings of data such as temperature and pH. When probeware is connected to a computer, the data can be calculated and analyzed instantly.

A **Infer How might probeware be used by a biologist studying the decline of fish in a certain lake?**

CONNECT TO

IMAGING

Biologists use several types of micrographs, or images from microscopes. Whenever you see a micrograph in this book, the abbreviation *LM* stands for light micrograph, the abbreviation *SEM* stands for scanning electron micrograph, and the abbreviation *TEM* stands for transmission electron micrograph.

Differentiated Instruction

ENGLISH LEARNERS

English learners may be at a disadvantage in comprehending the text's language, but they are as competent as native speakers in interpreting images. Start with **FIGURE 4.3.** Have students describe what they see. Ask how the images are alike and different. Then apply the same technique to **FIGURE 4.4.**

Teacher Toolkit, Section C, Connect to Content through Visuals

Integrating Forensic Science

The term *forensic science* is used to describe the actions taken by investigators during the examination of crime scenes and the gathering of evidence to be used in the prosecution of criminals. The SEM is an important tool in modern forensic science due to its wide range of applications. The SEM allows the rapid analysis of very small specimens of many materials that are important as evidence. Paint particles, natural and artificial fibers, fingerprints, gunshot residue, counterfeit money, and forged documents are all examples of specimens that can be analyzed with a SEM.

Take It Further

A **scanning electron microscope** (SEM) uses a beam of electrons instead of light, but it yields information similar to that of a light microscope. SEMs, however, can magnify objects up to 500,000 times. Different types of SEMs can yield four types of information:

- topography (surface features of an object)
- morphology (shape, size, and arrangement of an object's particles)
- composition (elements and compounds and their relative ratios)
- crystallographic information (arrangement and degree of order of the atoms)

Answers

A **Infer** A biologist studying the decline of fish in a lake may use probeware to assess the temperature, dissolved oxygen, nutrients, amount of light, or other factors that affect fish and their ecosystem over time.

▼ Teach

Take It Further

Lead students in a debate about using probeware and computers to collect and analyze data. For each of the statements below, ask a small group of students to refute each statement and another group to support each statement.

- Using probeware removes skill-building opportunities for students, such as measuring and using mathematics, by automating such steps.
- Purchasing probeware is too expensive to be useful to real scientists.
- Using probeware is inefficient because it requires time-consuming set ups and programming.
- Using probeware eliminates the needs for other science tools.

Students should recognize some advantages and disadvantages to using probeware in education and in scientific research. Students should realize that each statement can be supported or refuted depending on the circumstances of the learning or research situation.

Answers

Ⓐ **Conclude** Some phenomena cannot be studied directly due to ethics, practicality, scale, complexity, or safety.

MAIN IDEA

Complex systems are modeled on computers.

Normal heartbeat

Heart attack

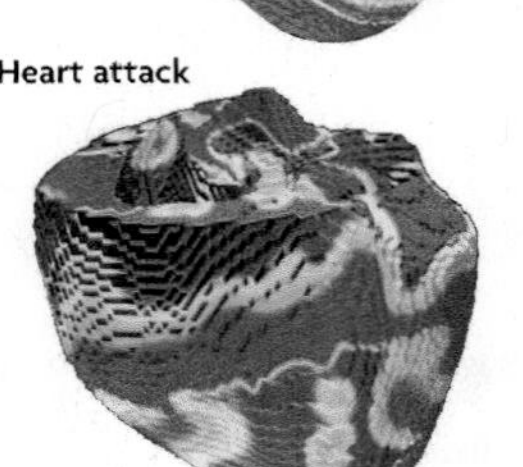

FIGURE 4.5 This computer-generated model shows that heart activity (red) is tightly regulated during a normal heartbeat. During a heart attack, heart activity is widespread and disorganized.

Computer-based technology has greatly expanded biological research. As computers have become faster and more powerful, biologists have found ways to use them to model living systems that cannot be studied directly. A computer model simulates the interactions among many different variables to provide scientists with a general idea of how a biological system may work.

Computers can model complex systems within organisms. For example, computer models are used to study how medicines might affect the body or, as you can see in **FIGURE 4.5**, the effects of a heart attack. Scientists have even used computer models to find out how water molecules travel into and out of cells. The scientists made a computer program that took into account more than 50,000 virtual atoms in a virtual cell. The computer model showed that water molecules must spin around in the middle of a channel, or a passage into the cell, to fit through the channel. Water molecules had a specific fit that other molecules could not match.

Computer models can also help biologists study complex systems on a much larger scale. Epidemiology, which is the study of how diseases spread, depends on computer models. For example, the computer model in **FIGURE 4.6** can predict how fast and how far a disease might spread through a herd of cattle. A model can calculate the number of cattle who might get sick and suggest where the disease could be spread to humans through eating contaminated meat or other sources. This study cannot be done with real cattle and people. Computer models are used when actual experiments are not safe, ethical, or practical. However, all models have limitations, and they are not able to replicate exactly all aspects of the system they are showing.

Ⓐ Conclude **What are some reasons why biologists use computer models?**

FIGURE 4.6 Computer Simulation

Computer simulations can help epidemiologists to predict the spread of disease and to develop a response plan.

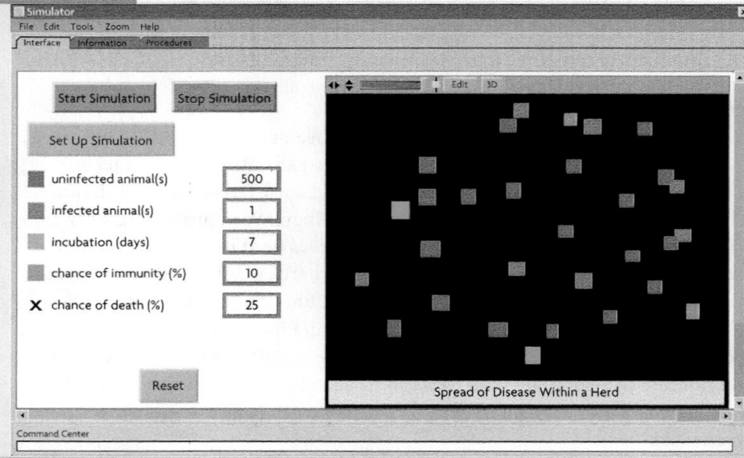

Differentiated Instruction

BELOW LEVEL

Remind students of the importance of making observations in science. Have students write for five minutes on the question of how technology affects our ability or capacity to make observations, using examples from this section. Tell students to write continually during the whole time and not to worry about style.

Teacher Toolkit, Section C, Quick-Write

MAIN IDEA

The tools of molecular genetics give rise to new biological studies.

Computer-based technologies, such as those shown in **FIGURE 4.7**, have led to major changes in biology. But perhaps the greatest leap forward in our knowledge of life has happened in genetics. In just 40 years, we have gone from learning how the genetic code works, to changing genes, to implanting genes from one species into another.

What is a gene? A **gene** is a segment of DNA that stores genetic information. Our understanding of the DNA molecule has led to many technologies that were unimaginable a few decades ago—genetically modified foods, transgenic plants and animals, even replacement of faulty genes. These advances come from molecular genetics. **Molecular genetics** is the study and manipulation of DNA on a molecular level. Molecular genetics is used to study evolution, ecology, biochemistry, and many other areas of biology.

Entirely new areas of biology have arisen from combining molecular genetics with computer technology. For example, computers are used to quickly find DNA sequences. Through the use of computers, the entire DNA sequences, or genomes, of humans and other organisms have been found. **Genomics** (juh-NOH-mihks) is the study and comparison of genomes both within and across species.

All of the information from genomics is managed by computer databases. By searching computer databases, a process called data mining, a biologist can find patterns, similarities, and differences in biological data. Suppose a biologist identifies a molecule that prevents the growth of cancerous tumors. The biologist could use computer databases to search for similar molecules.

This is the cutting edge of biology today. Where will biology be when your children are in high school?

A Connect **What does the term genetics mean to you? Why?**

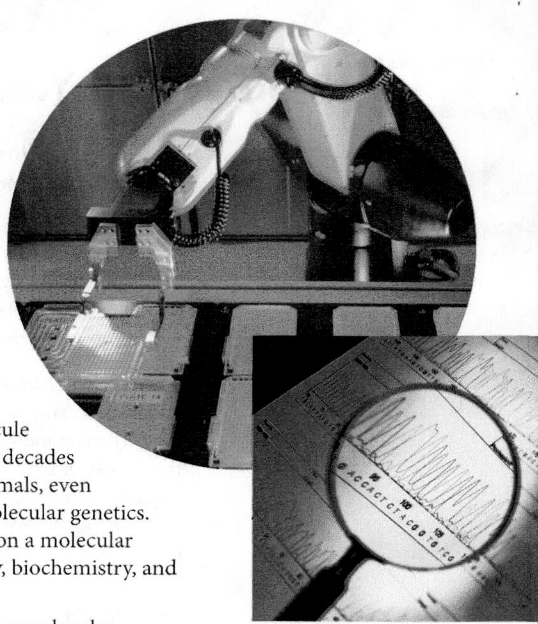

FIGURE 4.7 Robots are used to speed up research into the human genome (top). Computers are used to sequence human DNA (bottom).

CONNECT TO

GENETICS

You will learn much more about these and other genetics topics in the **Genetics** unit.

SELF-CHECK Online
HMHScience.com
GO ONLINE

1.4 Formative Assessment

REVIEWING MAIN IDEAS

1. What are two ways scientists can describe the quality of **measurements**?
2. Why is computer modeling used in biological studies?
3. Why do computer models have limitations?

CRITICAL THINKING

4. **Apply** Viruses are smaller than cells. What types of microscopes could be used to study them? Explain.
5. **Synthesize** Provide an example of how technology has helped biologists gain a better understanding of life.

CONNECT TO

EVOLUTION

6. **Genomics** can be used to study the *genetic* relationships among species. Why might genomics be important for research on evolution? Explain.

Integrating Genetics

The **Human Genome Project** (HGP) is the international research program with the goal of completely mapping all the genes of human beings. The HGP has revealed that there are approximately 30,000 human genes. This is the basic set of inheritable instructions for the development and function of a human being. The full sequence of genetic information (all of the DNA in the human genome) was completed in April 2003, many years ahead of schedule due mainly to the simultaneous development of computer programs that could very quickly analyze the genetic information. Another major component of the HGP is devoted to the analysis of the ethical, legal, and social implications of this new genetic knowledge. The Human Genome Project is discussed in more detail in Frontiers of Biotechnology.

Answers

A **Connect** Answers may include topics from popular culture, such as cloning, forensics, and mutation.

Assess and Reteach

Assess Use the Section Self-Check or Section Quiz, both available at **HMHScience.com**.

Reteach Remind students that one way to define technology is an innovation that allows humans to manipulate their environment. Have students go through the different forms of technology discussed in this section and describe what form that manipulation takes and how it benefits us.

1.4 FORMATIVE ASSESSMENT

1. accuracy and precision
2. to model anything that is not practical or ethical to do in the real world
3. Computer models, like all models, cannot exactly replicate the system it is showing, thus the model is limited.
4. Light microscopes are not powerful enough to clearly view viruses, so electron microscopes would need to be used.
5. Answers could include imaging technologies showing more details of cells, computer analysis of genes and genomes, and computer models.
6. By comparing the genomes of different species, scientists can establish how closely related species are by finding occurrences of shared DNA sequences and genes.

SECTION 1.5

▼ Plan and Prepare

Activate Prior Knowledge Discuss the steps that people take when making important decisions. **Ask,** How would you characterize some of the factors you take into account when making an important decision? social, economic, ethical, moral Explain that knowing as much as they can about biology can help them make informed decisions about their health, the environment, how they vote, and how they act as citizens.

▼ Teach

Take It Further

Allergic reactions to peanuts range from itching or swelling of the lips, tongue, or mouth to shortness of breath and a drop in blood pressure. Sometimes the allergy is so severe that even cross-contaminated equipment in the food processing facility can cause a deadly reaction. Because of this, companies sometimes put warning statements such as "may contain peanuts" on the label. Foods with these labels could be unsafe for people with a peanut allergy.

1.5 Biology and Your Future

KEY CONCEPT **Understanding biology can help you make informed decisions.**

VOCABULARY
biotechnology
transgenic

MAIN IDEAS
- Your health and the health of the environment depend on your knowledge of biology.
- Biotechnology offers great promise but also raises many issues.
- Biology presents many unanswered questions.

Connect to Your World

Should brain imaging technology be used to tell if someone is lying? Is an endangered moth's habitat more important than a new highway? Would you vote for or against the pursuit of stem cell research? An informed answer to any of these questions requires an understanding of biology and scientific thinking. And although science alone cannot answer these questions, gathering evidence and analyzing data can help every decision maker.

MAIN IDEA

Your health and the health of the environment depend on your knowledge of biology.

Decisions are based on opinions, emotions, education, experiences, values, and logic. Many of your decisions, now and in the future, at both personal and societal levels, involve biology. Your knowledge of biology can help you make informed decisions about issues involving endangered species, biotechnology, medical research, and pollution control, to name a few. How will your decisions affect the future of yourself and others?

Biology and Your Health

What you eat and drink is directly related to your health. But you may not think twice about the possibility of contaminated food or water, or a lack of vitamins in your diet. Not long ago, diseases caused by vitamin deficiencies were still fairly common. The first vitamins were identified less than 100 years ago, but today the vitamins found in foods are printed on labels.

Even today we still face food-related causes of illness. For example, you might hear about an outbreak of food poisoning, and mad cow disease was only recognized in the late 1980s. Of perhaps greater concern to you are food allergies. Many people suffer from severe, even life-threatening, allergies to foods such as peanuts and shellfish. Beyond questions about the sources of food are questions and concerns about what people eat and how much they eat. For example, scientists estimate that more than 69% of adults in the United States are overweight or obese. The health consequences of obesity include increased risks of diabetes, stroke, heart disease, breast cancer, colon cancer, and other health problems. Biology can help you to better understand all of these health-related issues.

READING TOOLBOX

TAKING NOTES

Use a mind map to take notes about the importance of studying biology.

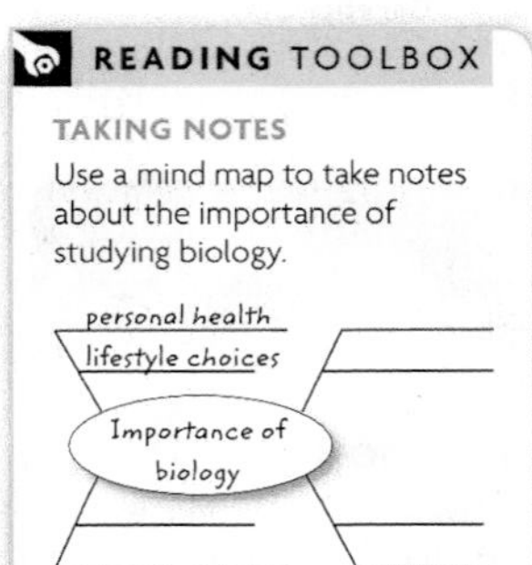

Differentiated Instruction

PRE-AP

Have students brainstorm designing a decision-making model with at least four steps. Give students the first step: Identify the issue or question. Subsequent steps could include gathering information about both sides of the issue, identifying options, listing benefits and consequences, considering personal values, deciding, and acting. Display the model, and suggest a question to which students can apply the model.

Teacher Toolkit, Section C, Brainstorming

An understanding of biology on many different levels—genetic, chemical, and cellular, for example—can help you make any number of lifestyle choices that affect your health. Why is it important to use sunscreen? What are the benefits of exercise? What are the effects of using alcohol, illegal drugs, and tobacco? Cigarette smoke does not just affect the lungs, as shown in **FIGURE 5.1**; it can also change a person's body chemistry. Lower levels of monoamine oxidase in the brain can affect mood, and lower levels in the liver could contribute to high blood pressure.

FIGURE 5.1 As compared with nonsmokers, smokers have visibly damaged lung tissue that is blackened by tar deposits.

Biology and the World Around You

In 1995, some middle school students from Minnesota were walking through a wetland and collecting frogs for a school project. The students stopped to look at the frogs, and what they saw shocked them. Many of the frogs had deformities, including missing legs, extra legs, and missing eyes. What caused the deformities? Scientists investigated that question by testing several hypotheses. They studied whether the deformities could have been caused by factors such as a chemical in the water, ultraviolet radiation, or some type of infection.

Why would frog deformities such as that in **FIGURE 5.2** provoke such scientific interest? The frogs are a part of an ecosystem, so whatever affected them could affect other species in the area. If the deformities were caused by a chemical in the water, might the chemical pose a risk to people living in the area? In other regions of the United States, parasites caused similar deformities in frogs. Might that parasite also be present in Minnesota? If so, did it pose a risk to other species?

At first, parasites were not found in the frogs. However, scientists now suggest that the frog deformities were due to a combination of infection by parasites, called trematodes, and predation by dragonfly nymphs. Science has answered some questions about the cause of the leg deformities. However, scientists now think that a chemical may be connected to the increased number of parasite infections.

FIGURE 5.2 Deformities in frogs can be an indication of chemical pollution in an ecosystem.

Suppose that the chemical comes from a factory in the area. Is it reasonable to ban the chemical? Should the factory be closed or fined? In any instance like this, political, legal, economic, and biological concerns have to be considered. What is the economic impact of the factory on the area? Is there any evidence of human health problems in the area? Is there a different chemical that could be used? Without an understanding of biology, how could you make an informed decision related to any of these questions?

These are the types of questions that people try to answer every day. Biologists and other scientists research environmental issues such as pollution, biodiversity, habitat preservation, land conservation, and natural resource use, but decisions about the future are not in the hands of scientists. It is up to everyone to make decisions based on evidence and conclusions from many different sources.

A Connect **How might biology help you to better understand environmental issues?**

ENGLISH LEARNERS

Use the section Biology and the World Around You to model how to interpret text. Ask volunteers to read the text aloud and then read through parts of it again to establish what happened, why it was important, what concerns were raised, and what we know so far. Use direct sentence structure when talking about or paraphrasing the material. Place main clauses before subordinate ones, use short and simple sentences, and avoid interrupting clauses.

TEACH FROM VISUALS

FIGURE 5.2 Tell students that research has shown that abnormalities are rare among laboratory-reared frogs—less than 0.05%. **Ask,** What can you infer from this fact? An environmental factor is the cause of the abnormalities.

Take It Further

In the two years that followed the discovery of the Minnesota **frog deformities** in 1995, reports of deformities increased but were restricted to one species, the northern leopard frog. In 1997, the number of reports and species involved increased. Six species of deformed frogs were documented at more than 150 sites across 54 counties in Minnesota. The malformations found included increases or decreases in the number of feet, legs, toes, and eyes, as well as musculoskeletal and urogenital defects. Among some populations, as many as 60% of frogs had abnormalities.

Integrating Epidemiology

Epidemiology is the study of factors that cause illness and disease in populations. Epidemiologists are consulted when acute conditions or diseases affect a small number of people in the same community because most diseases are not randomly distributed. For example, epidemiologists investigated cancer clusters reported in Toms River, New Jersey, and Woburn, Massachusetts, that were thought to be caused by industrial pollutants. An epidemiologist uses scientific inquiry and experimentation to determine the relationship between a disease and its cause and the implications for public health. Principles of science, statistics, philosophy, anthropology, psychology, and social policy are integrated into epidemiological investigations.

Answers

A Connect Answers should indicate a knowledge of the interactions among living things in an ecosystem.

Take It Further

In 1963, **Thomas Starzl** performed the first liver transplant. Starzl has since become known as the father of transplantation. More than 60,000 people are alive today due to organ transplants, with more than 111,000 Americans on waiting lists.

To address the lack of human organs available for transplant, Starzl researched **xenotransplantation,** which is the transfer of cells, tissues, or organs from one species to another. Between 1963 and 1993, Starzl transplanted into humans six baboon kidneys, three chimpanzee livers, and two baboon livers. All of the transplants were unsuccessful. Starzl does not view xenotransplants as permanent replacements, just temporary fixes until an appropriate human organ is located. The risks of xenotransplants are organ rejection and infection spread from donor animals to humans.

MAIN IDEA

Biotechnology offers great promise but also raises many issues.

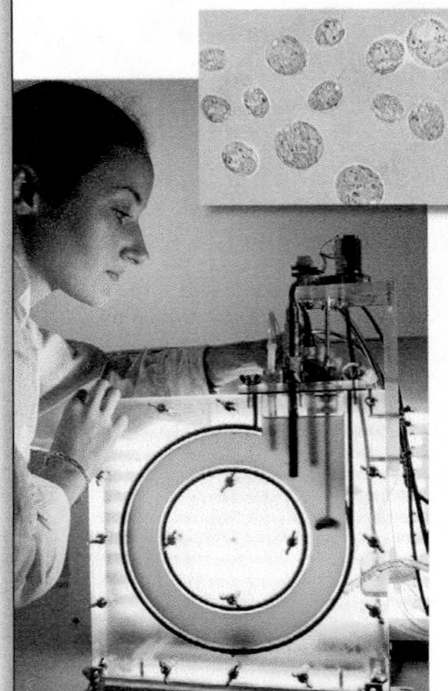

FIGURE 5.3 Biotechnology is being used in the search for alternative energy sources, as shown in this bioreactor that uses algae (inset) to produce hydrogen gas. (LM; magnification 400×)

Biotechnology is the use and application of living things and biological processes. Biotechnology includes a very broad range of products, processes, and techniques. In fact, some forms of biotechnology have been around for centuries, such as the use of microorganisms to make bread and cheese. Today, biotechnology is used in medicine, agriculture, forensic science, and many other fields. For example, people wrongly convicted of crimes have been freed from prison when DNA testing has shown that their DNA did not match DNA found at crime scenes. Biotechnology has great potential to help solve a variety of modern problems, such as the search for alternative energy sources using algae, as shown in **FIGURE 5.3.** However, along with the advances in biotechnology come questions about its uses.

Benefits and Biological Risks

All domestic plants and animals are the result of centuries of genetic manipulation through selective breeding. Today, genetic manipulation can mean the transfer of genetic information from one organism to a very different organism. Organisms that have genes from more than one species, or have altered copies of their own genes, are called **transgenic** organisms. Transgenic bacteria can make human insulin to treat people with diabetes. Transgenic sheep and cows can make human antibodies and proteins. When you hear about genetically modified foods, you are hearing about transgenic organisms.

Genetically modified foods have many potential benefits. Crop plants are changed to increase the nutrients and yield of the plants and to resist insects. Insect-resistant crops could reduce or end the need for chemical pesticides. However, the long-term effects of genetically modified crops are not fully known. Is it safe to eat foods with genetically modified insect resistance? What if genetically modified plants spread undesirable genes, such as those for herbicide resistance, to wild plants? Around the world, the benefits and risks of biotechnology are debated. Understanding these benefits and risks requires knowledge of ecosystems, genetic principles, and even the functions of genes.

Benefits and Ethical Considerations

Another form of biotechnology is human genetic screening, which is the analysis of a person's genes to identify genetic variations. Genetic screening can indicate whether individuals or their potential offspring may be at risk for certain diseases or genetic disorders. Genetic screening has the potential for early diagnosis of conditions that can be treated before an illness occurs.

Genetic screening also raises ethical concerns. For example, who should have access to a person's genetic information? Some people are concerned that insurance companies might refuse health insurance to someone with a gene that might cause a disease. Suppose genetic screening reveals that a child might have a genetic disorder. How should that information be used? Genetic screening has the potential to eliminate some disorders, but what should be

CONNECT TO

GENETICS

You will learn more about genetic screening and how it is used in the chapter **Frontiers of Biotechnology.**

Differentiated Instruction

HANDS-ON ACTIVITY

Introduce social issues and current science topics into the science classroom by having students bring in articles on life science and biotechnology from newspapers and magazines. An example of this might be having students bring in articles about stem cells. Set aside class time regularly to discuss the articles.

Tell students that the study of life science will introduce topics about which there will be different points of view. Solicit their help in creating an environment in which students are expected to respect the right of others to express those views.

considered a disorder? Of greater concern is the possibility that people might use genetic screening to choose the characteristics of their children. Is it ethical to allow people to choose to have only brown-eyed male children who would be at least 6 feet (ft) tall?

A Predict **How might genetically modified crops affect biodiversity?**

Bioethics

For more on bioethics, see the WebQuest at **HMHScience.com**.

MAIN IDEA

Biology presents many unanswered questions.

The structure of DNA was described in 1953. By 2003, the entire human DNA sequence was known. Since 1953, our biological knowledge has exploded. But even today there are more questions than answers. Can cancer be prevented or cured? How do viruses mutate? How are memories stored in the brain? One of the most interesting questions is whether life exists on planets other than Earth. Extreme environments on Earth are home to living things like the methane worms in **FIGURE 5.4.** Thus, it is logical to suspect that other planets may also support life. But even if life exists elsewhere in the universe, it may be completely different from life on Earth. How might biological theories change to take into account the characteristics of those organisms?

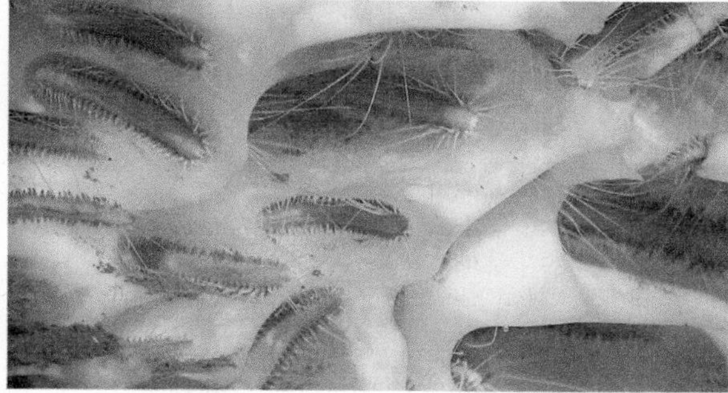

FIGURE 5.4 Methane hydrate ice worms live in frozen methane gas at the bottom of the Gulf of Mexico. Because some organisms can live in such extreme environments, some scientists hypothesize that life exists, or once existed, on the planet Mars.

A large number of questions in biology are not just unanswered—they are unasked. Before the microscope was developed, no one investigated anything microscopic. Before the middle of the 20th century, biologists did not know for sure what the genetic material in organisms was made of. As technology and biology advance, who knows what will be discovered in the next 20 years?

B Evaluate **Do you think technology can help answer all biological questions? Explain your views.**

Take It Further

Discuss with students that like the methane worms in **FIGURE 5.4,** many organisms alive on Earth today are hardy enough to withstand, even flourish, in extremely harsh environments. *Thermophilic bacteria* live in pools of boiling water at Yellowstone National Park, where water boils at 92°C (198°F). Dense colonies of mussels form around the edge of extremely salty holes in the ocean floor. The **brine pools** are so salty and dense that a submersible vehicle such as the Alvin can sit on top of them with its engines off.

Answers

A Predict If only a few varieties of crop plants are used, biodiversity will decrease.

B Evaluate No, because at this time we can only directly study a limited number of biological phenomena, even with advances in technology. There are always questions to be asked and investigated, and technology is a part of the search for answers.

1.5 Formative Assessment

SELF-CHECK Online
HMHScience.com
GO ONLINE

REVIEWING MAIN IDEAS

1. Give three examples of ways in which biology can help inform everyday decisions.
2. What are some of the potential benefits and potential risks of **biotechnology**?
3. What are some of the unanswered questions in biology?

CRITICAL THINKING

4. **Synthesize** Scientists disagree on whether genetically modified foods are safe to eat. What type of scientific evidence would be needed to show that a genetically modified food is unsafe?
5. **Connect** How might your study of biology help inform you about your lifestyle choices?

CONNECT TO ECOLOGY

6. What effects might genetically modified plants and animals have on an ecosystem if they breed with wild plants and animals?

1.5 FORMATIVE ASSESSMENT

1. *Sample answer:* Knowledge of biology can inform decisions about diet, use of sunscreen, and exercise.
2. benefits: treatment and prevention of disease and illness, improving crop growth; risks: ethical concerns, privacy, potential negative health and environmental effects
3. Answers could include questions about life on other planets, cancer, viruses, or memory.
4. *Sample answer:* Evidence may include long-term feeding trials comparing health of animals that do and do not eat GM foods. The best evidence will be collected over time with humans. Over several years, there will be more data about the health of people who eat GM foods compared with people who do not.
5. A knowledge of biology helps you make informed decisions about lifestyle choices that could affect your health and quality of life and the health of the environment.
6. They could decrease biodiversity and affect an ecosystem in unpredictable ways.

Assess and Reteach

Assess Use the Section Self-Check or Section Quiz, both available at **HMHScience.com.**

Reteach Have students recall recent news stories of developments in the biological sciences. Discuss whether these developments have the potential to raise social or ethical questions, as well as scientific ones. Discuss the question of science literacy in evaluating these stories.

GO ONLINE

Encourage students to go to **HMHScience.com** for a detailed review of each section, including visuals and vocabulary practice.

Online Student Resources, Vocabulary Practice Worksheet

CHAPTER 1 Summary

BIG IDEA Biology is the scientific study of all aspects of living things and it shapes our understanding of our world, from human health to biotechnology to environmental preservation.

KEY CONCEPTS

1.1 The Study of Life

Science is the knowledge obtained through observation of natural events and conditions in order to discover facts and formulate laws or principles that can be verified or tested. Biology is the study of all forms of life and their interactions with each other and the environment. Everywhere that organisms are found on Earth is considered to be the biosphere. Biology has been studied throughout history.

1.2 Unifying Themes of Biology

Unifying themes connect concepts from many fields of biology. Organisms are made of one or more cells, need energy for all of their functions, respond to their environment, and reproduce by passing their genetic information to offspring. Interactions occur at various levels, from chemical processes within cells to interactions between species within an ecosystem. Individual organisms depend on the relationship between structure and function, and on the ability to maintain homeostasis. Over billions of years, evolution and adaptation have given rise to all of the species on Earth.

1.3 Scientific Thinking and Processes

Science is a way of thinking, questioning, and gathering evidence. Scientists test hypotheses, or proposed explanations, through observation and experimentation. In a scientific experiment, a scientist controls constants, manipulates independent variables, and measures dependent variables. A scientific theory explains a wide range of observations and experimental results. A theory is supported by a wide range of evidence, and it is widely accepted by the scientific community.

1.4 Biologists' Tools and Technology

Technology continually changes the way biologists work. Observation and measurement result in the data that are analyzed in scientific study. Tools for observation and measurement improve as technology improves. The development of fast, powerful computers and probeware has given scientists the ability to quickly and accurately analyze data and model aspects of life that cannot be studied directly.

1.5 Biology and Your Future

Understanding biology can help you make informed decisions. An understanding of biology can help you to make important decisions about your own health and lifestyle, as well as decisions that will shape the world around you. The development of biotechnology and genetic manipulation is just one issue in biology that will affect you and the rest of society in the coming years.

READING TOOLBOX SYNTHESIZE YOUR NOTES

Content Frame Identify relationships between the characteristics of living things and the unifying themes of biology. Use your notes to make content frame organizers like the one below to summarize the relationships.

Characteristic	Theme	Example
Cells	Systems	Cells work together in multicellular organisms.
	Structure and Function	

Concept Map Use concept maps like the one below to visualize general relationships among topics in biology.

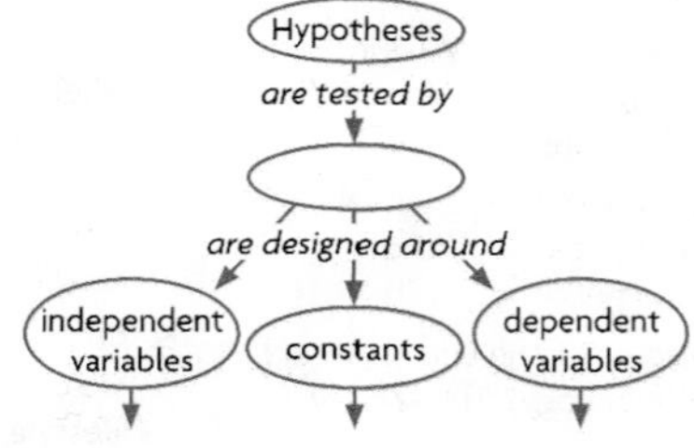

Reviewing Vocabulary

1. Organisms live in both; the biosphere contains all ecosystems.
2. Both try to answer a scientific question, but a theory encompasses a large quantity of observations and experimental results, and a hypothesis applies to just one experiment.
3. Both describe the quality of a set of measurements. Accuracy describes how close measurements are to the actual value,; precision describes how close the measurements are to each other.
4. What is it that natural selection acts upon to bring about evolution?
5. Observations are typically qualitative in nature: what do scientists collect to measure natural phenomena?
6. What part of the DNA sequence in a genome contains genetic information?
7. All of the terms relate to the study of living things.
8. stopping change to internal conditions, keeping them at the same point

1 Review

INTERACTIVE Review
HMHScience.com
GO ONLINE
Review Games • Concept Map • Section Self-Checks

CHAPTER VOCABULARY

1.1 biosphere, biodiversity, species, biology, science

1.2 organism, cell, metabolism, DNA, system, ecosystem, homeostasis, evolution, adaptation

1.3 observation, data, hypothesis, experiment, independent variable, dependent variable, constant, theory

1.4 measurement, accuracy, precision, microscope, gene, molecular genetics, genomics

1.5 biotechnology, transgenic

Reviewing Vocabulary

Compare and Contrast

Describe one similarity and one difference between the two terms in each of the following pairs.

1. biosphere, ecosystem
2. hypothesis, theory
3. accuracy, precision

Write Your Own Questions

Think about the relationship between each word pair below. Then write a question about the first term that uses the second term as the answer. For the terms *organism, cell,* the question could be "What is the basic building block of all organisms?" Answer: the cell

4. evolution, adaptation
5. observation, data
6. DNA, gene

READING TOOLBOX GREEK AND LATIN WORD ORIGINS

7. The prefix *bio-* means "life." How does this meaning relate to the definitions of terms in the chapter that contain the prefix *bio-*?

8. The prefix *homeo-* comes from a Greek word that means "same." The suffix *-stasis* comes from a Greek word that means "stoppage," or "standstill." How are these definitions related to the meaning of the word *homeostasis?*

Reviewing MAIN IDEAS

9. Why is it important that biology studies the interactions of organisms with both their environments and other organisms?

10. Explain why domestication of plants and animals was likely one of the first areas of biology.

11. Briefly describe the basic characteristics that all living things on Earth have in common.

12. Give an example of how structure and function are related in an organism.

13. How does negative feedback act to maintain homeostasis in living things?

14. Explain how scientists use observations and data to develop a hypothesis.

15. What is the difference between a scientific hypothesis and a scientific theory?

16. Explain the difference between tools that enhance senses and tools that are used for measurements.

17. Briefly describe why the development of the microscope was important in biology.

18. How can an understanding of biology play a role in your health? in the health of your environment?

19. Describe an example of biotechnology, including its benefits and risks.

CHAPTER REVIEW

Reviewing Main Ideas

9. The biosphere includes all living things and all the places they are found. Organisms interact with and depend on biotic (living) and abiotic (nonliving) factors in their environment, so it is important that both are studied.
10. Domestication of plants and animals would allow humans to raise crops and livestock for food and materials instead of using a hunter-gatherer method. Farming is much more efficient than hunting and gathering. Farming enables people to stay in one place and develop other societal skills and characteristics.
11. They all have one or more cells, which are the basic units of life. They all need energy to carry out cell functions. They all need to respond to the environment to survive. They must be able to reproduce to maintain the species.
12. Molecules with different structures have different functions; specialized cells have structures that allow them to perform their functions; different parts of multicellular organisms are specialized to perform different functions.
13. It acts to reverse a change in conditions to bring the conditions back to normal levels.
14. Scientists propose explanations for observations and data to form hypotheses.
15. A hypothesis addresses one scientific question (observation or experiment); a theory is a proposed explanation for a wide range of observations and experimental results that are supported by evidence.
16. Tools that enhance the senses, such as hand lenses, microscopes, and recording devices, allow scientists to make qualitative observations that would otherwise be difficult or impossible. Tools that are used for measurement allow the collection of quantitative data.
17. Microscopes have allowed for great advances in the study of living things. For example, different types of microscopes allow for the study of things too small to be seen with the human eye. The development of the microscope led to the discovery of cells and microorganisms. Modern microscopes show the internal structure of cells.
18. It allows you to make informed decisions on health and environmental concerns such as smoking, diet, exercise, sunscreen use, pollution, habitat preservation, and natural-resource use.
19. *Sample answers:* GM foods (benefits: improved crop yield; risks: loss of biodiversity and possible long-term health effects); genetic screening (benefits: detection of genetic diseases; risk: privacy).

Critical Thinking

20. Banning DDT allowed affected populations of fish and birds to recover. Humans are part of the same ecosystems as fish and birds, and toxins that affect those animals may also affect humans. Removing a toxic chemical from the environment decreases risks to human health.
21. The student can review the scientific information to find evidence that supports claims; this supports the validity of the claims. The student can also review the information for bias, including how the source could benefit from making the claim. The student can compare the information to other research from previous existing projects.
22. *Sample answer:* Scientific research can teach us about human health and the environment in order to treat human illnesses and protect the environment from human impact. Scientific research is expensive and does not always provide answers. Sometimes research can uncover more challenges to a problem.
23. No, because two variables were manipulated, it is not possible to determine which one produced the effect.
24. Science is limited to studying phenomena that can be tested because scientific knowledge depends on proof and evidence. Answers will vary but could include any two questions that are outside the realm of science, such as those that are based on the supernatural.

Interpreting Visuals

25. At all points of the scientific thinking cycle; observations help scientists carefully consider information and data.
26. during the "Evaluating Results" step

Critical Thinking

20. Synthesize In 1973, the insecticide called DDT was banned in the United States due to scientific research showing it was toxic to fish and that it may have affected birds. There is little scientific evidence that DDT is directly harmful to humans. How could banning DDT be beneficial to human health and society?

21. Apply A student is trying to predict the effects on wildlife of a proposed construction project in an undeveloped area nearby. Describe how the student can evaluate scientific information extracted from news reports, marketing materials, and online resources.

22. Evaluate Discuss the impact of scientific research on society and the environment. Consider the benefits and risks of scientific research and the challenges that unanswered questions leave for biologists and other scientists to wrestle with.

23. Evaluate Suppose a scientist is investigating plant growth. During the experiment, both the type of light and the type of plant are manipulated. The scientist concludes that the results are caused only by changes in the light. Is this an appropriate conclusion? Why or why not?

24. Justify Why is science limited to studying phenomena that are scientifically testable? Give two examples of questions that are outside the realm of science.

Interpreting Visuals

Use the diagram below to answer the next two questions.

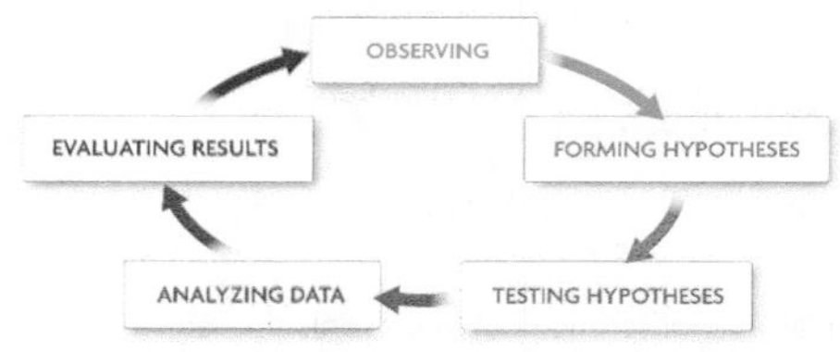

25. Apply Observing is shown at only one point during the cycle. At what other points during the cycle is observing necessary? Explain.

26. Distinguish Where in the process are scientists most likely to make inferences and predict trends from data?

Analyzing Data Identify Data Types

Use the information below to answer the next three questions.

Suppose a team of scientists is studying the migration of animal species in Africa. One of the scientists takes the photograph below.

27. Apply Give three examples each of quantitative and qualitative data that could be collected during this research.

28. Identify What are four tools that the team of scientists likely used while conducting, analyzing, and communicating their work? Explain your answer.

29. Evaluate Suppose the scientists wanted to change the number of species present in this study. What are some limitations and advantages of using a computer model to simulate the change?

Making Connections

30. Defend Much of the work and ideas of early scientists, such as Hippocrates's four humours and Aristotle's classification system for animals, were shown to be incorrect and have been discarded or replaced. Why, then, are early Greeks credited as the fathers or inventors of science?

31. Analyze The yellow fever mosquito shown on the Chapter Opener is just one type of mosquito that can pass disease-causing viruses to people. Mosquitoes can also carry other diseases such as malaria, Dengue fever, and West Nile virus. And even if mosquitoes do not carry dangerous viruses, they are certainly pests. On the other hand, mosquitoes are a source of food for many types of animals. Suppose you developed a way to rid Earth of mosquitoes. Do you think it should be used? Why or why not?

Analyzing Data

27. Answers could include any three qualitative observations, such as a description of landscape and climate, and behavior of animals and their distribution, and any three quantitative or measurable observations, such as the number of different species and number of animals of each species, and relative proportion of one species to another.
28. Answers could include any tools and descriptions of use that are appropriate to the situation, such as binoculars for better visuals, lab notebook for writing observations, camera for taking photographs, thermometer for measuring temperature, or computer software for writing a report of the investigation.
29. The computer model is limited because it cannot show exactly what would happen in a real situation. However, the advantages of using a computer model to alter an ecosystem include the ability to manipulate the variables, which might be unrealistic or unethical in real life.

Standards-Based Assessment

Record your answers on a separate piece of paper.

MULTIPLE CHOICE

1 Finch species in the Galapagos Islands have a wide variety of beak shapes. The theory of natural selection suggests that these differences arose because —

A changes occurred over a short period of time
B finches with certain beak shapes survived in greater numbers
C conscious decisions allowed certain finches to survive
D individual finches adapted to their environment

2

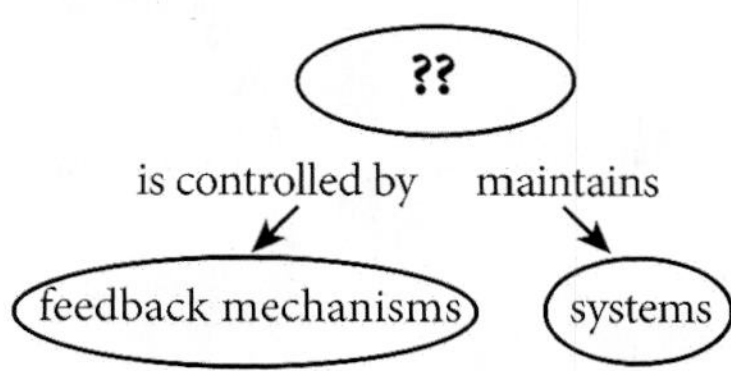

Which of the following ***best*** completes this concept map?

A biodiversity
B homeostasis
C evolution
D adaptation

3 Based on their limitations, which of the following models is the ***best*** representation of how the human skeletal and muscular systems work together to produce motion?

A a detailed illustration in a textbook
B a skeleton made up of human bones that can be manually manipulated
C a computer simulation of the skeletal and muscular systems in motion
D a human running on a treadmill

4 A student is provided with a sample of pond water that contains a variety of single-celled organisms. How might the student determine if any of the organisms in the sample are in the process of reproducing?

A Examine the pond water with a hand lens to determine if the water in the sample is moving.
B Examine a sample of the pond water with a compound microscope to determine if any of the cells are dividing into two cells.
C Observe a drop of pond water with a compound microscope, return the drop back to the larger sample, and then repeat the process every hour for three hours to see if the population size changes.
D Examine the pond water with a compound microscope to determine whether the single-celled organisms it contains are moving.

5 Students hypothesized that water pollution affects the growth of fish. In an experiment, they added the same amount of food to ponds polluted by fertilizers and industrial waste. They measured fish growth and found that most fish grow slowly in each of these environments. Why is their conclusion not reliable?

A They did not have a control.
B They did not have a clear hypothesis.
C They only tested one independent variable.
D They did not have a dependent variable.

THINK THROUGH THE QUESTION

When scientists study how one thing affects another, the investigation generally has a control, a testable hypothesis, one manipulated (independent) variable, and one measured (dependent) variable. Are these components present in the student's experiment?

Standards-Based Assessment

The Standards-Based Assessment questions will help students prepare for their final examination in the course. If you wish to give students practice in coding their answers, look for the Standards-Based Assessment Answer Sheet at **HMHScience.com**. To give students practice under timed testing conditions, allow them five minutes per question.

Question	Answer	Depth of Knowledge	Cognitive Complexity
1	B	II	M
2	B	I	M
3	C	II	M
4	B	IV	M
5	A	II	M

KEY

Depth of Knowledge		Cognitive Complexity	
I	Recall	L	Low
II	Skill/Concept	M	Moderate
III	Strategic Thinking	H	High
IV	Extended Thinking		

Making Connections

30. Early Greeks are credited with originating the practices and processes of modern science. While their discoveries have since been overturned, their methods of discovery are still used.
31. Students should describe the effects of removing mosquitoes from Earth in terms of biodiversity, ecosystems, the biosphere, and risks and benefits.

CHAPTER 2

Instruction and Intervention Support

Chemistry of Life

① Core Instruction

The **Core Instruction** resources below can be used for all students. Core instruction should be followed by ongoing assessment to determine which students need further help.

Available in both English and Spanish

Available Online

Section	Instruction	PRINT	ONLINE	Labs
2.1	Textbook **Atoms, Ions, and Molecules**	■	●	
	Animated Biology Ionic Bonding in Salt, Atoms and Bonding		●	
	Teaching Visuals Atom Models (Fig. 1.2), Ionic and Covalent Bonds (Fig. 1.3, 1.4)		●	
	PowerPresentation and Notes 2.1		●	
2.2	Textbook **Properties of Water**	■	●	Testing pH Acids and Bases (Probeware Lab)
	Animated Biology Hydrogen Bonding		●	
	Teaching Visuals Hydrogen Bonds (Fig. 2.2), Understanding pH (Fig. 2.5)		●	
	PowerPresentation and Notes 2.2		●	
2.3	Textbook **Carbon-Based Molecules**	■	●	Modeling Biochemical Compounds
	Teaching Visuals Carbon-Based Molecules (Fig. 3.3, 3.5, 3.7)		●	
	PowerPresentation and Notes 2.3		●	
2.4	Textbook **Chemical Reactions**	■	●	Chemical Reactions (Open Inquiry) The Biochemistry of Compost Bins (Challenge Lab, Design Your Own) **QuickLab** Chemical Bonding **Virtual Lab** Calorimetry
	Animated Biology Energy and Chemical Reactions, Reaction Conditions		●	
	Teaching Visuals Energy and Chemical Reactions (Fig. 4.3)		●	
	PowerPresentation and Notes 2.4		●	
2.5	Textbook: Enzymes	■	●	Enzymatic Activity Enzymes Action of Yeast (Challenge Lab) Enzyme Action: Testing Catalase Activity (Probeware Lab) **Video Lab** Enzymes in Detergents
	Animated Biology Enzyme Action		●	
	Teaching Visuals Enzymes (Fig. 5.1)		●	
	PowerPresentation and Notes 2.5		●	

Additional online resources available for this chapter include **Interactive Whiteboard Resources.**

GO ONLINE! for all your teacher resources at HMHScience.com

2 Support and Intervention

Support and Intervention resources are useful for students who need targeted help beyond the Core Instruction

Resources	PRINT	ONLINE
Assess and Reteach (TE wrap)	■	●
Concept Map		●
Interactive Reader	■	●
Interactive Review Games		●
Section Self-Checks		●
Study Guide B		●
Virtual Investigation Macromolecules of Life		●
Vocabulary Practice Worksheets		●

3 Specialized Support

Students who need more intensive personalized intervention benefit from **Specialized Support** resources.

Resources	PRINT	ONLINE
Chapter Audio Files		●
Differentiated Instruction Inclusion, Below Level, and English Learners (TE wrap)	■	●
ELL Strategies	■	●
Modified Lesson Plans for English Learners		●
Reinforcement Worksheets		●
Study Guide A		●

Extension and Assessment

Enrichment and Challenge

Resources	PRINT	ONLINE
Active Reading Worksheet		●
Data Analysis Practice Worksheet		●
Differentiated Instruction Pre-AP (TE wrap)	■	●
Pre-AP Activity Surface Tension and Cohesion, Enzyme Action		●
The Inside Story and **Take It Further** (TE wrap)	■	●
Unit Project		●
WebLinks		●
WebQuest Prions and Public Health (2.3)		●

Assessment

Resources	PRINT	ONLINE
Alternative Assessment		●
Chapter Tests A and B		●
Diagnostic Test		●
ExamView Banks		●
Extended Response Test		●
Online Assessment System		●
Section Quizzes		●
Standards-Based Assessment	■	●

CHAPTER 2

Chapter Overview

- **Section 1** introduces atomic structure and the essential elements and compounds common to living things.
- **Section 2** discusses the properties of water and its importance to life processes.
- **Section 3** compares the structures and functions of biomolecules.
- **Section 4** provides coverage of chemical reactions.
- **Section 5** discusses the role of enzymes as catalysts in chemical reactions.

▼ Focus and Motivate

How can this plant digest a frog?

Have students read the explanation in the caption. **Ask,** If plants can make their own food through photosynthesis, why would a plant species evolve a mechanism to capture and eat animals? The animal must be supplying nutrients that the plant cannot get from other sources.

Discuss with students that not all the materials a plant needs are supplied by photosynthesis. The end product of photosynthesis is a simple sugar called glucose, which is broken down to yield energy. Most plants absorb additional nutrients from the soil, such as compounds containing nitrogen and phosphorus, which are needed to make molecules that make up a plant's cells and tissues. Venus flytraps grow in swampy areas that have nitrogen-poor soil. These plants get the nitrogen they need by trapping and digesting animals.

Students can access BioZine at **HMHScience.com** to check the daily science news feeds.

CHAPTER 2

Chemistry of Life

BIG IDEA Living things depend on chemical reactions that require water, carbon-based molecules, and other molecules including enzymes to regulate chemical reactions.

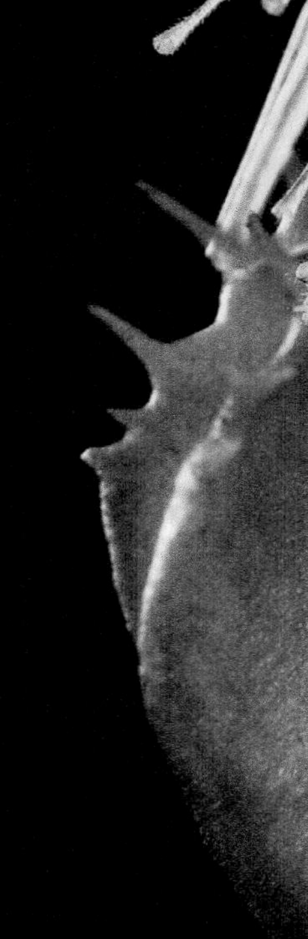

ONLINE BIOLOGY HMHScience.com

ONLINE Labs

- **QuickLab** Chemical Bonding
- Enzymatic Activity
- Testing pH
- Enzymes
- Modeling Biochemical Compounds
- The Biochemistry of Compost Bins
- Action of Yeast
- Acids and Bases
- Enzyme Action: Testing Catalase Activity
- **Virtual Lab** Calorimetry
- **Video Lab** Enzymes in Detergents
- **Open Inquiry Lab** Chemical Reactions

Teacher Demo

Eye Opener **Demonstrate the dehydration of sucrose.**

Materials

- 100-mL beaker of heat-resistant glass
- 20 g powdered sugar
- 5 mL concentrated sulfuric acid
- safety goggles

Safety Make sure the beaker has no cracks. The reaction is exothermic, producing fumes from burning sugar. Perform in a well-ventilated area, where the beaker can be left untouched as it cools. Do not touch the beaker once the reaction begins. Refer to the MSDS on sulfuric acid.

How can this plant digest a grasshopper?

Like other carnivores, the Venus flytrap eats animals to get nutrients that it needs to make molecules such as proteins and nucleic acids. Other chemical compounds made by the plant's cells enable the Venus flytrap to digest the animals that it eats. These chemicals are similar to the chemicals that allow you to digest the food that you eat.

READING TOOLBOX **This reading tool can help you learn the material in the following pages.**

USING LANGUAGE

Quantifiers Quantifiers are words that describe how much, how large, and how often. Quantifiers can also describe the order in which things occur. Words that describe an order include first, second, third, fourth, primary, secondary, tertiary, and quaternary.

YOUR TURN

Use what you have learned about quantifiers to answer the following questions.

1. Place the following months in order of fourth, third, second, and first: January, March, April, February.
2. Would a student attending primary school be younger or older than a student attending secondary school?

Demonstrate Place sugar into the beaker. As you proceed, point out the safety precautions you are taking. With goggles on, slowly add sulfuric acid to the sugar. A column of carbon will rise up from the beaker, as steam is released.

Discuss Point out that students have just observed a chemical reaction involving the dehydration of the organic compound sucrose, a sugar. **Ask**

- What effect did the sulfuric acid have upon sugar? caused the release of water in the form of steam—dehydration, leaving behind a mass of carbon material
- What is the defining characteristic of an organic compound? contains carbon
- Was the reaction exothermic or endothermic, and what does that indicate? exothermic, releases energy

Activate Prior Knowledge

Point out that sometimes to understand how something works, one needs to get down to basics. **Ask,** What does it take to master a computer game, perform a dance move, or sink a penalty shot in the back of the net? One needs to know how it works, break it down into components, study it. Discuss the fact that much of what happens in biology, at a basic level, relates to chemistry.

Preview Vocabulary

Word Origins Sometimes word parts can help students remember meaning:

mono = one   *poly* = many

Other times, word roots are too similar, which is true for *solvent/solute/solution.* In such instances, students should look for other ways to associate meaning with words so similar in appearance.

English Learners Tell students that in this chapter they will be dealing with words that are not a regular part of everyday conversation. Suggest that students use the strategy of word squares to help them learn key vocabulary. This strategy, described in Section D of the *Teacher Toolkit,* includes a picture, a student definition as well as a dictionary definition, and use in a sentence. Have English learners pair up to teach one another the words.

Integrating Biomechanics

The Venus flytrap can capture prey even though it has no muscles or nervous system. When one of six tiny trigger hairs is touched, the plant responds by moving water in its cells to change the curvature of the leaves. The convex leaf halves become concave and snap shut in less than 0.5 seconds.

Answers

1. April, March, February, January
2. younger

SECTION 2.1

B.1.1 Compare and contrast the shape and function of the essential biological macromolecules (i.e. carbohydrates, lipids, proteins, and nucleic acids), as well as, how chemical elements (i.e. carbon, hydrogen, oxygen, nitrogen, phosphorus, and sulfur) can combine to form these biomolecules.

B.1.2 Analyze how the shape of a molecule determines its role in the many different types of cellular processes (e.g., metabolism, homeostasis, growth and development, and heredity) and understand that the majority of these processes involve proteins that act as enzymes.

▼ Plan and Prepare

Activate Prior Knowledge Tell students that six elements are found in substantial quantities in the human body, with traces of 22 others. **Ask,** What are some examples of things that are complex yet made up of simple units? Students might mention 0s and 1s of binary computer code or the 26 letters of the alphabet. Discuss that chemical reactions that occur in living matter produce almost unlimited variety.

▼ Teach

Science Trivia

- The four most common elements in the human body and their mass percents are oxygen (65.0), carbon (18.0), hydrogen (10.0), and nitrogen (3.0).
- The mass percent of the most common trace elements in the body are calcium (1.5), phosphorus (1.0), potassium (0.35), sulfur (0.25), and sodium (0.15).

2.1 Atoms, Ions, and Molecules

KEY CONCEPT All living things are based on atoms and their interactions.

VOCABULARY

atom
element
compound
ion
ionic bond
covalent bond
molecule

MAIN IDEAS

- Living things consist of atoms of different elements.
- Ions form when atoms gain or lose electrons.
- Atoms share pairs of electrons in covalent bonds.

Connect to Your World

The Venus flytrap produces chemicals that allow it to consume and digest insects and other small animals, including an unlucky frog. Frogs also produce specialized chemicals that allow them to consume and digest their prey. In fact, all organisms depend on many chemicals and chemical reactions. For this reason, the study of living things also involves the study of chemistry.

MAIN IDEA

Living things consist of atoms of different elements.

READING TOOLBOX

TAKING NOTES

Use a main idea web to help you make connections among elements, atoms, ions, compounds, and molecules.

atom: . . .
element
ion: . . .

What do a frog, a skyscraper, a car, and your body all have in common? Every physical thing you can think of, living or not, is made of incredibly small particles called atoms. An **atom** is the smallest basic unit of matter. Millions of atoms could fit in a space the size of the period at the end of this sentence. And it would take you more than 1 trillion (1,000,000,000,000, or 10^{12}) years to count the number of atoms in a single grain of sand.

Atoms and Elements

Although there is a huge variety of matter on Earth, all atoms share the same basic structure. Atoms consist of three types of smaller particles: protons, neutrons, and electrons. Protons and neutrons form the dense center of an atom—the atomic nucleus. Electrons are much smaller particles outside of the nucleus. Protons have a positive electrical charge, and electrons have a negative electrical charge. Neutrons, as their name implies, are neutral—they have no charge. Because an atom has equal numbers of positively charged protons and negatively charged electrons, it is electrically neutral.

An **element** is one particular type of atom, and it cannot be broken down into a simpler substance by ordinary chemical means. An element can also refer to a group of atoms of the same type. A few familiar elements include the gases hydrogen and oxygen and the metals aluminum and gold. Because all atoms are made of the same types of particles, what difference among atoms makes one element different from other elements? Atoms of different elements differ in the number of protons they have. All atoms of a given element have a specific number of protons that never varies. For example, all hydrogen atoms have one proton, and all oxygen atoms have eight protons.

Differentiated Instruction

ENGLISH LEARNERS

Remind students to preview each section by first looking for main ideas and key vocabulary. Vocabulary terms appear at the top of the first page of each section and are highlighted in yellow in the text. The blue headings in each section are the main ideas written as sentences; each is signaled by a small red triangle and the words "Main Idea." The paragraphs under them further explain the ideas, and the smaller black headings are key supporting details.

Teacher Toolkit, Section C, Section Preview

PRE-AP

Tell students that they will see different types of models used to show atoms and molecules. The model used depends on the characteristic that is of interest: specifically chemical formula, orbital configuration, or three-dimensional shape. Have students set up a table to compare different models used in this section and throughout the chapter.

Teacher Toolkit, Section C, Content Frame

The electrons in the atoms of each element determine the properties of that element. As **FIGURE 1.1** shows, electrons are considered to be in a cloud around the nucleus. The simplified models of a hydrogen atom and an oxygen atom on the left side of **FIGURE 1.2** illustrate how electrons move around the nucleus in regions called energy levels. Different energy levels can hold different numbers of electrons. For example, the first energy level can hold two electrons, and the second energy level can hold eight electrons. Atoms are most stable when they have a full valence, or outermost energy level.

Of the 91 elements that naturally occur on Earth, only about 25 are found in organisms. Just 4 elements—carbon (C), oxygen (O), nitrogen (N), and hydrogen (H)—make up 96% of the human body's mass. The other 4% consists of calcium (Ca), phosphorus (P), potassium (K), sulfur (S), sodium (Na), and several other trace elements. Trace elements are found in very small amounts in your body, but you need them to survive. For example, iron (Fe) is needed to transport oxygen in your blood. Chromium (Cr) is needed for your cells to break down sugars for usable energy.

FIGURE 1.1 The exact position of electrons cannot be known. They are somewhere in a three-dimensional electron cloud around the nucleus.

FIGURE 1.2 Representing Atoms

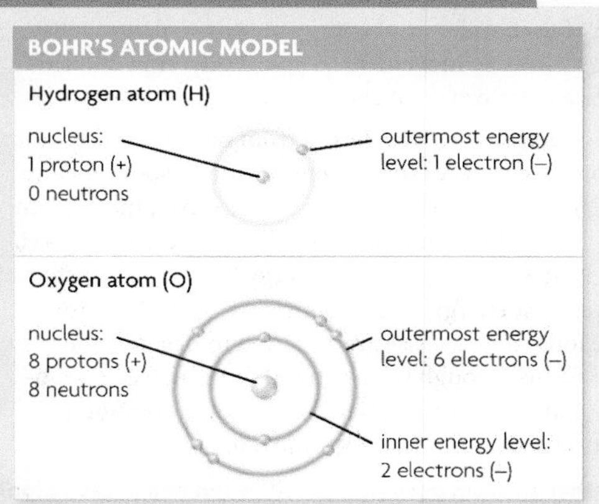

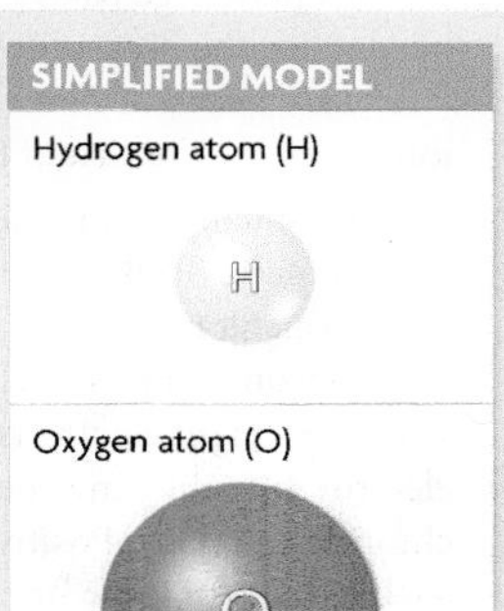

The model of the atom developed by Niels Bohr (left) shows that an atom's electrons are located outside the nucleus in regions called energy levels. Different types of atoms have different numbers of electrons and energy levels.

Often, atoms are shown as simplified spheres (right). Different types of atoms are shown in different sizes and colors.

A Evaluate **What information does the Bohr atomic model provide that the simplified model does not provide? What is a limitation of both models?**

Compounds

The atoms of elements found in organisms are often linked, or bonded, to other atoms. A **compound** is a substance made of atoms of different elements bonded together in a certain ratio. Common compounds in living things include water (H_2O) and carbon dioxide (CO_2). A compound's properties are often different from the properties of the elements that make up the compound. At temperatures on Earth, for example, hydrogen and oxygen are both gases. Together, though, they can form water. Similarly, a diamond is pure carbon, but carbon atoms are also the basis of sugars, proteins, and millions of other compounds.

B Contrast **How are elements different from compounds?**

BELOW LEVEL

Work with students to create a concept map that shows the relationship between atoms, elements, compounds, and molecules. Have them suggest ways to incorporate all the key vocabulary of the section.

Teacher Toolkit, Section C, Concept Map

History of Science

Over the past 200 years, various models of the atom have been proposed. In 1808, **John Dalton** proposed that all matter is composed of tiny indivisible particles called atoms. Then in 1897, **J. J. Thomson** discovered the electron and announced that atoms are divisible into even smaller particles. He proposed a model of a spherical, positively charged atom in which negatively charged electrons were embedded like raisins in plum pudding.

In 1910, **Ernest Rutherford's** experiments showed that an atom is mostly empty space. Within the space is a tiny, dense nucleus that contains almost all the atom's mass. **Niels Bohr** introduced his model of the atom in 1913, and along with it, the concept of energy levels.

The current **quantum-mechanical model** describes an atom with electrons that move with wavelike motion in locations that cannot be exactly known. Just as different tools are needed for different jobs, each model adds different information to the scientific understanding of the atom.

Answers

A Evaluate Bohr's model provides the number of electrons and energy levels of an atom, which the simplified model does not provide; Bohr's model is only two-dimensional and the simplified model does not provide any detail other than the representative size and color of an atom.

B Contrast Elements are composed of only one type of atom; compounds are composed of different types of atoms.

Chapter 2: Chemistry of Life 39

▼ Teach *continued*

TEACH FROM VISUALS

FIGURE 1.3 Explain that the relative sizes of the subatomic particles shown in the figure are not accurate. They are drawn this way to illustrate the concepts of ion formation. Actually, electrons are about 1000 times smaller than protons and neutrons and are much farther away from the nucleus than shown in the diagram. **Ask**

- Why is the sodium ion shown smaller than the sodium atom? It has lost its outer energy level.
- How does the size of the chlorine atom compare with the size of the chloride ion? The ion is much larger than the atom.

Explain to students that when an atom loses an electron, the nuclear charge pulls the remaining electrons closer. When an atom gains an electron, the electron cloud takes up more space.

Address Misconceptions

Common Misconception Students often think that a positive ion can bond only with the negative ion to which it donated its electron.

Correcting the Misconception A positive ion can bond with any negative ion. An ionic bond is simply the electrostatic attraction between oppositely charged ions. Make sure students do not think an ionic bond is a physical connection between two ions.

Answers

A Apply Atoms with few outer electrons tend to lose electrons and so form positive ions; atoms with almost full outer energy levels tend to gain electrons and form negative ions.

MAIN IDEA

Ions form when atoms gain or lose electrons.

CONNECT TO

CELL STRUCTURE AND FUNCTION

Several different ions are transported across cell membranes during cell processes. You will learn how this transport occurs in the chapters **Cell Structure and Function** and **Cells and Energy.**

An **ion** is an atom that has gained or lost one or more electrons. An ion forms because an atom is more stable when its outermost energy level is full; the gain or loss of electrons results in a full outermost energy level. An atom becomes an ion when its number of electrons changes, and it gains an electrical charge. This charge gives ions certain properties. For example, compounds consisting only of ions—ionic compounds—easily dissolve in water.

Some ions are positively charged, and other ions are negatively charged. The type of ion that forms depends on the number of electrons in an atom's outer energy level. An atom with few electrons in its outer energy level tends to lose those electrons. An atom that loses one or more electrons becomes a positively charged ion because it has more protons than electrons. In contrast, an atom with a nearly full outer energy level tends to gain electrons. An atom that gains one or more electrons becomes a negatively charged ion because it has more electrons than protons.

Ions play large roles in organisms. For example, hydrogen ions (H^+) are needed for the production of usable chemical energy in cells. Calcium ions (Ca^{2+}) are necessary for every muscle movement in your body. And chloride ions (Cl^-) are important for a certain type of chemical signal in the brain.

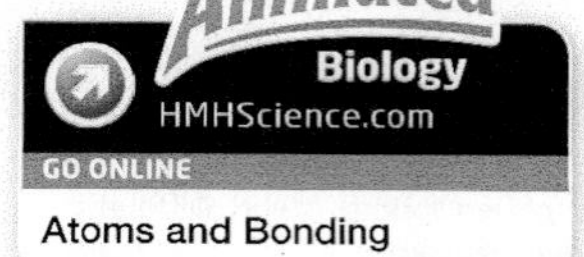

Atoms and Bonding

Ions usually form when electrons are transferred from one atom to another. For example, **FIGURE 1.3** shows the transfer of an electron from a sodium atom (Na) to a chlorine atom (Cl). When it loses its one outer electron, the sodium atom becomes a positively charged sodium ion (Na^+). Its second energy level, which has eight electrons, is now a full outermost energy level. The transferred electron fills chlorine's outermost energy level, forming a negatively charged chloride ion (Cl^-). Positive ions, such as Na^+, are attracted to negative ions, such as Cl^-. An **ionic bond** forms through the electrical force between oppositely charged ions. Salt, or sodium chloride (NaCl), is an ionic compound of Na^+ and Cl^-. Sodium chloride is held together by ionic bonds.

A Apply What determines whether an atom becomes a positive ion or a negative ion?

FIGURE 1.3 IONS AND IONIC BONDS

1 The sodium atom (Na) loses its one outer electron to the chlorine atom (Cl).

Na loses an electron to Cl

Sodium atom (Na) Chlorine atom (Cl)

2 The positive sodium ion (Na^+) and negative chloride ion (Cl^-) attract each other and form an ionic bond.

ionic bond

gained electron

Sodium ion (Na^+) Chloride ion (Cl^-)

Differentiated Instruction

INCLUSION

Physical representations of **FIGURES 1.3** and **1.4** can be made to help students who are visually impaired. Copy the figures onto a piece of cardboard. Squeeze white glue onto the electrons and their energy levels, then sprinkle with coarse sand. When the glue dries, this will be a tactile learning tool.

MAIN IDEA

Atoms share pairs of electrons in covalent bonds.

Not all atoms easily gain or lose electrons. Rather, the atoms of many elements share pairs of electrons. The shared pairs of electrons fill the outermost energy levels of the bonded atoms. A **covalent bond** forms when atoms share a pair of electrons. Covalent bonds are generally very strong, and depending on how many electrons an atom has, two atoms may form several covalent bonds to share several pairs of electrons. **FIGURE 1.4** illustrates how atoms of carbon and oxygen share pairs of electrons in covalent bonds. All three atoms in a molecule of carbon dioxide (CO_2) have full outer energy levels.

FIGURE 1.4 COVALENT BONDS

A carbon atom needs four electrons to fill its outer energy level. An oxygen atom needs two electrons to fill its outer energy level. In carbon dioxide, carbon makes a double bond, or shares two pairs of electrons, with each oxygen atom.

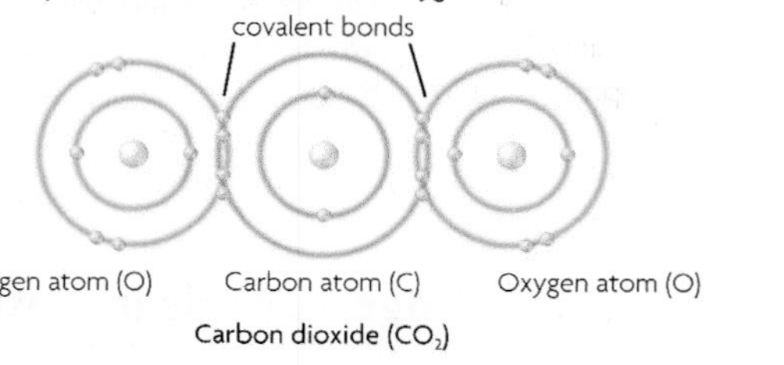

A **molecule** is two or more atoms held together by covalent bonds. In the compound carbon dioxide, each oxygen atom shares two pairs of electrons (four electrons) with the carbon atom. Some elements occur naturally in the form of diatomic, or "two-atom," molecules. For example, a molecule of oxygen (O_2) consists of two oxygen atoms that share two pairs of electrons. Almost all of the substances that make up organisms, from lipids to nucleic acids to water, are molecules held together by covalent bonds.

Summarize **What happens to electrons in outer energy levels when two atoms form a covalent bond?**

READING TOOLBOX

VOCABULARY

The prefix *co-* means "together," and the term *valent* comes from a Latin word that means "power" or "strength."

2.1 Formative Assessment

REVIEWING MAIN IDEAS

1. What distinguishes one **element** from another?
2. Describe the formation of an **ionic compound.**
3. What is the difference between an **ionic bond** and a **covalent bond**?

CRITICAL THINKING

4. **Compare and Contrast** How does a **molecule** differ from an **atom**?
5. **Apply** Explain why a hydrogen atom can become either an **ion** or a part of a molecule.
6. **Evaluate** Explain the benefits and limitations of atomic models.

SELF-CHECK Online
HMHScience.com
GO ONLINE

CONNECT TO

CHEMISTRY

7. A sodium atom has one outer electron, and a carbon atom has four outer electrons. How might this difference be related to the types of compounds formed by atoms of these two elements?

ONLINE Biology
HMHScience.com

Students can simulate building their own atoms in the Animated Biology at **HMHScience.com.**

TEACH FROM VISUALS

FIGURE 1.4 Have students look closely at the energy levels. **Ask**

- How many electrons does a single oxygen atom have in its outer energy level? 6 a carbon atom? 4
- What is the significance of the number of electrons in the outer energy levels of oxygen and carbon in a molecule of carbon dioxide? Each atom shares enough electrons to complete the outer level; oxygen gains 2 and carbon gains 4.

Answers

A **Summarize** Atoms share pairs of outer energy level electrons.

Assess and Reteach

Assess Use the Section Self-Check or Section Quiz, both available at **HMHScience.com.**

Reteach Use **FIGURES 1.3** and **1.4** to review the material in the section. Have students describe what is happening in each figure, using the key vocabulary from the section.

2.1 FORMATIVE ASSESSMENT

1. The number of protons in the nucleus
2. *Sample answer:* In sodium chloride, a sodium atom loses an electron to a chlorine atom. The oppositely charged ions are attracted to each other and form an ionic bond.
3. An ionic bond is formed due to the electrical attraction between oppositely charged ions. A covalent bond is formed by shared pairs of electrons.
4. A molecule is made up of two or more atoms held together by covalent bonds.
5. A hydrogen atom has one unpaired electron in its outer energy level. The electron can be lost to form an ion or shared to form a covalent bond.
6. Benefits: show the number of electrons and energy levels of atoms, electron arrangements in different types of bonds, compare size of different types of atoms; Limitations: two-dimensional or simplified spheres
7. An atom that has a nearly full or nearly empty outer energy level (such as sodium) tends to form ions. An atom in between (such as carbon) tends to share electrons.

SECTION 2.2

▼ Plan and Prepare

Activate Prior Knowledge When astronomers look for evidence of life on other planets, they typically search for evidence of water. **Ask,** Why is water so important to life? Students may recognize water as the main component of cytoplasm and blood. Discuss that water is also the medium in which the chemical reactions in cells take place.

▼ Teach

Vocabulary

Academic Vocabulary A **pole** is, in simple terms, a rod. When applied to a rotating body, as in the rotation of Earth, the pole becomes an **axis** around which a body rotates. The word **polar** is often used to describe the extreme ends of a body. This relates to the description of water as a *polar* molecule.

With a magnet, each end of the pole has an opposite charge, which is analogous to what happens with a polar molecule. Because of the two different charges, the pole is often referred to as a **dipole.**

2.2 Properties of Water

KEY CONCEPT **Water's unique properties allow life to exist on Earth.**

VOCABULARY

- hydrogen bond
- cohesion
- adhesion
- solution
- solvent
- solute
- acid
- base
- pH

MAIN IDEAS

- Life depends on hydrogen bonds in water.
- Many compounds dissolve in water.
- Some compounds form acids or bases.

Connect to Your World

When you are thirsty, you need to drink something that is mostly water. Why is the water you drink absolutely necessary? Your cells, and the cells of every other living thing on Earth, are mostly water. Water gives cells structure and transports materials within organisms. All of the processes necessary for life take place in that watery environment. Water's unique properties, which are related to the structure of the water molecule, are important for living things.

MAIN IDEA

Life depends on hydrogen bonds in water.

How do fish survive a cold winter if their pond freezes? Unlike most substances, water expands when it freezes. Water is less dense as a solid (ice) than as a liquid. In a pond, ice floats and covers the water's surface. The ice acts as an insulator that allows the water underneath to remain a liquid. Ice's low density is related to the structure of the water molecule.

Water and Hydrogen Bonds

Water is a polar molecule. You can think about polar molecules in the same way that you can think about a magnet's poles. That is, polar molecules have a region with a slight positive charge and a region with a slight negative charge. Polar molecules, such as the water molecule shown in **FIGURE 2.1,** form when atoms in a molecule have unequal pulls on the electrons they share. In a molecule of water, the oxygen nucleus, with its eight protons, attracts the shared electrons more strongly than do the hydrogen nuclei, with only one proton each. The oxygen atom gains a small negative charge, and the hydrogen atoms gain small positive charges. Other molecules, called nonpolar molecules, do not have these charged regions. The atoms in nonpolar molecules share electrons more equally.

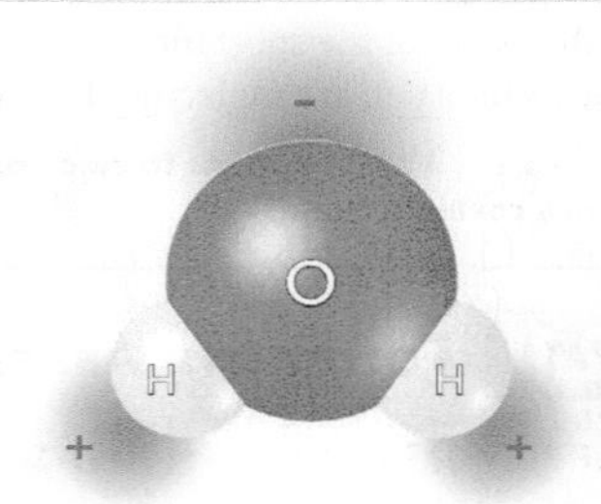

FIGURE 2.1 In water molecules, the oxygen atom has a slightly negative charge, and the hydrogen atoms have slightly positive charges.

Differentiated Instruction

PRE-AP

Have students use Cornell notes to outline the section. They should include a diagram for each key vocabulary term.

Teacher Toolkit, Section C, Cornell Notes

BELOW LEVEL

Point out to students that among the vocabulary terms in this section are words that can be paired and compared.

cohesion	*adhesion*
solvent	*solute*
acid	*base*

Suggest students use diagrams to compare and contrast these terms.

Teacher Toolkit, Section C, Combination Notes

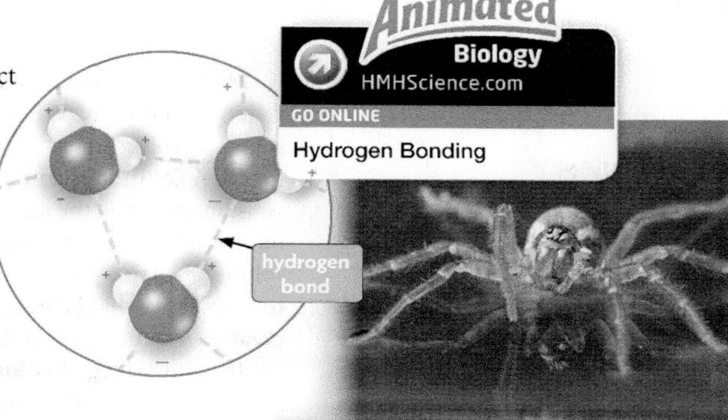

Opposite charges of polar molecules can interact to form hydrogen bonds. A **hydrogen bond** is an attraction between a slightly positive hydrogen atom and a slightly negative atom, often oxygen or nitrogen. Hydrogen bonding is shown among water molecules in **FIGURE 2.2**, but these bonds are also found in many other molecules. For example, hydrogen bonds are part of the structures of proteins and of DNA, which is the genetic material for all organisms.

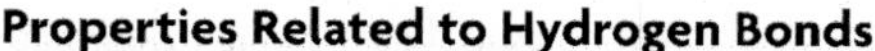

FIGURE 2.2 Water's surface tension comes from hydrogen bonds (left) that cause water molecules to stick together.

Properties Related to Hydrogen Bonds

Individual hydrogen bonds are about 20 times weaker than typical covalent bonds, but they are relatively strong among water molecules. As a result, a large amount of energy is needed to overcome the attractions among water molecules. Without hydrogen bonds, water would boil at a much lower temperature than it does because less energy would be needed to change liquid water into water vapor. Water is a liquid at the temperatures that support most life on Earth only because of hydrogen bonds in water. Hydrogen bonds are responsible for three important properties of water.

- **High specific heat** Hydrogen bonds give water an abnormally high specific heat. This means that water resists changes in temperature. Compared to many other compounds, water must absorb more heat energy to increase in temperature. This property is very important in cells. The processes that produce usable chemical energy in cells release a great deal of heat. Water absorbs the heat, which helps to regulate cell temperatures.
- **Cohesion** The attraction among molecules of a substance is **cohesion.** Cohesion from hydrogen bonds makes water molecules stick to each other. You can see this when water forms beads, such as on a recently washed car. Cohesion also produces surface tension, which makes a kind of skin on water. Surface tension keeps the spider in **FIGURE 2.2** from sinking.
- **Adhesion** The attraction among molecules of different substances is called **adhesion.** In other words, water molecules stick to other things. Adhesion is responsible for the upward curve on the surface of the water in **FIGURE 2.3** because water molecules are attracted to the glass of the test tube. Adhesion helps plants transport water from their roots to their leaves because water molecules stick to the sides of the vessels that carry water.

FIGURE 2.3 The water's surface (left, dyed red) is curved down because water has greater adhesion than cohesion. The surface of the mercury (right) is curved up because mercury has greater cohesion than adhesion.

A Compare How are hydrogen bonds similar to ionic bonds?

MAIN IDEA

Many compounds dissolve in water.

Molecules and ions cannot take part in chemical processes inside cells unless they dissolve in water. Important materials such as sugars and oxygen cannot be transported from one part of an organism to another unless they are dissolved in blood, plant sap, or other water-based fluids.

Integrating Physics

Hydrogen bonding is a special case of **dipole-dipole attractions** that occur between polar molecules. Hydrogen bonds form between molecules that consist of hydrogen atoms and atoms with high electronegativities, such as oxygen and nitrogen. The bonds within these molecules are very polar, and the hydrogen atom is so small that the molecules can get very close to one another. A hydrogen bond is not as strong as an ionic bond. In relative terms, it is only about 1/10 as strong.

Vocabulary

Greek and Latin Word Origins The Latin root that is the base of **adhere** and **cohere** is

haerere = to cling

The prefixes that differentiate the two words might not seem to offer much help: *ad-* means "toward," and *co-* means "together." Students could think of *adhesive* tape as holding together two separate and different things.

Students might think of a different set of words. An *adversary* is one who opposes or differs in point of view. Compare this to a *coworker, copilot,* or *cocaptain,* who are people who share similar views and goals.

Answers

A Compare Hydrogen bonds are attractions due to charged regions; ionic bonds are bonds formed by the attraction of oppositely charged ions.

INCLUSION

For students who are literal thinkers, help them visualize hydrogen bonding by using cardboard cutouts of water molecules, labeling the positive and negative ends. Have students arrange the cutouts with opposite charges together to make an array of molecules that represent the organization of water.

Vocabulary

Word Origins The words **solution, solvent,** and **solute** all share the same root, meaning "to loosen." To distinguish among the words, have students make associations that will help them remember the terms. For example, *dilute/solute* suggests a small amount spread out. Students can associate the *v* in *solvent* with a wedge that splits and separates the *solute.* Once they have sorted that out, they have their *solution.*

Address Misconceptions

Common Misconception Students often think that all solutes are solids and all solvents are liquids.

Correcting the Misconception Solutions can involve different states of matter.

- Air is made up of roughly 78 percent nitrogen, 21 percent oxygen, and a mix of argon, carbon dioxide, and other gases. **Ask,** Which gas is the solvent, and why? nitrogen, because it is present in the greatest amount
- Brass is a metal alloy, a solid dissolved in a solid, typically 67 percent copper and 33 percent zinc. **Ask,** Which is the solvent? copper the solute? zinc
- Vinegar contains about 5 percent acetic acid and 95 percent water. **Ask,** Which is the solute? acetic acid

Take It Further

Solutes that dissolve in water disrupt the hydrogen bonds between water molecules, replacing them with attractions between solute and water. If the attractions between solute particles are stronger than those between solute and water, the compound will not dissolve. Nonpolar molecules do not dissolve in water because the attraction among the nonpolar molecules is greater than the attraction between water molecules and the nonpolar molecules.

Answers

Ⓐ **Connect** Answers will vary, but typically the solvent is water; the solutes include sugars, ions, and proteins.

Many substances dissolve in the water in your body. When one substance dissolves in another, a solution forms. A **solution** is a mixture of substances that is the same throughout—it is a homogeneous mixture. A solution has two parts. The **solvent** is the substance that is present in the greater amount and that dissolves another substance. A **solute** is a substance that dissolves in a solvent. The amount of solute dissolved in a certain amount of solvent is a solution's concentration. One spoonful of a drink mix in water has little flavor because it has a low concentration. But a solution with four spoonfuls in the same amount of water tastes stronger because it has a higher concentration.

VISUAL VOCAB

The **solvent** is the substance that is present in the greatest amount and is the substance that dissolves solutes.

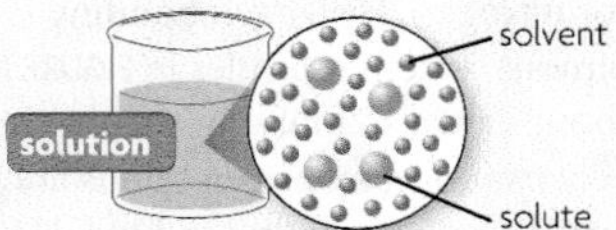

A **solute** is the substance that dissolves.

The liquid part of your blood, called plasma, is about 95% water. Therefore, the solvent in plasma is water, and all of the substances dissolved in it are solutes. Most of these solutes, such as sugars and proteins, dissolve in the water of blood plasma because they are polar. Polar molecules dissolve in water because the attraction between the water molecules and the solute molecules is greater than the attraction among the molecules of the solute. Similarly, ionic compounds, such as sodium chloride, dissolve in water because the charges of the water molecules attract the charges of the ions. The water molecules surround each ion and pull the compound apart.

Nonpolar substances, such as fats and oils, rarely dissolve in water. Nonpolar molecules do not have charged regions, so they are not attracted to polar molecules. Polar molecules and nonpolar molecules tend to remain separate, which is why we say, "Oil and water don't mix." But nonpolar molecules will dissolve in nonpolar solvents. For example, some vitamins, such as vitamin E, are nonpolar and dissolve in fat in your body.

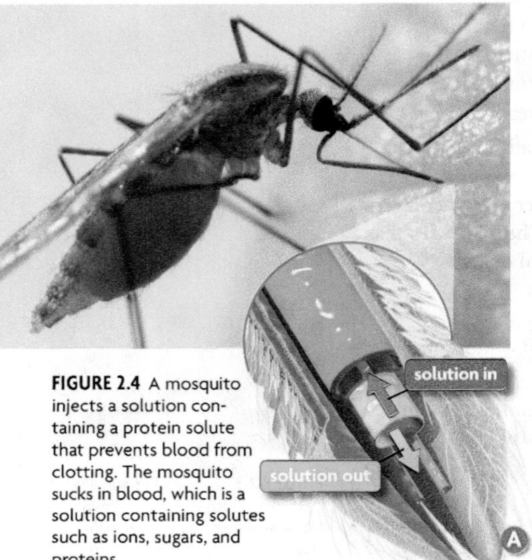

FIGURE 2.4 A mosquito injects a solution containing a protein solute that prevents blood from clotting. The mosquito sucks in blood, which is a solution containing solutes such as ions, sugars, and proteins.

Ⓐ Connect **What are the solvent and solutes in a beverage you drink?**

MAIN IDEA

Some compounds form acids or bases.

Some compounds break up into ions when they dissolve in water. An **acid** is a compound that releases a proton—a hydrogen ion (H^+)—when it dissolves in water. An acid increases the concentration of H^+ ions in a solution. **Bases** are compounds that remove H^+ ions from a solution. When a base dissolves in water, the solution has a low H^+ concentration. A solution's acidity, or H^+ ion concentration, is measured by the **pH** scale. In **FIGURE 2.5**, you can see that pH is usually between 0 and 14. A solution with a pH of 0 is very acidic, with a high H^+ concentration. A solution with a pH of 14 is very basic, with a low H^+ concentration. Solutions with a pH of 7 are neutral—neither acidic nor basic.

Differentiated Instruction

ENGLISH LEARNERS

Point out that the **VISUAL VOCAB** note reinforces definitions given in the text. Use questions to work through this figure as well as **FIGURE 2.5.** Ask questions to help students interpret the diagram, discussing the use of color, number, shape, and direction. Have them sketch the diagram of the pH scale in their science notebooks and then add labels. Point out that a low pH is associated with a high number of hydrogen ions.

Teacher Toolkit, Section C, Connect to Content Through Visuals

FIGURE 2.5 Understanding pH

The pH of a solution depends on the concentration of H^+ ions.

The concentration of H^+ ions varies depending on how acidic or basic a solution is.

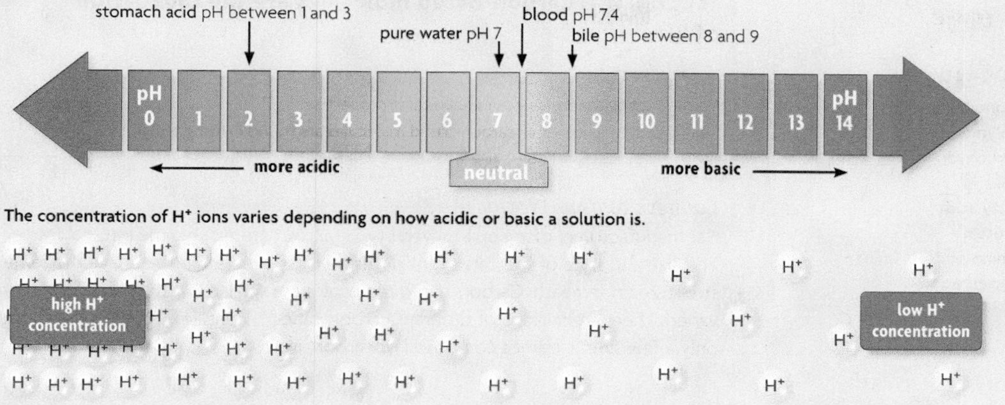

A **Summarize** **Describe the relationship between the H^+ concentration and the pH value.**

Most organisms, including humans, need to keep their pH within a very narrow range around neutral (pH 7.0). However, some organisms need a very different pH range. The azalea plant thrives in acidic (pH 4.5) soil, and a microorganism called *Picrophilus* survives best at an extremely acidic pH of 0.7. For all of these different organisms, pH must be tightly controlled.

One way pH is regulated in organisms is by substances called buffers. A buffer is a compound that can bind to an H^+ ion when the H^+ concentration increases, and can release an H^+ ion when the H^+ concentration decreases. In other words, a buffer "locks up" H^+ ions and helps to maintain homeostasis. For example, the normal pH of human blood is between 7.35 and 7.45, so it is slightly basic. Just a small change in pH can disrupt processes in your cells, and a blood pH greater than 7.8 or less than 6.8, for even a short time, is deadly. Buffers in your blood help prevent any large changes in blood pH.

B **Apply** **Cells have higher H^+ concentrations than blood. Which has a higher pH? Why?**

CONNECT TO

HUMAN BIOLOGY

In the human body, both the respiratory system and the excretory system help regulate pH. You will learn about human systems and homeostasis in the chapter **Human Systems and Homeostasis.**

2.2 Formative Assessment

REVIEWING MAIN IDEAS

1. How do polar molecules form **hydrogen bonds**?
2. What determines whether a compound will dissolve in water?
3. Make a chart that compares **acids** and **bases.**

CRITICAL THINKING

4. **Compare and Contrast** How do polar molecules differ from nonpolar molecules? How does this difference affect their interactions?
5. **Connect** Describe an example of **cohesion** or **adhesion** that you might observe during your daily life.

SELF-CHECK Online HMHScience.com GO ONLINE

CONNECT TO

CELLULAR RESPIRATION

6. When sugars are broken down to produce usable energy for cells, a large amount of heat is released. Explain how the water inside a cell helps to keep the cell's temperature constant.

TEACH FROM VISUALS

FIGURE 2.5 To explain why the concentration of hydrogen ions decreases the larger the pH number becomes, explain that the pH scale is a negative logarithm. A pH of 1 is equal to the log of a H^+ ion concentration of 10^{-1}, whereas a pH of 10 is equal to the log of a H^+ ion concentration of 10^{-10}. There is a tenfold difference in H^+ ion concentration from one pH value to the next. **Ask,** What is the difference in H^+ ion concentration between lemon juice (pH 2) and tomato juice (pH 4)? Lemon juice has a H^+ concentration 100 times greater than tomato juice.

Answers

A **Summarize** The higher the H^+ concentration, the lower the pH.

B **Apply** blood, because a lower H^+ concentration means a higher pH

Assess and Reteach

Assess Use the Section Self-Check or Section Quiz, both available at **HMHScience.com**.

Reteach Have students use the example of dropping a sugar cube into a glass of water to diagram the interaction of a solute and solvent. Then have students compare this to pouring oil into water.

2.2 FORMATIVE ASSESSMENT

1. The oppositely charged regions of a polar molecule attract other polar molecules, allowing a positively charged hydrogen atom to bond to a negatively charged atom.
2. Compounds that have charges, such as ionic compounds and polar molecules, will dissolve in water.
3. Answers will vary but should indicate the following: acids donate protons (hydrogen ions), and bases accept hydrogen ions in solution; acids in solution have a high hydrogen ion concentration and a pH below 7; bases in solution have a low hydrogen ion concentration and a pH above 7.
4. Polar molecules have charged regions due to unequal sharing of electrons. Nonpolar molecules do not have charged regions because electrons are shared more equally. The charge differences tend to keep the molecules separate.
5. *Sample answer:* Cohesion: water beading on a surface; adhesion: water sticking to the side of a glass.
6. Water has a high specific heat; water in a cell can absorb a large amount of energy before its temperature increases.

SECTION 2.3

B.1.1 Compare and contrast the shape and function of the essential biological macromolecules (i.e. carbohydrates, lipids, proteins, and nucleic acids), as well as, how chemical elements (i.e. carbon, hydrogen, oxygen, nitrogen, phosphorus, and sulfur) can combine to form these biomolecules.

B.1.2 Analyze how the shape of a molecule determines its role in the many different types of cellular processes (e.g., metabolism, homeostasis, growth and development, and heredity) and understand that the majority of these processes involve proteins that act as enzymes.

B.4.3 Construct a model to explain that the unique shape and function of each protein is determined by the sequence of its amino acids, and thus is determined by the sequence of the DNA that codes for this protein.

▼ Plan and Prepare

Activate Prior Knowledge Students may not realize that the word *organic* is related to carbon-based molecules. **Ask,** What do you think of when you hear the word *organic?* Students may mention organic food and farming. For a long time, the term *organic* was strictly associated with the chemistry of life. Until scientists gained the ability to synthesize carbon compounds, the only "factories" making carbon compounds were living organisms, hence the connection to "all natural."

▼ Teach

TEACH FROM VISUALS

FIGURE 3.1 Tell students the molecular formulas in the figure do not show all bonds as lines. For example, CH_3 has three hydrogens bonded to carbon. **Ask,** What is common to all the carbons shown in the figure? Each has four bonds.

2.3 Carbon-Based Molecules

KEY CONCEPT **Carbon-based molecules are the foundation of life.**

VOCABULARY

- monomer
- polymer
- carbohydrate
- lipid
- fatty acid
- protein
- amino acid
- nucleic acid

MAIN IDEAS

- Carbon atoms have unique bonding properties.
- Four main types of carbon-based molecules are found in living things.

Connect to Your World

Car manufacturers often build several types of cars from the same internal frame. The size and style of the cars might differ on the outside, but they have the same structure underneath. Carbon-based molecules are similar, but they are much more varied. There are millions of different carbon-based molecules, but they form around only a few simple frames composed of carbon atoms.

MAIN IDEA

Carbon atoms have unique bonding properties.

Carbon is often called the building block of life because carbon atoms are the basis of most molecules that make up living things. These molecules form the structure of living things and carry out most of the processes that keep organisms alive. Carbon is so important because its atomic structure gives it bonding properties that are unique among elements. Each carbon atom has four unpaired electrons in its outer energy level. Therefore, carbon atoms can form covalent bonds with up to four other atoms, including other carbon atoms.

As **FIGURE 3.1** shows, carbon-based molecules have three fundamental structures—straight chains, branched chains, and rings. All three types of molecules are the result of carbon's ability to form four covalent bonds. Carbon chains can bond with carbon rings to form very large, complex molecules. These large molecules can be made of many small molecules that are bonded together. In a sense, the way these molecules form is similar to the way in which individual links of metal come together to make a bicycle chain.

FIGURE 3.1 CARBON CHAINS AND RINGS

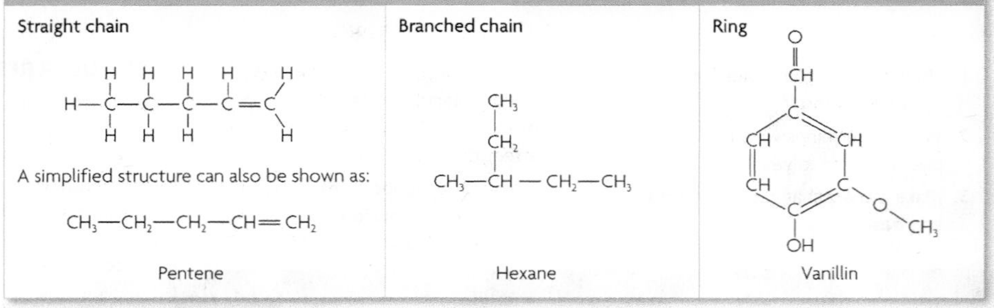

Differentiated Instruction

BELOW LEVEL

To reinforce the concept of polymers (many) made from repeating monomers (one), write this chart on the board. Have students expand the chart in their science notebooks to include Example and Function as suggested in their text on the next page.

Monomer	Polymer
monosaccharides (simple sugars)	polysaccharides
amino acid	proteins
nucleotides	nucleic acids
fatty acids	lipids (triglycerides)*

*Tell students that lipids are smaller than true polymers and are not all made of repeating units.

Teacher Toolkit, Section C, Content Frames

In many carbon-based molecules, small molecules are subunits of an entire molecule, like links in a chain. Each subunit in the complete molecule is called a **monomer.** When monomers are linked, they form molecules called polymers. A **polymer** is a large molecule, or macromolecule, made of many monomers bonded together. All of the monomers in a polymer may be the same, as they are in starches, or they may be different, as they are in proteins.

VISUAL VOCAB

Each smaller molecule is a subunit called a **monomer.**

mono- = one
poly- = many

monomer

polymer

A **polymer** is a molecule that contains many monomers bonded together.

A Synthesize **Write your own analogy for the formation of a polymer from monomers.**

MAIN IDEA

Four main types of carbon-based molecules are found in living things.

All organisms are made of four types of carbon-based molecules: carbohydrates, lipids, proteins, and nucleic acids. These molecules have different structures and functions, but all are formed around carbon chains and rings.

READING TOOLBOX

TAKING NOTES

Use a content frame to help you understand monomers and polymers in carbon-based molecules.

Monomer	Polymer	Example	Function

Carbohydrates

Fruits and grains are in different food groups, but they both contain large amounts of carbohydrates. **Carbohydrates** are molecules composed of carbon, hydrogen, and oxygen, and they include sugars and starches. Carbohydrates can be broken down to provide a source of usable chemical energy for cells. Carbohydrates are also a major part of plant cell structure.

The most basic carbohydrates are simple sugars, or monosaccharides (MAHN-uh-SAK-uh-RYDZ). Many simple sugars have either five or six carbon atoms. Fruits contain a six-carbon sugar called fructose. Glucose, one of the sugars made by plant cells during photosynthesis, is another six-carbon sugar. Simple sugars can be bonded to make larger carbohydrates. For example, two sugars bonded together make the disaccharide table sugar, shown in **FIGURE 3.2.** Many glucose molecules can be linked to make polysaccharides (PAHL-ee-SAK-uh-RYDZ), which are polymers of monosaccharides.

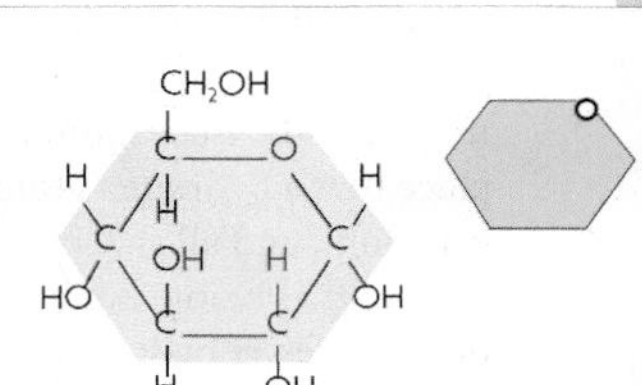

Glucose ($C_6H_{12}O_6$) can be ring shaped and is often shown as a simplified hexagon. During photosynthesis, six molecules of CO_2 combine with six molecules of H_2O to form one molecule of glucose and six molecules of O_2.

Starches, glycogen, and cellulose are polysaccharides. Most starches are branched chains of glucose molecules. Starches are made and stored by plants, and they can be broken down as a source of energy by plant and animal cells. Glycogen, which is made and stored in animals, is more highly branched than plant starches.

FIGURE 3.2 Household sugar (sucrose) is a disaccharide, or two-sugar molecule, of glucose (inset) and fructose.

The Inside Story

Early chemists believed in **vitalism**—the idea that a spiritual, vital force existed inside the molecules of living things. Then in 1828, **Friedrich Wöhler** heated ammonium and cyanate ions—inorganic "mineral-world" substances—and produced urea, an organic "living-world" compound. Wöhler wrote, "I must tell you that I can prepare urea without requiring a kidney of an animal, either man or dog." This was the beginning of organic chemistry.

TEACH FROM VISUALS

FIGURE 3.2 Have students study the inset of the glucose molecule. Have them use the information in the caption to account for all of the carbon, hydrogen, and oxygen atoms in a molecule of glucose formed through photosynthesis.

Answers

A Synthesize Answers should indicate an understanding of linking units together to make a whole, such as a string of holiday lights, beads on a necklace or bracelet, or links in a chain.

Vocabulary

carbohydrate The word *carbohydrate* literally means "watered carbon." This can be explained by the ratio of carbon atoms to hydrogen and oxygen atoms in a carbohydrate: 1:2:1. However, the general formula CH_2O creates a false impression that the oxygen is supplied by water. The oxygen in a carbohydrate comes from oxygen gas. The hydrogens come from a molecule of water, but only after releasing the oxygen.

Integrating Chemistry

Some polymers form through a process of **dehydration,** that is, a molecule of water is released as one monomer bonds to another. One provides a hydrogen (—H) and the other provides a hydroxyl group (—OH). Some polymers can also be broken down in a reverse reaction, called **hydrolysis.** The bonds between the monomers are broken by the addition of water molecules.

ENGLISH LEARNERS

Suggest that students use context clues to identify which terms used in the text relate to monomers and which to the polymer itself. Model for students how you interpret the text describing carbohydrates on this student page. Point out the words associated with *monomer: monosaccharides, fructose, glucose;* and those associated with *polymer: polysaccharides, starch, glycogen, cellulose.* You might want to use a cluster diagram to show the relationship.

Teacher Toolkit, Section D, Context Clues

INCLUSION

You can help students who are hearing-impaired as you discuss the material in the section if you signal for them the key ideas or identify the particular compounds you want them to know. Arrange with them a phrase that will act as the signal, such as "important idea." Be consistent in using the phrase, being sure to look directly at students when you speak.

▼ Teach *continued*

Take It Further

Few animals have the enzymes that allow them to hydrolyze **cellulose.** The structure of cellulose plays a role, but it is the amount and type of available enzymes that determine whether or not cellulose is broken down. Cows and termites are able to obtain energy from grass, hay, or wood because protists and bacteria that live in their bodies hydrolyze the cellulose to glucose. Although humans cannot digest cellulose, it does play an important role in our diets as insoluble fiber.

Science Trivia

- Cellulose is the most abundant organic molecule on Earth.
- Plants produce almost 10^{11} (100 billion) tons of cellulose a year.

Integrating Chemistry

Point out that biological macromolecules such as starches are similar in structure to polymers that students use every day. Many of these polymers are based on organic molecules from petroleum. **Ask,** What polymers do you commonly use? Plastics, nylon, polyesters, and Teflon are examples.

Vocabulary

Academic Vocabulary The word **saturate** shares the same sense of being full or complete as the words **satiate** and **satisfy.** However, *satiate* means to "satisfy fully, to excess," whereas *satisfy* suggests something that is "sufficient, adequate" in filling a need.

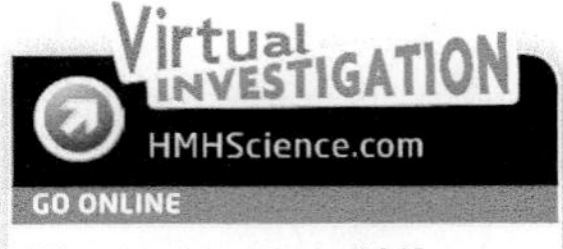

Macromolecules of Life

CONNECT TO

CELL STRUCTURE

A cell wall made of cellulose surrounds the membrane of plant cells. You will learn more about cell walls in the chapter **Cell Structure and Function.**

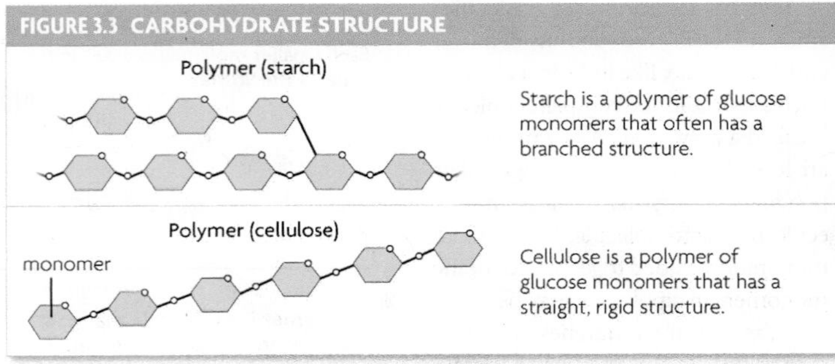

Polymer (starch)
Starch is a polymer of glucose monomers that often has a branched structure.
Polymer (cellulose)
monomer
Cellulose is a polymer of glucose monomers that has a straight, rigid structure.

FIGURE 3.3 CARBOHYDRATE STRUCTURE

Cellulose is somewhat different from starch and glycogen. Its straight, rigid structure, shown in **FIGURE 3.3,** makes the cellulose molecule a major building block in plant cell structure. Cellulose makes up the cell wall that is the tough, outer covering of plant cells. You have eaten cellulose in the stringy fibers of vegetables such as celery, so you know that it is tough to chew and break up.

Lipids

Lipids are nonpolar molecules that include fats, oils, and cholesterol. Like carbohydrates, most lipids contain chains of carbon atoms bonded to oxygen and hydrogen atoms. Some lipids are broken down as a source of usable energy for cells. Other lipids are parts of a cell's structure.

Fats and oils are two familiar types of lipids. They store large amounts of chemical energy in organisms. Animal fats are found in foods such as meat and butter. You know plant fats as oils, such as olive oil and peanut oil. The structures of fats and oils are similar. They both consist of a molecule called glycerol (GLIHS-uh-RAWL) bonded to molecules called fatty acids. **Fatty acids** are chains of carbon atoms bonded to hydrogen atoms. Two different types of fatty acids are shown in **FIGURE 3.4.**

Many lipids, both fats and oils, contain three fatty acids bonded to glycerol. They are called triglycerides. Most animal fats are saturated fats, which means they have the maximum number of hydrogen atoms possible. That is, every place that a hydrogen atom can bond to a carbon atom is filled with a hydrogen atom, and all carbon–carbon bonds are single bonds. You can think of the fatty acid as being "saturated" with hydrogen atoms. In contrast, fatty acids in oils have fewer hydrogen atoms because there is at least one double bond between carbon atoms. These lipids are called unsaturated fats because the fatty acids are not saturated with hydrogen atoms. Fats and oils are very similar, but why are animal fats solid and plant oils liquid? The double bonds in unsaturated fats make kinks in the fatty acids. As a result, the molecules cannot pack together tightly enough to form a solid.

FIGURE 3.4 Fatty acids can be either saturated or unsaturated.

Saturated fatty acid

Saturated fats contain fatty acids in which all carbon–carbon bonds are single bonds.

Unsaturated fatty acid

Unsaturated fats have fatty acids with at least one carbon–carbon double bond.

Differentiated Instruction

PRE-AP

Remind students to expand their table describing models used for atoms and molecules, as suggested in the Pre-AP note in Section 1. Have them include the molecular formulas shown in this section.

All cell membranes are made mostly of another type of lipid, called a phospholipid (FAHS-foh-LIHP-ihd). A phospholipid consists of glycerol, two fatty acids, and a phosphate group (PO_4^-) that is part of the polar "head" of the molecule. The fatty acids are the nonpolar "tails" of a phospholipid. Compare the structure of a phospholipid to the structure of a triglyceride in **FIGURE 3.5.**

FIGURE 3.5 LIPID STRUCTURE

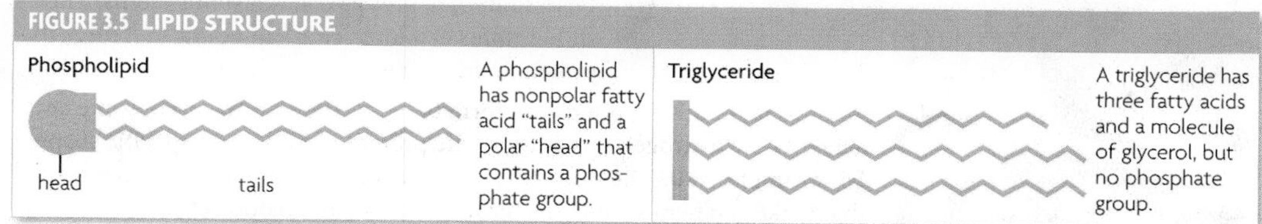

A phospholipid has nonpolar fatty acid "tails" and a polar "head" that contains a phosphate group.

A triglyceride has three fatty acids and a molecule of glycerol, but no phosphate group.

Cholesterol (kuh-LEHS-tuh-RAWL) is a lipid that has a ring structure. You may hear about dangers of eating foods that contain a lot of cholesterol, such as eggs, but your body needs a certain amount of it to function. For example, cholesterol is a part of cell membranes, and your body uses it to make chemicals called steroid hormones. Cholesterol-based steroids have many functions. Some regulate your body's response to stress. Others, such as testosterone and estrogen, control sexual development and the reproductive system.

Proteins

Proteins are the most varied of the carbon-based molecules in organisms. In movement, eyesight, or digestion, proteins are at work. A **protein** is a polymer made of monomers called amino acids. **Amino acids** are molecules that contain carbon, hydrogen, oxygen, nitrogen, and sometimes sulfur. Organisms use 20 different amino acids to build proteins. Your body can make 12 of the amino acids. The others come from foods you eat, such as meat, beans, and nuts.

FIGURE 3.6 Serine is one of 20 amino acids that make up proteins in organisms.

Look at **FIGURE 3.6** to see the amino acid serine. All amino acids have similar structures. As **FIGURE 3.7** shows, each amino acid monomer has a carbon atom that is bonded to four other parts. Three of these parts are the same in every amino acid: a hydrogen atom, an amino group (NH_2), and a carboxyl group (COOH). Amino acids differ only in their side group, or the R-group.

Amino acids form covalent bonds, called peptide bonds, with each other. The bonds form between the amino group of one amino acid and the carboxyl group of another amino acid. Through peptide bonds, amino acids are linked into chains called polypeptides. A protein is one or more polypeptides.

FIGURE 3.7 AMINO ACID AND PROTEIN STRUCTURE

All amino acids have a carbon atom bonded to a hydrogen atom, an amino group (NH_2), and a carboxyl group (COOH). Different amino acids have different side groups (R).

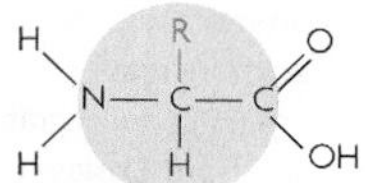

Monomer (amino acid)

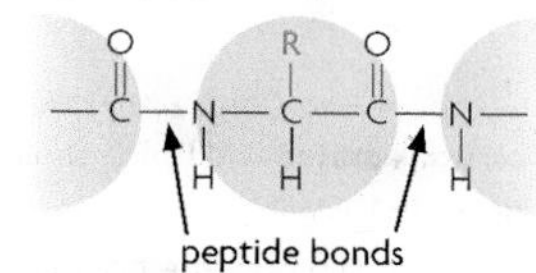

Peptide bonds form between the amino group of one amino acid and the carboxyl group of another amino acid.

Polymer (protein)

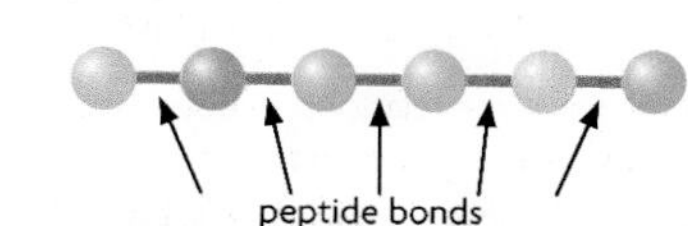

A polypeptide is a chain of precisely ordered amino acids linked by peptide bonds. A protein is made of one or more polypeptides.

TEACH FROM VISUALS

FIGURE 3.5 Point out the two parts of a phospholipid. **Ask**

- How would the polar head of a phospholipid respond to water molecules? attracted to water
- How would the nonpolar tails respond to water molecules? repelled by water

Point out that the phosphate group is a polyatomic ion. A group of atoms that are covalently bonded together may collectively lose or gain one or more electrons. A polyatomic ion stays together as a unit during reactions.

Integrating Medical Science

Lipoproteins are clusters of lipids (including cholesterol) and proteins that travel in blood plasma. They carry lipids to the cells in the body, where they are used to make membranes and steroid hormones. There are two main kinds of lipoproteins, distinguished by how dense, or compact, they are. **Low-density lipoproteins** (LDLs), commonly called "bad cholesterol," have been implicated in high blood pressure and heart disease because they are deposited on the walls of arteries as plaque and can block the flow of blood through the arteries. **High-density lipoproteins** (HDLs), called "good cholesterol," are beneficial. HDLs remove cholesterol from the arteries and return it to the liver.

TEACH WITH TECHNOLOGY

Computer-generated molecular models can help students visualize the types of macromolecules discussed in this section. Exploring carbohydrates and proteins in three dimensions will add to students' understanding. Computer programs such as Chem3D allow representation of molecules in three dimensions.

Teach *continued*

Take It Further

Proteins have several levels of structure. The **primary structure** is the sequence of amino acids in the chain. The **secondary structure** is the arrangement of the amino acid chain in space. The two most common arrangements are the alpha helix, in which hydrogen bonding occurs between every fourth amino acid, and the beta sheet, in which amino acids in two parallel regions of the chain form hydrogen bonds. The **tertiary structure** is the overall shape of the protein after the secondary structure folds. Shape can be partially due to covalent bonding between sulfur atoms in some side groups, as well as to hydrogen bonding.

Have students do the WebQuest on prions to learn what happens when proteins are malformed.

Answers

A Apply Proteins are polymers of amino acids that are assembled based on genetic information in nucleic acids.

Assess and Reteach

Assess Use the Section Self-Check or Section Quiz, both available at **HMHScience.com**.

Reteach Use the figures to reteach the section, referring to the different ways molecules are represented. Each model serves a different purpose: to show the three-dimensional shape, the atomic structure of a molecule, or bonding, or even to provide a simplified symbol for easier identification. Have students look at the figures and explain how the different models are used.

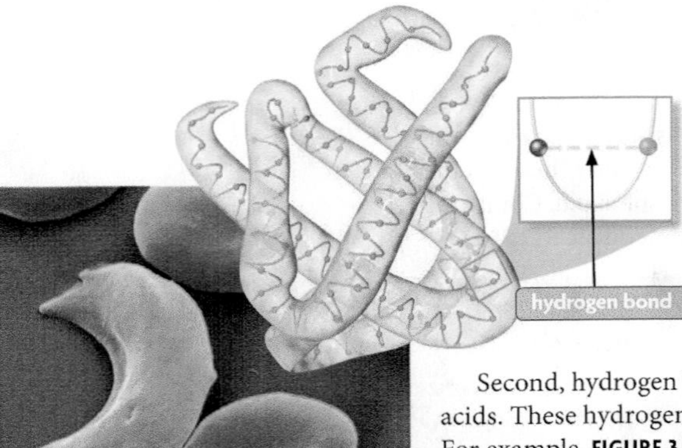

FIGURE 3.8 Hemoglobin in red blood cells transports oxygen. The structure of hemoglobin depends on hydrogen bonds between specific amino acids. Just one amino acid change causes red blood cells to have the curved shape characteristic of sickle cell anemia. (colored SEM; magnification 3500×)

Prions and Public Health

Proteins differ in the number and order of amino acids. The specific sequence of amino acids determines a protein's structure and function. Two types of interactions between the side groups of some amino acids are especially important in protein structure. First, some side groups contain sulfur atoms. The sulfur atoms can form covalent bonds that force the protein to bend into a certain shape.

Second, hydrogen bonds can form between the side groups of some amino acids. These hydrogen bonds cause the protein to fold into a specific shape. For example, **FIGURE 3.8** shows the structure of one of the four polypeptides that makes up hemoglobin, the protein in your red blood cells that transports oxygen. Each of the four polypeptides contains an iron atom that bonds to an oxygen molecule. The four polypeptides are folded in a way that puts the four oxygen-carrying sites together in a pocketlike structure inside the molecule. If a protein has incorrect amino acids, the structure may change in a way that prevents the protein from working properly. Just one wrong amino acid of the 574 amino acids in hemoglobin causes the disorder sickle cell anemia.

Nucleic Acids

Detailed instructions to build proteins are stored in extremely long carbon-based molecules called nucleic acids. **Nucleic acids** are polymers that are made up of monomers called nucleotides. A nucleotide is composed of a sugar, a phosphate group, and a nitrogen-containing molecule called a base. There are two general types of nucleic acids: DNA and RNA.

Nucleic acids work together to make proteins. DNA contains the code that determines the sequence of animo acids that make up a protein. The code is transcribed to RNA, which moves to ribosomes for protein synthesis. The sequence of animo acids determines the shape of a protein. The shape of a protein is essential to its ability to perform its function. Offspring are similar to their parents because they inherit their parents' genes, which contain codes on DNA to make proteins. The same proteins, which perform the same functions, are made from similar genes in offspring through the same processes as in the parents.

A Apply What is the relationship between proteins and nucleic acids?

2.3 Formative Assessment

REVIEWING MAIN IDEAS

1. What is the relationship between a **polymer** and a **monomer**?
2. Explain how both **nucleic acids** and **proteins** are polymers. Be sure to describe the monomers that make up the polymers.

CRITICAL THINKING

3. **Compare and Contrast** How are **carbohydrates** and **lipids** similar? How are they different?
4. **Infer** Explain how the bonding properties of carbon atoms result in the large variety of carbon-based molecules in living things.

CONNECT TO BIOCHEMISTRY

5. Why might **fatty acids, amino acids,** and nucleic acids increase the hydrogen ion (H^+) concentration of a solution? Explain your answer.

2.3 FORMATIVE ASSESSMENT

1. A polymer is a large molecule made up of smaller units, called monomers, which are linked together.
2. Both are made of smaller units that are bonded together. Proteins are polymers of amino acids; nucleic acids are polymers of nucleotides.
3. Answers should include the following information: both are made of carbon, hydrogen, and oxygen; both are broken down as a source of energy; both have some structural functions; carbohydrates include sugars and starches, and lipids include fats and oils.
4. Carbon atoms are able to form four covalent bonds with other atoms including other carbon atoms; many other types of atoms can bond to carbon, and many different combinations are possible.
5. The molecules are acids; acids increase the H^+ ion concentration in a solution and lower the pH.

Identifying Variables

Smart Grapher
HMHScience.com
GO ONLINE
Create animated charts and graphs using Smart Grapher.

In an experiment, a scientist determines the effect one variable has on another. A scientist changes, or manipulates, the **independent variable** and measures or observes the **dependent variables**. Therefore, data from an experiment are measurements of dependent variables. Changes in dependent variables "depend upon" the independent variable.

Model

A scientist studied the effect of jogging on the number of Calories used. (The Calories in food are kilocalories, or 1000 calories.) People jogged for three different lengths of time—10 minutes, 20 minutes, and 30 minutes. The number of Calories used was measured, recorded, and plotted on a graph like the one shown on the right. What are the independent and dependent variables?

- The independent variable is the length of time spent jogging (10 minutes, 20 minutes, or 30 minutes).
- The dependent variable is the number of Calories used while jogging—the number of Calories "depends on" time.

GRAPH 1. JOGGING AND CALORIES

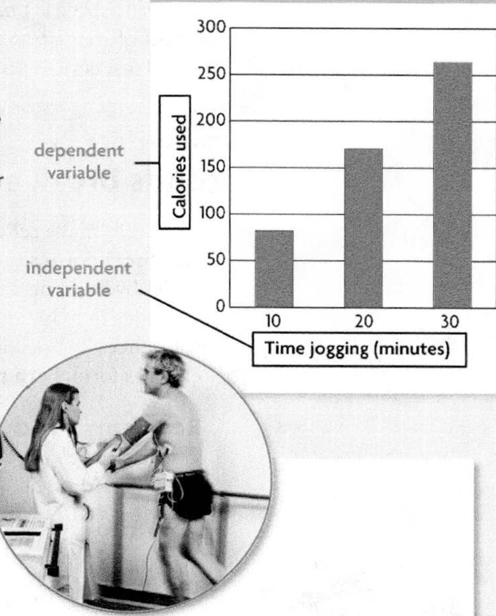

Practice Identify Variables

A company that makes nutritional products is developing a new type of protein drink for athletes. A scientist at the company is studying the pH at which a digestive enzyme best breaks down the different proteins in the drink. The scientist uses the following experimental procedure:

- Five test tubes each contain 2 mL of the protein drink.
- Five different solutions contain the digestive enzyme, but each solution has a different pH—1.5, 2.0, 2.5, 3.0, and 3.5.
- One enzyme solution is added to each test tube of protein drink.
- Protein levels are measured in each of the five test tubes.

1. **Identify** What are the independent and dependent variables in the experiment? Explain your answers.
2. **Apply** Time is often used as a dependent variable in experiments. Describe how time could be used as a dependent variable in this experiment.

Answers

1. The independent variable is pH because pH is manipulated. The dependent variable is the protein concentration because it is the variable that is measured.
2. Time could be used as a dependent variable if the amount of time needed to break down the protein was measured.

DATA ANALYSIS

Introduce

Explain what is implied by the term *rate*. **Ask**

- How many units of measure are involved in a rate? at least two
- What measurements should you make to find your heart rate? number of beats and time

Have students measure their heart rate by taking their pulse. Show students how to place their second and third fingers (not the thumb) of one hand on the inside of the wrist of the other hand. **Ask,** In what units should you express your heart rate? beats per minute

Discuss

Discuss the variables in the example. **Ask**

- What variables must be held constant in this experiment for the results to be valid? how fast the subject jogs
- What would the graph look like if *Time* was plotted on the vertical axis and *Calories* on the horizontal axis? The bars would be horizontal.
- What do the data tell you? The longer you jog, the more energy is used.

Online Student Resources, Data Analysis Practice

SECTION 2.4

▼ Plan and Prepare

Activate Prior Knowledge Have students think of pedaling a bike along a level surface, then up a hill, and then down. Make the analogy to the energy involved in a chemical reaction. **Ask,** At what point is more energy needed? when leaving the level surface to reach the top of the hill Relate this to the energy of activation. **Ask,** How does it feel when you crest the hill and head down? Extra energy is no longer needed to cover the distance back down.

▼ Teach

Take It Further

Point out that the chemical equation shown in the text for cellular respiration describes the overall process. The equation is a summary of many chemical reactions. The products of the first reaction, in which some of the bonds in glucose are broken, become the reactants in the next reaction, and so on. Oxygen does not take part in the process until the final reaction.

2.4 Chemical Reactions

VOCABULARY

chemical reaction
reactant
product
bond energy
equilibrium
activation energy
exothermic
endothermic

KEY CONCEPT **Life depends on chemical reactions.**

MAIN IDEAS

- Bonds break and form during chemical reactions.
- Chemical reactions release or absorb energy.

Connect to Your World

When you hear the term *chemical reaction,* what comes to mind? Maybe you think of liquids bubbling in beakers. You probably do not think of the air in your breath, but most of the carbon dioxide and water vapor that you breathe out are made by chemical reactions in your cells.

MAIN IDEA

Bonds break and form during chemical reactions.

Plant cells make cellulose by linking simple sugars together. Plant and animal cells break down sugars to get usable energy. And all cells build protein molecules by bonding amino acids together. These are just a few of the chemical reactions in living things. **Chemical reactions** change substances into different substances by breaking and forming chemical bonds. Although the matter changes form, both matter and energy are conserved in a chemical reaction.

Reactants, Products, and Bond Energy

Your cells need the oxygen molecules that you breathe in. Oxygen (O_2) plays a part in a series of chemical reactions that provides usable energy for your cells. These reactions, which are described in detail in the chapter Cells and Energy, break down the simple sugar glucose ($C_6H_{12}O_6$). The process uses oxygen and glucose and results in carbon dioxide (CO_2), water (H_2O), and usable energy. Oxygen and glucose are the reactants. **Reactants** are the substances changed during a chemical reaction. Carbon dioxide and water are the products. **Products** are the substances made by a chemical reaction. Chemical equations are used to show what happens during a reaction. The overall equation for the process that changes oxygen and glucose into carbon dioxide and water is

$$6O_2 + C_6H_{12}O_6 \longrightarrow 6CO_2 + 6H_2O$$

Reactants — Direction — Products

The reactants are on the left side of the equation, and the products are on the right side. The arrow shows the direction of the reaction. This process, which is called cellular respiration, makes the carbon dioxide and water vapor that you breathe out. But for carbon dioxide and water to be made, bonds must be broken in the reactants, and bonds must form in the products. What causes bonds in oxygen and glucose molecules to break? And what happens when new bonds form in carbon dioxide and water?

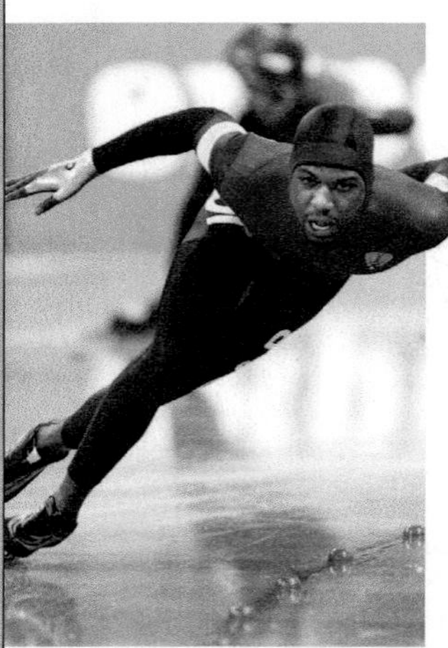

FIGURE 4.1 The breakdown of glucose provides chemical energy for all activities, including speed skating.

Differentiated Instruction

ENGLISH LEARNERS

Students who have been educated in their home languages can transfer some content language because many science terms derived from Latin are similar across languages. For example, ask students how the terms *equilibrium, exothermic,* and *endothermic* are expressed in their home language to check for cognates, or shared roots.

PRE-AP

Explain that the coefficients in the equation for cellular respiration show the number of molecules taking part in the reaction. The law of conservation of mass states that matter cannot be created or destroyed in a chemical reaction. Have students take five minutes to describe how this relates to the chemical equation shown in the text.

Teacher Toolkit, Section C, Quick-Write

QUICKLAB MODELING

Chemical Bonding

You use energy to put things together, but chemical bonding is different. Energy is added to break bonds, and energy is released when bonds form.

MATERIALS
2 flat magnets

PROBLEM How is chemical bonding similar to the interaction between two magnets?

PROCEDURE

1. Bring the magnets close to each other until they snap together.
2. Pull the magnets away from each other.

ANALYZE AND CONCLUDE

1. **Infer** How is bond formation represented by the snapping sound?
2. **Apply** How is bond energy related to the separation of the magnets?

First, energy is added to break bonds in molecules of oxygen and glucose. **Bond energy** is the amount of energy that will break a bond between two atoms. Bonds between different types of atoms have different bond energies. Energy is released when bonds form, such as when molecules of water and carbon dioxide are made. When a bond forms, the amount of energy released is equal to the amount of energy that breaks the same bond. For example, energy is released when hydrogen and oxygen atoms bond to form a water molecule. The same amount of energy is needed to break apart a water molecule.

Chemical Equilibrium

Some reactions go from reactants to products until the reactants are used up. However, many reactions in living things are reversible. They move in both directions at the same time. These reactions tend to go in one direction or the other depending on the concentrations of the reactants and products. One such reaction lets blood, shown in **FIGURE 4.2,** carry carbon dioxide. Carbon dioxide reacts with water in blood to form a compound called carbonic acid (H_2CO_3). Your body needs this reaction to get rid of carbon dioxide waste from your cells.

$$CO_2 + H_2O \rightleftarrows H_2CO_3$$

The arrows in the equation above show that the reaction goes in both directions. When the carbon dioxide concentration is high, as it is around your cells, the reaction moves toward the right and carbonic acid forms. In your lungs, the carbon dioxide concentration is low. The reaction goes in the other direction, and carbonic acid breaks down.

When a reaction takes place at an equal rate in both directions, the reactant and product concentrations stay the same. This state is called equilibrium. **Equilibrium** (EE-kwuh-LIHB-ree-uhm) is reached when both the reactants and products are made at the same rate.

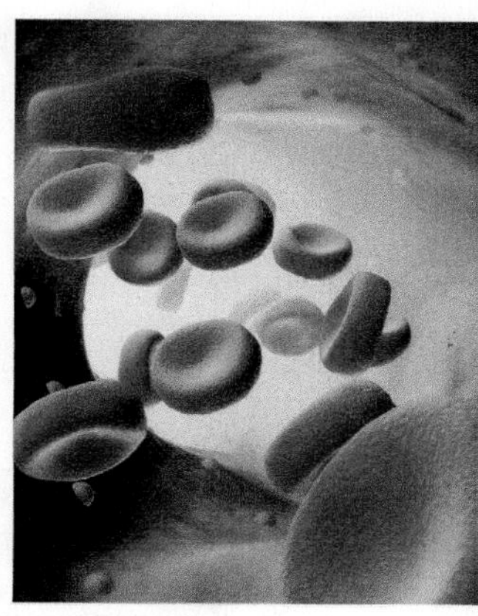

FIGURE 4.2 Blood cells and plasma transport materials throughout the body. Carbonic acid dissolves in the blood so that carbon dioxide can be transported to the lungs.

A Apply **Explain why concentration is important in a chemical reaction.**

BELOW LEVEL

Explain that the term *equilibrium* means "balanced." Have two students pull with equal force on opposite ends of a rope so they are balanced. **Ask,** Are the students in equilibrium? Explain why or why not. The students are in equilibrium because they are pulling with balanced forces. **Ask,** Is it correct to say that nothing is happening? Explain why or why not. No, the students are exerting forces. Because the forces are balanced, neither student moves.

QUICKLAB

Time 10 minutes

Purpose Model the formation and breaking of a chemical bond.

LAB MANAGEMENT

- Make sure students understand the nature of the model. Atoms do not make a snapping sound when they form a bond; the sound is symbolic.

Analyze and Conclude

1. The sound represents the energy released when a bond forms.
2. In order to pull the magnets apart, effort (energy) is needed. Similarly, energy is required to break bonds.

Address Misconceptions

Common Misconception Students often think that energy is released when chemical bonds are broken.

Correcting the Misconception The opposite is true. Energy is always required to break bonds, and energy is always released when new bonds form. However, the net change in energy can be either an overall release or absorption of energy. You can compare bond breaking within molecules to the physical energy required in opening a sealed jar.

Answers

A **Apply** Concentration can alter the equilibrium of a chemical reaction. A higher concentration of reactants means that more of the reactants are available to react.

▼ Teach *continued*

Take It Further

Point out that living systems maintain a **dynamic equilibrium.** Reactants are always being delivered to cells and products removed. If this movement of materials stops, the cell dies. For example, as long as a cell receives a steady supply of oxygen and glucose and gets rid of carbon dioxide waste, the product of one reaction in cellular respiration becomes the reactant of the next reaction. Cells do not reach a state of equilibrium, but carry on chemical activity continually.

TEACH FROM VISUALS

FIGURE 4.3 Explain that the energy curves in these graphs are steeper than they are in actual reactions. The graphs represent idealized situations.

Point out on the graphs that the energies of the products are not equal to the energies of the reactants. Tell students that a decrease in total energy actually indicates an increase in bond energy, and vice versa. **Ask,** How does the bond energy of the products compare with the bond energy of the reactants in each type of reaction? Bond energy of products is higher in an exothermic reaction and lower in an endothermic reaction.

Answers

A Critical Viewing No, the bond energies of reactants and products determine whether a reaction is exothermic or endothermic.

Have students use the Virtual Lab to explore how much energy food provides.

FIGURE 4.3 Energy and Chemical Reactions

Energy is required to break bonds in reactants, and energy is released when bonds form in products. Overall, a chemical reaction either absorbs or releases energy.

GO ONLINE

Energy and Chemical Reactions

ACTIVATION ENERGY

When enough activation energy is added to the reactants, bonds in the reactants break and the reaction begins.

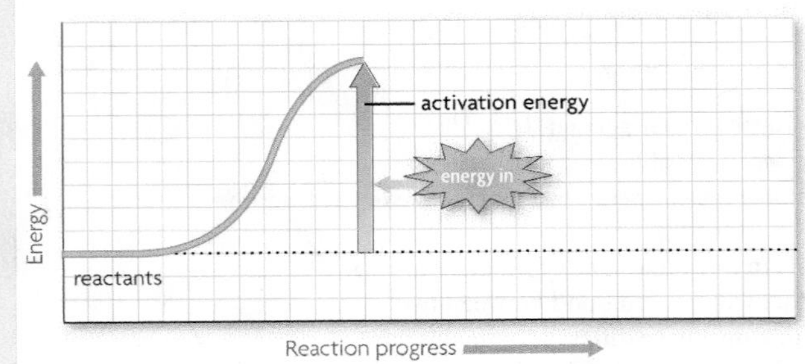

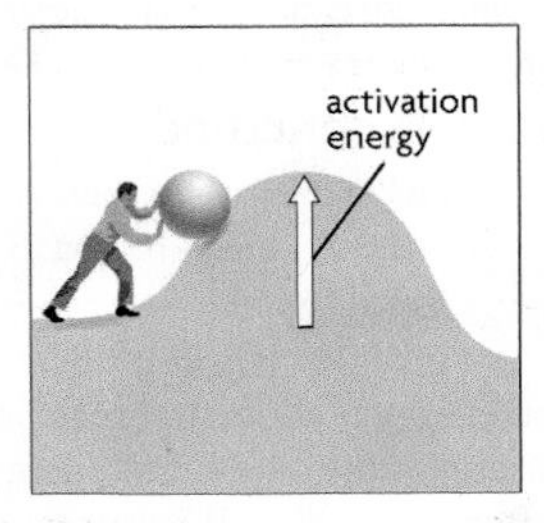

EXOTHERMIC REACTION Energy Released

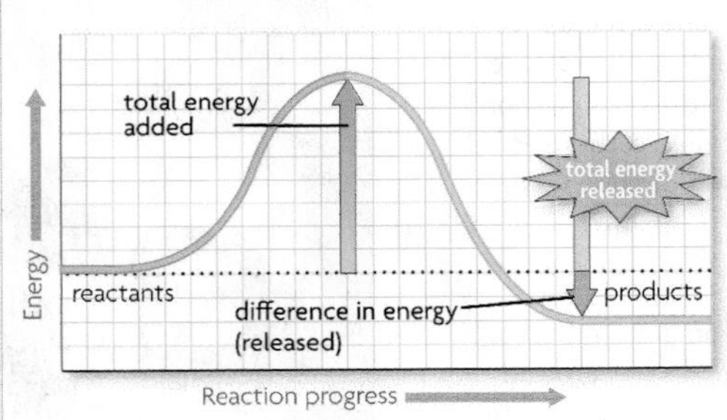

The products in an exothermic reaction have a higher bond energy than the reactants, and the difference in energy is released to the surroundings.

ENDOTHERMIC REACTION Energy Absorbed

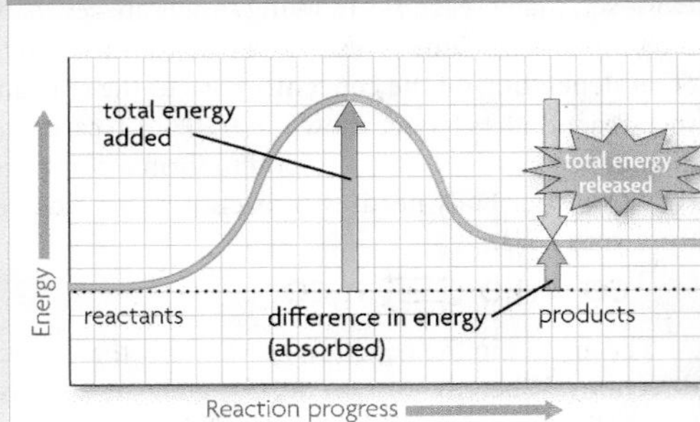

The products in an endothermic reaction have a lower bond energy than the reactants, and the difference in energy is absorbed from the surroundings.

A CRITICAL VIEWING **Is the amount of activation energy related to whether a reaction is exothermic or endothermic? Why or why not?**

Differentiated Instruction

TEACH WITH TECHNOLOGY

Use a temperature probe to demonstrate an exothermic or endothermic reaction.

Exothermic Place a temperature probe in a jar. Cover jar. After five minutes, record temperature. Remove probe. Soak a piece of steel wool in vinegar for one minute. Then squeeze out the excess vinegar. Wrap the wool around the probe, and place the wool/probe in jar. Cover jar. After five minutes, record the temperature. (When iron rusts, four atoms of solid iron react with three molecules of oxygen gas to form two molecules of solid iron oxide).

Endothermic Pour 25 mL of a citric acid solution (any strength) into a plastic-foam coffee cup. Use a temperature probe to record the initial temperature. Stir in about 15 g of baking soda (sodium bicarbonate). Record the change in temperature. The reaction mixture can be rinsed down the drain. (In this reaction, one molecule of citric acid reacts with three molecules of sodium bicarbonate to form three molecules of carbon dioxide, three molecules of water, and one molecule of sodium citrate.)

MAIN IDEA

Chemical reactions release or absorb energy.

All chemical reactions involve changes in energy. Energy that is added to the reactants breaks their chemical bonds. When new bonds form in the products, energy is released. This means that energy is both absorbed and released during a chemical reaction. Some chemical reactions release more energy than they absorb. Other chemical reactions absorb more energy than they release. Whether a reaction releases or absorbs energy depends on bond energy.

Some energy must be absorbed by the reactants in any chemical reaction. **Activation energy** is the amount of energy that needs to be absorbed for a chemical reaction to start. Activation energy is like the energy you would need to push a rock up a hill. Once the rock is at the top of the hill, it rolls down the other side by itself. A graph of the activation energy that is added to start a chemical reaction is shown at the top of **FIGURE 4.3.**

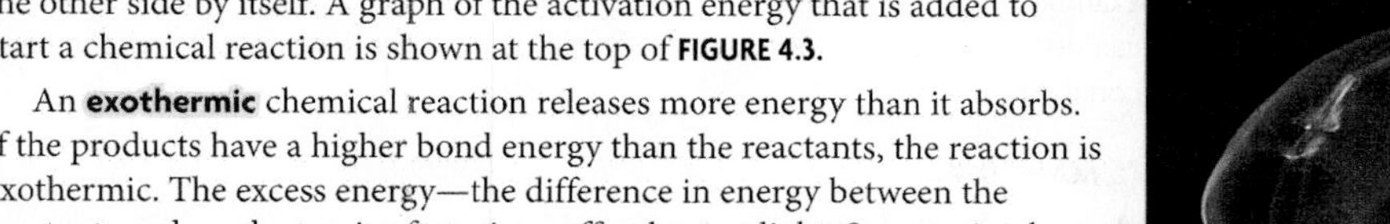

An **exothermic** chemical reaction releases more energy than it absorbs. If the products have a higher bond energy than the reactants, the reaction is exothermic. The excess energy—the difference in energy between the reactants and products—is often given off as heat or light. Some animals, such as squids and fireflies, give off light that comes from exothermic reactions, as shown in **FIGURE 4.4**. Cellular respiration, the process that uses glucose and oxygen to provide usable energy for cells, is also exothermic. Cellular respiration releases not only usable energy for your cells but also heat that keeps your body warm.

An **endothermic** chemical reaction absorbs more energy than it releases. If products have a lower bond energy than reactants, the reaction is endothermic. Energy must be absorbed to make up the difference. One of the most important processes for life on Earth, photosynthesis, is endothermic. During photosynthesis, plants absorb energy from sunlight and use that energy to make simple sugars and complex carbohydrates.

A Analyze **How is activation energy related to bond energy?**

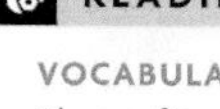

READING TOOLBOX

VOCABULARY

The prefix *exo-* means "out," and the prefix *endo-* means "in." Energy moves out of an exothermic reaction, and energy moves into an endothermic reaction.

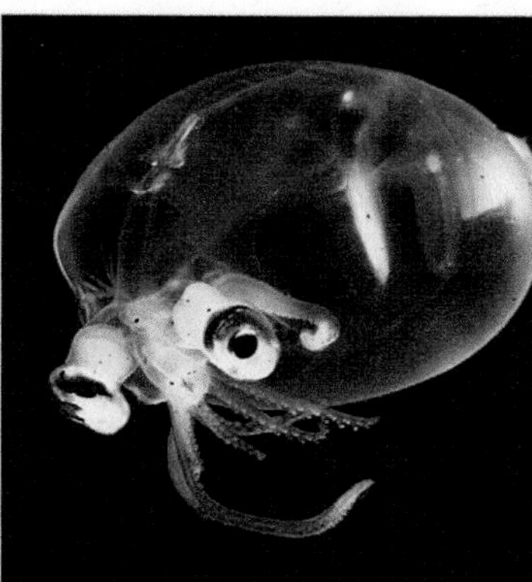

FIGURE 4.4 The glow of the bugeye squid comes from an exothermic reaction that releases light.

Integrating Physics

When a bond is made, not all of the activation energy that is used to make the bond ends up in the bond. Some spreads out into the surroundings as heat, according to the **second law of thermodynamics.** If this energy did not disperse, it would simply flow back into the bond and undo it. Heat dispersal ensures that the molecules that are formed stay together in a stable state.

Answers

A Analyze The amount of activation energy required depends on the bond energy of the reactants.

Assess and Reteach

Assess Use the Section Self-Check or Section Quiz, both available at **HMHScience.com**.

Reteach Have students give examples of an exothermic and an endothermic reaction. Exothermic: the burning of paper, cellular respiration; endothermic: reaction in a cold pack, photosynthesis. Have students draw an energy graph for each reaction. **Ask,** What form does the energy take in each reaction? The burning of paper releases both heat and light; cellular respiration releases heat and chemical energy (ATP). A cold pack absorbs heat; photosynthesis absorbs light energy from sunlight.

2.4 Formative Assessment

SELF-CHECK Online
HMHScience.com
GO ONLINE

REVIEWING MAIN IDEAS

1. Hydrogen peroxide (H_2O_2) breaks down into water (H_2O) and oxygen (O_2). Explain why this is a **chemical reaction**. What are the **reactants** and the **products** in the reaction?
2. How do **endothermic** and **exothermic** reactions differ?

CRITICAL THINKING

3. **Infer** The process below is exothermic. What must be true about the **bond energies** of the reactants and the products? Explain.

$$6O_2 + C_6H_{12}O_6 \longrightarrow 6CO_2 + 6H_2O$$

4. **Evaluate** Why might it not always be possible to determine the reactants and the products in a reaction? Explain your answer in terms of chemical **equilibrium.**

CONNECT TO

BIOCHEMISTRY

5. A chemical reaction can start when enough **activation energy** is added to the reactants. Do you think the activation energy for chemical reactions in living things is high or low? Explain your answer.

2.4 FORMATIVE ASSESSMENT

1. It is a chemical reaction because different substances are formed. The reactant is hydrogen peroxide, and the products are oxygen and water.
2. Endothermic reactions absorb energy because the products have a higher total energy than the reactants have. Exothermic reactions release energy because the products have a lower total energy than the reactants have.
3. The bond energies of the products must be higher than those of the reactants because excess total energy is released.
4. Depending on the concentrations of the reactants and the products, both reactants and products may be formed at the same time if the reaction is reversible. At equilibrium, reactants and products are formed at the same rate.
5. The activation energy for reactions must be relatively low because temperature cannot be greatly increased in living things.

SECTION 2.5

B.1.2 Analyze how the shape of a molecule determines its role in the many different types of cellular processes (e.g., metabolism, homeostasis, growth and development, and heredity) and understand that the majority of these processes involve proteins that act as enzymes.

▼ Plan and Prepare

Activate Prior Knowledge Discuss how leaving a newspaper in sunlight will eventually cause the paper to yellow. If you set a match to the newspaper, it burns quickly. **Ask,** What does adding energy to a reaction do? It increases the kinetic energy of the reactant molecules, so more frequent and forceful collisions result in a faster reaction. Discuss that adding energy to reactions in a cell could destroy the cell. A solution to the problem is to lower the amount of energy needed to start the reaction.

▼ Teach

TEACH FROM VISUALS

FIGURE 5.1 Point out that a catalyst lowers the activation energy of a slowly occurring reaction so that it occurs more quickly. It cannot cause a reaction that would never occur otherwise.

2.5 Enzymes

KEY CONCEPT **Enzymes are catalysts for chemical reactions in living things.**

VOCABULARY

catalyst
enzyme
substrate

MAIN IDEAS

- A catalyst lowers activation energy.
- Enzymes allow chemical reactions to occur under tightly controlled conditions.

Connect to Your World

How can a Venus flytrap digest a frog? It happens through the action of proteins called enzymes. Enzymes help to start and run chemical reactions in living things. For example, enzymes are needed to break down food into smaller molecules that cells can use. Without enzymes, a Venus flytrap couldn't break down its food, and neither could you.

MAIN IDEA

A catalyst lowers activation energy.

Remember what you learned about activation energy in Section 4. Activation energy for a chemical reaction is like the energy that is needed to push a rock up a hill. When enough energy is added to get the rock to the top of a hill, the rock can roll down the other side by itself. Activation energy gives a similar push to a chemical reaction. Once a chemical reaction starts, it can continue by itself, and it will go at a certain rate.

Often, the activation energy for a chemical reaction comes from an increase in temperature. But even after a chemical reaction starts, it may happen very slowly. The reactants may not interact enough, or they may not be at a high enough concentration, to quickly form the products of the reaction. However, both the activation energy and rate of a chemical reaction can be changed by a chemical catalyst, as shown in **FIGURE 5.1.** A **catalyst** (KAT-l-ihst) is a substance that decreases the activation energy needed to start a chemical reaction and, as a result, also increases the rate of the chemical reaction.

FIGURE 5.1 CATALYSTS AND ACTIVATION ENERGY

Under normal conditions, a certain amount of activation energy is needed to start a chemical reaction. A catalyst decreases the activation energy needed.

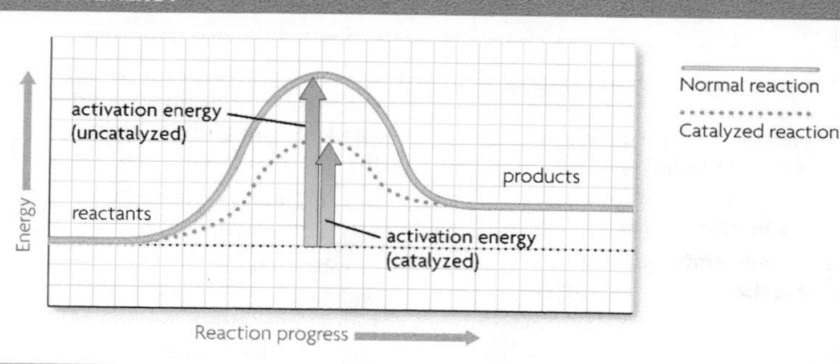

Differentiated Instruction

ENGLISH LEARNERS

Have students use a 2 × 2 word square for the vocabulary in this section. They should place the term at the center of the square and then in the four cells include a definition, characteristics, examples, and nonexamples.

Teacher Toolkit, Section D, Frayer Model

BELOW LEVEL

Have students review the three parts of the lock-and-key model shown on the last page of this section. Have them write for five minutes, describing the analogy. They should consider why the model is described as a lock and key. Have them identify the different parts and what happens to each part after the reaction is completed.

Teacher Toolkit, Section C, Quick-Write

Compare the activation energies and the reaction rates in the graph in **FIGURE 5.1.** Under normal conditions, the reaction requires a certain amount of activation energy, and it occurs at a certain rate. When a catalyst is present, less energy is needed and the products form faster. Although catalysts take part in chemical reactions, catalysts are not considered to be either reactants or products because catalysts are not changed or used up during a reaction.

A Summarize **Describe two functions of catalysts in chemical reactions.**

MAIN IDEA

Enzymes allow chemical reactions to occur under tightly controlled conditions.

Chemical reactions in organisms have to take place at an organism's body temperature. Often, reactants are found in low concentrations. Because the reactions must take place very quickly, they usually need a catalyst. **Enzymes** are catalysts for chemical reactions in living things. Enzymes, like other catalysts, lower the activation energy and increase the rate of chemical reactions. In reactions that are reversible, such as the carbon dioxide and carbonic acid reaction described in Section 4, enzymes do not affect chemical equilibrium. This means that enzymes do not change the direction of a reaction—they just change the amount of time needed for equilibrium to be reached.

Enzymes are involved in almost every process in organisms. From breaking down food to building proteins, enzymes are needed. For example, amylase is an enzyme in saliva that breaks down starch into simpler sugars. This reaction occurs up to a million times faster with amylase than without it. Enzymes are also an important part of your immune system, as shown in **FIGURE 5.2.**

Almost all enzymes are proteins. These enzymes, like other proteins, are long chains of amino acids. Each enzyme also depends on its structure to function properly. Conditions such as temperature and pH can affect the shape and function, or activity, of an enzyme. Enzymes work best in a small temperature range around the organism's normal body temperature. At only slightly higher temperatures, the hydrogen bonds in an enzyme may begin to break apart. The enzyme's structure changes, and it loses its ability to function. This is one reason why a very high fever is so dangerous to a person. A change in pH can also affect the hydrogen bonds in enzymes. Many enzymes in humans work best at the nearly neutral pH that is maintained within cells of the human body.

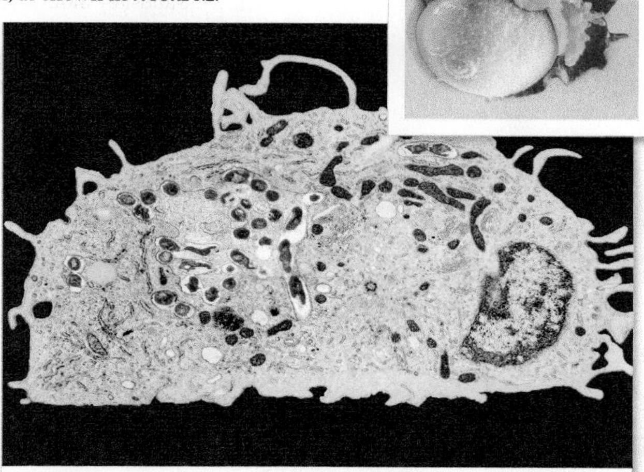

FIGURE 5.2 The inset micrograph (top) shows a white blood cell engulfing an invading pathogen. The larger micrograph shows a pathogen after it has been captured. Once inside a white blood cell, enzymes are used to destroy the pathogen.

TEACH WITH TECHNOLOGY

Use an oxygen probe to track the effect of an enzyme on a reaction. One such reaction uses liver extract, which contains the enzyme catalase, to convert hydrogen peroxide (H_2O_2) to oxygen gas and water. In another reaction, an extract of ground raw potato becomes darkened in the presence of catechol and oxygen, in the same way a cut potato darkens. The change in absorbance (optical density) at 540 nm can be tracked with a probe.

Answers

A Summarize Catalysts decrease activation energy and increase reaction rate.

Vocabulary

Academic Vocabulary The word **catalyst** is used in everyday language to describe someone or something that sets a process in motion. The root of the word means "to loosen." A related concept is that of a **threshold.** In everyday terms, a *threshold* is a point of entry. When applied in science, it refers to the point at which an effect can be seen or differentiated. An enzyme acting as a catalyst effectively lowers the threshold for the energy of activation in a chemical reaction.

History of Science

All enzymes were thought to be proteins until 1982, when **Thomas Cech** and **Sidney Altman** discovered the catalytic activity of RNA. These RNAs were named **ribozymes.** They resemble enzymes in their action and the presence of an active site. More than 500 ribozymes are now known. Altman and Cech were awarded the Nobel Prize in Chemistry in 1989 for their work.

Integrating Genetics

By switching genes on and off, a cell can control which metabolic reactions take place in that cell. In addition, some genes code for enzyme inhibitors and regulatory molecules. Some inhibitors work on specific enzymes, others are nonspecific, and still others compete with the substrate for the active site. By controlling the production of enzymes and inhibitors, the cell regulates its metabolism.

▼ Teach *continued*

Take It Further

The lock-and-key model is a good way to begin to understand enzyme function, but it has been largely replaced by the **inducible fit model,** which is described in the last paragraph of the text. The main difference is the understanding that the enzyme itself changes shape as it interacts with its substrate. In the inducible fit model, the bending of the enzyme gives insight into one mechanism by which bonds in the substrate are weakened. The enzyme resists bending and puts a molecular force on the substrate. (Electrostatic and hydrophobic/hydrophilic interactions between side chains of the protein also weaken bonds.)

Answers

A Apply If the structure of an enzyme changes, its function will change.

▼ Assess and Reteach

Assess Use the Section Self-Check or Section Quiz, both available at **HMHScience.com**.

Reteach Relate the lock-and-key model shown on this page to **FIGURE 5.1** to summarize how an enzyme acts as a catalyst.

CONNECT TO
BIOCHEMISTRY
The order of amino acids determines the structure and function of an enzyme. An enzyme's structure often depends on hydrogen bonds between amino acids.

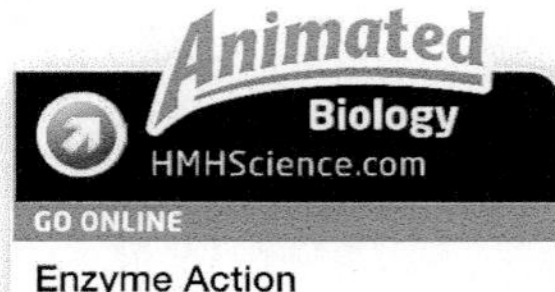

Enzyme Action

Enzyme structure is important because each enzyme's shape allows only certain reactants to bind to the enzyme. The specific reactants that an enzyme acts on are called **substrates.** For example, amylase only breaks down starch. Therefore, starch is the substrate for amylase. Substrates temporarily bind to enzymes at specific places called active sites. In the same way that a key fits into a lock, substrates exactly fit the active sites of enzymes. This is why, if an enzyme's structure changes, it may not work at all. This idea of enzyme function, which is called the lock-and-key model, is shown below.

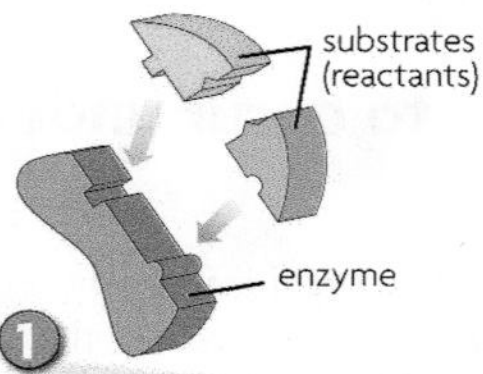

1 Substrates bind to an enzyme at certain places called active sites.

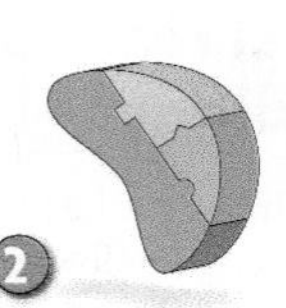
2 The enzyme brings substrates together and weakens their bonds.

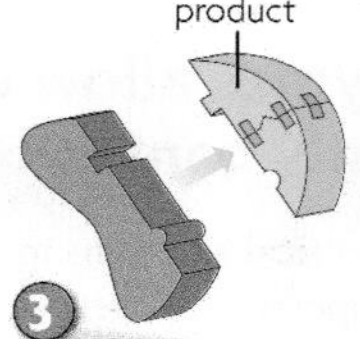

3 The catalyzed reaction forms a product that is released from the enzyme.

The lock-and-key model helps explain how enzymes work. First, enzymes bring substrate molecules close together. Because of the low concentrations of reactants in cells, many reactions would be unlikely to take place without enzymes bringing substrates together. Second, enzymes decrease activation energy. When substrates bind to the enzyme at the enzyme's active site, the bonds inside these molecules become strained. If bonds are strained, or stretched slightly out of their normal positions, they become weaker. Less activation energy is needed for these slightly weakened bonds to be broken.

The lock-and-key model is a good starting point for understanding enzyme function. However, scientists have found that the structures of enzymes are not fixed in place. Instead, enzymes actually bend slightly when they are bound to their substrates. In terms of a lock and key, it is as if the lock bends around the key to make the key fit better. The bending of the enzyme is one way in which bonds in the substrates are weakened.

A Apply How does the structure of an enzyme affect its function?

2.5 Formative Assessment

REVIEWING ▶ MAIN IDEAS

1. How does a **catalyst** affect the activation energy of a chemical reaction?
2. Describe how the interaction between an **enzyme** and its **substrates** changes a chemical reaction.

CRITICAL THINKING

3. **Infer** Some organisms live in very hot or very acidic environments. Would their enzymes function in a person's cells? Why or why not?
4. **Predict** Suppose that the amino acids that make up an enzyme's active site are changed. How might this change affect the enzyme?

CONNECT TO
HOMEOSTASIS

5. Organisms need to maintain homeostasis, or stable internal conditions. Why is homeostasis important for the function of enzymes?

Unit 1: Introducing Biology

2.5 FORMATIVE ASSESSMENT

1. A catalyst reduces the activation energy required to start the reaction.
2. An enzyme brings substrates close together so that they can react, and slightly alters (weakens) the bonds within the substrates by changing the shapes of the molecules.
3. No, those enzymes function under different conditions than are found in humans.
4. The substrates would likely not bond to the enzyme because the shape of the active site would change.
5. If homeostatic conditions, such as temperature or pH, are not maintained, then the hydrogen bonds that keep an enzyme in its correct shape will weaken or break and the enzyme's structure will change. This will affect its function.

Mars Water

S.T.E.M. Interactions

Ever since astronomers in the 1870s noticed markings that looked like canals on the surface of Mars, people have wondered if water could exist there. Life on Earth can't exist without water. If Mars has water, does it have life too?

Since then, astronomers have been trying to confirm that water is present on Mars—or was present in the past. The Compact Reconnaissance Imaging Spectrometer for Mars (CRISM) was built to answer the question. CRISM is an imaging spectrometer, an instrument that uses reflected sunlight to measure the chemistry of Mars's surface and atmosphere. Astronomers' primary goal is to use CRISM to search for clues that might reveal the presence of water. Images received from CRISM since 2006 seem to confirm that Mars had large amounts of water in its ancient history. What is this evidence? CRISM has detected clay on the surface of Mars. Clay is a type of soil that has a large water content. It forms when rock is weathered and changed by water that becomes trapped within the rock structure. Much of the clay on Mars is found in and around large craters. Scientists think that the clay formed billions of years ago and became buried over time. It was likely brought to the surface by the impact of a space rock hitting Mars and creating the crater.

Using data from CRISM, NASA has confirmed that liquid water is flowing on present-day Mars. Images of Mars's surface show dark, narrow, 100-meter-long streaks on steep slopes. The streaks get longer and wider and appear to flow downhill during warm seasons. In cooler seasons, the streaks get shorter and narrower. Then they disappear. Chemical analyses of the streaks show that they contain hydrated minerals (salts), but only when the streaks are relatively wide. When narrow streaks were analyzed, the hydrated salts were gone. Hydrated salts have water molecules in their crystal structure. The salts lower the freezing point of water, just as salt does when it is spread on roads to melt snow and ice. The presence of these salts may explain how liquid water could exist on a planet that is much colder than ours.

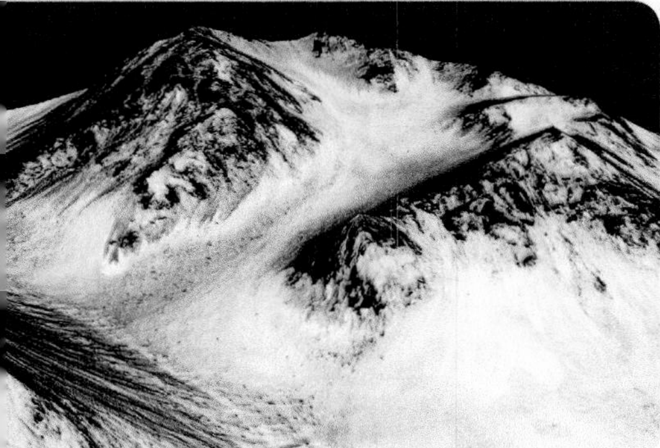

If liquid water is flowing today on the surface of Mars, could life exist there? The hydrated salts make the water too briny for humans to drink. Only time and more research will tell if Mars can be a habitable planet for humans.

Questions

1. The Mars Analog Research and Technology Experiment (MARTE) was an international project looking at science and technologies needed for a future drilling mission to Mars. What major challenges would a team face in researching a site they cannot visit?
2. Research MARTE to learn how the research team overcame this challenge.
3. What are the constraints of conducting research in a simulated environment?

Introduce

Explain to students that many discoveries about Mars have been made since spacecraft have orbited and rovers have explored its surface and atmosphere, but one discovery has generated the most interest: the possibility that liquid water exists now or existed in the distant past. **Ask,** Why are scientists so eager to find water on Mars? Explain that water is essential to life. Everywhere on Earth that water is found, life is also found. Might that also be true on Mars?

Discuss

Tell students that about 3.8 to 3.5 billion years ago, Mars and Earth were much more similar than they are now. Evidence shows that Mars may have been warmer and wetter than it is today. Discuss what environmental conditions and resources would have been needed for life to arise. What form could this life possibly have taken—unicellular and microscopic? Discuss the possibility that if life were present in Mars's past, it might still exist.

Then discuss how CRISM might be used to find Martian life. Encourage students to find out the kinds of compounds CRISM can detect and whether these compounds are associated with life on Earth. Tell students that there are many Mars studies being conducted today. The Mars Odyssey, Mars Exploration Rovers, Mars Reconnaissance Orbiter, and Mars Phoenix Lander were all designed to make discoveries under the previous Mars Exploration Program theme of "Follow the Water." Now that water has been discovered, the next steps toward finding evidence of life itself can be taken. Tell students that the new initiative is called "Seek Signs of Life." Rovers are currently searching for evidence of organic compounds, the building blocks of life. Scientists hope that areas with water and the chemistry needed for life might provide habitable conditions for life on Mars.

CHAPTER REVIEW

GO ONLINE

Encourage students to go to **HMHScience.com** for a detailed review of each section, including visuals and vocabulary practice.

Online Student Resources, Vocabulary Practice Worksheet

CHAPTER 2 Summary

BIG IDEA Living things depend on chemical reactions that require water, carbon-based molecules, and other molecules including enzymes to regulate chemical reactions.

KEY CONCEPTS

2.1 Atoms, Ions, and Molecules

All living things are based on atoms and their interactions. All matter is composed of atoms that interact. Atoms can become ions by gaining or losing electrons. Compounds and molecules form when atoms form bonds.

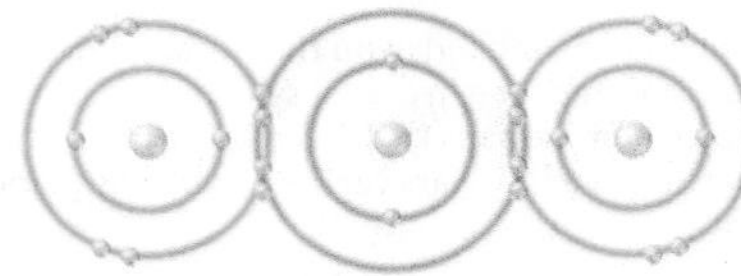

Carbon dioxide

2.2 Properties of Water

Water's unique properties allow life to exist on Earth. Water is a polar molecule. The slightly charged regions of water molecules form hydrogen bonds that give water properties such as cohesion and adhesion. Many substances dissolve in water to form solutions.

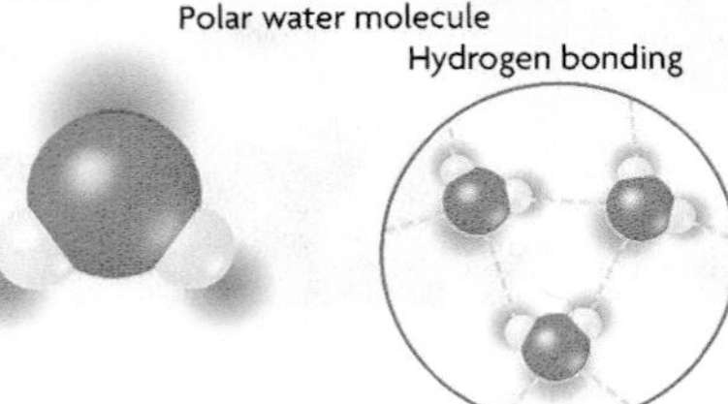

2.3 Carbon-Based Molecules

Carbon-based molecules are the foundation of life. The four main types of carbon-based molecules in living things are carbohydrates, lipids, proteins, and nucleic acids. The molecules have different functions that are based on their different structures.

2.4 Chemical Reactions

Life depends on chemical reactions. A chemical reaction changes reactants into products. Bonds break in the reactants, and new bonds form in the products. Chemical reactions either release energy (exothermic reactions) or absorb energy (endothermic reactions).

2.5 Enzymes

Enzymes are catalysts for chemical reactions in living things. Enzymes increase the rate of reactions and decrease the activation energy for reactions. Each enzyme catalyzes a specific reaction, and a change in an enzyme's structure changes its function.

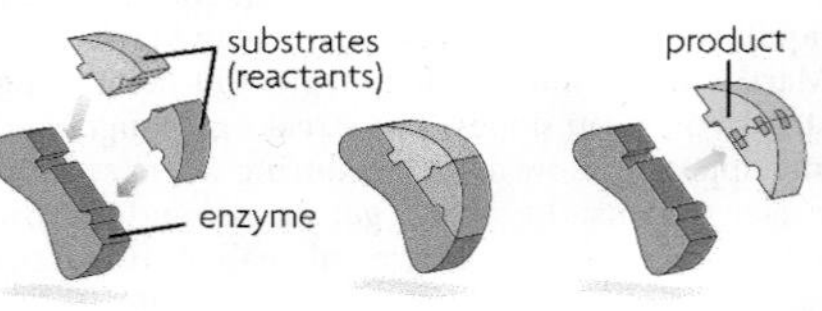

READING TOOLBOX SYNTHESIZE YOUR NOTES

Supporting Main Ideas Use your notes to make a detailed version of the graphic organizer shown below. Make organizers for each key concept in the chapter. Be sure to include important details and to mark important vocabulary terms.

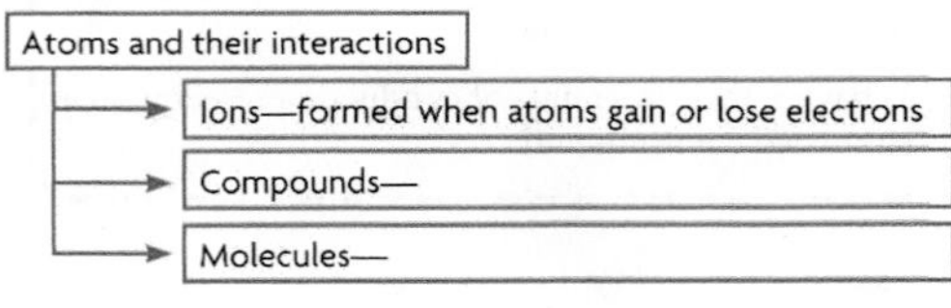

Concept Map Use concept maps like the one below to visualize the relationships among chapter concepts.

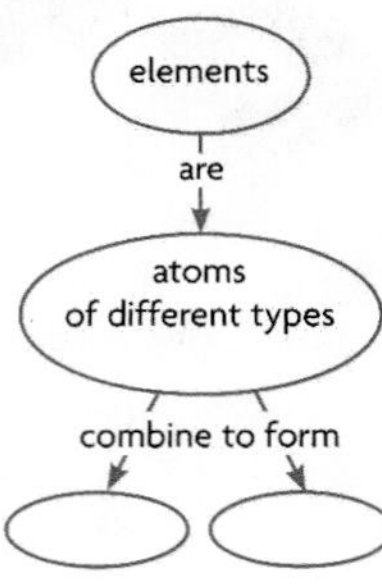

Reviewing Vocabulary

1. Atoms are the basic unit of matter. An atom that gains or loses electrons and has a charge is an ion.
2. Cohesion in water is the result of hydrogen bonds that form from one polar water molecule being attracted to another.
3. A solvent dissolves other substances to form a solution.
4. Acids have a high concentration of hydrogen ions and a low pH. Bases have a low concentration of hydrogen ions and a high pH.
5. Exothermic reactions release more energy than they absorb. Endothermic reactions absorb more energy than they release.
6. A catalyst is a substance that increases the rate of a chemical reaction. Enzymes are biological catalysts.
7. An atom is the basic unit of matter. It cannot be broken down by normal chemical means.
8. It is the strength or concentration of hydrogen ions that makes a solution acidic or basic.
9. A monounsaturated lipid has one unsaturated carbon in its fatty acid tail(s); a polyunsaturated lipid has two or more unsaturated carbons in its fatty acid tail(s).

CHAPTER REVIEW

2 Review

INTERACTIVE Review
HMHScience.com
GO ONLINE
Review Games • Concept Map • Section Self-Checks

CHAPTER VOCABULARY

2.1 atom, element, compound, ion, ionic bond, covalent bond, molecule

2.2 hydrogen bond, cohesion, adhesion, solution, solvent, solute, acid, base, pH

2.3 monomer, polymer, carbohydrate, lipid, fatty acid, protein, amino acid, nucleic acid

2.4 chemical reaction, reactant, product, bond energy, equilibrium, activation energy, exothermic, endothermic

2.5 catalyst, enzyme, substrate

Reviewing Vocabulary

Vocabulary Connections

The vocabulary terms in this chapter are related to each other in various ways. For each group of words below, write a sentence or two to clearly explain how the terms are connected. For example, for the terms *covalent bond* and *molecule*, you could write "A molecule is made of atoms connected by covalent bonds."

1. atom, ion
2. hydrogen bond, cohesion
3. solution, solvent
4. acid, base, pH
5. exothermic, endothermic
6. catalyst, enzyme

READING TOOLBOX WORD ORIGINS

7. The word *atom* comes from the Greek word *atomos,* which means "indivisible." Describe the relationship between the Greek term and your understanding of atoms.
8. The letter *p* in the term *pH* stands for the German word *Potenz,* which means "power" or "potential." The letter *H* represents hydrogen ions (H^+). How are these related to the definition of pH?
9. The prefix *mono-* means "one" and the prefix *poly-* means "many." Some lipids are monounsaturated, and others are polyunsaturated. Explain the difference between the fatty acids in these different types of lipids.

Reviewing MAIN IDEAS

10. Explain how the combination of electrons, protons, and neutrons results in the neutral charge of an atom.
11. Potassium ions (K^+) have a positive charge. What happens to a potassium atom's electrons when it becomes an ion?
12. Some types of atoms form more than one covalent bond with another atom. What determines how many covalent bonds two atoms can make? Explain.
13. How is hydrogen bonding related to the structure of the water molecule?
14. Explain the difference between solvents and solutes.
15. Describe the relationship between hydrogen ions (H^+) and pH. How is pH related to a solution's acidity?
16. Carbon forms a very large number of compounds. What characteristic of carbon atoms allows the formation of all of these compounds? Explain.
17. Describe examples of monomers and polymers in carbohydrates, proteins, and nucleic acids.
18. Explain the relationship between a protein's structure and its ability to function.
19. What are the components of a chemical reaction?
20. Explain the difference between exothermic and endothermic reactions.
21. Describe the effect of a catalyst on activation energy and reaction rate.
22. What is the role of enzymes in organisms?

Reviewing Main Ideas

10. Neutrons have no charge. Each proton has a charge of +1, and each electron has a charge of −1. Atoms are neutral when the number of protons and electrons are equal.
11. loses one electron
12. If atoms need more than one electron to fill their outermost energy levels, they can share more than one electron pair.
13. The larger oxygen atom pulls electrons away from the hydrogen atoms, producing charged regions that result in hydrogen bonding.
14. Solvents are present in greater concentrations and dissolve solutes.
15. There is an inverse relationship—the greater the hydrogen ion concentration, the lower the pH, and the more acidic the solution.
16. Carbon atoms have four unpaired electrons in their outermost energy level, so they can form four covalent bonds.
17. Carbohydrates—Simple sugars (for example, glucose) are monomers that are bonded to form polysaccharides (for example, cellulose). Proteins—Amino acids are monomers that are bonded to form proteins. Nucleic acids—Nucleotides are monomers that are bonded to form nucleic acids.
18. The specific function of a protein is dependent on its precise structure. A change in protein structure changes its function.
19. Substances that are changed in a chemical reaction are reactants; substances made are products.
20. If a reaction has a net gain of energy (that is, it absorbs more energy than it releases), it is an endothermic reaction and the products have a lower bond energy than the reactants have. If a reaction has a net release of energy (that is, it releases more energy than it absorbs), it is an exothermic reaction and the products have a higher bond energy than the reactants have.
21. A catalyst decreases activation energy and increases reaction rate.
22. Enzymes allow reactions to occur at high rates under the tightly controlled conditions found in organisms.

Critical Thinking

23. Phospholipids have fatty acid chains bonded to glycerol, as do triglycerides; however, a third fatty acid is replaced by a phosphate group, which gives the molecule a polar head and two nonpolar tails.
24. Both bonds involve attraction between positive and negative charges. Ionic bonds are very strong attractions between oppositely charged ions that result in a compound. Hydrogen bonds are relatively weak attractions between partial positive and negative charges that do not form a compound.
25. For medication to travel in the body, it must dissolve in the blood. To dissolve easily, the molecules of the medication must be polar.
26. A protein's function might be disrupted if hydrogen bonds break and the protein's structure changes due to changes in pH or temperature.
27. Starch and cellulose are both polysaccharides of glucose. Starches are branched and are used by plants to store chemical energy. Cellulose has a straight, rigid structure and makes up plant cell walls.
28. Lipids are a major component of cell membranes, they store energy, and they are used to make hormones.
29. In raw foods, enzyme structures are still intact and can be reused. When foods are cooked, the enzyme structure is destroyed, and it loses its function.

Interpreting Visuals

30. A substrate (B) binds to the active site of the enzyme (A); a chemical reaction occurs due to the reactants' weakened bonds; products (C and D) are released from the enzyme.
31. It decreases the amount of activation energy needed because the weakened bonds of the substrate are easier to break.
32. Buffers help keep pH stable. Conditions such as pH need to be tightly controlled so that hydrogen bonds between amino acids in enzymes can remain intact.

Critical Thinking

23. Compare and Contrast How are phospholipids similar to lipids such as triglycerides? How are they different?

24. Compare and Contrast Briefly describe the similarities and differences between hydrogen bonds and ionic bonds. Which type of bond do you think is stronger? Why?

25. Infer Suppose that you have a cold. What characteristics must cold medicine have that allow it to be transported throughout your body? Explain.

26. Predict Homeostasis involves the maintenance of constant conditions in an organism. What might happen to a protein if homeostasis is disrupted? Why?

27. Compare and Contrast Describe the structures and functions of starch and cellulose. How are the molecules similar? How are they different?

28. Apply Suppose you had a friend who wanted to entirely avoid eating fats. What functions of lipids could you describe to convince that person of the importance of fats to his or her health?

29. Infer The human body can reuse some of the enzymes found in raw fruits and vegetables. Why is this not the case for cooked fruits and vegetables?

Interpreting Visuals

The diagram below shows the lock-and-key model of enzyme function. Use it to answer the next three questions.

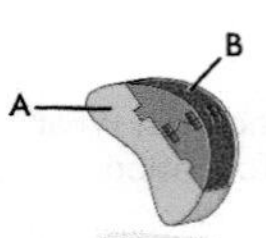

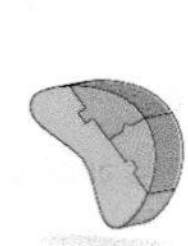
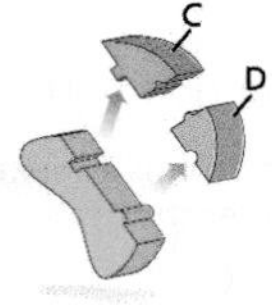

30. Summarize Briefly explain what is happening at each step of the process. Be sure to identify each of the substances (A–D) shown in each step of the process.

31. Apply How does Substance A affect the amount of activation energy needed by the process? Explain.

32. Synthesize Describe the importance of buffers in solutions in allowing the process shown above to take place.

Analyzing Data Identify Variables

Use the graph below to answer the next three questions.

ENERGY IN A CHEMICAL REACTION

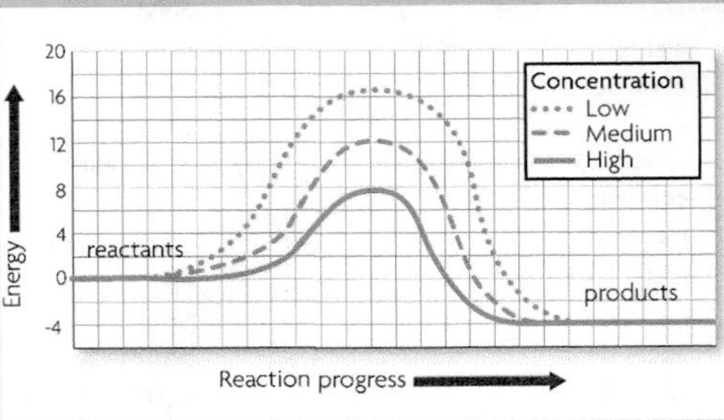

33. Apply Suppose the graph was constructed from data collected during an experiment. What were the independent and dependent variables in the experiment? Explain.

34. Analyze How much activation energy is needed to start the chemical reaction represented by each line on the graph? How much energy is released from each reaction?

35. Apply Explain whether each of the chemical reactions shown on the graph is endothermic or exothermic.

Making Connections

36. Write About Chemical Equilibrium Carbon dioxide reacts with water in blood plasma to form carbonic acid. The equation for this reaction is shown on the second page of Section 4. Imagine that you are a molecule of carbon dioxide. Describe the chemical reactions that take place when you enter the blood and when you leave the blood. Explain what determines how these reactions occur. Be sure to include all terms from the chapter that are related to the chemical reaction.

37. Apply The Venus flytrap shown in the photograph on the chapter opener uses enzymes to digest its prey. Describe how pH, solutions, and chemical reactions all play important roles inside the trap of this carnivorous plant.

Analyzing Data

33. The independent variable is enzyme (or catalyst) concentration; the dependent variable is energy required.
34. 17 units needed/21 units released; 12 units needed/16 units released; 8 units needed/ 12 units released
35. They are all exothermic because they release more energy than they absorb.

62 Unit 1: Introducing Biology

Standards-Based Assessment

Record your answers on a separate piece of paper.

MULTIPLE CHOICE

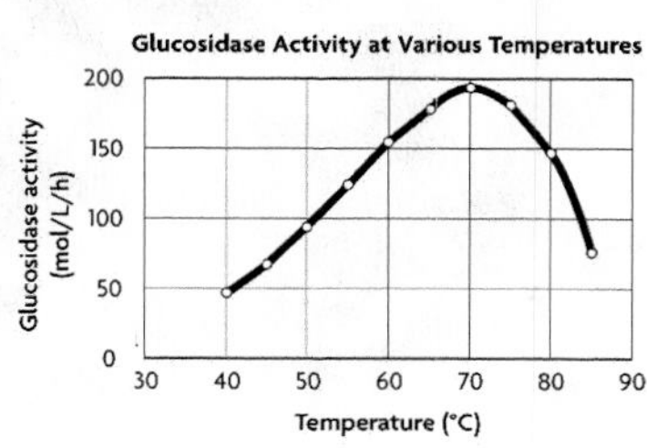

1 The graph above shows the activity of an enzyme called glucosidase. What can you conclude from these data?

A Glucosidase breaks down glucose substrates.

B Glucosidase functions best around 70°C.

C Glucosidase does not function below 70°C.

D Glucosidase is not affected by temperature.

2 Proteins are long molecules that are built from various combinations of —

A carbohydrates

B nucleic acids

C lipids

D amino acids

3

The diagram above shows how an enzyme (black) binds to a substrate (white) when catalyzing a chemical reaction. When this reaction is complete, the —

A enzyme's shape will be different

B surrounding temperature will have increased

C hydrogen ion concentration will have decreased

D substrate will be a different molecule

4 Complex carbohydrates, such as starch, are examples of polymers. Which scientific explanation below ***best*** describes a polymer?

A Polymers are individual parts of a large molecule that are different.

B Polymers are any molecules in which the atoms are held together by bonds.

C Polymers are made of many small molecules that are similar or different.

D Amino acids and nucleotides are examples of polymers.

THINK THROUGH THE QUESTION

Many terms in biology are based on roots, prefixes, or suffixes. The prefix *poly-* means "many." Consider how this meaning gives a clue to the answer.

5 The primary function of DNA is to —

A provide energy for a cell

B transmit messages between cells

C make up cell membranes

D store information for building proteins

6 Scientists have conducted studies to determine how much energy is required to make aluminum cans from bauxite ore, as opposed to making the same cans from aluminum that has been used for other purposes and then discarded. Based on this research, they have determined that much more energy is needed to produce an aluminum can from bauxite ore than from previously discarded aluminum products. What is one beneficial impact that this research has had on society?

A It has encouraged an increase in mining for aluminum ore.

B It has resulted in greater quantities of aluminum products being discarded in landfills.

C It has led to an increase in the recycling of aluminum products.

D It has led to a decrease in the use of aluminum in the making of cans.

Standards-Based Assessment

The Standards-Based Assessment questions will help students prepare for their final examination in the course. If you wish to give students practice in coding their answers, look for the Standards-Based Assessment Answer Sheet at **HMHScience.com**. To give students practice under timed testing conditions, allow them five minutes per question.

Question	Answer	Depth of Knowledge	Cognitive Complexity
1	B	II	M
2	D	I	L
3	D	II	L
4	C	III	M
5	D	I	L
6	C	IV	H

KEY

Depth of Knowledge		Cognitive Complexity	
I	Recall	L	Low
II	Skill/Concept	M	Moderate
III	Strategic Thinking	H	High
IV	Extended Thinking		

Making Connections

36. Answers will vary, but they should include information about reactants (H_2O, CO_2 or H_2CO_3), products (H_2CO_3 or H_2O, CO_2), solvent (water), solute (carbon dioxide), solution (blood), chemical equilibrium, and concentration. Answers should imply that the carbon dioxide molecule enters the blood at the cells and leaves at the lungs.

37. Answers will vary, but they should say that enzymes work at specific pH, that the enzymes and the digestive products are in solution, and that chemical reactions take place in the trap. Additional information about enzyme structure and function and about the role of enzymes in chemical reactions in living things could be included.

UNIT
1

Introduce

Tell students that advances in knowledge and technology have been tied to ethical considerations since ancient times. The Hippocratic Oath, written in ancient Greece, described the ethical obligations of physicians. Today physicians traditionally take a modern version of the Hippocratic Oath. Sometimes codes of ethics are written in response to ethical issues that arise. For example, the Nuremberg Code was written to establish ethics involving research on humans in response to abuses during World War II.

Scientists, especially those with careers in fields such as biotechnology, genetics, and medicine, must take the ethical issues of their work into account. Some scientists make decisions about their work based on their own values. Other decisions are based on guidelines and laws that regulate research or how knowledge gained from research is used.

As more complicated ethical, legal, and social issues arise, time and money are spent in studying and debating these issues. Individuals and groups take grievances into the court system, bills are introduced into Congress, congressional hearings are held, and, for some issues, state and federal laws are passed. As students read about scientific advances, they should consider the ethical issues that could be involved.

Discuss with students how ethical issues affect scientists and how scientific research raises ethical issues. **Ask**

- What might limit the research a scientist can do? personal values, guidelines and laws
- How might the work a scientist does raise ethical issues? Students might answer that the knowledge scientists gain in their research creates new ethical issues.

UNIT 1: INTRODUCING BIOLOGY

BIOZINE at HMHSCIENCE.COM

INTERNET MAGAZINE

Go online for the latest biology news and updates on all BioZine articles.

Expanding the Textbook

News Feeds

Science Daily

CNN

BBC

Careers

Bio Bytes

Opinion Poll

Strange Biology

Scientists can change an organism's genes. Should they?

When Knowledge and Ethics Collide

Our ability to change living things grows as we learn more about life. But sometimes biotechnology makes us question whether or not we should change organisms. Maybe the technology is dangerous, or maybe it challenges our values. Consider the greenish pig in the photo. A GFP (green fluorescent protein) from a jellyfish was added to its genome by genetic engineering for medical research. But how and when should we alter an organism's genes?

64 Unit 1: Introducing Biology

Strange Biology

A fluorescent pig is pretty strange! Have students go to BioZine at **HMHScience.com** and check out the feature called Strange Biology. Have them relate the information they find there to a concept they learned about in the **Introducing Biology** unit.

Bioethics

Bioethics is the study of moral questions that are raised as a result of biology research and its applications. But what do questions of ethics have to do with biology? It might seem better to leave questions about values in a philosophy or social studies class. Keep your mind open as you learn more about the power of biological research. You might find that your biology class is the perfect place to consider any number of ethical questions.

Ethical questions require all of us to make decisions about "the right thing to do." Often, the right thing to do is very clear. Do we cheat on a test, or do we study and learn the material for ourselves? A good decision can benefit ourselves, our families, and even our society—and it often follows the accepted values of society. However, many times the "right" and "wrong" about an ethical issue are not so obvious. Strong feelings on both sides of an ethical question can produce conflicts—in ourselves, and for everyone involved. Can we rely upon biology, or any other scientific field, for our decisions?

Potential Benefits

There are some obvious benefits to having biological information more easily accessible. The Innocence Project, for example, as of 2010 has freed more than 260 prisoners—some of them on death row—who were wrongfully convicted based on incorrect or incomplete evidence. In such cases, DNA technology can add new facts to an old story and actually save a person's life.

In less dramatic ways, biological information can help people live longer and healthier lives. Tests can reveal whether someone is prone to gum disease, heart attacks, Alzheimer's, or certain kinds of cancer. With this information—now available through at-home saliva tests—people can tailor their exercise, diet, and other lifestyle choices to guard against actually contracting these diseases. Access to biological information, in these cases, can be empowering, and can help people live healthier lives.

TECHNOLOGY S.T.E.M.

Genetic Testing

Genetic testing is used in many ways. We can identify disease-causing genes, determine the guilt or innocence of crime suspects, and reunite families that have been separated. But should genetic testing be used by employers to make decisions about employees?

Suppose that a company secretly obtained and tested DNA samples from some of its employees. Because of rising medical insurance claims, the company wanted to know if the employees had a gene that increased their risk for developing a certain medical condition. Does this seem like a plot for a television show? It isn't. In 2002, a company had to pay more than $2 million in damages for testing the DNA of employees without their knowledge.

Consider another case. In 2005, a basketball player named Eddy Curry missed the end of the season because of a potential heart problem. His team wanted to use a genetic test to find out if he had a life-threatening condition. Curry refused because the test results could have ended his career. The team refused to let him play. Both the team and Curry made choices. Who do you think was right?

Read More >> at HMHScience.com

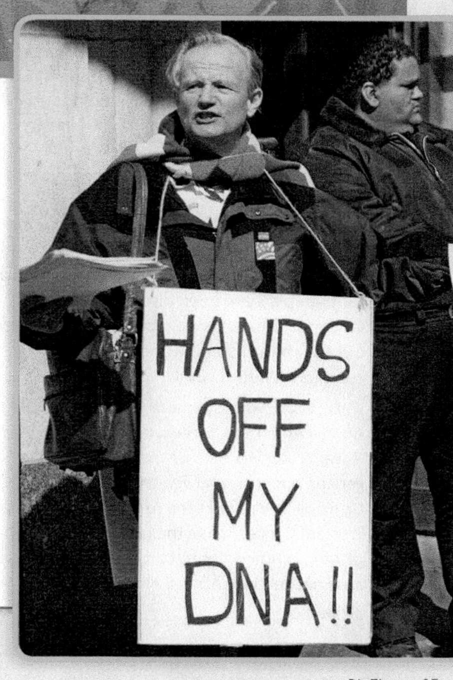

Vocabulary of Ethics

Students may need clarification of some of the terms used to discuss ethical issues.

morals—rules or habits of conduct, with reference to standards of right and wrong

value—a principle, standard, or quality considered worthwhile or desirable

ethics—rules or standards governing the conduct of a person or the member of a profession; the study of moral choices

bioethics—the study of the ethical and moral issues that arise from new biological discoveries and medical advances, often in the field of genetic engineering

biotechnology—the use and application of living things and biological processes

genetic engineering—changing the genetic makeup of an organism, often by adding a gene from a different species

genetic testing—the analysis of an individual's DNA to detect the presence of a gene or genes that are associated with an inherited disorder or an increased risk for a disease, such as cancer; also called genetic screening

Current News

Using the Current News section of BioZine at **HMHScience.com**, have students look for stories about current biological research. Have students consider these questions:

- What question or questions were scientists trying to answer?
- What experimental procedures and methods did the scientists use?
- What kind of language is being used to describe the research and experimentation?
- Are there any ethical issues that might arise from the research?

UNIT 1

Take It Further

The Equal Employment Opportunity Commission (EEOC) settled the first lawsuit involving genetic discrimination in the workplace in 2001. The lawsuit was filed on behalf of employees of the Burlington Northern Santa Fe Railroad who had submitted claims of work-related carpal tunnel syndrome. Without the employees' knowledge, they were tested for a rare genetic condition, HNPP (Hereditary Neuropathy with liability to Pressure Palsies). It is caused by a deletion on chromosome 17, which may predict some forms of carpal tunnel syndrome. Workers were also screened for alcoholism and diabetes. Because these conditions are not job related, testing for them violates the Americans with Disabilities Act and is illegal. The railroad quickly agreed to a settlement.

Hundreds of cases of genetic discrimination have been documented. These cases include a child's health insurance coverage being dropped after a genetic test found an inherited disorder—Fragile X syndrome, and a woman losing her job after her employer discovered that her mother died from Huntington's disease—a fatal genetic disorder. As our ability to gather and process genetic information grows, society will be faced with questions of how to define legitimate and illegitimate uses for this information.

Controversial Issues

With genetic information much more easily accessible, new questions arise. Can a DNA-testing facility, for example, be trusted to keep your results private? This issue of right to information has taken many turns during the past decade. In 2008, the United States passed a law called the Genetic Information Nondiscrimination Act (GINA). This law protects all citizens from potential discrimination by employers and insurers: Even if genetic testing does reveal an individual's likelihood for developing certain health problems, an insurer cannot deny this person coverage based on this information. Do you think this law is necessary? Would you be more likely to get DNA testing knowing that this law is in place?

Aside from issues of privacy, what do lifestyle and health decisions look like if you do test positive for an incurable fatal disease? DNA testing is more accurate than many other tests, but there is still a possibility of incorrect results. Even if they are correct, there is the possibility that a cure will come for that fatal disease within your lifetime. The decision to be tested has many pros and cons. For example, in families with members who have a neurological disorder called Huntington's disease, some individuals do not elect to be tested for the gene. They do not want this information—bad or good—to affect their lives. How can this information improve or limit your choices?

As biotechnology continues to advance, you will face new bioethics questions. Will you be ready?

Science can only provide information and possibilities. We can add new genes to an organism's DNA. We can clone animals and may someday clone humans. We can extend human life expectancies and test people's risk for diseases. But should we do all these things? Should government continue to make laws regarding bioethical issues? Should people be able to make their own decisions about personal health and privacy? As biotechnology continues to advance, you will face new bioethics questions. Will you be ready?

CAREERS

Geneticist in Action

DR. CHARMAINE ROYAL

TITLE Professor, Pediatrics, Howard University

EDUCATION Ph.D., Human Genetics, Howard University

Many bioethicists focus on the ethical implications of technology. Dr. Charmaine Royal, however, is concerned with the ethics of experimental design and the applications and implications of biological research. Dr. Royal, who is a geneticist at the Human Genome Center of Howard University, points out that some scientists in the past tried to use genetic research to justify treating non-Caucasians as inferior. She also notes that although there is no biological basis for any meaningful differences among races, many African Americans are still suspicious of genetic research. Many, for example, have been discriminated against when an insurance company or a prospective employer finds out they have sickle cell anemia, which is a relatively common genetic disorder in African Americans.

Dr. Royal, who is Jamaican, wants to ensure that African Americans are included and treated fairly in research studies and that they receive the benefits of genetic screening and genetic counseling. In 1998 Dr. Royal helped start the African American Hereditary Prostate Cancer Study, the first large-scale genetic study of African Americans to be designed and carried out by an almost entirely African American research team.

Read More >> at HMHScience.com

Questions to Consider

- Should scientists do all of the things that technology has made it possible for them to do?
- Should individuals or the government decide how biotechnology is used?
- Should scientific knowledge or personal beliefs be more important in decisions about biotechnology?

Read More >> at HMHScience.com

Careers

Have students check out BioZine at **HMHScience.com** to learn about different careers in biology. For each career they read about, have students write a brief paragraph that addresses the following questions:

- What topic(s) does this scientist study?
- What are the benefits and risks associated with this type of research?
- How could this scientist's work affect my life or the environment?
- Are there any controversial or ethical issues related to this type of research?
- How do the ethical issues compare with those in other biology-related careers?

UNIT 2

Cells

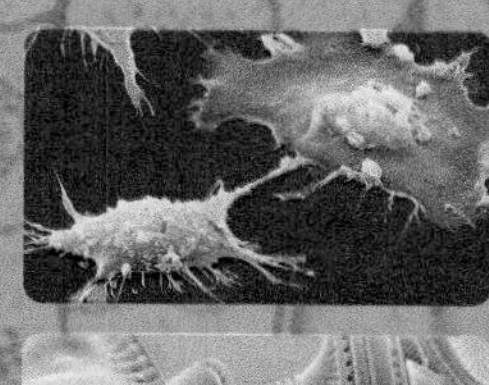

BIOZINE
HMHScience.com

Stem Cell Research—Potential Solutions, Practical Challenges

TECHNOLOGY **Somatic Cell Nuclear Transfer**

CAREER **Cell Biologist**

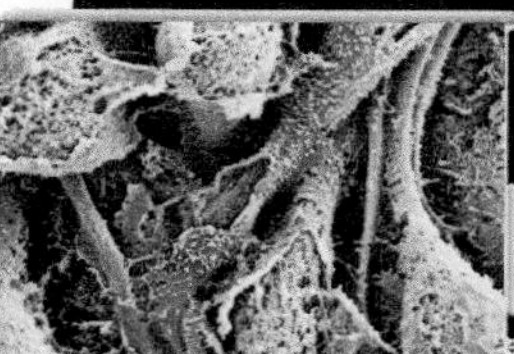

Unit Project

Purpose **Demonstrate an understanding of the structure and function of cell organelles and the relationships between them.**

Overview Students prepare a blueprint and write a proposal for a miniature golf course that provides a tour of a cell and its organelles. Students will

- incorporate the main cell organelles from either a plant or an animal cell
- identify the size, structure, and function of each organelle
- identify and explain the relationships between different organelles

Preparation Make a copy of the project description and rubric for each student. Tell students that they will be evaluated not just on their knowledge of cell structure but also on their design. An optional student handout is available, providing information on cell structures and their size.

Project Management Allow three weeks for the completion of the project. Check on students' progress at the end of each week leading up to the completion date.

Online Student Resources Unit 2 Project

CHAPTER 3

Instruction and Intervention Support

Cell Structure and Function

① Core Instruction

The **Core Instruction** resources below can be used for all students. Core instruction should be followed by ongoing assessment to determine which students need further help.

Available in both English and Spanish

Available Online

Section	Instruction	PRINT	ONLINE	Labs
3.1	Textbook **Cell Theory**	■	●	Estimating a Cell Count (Challenge Lab)
	PowerPresentation and Notes 3.1		●	
3.2	Textbook **Cell Organelles**	■	●	Comparing Cells Modeling the Cell Cell Motility and the Cytoskeleton Staining Biological Specimens (Biotechnology Lab) Cytoplasmic Streaming in Elodea (Challenge Lab, Design Your Own) **Video Lab** Plant Cell Observation
	Animated Biology Cell Structures, Making and Exporting Proteins		●	
	Teaching Visuals Plant Cell (Fig. 2.2), Animal Cell (Fig. 2.2), Cell Organelles (Fig. 2.1, 2.3–2.12)		●	
	PowerPresentation and Notes 3.2		●	
3.3	Textbook **Cell Membrane**	■	●	**QuickLab** Modeling the Cell Membrane
	Teaching Visuals Fluid Mosaic Model (Fig. 3.1), Selective Permeability (Fig. 3.2), Cell Receptors (Fig. 3.3, 3.4)		●	
	PowerPresentation and Notes 3.3		●	
3.4	Textbook **Diffusion and Osmosis**	■	●	Diffusion Across a Membrane (Design Your Own) Diffusion and Dialysis Diffusion Through Membranes (Probeware Lab) The Effect of Alcohol on Biological Membranes (Probeware Lab) Biological Membranes (Probeware Lab) **Video Lab** Cell Size and Diffusion
	Animated Biology Facilitated Diffusion		●	
	Teaching Visuals Passive and Active Transport (Fig. 4.1, 5.1)		●	
	PowerPresentation and Notes 3.4		●	
3.5	Textbook **Active Transport, Endocytosis, and Exocytosis**	■	●	
	Animated Biology Get Through a Cell Membrane, Sodium-Potassium Pump		●	
	Teaching Visuals Endocytosis and Exocytosis		●	
	PowerPresentation and Notes 3.5		●	

Additional online resources available for this chapter include **Interactive Whiteboard resources.**

GO ONLINE! for all your teacher resources at HMHScience.com

2 Support and Intervention

Support and Intervention resources are useful for students who need targeted help beyond the Core Instruction

Resources	PRINT	ONLINE
Assess and Reteach (TE wrap)	■	⊙
Concept Map		⊙
Interactive Reader	■	⊙
Interactive Review Games		⊙
Section Self-Checks		⊙
Study Guide B		⊙
Virtual Investigation Virtual Tour of Animal Cell		⊙
Vocabulary Practice Worksheets		⊙

3 Specialized Support

Students who need more intensive personalized intervention benefit from **Specialized Support** resources.

Resources	PRINT	ONLINE
Chapter Audio Files		⊙
Differentiated Instruction Inclusion, Below Level, and English Learners (TE wrap)	■	⊙
ELL Strategies	■	⊙
Modified Lesson Plans for English Learners		⊙
Reinforcement Worksheets		⊙
Study Guide A		⊙

Extension and Assessment

Enrichment and Challenge

Resources	PRINT	ONLINE
Active Reading Worksheet		⊙
Data Analysis Practice Worksheet		⊙
Differentiated Instruction Pre-AP (TE wrap)	■	⊙
The Inside Story and **Take It Further** (TE wrap)	■	⊙
Pre-AP Activity Modeling Cell Receptors, Experiment with Osmosis		⊙
Unit Project		⊙
WebLinks		⊙
WebQuest Organelle Dysfunction (3.2)		⊙

Assessment

Resources	PRINT	ONLINE
Alternative Assessment		⊙
Chapter Tests A and B		⊙
Diagnostic Test		⊙
ExamView Banks		⊙
Extended Response Test		⊙
Online Assessment System		⊙
Section Quizzes		⊙
Standards-Based Assessment	■	⊙

CHAPTER 3

Chapter Overview

- **Section 1** differentiates between prokaryotes and eukaryotes and outlines the scientific developments that led to the cell theory.
- **Section 2** covers eukaryotic cell structure, including organelles and their functions.
- **Section 3** discusses the structure and function of a cell membrane.
- **Section 4** describes passive transport and distinguishes among osmosis, diffusion, and facilitated diffusion.
- **Section 5** describes active transport and distinguishes among endocytosis, phagocytosis, and exocytosis.

▼ Focus and Motivate

How do cells help defend against invaders?

Tell students that macrophages, like many other cells in the body, can crawl. They crawl to sites of infection and engulf invading bacterial cells. Cell movement is a complex process that involves the cell membrane and a skeleton-like system of fibers that stretch throughout the cell. Students will learn more about a cell and its inner structure in this chapter.

Ask, What can you learn by looking at cells? get a sense of structure and shape; also a sense of relative size, in this case the size of a macrophage to a bacterium

BIOZINE
HMHScience.com

Students can access BioZine at **HMHScience.com** to learn about the variety of careers open to biologists.

CHAPTER 3 Cell Structure and Function

BIG IDEA Cells are the smallest unit of living matter that can carry out all processes required for life.

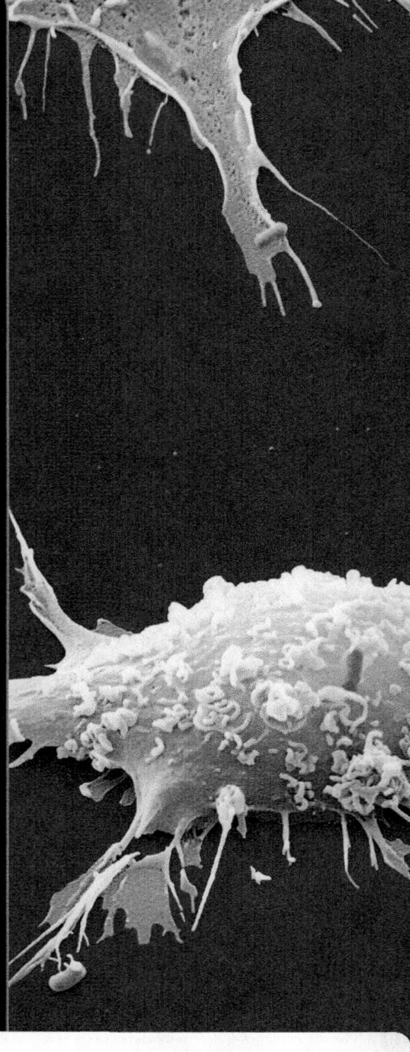

ONLINE BIOLOGY HMHScience.com

ONLINE Labs
- **QuickLab** Modeling the Cell Membrane
- Diffusion Across a Membrane
- Comparing Cells
- Modeling the Cell
- Cell Motility and the Cytoskeleton
- Staining Biological Specimens
- Diffusion and Dialysis
- Estimating a Cell Count
- Cytoplasmic Streaming in *Elodea*
- Diffusion Through Membranes
- The Effect of Alcohol on Biological Membranes
- Biological Membranes
- **Video Lab** Plant Cell Observation
- **Video Lab** Cell Size and Diffusion

Teacher Demo

Eye Opener **Use a bubble frame to explore the properties of a bilayer and how it interacts with polar and nonpolar molecules. A bubble frame can be made from straws and two lengths of string.**

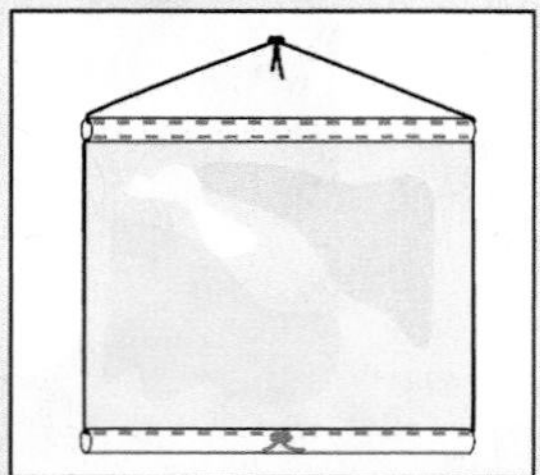

Materials
- bubble solution
- bubble frame or loop
- aluminum pan
- 1-inch flexible PVC pipe
- scissors
- small container of water

If using store-bought solution, add extra detergent or glycerin for a thicker film. To make your own solution, mix 2/3 cup of liquid dish detergent with 3 tablespoons of glycerin per gallon of water; let it sit overnight.

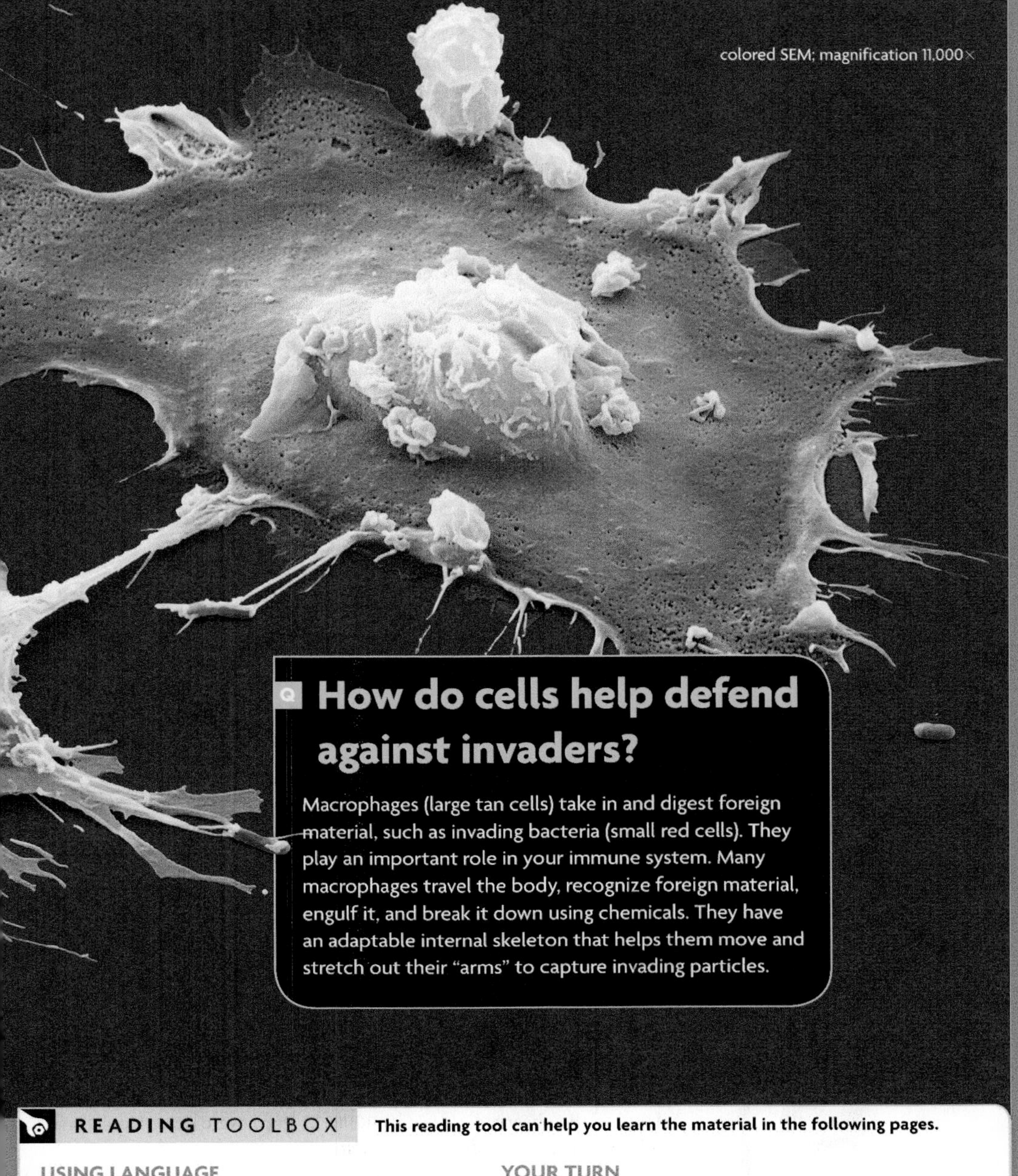

How do cells help defend against invaders?

Macrophages (large tan cells) take in and digest foreign material, such as invading bacteria (small red cells). They play an important role in your immune system. Many macrophages travel the body, recognize foreign material, engulf it, and break it down using chemicals. They have an adaptable internal skeleton that helps them move and stretch out their "arms" to capture invading particles.

READING TOOLBOX **This reading tool can help you learn the material in the following pages.**

USING LANGUAGE

Similes Similes help relate new ideas to ideas that you already know. Often, similes use the terms *like* or *as*. For example, if you were describing a motorcycle to someone who had never seen one, you might say that it is like a bicycle that has a motor.

YOUR TURN

Use the information in the chapter to perform the following tasks.

1. Find a simile to describe the endoplasmic reticulum.
2. Write a simile to describe the function of a mitochondrion.

Activate Prior Knowledge

Direct students' attention to the chapter title. **Ask,** Have you ever heard the expression "form follows function"? What does it mean? Students will probably relate physical shape to a job done.

Give the examples of a diesel engine and a gasoline engine. Both have the same shape, yet they operate in different ways. **Ask,** What's the difference? The engines have different internal structures and use different fuels. Give students another example: motor oil doesn't look much different from maple syrup. **Ask,** What's the difference? chemical makeup

Discuss that structure and function can relate to shape, internal structure, or chemical makeup.

Preview Vocabulary

Academic Vocabulary The words *structure* and *function* are ones most students are familiar with. Ask students to define them.

structure, the way in which parts are put together to form a whole

function, the action for which something is particularly fitted

Discuss with students that the working parts of cellular structure include atoms, molecules, and organelles. Function relates directly to the properties of a cell's parts.

Greek and Latin Word Origins In this chapter, students will see scientific terms constructed from Greek and Latin roots. Have students watch for applications of these word parts:

cyto- = cell
endo- = within
iso- = equal
hypo- = below
kary- = kernel
exo- = out of
hyper- = above

Demonstrate

- Place the bubble frame in the solution, then slowly lift the frame from the solution.
- Wet your finger in the solution and gently press it into the film. Move your finger around within the film.
- Repeat the process with your finger dipped in water and then with your finger dry.
- Cut a short length of PVC pipe and wet it in solution. Pull up the frame and move the pipe into and around the film. Have two students come up to pass a pencil through the pipe, from one side to the other.

Discuss Relate the bubble film to a cell membrane. The solution of soap and water forms a bilayer. Lipid molecules (soap) are positioned on either side of an inner layer of water molecules. Their polar heads point inward, attracted to water molecules; their nonpolar tails point outward. **Ask**

- Why could I move my finger within the film when covered in solution or water? With solution, the bilayer was maintained; water is a polar molecule.
- How might nonpolar or large molecules move across a bilayer? through a channel; in cells, through protein channels

Answers

1. The folds of a sleeping bag allow it to fit inside a tiny little sack. Likewise, the ER's many folds enable it to fit within the cell.
2. A mitochondrion is like an electric plant that converts the chemical energy stored in coal into electrical energy, a more easily used form of energy.

SECTION 3.1

B.4.2 Construct an explanation for how the structure of DNA determines the structure of proteins which carry out the essential functions of life through systems of specialized cells.

▼ Plan and Prepare

Activate Prior Knowledge Point out that living things come in all sizes. For example, compare a tadpole to a blue whale. **Ask,** How does the size of a cell in a tadpole compare to the size of a cell in a whale? Most cells in a whale are similar in size to those in a tadpole. **Ask,** What makes a whale so much larger than a tadpole? A whale has far more cells than a tadpole and more cells than the frog a tadpole grows into. Discuss that most cells are microscopic and that we can't see a whale cell any easier than we can see a tadpole cell.

▼ Teach

Science Trivia

- Hooke's microscope magnified objects only 30 times (30×) even though it had three lenses.
- Leeuwenhoek's microscopes had only one lens, but they magnified objects up to 300 times (300×).
- Many of the cells shown in this book have been magnified thousands of times by an electron microscope.

3.1 Cell Theory

KEY CONCEPT **Cells are the basic unit of life.**

MAIN IDEAS

- Early studies led to the development of the cell theory.
- Prokaryotic cells lack a nucleus and most internal structures of eukaryotic cells.

VOCABULARY

cell theory
cytoplasm
organelle
prokaryotic cell
eukaryotic cell

Connect to Your World

You and all other organisms are made of cells. As you saw on the previous page, a cell's structure is closely related to its function. Today, we know that cells are the smallest unit of living matter that can carry out all processes required for life. But before the 1600s, people had many other ideas about the basis of life. Like many breakthroughs, the discovery of cells was aided by the development of new technology—in this case, the microscope.

READING TOOLBOX

TAKING NOTES

As you read, make an outline using the headings as topics. Summarize details that further explain those ideas.

I. Main Idea
 A. Supporting idea
  1. Detail
  2. Detail
 B. Supporting idea

MAIN IDEA

Early studies led to the development of the cell theory.

Almost all cells are too small to see without the aid of a microscope. Although glass lenses had been used to magnify images for hundreds of years, the early lenses were not powerful enough to reveal individual cells. The invention of the compound microscope in the late 1500s was an early step toward this discovery. The Dutch eyeglass maker Zacharias Janssen, who was probably assisted by his father, Hans, usually gets credit for this invention.

A compound microscope contains two or more lenses. Total magnification, the product of the magnifying power of each individual lens, is generally much more powerful with a compound microscope than with a single lens.

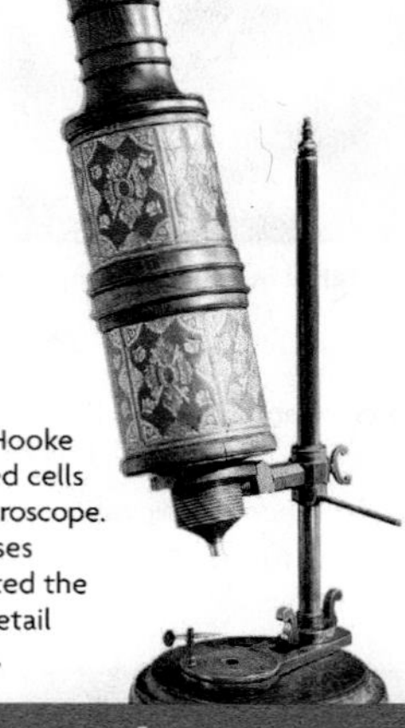

FIGURE 1.1 Hooke first identified cells using this microscope. Its crude lenses severely limited the amount of detail he could see.

Discovery of Cells

In 1665, the English scientist Robert Hooke used the three-lens compound microscope shown in **FIGURE 1.1** to examine thin slices of cork. Cork is the tough outer bark of a species of oak tree. He observed that cork is made of tiny, hollow compartments. The compartments reminded Hooke of small rooms found in a monastery, so he gave them the same name: cells. The plant cells he observed, shown in **FIGURE 1.2** (top), were dead. Hooke was looking only at cell walls and empty space.

Around the same time, Anton van Leeuwenhoek, a Dutch tradesman, was studying new methods for making lenses to examine cloth. As a result of his research, his single-lens microscopes were much more powerful than Hooke's crude compound microscope. In 1674, Leeuwenhoek became one of the first people to describe living cells when he observed numerous single-celled organisms swimming in a drop of pond water. Sketches of his "animalcules" are pictured in **FIGURE 1.2** (bottom).

Differentiated Instruction

ENGLISH LEARNERS

Remind students to use the tools they find in their book, for example, the note-taking strategy shown on this page. Have them label their outlines with the section title and the key concept shown at the top of the page. Point out that the main ideas are already labeled for them (blue headings). Connect the lettered items in the outline to the black headings in the text. Have students include all key vocabulary within the details of their outlines.

Teacher Toolkit, Section C, Main Idea/Detail Notes

HANDS-ON ACTIVITY

Provide students with a variety of hand magnifiers and a microscope. Have students use soft rulers that can bend along the lens, to determine the magnification of each lens. Students will need to divide the actual size of the object into the magnified size. Printed letters work well as the object. Have students look at the same object under a microscope. **Ask,** What is different about the image in the microscope? bigger, and also inverted

Safety Remind students that any lens that touches the eye must be cleaned after use.

As people continued to improve the microscope over the next century and a half, it became sturdier, easier to use, and capable of greater magnification. This combination of factors led people to examine even more organisms. They observed a wide variety of cell shapes, and they observed cells dividing. Scientists began to ask important questions: Is all living matter made of cells? Where do cells come from?

Cell Theory

The German scientist Matthias Schleiden also used compound microscopes to study plant tissue. In 1838, he proposed that plants are made of cells. Schleiden discussed the results of his work with another German scientist, Theodor Schwann, who was struck by the structural similarities between plant cells and the animal cells he had been studying. Schwann concluded that all animals are made of cells. Shortly thereafter, in 1839, he published the first statement of the cell theory, concluding that all living things are made of cells and cell products. This theory helped lay the groundwork for all biological research that followed. However, it had to be refined over the years as additional data led to new conclusions. For example, Schwann stated in his publication that cells form spontaneously by free-cell formation. As later scientists studied the process of cell division, they realized that this part of Schwann's idea was wrong. In 1855, Rudolf Virchow, another German scientist, reported that all cells come from preexisting cells. These early contributors are shown in **FIGURE 1.3.**

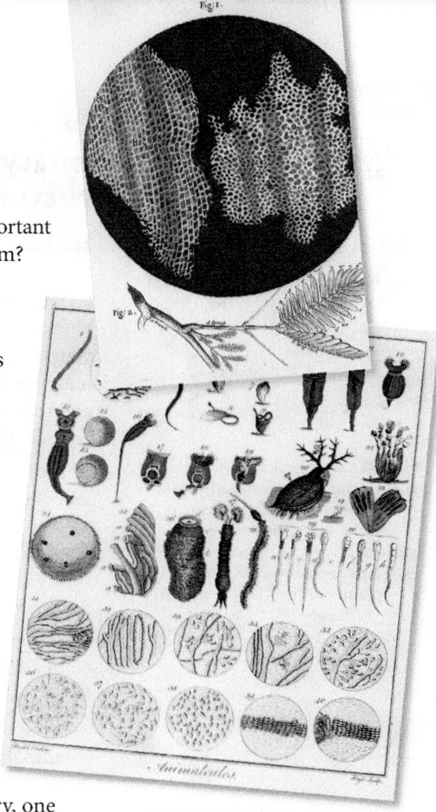

FIGURE 1.2 Hooke observed the cell walls of dead plant cells (top). In contrast, Leeuwenhoek observed and drew microscopic life, which he called "animalcules," in pond water (bottom).

This accumulated research can be summarized in the cell theory, one of the first unifying concepts developed in biology. The major principles of the **cell theory** are the following:

- All organisms are made of cells.
- All existing cells are produced by other living cells.
- The cell is the most basic unit of life.

A Summarize **Explain the three major principles of cell theory in your own words.**

FIGURE 1.3 Contributors to Cell Theory

HOOKE

1665 Hooke was the first to identify cells, and he named them.

LEEUWENHOEK

1674 Because he made better lenses, Leeuwenhoek observed cells in greater detail.

SCHLEIDEN

1838 Schleiden was the first to note that plants are made of cells.

SCHWANN

1839 Schwann concluded that all living things are made of cells.

VIRCHOW

1855 Virchow proposed that all cells come from other cells.

INCLUSION

You can use length to demonstrate powers of magnification to a student who is visually impaired. Take an object such as a pencil and measure its length with a tape measure. Then extend the tape measure 10 times the length. Have the student walk the extended length. **Ask,** Where would a magnification of 100 put us? outside the classroom A magnification of 1000? maybe outside the school

PRE-AP

Have students draw a timeline that includes the five dates shown in **FIGURE 1.3.** Then have students use library references or the Internet to include dates in a topic area of interest to them. You may want to compile the information that students gather into a single timeline in the classroom.

Teacher Toolkit, Section C, Timeline

History of Science

The observations that led to the development of the cell theory **(FIGURE 1.3)** spanned two centuries. Put this into context. **Ask,** in what year did the following events occur?

- the landing of the *Mayflower* 1620
- Declaration of Independence 1776
- Louisiana Purchase 1803
- Emancipation Proclamation 1863

Ask, Why did it take so long after cells were discovered for the cell theory to be developed? Better and more powerful microscopes were needed to make many different observations that contributed to the cell theory.

The Inside Story

In the early days of biology, many of those we describe as scientists came to science in roundabout ways. For example, among the scientists shown in **FIGURE 1.3,** only **Hooke** started life as a scientist. **Schleiden** originally studied law; **Schwann** and **Virchow** were medical doctors.

Born the son of a basket maker, **Leeuwenhoek** was trained as a draper, a fabric merchant. He was accustomed to using magnifying lenses to examine threads. At the age of 28, this successful merchant was appointed to a government position that ensured his financial security. Free to train his microscope on the invisible world of living matter, Leeuwenhoek's work earned him the title of the Father of Microbiology. Such was his celebrity that several reigning monarchs visited him, including Czar Peter the Great of Russia.

Answers

A Summarize All organisms are made of cells. All cells are made by other living cells. The cell is the basic unit that can carry out all life functions.

Chapter 3: Cell Structure and Function **71**

▼ Teach *continued*

Vocabulary

Greek and Latin Word Origins The key to understanding the terms **prokaryotic** and **eukaryotic** is the Greek root *karuon,* which means "nut" or "kernel," the center of a seed. Here *kernel* refers to the nucleus. A cell with a true nucleus is *eukaryotic.*

eu- = true *pro-* = before

In contrast, prokaryotic cells belong to an ancient class of cells that appeared on Earth long before eukaryotic cells: "before the nucleus."

Answers

A Compare Most cells are microscopic, composed of similar building blocks, and are enclosed by a membrane that controls the movement of materials into and out of the cell.

▼ Assess and Reteach

Assess Use the Section Self-Check or Section Quiz, both available at **HMHScience.com.**

Reteach Make use of the note-taking strategy presented on the first page of this section to help students summarize the material in this section.

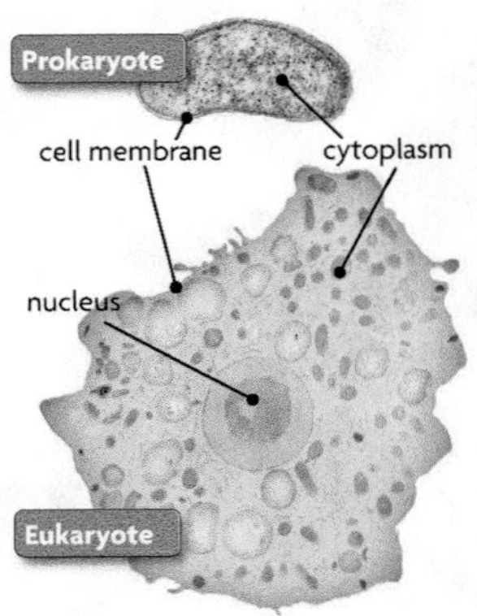

FIGURE 1.4 In prokaryotic cells, such as this bacterium (top), DNA is suspended in the cytoplasm. In eukaryotic cells, such as this protozoan (bottom), the nuclear envelope separates DNA from the cytoplasm. (colored TEMs; magnifications: protozoan 3200×; bacterium 19,000×)

CONNECT TO

PROKARYOTES

You will learn more about prokaryotes in the chapter **Viruses and Prokaryotes,** which discusses their requirements to sustain life, their role in the ecosystem, and their role in human disease.

MAIN IDEA

Prokaryotic cells lack a nucleus and most internal structures of eukaryotic cells.

The variety of cell types found in living things is staggering. Your body alone is made of trillions of cells of many different shapes, sizes, and functions. They include long, thin, nerve cells that transmit sensory information, as well as short, blocky, skin cells that cover and protect the body. Despite this variety, the cells in your body share many characteristics with one another and with the cells that make up every other organism. In general, cells tend to be microscopic in size and have similar building blocks. They are also enclosed by a membrane that controls the movement of materials into and out of the cell.

Within the membrane, a cell is filled with cytoplasm. **Cytoplasm** is a jellylike substance that contains dissolved molecular building blocks—such as proteins, nucleic acids, minerals, and ions. Cytoplasm also contains ribosomes—molecules where proteins are assembled. In some types of cells, the cytoplasm also contains **organelles,** which are structures specialized to perform distinct processes within a cell. Most organelles are surrounded by a membrane. In many cells, the largest and most visible organelle is the nucleus.

As shown in **FIGURE 1.4**, cells can be separated into two broad categories based on their internal structures: prokaryotic cells and eukaryotic cells.

- **Prokaryotic cells** (pro-KAR-ee-AHT-ihk) do not have a nucleus or other membrane-bound organelles. Instead, the cell's DNA is suspended in the cytoplasm. Most prokaryotes are microscopic, single-celled organisms.
- **Eukaryotic cells** (yoo-KAR-ee-AHT-ihk) have a nucleus and other membrane-bound organelles. The nucleus, the largest organelle, encloses the genetic information. Eukaryotes may be multicellular or single-celled organisms.

VISUAL VOCAB

Prokaryotic cells do not have a nucleus or other membrane-bound organelles.

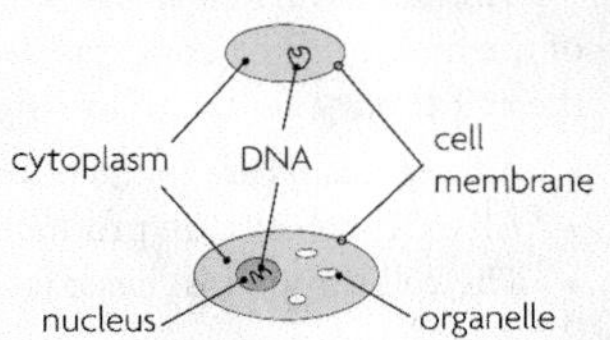

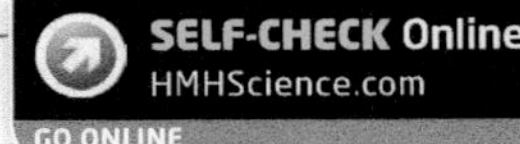

Eukaryotic cells have a nucleus and other membrane-bound organelles.

A Compare What characteristics are shared by most cells?

3.1 Formative Assessment

SELF-CHECK Online
HMHScience.com
GO ONLINE

REVIEWING MAIN IDEAS

1. How did improvements in the microscope help scientists form the **cell theory**?
2. How do **prokaryotic** and **eukaryotic cells** differ?

CRITICAL THINKING

3. **Analyze** Today, scientists can study human cells grown in petri dishes. Explain how this technique builds on the work of early scientists.
4. **Compare** In what way are cells similar to atoms?

CONNECT TO

MEDICINE

5. Suppose a certain poison kills human cells by blocking pores in the nuclear membrane. Explain why it would or would not kill bacteria.

3.1 FORMATIVE ASSESSMENT

1. Improvements allowed scientists to see cells in greater and greater detail and enabled them to discover cells in all types of living matter.
2. Eukaryotic cells have a nucleus and membrane-bound organelles; prokaryotic cells do not.
3. Once it was understood that cells were the basic building blocks of living matter, scientists could concentrate on describing different types of cells and discovering the relationship between cell type and cell function. One way to do this is to isolate the cell itself.
4. Both are basic units, or building blocks. The atom is the basic unit of matter; the cell is the basic unit of living organisms.
5. It would not kill bacteria because bacteria do not have a nucleus, so there are no nuclear pores to be blocked.

3.2 Cell Organelles

VOCABULARY

cytoskeleton
nucleus
endoplasmic reticulum
ribosome
Golgi apparatus
vesicle
mitochondrion
vacuole
lysosome
centriole
cell wall
chloroplast

KEY CONCEPT Eukaryotic cells share many similarities.

MAIN IDEAS

- Cells have an internal structure.
- Several organelles are involved in making and processing proteins.
- Other organelles have various functions.
- Plant cells have cell walls and chloroplasts.

Connect to Your World

Your body is highly organized. It contains organs that are specialized to perform particular tasks. For example, your skin receives sensory information and helps prevent infection. Your intestines digest food, your kidneys filter wastes, and your bones protect and support other organs. On a much smaller scale, your cells have a similar division of labor. They contain specialized structures that work together to respond to stimuli and efficiently carry out other necessary processes.

MAIN IDEA

Cells have an internal structure.

Like your body, eukaryotic cells are highly organized structures. They are surrounded by a protective membrane that receives messages from other cells. They contain membrane-bound organelles that perform specific cellular processes, divide certain molecules into compartments, and help regulate the timing of key events. But the cell is not a random jumble of suspended organelles and molecules. Rather, certain organelles and molecules are anchored to specific sites, which vary by cell type. If the membrane were removed from a cell, the contents wouldn't collapse and ooze out in a big puddle. How does a cell maintain this framework?

Each eukaryotic cell has a **cytoskeleton,** which is a flexible network of proteins that provide structural support for the cell. It is made of small protein subunits that form long threads, or fibers, that crisscross the entire cell, as shown in **FIGURE 2.1.** Three main types of fibers make up the cytoskeleton and allow it to serve a wide range of functions.

FIGURE 2.1 The cytoskeleton supports and shapes the cell. The cytoskeleton includes microtubules (green) and microfilaments (red).

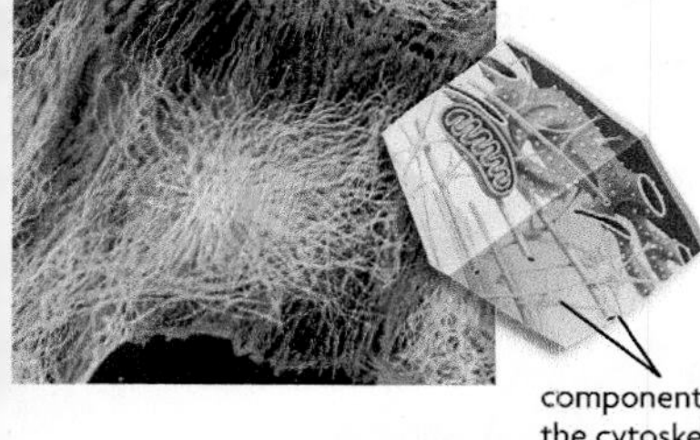

components of the cytoskeleton

- Microtubules are long, hollow tubes. They give the cell its shape and act as "tracks" for the movement of organelles. When cells divide, microtubules form fibers that pull half of the DNA into each new cell.
- Intermediate filaments, which are somewhat smaller than microtubules, give a cell its strength.
- Microfilaments, the smallest of the three, are tiny threads that enable cells to move and divide. They play an important role in muscle cells, where they help the muscle contract and relax.

Differentiated Instruction

ENGLISH LEARNERS

Have students work in pairs in their home language to set up a matrix that will enable them to compare the different structures in a cell, as described in the accompanying Pre-AP note. Students should use the Multilanguage Glossary because many of the cell structures are included as key terms.

Teacher Toolkit, Section C, Think-Pair-Share

PRE-AP

Have students leaf through the section and then choose a graphic organizer that will help them organize the information. Note the hierarchy of information that is possible:

- type of cell: prokaryotic/eukaryotic
- type of organism: animal/plant
- type of organelle: location/function

Teacher Toolkit, Section D, Semantic Feature Analysis

SECTION 3.2

B.1.4 Develop and use models to illustrate how specialized structures within cells (i.e. nuclei, ribosomes, Golgi, endoplasmic reticulum) interact to produce, modify, and transport proteins.

B.4.2 Construct an explanation for how the structure of DNA determines the structure of proteins which carry out the essential functions of life through systems of specialized cells.

Plan and Prepare

Activate Prior Knowledge Hold up an "instant" cold pack, the type with two compartments. **Ask,** Have you ever used a cold pack like this? How does it work? Breaking the seal between the compartments causes two substances (water and ammonium nitrate) to mix, producing "instant" cold. Relate this to the way compartments within a eukaryotic cell enable it to carry on different chemical activities at the same time with no mixing.

Teach

Vocabulary

cytoskeleton Tell students that the prefix *cyto-* comes from the Greek root *kytos,* meaning "hollow vessel." Remind students that Hooke chose the word *cell* because he thought it was a good description for the empty or hollow compartments he saw. Tell students that the prefix *cyto-* signals something that belongs to a cell. As you go through the section, students will see that cells are anything but empty.

▼ Teach *continued*

TEACH FROM VISUALS

FIGURE 2.2 Explain that the cell diagrams represent idealized versions of each cell type. For example, only a very small portion of the cytoskeleton has been shown in each diagram so that other cell parts can be seen more easily. In reality, the cytoskeleton fills a living cell. Have students compare the diagrams to the micrograph in **FIGURE 2.1.**

Address Misconceptions

Common Misconception Because of the ways cells are portrayed, with only a few representatives of each organelle shown, students may think of a cell as a bag of cytoplasm with a loose assortment of organelles floating about.

Correcting the Misconception Quantitative analysis of cell material shows that the parts of a cell are so numerous that they constantly bump up against one another and against the cell membrane and cytoskeleton.

Answers

Ⓐ Critical Viewing The plant cell has chloroplasts, a central vacuole, and a cell wall. The animal cell has centrioles and lysosomes.

FIGURE 2.2 Cell Structure

Eukaryotic cells have highly organized structures, including membrane-bound organelles. Plant and animal cells share many of the same types of organelles, but both also have organelles that are unique to their needs.

PLANT CELL

FOUND IN PLANT CELLS

chloroplast
central vacuole
cell wall

FOUND IN BOTH

cytoskeleton
vesicle
nucleus
nucleolus
endoplasmic reticulum (rough)
ribosome
centrosome
endoplasmic reticulum (smooth)
cell membrane
Golgi apparatus
mitochondrion
vacuole

ANIMAL CELL

FOUND IN ANIMAL CELLS

centriole
lysosome

cytoskeleton
vesicle
nucleus
nucleolus
endoplasmic reticulum (rough)
ribosome
centrosome
endoplasmic reticulum (smooth)
cell membrane
Golgi apparatus
mitochondrion
vacuole

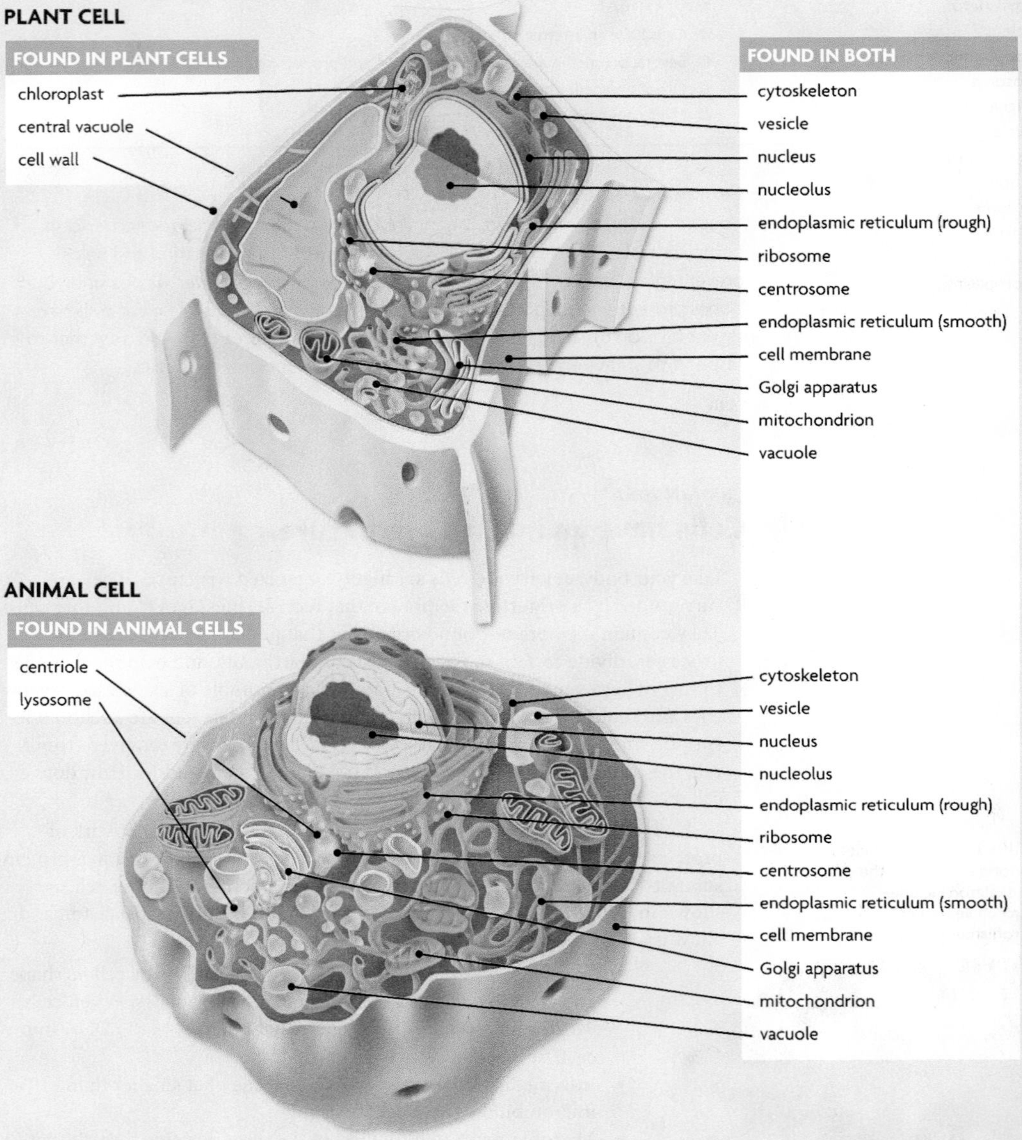

Ⓐ CRITICAL VIEWING **What differences do you observe between animal and plant cells?**

Differentiated Instruction

BELOW LEVEL

Have students copy an outline of the two cells from **FIGURE 2.2** into their science notebooks. As students learn about each organelle, have them draw it into the diagrams, including definitions and notes. Once it is complete, students will have a good tool for review.

Teacher Toolkit, Section C, Combination Notes

TEACH WITH TECHNOLOGY

Students may be interested in viewing the art of David Goodsell, a molecular biologist and artist whose drawings are meant to depict cellular structures in a realistic way. Go online to find examples of his work and then project it on the board. Compare his work with the idealized models above.

Cytoplasm, which you read about in Section 1, is itself an important contributor to cell structure. In eukaryotes, it fills the space between the nucleus and the cell membrane. The fluid portion, excluding the organelles, is called cytosol and consists mostly of water. The makeup of cytoplasm shows that water is necessary for maintaining cell structure. This is only one of many reasons that water is an essential component for life, however. Many chemical reactions occur in the cytoplasm, where water acts as an important solvent.

The remainder of this chapter highlights the structure and function of the organelles found in eukaryotic cells. As **FIGURE 2.2** shows, plant and animal cells use many of the same types of organelles to carry out basic functions. Both cell types also have organelles that are unique to their needs.

Infer **What problems might a cell experience if it had no cytoskeleton?**

READING TOOLBOX

TAKING NOTES

Make a chart to correlate each organelle with its function.

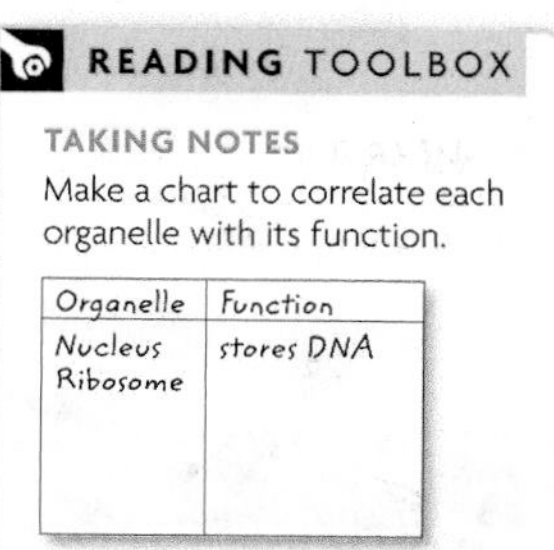

Organelle	Function
Nucleus	stores DNA
Ribosome	

MAIN IDEA

Several organelles are involved in making and processing proteins.

Much of the cell is devoted to making proteins. Proteins are made of 20 types of amino acids that have unique characteristics of size, polarity, and acidity. They can form very long or very short protein chains that fold into different shapes. And multiple protein chains can interact with each other. This almost limitless variety of shapes and interactions makes proteins very powerful. Proteins carry out many critical functions, so they need to be made correctly.

CONNECT TO

BIOCHEMISTRY

Recall from the chapter **Chemistry of Life** that certain amino acids within a protein molecule may form hydrogen bonds with other amino acids. These bonds cause the protein to form a specific shape.

Nucleus

The **nucleus** (NOO-klee-uhs) is the storehouse for most of the genetic information, or DNA (deoxyribonucleic acid), in your cells. DNA contains genes that are instructions for making proteins. There are two major demands on the nucleus: (1) DNA must be carefully protected, and (2) DNA must be available for use at the proper times. Molecules that would damage DNA need to be kept out of the nucleus. But many proteins are involved in turning genes on and off, and they need to access the DNA at certain times. The special structure of the nucleus helps it meet both demands.

The nucleus is composed of the cell's DNA enclosed in a double membrane called the nuclear envelope. Each membrane in the nuclear envelope is similar to the membrane surrounding the entire cell. As **FIGURE 2.3** shows, the nuclear envelope is pierced with holes called pores that allow large molecules to pass between the nucleus and cytoplasm.

The nucleus also contains the nucleolus. The nucleolus is a dense region where tiny organelles essential for making proteins are assembled. These organelles, called ribosomes, are a combination of proteins and RNA molecules. They are discussed on the next page, and a more complete description of their structure and function is given in the chapter From DNA to Proteins.

FIGURE 2.3 The nucleus stores and protects DNA. (colored SEM; magnification 90,000×)

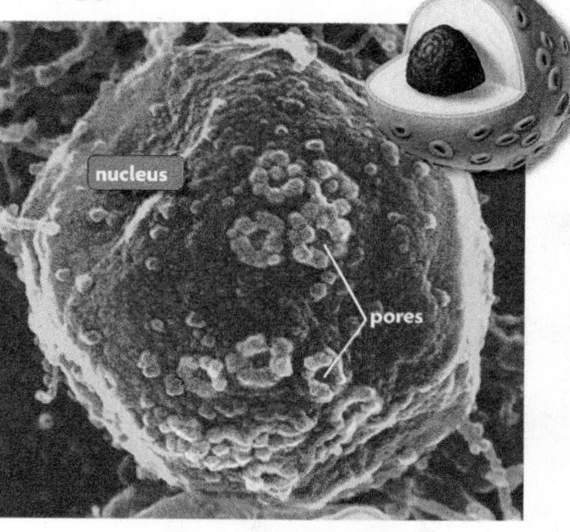

ENGLISH LEARNERS

Point out that the same words can be used to mean different things, depending on context. For example, in the chapter Chemistry of Life, the nucleus was described as being the center of an atom, where protons and neutrons are located. Here the nucleus is an organelle that houses genetic material. Students may find that to be true in their home language. For example, *el núcleo* is used for both in Spanish.

INCLUSION

Students who are hearing impaired benefit by having visual cues accompany an oral presentation. Project the cell diagrams of **FIGURE 2.2** from the Teaching Visuals and point to each cell part as you discuss it with the class. As with English learners, students who are hearing impaired need plenty of cues from your mouth and facial expressions. When possible, face students as you speak and speak slowly and clearly.

TEACH FROM VISUALS

FIGURE 2.3 Have students look carefully at the colorized micrograph. The nuclear pores highlighted in pink represent only a tiny portion of pores that are present on this nucleus. If students look closely, they will see that pores cover the entire surface of the nucleus. **Ask,** What is distinctive about the nuclear membrane? Why is it described as an envelope? It is a double membrane with a bilipid membrane folded upon itself, creating a space in between, which is the inside of the envelope.

Suggest the analogy of the nucleus as a castle keep, the stronghold of a castle. **Ask,** What are the nuclear envelope and nuclear pores analogous to? The interior space of the double membrane acts almost like a moat, forcing materials to move across a few thousand tiny drawbridges, the nuclear pores.

Take It Further

Being isolated in the nucleus—away from other organelles and enzymes that can inflict damage—protects the genetic information in **eukaryotes.** Students may ask how **prokaryotes** can survive if their DNA is not so well protected. Some scientists think that the movement of organelles within a cell or the movement of the cell itself by the action of the cytoskeleton may create shearing forces that could damage or destroy the DNA. The nucleus may protect DNA from the cytoskeleton. Because prokaryotes have no cytoskeleton, their DNA does not need the protection of a nucleus.

Answers

A **Infer** The cell would be disorganized. It would be weak and might fall apart. The cell would also be unable to move, divide, and transport organelles.

▼ Teach *continued*

TEACH FROM VISUALS

FIGURES 2.4–2.8 Have students look at the micrographs on these pages. It should be clear from these images that much of the work of a cell is done in separate compartments. **Ask**

- What do all the organelles shown in the micrographs on these pages have in common? They are not only surrounded by membranes, but many have internal membranes.
- What are these membranes composed of? lipid bilayer
- What does the membrane do? It isolates an organelle's contents from the surrounding cytoplasm and controls the internal environment in which its chemical activities take place.

Mention that the only organelle not bound by a membrane is the ribosome.

The Inside Story

The **Golgi apparatus** was discovered by medical researcher **Camillo Golgi** in 1898, while working with a new staining technique he had developed. In the days before the electron microscope, discoveries of cell structure were limited by the ability of scientists to find stains that would clarify the finer details of cells and tissue using just a light microscope. In 1906, Golgi won a Nobel Prize for his work in detailing structures of the nervous system. Golgi's celebrity today, however, is maintained because an organelle was named after him.

What would it be like to study cell structure if the structures were identified by the people who discovered them? The cell might be called a Hooke and the nucleus a Brown body. The endoplasmic reticulum would be the Claude-Porter apparatus, and the ribosome would be known as a Palade.

FIGURE 2.4 The endoplasmic reticulum aids in the production of proteins and lipids.

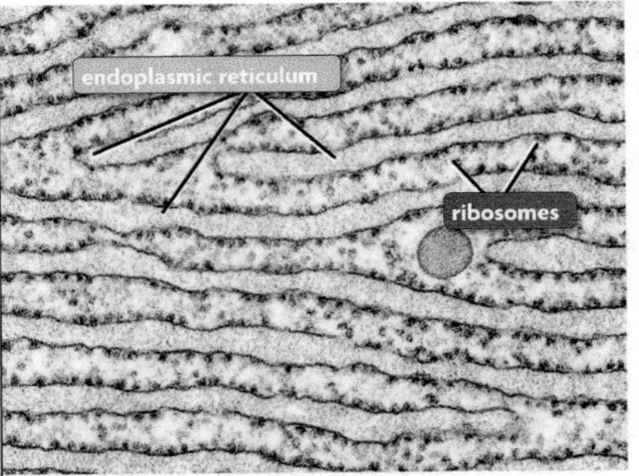

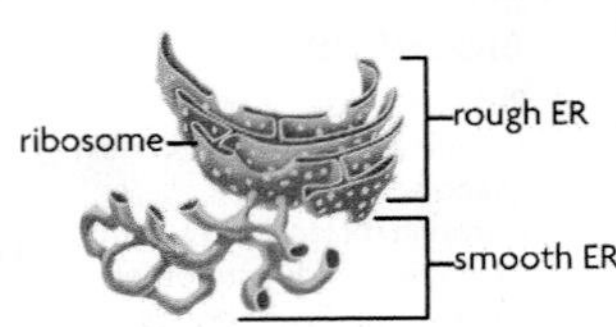

Endoplasmic Reticulum and Ribosomes

A large part of the cytoplasm of most eukaryotic cells is filled by the endoplasmic reticulum, shown in **FIGURE 2.4**. The **endoplasmic reticulum** (EHN-duh-PLAZ-mihk rih-TIHK-yuh-luhm), or the ER, is an interconnected network of thin, folded membranes. The composition is very similar to that of the cell membrane and nuclear membranes. The ER membranes form a maze of enclosed spaces. The interior of this maze is called the lumen. Numerous processes, including the production of proteins and lipids, occur both on the surface of the ER and inside the lumen. The ER must be large enough to accommodate all these processes. How does it fit inside a cell?

The ER membrane has many creases and folds. If you have ever gone camping, you probably slept in a sleeping bag that covered you from head to foot. The next morning, you stuffed it back into a tiny little sack. How does the entire sleeping bag fit inside such a small sack? The surface area of the sleeping bag does not change, but the folds allow it to take up less space. Likewise, the ER's many folds enable it to fit within the cell.

In some regions, the ER is studded with **ribosomes** (RY-buh-SOHMZ), tiny organelles that link amino acids together to form proteins. Ribosomes are both the site of protein synthesis and active participants in the process. Ribosomes are themselves made of proteins and RNA. After assembly in the nucleolus, ribosomes pass through the nuclear pores into the cytoplasm, where most protein synthesis occurs.

Surfaces of the ER that are covered with ribosomes are called rough ER because they look bumpy when viewed with an electron microscope. As a protein is being made on these ribosomes, it enters the lumen. Inside the lumen, the protein may be modified by having sugar chains added to it, which can help the protein fold or give it stability.

Not all ribosomes are bound to the ER; some are suspended in the cytoplasm. In general, proteins made on the ER are either incorporated into the cell membrane or secreted. In contrast, proteins made on suspended ribosomes are typically used in chemical reactions occurring within the cytoplasm.

Surfaces of the ER that do not contain ribosomes are called smooth ER. Smooth ER makes lipids and performs a variety of other specialized functions, such as breaking down drugs and alcohol.

FIGURE 2.5 The Golgi apparatus modifies, packages, and transports proteins.

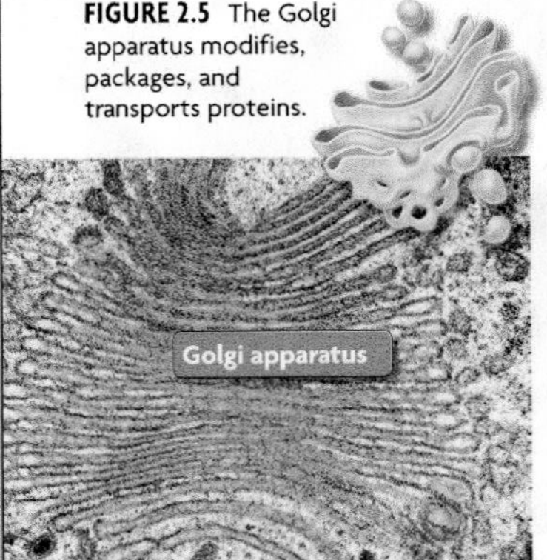

Golgi Apparatus

From the ER, proteins generally move to the Golgi apparatus, shown in **FIGURE 2.5**. The **Golgi apparatus** (GOHL-jee) consists of closely layered stacks of membrane-enclosed spaces that process, sort, and deliver proteins. Its membranes contain enzymes that make additional changes to proteins. The Golgi apparatus also packages proteins. Some of the packaged proteins are stored within the Golgi apparatus for later use. Some are transported to other organelles within the cell. Still others are carried to the membrane and secreted outside the cell.

Differentiated Instruction

BELOW LEVEL

To help students understand how a large surface area can fit into a small space, show them a pocket-sized package of facial tissues. Carefully pull out the tissues, unfold them, and spread them out in a single layer on a desk. Students will see how folding a membrane allows a large surface area to fit into a small space.

PRE-AP

Have groups of students work out a pathway from the nucleus to the cell membrane that would keep a protein from ever entering the cytoplasm. They can start with information passed from the nucleus to the ER, then on to the Golgi apparatus and lysosomes. Have each group present its ideas to the class. Discuss that some products produced by the cell are exported in this way.

Teacher Toolkit, Section C, Think-Pair-Share

Vesicles

Cells need to separate reactants for various chemical reactions until it is time for them to be used. **Vesicles** (VEHS-ih-kuhlz), shown in **FIGURE 2.6**, are a general name used to describe small, membrane-bound sacs that divide some materials from the rest of the cytoplasm and transport these materials from place to place within the cell. Vesicles are generally short-lived and are formed and recycled as needed.

After a protein has been made, part of the ER pinches off to form a vesicle surrounding the protein. Protected by the vesicle, the protein can be safely transported to the Golgi apparatus. There, any necessary modifications are made, and the protein is packaged inside a new vesicle for storage, transport, or secretion.

 Compare and Contrast **How are the nucleus and a vesicle similar and different in structure and function?**

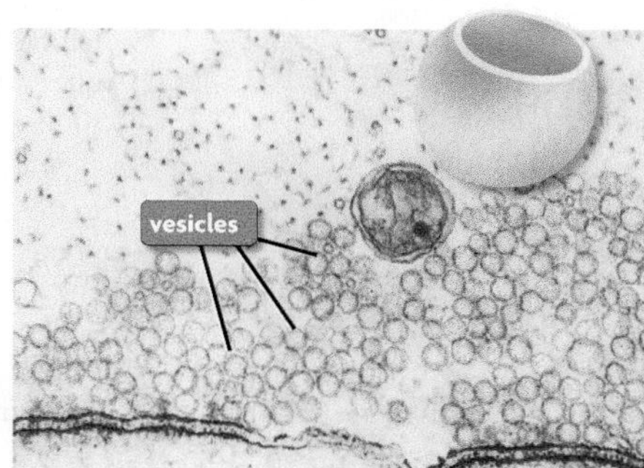

FIGURE 2.6 Vesicles isolate and transport specific molecules.

MAIN IDEA

Other organelles have various functions.

Mitochondria

Mitochondria (MY-tuh-KAHN-dree-uh) supply energy to the cell. Mitochondria (singular, *mitochondrion*) are bean shaped and have two membranes, as shown in **FIGURE 2.7**. The inner membrane has many folds that greatly increase its surface area. Within these inner folds and compartments, a series of chemical reactions converts molecules from the food you eat into usable energy. You will learn more about this process in Cells and Energy.

Unlike most organelles, mitochondria have their own ribosomes and DNA. This fact suggests that mitochondria were originally free-living prokaryotes that were taken in by larger cells. The relationship must have helped both organisms to survive.

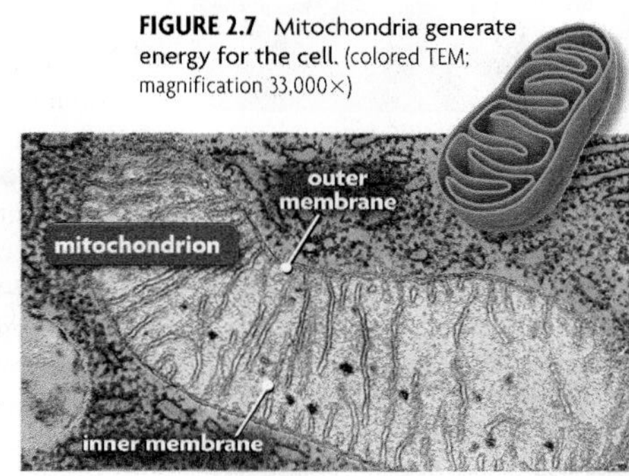

FIGURE 2.7 Mitochondria generate energy for the cell. (colored TEM; magnification 33,000×)

Vacuole

A **vacuole** (VAK-yoo-OHL) is a fluid-filled sac used for the storage of materials needed by a cell. These materials may include water, food molecules, inorganic ions, and enzymes. Most animal cells contain many small vacuoles. The central vacuole, shown in **FIGURE 2.8**, is a structure unique to plant cells. It is a single, large vacuole that usually takes up most of the space inside a plant cell. It is filled with a watery fluid that strengthens the cell and helps to support the entire plant. When a plant wilts, its leaves shrivel because there is not enough water in each cell's central vacuole to support the leaf's normal structure. The central vacuole may also contain other substances, including toxins that would harm predators, waste products that would harm the cell itself, and pigments that give color to cells—such as those in the petals of a flower.

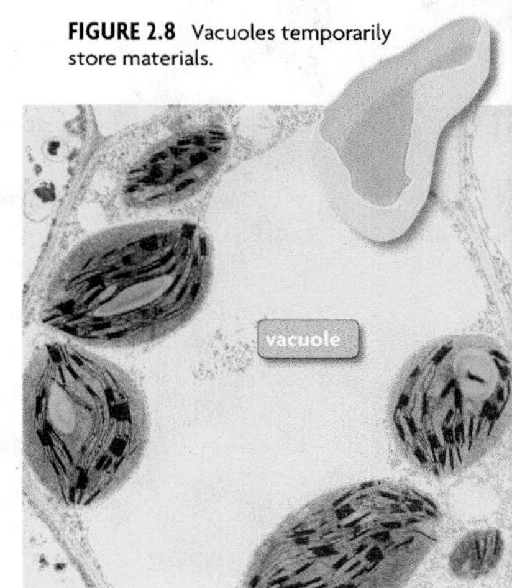

FIGURE 2.8 Vacuoles temporarily store materials.

Vocabulary

Word Origins Words can have diminutive forms, which suggest a smaller version of something large. For example, *duck* becomes *duckling*. A similar thing happens with several of the terms introduced in this section. In each instance, a suffix is added to the original to produce the diminutive.

organ	*organelle*
nucleus	*nucleolus*
vessel	*vesicle*
vacuum	*vacuole*
center	*centriole*

Integrating Anthropology

Anthropologists use **mitochondrial DNA** to trace human ancestry. When cells divide, not only is the genetic material shared between two cells, but so are the organelles. With sexual reproduction, mitochondria are passed to offspring only through the egg—sperm contain little cytoplasm—so a direct female lineage can be traced. Research indicates that modern humans originated in Africa between 100,000 and 200,000 years ago.

Answers

A **Compare and Contrast** Both are membrane-bound compartments that store and separate certain materials. The nucleus is an almost permanent structure protected by a double membrane bilayer, whereas a vesicle is a temporary organelle.

ENGLISH LEARNERS

Point out the irregular plural forms of key vocabulary in this section:

nucleus	*nuclei*
mitochondrion	*mitochondria*

You may also want to point out that *endoplasmic reticulum* and *Golgi apparatus* are structures that are referred to only in the singular.

▼ Teach continued

Take It Further

Lysosomes, which contain about 40 different digestive enzymes, are the recycling centers of the cell. What the cell is recycling, in large part, is itself. The process is called **autophagy,** meaning to "eat oneself." For example, in a liver cell, a mitochondrion has an average lifespan of 10 days. A lysosome engulfs the organelle, breaks it down, and then releases the recycled materials to the cytoplasm, providing raw material for the manufacture of more organelles. In fact, cells continually break down and rebuild themselves.

Integrating Chemistry

The digestive enzymes in a lysosome, like all enzymes, have an **optimum pH** at which they work best. Enzymes of the lysosome function best in an acidic environment with a pH of 5. The pH of cytoplasm is about 7. **Ask,** How does this difference in pH offer some protection to the cell if a lysosome should leak? The enzymes would not be very active, so they would not cause much damage to the cell's contents.

Have students do the WebQuest to see what happens when an organelle fails to function as it should.

Answers

A Compare All are membrane-bound organelles that store or separate certain substances.

FIGURE 2.9 Lysosomes digest and recycle foreign materials or worn-out parts. (colored TEM; magnification 21,000×)

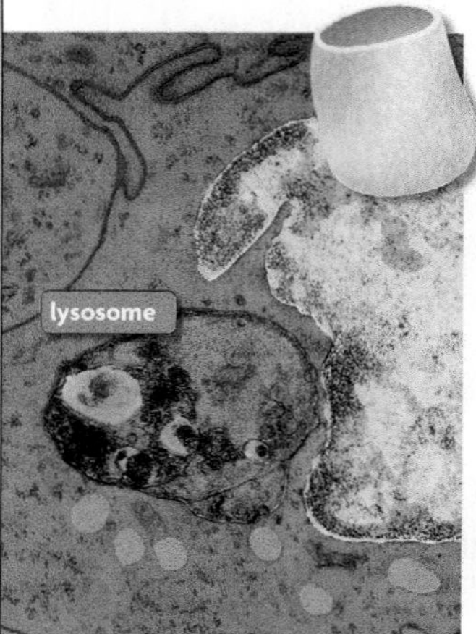

FIGURE 2.10 Centrioles divide DNA during cell division.

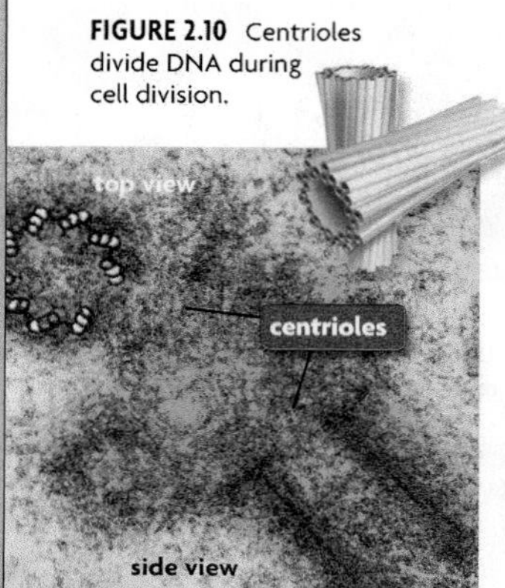

Lysosomes

Lysosomes (LY-suh-SOHMZ), shown in **FIGURE 2.9,** are membrane-bound organelles that contain enzymes. They defend a cell from invading bacteria and viruses. They also break down damaged or worn-out cell parts. Lysosomes tend to be numerous in animal cells. Their presence in plant cells is still questioned by some scientists, but others assert that plant cells do have lysosomes, though fewer than are found in animal cells.

Recall that all enzymes are proteins. Initially, lysosomal enzymes are made in the rough ER in an inactive form. Vesicles pinch off from the ER membrane, carry the enzymes, and then fuse with the Golgi apparatus. There, the enzymes are activated and packaged as lysosomes that pinch off from the Golgi membrane. The lysosomes can then engulf and digest targeted molecules. When a molecule is broken down, the products pass through the lysosomal membrane and into the cytoplasm, where they are used again.

Lysosomes provide an example of the importance of membrane-bound structures in the eukaryotic cell. Because lysosomal enzymes can destroy cell components, they must be surrounded by a membrane that prevents them from destroying necessary structures. However, the cell also uses other methods to protect itself from these destructive enzymes. For example, the enzymes do not work as well in the cytoplasm as they do inside the lysosome.

Centrosome and Centrioles

The centrosome is a small region of cytoplasm that produces microtubules. In animal cells, it contains two small structures called centrioles. **Centrioles** (SEHN-tree-OHLZ) are cylinder-shaped organelles made of short microtubules arranged in a circle. The two centrioles are perpendicular to each other, as shown in **FIGURE 2.10.** Before an animal cell divides, the centrosome, including the centrioles, doubles and the two new centrosomes move to opposite ends of the cell. Microtubules grow from each centrosome, forming spindle fibers. These fibers attach to the DNA and appear to help divide it between the two cells.

Centrioles were once thought to play a critical role in animal cell division. However, experiments have shown that animal cells can divide even if the centrioles are removed, making their role questionable. In addition, although centrioles are found in some algae, they are not found in plants.

Centrioles also organize microtubules to form cilia and flagella. Cilia look like little hairs; flagella look like a whip or a tail. Their motion forces liquids past a cell. For single cells, this movement results in swimming. For cells anchored in tissue, this motion sweeps liquid across the cell surface.

A Compare **In what ways are lysosomes, vesicles, and the central vacuole similar?**

MAIN IDEA

Plant cells have cell walls and chloroplasts.

Plant cells have two features not shared by animal cells: cell walls and chloroplasts. Cell walls are structures that provide rigid support. Chloroplasts are organelles that help a plant convert solar energy to chemical energy.

Differentiated Instruction

PRE-AP

Have students read through the sequence of events described in the last two paragraphs of the section on lysosomes, where the text describes how lysosomes are formed. Refer to the diagram of the animal cell in **FIGURE 2.2** and the micrographs in **FIGURES 2.5** and **2.6.** Have students diagram the process described. Tell students to think in terms of an assembly line.

Teacher Toolkit, Section C, Sequence Diagram

Cell Walls

In plants, algae, fungi, and most bacteria, the cell membrane is surrounded by a strong **cell wall**, which is a rigid layer that gives protection, support, and shape to the cell. The cell walls of multiple cells, as shown in **FIGURE 2.11**, can adhere to each other to help support an entire organism. For instance, much of the wood in a tree trunk consists of dead cells whose cell walls continue to support the entire tree.

Cell wall composition varies and is related to the different needs of each type of organism. In plants and algae, the cell wall is made of cellulose, a polysaccharide. Because molecules cannot easily diffuse across cellulose, the cell walls of plants and algae have openings, or channels. Water and other molecules small enough to fit through the channels can freely pass through the cell wall. In fungi, cell walls are made of chitin, and in bacteria, they are made of peptidoglycan.

FIGURE 2.11 Cell walls shape and support individual cells and entire organisms. (LM; magnification 3000×)

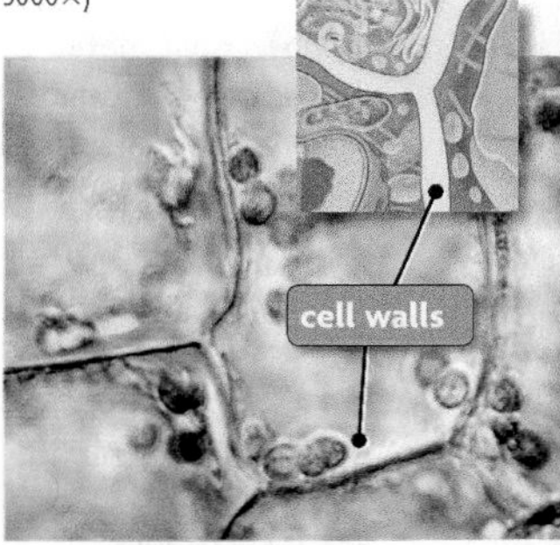

Chloroplasts

Chloroplasts (KLAWR-uh-PLASTS) are organelles that carry out photosynthesis, a series of complex chemical reactions that convert solar energy into energy-rich molecules the cell can use. Photosynthesis will be discussed more fully in Cells and Energy. Like mitochondria, chloroplasts are highly compartmentalized. They have both an outer membrane and an inner membrane. They also have stacks of disc-shaped sacs within the inner membrane, shown in **FIGURE 2.12**. These sacs, called thylakoids, contain chlorophyll, a light-absorbing molecule that gives plants their green color and plays a key role in photosynthesis. Like mitochondria, chloroplasts also have their own ribosomes and DNA. Scientists have hypothesized that they, too, were originally free-living prokaryotes that were taken in by larger cells.

Both chloroplasts and mitochondria are present in plant cells, where they work together to capture and convert energy. Chloroplasts are found in the cells of certain other organisms as well, including green algae.

FIGURE 2.12 Chloroplasts convert solar energy into chemical energy through photosynthesis. (colored TEM; magnification 21,000×)

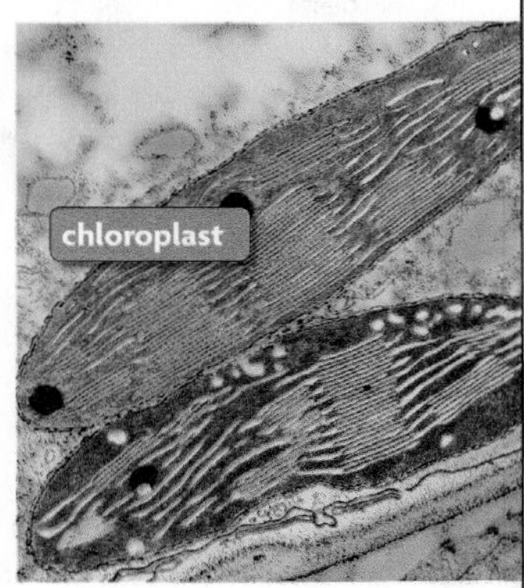

A Analyze **Would it be accurate to say that a chloroplast makes energy for a plant cell? Explain your answer.**

SELF-CHECK Online HMHScience.com GO ONLINE

3.2 Formative Assessment

REVIEWING MAIN IDEAS

1. What are the functions of the **cytoskeleton**?
2. Describe the structure of the **nucleus.**
3. Explain the structure and function of the **mitochondrion.**
4. What function does the **cell wall** perform in a plant?

CRITICAL THINKING

5. **Compare** What similarities do mitochondria and **chloroplasts** share?
6. **Compare** Describe how the **endoplasmic reticulum,** mitochondrion, and **Golgi apparatus** are structurally similar.

CONNECT TO HEALTH

7. Medicine, alcohol, and many drugs are detoxified in liver cells. Why do you think the liver cells of some people who abuse alcohol and drugs have an increased amount of smooth ER?

TEACH FROM VISUALS

FIGURES 2.11 AND 2.12 Have students compare the two micrographs. **Ask**

- How are the two images related? Both show plant cells. More of the cell is seen in Figure 2.11, given the lower magnification. Students may recognize that the smaller structures within the cell are the chloroplasts detailed in Figure 2.12.
- How are the two images different? Figure 2.11 is a light micrograph at low resolution; Figure 2.12 is an electron micrograph at high resolution. The second image shows more detail than the first.

Answers

A **Analyze** No, energy cannot be made or destroyed. The chloroplast converts light energy to a form that a cell can use.

Assess and Reteach

Assess Use the Section Self-Check or Section Quiz, both available at **HMHScience.com**.

Reteach Have students choose an organelle and write an advertisement that explains why a cell needs to "buy" that organelle and why the cell cannot live without one. Make sure every organelle is covered. Then post the ads in the classroom.

3.2 FORMATIVE ASSESSMENT

1. The cytoskeleton supports and shapes a cell, helps position and move organelles, provides strength, assists in cell division, and aids cell movement.
2. The nucleus is surrounded by a double membrane with pores that connect its interior to the cytoplasm. DNA and the nucleolus are located inside the nucleus.
3. A mitochondrion supplies energy to a cell by releasing the energy stored in food molecules. The outer membrane surrounds a highly folded inner membrane where the chemical activity occurs. It has its own ribosomes and DNA.
4. The cell wall protects, supports, and shapes a plant cell, and regulates what moves into the cell. The cell walls of multiple cells can help support the entire plant.
5. Both membrane-bound organelles have their own DNA and help make energy available to the cell.
6. All are composed of membrane-enclosed chambers. The surface area of each is greatly increased by folds and layers.
7. Increased amounts of smooth ER in the liver cells suggests that the cells have responded to increased amounts of toxins by producing more smooth ER to handle the processing.

DATA ANALYSIS

Introduce

Discuss with students how an operational definition differs from a regular definition. In general terms, a definition gives the precise meaning of something or describes its basic qualities. An operational definition provides a way to test for those qualities. **Ask**

- How is an operational definition used in an experiment? It describes a phenomenon in terms of how it is to be measured and so can be used to test for that phenomenon.
- In the example given, what is being measured? number of chloroplasts at different times of year
- What does the relative number of chloroplasts represent to the scientists doing the research? level of photosynthetic activity

Discuss

Talk about the fact that in both examples given, the objects of interest to the scientists—photosynthesis and immunity—are not something that can be observed directly. Yet scientists can use physical evidence—number of chloroplasts or bacteria—to test their hypotheses.

Online Student Resources, Data Analysis Practice

DATA ANALYSIS

Defining Variables

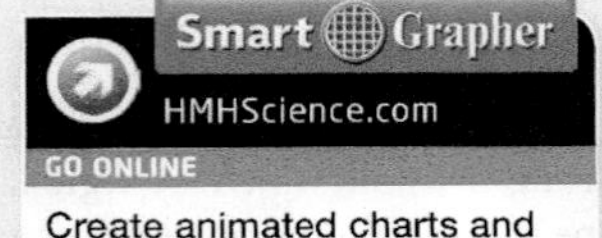

Create animated charts and graphs using Smart Grapher.

The operational definition of a dependent variable is a description of what is to be observed and measured in an experiment and what that measurement represents. It is important for scientists to include in their reports the operational definition of the dependent variable so that different scientists repeating the experiment will collect and record data in exactly the same way.

Model

Chloroplasts are organelles that can have a variety of pigments. Only chloroplasts that contain chlorophyll, a type of pigment, can carry out photosynthesis. The rate of photosynthesis increases as the number of chloroplasts with chlorophyll increases. Students wanted to determine if the rate of photosynthesis was greater in summer or fall. They collected leaves from many trees in both summer and fall and counted the number of chloroplasts with chlorophyll.

In this experiment, the number of chloroplasts with chlorophyll is what is being measured. The operational definition is the number of chloroplasts with chlorophyll in the leaf. This number represents the rate at which a plant can carry out photosynthesis.

TABLE 1. CHLOROPLASTS WITH CHLOROPHYLL

Tree	Leaf Chloroplasts with Chlorophyll (no./cell)	
	Summer	Fall
Birch	192	44
Linden	182	32
Maple	183	28
Weeping willow	177	35

Practice

Form an Operational Definition

Some studies suggest that drinking cranberry juice may help prevent the development of urinary tract infections caused by bacterial cells, which are prokaryotes. Researchers hypothesize that a chemical in cranberry juice may stop the bacteria from attaching to cells in the wall of the urinary bladder. Researchers grew eukaryotic bladder cells in culture and exposed them to a solution containing bacteria. The cells were then treated with a solution of different juices or water to determine if the juices interfered with bacterial attachment. The results are shown in the graph.

GRAPH 1. EFFECT OF JUICE TYPES ON BACTERIAL GROWTH

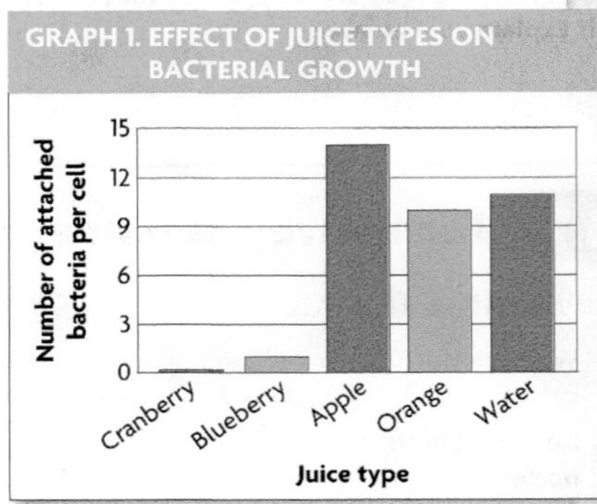

1. **Apply** What is the operational definition of the dependent variable in this experiment?
2. **Conclude** Which juices may be effective in preventing urinary tract infections?

Answers

1. The operational definition is the number of attached bacteria per cell. It indicates whether a particular juice interferes with bacterial attachment.
2. cranberry and blueberry

3.3 Cell Membrane

KEY CONCEPT **The cell membrane is a barrier that separates a cell from the external environment.**

MAIN IDEAS
- Cell membranes are composed of two phospholipid layers.
- Chemical signals are transmitted across the cell membrane.

VOCABULARY
cell membrane
phospholipid
fluid mosaic model
selective permeability
receptor

Connect to Your World
Think about how the products you buy are packaged—a pint of berries, perhaps, or a tube of toothpaste. The berries are probably in a plastic container that has holes to allow air circulation. The toothpaste is in a tube strong enough to be squeezed without ripping. Both containers protect their contents but do so in different ways. Like these products, the cell needs protection, but it must also be able to respond to its surroundings. It is constantly taking in and getting rid of various molecules. The structure of the cell membrane allows it to perform all those functions.

MAIN IDEA
Cell membranes are composed of two phospholipid layers.

The **cell membrane,** or the plasma membrane, forms a boundary between a cell and the outside environment and controls the passage of materials into and out of a cell. The cell membrane consists of a double layer of phospholipids interspersed with a variety of other molecules. A **phospholipid** (FAHS-foh-LIHP-ihd) is a molecule composed of three basic parts:

- a charged phosphate group
- glycerol
- two fatty acid chains

Together, the glycerol and the phosphate group form the "head" of a phospholipid; the fatty acids form the "tail." Because the head bears a charge, it is polar. Recall that water molecules are also polar. Therefore, the polar head of the phospholipid forms hydrogen bonds with water molecules. In contrast, the fatty acid tails are nonpolar and cannot form hydrogen bonds with water. As a result, the nonpolar tails are attracted to each other and repelled by water.

Because the membrane touches the cytoplasm inside the cell and the watery fluid outside the cell, the properties of polar heads and nonpolar tails cause the phospholipids to arrange themselves in layers, like a sandwich.

VISUAL VOCAB
A **phospholipid** is composed of three basic parts:

CONNECT TO
BIOCHEMISTRY
Recall from the chapter **Chemistry of Life** that a hydrogen bond is a weak chemical bond that forms between a slightly positive hydrogen atom and a negatively charged region of another molecule.

Differentiated Instruction

ENGLISH LEARNERS
Help students structure a main idea web by placing the key concept in a central box: "The cell membrane is a barrier that separates a cell from the external environment." Show students how to connect the main ideas of the section to this key concept. Suggest they break down the main ideas into smaller parts if appropriate. For example, the second level of ideas might be structured as "membrane structure," "membrane behavior," and "moving across the membrane."

Teacher Toolkit, Section C, Main Idea Web

INCLUSION
Make a model of a phospholipid for a student who is visually impaired. You could, for example, stick two pipe cleaners into a gumdrop. Use the model to help the student distinguish between its polar and nonpolar regions. Three gumdrops attached by toothpicks can also be used to make a water molecule to demonstrate how a polar water molecule interacts with a phospholipid.

SECTION 3.3

B.1.3 Develop and use models that illustrate how a cell membrane regulates the uptake of materials essential for growth and survival while removing or preventing harmful waste materials from accumulating through the processes of active and passive transport.

Plan and Prepare

Activate Prior Knowledge Mention to students that a cell is about 80 percent water by weight. **Ask,** What property do water molecules have? They are polar. Students may associate polarity with magnetic force. **Ask,** What type of force is at work in a water molecule? electric force Tell students that the way other substances react with water is critical to understanding cell structure and activity.

Teach

Vocabulary
Academic Vocabulary The words **compose** and **comprise** are sometimes mistakenly used interchangeably. Use the main idea on this page to help students distinguish between them.

compose, to make up the parts of
comprise, to include or contain

A membrane is *composed* of phospholipids; a membrane *comprises* a double layer of phospholipids. The parts *compose* the whole; the whole *comprises* the parts.

▼ Teach *continued*

TEACH FROM VISUALS

FIGURE 3.1 Point out the parts of the membrane. **Ask**

- How are cytoskeleton proteins involved in the membrane? They are attached to the inside of the membrane and help support it.
- What is the function of the protein channels? They provide passageways for materials to cross the membrane.
- Which part of the membrane is nonpolar? the inside

Take It Further

The distinctive structure of phospholipid molecules causes them to organize spontaneously into a bilayer in the presence of water. This structure is sometimes described explicitly in terms of their relationship to water. The phospholipid head is **hydrophilic,** or "water-loving." The phospholipid tail is **hydrophobic,** or "water-fearing."

Phospholipids bury their nonpolar tails within the bilayer, leaving their polar heads at the surface. They naturally form into a self-enclosed shape, so no hydrophobic edge of the bilayer is exposed to water. This property makes the bilayer self-healing because phospholipids will quickly rearrange themselves to cover any surface break that exposes the hydrophilic tails to water.

Science Trivia

- A typical human body cell measures 10–30 microns in diameter.
- The cell membrane is a little less than 10 nanometers thick.
- If the cell were the size of a large baseball field (Wrigley), then the membrane surrounding it would measure about 6 centimeters thick.

Answers

A Infer Nonpolar. If cholesterol were polar, it would form hydrogen bonds with the polar heads and water. Instead, cholesterol is located between the fatty acid chains.

The polar heads are like the bread. They form the outer surfaces of the membrane, where they interact with the watery environment both outside and inside a cell. The nonpolar tails are like the filling. They are sandwiched between the layers of polar heads, where they are protected from the watery environment.

FIGURE 3.1 shows other molecules embedded within the phospholipid layers. They give the membrane properties and characteristics it would not otherwise have. These molecules serve diverse functions. Here are a few examples:

- Cholesterol molecules strengthen the cell membrane.
- Some proteins extend through one or both phospholipid layers and help materials cross the membrane. Other proteins are key components of the cytoskeleton. Different cell types have different membrane proteins.
- Carbohydrates attached to membrane proteins serve as identification tags, enabling cells to distinguish one type of cell from another.

FIGURE 3.1 Cell Membrane

The cell membrane is made of two phospholipid layers embedded with other molecules, such as proteins, carbohydrates, and cholesterol.

carbohydrate chain
proteins
protein
cholesterol
cytoskeletal proteins
protein channel
Phospholipid

A Infer Note that cholesterol is located between the fatty acid chains. Do you think cholesterol is polar or nonpolar? Explain your answer.

Fluid Mosaic Model

Scientists have developed the **fluid mosaic model,** which describes the arrangement of the molecules that make up a cell membrane. This model of cell membrane structure takes its name from two characteristics. First, the cell membrane is flexible, not rigid. The phospholipids in each layer can move from side to side and slide past each other. As a result, the membrane behaves like a fluid, similar to a film of oil on the surface of water. However, proteins embedded in the membrane do not flip vertically. If one part of a protein is outside the membrane, it will stay outside the membrane. Second, the variety of molecules studding the membrane is similar to the arrangement of colorful tiles with different textures and patterns that make up a mosaic.

Differentiated Instruction

HANDS-ON ACTIVITY

Bring in a couple of boxes of metal fasteners, the type with a round head and double-pronged shank. Have students form into teams, and give each team 25 fasteners. Allow them five minutes to come up with three possible configurations that lipids might form in the presence of water. The only rule that applies is that the "tails" must be kept separate from water. Allow for the possibility of a second nonpolar substance being present. Sample configurations:

1. A micelle forms if the lipid tails are small enough to pack in tightly toward the center.
2. A monolayer forms if a second nonpolar substance is present, as happens with soap bubbles or when detergent surrounds a drop of oil.
3. A bilayer forms if water surrounds the lipids, inside and out.

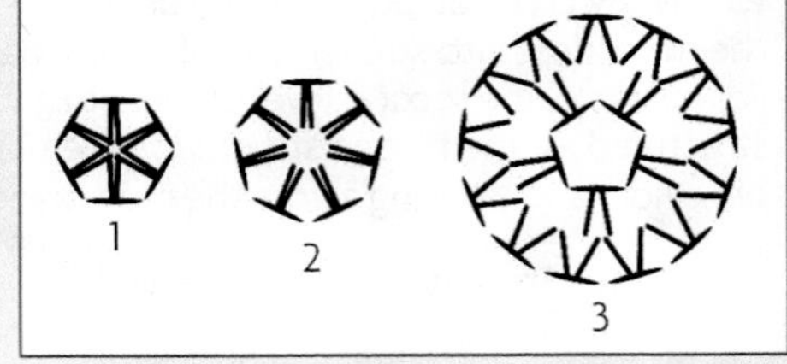

QUICKLAB MODELING

Modeling the Cell Membrane

The cell membrane regulates what moves into and out of the cell.

PROBLEM How does the cell membrane regulate what moves into and out of the cells?

MATERIALS
- 50 cotton swabs
- 1 thick, medium-sized rubber band
- 2 pipe cleaners, each a different color
- 1 drinking straw
- scissors

PROCEDURE
1. Bundle the swabs as shown.
2. Make a receptor from one pipe cleaner. It should extend through the bunch of swabs and have a region that would bind to a signal molecule. Use the other pipe cleaner to make a carbohydrate chain. Insert the chain into the "membrane" of the bunch of swabs.
3. Cut the drinking straw in half and insert both halves into the bunch of swabs.

ANALYZE AND CONCLUDE
1. **Explain** How do the swabs represent the polar and nonpolar characteristics of the cell membrane?
2. **Evaluate** In this model, the swabs and proteins can be moved around. Explain whether this is an accurate representation of actual cell membranes.

Selective Permeability

The cell membrane has the property of **selective permeability,** which means it allows some, but not all, materials to cross. Selective permeability is illustrated in **FIGURE 3.2.** The terms *semipermeable* and *selectively permeable* also refer to this property. As an example, outdoor clothing is often made of semipermeable fabric. The material is waterproof yet breathable. Molecules of water vapor from sweat are small enough to exit the fabric, but water droplets are too large to enter.

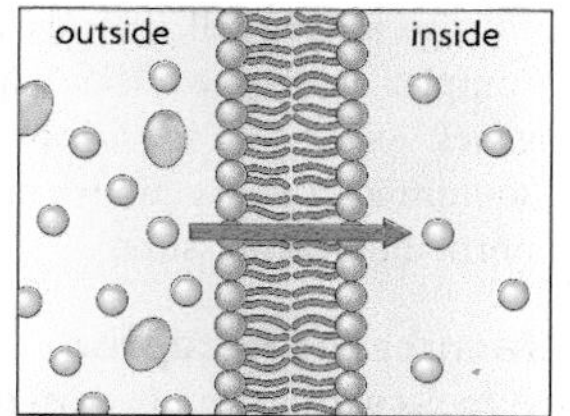

FIGURE 3.2 A selectively permeable membrane allows some, but not all, molecules to cross.

Selective permeability enables a cell to maintain homeostasis in spite of unpredictable, changing conditions outside the cell. Because a cell needs to maintain certain conditions to carry out its functions, it must control the import and export of certain molecules and ions. Thus, even if ion concentrations change drastically outside a cell, these ions won't necessarily interfere with vital chemical reactions inside a cell.

Molecules cross the membrane in several ways. Some of these methods require the cell to expend energy; others do not. How a particular molecule crosses the membrane depends on the molecule's size, polarity, and concentration inside versus outside the cell. In general, small nonpolar molecules easily pass through the cell membrane, small polar molecules are transported via proteins, and large molecules are moved in vesicles.

CONNECT TO

HOMEOSTASIS

Recall from the chapter **Biology in the 21st Century** that homeostasis must be maintained in all organisms because vital chemical reactions can take place only within a limited range of conditions.

Connect **Describe a semipermeable membrane with which you are already familiar.**

BELOW LEVEL

To demonstrate selective permeability, make a mixture of sand and gravel. Pour the mixture through a piece of screen or sieve. The sand will pass through, but the gravel will not. **Ask,** In what way is the screen or sieve permeable? allows passage of materials **Ask,** In what way is the screen or sieve selective? only small particles pass through Discuss other types of selectivity, such as chemical selectivity.

PRE-AP

Have students compare the diagram in **FIGURE 3.2** with those of **FIGURES 3.3** and **3.4.** Have them redraw the diagrams in their science notebook, noting similarities and differences. Point out that both types of signaling discussed on the next page fall under the broad category of the effects of a membrane's selective permeability. Students can continue to add to their notes in the next two sections with the discussion of different types of transport.

Teacher Toolkit, Section C, Combination Notes

QUICKLAB

Time 15 minutes

Purpose Model the structure of a cell membrane.

LAB MANAGEMENT

- Cotton swabs should be tightly packed so they do not fall out of the rubber band, yet not so tightly packed that students cannot insert the other materials. Vary the number of swabs according to the size of the rubber band used.
- Discuss that the cotton swab is representing two phospholipids, not one. This is a limitation of the model.

Analyze and Conclude

1. The swab tips represent the polar heads, and the sticks represent the nonpolar tails of the phospholipids making up the interior of the membrane. The spaces between the tips and sticks represent the semipermeable nature of the membrane.
2. This is accurate because the cell membrane is fluid. Proteins and phospholipids slide past each other.

Vocabulary

Academic Vocabulary The words **permeate** and **pervade** have similar roots, meaning to "pass or move through," and are used synonymously in everyday language. *Permeability,* when used in reference to membranes, describes a physical quality. Materials that are able to pass through a cell membrane are penetrating a physical barrier.

Answers

A Connect *Sample answer:* A strainer is semipermeable because it allows water to pass through but holds back the spaghetti.

▼ Teach *continued*

Integrating Pharmacology

Many drugs used for medical treatment act by binding to **receptors** and inhibiting or enhancing their activity. Drugs that bind to a membrane receptor do not have to enter the cell; they can control intracellular reactions from outside the cell. Researchers can now use computers to design drugs with structures that fit the docking site of the specific receptor they want to inhibit.

Answers

A Contrast Intracellular receptors are located within a cell and bind to molecules that cross directly through the membrane. Membrane receptors are located in the membrane, bind to molecules that cannot cross it, and transmit the signal to the cell interior by changing shape.

▼ Assess and Reteach

Assess Use the Section Self-Check or Section Quiz, both available at **HMHScience.com**.

Reteach Use **FIGURE 3.1** to go over the key points of the section. Have students make a table of the components of the cell membrane, including a description of the functions of each.

MAIN IDEA

Chemical signals are transmitted across the cell membrane.

Recall that cell membranes may secrete molecules and may contain identifying molecules, such as carbohydrates. All these molecules can act as signals to communicate with other cells. How are these signals recognized?

A **receptor** is a protein that detects a signal molecule and performs an action in response. It recognizes and binds to only certain molecules, ensuring that the right cell gets the right signal at the right time. The molecule a receptor binds to is called a ligand. When a receptor and a ligand bind, they change shape. This change is critical because it affects how a receptor interacts with other molecules. Two major types of receptors are present in your cells.

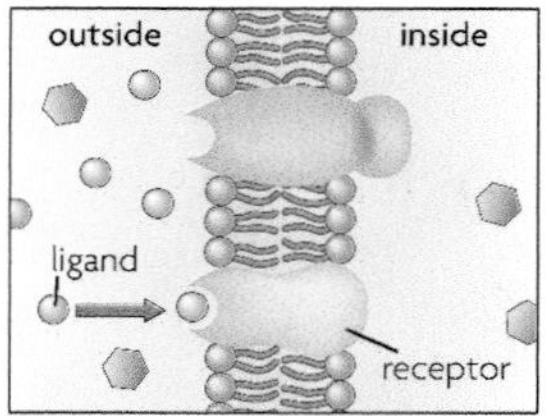

FIGURE 3.3 Intracellular receptors are located inside the cell. They are bound by molecules that can cross the membrane.

outside
inside
ligand
receptor

FIGURE 3.4 Membrane receptors bind to molecules that cannot enter the cell. When bound, the receptor transmits the signal inside the cell by changing shape.

Intracellular Receptor

A molecule may cross the cell membrane and bind to an intracellular receptor, as shown in **FIGURE 3.3.** The word *intracellular* means "within, or inside, a cell." Molecules that cross the membrane are generally nonpolar and may be relatively small. Many hormones fit within this category. For example, aldosterone can cross most cell membranes. However, it produces an effect only in cells that have the right type of receptor, such as kidney cells. When aldosterone enters a kidney cell, it binds to an intracellular receptor. The receptor-ligand complex enters the nucleus, interacts with the DNA, and turns on certain genes. As a result, specific proteins are made that help the kidneys absorb sodium ions and retain water, both of which are important for maintaining normal blood pressure.

Membrane Receptor

A molecule that cannot cross the membrane may bind to a receptor in the cell membrane, as shown in **FIGURE 3.4.** The receptor then sends the message to the cell interior. Although the receptor binds to a signal molecule outside the cell, the entire receptor changes shape—even the part inside the cell. As a result, it causes molecules inside the cell to respond. These molecules, in turn, start a complicated chain of events inside the cell that tells the cell what to do. For instance, band 3 protein is a membrane receptor in red blood cells. When activated, it triggers processes that carry carbon dioxide from body tissues to the lungs. A

Contrast **How do intracellular receptors differ from membrane receptors?**

3.3 Formative Assessment

REVIEWING MAIN IDEAS

1. Why do **phospholipids** form a double layer?
2. Explain how membrane **receptors** transmit messages across the **cell membrane.**

CRITICAL THINKING

3. **Compare** Describe the similarities between enzymes and receptors.
4. **Infer** If proteins were rigid, why would they make poor receptors?

CONNECT TO

HUMAN BIOLOGY

5. Insulin helps cells take up sugar from the blood. Explain the effect on blood sugar levels if insulin receptors stopped working.

3.3 FORMATIVE ASSESSMENT

1. Phospholipids form a double layer in response to the presence of polar water molecules surrounding them. The polar heads of phospholipids interact with the water inside and outside the cell, forming transient hydrogen bonds. The nonpolar tails are repelled by water and interact with each other inside the membrane.
2. Membrane receptors bind to a signal molecule on the outside of a cell. Upon binding, the membrane receptor changes shape, which sends a message inside the cell.
3. Both enzymes and receptors are proteins that bind to a specific ligand or substrate, change shape in response to binding, and cause some sort of action or response.
4. If proteins were rigid, they would be unable to change shape. Therefore, they could not effectively transmit a message to the cell interior.
5. The body would no longer receive the message from insulin. Cells would not take up sugar, blood sugar levels would rise, and death would result.

3.4 Diffusion and Osmosis

KEY CONCEPT **Materials move across membranes because of concentration differences.**

MAIN IDEAS
- Diffusion and osmosis are types of passive transport.
- Some molecules diffuse through membrane proteins.

VOCABULARY

passive transport
diffusion
concentration gradient
osmosis
isotonic
hypertonic
hypotonic
facilitated diffusion

Connect to Your World

If you have ever been stuck in traffic behind a truck full of pigs, you know that "unpleasant" fails to fully describe the situation. That is because molecules travel from the pigs to receptors in your nose, and your brain interprets those molecules to be a really bad odor. Or, perhaps you have tie-dyed a T-shirt and have seen dye molecules spread throughout the pot of water, turning it neon green or electric blue. Why does that happen? Why don't the molecules stay in one place?

MAIN IDEA

Diffusion and osmosis are types of passive transport.

outside inside

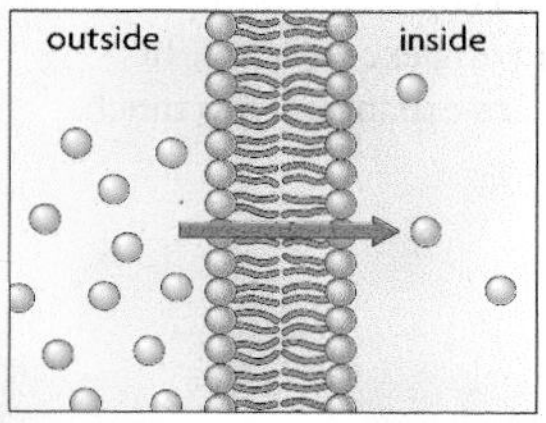

FIGURE 4.1 Passive transport is the movement of molecules across the membrane from areas of higher concentration to areas of lower concentration. It does not require energy input from the cell.

Cells almost continually import and export substances. If they had to expend energy to move every molecule, cells would require an enormous amount of energy to stay alive. Fortunately, some molecules enter and exit a cell without requiring the cell to work. As **FIGURE 4.1** shows, **passive transport** is the movement of molecules across a cell membrane without energy input from the cell. It may also be described as the diffusion of molecules across a membrane.

Diffusion

Diffusion is the movement of molecules in a fluid or gas from a region of higher concentration to a region of lower concentration. It results from the natural motion of particles, which causes molecules to collide and scatter. Concentration is the number of molecules of a substance in a given volume, and it can vary from one region to another. A **concentration gradient** is the difference in the concentration of a substance from one location to another. Molecules diffuse down their concentration gradient—that is, from a region of higher concentration to a region of lower concentration.

In the tie-dye example, dye molecules are initially at a high concentration in the area where they are added to the water. Random movements of the dye and water molecules cause them to bump into each other and mix. Thus, the dye molecules move from an area of higher concentration to an area of lower concentration. Eventually, they are evenly spread throughout the solution. This means the molecules have reached a dynamic equilibrium. The concentration of dye molecules is the same throughout the solution (equilibrium), but the molecules continue to move (dynamic).

CONNECT TO

HUMAN BIOLOGY

As you will learn in the chapter **Respiratory and Circulatory Systems,** diffusion plays a key role in gas exchange in the lungs and other body tissues.

SECTION 3.4

B.1.3 Develop and use models that illustrate how a cell membrane regulates the uptake of materials essential for growth and survival while removing or preventing harmful waste materials from accumulating through the processes of active and passive transport.

Plan and Prepare

Activate Prior Knowledge Have students picture a cup of water and a container of drink mix and then create a solution by mixing the two. **Ask,** Which is the solute? drink mix Which is the solvent? water **Ask,** What happens to the concentration of each if you continue to add the mix? The solute becomes more concentrated and the solvent less concentrated. Tell students that concentration is a factor that affects what happens across a cell membrane.

Teach

TEACH FROM VISUALS

FIGURE 4.1 Point out that the cell membrane determines what particles will pass through it but not the direction of the movement. **Ask**

- Are the particles shown likely to be polar or nonpolar? nonpolar because they are passing freely through the cell membrane
- Do the particles to the right of the membrane also move? If so, in which direction? The particles move back and forth across the membrane.

Differentiated Instruction

ENGLISH LEARNERS

Have students use a 2 × 2 word square for each type of passive diffusion. In the first square, have them write the word and its translation from the Multilanguage Glossary. In the second, they should draw a diagram of the process. In the third, have them describe the process in their own words and then write the English Glossary definition. In the fourth, have them write a sentence using the word. Repeat this activity for types of transport in the next section.

Teacher Toolkit, Section D, Word Squares

HANDS-ON ACTIVITY

Demonstrate that diffusion can occur in a solid—not just liquids and gases—though at a slower rate. At the beginning of class, place a drop of potassium permanganate on the surface of solidified agar or gelatin in a jar. Check it periodically. Students will see the purple permanganate diffuse slowly through the solid. Remind students that particles are in motion in all states of matter. Only at absolute zero, −273.15°C, would atoms have no motion or energy—a condition never reached.

▼ Teach *continued*

Integrating Physics

In any system, there is a tendency for **entropy,** or disorder, to increase. Diffusion increases as localized concentrations of solute particles move to a state in which the particles are randomly mixed. An input of energy would be required to reverse the process. Diffusion is a spontaneous process that occurs without any input of energy.

TEACH FROM VISUALS

FIGURE 4.3 Describe osmosis as a special case of diffusion in which the solvent moves across a semipermeable membrane. Be sure students recognize that *isotonic, hypertonic,* and *hypotonic* refer to the concentration of the solute, even though it is the solvent, in this case water, that moves in response to the solute's concentration gradient. To help students remember, have them think of the *v* in *sol**v**ent* as an arrow of the solvent's movement or relate it to the *v* in *move*.

FIGURE 4.4 Be sure students understand that diffusion describes the net movement of particles in response to concentration. This may or may not happen across a membrane.

Take It Further

Plant cells are less likely than animal cells to burst in a hypotonic solution because they have rigid cell walls. In fact, plant cells are healthiest in a hypotonic environment. A plant cell swells to the point where it exerts a backward pressure, called **turgor pressure,** which prevents further uptake of water. Animal cells do best in an isotonic environment.

Answers

Ⓐ **Apply** The cell would lose water and shrink.

FIGURE 4.2 Diffusion results from the natural motion of particles.

In cells, diffusion plays an important role in moving substances across the membrane. Small lipids and other nonpolar molecules, such as carbon dioxide and oxygen, easily diffuse across the membrane. For example, most of your cells continually consume oxygen, which means that the oxygen concentration is almost always higher outside a cell than it is inside a cell. As a result, oxygen generally diffuses into a cell without the cell expending any energy.

Osmosis

Water molecules, of course, also diffuse. They move across a semipermeable membrane from an area of higher water concentration to an area of lower water concentration. This process is called **osmosis.** It is important to recognize that the higher the concentration of dissolved particles in a solution, the lower the concentration of water molecules in the same solution. So, if you put 1 teaspoon of salt in a cup of water and 10 teaspoons of salt in a different cup of water, the first cup would have the higher water concentration.

A solution may be described as isotonic, hypertonic, or hypotonic relative to another solution. Note that these terms are comparisons; they require a point of reference, as shown in **FIGURE 4.3.** An **isotonic** solution has a solute concentration equal to the solute concentration inside a cell. A **hypertonic** solution has a solute concentration higher than the solute concentration inside a cell. A **hypotonic** solution has a solute concentration lower than the solute concentration inside a cell.

Some animals and single-celled organisms can survive in hypotonic environments. Their cells have adaptations for removing excess water. In plants, the rigid cell wall prevents the membrane from expanding too much.

FIGURE 4.3 Effects of Osmosis

Osmosis is the diffusion of water across a semipermeable membrane from an area of higher water concentration to an area of lower water concentration.

ISOTONIC SOLUTION

isotonic

H_2O isotonic H_2O

A solution is isotonic to a cell if it has the same concentration of solutes as the cell. Equal amounts of water enter and exit the cell, so its size stays constant.

HYPERTONIC SOLUTION

hypertonic

H_2O H_2O hypotonic

A hypertonic solution has more solutes than a cell. Overall, more water exits a cell in a hypertonic solution, causing the cell to shrivel or even die.

HYPOTONIC SOLUTION

hypotonic

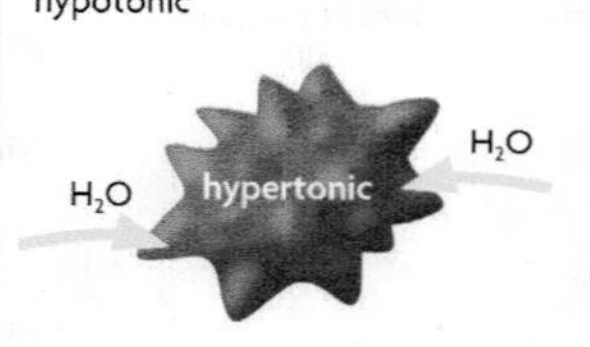

A hypotonic solution has fewer solutes than a cell. Overall, more water enters a cell in a hypotonic solution, causing the cell to expand or even burst.

Ⓐ Apply **How would adding salt to the isotonic solution above affect the cell?**

Differentiated Instruction

PRE-AP

Have students redraw the three cells shown in **FIGURE 4.3** onto a sheet of paper and then draw differently colored dots for both solute and solvent to represent the relative amounts of each. Ask students to write a paragraph explaining how relative concentrations relate to the arrows shown in each part of the figure.

Teacher Toolkit, Section C, Quick-Write

Remember from Section 2 that pressure exerted on the cell wall by fluid inside the central vacuole provides structural support for each cell and for the plant as a whole.

Apply **What will happen to a houseplant if you water it with salt water (a hypertonic solution)?**

MAIN IDEA

Some molecules diffuse through membrane proteins.

Biologists have long known that osmosis alone cannot account for the rapid movement of water into and out of cells, especially cells such as red blood cells and certain kidney cells. More recent research has revealed that a group of membrane proteins called aquaporins also play an important role in the transport of water into and out of these cells. Aquaporin molecules form channels, or tunnels, through the cell membrane. The structure of these channels allows water molecules to pass through in a single file. However, no charged particles, not even hydrogen ions, can pass through.

The transport of water by aquaporins is one example of **facilitated diffusion,** the diffusion of molecules across a membrane through transport proteins. The word *facilitate* means "to make easier." Transport proteins make it easier for molecules to enter or exit a cell. But the process is still a form of passive transport. The molecules move down a concentration gradient, requiring no energy expenditure by the cell.

There are many types of transport proteins. Like aquaporins, most types allow only a certain type of molecule or ion to pass. As **FIGURE 4.4** shows, some transport proteins are simple channels through which particles such as ions can pass. Others act more like enzymes. When a specific molecule binds with the protein, the protein changes shape in a way that allows the molecule to travel the rest of the way into the cell.

Explain **What role do transport proteins play in the cell membrane?**

READING TOOLBOX

VOCABULARY

The words *isotonic, hypertonic,* and *hypotonic* share the root word *tonic*, which means "pressure." Their prefixes give them different comparative meanings.

iso- = equal, same
hyper- = over, above
hypo- = under, below

Facilitated Diffusion

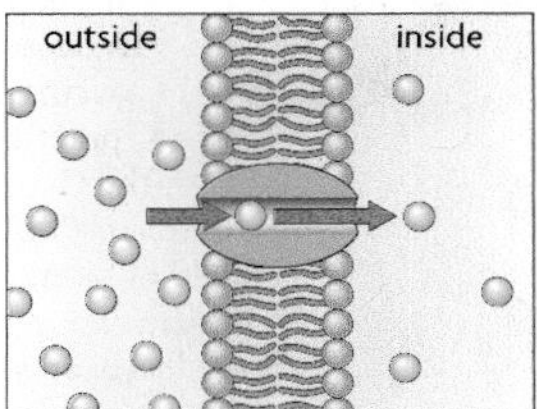

FIGURE 4.4 Facilitated diffusion enables molecules that cannot directly cross the phospholipid bilayer to diffuse through transport proteins in the membrane.

3.4 Formative Assessment

REVIEWING MAIN IDEAS

1. Explain what a **concentration gradient** is and what it means for a molecule to diffuse down its concentration gradient.
2. Explain why **facilitated diffusion** does not require energy from a cell.

CRITICAL THINKING

3. **Apply** A cell is bathed in fluid. However, you notice that water is flowing out of the cell. In what kind of solution is this cell immersed: **isotonic, hypotonic,** or **hypertonic**?
4. **Compare** How are receptors and transport proteins similar?

SELF-CHECK Online
HMHScience.com
GO ONLINE

CONNECT TO

HEALTH

5. When a person becomes dehydrated due to the loss of fluids and solutes, saline solution (water and salts) is infused into the bloodstream by medical personnel. Why is saline solution used instead of pure water?

History of Science

For many years, cell biologists wondered how polar water molecules were able to diffuse across the lipid cell membrane so rapidly. They suspected that water-channel proteins similar to the one in **FIGURE 4.4** might be at work. In the mid-1980s, **Peter Agre** started to search. In 1992, he found water channels in red blood cells and named them aquaporins.

A single human aquaporin-1 channel facilitates water transport at a rate of roughly 3 billion molecules per second. Aquaporins have also been found in bacteria, plants, and animals. In 2003, Agre won the Nobel Prize for his work.

Answers

A Apply Water will diffuse out of the plant cells, and the plant will wilt.

B Explain Some molecules cannot easily diffuse across the membrane. Transport proteins provide a way for some of these molecules to enter cells without having to interact with phospholipids. Some form channels; others act more like enzymes and change shape.

Assess and Reteach

Assess Use the Section Self-Check or Section Quiz, both available at **HMHScience.com**.

Reteach Create a game that models diffusion, osmosis, and facilitated diffusion by using students to represent solute particles (girls) and solvent particles (boys). A row of 10 students can model the cell membrane.

3.4 FORMATIVE ASSESSMENT

1. A concentration gradient is the difference in concentration of a substance from one location to another. A molecule diffuses down its concentration gradient by moving from a region of higher concentration to a region of lower concentration.
2. No energy is needed because the molecules move down a concentration gradient.
3. hypertonic
4. Both are proteins and may work with only specific molecules. In addition, both may require a change in shape to accomplish their function.
5. Pure water would be hypotonic relative to the contents of blood cells, so water would rush into the blood cells and could cause the cells to burst. The saline solution is isotonic relative to the cell contents.

Introduce

Direct students' attention to the photos of a high-speed bullet train and a kingfisher. **Ask,** What do this train and bird have in common? From the photos, students may conclude that the shape of the kingfisher's bill inspired the shape of the train's nose.

Explain that Japanese engineers used the kingfisher, a diving bird, to solve a design flaw of high-speed trains. When the first generation of bullet trains emerged from tunnels, they produced an ear-splitting sound similar to a sonic boom. It took an engineer who was also an avid bird-watcher to recognize that the unique shape of a kingfisher's bill allowed it to travel through air into water without making a splash. Modeling the nose of the bullet train after that bill shape allowed trains to move quickly and quietly with less fuel required, and without generating pressure waves in tunnels.

Discuss

Discuss other examples of biomimicry that students may be familiar with. Encourage them to research some examples to add to the discussion. Prompt students to point out the problem being solved and how nature provided the inspiration for the solution. Explain that exploring interactions that occur in nature can be the basis for solutions to human problems. Further examples include improving computer screen color by modeling butterfly wings, making hypodermic needles less painful by simulating a mosquito's bite, and improving liquid-dispensing equipment by imitating spitting reptiles.

S.T.E.M. Interactions

Biomimicry

People have looked to the natural world to help solve problems for centuries. The dream of building airplanes likely came from watching birds in flight. In the mid-1900s, the hook-and-loop fastener, commonly called by its brand name, Velcro®, was invented after a Swiss engineer noticed how burs have little hooks that stick to fur and clothing. Over time, using nature as a guide for solving human problems has moved from an occasional or accidental occurrence to an intentional practice called biomimicry, from the Greek words *bio* ("life") and *mimesis* ("to imitate"). The growing field of biomimicry recognizes that humans are grappling with problems that nature has been solving for millions of years.

Today, examples of biomimicry can be found in almost every industry—even in sports. At the 2008 Summer Olympic Games in Beijing, the vast majority of swimmers who broke world records were wearing suits modeled after sharkskin. The technology proved to be such an advantage that the material has been banned, at least in its full-length version, from future competitions. It turns out that sharks are not just fast, they are microbe-free. Researchers are developing plastic films that mimic sharkskin—made of tiny denticles, or teethlike scales. This type of material can be used to keep bacteria off surfaces in restaurants and hospitals.

The health-care industry has looked to biomimicry for other solutions as well. Water purification once was limited to pushing water through a membrane, a process that required a lot of energy and frequently required membranes to be unclogged or replaced. New technology looks to our own cells for solutions to these problems, using aquaporin proteins to escort water molecules across a membrane and leaving contaminants behind.

Because natural processes are inherently sustainable, some industries are using biomimicry in efforts to be more environmentally friendly. One manufacturer of carpets has looked to nature to solve several issues. Inspiration from the forest floor has led to carpet colors and patterns that are purposely less uniform than traditional designs, leading to less waste during manufacturing and fewer quality-control checks. Instead of using conventional glues that release toxic chemicals into the air, manufacturers use Earth's gravity to hold the carpets down. Creating carpet pieces that hook to each other with tiny hairs, similar to the hairs that allow a gecko to cling to a wall, provides enough weight to hold carpets in place. Reducing the use of glue has the additional benefit of allowing the carpet to be more easily recycled at the end of its use.

Considering how products can be used and then broken down into their components and reused is not only sustainable, but it is also more evidence of biomimicry in action. Nature's cycling of matter ensures that nothing goes to waste, and the field of life-cycle engineering looks not only at the development of a product and how it will be used but also at how waste can be reduced or eliminated after the product is no longer useful. From engineering to design to waste management, taking the time to explore the natural world can provide inspiration for the next innovative solution in virtually any field you choose to pursue.

The shape of the kingfisher beak creates very little splash when the bird dives into water. Engineers used a similar shape for the nose of a bullet train to reduce booming sounds when the train exits a tunnel.

3.5 Active Transport, Endocytosis, and Exocytosis

KEY CONCEPT **Cells use energy to transport materials that cannot diffuse across a membrane.**

MAIN IDEAS
- Proteins can transport materials against a concentration gradient.
- Endocytosis and exocytosis transport materials across the membrane in vesicles.

VOCABULARY
active transport
endocytosis
phagocytosis
exocytosis

Connect to Your World

If you want to go up to the second floor of the mall, you're going to need help beating gravity. You could take an escalator, which uses energy to move you against gravity, much like transport proteins involved in active transport use energy to move molecules against a gradient. Alternatively, you might take the elevator, entering on the first floor and hopping out when the doors open on the second. In endocytosis and exocytosis, vesicles act like that elevator, surrounding molecules on one side of a membrane and releasing them into the other.

MAIN IDEA
Proteins can transport materials against a concentration gradient.

You just learned that some transport proteins let materials diffuse into and out of a cell down a concentration gradient. Many other transport proteins, often called pumps, move materials against a concentration gradient. **Active transport** drives molecules across a membrane from a region of lower concentration to a region of higher concentration. This process, shown in **FIGURE 5.1**, uses transport proteins powered by chemical energy. Cells use active transport to get needed molecules regardless of the concentration gradient and to maintain homeostasis.

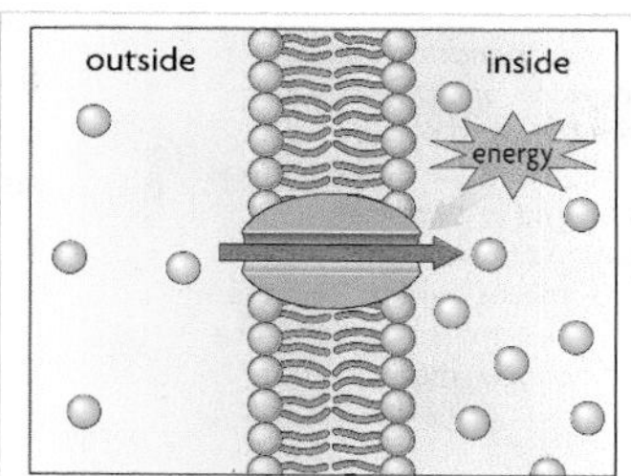

FIGURE 5.1 During active transport, a cell uses energy to move substances against a concentration gradient—that is, from a lower to a higher concentration.

Before we discuss active transport proteins, let's look at transport proteins in general. All transport proteins span the membrane, and most change shape when they bind to a target molecule or molecules. Some transport proteins bind to only one type of molecule. Others bind to two different types. Some proteins that bind to two types of molecules move both types in the same direction. Others move the molecules in opposite directions.

CONNECT TO
HUMAN BIOLOGY
As you will learn in the chapter **Digestive and Excretory Systems,** active transport is a necessary part of nutrient absorption.

Differentiated Instruction

ENGLISH LEARNERS

If students created word squares for types of transport in Section 4 (English Learners note), have them do the same for this section. You can also have students form into groups of three, counting off within the group from one to three. Then assemble all ones, twos, and threes into expert panels, each panel studying a type of transport in this section and preparing a lesson plan for the group. Reconvene the home groups and have each expert teach the group.

Teacher Toolkit, Section C, Jigsaw Reading

BELOW LEVEL

Have students prepare a table to compare different types of cellular transport. Help them choose categories for comparison, such as whether the transport is passive or active, whether it moves toward or against a gradient, and whether it involves a channel or pump. Make sure students understand that endocytosis and exocytosis are not types of active transport even though they require energy input.

Teacher Toolkit, Section D, Semantic Feature Analysis

SECTION 3.5

B.1.3 Develop and use models that illustrate how a cell membrane regulates the uptake of materials essential for growth and survival while removing or preventing harmful waste materials from accumulating through the processes of active and passive transport.

Plan and Prepare

Activate Prior Knowledge Use the analogies of a water pump and a waterfall to represent active or passive transport. **Ask,** Which is active transport and which is passive transport and why? The waterfall is passive because no input of energy is required to move water; the pump is active because energy is needed to move water. Explain that cells often need to gather ions and other substances against a gradient. Cellular systems that move materials against a gradient are referred to as pumps.

Teach

TEACH FROM VISUALS

FIGURE 5.1 Have students compare the inside and the outside of the cell in the diagram. **Ask,** What is the result of the process shown? More particles accumulate inside the cell than outside the cell. Have students compare this diagram to **FIGURE 4.4** and describe the differences.

▼ Teach continued

Take It Further

Many types of cells have **proton pumps,** which are essential for cellular respiration and photosynthesis. Energy extracted by electron transport chains in these processes is used to pump protons up their concentration gradient. The protons then flow back down their gradient by diffusion, providing energy to transform the molecule ADP into the energy carrier ATP. Students will learn about ATP in the chapter **Cells and Energy.**

The Inside Story

The biologist **Elie Metchnikoff** originated the theory on which modern cellular immunology is based—that the body is protected by mobile cells (white blood cells) that engulf bacteria and other pathogens. He coined the term **phagocytosis** and won a Nobel Prize for his work in 1908.

The official biography of the Nobel Foundation describes Metchnikoff in this way: "Photographs taken of him when he was working at the Pasteur Institute show him with long hair and an unkempt beard. It is said of him that at this time he usually wore overshoes in all weathers and carried an umbrella, his pockets being overfull with scientific papers, and that he always wore the same hat, and often, when he was excited, sat on it."

Answers

A Synthesize Both are proteins that recognize only specific target molecules and change shape when they bind.

FIGURE 5.2 Just as a cell uses energy in the process of active transport, this boy uses energy to pump air against a concentration gradient.

The key feature of active transport proteins is that they can use chemical energy to move a substance against its concentration gradient. Most use energy from a molecule called ATP, either directly or indirectly. For example, nerve cells, or neurons, need to have a higher concentration of potassium ions and a lower concentration of sodium ions than the fluid outside the cell. The sodium-potassium pump uses energy directly from the breakdown of ATP. It pumps three sodium ions out of the cell for every two potassium ions it pumps in. The proton pump, another transport protein, uses energy from the breakdown of ATP to move hydrogen ions (or protons) out of the cell. This action forms a concentration gradient of hydrogen ions (H^+), which makes the fluid outside the cell more positively charged than the fluid inside. In fact, this gradient is a form of stored energy that is used to power other active transport proteins. In plant cells, this gradient causes yet another protein to transport sucrose into the cell—an example of indirect active transport.

A Synthesize **In what ways are active transport proteins similar to enzymes?**

MAIN IDEA

Endocytosis and exocytosis transport materials across the membrane in vesicles.

A cell may also use energy to move a large substance or a large amount of a substance in vesicles. Transport in vesicles lets substances enter or exit a cell without crossing through the membrane.

READING TOOLBOX

VOCABULARY

The words *endocytosis, exocytosis,* and *phagocytosis* share the word part *cyto-,* which means "cell." The prefixes *endo-* and *exo-* indicate location or direction. The prefix *endo-* means "within," and the prefix *exo-* means "out of." The prefix *phago-* means "eating."

Endocytosis

Endocytosis (EN-doh-sy-TOH-sihs) is the process of taking liquids or fairly large molecules into a cell by engulfing them in a membrane. In this process, the cell membrane makes a pocket around a substance. The pocket breaks off inside the cell and forms a vesicle, which then fuses with a lysosome or a similar type of vesicle. Lysosomal enzymes break down the vesicle membrane and its contents (if necessary), which are then released into the cell.

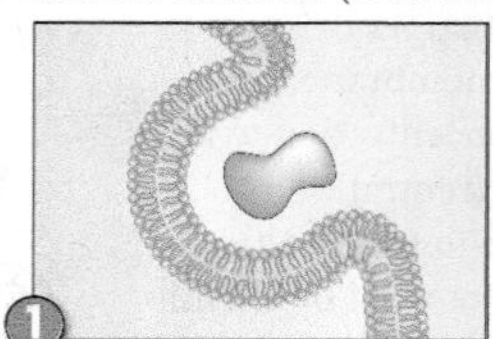

1 During endocytosis, the cell membrane folds inward and fuses together, surrounding the substance in a pocket.

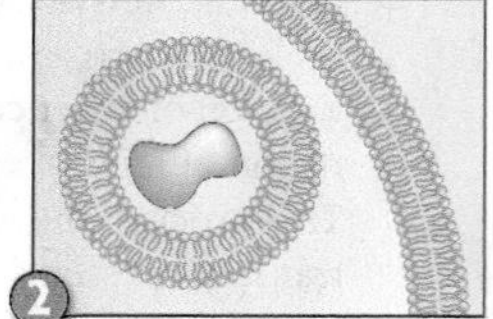

2 The pocket pinches off inside the cell, forming a vesicle.

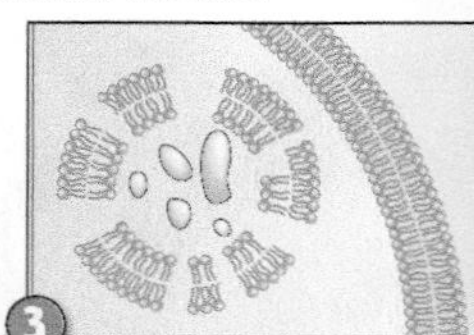

3 The vesicle fuses with a lysosome or a similar vesicle, where enzymes break down the membrane and its contents.

Phagocytosis (FAG-uh-sy-TOH-sihs) is a type of endocytosis in which the cell membrane engulfs large particles. The word literally means "cell eating." Phagocytosis plays a key role in your immune system. Some white blood cells called macrophages help your body fight infection. They find foreign materials, such as bacteria, and engulf and destroy them.

Differentiated Instruction

HANDS-ON ACTIVITY

Help students develop a sense of scale by comparing the size of a small eukaryotic cell and its organelles to an *E. coli* bacterium that measures 500 × 1500 nm. Have students prepare a classroom display that can encompass these measures: cell 20,000 nm; nucleus 7000 nm; chloroplast 2000 × 5000 nm; mitochondrion 500 × 1500 nm; ribosome 25 nm; thickness of cell membrane 10 nm; protein 7 nm; water molecule 0.4 nm. Tell students that cells, organelles, proteins, and bacteria vary in size but that these numbers are within a normal range.

PRE-AP

Some scientists think that mitochondria and chloroplasts are descendants of primitive prokaryotes. Have students write a paragraph that cites evidence from this chapter that supports this conclusion. Students should mention the similar size of those organelles to a prokaryote, that both mitochondria and chloroplasts have their own DNA and double membranes, and that cells demonstrate the ability to engulf bacteria by phagocytosis.

Teacher Toolkit, Section C, Quick Write

Exocytosis

Exocytosis (EHK-soh-sy-TOH-sihs), the opposite of endocytosis, is the release of substances out of a cell by the fusion of a vesicle with the membrane. During this process, a vesicle forms around materials to be sent out of the cell. The vesicle then moves toward the cell's surface, where it fuses with the membrane and releases its contents.

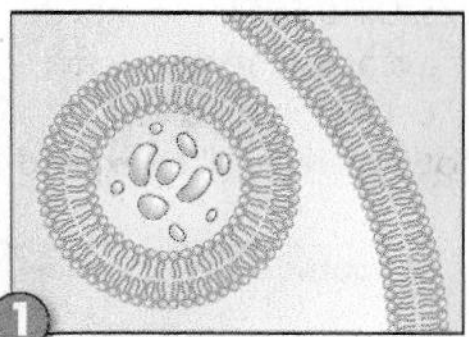

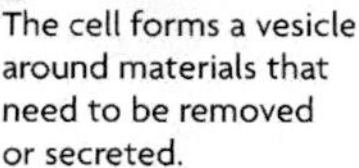

1 The cell forms a vesicle around materials that need to be removed or secreted.

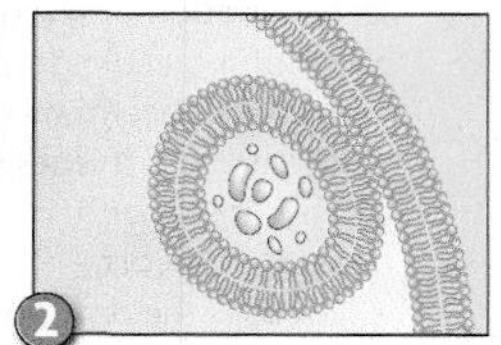

2 The vesicle is transported to the cell membrane.

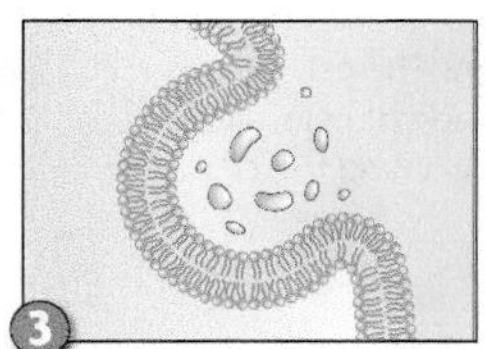

3 The vesicle membrane fuses with the cell membrane and releases the contents.

Exocytosis happens all the time in your body. In fact, you couldn't think or move a muscle without it. When you want to move your big toe, for example, your brain sends a message that travels through a series of nerve cells to reach your toe. This message, or nerve impulse, travels along each nerve cell as an electrical signal, but it must be converted to a chemical signal to cross the tiny gap that separates one nerve cell from the next. These chemicals are stored in vesicles within the nerve cells. When a nerve impulse reaches the end of a cell, it causes the vesicles to fuse with the cell membrane and release the chemicals outside the cell. There they attach to the next nerve cell, which triggers a new electrical impulse in that cell.

Hypothesize What might happen if vesicles in your neurons were suddenly unable to fuse with the cell membrane?

CONNECT TO

ENDOCRINE SYSTEM

As you will learn in the chapter **Nervous and Endocrine Systems,** thyroid hormones play an important role in controlling your growth and development. These hormones are released into the blood by exocytosis.

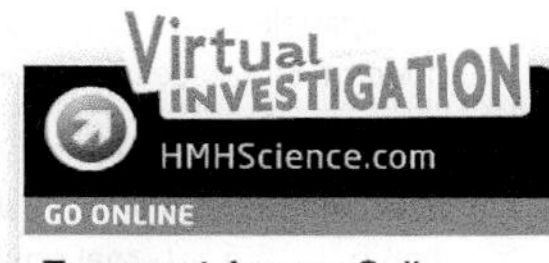

Virtual INVESTIGATION

HMHScience.com

GO ONLINE

Transport Across Cell Membrane

3.5 Formative Assessment

SELF-CHECK Online

HMHScience.com

GO ONLINE

REVIEWING MAIN IDEAS

1. How do transport proteins that are pumps differ from those that are channels?
2. How do **endocytosis** and **exocytosis** differ from diffusion?

CRITICAL THINKING

3. **Apply** Small lipid molecules are in high concentration outside a cell. They slowly cross the membrane into the cell. What term describes this action? Does it require energy?
4. **Apply** Ions are in low concentration outside a cell. They move rapidly into the cell via protein molecules. What term describes this action? Does it require energy?

CONNECT TO

DIFFUSION

5. Suppose molecules were unable to diffuse into and out of cells. How might life be different if cells had to use **active transport** to move every substance? Explain your reasoning.

3.5 FORMATIVE ASSESSMENT

1. Pumps require energy, transport a molecule against its concentration gradient, and change shape upon binding. A protein channel does not change shape or require energy. It allows certain molecules to diffuse through it, down their concentration gradient.
2. They require energy input; diffusion does not. They also enable larger particles to enter a cell, particles that are too large to diffuse across a cell membrane.
3. diffusion, no
4. active transport, yes
5. Cells would require vast amounts of energy to perform even simple functions. Perhaps organisms would have to take in more food to provide more energy. If food were limited, perhaps only photosynthetic organisms would be able to survive. Perhaps organisms would move and respond more slowly and be more sedentary. Perhaps organisms would be simpler, and highly specialized organs would not have developed.

ONLINE Biology

HMHScience.com

Have students try different mechanisms for moving materials across a cell membrane. See the Animated Biology titled Get Through a Cell Membrane on **HMHScience.com**.

Take It Further

There are three types of endocytosis. In **phagocytosis,** cells engulf a particle or another cell and enclose it within a sac. In **pinocytosis,** cells gulp droplets of extracellular fluid and any solutes that are dissolved in it. **Receptor-mediated endocytosis** is much more specific. It requires a specific receptor protein, which helps to form the vesicle in which the substance is brought into the cell. Cholesterol enters a cell when a cholesterol-LDL complex binds to an LDL receptor on the cell membrane.

Answers

A **Hypothesize** The neurons would be unable to transmit signals, so you would be unable to respond to stimuli.

Assess and Reteach

Assess Use the Section Self-Check or Section Quiz, both available at **HMHScience.com**.

Reteach Use the Animated Biology titled Get Through a Cell Membrane to review the material in this section. Have students prepare or share comparison tables, as suggested in the Below Level Instruction option on the first page of this section.

GO ONLINE

Encourage students to go to **HMHScience.com** for a detailed review of each section, including visuals and vocabulary practice.

Online Student Resources, Vocabulary Practice Worksheet

CHAPTER 3 **Summary**

BIG IDEA Cells are the smallest unit of living matter that can carry out all processes required for life.

KEY CONCEPTS

3.1 Cell Theory

Cells are the basic unit of life. The contributions of many scientists led to the discovery of cells and the development of the cell theory. The cell theory states that all organisms are made of cells, all cells are produced by other living cells, and the cell is the most basic unit of life.

3.2 Cell Organelles

Eukaryotic cells share many similarities. They have a nucleus and other membrane-bound organelles that perform specialized tasks within the cell. Many of these organelles are involved in making proteins. Plant and animal cells share many of the same types of organelles, but both also have organelles that are specific to the cells' unique functions.

3.3 Cell Membrane

The cell membrane is a barrier that separates a cell from the external environment. It is made of a double layer of phospholipids and a variety of embedded molecules. Some of these molecules act as signals; others act as receptors. The membrane is selectively permeable, allowing some but not all materials to cross.

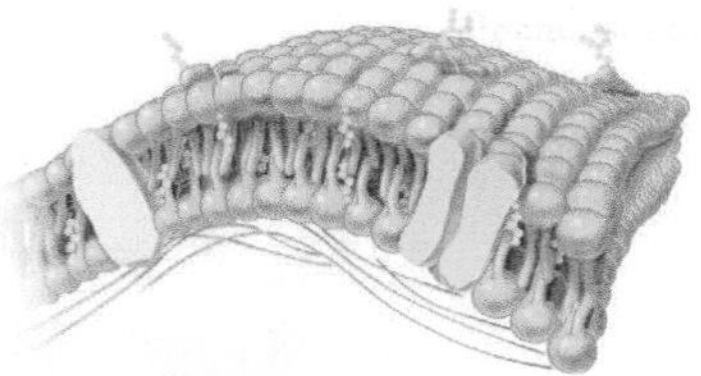

3.4 Diffusion and Osmosis

Materials move across membranes because of concentration differences. Diffusion is the movement of molecules in a fluid or gas from a region of higher concentration to a region of lower concentration. It does not require a cell to expend energy; it is a form of passive transport. Osmosis is the diffusion of water. Net water movement into or out of a cell depends on the concentration of the solution.

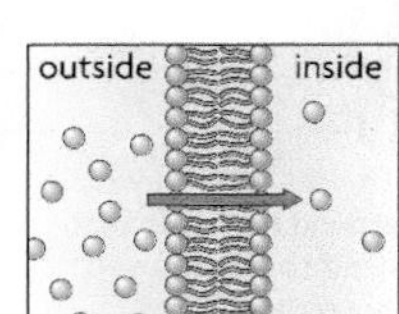

Passive transport

3.5 Active Transport, Endocytosis, and Exocytosis

Cells use energy to transport materials that cannot diffuse across a membrane. Active transport is the movement of molecules across a membrane from a region of lower concentration to a region of higher concentration—against a concentration gradient. The processes of endocytosis and exocytosis move substances in vesicles and also require energy.

Endocytosis

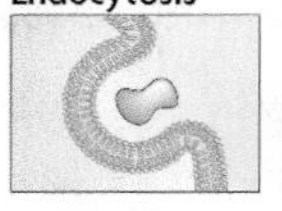
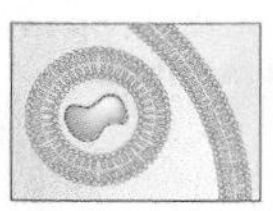

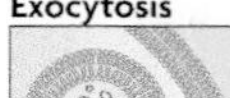

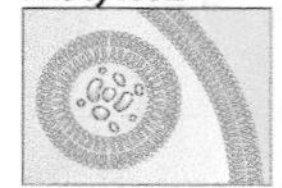
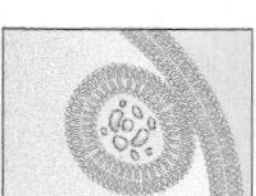
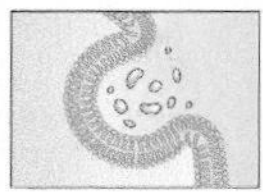

READING TOOLBOX SYNTHESIZE YOUR NOTES

Main Idea Web Plant and animal cells, though similar, each have some unique features. Identify how these cell types differ by placing plant cell characteristics on the left side of the main idea web and animal cell characteristics on the right.

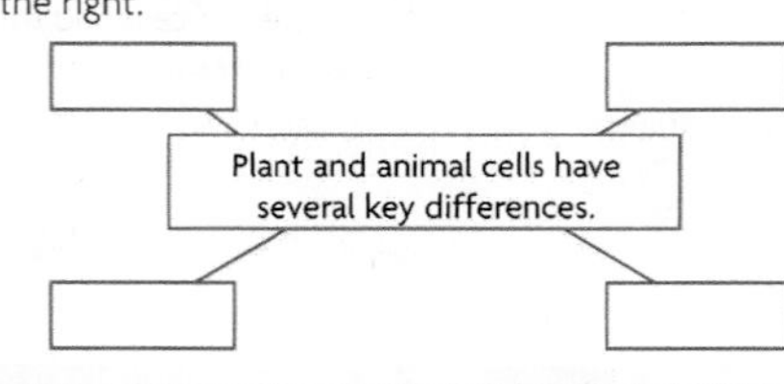

Concept Map Fill in a concept map like the one below to summarize what you know about forms of transport.

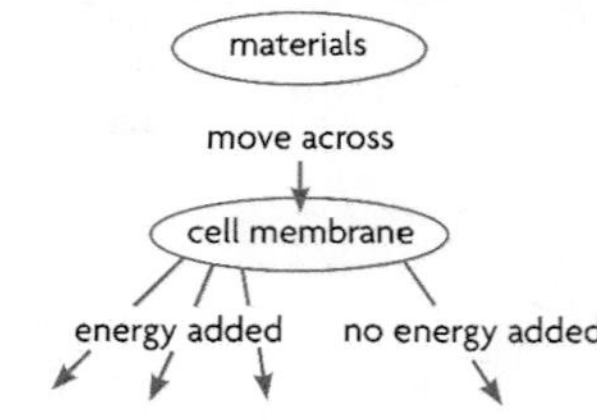

active transport
passive transport
diffusion
endocytosis
materials
exocytosis
osmosis
cell membrane

Reviewing Vocabulary

1. cell membrane
2. rough endoplasmic reticulum (also accept ribosomes)
3. nucleus
4. centriole
5. mitochondrion
6. Golgi apparatus
7. cytoskeleton
8. endoplasmic reticulum (smooth)
9. Eukaryotic and prokaryotic cells are surrounded by a cell membrane. Only eukaryotic cells have a nucleus and membrane-bound organelles.
10. Both the cell wall and cell membrane surround the cell. The cell wall is a rigid structure, while the cell membrane is not.
11. Both diffusion and facilitated diffusion allow materials to cross a semipermeable membrane without the use of energy. In simple diffusion, a molecule capable of crossing the cell membrane will pass through on its own. Facilitated diffusion requires a transport protein and allows only specific types of molecules to pass.
12. An organelle carries out a specific function or set of functions within a cell.
13. Prokaryotes do not have a nucleus, or "nut." Eukaryotes do have a nucleus.

3 Review

INTERACTIVE Review
HMHScience.com
GO ONLINE
Review Games • Concept Map • Section Self-Checks

CHAPTER VOCABULARY

3.1 cell theory, cytoplasm, organelle, prokaryotic cell, eukaryotic cell

3.2 cytoskeleton, nucleus, endoplasmic reticulum, ribosome, Golgi apparatus, vesicle, mitochondrion, vacuole, lysosome, centriole, cell wall, chloroplast

3.3 cell membrane, phospholipid, fluid mosaic model, selective permeability, receptor

3.4 passive transport, diffusion, concentration gradient, osmosis, isotonic, hypertonic, hypotonic, facilitated diffusion

3.5 active transport, endocytosis, phagocytosis, exocytosis

Reviewing Vocabulary

Labeling Diagrams

In your science notebook, write the vocabulary term that matches each numbered item below.

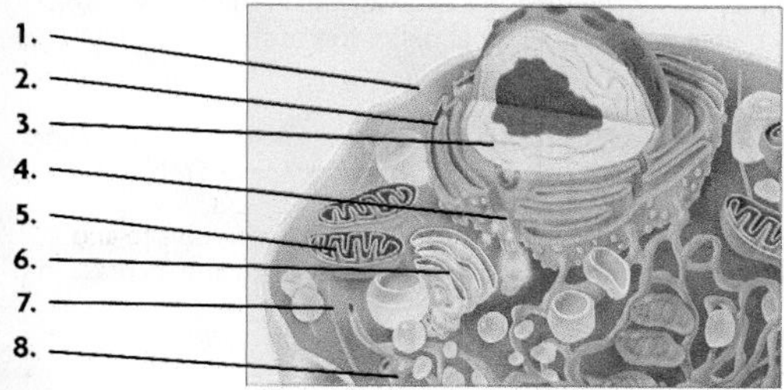

Labeling Diagrams

Describe one similarity and one difference between the two terms in each of the following pairs.

9. eukaryotic, prokaryotic

10. cell wall, cell membrane

11. diffusion, facilitated diffusion

READING TOOLBOX GREEK AND LATIN WORD ORIGINS

12. The word *organelle* is the diminutive, or "tiny," form of the Latin word for organs of the body. How is an organelle like a tiny organ?

13. The Greek word *karuon* means "nut." The prefix *pro-* means "before," and the prefix *eu-* means "true." Thus, *prokaryote* means "before nut," and *eukaryote* means "true nut." How do these meanings relate to structural differences between these two cell types?

Reviewing MAIN IDEAS

14. According to the cell theory, what is required for an object to be considered alive?

15. What role do membranes play in prokaryotic cells? in eukaryotic cells?

16. How do the cytoskeleton and the cytoplasm contribute to a cell's shape?

17. You know that many organelles are involved in protein production. Briefly explain where proteins are made, modified, and packaged within a cell.

18. Explain what mitochondria do and why evidence suggests that they might have descended from free-living prokaryotes in the evolutionary past.

19. If you were looking through a microscope at an unknown cell, how might you determine whether it was a plant cell or an animal cell?

20. Cells are surrounded by a watery fluid, and they contain cytoplasm. Explain how the structure of the lipid bilayer is related to these two watery environments.

21. How are cells able to respond to signal molecules that are too large to enter the cytoplasm?

22. How do transport proteins make it easier for certain molecules to diffuse across a membrane?

23. Under what conditions would a molecule need to be actively transported across a membrane?

24. Do you think that endocytosis and exocytosis can occur within the same cell? Explain your reasoning.

Reviewing Main Ideas

14. It must be made of cells that are produced by other living cells and that carry out life functions, such as metabolism and maintaining homeostasis.

15. Both cell types have a cell membrane that forms a protective barrier between the cell and its environment and controls the passage of materials in and out. Eukaryotic cells have membrane-bound organelles; prokaryotic cells do not.

16. The cytoskeleton is made up of a network of proteins that gives the cell a strong structure while constantly changing in response to the cell's changing needs. The cytoplasm fills in the areas around the cytoskeleton, keeping the membrane from collapsing onto the cytoskeleton.

17. The nucleus has the DNA, which codes for proteins, and the nucleolus, which is where ribosomes are made. Ribosomes exit through nuclear pores, and some associate with the ER. Proteins made on the ribosomes may undergo modification in the ER. From the ER, they may be packaged into vesicles and sent to the Golgi apparatus for further modifications. A completed protein can be stored, released into the cell for use, released to the cell membrane for use, or excreted outside of the cell.

18. Mitochondria produce chemical reactions that convert simple food molecules into energy. They are similar to prokaryotes in that they contain their own DNA and ribosomes but no membrane-bound organelles.

19. Look for cell walls and chloroplasts (plant cell features) or centrioles (animal cell features).

20. The polar heads of the phospholipids can form hydrogen bonds with the polar water molecules. The nonpolar tails are sandwiched inside the membrane where they can't react with the water.

21. Membrane receptors allow large ligands to bind to the outside of the cell. The receptor then changes physically, including the part inside the cell, which triggers a response.

22. Transport proteins can form a larger opening or pore that allows molecules to pass.

23. A molecule would need to be actively transported when the concentration of the molecule is higher on the other side of the membrane.

24. Yes, both are needed to move substances in and out of a cell and to maintain the cell's volume.

Critical Thinking

25. The cell theory depended on the invention of microscopes that allowed scientists to see cells.
26. Eukaryotic cells contain everything a prokaryotic cell contains and more, suggesting that these characteristics developed over time. The presence of mitochondria and chloroplasts, which have their own DNA and membranes, suggests that these organelles descended from prokaryotes that were engulfed by a larger cell.
27. The ER manufactures more phospholipid membrane.
28. Vesicles are used for temporary transport and storage. Vacuoles tend to be more permanent features of a cell.
29. Only cells with the proper receptors will respond to a specific ligand.
30. *Sample answer:* transporting proteins and removing wastes
31. Like active transport, facilitated diffusion requires membrane proteins. Like passive transport, facilitated diffusion occurs down a concentration gradient and does not require energy.

Interpreting Visuals

32. Protein synthesis and secretion. We see the vesicle-wrapped proteins leaving the ribosomes and ER, getting processed and repackaged in the Golgi apparatus, and being released by exocytosis.
33. The cell would run out of the amino acids needed for protein synthesis.
34. They must be the same or very similar in order to fuse.

Critical Thinking

25. Summarize How was the development of cell theory closely tied to advancements in technology?

26. Analyze What structural features suggest that eukaryotic cells evolved from prokaryotic cells?

27. Synthesize If vesicles are almost constantly pinching off from the ER to carry proteins to the Golgi apparatus, why does the ER not shrink and finally disappear?

28. Compare and Contrast You know that both vesicles and vacuoles are hollow compartments used for storage. How do they differ in function?

29. Infer When cells release ligands, they are sent through the bloodstream to every area of the body. Why do you think that only certain types of cells will respond to a particular ligand?

30. Provide Examples What are two ways in which exocytosis might help a cell maintain homeostasis?

31. Compare How is facilitated diffusion similar to both passive transport and active transport?

Interpreting Visuals

Use the diagram to answer the next three questions.

32. Apply What process is occurring in the diagram, and how do you know?

33. Predict If the transport proteins that carry amino acids into this cell stopped working, how might the process shown be affected?

34. Infer What might you conclude about the membrane structure of the final vesicle and the cell membrane?

Analyzing Data Form an Operational Definition

Use the text and table below to answer the next three questions. Reactive oxygen species, or ROS, are clusters of highly reactive oxygen atoms that can damage the body. As people age, the amount of ROS in the body increases, causing a condition called oxidative stress. In one study, researchers studied how the number of mitochondria might be involved in this situation.

- Muscle tissue was obtained from patients.
- Radioactive probes labeled the mitochondria.
- A machine counted the mitochondria per cell.

AGE AND MUSCLE CELL MITOCHONDRIA

Patient	Age	Mitochondria per Muscle Cell
1	47	2026
2	89	2987
3	65	2752
4	38	1989

35. Apply If the independent variable in this study is age, what is the operational definition of the dependent variable?

36. Analyze What do the data show about the relationship between age and number of mitochondria?

37. Infer What might the relationship between age and number of mitochondria indicate about the increase in ROS levels?

Making Connections

38. Write an Analogy The cell membrane regulates what can enter and exit a cell. In eukaryotes, it encloses a complex group of organelles that carry out special jobs. Make an analogy to describe the cell membrane and the variety of organelles and processes that take place inside it. Explain any limitations of your analogy.

39. Connect On the chapter opener, you saw a picture of macrophages eating up bacteria. Identify the ways in which the cytoskeleton helps the macrophage carry out this job.

Analyzing Data

35. The number of radioactive-labeled mitochondria per muscle cell in people of different ages, as counted by machine.
36. As people age, the number of mitochondria per muscle cell increases.
37. *Sample answer:* As people age, ROS levels might increase because there are more mitochondria. It is possible that the mitochondria make ROS as a byproduct.

Standards-Based Assessment

Record your answers on a separate piece of paper.

MULTIPLE CHOICE

1 The cell theory states that the cell is the most basic unit of life, all organisms are made of cells, and all cells come from cells. What makes the cell theory a scientific theory?

A It is based on a scientific publication that is read by scientists worldwide.
B It is based on the work of many scientists and leads to accurate predictions.
C It is based on ideas that have been proven true and that are not subject to revision.
D It is based on preliminary evidence but still needs to be confirmed with experiments.

2 A student observes four cells with a compound microscope and records her observations in the table shown.

Observed Structures	Cell 1	Cell 2	Cell 3	Cell 4
Cell Wall	yes	no	yes	no
Nucleus	yes	yes	no	yes
Chloroplasts	yes	no	no	no
Mitochondrion	yes	yes	no	yes

Based on these data, how should the cells be classified?

A Cells 1 and 3 are prokaryotic cells, and Cells 2 and 4 are eukaryotic cells.
B All four cells are prokaryotic cells.
C Cell 3 is a prokaryotic cell, and Cells 1, 2, and 4 are eukaryotic cells.
D All four cells are eukaryotic cells.

3 As the concentration of molecules outside a cell increases, more molecules will enter the cell because —

A the molecules are moving down their concentration gradient
B the molecules are moving from an area of low concentration to an area of high concentration
C energy is available to move them using active transport
D they have reached dynamic equilibrium

THINK THROUGH THE QUESTION

Are the molecules that are moving into the cell moving from an area of high concentration to low concentration, or vice versa?

4 Some viruses attack cells by inserting their own DNA into the host cells' DNA. Why might it be simpler for these viruses to attack prokaryotic cells than eukaryotic cells?

A Prokaryotic cells have less DNA than do eukaryotic cells.
B Unlike eukaryotic cells, prokaryotic cells do not have a nucleus.
C The cell wall in prokaryotic cells is a less effective barrier.
D The rapid growth of prokaryotic cells generates more viruses.

5 The diagram below shows how glucose molecules move down a concentration gradient to enter a cell with the help of transport proteins.

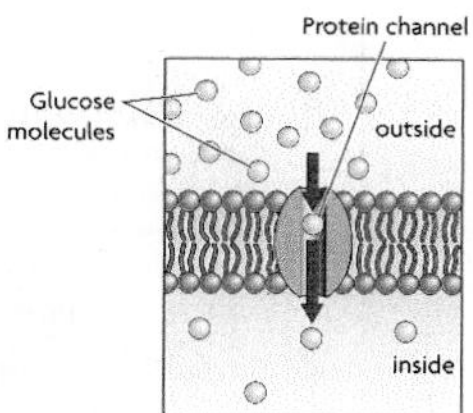

What type of transport is shown above?

A facilitated diffusion
B active transport
C osmosis
D pinocytosis

CHAPTER REVIEW

Standards-Based Assessment

The Standards-Based Assessment questions will help students prepare for their final examination in the course. If you wish to give students practice in coding their answers, look for the Standards-Based Assessment Answer Sheet at **HMHScience.com**. To give students practice under timed testing conditions, allow them five minutes per question.

Question	Answer	Depth of Knowledge	Cognitive Complexity
1	B	I	L
2	C	II	M
3	A	III	M
4	B	II	M
5	A	III	H

KEY

Depth of Knowledge		Cognitive Complexity	
I	Recall	L	Low
II	Skill/Concept	M	Moderate
III	Strategic Thinking	H	High
IV	Extended Thinking		

Making Connections

38. An analogy that could work in this case would compare a cell to a city that has various industries and modes of transport, and a defined but permeable border. The cell nucleus could be compared to a city government. A limitation of this analogy would be that industries may be able to function or produce their products without instruction or material from the government.

39. The cytoskeleton enables macrophages to move and capture the bacteria.

A BOOK EXPLAINING COMPLEX IDEAS USING ONLY THE 1,000 MOST COMMON WORDS

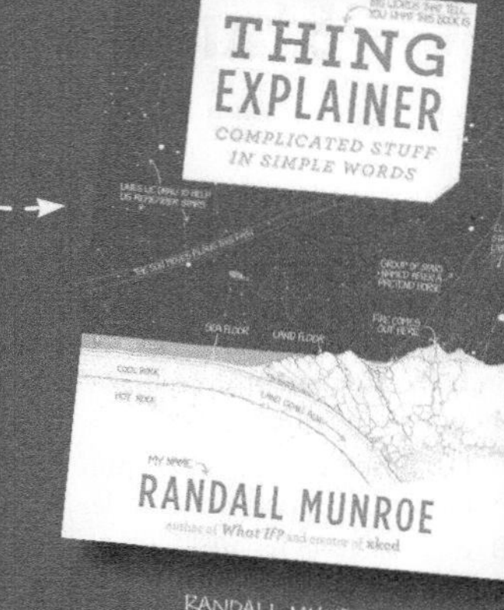

RANDALL MUNROE
XKCD.COM

TINY BAGS OF WATER YOU'RE MADE OF

The very tiny parts of people and other animals

You've learned that a cell is the basic unit of life. Organisms are made of one or more cells, need energy for all of their functions, respond to their environment, and reproduce by passing their genetic information to offspring. Here's a description of animal cells in simple language.

THE STORY OF WHAT LIVING THINGS ARE MADE OF

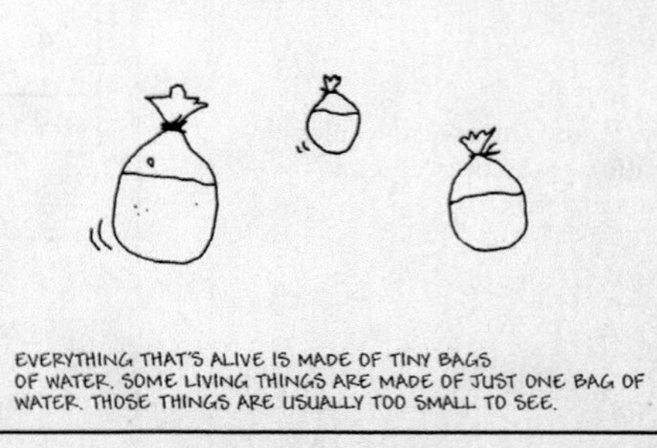

EVERYTHING THAT'S ALIVE IS MADE OF TINY BAGS OF WATER. SOME LIVING THINGS ARE MADE OF JUST ONE BAG OF WATER. THOSE THINGS ARE USUALLY TOO SMALL TO SEE.

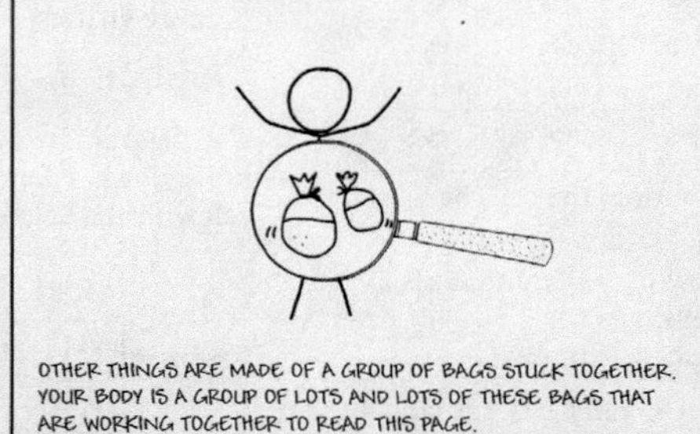

OTHER THINGS ARE MADE OF A GROUP OF BAGS STUCK TOGETHER. YOUR BODY IS A GROUP OF LOTS AND LOTS OF THESE BAGS THAT ARE WORKING TOGETHER TO READ THIS PAGE.

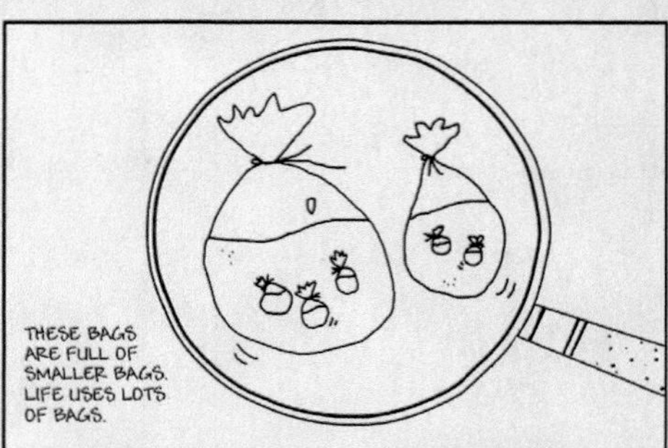

THESE BAGS ARE FULL OF SMALLER BAGS. LIFE USES LOTS OF BAGS.

ALL LIFE IS MADE FROM DIFFERENT KINDS OF WATER, AND A BAG KEEPS THE STUFF INSIDE IT FROM TOUCHING THE STUFF ON THE OUTSIDE. BY USING BAGS, LIVING THINGS CAN KEEP DIFFERENT KINDS OF WATER IN ONE PLACE WITHOUT IT ALL COMING TOGETHER.
OH MY!
SO SORRY!
AFTER YOU!

SOME OF THE LITTLE BAGS YOU SEE HERE WERE ONCE LIVING THINGS ON THEIR OWN. LONG AGO, SOME LITTLE GREEN BAGS LEARNED TO GET POWER FROM THE SUN. THEN THEY GOT STUCK INSIDE OTHER BAGS, AND THOSE BECAME FLOWERS AND TREES. THE GREEN COLOR OF LEAVES COMES FROM THE CHILDREN OF THOSE LITTLE GREEN BAGS.

SIZE

These bags are almost always too small to see. In fact, they're almost as small as the waves of light we see with:

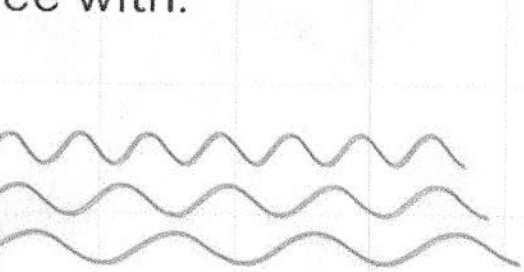

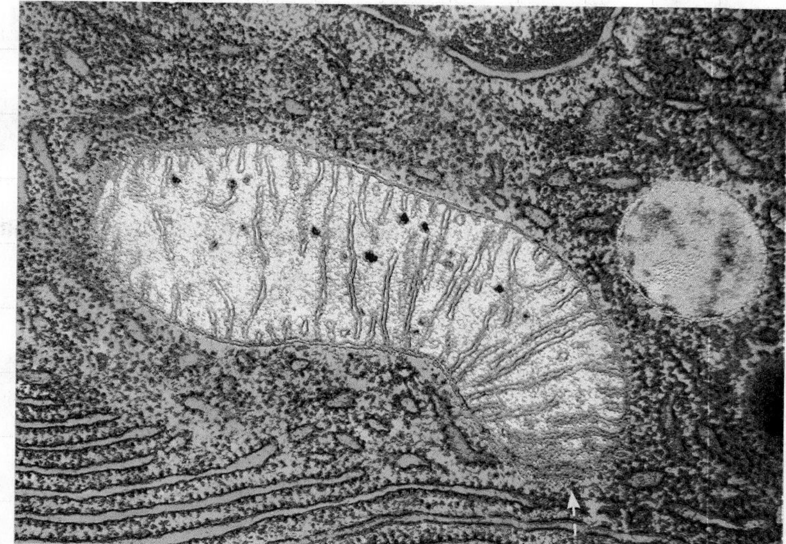

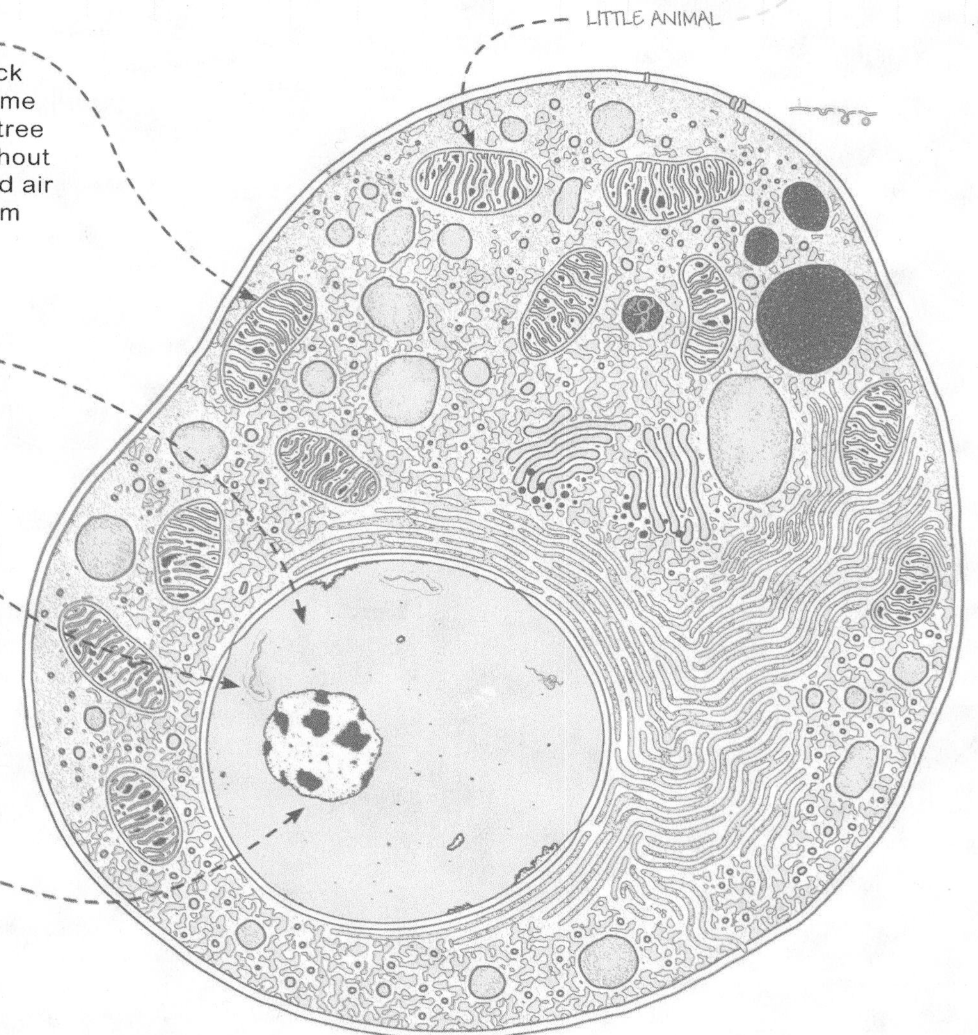

LITTLE ANIMALS

These are living things (not really "animals") that got stuck in our bags of water a long time ago, like the green things in tree leaves. Now we can't live without each other. They get food and air from our bodies and turn them into power for our bags.

INFORMATION

The information for how to make different body parts is stored here.

READERS

These machines read the information about how to make parts and write it on little notes, then send them out through the holes in the wall.

MACHINE MAKER

This part makes the little machines that sit outside the control area.

TINY BAGS OF WATER YOU'RE MADE OF

OUTSIDE WALL

The water bags that make up animals have soft walls. The bags in trees and flowers, which don't need to move around as much as us, have a less soft outside layer.

GETTING IN AND OUT

Some things can go through the bag's wall on their own. Other things can only go through if the bag helps them, either by letting them through an opening, or by making part of the wall into a new bag to hold them.

BAG FILLER

This machine fills little bags with stuff and then sends them out into the water. Some stuff gets sent out of the big bag to another part of your body.

The machine also fills bags with death water, marking them very carefully before sending them out so they don't get used in the wrong place.

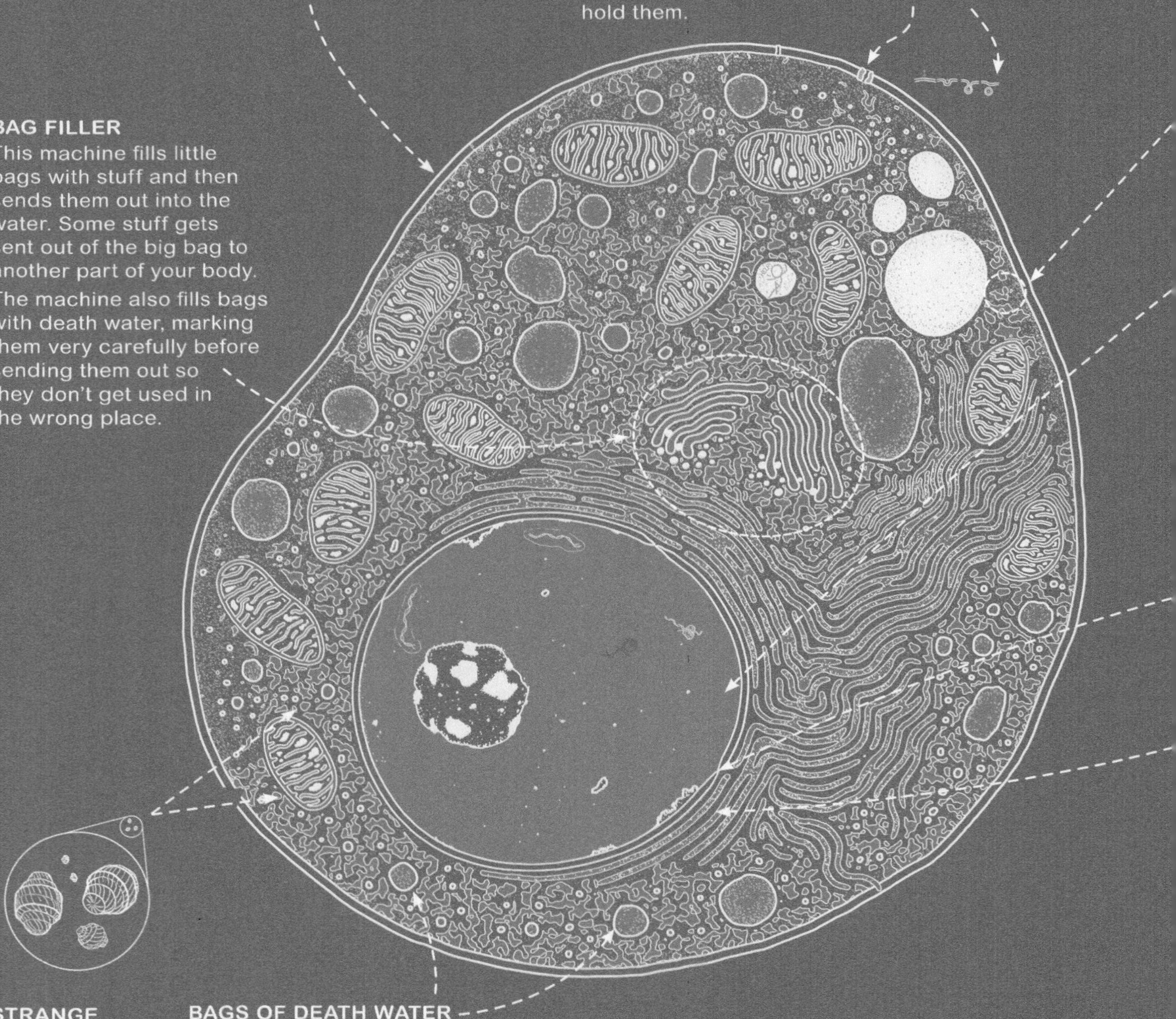

STRANGE BOXES

There are lots of these little boxes in our water bags. We don't know what they do.

BAGS OF DEATH WATER

These little bags are full of a kind of water that breaks things into tiny pieces. If something is put inside them, the water breaks it down into whatever it's made of.

If something goes wrong, these little bags tear open and all their bad water falls out. That makes the whole bag around it fall to pieces and die.

"Bags falling to pieces" sounds bad, since bags are what you're made of. But if a bag was having problems, it could hurt you. The death water helps clear it away so your body can make a new one.

BAG SHAPERS

The space between bag parts is full of lots of very thin hair-like lines. These are like bones for the bag; they help hold its shape, and do some other things.

Some of these shapers also have holes down the middle, and can carry things from one part of the bag to another.

EMPTY POCKETS

This part of the bag has pockets to hold stuff that it might need later. It also makes a few things.

One of the things it makes is that stuff that helps your arms and legs get stronger. Sometimes, people who want to run or ride fast will put bottles of that stuff into their body and then lie about it.

CONTROL AREA

This area in the middle holds information about how to make the different parts of your body. It writes this information in notes and sends them out into the bag.

Bags make more bags by breaking in half. When this happens, the control area also breaks in half, and each half gets a full set of the bag's information.

Not all bags have these control areas. The bags in human blood don't (which means blood can't grow) but the bags in bird blood do.

This control area may have once been a living thing on its own, just like the green things in leaves.

CONTROL AREA HOLES

Notes and workers go out through these openings.

LITTLE BUILDERS

This area is covered in little building machines that build new parts for the bag. The builders sit just outside the control area, reading the notes from inside that tell them what to build.

After the builder makes a part, the part falls away into the bag. Each part has a job to do. Maybe its job is to tell another part it's time to stop working. Maybe its job is to turn one kind of part into another. Maybe it makes another part do something different. Or maybe it has a job, but waits until it sees *another* part before it starts working.

The strange thing is, no one tells the part where to go. It just falls out into the room with all the other parts, and hangs around until it runs into whatever part it's supposed to grab. (Or until another part grabs *it!*) This sounds strange, and it is! There are so many parts, and they're all grabbing each other and stopping each other and helping each other.

The insides of these bags are harder to understand than almost anything else in the world.

THINGS THAT MAKE YOU SICK

These tiny things can get into your bags and take control of them. When they do that, they use the bag to build more of them.

When the kind shown here gets into you, your body gets hot, your legs hurt, and you have to lie down. Your whole body feels bad, and it makes you hate everything. You feel like you're going to die but usually don't.

We say all life is made of bags, but these things aren't. They also can't make more of themselves; they have to get a bag to make them. So we don't know if it makes sense to say they're "alive." They're more like an idea that spreads itself.

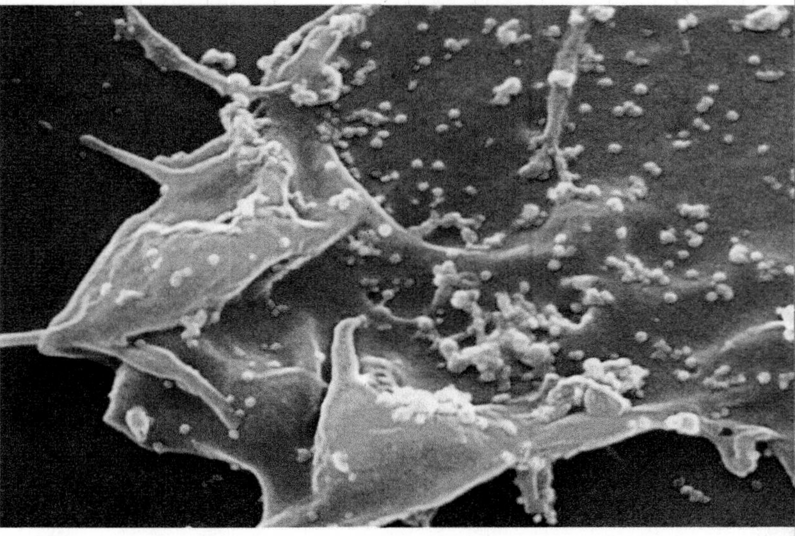

CHAPTER 4

Instruction and Intervention Support

Cells and Energy

① Core Instruction

The **Core Instruction** resources below can be used for all students. Core instruction should be followed by ongoing assessment to determine which students need further help.

Available in both English and Spanish

Available Online

Section	Instruction	PRINT	ONLINE	Labs
4.1	Textbook **Chemical Energy and ATP**	■	●	
	Animated Biology Photosynthesis and Respiration		●	
	PowerPresentation and Notes 4.1		●	
4.2	Textbook **Overview of Photosynthesis**	■	●	Rates of Photosynthesis
	Animated Biology Photosynthesis		●	
	PowerPresentation and Notes 4.2		●	
4.3	Textbook **Photosynthesis in Detail**	■	●	
	That's Amazing! Video Inquiry Lungs of the Planet		●	
	Animated Biology Electron Transport Chains of Photosynthesis		●	
	PowerPresentation and Notes 4.3		●	
4.4	Textbook **Overview of Cellular Respiration**	■	●	Cellular Respiration Photosynthesis and Respiration (Probeware Lab) **Virtual Lab** Carbon Transfer Through Snails and Elodea
	Animated Biology Cellular Respiration		●	
	PowerPresentation and Notes 4.4		●	
4.5	Textbook **Cellular Respiration in Detail**	■	●	Designing an Experiment to Test a Hypothesis **Video Lab** Cellular Respiration
	Animated Biology Mirror Processes, Glycolysis, Krebs Cycle, Electron Transport Chain		●	
	PowerPresentation and Notes 4.5		●	
4.6	Textbook **Fermentation**	■	●	Investigating Fermentation in Foods **QuickLab** Fermentation (Design Your Own) The Effect of Temperature on Respiration (Probeware Lab)
	Teaching Visuals Fermentation		●	
	PowerPresentation and Notes 4.6		●	

Additional online resources available for this chapter include **Interactive Whiteboard Resources.**

GO ONLINE! for all your teacher resources at HMHScience.com

② Support and Intervention

Support and Intervention resources are useful for students who need targeted help beyond the Core Instruction

Resources	PRINT	ONLINE
Assess and Reteach (TE wrap)	■	●
Concept Map		●
Interactive Reader	■	●
Interactive Review Games		●
Section Self-Checks		●
Study Guide B		●
Virtual Investigation Photosynthesis and Cellular Respiration		●
Vocabulary Practice Worksheets		●

③ Specialized Support

Students who need more intensive personalized intervention benefit from **Specialized Support** resources.

Resources	PRINT	ONLINE
Chapter Audio Files		●
Differentiated Instruction Inclusion, Below Level, and English Learners (TE wrap)	■	●
ELL Strategies	■	●
Modified Lesson Plans for English Learners		●
Reinforcement Worksheets		●
Study Guide A		●

Extension and Assessment

Enrichment and Challenge

Resources	PRINT	ONLINE
Active Reading Worksheets		●
Data Analysis Practice Worksheet		●
Differentiated Instruction Pre-AP (TE wrap)	■	●
Pre-AP Activity Leaf Structure: Built for Photosynthesis, Order Versus Disorder in Living Matter		●
The Inside Story and **Take It Further** (TE wrap)	■	●
Unit Project		●
WebLinks		●
WebQuest Energy and Athletic Training (4.6)		●

Assessment

Resources	PRINT	ONLINE
Alternative Assessment		●
Chapter Tests A and B		●
Diagnostic Test		●
ExamView Banks		●
Extended Response Test		●
Online Assessment System		●
Section Quizzes		●
Standards-Based Assessment	■	●

CHAPTER 4

Chapter Overview

- **Section 1** explains how cells use chemical energy to conduct cell processes.
- **Section 2** provides an overview of photosynthesis.
- **Section 3** details the light-dependent and light-independent reactions of photosynthesis.
- **Section 4** provides an overview of cellular respiration.
- **Section 5** details the processes of cellular respiration and compares photosynthesis and cellular respiration in terms of energy and matter.
- **Section 6** discusses the role of fermentation in cellular processes and in the production of some foods.

▼ Focus and Motivate

What makes these cells so important to many other organisms?

Have students read the caption. **Ask,** What are three things mentioned that are critical to your life? energy, sugar, and oxygen Tell students that diatoms are responsible for up to 25 percent of all carbon fixation on Earth. **Ask**

- What is another name for carbon fixation? photosynthesis
- Why does carbon need to be fixed? Organisms cannot use inorganic carbon. It must be "fixed" and incorporated into the organic molecules necessary for life.

BIOZINE
HMHScience.com

Students can access BioZine at **HMHScience.com** to receive updates to featured topics in the book.

CHAPTER 4

Cells and Energy

BIG IDEA All living things require energy in the form of ATP to carry on cell processes, and ATP is most often produced by the linked reactions of photosynthesis and respiration.

ONLINE BIOLOGY HMHScience.com

ONLINE Labs

- Rates of Photosynthesis
- **QuickLab** Fermentation
- Cellular Respiration
- Investigate Fermentation in Foods
- Designing an Experiment to Test a Hypothesis
- Photosynthesis and Respiration
- The Effect of Temperature on Respiration
- **Virtual Lab** Carbon Dioxide Transfer Through Snails and *Elodea*
- **Video Lab** Cellular Respiration

Student Activity

Purpose **Using a drinking straw to exhale into limewater, students will observe that one of the end products of cellular respiration is carbon dioxide.**

Safety Note Warn students to be careful not to inhale through the straw when doing this activity.

Materials (per team)

100 mL limewater

1 drinking straw per student

500-mL (1-pint) jar or glass

Prepare Dissolve one tablespoon of lime (calcium hydroxide, garden lime, or pickling lime) in about 1 L of water. Cover and let stand overnight. Pour off clear liquid (limewater) into a second jar, discard the residue, and cover.

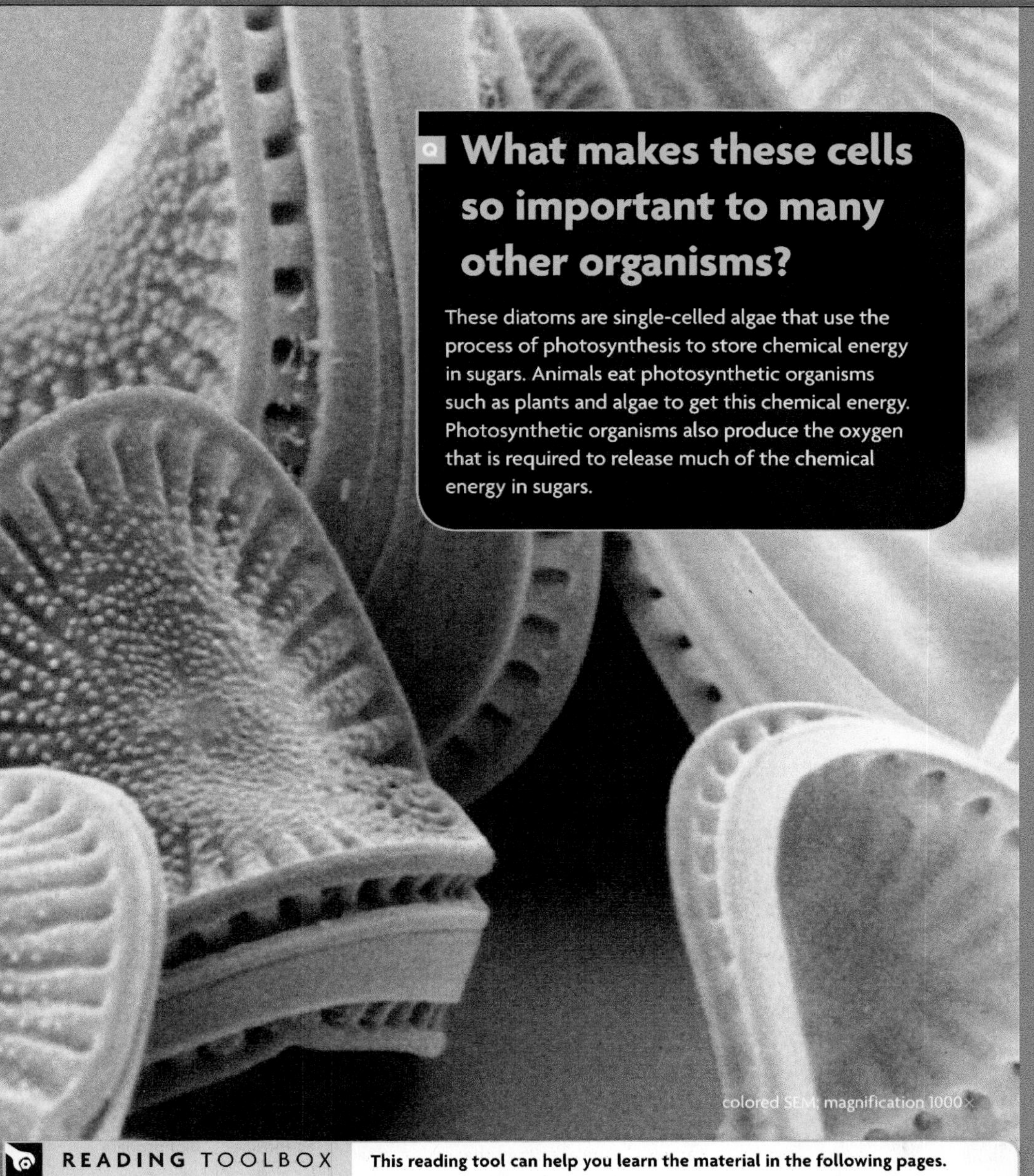

What makes these cells so important to many other organisms?

These diatoms are single-celled algae that use the process of photosynthesis to store chemical energy in sugars. Animals eat photosynthetic organisms such as plants and algae to get this chemical energy. Photosynthetic organisms also produce the oxygen that is required to release much of the chemical energy in sugars.

colored SEM; magnification 1000×

READING TOOLBOX **This reading tool can help you learn the material in the following pages.**

USING LANGUAGE

Describing Space As you read the chapter, look for language clues that answer the question, Where does this process take place? Words such as *inside, outside,* and *between* can help you learn where these processes take place to help you better understand them.

YOUR TURN

Describe as precisely as you can where the following processes happen.

1. photosynthesis
2. cellular respiration

Introduce Tell students that limewater turns milky white when combined with carbon dioxide. Have them take turns using their straws to blow gently into the limewater. As they do so, ask students to think about what happens every time they take a breath. They should continue blowing into the limewater until it turns a milky white. **Ask,** How is the air you exhale different from the air you inhale? Exhaled breath has much more carbon dioxide than air that is inhaled.

Discuss Point out that limewater turns milky white because it combines with carbon dioxide to form a white compound called calcium carbonate, or limestone, which is insoluble in water. If the white solution is allowed to stand for several hours, the calcium carbonate will settle to the bottom of the jar.

Ask, Where do you think the carbon dioxide comes from? It is given off by cells as a product of cellular respiration, transported to the lungs, and exhaled.

Activate Prior Knowledge

Direct students to the chapter title. **Ask,** What cellular activities require energy? Students may offer obvious suggestions such as contraction of muscle cells, repair of body tissue, or transmission of nerve impulses, but practically all cellular activity requires an input of energy. Have students think about the energy drinks and power bars that are widely consumed. **Ask,** Do energy drinks and power bars do something different from any other food that you eat? Explain. They may contain certain types of carbohydrates that can be used more quickly and thus supply energy faster. Point out that an energy bar provides no more energy than a bagel or a banana. The human body has enough stored energy in fat and glycogen to allow someone to run several back-to-back marathons.

Preview Vocabulary

Academic Vocabulary

Tell students that the processes described in this chapter can be summed up by one word: *metabolism.* Metabolism is the total of all the chemical processes that occur in an organism.

Metabolic processes take one of two directions. Either they are *synthetic* processes that build up material and store energy, or they are *catabolic* processes that break material down, often releasing energy. (The root *cata-* means to "fall or drop down," whereas *meta-* means "change.")

Chemosynthesis and *photosynthesis* are synthetic processes that capture the energy needed for life and store it in sugars. *Cellular respiration* and *fermentation* are catabolic processes that break down sugars and deliver energy to sustain life.

Answers

1. in chloroplasts
2. in mitochondria

SECTION 4.1

B.2.1 Use a model to illustrate how photosynthesis transforms light energy into stored chemical energy.

B.2.2 Use a model to illustrate that cellular respiration is a chemical process whereby the bonds of food molecules and oxygen molecules are broken and the bonds in new compounds are formed resulting in a net transfer of energy.

▼ Plan and Prepare

Activate Prior Knowledge Ask students to think about how smaller units are sometimes more convenient. **Ask,** Would you rather have fifty $1 bills or one $50 bill? One-dollar bills have more practical use, in vending machines for example; $50 bills are less readily accepted. Tell students that energy in organisms is packaged in small units. These "energy packets" will be introduced in this chapter.

▼ Teach

TEACH FROM VISUALS

VISUAL VOCAB Have students compare the molecular structures of ATP and ADP. **Ask**

- How are ATP and ADP alike? Both contain adenosine and phosphate groups.
- How are they different? ATP has three phosphate groups; ADP two.
- Why is this difference important? The extra bond is a source of energy.

4.1 Chemical Energy and ATP

KEY CONCEPT **All cells need chemical energy.**

VOCABULARY

ATP
ADP
chemosynthesis

MAIN IDEAS

- The chemical energy used for most cell processes is carried by ATP.
- Organisms break down carbon-based molecules to produce ATP.
- A few types of organisms do not need sunlight and photosynthesis as a source of energy.

Connect to Your World

The cells of all organisms—from algae to whales to people—need chemical energy for all of their processes. Some organisms, such as diatoms and plants, absorb energy from sunlight. Some of that energy is stored in sugars. Cells break down sugars to produce usable chemical energy for their functions. Without organisms that make sugars, living things on Earth could not survive.

MAIN IDEA

The chemical energy used for most cell processes is carried by ATP.

Sometimes you may feel that you need energy, so you eat food that contains sugar. Does food, which contains sugar and other carbon-based molecules, give you energy? The answer to this question is yes and no. All of the carbon-based molecules in food store chemical energy in their bonds. Carbohydrates and lipids are the most important energy sources in foods you eat. However, this energy is only usable after these molecules are broken down by a series of chemical reactions. Your energy does come from food, but not directly.

All cells, like that in **FIGURE 1.1**, use chemical energy carried by ATP—adenosine triphosphate. **ATP** is a molecule that transfers energy from the breakdown of food molecules to cell processes. You can think of ATP as a wallet filled with money. Just as a wallet carries money that you can spend, ATP carries chemical energy that cells can use. Cells use ATP for functions such as building molecules and moving materials by active transport.

VISUAL VOCAB

ATP transfers energy to cell processes.

adenosine triphosphate tri = 3

ADP is a lower-energy molecule that can be converted into ATP.

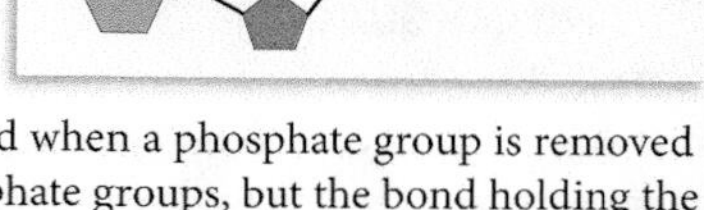

The energy carried by ATP is released when a phosphate group is removed from the molecule. ATP has three phosphate groups, but the bond holding the third phosphate group is unstable and is very easily broken. The removal of the third phosphate group usually involves a reaction that releases energy.

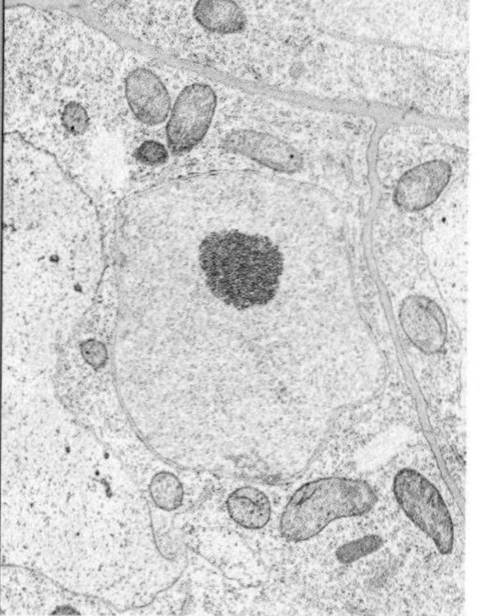

FIGURE 1.1 All cells, including plant cells, use ATP for energy. (colored TEM; magnification 9000×)

Differentiated Instruction

ENGLISH LEARNERS

Point out the wallet-money analogy used in the text. Have students look at the wording to see how the comparison is made. The word *as* signals the analogy: "Just as a wallet carries money. . ., ATP carries chemical energy. . ."

Prompt students to develop the analogy further. For example, energy and money are resources that can be "spent." They both must be "earned" and "stored." Both have value.

Teacher Toolkit, Section D, Analogies

PRE-AP

The material in this chapter first looks at energy processes in overview and then in detail. Suggest to students that they use Cornell Notes to outline this chapter, and to incorporate drawings into their notes. In their summaries, have students think about how material in one section relates to another.

Teacher Toolkit, Section C, Cornell Notes

FIGURE 1.2 ATP and ADP

Adding a phosphate group to ADP forms ATP.

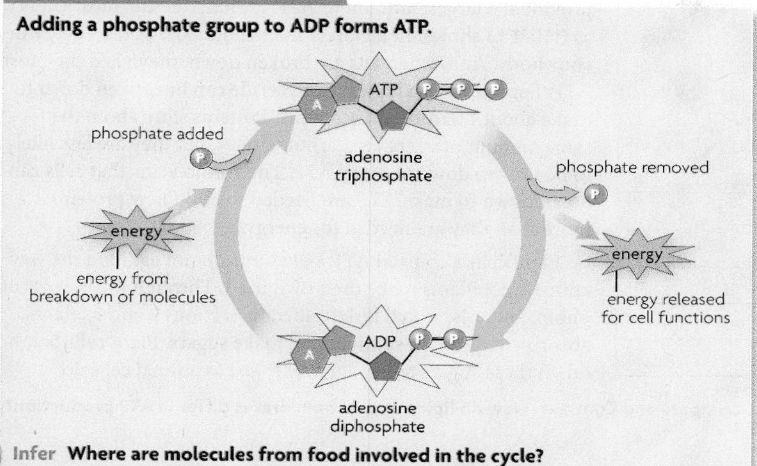

A Infer **Where are molecules from food involved in the cycle?**

When the phosphate is removed, energy is released and ATP becomes ADP—adenosine diphosphate. **ADP** is a lower-energy molecule that can be converted into ATP by the addition of a phosphate group. If ATP is a wallet filled with money, ADP is a nearly empty wallet. The breakdown of ATP to ADP and the production of ATP from ADP can be represented by the cycle shown in **FIGURE 1.2.** However, adding a phosphate group to ADP to make ATP is not a simple process. A large, complex group of proteins is needed to do it. In fact, if just one of these proteins is faulty, ATP is not produced.

B Synthesize **Describe the relationship between energy stored in food and ATP.**

CONNECT TO

BIOCHEMISTRY

As you learned in the chapter **Chemistry of Life,** carbon-based molecules in living things—carbohydrates, lipids, proteins, and nucleic acids—have different structures and functions.

MAIN IDEA

Organisms break down carbon-based molecules to produce ATP.

Foods that you eat do not contain ATP that your cells can use. First, the food must be digested. One function of digestion is to break down food into smaller molecules that can be used to make ATP. You probably know that different foods have different amounts of calories, which are measures of energy. Different foods also provide different amounts of ATP. The number of ATP molecules that are made from the breakdown of food is related to the number of calories in food, but not directly.

The number of ATP molecules produced depends on the type of molecule that is broken down—carbohydrate, lipid, or protein. Carbohydrates are not stored in large amounts in your body, but they are the molecules most commonly broken down to make ATP. The breakdown of the simple sugar glucose yields about 36 molecules of ATP.

READING TOOLBOX

TAKING NOTES

Use a supporting main ideas chart to organize concepts related to chemical energy.

All cells need chemical energy.
→ ATP carries energy.
→
→

TEACH FROM VISUALS

FIGURE 1.2 Have students connect the diagram to **VISUAL VOCAB** and follow the triphosphate-diphosphate cycle. **Ask,** When is energy available for cell processes? after a phosphate is removed from ATP

Integrating Chemistry

Remind students that a phosphate group is a **polyatomic ion,** that is, a charged group of atoms that are held together by covalent bonds. Each phosphate group in ATP is negatively charged. Because the groups are crowded together, yet repel each other due to their like charges, the bonds between phosphate groups are unstable.

ATP can be thought of as a compressed spring that stores potential energy. When the third phosphate group is removed, the "spring" relaxes and energy is released. ADP is analogous to the relaxed spring that has released its potential energy but can be compressed again.

Vocabulary

Calorie A food Calorie (also called a kilocalorie; 1000 calories) is the amount of heat required to raise the temperature of one kilogram of water by 1°C. When a mole of ATP is converted to ADP in a cell, about 7.3 Calories (7.3 kilocalories) of energy are released.

Answers

A Infer Food molecules are supplying the energy to add phosphate to ADP (shown to the left) and convert it to ATP.

B Synthesize Food molecules store chemical energy in their bonds. Food is broken down into smaller molecules that are broken down further to transfer this energy to ATP.

ENGLISH LEARNERS

Show students how a cycle diagram can be a useful tool for understanding what they have read and for summarizing scientific information. Have students list the events in the ADP/ATP cycle. Point out that there are two distinct sets of arrows: blue for phosphate and gold for energy. Have students talk about the diagram, making statements about the cycle of events.

Teacher Toolkit, Section C, Cycle Diagram

BELOW LEVEL

Model using a graphic organizer, such as a mind map, to organize material in this section. Start with ATP in a central circle, then on four diagonal lines branching from the center, have students suggest statements that relate to the ATP. Possible statements: It is an energy carrier; it gets energy from the breakdown of food molecules; it is produced when phosphate is added to ADP; and it releases energy when converted back to ADP. Have students copy the map into their notebooks.

Teacher Toolkit, Section C, Mind Map

▼ Teach *continued*

Integrating Physics

Most **wavelengths of light** are either absorbed or scattered by water. In clear ocean water, visible light decreases about 10-fold with each 75 meters (246 feet) of depth. Only 1 percent of the light at the surface reaches a depth of 150 meters (492 feet). Some photosynthetic organisms, such as red algae, can live at greater depths because they contain light-absorbing molecules that absorb the blue and green wavelengths that penetrate deeper into the water. Below 150 meters (492 feet), producers capture energy from chemical compounds through the process of chemosynthesis.

Answers

A Compare and Contrast Lipids provide more ATP than carbohydrates do.

B Compare Both chemosynthetic organisms and plants make their own food and both are eaten by other organisms that cannot make their own food.

▼ Assess and Reteach

Assess Use the Section Self-Check or Section Quiz, both available at **HMHScience.com**.

Reteach As a class, review **FIGURE 1.2.** Have students close their books and draw and label the diagram from memory.

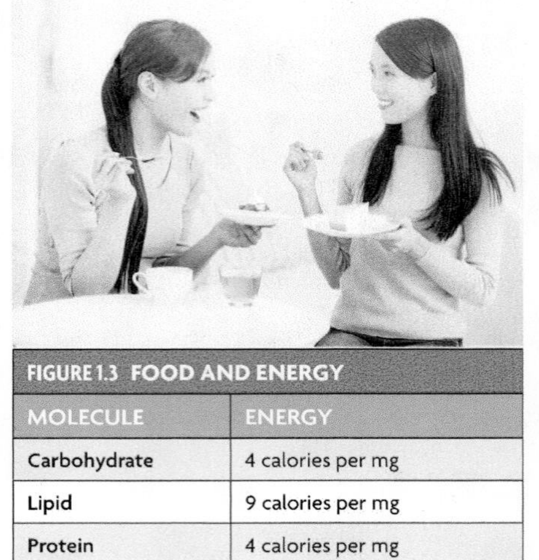

FIGURE 1.3 FOOD AND ENERGY

MOLECULE	ENERGY
Carbohydrate	4 calories per mg
Lipid	9 calories per mg
Protein	4 calories per mg

You might be surprised to learn that carbohydrates do not provide the largest amount of ATP. Lipids store the most energy, as **FIGURE 1.3** shows. In fact, fats store about 80% of the energy in your body. And, when fats are broken down, they yield the most ATP. For example, a typical triglyceride can be broken down to make about 146 molecules of ATP. Proteins store about the same amount of energy as carbohydrates, but they are less likely to be broken down to make ATP. The amino acids that cells can break down to make ATP are needed to build new proteins more than they are needed for energy.

Plant cells also need ATP, but plants do not eat food the way animals do. Plants make their own food. Through the process of photosynthesis, which is described in Sections 2 and 3, plants absorb energy from sunlight and make sugars. Plant cells break down these sugars to produce ATP, just as animal cells do.

A Compare and Contrast **How do lipids and carbohydrates differ in ATP production?**

MAIN IDEA

A few types of organisms do not need sunlight and photosynthesis as a source of energy.

Most, but not all, organisms rely directly or indirectly on sunlight and photosynthesis as their source of chemical energy. In places that never get sunlight, such as in the deep ocean, there are areas with living things. Some organisms live in very hot water near cracks in the ocean floor called hydrothermal vents. These vents release chemical compounds, such as sulfides, that can serve as an energy source. **Chemosynthesis** (KEE-mo-SIHN-thih-sihs) is a process by which some organisms use chemical energy to make energy-storing carbon-based molecules. These organisms still need ATP for energy. The processes that make their ATP are very similar to those in other organisms. Like plants, chemosynthetic organisms make their own food, but the raw materials differ.

B Compare **How are chemosynthetic organisms and plants similar as energy sources?**

SELF-CHECK Online
HMHScience.com
GO ONLINE

4.1 Formative Assessment

REVIEWING MAIN IDEAS

1. How are **ATP** and **ADP** related?
2. What types of molecules are broken down to make ATP?
3. How are some organisms able to survive without sunlight and photosynthesis?

CRITICAL THINKING

4. **Apply** Describe how you get energy indirectly from the food that you eat.
5. **Compare and Contrast** How are the energy needs of plant cells similar to those of animal cells? How are they different?

CONNECT TO

CHEMICAL REACTIONS

6. A water molecule is added to an ATP molecule to break ATP down into ADP and a phosphate group. Write the chemical equation for this reaction.

4.1 FORMATIVE ASSESSMENT

1. High-energy ATP molecules are converted into lower-energy ADP molecules when a phosphate is removed and energy is released. ADP is converted back into ATP by the addition of a phosphate.
2. Carbohydrates, lipids, and proteins; lipids and carbohydrates are the main sources of ATP.
3. Chemosynthetic organisms use chemicals from their environment to make high-energy carbon-based molecules.
4. Food is not directly used for energy, but it is broken down to make ATP, which provides energy.
5. Both plants and animals use ATP to power cell functions. Plants make their own food to be broken down to make ATP; animals must consume other organisms for the food that is broken down to make ATP.
6. $H_2O + ATP \rightarrow ADP + P$

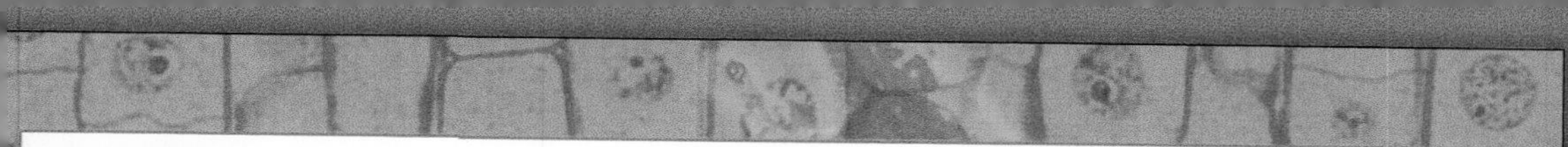

4.2 Overview of Photosynthesis

KEY CONCEPT **The overall process of photosynthesis produces sugars that store chemical energy.**

MAIN IDEAS
- Photosynthetic organisms are producers.
- Photosynthesis in plants occurs in chloroplasts.

VOCABULARY
photosynthesis
chlorophyll
thylakoid
light-dependent reactions
light-independent reactions

Connect to Your World
Solar-powered calculators, homes, and cars are just a few things that use energy from sunlight. In a way, you are also solar-powered. Of course, sunlight does not directly give you the energy you need to play a sport or read this page. That energy comes from ATP. Molecules of ATP are often made from the breakdown of sugars, but how are sugars made? Plants capture some of the energy in sunlight and change it into chemical energy stored in sugars.

MAIN IDEA
Photosynthetic organisms are producers.

Some organisms are called producers because they produce the source of chemical energy for themselves and for other organisms. Plants, as well as some bacteria and protists, are the producers that are the main sources of chemical energy for most organisms on Earth. Certainly, animals that eat only plants obtain their chemical energy directly from plants. Animals that eat other animals, and bacteria and fungi that decompose other organisms, get their chemical energy indirectly from plants. When a wolf eats a rabbit, the tissues of the rabbit provide the wolf with a source of chemical energy. The rabbit's tissues are built from its food source—the sugars and other carbon-based molecules in plants. These sugars are made through photosynthesis.

Photosynthesis is a process that captures energy from sunlight to make sugars that store chemical energy. Therefore, directly or indirectly, the energy for almost all organisms begins as sunlight. Sunlight includes a wide range of radiant energy, such as ultraviolet radiation, microwaves, and the visible light that lets you see. Plants absorb visible light for photosynthesis. Visible light appears white, but it is made up of several colors, or wavelengths, of light.

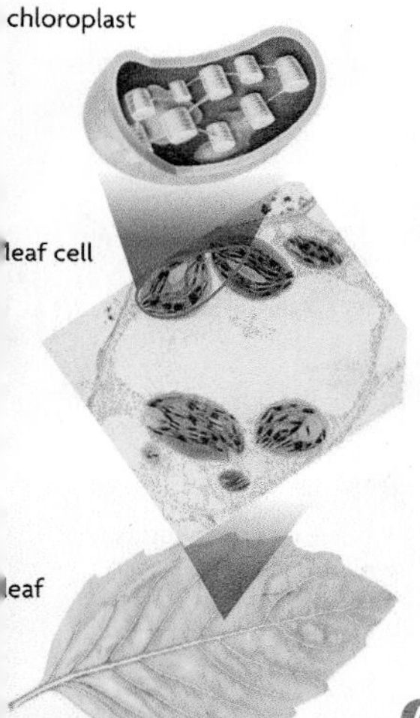

Chlorophyll (KLAWR-uh-fihl) is a molecule in chloroplasts, shown in **FIGURE 2.1**, that absorbs some of the energy in visible light. Plants have two main types of chlorophyll, called chlorophyll *a* and chlorophyll *b*. Together, these two types of chlorophyll absorb mostly red and blue wavelengths of visible light. Neither type absorbs much green light. Plants have other light-absorbing molecules that absorb green light, but there are fewer of these molecules. As a result, the green color of plants comes from the reflection of light's green wavelengths by chlorophyll.

FIGURE 2.1 Chloroplasts in plant cells contain a light-absorbing molecule called chlorophyll.

chloroplast

leaf cell

leaf

(A) Apply **Describe the importance of producers and photosynthesis.**

Differentiated Instruction

ENGLISH LEARNERS
Effective questioning helps students think more deeply as they read and develop their own questions about language and meaning. List some key questions to ask before, during, and after reading. Before: What do you already know about photosynthesis? What do you need to find out? During: What have you learned so far? What is new to you? After: What was the most important part of the reading? What questions do you still have?

Teacher Toolkit, Section C, Questions to Guide Reading

SECTION 4.2

B.2.1 Use a model to illustrate how photosynthesis transforms light energy into stored chemical energy.

Plan and Prepare

Activate Prior Knowledge Have students think about the word *producer* in a different context. **Ask,** What do film, radio, television, and music-recording producers do? oversee production of something they do not actually make Relate this to photosynthesis. Plants do not make energy; they capture it, store it, and deliver it. **Ask,** What law says that energy can be transformed but never created or destroyed? first law of thermodynamics

Teach

Vocabulary
chloroplast, chlorophyll Tell students that these terms relate to plant color:

chloro- = "green"

The root *-phyll* or *phyllon* means "leaf," and the root *-plast* or *plastos* means "molded," as into an organized body.

Answers
(A) **Apply** Photosynthesis enables producers to capture energy from sunlight and make sugars that store chemical energy. The food produced becomes a source of energy for nonproducers.

▼ Teach

TEACH FROM VISUALS

FIGURE 2.2 Point out that the numbers in the figure correspond to the numbered list on the next page. **Ask**

- Where do the light-dependent and light-independent reactions occur? thylakoid membranes, stroma
- What two reactants are shown entering the chloroplast? water and carbon dioxide
- What two products are shown leaving the chloroplast? oxygen and sugar

Integrating Physics

The sunlight used in photosynthesis is a form of electromagnetic, or radiant, energy. The sun produces a full spectrum of **electromagnetic radiation,** but Earth's atmosphere filters out much of it. The radiation that the atmosphere does allow in appears toward the middle of the spectrum, and this is what we see as color, or **visible light.**

Within the spectrum of visible light are different wavelengths that we associate with different colors. The wavelengths range from 400 to 700 nanometers (nm) on the electromagnetic spectrum, with blue light being the shortest wavelength at 400 nm and red light being the longest at 700 nm.

Light that comes to Earth may be reflected or absorbed. A substance that absorbs light is called a **pigment.** The colors we see result from reflected light that is not absorbed by pigments. A leaf appears green because it reflects green light, while absorbing red and blue light.

Answers

A **Identify** The reactants are water and carbon dioxide. The products are sugar and oxygen.

MAIN IDEA

Photosynthesis in plants occurs in chloroplasts.

Chloroplasts are the membrane-bound organelles where photosynthesis takes place in plants. Most of the chloroplasts are in leaf cells that are specialized for photosynthesis, which has two main stages as shown in **FIGURE 2.2.** The two main parts of chloroplasts needed for photosynthesis are the grana and the stroma. Grana (singular, *granum*) are stacks of coin-shaped, membrane-enclosed compartments called **thylakoids** (THY-luh-KOYDZ). The membranes of the thylakoids contain chlorophyll, other light-absorbing molecules, and proteins. The stroma is the fluid that surrounds the grana inside a chloroplast.

FIGURE 2.2 Photosynthesis Overview

Chloroplasts absorb energy from sunlight and produce sugars through the process of photosynthesis.

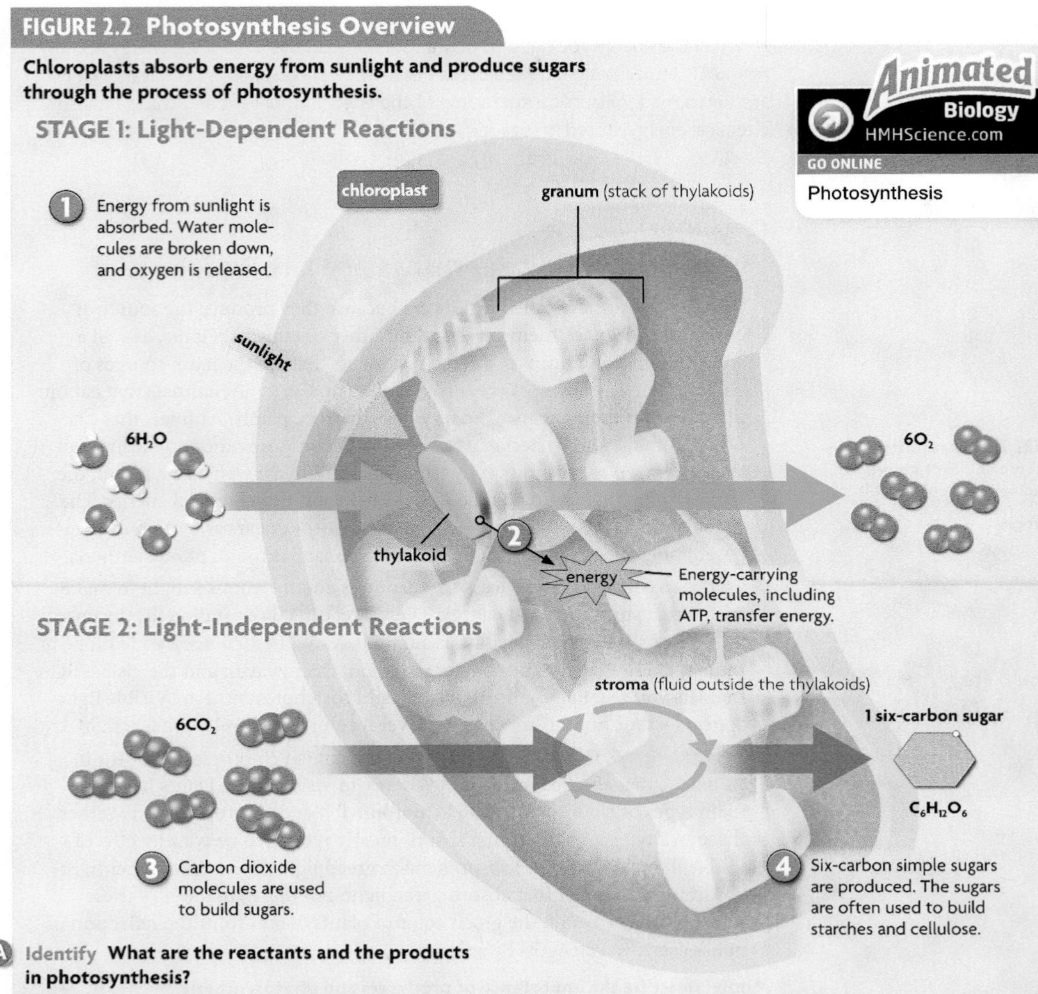
STAGE 1: Light-Dependent Reactions
Animated Biology
HMHScience.com
GO ONLINE
Photosynthesis
1 Energy from sunlight is absorbed. Water molecules are broken down, and oxygen is released.
chloroplast
granum (stack of thylakoids)
sunlight
$6H_2O$
$6O_2$
thylakoid
2
energy
Energy-carrying molecules, including ATP, transfer energy.
STAGE 2: Light-Independent Reactions
stroma (fluid outside the thylakoids)
$6CO_2$
1 six-carbon sugar
$C_6H_{12}O_6$
3 Carbon dioxide molecules are used to build sugars.
4 Six-carbon simple sugars are produced. The sugars are often used to build starches and cellulose.

A Identify **What are the reactants and the products in photosynthesis?**

Differentiated Instruction

BELOW LEVEL

Have students write about the process of photosynthesis. Ask them to break it down into the *photo-* part (light-dependent reactions that capture energy from sunlight) and the *-synthesis* part (light-independent reactions that produce sugars). Tell students to write continuously for five minutes, even if they simply end up writing the same thing over and over again. Suggest that they look at **FIGURE 2.2** as they write.

Teacher Toolkit, Section C, Quick Write

TEACH WITH TECHNOLOGY

If a PC microscope is available, project a prepared slide of plant cells or a wet mount of an *Anacharis* leaf. Point out the green chloroplasts. Have students locate the mesophyll cells that contain the most chloroplasts and recognize that these cells are where most photosynthesis occurs in a plant. As a comparison, project a slide of a root tip. **Ask,** Why do you think there are no chloroplasts in root cells? Root cells grow underground; they are not exposed to sunlight.

The **light-dependent reactions** capture energy from sunlight. These reactions take place within and across the membrane of the thylakoids. Water (H_2O) and sunlight are needed for this stage of photosynthesis.

1. Chlorophyll absorbs energy from sunlight. The energy is transferred along the thylakoid membrane. Water molecules (H_2O) are broken down. Oxygen molecules (O_2) are released.
2. Energy carried along the thylakoid membrane is transferred to molecules that carry energy, such as ATP.

The **light-independent reactions** use energy from the light-dependent reactions to make sugars. These reactions occur in the stroma of chloroplasts. Carbon dioxide molecules (CO_2) are needed during this stage of photosynthesis.

3. CO_2 is added to a cycle of chemical reactions to build larger molecules. Energy from the light-dependent reactions is used in the reactions.
4. A molecule of a simple sugar is formed. The sugar, usually glucose ($C_6H_{12}O_6$), stores some of the energy that was captured from sunlight.

CONNECT TO

CALVIN CYCLE

The light-independent reactions include a series of chemical reactions called the Calvin cycle. You can read more about the Calvin cycle in **Section 3.**

The equation for the whole photosynthesis process is shown below. As you can see, there are many arrows between the reactants—CO_2 and H_2O—and the products—a six-carbon sugar and O_2. Those arrows tell you that photosynthesis has many steps. For example, the light-independent reactions need only one molecule of CO_2 at a time, and the six-carbon sugar comes from a reaction that combines two three-carbon sugars. Also, enzymes and other chemicals are needed, not just light, carbon dioxide, and water.

$$\underset{\text{carbon dioxide}}{6CO_2} + \underset{\text{water}}{6H_2O} \xrightarrow{} \xrightarrow{} \xrightarrow{\text{light, enzymes}} \xrightarrow{} \xrightarrow{} \xrightarrow{} \underset{\text{a sugar}}{C_6H_{12}O_6} + \underset{\text{oxygen}}{6O_2}$$

Glucose and other simple sugars, such as fructose, are not the only carbohydrates that come from photosynthesis. Plants need the simple sugars to build starch and cellulose molecules. In effect, plants need photosynthesis for their growth and development. You will learn more about the importance of another product of photosynthesis—oxygen—in Sections 4 and 5.

Summarize **How is energy from sunlight used to make sugar molecules?**

4.2 Formative Assessment

SELF-CHECK Online
HMHScience.com
GO ONLINE

REVIEWING MAIN IDEAS

1. What are the roles of chloroplasts and **chlorophyll** in **photosynthesis**?
2. Describe the stages of photosynthesis. Use the terms **thylakoid, light-dependent reactions,** and **light-independent reactions** in your answer.

CRITICAL THINKING

3. **Apply** Suppose you wanted to develop a light to help increase plant growth. What characteristics should the light have? Why?
4. **Analyze** Explain why photosynthesis is important for building the structure of plant cells.

CONNECT TO

CHEMICAL REACTIONS

5. Overall, do you think photosynthesis is endothermic or exothermic? Explain your answer.

Chapter 4: Cells and Energy 103

4.2 FORMATIVE ASSESSMENT

1. Photosynthesis occurs in chloroplasts, powered by energy absorbed by chlorophyll. Chlorophyll is a light-absorbing molecule located in chloroplasts.
2. The first stage of photosynthesis is the light-dependent reactions that take place in the thylakoids. Energy is absorbed from sunlight and transferred through the thylakoid membrane. The energy is used in the light-independent reactions to produce sugars.
3. The light should emit the optimal wavelengths, such as blue and red, to be absorbed by the pigments in plants.
4. In plants, the cell wall is responsible for structure and support. Cell walls are made from cellulose, which is a carbohydrate that is built up from sugars produced during photosynthesis.
5. Endothermic; it absorbs energy to produce sugars.

Vocabulary

light-dependent, light-independent Explain that these reactions were previously known as light reactions and dark reactions, respectively. These terms are no longer used, but students may still find them in books.

Address Misconceptions

Common Misconception Students often think that photosynthesis is a single reaction in which CO_2 and H_2O combine to form sugar and O_2.

Correcting the Misconception Have students look at **FIGURE 2.2,** then direct their attention to the equation on this page. Explain that the many arrows represent many steps.

Answers

A **Summarize** Energy from sunlight is absorbed to generate energy-carrying molecules. The energy-carrying molecules are transferred to the reactions that make sugars.

Assess and Reteach

Assess Use the Section Self-Check or Section Quiz, both available at **HMHScience.com**.

Reteach Draw an oval on the board to represent a chloroplast. Tell students to take a quick look at **FIGURE 2.2,** and then close their books. Have students provide the details of photosynthesis to complete the representation.

Discuss

Review the light reactions and the Calvin cycle with students. **Ask,** How can you divide artificial photosynthesis into two separate parts, similar to the parts of the process of natural photosynthesis? collect sunlight to split water and reduce, or fix, carbon Engage students' interest in artificial photosynthesis by having them compare the artificial process with the natural process. Have them make a table comparing the two processes, such as listing methane and glucose as the final products of artificial and natural photosynthesis, respectively. Emphasize that both are fuels. **Ask,** What does glucose fuel? metabolic processes

Explain to students that the reaction that uses electricity to split water into its components, hydrogen and oxygen, is known as hydrolysis (*hydro* = "water"; *lysis* = "splitting"). The electrochemical splitting of water usually requires a catalyst to start the reaction. Catalysts are substances that speed up a chemical reaction but are not themselves changed by the reaction. Many catalysts used in hydrolysis reactions in the lab are expensive precious metals, but some scientists have discovered that nickel works well in artificial photosynthesis. In plants, manganese acts as a catalyst to get photosynthesis started, but it cannot be used in artificial photosynthesis because it is too unstable.

Splitting water using electricity is not economical. Compared with the cost of energy that has to be input into the system, the rate at which hydrogen is produced is low. However, the use of solar power might be an ideal way to produce hydrogen because solar energy is essentially free.

Artificial Photosynthesis

As the world population and demand for energy increase, the reserves of fossil fuels are being depleted. The development of power from alternative energy sources such as wind, water, and the sun has helped slow the depletion of fossil fuels. However, these renewable energy sources haven't replaced fossil fuels. And as coal, oil, and natural gas are burned to release needed energy, they also release carbon dioxide. Increasing amounts of carbon dioxide in the atmosphere are implicated in Earth's climate change.

To help address the twin problems of decreasing fossil fuel reserves and increasing carbon dioxide emissions, scientists are attempting to do what plants and other green organisms have been doing for billions of years—convert solar energy into chemical energy. In nature, plants capture energy from sunlight in chlorophyll molecules within the chloroplasts. The solar energy is used to transfer electrons from water molecules to carbon dioxide molecules, reducing the carbon dioxide and storing the energy in the chemical bonds of a fuel. In plant photosynthesis, that fuel is a carbohydrate, glucose. Oxygen also forms.

Researchers in Berkeley, California, have made important advances in the field of artificial photosynthesis using nanotechnology to mimic natural photosynthesis. Unlike the process in plants that uses chlorophyll, artificial photosynthesis uses a membrane of semiconducting nanowires to harness solar energy. Bacteria embedded in the membrane use this solar energy to convert carbon dioxide and water into acetate rather than glucose. Acetate is a chemical building block that scientists use to make more-complex molecules that make up biodegradable plastics, medicines, and even fuels. For example, the Berkeley scientists have produced methane, CH_4, the main component of natural gas.

The basis of their artificial photosynthesis system is an array of silicon and titanium oxide nanowires that functions much like a chloroplast. The structure of the wire array protects oxygen-sensitive bacteria that are embedded among the wires in the membrane. When the wires absorb solar energy, light-excited electrons are generated. The electrons are delivered to the bacteria, which use them to reduce carbon dioxide and combine it with water molecules to make acetate and oxygen. Once acetate has formed, other bacteria that have been genetically engineered for the process are used to synthesize desired chemical products such as fuels.

The same group of scientists has achieved a more recent breakthrough. They have now developed a new hybrid system with nanowires that are made of different materials. These materials also harness solar energy and use it to split water molecules into oxygen and hydrogen molecules. This process is called the hydrogen evolution reaction (HER). Then the hydrogen is passed to bacteria that use it to reduce carbon dioxide to methane. Since most of the methane currently used comes from natural gas, this new ability to generate methane from a renewable hydrogen source may decrease our reliance on fossil fuels in the future.

The diagram below summarizes the new process, a form of solar-to-chemical conversion similar to photosynthesis. After the membrane made of semiconductor nanowires absorbs solar energy, the energy is used to split water molecules, generating hydrogen gas. Then, bacteria in the membrane combine the hydrogen produced in the HER with carbon dioxide from the atmosphere to produce methane.

The new system has two advantages over the scientists' original system. First, hydrogen molecules, rather than electrons, are used as the energy carrier. This approach opens up the possibility that carbon dioxide fixation can use hydrogen from other sustainable sources, such as wind, hydrothermal, or nuclear energy. Second, now that scientists know that one species of bacteria can use renewable hydrogen, they can expand their search to find other organisms and use them in the production of other valuable chemical products.

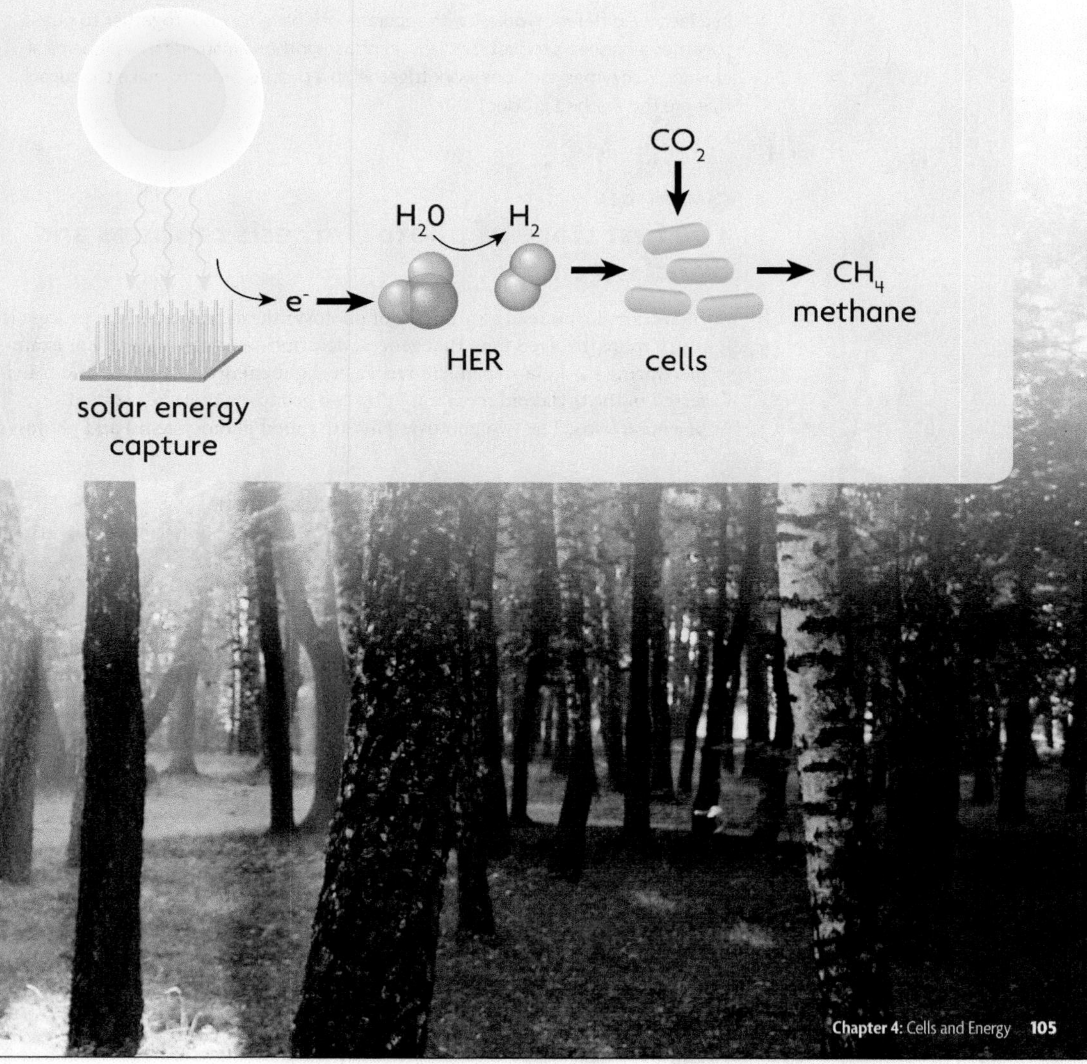

Discuss the following questions.

1. How is the nanowire array similar to a chloroplast? How is it different? The array is similar because the harnessing of solar energy takes place within a membrane. It is different because chlorophyll is used.
2. Can you think of a device that converts solar energy to electrical energy? Answers should include any photovoltaic cell, such as the cell in a solar calculator.
3. If solar energy from artificial photosynthesis is to be a major energy source, it must be stored so it is available at all times. In plant photosynthesis, the solar energy is stored in the chemical bonds of glucose. How could solar energy from artificial photosynthesis be stored? Sample answer: The energy could be stored in the form of chemical bonds of a high-energy density fuel such as liquid hydrogen.

SECTION 4.3

B.2.1 Use a model to illustrate how photosynthesis transforms light energy into stored chemical energy.

▼ Plan and Prepare

Activate Prior Knowledge Remind students of atomic structure. **Ask,** Of all the particles that make up an atom, which has the ability to move in or out of an atom? only the electron, assuming no radioactive decay Discuss that energy is associated with the transfer of electrons in the making or breaking of bonds. In photosynthesis, electrons take on a special role in getting energy into a living system.

▼ Teach

Vocabulary

Academic Vocabulary Two words used in this section are **transport** and **transfer.** They are similar but not synonymous. *Transport* refers to an object being moved or carried, such as electrons in *electron transport* or ions and molecules in *active* or *passive transport*. The word *transfer* refers to a change in location, as in energy being transferred from sunlight to electrons to ATP or NADPH. It may help students to think of a bus transfer, as opposed to a bus as a means of transport.

4.3 Photosynthesis in Detail

KEY CONCEPT **Photosynthesis requires a series of chemical reactions.**

VOCABULARY

photosystem
electron transport chain
ATP synthase
Calvin cycle

MAIN IDEAS

- The first stage of photosynthesis captures and transfers energy.
- The second stage of photosynthesis uses energy from the first stage to make sugars.

Connect to Your World

In a way, the sugar-producing cells in leaves are like tiny factories with assembly lines. In a factory, different workers with separate jobs have to work together to put together a finished product. Similarly, in photosynthesis many different chemical reactions, enzymes, and ions work together in a precise order to make the sugars that are the finished product.

MAIN IDEA

The first stage of photosynthesis captures and transfers energy.

In Section 2, you read a summary of photosynthesis. However, the process is much more involved than that general description might suggest. For example, during the light-dependent reactions, light energy is captured and transferred in the thylakoid membranes by two groups of molecules called **photosystems.** The two photosystems are called photosystem I and photosystem II.

Overview of the Light-Dependent Reactions

The light-dependent reactions are the *photo-* part of photosynthesis. During the light-dependent reactions, chlorophyll and other light-absorbing molecules capture energy from sunlight. Water molecules are broken down into hydrogen ions, electrons, and oxygen gas. The oxygen is given off as a waste product. Sugars are not made during this part of photosynthesis.

The main functions of the light-dependent reactions are to capture and transfer energy. In these reactions, as in the solar car in **FIGURE 3.1,** energy is transferred to electrons. The electrons are only used for energy in a few specific processes. Recall a time when you went to an amusement park. To go on rides, you needed special tickets that could be used only there. Similarly, the electrons are used for energy during photosynthesis but not for the cell's general energy needs.

Energy from the electrons is used to make molecules that act as energy carriers. These energy carriers are ATP and another molecule called NADPH. The ATP from the light-dependent reactions is usually not used for a cell's general energy needs. In this case, ATP molecules, along with NADPH molecules, go on to later stages of photosynthesis.

FIGURE 3.1 The light-dependent reactions capture energy from sunlight and transfer energy through electrons. The solar cells that power a solar car do the same thing.

Differentiated Instruction

ENGLISH LEARNERS

Before beginning this section, have a brainstorming session in which you work with students to produce a graphic organizer, such as a cluster diagram. This will enable you to review what they have learned about photosynthesis so far. A cluster diagram is a fairly unstructured way of generating ideas, as well as getting a lot of student feedback in a short amount of time. This information could later be reformatted into a concept map.

Teacher Toolkit, Section C, Cluster Diagram

BELOW LEVEL

Have students preview the material in this section by creating an outline. Be sure they start with the key concept and then add the headings and numbered items. Point out that the headings "Summary of the Light-Dependent Reactions" and "Summary of the Light-Independent Reactions" contain the steps outlined in each part.

Teacher Toolkit, Section C, Section Review

Photosystem II and Electron Transport

In photosystem II, chlorophyll and other light-absorbing molecules in the thylakoid membrane absorb energy from sunlight. The energy is transferred to electrons. As shown in **FIGURE 3.2**, photosystem II needs water to function.

1. **Energy absorbed from sunlight** Chlorophyll and other light-absorbing molecules in the thylakoid membrane absorb energy from sunlight. The energy is transferred to electrons (e^-). High-energy electrons leave the chlorophyll and enter an **electron transport chain,** which is a series of proteins in the membrane of the thylakoid.
2. **Water molecules split** Enzymes break down water molecules. Oxygen, hydrogen ions (H^+), and electrons are separated from each other. The oxygen is released as waste. The electrons from water replace those electrons that left chlorophyll when energy from sunlight was absorbed.
3. **Hydrogen ions transported** Electrons move from protein to protein in the electron transport chain. Their energy is used to pump H^+ ions from outside to inside the thylakoid against a concentration gradient. The H^+ ions build up inside the thylakoid. Electrons move on to photosystem I.

Photosystem I and Energy-Carrying Molecules

In photosystem I, chlorophyll and other light-absorbing molecules in the thylakoid membrane also absorb energy from sunlight. The energy is added to electrons, some of which enter photosystem I from photosystem II.

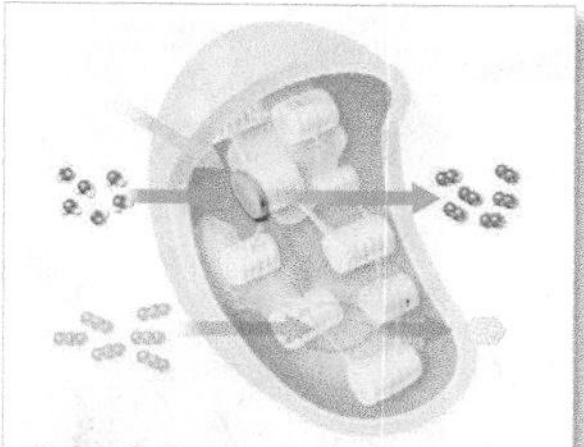

Light-dependent reactions take place in and across the thylakoid membrane.

FIGURE 3.2 Light-Dependent Reactions

Photosystems II and I absorb energy from sunlight and transfer energy to the Calvin cycle.

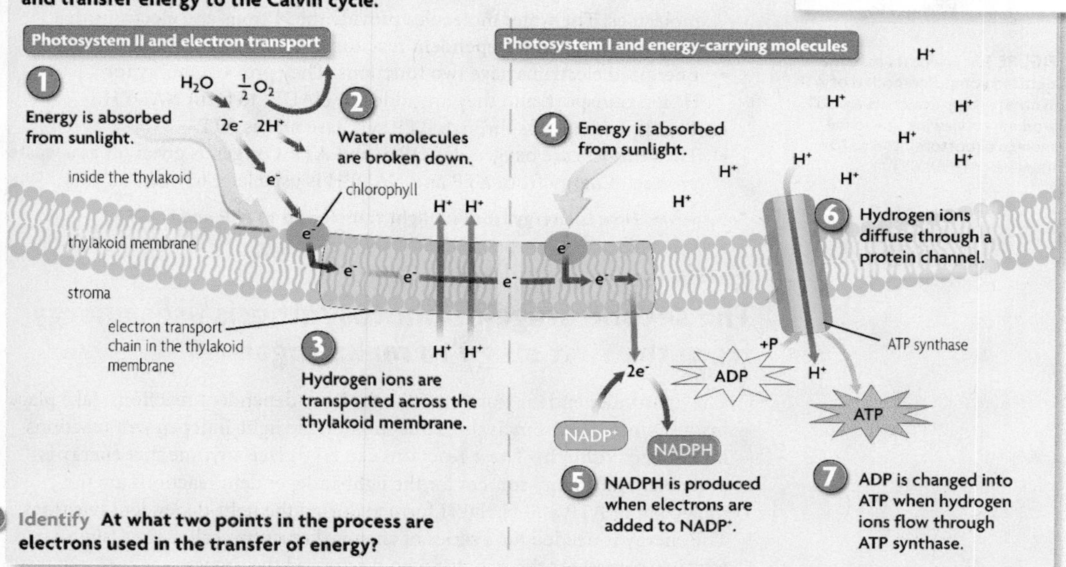

A Identify At what two points in the process are electrons used in the transfer of energy?

TEACH FROM VISUALS

FIGURE 3.2 Use the figure to walk students through the steps of the light-dependent reactions. Point out that the numbered steps in the text on these pages correspond to the numbered steps in the figure. **Ask**

- Where do the light-dependent reactions occur? thylakoid membrane of chloroplast
- What is the source of the electrons in the electron transport chain? chlorophyll
- How are electrons that are released from the water molecules used? to replace energized electrons that leave the chlorophyll molecules
- What role do these electrons play? provide energy to move hydrogen ions into the thylakoid and to produce molecules of NADPH
- What two energy carriers are produced? NADPH, ATP
- In what step is active transport occurring? step 3 passive transport? step 6

Students may wonder why the photosystems seem to be out of order in the process. Explain that photosystem I was discovered before photosystem II. Both photosystems occur simultaneously, although they are described as happening in a sequence.

Integrating Chemistry

Students may wonder what $\frac{1}{2}O_2$ in **FIGURE 3.2** signifies. Explain that the coefficients in the process, including the chemical equation of photosynthesis, reflect the number of **moles** of the molecules involved (6.02×10^{23}), not the number of molecules.

ENGLISH LEARNERS

Students must deal with many abbreviated chemical names and acronyms such as ATP, ADP, $NADP^+$, and NADPH. Compare these acronyms to more common linguistic shortcuts, such as CDs and DVDs. Point out that parts of the names of these compounds signal important distinctions (for example, *tri-* versus *di-*).

INCLUSION

Help students with short attention spans to organize the material in this section by using index cards. On each card, they should write a step of a reaction in as simple a statement as possible. (Examples: Light is absorbed by chlorophyll molecules in a plant cell. Water molecules break down.) Students should put the cards in order and number them.

Teacher Toolkit, Section C, Summarizing

Answers

A Identify In photosystem II, electrons provide energy to transport hydrogen ions across the thylakoid membrane. In photosystem I, electrons are used to produce NADPH.

▼ Teach *continued*

History of Science

Jan Baptista van Helmont was the first to try to scientifically address the question of where plants got their food. His experiment, which was conducted in the 1600s, tested the idea that all of a plant's nutrients came from soil. He planted a willow-tree seedling in a pot of soil, after weighing both the tree and the soil. After five years, the tree had gained 74 kilograms (164 pounds), but the soil had lost only 57 grams (2 ounces). He wrongly concluded that the nutrients were coming from the water he provided.

In the late 1700s, **Joseph Priestley** was able to demonstrate that a plant produces oxygen, or "restores air." Several years later, **Jan Ingenhousz** showed that air was "restored" only when the green parts of the plant were exposed to sunlight. At this point, the assumption was that plants were able to absorb carbon dioxide from the air and then split it to produce carbon, which was then joined to water to form carbohydrates.

It was not until the late 1930s that a complete understanding of photosynthesis was achieved. **C. B. van Niel** realized that it was not carbon dioxide being split, but water. In the presence of sunlight, hydrogen split from water was added to carbon dioxide to produce sugar, with oxygen as a byproduct.

Answers

A Summarize Electrons absorb energy from sunlight. Some of the energy is used to pump hydrogen ions against a concentration gradient. The hydrogen ions then flow back through a protein channel to enable ATP synthase to add a phosphate group to ADP to produce ATP. Energized electrons also provide energy to add hydrogen ions to $NADP^+$ to produce NADPH.

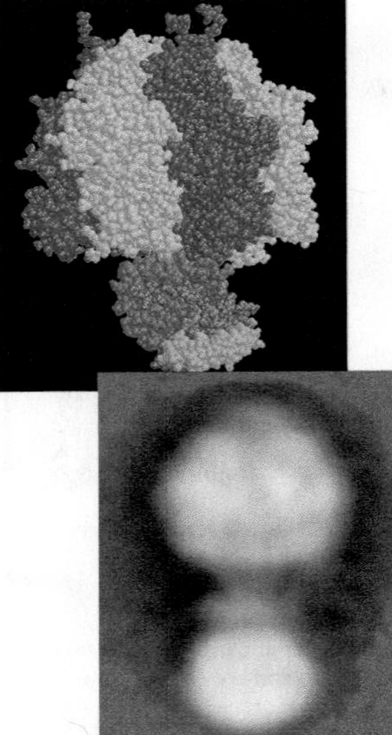

FIGURE 3.3 Scientists have made detailed computer models of ATP synthase (top). Scientists are still working on viewing the actual molecule (bottom). (colored TEM; magnification 1,800,000×)

4. **Energy absorbed from sunlight** As in photosystem II, chlorophyll and other light-absorbing molecules inside the thylakoid membrane absorb energy from sunlight. Electrons are energized and leave the molecules.

5. **NADPH produced** The energized electrons are added to a molecule called $NADP^+$, forming a molecule called NADPH. In photosynthesis, $NADP^+$ functions like ADP, and NADPH functions like ATP. The molecules of NADPH go to the light-independent reactions.

ATP Production

The final part of the light-dependent reactions makes ATP. The production of ATP depends on the H^+ ions that build up inside the thylakoid from photosystem II, and on a complex enzyme in the thylakoid membrane.

6. **Hydrogen ion diffusion** Hydrogen ions flow through a protein channel in the thylakoid membrane. Recall that the concentration of H^+ ions is higher inside the thylakoid than it is outside. This difference in H^+ ion concentration is called a chemiosmotic gradient, which stores potential energy. Therefore, the ions flow through the channel by diffusion.

7. **ATP produced** The protein channel in Step 6 is part of a complex enzyme called **ATP synthase,** shown in **FIGURE 3.3.** As the ions flow through the channel, ATP synthase makes ATP by adding phosphate groups to ADP.

Summary of the Light-Dependent Reactions

- Energy is captured from sunlight by light-absorbing molecules. The energy is transferred to electrons that enter an electron transport chain.
- Water molecules are broken down into H^+ ions, electrons, and oxygen molecules. The water molecules provide the H^+ ions and electrons that are used in the light-dependent reactions.
- Energized electrons have two functions. They provide energy for H^+ ion transport, and they are added to $NADP^+$ to form NADPH.
- The flow of H^+ ions through ATP synthase makes ATP.
- The products are oxygen, NADPH, and ATP. Oxygen is given off as a waste product. Energy from ATP and NADPH is used later to make sugars.

A Summarize **How is energy from sunlight transferred to ATP and NADPH?**

MAIN IDEA

The second stage of photosynthesis uses energy from the first stage to make sugars.

The light-independent reactions, like the light-dependent reactions, take place inside chloroplasts. But as the name implies, the light-independent reactions do not need sunlight. These reactions can take place anytime that energy is available. The energy sources for the light-independent reactions are the molecules of ATP and NADPH formed during the light-dependent reactions. The energy is needed for a series of chemical reactions called the Calvin cycle, which is named for the scientist who discovered the process.

Differentiated Instruction

HANDS-ON ACTIVITY

Have students submerge a freshly picked leaf in water. They should observe the leaf after about 30 minutes. Students should see bubbles of oxygen forming on the underside of the leaf, demonstrating that the light-dependent reactions continued after the leaf was picked. **Ask,** Where did the oxygen come from? water molecules

The Calvin Cycle

The Calvin cycle cannot take place without the ATP and NADPH from the light-dependent reactions. The chemical reactions of the **Calvin cycle** use carbon dioxide (CO_2) gas from the atmosphere and the energy carried by ATP and NADPH to make simple sugars. Because the light-independent reactions build sugar molecules, they are the *synthesis* part of photosynthesis. Only one molecule of CO_2 is actually added to the Calvin cycle at a time. The simplified cycle in **FIGURE 3.4** shows three CO_2 molecules added at once.

1. **Carbon dioxide added** CO_2 molecules are added to five-carbon molecules already in the Calvin cycle. Six-carbon molecules are formed.
2. **Three-carbon molecules formed** Energy—ATP and NADPH—from the light-dependent reactions is used by enzymes to split the six-carbon molecules. Three-carbon molecules are formed and rearranged.
3. **Three-carbon molecules exit** Most of the three-carbon molecules stay in the Calvin cycle, but one high-energy three-carbon molecule leaves the cycle. After two three-carbon molecules have left the cycle, they are bonded together to build a six-carbon sugar molecule such as glucose.
4. **Three-carbon molecules recycled** Energy from ATP molecules is used to change the three-carbon molecules back into five-carbon molecules. The five-carbon molecules stay in the Calvin cycle. These molecules are added to new CO_2 molecules that enter the cycle.

READING TOOLBOX

VOCABULARY

The light-dependent reactions are the *photo-* part of photosynthesis. The light-independent reactions are the *synthesis* part of photosynthesis.

FIGURE 3.4 Light-Independent Reactions (Calvin Cycle)

The Calvin cycle produces sugars.

1 Carbon dioxide (CO_2) molecules enter the cycle and are added to five-carbon molecules. Six-carbon molecules are formed.
3 C from CO_2
3 CCCCCC
6 ATP
6 ADP
6 NADPH
6 NADP+
2 Energy is added. The six-carbon molecules split to form three-carbon molecules. More energy is added, and the molecules are rearranged into higher-energy molecules.
6 CCC
CCC
CCC
CCCCCC
3 A high-energy three-carbon molecule exits for every 3 CO_2 molecules that enter. After 2 three-carbon molecules have exited, they bond to form 1 six-carbon sugar.
5 CCC
3 CCCCC
3 ATP
3 ADP
4 Three-carbon molecules are changed back to five-carbon molecules by energy from ATP.
Light-independent reactions take place in the stroma.

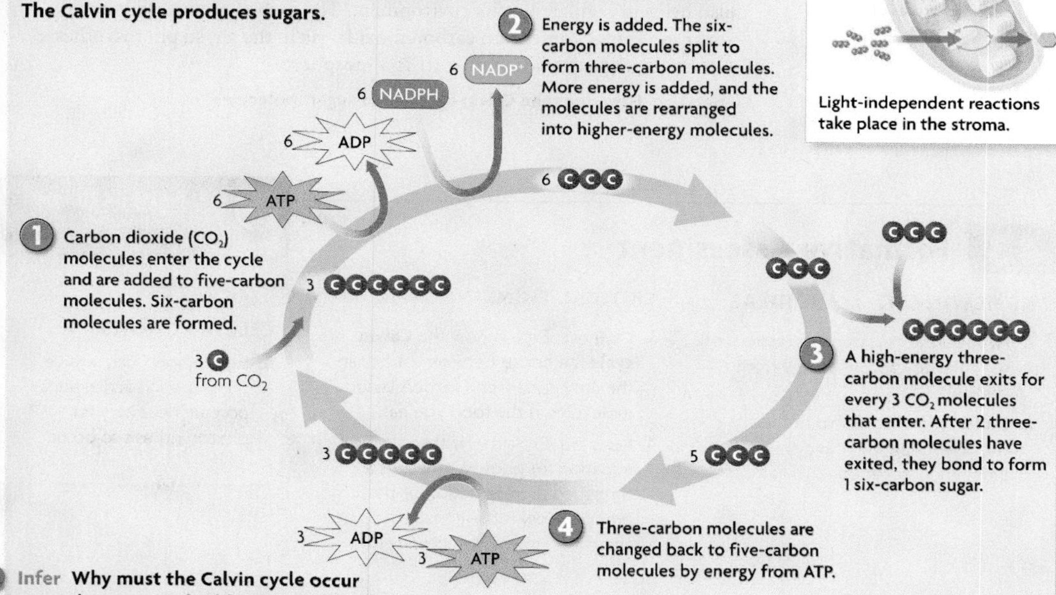

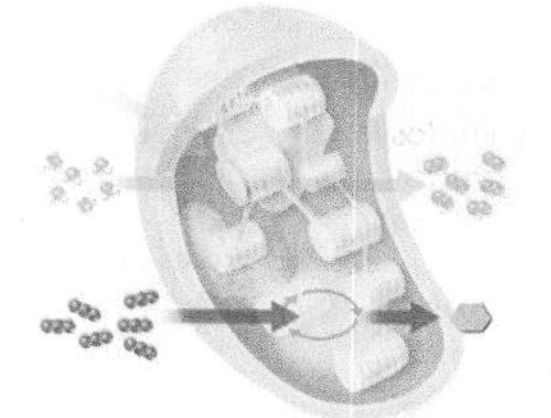

Infer **Why must the Calvin cycle occur more than once to build a sugar molecule?**

BELOW LEVEL

Students who have mastered the details of photosynthesis can act as teachers for those who are struggling. Set up student pairs: the teacher reads through the text, encouraging the struggling student to ask questions. Set the goal for each pair to make an enlarged drawing of a plant cell, showing light-dependent reactions in thylakoid and light-independent reactions in stroma.

Teacher Toolkit, Section C, Reciprocal Teaching

TEACH FROM VISUALS

FIGURE 3.4 Use the figure to teach an overview of the Calvin cycle. Point out that the numbered steps in the text correspond to the numbered steps in the figure. **Ask**

- Where in the chloroplast do light-independent reactions occur? stroma of chloroplast
- Where are the ATP and NADPH coming from? light-dependent reactions
- Why are these reactions called a cycle? The five-carbon molecule of the process is regenerated, so the cycle continues.

Point out that the molecule produced in the Calvin cycle is actually a three-carbon sugar, not a six-carbon glucose. Two molecules of the three-carbon sugar combine to form one molecule of a six-carbon glucose, but this reaction is not part of the Calvin cycle.

Science Trivia

- Rubisco, which is an enzyme that sets up the Calvin cycle, is thought to be the most abundant protein on Earth. It has been estimated that there are 22 pounds of Rubisco for every human on Earth.
- Rubisco is very slow and inefficient. It catalyzes between 2 and 8 molecules of CO_2 per second compared to thousands per second for most enzymes.

Vocabulary

Academic Vocabulary The process that occurs in the Calvin cycle is often referred to as carbon **fixation.** The carbon is *fixed* or "fastened" into an organic compound, which for organisms is its usable form. This expression is also used for nitrogen: nitrogen fixation.

Answers

A **Infer** As described in the text, only one carbon dioxide molecule, and so just one carbon, is added to the Calvin cycle with each turn.

▼ Teach *continued*

History of Science

The details of the Calvin cycle were worked out by **Melvin Calvin** and his colleague **A. A. Benson.** They used radioactive carbon (C-14) and paper chromatography, new scientific tools in the late 1940s, to trace the incorporation of the carbon atom in CO_2 into sugar. The cycle is often called the Calvin-Benson cycle, although only Calvin won a Nobel Prize for the work in 1961.

Answers

A Summarize Carbon dioxide is added to five-carbon molecules in the cycle. Energy from ATP and NADPH is used in a series of chemical reactions that build the three-carbon molecules needed to form a six-carbon sugar.

▼ Assess and Reteach

Assess Use the Section Self-Check or Section Quiz, both available at **HMHScience.com**.

Reteach Work with students to put together a concept map of the photosynthetic process. Start the concept map with the word *sunlight*. Tell students that the concept map must end with *glucose*.

Lungs of the Planet

CONNECT TO

ECOLOGY

Photosynthesis is a major part of the carbon cycle. You will learn more about the carbon cycle in the chapter **Principles of Ecology.**

Summary of the Light-Independent Reactions

- Carbon dioxide enters the Calvin cycle.
- ATP and NADPH from the light-dependent reactions transfer energy to the Calvin cycle and keep the cycle going.
- One high-energy three-carbon molecule is made for every three molecules of carbon dioxide that enter the cycle.
- Two high-energy three-carbon molecules are bonded together to make a sugar. Therefore, six molecules of carbon dioxide must be added to the Calvin cycle to make one six-carbon sugar.
- The products are a six-carbon sugar such as glucose, $NADP^+$, and ADP. The $NADP^+$ and ADP molecules return to the light-dependent reactions.

Functions of Photosynthesis

Photosynthesis is much more than just a biochemical process. Photosynthesis is important to most organisms on Earth, as well as to Earth's environment. Recall that plants produce food for themselves and for other organisms through photosynthesis. Both plant cells and animal cells release the energy stored in sugars through cellular respiration. Cellular respiration, which uses the oxygen that is a waste product of photosynthesis, is the process that makes most of the ATP used by plant and animal cells.

Photosynthesis does more than make sugars. It also provides materials for plant growth and development. The simple sugars from photosynthesis are bonded together to form complex carbohydrates such as starch and cellulose. Starches store sugars until they are needed for energy. Cellulose is a major part of plant structure—it is the building block of plant cell walls. Photosynthesis also helps to regulate Earth's environment. The carbon atoms used to make sugar molecules come from carbon dioxide gas in the air, so photosynthesis removes carbon dioxide from Earth's atmosphere.

 Summarize **How does the Calvin cycle build sugar molecules?**

4.3 Formative Assessment

SELF-CHECK Online
HMHScience.com
GO ONLINE

REVIEWING MAIN IDEAS

1. How do the two **photosystems** work together to capture energy from sunlight?
2. Explain the relationship between the light-dependent and the light-independent reactions.

CRITICAL THINKING

3. **Connect** Explain how the **Calvin cycle** is a bridge between carbon in the atmosphere and carbon-based molecules in the food you eat.
4. **Evaluate** Explain why the chemical equation for photosynthesis is a simplified representation of the process. How is the equation accurate? How is it inaccurate?

CONNECT TO

CELL FUNCTIONS

5. Explain how both passive transport and active transport are necessary for photosynthesis to occur.

4.3 FORMATIVE ASSESSMENT

1. Photosystem II absorbs energy and energizes electrons. The electrons are passed along to photosystem I, which absorbs more energy and adds it to the electrons.
2. The light-dependent reactions absorb energy from sunlight and transfer the energy to the light-independent reactions that produce sugars.
3. Carbon dioxide is removed from the atmosphere by plants for photosynthesis. The carbon is incorporated into sugars and other carbon-based molecules that are eaten by other organisms.
4. The equation shows the general reactants and products of the process. However, it does not show intermediate steps. For example, carbon dioxide and water do not actually react with each other.
5. Active transport moves hydrogen ions against the concentration gradient in photosystem II. Passive transport occurs when hydrogen ions flow through the channel bound to ATP synthase.

4.4 Overview of Cellular Respiration

KEY CONCEPT **The overall process of cellular respiration converts sugar into ATP using oxygen.**

MAIN IDEAS
- Cellular respiration makes ATP by breaking down sugars.
- Cellular respiration is like a mirror image of photosynthesis.

VOCABULARY
ellular respiration
erobic
lycolysis
naerobic
Krebs cycle

Connect to Your World

The term *cellular respiration* may lead you to form a mental picture of cells breathing. This image is not correct, but it is useful to remember. Your cells need the oxygen that you take in when you breathe. That oxygen helps your body release the energy in sugars and other carbon-based molecules. Indirectly, your breathing is connected to the ATP that your cells need for everything you do.

MAIN IDEA

Cellular respiration makes ATP by breaking down sugars.

Plants use photosynthesis to make their own food. Animals eat other organisms as food. But food is not a direct source of energy. Instead, plants, animals, and other eukaryotes break down molecules from food to produce ATP. **Cellular respiration** releases chemical energy from sugars and other carbon-based molecules to make ATP when oxygen is present. Cellular respiration is an **aerobic** (air-OH-bihk) process, meaning that it needs oxygen to take place. Cellular respiration takes place in mitochondria, which are often called the cell's "powerhouses" because they make most of a cell's ATP.

A mitochondrion, shown in **FIGURE 4.1**, cannot directly make ATP from food. First, foods are broken down into smaller molecules such as glucose. Then, glucose is broken down, as shown below. **Glycolysis** (gly-KAHL-uh-sihs) splits glucose into two three-carbon molecules and makes two molecules of ATP. Glycolysis takes place in a cell's cytoplasm and does not need oxygen. Glycolysis is an **anaerobic** process because it does not need oxygen to take place. However, glycolysis is necessary for cellular respiration. The products of glycolysis are broken down in mitochondria to make many more ATP.

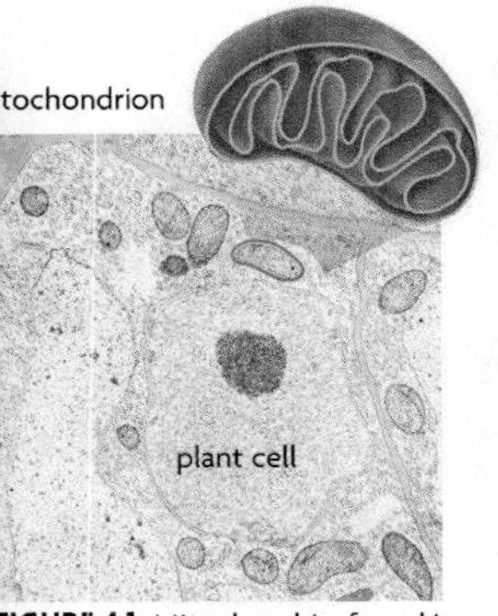

FIGURE 4.1 Mitochondria, found in both plant and animal cells, produce ATP through cellular respiration. (colored TEM; magnification 7000×)

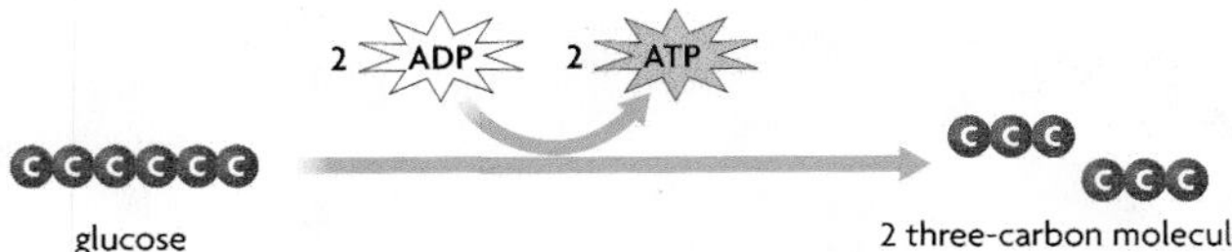

A Explain **What is the function of cellular respiration?**

Differentiated Instruction

ENGLISH LEARNERS

Have students preview this section by comparing it to **Section 4.2.** Point out the similarities between the two sections: the process diagrams corresponding to numbered text, the same chemical compounds, for example, H_2O, CO_2, O_2, and ATP. Now read the main idea on the next page: "Cellular respiration is like a mirror image of photosynthesis." Discuss what this sentence means in the context of these two sections.

Teacher Toolkit, Section C, Compare/Contrast Chart

TEACH WITH TECHNOLOGY

If you have materials and probeware available, have students observe cellular respiration. They can measure the rate of cellular respiration in germinating seeds and the effect of temperature on rate.

SECTION 4.4

B.2.2 Use a model to illustrate that cellular respiration is a chemical process whereby the bonds of food molecules and oxygen molecules are broken and the bonds in new compounds are formed resulting in a net transfer of energy.

Plan and Prepare

Activate Prior Knowledge Tell students that by the time a person reaches age 16, he or she will have probably taken more than 200 million breaths. **Ask**

- Why is breathing vital to life? supplies oxygen needed for cellular respiration and release of energy
- How is the air you breathe in different from the air you breathe out? more oxygen, less carbon dioxide

Teach

Vocabulary

Greek and Latin Word Origins Tell students that **glycolysis** comes from the Greek *glukus,* meaning "sweet" and *lysis,* meaning "to loosen" or "split." *Glycolysis* literally means "to split the sweet."

Answers

A Explain Cellular respiration breaks down sugars to produce ATP for cell activities.

▼ Teach *continued*

TEACH FROM VISUALS

FIGURE 4.2 Remind students to refer to the numbered list on the next page when studying the figure. **Ask**

- What process leads to cellular respiration, and where does it take place? glycolysis, which occurs in cytoplasm
- Where does cellular respiration take place? mitochondria
- What two reactants are shown entering the mitochondrion? three-carbon molecules and oxygen
- Where do the three-carbon molecules go when they enter the mitochondrion? into the matrix
- What two products are shown leaving the mitochondrion? carbon dioxide, water

Address Misconceptions

Common Misconception Students often think that cellular respiration takes place only in animal cells.

Correcting the Misconception Cellular respiration takes place in almost all organisms. Note that the cells of all eukaryotes have mitochondria. Cellular respiration takes place in many prokaryotic organisms as well, although they do not have mitochondria. The enzymes and transport proteins are found free in the cytoplasm and attached to the cell membrane.

Answers

A Identify The reactants are three-carbon molecules and oxygen. The products are water and carbon dioxide.

MAIN IDEA

Cellular respiration is like a mirror image of photosynthesis.

CONNECT TO

PHOTOSYNTHESIS

Review the overall process of photosynthesis in **Section 2**, and compare photosynthesis to cellular respiration.

Photosynthesis and cellular respiration are not true opposites, but you can think about them in that way. For example, chloroplasts absorb energy from sunlight and build sugars. Mitochondria release chemical energy to make ATP. The chemical equation of cellular respiration is also basically the reverse of photosynthesis. But the structures of chloroplasts and mitochondria are similar. A mitochondrion is surrounded by a membrane. It has two parts that are involved in cellular respiration: the matrix and the inner mitochondrial membrane. In mitochondria, cellular respiration takes place in two main stages, as shown in **FIGURE 4.2.**

FIGURE 4.2 Cellular Respiration Overview

When oxygen is available, ATP is produced by cellular respiration in mitochondria.

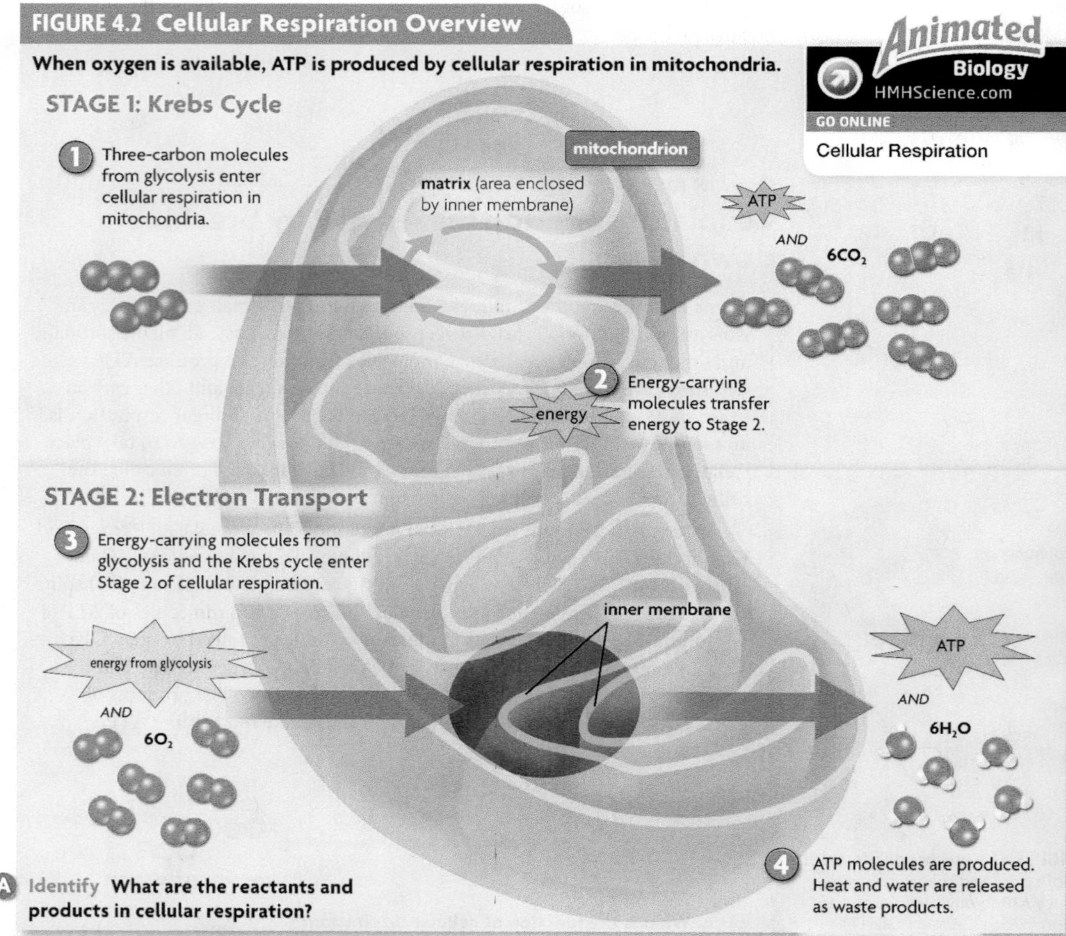

STAGE 1: Krebs Cycle
1 Three-carbon molecules from glycolysis enter cellular respiration in mitochondria.
mitochondrion
matrix (area enclosed by inner membrane)
ATP
AND
$6CO_2$
2 Energy-carrying molecules transfer energy to Stage 2.
energy
STAGE 2: Electron Transport
3 Energy-carrying molecules from glycolysis and the Krebs cycle enter Stage 2 of cellular respiration.
inner membrane
energy from glycolysis
AND
$6O_2$
ATP
AND
$6H_2O$
4 ATP molecules are produced. Heat and water are released as waste products.

Animated Biology HMHScience.com GO ONLINE Cellular Respiration

A Identify What are the reactants and products in cellular respiration?

Differentiated Instruction

PRE-AP

Have students compare the diagrams shown in **FIGURE 2.2** with **FIGURE 4.2**. Ask them to write a few paragraphs explaining how the membranous structures in chloroplasts (thylakoids) and mitochondria (inner membrane) contribute to the processes that take place in each. Students should mention both separation and increased surface area.

Teacher Toolkit, Section C, Quick Write

INCLUSION

To help students with visual impairments, have students work in pairs to compare the diagrams shown in **FIGURE 2.2** and **FIGURE 4.2.** Have one student act as a "tour guide" and describe what is happening. The second student may ask questions until he or she has a full picture.

Teacher Toolkit, Section C, Think-Pair-Share

The **Krebs cycle** produces molecules that carry energy to the second part of cellular respiration. The Krebs cycle, named for the scientist who discovered the process, takes place in the interior space, or matrix, of the mitochondrion.

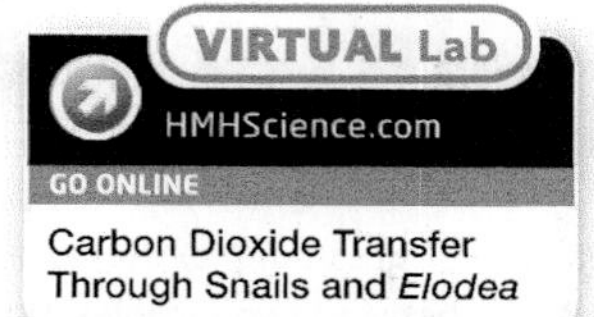

VIRTUAL Lab
HMHScience.com
GO ONLINE
Carbon Dioxide Transfer Through Snails and *Elodea*

1. Three-carbon molecules from glycolysis are broken down in a cycle of chemical reactions. A small number of ATP molecules are made. Other types of energy-carrying molecules are also made. Carbon dioxide is given off as a waste product.
2. Energy is transferred to the second stage of cellular respiration.

An electron transport chain made of proteins needs energy-carrying molecules from the Krebs cycle and oxygen to make ATP. This part of the process takes place in and across the inner mitochondrial membrane.

3. Energy is transferred to a chain of proteins in the inner membrane of the mitochondrion.
4. A large number of ATP molecules are made. Oxygen enters the process and is used to make water molecules. Water and heat are given off as waste products.

Up to 38 ATP molecules are made from the breakdown of 1 glucose molecule—2 from glycolysis and 34 or 36 from cellular respiration. The equation for cellular respiration is shown below, but it actually has many more steps. For example, the cellular respiration equation includes glycolysis. And many enzymes are also part of the process.

$$C_6H_{12}O_6 + 6O_2 \rightarrow \rightarrow \rightarrow \rightarrow 6CO_2 + 6H_2O$$

a sugar — oxygen — carbon dioxide — water

Use **FIGURE 4.3** to compare cellular respiration with photosynthesis. As you can see, photosynthesis uses the products of cellular respiration. It converts energy from sunlight into sugars. Cellular respiration needs the products of photosynthesis. It releases stored energy from sugars to make ATP that can be used by cells.

FIGURE 4.3 COMPARING PROCESSES

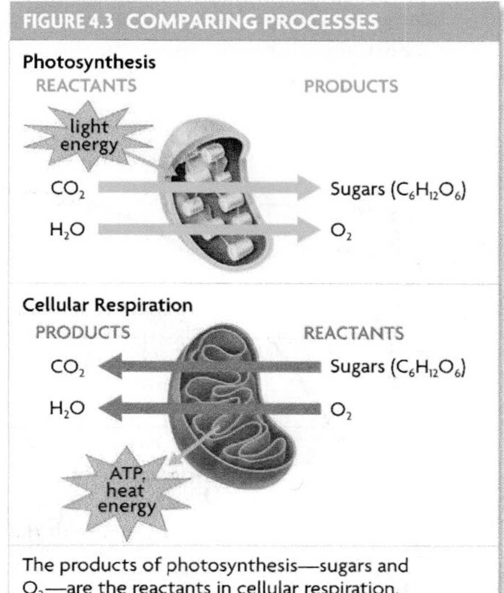

The products of photosynthesis—sugars and O_2—are the reactants in cellular respiration.

Apply **Does glucose actually react with oxygen during cellular respiration? Explain.**

4.4 Formative Assessment

REVIEWING MAIN IDEAS

1. How are **cellular respiration** and **glycolysis** related?
2. Summarize the **aerobic** stages of cellular respiration. Be sure to discuss the **Krebs cycle** and the electron transport chain in your answer.

CRITICAL THINKING

3. **Analyze** Describe the relationship between cellular respiration and photosynthesis. Discuss the functions of chloroplasts and mitochondria.
4. **Apply** Is glucose a reactant in the aerobic stages of cellular respiration? Explain.

SELF-CHECK Online
HMHScience.com
GO ONLINE

CONNECT TO

CHEMICAL REACTIONS

5. Is the process of cellular respiration exothermic or endothermic? Explain your answer.

ONLINE Biology
HMHScience.com

Students can do a virtual lab involving snails and *Elodea* to see how carbon dioxide cycles through a living system.

Take It Further

Glycolysis was probably among the first biochemical processes to evolve. It is likely that early forms of life produced ATP from glycolysis, because the process takes place in the cytoplasm and does not require oxygen. According to the **endosymbiosis theory,** mitochondria were once prokaryotes that were engulfed by other prokaryotes. This process may have led to the evolution of cellular respiration.

Answers

A Apply No, glucose is split by glycolysis prior to the aerobic parts of cellular respiration, when oxygen enters the process.

Assess and Reteach

Assess Use the Section Self-Check or Section Quiz, both available at **HMHScience.com.**

Reteach Draw an oval on the board to represent a mitochondrion. Tell students to take a quick look at **FIGURE 4.2,** and then close their books. Have students provide the details of cellular respiration to complete the representation.

4.4 FORMATIVE ASSESSMENT

1. Glycolysis breaks down glucose in the cytoplasm before cellular respiration occurs in the mitochondria. The aerobic processes in mitochondria use the products of glycolysis.
2. Answers should indicate that the products of glycolysis are broken down by the Krebs cycle to make energy-carrying molecules and carbon dioxide. Energy from the Krebs cycle is used by the electron transport chain to make ATP.
3. The reactants and products of the overall processes are essentially a mirror image of each other. The chloroplasts and mitochondria also have approximately opposite functions. Chloroplasts absorb energy and build carbon-based molecules, and mitochondria break down carbon-based molecules to release energy.
4. No, glucose is broken down during glycolysis, which is an anaerobic process.
5. Exothermic; energy is released as heat and ATP.

DATA ANALYSIS

Introduce

Have students compare the two graphs on the page and discuss the type of general information one can observe from the graphs before looking at them in any detail. **Ask**

- What do the differences in the appearance of the graphs suggest about the nature of the phenomena that are being measured? Graph 1 suggests a phenomenon that builds over time and then levels off. The phenomenon in Graph 2 appears to be cyclical.
- Looking at Graph 1, why might sugar production peak between 3000 and 4000 mm of precipitation? Answers will vary, but students should suggest that there is a physical limit to a plant's production, as well as to its absorption or use of water. This can be compared to the amount of weight a human can gain by eating. At some point it becomes physically impossible for someone to keep eating.

Discuss

Tell students that Biosphere 2 was designed to model the interactions and functions of Earth's different ecosystems, such as forests and oceans, and the ways they affect the atmosphere. Sunlight was allowed into Biosphere 2, much like it is allowed through the glass of a greenhouse. Have students look at Graph 2. **Ask,** What effect does sunlight have on the fluctuating amount of carbon dioxide? Photosynthesis requires sunlight, so when sunlight is absent or less abundant, less carbon dioxide will be taken up by plants for photosynthesis. Discuss how the graph might appear for the days that follow.

Online Student Resources, Data Analysis Practice

DATA ANALYSIS

Interpreting Graphs

GO ONLINE

Create animated charts and graphs using Smart Grapher.

After scientists record their data in tables, they usually make graphs to display the results. Graphs show the relationship between two variables. The pattern of curve or line that is drawn helps scientists form conclusions about their data.

Model

Scientists study the net amount of sugar production per square meter per year in forest plants. Look at the graph below. Notice that the net amount of sugar produced increases rapidly at first, then levels off after about 2500 mm of precipitation. Scientists can conclude that forests need about 2500 mm of rain annually for maximum net sugar production.

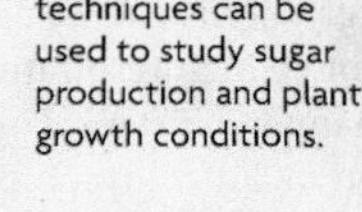

Infrared imaging techniques can be used to study sugar production and plant growth conditions.

GRAPH 1. NET SUGAR PRODUCTION

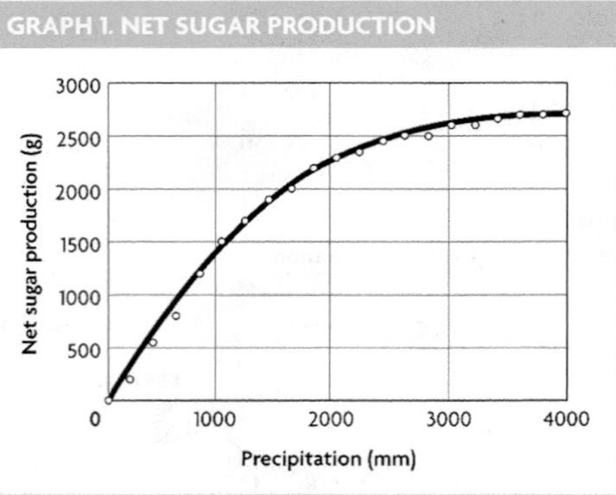

Source: H. Leith, *Human Ecology*

Practice **Interpret a Graph**

Look at the graph to the right. It shows the amount of carbon dioxide in the air during different times of the day in Biosphere 2, an enclosed research and education center in Arizona.

1. **Interpret** What is the relationship between the time of day and the amount of carbon dioxide in the research facility?
2. **Infer** Using your knowledge of the process of photosynthesis, draw a conclusion about the pattern of the data.

GRAPH 2. CO_2 LEVELS OVER TIME

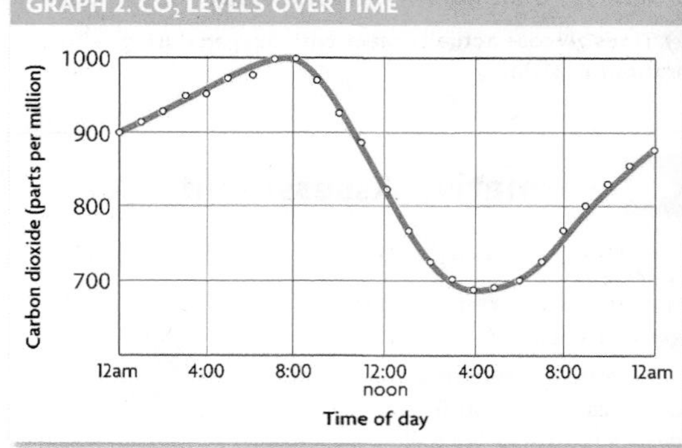

114 Unit 2: Cells

Answers

1. During daylight hours, the concentration of carbon dioxide in the air decreases. During the night, the carbon dioxide concentration increases.
2. During daylight hours, plants remove carbon dioxide from the air for use in photosynthesis. During the night, when there is no sunlight, photosynthesis decreases and less carbon dioxide is removed from the air.

4.5 Cellular Respiration in Detail

KEY CONCEPT **Cellular respiration is an aerobic process with two main stages.**

MAIN IDEAS

- Glycolysis is needed for cellular respiration.
- The Krebs cycle is the first main part of cellular respiration.
- The electron transport chain is the second main part of cellular respiration.

Connect to Your World

If chloroplasts are like tiny factories that make products, mitochondria are like power plants that burn fuel to produce electricity. In a power plant, a processed fuel is burned in the presence of oxygen, and energy is released as useful electricity. During cellular respiration, oxygen and digested molecules from food are used to produce useful energy in the form of ATP.

MAIN IDEA

Glycolysis is needed for cellular respiration.

In Section 4, you read a summary of the way cellular respiration produces ATP molecules. But cellular respiration, like photosynthesis, is a very complex process. For example, glucose and oxygen do not react directly with each other, and many chemical reactions, such as glycolysis, must take place.

Glycolysis is an ongoing process in all cells, including yours. It takes place in the cytoplasm before cellular respiration, and it does not require oxygen. Glycolysis makes a small number of ATP molecules, but its other products are much more important. If oxygen is available, the products of glycolysis are used to produce many more ATP molecules through cellular respiration. The process of glycolysis can be summarized as follows.

1. Two ATP molecules are used to energize a glucose molecule. The glucose molecule is split into two three-carbon molecules. A series of enzymes and chemical reactions rearranges the three-carbon molecules.
2. Energized electrons from the three-carbon molecules are transferred to molecules of NAD^+, forming NADH molecules. A series of reactions converts the three-carbon molecules to pyruvate (py-ROO-vayt), which enters cellular respiration. This process also forms four ATP molecules.

Animated Biology HMHScience.com GO ONLINE Glycolysis

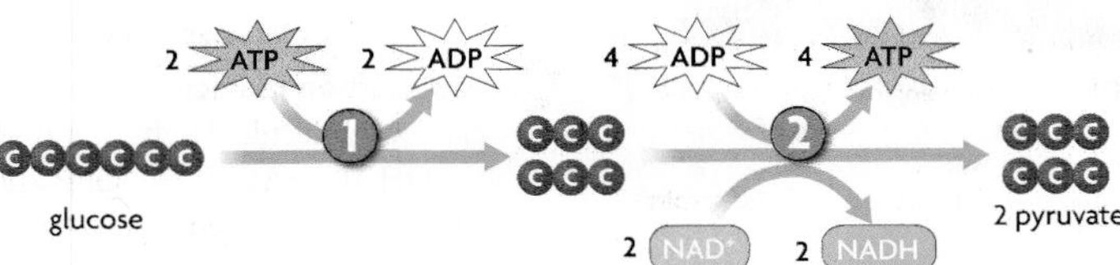

SECTION 4.5

B.2.2 Use a model to illustrate that cellular respiration is a chemical process whereby the bonds of food molecules and oxygen molecules are broken and the bonds in new compounds are formed resulting in a net transfer of energy.

Plan and Prepare

Activate Prior Knowledge Have students compare cellular respiration to combustion. **Ask,** How are combustion and cellular respiration alike? How are they different? Both are chemical reactions that use oxygen to release energy; both produce heat. Cellular respiration releases energy slowly, with many reactions, while combustion releases energy as heat and light all at once.

Teach

TEACH FROM VISUALS

Have students look at the equation at the bottom of the page. **Ask,** How do you know that glycolysis releases energy? Two ATP molecules (net) and two NADH molecules are produced.

Differentiated Instruction

ENGLISH LEARNERS

Before beginning this section, have a brainstorming session in which you work with students to produce a cluster diagram on cellular respiration. Have them compare this diagram to the one they made for photosynthesis in **Section 3.**

Teacher Toolkit, Section C, Cluster Diagram

BELOW LEVEL

As suggested on the first page of **Section 3,** have students preview the section by creating an outline. Have them include the numbered steps as well as the bulleted items detailing the products of glycolysis and cellular respiration.

Teacher Toolkit, Section C, Section Preview

▼ Teach *continued*

Answers

A Summarize Glycolysis makes four ATP molecules but two ATP are used to split the glucose molecule, yielding a net gain of two ATP.

Integrating Chemistry

Point out that pyruvate does not directly enter the Krebs cycle. As students can see in **FIGURE 5.2,** one carbon is split off from the molecule; a two-carbon molecule, called **acetyl-CoA,** enters the Krebs cycle.

Acetyl-CoA is one of the most important molecules in the body. Almost all nutrients—proteins, lipids, and carbohydrates—generate acetyl-CoA when they are broken down. The large amounts of acetyl-CoA produced are channeled into the Krebs cycle if the body is in need of energy, or into the synthesis of fat to be stored for future energy needs.

History of Science

In the 1930s, biochemists wondered about the nature of the pathway that produced the large amounts of ATP needed by the body. They reasoned that the body's supply of the compound that started the pathway would be used up rapidly.

Hans Krebs solved the mystery in 1937 when he determined that the pathway is cyclic. The four-carbon molecule that starts the cycle when it combines with acetyl-CoA is regenerated to keep the cycle going. The pathway, named for Krebs, is also called the citric acid cycle because citric acid is the first substance formed. Krebs won the Nobel Prize for his work in 1953.

CONNECT TO

FERMENTATION

When cells do not have a supply of oxygen for the aerobic processes of cellular respiration, the anaerobic processes of fermentation take place. You will learn about fermentation in **Section 6.**

Although glycolysis makes four ATP molecules, recall that two ATP molecules are used to first split the glucose molecule. So the breakdown of one glucose molecule by glycolysis gives a net gain of two ATP molecules. The pyruvate and NADH produced by glycolysis are used for cellular respiration when oxygen is present. NADH is an electron carrier like NADPH, the electron carrier in photosynthesis.

A Summarize **How does glycolysis result in a net gain of two ATP molecules?**

MAIN IDEA

The Krebs cycle is the first main part of cellular respiration.

Cellular respiration makes many more ATP molecules than does glycolysis. It begins with the breakdown of pyruvate in Steps 1 and 2 below. The process continues with the Krebs cycle, shown in **FIGURE 5.2.** Notice that Steps 1, 4, and 5 below are very similar. In those steps, a carbon-based molecule is split, a molecule of carbon dioxide is formed, and energy-carrying NADH molecules are made. In fact, the main function of the Krebs cycle is to transfer high-energy electrons to molecules that carry them to the electron transport chain. The Krebs cycle is also sometimes called the citric acid cycle because citric acid is the first molecule formed, as you can see in Step 3 below.

FIGURE 5.1 Gasoline engines burn carbon-based molecules in the presence of oxygen, and they release water, carbon dioxide, and energy. The overall process of cellular respiration is similar.

1. **Pyruvate broken down** A pyruvate molecule is split into a two-carbon molecule and a molecule of carbon dioxide, which is given off as a waste product. High-energy electrons are transferred from the two-carbon molecule to NAD^+, forming a molecule of NADH. The NADH moves to the electron transport chain.
2. **Coenzyme A** A molecule called coenzyme A bonds to the two-carbon molecule made from the breakdown of pyruvate. This intermediate molecule goes to the Krebs cycle.
3. **Citric acid formed** The two-carbon part of the intermediate molecule is added to a four-carbon molecule to form a six-carbon molecule called citric acid. Coenzyme A goes back to Step 2.
4. **Citric acid broken down** The citric acid molecule is broken down by an enzyme, and a five-carbon molecule is formed. A molecule of NADH is made and moves out of the Krebs cycle. A molecule of carbon dioxide is given off as a waste product.
5. **Five-carbon molecule broken down** The five-carbon molecule is broken down by an enzyme. A four-carbon molecule, a molecule of NADH, and a molecule of ATP are formed. The NADH leaves the Krebs cycle. Carbon dioxide is given off as a waste product.
6. **Four-carbon molecule rearranged** Enzymes rearrange the four-carbon molecule. High-energy electrons are released. Molecules of NADH and $FADH_2$, which is another electron carrier, are made. They leave the Krebs cycle, and the four-carbon molecule remains.

Differentiated Instruction

INCLUSION

As suggested for **Section 3,** have students who have difficulty processing multiple levels of information organize material by using index cards. Tell them to work with the numbered lists in this section, and write the steps in as simple a statement as possible. For example, on cards labeled *glycolysis,* they could write (1) ATP is used to split a molecule of glucose (6C). (2) Pyruvate (3C), ATP, and NADH are produced.

Teacher Toolkit, Section C, Summarizing

FIGURE 5.2 The Krebs Cycle

The Krebs cycle breaks down citric acid and transfers energy to the electron transport chain.

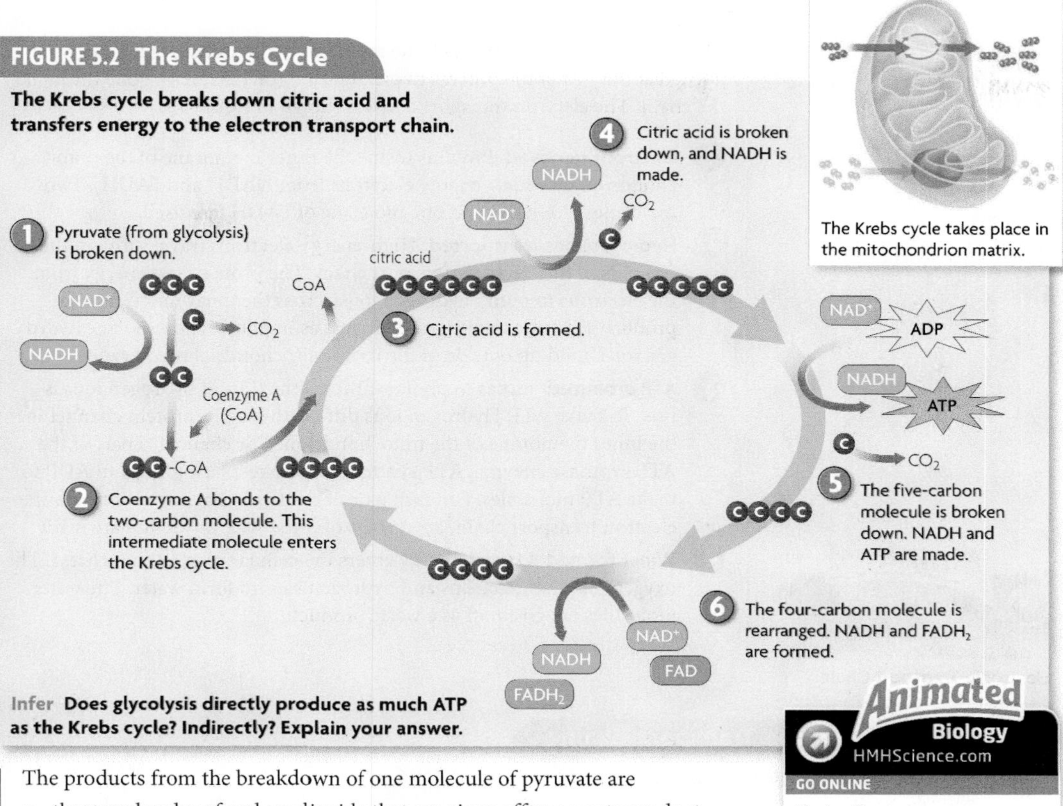

1 Pyruvate (from glycolysis) is broken down.
NAD+
NADH
CO2
CoA
Coenzyme A (CoA)
-CoA
2 Coenzyme A bonds to the two-carbon molecule. This intermediate molecule enters the Krebs cycle.
citric acid
3 Citric acid is formed.
NAD+
NADH
4 Citric acid is broken down, and NADH is made.
CO2
NAD+
ADP
NADH
ATP
CO2
5 The five-carbon molecule is broken down. NADH and ATP are made.
6 The four-carbon molecule is rearranged. NADH and FADH2 are formed.
NAD+
NADH
FAD
FADH2
The Krebs cycle takes place in the mitochondrion matrix.
Animated Biology
HMHScience.com
GO ONLINE
Krebs Cycle

Infer Does glycolysis directly produce as much ATP as the Krebs cycle? Indirectly? Explain your answer.

The products from the breakdown of one molecule of pyruvate are

- three molecules of carbon dioxide that are given off as a waste product
- one molecule of ATP
- four molecules of NADH to the electron transport chain
- one molecule of $FADH_2$ to the electron transport chain

Remember, glycolysis produces two pyruvate molecules. Therefore, the products above are half of what comes from one glucose molecule. The totals are six carbon dioxide, two ATP, eight NADH, and two $FADH_2$ molecules.

Analyze How are the products of the Krebs cycle important for making ATP?

MAIN IDEA

The electron transport chain is the second main part of cellular respiration.

The electron transport chain takes place in and across the inner membrane of a mitochondrion. As with electron transport in photosynthesis, proteins make up the electron transport chain in cellular respiration. The proteins use energy from the electrons supplied by NADH and $FADH_2$ to pump hydrogen ions against a concentration gradient and across the inner mitochondrial membrane.

TEACH FROM VISUALS

FIGURE 5.2 Use the figure to teach the details of the Krebs cycle, referring to the numbered items in the text to help clarify. Remind students that the diagram has been simplified and is not balanced in terms of electrons and ions.

Ask

- What event starts the Krebs cycle? Pyruvate (from glycolysis) is broken down and a two-carbon molecule bonded to Coenzyme A (acetyl-CoA) enters the Krebs cycle.
- Where does the Krebs cycle take place? mitochondrion matrix
- How many membranes does a pyruvate molecule cross? two: outer and inner membranes of mitochondrion

Take It Further

In glycolysis, most of the chemical energy from glucose remains in the bonds of pyruvate. In the Krebs cycle, the six molecules of carbon dioxide that are formed are much lower in energy. Most of the energy from glucose has been transferred to NADH and $FADH_2$.

Answers

A Infer Glycolysis and the Krebs cycle directly produce equal amounts of ATP. Indirectly, the Krebs cycle is responsible for more ATP production through the transfer of energy to the electron transport chain.

B Analyze The Krebs cycle produces two ATP and energy-carrying molecules that are used to produce more ATP in the electron transport chain.

BELOW LEVEL

Have students work in small groups to make a summary diagram of glycolysis and cellular respiration. They should draw a mitochondrion, including the folded inner membrane; then start the sequence with a molecule of glucose in the cytoplasm and end it with the production of water and ATP. Tell students to keep the diagram simple, using boxes to represent a reaction. Suggest that they show reactants and products, but not include any numbers of molecules.

Teacher Toolkit, Section C, Sequence Diagram

▼ Teach *continued*

TEACH FROM VISUALS

FIGURE 5.3 Use the figure to teach the electron transport chain. Explain that the ions and electrons in the diagram are not balanced, for the sake of simplicity. **Ask**

- Where do hydrogen ions accumulate? outside of the inner mitochondrial membrane
- Where does the energy that pumps H^+ against their gradient come from? from electrons removed from NADH and $FADH_2$

Take It Further

Remind students that a hydrogen atom consists of one proton and one electron. When that electron is lost, the hydrogen atom becomes a hydrogen ion. A **hydrogen ion** is simply a naked proton.

Integrating Genetics

The proteins in the electron transport chain, called **cytochromes,** are found in vastly different organisms. Cytochrome c is found in all aerobic organisms, indicating that all aerobic organisms probably descended from a common ancestor that used this molecule for cellular respiration. The amino acid sequence of cytochrome c differs slightly in different species. Closely related species have more similar sequences than distantly related species.

Answers

A Explain Hydrogen ions are transported across the inner membrane. They then flow through ATP synthase to produce ATP.

The ions later flow back through the membrane to produce ATP. Oxygen is needed at the end of the process to pick up electrons that have gone through the chain. The electron transport chain is shown in **FIGURE 5.3.**

1. **Electrons removed** Proteins inside the inner membrane of the mitochondrion take high-energy electrons from NADH and $FADH_2$. Two molecules of NADH and one molecule of $FADH_2$ are used.
2. **Hydrogen ions transported** High-energy electrons travel through the proteins in the electron transport chain. The proteins use energy from the electrons to pump hydrogen ions across the inner membrane to produce a chemiosmotic gradient, just as in photosynthesis. The hydrogen ions build up outside of the inner mitochondrial membrane.
3. **ATP produced** Just as in photosynthesis, the flow of hydrogen ions is used to make ATP. Hydrogen ions diffuse through a protein channel in the inner membrane of the mitochondrion. The channel is part of the ATP synthase enzyme. ATP synthase adds phosphate groups to ADP to make ATP molecules. For each pair of electrons that passes through the electron transport chain, an average of three ATP molecules are made.
4. **Water formed** Oxygen finally enters the cellular respiration process. The oxygen picks up electrons and hydrogen ions to form water. The water molecules are given off as a waste product.

FIGURE 5.3 The Electron Transport Chain

Energy from the Krebs cycle is used to produce ATP.

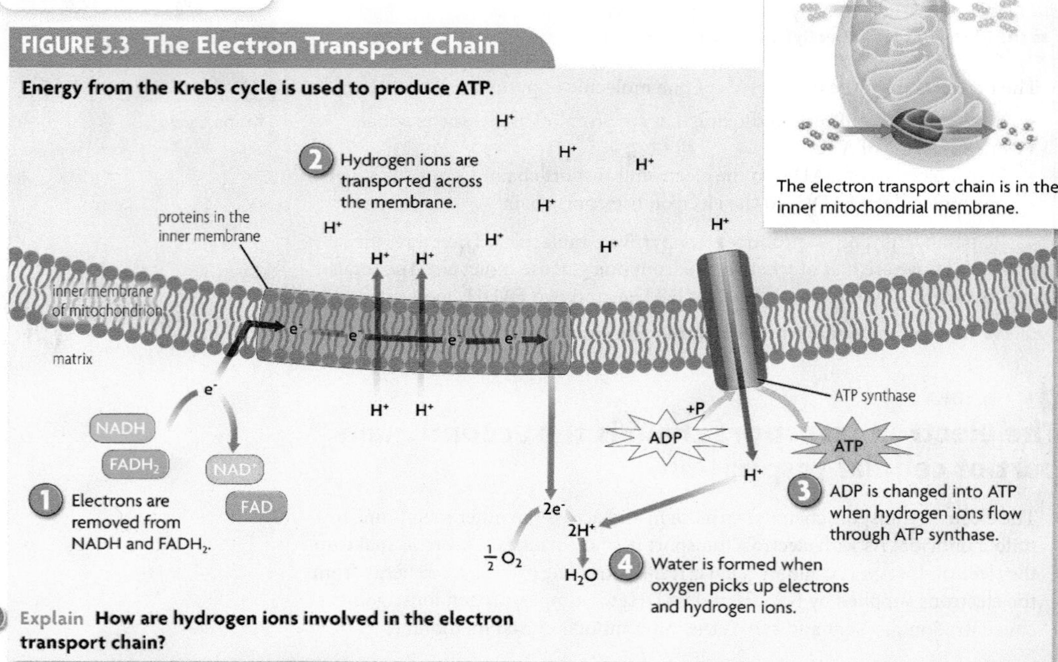

A Explain How are hydrogen ions involved in the electron transport chain?

Differentiated Instruction

PRE-AP

Give students five minutes to write about the function of oxygen in providing energy to a cell. They should refer to **FIGURES 5.2** and **5.3.** Ask them also to consider the role of hydrogen. Students should realize that it is the electrons and hydrogen ions that are used to produce ATP. Oxygen is used as an electron acceptor.

Teacher Toolkit, Section C, Quick Write

The products of cellular respiration—including glycolysis—are

- Carbon dioxide from the Krebs cycle and from the breakdown of pyruvate before the Krebs cycle
- Water from the electron transport chain
- A net gain of up to 38 ATP molecules for every glucose molecule—2 from glycolysis, 2 from the Krebs cycle, and up to 34 from the electron transport chain

Comparing Cellular Respiration and Photosynthesis

Again, think about how photosynthesis and cellular respiration are approximately the reverse of each other. Photosynthesis stores energy from sunlight as chemical energy. In contrast, cellular respiration releases stored energy as ATP and heat. Look at **FIGURE 5.5**, and think about other similarities and differences between the processes.

FIGURE 5.5 PHOTOSYNTHESIS AND CELLULAR RESPIRATION

	PHOTOSYNTHESIS	CELLULAR RESPIRATION
Organelle for process	chloroplast	mitochondrion
Reactants	CO_2 and H_2O	sugars ($C_6H_{12}O_6$) and O_2
Electron transport chain	proteins within thylakoid membrane	proteins within inner mitochondrial membrane
Cycle of chemical reactions	Calvin cycle in stroma of chloroplasts builds sugar molecules	Krebs cycle in matrix of mitochondria breaks down carbon-based molecules
Products	sugars ($C_6H_{12}O_6$) and O_2	CO_2 and H_2O

Recall the roles of electrons, hydrogen ions, and ATP synthase. In both processes, high-energy electrons are transported through proteins. Their energy is used to pump hydrogen ions across a membrane. And the flow of hydrogen ions through ATP synthase produces ATP. As you can see, the parts of the processes are very similar, but their end points are very different.

A Analyze How does the electron transport chain depend on the Krebs cycle?

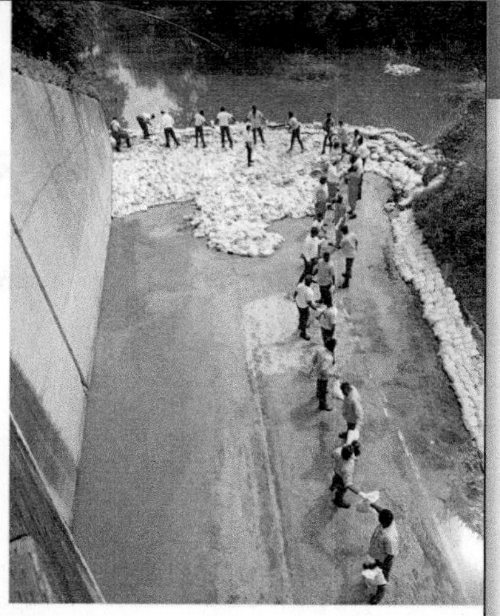

FIGURE 5.4 Like sandbags passed down a line of people, high-energy electrons are passed along a chain of proteins in the inner mitochondrial membrane.

Mirror Processes

4.5 Formative Assessment

REVIEWING MAIN IDEAS

1. What is the role of pyruvate in cellular respiration?
2. Describe in your own words the function of the Krebs cycle.
3. Explain the functions of electrons, hydrogen ions, and oxygen in the electron transport chain.

CRITICAL THINKING

4. **Compare** Describe the relationship between cellular respiration and photosynthesis in terms of energy and matter.
5. **Evaluate** Is oxygen necessary for the production of all ATP in your cells? Why or why not?

SELF-CHECK Online
HMHScience.com
GO ONLINE

CONNECT TO
COMMON ANCESTRY

6. Protein molecules called cytochromes are part of the electron transport chain. They are nearly identical in every known aerobic organism. How do these molecules show the unity of life on Earth?

Integrating Ecology

About 40 percent of the energy in glucose is converted to ATP during cellular respiration. The rest is lost as heat. Much of this heat keeps the body warm. This loss of energy explains why so little energy is available at each **trophic level** and why the length of **food chains** is limited. It also explains why people feel so warm when they exercise.

ONLINE Biology
HMHScience.com

Have students view the interactive animation that compares photosynthesis to respiration. See the Animated Biology titled Mirror Processes at **HMHScience.com**.

Answers

A Analyze Energy from the Krebs cycle is necessary for the electron transport chain to function.

Assess and Reteach ▼

Assess Use the Section Self-Check or Section Quiz, both available at **HMHScience.com**.

Reteach Work with students to put together a concept map of cellular respiration. Start the concept map with the word *glycolysis*. Tell students that the concept map must end with the word *water*.

4.5 FORMATIVE ASSESSMENT

1. Pyruvate, produced by the breakdown of glucose, is needed for the Krebs cycle, which is a part of cellular respiration.
2. The Krebs cycle breaks down and extracts energy from carbon-based molecules, transfers it to the electron transport chain, makes a small amount of ATP, and releases carbon dioxide.
3. The electron transport chain pumps hydrogen ions across the inner mitochondrial membrane. Hydrogen ions then flow through a channel that is bound to ATP synthase. Oxygen picks up electrons and hydrogen ions so that the electron transport chain can continue to function.
4. The reactants and products (matter) of the overall processes are essentially the reverse of each other. Photosynthesis uses light energy to build carbon-based molecules and releases oxygen; cellular respiration uses oxygen to break down carbon-based molecules to release energy.
5. No, ATP is also formed during glycolysis, which can continue without oxygen.
6. The similarity of cytochromes in many different organisms suggests a common ancestor.

SECTION 4.6

▼ Plan and Prepare

Activate Prior Knowledge Have students consider a long-distance runner. **Ask**

- How do long-distance runners, such as marathoners, provide the energy their bodies need for a race? by carb-loading, eating carbohydrate-rich foods
- When a runner "hits the wall," what has happened? The carbohydrates are depleted. The body now burns more fat, which requires more oxygen, energy, and time to burn.

"Hitting the wall" means a runner is making ATP through glycolysis and fermentation.

▼ Teach

Vocabulary

Greek and Latin Origins Remind students that the Greek and Latin prefix *an-* means "not." In combination with the Greek root *aer,* meaning "air," **anaerobic** means "not aerobic" or "not in air." Tell students that the *aer-* of **aerobic** is the *air* that they inhale.

4.6 Fermentation

KEY CONCEPT **Fermentation allows the production of a small amount of ATP without oxygen.**

VOCABULARY
fermentation
lactic acid

MAIN IDEAS
- Fermentation allows glycolysis to continue.
- Fermentation and its products are important in several ways.

Connect to Your World

Think about a time when you worked or exercised hard. Maybe you moved heavy boxes or furniture. Maybe, playing basketball, you found yourself repeatedly running up and down the court. Your arms and legs began to feel heavy, and they seemed to lose strength. Your muscles became sore, and even when you rested you kept breathing hard. Your muscles were using fermentation.

MAIN IDEA

Fermentation allows glycolysis to continue.

The cells in your body cannot store large amounts of oxygen for cellular respiration. The amount of oxygen that is provided by breathing is enough for your cells during normal activities. When you are reading or talking to friends, your body can maintain its oxygen levels. When you are doing high levels of activity, as the sprinter is in **FIGURE 6.1**, your body cannot bring in enough oxygen for your cells, even though you breathe faster. How do your cells function without enough oxygen to keep cellular respiration going?

Recall that glycolysis yields two ATP molecules when it splits glucose into two molecules of pyruvate. Glycolysis is always occurring and does not require oxygen. If oxygen is available, the products of glycolysis—pyruvate and the electron carrier NADH—are used in cellular respiration. Then, oxygen picks up electrons at the end of the electron transport chain in cellular respiration. But what happens when oxygen is not there to pick up electrons? The production of ATP without oxygen continues through the anaerobic processes of glycolysis and fermentation.

FIGURE 6.1 Muscle cells use anaerobic processes during hard exercise.

Fermentation does not make ATP, but it allows glycolysis to continue. Fermentation removes electrons from NADH molecules and recycles NAD^+ molecules for glycolysis. Why is this process important? Because glycolysis, just like cellular respiration, needs a molecule that picks up electrons. It needs molecules of NAD^+.

VISUAL VOCAB

Fermentation is an anaerobic process that allows glycolysis to continue.

glycolysis — with O_2 → cellular respiration
glycolysis — without O_2 → fermentation

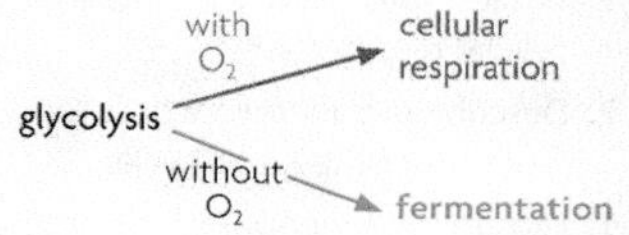

Differentiated Instruction

ENGLISH LEARNERS

If you used the strategy of a brainstorming session with students for **Sections 3** and **5,** continue the practice here. Produce a cluster diagram to organize information about the process of fermentation. Compare this diagram to the ones made earlier. Point out the details that are critical for students to know.

Teacher Toolkit, Section C, Cluster Diagram

BELOW LEVEL

Rather than have students use an outline for this section, suggest they use a two-column graphic organizer to compare lactic acid and alcoholic fermentation. To get them started, have them consider these questions:

- What are the reactants?
- What are the products?
- What consumer products are made from the process?

Teacher Toolkit, Section C, T-Chart

Without NAD^+ to pick up high-energy electrons from the splitting of glucose, glycolysis would stop. When the high-energy electrons are picked up, though, a eukaryotic cell can continue breaking down glucose and other simple sugars to make a small amount of ATP.

Suppose that a molecule of glucose has just been split by glycolysis in one of your muscle cells, but oxygen is unavailable. A process called lactic acid fermentation takes place. Lactic acid fermentation occurs in your muscle cells, the cells of other vertebrates, and in some microorganisms. **Lactic acid,** $C_3H_6O_3$, is what causes your muscles to "burn" during hard exercise.

1. Pyruvate and NADH from glycolysis enter the fermentation process. Two NADH molecules provide energy to convert pyruvate into lactic acid. As the NADH is used, it is converted back into NAD^+.
2. Two molecules of NAD^+ are recycled back to glycolysis. The recycling of NAD^+ allows glycolysis to continue.

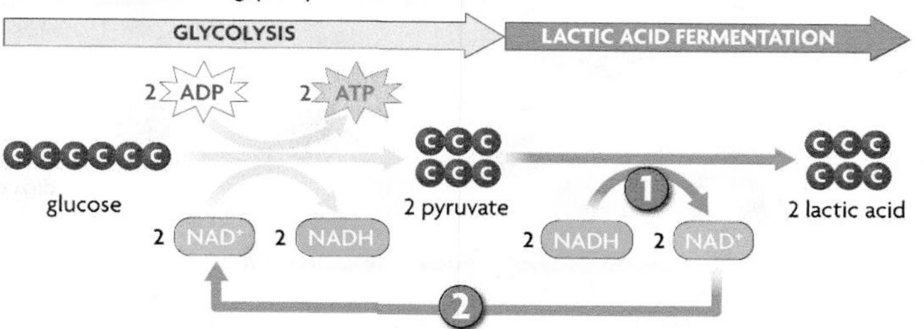

As you can see, the role of fermentation is simply to provide glycolysis with a steady supply of NAD^+. By itself, fermentation does not produce ATP. Instead, it allows glycolysis to continue to produce ATP. However, fermentation does produce the lactic acid waste product that builds up in muscle cells and causes a burning feeling. Once oxygen is available again, your cells return to using cellular respiration. The lactic acid is quickly broken down and removed from the cells. This is why you continue to breathe hard for several minutes after you stop exercising. Your body is making up for the oxygen deficit in your cells, which allows the breakdown of lactic acid in your muscles.

Sequence **Which process must happen first, fermentation or glycolysis? Explain.**

MAIN IDEA

Fermentation and its products are important in several ways.

How would your diet change without cheese, bread, and yogurt? How would pizza exist without cheese and bread? Without fermentation, a pizza crust would not rise and there would be no mozzarella cheese as a pizza topping. Cheese, bread, and yogurt are just a few of the foods made by fermentation. Milk is changed into different cheeses by fermentation processes carried out by different types of bacteria and molds. Waste products of their fermentation processes give cheeses their different flavors and textures. Additionally, some types of bacteria that use lactic acid fermentation sour the milk in yogurt.

READING TOOLBOX

TAKING NOTES

Use a mind map to take notes on the processes involved in fermentation.

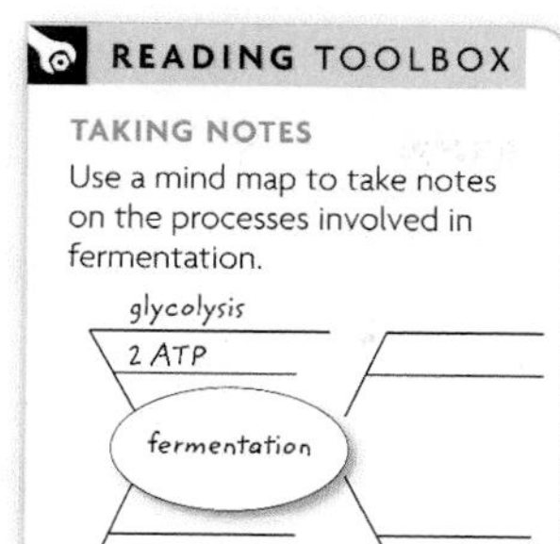

CONNECT TO

HUMAN BIOLOGY

Muscle cells need ATP to contract. You will learn how the muscular system works with other systems of the body to allow movement in the chapter **Human Systems and Homeostasis.**

GO ONLINE

Energy and Athletic Training

HANDS-ON ACTIVITY

Students may be interested in making yogurt. There are many recipes available on the Internet. The yogurt can be incubated using a commercial yogurt machine, or it can be heated on a stove or hot plate, following directions in the recipe. A small amount of commercial yogurt that contains living cultures is used as a starter.

ONLINE Biology

HMHScience.com

Have students do the WebQuest to learn more about the way lactic acid fermentation affects muscles.

Take It Further

Oxygen greatly increases the amount of energy available to an organism. An anaerobic organism gets only two ATP molecules out of a molecule of glucose. By comparison, an aerobic organism can get up to 38 molecules of ATP from one molecule of glucose.

The Inside Story

Ideas about healthy eating and long life have been around for quite a while. So have health-food fads. In 1908, Russian biologist **Elie Metchnikoff** published a book called *The Prolongation of Human Life.* In his book, Metchnikoff suggested that the long life spans associated with Bulgarian people were due to their high consumption of foods cultured with *Lactobacillus* bacteria. More simply put, they ate a lot of **yogurt.**

The production of yogurt by lactic acid fermentation is believed to have been discovered by Balkan tribes as many as 4500 years ago. Until 1908, yogurt was eaten mainly by people in eastern European and Middle Eastern countries. Metchnikoff devoted the last ten years of his life to the study of lactic acid fermentation and longevity. He named the bacterium that produces yogurt *Lactobacillus bulgaricus* in honor of the Bulgarian people.

Answers

A **Sequence** Gycolysis must occur first because fermentation requires pyruvate and NADH.

Chapter 4: Cells and Energy 121

▼ Teach *continued*

TEACH FROM VISUALS

Have students compare the diagram shown on this page with the one shown on the previous page. **Ask**

- How are alcoholic fermentation and lactic acid fermentation similar? Both begin with glycolysis of glucose; both produce ATP and NAD^+.
- How are they different? Lactic acid fermentation produces lactic acid; alcoholic fermentation produces alcohol and carbon dioxide.

QUICKLAB

Time 20–30 minutes

Purpose Measure the amount of fermentation in various beverages.

LAB MANAGEMENT

- Be sure to use fresh yeast. Check the expiration date.
- Students can use duct tape to seal the balloon onto the bottle neck.
- Students should measure the circumference of the balloon as a measure of fermentation.

Expected Results

Beverages that contain the most sugar will yield the most carbon dioxide.

Analyze and Conclude

1. independent variable: type or temperature of beverage; dependent variable: inflation of balloon indicating the amount of carbon dioxide produced; constants: amount of beverage and yeast, size of balloon
2. The type of beverage affected how much carbon dioxide was produced because different beverages have different amounts of sugar. A higher sugar concentration increases the rate of fermentation.
3. inconsistent methods, poorly controlled constants, random error (for example, different yeast activity, differences in balloons used)

Lactic acid fermentation is not the only anaerobic process. Alcoholic fermentation occurs in many yeasts and in some types of plants. Alcoholic fermentation begins at the same point as lactic acid fermentation. That is, glycolysis splits a molecule of glucose and produces two net ATP molecules, two pyruvate molecules, and two NADH molecules. Pyruvate and NADH enter alcoholic fermentation.

1. Pyruvate and NADH from glycolysis enter alcoholic fermentation. Two NADH molecules provide energy to break down pyruvate into an alcohol and carbon dioxide. As the NADH molecules are used, they are converted back into molecules of NAD^+.
2. The molecules of NAD^+ are recycled back to glycolysis. The recycling of NAD^+ allows glycolysis to continue.

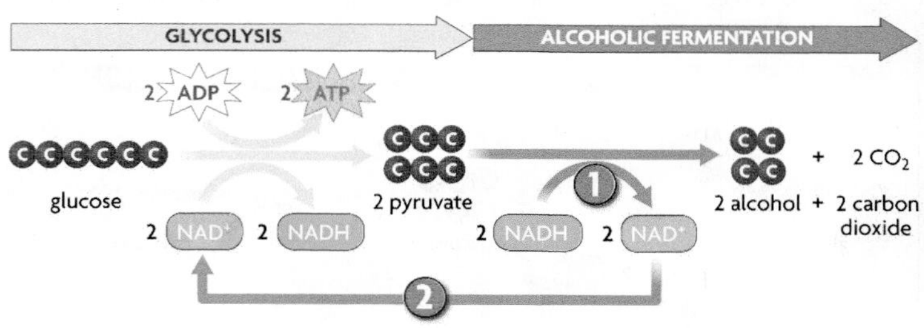

The products of this process are two molecules of an alcohol, often ethyl alcohol, two molecules of carbon dioxide, and two molecules of NAD^+. Just like lactic acid fermentation, alcoholic fermentation recycles NAD^+ and so allows glycolysis to keep making ATP.

QUICKLAB DESIGN YOUR OWN

Fermentation

One waste product of alcoholic fermentation is carbon dioxide. In this lab, you will determine which beverage causes yeast to undergo a higher rate of fermentation.

PROBLEM What factors affect the rate of fermentation in yeast?

PROCEDURE

1. Write an operational definition for the dependent variable that you will use to measure the rate of fermentation.
2. Develop a technique using a balloon to measure fermentation rate.
3. Design your experiment. Have your teacher approve your experimental design. Write your experimental procedure and conduct your experiment.
4. Construct a data table to record your data. Construct a graph to display your data.

ANALYZE AND CONCLUDE

1. **Identify** What are the independent variable, dependent variable, and constants?
2. **Analyze** How did the independent variable affect the rate of fermentation? Why?
3. **Experimental Design** Identify possible reasons for any inconsistent results you observed.

MATERIALS

- 2 empty plastic bottles
- 1 package of yeast
- 2 100-mL graduated cylinders
- 2 250-mL beakers
- 2 beverages
- 2 round balloons
- 30 cm string
- metric ruler

Differentiated Instruction

TEACH WITH TECHNOLOGY

If you have access to probeware, have students make a quantitative measure of the carbon dioxide produced by alcoholic fermentation.

ENGLISH LEARNERS

Remember to take extra time early in the year to walk students through the laboratory directions. Students should prepare word squares for terms specifically associated with experimental procedures: *variable, independent variable, dependent variable, constant,* and *operational definition.* Search the QuickLab instructions for difficult vocabulary or constructions. You might want to read the materials list aloud, holding up each item as you say its name.

Teacher Toolkit, Section D, Word Squares

FIGURE 6.2 Fermentation by molds and bacteria produces the different flavors and textures of various cheeses.

Alcoholic fermentation in yeast is particularly useful. When bread or pizza crust is made, yeast is used to cause the dough to rise. The yeast breaks down sugars in the dough through glycolysis and alcohol fermentation. The carbon dioxide gas produced by alcoholic fermentation causes the dough to puff up and rise. When the dough is baked, the alcohol that is produced during fermentation evaporates into the air. The yeast in dough is killed by the heat of baking.

Bacteria that rely upon fermentation play a very important role in the digestive systems of animals. Microorganisms in the digestive tracts of animals, including humans, must obtain their ATP from anaerobic processes because oxygen is not available. Without them, neither you nor other animals would be able to fully digest food. Why? These bacteria continue the breakdown of molecules by taking in undigested material for their needs. The additional breakdown of materials by digestive bacteria allows the host animal to absorb more nutrients from food.

Photosynthesis and Cellular Respiration

A Apply **Explain the importance of alcoholic fermentation in the production of bread's light, fluffy texture.**

SELF-CHECK Online
HMHScience.com
GO ONLINE

4.6 Formative Assessment

REVIEWING MAIN IDEAS

1. What is the relationship between glycolysis and **fermentation**?
2. Summarize the process of alcoholic fermentation in yeast.

CRITICAL THINKING

3. **Compare and Contrast** How are **lactic acid** fermentation and alcoholic fermentation similar? How are they different?
4. **Compare and Contrast** Describe the similarities and differences between cellular respiration and fermentation.

CONNECT TO
CELLULAR RESPIRATION

5. How is the role of oxygen in cellular respiration similar to the role of NAD^+ in fermentation ?

Vocabulary

Word Origins The word **fermentation** and the word **brew** share the same root, *bhreu-*, meaning "boil" or "bubble." This relates to the gas released by yeast during the process of alcoholic fermentation. In German, the root word was reduced to *bher-* and later *bhermen*, which eventually became *ferment*.

Answers

A **Apply** Carbon dioxide produced from alcoholic fermentation creates gas pockets in the bread, which cause the bread to rise.

Assess and Reteach

Assess Use the Section Self-Check or Section Quiz, both available at **HMHScience.com**.

Reteach Have students identify products that are made by fermentation. Choose among the products and ask different students to write the fermentation process associated with the product on the board.

4.6 FORMATIVE ASSESSMENT

1. Glycolysis leads to fermentation if no oxygen is available. NAD^+ produced by fermentation allows glycolysis to continue.
2. Sugars are broken down by glycolysis. Pyruvate and NADH enter alcoholic fermentation, producing alcohol and carbon dioxide. NAD^+ is recycled back to glycolysis.
3. Both are anaerobic processes that break down glucose to make ATP and recycle NAD^+ to glycolysis. Lactic acid fermentation produces lactic acid; alcoholic fermentation produces an alcohol and carbon dioxide.
4. Both produce ATP through the breakdown of carbon-based molecules, and both allow glycolysis to continue by recycling electron acceptors. Cellular respiration requires oxygen and produces much more ATP than fermentation does.
5. Both oxygen and NAD^+ pick up electrons and allow ATP production to continue.

CHAPTER REVIEW

GO ONLINE

Encourage students to go to **HMHScience.com** for a detailed review of each section, including visuals and vocabulary practice.

Online Student Resources, Vocabulary Practice Worksheet

CHAPTER 4 Summary

BIG IDEA All living things require energy in the form of ATP to carry on cell processes, and ATP is most often produced by the linked reactions of photosynthesis and respiration.

KEY CONCEPTS

4.1 Chemical Energy and ATP

All cells need chemical energy. Adenosine triphosphate (ATP) is the primary source of energy in all cells. ATP transfers energy for cell processes such as building new molecules and transporting materials.

4.2 Overview of Photosynthesis

The overall process of photosynthesis produces sugars that store chemical energy. Photosynthesis uses energy captured from sunlight to change carbon dioxide and water into oxygen and sugars. Sunlight is absorbed during the light-dependent reactions, and sugars are made during the light-independent reactions.

4.3 Photosynthesis in Detail

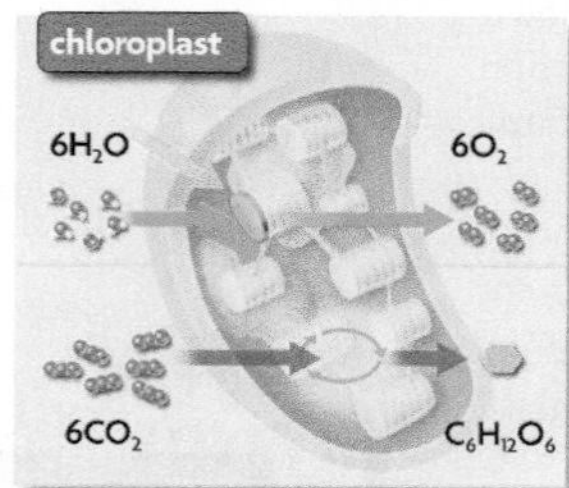

Photosynthesis requires a series of chemical reactions. Energy from sunlight is absorbed in the thylakoid membrane by photosystems II and I in the light-dependent reactions. The energy is transferred to the Calvin cycle, which builds sugar molecules from carbon dioxide.

4.4 Overview of Cellular Respiration

The overall process of cellular respiration converts sugar into ATP using oxygen. Glycolysis splits glucose; the products of glycolysis are used in cellular respiration when oxygen is present. The Krebs cycle transfers energy to the electron transport chain, which produces most of the ATP in eukaryotic cells.

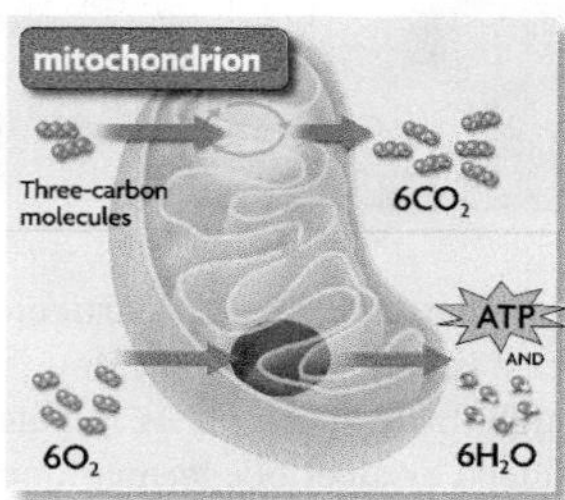

4.5 Cellular Respiration in Detail

Cellular respiration is an aerobic process with two main stages. The Krebs cycle breaks down carbon-based molecules and transfers energy to electron carriers. The electron carriers provide energy to the electron transport chain. ATP is produced by the electron transport chain when hydrogen ions flow through ATP synthase.

4.6 Fermentation

Fermentation allows the production of a small amount of ATP without oxygen. Fermentation allows glycolysis to continue producing ATP when oxygen is unavailable. Lactic acid fermentation occurs in many cells, including human muscle cells.

READING TOOLBOX SYNTHESIZE YOUR NOTES

Two-Column Chart Compare and contrast photosynthesis and cellular respiration. Use your notes to make detailed charts that include details about both processes. Highlight important vocabulary and processes.

Photosynthesis	Cellular Respiration
absorbs sunlight occurs in chloroplasts $6CO_2+6H_2O \rightarrow C_6H_{12}O_6+6O_2$	produces ATP occurs in mitochondria $C_6H_{12}O_6+6O_2 \rightarrow 6CO_2+6H_2O$

Concept Map Use a concept map like the one below to summarize and organize the processes of photosynthesis, cellular respiration, and fermentation.

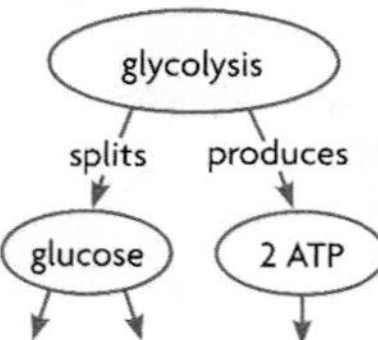

Reviewing Vocabulary

1. builds sugars
2. absorb and transfer energy
3. produces ATP when oxygen is available
4. with oxygen
5. breaks down pyruvate
6. allows glycolysis to continue
7. Photosynthesis uses light to put sugars together.
8. Aerobic processes require oxygen, anaerobic processes do not.
9. Oxygen taken in through breathing is needed for cellular respiration.

Review Games • Concept Map • Section Self-Checks

4 Review

CHAPTER VOCABULARY

4.1 ATP, ADP, chemosynthesis

4.2 photosynthesis, chlorophyll, thylakoid, light-dependent reactions, light-independent reactions

4.3 photosystem, electron transport chain, ATP synthase, Calvin cycle

4.4 cellular respiration, aerobic, glycolysis, anaerobic, Krebs cycle

4.6 fermentation, lactic acid

Reviewing Vocabulary

Keep It Short

For each vocabulary term below, write a short, precise phrase that describes its meaning. For example, a short phrase to describe the term *ATP* could be "energy for cells."

1. photosynthesis
2. light-dependent reactions
3. cellular respiration
4. aerobic
5. Krebs cycle
6. fermentation

READING TOOLBOX GREEK AND LATIN WORD PARTS

Use the definitions of the word parts to answer the next three questions.

Prefix or Root	Meaning
photo-	light
syn-	together
aero-	air
spirare	to breathe

7. Describe how the meaning of the term *photosynthesis* is a combination of the meanings of the prefixes *photo-* and *syn-*.
8. Explain how the prefix *aero-* is related to the terms *aerobic* and *anaerobic*.
9. Why is the root *spirare* the basis of the term *cellular respiration*? Explain your answer.

Reviewing MAIN IDEAS

10. Describe the roles of ADP and ATP in the transfer and use of energy in cells.
11. What types of carbon-based molecules are most often broken down to make ATP? Explain how ATP production differs depending on the type of carbon-based molecule that is broken down.
12. Describe how and where energy from light is absorbed during photosynthesis. What happens to the energy after it is absorbed?
13. Write the chemical equation for photosynthesis and explain what it represents.
14. What roles do electrons and hydrogen ions play in the light-dependent reactions of photosynthesis?
15. Describe how the light-independent reactions are the synthesis part of photosynthesis.
16. How does glycolysis contribute to the overall process of cellular respiration?
17. Write the chemical equation for cellular respiration and explain what it represents.
18. What is the function of the Krebs cycle? In your answer, describe the products of the Krebs cycle and what happens to them.
19. Explain the function of the electron transport chain in cellular respiration. Why is oxygen needed for the electron transport chain?
20. Fermentation does not produce ATP. Why is fermentation such an important process in cells?
21. How is alcoholic fermentation similar to lactic acid fermentation? How is it different?

Reviewing Main Ideas

10. ATP, a high-energy molecule, transfers energy to cell processes. ADP, a lower-energy molecule, can be converted into ATP.
11. Carbohydrates; breakdown of lipids produces the most ATP, followed by carbohydrates and proteins.
12. Molecules absorb energy in the chloroplast and transfer the energy to electrons that move through the thylakoid membrane. These are used to produce energy-carrying molecules.
13. $6CO_2 + 6H_2O \rightarrow C_6H_{12}O_6 + 6O_2$; the equation is for the overall process and shows the overall reactants and products.
14. Electrons transfer energy, and hydrogen ions flow through ATP synthase to produce ATP.
15. The light-independent reactions build or "put together" sugars from carbon dioxide.
16. Glycolysis breaks down glucose, the products of which enter cellular respiration when oxygen is present.
17. $C_6H_{12}O_6 + 6O_2 \rightarrow 6CO_2 + 6H_2O$; the equation is for the overall process and shows the overall reactants and products.
18. The Krebs cycle breaks down pyruvate and produces electron carriers (NADH and $FADH_2$) and carbon dioxide waste. The electron carriers are used to provide energized electrons to the electron transport chain.
19. The electron transport chain uses energy from energized electrons to pump H^+ ions across the inner mitochondrial membrane. The H^+ ions flow back across, through ATP synthase, to produce ATP. Oxygen picks up the electrons after they pass through the chain.
20. Fermentation allows glycolysis to continue to produce a small amount of ATP when oxygen is unavailable.
21. Both recycle NAD^+ to glycolysis and both break down pyruvate, but the products of the two fermentation processes differ (lactic acid vs. alcohol and CO_2).

Critical Thinking

22. because the cells will not be able to produce ATP to continue to function
23. Examples could include the electron transport chains, the transfer of electron carriers, and the flow of H^+ ions down a concentration (chemiosmotic) gradient.
24. Photosynthesis stores energy in sugars; cellular respiration releases energy (as ATP and heat) from the breakdown of sugars.
25. Both require the products of glycolysis; glycolysis requires either process to pick up the products and supply molecules to pick up electrons.
26. The light-dependent reactions and electron transport chain are nearly identical because both use energized electrons to pump H^+ ions across a membrane and produce ATP and other electron carriers. The Krebs cycle and Calvin cycle are nearly opposite; the Krebs cycle breaks down carbon-based molecules and supplies energy, and the Calvin cycle uses energy to build sugars.

Interpreting Visuals

27. Photosynthesis stores energy absorbed from sunlight; cellular respiration releases energy as ATP and heat.
28. photosynthesis produces sugars and oxygen needed for cellular respiration, and cellular respiration produces the carbon dioxide and water needed for photosynthesis
29. photosynthesis, because it produces the sugars and oxygen needed for cellular respiration

Critical Thinking

22. Infer Human brain cells do not use fermentation. Explain why a lack of oxygen for even a short period of time might result in the death of brain cells.

23. Apply Energy is transferred in several different ways during photosynthesis and cellular respiration. Give two examples of the way energy is transferred in the processes. Explain both examples.

24. Analyze How do photosynthesis and cellular respiration form a cycle of energy storage and use?

25. Synthesize How do cellular respiration and fermentation depend on glycolysis? How does glycolysis depend on aerobic and anaerobic processes?

26. Analyze Consider the following two groups of processes:
- light-dependent reactions and electron transport chain
- Calvin cycle and Krebs cycle

Which pair is nearly identical? Which is nearly opposite? Explain.

Interpreting Visuals

Use the diagram to answer the next three questions.

27. Apply Which process stores energy? Which process releases energy? How do you know?

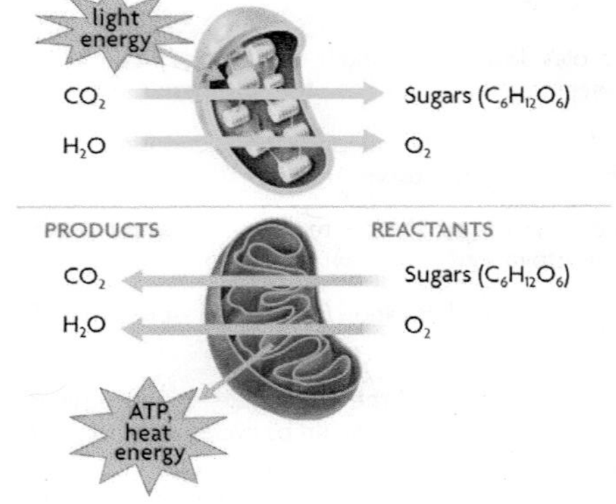

28. Infer Use information in the visual to explain how matter, in the form of reactants and products, is cycled through these processes.

29. Infer Which of the processes in the diagram is necessary for most living things to survive? Explain.

Analyzing Data Interpret a Graph

Use information in the text and the graph below to answer the next two questions.

Plants have several different molecules that together absorb all of the different wavelengths of visible light. Visible light ranges between the wavelengths of about 400 and 700 nanometers (nm).

ABSORPTION OF LIGHT BY CHLOROPHYLL

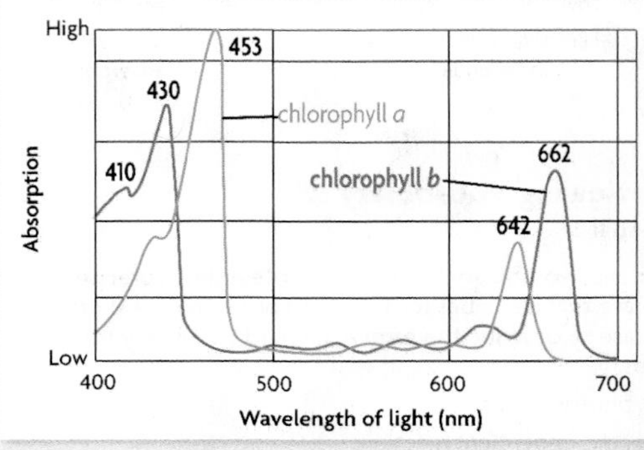

30. Analyze Data What range of wavelengths is absorbed by chlorophyll *a*? chlorophyll *b*?

31. Synthesize Suppose a type of plant has only chlorophylls *a* and *b* and is exposed to different wavelengths of light. At which wavelengths would there be the greatest amounts of carbon dioxide in the air around the plants? the least? Explain your answers.

Making Connections

32. Write an Analogy Suppose that photosynthesis and cellular respiration take place in a factory. You are a tour guide at the factory, explaining each step of the process to a group of visitors. Use analogies to describe what happens at each step. For example, you could describe the photosystems of photosynthesis as "the green machines next to windows to absorb light." Be sure to include important details of the process you select.

33. Analyze Look at the micrograph of diatoms on the chapter opener. Write a paragraph that explains the role of these single-celled organisms in a marine food web.

Analyzing Data

30. 400–460 and 620–660; 400–450 and 630–680
31. greatest CO_2, 460–620, because little energy is being absorbed from light and less oxygen is being produced; least CO_2, 400–460 and 620–680, because the chlorophylls absorb energy for photosynthesis at those wavelengths and produce more oxygen

Making Connections

32. Answers should indicate knowledge of the steps of photosynthesis or cellular respiration and where they occur in cells.
33. Answers should indicate that diatoms are producers that form the base of marine food webs.

Standards-Based Assessment

Record your answers on a separate piece of paper.

MULTIPLE CHOICE

1 A group of students wants to find out how much carbon dioxide is used by plants during the daytime. What control could be used in this experiment?

A the amount of water used during the daytime
B the amount of oxygen released at night
C the amount of carbon dioxide used at night
D the amount of oxygen used during the daytime

2 The concept map below shows some of the carbon-based molecules in cells. Some of these molecules can be broken down to produce usable chemical energy.

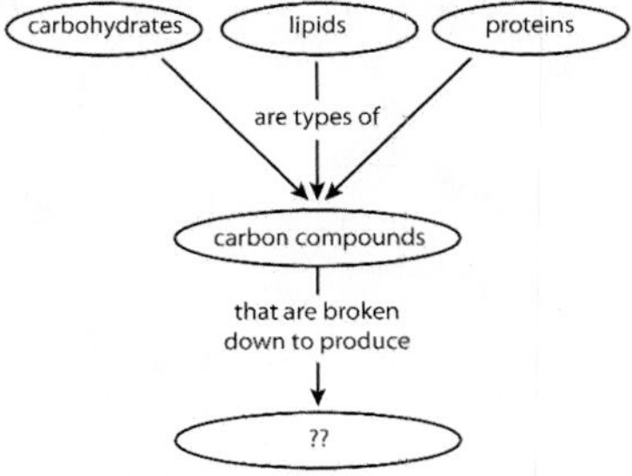

Which of the following terms ***best*** completes this concept map?

A glucose
B ATP
C lactic acid
D oxygen

3 Photosynthesis is a part of various cycles that help to move oxygen and carbon through the environment. What form of abiotic carbon do plants remove from the environment?

A glucose
B starch
C carbon dioxide
D ATP

THINK THROUGH THE QUESTION

Some terms in questions, such as biotic or abiotic, may be unfamiliar to you. Often, terms like these are used to present an example but are not necessary to answer the question. Find the important pieces of information in the question and focus on those points.

4

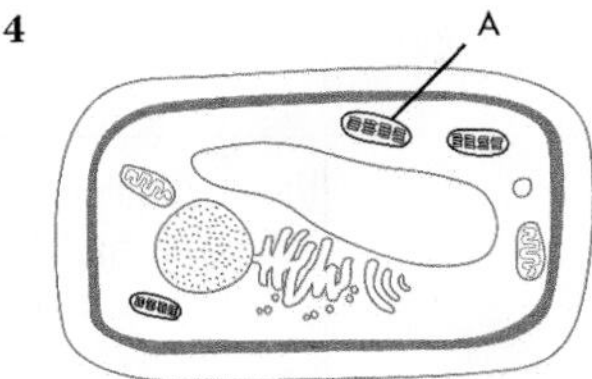

Which of the following ***best*** represent the final products of the chemical reactions that take place inside the organelle labeled A in the diagram above?

A sugars, oxygen
B ATP, electrons
C ATP, sugars
D carbon dioxide, water

5 Which process is represented by the following chemical equation?

$6CO_2 + 6H_2O \longrightarrow C_6H_{12}O_6 + 6O_2$

A photosynthesis
B fermentation
C glycolysis
D cellular respiration

Standards-Based Assessment

The Standards-Based Assessment questions will help students prepare for their final examination in the course. If you wish to give students practice in coding their answers, look for the Standards-Based Assessment Answer Sheet at **HMHScience.com**. To give students practice under timed testing conditions, allow them five minutes per question.

Question	Answer	Depth of Knowledge	Cognitive Complexity
1	C	II	M
2	B	I	M
3	C	I	M
4	A	III	M
5	A	I	L

KEY

Depth of Knowledge
I Recall
II Skill/Concept
III Strategic Thinking
IV Extended Thinking

Cognitive Complexity
L Low
M Moderate
H High

Chapter 4: Cells and Energy 127

CHAPTER 5

Instruction and Intervention Support

Cell Growth and Division

① Core Instruction

The **Core Instruction** resources below can be used for all students. Core instruction should be followed by ongoing assessment to determine which students need further help.

Available in both English and Spanish

Available Online

Section	Instruction	PRINT	ONLINE	Labs
5.1	Textbook **The Cell Cycle**	■	●	Modeling Cell Surface Area–to-Volume Ratio
	Teaching Visuals The Cell Cycle (Fig. 1.1)		●	
	PowerPresentation and Notes 5.1		●	
5.2	Textbook **Mitosis and Cytokinesis**	■	●	Mitosis in Onion Root Cells Animating Mitosis **Video Lab** Mitosis in Plant Cells
	Animated Biology Mitosis Stage Matching, Stages of Mitosis		●	
	Teaching Visuals Chromosome Structure (Fig. 2.2), Mitosis and Cytokinesis (Fig. 2.4)		●	
	PowerPresentation and Notes 5.2		●	
5.3	Textbook **Regulation of the Cell Cycle**	■	●	Apoptosis **QuickLab** Cancer
	PowerPresentation and Notes 5.3		●	
5.4	Textbook **Asexual Reproduction**	■	●	**Virtual Lab** Investigating Bacterial Growth
	Animated Biology Binary Fission		●	
	PowerPresentation and Notes 5.4		●	
5.5	Textbook **Multicellular Life**	■	●	S.T.E.M. Lab Multicellular Life: Stem Cells
	Teaching Visuals Harvesting Stem Cells (Fig. 5.4)		●	
	PowerPresentation and Notes 5.5		●	

Additional online resources available for this chapter include **Interactive Whiteboard Resources.**

GO ONLINE! for all your teacher resources at HMHScience.com

2 Support and Intervention

Support and Intervention resources are useful for students who need targeted help beyond the Core Instruction

Resources	PRINT	ONLINE
Assess and Reteach (TE wrap)	■	●
Concept Map		●
Interactive Reader	■	●
Interactive Review Games		●
Section Self-Checks		●
Study Guide B		●
Virtual Investigation Phases of Mitosis		●
Vocabulary Practice Worksheets		●

3 Specialized Support

Students who need more intensive personalized intervention benefit from **Specialized Support** resources.

Resources	PRINT	ONLINE
Chapter Audio Files		●
Differentiated Instruction Inclusion, Below Level, and English Learners (TE wrap)	■	●
ELL Strategies	■	●
Modified Lesson Plans for English Learners		●
Reinforcement Worksheets		●
Study Guide A		●

Extension and Assessment

Enrichment and Challenge

Resources	PRINT	ONLINE
Active Reading Worksheets		●
Data Analysis Practice Worksheet		●
Differentiated Instruction Pre-AP (TE wrap)	■	●
Pre-AP Activity Spindles and Mitosis, HeLa Cells		●
The Inside Story and **Take It Further** (TE wrap)	■	●
Unit Project		●
WebLinks		●
WebQuest Skin Cancer (5.3)		●

Assessment

Resources	PRINT	ONLINE
Alternative Assessment		●
Chapter Tests A and B		●
Diagnostic Test		●
ExamView Banks		●
Extended Response Test		●
Online Assessment System		●
Section Quizzes		●
Standards-Based Assessment	■	●

CHAPTER 5

Chapter Overview

- **Section 1** describes the stages of the cell cycle and the factors that affect cell size and the rate at which cells divide.
- **Section 2** describes the structure of chromosomes and provides details about the processes of mitosis and cytokinesis.
- **Section 3** discusses the factors that regulate cell division and differentiation and explains how cancer is related to the cell cycle.
- **Section 4** provides coverage of organisms that reproduce asexually through binary fission and mitosis.
- **Section 5** details how cells become differentiated to perform specific functions.

▼ Focus and Motivate

What does it mean for a cell to be immortal?

Have students define *immortal*. Most students will say it means to live forever. Have students read the explanation. **Ask**

- How do scientists define *immortality* for cells? division without limits
- What can you infer about cell division in a normal cell versus in a cancer cell? Division in normal cells is limited, or regulated, in some way.

Explain that uncontrolled cell growth can be unhealthy for an organism. The division of normal cells is controlled by the body in response to injury, infection, developmental changes, or maintenance. Recognize that it is really the cell line, not a single cell, that is immortal.

BIOZINE
HMHScience.com

Students can access BioZine at **HMHScience.com** to learn about some of the latest research in the biological sciences.

CHAPTER 5

Cell Growth and Division

BIG IDEA Cells have their own life cycle that includes reproduction, growth, and regulation, which allows organisms to carry out life functions and grow.

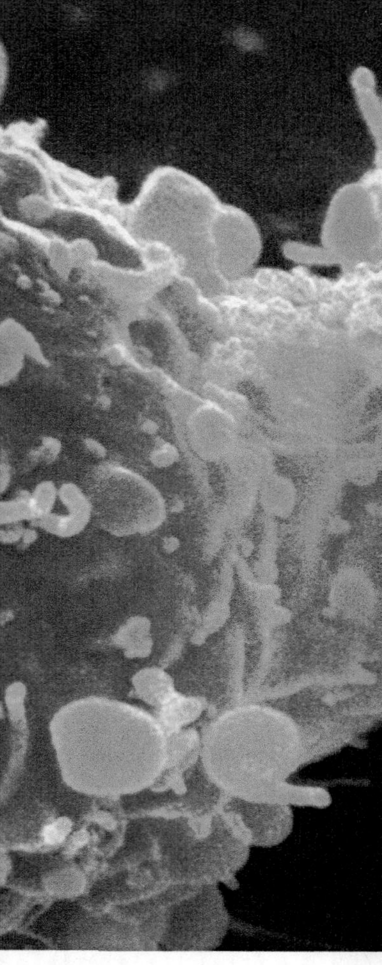

ONLINE BIOLOGY HMHScience.com

ONLINE Labs
- Mitosis in Onion Root Cells
- **Quick Lab** Cancer
- Modeling Cell Surface Area–to-Volume Ratio
- Apoptosis
- Animating Mitosis
- **Virtual Lab** Investigating Bacterial Growth
- **Video Lab** Mitosis in Plant Cells
- **S.T.E.M. Lab** Modeling Induction in Embryos

Student Activity

Purpose **Have students compare a diagram of an interphase cell with one of separating telophase cells and infer the sequence of events needed to connect the two stages.**

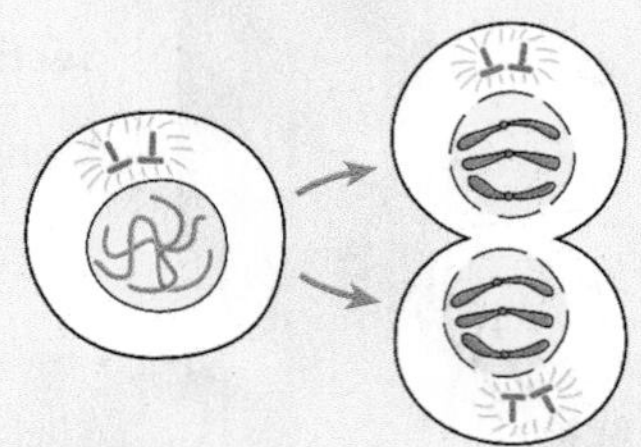

Materials (per team)
- colored pencils
- 6 index cards

Draw on the board the diagrams shown. Label DNA, nuclear envelope, and centrosome.

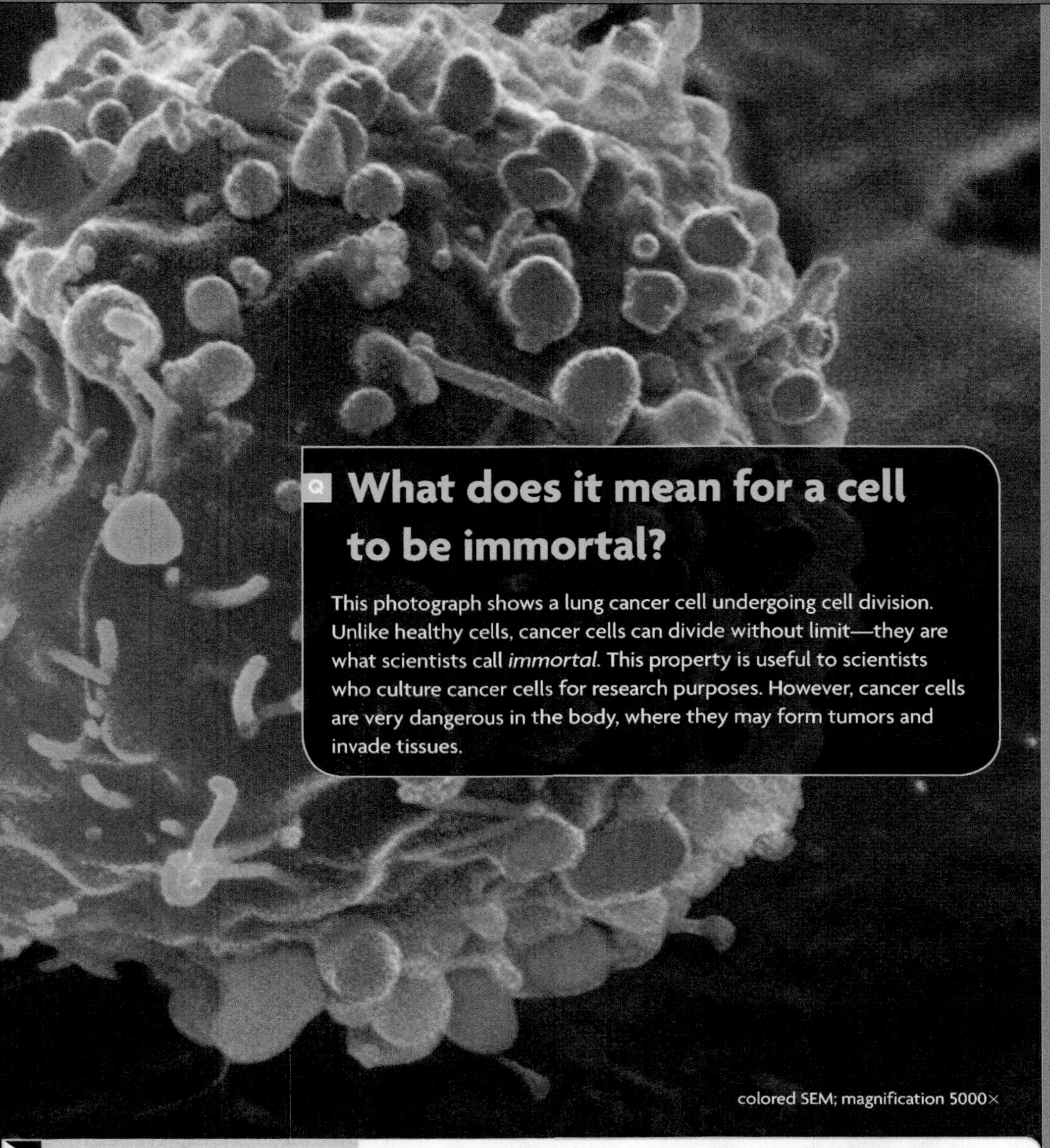

What does it mean for a cell to be immortal?

This photograph shows a lung cancer cell undergoing cell division. Unlike healthy cells, cancer cells can divide without limit—they are what scientists call *immortal*. This property is useful to scientists who culture cancer cells for research purposes. However, cancer cells are very dangerous in the body, where they may form tumors and invade tissues.

colored SEM; magnification 5000×

READING TOOLBOX This reading tool can help you learn the material in the following pages.

USING LANGUAGE

Cause and Effect In biological processes, one step leads to another step. When reading, you can often recognize these cause-and-effect relationships by words that indicate a result, such as *so, consequently, if-then,* and *as a result.*

YOUR TURN

Identify the cause and effect in the following sentences.

1. People often shiver as a result of being cold.
2. The light got brighter, so the pupil of the eye got smaller.
3. If the cell passes the G_2 checkpoint, then the cell may begin to divide.

Introduce Tell students that the diagrams on the board represent the before and after diagrams of a cell dividing. Have students form small groups, and give them five minutes to sort out the steps needed to get from the initial phase to the ending phase. Suggest they use scrap paper to do their problem solving. After five minutes, have one member of each group draw out the steps onto as many of the index cards as needed to complete the picture.

Discuss Have each group describe the steps they outlined. **Ask**

- What changes were critical in getting your cell to divide successfully? doubling of DNA, DNA condensing to form chromosomes, separation of duplicated chromosomes and centrosomes, and the division and re-formation of the nuclear envelope and cell membrane
- What happens to the organelles in the cytoplasm during cell division? Organelles also need to be divided equally between the two new cells.

Activate Prior Knowledge

To get students thinking about doubling and division, have them think about baking cookies. **Ask,** If you want two batches of cookies, not just one, what do you need to do to the recipe? Double it. Discuss that doubling a recipe means doubling all the ingredients in the original recipe.

Have students apply this idea to cell division. **Ask,** For cells to be functional after division, what needs to be present? complete set of DNA, organelles, cytoplasm, cell membrane, cell wall if a plant cell

Preview Vocabulary

Greek and Latin Word Origins Students will be studying *cycles, phases,* and *stages* in this chapter. A cycle is a repeating series of events. It has an obvious relationship to the Latin word *cyclus,* meaning "circle." The word *phase* comes from the Greek *phasis,* meaning "appearance." Remind students of the phases of the moon. Each phase of mitosis has a distinctive appearance. The word *stage* comes from the Latin *status,* or "stand." Students may think in terms of stagecoaches and the stopping points, or stands, along a journey. A cell must move through the stages in the cell cycle to reach the point where it can successfully divide.

English Learners Students may find the use of the familiar terms parent and daughter potentially confusing when applied to cell division. The idea that daughter cells originate from the same parent is straightforward. Point out to students that what is distinctive about this use is that the parent no longer exists once the daughters come into being.

Answers

1. cause: being cold; effect: to shiver
2. cause: increasing brightness of light; effect: pupil gets smaller
3. cause: cell passing G_2; effect: cell begins to divide

SECTION 5.1

B.4.4 Use a model to illustrate the role of cellular division (mitosis) and differentiation in producing and maintaining complex organisms.

▼ Plan and Prepare

Activate Prior Knowledge Link growth to cell division. **Ask,** Why do you always have to cut your hair, your fingernails, and the lawn? growth caused by new cells being made Tell students that in this section, they will learn how new cells are produced.

▼ Teach

TEACH FROM VISUALS

FIGURE 1.1 Point out the clockwise arrangement of the diagram. Relate the outer arrows to the inner descriptions. **Ask**

- What are the four main stages of the cell cycle? gap 1, synthesis, gap 2, mitosis
- What can you infer about the relative amount of time a cell spends in each stage? An actively dividing cell spends the least amount of time in the mitosis stage. The length of gap 1 varies the most and is usually the longest.

5.1 The Cell Cycle

KEY CONCEPT **Cells have distinct phases of growth, reproduction, and normal functions.**

VOCABULARY

cell cycle
mitosis
cytokinesis

MAIN IDEAS

- The cell cycle has four main stages.
- Cells divide at different rates.
- Cell size is limited.

Connect to Your World

Many of life's little chores can be quietly satisfying and rather fun. Washing dishes by hand, however, is not so fun, which is why some clever person made the dishwasher. This handy invention soaks, washes, and rinses your dishes to a spot-free, sanitary sparkle. You unload the dishes, and the machine is ready to start the cycle all over again. A cell goes through a cycle, too. This cycle of growth, DNA synthesis, and division is essential for an organism to grow and heal. If it goes out of control, abnormal cell growth may occur, resulting in cancer cells like those shown on the previous page.

MAIN IDEA

The cell cycle has four main stages.

Just as all species have life cycles, from tiny chihuahuas to massive beluga whales, cells also have a life cycle. The **cell cycle** is the regular pattern of growth, DNA duplication, and cell division that occurs in eukaryotic cells. **FIGURE 1.1** shows its four main stages: gap 1, synthesis, gap 2, and mitosis. Gap 1, synthesis, and gap 2 together make up what is called interphase.

The stages of the cell cycle get their names from early studies of cell division. Scientists' observations were limited by the microscopes of the time. When a cell was not actively dividing, they could not see activity in it. Thus, they originally divided the cell cycle into two parts: interphase, when the cell appeared to be at rest, and mitosis, when the cell was dividing. Improved techniques and tools later allowed scientists to detect the copying of DNA (DNA synthesis), and they changed their description of the cell cycle to include the synthesis stage. Since they still could not see anything happening during the other parts of interphase, scientists named the periods between mitosis and synthesis "gap 1" and "gap 2." Eventually scientists learned that, during interphase, cells carry out their normal functions and undergo critical growth and preparation for cell division.

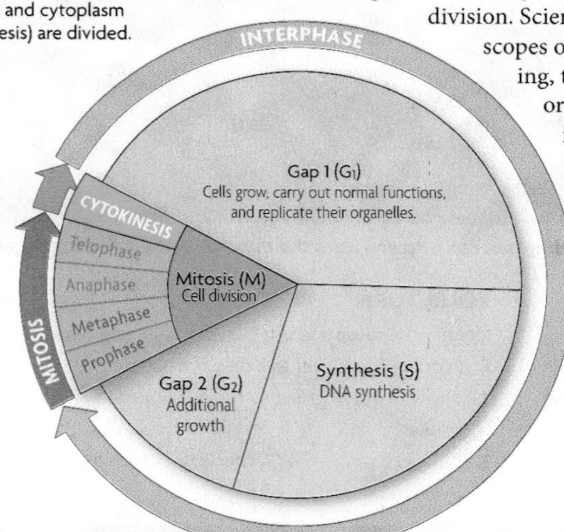

FIGURE 1.1 Cells grow and copy their DNA during interphase. They also carry out cell-specific functions in G_1 and G_2. During M stage, both the nucleus (in mitosis) and cytoplasm (in cytokinesis) are divided.

Differentiated Instruction

BELOW LEVEL

Help students understand the vocabulary involved in the cell cycle by using a word-sort activity. Prepare cards with the terms *gap 1, synthesis, gap 2,* and *mitosis* on the front and a brief description about that stage on the back. Have students arrange the cards in the correct sequence and discuss what happens during each stage, using the back of the cards if they need a reminder.

Teacher Toolkit, Section D, Word Sort

ENGLISH LEARNERS

Students might find it easier to understand the cell cycle if they think of it as a linear sequence of events. Help them visualize what is occurring at each step, using **FIGURE 2.2** from the chapter Cell Structure and Function to remind them of a eukaryote's cell structure. Have them draw out the sequence in their science notebooks.

Teacher Toolkit, Section C, Connect to Content Through Visuals

Gap 1 (G_1)

The first stage of the cell cycle is gap 1 (G_1). During G_1, a cell carries out its normal functions. If it is a skeletal muscle cell, it contracts to move joints. If it is an adrenal cell, it secretes hormones such as adrenaline. If it is an intestinal cell, it absorbs nutrients. During G_1, cells also increase in size, and organelles increase in number. A cell spends most of its time in the G_1 stage, although the length of this stage varies by cell type.

During G_1, the cell must pass a critical checkpoint before it can proceed to the synthesis stage. Just as it would be dangerous for you to run a marathon if you had not slept or eaten for several days, it would also be dangerous for your cells to continue dividing if certain conditions were not met. For instance, most animal cells need enough nutrition, adequate size, and relatively undamaged DNA to divide successfully. They also need specific signals from other cells, telling them whether more cell division is needed.

Synthesis (S)

The second stage of the cell cycle is the synthesis (S) stage. *Synthesis* means "the combining of parts to make a whole." During the S stage, the cell makes a copy of its nuclear DNA. In eukaryotes, DNA is located in the nucleus. During interphase, it is loosely organized and appears grainy in photographs. By the end of the S stage, the cell nucleus contains two complete sets of DNA.

Gap 2 (G_2)

Gap 2 (G_2) is the third stage of the cell cycle. During G_2, cells continue to carry out their normal functions, and additional growth occurs. Like G_1, this stage includes a critical checkpoint. Everything must be in order—adequate cell size, undamaged DNA—before the cell goes through mitosis and division.

Mitosis (M)

Mitosis (M), the fourth stage of the cell cycle, includes two processes: mitosis and cytokinesis. **Mitosis** (my-TOH-sihs) is the division of the cell nucleus and its contents. During mitosis, the nuclear membrane dissolves, the duplicated DNA condenses around proteins and separates, and two new nuclei form. Lastly, **cytokinesis** (SY-toh-kuh-NEE-sihs) is the process that divides the cell cytoplasm. The result is two daughter cells that are genetically identical to the original cell.

VISUAL VOCAB

Mitosis is the division of the cell nucleus and its contents.

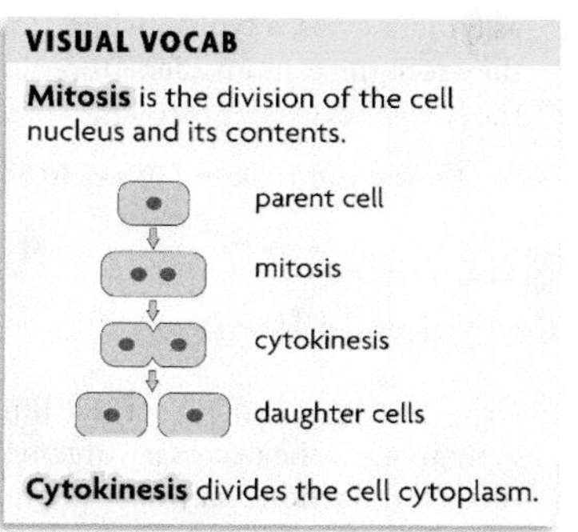

Cytokinesis divides the cell cytoplasm.

The stages of the cell cycle and the proteins that control it are similar in all eukaryotes. For example, scientists have demonstrated that some of the molecules that regulate checkpoints in the yeast cell cycle can work in human cells, too. Such similarities suggest that eukaryotes share a common ancestry.

A Predict What might happen if the G_2 checkpoint stopped working in cells?

READING TOOLBOX

TAKING NOTES

Construct your own cycle diagram to take notes about processes such as the cell cycle.

G_1 Growth → S Synthesis

CONNECT TO

DNA REPLICATION

As you will learn in the chapter **From DNA to Proteins,** DNA synthesis is also called DNA replication. During this process, the DNA molecule unzips and each strand is used as a pattern for a new DNA strand.

PRE-AP

As described on this student page, the proteins that control the cell cycle, and therefore the DNA that codes for them, are highly conserved. Similar proteins are found in many organisms, not just in eukaryotes, but also in bacteria. Have students write for five minutes to explain why a control mechanism that limits growth rather than encourages it would be an advantageous adaptation. Suggest that they think about the cancer cells pictured on the chapter opener.

Teacher Toolkit, Section C, Quick-Write

Vocabulary

Academic Vocabulary The word **gap** suggests a break or an interruption. Scientists named the two stages of the cell cycle *gaps* because they did not know the cell was active during these stages.

Take It Further

Three important **checkpoints** in a cell cycle ensure that specific events occur correctly and in the proper order, thus signaling readiness for cell division.

- The first checkpoint begins at the end of gap 1, during which a cell checks the DNA for any damage before copying begins and also makes sure that conditions are right for division.
- By the second checkpoint, at the end of gap 2, both DNA and the centrosome need to have been successfully copied, and those parts of the cytoskeleton that help to pull the two halves apart must be in place.
- The third and final checkpoint occurs halfway through mitosis, when the two copies of DNA must be properly attached to the cytoskeleton that will separate them.

Address Misconceptions

Common Misconception Students often think that cytokinesis is part of the process of mitosis, especially given its inclusion as part of the M stage of the cell cycle.

Correcting the Misconception Use the Visual Vocab to reinforce the point that mitosis and cytokinesis are two distinct processes. Mitosis is the division of the cell nucleus and its contents, resulting in two identical nuclei. Cytokinesis is the division of the cell cytoplasm, resulting in two cells, each of which contains one of the nuclei from mitosis. The two processes overlap. The cytoplasm begins to divide during the last phases of mitosis. Together mitosis and cytokinesis make up the mitosis stage of the cell cycle.

Answers

A Predict Cells may be the wrong size, have damaged DNA, and fail to divide.

Chapter 5: Cell Growth and Division 131

▼ Teach *continued*

Take It Further

It might be helpful for students to think in terms of a cell population when relating the rate of cell division to the length of cell life spans. For example, from the information supplied in **FIGURE 1.2,** we would expect a population of muscle cells to divide at a much slower rate than a population of skin cells.

Explain to students that specialization in cells sometimes includes cells whose job it is to divide to supply new cells. These are **stem cells,** which are discussed in **Section 5.** Many of the cells in the human body that need constant replacement, such as blood cells and surface skin cells, are unable to divide. Stem cells that are part of the cell population provide new cells that, once produced, differentiate into the type of cell needed.

Answers

A Infer A skin cell would probably have a short G_1. Skin cells undergo a lot of wear and tear because they are exposed on the outside of the body. Therefore, they are probably replaced quickly.

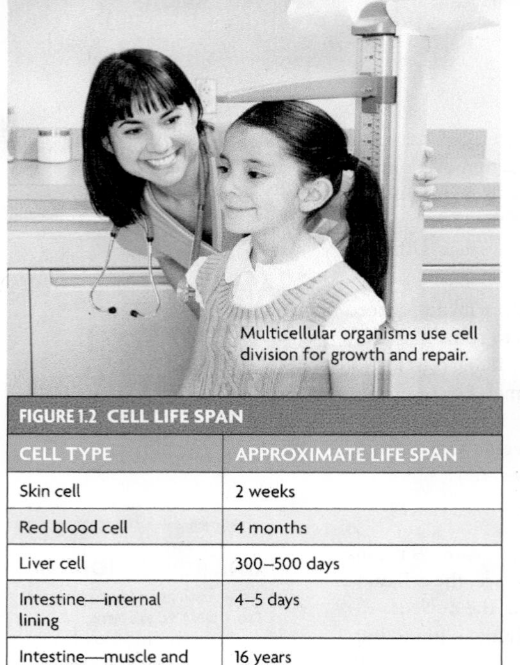

Multicellular organisms use cell division for growth and repair.

FIGURE 1.2 CELL LIFE SPAN

CELL TYPE	APPROXIMATE LIFE SPAN
Skin cell	2 weeks
Red blood cell	4 months
Liver cell	300–500 days
Intestine—internal lining	4–5 days
Intestine—muscle and other tissues	16 years

Source: Spaulding et al., *Cell* 122:1.

CONNECT TO

LYMPHOCYTES

As you will learn in the chapter **Immune System and Disease,** lymphocytes are a part of your immune system. There are two major types of lymphocytes, B and T cells. Both types recognize specific antigens.

MAIN IDEA

Cells divide at different rates.

Rates of cell division vary widely, as shown in **FIGURE 1.2.** The prokaryotic cell cycle is similar but not identical to that of eukaryotic cells. Recall that prokaryotes do not have the membrane-bound organelles and cytoskeleton found in eukaryotes. Thus, prokaryotic cells typically divide much faster than do eukaryotic cells.

The rate at which your cells divide is linked to your body's need for those cells. In human cells, the S, G_2, and M stages together usually take about 12 hours. The length of the G_1 stage differs most from cell type to cell type. The rate of cell division is greater in embryos and children than it is in adults. Children have a shorter cell cycle, and many of their organs are still developing. But the rate of cell division also varies within different tissues of the adult body. The internal lining of your digestive tract receives a lot of wear and tear. As a result, cells that line your stomach and intestine are replaced every few days. In contrast, cells that make up the rest of your intestine (mainly smooth muscle) and many of your internal organs, such as lungs, kidneys, and liver, divide only occasionally, in response to injury or cell death.

Cells that divide only rarely are thought to enter a stage that some scientists call G_0. In G_0, cells are unlikely to divide, although they continue to carry out their normal functions. Some cells, such as neurons, appear to stay permanently in the G_0 stage. However, some data suggest that neurons actually can divide, and this question continues to be actively researched. Other cells, such as lymphocytes, a type of white blood cell, may remain in G_0 for years until they recognize an invader. Once the invader binds to a lymphocyte receptor, the lymphocyte goes through rapid cell divisions to help fight infection.

A Infer **Do you think a skin cell would have a long or short G_1 stage? Explain why.**

MAIN IDEA

Cell size is limited.

Cells have upper and lower size limits. If cells were too small, they could not contain all of the necessary organelles and molecules. For instance, a cell with too few mitochondria would not have enough energy to live. However, cells cannot grow beyond a certain size, even if surrounded by plenty of nutrients. The upper limit on cell size is due to the ratio of cell surface area to volume. Recall that oxygen, nutrients, and wastes move across the cell membrane, or the surface of the cell. These materials must be transported in adequate amounts and with adequate speed to keep the inside of the cell functioning. But as a cell increases in size, its volume increases faster than its surface area, as shown in **FIGURE 1.3.** Therefore, a further increase in size could result in a surface area too small for the adequate exchange of materials.

Differentiated Instruction

INCLUSION

Use cubic cell models to help literal thinkers understand the relationship between surface area and volume. Two sizes of cutouts are provided in the Teacher Resources at **HMHScience.com.** Use eight cutouts of the smaller cube (2 cm^3) to fill the interior of the larger cube (4 cm^3). Work with students to calculate the ratio of surface area–to–volume for each cube. Then have students compare the surface area of eight smaller cubes to that of one large cube. Make sure students understand that the sides represent cell membrane.

Remind students that cells work together. Have students consider the advantages of eight smaller cells of a given volume working together compared to one larger cell of equal volume.

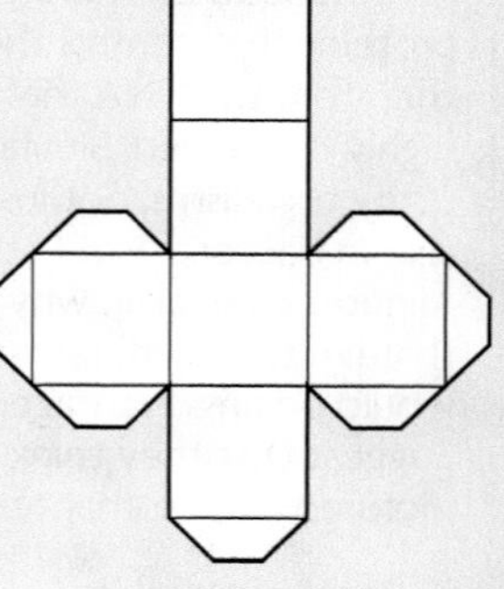

FIGURE 1.3 Ratio of Surface Area to Volume in Cells

As a cell grows, its volume increases more rapidly than its surface area. When the surface area–to-volume ratio is too small, the cell cannot move materials into and out of the cell at a sufficient rate or in sufficient quantities.

Relative size	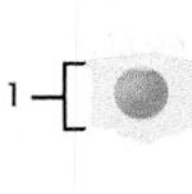 1	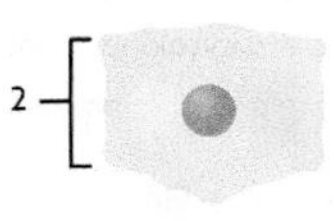 2	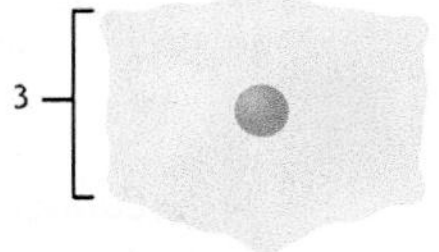 3
Surface area (length × width × number of sides)	6	24	54
Volume (length × width × height)	1	8	27
Ratio of surface area to volume	$\frac{6}{1} = 6:1$	$\frac{24}{8} = 3:1$	$\frac{54}{27} = 2:1$

Compare **Which cell has the largest surface area? Which cell has the largest surface area–to-volume ratio?**

Some cells, however, must be large. A neuron running down a giraffe's neck to its legs may be several meters long, for instance. But it is not shaped like a cube or a sphere. Instead, it is extremely long and thin. This structure gives the neuron a large surface area with a relatively small increase in volume.

To maintain a suitable cell size, growth and division must be coordinated. If a cell more than doubled its size before dividing, the daughter cells would be larger than the original cell. If this happened with each generation, cells would quickly become too large to live. Similarly, if a cell did not double its size before dividing, the daughter cells would be smaller than the original cell. If this happened with each generation, cells would become too small to live.

Connect **Which has the larger ratio of surface area to volume, a tennis ball or a soccer ball? Explain your reasoning.**

5.1 Formative Assessment

REVIEWING ◉ MAIN IDEAS

1. During which stage of the **cell cycle** is the DNA copied?
2. Which stages of the cell cycle generally require about the same amount of time in all human cells?
3. What limits the maximum size of a cell?

CRITICAL THINKING

4. **Infer** Suppose you were to draw a diagram representing the cell cycle of a neuron. Explain where and how you would represent G_0.
5. **Predict** Suppose you treat cells with chemicals that block **cytokinesis.** Describe what you think the cells would look like.

SELF-CHECK Online
HMHScience.com
GO ONLINE

CONNECT TO

SCIENTIFIC PROCESS

6. Predict how the rate of cell division would differ between single-celled algae living in a sunny, nutrient-rich pond versus algae living in a shady, nutrient-poor pond. How could you test your prediction?

TEACH FROM VISUALS

FIGURE 1.3 Go over the math needed to calculate the ratio of surface area to volume of a cell. **Ask,** What formula is used to calculate the surface area of a cell? length × width × number of sides What formula is used to calculate the volume of a cell? length × width × height

Point out that the surface area of a cube increases by the length squared and its volume increases by length cubed. Calculate and list on the board the squares and cubes of the numbers 1 through 9 to show how much more rapidly the cube (volume) increases compared to the square (surface area) of the number.

Answers

A **Compare** Cell 3 has the largest surface area; Cell 1 has the largest surface area-to-volume ratio.

B **Connect** a tennis ball, because volume increases more rapidly than does surface area as a ball gets larger

Assess and Reteach ▼

Assess Use the Section Self-Check or Section Quiz, both available at **HMHScience.com**.

Reteach Randomly write on the board the events of the cell cycle and have students indicate the proper order.

5.1 FORMATIVE ASSESSMENT

1. synthesis (S)
2. S, G_2, and M stages
3. the ratio of cell surface area to volume
4. Students should suggest representing G_0 as an offshoot of G_1, because during G_0, a cell carries out normal functions but does not divide. G_1 is the only stage that does not involve DNA synthesis, duplicated DNA, or cell division.
5. The cells would probably look large and have two nuclei located at opposite sides of the cell.
6. It is likely that the algae in the sunny pond would have a faster rate of cell division than the algae in the shady pond. Any feasible way of testing the prediction is acceptable. One example could be to gather algae from the two ponds and evaluate what percentages of the samples were in each stage of the cell cycle. Presumably, a higher percentage of the algae in the shady pond would be in G_1 compared to the algae in the sunny pond.

SECTION 5.2

B.4.4 Use a model to illustrate the role of cellular division (mitosis) and differentiation in producing and maintaining complex organisms.

▼ Plan and Prepare

Activate Prior Knowledge Have students think about packing for a trip. **Ask**

- What would you do if you had to put a lot of clothes into a small suitcase? compress the clothes
- If you were sharing the suitcase with your twin brother or sister, what would you need to do? compress the clothes, and later separate them

Tell students that strands of DNA need to be both condensed and separated for a cell to divide.

▼ Teach

Vocabulary

Academic Vocabulary Have students compare these words:

condense, to reduce the volume of
compress, to press together

The words share a prefix that means "together." The root *densare* of *condense* means to "thicken." Tell students that *condense* and *compress* are not synonymous, but the result is an object that is made more **compact.**

5.2 Mitosis and Cytokinesis

KEY CONCEPT **Cells divide during mitosis and cytokinesis.**

MAIN IDEAS
- Chromosomes condense at the start of mitosis.
- Mitosis and cytokinesis produce two genetically identical daughter cells.

VOCABULARY

chromosome
histone
chromatin
chromatid
centromere
telomere
prophase
metaphase
anaphase
telophase

Connect to Your World

When you were a child, perhaps you attended a birthday party where goody bags were handed out. Whoever stuffed the bags had to make sure that each bag had exactly the same number of erasers, candies, and stickers. Otherwise, some ill-mannered child (not you, of course) might have raised a fuss if an item was missing. In a similar way, your cells must receive a full set of DNA—no more, no less—to work properly. Dividing DNA is a complicated task because the DNA is so long and stringy. Mitosis is an amazing process that efficiently sorts two sets of DNA and divides them between two nuclei.

MAIN IDEA

Chromosomes condense at the start of mitosis.

DNA is a double-stranded molecule made of four different subunits called nucleotides. A **chromosome** is one long continuous thread of DNA that consists of numerous genes along with regulatory information. Your body cells have 46 chromosomes each. If stretched out straight and laid end to end, the DNA in just one of your cells would be about 3 meters (10 feet) long. How does it fit inside the nucleus of a microscopic cell?

DNA wraps around proteins that help organize and condense it. During interphase, or when a cell is not dividing, DNA is loosely organized—it looks a bit like spaghetti. During mitosis, however, your chromosomes are tightly condensed, as shown in **FIGURE 2.1.** These changes in DNA's organization allow a cell to carry out its necessary functions. During all of interphase, proteins must access specific genes for a cell to make specific proteins or to copy the entire DNA sequence. During mitosis, the duplicated chromosomes must condense to be divided between two nuclei. If chromosomes remained stringy during mitosis, they could become entangled. Perhaps a cell would get two copies of one chromosome and no copies of a different one. **FIGURE 2.2** shows the process that converts a chromosome from a linear strand of DNA to its highly condensed form. The key to this process is the association between DNA and proteins.

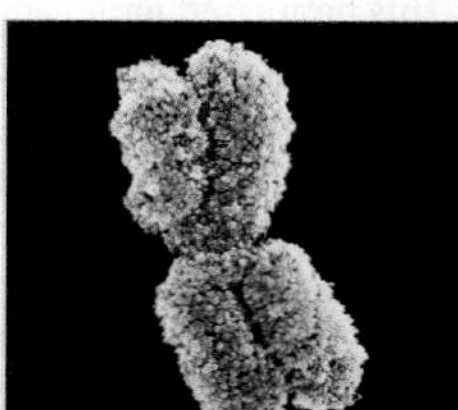

FIGURE 2.1 This duplicated chromosome is tightly condensed. (colored SEM; magnification unknown)

CONNECT TO

BIOCHEMISTRY

As you will learn in the chapter **From DNA to Proteins,** a nucleotide is made of three parts: a sugar, a phosphate group, and a nitrogen-containing molecule called a base. When the sugars and phosphate groups bond, they form the backbones of the long chains called nucleic acids.

phosphate
base
sugar

Differentiated Instruction

ENGLISH LEARNERS

Point to the vocabulary list for the section. Tell students that the first six words relate to DNA. Point out that three of the words (*chromosome, chromatin, chromatid*) are various forms of DNA. Tell them that the *-phase* words are the steps of mitosis they were introduced to in **Section 1.** Suggest that students use diagrams with their notes to work out the relationship between the terms.

Teacher Toolkit, Section C, Combination Notes

BELOW LEVEL

Have students use the technique of directed reading-thinking to preview the section and identify material that is familiar to them. Have them set up a table and fill in the following categories as they preview, read, and review:

- What I know I know
- What I think I know
- What I think I'll learn
- What I learned

Teacher Toolkit, Section C, DRTA

FIGURE 2.2 Chromosome Structure

DNA condenses tightly during the early stages of mitosis.

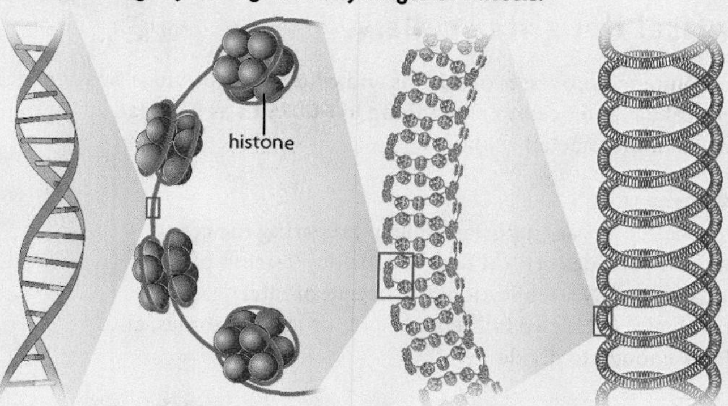

chromatid

telomere

centromere

telomere

DNA double helix Each continuous, double-stranded DNA molecule makes one chromosome.

DNA and histones DNA wraps at regular intervals around proteins called histones, forming chromatin.

Chromatin Interactions between parts of the histones further compact the DNA.

Supercoiled DNA The chromatin coils more and more tightly around organizing proteins.

Condensed, duplicated chromosome The condensed, duplicated chromosomes can be aligned and separated during mitosis.

Infer **Overall, DNA has a negative charge. Look at the histone proteins in the figure. What type of overall charge do you think they have? Explain.**

At almost all times during the cell cycle, each of your chromosomes is associated with a group of proteins called **histones.** DNA wraps around histones at regular intervals, similar to beads on a string. The complex of protein and DNA that makes up the chromosome is called **chromatin.** Parts of the histones interact with each other, further compacting the DNA. At the "spaghetti" stage, the combination of DNA and proteins is loose. The word "loose" describes how much the DNA strand folds back on itself; it does not mean the DNA is loosely wrapped around the histones.

As a cell progresses into mitosis, chromatin further condenses. It continues to coil more and more tightly around organizing proteins, finally forming small, thick rods. Recall that each chromosome has already been copied during the previous S stage. Thus, the chromosome looks similar to an "X" in which the left and right halves are two identical DNA double helixes. One half of a duplicated chromosome is called a **chromatid** (KROH-muh-tihd). Together, the two identical chromatids are called sister chromatids. Sister chromatids are held together at the **centromere** (SEHN-truh-MEER), a region of the condensed chromosome that looks pinched.

In addition, the ends of DNA molecules form structures called **telomeres** (TEHL-uh-MEERS), which are made of repeating nucleotides that do not form genes. They prevent the ends of chromosomes from accidentally attaching to each other, and they help prevent the loss of genes. A short section of nucleotides is lost from a new DNA molecule each time it is copied. It is important that these nucleotides are lost from telomeres, not from the genes themselves.

Apply **What is the relationship between a molecule of DNA and a chromosome?**

READING TOOLBOX

TAKING NOTES

Use a main idea web to help you study the makeup and organization of chromosomes.

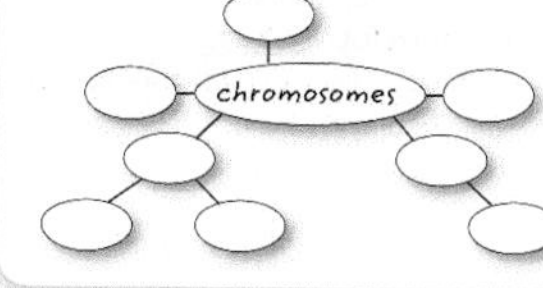

INCLUSION

For students who have difficulty working with layers of information, model for them how you read the text on these pages for understanding. Relate descriptions in the text to the various parts of **FIGURE 2.2**, demonstrating for students how to connect the two.

TEACH FROM VISUALS

FIGURE 2.2 Have students look carefully at the diagram, starting with the DNA double helix on the left. Discuss how that structure relates to each successive structure. **Ask**

- Starting with the DNA double helix on the left, how does that part of the diagram relate to the next part of the diagram, and how can you tell? The first is a much more detailed version of the DNA strand in the "DNA and histones" diagram. The outline of a square shows which part of the diagram has been magnified.
- Where do you see helices (spirals) in this figure? There are spiraling shapes in each of the DNA diagrams. Students may perceive spiraling in the chromatids.

Make sure students understand that the two spiraling strands of the DNA double helix represent a single molecule. **Ask,** What happens to DNA by the time it reaches the structure shown on the right? DNA has been copied during interphase. Each copy of the DNA molecule wraps around histones to form a coil that then coils again to form a supercoil.

Vocabulary

Greek and Latin Word Origins Tell students that many of the vocabulary words in this section come from Greek prefixes and suffixes, producing names that are descriptive. **Telomere** and **centromere** refer to parts of a chromosome:

-mere = part or segment
telo- = end
centro- = center

The Greek root *chromo* means "color" and refers to the fact that DNA in its various forms readily attracted the stains that made it visible under the microscope. The rest of the word **chromosome** completes the description:

soma = body

Answers

A Infer Positive; negative and positive charges attract each other. If the histones were negatively charged, they would repel DNA.

B Apply A chromosome is made of one continuous DNA molecule.

▼ Teach *continued*

History of Science

With the **cell theory** established by the mid-1800s, attention turned to the mechanism by which one cell becomes two. Advances in staining techniques and the development of better microscopes were required to get a clear picture of what was happening during **mitosis.** In studying eukaryotic cells, scientists were puzzled because the nucleus seemed to disappear from the parent cell and then reappear in each daughter cell.

In 1882, German scientist **Walther Flemming** published the definitive paper detailing the steps of mitosis in eukaryotic cells. Using a new staining technique and greatly enhanced microscope technology, he put together the sequence by studying the fixed and stained cells from a salamander larva. He saw that as the nucleus disappeared, threadlike structures came to the center of the cell to divide. Flemming coined the term *mitosis* for the process, the Greek word *mitos,* meaning "thread." He went on to observe this process in both living and fixed cells of many different types of organisms. He concluded that it was a universal feature of organisms.

Vocabulary

Greek and Latin Roots The word **phase** comes from the Greek root meaning "appearance."

inter- = between
pro- = before
meta- = after
ana- = back
telo- = end

Ask, What do you think the prefixes used are referring to? appearance of chromosomes

FIGURE 2.3 The nucleus and chromosomes go through dramatic changes in a dividing cell.

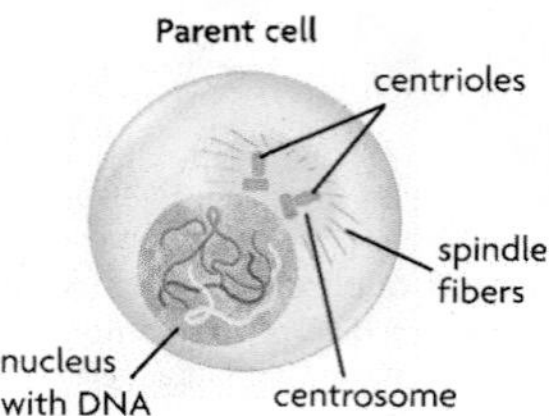

CONNECT TO

CELLS

As you will learn in the chapter **Meiosis and Mendel,** your body has two major cell types. Germ cells develop into eggs or sperm. Somatic cells make up the rest of your body.

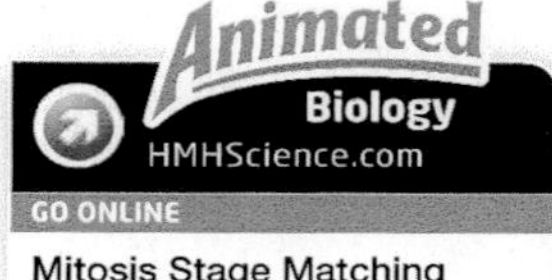

Mitosis Stage Matching

MAIN IDEA

Mitosis and cytokinesis produce two genetically identical daughter cells.

The combined processes of mitosis and cytokinesis produce two genetically identical daughter cells. Follow along in **FIGURE 2.4** as you read about the process in more detail below.

Interphase

INTERPHASE

Interphase plays an important role in preparing the cell to divide. It provides critical time for the duplication of organelles and for DNA replication. By the end of interphase, an individual cell has two full sets of DNA, or chromosomes, and is large enough to divide.

Mitosis

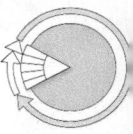

MITOSIS

Mitosis divides a cell's nucleus into two genetically identical nuclei, each with its own single, full set of DNA. This process occurs in all of your body cells—except those that form eggs or sperm—and prepares them for cytokinesis. Although mitosis and cytokinesis are continuous processes, scientists have divided them into phases to make them easier to understand and discuss. The four main phases of mitosis are prophase, metaphase, anaphase, and telophase. Cytokinesis begins during late anaphase or telophase.

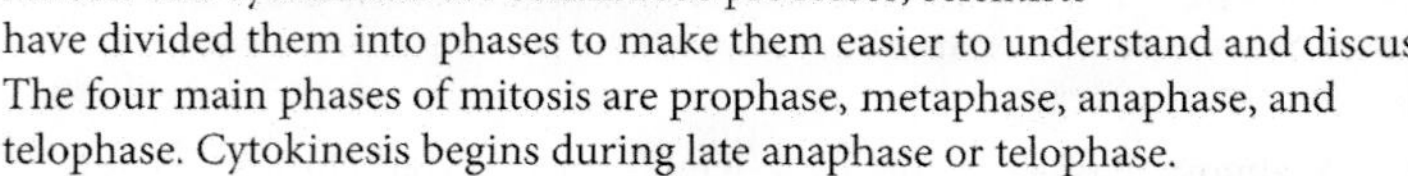

1. During **prophase,** chromatin condenses into tightly coiled chromosomes. Each consists of two identical sister chromatids. The nuclear envelope breaks down, the nucleolus disappears, and the centrosomes and centrioles begin to migrate to opposite sides of the cell. Organized microtubules called spindle fibers grow from the centrioles and radiate toward the center of the cell.

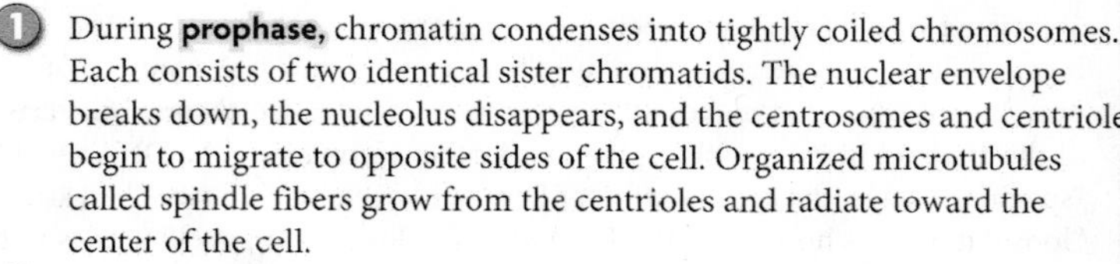

2. In **metaphase,** the spindle fibers attach to a protein structure on the centromere of each chromosome and align the chromosomes along the cell equator, around the middle of the cell.
3. During **anaphase,** sister chromatids separate from each other. The spindle fibers begin to shorten, pulling the sister chromatids away from each other and toward opposite sides of the cell.
4. In **telophase,** a complete set of identical chromosomes is positioned at each pole of the cell. The nuclear membranes start to form, the chromosomes begin to uncoil, and the spindle fibers fall apart.

Cytokinesis

Cytokinesis divides the cytoplasm into two cells and completes a full stage of the cell cycle. Cytokinesis differs in animal and plant cells. In animal cells, the membrane forms a furrow, or trench, that is pulled inward by tiny filaments, like a drawstring. Gradually, the membrane pinches closed, forming a separate cell around each nucleus.

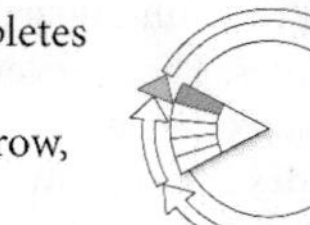

Differentiated Instruction

BELOW LEVEL

Remind students that mnemonic devices, or memory aids, can help with recall. To remember the order of phases in mitosis, ask students to come up with an expression that uses the first letter of each phase. Examples: People may answer telephones or peas make awful tarts.

FIGURE 2.4 The Cell Cycle in Detail

Following interphase, mitosis divides duplicated chromosomes between two nuclei. Cytokinesis divides the cytoplasm. In this diagram, the mitosis stage is greatly expanded to highlight its four major phases. (micrographs; magnification about 100×)

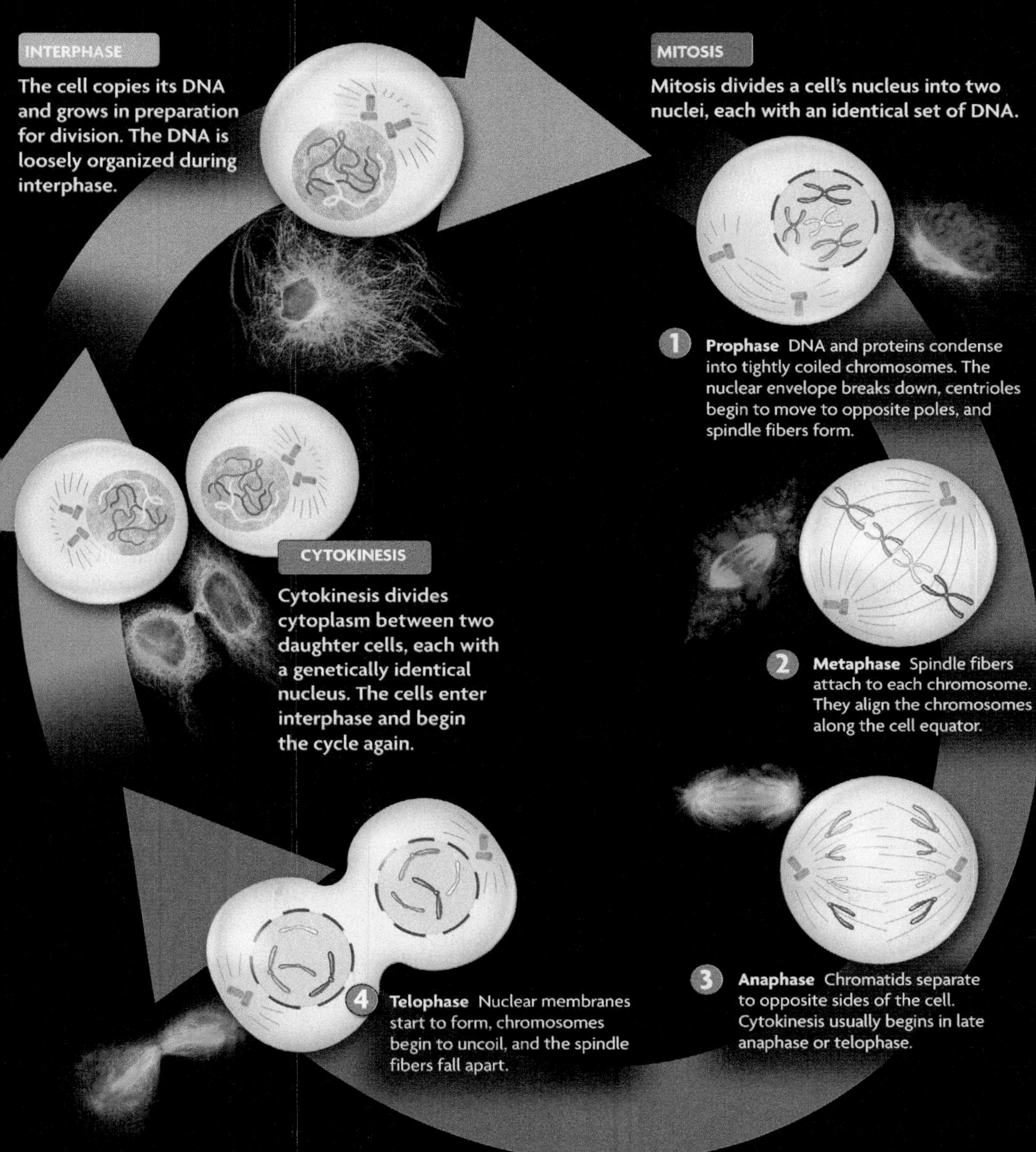
INTERPHASE
The cell copies its DNA and grows in preparation for division. The DNA is loosely organized during interphase.
MITOSIS
Mitosis divides a cell's nucleus into two nuclei, each with an identical set of DNA.
1 Prophase DNA and proteins condense into tightly coiled chromosomes. The nuclear envelope breaks down, centrioles begin to move to opposite poles, and spindle fibers form.
2 Metaphase Spindle fibers attach to each chromosome. They align the chromosomes along the cell equator.
3 Anaphase Chromatids separate to opposite sides of the cell. Cytokinesis usually begins in late anaphase or telophase.
4 Telophase Nuclear membranes start to form, chromosomes begin to uncoil, and the spindle fibers fall apart.
CYTOKINESIS
Cytokinesis divides cytoplasm between two daughter cells, each with a genetically identical nucleus. The cells enter interphase and begin the cycle again.

CRITICAL VIEWING **How many chromosomes does the cell have at the start of mitosis? How many does it have after cytokinesis?** (A)

TEACH FROM VISUALS

FIGURE 2.4 Point out that the diagrams have been greatly simplified. They show only 4 chromosomes, whereas the accompanying TEMs show 46. Have students relate the chromosomes in each phase of mitosis with the chromosome structures shown in **FIGURE 2.2**. Have students identify points where DNA is single and where it is doubled. **Ask**

- How are the chromosomes shown in step 1 (prophase) different from those in step 4 (telophase)? Sister chromatids have separated by step 4. The daughter chromosomes have just one copy of DNA.
- What type of chromosome is pictured in **FIGURE 2.1**? metaphase chromosome
- What other cellular structure, besides DNA, must double for another round of mitosis to occur? centrosome

Take It Further

The **centrosome** is the organizing center for the microtubules that make up the mitotic spindle. The microtubules are colored bright green in the TEMs shown in **FIGURE 2.4.** The **tubulin** units that make up microtubules can rapidly assemble, as they do during metaphase, or disassemble, as they do during telophase. The **centrioles,** also made up of microtubules, appear to play a role in the duplication of the centrosome in animal cells. Plant cells do not have centrioles.

TEACH WITH TECHNOLOGY

Walther Flemming published many drawings of mitosis. Some are available on the Internet. Project the images for students and have them compare the drawings. Discuss the importance of these images as a source of information.

Answers

(A) **Critical Viewing** four (duplicated) chromosomes; four (unduplicated) chromosomes

▼ Teach *continued*

DATA ANALYSIS

Introduce

Remind students that units of measure typically go into the column headings, reserving the cells of a table for numbers alone. All values in a column must be in the same unit of measure.

Answers

1. Students will list the given temperatures in the first column and the number of daily doublings in the second column. An appropriate title would be "Effect of Temperature on Cell Division in *Chlorella*."
2. The independent variable is temperature, and the dependent variable is the number of daily doublings.

Online Student Resources, Data Analysis Practice

Answers

Ⓐ **Contrast** In animal cells, the membrane pinches together to separate the cytoplasm. In plant cells, a cell plate forms and divides the cell, along which the cell membrane and cell wall re-form.

▼ Assess and Reteach

Assess Use the Section Self-Check or Section Quiz, both available at **HMHScience.com**.

Reteach Have students view mitosis diagrams from the Media Gallery. Then have students draw and label their own diagrams of the four major phases of mitosis and of cytokinesis. Have them relate chromosome structure to the stages of the cell cycle.

DATA ANALYSIS

CONSTRUCTING DATA TABLES

Scientists use data tables to record their data. Data tables are organized by the independent and dependent variables. Usually the independent variable is listed in the left column, and the other columns list the dependent variables. Each separate observation is listed in its own row. When measurements are taken using units, they are listed in the column headings in parentheses. All tables should have numbers and titles.

TABLE 1. EFFECT OF HORMONES ON CELL DIVISION

Concentration of Hormone Solution (%)	Size of Cell Clump After 24 Hours (mm)
0	3
25	4
50	8
75	9
100	9

independent variable — dependent variable — observations

Table 1 shows data from a hypothetical experiment in which growth hormones were added to clumps of cells in a laboratory, and the growth of the cell clumps was measured.

1. **Display Data** Suppose a scientist decided to measure the effect of temperature on cell division in *chlorella*, a type of green algae. Set up a table that could be used to record the results for the number of daily doublings of the cells: 20°C, 3 doublings; 30°C, 7 doublings; 40°C, 12 doublings; 50°C, 0 doublings.
2. **Apply** Label the independent and dependent variables on your table.

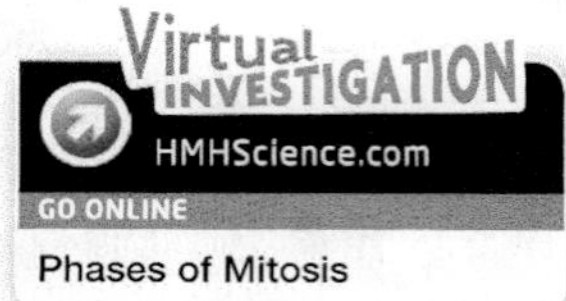

During cytokinesis in plant cells, the membrane cannot pinch inward because of the cell wall. Instead, a cell plate forms between the two nuclei. It is made by the Golgi apparatus, which supplies the new plasma membrane. A new wall then grows as cellulose and other materials are laid down. Typically, cytoplasm is divided evenly between daughter cells in both plant and animal cells.

The formation of new cells is critical in both multicellular and single-celled organisms. Single-celled organisms use cell division to reproduce, whereas multicellular organisms use it for growth, development, and repair.

 **Contrast** **How does cytokinesis differ in animal and plant cells?**

5.2 Formative Assessment

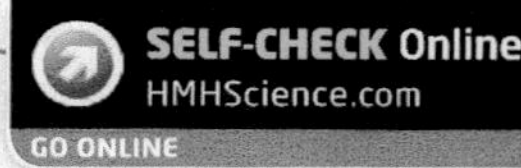

REVIEWING ⊙ MAIN IDEAS

1. Draw what a **chromosome** looks like during **metaphase.** Identify the **chromatids** and the **centromere.**
2. Briefly explain why the daughter cells resulting from mitosis are genetically identical to each other and to the original cell.

CRITICAL THINKING

3. **Contrast** How do **prophase** and **telophase** differ?
4. **Apply** Using a light microscope, you observe a cell that has no nucleus. What features would you look for to determine whether it is a eukaryotic cell undergoing mitosis or a prokaryotic cell?

CONNECT TO

PROTEIN SYNTHESIS

5. For a cell to make proteins, enzymes must access its genes. When **histones** are modified with acetyl groups (-$COCH_3$), their positive charge is neutralized, so they wrap DNA less tightly. How might this affect the rate of protein synthesis?

5.2 FORMATIVE ASSESSMENT

1. Accept all reasonable sketches. Refer to Step 2 in Figure 2.4 for an example.
2. During interphase, the original cell copies its DNA. During mitosis, the two copies separate to opposite poles of the cell. After cytokinesis, each daughter cell has a copy of the original cell's DNA.
3. Prophase and telophase are opposites. In prophase, the nuclear envelope fragments, chromosomes condense, and spindle fibers start to assemble. In telophase, the reverse occurs: the nuclear envelope re-forms, chromosomes uncoil, and spindle fibers disassemble.
4. Condensed chromosomes and spindle fibers would be visible in a eukaryotic cell undergoing mitosis. The other organelles of a eukaryotic cell would also be visible.
5. Acetylation (adding an acetyl group) could increase the rate of protein synthesis because the looser DNA wrapping may make it easier for enzymes to access the genes.

Exploring Elephants' Low Cancer Rates

S.T.E.M. Interactions

More than eight million people around the globe succumb to cancer every year, including more than half a million deaths in the United States alone. Researchers have been working for decades to understand the disease better and to discover improved treatments, diagnosis, and prevention. One way to do this is to study cancer in other animals.

Recent genetic studies have shed light on one of science's long-standing questions: How can animals as large as elephants have such a low incidence of cancers? The answer potentially lies in a particular protein encoded in a gene called TP53.

In 1977, British epidemiologist and statistician Richard Peto pointed out that most animals, regardless of their size, have roughly the same rates of cancer occurrence. He found this surprising because of the way cancer spreads in the body. Basically, when a cell divides, a mutation that makes the cell grow more quickly may occur. The more times the cell divides, the more chances there are for more mutations to occur. Therefore, larger animals—which have more cells than smaller animals and whose cells have divided many more times than those of smaller animals—should have higher rates of cancer occurrence than smaller animals. Yet, they don't. This puzzle is known as Peto's paradox.

Elephants are one of the world's longest-lived animals, with an average lifespan of 60 to 70 years, depending on the species. They are also the world's largest land animals, with an average weight of 5,000 to 8,000 kg (~ 11,000 to 17,000 lbs) and an average height of 3 to 4 m (9 to 13 ft). Their size and age mean they have trillions of cells that have divided many times, so they would seem to be prime candidates for cancer. Yet, only 5 percent of elephant deaths are caused by cancer, compared with a much higher cancer death rate in humans: 11 to 25 percent.

Several different teams of scientists recently set out to investigate Peto's paradox as it applies to African and Asian elephants. The teams independently found evidence that the secret of the elephant's resistance to cancer might lie in the TP53 gene, which makes proteins that work to suppress tumors. These proteins repair damage to a cell's DNA. If the damage is too great, the proteins can stop the cell from dividing or even trigger the death of the cell. Because cancer is caused by out-of-control cell division, the deaths of damaged cells are beneficial to the organism, because the cells are prevented from dividing further.

While humans (and some other animals) have only one copy of the TP53 gene, elephants have evolved to have 20 copies, which appears to multiply their cancer-fighting abilities. Damaged elephant cells self-destruct at a much higher rate than do those of humans, which further boosts elephants' resistance to cancer.

The findings of the recent studies must be replicated, and more research must be done, before scientists can say with any certainty what role TP53 plays in the low incidence of deaths from cancer in elephant populations. However, the initial evidence points to an intriguing evolutionary solution to the problem of cancer.

Introduce

Engage students' interest in the TP53 gene by telling them about another component of one of the studies discussed in the feature. One of the teams of scientists investigating the TP53 gene in elephants compared the genomes of elephants with the genomes of woolly mammoths and mastodons (using fossil DNA) and with the genomes of manatees and hyraxes, which are smaller, living relatives of elephants. The scientists found that the elephant's extinct relatives had more than 12 copies of the TP53 gene, while the manatees and hyraxes had only one copy. **Ask,** What does this tell you about the evolution of the elephant and its relatives? Students may conclude that the pattern of inheritance that allows for multiple copies of TP53 in a genome evolved only for larger animals. Discuss an evolutionary reason for this pattern of inheritance.

Discuss

Discuss with students why further investigation is needed into the role of TP53 in the elephant's apparent resistance to cancer. Encourage them to think about the steps of the scientific method and the role of replication of scientific research. Prompt them to point out that every investigation must be replicated many times to establish the validity of conclusions drawn from the initial investigation. Invite students to speculate about other possible roles of TP53 in cancer resistance and to suggest ways to test their ideas.

SECTION 5.3

▼ Plan and Prepare

Activate Prior Knowledge Determine what students know about cancer. **Ask,** What is cancer? Cancer is uncontrolled cell division. Tell students that cancers are caused by a variety of factors and that most affect the cell cycle.

▼ Teach

TEACH FROM VISUALS

FIGURE 3.1 Point out that the tan-colored cells growing in the culture dishes are just a single layer. **Ask**

- What would a cross-sectional view of each dish look like? top dish: one layer of a cell; bottom dish: clump of cells spreading up and across the single layer of normal cells
- What external factor is helping to regulate normal cell division? contact with other cells

5.3 Regulation of the Cell Cycle

KEY CONCEPT **Cell cycle regulation is necessary for healthy growth.**

VOCABULARY

growth factor
apoptosis
cancer
benign
malignant
metastasize
carcinogen

MAIN IDEAS

- Internal and external factors regulate cell division.
- Cell division is uncontrolled in cancer.

Connect to Your World

Have you ever watched a movie in which people play with the elements of nature? They might bring back dinosaurs or make a newfangled robot. And have you noticed that these movies are always scary? That's because things go out of control. The robots take over, or the dinosaurs start eating humans. If cell growth goes out of control in your body, the result can be even scarier. Cancer is uncontrolled cell growth and results from many factors that affect the cell cycle. So how does your body regulate all the millions of cell divisions happening in your body?

MAIN IDEA

Internal and external factors regulate cell division.

Both external and internal factors regulate the cell cycle in eukaryotic cells. External factors come from outside the cell. They include messages from nearby cells and from distant parts of the organism's body.

Internal factors come from inside the cell and include several types of molecules found in the cytoplasm. Both types of factors work together to help your body control the process of cell division.

FIGURE 3.1 Normal animal cells (top) respond to external factors and stop dividing when they touch each other. Cancer cells (bottom) fail to respond and form clumps.

Normal cell growth

Cancerous cell growth

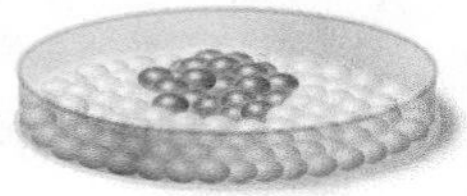

External Factors

External factors that help regulate the cell cycle include physical and chemical signals. One example of a physical signal is cell-to-cell contact. Most mammal cells grown in the laboratory form a single layer on the bottom of a culture dish, as shown in **FIGURE 3.1.** Once a cell touches other cells, it stops dividing. The exact reason for this phenomenon is unknown. One hypothesis is that receptors on neighboring cells bind to each other and cause the cells' cytoskeletons to form structures that may block the signals that trigger growth.

Many cells also release chemical signals that tell other cells to grow. For example, **growth factors** are a broad group of proteins that stimulate cell division. Growth factors bind to receptors that activate specific genes to trigger cell growth. In general, cells grow and divide in response to a combination of different growth factors, not just one.

Differentiated Instruction

BELOW LEVEL

Have students organize notes around the key concept, placing it in a box. From this, students should draw a vertical line to which they attach the headings and subheadings for this section and show how the material in the text supports the key concept.

Teacher Toolkit, Section C, Supporting Main Ideas

ENGLISH LEARNERS

Divide students into small groups and have students number off. Ask students questions about the factors that regulate the cell cycle and what happens to surrounding cells if a cell starts to divide in an unregulated way. After each question, give the groups time to develop their answer. Then call out a number to identify a spokesperson for the group.

Teacher Toolkit, Section C, Numbered Heads Together

Some growth factors affect many types of cells. For example, platelets are sticky fragments of bone marrow cells. They form clots that help stop bleeding. Platelets store a type of growth factor that helps your body repair wounds by triggering the growth of many cell types. Other growth factors have more specific targets. For instance, erythropoietin (ih-RIHTH-roh-poy-EE-tihn) stimulates the production only of cells that will become red blood cells. Red blood cells carry oxygen. If you moved from the coast to the mountains, your blood oxygen levels would be lower because the air pressure is lower at higher altitudes. The decrease in blood oxygen levels would cause your body to produce more erythropoietin. That factor would increase the number of red blood cells and raise your blood oxygen levels.

Various hormones may also stimulate the growth of certain cell types. In particular, growth hormone results in bone growth and also affects your protein and fat metabolism.

Internal Factors

When external factors bind to their receptors, they can trigger internal factors that affect the cell cycle. Two of the most important and well-studied internal factors involved in the eukaryotic cell cycle are kinases and cyclins. A kinase is an enzyme that, when activated, transfers a phosphate group from one molecule to a specific target molecule. This action typically increases the energy of the target molecule or changes its shape. Your cells have many types of kinases, and they are almost always present in the cell. Those kinases that help control the cell cycle are activated by cyclins. Cyclins are a group of proteins that are rapidly made and destroyed at certain points in the cell cycle. These two factors help a cell advance to different stages of the cell cycle when cells bind to each other.

Apoptosis

Just as some cells need to grow and divide, other cells need to die. **Apoptosis** (AP-uhp-TOH-sihs) is programmed cell death. It occurs when internal or external signals activate genes that help produce self-destructive enzymes. Many questions remain about this process. What is known is that the nucleus of an apoptotic cell tends to shrink and break apart, and the cell is recognized by specialized cells in the immune system. These cells very tidily gobble up the apoptotic cell and recycle its chemical parts for use in building other molecules. **FIGURE 3.2** shows a classic example of apoptosis. In the early stages of development, human embryos have webbing between their fingers and toes, or digits. Before a baby is born, those cells typically go through apoptosis. Most babies are born with little unwebbed fingers and toes they love to put in their mouths.

FIGURE 3.2 Human embryos have webbed digits early in their development. The cells between the digits undergo apoptosis during later stages of development. As a result, the baby is born with unwebbed fingers and toes.

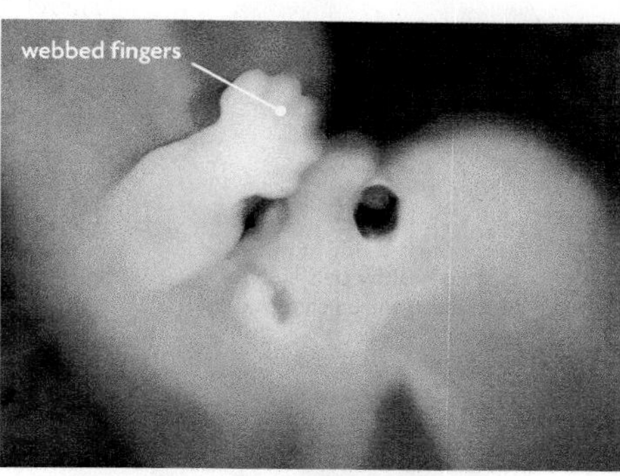

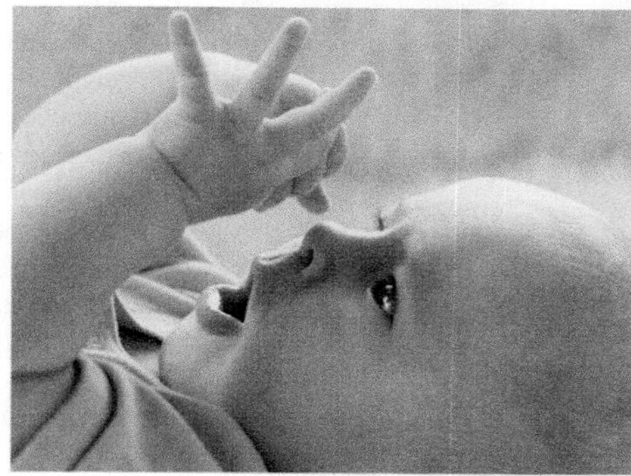

A Predict Suppose a child was born with growth hormone receptors that did not work properly. How do you think this would affect the child's development?

PRE-AP

Tell students that as they are sitting in class, millions of their skin cells are dying. Have students speculate about the series of events that occur when a single cell dies. Have them think of causes and effects, including the internal and external factors involved.

Teacher Toolkit, Section C, Cause-and-Effect Chain

Vocabulary

kinase One internal factor that regulates the cell cycle is a group of proteins called kinases. Tell students that the word *kinase* is a combination of *kin(etic)* and *-ase*. *Kinetic* comes from the Greek *kinein,* which means "to move." The suffix *-ase* means "enzyme." Kinase moves a phosphate group from one molecule to a specific target molecule, and thus affects that molecule's activity.

cyclin An internal factor that controls kinases is cyclins. The *cyclic* nature of these proteins is that they can rapidly be made or destroyed, thus controlling the cell cycle.

Take It Further

The process of **apoptosis** is not just a function of embryonic development. In adults, cell death is balanced by cell division, which keeps body tissue from growing or shrinking as cells reach the end of their life span. Cells that die through injury, a process called **cell necrosis,** may swell and burst, damaging surrounding cells. In contrast, during apoptosis, cells collapse inward, without spilling their contents.

Apoptosis also takes place in plants. The leaves of deciduous trees fall off before winter due to apoptosis. *Apoptosis* is a Greek word that means "a falling off."

Answers

A Predict The child's ability to produce new cells and, therefore, tissues at the proper rate would be affected. This in turn would affect developing tissues and organs, and also could affect height and weight.

▼ Teach *continued*

Take It Further

According to the American Cancer Society, **skin cancer** is the most common of all cancers. It is very treatable if found early, so people are encouraged to examine their skin every few months to look for changes in moles, freckles, and other marks on the skin. The American Academy of Dermatology suggests using the ABCD rule. These letters can be used as a mnemonic to help people remember what to look for. Asymmetry is irregular shape. Border is an irregular border. Color is for change in color, many colors, or uneven distribution of colors. Dimension is for diameter larger than 6 millimeters (1/4 in.). New growth, changes in growths, or a sore that does not heal are warning signs and need to be checked by a physician. Have students find the ABCD of the cancerous mole in **FIGURE 3.4.**

Vocabulary

Academic Vocabulary The words **benign** and **malignant** are a part of everyday language:

benign, of a kind, gentle disposition
malignant, disposed to do evil

The words **cancerous** and **metastasize** are also used in everyday language, to suggest "spreading evil." You might want to introduce students to the word **connotation** in this context:

connotation = an idea or meaning suggested by a word or thing

Have students do the WebQuest to learn more about skin cancer.

MAIN IDEA

Cell division is uncontrolled in cancer.

FIGURE 3.3 Cancer cells form tumors that may metastasize to other parts of the body.

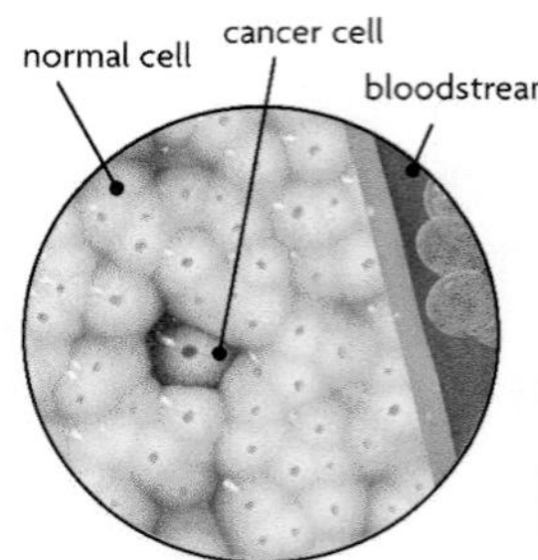

1. A healthy cell may become a cancer cell if certain genes are damaged.

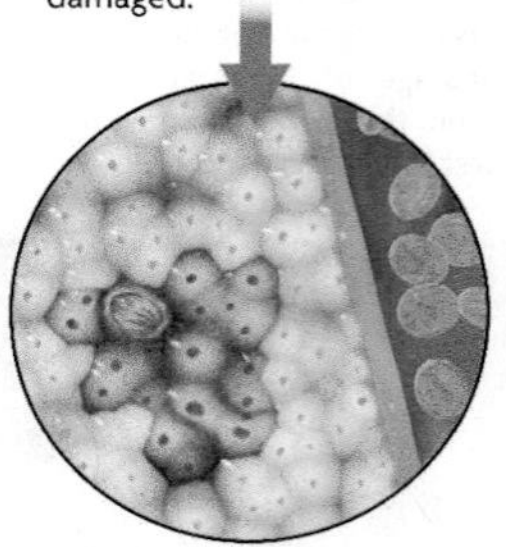

2. Cancer cells divide more often than do healthy cells and may form disorganized clumps called tumors.

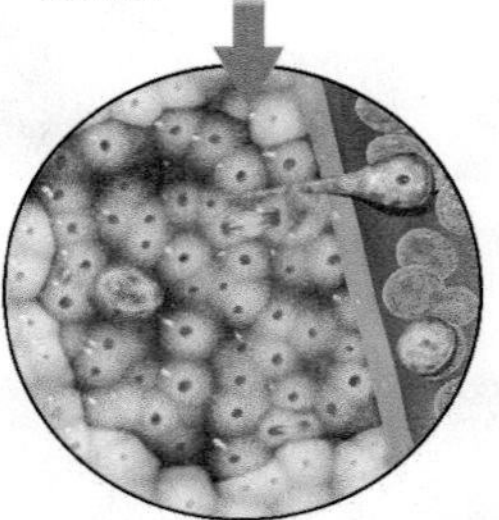

3. Sometimes, cancer cells break away from the tumor. They can be carried in the bloodstream to other parts of the body, where they form new tumors.

Cancer is the common name for a class of diseases characterized by uncontrolled cell division. It arises when regulation of the cell cycle is disrupted. Unlike healthy cells, cancer cells grown in a culture dish continue to divide, even when surrounded by neighboring cells. Cancer cells can also continue to divide in the absence of many of the growth factors required for division in healthy cells. As a result, they divide much more often than do healthy cells.

Cancer cells form disorganized clumps called tumors. In a **benign** tumor, the cancer cells typically remain clustered together. This means the tumor may be relatively harmless and can probably be cured by removing it. However, if a tumor is **malignant,** some of the cancer cells can break away, or **metastasize** (mih-TAS-tuh-SYZ), from the tumor. These breakaway cells can be carried in the bloodstream or lymphatic system to other parts of the body, as shown in **FIGURE 3.3,** where they can form more tumors, called metastases. Once a tumor metastasizes, it is much more difficult to entirely rid the body of tumors.

But why are tumors harmful? Cancer cells do not perform the specialized functions needed by the body. In the lung, for example, cancer cells do not exchange oxygen and carbon dioxide. In the brain, they do not transmit the carefully ordered electrical messages needed to interpret information. Therefore, the body has large clumps of rapidly dividing cells that require lots of food and a hearty blood supply but that contribute nothing to the body's function. In addition, a growing tumor can exert great pressure on surrounding organs. For instance, a tumor growing inside the skull will cramp the brain for space, and some regions will be unable to function properly. If cancer cells continue to grow unchecked, they will eventually kill the organism.

Cancer cells come from normal cells that have suffered damage to the genes that help make proteins involved in cell-cycle regulation. Most cancer cells carry mutations, or errors, in two types of genes. One type, called oncogenes, accelerate the cell cycle. The second type act as cell-cycle brakes. Mutations in these genes can be inherited. For instance, some breast cancers appear to be caused by inherited errors in specific genes. Other mutations can be caused by exposure to radiation or chemicals. For example, some skin cancers are due to DNA damage caused by ultraviolet radiation from sunlight. Substances known to produce or promote the development of cancer are called **carcinogens** (kahr-SIHN-uh-juhnz). These include tobacco smoke and certain air pollutants, which are both associated with lung cancer. Some mutated forms of oncogenes are even carried by viruses; one such virus can cause cervical cancer.

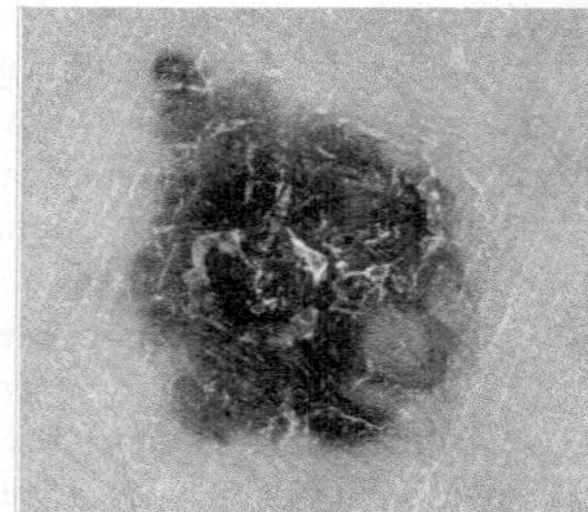

FIGURE 3.4 This cancerous mole is an example of a skin cancer, which may metastasize quickly.

Differentiated Instruction

BELOW LEVEL

Have students create a Y diagram to compare benign and malignant growth. Tell them to write *Benign* at the top the left arm of the Y and *Malignant* at the top of the right. Students should list the characteristics of each type of tumor under each heading. Once they have finished, have them cross out the characteristics shared by both benign and malignant growth, and list those characteristics in the stem.

Teacher Toolkit, Section C, Y Diagram

ENGLISH LEARNERS

Have students prepare two-by-two word squares for the vocabulary on this page. They should include the word and a translation in their own language, a definition in their own words, and their use of it in a sentence. Help them come up with a drawing that will help to recall the word.

Teacher Toolkit, Section D, Word Squares

QUICKLAB OBSERVING

Cancer

In this lab, you will compare normal cells with cancerous cells and observe the differences between them.

PROBLEM How do normal and cancerous cells compare?

PROCEDURE

1. Examine the slides of normal cells under the microscope. Draw and describe your observations.
2. Repeat step 1 with slides of cancer cells.

ANALYZE AND CONCLUDE

1. **Compare** How does the structure of the normal cells compare with the structure of the cancerous cells for each of the slides you viewed?
2. **Infer** Cancer cells not only appear different from normal cells but they also divide more rapidly. Why do you think chemotherapy, a common treatment for cancer, results in the loss of hair?

MATERIALS

- microscope
- slides of normal cells
- slides of cancerous cells

Standard cancer treatment often involves both radiation and chemotherapy. Radiation therapy is the use of radiation to kill cancer cells and shrink tumors. It works by damaging a cell's DNA so much that the cell cannot divide. Radiation is usually localized—that is, its use is targeted to a specific region—because it can also hurt healthy cells. Chemotherapy uses certain drugs, often in combination, to kill actively dividing cells. Like radiation, it kills both cancerous and healthy cells. However, chemotherapy is systemic—drugs travel throughout the entire body.

Skin Cancer

Medical researchers use laboratory-grown cancer cells in their search for cancer treatments. Much of what is known about the cell cycle has come from studies that use cancer cells. The most famous cancer cells used for research are called HeLa cells. HeLa cells were originally obtained in 1951 from a cervical tumor removed from a woman named Henrietta Lacks. This cell line continues to be grown and studied in laboratories all over the world.

Analyze **HeLa cells are also used to study cell signaling processes. What might be a disadvantage of using cancer cells to study processes occurring in healthy cells?**

5.3 Formative Assessment

SELF-CHECK Online HMHScience.com GO ONLINE

REVIEWING MAIN IDEAS

1. Describe what a **growth factor** is and how it influences the cell cycle.
2. Explain how **cancer** cells differ from healthy cells.

CRITICAL THINKING

3. **Contrast** How do **benign** and **malignant** tumors differ?
4. **Hypothesize** Suppose chromosomes in a skin cell are damaged by ultraviolet radiation. If the damaged genes do not affect cell cycle regulation, do you think the cell will become cancerous? Explain.

CONNECT TO

CELL ORGANELLES

5. Some anticancer drugs prevent microtubules from forming spindle fibers. Why do you think these drugs might be effective treatments for cancer?

5.3 FORMATIVE ASSESSMENT

1. A growth factor is an external signal that stimulates growth and division of cells.
2. Cancer cells have uncontrolled division, grow rapidly without many growth factors, can form tumors, can metastasize, and do not contribute to the body's function.
3. Benign tumors—cancer cells that are clustered together and relatively harmless; Malignant tumors—cancer cells that can metastasize and form more tumors.
4. No, if the damage does not affect the cell cycle, the cell will probably continue to divide normally and will not become cancerous.
5. Without microtubules and spindle fibers, mitosis cannot take place.

QUICKLAB

Time 20 minutes

Purpose Observe and compare normal cells and cancerous cells.

LAB MANAGEMENT

- When making comparisons, students should look for the following traits in the cancerous cells or tumors: a large number of dividing cells, changes to the nucleus such as size and shape, and changes in cell size and shape.

Safety Caution students to be careful when handling the slides. Remind them to wipe down the eyepieces of the microscope with alcohol wipes after use.

Teacher Note "I would have students hypothesize consequences for different cell types if mutations occur."

Answers

Analyze and Conclude

1. In general, cancerous cells differ from normal cells in size, shape, color, and in the shape and size of the nucleus.
2. Chemotherapy affects rapidly dividing cells, both cancerous and normal. Cells in the hair follicles probably divide rapidly, so they are killed by chemotherapy.

Answers

A Analyze Cancer cells may not have exactly the same processes as healthy cells. This could lead to errors.

Assess and Reteach

Assess Use the Section Self-Check or Section Quiz, both available at **HMHScience.com**.

Reteach Make a T-chart on the board, one side for cancer cells and one side for normal cells. Have students list the characteristics of cancer cells, and then define a normal cell by how it differs from a cancer cell.

SECTION 5.4

▼ Plan and Prepare

Activate Prior Knowledge Spider plants are common household plants that produce plantlets, or "babies," which can grow independently when removed and placed in soil. **Ask,** Why can this form of reproduction be called asexual? The genetic material for the baby comes from only one parent.

▼ Teach

Vocabulary

binary fission Point out that the word *binary* means "consisting of two parts." The word *fission* means "the act or process of splitting into two parts." Point out that despite various forms of asexual reproduction that occur in multicellular organisms, binary fission is a term reserved for single-celled, prokaryotic organisms.

5.4 Asexual Reproduction

VOCABULARY

asexual reproduction
binary fission

KEY CONCEPT **Many organisms reproduce by cell division.**

MAIN IDEAS

- Binary fission is similar in function to mitosis.
- Some eukaryotes reproduce through mitosis.

Connect to Your World

In this flashy world of ours, you may think that the humble bacterium would have little chance of finding a mate. No dazzling smile, no fancy hair products, no shiny car, and—if we are brutally honest—not even a brain. With all of these limitations, it may seem that our bacteria friends would be destined to die out. And yet, bacteria are found in abundance and live just about everywhere on Earth. How can there be so many bacteria?

MAIN IDEA

Binary fission is similar in function to mitosis.

Reproduction is a process that makes new organisms from one or more parent organisms. It happens in two ways—sexually and asexually. Sexual reproduction involves the joining of two specialized cells called gametes (eggs and sperm cells), one from each of two parents. The offspring that result are genetically unique; they have a mixture of genes from both parents. In contrast, **asexual reproduction** is the production of offspring from a single parent and does not involve the joining of gametes. The offspring that result are, for the most part, genetically identical to each other and to the single parent.

Binary Fission and Mitosis

Most prokaryotes reproduce through **binary fission** (BY-nuh-ree FIHSH-uhn), the asexual reproduction of a single-celled organism by which the cell divides into two cells of the same size. Binary fission and mitosis have similar results. That is, both processes form two daughter cells that are genetically identical to the parent cell. However, the actual processes are different in several important ways.

As you already learned, prokaryotes such as bacteria do not have nuclei. They also do not have spindle fibers. And although they have DNA, prokaryotes have much less DNA than do most eukaryotes. The DNA of most bacteria is in the form of a single circular chromosome.

CONNECT TO

CELL STRUCTURE

Recall from the chapter **Cell Structure and Function** that many scientists hypothesize that mitochondria and chloroplasts were originally free-living prokaryotes. One piece of evidence that supports this hypothesis is the fact that these two organelles replicate much as bacteria do, through fission.

VISUAL VOCAB

Binary fission is the asexual reproduction of a single-celled organism by division into two roughly equal parts.

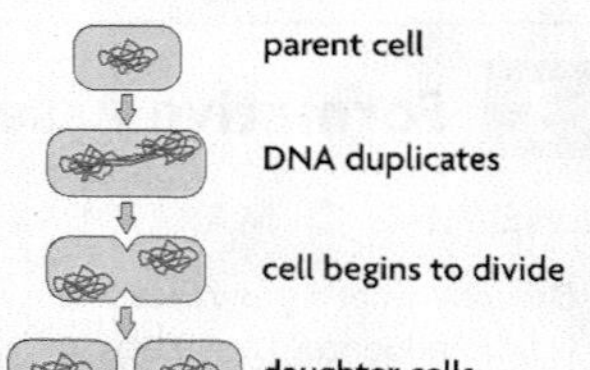

Differentiated Instruction

BELOW LEVEL

Have students make a chart to compare and contrast binary fission and mitosis. Have them place the terms in two boxes with an arrow pointing from each to a single box that describes the shared characteristics. Then have them draw arrows from this box to two separate boxes that detail the differences. Refer students to **Section 1** to review mitosis if necessary.

Teacher Toolkit, Section C, Compare/Contrast Chart

ENGLISH LEARNERS

Ask students to record in a T-chart the advantages and disadvantages of asexual reproduction. Model finding items for each column. Encourage students to work together to complete the charts. A key principle of language learning is that language develops best when students focus on accomplishing something with others rather than focus on language itself.

Teacher Toolkit, Section C, T-Chart

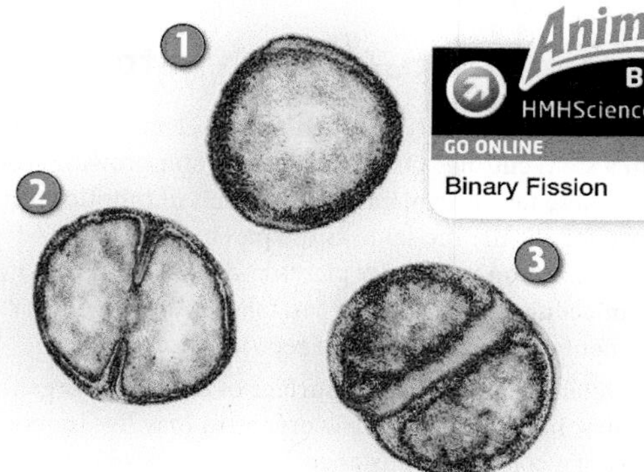

Animated Biology
HMHScience.com
GO ONLINE
Binary Fission

FIGURE 4.1 This micrograph shows three individual bacteria, each at a different stage of binary fission. First, a cell elongates (1), and the DNA is replicated. Next, the cell membrane pinches inward (2). Finally, the membrane meets, and a new cell wall forms, separating the two cells (3).

Binary fission, shown in **FIGURE 4.1**, starts when the bacterial chromosome is copied. Both chromosomes are attached to the cell membrane. As the cell grows and gets longer, the chromosomes move away from each other. When the cell is about twice its original size, it undergoes cytokinesis. The membrane pinches inward, and a new cell wall forms between the two chromosomes, which completes the separation into two daughter cells.

FIGURE 4.2 BACTERIA GROWTH

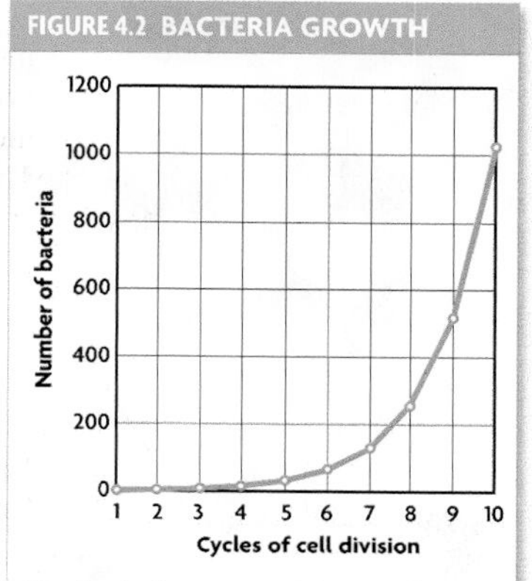

One bacterium can result in a total of 1024 cells after only 10 rounds of cell division.

Advantages and Disadvantages of Asexual Reproduction

Very often, whether something is helpful or harmful depends on the situation. In favorable environments that do not change much, asexual reproduction can be more efficient than sexual reproduction. Recall that asexual reproduction results in genetically identical offspring. If they are well suited to the environment, genetic variation could be more harmful than helpful. In other words, if it ain't broke, don't fix it.

However, asexual reproduction may be a disadvantage in changing conditions. Genetically identical offspring will respond to the environment in the same way. If population members lack traits that enable them to reproduce in a changed environment, the entire population could die off. In contrast, sexual reproduction increases genetic diversity, which raises the chance that some individuals will survive in changing conditions.

Keep in mind, however, that the act of asexual reproduction itself is not more efficient; rather, the associated costs of sexual reproduction are greater. For example, all asexually reproducing organisms can potentially reproduce. Suppose two organisms each have ten offspring. If one organism reproduces asexually, all ten offspring can have offspring of their own. If the other organism reproduces sexually, having five females and five males, only the five females can bear offspring. In addition, sexually reproducing organisms must attract a mate. This effort involves not only the time and energy needed to find a mate but also many structures, signals, and behaviors that have evolved to attract mates. Organisms that reproduce asexually do not have these costs.

CONNECT TO

EVOLUTION

As you will learn in the chapter **Viruses and Prokaryotes**, the misuse of antibiotics has resulted in multidrug-resistant bacteria. The bacteria not killed by antibiotics can reproduce quickly, passing the genes for antibiotic resistance on to their offspring.

A **Summarize** **How is asexual reproduction an advantage in some conditions?**

PRE-AP

Have students read the last paragraph on this page, about the costs associated with sexual reproduction. Ask them to write for five minutes on the question of who (or what) benefits despite the costs associated with sexual reproduction.

Teacher Toolkit, Section C, Quick-Write

HANDS-ON ACTIVITY

Have students model bacterial growth by binary fission, using a pile of beads. Tell students to start with one bead and add a second to represent the two bacteria that result from one cycle of division. Have students continue to add one bead for each bacterium after each cycle of division. Tell students to keep track of the number of cycles of cell division that occur before they run out of beads.

ONLINE Biology
HMHScience.com

Students can do a virtual lab on bacterial growth to explore some of the external factors that affect the rate of reproduction/division for these single-celled organisms.

TEACH FROM VISUALS

FIGURE 4.2 Have students compare the units on the axes to see how quickly a population of bacteria can grow by binary fission. With each division, the number of bacteria doubles. Point out that the increase in the total number of bacteria at each successive cycle is exponential:

$$\text{number of bacteria} = 2^x$$

where x is the number of the cycle. Point out that the shape of the graph line is typical of exponential growth—a modest beginning followed by explosive growth.

Take It Further

Because bacterial reproduction is asexual, a population of bacteria is genetically identical. However, once a genetic mutation occurs within a population, it can spread rapidly because of exponential growth.

Genetic diversity can occur by other means within a population of bacteria. For example, a virus that infects one bacterium can transfer genetic material from that bacterium to another, a process called **transduction.** Bacterial cells can also share genetic material directly by the process of **conjugation.** The donor of genetic material is able to attach to a second bacterial cell by way of a tubular structure called a pilus. The "male" transfers DNA by way of the pilus to the "female."

Answers

A **Summarize** Asexual reproduction results in genetically identical offspring that are well suited to an unchanging environment.

▼ Teach *continued*

TEACH FROM VISUALS

FIGURE 4.3 Have students find the bud on the yeast and the hydra. **Ask,** What is distinctive about the cells of the budding hydra compared to those of the budding yeast? In the hydra, there is some differentiation among the cells of the bud, whereas for the yeast, the cells are identical.

Explain that when the hydra bud breaks off, it will continue to grow by mitosis to be the same size as the parent.

Answers

A Synthesize Since asexually reproduced plants are clones, we can theoretically grow a particular plant in abundance under certain conditions. However, if conditions change, a significant portion of our food supply could be adversely affected.

▼ Assess and Reteach

Assess Use the Section Self-Check or Section Quiz, both available at **HMHScience.com**.

Reteach Have students summarize the ways in which asexual reproduction of a bacterial or yeast cell is the same as and different from the mitotic division of cells that occurs in a multicellular organism.

MAIN IDEA

Some eukaryotes reproduce through mitosis.

Some eukaryotes also reproduce asexually, through mitosis. Have you ever grown a new plant from a stem cutting? Or seen a new sea star growing from the arm of another one? These new organisms are the result of mitotic reproduction and are therefore genetically the same as the parent organism. Mitotic reproduction is especially common in simpler plants and animals. It occurs in both multicellular and unicellular eukaryotes. It can take several forms, including budding, fragmentation, and vegetative reproduction.

In budding, a small projection grows on the surface of the parent organism, forming a separate new individual. The new organism may live independently or attached as part of a colony. For instance, hydras and some types of yeast reproduce by budding. Examples are shown in **FIGURE 4.3.**

In fragmentation, a parent organism splits into pieces, each of which can grow into a new organism. Flatworms and sea stars both reproduce by fragmentation. Many plants, including strawberries and potatoes, reproduce via vegetative reproduction. In general, vegetative reproduction involves the modification of a stem or underground structures of the parent organism. The offspring often stay connected to the original organism, through structures called runners, for example.

Many organisms can reproduce both asexually and sexually. The form of reproduction may depend on the current conditions. The sea anemone can reproduce in many ways. It can reproduce asexually by dividing in half, by breaking off small pieces from its base, or by budding. It can also reproduce sexually by making eggs and sperm. Some species of anemone have separate males and females. In other anemone species, the same organism can produce both eggs and sperm cells.

FIGURE 4.3 Yeast and hydras can reproduce by budding.

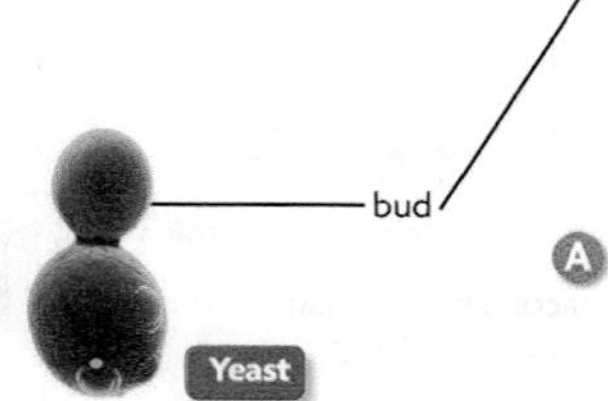

A Synthesize How might the asexual reproduction of genetically identical plants be useful to humans? How could it prove harmful to our food supply?

5.4 Formative Assessment

REVIEWING MAIN IDEAS

1. Explain how mitosis differs from **binary fission.**
2. Briefly explain why cutting a flatworm into pieces would not kill it.

CRITICAL THINKING

3. **Infer** How does an organism benefit by being able to reproduce both sexually and asexually?
4. **Apply** Yeasts are growing in two dishes. You treat one dish with a chemical that blocks DNA replication but forget to label it. How can you identify the treated dish?

SELF-CHECK Online
HMHScience.com
GO ONLINE

CONNECT TO
ECOLOGY

5. Two populations live in the same habitat and compete for food. The first group is larger and multiplies through **asexual reproduction**; the second reproduces sexually. What could happen to cause the second group to outnumber the first?

5.4 FORMATIVE ASSESSMENT

1. Mitosis is carried out only in eukaryotes; it involves the division of DNA in the nucleus by way of spindle fibers to ensure that both daughter cells receive a full set of chromosomes. Organisms that undergo binary fission do not have a nucleus; most have a single, circular chromosome, so division of the DNA is simpler.
2. The flatworm can reproduce asexually by fragmentation.
3. Sexual reproduction provides greater genetic diversity and adaptability; asexual reproduction allows for rapid population growth under certain conditions without a mate.
4. Yeast in the untreated dish will be growing and budding; yeast in the treated dish will be unable to bud.
5. Change in environmental conditions could severely limit the growth of the first population. The second population would be more likely to have individuals that could adapt to the change. These individuals would be able to reproduce successfully in the new conditions and increase the population.

5.5 Multicellular Life

KEY CONCEPT **Cells work together to carry out complex functions.**

MAIN IDEAS

- Multicellular organisms depend on interactions among different cell types.
- Specialized cells perform specific functions.
- Stem cells can develop into different cell types.

VOCABULARY

tissue
organ
organ system
cell differentiation
stem cell

Connect to Your World

Each of us enters this world as a helpless infant. At first, your ability to eat solid foods or take your first steps elicits a great deal of praise. Over time, however, your development of normal skills gets far less attention. By the time you reach the age of 18, people want to know what you plan to do with your life. Will you build houses or design clothing or treat patients? What will your specialty be? Cells, too, undergo specialization to carry out the complex functions required by the body.

MAIN IDEA

Multicellular organisms depend on interactions among different cell types.

Within multicellular organisms, cells communicate and work together in groups that form increasingly larger, more complex structures. This arrangement progresses from cells to tissues to organs to organ systems, as shown in **FIGURE 5.1**. **Tissues** are groups of cells that work together to perform a similar function. Groups of tissues that work together to perform a specific function or related functions are called **organs.** For instance, plants have photosynthetic tissues made of chlorophyll-containing cells. Conductive tissues transport sugars, water, and minerals to and from other parts of the plant. Protective tissues help prevent water loss. Together, these and other tissues form a leaf, the plant's food-producing organ.

Organs that carry out similar functions are further grouped into **organ systems.** In plants, the shoot system is above the ground. It includes stems that support the plant, leaves that capture radiant energy, and flowers that aid reproduction. Beneath the ground, the root system has different types of roots and root hairs that anchor the plant and absorb water and minerals.

As organ systems work together, they help an organism maintain homeostasis. For example, plants need to maintain a certain level of water within their cells, otherwise they will wilt and die. They absorb water through their roots and expel it as water vapor through openings in their leaves called stomata. Stomata are controlled by special cells called guard cells, which close the stomata when a plant's water intake cannot keep up with its water loss.

CONNECT TO

HOMEOSTASIS

As you learned in the chapter **Biology in the 21st Century,** homeostasis is the maintenance of a stable internal environment. Both an organism's physiology and its behavior help it achieve homeostasis.

Ⓐ Apply **Suppose your family goes out of town and forgets to ask your neighbor to water the plants. Do you think the plants' stomata will be open or closed? Explain.**

Differentiated Instruction

BELOW LEVEL

Have students use an outline to organize their notes for this section. Suggest that they include definitions of key vocabulary with their outlines. This should help them see the relationship between the vocabulary in each subsection.

Teacher Toolkit, Section C, Outline

SECTION 5.5

B.1.5 Develop and use a model to illustrate the hierarchical organization of interacting systems (cell, tissue, organ, organ system) that provide specific functions within multicellular organisms.

B.4.4 Use a model to illustrate the role of cellular division (mitosis) and differentiation in producing and maintaining complex organisms.

Plan and Prepare

Activate Prior Knowledge Have students look at one of their hands. **Ask**

- What are some of the different types of cells in your hand? those making up skin, hair, fingernails, muscle, bone, blood, nerves
- Are the cells in the trunk of your body the same or different? similar types of cells, but many more also associated with internal organs

Discuss differentiation as how cells are different and how they are allocated.

Teach

Vocabulary

Academic Vocabulary Tell students that there are two views of multicellular organisms:

anatomy, the study of the bodily structures of an organism or its parts

physiology, the study of the functions of an organism or any of its parts

Answers

Ⓐ Apply Because the plants are not receiving any water, they will need to conserve the water that they have. The stomata will most likely be closed.

▼ Teach *continued*

Answers

A Apply Roots branch into smaller and smaller structures that increase the surface area, thereby allowing increased absorption of water and nutrients and better anchoring of the plant.

Science Trivia

- A human has about 200 different types of cells.
- At any one time, a human cell probably expresses about 20% of its genes.

Vocabulary

apical The words *apical* and *apex* share the same root and refer to the tip or high point.

basal The words *basal* and *base* share the same root and refer to the bottom.

migrate The word *migrate* means "to change location periodically," which suggests a lack of permanence. For most animal cells, this applies only up to the point when differentiation occurs.

FIGURE 5.1 Levels of Organization

Cells work together in groups that form larger, specialized structures.

CELL

Vessel elements are tube-shaped cells.

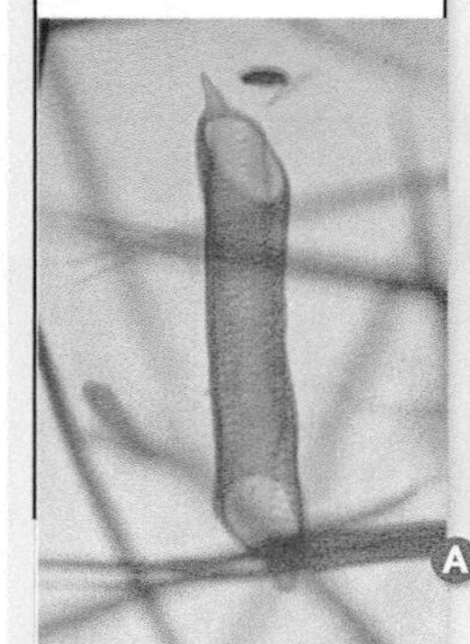

TISSUE

Vessel elements, tracheids, and parenchyma cells form xylem. (colored SEM; magnification 240×)

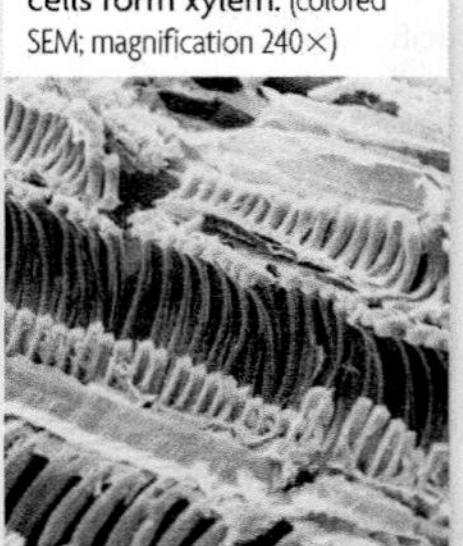

ORGAN

Xylem and other tissues form roots that absorb water and nutrients.

SYSTEMS

stem
leaf
vascular tissue
lateral roots
primary root
shoot system
root system

A Apply **How is the shape of this plant's roots suited to their function?**

CONNECT TO

GAMETOGENESIS

As you will learn in the chapter **Meiosis and Mendel**, the egg is stocked with organelles and molecules that are necessary for an embryo to grow. Many of these molecules are not evenly distributed throughout the cell; they form gradients.

MAIN IDEA

Specialized cells perform specific functions.

It is easy to see that a skin cell can divide to make a new skin cell, or that a single bacterium can generate another bacterium. But how does a complex organism like you develop? Your body began as a single fertilized egg. If the egg simply divided to make lots of identical cells, it would not form a baby. To form the intricate structures that make up your body and the bodies of countless organisms around you, cells must specialize.

Cell differentiation is the process by which a cell becomes specialized for a specific structure or function during multicellular development. While almost every cell in your body has a full set of DNA, each type of cell expresses only the specific genes it needs to carry out its function. That is, a cell differentiates among the genes and uses only certain ones. You can think of your DNA as a cookbook. When you want to make a specific dish, you select that recipe and carry out its instructions. If you need to make a dessert, you might choose brownies. If you need to make a main course, you might fix lentil stew. The dishes are very different, but they all come from the same cookbook.

A cell's location within the embryo helps determine how it will differentiate. In plant cells, the first division of a fertilized egg is unequal, or asymmetric, as shown in **FIGURE 5.2**. The apical cell forms most of the embryo, including the growth point for stems and leaves. The major role of the basal cell is to provide nutrients to the embryo; it also creates the growth point for the roots. Plant cells cannot easily migrate because of the cell wall, but they adapt to changing conditions and continue to develop throughout their lifetime.

Differentiated Instruction

ENGLISH LEARNERS

Point out the analogy on this page comparing DNA to a cookbook. Model for students how to make the associations between the different elements of this analogy:

DNA = cookbook

different genes = different ingredients

differentiated cells = different recipes

The analogy is based on the idea that both DNA and a cookbook represent sets of instructions contained in a single place.

Teacher Toolkit, Section D, Analogies

As the plant grows, new cells continue to differentiate based on their location. For example, cells on the outer layer of a leaf may become epidermal cells that secrete a waxy substance that helps prevent water loss. Cells on the lower leaf surface may become guard cells that control the exchange of water, air, and carbon dioxide.

FIGURE 5.2 Cell Differentiation in Seed Plants

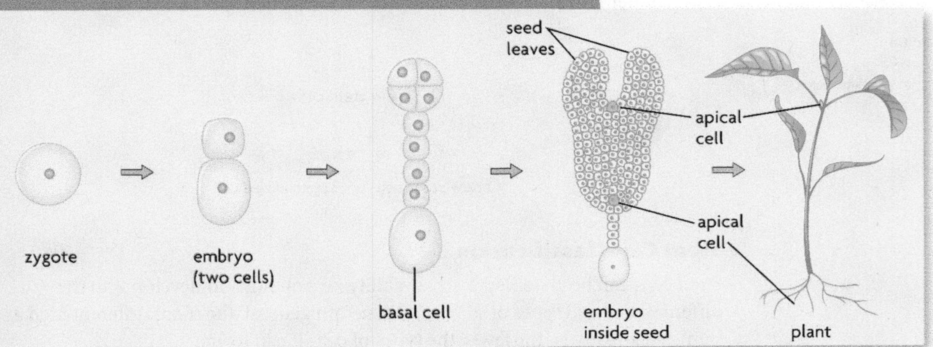

In animals, an egg undergoes many rapid divisions after it is fertilized. The resulting cells can migrate to a specific area, and the cells quickly begin to differentiate. The early animal embryo generally takes the shape of a hollow ball. As the embryo develops, part of the ball folds inward, forming an inner layer and creating an opening in the outer cell layer. A middle layer of cells then forms. As shown in **FIGURE 5.3**, in vertebrates, the outer cell layer differentiates to form the outer layer of skin and elements of the nervous system, such as the brain and spinal cord. The middle cell layer forms bones, muscles, kidneys, and the inner layer of skin. The inner cell layer forms internal organs, such as the pancreas, lungs, and digestive system lining.

A Analyze **Why is regulation of the differentiation process during the early stages of development so critical?**

FIGURE 5.3 Cell Differentiation in Animals

Cell differentiation in the developing animal embryo is based on location.

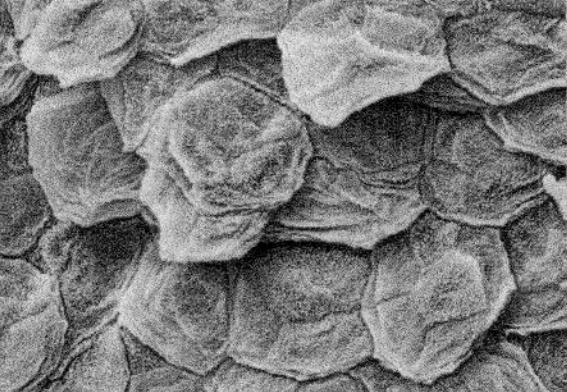

Outer Skin cells help prevent infection and dehydration. (colored SEM; magnification 500×)

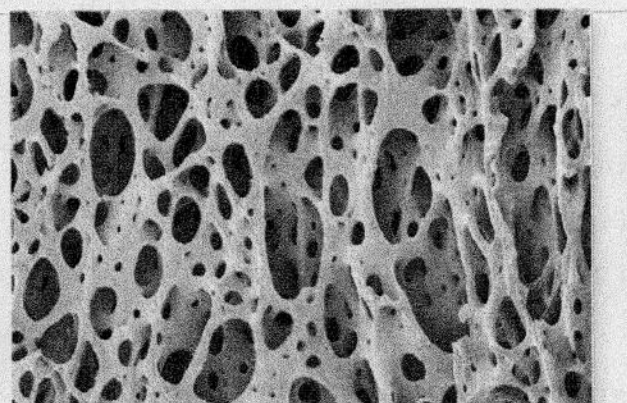

Middle Bone cells form a hard matrix (shown) that supports and protects organs. (colored SEM; magnification 15×)

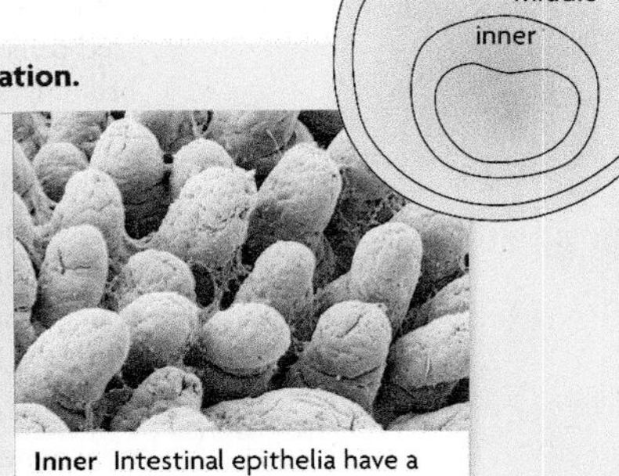

Inner Intestinal epithelia have a large surface area that increases absorption.

PRE-AP

Tell students that during development of a human embryo, a portion of the outer layer of cells pushes in to the center to form the endoderm, an inner layer of cells surrounding an inner cavity. This creates a middle layer of cells, the mesoderm, surrounded by the remaining outer layer of cells, the ectoderm. Have students speculate on the fate of each layer's cells and which structures they likely form, based on their location. Have students consider the fate of the central cavity.

Teacher Toolkit, Section C, Think-Pair-Share

BELOW LEVEL

Using the text on these pages, have students draw a sequence diagram that follows the development of an embryo, starting with the fertilized egg. Have students include the highlighted vocabulary of the first two subsections. Go over the diagrams to help students clarify the sequence.

Teacher Toolkit, Section C, Sequence Diagram

TEACH FROM VISUALS

FIGURE 5.3 Have students find the three layers in the cross-sectional diagram of the animal embryo. **Ask,** What is the shape of the embryo that this cross section represents? a hollow ball

Point out the embryo's outer layer of cells. Have students locate the photograph of cells that came from this layer. **Ask**

- What other type of cell differentiates in the outer layer? nerve cell
- What forms in the middle layer? bones, muscles, kidneys, inner layer of skin
- What forms in the inner layer? pancreas, lungs, digestive system lining

Integrating Embryology

Three processes affect the embryonic development of seed plants and animals. Embryonic development involves cell division, cell differentiation, and **morphogenesis.** Morphogenesis is the process by which cells are organized into tissues and organs that give an organism its shape, determining characteristics such as which end of a plant turns into the shoot system or which end of an animal turns into the head.

In humans, disruption of the process can lead to conditions such as **cleft palate** or **cleft lip.** This occurs between weeks 6–10 of embryonic development if the bones that make up the palate fail to join properly.

Answers

A **Analyze** The early stages of differentiation lead to the development of progressively more specialized tissues and organs. Disruption of cell differentiation in the early stages could cause severe abnormalities in an organism's body structure.

Chapter 5: Cell Growth and Division 149

▼ Teach continued

History of Science

The term *stem cell* was coined by biologist **Gail Martin** in 1981 when she and fellow scientists working at the University of California at San Francisco were able to establish a culture of pluripotent cells from a mouse embryo. She used the term because these are the cells that all other cells "stem" from. In 1988, at the University of Wisconsin-Madison, four embryonic stem cell lines from a species of hamster were established. In 1995, researchers at the university's primate research center established the first embryonic stem cell line from a primate species, the rhesus monkey. Then, in 1998, **James Thomson** and his colleagues developed five lines of human embryonic stem cells.

For more on stem cell research, see the Unit 2 BioZine feature article.

Take It Further

Adult stem cells are necessary for survival. These stem cells replace specialized cells in the body that cannot reproduce themselves. Erythrocytes, leukocytes, platelets, and cells lining the intestines all need frequent replacement. For example, an erythrocyte, or red blood cell, lives only about three or four months. **Ask,** What could cause an immediate need for adult stem cells to make red blood cells? bleeding, blood donation white blood cells? an infection or a wound

CONNECT TO

VOCABULARY

Potent comes from a Latin word meaning "to be able."
The addition of prefixes defines the level of power or ability.
toti- = all
pluri- = more, several
multi- = many

MAIN IDEA

Stem cells can develop into different cell types.

Stem cells are a unique type of body cell that can (1) divide and renew themselves for long periods of time, (2) remain undifferentiated in form, and (3) differentiate into a variety of specialized cell types. When a stem cell divides, it forms either two stem cells or one stem cell and one specialized cell.

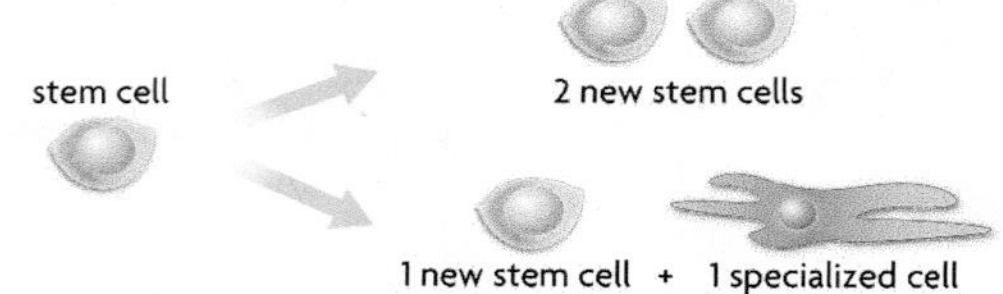

Stem Cell Classification

Stem cells can be classified by their ability, or potential, to develop into the differentiated cell types of different tissues. In general, the more differentiated a stem cell already is, the fewer the types of cells it can form.

- Totipotent stem cells can grow into any other cell type. Only a fertilized egg and the cells produced by the first few divisions of an embryo are totipotent.
- Pluripotent stem cells can grow into any cell type except for totipotent stem cells.
- Multipotent stem cells can grow only into cells of a closely related cell family.

Stem cells are also classified by their origin, as either adult or embryonic. Adult stem cells have been studied for decades, but the ability to grow human embryonic stem cells was not developed until 1998. Since that time, embryonic stem cells have attracted great attention because of their potential to form almost any cell type.

Adult Stem Cells

Adult stem cells are partially undifferentiated cells located among the specialized cells of many organs and tissues. They are found all over the body, in the brain, liver, bone marrow, skeletal muscle, dental pulp, and even fat. These stem cells are also found in children and in umbilical cord blood, so the term *somatic stem cell* is more accurate although less frequently used.

A major advantage of adult stem cells is that they can be taken from a patient, grown in culture, and put back into the patient. Thus, the risk of transplant rejection by a patient's immune system is very low. This method also avoids many ethical issues associated with using embryonic stem cells.

Adult stem cells currently pose many disadvantages as well. They are few in number, difficult to isolate, and sometimes tricky to grow. They may also contain more DNA abnormalities than do embryonic stem cells. For years, much evidence suggested that adult stem cells were multipotent. This would mean that a stem cell from fat would produce only fat cells, never muscle cells.

Differentiated Instruction

ENGLISH LEARNERS

To test students' understanding, question students about cell differentiation and how it relates to different types of stem cells. Have students react to the statements as being true or false using thumbs-up/thumbs-down signals. Or use cards to have students provide their own responses.

Teacher Toolkit, Section C, Card Responses

Newer data suggest otherwise. Adult stem cells treated with the right combination of molecules may give rise to a completely different type of tissue. This process, called transdifferentiation, remains an active area of research.

Embryonic Stem Cells

Most embryonic stem cells come from donated embryos grown in a clinic. These embryos are the result of in vitro fertilization, a process by which eggs are fertilized outside a woman's body. The stem cells are taken from a cluster of undifferentiated cells in the three-to-five-day-old embryo. These cells, called the inner cell mass, do not have the characteristics of any specific cell type. Because they are pluripotent, they can form any of the 200 cell types of the body. They can also be grown indefinitely in culture. These qualities offer hope that many diseases will be treatable or even curable. Stem cells have long been used to treat patients with leukemia and lymphoma, and people with diabetes might someday be cured if nonworking cells in the pancreas are replaced with healthy, growing cells. Even damaged organs might be strengthened by an injection of healthy cells.

Embryonic stem cells also have a downside. If these cells are used in treatment, a patient's body might reject them as foreign material. A different possibility is that the stem cells could grow unchecked in a patient's body and form a tumor. The use of embryonic stem cells also raises many ethical questions. **FIGURE 5.4** shows the most common method of obtaining embryonic stem cells. This method currently involves destruction of the embryo, which some people consider ethically unacceptable.

FIGURE 5.4 HARVESTING EMBRYONIC STEM CELLS

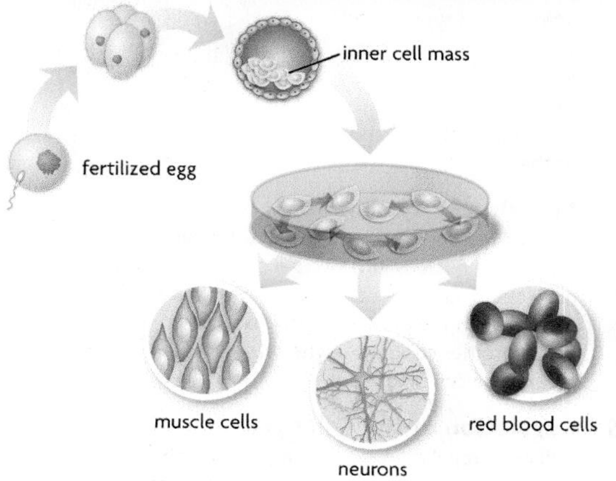

First, an egg is fertilized by a sperm cell in a petri dish. The egg divides, forming an inner cell mass. These cells are then removed and grown with nutrients. Scientists try to control how the cells specialize by adding or removing certain molecules.

A Compare and Contrast **List treatment benefits and risks of both types of stem cells.**

Integrating Medical Science

Although embryonic stem cell research is still in experimental stages, adult stem cells are currently used for some cancer treatments. An **autologous stem cell transplant** is used to treat lymphomas and some other cancers. A person's own stem cells are harvested from bone marrow or blood and frozen and returned to the body after chemotherapy or radiation treatment. An **allogeneic stem cell transplant** is used to treat leukemias and other bone marrow disorders, using stem cells from a donor. In both types of transplants, the stem cells are added to the person's blood and move to the bone marrow, where they begin making blood cells.

Answers

A Compare and Contrast Adult stem cells taken from a patient's own body are less likely to be rejected than those from a donor. However, they can be difficult to isolate and grow, and have limited potential as far as what tissue can develop. Embryonic stem cells can develop into almost any cell type. However, they may be rejected by a patient's body.

5.5 Formative Assessment

SELF-CHECK Online HMHScience.com GO ONLINE

REVIEWING MAIN IDEAS

1. How does communication between cells help maintain homeostasis?
2. Why is **cell differentiation** an important part of the development of a multicellular organism?
3. What are the defining characteristics of **stem cells**?

CRITICAL THINKING

4. **Compare** Describe how cells, **tissues, organs,** and **organ systems** are related.
5. **Evaluate** What role does the location of a cell in a developing embryo play in cell differentiation?

CONNECT TO ETHICS IN BIOLOGY

6. Explain which factor you think is most important in deciding whether stem cell research should be legal and government-funded.

5.5 FORMATIVE ASSESSMENT

1. Different cells are needed for different functions, and their activities need to be coordinated to maintain the body's internal environment.
2. It is essential for different functions because one kind of cell cannot perform all the activities required for life.
3. Stem cells divide continually, while remaining undifferentiated for long periods of time. Yet they can develop into specialized cell types.
4. Tissues are groups of specialized cells that make up organs, and organs work together in organ systems.
5. In a developing embryo, a cell's location helps determine what structure and function the cell will have. Cell differentiation leads to the development of progressively more specialized tissues and organs.
6. Answers will vary.

Assess and Reteach

Assess Use the Section Self-Check or Section Quiz, both available at **HMHScience.com**.

Reteach Have pairs of students quiz each other on key material in this section. Have them write down their questions and answers. Then collect the questions for review with the class.

CHAPTER REVIEW

GO ONLINE

Encourage students to go to **HMHScience.com** for a detailed review of each section, including visuals and vocabulary practice.

Online Student Resources, Vocabulary Practice Worksheet

CHAPTER

5 Summary

BIG IDEA Cells have their own life cycle that includes reproduction, growth, and regulation, which allows organisms to carry out life functions and grow.

KEY CONCEPTS

5.1 The Cell Cycle

Cells have distinct phases of growth, reproduction, and normal functions. The cell cycle has four main stages: G_1, S, G_2, and M. The length of the cell cycle can vary, resulting in different rates of cell division. This variability is based on the body's need for different cell types. Cells also divide because they need a sufficient surface area–to–volume ratio to move materials into and out of the cell.

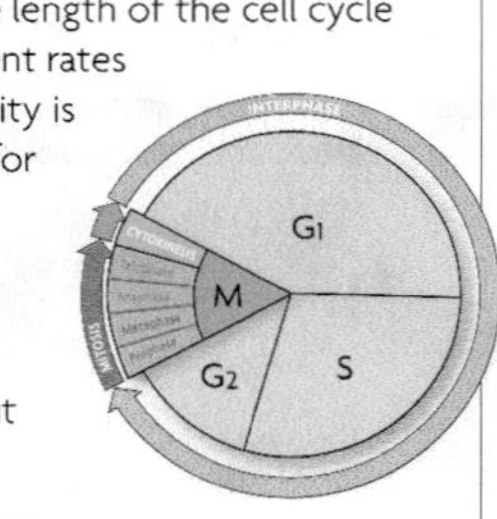

5.2 Mitosis and Cytokinesis

Cells divide during mitosis and cytokinesis. Mitosis divides the nucleus into two genetically identical nuclei in a four-phase process: prophase, metaphase, anaphase, and telophase. In prophase, the duplicated chromosomes condense tightly. Cytokinesis actually divides the cell cytoplasm.

5.3 Regulation of the Cell Cycle

Cell cycle regulation is necessary for healthy growth. Cell growth and division are regulated by both external factors, such as hormones and growth factors, and internal factors, such as cyclins and kinases. When proper regulation of cell growth is disrupted, a cell may become cancerous. Cancer cells grow more rapidly than do normal cells and form clumps called tumors that may metastasize to other regions of the body.

5.4 Asexual Reproduction

Many organisms reproduce by cell division. Most prokaryotes reproduce through a process called binary fission, in which a cell divides into two approximately equal parts. Some eukaryotes reproduce through mitosis. The offspring that result from asexual reproduction are genetically identical to the parent organism, except when mutations occur. Whether being identical is an advantage or a disadvantage depends on the environment.

5.5 Multicellular Life

Cells work together to carry out complex functions. Within multicellular organisms, cells form tissues, tissues form organs, and organs form organ systems. The cells differentiate to perform specific functions. Much of this specialization is determined by a cell's location within the developing embryo. Stem cells are a special type of cell that continue to divide and renew themselves for long periods of time.

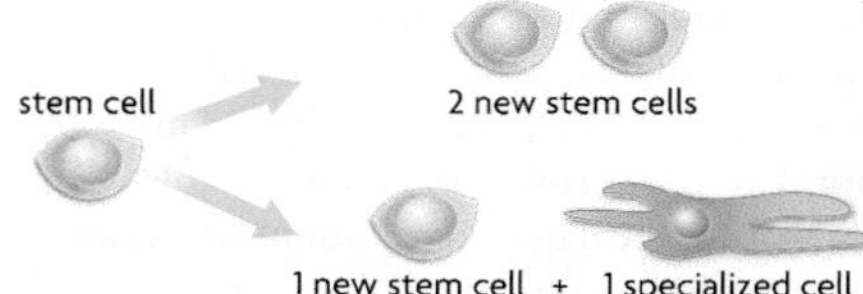

READING TOOLBOX SYNTHESIZE YOUR NOTES

Concept Map Use a concept map like the one below to summarize what you know about mitosis.

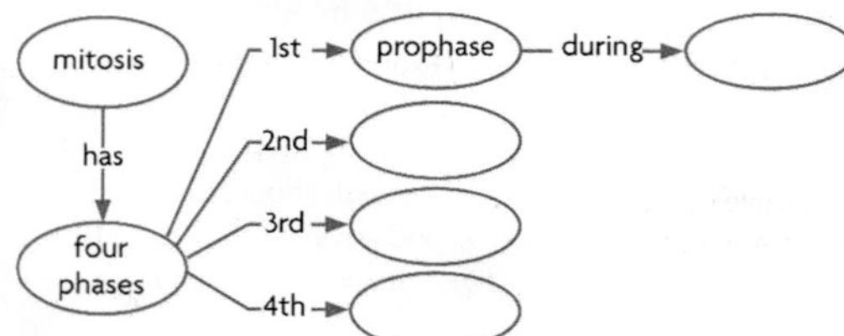

Venn Diagram Draw a Venn diagram like the one below to summarize the similarities and differences between embryonic and adult stem cells.

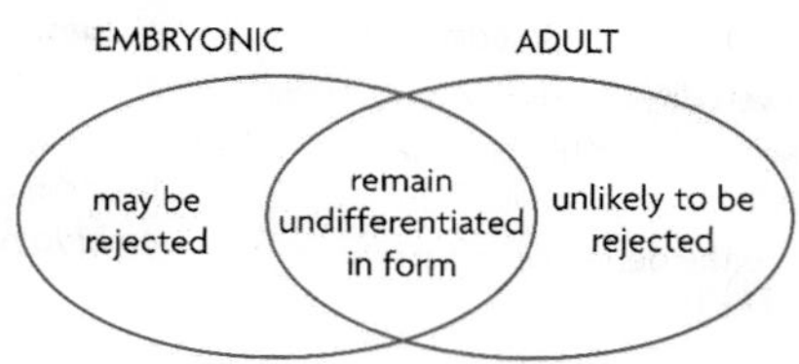

Reviewing Vocabulary

1. sketch of a cell with nucleus starting to disintegrate and chromosomes in condensed, duplicated form
2. sketch of a cell with chromosomes lined up in the middle with one chromatid facing each pole
3. sketch of a cell with chromatid pairs pulled apart by spindle fibers and being pulled toward the poles
4. sketch of a cell forming into two, each with a nucleus forming and with single chromosomes
5. sketch of two separate identical cells, each with intact nucleus
6. sketch of central point in a condensed, duplicated chromosome where sister chromatids are joined
7. sketch of a chromosome with end regions shaded or distinguished and labeled
8. Prophase is the first, and therefore earliest, stage of mitosis, before chromosomes line up at the middle of the cell.
9. Telophase is the last, and therefore ending, phase of mitosis. The telomere is the region of DNA located at each end of a chromosome.
10. The chromosomes themselves appear to be threadlike when viewed through a microscope. Some students may think the spindle fibers look like threads.

INTERACTIVE Review
HMHScience.com
GO ONLINE
Review Games • Concept Map • Section Self-Checks

5 Review

CHAPTER VOCABULARY

5.1 cell cycle, mitosis, cytokinesis

5.2 chromosome, histone, chromatin, chromatid, centromere, telomere, prophase, metaphase, anaphase, telophase

5.3 growth factor, apoptosis, cancer, benign, malignant, metastasize, carcinogen

5.4 asexual reproduction, binary fission

5.5 tissue, organ, organ system, cell differentiation, stem cell

Reviewing Vocabulary

Visualize Vocabulary

For each term below, draw a simple picture that represents the meaning of the word. Here is an example for *mitosis*.

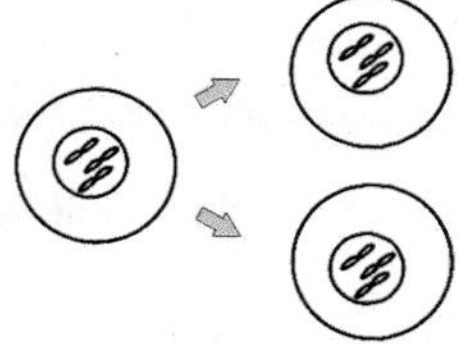

1. prophase
2. metaphase
3. anaphase
4. telophase
5. cytokinesis
6. centromere
7. telomere

READING TOOLBOX WORD ORIGINS

8. The prefix *pro-* means "earlier than" or "prior to." Explain how this meaning relates to the word *prophase*.
9. The prefix *telo-* means "distant, far, or end." How does this meaning relate to the words *telophase* and *telomere*?
10. The term *mitosis* comes from the Greek root *mitos*, which means "thread." How does this meaning relate to the process of mitosis?

Reviewing MAIN IDEAS

11. The cell cycle has four main stages—G_1, S, G_2, and M. What occurs in the cell during each stage?
12. Compare the rates of cell division occurring in your neurons and your hair follicles.
13. What is the relationship between a cell's surface area and its volume?
14. You know that a chromosome is a very long, continuous strand of DNA. How do proteins help condense chromosomes?
15. Describe what happens in each main phase of mitosis—prophase, metaphase, anaphase, and telophase.
16. How does the process of cytokinesis differ from the process of mitosis?
17. Increased levels of cyclin help trigger a cell to divide. Do you think a growth factor would increase or decrease cyclin levels? Explain.
18. Describe how uncontrolled cell division is dangerous in organisms.
19. List one similarity and one difference between binary fission and mitosis.
20. You pull a leaf from a plant and place it in a cup of water. After a week, roots start to grow from the leaf. What type of reproduction has occurred, and what role does mitosis play in it?
21. Briefly describe how cell differentiation occurs in the developing animal embryo.
22. List three characteristics of all stem cells.

Reviewing Main Ideas

11. A cell grows and carries out its normal functions in G_1. During the S stage, DNA is copied. The cell continues to grow during G_2. During the four phases of mitosis, the cell's nucleus breaks down, and the duplicated chromosomes line up at the cell's center and then separate. The cell membrane starts to pinch together as the last part of mitosis, known as cytokinesis, brings about the division of one cell into two. Each of those cells return to interphase.
12. Cell division occurs much more rapidly in hair follicles than in neurons.
13. The larger a cell, the smaller is the surface area of cell membrane available to support a given volume of the cell's interior. Assuming a cell is shaped like a cube or sphere, surface area increases by the power of 2 compared to an increase in volume by the power of 3.
14. DNA strands are wrapped around proteins called histones, which keep the strands from getting tangled. The tighter the coils, the more condensed the DNA becomes, enabling duplicated DNA to be separated and evenly distributed between two cells during mitosis.
15. Prophase: chromosomes condense, nuclear envelope starts to break down, spindle fibers form. Metaphase: spindle fibers align the chromosomes at the center of the cell. Anaphase: spindle fibers pull the sister chromatids apart and toward opposite sides of the cell. Telophase: chromosomes uncoil, spindle fibers break down, and the nuclear membrane re-forms.
16. Cytokinesis is the division of the cytoplasm, whereas mitosis is the division of the chromosomes. Cytokinesis occurs when the cell membrane closes in to form two new animal cells or when the cell wall closes in to form two new plant cells.
17. A growth factor would likely increase cyclin levels because cyclin helps stimulate the cell division cycle.
18. A body needs a certain number of specific types of cells to function properly and maintain a stable environment and homeostasis. Uncontrolled cell division throws off this balance. More cells means more energy and resources than might be available, possibly depriving other cells of what they need to function.
19. Both mitosis and binary fission are types of cell division that result in identical daughter cells. Binary fission occurs in prokaryotes, where no nucleus is present, and results in two new organisms. Mitosis requires breakdown of the nucleus. It is used for growth and repair in multicellular organisms.
20. It is vegetative reproduction, a form of asexual reproduction. The newly formed plant grows new roots and stems by mitosis.
21. Dividing cells in the developing embryo form into three layers, and cells in those layers develop into specific types of tissues and organs.
22. Stem cells have the ability to divide and renew themselves for long periods of time; they can remain undifferentiated in form for long periods of time; and they have the capacity to develop into a variety of specialized cell types.

Critical Thinking

23. Regulatory proteins control cell division by acting as stop or go signals. They can delay cell division if external conditions are not favorable or if new cells are not needed, reserving resources for other functioning cells. Regulatory proteins can promote cell division if conditions require it. They also ensure that DNA has been properly copied so that the new cells produced function properly.
24. A cell's location within the embryo determines how it will differentiate. For example, the outer layer of cells in the hollow, ball-shaped animal embryo will differentiate to form the outer layer of the skin or the brain or spinal cord.
25. This technique would allow faster growth of potatoes because the plants are not grown from seed, and there may be a greater yield. However, because it is an asexual form of reproduction, the entire crop is genetically identical. If the original potato plants are susceptible to a particular disease or pest, then the whole crop is at risk.
26. It provides a source of variation that may help them survive.
27. After the S phase, each pair would have doubled, so there would be 48 chromatids in the cell.
28. If DNA does not attach to the histones in the right way, then DNA might become tangled or damaged. This might interfere with the DNA being copied correctly or prevent the duplicated DNA from dividing equally between the two new cells during mitosis.

Critical Thinking

23. Synthesize How do regulatory proteins of the cell cycle help maintain homeostasis?

24. Describe How is the location of a cell in an embryo related to differentiation of that cell?

25. Analyze A scientist wants to use asexually reproducing vegetables to increase crop yields. He plans to distribute budding potatoes and teach farmers how to separate them into new plants. What are some potential benefits and risks that could result from this situation?

26. Analyze The rates of DNA mutations in bacteria are known to increase when they are under stressed environmental conditions. Why do you think this is important for an organism that reproduces asexually?

27. Apply Suppose an organism usually has 24 chromosomes in its nucleus. How many chromatids would it have just after the S phase of the cell cycle?

28. Predict If a mutation made histone proteins bind less tightly to DNA, how might the cell cycle be affected?

Interpreting Visuals

Use the picture of onion root cells shown below to answer the next three questions.

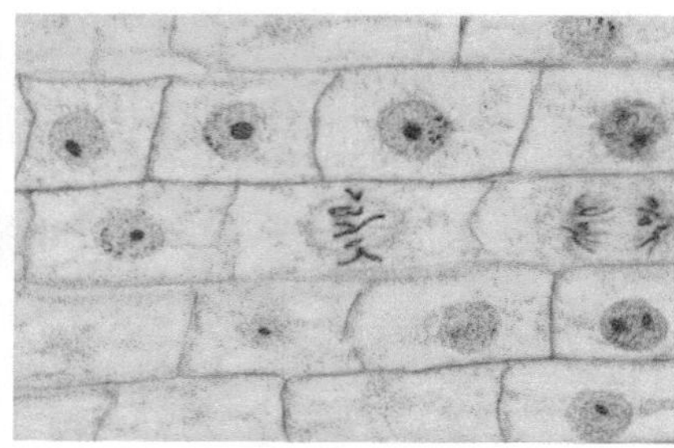

magnification 120×

29. Apply In what stage of the cell cycle are most of these cells? Explain.

30. Apply How can you visually distinguish between newly formed cells and older cells?

31. Synthesize If these cells were immersed in salt water, how would the cells undergoing mitosis be affected? (Hint: Think about the process of osmosis.)

Analyzing Data Construct a Data Table

The graph below shows the five-year survival rate, expressed as percentages, of patients diagnosed with cancer from 1985 through 1997. This data is for all types of invasive cancers and includes males and females of all races. Use the graph to answer the next two questions.

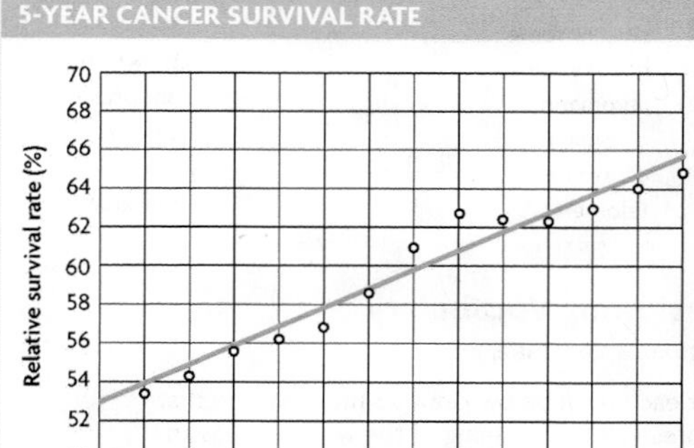

Source: The National Cancer Institute

32. Analyze Which points do not follow the best-fit line for the data?

33. Interpret What is the trend in the data of cancer survival during the span of time given?

Making Connections

34. Write a Narrative Imagine that you are a single chromosome about to undergo replication and mitosis. Describe what will happen to you starting from the S phase through mitosis. Be creative. Use humor and a first-person point of view. Come up with sounds or perspectives that illustrate what is happening. Be sure to include all details of the process and related terms.

35. Design an Experiment Cancer cells, such as those shown on the chapter opener, are frequently grown in labs for research uses. Suppose you wanted to determine whether a certain substance was a carcinogen. Outline a plan for an experiment to describe what questions you would want to answer, what experiments you would perform, and what the different possible results would suggest.

Interpreting Visuals

29. Most of these cells appear to be in interphase, which is indicated by the presence of the nucleus. Cells spend most of their time in interphase.
30. The newly formed cells are smaller in volume, and the nucleus takes up most of the cytoplasm. Older cells have more cytoplasmic space in relation to nuclear space.
31. If the cells were immersed in salt water, there would be a higher concentration of salt outside the cells than inside, causing the cells to lose water by the process of osmosis. Cells generally do not divide when they are in adverse conditions.

Analyzing Data

32. Points for years 1989, 1991, and 1992 are well off the line; to a lesser degree, so are years 1986, 1988, 1993, 1995, 1996, and 1997.
33. During the period shown, the number of people who survived cancer for at least five years increased.

Standards-Based Assessment

Record your answers on a separate piece of paper.

MULTIPLE CHOICE

1 Scientists researching anticancer drugs treat a cell culture with a compound. Following treatment, they notice that the culture stopped growing. Untreated cells from the same culture, however, have continued to grow. These results indicate that the compound blocks the normal cell cycle. What else could have caused these results?

A The compound had degraded.

B The compound prevented cells from mutating.

C The compound killed the treated cells.

D The compound had no effect.

THINK THROUGH THE QUESTION

The untreated cells serve as a control in this experiment. Therefore, differences between the treated and untreated cells should be the result of the drug. If the drug has no effect, the two groups of cells should be the same.

2 Which describes the role of DNA in cell differentiation?

A It regulates cell differentiation.

B It carries the code from which each cell type expresses specific genes.

C It removes genes that are unneeded from differentiated cells.

D It prevents a full set of DNA from being passed on to stem cells.

3 One environmental factor that plays a key role in cell differentiation in multicellular organisms is the location of the developing cell with respect to other cells. In human development, from which cell layer in the embryo will a nerve cell develop?

A within the nucleus

B outer layer

C middle layer

D inner layer

4

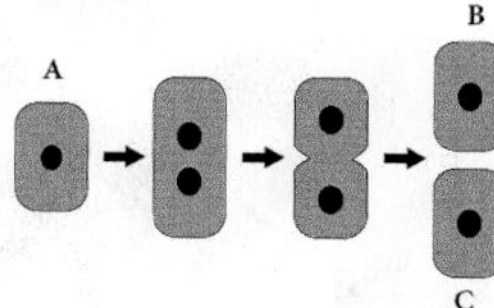

In the diagram above, cell A is undergoing mitosis. If cell A has 6 chromosomes, how many chromosomes will cells B and C have?

A none

B 3 each

C 6 each

D 12 each

5

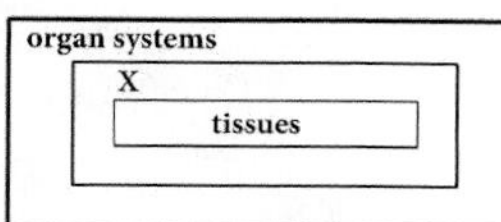

The figure above represents some levels of organization in multicellular organisms. Which term fits in the box marked "X"?

A cells

B organelles

C organs

D organisms

6 Unlike stem cells, most body cells cannot form different types of cells. For example, skin cells can only make skin cells, and nerve cells only make nerve cells. Which statement ***best*** explains why skin cells will never become nerve cells?

A Each type of cell gets a different message from the central DNA, which is stored in DNA cells.

B Each type of cell has only the part of the DNA necessary for making that type of cell.

C Each cell type is determined by messages sent from the brain, which directs development.

D Both types of cells have the same DNA, but each cell uses only part of the DNA message.

Standards-Based Assessment

The Standards-Based Assessment questions will help students prepare for their final examination in the course. If you wish to give students practice in coding their answers, look for the Standards-Based Assessment Answer Sheet at **HMHScience.com**. To give students practice under timed testing conditions, allow them five minutes per question.

Question	Answer	Depth of Knowledge	Cognitive Complexity
1	C	III	H
2	B	II	L
3	B	IV	M
4	C	I	M
5	C	I	L
6	D	II	M

KEY

Depth of Knowledge
- I Recall
- II Skill/Concept
- III Strategic Thinking
- IV Extended Thinking

Cognitive Complexity
- L Low
- M Moderate
- H High

Making Connections

34. The narrative should describe DNA being duplicated creating a "twin," increased coiling as chromatin takes the form of a chromosome, being pulled to the center as nuclear membrane breaks down, being separated from the twin and pulled away, and finally separated as new cells form.

35. The point of the experiment would be to discover if the substance might cause changes in an organism's DNA or affect the cell cycle. A test animal could be exposed to various levels of the material to determine where changes might occur. Tumors would be an obvious sign of cancer; samples of tissues might also show signs of change. The test might show that some organs and tissues are more likely to be affected. The DNA of the test animal could be compared to that of a normal animal for possible mutations—how many and to what genes.

UNIT 2

Introduce

Tell students that there are generally four types of sources for science information.

Primary sources are the professional print and web journals principally intended for science professionals, for example, *Science* and *Nature* magazines.

Secondary sources are science magazines, books, and Web pages intended for a science-literate public, for example, *Scientific American* and *Science News*.

General sources include national newspapers and magazines that have staff writers who report on science for the general public, for example, *The New York Times*, *Time*, and *Newsweek*.

Local and mass media offer reports that are limited in scope and often contain information gathered from general sources.

Discuss these sources with students. **Ask**

- If you were doing a report for school, which source would you choose? Most students would probably use secondary and general sources.
- Why might it be useful to look at a primary source when evaluating a story you read in a secondary or general source? The primary source gives more information on the research itself, often indicating limitations or reservations the researchers have. Dissenting views are sometimes published in the primary source.

UNIT 2: CELLS

BIOZINE at HMHSCIENCE.COM

INTERNET MAGAZINE

Go online for the latest biology news and updates on all BioZine articles.

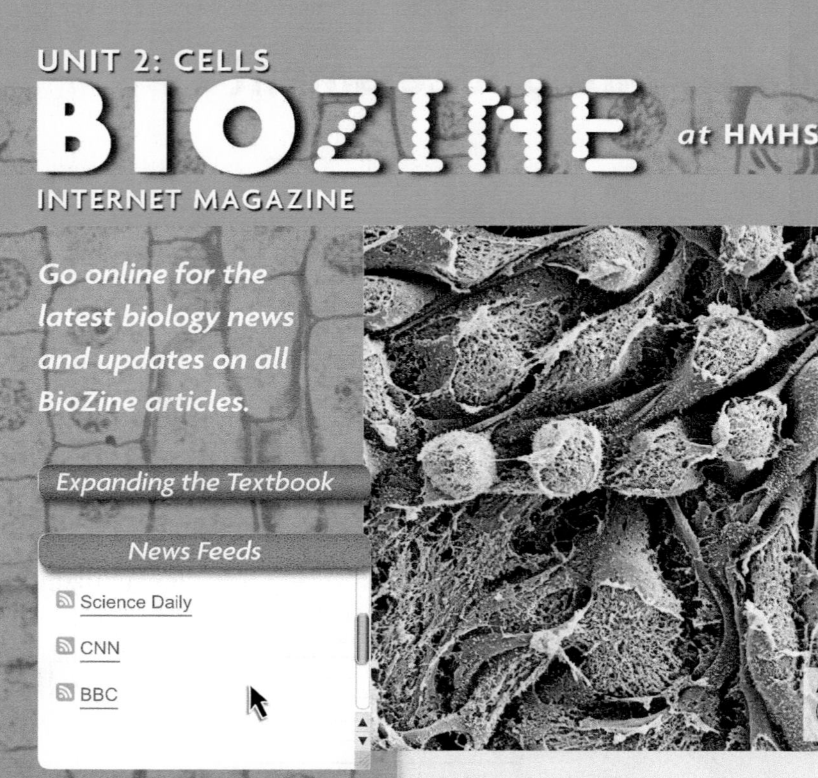

A group of embryonic stem cells (colored SEM, magnification 1,000×)

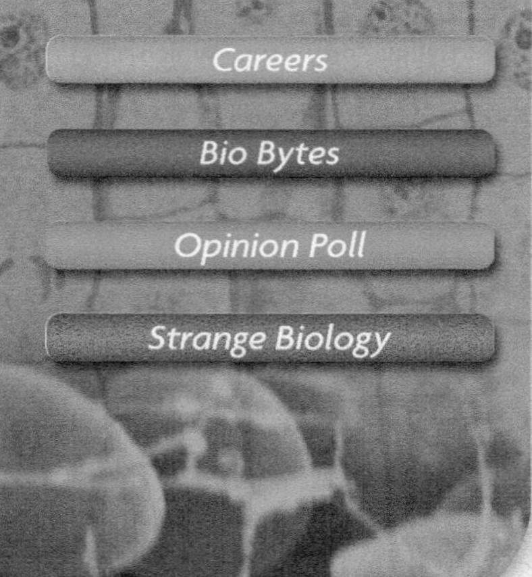

Stem Cell Research—Potential Solutions, Practical Challenges

A news program asks viewers to vote online: "Should stem cell research be banned? Yes or no?" Some people claim that stem cell therapy will revolutionize medicine. Others believe that some types of stem cell research violate ethical standards and are not justified by the potential benefits. Between these two positions exists a wide range of ideas about what is or is not acceptable. Would you know how to vote?

156 Unit 2: Cells

Current News

Using an interactive whiteboard or the computer lab, have students compare the stories being covered by the media sources featured in the Current News section of BioZine online. Have students consider these questions:

- What stories about biology are making headlines at these different news sources?
- How does the coverage of the same story by different news sources compare?
- To whom do reporters go for verification and for commentary?

Opinion Poll

Have students go to the BioZine at **HMHScience.com** to take the online poll for that day. Check the results and report the outcome to the class. **Ask**

- Did the poll, as worded, enable you to express your opinion fully? If not, explain.
- How might the way in which a question is worded influence a response? Give some examples.
- Why is it important to know who is conducting a poll?

Using Stem Cells

Stem cells are undifferentiated cells that can regenerate themselves and develop into specialized types of cells. Stem cell research offers the hope of understanding basic cell processes and treating or even curing many diseases. However, many technical challenges must be overcome before stem cell therapy is a realistic option, and ethical issues continue to surround stem cell research.

Potential Benefits

Stem cell research offers many potential benefits.

- Studying adult stem cells may help scientists better understand how tissues develop and what goes wrong when those tissues become diseased.
- A better understanding of the properties of stem cells may give scientists more information about how cancer cells replace themselves and thus help scientists develop more-targeted cancer therapies.
- Stem cells could be used to grow human tissues to test the effects of drugs and chemicals.
- Stem cells may be used to replace healthy cells that are killed by radiation treatment for cancer.
- Stem cells may be used to regenerate tissues. For example, chemotherapy kills blood-producing cells in bone marrow. To replace these cells, stem cells could be used instead of the patient's own marrow, which may contain cancer cells.
- Stem cells may be used to treat spinal cord injuries and neurodegenerative diseases, such as Parkinson's.

TECHNOLOGY S.T.E.M.

Somatic Cell Nuclear Transfer

Somatic cell nuclear transfer (SCNT), also called therapeutic cloning, is a method for obtaining stem cells that has been used to clone animals. The process is still under development, however, and it has not yet been used to produce stem cells for humans. SCNT offers the hope of using a patient's own DNA to produce stem cells that can form many types of specialized cells. Many SCNT studies have been done in mice and pigs; the diagram to the right shows how the SCNT process might be applied in human cells.

1. An unfertilized egg is taken from a female's body, and the nucleus—containing the DNA—is removed. A cell is then taken from a patient's body. The nucleus is removed and inserted into the egg.
2. The egg is given a mild electrical stimulation, which makes it divide. The DNA comes from the patient's nucleus, and the materials needed for division come from the egg.
3. The stem cells could then be cultured and caused to differentiate into any tissue or organ needed by the patient.

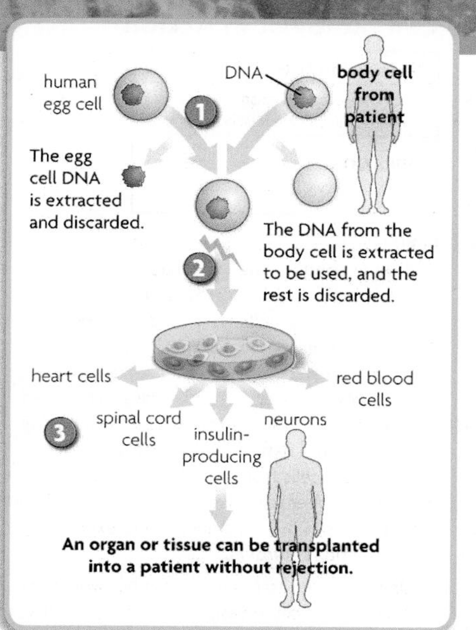

human egg cell
DNA
body cell from patient
1
The egg cell DNA is extracted and discarded.
The DNA from the body cell is extracted to be used, and the rest is discarded.
2
heart cells
red blood cells
spinal cord cells
neurons
insulin-producing cells
3
An organ or tissue can be transplanted into a patient without rejection.

Once a stem cell line is established, in theory it can continue to grow indefinitely. Researchers could use these cell lines without having to harvest more stem cells. The cell lines also could be frozen and shipped to other researchers around the world.

Read More >> at HMHScience.com

Vocabulary of Stem Cells

Students may need clarification of some of the terms used in stem cell research.

stem cell—an undifferentiated cell that can divide to produce one or more specialized cells. When a stem cell divides, it can produce more stem cells or differentiate into specialized cells, such as blood or muscle cells. Controlling stem cell differentiation is one the biggest challenges of stem cell research.

totipotent—quality of a fertilized egg to give rise to all cells in the body and thus form an entire organism.

differentiation—the process by which a cell develops physical characteristics that make it suited to a particular function. The process occurs in response to biochemical signals or environmental conditions.

blastocyst—a hollow ball of undifferentiated cells formed just after fertilization in the embryos of some animals. In humans, the outer layer of cells develops into the placenta and the inner cell mass becomes the fetus.

embryonic stem cell—cells of the inner cell mass of a blastocyst, before they begin to differentiate. In humans, this stage is reached less than a week after fertilization. The blastocyst is made up of 100 to 150 cells.

pluripotent—the quality of an embryonic stem cell that enables it to differentiate into almost any type of cell.

adult stem cell—undifferentiated cells of a certain type of tissue that are used for growth and repair. For example, stem cells in human skin divide and differentiate into the specific skin cells found in different layers of the skin.

multipotent—quality of an adult stem cell that limits its differentiation to cells of a certain tissue type.

cell line—a group of stem cells developed by repeated division of a single cell. Once established, a cell line can be used to produce an unlimited supply of undifferentiated cells. It can also be frozen and kept in a cell bank.

Expanding the Textbook

Have students check out the BioZine at **HMHScience.com** to read more about stem cells. Have students take notes on different types of stem cells. Students should come to class prepared to discuss the advantages and disadvantages of each type. Have students identify the conditions or diseases that are most often cited as possibly benefiting from stem cell research or treatment.

You could extend the discussion to include students' understanding of the ethical questions surrounding stem cell research. What do students think is the appropriate role of government in regulating such research? Students can research current state and federal regulations and funding for stem cell research.

Take It Further

According to the National Academies of Science, stem cell–based therapies have the potential to help some of the millions of people who are treated for the following conditions and diseases:

- cardiovascular disease: roughly 70 million Americans live with this disease
- autoimmune diseases: approximately 14 to 22 million people are affected
- diabetes: there are approximately 14.7 million patients
- osteoporosis: approximately 10 million patients are treated per year
- Alzheimer's disease: approximately 4.5 million Americans have this disease
- Parkinson's disease: approximately 1.5 million Americans currently have this disease
- spinal-cord injuries: approximately 0.25 million patients are treated each year

Technical Challenges

Adult stem cells have been used therapeutically for years in the form of bone marrow transplants. Nevertheless, many technical challenges must still be overcome before stem cells can be used to treat a wide range of disorders. Examples are highlighted below.

Supply Stem cells can be taken from a variety of sources, including an embryo, a patient in need of treatment, a patient's relative, or an established embryonic stem cell line. Embryonic stem cells are taken from embryos fertilized in an in vitro fertilization clinic, whereas established stem cell lines are cultures of embryonic stem cells used to grow additional stem cells that match the ones that came from the original embryo. Each source presents its own special set of ethical considerations.

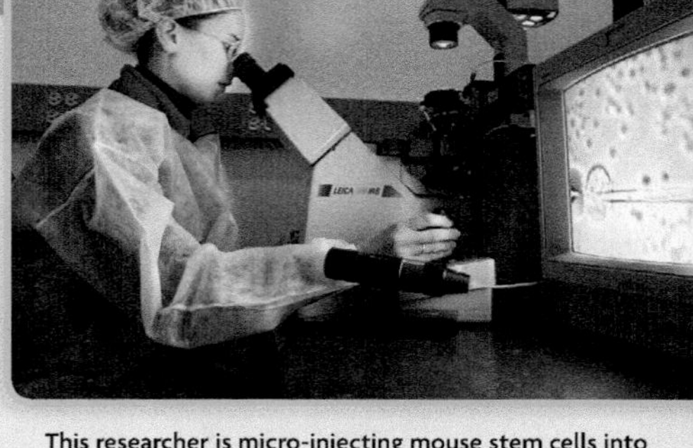

This researcher is micro-injecting mouse stem cells into fertilized mouse eggs to be used in drug research.

Transplantation into the target area The delivery of stem cells to targeted tissues can be complex, especially if the tissues are deep inside the body. And once delivered, stem cells must "learn" to work with other cells. For instance, inserted cardiac cells must contract in unison with a patient's heart cells.

Prevention of rejection Stem cells may be rejected if a patient's body sees them as foreign. This problem can remain even when certain identifying proteins are removed from the cells' membranes. The development of SCNT technology in humans could help solve this problem so that patients would not have to take drugs to suppress their immune system.

Suppression of tumor formation By their very nature, stem cells remain undifferentiated and continue to divide for long periods of time. When transplanted into an organism, many embryonic stem cells tend to form tumors. This risk must be removed before the cells can be used therapeutically.

CAREERS

Cell Biologist in Action

DR. GAIL MARTIN
TITLE Professor, Anatomy, University of California, San Francisco
EDUCATION Ph.D., Molecular Biology, University of California, Berkeley

In 1974 Dr. Gail Martin was working at the University College in London when she made a huge advance. She developed a way to grow stem cells in a petri dish. These fragile cells were hard to work with, so Dr. Martin's breakthrough removed a big obstacle to stem cell research. Seven years later, she made another key discovery while working in her own laboratory at the University of California, San Francisco, in her native United States—how to harvest stem cells from mouse embryos. Her work has helped other scientists develop ways to harvest stem cells from human embryos and explore their use in treating disorders.

Dr. Martin likes to point out that her work shows how small advances in basic biology can pay off years later in unexpected ways. She states that many people focus on cures for specific diseases, not realizing that these cures "may come from basic research in seemingly unrelated areas. What is really going to be important 20 years from now isn't clear."

Read More >> at HMHScience.com

Unanswered Questions

Stem cell research and therapy do not only involve questions of what we can do. They also involve questions about what we should do, who should benefit, and who should pay.

- Should human embryos be a source of stem cells?
- How should stem cell research be funded?
- How can the benefits of stem cell research best be shared by all people, regardless of income?
- Should insurance cover costly stem cell procedures?

Read More >> at HMHScience.com

BIOZINE HMHScience.com

Have students use the resources available in the BioZine for this unit at **HMHScience.com** to report about a recent discovery in cell biology. In addition to the secondary and general sources available in BioZine, have students work with a librarian to locate the original, primary source. Have students compare the reports. **Ask**

- How well did the secondary and general sources do in describing the discovery or event?
- What was left out of the reports written for the general public?
- How do the different sources vary in describing the potential benefits or applications of the discovery?
- What concerns, if any, are expressed by the people who report on the discovery, and how do those concerns differ among the various reports you read?

GO ONLINE! for all your teacher resources at HMHScience.com

② Support and Intervention

Support and Intervention resources are useful for students who need targeted help beyond the Core Instruction

Resources	PRINT	ONLINE
Assess and Reteach (TE wrap)	■	➚
Concept Map		➚
Interactive Reader	■	➚
Interactive Review Games		➚
Section Self-Checks		➚
Study Guide B		➚
Virtual Investigation Phases of Meiosis		➚
Vocabulary Practice Worksheets		➚

③ Specialized Support

Students who need more intensive personalized intervention benefit from **Specialized Support** resources.

Resources	PRINT	ONLINE
Chapter Audio Files		➚
Differentiated Instruction Inclusion, Below Level, and English Learners (TE wrap)	■	➚
ELL Strategies	■	➚
Modified Lesson Plans for English Learners		➚
Reinforcement Worksheets		➚
Study Guide A		➚

Extension and Assessment

Enrichment and Challenge

Resources	PRINT	ONLINE
Active Reading Worksheets		➚
Data Analysis Practice Worksheet		➚
Differentiated Instruction Pre-AP (TE wrap)	■	➚
Pre-AP Activity Viewing Mendel Through a Modern Lens, Chi Square Tests		➚
The Inside Story and **Take It Further** (TE wrap)	■	➚
Unit Project		➚
WebLinks		➚
WebQuest Selective Breeding (6.6)		➚

Assessment

Resources	PRINT	ONLINE
Alternative Assessment		➚
Chapter Tests A and B		➚
Diagnostic Test		➚
ExamView Banks		➚
Extended Response Test		➚
Online Assessment System		➚
Section Quizzes		➚
Standards-Based Assessment	■	➚

CHAPTER 6

Chapter Overview

- **Section 1** compares body cells and gametes, and introduces meiosis.
- **Section 2** details the process of meiosis.
- **Section 3** introduces Mendel's genetic research, which revealed patterns of inheritance.
- **Section 4** explains how genes influence the development of traits, and how a single gene can have multiple versions.
- **Section 5** describes monohybrid and dihybrid crosses, as well as how patterns in heredity can be calculated using mathematics.
- **Section 6** discusses meiosis and genetic variation.

Focus and Motivate

What makes you who you are?

Students should recognize that there is no simple answer to the question posed; the development of a human being involves the genetic component as well as environmental factors. **Ask**

- What is distinctive about sex cells, as compared to all other cells found in the body? Sperm and egg cells contain only a single set of chromosomes, not chromosome pairs.
- What role do sex cells play in the well-being of a human? Sex cells do not contribute to general maintenance. Rather, they control sexual determination and development.

BIOZINE HMHScience.com

Students can access BioZine at **HMHScience.com** to receive updates about featured topics in the book.

CHAPTER 6 Meiosis and Mendel

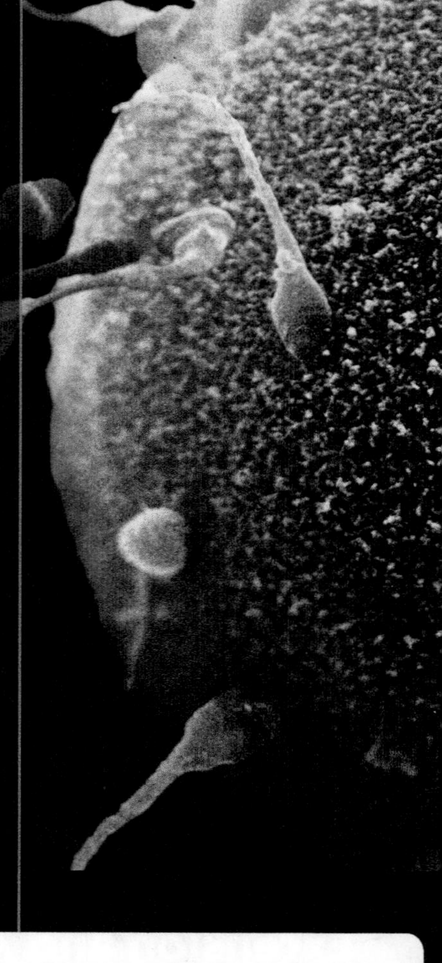

BIG IDEA In meiosis, genetic material from two parent organisms results in offspring with traits that follow a pattern of inheritance.

ONLINE BIOLOGY HMHScience.com

ONLINE Labs

- **QuickLab** Using a Testcross
- Allele Combinations and Punnett Squares
- Modeling Meiosis
- S.T.E.M. Lab Modeling Chromosomes in Meiosis
- Probability Practice
- Modeling Monohybrid and Dihybrid Crosses
- **Virtual Lab** Breeding Mutations in Fruit Flies
- **Video Lab** Meiosis Model

Teacher Demo

Modeling **Use a simple model to preview how different combinations of alleles are formed through the process of crossing over.**

Materials

- 4 toothpicks
- 4 red gumdrops
- 4 green gumdrops
- 2 twist ties

Prepare Thread two red gumdrops onto each of two toothpicks. With the gumdrops facing in opposite directions, tie the toothpicks together with a twist tie. Do the same thing with the green gumdrops. The gumdrops on each toothpick represent the genetic information supplied by each parent. Each toothpick pair represents one duplicated chromosome (two sister chromatids) of a homologous pair. The twist tie represents the centromere.

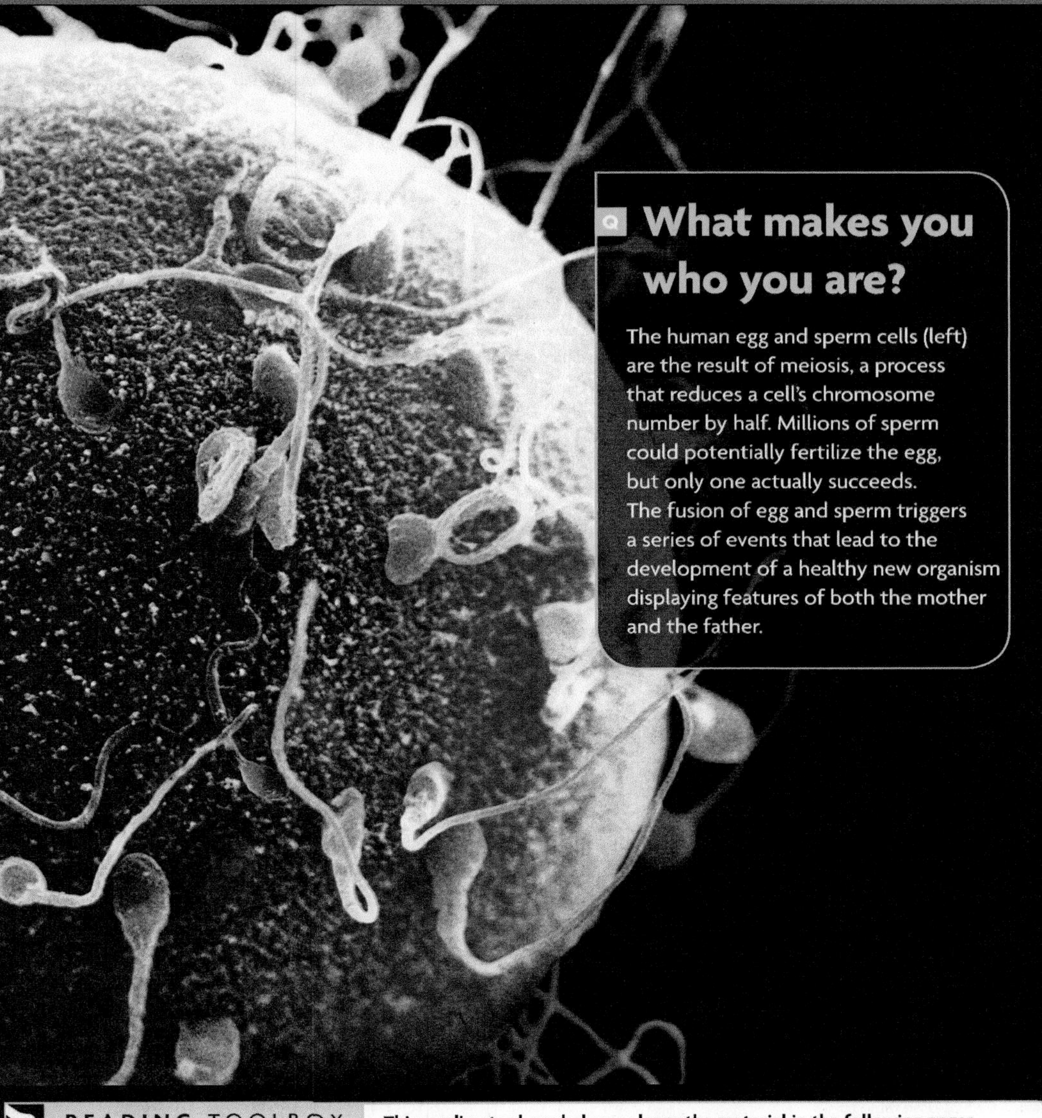

What makes you who you are?

The human egg and sperm cells (left) are the result of meiosis, a process that reduces a cell's chromosome number by half. Millions of sperm could potentially fertilize the egg, but only one actually succeeds. The fusion of egg and sperm triggers a series of events that lead to the development of a healthy new organism displaying features of both the mother and the father.

READING TOOLBOX **This reading tool can help you learn the material in the following pages.**

USING LANGUAGE

Comparisons Comparing is a way of looking for the similarities between different things. Contrasting is a way of looking for differences. Certain words and phrases can help you determine if things are being compared or contrasted. Comparison words include *and, like, just as,* and *in the same way.* Contrast words include *however, unlike, in contrast,* and *on the other hand.*

YOUR TURN

In the following sentences, find the things that are being compared or contrasted.

1. Like mitosis, meiosis is a process that reproduces new cells.
2. In contrast to many other reptiles, the Burmese python does not reproduce sexually.

Introduce Position the gumdrop models together to illustrate pairs of homologous chromosomes, as in prophase I. Line them up, side by side, as in metaphase I. Exchange one red and one green gumdrop, maintaining their original positions on the respective inner chromatids, to illustrate the way DNA on homologous chromatids can cross over in anaphase I. Separate the pairs, as in telophase I. Then show the separation of the chromatids into individual chromosomes, as in meiosis II.

Discuss Point out that during meiosis, genetic recombination can occur between homologous chromosomes. **Ask,** How is the genetic material that is exchanged during meiosis alike and how is it different? The exchanged DNA is located at the same position on each chromatid, meaning that it codes for the same cell functions. However, genetic material from one parent can differ from that of the other even though it provides for the same cell functions. The exchange introduces genetic diversity into the chromosomes.

Activate Prior Knowledge

The chapter introduces how the genetic material from two parents results in a single offspring, and how this material is physically represented as traits in the offspring. **Ask,** If you were looking at a couple who are expecting a child, what traits could you predict for the child just by observing the parents? Student answers may include color of hair, eyes, and skin; height and body type; and facial features. Discuss traits that seem to be a combination of the two parents, compared with traits that seem to come directly from one parent and not the other. **Ask,** What affects the traits and development of an offspring after he or she is born? his or her environment

Preview Vocabulary

Greek and Latin Word Origins

Students will see a number of words in this chapter that relate to giving birth or bearing offspring. The Latin root *gen,* which means "to give birth to," is the root of these words:

genetics, gene, generation

The Latin root *ferre,* which means "to bear" as in "bear fruit," is the root of the word *fertilize.*

Academic Vocabulary Tell students that one of Mendel's great strengths as a scientist was his skill as a statistician. Have students review these words related to statistics:

probability	*predict*
ratio	*average*
outcome	*event*

Answers

1. Meiosis and mitosis are being compared.
2. The Burmese python is being contrasted to other reptiles.

SECTION 6.1

B.4.4 Use a model to illustrate the role of cellular division (mitosis) and differentiation in producing and maintaining complex organisms.

B.4.6 Apply concepts of statistics and probability to explain the variation and distribution of expressed traits in a population.

▼ Plan and Prepare

Activate Prior Knowledge Remind students that the human egg and sperm are different from all other human cells. **Ask,** What makes sex cells different from all others? Is it that they carry X and Y chromosomes? Explain. No, they carry only a single set of chromosomes, not chromosome pairs. Body cells have some pairing of X and Y chromosomes; eggs have a single X; sperm have a single X or Y.

▼ Teach

Vocabulary

Greek and Latin Word Origins

The word **gamete** comes from the Greek word *gamos,* meaning "marriage." The words that follow share the same root; note the prefix indicating number:

polygamy	*polygamous*
monogamy	*monogamous*
bigamy	*bigamous*

Answers

Ⓐ **Identify** somatic, or body, cells

6.1 Chromosomes and Meiosis

KEY CONCEPT **Gametes have half the number of chromosomes that body cells have.**

VOCABULARY

- somatic cell
- gamete
- homologous chromosome
- autosome
- sex chromosome
- sexual reproduction
- fertilization
- diploid
- haploid
- meiosis

MAIN IDEAS

- You have body cells and gametes.
- Your cells have autosomes and sex chromosomes.
- Body cells are diploid; gametes are haploid.

Connect to Your World

Perhaps you are familiar with the saying, "Everything old is new again." This phrase usually indicates that a past style is again current. However, it applies equally well to you. The fusion of a single egg and sperm cell resulted in the complex creature that is you. There's never been anyone quite like you. And yet the DNA that directs your cells came from your mother and father. And their DNA came from their mother and father, and so on and so on. In this chapter, you will examine the processes that went into making you who you are.

MAIN IDEA

You have body cells and gametes.

You have many types of specialized cells in your body, but they can be divided into two major groups: somatic cells and germ cells. **Somatic cells** (soh-MAT-ihk), also called body cells, make up most of your body tissues and organs. For example, your spleen, kidneys, and eyeballs are all made entirely of body cells. DNA in your body cells is not passed on to your children. Germ cells, in contrast, are cells in your reproductive organs, the ovaries or the testes, that develop into gametes. **Gametes** are sex cells—ova, or eggs, in the female, and spermatozoa, or sperm cells, in the male. DNA in your gametes can be passed on to your children.

Each species has a characteristic number of chromosomes per cell. This number is typically given for body cells, not for gametes. Chromosome number does not seem to be related to the complexity of an organism. For example, yeast have 32 chromosomes, which come in 16 pairs. The fruit flies commonly used in genetic experiments have 8 chromosomes, which come in 4 pairs. A fern holds the record for the most chromosomes—more than 1200. Each of your body cells contains a set of 46 chromosomes, which come in 23 pairs. These cells are genetically identical to each other unless mutations have occurred. As you have learned, cells within an organism differ from one another because different genes are expressed, not because they have different genes.

Ⓐ Identify **Which cell type makes up the brain?**

READING TOOLBOX

TAKING NOTES

Make a two-column table to keep track of the vocabulary in this chapter.

Differentiated Instruction

ENGLISH LEARNERS

Use questions to guide students' reading on major concepts and determine their prior knowledge. **Ask,** How does a gamete differ from a body cell? Ask the question before the section, and remind students of it as they read and after they finish. Model for students how to ask more questions. **Ask,** Why does a gamete have only half the number of chromosomes as a body cell? Encourage students to ask each other questions.

Teacher Toolkit, Section C, Questions to Guide Reading

BELOW LEVEL

Point out that there are many vocabulary terms in this section that work as pairs, for example, *haploid* and *diploid*. Suggest that students look for logical pairings, writing their own definition, adding a glossary definition, and then including a picture to reinforce the meaning. They can use this technique for any unfamiliar terms, not just key vocabulary.

Teacher Toolkit, Section D, Student Vocabulary

MAIN IDEA

Your cells have autosomes and sex chromosomes.

Suppose you had 23 pairs of gloves. You would have a total of 46 gloves that you could divide into two sets, 23 right and 23 left. Similarly, your body cells have 23 pairs of chromosomes for a total of 46 that can be divided into two sets: 23 from your mother and 23 from your father. Just as you use both gloves when it's cold outside, your cells use both sets of chromosomes to function properly.

Together, each pair of chromosomes is referred to as a homologous pair. In this context, the word *homologous* means "having the same structure." **Homologous chromosomes** are two chromosomes—one inherited from the mother, one from the father—that have the same length and general appearance. More importantly, these chromosomes have copies of the same genes, although the two copies may differ. For example, if you have a gene that influences blood cholesterol levels on chromosome 8, you will have one copy from your mother and one copy from your father. It is possible that one of these copies is associated with high cholesterol levels, while the other is associated with low cholesterol levels. For convenience, scientists have assigned a number to each pair of homologous chromosomes, ordered from largest to smallest. As **FIGURE 1.1** shows, the largest pair of chromosomes is number 1, the next largest pair is number 2, and so forth.

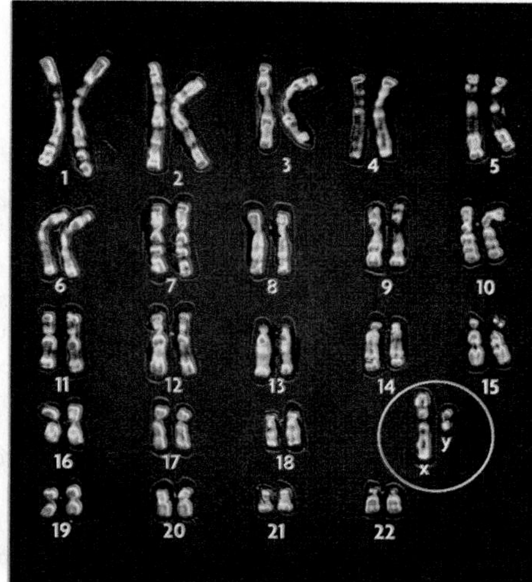

FIGURE 1.1 Human DNA is organized into two sets of 23 chromosomes. Each set contains 22 autosomes and 1 sex chromosome. Females have two X chromosomes. Males have an X and a Y chromosome (circled). (colored LM; magnification 4400×)

Collectively, chromosome pairs 1 through 22 make up your **autosomes,** chromosomes that contain genes for characteristics not directly related to the sex of an organism. But what about the 23rd chromosome pair?

Most sexually reproducing species also have **sex chromosomes** that directly control the development of sexual characteristics. Humans have two very different sex chromosomes, X and Y. How sex is determined varies by species. In all mammals, including humans, an organism's sex is determined by the XY system. An organism with two X chromosomes is female. An organism with one X and one Y chromosome is male. Sex chromosomes make up your 23rd pair of chromosomes. Although the X and Y chromosomes pair with each other, they are not homologous. The X chromosome is the larger sex chromosome and contains numerous genes, including many that are unrelated to sexual characteristics. The Y chromosome is the sex chromosome that contains genes that direct the development of the testes and other male traits. It is the smallest chromosome and carries the fewest genes.

"The parents are both geneticists."

A Summarize **Are homologous chromosomes identical to each other? Explain.**

Take It Further

Tell students that in birds, butterflies, and some fish species, the female gamete determines the gender of the individual. In these species, female gametes contain either a **Z chromosome** or a **W chromosome.** Male gametes have only a Z chromosome. A ZW offspring is female; ZZ is male.

While **sex determination** is chromosomal in many species, there are exceptions. The sex of some reptiles, such as the American alligator, is determined by the temperature of the environment surrounding incubating eggs. Temperatures in the low 90s (Fahrenheit) make the young alligators male, while temperatures in the mid-80s yield females.

Vocabulary

Academic Vocabulary The complete set of chromosomes for an organism is sometimes referred to as a *chromosome complement.* The word **complement** has different meanings, but it typically refers to a **complete** set or pairing. In grammar, for example, the word used after a verb to complete the predicate is its complement. In logic, the complement is a universal set, the set of all elements.

Answers

A Summarize No, they are very similar in size and shape and carry the same type of genes, but the version of the genes may differ.

INCLUSION

For students who have difficulty processing information, you may want to project **FIGURE 1.1** from the Media Gallery and relate what is discussed in the text on this page to the image. Model the way you interpret the text as you read and how you relate that information to the photograph. Point out that the chromosomes shown are metaphase chromosomes, meaning that each has a pair of chromatids. However, the term *chromosome pair* refers to both homologous chromosomes, not the chromatid pairs.

▼ Teach

TEACH FROM VISUALS

VISUAL VOCAB Have students study the figure. **Ask**

- If these cells were human cells, how many chromosomes would the haploid cell have? 23
- How many chromosomes would the diploid cell have? 46

Take It Further

Not all eukaryotic organisms have just two sets of chromosomes. **Polyploidy** is a condition in which an organism has multiple sets of chromosomes. Polyploidy occurs in some animal species, such as species of salmon, goldfish, and salamanders. It is much more common in certain types of plants. For example, some species of chrysanthemums are **tetraploid** with 36 chromosomes in four sets, **hexaploid** with 54 chromosomes in six sets, **octaploid** with 72 chromosomes in eight sets, and **decaploid** with 90 chromosomes in ten sets. Naturally occurring polyploidy plants almost always have an even number of chromosome sets.

Science Trivia

The haploid cells resulting from meiosis are initially quite small. After processing in the testes or ovaries, they can end up much larger than somatic cells.

- Ostrich eggs are about 180 mm long and 140 mm wide, and weigh 1.2 kg, making them over 2000 times larger than the smallest hummingbird egg.
- The sperm of *Drosophila bifurca,* a fruit fly, can reach up to 6 cm in length.

MAIN IDEA

Body cells are diploid; gametes are haploid.

Sexual reproduction involves the fusion of two gametes, resulting in offspring that are a genetic mixture of both parents. The actual fusion of an egg and a sperm cell is called **fertilization.** When fertilization occurs, the nuclei of the egg and sperm cell fuse to form one nucleus. This new nucleus must have the correct number of chromosomes for a healthy new organism to develop. Therefore, both the egg and the sperm cell need only half the usual number of chromosomes—one chromosome from each homologous pair.

Diploid and Haploid Cells

Body cells and gametes have different numbers of chromosomes. Your body cells are diploid. **Diploid** (DIHP-LOYD) means that a cell has two copies of each chromosome: one copy from the mother, and one copy from the father. Diploid cells can be represented as $2n$. In humans, the diploid chromosome number is 46.

Gametes are not diploid cells; they are haploid cells, represented as n. **Haploid** (HAP-LOYD) means that a cell has only one copy of each chromosome. Each human egg or sperm cell has 22 autosomes and 1 sex chromosome. In the egg, the sex chromosome is always an X chromosome. In the sperm cell, the sex chromosome can be an X chromosome or a Y chromosome. The reason for this difference will be discussed in the following sections.

READING TOOLBOX

VOCABULARY

The word *diploid* comes from the Greek word *diplous,* which means "double." The word *haploid* comes from the Greek word *haplous,* which means "single."

VISUAL VOCAB

Diploid cells have two copies of each chromosome: one copy from the mother and one from the father.

Body cells are diploid (*2n*).

Gametes (sex cells) are haploid (*n*).

Haploid cells have only one copy of each chromosome.

Maintaining the correct number of chromosomes is important to the survival of all organisms. Typically, a change in chromosome number is harmful. However, increasing the number of sets of chromosomes can, on occasion, give rise to a new species. The fertilization of nonhaploid gametes has played an important role in plant evolution by rapidly making new species with more than two sets of chromosomes. For example, some plants have four copies of each chromosome, a condition called tetraploidy ($4n$). This type of event has occurred in many groups of plants, but it is very rare in animals.

Meiosis

Germ cells in your reproductive organs undergo the process of meiosis to form gametes. **Meiosis** (my-OH-sihs) is a form of nuclear division that divides a diploid cell into haploid cells. This process is essential for sexual reproduction. The details of meiosis will be presented in the next section. **FIGURE 1.2** highlights some differences between mitosis and meiosis in advance to help you keep these two processes clear in your mind.

CONNECT TO

EVOLUTION

As you will learn in **Principles of Evolution,** the passing on of traits to offspring during reproduction is a key factor in species changing over time.

Differentiated Instruction

TEACH WITH TECHNOLOGY

If your classroom is equipped with a personal response system, use it to test students on haploid, diploid, and polyploid cells; mitosis and meiosis; and autosomes and sex chromosomes. Testing might also cover the number of chromosome sets in each type of cell, the location in the body where each cell type or process occurs, and the importance of each cell or chromosome type.

FIGURE 1.2 Comparing Mitosis and Meiosis

MITOSIS	MEIOSIS
Produces genetically identical cells	Produces genetically unique cells
Results in diploid cells	Results in haploid cells
Takes place throughout an organism's lifetime	Takes place only at certain times in an organism's life cycle
Involved in asexual reproduction	Involved in sexual reproduction

A Compare Using the diagrams above, explain how you think the process of meiosis differs from mitosis.

You have already learned about mitosis, another form of nuclear division. Recall that mitosis is a process that occurs in body cells. It helps produce daughter cells that are genetically identical to the parent cell. In cells undergoing mitosis, DNA is copied once and divided once. Both the parent cell and the daughter cells are diploid. Mitosis is used for development, growth, and repair in all types of organisms. It is also used for reproduction in asexually reproducing eukaryotes.

In contrast, meiosis occurs in germ cells to produce gametes. This process is sometimes called a "reduction division" because it reduces a cell's chromosome number by half. In cells undergoing meiosis, DNA is copied once but divided twice. Meiosis makes genetically unique haploid cells from a diploid cell. These haploid cells then undergo more processing in the ovaries or testes, finally forming mature gametes.

B Apply Why is it important that gametes are haploid cells?

6.1 Formative Assessment

REVIEWING MAIN IDEAS

1. Where are germ cells located in the human body?
2. What is the difference between an **autosome** and a **sex chromosome**?
3. Is the cell that results from **fertilization** a **haploid** or **diploid** cell? Explain.

CRITICAL THINKING

4. **Infer** Does mitosis or **meiosis** occur more frequently in your body? Explain your answer.
5. **Analyze** Do you think that the Y chromosome contains genes that are critical for an organism's survival? Explain your reasoning.

CONNECT TO TELOMERES

6. The ends of DNA molecules form telomeres that help keep the ends of chromosomes from sticking to each other. Why might this be especially important in germ cells, which go through meiosis and make haploid **gametes**?

6.1 FORMATIVE ASSESSMENT

1. in the reproductive organs (ovaries and testes)
2. Autosomes directly affect only body traits, whereas sex chromosomes directly affect the sexual characteristics of an organism.
3. Diploid; the combination of 23 chromosomes from the mother and 23 from the father restores the diploid number of chromosomes (46).
4. Mitosis occurs throughout an organism's lifetime throughout many cells of the entire body, compared to meiosis, which occurs only at certain times and only in the reproductive organs.
5. No, females do not have a Y chromosome, yet they are able to survive.
6. If the ends of two chromosomes stick together, the chromosomes will not separate correctly during meiosis. One of the resulting gametes will have an extra chromosome, and the other will be missing a chromosome.

TEACH FROM VISUALS

FIGURE 1.2 Have students study the table, which points out the differences between mitosis and meiosis. **Ask**

- How are mitosis and meiosis alike? Both involve division of the nucleus followed by the formation of new cells.
- What word pairs in the accompanying descriptions of mitosis and meiosis point to the differences between the two types of division? identical/unique, diploid/haploid, asexual/sexual

Vocabulary

Greek and Latin Word Origins The word **meiosis** comes from the Greek *meiōn,* meaning "less." This is the same root as the word **minor.**

Answers

A Compare In meiosis, a cell undergoes two cell divisions and produces four cells, each with half the original number of chromosomes. In mitosis, a cell undergoes only one division and produces two cells that have the same number of chromosomes as the original cell.

B Apply Gametes fuse to form a new organism. Because each gamete has half the chromosomes of the parent cell, fertilization produces a new organism with the correct number of chromosomes.

Assess and Reteach

Assess Use the Section Self-Check or Section Quiz, both available at **HMHScience.com**.

Reteach Work with students to prepare a compare-and-contrast chart for mitosis and meiosis. Ask them to include all the key vocabulary from this section.

Introduce

Bar graphs compare data or show data that are not continuous. Multiple sets of data can be compared by drawing several bars next to each other, using a large enough scale for the dependent variable to account for all data. **Ask**

- Why can't a line graph be used to show the frequency of genetic disorders? They are distinct disorders. The data do not show a continuous process.
- Why can't a line graph be used to show the number of chromosomes in different organisms? The chromosome numbers are independent of one another.

Take It Further

Down, Patau, and Edwards syndromes are all genetic disorders caused by **trisomy,** the presence of an extra chromosome. Down syndrome is caused by trisomy 21, the presence of a third chromosome 21. Edwards syndrome results from trisomy 18, and Patau syndrome from trisomy 13.

Explain to students that a **syndrome** is a group of symptoms that occur together and characterize a disorder. For example, Down syndrome is characterized by mental retardation, congenital heart defects, decreased muscle tone, slanting eyes, and a short stature.

Discuss

Have students focus on Graph 2. **Ask**

- What is the range of chromosome number shown in the graph? about 10 to over 200
- What organisms shown in the graph have a chromosome number most similar to that of humans? bats, porpoises, potatoes

Online Student Resources, Data Analysis Practice

DATA ANALYSIS

Interpreting Bar Graphs

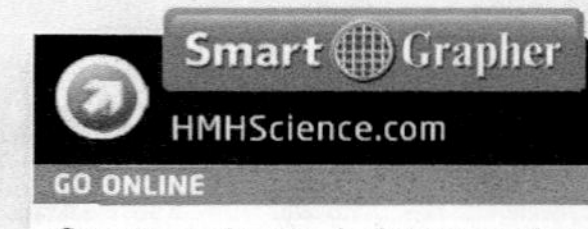

Create animated charts and graphs using Smart Grapher.

Bar graphs show data with bars. In a bar graph, the independent variable is usually graphed on the *x*-axis and the dependent variable is usually graphed on the *y*-axis. Both axes are labeled with the name and unit of the variable.

Model

The bar graph below contains data about the frequency of some genetic disorders in the human population. Each of the disorders listed is the result of nondisjunction, the failure of two chromosomes to separate properly during meiosis. This results in one extra chromosome or one less chromosome being passed on to the offspring.

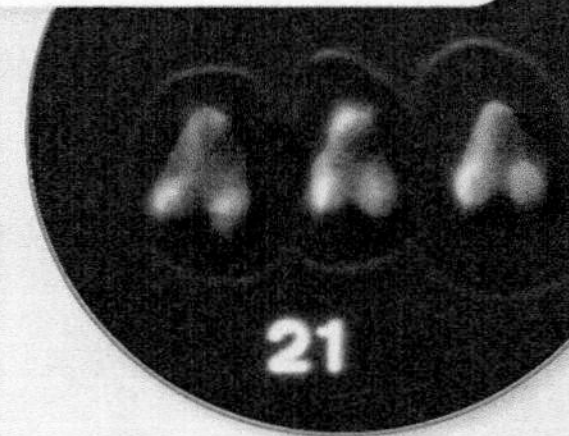

In most cases, Down syndrome results from an extra chromosome 21.
(colored LM; magnification 2000×)

For each syndrome on the *x*-axis, the bar extends vertically on the *y*-axis to represent the incidence per 100,000 births. For example, out of 100,000 births, 111 children are born with Down syndrome.

GRAPH 1. FREQUENCY OF GENETIC DISORDERS

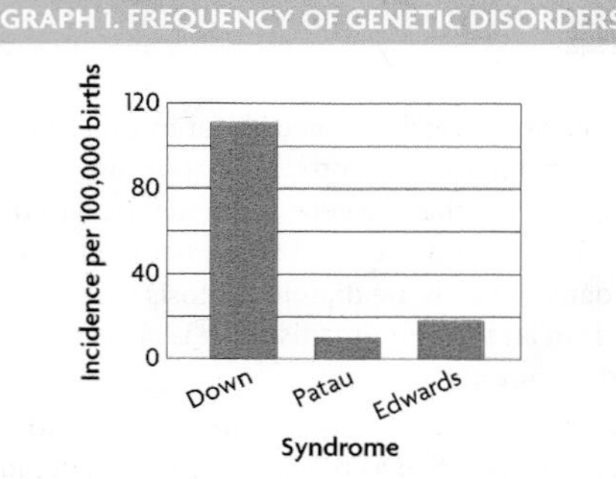

Source: U.S. National Library of Medicine

Practice **Interpret a Bar Graph**

The bar graph below contains data about the diploid number of chromosomes in different organisms.

1. **Analyze** Which organism has the greatest number of chromosomes? the least?
2. **Evaluate** Does chromosome number appear to correlate to the type of organism? Explain.
3. **Hypothesize** Do you think there is an upper limit to chromosome number? Explain.

GRAPH 2. DIPLOID NUMBER OF CHROMOSOMES IN VARIOUS ORGANISMS

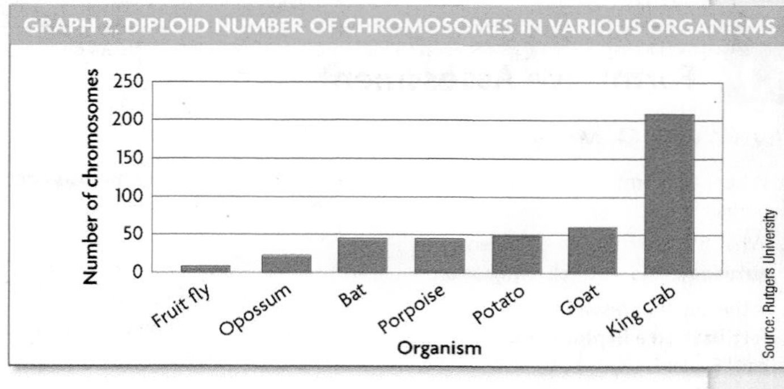

Source: Rutgers University

166 Unit 3: Genetics

Answers

1. king crab; fruit fly
2. No, the two arthropods have the greatest difference of chromosome number, and it appears that the potato (a plant) has a number closer to that of the humans than opossums.
3. yes, because the chromosomes need to be able to fit within the nucleus of a cell

6.2 Process of Meiosis

KEY CONCEPT **During meiosis, diploid cells undergo two cell divisions that result in haploid cells.**

MAIN IDEAS
- Cells go through two rounds of division in meiosis.
- Haploid cells develop into mature gametes.

VOCABULARY
gametogenesis
sperm
egg
polar body

Connect to Your World

Sometimes division, such as splitting the bill at a restaurant or dividing people into teams for basketball, is difficult. Luckily, understanding how meiosis divides chromosomes between cells is not that hard. Meiosis begins with a diploid cell that has already undergone DNA replication. The cell copies the chromosomes once and divides them twice, making four haploid cells.

MAIN IDEA

Cells go through two rounds of division in meiosis.

Meiosis is a form of nuclear division that creates four haploid cells from one diploid cell. This process involves two rounds of cell division—meiosis I and meiosis II. Each round of cell division has four phases, which are similar to those in mitosis. To keep the two processes distinct in your mind, focus on the big picture. Pay attention to the way meiosis reduces chromosome number and creates genetic diversity.

CONNECT TO

MITOSIS

As you learned in the chapter **Cell Growth and Division**, a condensed, duplicated chromosome is made of two chromatids. Sister chromatids separate during anaphase in mitosis.

Homologous Chromosomes and Sister Chromatids

To understand meiosis, you need to distinguish between homologous chromosomes and sister chromatids. As **FIGURE 2.1** shows, homologous chromosomes are two separate chromosomes: one from your mother, one from your father. Homologous chromosomes are very similar to each other, since they have the same length and carry the same genes. But they are not copies of each other. In contrast, each half of a duplicated chromosome is called a chromatid. Together, the two chromatids are called sister chromatids. Thus, the term *sister chromatids* refers to the duplicated chromosomes that remain attached (by the centromere). Homologous chromosomes are divided in meiosis I. Sister chromatids are not divided until meiosis II.

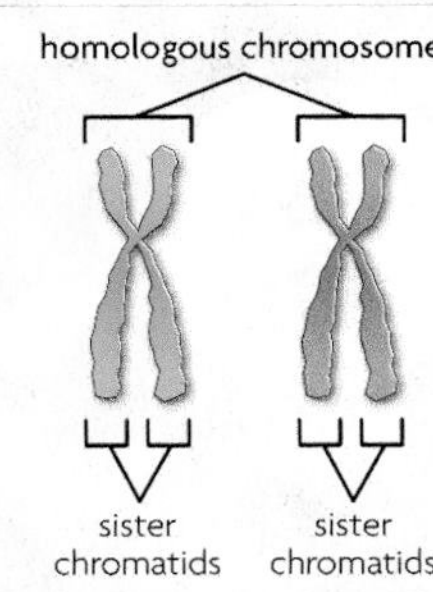

FIGURE 2.1 Homologous chromosomes (shown duplicated) are two separate chromosomes—one inherited from the mother, and one from the father.

READING TOOLBOX

TAKING NOTES

Draw a Venn diagram like the one below to summarize the similarities and differences between meiosis I and meiosis II.

Meiosis I | Meiosis II
divides homologous chromosomes | chromosomes condense | divides sister chromatids

SECTION 6.2

B.4.6 Apply concepts of statistics and probability to explain the variation and distribution of expressed traits in a population.

Plan and Prepare

Activate Prior Knowledge Discuss meiosis as though it is a simple equation wherein the DNA of two parents combines to form the DNA of one offspring. **Ask,** In order to make 1 + 1 = 1, what needs to happen to the DNA of the parents? It needs to be reduced by half.

Teach

TEACH FROM VISUALS

FIGURE 2.1 Have students study the homologous chromosomes. **Ask**

- What can you say about the genetic material on two sister chromatids? It is identical.
- What can you say about the genetic material on the homologous chromosomes? The genes on homologous chromosomes contain instructions for the same features and functions, but some of the instructions may be different. These differences yield variations in traits and functions.

Differentiated Instruction

ENGLISH LEARNERS

Have students make a sequence diagram for meiosis I and meiosis II with a single pair of homologous chromosomes, like those in **FIGURE 2.1.** Tell students that meiosis is considered a reduction division because the chromosome number is reduced. Then have students make a sequence diagram of mitosis, referring to **FIGURE 2.4** (parts 1–4) from the chapter Cell Growth and Division. Tell students to compare the two diagrams.

Teacher Toolkit, Section C, Compare/Contrast Chart

PRE-AP

Prepare a number of true/false questions on the different phases of meiosis I and II. See how well students can apply what they have learned about the basic phases of division in mitosis to the phases in meiosis. Students should re-read the section and correct their answers as needed.

Teacher Toolkit, Section C, Anticipation Guide

▼ Teach *continued*

Vocabulary

Academic Vocabulary The steps of mitosis and meiosis are referred to as **phases.** A phase is one of a series of gradual changes, such as the phases of the moon.

An **equator** is a line that divides an object into two equal parts. Earth's equator divides Earth into the Northern and Southern Hemispheres. During metaphase of meiosis and mitosis, chromosomes line up along the cell equator. This allows the chromosomes to be divided equally to the two halves of the cell.

Greek and Latin Word Origins The prefixes of the four phases in meiosis I and meiosis II come from Greek word parts:

pro- = before
meta- = beside, after
ana- = up
telo- = end

TEACH FROM VISUALS

FIGURE 2.3 Have students examine steps 1–8. **Ask**

- In what way are the chromosomes in telophase I of meiosis different from those in telophase of mitosis? In telophase I of meiosis, the sister chromatids are not separated. In telophase of mitosis, the sister chromosomes have already separated, forming single chromosomes.
- Tell students that meiosis is often called reduction division. What is reduced in the first division? the number of chromosomes in each cell
- What is reduced in the second division? the amount of DNA in each cell
- In which division do the cells become haploid? in the first division

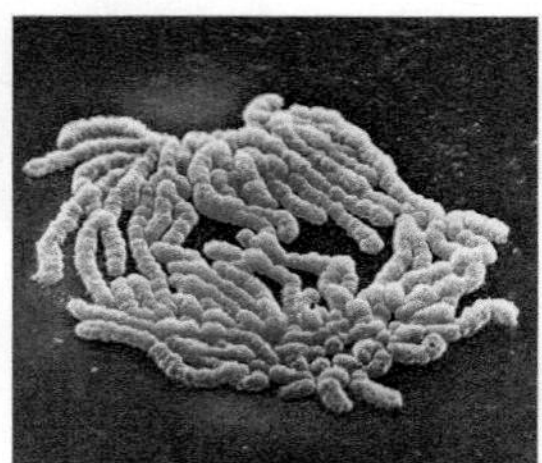

FIGURE 2.2 Homologous chromosomes separate during anaphase I. (colored SEM; magnification 2200×)

Meiosis I

Before meiosis begins, DNA has already been copied. Meiosis I divides homologous chromosomes, producing two haploid cells with duplicated chromosomes. Like mitosis, scientists describe meiosis in terms of phases, illustrated in **FIGURE 2.3** below. The figure is simplified, showing only four chromosomes.

1. **Prophase I** Early in meiosis, the nuclear membrane breaks down, the centrosomes and centrioles move to opposite sides of the cell, and spindle fibers start to assemble. The duplicated chromosomes condense, and homologous chromosomes pair up. They appear to pair up precisely, gene for gene, down their entire length. The sex chromosomes also pair with each other, and some regions of their DNA appear to line up as well.
2. **Metaphase I** The homologous chromosome pairs are randomly lined up along the middle of the cell by spindle fibers. The result is that 23 chromosomes—some from the father, some from the mother—are lined up along each side of the cell equator. This arrangement mixes up the chromosomal combinations and helps create and maintain genetic diversity. Since human cells have 23 pairs of chromosomes, meiosis may result in 2^{23}, or 8,388,608, possible combinations of chromosomes.
3. **Anaphase I** Next, the paired homologous chromosomes separate from each other and move toward opposite sides of the cell. The sister chromatids remain together during this step and throughout meiosis I.
4. **Telophase I** The nuclear membrane forms again in some species, the spindle fibers disassemble, and the cell undergoes cytokinesis. The end result is two cells that each have a unique combination of 23 duplicated chromosomes coming from both parents.

FIGURE 2.3 Meiosis

Meiosis I divides homologous chromosomes.

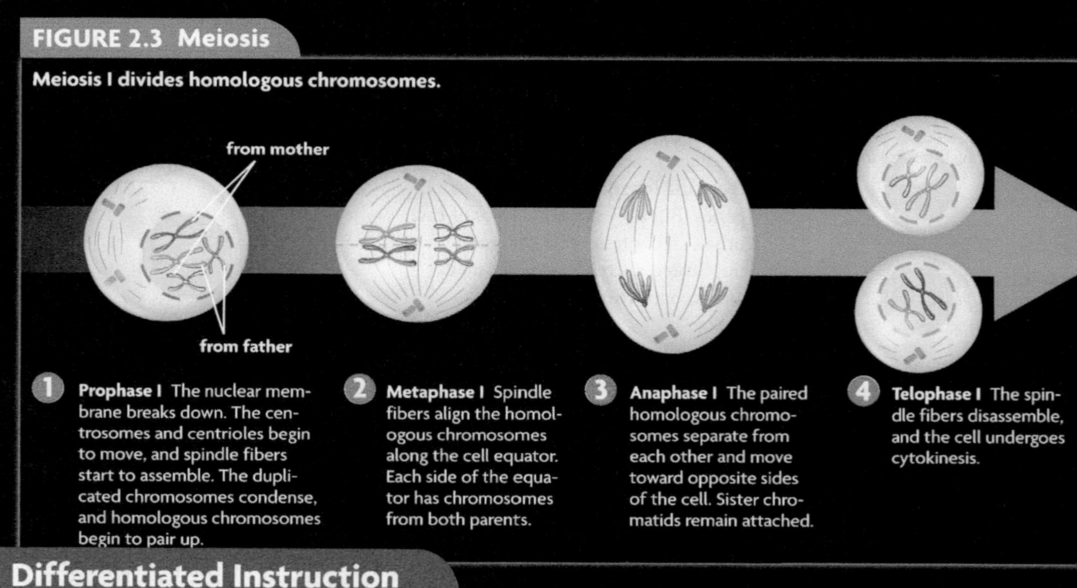

1. **Prophase I** The nuclear membrane breaks down. The centrosomes and centrioles begin to move, and spindle fibers start to assemble. The duplicated chromosomes condense, and homologous chromosomes begin to pair up.
2. **Metaphase I** Spindle fibers align the homologous chromosomes along the cell equator. Each side of the equator has chromosomes from both parents.
3. **Anaphase I** The paired homologous chromosomes separate from each other and move toward opposite sides of the cell. Sister chromatids remain attached.
4. **Telophase I** The spindle fibers disassemble, and the cell undergoes cytokinesis.

Differentiated Instruction

HANDS-ON ACTIVITY

Students can model meiosis I by using four pairs of shoes with laces. For example, students can use two pairs of sneakers and two pairs of leather shoes to represent two pairs of homologous chromosomes. Have students tie each pair of shoes together to represent sister chromatids held together by a centromere. They should place tags on each pair of shoes to indicate whether it came from the mother or the father. Tell students to use two equal lengths of yarn or string to mark a cell's perimeter on the floor. Then have them move the shoes around inside the circle to model the phases of meiosis I. After telophase I, have students form two cells from the two lengths of string. Students should observe that each cell contains a mixture of maternal and paternal chromosomes.

Meiosis II

Meiosis II divides sister chromatids and results in undoubled chromosomes. The following description of this process applies to both of the cells produced in meiosis I. Note that DNA is not copied again between these two stages.

5 **Prophase II** The nuclear membrane breaks down, centrosomes and centrioles move to opposite sides of the cell, and spindle fibers assemble.

6 **Metaphase II** Spindle fibers align the 23 chromosomes at the cell equator. Each chromosome still has two sister chromatids at this stage.

7 **Anaphase II** Next, the sister chromatids are pulled apart from each other and move to opposite sides of the cell.

8 **Telophase II** Finally, nuclear membranes form around each set of chromosomes at opposite ends of the cell, the spindle fibers break apart, and the cell undergoes cytokinesis. The end result is four haploid cells with a combination of chromosomes from both the mother and father.

Now that you've seen how meiosis works, let's review some key differences between the processes of meiosis and mitosis.

- Meiosis has two cell divisions. Mitosis has only one cell division.
- During meiosis, homologous chromosomes pair up along the cell equator. During mitosis, homologous chromosomes never pair up.
- In anaphase I of meiosis, sister chromatids remain together. In anaphase of mitosis, sister chromatids separate.
- Meiosis results in haploid cells. Mitosis results in diploid cells.

Contrast **What is the major difference between metaphase I and metaphase II?**

Virtual INVESTIGATION
HMHScience.com
GO ONLINE
Phases of Meiosis

CONNECT TO

CYTOKINESIS

As you learned in the chapter **Cell Growth and Division**, cytokinesis is the division of the cell cytoplasm. This process is the same in cells undergoing either mitosis or meiosis.

Meiosis II divides sister chromatids. The overall process produces haploid cells.

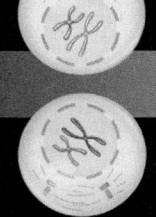

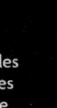

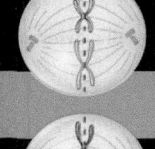

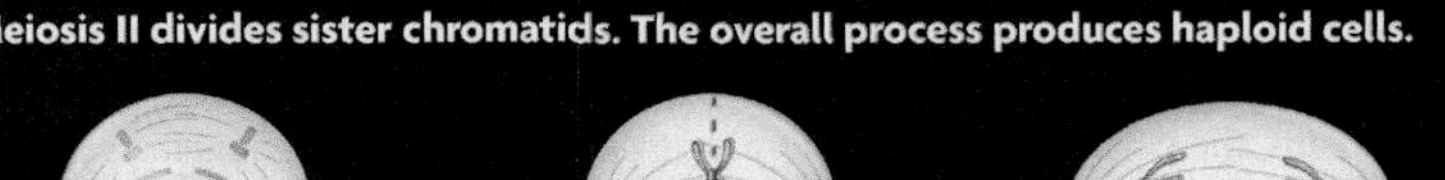

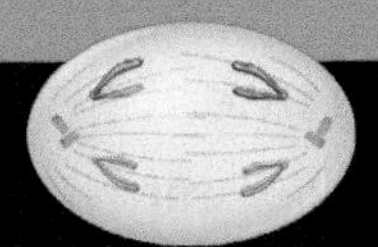
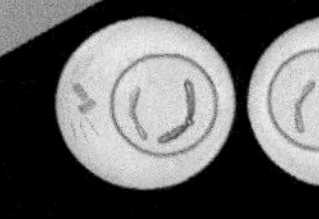

5 **Prophase II** The centrosomes and centrioles move to opposite sides of the cell, and spindle fibers start to assemble.

6 **Metaphase II** Spindle fibers align the chromosomes along the cell equator.

7 **Anaphase II** The sister chromatids are pulled apart from each other and move to opposite sides of the cell.

8 **Telophase II** The nuclear membranes form again around the chromosomes, the spindle fibers break apart, and the cell undergoes cytokinesis.

HANDS-ON ACTIVITY

Students can model meiosis II by continuing the activity from the previous page. As prophase II begins, there are two pairs of shoes in each cell, each representing sister chromatids. During metaphase II, the pairs of shoes line up at the equators of the cells. In anaphase II, the shoelaces are untied, and the two shoes in each pair separate and move to opposite sides of the cells. In telophase II (cut strings in half), four cells form, each with two single shoes. **Ask**

- How does the final distribution of the shoes compare with the original distribution? Each cell has one shoe of each type.
- How are the maternal and paternal shoes distributed in the haploid cells? They are mixed up. Most likely, none of the four cells has all maternal or all paternal shoes.

Address Misconceptions

Common Misconception Students may think that only animal reproductive cells undergo meiosis.

Correcting the Misconception Emphasize that if an organism is to reproduce sexually by combining its genetic material with that of another, the number of chromosomes must be halved. The reproductive cells of all organisms that reproduce sexually must undergo meiosis.

Science Trivia

- The duration of meiosis is highly variable in nature.
- In a male mouse, meiosis lasts for about 12 days, most of that time in meiosis I.
- In the male reproductive organs of a lily, meiosis takes about 7 days, 6 of which are in meiosis I.
- Meiosis in a human male takes 24 days; in a female, it takes years and is not completed until fertilization occurs.
- In all sexually reproducing species, prophase I is always much longer than all the other meiotic stages combined.

Answers

A Contrast In metaphase I, pairs of homologous chromosomes line up at the equator. In metaphase II, the chromosomes are not paired.

▼ Teach continued

TEACH FROM VISUALS

FIGURE 2.4 Have students compare the processes of sperm production and egg production. **Ask,** In gametogenesis, how does the number of sperm formed in a male compare with the number of eggs formed in a female? For every egg cell produced during gametogenesis, four sperm cells are produced. Tell students that just because a male germ cell becomes four sperm while a female germ cell becomes one egg does not mean the ratio of sperm to egg is 4:1. In all sexually reproducing animals, the number of sperm in a male is far greater than the number of eggs in a female.

Take It Further

During **embryonic development** in human females, about one million **primary oocytes** are formed by mitosis in each ovary. These cells begin but do not complete prophase I before the female is born. Years later, after puberty, one egg per month undergoes the rest of meiosis I. After metaphase II, the process stops again and will not continue for that egg unless it is fertilized.

Answers

A Apply The sperm cell's primary contribution to an embryo is DNA. By losing cytoplasm and gaining a tail and numerous mitochondria, the sperm cell can swim through the uterus and donate DNA to the egg.

▼ Assess and Reteach

Assess Use the Section Self-Check or Section Quiz, both available at **HMHScience.com**.

Reteach Draw the phases of meiosis I and have students provide you with information to label and summarize each phase. Then have volunteers draw the phases of meiosis II, and again have students provide you with information for labeling and summarizing the phases.

MAIN IDEA

Haploid cells develop into mature gametes.

FIGURE 2.4 GAMETOGENESIS

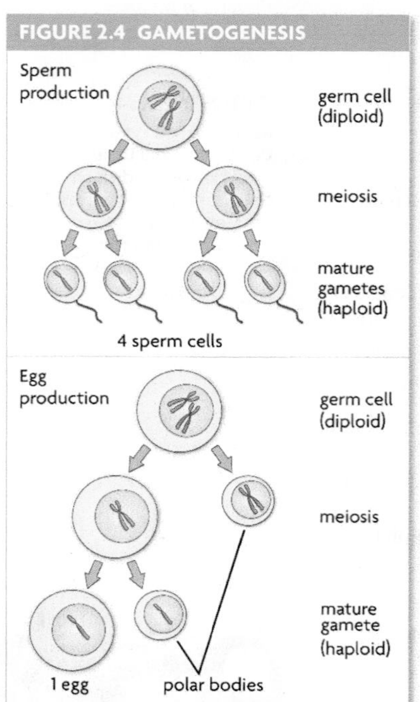

Haploid cells are the end result of meiosis. Yet these cells are incapable of fertilization until they go through more changes to form mature gametes. **Gametogenesis** (guh-MEE-tuh-JEHN-ih-sihs) is the production of gametes. As **FIGURE 2.4** shows, gametogenesis includes both meiosis and other changes that produce a mature cell. The final stages of gametogenesis differ between the sexes.

The **sperm** cell, the male gamete, is much smaller than the **egg,** the female gamete. The sperm cell's main contribution to an embryo is DNA. Yet it must swim to an egg to fertilize it, so the ability to move is critical. Sperm formation starts with a round cell and ends by making a streamlined cell that can move rapidly. During this process, significant changes occur. DNA is tightly packed and much of the cytoplasm is lost, resulting in a compact head. The sperm cell develops a whiplike flagellum and connecting neck region packed with mitochondria that drive the cell. Other changes, such as the addition of new proteins to the cell membrane, also take place.

The formation of an egg is a complicated process. It begins before birth, inside the developing body of a female embryo, and is not finished until that egg is fertilized by a sperm many years later. The process includes periods of active development and long periods of inactivity.

An egg not only gives its share of DNA to an embryo, but also contributes the organelles, molecular building blocks, and other materials an embryo needs to begin life. Only one of the four cells produced by each round of meiosis actually makes an egg. One cell—the egg—receives most of the organelles, cytoplasm, and nutrients. Many molecules are not evenly distributed throughout the egg's cytoplasm. This unequal distribution of molecules helps cells in the developing embryo to specialize. The other cells produced by meiosis become **polar bodies,** cells with little more than DNA that are eventually broken down. In many species, including humans, the polar body produced by meiosis I does not undergo meiosis II.

A Apply **Briefly explain how a sperm cell's structure is related to its function.**

6.2 Formative Assessment

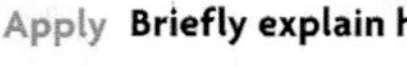

SELF-CHECK Online HMHScience.com GO ONLINE

REVIEWING MAIN IDEAS

1. How do homologous chromosomes differ from sister chromatids?
2. Explain why an **egg** is so much larger than a **sperm** cell.

CRITICAL THINKING

3. **Predict** If, during metaphase I, all 23 maternal chromosomes lined up on one side of the cell, would genetic diversity increase? Explain.
4. **Contrast** List the key differences between meiosis I and meiosis II.

CONNECT TO CELL BIOLOGY

5. Both mitosis and meiosis are types of nuclear division, but they result in different cell types. Describe how the steps of meiosis I differ from those of mitosis.

6.2 FORMATIVE ASSESSMENT

1. homologous chromosomes have the same genes but different versions of them; sister chromatids are copies of each other, and are produced by DNA replication
2. An egg needs to provide the nutrients and building blocks for life to begin; a sperm only needs to reach the egg and deliver its DNA, so it is streamlined and small.
3. Genetic diversity would not increase because the maternal and paternal chromosomes would not become arranged in new combinations.
4. meiosis I: begins with a diploid cell, homologous chromosomes separate; meiosis II: begins with two haploid cells, sister chromatids separate.
5. mitosis: chromosomes are duplicated and the copies are separated, one for each cell; meiosis I: duplicated chromosomes remain attached to each other, each new cell gets half of each homologous pair.

6.3 Mendel and Heredity

KEY CONCEPT **Mendel's research showed that traits are inherited as discrete units.**

MAIN IDEAS
- Mendel laid the groundwork for genetics.
- Mendel's data revealed patterns of inheritance.

VOCABULARY
trait
genetics
purebred
cross
law of segregation

Connect to Your World

When a magician makes a coin disappear, you know that the coin has not really vanished. You simply cannot see where it is. Maybe it is up a sleeve or in a pocket. When organisms reproduce, some traits seem to disappear, too. For centuries, no one could explain why. Then a careful, observant scientist showed that behind this phenomenon were inherited units, or genes.

MAIN IDEA
Mendel laid the groundwork for genetics.

When we think of how offspring resemble or differ from their parents, we typically refer to specific traits. **Traits** are distinguishing characteristics that are inherited, such as eye color, leaf shape, and tail length. Scientists recognized that traits are hereditary, or passed from one generation to the next, long before they understood how traits are passed on. **Genetics** is the study of biological inheritance patterns and variation in organisms.

The groundwork for much of our understanding of genetics was established in the middle of the 1800s by an Austrian monk named Gregor Mendel, shown in **FIGURE 3.1.** Scientists of the time commonly thought that parents' traits were blended in offspring, like mixing red and white paint to get pink paint. But this idea failed to explain how certain traits remained without being "diluted." Mendel, a shrewd mathematician, bred thousands of plants, carefully counting and recording his results. From his data, Mendel correctly predicted the results of meiosis long before chromosomes were discovered. He recognized that traits are inherited as discrete units from the parental generation, like different colored marbles mixed together that can still be picked out separately. By recognizing that organisms inherit two copies of each discrete unit, what we now call genes, Mendel described how traits were passed between generations.

A Connect Give two examples of traits not listed above.

FIGURE 3.1 Gregor Mendel is called "the father of genetics" for discovering hereditary units. The significance of his work went unrecognized for almost 40 years.

MAIN IDEA
Mendel's data revealed patterns of inheritance.

Mendel studied plant variation in a monastery garden. He made three key choices about his experiments that played an important role in the development of his laws of inheritance: control over breeding, use of purebred plants, and observation of "either-or" traits that appeared in only two alternate forms.

SECTION 6.3

B.4.1 Develop and revise a model that clarifies the relationship between DNA and chromosomes in coding the instructions for characteristic traits passed from parents to offspring.

B.4.6 Apply concepts of statistics and probability to explain the variation and distribution of expressed traits in a population.

Plan and Prepare

Activate Prior Knowledge Students need to realize that genes don't change even though they can produce a range of variation, as in skin color or height. **Ask,** How is it that the same song can sound completely different when played by two different groups? differences in the makeup of the band, interpretation of the music Explain that the expression of genes can vary.

Teach

Vocabulary

Academic Vocabulary The words **express** and **expression** are commonly used to describe a quality of communication, such as how a writer expresses ideas or a painter expresses emotion. In genetics, the words are applied to the effect that genes have in the traits an organism exhibits, or *expresses.*

Answers

A Connect Examples include hair color, flower color, height, earlobe type, and blood type.

Differentiated Instruction

ENGLISH LEARNERS

Let students work in small groups to create a graphic organizer for the second part of the section, "Mendel's Data . . ." Have them write the heading as a main idea in a box, with diverging boxes labeled with key terms and elements of Mendel's experiments.

Teacher Toolkit, Section C, Supporting Main Ideas

PRE-AP

Have students write a short essay evaluating Mendel's experimental design. Students should consider the following questions:

- Why was Mendel's use of pea plants a good choice?
- Why was it necessary for Mendel to use purebred plants in his experiments?

Teacher Toolkit, Section C, Quick-Write

▼ Teach *continued*

TEACH FROM VISUALS

FIGURE 3.2 Obtain flowers so that students can see the parts of a flower Mendel manipulated. **Ask,** Why did Mendel remove the stamens from his plants? to prevent the plant from self-pollinating

FIGURE 3.3 Explain that, before Mendel, many scientists thought the traits of parents always became blended in their offspring. **Ask,** If this were true, what flower color would you expect to observe in the F_1 generation? light purple

History of Science

Gregor Mendel and **Charles Darwin** lived at the same time, but it wasn't until after their deaths that the compatibility of their ideas was discovered. Mendel had read Darwin's books and accepted the theory of natural selection; Darwin, on the other hand, was either unaware of Mendel's work or did not grasp its potential relevance to his own.

Because no one understood the significance of his work, Mendel stopped publishing the results of his experiments. He died in 1884, unrecognized for his scientific discoveries. In 1900, Mendel's work was recognized independently by three botanists. By this time, cells and chromosomes were sufficiently understood, providing a physical framework for Mendel's abstract ideas.

FIGURE 3.2 MENDEL'S PROCESS

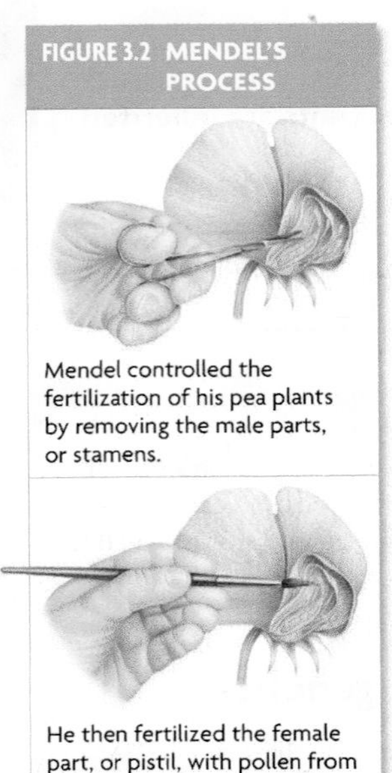

Mendel controlled the fertilization of his pea plants by removing the male parts, or stamens.

He then fertilized the female part, or pistil, with pollen from a different pea plant.

READING TOOLBOX

VOCABULARY

In Latin, the word *filius* means "son" and the word *filia* means "daughter."

Experimental Design

Mendel chose pea plants for his experiments because they reproduce quickly, and he could easily control how they mate. The sex organs of a plant are in its flowers, and pea flowers contain both male and female reproductive organs. In nature, the pea flower typically self-pollinates; that is, the plant mates with itself. If a line of plants has self-pollinated for long enough, that line becomes genetically uniform, or **purebred.** As a result, the offspring of purebred parents inherit all of the parent organisms' characteristics. Mendel was able to mate plants with specific traits by interrupting the self-pollination process. As you can see in **FIGURE 3.2,** he removed the male parts of flowers and fertilized the female parts with pollen that contained sperm cells from a different plant. Because he started with purebred plants, Mendel knew that any variations in offspring resulted from his experiments.

Mendel chose seven traits to follow: pea shape, pea color, pod shape, pod color, plant height, flower color, and flower position. All of these traits are simple "either-or" characteristics; they do not show intermediate features. The plant is tall or short. Its peas are wrinkled or round. What Mendel did not know was that most of the traits he had selected were controlled by genes on separate chromosomes. The selection of these particular traits played a crucial role in enabling Mendel to identify the patterns he observed.

Results

In genetics, the mating of two organisms is called a **cross.** An example of one of Mendel's crosses is highlighted in **FIGURE 3.3.** In this example, he crossed a purebred white-flowered pea plant with a purebred purple-flowered pea plant. These plants are the parental, or P, generation. The resulting offspring, called the first filial—or F_1—generation, all had purple flowers. The trait for white flowers seemed to disappear. When Mendel allowed the F_1 generation to self-fertilize, the resulting F_2 generation produced both plants with purple flowers and plants with white flowers. Therefore, the trait for white flowers had not disappeared; it had been hidden, or masked.

FIGURE 3.3 Mendel's Experimental Cross

Traits that were hidden when parental purebred flowers were crossed reappeared when the F_1 generation was allowed to self-pollinate.

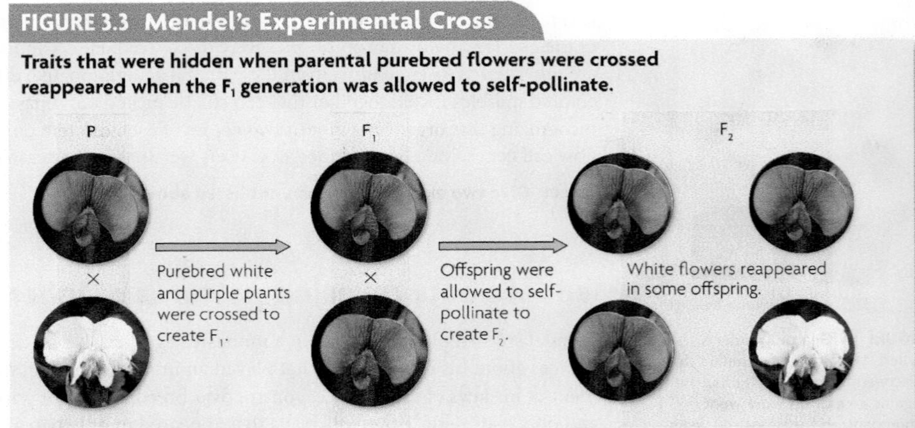
P
F1
F2
×
Purebred white and purple plants were crossed to create F1.
×
Offspring were allowed to self-pollinate to create F2.
White flowers reappeared in some offspring.

Differentiated Instruction

BELOW LEVEL

Ratios and proportions can be difficult for students to understand, even though they are used every day. Review fractions by using a common example such as the number of each color of coated candies in a bag compared to the total number of candies. Then explain that a ratio is a comparison using division of two numbers. Tell students that ratios can be written in three ways, for example, 1:3, 1 to 3, and 1/3.

INCLUSION

Teach Mendelian genetics to students who are visually impaired by making peas of round and wrinkled types, using table tennis balls and balls of aluminum foil or crumpled paper. Other traits can be modeled with fabric of different textures or actual flowers that are either terminal or axial.

Mendel did not cross only two plants, however; he crossed many plants. As a result, he was able to observe patterns. He noticed that each cross yielded similar ratios in the F_2 generation: about three-fourths of the plants had purple flowers, and about one-fourth had white flowers. A ratio is a comparison that tells how two or more things relate. This ratio can be expressed as 3:1 (read "three to one") of purple:white flowers. As you can see in **FIGURE 3.4,** Mendel's data show this approximately 3:1 ratio for each of his crosses.

FIGURE 3.4 MENDEL'S MONOHYBRID CROSS RESULTS

F_2 TRAITS	DOMINANT	RECESSIVE	RATIO
Pea shape	5474 round	1850 wrinkled	2.96:1
Pea color	6022 yellow	2001 green	3.01:1
Flower color	705 purple	224 white	3.15:1
Pod shape	882 smooth	299 constricted	2.95:1
Pod color	428 green	152 yellow	2.82:1
Flower position	651 axial	207 terminal	3.14:1
Plant height	787 tall	277 short	2.84:1

Source: Mendel, *Abhandlungen* (1865).

Conclusions

From these observations, Mendel drew three important conclusions. He demonstrated that traits are inherited as discrete units, which provided an explanation for individual traits that persisted without being blended or diluted over successive generations. Mendel's two other key conclusions are collectively called the **law of segregation,** or Mendel's first law.

- Organisms inherit two copies of each gene, one from each parent.
- Organisms donate only one copy of each gene in their gametes. Thus, the two copies of each gene segregate, or separate, during gamete formation.

Section 5 covers Mendel's second law, the law of independent assortment.

Infer **Explain why Mendel's choice of either-or characteristics aided his research.**

CONNECT TO

MEIOSIS

As you learned in **Section 2,** homologous chromosomes pair up in prophase I and are separated in anaphase I of meiosis. The overall process produces haploid cells that have a random assortment of chromosomes.

6.3 Formative Assessment

REVIEWING MAIN IDEAS

1. Mendel had no understanding of DNA as the genetic material, yet he was able to correctly predict how **traits** were passed between generations. What does Mendel's work in **genetics** show about the value of scientific observation?
2. Why is it important that Mendel began with **purebred** plants?

CRITICAL THINKING

3. **Analyze** Mendel saw purple flowers in the F_1 generation, but both purple and white flowers in F_2. How did this help him see that traits are inherited as discrete units?
4. **Evaluate** If Mendel had examined only one trait, do you think he would have developed the **law of segregation**? Explain.

SELF-CHECK Online
HMHScience.com
GO ONLINE

CONNECT TO

SCIENTIFIC PROCESS

5. You have learned that scientific thinking involves observing, forming hypotheses, testing hypotheses, and analyzing data. Use examples from Mendel's scientific process to show how his work fit this pattern.

Vocabulary

Academic Vocabulary The word **segregate** means "to separate" or "to isolate." In genetics, the function of segregation relates to the fact that genes are **discrete** or "separate" units.

Answers

A **Infer** Mendel could easily observe and quantify the effects of alleles because there were only two possible outcomes. The application of mathematical analysis helped him see that there were two factors influencing the traits.

Assess and Reteach

Assess Use the Section Self-Check or Section Quiz, both available at **HMHScience.com**.

Reteach Project the image of **FIGURE 3.3** from the Media Gallery. Have students relate the traits exhibited by the offspring of the purebred pea plants to the law of segregation.

6.3 FORMATIVE ASSESSMENT

1. Careful observation can lead to conclusions, even though the underlying reason or mechanism behind a phenomenon is unknown.
2. Self-pollination of purebred plants always yields the same traits, so Mendel could be sure that any changes he saw were the result of the crosses he made.
3. The units of color (purple and white) were both individually present. They had neither blended together nor vanished.
4. *Sample answer:* Probably not, because by experimenting with multiple traits, he could see that the ratio of dominant to recessive traits in monohybrid crosses was always 3:1.
5. Mendel observed the inheritance of certain either-or traits in pea plants and questioned how these traits were inherited over generations without becoming diluted. He hypothesized that he could answer this question by selectively breeding specific types of plants and observing the offspring. He then tested this hypothesis. Quantifying his results yielded data that helped him develop his law of segregation, which he then tested and demonstrated in other either-or traits of pea plants.

SECTION 6.4

B.4.1 Develop and revise a model that clarifies the relationship between DNA and chromosomes in coding the instructions for characteristic traits passed from parents to offspring.

B.4.6 Apply concepts of statistics and probability to explain the variation and distribution of expressed traits in a population.

▼ Plan and Prepare

Activate Prior Knowledge Discuss the different varieties of specific human physical traits. **Ask,** Why can siblings display diversity of traits, such as different eye or hair color? They inherited different forms of the genes that code for the development of those traits.

▼ Teach

Vocabulary

Greek and Latin Word Origins The suffix *-zygous* relates to the word **zygote,** which is the cell formed by the union of two gametes. Both come from the Greek word for yoke, the crossbar and halters that harness two farm animals together to work as one. Students can think of *homozygous* or *heterozygous* alleles as two horses side by side: their traits can be identical or very different.

Answers

Ⓐ **Compare and Contrast** An allele is an alternative form of a gene; it codes for a different form of the same trait. Alleles are found at the same location, or locus, on homologous chromosomes.

6.4 Traits, Genes, and Alleles

KEY CONCEPT **Genes encode proteins that produce a diverse range of traits.**

MAIN IDEAS
- The same gene can have many versions.
- Genes influence the development of traits.

VOCABULARY

gene
allele
homozygous
heterozygous
genome
genotype
phenotype
dominant
recessive

Connect to Your World

Most things come in many forms. Bread can be wheat, white, or rye. Cars can be two-door, four-door, hatchback, or convertible. Potatoes have more varieties than can be counted on two hands. Genes, too, come in many forms.

MAIN IDEA

The same gene can have many versions.

As you have learned, Mendel's discrete units of heredity are now called genes. But what are genes? You can think of a **gene** as a piece of DNA that provides a set of instructions to a cell to make a certain protein. This definition is not precise, but it gives you the main idea. Each gene has a locus, a specific position on a pair of homologous chromosomes. Just as a house is a physical structure and an address tells where that house is located, you can think of the locus as the "address" that tells where a gene is located on a chromosome.

Most genes exist in many forms. In Mendel's experiments, the effects of these different forms were easy to see: yellow or green, round or wrinkled. An **allele** (uh-LEEL) is any of the alternative forms of a gene that may occur at a specific locus. Your cells have two alleles for each gene, one on each of the homologous chromosomes on which the locus for that gene is found. Each parent gives one allele. The two alleles may be the same, or they may be different. The term **homozygous** (HOH-moh-ZY-guhs) describes two of the same alleles at a specific locus. For example, both might code for white flowers. The term **heterozygous** (HEHT-uhr-uh-ZY-guhs) describes two different alleles at a specific locus. Thus, one might code for white flowers, the other for purple flowers.

Ⓐ Compare and Contrast **Distinguish between the terms *allele* and *locus*.**

VISUAL VOCAB

Homozygous alleles are identical to each other.

Heterozygous alleles are different from each other.

Differentiated Instruction

ENGLISH LEARNERS

Write the key vocabulary for this section on cards and display them for the class. As you discuss the words in class, point to the terms and arrange them to show how they relate to one another. This arrangement can be used as the foundation for a cluster diagram.

Teacher Toolkit, Section D, Cluster Diagram

BELOW LEVEL

To reinforce the difference between a gene and an allele, have students make a chart with two columns labeled *Gene* and *Allele.* Ask them to place the terms in each of the following pairs in the correct column: hair color, brown hair; low cholesterol, cholesterol level; flower color, purple flowers; plant height, tall plant; long tail, tail length.

Teacher Toolkit, Section C, T-Chart

MAIN IDEA

Genes influence the development of traits.

You may have heard about the Human Genome Project. Its goal was to find out the sequence of the 3 billion nucleotide pairs that make up a human's genome. A **genome** is all of an organism's genetic material. Unless you have an identical twin, you have a unique genome that determines all of your traits. Some of your traits, such as the color of your eyes, can be seen. Other traits, such as the exact chemical makeup of your eyeball, cannot be seen.

In genetics, we often focus on a single trait or set of traits. A genome is all of an organism's genes, but a **genotype** (JEHN-uh-TYP) typically refers to the genetic makeup of a specific set of genes. The genotype of a pea plant includes both of the genes that code for flower color, even if one of these genes is masked. In contrast, the physical characteristics, or traits, of an individual organism make up its **phenotype** (FEE-nuh-TYP). A pea plant with purple flowers has a phenotype for purple flowers. The plant might have a hidden gene for white flowers, but that does not matter to its phenotype.

Dominant and Recessive Alleles

If an organism is heterozygous for a trait, which allele will be expressed? That is, if a plant has one allele for purple flowers and one for white flowers, what color will the flowers be? As Mendel learned, one allele may be dominant over another allele. A **dominant** allele is the allele that is expressed when two different alleles or two dominant alleles are present. A **recessive** allele is the allele that is expressed only when two copies are present. In Mendel's experiments, the allele for purple flowers was dominant to the allele for white flowers. All F_1 plants were purple even though they had only one allele for purple flowers.

VISUAL VOCAB

A **dominant** allele is expressed when two different alleles are present.

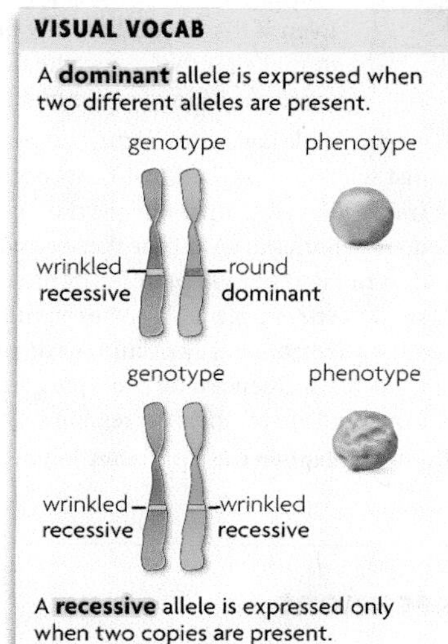

A **recessive** allele is expressed only when two copies are present.

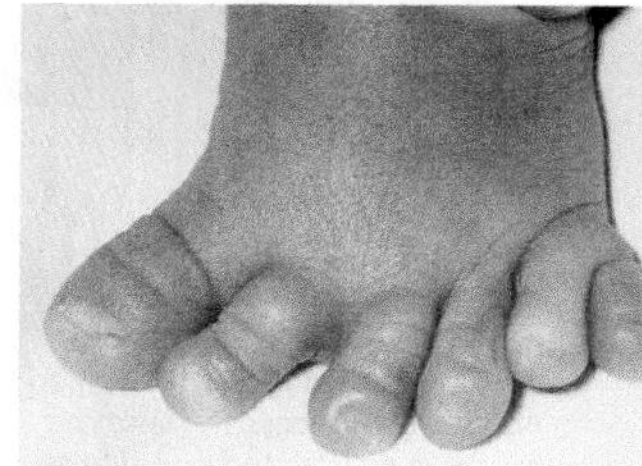

FIGURE 4.1 Polydactyly is the condition of having more than the typical number of fingers or toes. The allele for polydactyly is dominant.

Sometimes the word *dominant* is misunderstood. A dominant allele is not necessarily better or stronger than a recessive allele. It does not necessarily occur most often in the population. An allele is dominant in a heterozygote simply because it is expressed and the other allele is not.

Alleles are often represented on paper with individual letters. An organism's genotype for a trait can be shown with two letters—one per allele. Uppercase letters are used for dominant alleles, and lowercase letters are used for recessive alleles. For example, the dominant allele for height in pea plants is written as *T*, for tall. The recessive allele for short plants is written as *t*.

CONNECT TO

EXCEPTIONS TO MENDEL'S LAWS

Mendel's theory of inheritance cannot explain all patterns of inheritance. As you will learn in the chapter **Extending Mendelian Genetics,** incomplete dominance, codominance, polygenic traits, and environmental influences all provide exceptions.

PRE-AP

Have students structure the information in this section in the form of a concept map. Their concept maps should incorporate the Key Concept and Main Ideas of the section, as well as all of the key vocabulary.

Teacher Toolkit, Section C, Concept Map

Vocabulary

genotype, phenotype *Genotype* comes from the Greek word *genos,* meaning "race" or "kind." *Phenotype* comes from the Greek word meaning "to show." A genotype indicates the combination of alleles for a select group of traits, whereas the phenotype shows how those alleles are expressed in an individual.

dominant, recessive The word *dominant* comes from the same Latin root as *dominate,* meaning "to rule." The word *recessive* shares the same Latin root as *recede,* meaning "to go back," as in withdraw or retreat.

TEACH FROM VISUALS

FIGURE 4.1 Point out that most people have five fingers and toes on each hand and foot, even though having five digits is recessive. Tell students that this can be explained by the fact that the allele for polydactyly is rarely found in most populations, despite being a dominant allele.

Integrating Agricultural Science

Many agriculturally important crop plants are polyploids, meaning they have multiple sets of chromosomes. These include sugar cane, wheat, oats, bananas, potatoes, coffee, and cotton. The plants tend to be larger or healthier, or have larger flowers, than diploid plants. The basic set of chromosomes in a polyploid is the **monoploid** set. A plant breeder can isolate a desirable recessive trait in a monoploid set of chromosomes and then use a chemical called colchicine that interferes with spindle formation. As mitosis begins, the chromosomes are duplicated, but the cell doesn't divide. The result is a homozygous diploid plant with the desired characteristic.

▼ Teach *continued*

History of Science

The breakthrough that tied genes to the biochemistry of the cell came in 1941 when **George Beadle** and **Edward Tatum** rediscovered the work of **Archibald Garrod** (1909). The relationship between genotype and phenotype became clear when Beadle and Tatum's experimental results led them to the conclusion that each gene is responsible for the production of a single, specific enzyme. This became known as the **one gene/one enzyme** hypothesis. Further research in genetics has shown that not all proteins are enzymes and that some enzymes are made of more than one polypeptide chain. Thus, a more accurate way of expressing this foundation of modern genetics is **one gene/one polypeptide.**

Answers

A Contrast Genotype refers to the actual genes an organism carries. Phenotype typically refers to an organism's physical appearance or the expression of a certain gene.

▼ Assess and Reteach

Assess Use the Section Self-Check or Section Quiz, both available at **HMHScience.com**.

Reteach Work with students to create a concept map that uses as many of the vocabulary terms in this section as possible.

A plant's genotype might be homozygous dominant (*TT*), heterozygous (*Tt*), or homozygous recessive (*tt*).

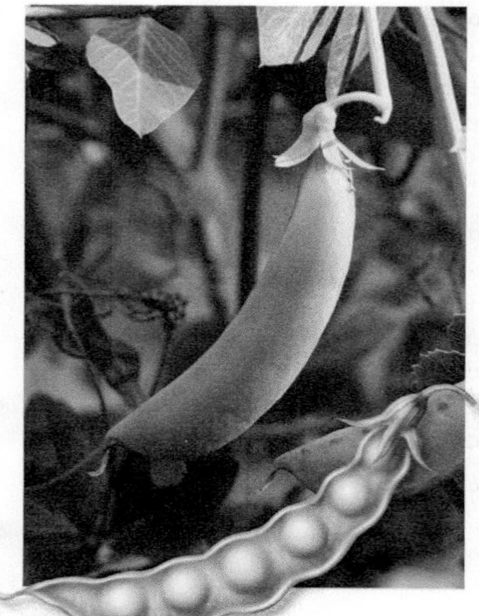

FIGURE 4.2 Both the homozygous dominant and heterozygous genotypes result in smooth, or inflated, pods (top). Only the homozygous recessive genotype results in constricted pods (inset).

Alleles and Phenotype

Because some alleles are dominant over others, two genotypes can produce the dominant phenotype. For example, smooth pods and constricted pods in pea plants, shown in **FIGURE 4.2**, are phenotypes. A plant with smooth pods could have a homozygous dominant (*SS*) or heterozygous (*Ss*) genotype. In contrast, a plant with constricted, or compressed, pods could have only a homozygous recessive (*ss*) genotype.

What actually makes one allele dominant over another? The answer is very complicated. It depends on the nature of the protein that is, or is not, made. Let's look at a fairly simple example. Pigment gives cells color. If *P* directs flower cells to make pigment, the flower may look purple. If *p* directs the cells not to make pigment, the flower looks white. So *P* codes for pigment to be present, but *p* codes for nothing, the absence of pigment. As a result, *P* has to be dominant. Even if the flower has only one *P* allele (*Pp*), that one allele tells its cells to make pigment, and the flower has color. Flower pigment is only one example. Many factors make one allele dominant over another.

As you know, most plants are not simply tall or short. Most flowers are not just white or purple. Most traits occur in a range. Other factors also affect traits. A lack of sunshine or vital nutrients could stunt a plant's growth. How does genetics account for these issues? Mendel studied traits that follow simple dominant-recessive patterns of inheritance, and each trait was the result of a single gene. In general, however, inheritance is much more complex. Most alleles are not simply dominant or recessive; some are codominant. Many traits are influenced by multiple genes. The environment also interacts with genes and affects their expression.

A Contrast Explain the difference between genotype and phenotype.

6.4 Formative Assessment

SELF-CHECK Online
HMHScience.com
GO ONLINE

REVIEWING ▶ MAIN IDEAS

1. How are the terms **gene**, locus, and **allele** related?
2. Explain why an organism's genotype may be **homozygous** dominant, homozygous recessive, or **heterozygous**, but never heterozygous recessive.

CRITICAL THINKING

3. **Apply** Suppose you are studying a fruit fly's DNA, and you discover a gene for antenna length on chromosome 2. What word describes its location, and where would it be found in other fruit flies' DNA?
4. **Predict** If a **recessive** allele helps an organism reproduce, but the **dominant** allele hinders reproduction, which will be more common in a population?

CONNECT TO

HUMAN BIOLOGY

5. Cystic fibrosis is a recessive disease that causes the production of abnormally thick, life-threatening mucus secretions. What is the **genotype** of a person with cystic fibrosis: *CC*, *Cc*, or *cc*? Explain.

Unit 3: Genetics

6.4 FORMATIVE ASSESSMENT

1. All have something to do with a particular segment of DNA, or nucleotides. A gene is a region of DNA, a series of nucleotides that codes for a protein. It can come in different forms, called alleles, that code for the same general type of information but with varying specifics. The locus tells where a particular gene or allele is located on a chromosome.
2. The only way a phenotype or genotype can be recessive is if both alleles are recessive.
3. locus; on chromosome 2 at the same locus
4. the recessive allele
5. The person's genotype is *cc*. If a disease or other trait is recessive, a person must have two recessive alleles for the trait to be expressed.

6.5 Traits and Probability

KEY CONCEPT **The inheritance of traits follows the rules of probability.**

MAIN IDEAS
- Punnett squares illustrate genetic crosses.
- A monohybrid cross involves one trait.
- A dihybrid cross involves two traits.
- Heredity patterns can be calculated with probability.

VOCABULARY
Punnett square
monohybrid cross
testcross
dihybrid cross
law of independent assortment
probability

Connect to Your World

If you have tried juggling, you know it can be a tricky thing. Keeping three flaming torches or clubs in motion at the same time is a challenge. Trying to keep track of what organism has which genotype and which gamete gets which allele can also be a lot to juggle. Fortunately, R. C. Punnett developed a method to keep track of all of the various combinations graphically.

MAIN IDEA
Punnett squares illustrate genetic crosses.

Shortly after Mendel's experiments became widely known among scientists, a poultry geneticist named R. C. Punnett developed the Punnett square. A **Punnett square** is a grid system for predicting all possible genotypes resulting from a cross. The axes of the grid represent the possible gamete genotypes of each parent. The grid boxes show all of the possible genotypes of offspring from those two parents. Because segregation and fertilization are random events, each combination of alleles is as likely to be produced as any other. By counting the number of squares with each genetic combination, we can find the ratio of genotypes in that generation. If we also know how the genotype corresponds to the phenotype, we can find the ratio of phenotypes in that generation as well.

VISUAL VOCAB

The **Punnett square** is a grid system for predicting possible genotypes of offspring.

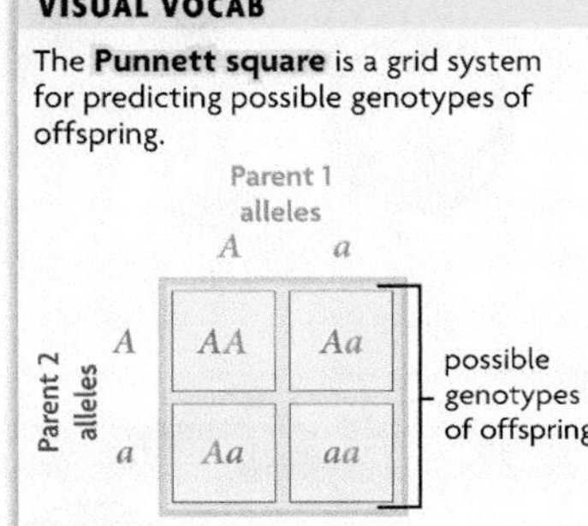

Let's briefly review what you've learned about meiosis and segregation to examine why the Punnett square is effective. Both parents have two alleles for each gene. These alleles are represented on the axes of the Punnett square. During meiosis, the chromosomes—and, therefore, the alleles—are separated.

SECTION 6.5

B.4.1 Develop and revise a model that clarifies the relationship between DNA and chromosomes in coding the instructions for characteristic traits passed from parents to offspring.

B.4.6 Apply concepts of statistics and probability to explain the variation and distribution of expressed traits in a population.

Plan and Prepare

Activate Prior Knowledge Discuss probability as it applies to everyday life. **Ask,** In what ways do you apply probability or likelihood in your everyday life? Students may mention card games, answering multiple-choice questions on tests, or sports in which players often guess what the opponent will do next. Discuss ways in which each of these examples is based on the chance or likelihood of a specific event happening.

Teach

TEACH FROM VISUALS

VISUAL VOCAB Emphasize that it makes no difference which parental genotype is shown on each axis of a Punnett square. On the board, draw two Punnett squares for the cross *Aa* × *aa*. On one, place the *Aa* across the top; on the other, place the *Aa* along the side. Fill in the grids. The results are the same, although the Punnett squares look different.

Differentiated Instruction

ENGLISH LEARNERS

After reading the section, do a jigsaw activity. With students assembled in home groups of four, assign topics by number: (1) Punnett square, (2) monohybrid cross, (3) test cross, (4) dihybrid cross. Have students move into expert groups to prepare a lesson on their topic. Then have the experts return to their home groups to teach their lessons to one another.

Teacher Toolkit, Section C, Jigsaw Reading

BELOW LEVEL

Use an overhead projector to display a blank Punnett square. Lead students through the steps in each of the monohybrid crosses illustrated in this section. Show how to write the possible gamete genotypes of each parent across the top and side of the Punnett square. Draw arrows to show how to record each allele in the appropriate box. Have students determine the genotype and phenotype of each possible offspring.

▼ Teach *continued*

Have students make crosses to determine how certain genes are inherited in fruit flies in the Virtual Lab, available at **HMHScience.com**.

TEACH FROM VISUALS

FIGURE 5.2 Point out that this is the cross that Mendel did to produce the F_1 generation. **Ask,** What did Mendel call a homozygous plant such as *FF* or *ff*? a purebred plant

FIGURE 5.3 Point out that this is the cross that Mendel did when he allowed the F_1 plants to self-pollinate to produce the F_2 generation. **Ask,** How did the white flower appear among the offspring if neither parent had white flowers? Each parent produced some gametes that contained the recessive allele for white flowers. When two such gametes came together, a white-flowered offspring was produced.

The Inside Story

Reginald C. Punnett was an authority on poultry breeding. He developed many new breeds of chickens by transferring genes located on the X chromosome of one breed to the chromosomes of another breed. This work was done in the 1920s and can be thought of as an early method of genetic engineering. His work ended in 1955, when his incubator house was destroyed by fire.

Answers

A Explain alleles of the parents

Each gamete gets one of the alleles. Since each parent contributes only one allele to the offspring, only one allele from each parent is written inside each grid box. Fertilization restores the diploid number in the resulting offspring. This is why each grid box has two alleles, one from the mother and one from the father. Since any egg has the same chance of being fertilized by any sperm cell, each possible genetic combination is equally likely to occur.

A Explain **What do the letters on the axes of the Punnett square represent?**

MAIN IDEA

A monohybrid cross involves one trait.

Thus far, we have studied **monohybrid crosses,** crosses that examine the inheritance of only one specific trait. Three example crosses are used below and on the next page to illustrate how Punnett squares work and to highlight the resulting ratios—for both genotype and phenotype.

FIGURE 5.2 HOMOZYGOUS-HOMOZYGOUS

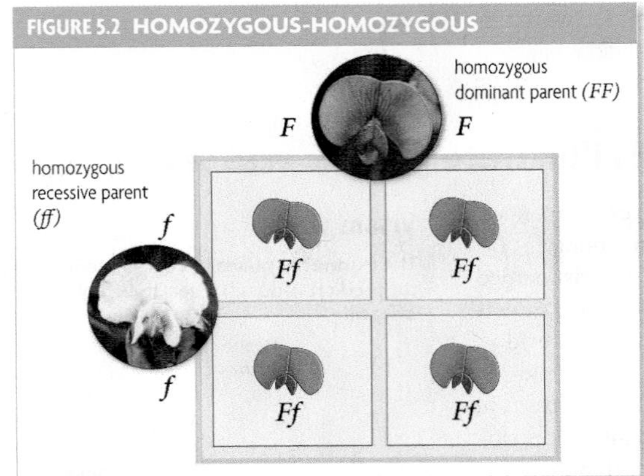

Homozygous-Homozygous

Suppose you cross a pea plant that is homozygous dominant for purple flowers with a pea plant that is homozygous recessive for white flowers. To determine the genotypic and phenotypic ratios of the offspring, first write each parent's genotype on one axis: *FF* for the purple-flowered plant, *ff* for the white-flowered plant. Every gamete from the purple-flowered plant contains the dominant allele, *F*. Every gamete from the white-flowered plant contains the recessive allele, *f*. Therefore, 100% of the offspring have the heterozygous genotype, *Ff*. And 100% of the offspring have purple flowers because they all have a copy of the dominant allele, as shown in **FIGURE 5.2.**

FIGURE 5.3 HETEROZYGOUS-HETEROZYGOUS

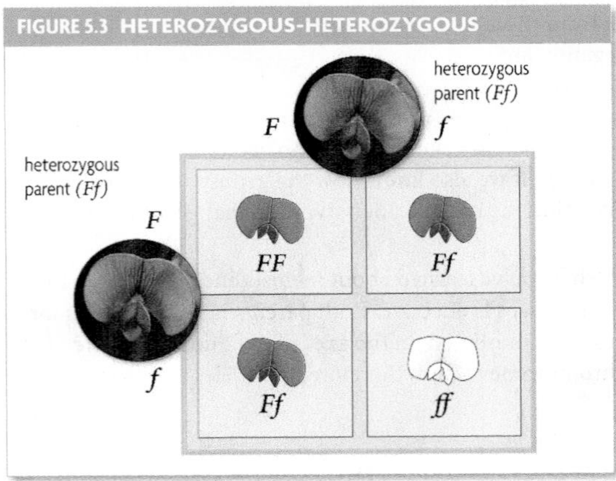

Heterozygous-Heterozygous

Next, in **FIGURE 5.3,** you can see a cross between two purple-flowered pea plants that are both heterozygous (*Ff*). From each parent, half the offspring receive a dominant allele, *F*, and half receive a recessive allele, *f*. Therefore, one-fourth of the offspring have a homozygous dominant genotype, *FF*; half have a heterozygous genotype, *Ff*; and one-fourth have a homozygous recessive genotype, *ff*. Both the *FF* and the *Ff* genotypes result in purple flowers. Only the *ff* genotype results in white flowers. Thus, the genotypic ratio is 1:2:1 of homozygous dominant:heterozygous:homozygous recessive. The phenotypic ratio is 3:1 of purple:white flowers.

Differentiated Instruction

BELOW LEVEL

Be sure students understand that a Punnett square shows the proportions of gamete combinations expected to occur, not the actual numbers of combinations that do occur. As an example, make a Punnett square showing two X chromosome gametes on one axis (from the female parent) and one X chromosome gamete and one Y chromosome gamete on the other axis (from the male parent). Fill in the boxes to show that equal numbers of males and females are to be expected. Compare this with actual ratios of males and females in students' families.

Heterozygous-Homozygous

Finally, suppose you cross a pea plant that is heterozygous for purple flowers (*Ff*) with a pea plant that is homozygous recessive for white flowers (*ff*). As before, each parent's genotype is placed on an axis, as shown in **FIGURE 5.4.** From the homozygous parent with white flowers, the offspring each receive a recessive allele, *f*. From the heterozygous parent, half the offspring receive a dominant allele, *F*, and half receive a recessive allele, *f*. Half the offspring have a heterozygous genotype, *Ff*. Half have a homozygous recessive genotype, *ff*. Thus, half the offspring have purple flowers, and half have white flowers. The resulting genotypic ratio is 1:1 of heterozygous:homozygous recessive. The phenotypic ratio is 1:1 of purple:white.

FIGURE 5.4 HETEROZYGOUS-HOMOZYGOUS

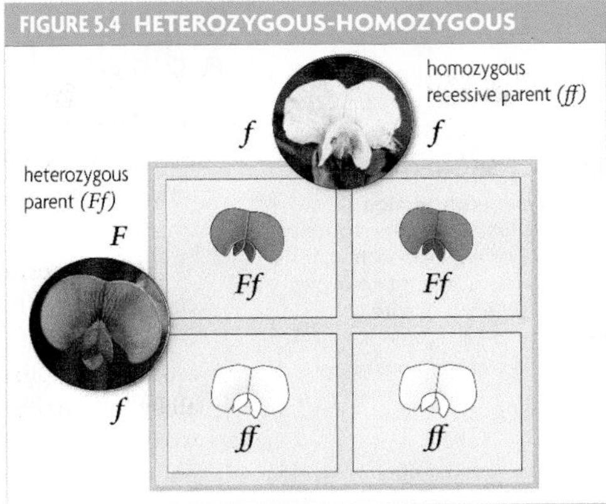

Suppose we did not know the genotype of the purple flower in the cross above. This cross would allow us to determine that the purple flower is heterozygous, not homozygous dominant. A **testcross** is a cross between an organism with an unknown genotype and an organism with the recessive phenotype. The organism with the recessive phenotype must be homozygous recessive. The offspring will show whether the organism with the unknown genotype is heterozygous, as above, or homozygous dominant.

Apply **From an *FF* × *Ff* cross, what percent of offspring would have purple flowers?**

QUICKLAB INFERRING

Using a Testcross

Suppose you work for a company that sells plant seeds. You are studying a plant species in which the dominant phenotype is pink flowers (*PP* or *Pp*). The recessive phenotype is white flowers (*pp*). Customers have been requesting more plants with pink flowers. To meet this demand, you need to determine the genotypes of some of the plants you are currently working with.

PROBLEM What is the genotype of each plant?

PROCEDURE

1. Suppose you are presented with Plant A of the species you are studying. It has pink flowers. You want to determine the genotype of the plant.
2. You cross Plant A with Plant B of the same species. This plant has white flowers and a known genotype of *pp*.
3. The resulting cross yields six plants with pink flowers and six plants with white flowers. Use Punnett squares to determine the genotype of Plant A.

MATERIALS

- pencil
- paper

ANALYZE AND CONCLUDE

1. Apply What is the genotype of Plant A? Explain how you arrived at your answer.
2. Apply What are the possible genotypes and phenotypes of offspring if Plant A is crossed with a plant that has a genotype of *PP*?
3. Calculate What ratio of dominant to recessive phenotypes would exist if Plant A were crossed with a plant that has a genotype of *Pp*?
4. Evaluate Is Plant A the best plant, in terms of genotype, that you can work with to produce as many of the requested seeds as possible? Why or why not? Which genotype would be best to work with?

Answers

A Apply 100 percent

QUICKLAB

Time 15 minutes

Purpose Determine the genotype of a plant by analyzing a testcross.

LAB MANAGEMENT

Tell students that they will need to work backwards from a Punnett square to determine the genotype of one of the parents.

Answers

1. Plant A has a *Pp* genotype. If it were *PP*, there would not have been any white offspring from the testcross.
2. All the offspring would have pink flowers. Half would have the *PP* genotype; the other half would have the *Pp* genotype.
3. 3:1 of pink:white
4. Plant A is not the best plant to work with. A homozygous dominant plant (*PP*) would be better because all crosses would produce only pink-flowered offspring.

PRE-AP

Have students imagine that they will be breeding guinea pigs. Black fur, a recessive trait, is most popular. Have students develop a plan for raising as many black guinea pigs as possible. **Ask,** Which cross will produce the most black guinea pigs? Black × black (both homozygous recessive) will produce all black offspring. **Ask,** Which cross is expected to produce black fur in about half the offspring? a cross between a black guinea pig and a heterozygous guinea pig

Teacher Toolkit, Section C, Quick-Write

▼ Teach *continued*

The Inside Story

Mendel either had good luck in his choice of traits to study or he did not report crosses with traits that did not show **independent assortment.** Garden peas have seven pairs of chromosomes. Genes for six of the seven traits Mendel chose are located on separate chromosomes. The gene for the seventh trait shares a chromosome with another gene Mendel studied, but it is so far away from that gene that the two genes sort independently.

TEACH FROM VISUALS

FIGURE 5.5 Have students examine the Punnett square. **Ask,** Would this Punnett square represent the expected results if the genes for the two traits were inherited together? No, if the genes were inherited together, you would not expect to see all the different combinations of alleles.

Vocabulary

Academic Vocabulary The **grid system** of a Punnett square makes it easy to determine all possible combinations of male and female gametes. Many cities have a street grid system, making it easy to find one's way in the city. Maps have a grid system that makes it easy to find specific locations on a map.

Answers

A Analyze Two alleles are shown because two different genes are being observed. Each gamete has one allele for each gene.

CONNECT TO

LAW OF SEGREGATION

As you learned in **Section 3,** Mendel's first law of inheritance is the law of segregation. It states that organisms inherit two copies of each gene but donate only one copy to each gamete.

MAIN IDEA

A dihybrid cross involves two traits.

All of the crosses discussed so far have involved only a single trait. However, Mendel also conducted **dihybrid crosses,** crosses that examine the inheritance of two different traits. He wondered if both traits would always appear together or if they would be expressed independently of each other.

Mendel performed many dihybrid crosses and tested a variety of different combinations. For example, he would cross a plant with yellow round peas with a plant with green wrinkled peas. Remember that Mendel began his crosses with purebred plants. Thus, the first generation offspring (F_1) would all be heterozygous and would all look the same. In this example, the plants would all have yellow round peas. When Mendel allowed the F_1 plants to self-pollinate, he obtained the following results: 9 yellow/round, 3 yellow/wrinkled, 3 green/round, 1 green/wrinkled.

Mendel continued to find this approximately 9:3:3:1 phenotypic ratio in the F_2 generation, regardless of the combination of traits. From these results, he realized that the presence of one trait did not affect the presence of another trait. His second law of genetics, the **law of independent assortment,** states that allele pairs separate independently of each other during gamete formation, or meiosis. That is, different traits appear to be inherited separately.

The results of Mendel's dihybrid crosses can also be illustrated with a Punnett square, like the one in **FIGURE 5.5.** Drawing a Punnett square for a dihybrid cross is the same as drawing one for a monohybrid cross, except that the grid is bigger because two genes, or four alleles, are involved. For example, suppose you cross two plants with yellow, round peas that are heterozygous for both traits (*YyRr*). The four allele combinations possible in each gamete—*YR*, *Yr*, *yR*, and *yr*—are used to label each axis. Each grid box can be filled in using the same method as that used in the monohybrid cross. A total of nine different genotypes may result from the cross in this example. However, these nine genotypes produce only four different phenotypes. These phenotypes are yellow round, yellow wrinkled, green round, and green wrinkled, and they occur in the ratio of 9:3:3:1. Note that the 9:3:3:1 phenotypic ratio results from a cross between organisms that are heterozygous for both traits. The phenotypic ratio of the offspring will differ (from 9:3:3:1) if one or both of the parent organisms are homozygous for one or both traits.

FIGURE 5.5 DIHYBRID CROSS

This dihybrid cross is heterozygous-heterozygous.

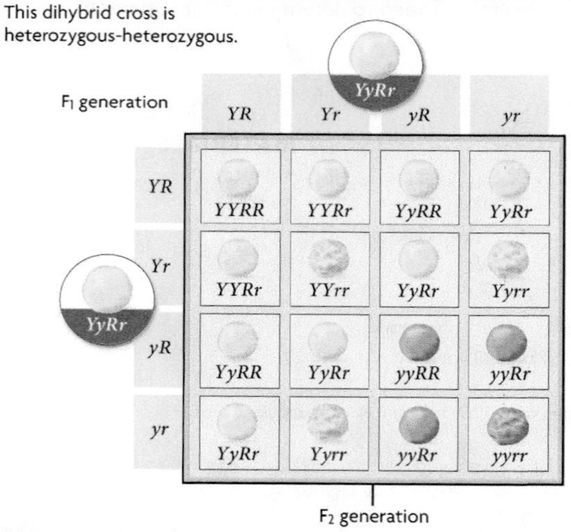

F1 generation: *YyRr* × *YyRr*

	YR	*Yr*	*yR*	*yr*
YR	*YYRR*	*YYRr*	*YyRR*	*YyRr*
Yr	*YYRr*	*YYrr*	*YyRr*	*Yyrr*
yR	*YyRR*	*YyRr*	*yyRR*	*yyRr*
yr	*YyRr*	*Yyrr*	*yyRr*	*yyrr*

F2 generation

A Analyze In FIGURE 5.5, the boxes on the axes represent the possible gametes made by each parent plant. Why does each box have two alleles?

Differentiated Instruction

BELOW LEVEL

Write the letters *YyRr* on the board to represent a parent's alleles for two traits. Show students how to determine the possible gametes that can form, as follows: Draw an arrow under the letters from the *Y* to the *R* and an arrow from the *Y* to the *r*. Write the gamete genotypes *YR* and *Yr* on the board. Now draw an arrow above the letters from the *y* to the *R* and an arrow from the *y* to the *r*. Write the gamete genotypes *yR* and *yr* on the board. Have students use this method to determine the possible gametes that can form when they make a Punnett square for a dihybrid cross.

HANDS-ON ACTIVITY

Give each student one large paper clip and one small paper clip, one large bean and one small bean. Tell students that the objects represent alleles for a paper-clip gene and a bean gene. Large paper clips and large beans are dominant alleles; small paper clips and small beans are recessive alleles. Have students model independent assortment of their "alleles" into gametes. Students should produce four kinds of "gametes": large paper clip and large bean, large paper clip and small bean, small paper clip and large bean, and small paper clip and small bean.

MAIN IDEA

Heredity patterns can be calculated with probability.

Probability is the likelihood that a particular event will happen. It predicts the average number of occurrences, not the exact number of occurrences.

$$\text{Probability} = \frac{\text{number of ways a specific event can occur}}{\text{number of total possible outcomes}}$$

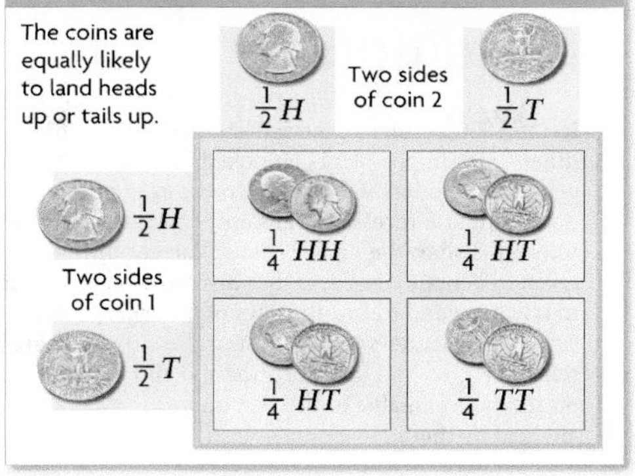

Suppose you flip a coin. The number of total possible outcomes is two: heads up or tails up. The probability that it would land heads up is 1/2, or one out of two. The probability that it would land tails up is also 1/2.

Next, suppose you flip two coins. How one coin lands does not affect how the other coin lands. To calculate the probability that two independent events will happen together, multiply the probability of each individual event. The probability that both coins will land heads up, for example, is $1/2 \times 1/2 = 1/4$.

These probabilities can be applied to meiosis. Suppose a germ cell undergoes meiosis in a plant that is heterozygous for purple flowers. The number of total possible outcomes is two because a gamete could get a dominant or a recessive allele. The probability that a gamete will get a dominant allele is 1/2. The probability that it will get a recessive allele is also 1/2.

If two plants that are heterozygous for purple flowers fertilize each other, the probability that both egg and sperm have a dominant allele is $1/2 \times 1/2 = 1/4$. So, too, the probability that both have a recessive allele is 1/4. There is also a 1/4 chance that a sperm cell with a dominant allele will fertilize an egg with a recessive allele, or that a sperm cell with a recessive allele will fertilize an egg with a dominant allele. These last two combinations are basically the same. In either case, the resulting plant will be heterozygous. Thus, the probability that a pea plant will be heterozygous for this trait is the sum of the probabilities: $1/4 + 1/4 = 1/2$.

Apply **Explain how Mendel's laws relate to probability.**

FIGURE 5.6 PROBABILITY AND HEREDITY

The coins are equally likely to land heads up or tails up.

	Two sides of coin 2: $\frac{1}{2}H$	$\frac{1}{2}T$
Two sides of coin 1: $\frac{1}{2}H$	$\frac{1}{4}HH$	$\frac{1}{4}HT$
$\frac{1}{2}T$	$\frac{1}{4}HT$	$\frac{1}{4}TT$

Integrating Statistics

Have students refer back to Mendel's data in **FIGURE 3.4** and look at the ratios in the last column. Students should recognize that Mendel's ratios approximate the expected 3:1 ratio. Tell them that the more observations that are made, the closer the actual ratio will approach the expected ratio. For example, if a coin was tossed 1000 times, we could expect the ratio of heads-to-tails to be closer to 1:1 than if the coin was tossed four times. In statistics, on which science relies heavily, the number of observations or data is referred to as the **sample size.** The larger the sample size, the more reliable is the data.

Compare the coin example with how the ratio of males to females in families is often very different from the expected 1:1 ratio.

Answers

A **Apply** Mendel's laws of segregation and probability are based on random events. The chance, or probability, that two particular events will occur together during meiosis is determined in the same way as any other set of random events.

6.5 Formative Assessment

REVIEWING MAIN IDEAS

1. What do the grid boxes in a **Punnett square** represent?
2. Why does the expected genotypic ratio often differ from the expected phenotypic ratio resulting from a **monohybrid cross**?
3. How did Mendel's **dihybrid crosses** help him develop his second law?

CRITICAL THINKING

4. **Calculate** What would be the phenotypic ratios of the offspring resulting from the following cross: *YYRr* × *YyRr*?
5. **Predict** If you are working with two tall pea plants and know that one is *Tt*, how could you determine the genotype of the other plant?

SELF-CHECK Online
HMHScience.com
GO ONLINE

CONNECT TO

ADAPTATION

6. You have seen that one-quarter of offspring resulting from two heterozygous parents are homozygous recessive. Yet for some genes, the recessive allele is more common in the population. Explain why this might be.

Assess and Reteach

Assess Use the Section Self-Check or Section Quiz, both available at **HMHScience.com**.

Reteach Work with students to calculate the probabilities of the genotypes and phenotypes of the offspring shown in the Punnett squares in **FIGURES 5.3** and **5.4.**

6.5 FORMATIVE ASSESSMENT

1. all the possible allele combinations of offspring resulting from a cross
2. Multiple genotypes can cause the same phenotype. For example, the homozygous dominant genotype and the heterozygous genotype yield the same phenotype in simple dominant-recessive cases.
3. Mendel was able to observe that the inheritance of one trait did not influence the inheritance of a second trait.
4. all *Y* (yellow); 3:1 *R* : *r* (round:wrinkled)
5. Cross the two plants together. If the offspring are tall:short in a 3:1 ratio, the unknown plant is heterozygous, *Tt*. If all the offspring are tall, the unknown plant is homozygous dominant, *TT*.
6. The recessive condition could be advantageous for survival in some way, or the dominant condition could be disadvantageous.

Introduce

Engage students' interest in single-gene conditions by explaining the barriers that prevent affected people from seeking treatment for their conditions. **Ask,** If you have a condition that many doctors have never seen before, what do you think will happen when you seek medical attention? Students may conclude that patients would have difficulty receiving an accurate diagnosis, and that without a diagnosis, it would be impossible to know what treatments or therapies might help treat the condition. Explain that people who cannot get an accurate diagnosis are also in danger of falling victim to unforeseen complications of their condition.

Discuss

Discuss Mendelian conditions with which students may be familiar, such as the ones mentioned: cystic fibrosis, muscular dystrophy, sickle cell disease, and Huntington's disease. Encourage students to research other examples. Invite students to speculate how future scientific and medical advances might address single-gene conditions. **Ask,** What types of technology could help people affected by Mendelian conditions?

Answers

A large amount of data sharing and research sharing has to continue on an international level for the CMG to succeed. Also, scientists and doctors have to continue to find people with suspected Mendelian conditions and ask them to submit DNA samples for the CMG work to continue.

Identifying Single-Gene Conditions

In the 1800s, Gregor Mendel's studies of patterns of inheritance in pea plants launched the scientific field of genetics. Mendel's work revealed the existence of dominant and recessive traits and explained how they interact. Today, the name "Mendelian conditions" is given to genetic disorders that involve a single mutation in one gene and follow the laws of inheritance demonstrated by Mendel's work. Most of these diseases are relatively rare, and little information and few therapy options are available to the vast majority of people affected by them.

To address this problem, in 2011 the National Human Genome Research Institute (NHGRI) and the National Heart, Lung, and Blood Institute (NHLBI) founded the Centers for Mendelian Genomics (CMG) program. Its mission is to uncover the genetic basis of all human Mendelian conditions in order to increase scientific knowledge of these diseases and to improve therapy options for affected patients.

The mission of CMG is a challenging one. Scientists estimate that there are at least 7,300 known Mendelian conditions, including well-known ones such as cystic fibrosis, muscular dystrophy, sickle cell disease, and Huntington's disease. Each disease may affect only a small number of people, but all Mendelian conditions together affect 20 million to 30 million people in the United States alone.

More than 500 scientists in 36 countries are working together on the CMG program, which is centered at four universities in the United States. People who have a known Mendelian condition—or whose physicians suspect they might—can submit DNA samples to the CMG program for whole genome sequencing, which includes protein-coding genes. Data collected from thousands of patients are shared with researchers so that important connections can be made.

In the years since the program was founded, CMG scientists have made connections between gene mutations and diseases that were not yet understood to be caused by gene mutations, suggesting possible therapies for affected people. Researchers have also:

- discovered that a single mutation in many different genes can cause the same or a similar disease;
- deduced that a gene can be mutated in more than one way, with each mutation causing a different disease;
- learned that a single mutation in one gene can have one effect on one family member and a similar, but weaker, effect on another family member; and
- realized that a person may inherit two different genetic changes that interact to cause one condition.

One of the more astounding findings of CMG research is that some Mendelian conditions are not inherited. Some affected people, researchers have found, are the only ones affected in their families. Researchers call these mutations *de novo*, or new, mutations.

So far scientists have identified the genomic causes for about half of the 7,300 conditions. The CMG research has led to more avenues of inquiry, such as whether exposure to chemicals or other environmental factors might cause an underlying Mendelian condition to be revealed. People affected by Mendelian conditions have reason to hope that CMG research will bring them even more information in the near future.

S.T.E.M. Activity

Consider the mission of the CMG program. What resources are needed for scientists to continue their work in this program? What constraints do you think might hinder their work?

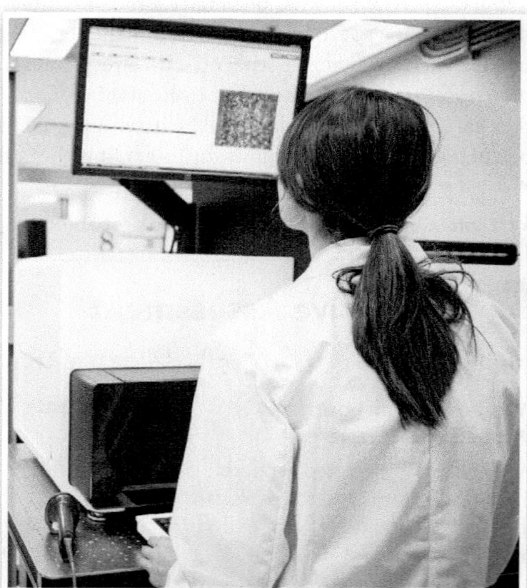

A scientist studies DNA sequencing.

6.6 Meiosis and Genetic Variation

KEY CONCEPT **Independent assortment and crossing over during meiosis result in genetic diversity.**

VOCABULARY

crossing over
genetic linkage

MAIN IDEAS

- Sexual reproduction creates unique gene combinations.
- Crossing over during meiosis increases genetic diversity.

Connect to Your World

A surprising number of people make their living as Elvis impersonators. They wear slicked-up hairdos, large sunglasses, and big white jumpsuits. They mimic his voice, his dancing, and his phrases. They copy every possible detail, but they still do not come close to being the King. Elvis, like all people, was unique, or one of a kind. This uniqueness arises more from the events of meiosis—from the tiny shufflings of chromosomes and the crossing over of DNA segments—than from our hairstyles or our clothing.

MAIN IDEA

Sexual reproduction creates unique gene combinations.

FIGURE 6.1 This photograph shows only a small sample of the great genetic potential for variety in the human population.

The major advantage of sexual reproduction is that it gives rise to a great deal of genetic variation within a species, as shown in **FIGURE 6.1**. This variation results largely from (1) the independent assortment of chromosomes during meiosis and (2) the mixing of alleles as gametes join during fertilization.

Recall that homologous chromosomes pair up randomly along the cell equator during meiosis I. In other words, it's a matter of chance which of the two chromosomes from any homologous pair ends up on a given side of the cell equator. As you've learned, human cells have 23 pairs of chromosomes, and each pair lines up independently. As a result, gametes with 2^{23}, or about 8 million, different combinations of chromosomes can be produced through meiosis from one human cell.

Now think about the fact that sexual reproduction produces offspring through the combination of gametes. In humans, for example, a sperm cell with one of 2^{23} (about 8 million) chromosome combinations fertilizes an egg cell, which also has one out of 2^{23} chromosome combinations. If sperm cells and eggs were combined at random, the total number of possible combinations is the product of $2^{23} \times 2^{23}$, or more than 70 trillion. In other words, a human couple can produce a child with one of about 70 trillion different combinations of chromosomes.

Differentiated Instruction

BELOW LEVEL

Review large numbers, such as millions, billions, and trillions so that students understand why each individual is unique. Write the numerals one million, one billion, and one trillion on the board. Help students to make these numbers more tangible. **Ask,** If the largest passenger plane can hold a thousand people, how many flights would you need to carry the 300 million people in the United States? 300,000

SECTION 6.6

B.4.5 Make and defend a claim based on evidence that inheritable genetic variations may result from: (1) new genetic combinations through meiosis, (2) viable errors occurring during replication, and (3) mutations caused by environmental factors.

Plan and Prepare

Activate Prior Knowledge Have students think about the kinds of genetic variation in humans. **FIGURE 6.1** can be used as a starting point. **Ask,** What are some examples of genetic variation in humans? eye color, hair color and texture, baldness, skin color, anatomical differences between the sexes, facial features, height, weight, musculature Point out that humans are able to alter many of their physical traits, but doing so does not alter the genotypes for those traits or the genes that will be passed on to offspring.

Teach

Vocabulary

Academic Vocabulary The everyday usage of the word **random** often simply means "I'm not sure why that happened." In a scientific context, *random* is a word applied to an event in which all possible outcomes are equally likely. In some instances, what seems random to us is not really random at all.

▼ Teach *continued*

Take It Further

Crossing over is a precise process, with each chromatid usually breaking at the same point. If exchange were not so precise, one chromatid might lose genes and the other chromatid might gain genes. Certain places on the chromatids, called **hotspots,** are more likely to break than other places. Sister chromatids may also exchange chromosome segments. However, these exchanges are not likely to create new gene combinations.

Address Misconceptions

Common Misconception Sister chromatids are always identical.

Correcting the Misconception Point out that this is only true for mitotic division. Emphasize that in meiosis, sister chromatids are identical copies of each other before prophase I, but after this phase, the sister chromatids can differ if crossing over has taken place.

Answers

A Calculate Each egg and sperm has 16 possible chromosome combinations, so the total number of possible combinations would be $16 \times 16 = 256$.

B Synthesize One chromosome will be all purple, one all green; the other two will have a segment of the other color at the base.

CONNECT TO

EVOLUTION

As you will learn in the chapter **Principles of Evolution,** natural selection is a mechanism by which individuals that have inherited beneficial adaptations produce more offspring on average than do other individuals. The rabbit-eared bandicoot (below) has adaptations that enable it to survive and reproduce in regions of Australia.

Independent assortment and fertilization play key roles in creating and maintaining genetic diversity in all sexually reproducing organisms. However, the number of possible chromosome combinations varies by species. The probability that a bald eagle or a rabbit-eared bandicoot will inherit a specific allele is determined in the same way that it is for a pea plant.

Sexual reproduction creates unique combinations of genes. This results in organisms with unique phenotypes. The offspring of sexual reproduction have a mixture of both parents' traits. For example, rabbit-eared bandicoot offspring all share many traits for the things that make them bandicoots, but they may also differ in many ways. Some may be colored more like the mother, others more like the father. Some may dig deeper burrows or hunt more skillfully; others may in time produce more milk for their own offspring or have more litters. Having some of these traits may allow one bandicoot to reproduce in conditions where another bandicoot could not.

A Calculate **Fruit fly gametes each have four chromosomes, representing 2^4, or 16, possible chromosome combinations. How many chromosome combinations could result from fertilization between a fruit fly egg and a sperm cell?**

MAIN IDEA

Crossing over during meiosis increases genetic diversity.

It is clear that independent assortment creates a lot of variation within a species. Another process, called crossing over, occurs during meiosis and helps create even greater variation. **Crossing over** is the exchange of chromosome segments between homologous chromosomes during prophase I of meiosis I. At this stage, each chromosome has been duplicated, the sister chromatids are still connected to each other, and homologous chromosomes have paired with each other. When homologous chromosomes are in this position, some of the chromatids are very close to each other. Part of one chromatid from each chromosome breaks off and reattaches to the other chromosome, as shown in **FIGURE 6.2.** Crossing over happens any time a germ cell divides. In fact, it can occur many times within the same pair of homologous chromosomes.

FIGURE 6.2 Crossing Over

Crossing over exchanges segments of DNA between homologous chromosomes.

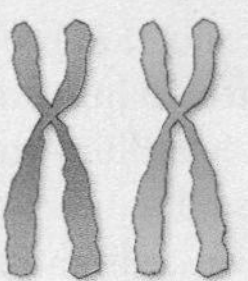

1. Two homologous chromosomes pair up with each other during prophase I in meiosis.

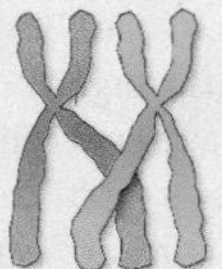

2. In this position, some chromatids are very close to each other and segments cross.

3. Some of these segments break off and reattach to the other homologous chromosome.

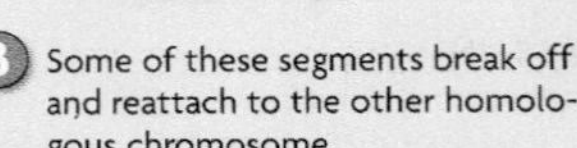

B Synthesize **Draw the four chromosomes that would result after the above chromosomes go through meiosis.**

Differentiated Instruction

ENGLISH LEARNERS

Have students address the question of how crossing over contributes to genetic diversity. Give individual students a chance to think and take notes about the question, telling them to pay special attention to **FIGURE 6.2.** Then have them pair up to compare ideas and prepare a final answer to share with the class.

Teacher Toolkit, Section C, Think-Pair-Share

Because crossing over results in new combinations of genes, it is also called recombination. The term *recombination* generally refers to any mixing of parental alleles, including recombination events.

Now that you know about crossing over, let's look again at some of Mendel's results and conclusions. As you know from his research, genes located on separate chromosomes assort independently. This independence is caused by the random assortment of chromosomes during meiosis. But you also know that a single chromosome can have hundreds of genes. What happens when two genes are both on the same chromosome? Will they display independent assortment as well? Or will they travel together as a unit?

The answer to these questions is, "It depends." Recall that each gene has its own locus, or place on a chromosome. As **FIGURE 6.3** shows, some genes on the same chromosome are close together; others are far apart. The farther apart two genes are located, the more likely they are to be separated when crossing over happens. Thus, genes located close together tend to be inherited together, which is called **genetic linkage.** Linked genes will be inherited in the same predicted ratios as would a single gene. In contrast, genes that are far apart are more likely to assort independently. For example, the alleles for flower and seed color are located on the same chromosome in pea plants, but they are not near each other. Because they are so far apart, Mendel observed independent assortment for these traits.

FIGURE 6.3 GENETIC LINKAGE

A and B are not linked to C and D because they are so far apart. Crossing over is likely to occur in the space between genes B and C, thereby separating A and B from C and D.

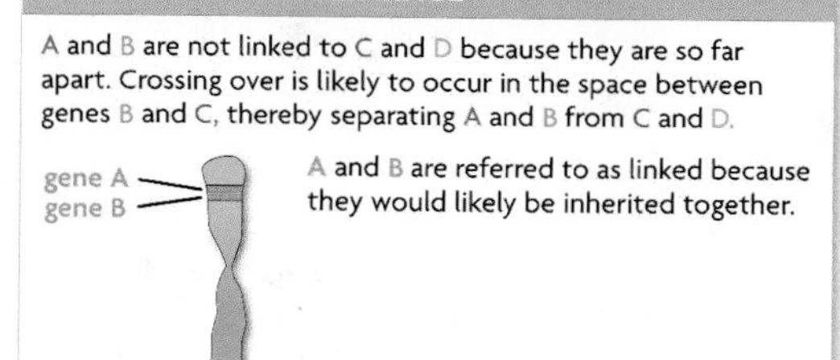
gene A
gene B
A and B are referred to as linked because they would likely be inherited together.
gene C
gene D
C and D are referred to as linked because they would likely be inherited together.

Genetic linkage has let scientists calculate the physical distance between two genes. By exploring relationships between many genes, scientists have been able to build a linkage, or genetic, map of many species.

A Predict **Suppose two genes are very close together on a chromosome. Are the genes likely to be separated by crossing over? Explain.**

WebQuest HMHScience.com GO ONLINE Selective Breeding

ONLINE Biology

HMHScience.com

Students can learn how dog breeders use Mendel's principles to enhance certain traits. See the WebQuest on selective breeding, available at **HMHScience.com**.

Take It Further

A **linkage map** can be prepared based on recombination frequencies. The distances between genes are called **map units,** with one map unit being defined as a recombination frequency of 1 percent. Creating such a map can help geneticists see and predict how certain genes are linked and passed on together. Students will learn more about this in Extending Mendelian Genetics.

Answers

A Predict The genes are not likely to be separated by crossing over. Genes that are close together tend to be inherited together.

6.6 Formative Assessment

SELF-CHECK Online HMHScience.com GO ONLINE

REVIEWING MAIN IDEAS

1. Briefly explain how sexual reproduction generates new allele combinations in offspring.
2. How does **crossing over** contribute to genetic diversity?

CRITICAL THINKING

3. **Infer** You know that you get half your DNA from your mom, half from your dad. Does this mean you got one-quarter of your DNA from each of your grandparents? Explain your reasoning.
4. **Synthesize** Suppose you know that two genes exist on the same chromosome. How could you determine if they are located close to each other?

CONNECT TO MITOSIS

5. Mitosis creates daughter cells that are genetically identical to the parent cell. If crossing over occurred between sister chromatids during mitosis, would it increase genetic diversity? Explain.

Assess and Reteach

Assess Use the Section Self-Check or Section Quiz, both available at **HMHScience.com**.

Reteach Have students draw a sequence diagram of meiosis, this time incorporating crossing over into the process. Refer them to **FIGURE 2.3**.

6.6 FORMATIVE ASSESSMENT

1. Each egg and sperm already have a mixture of chromosomes from both parents due to the independent assortment of chromosomes. Since any sperm could potentially fertilize any egg, the potential allele combinations are numerous even for simple organisms.
2. Crossing over makes new combinations of maternal and paternal genes. In this way, an egg or a sperm not only receives a unique combination of the maternal and paternal chromosomes, but those chromosomes themselves become a unique patchwork of maternal and paternal genes.
3. Not necessarily. The gametes that you inherited from each of your parents could have contained more chromosomes from one of their parents than the other.
4. Cross two organisms purebred for the two traits coded for by the genes. Then cross the F_1 generation. The more often the traits are inherited together, the closer the genes are on the chromosome.
5. No, sister chromatids are identical to each other, so an exchange of DNA segments would be meaningless.

GO ONLINE

Encourage students to go to **HMHScience.com** for a detailed review of each section, including visuals and vocabulary practice.

Online Student Resources, Vocabulary Practice Worksheet

CHAPTER 6

Summary

BIG IDEA In meiosis, genetic material from two parent organisms results in offspring with traits that follow a pattern of inheritance.

KEY CONCEPTS

6.1 Chromosomes and Meiosis

Gametes have half the number of chromosomes that body cells have. Your body cells have 23 pairs of homologous chromosomes, making 46 total chromosomes. Gametes have only 1 chromosome from each homologous pair—23 chromosomes in all.

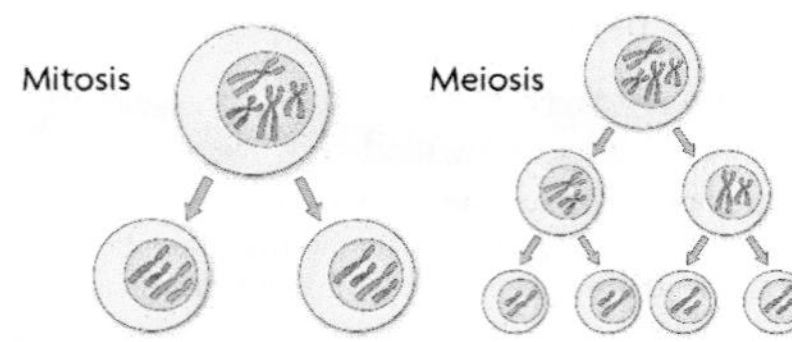

6.2 Process of Meiosis

During meiosis, diploid cells undergo two cell divisions that result in haploid cells. In meiosis I, homologous chromosomes pair up along the cell equator and are divided into separate cells. In meiosis II, sister chromatids are divided into separate cells, making a total of four haploid cells that are genetically unique.

6.3 Mendel and Heredity

Mendel's research showed that traits are inherited as discrete units. His large amount of data, control over breeding, use of purebred plants, and observation of "either-or" traits allowed him to see patterns in the inheritance of traits. He concluded that organisms inherit two copies of each gene and that organisms donate only one copy of each gene in their gametes.

6.4 Traits, Genes, and Alleles

Genes encode proteins that produce a diverse range of traits. Every diploid organism has two alleles for each gene: one from the mother, one from the father. These two alleles may be the same (homozygous) or different (heterozygous). One allele may be dominant over another.

6.5 Traits and Probability

The inheritance of traits follows the rules of probability. Punnett squares are a grid system for predicting all possible genotypes resulting from a cross. When Mendel performed two-trait crosses, he discovered that different traits appear to be inherited separately—the law of independent assortment. The patterns of inheritance that he observed can be predicted by using mathematical probabilities.

6.6 Meiosis and Genetic Variation

Independent assortment and crossing over during meiosis result in genetic diversity. Independent assortment produces unique combinations of parental chromosomes. Crossing over between homologous chromosomes creates a patchwork of genes from both parents. Genetic linkage describes genes that are close together and tend to be inherited as a unit.

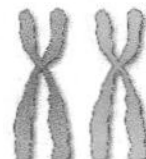

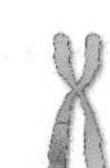

READING TOOLBOX SYNTHESIZE YOUR NOTES

"Y" Diagram Use a "Y" diagram to summarize what you know about meiosis I and meiosis II.

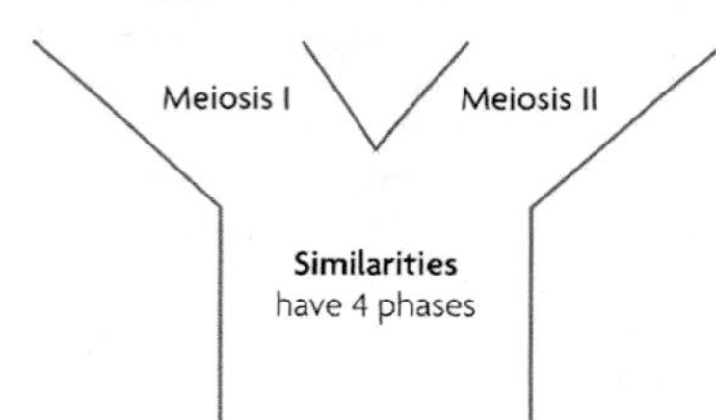

Cycle Diagram Fill in a cycle diagram like the one below to show the relationship between diploid and haploid cells.

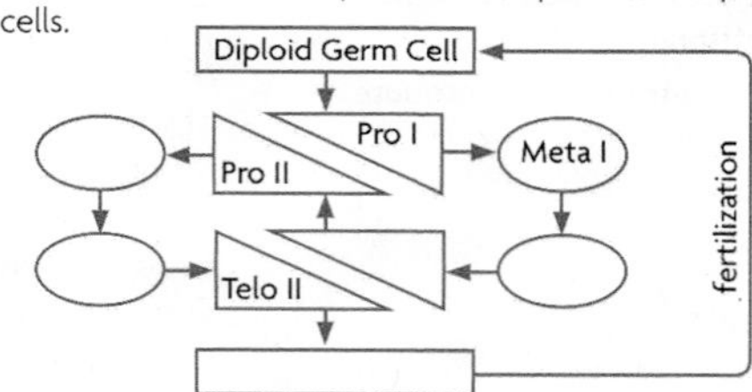

Reviewing Vocabulary

1. gene: could be a drawing of a chromosome, with a small segment indicated
2. fertilization: could be a drawing of a sperm burrowing into an egg
3. crossing over: could be a drawing of a pair of homologous chromosomes that are duplicated, lined up as in metaphase I of meiosis, with parts crossed, as in Figure 6.2.
4. genetic linkage: could be a drawing of a chromosome with two different genes indicated (or the loci for two different genes indicated)
5. haploid: could be a drawing of a gamete cell with only one set of chromosomes (not homologous pairs of chromosomes)
6. Meiosis is a reductive process that diminishes, or reduces, the amount of DNA. It begins with a diploid cell and ends with haploid cells.
7. Haploid cells have a single set of chromosomes, whereas diploid cells have a double set of chromosomes.
8. Homologous chromosomes have the same genes at each locus. *Homozygous* means that the two alleles at a locus are the same.
9. Both are crosses that Mendel used to study inheritance. A monohybrid cross focuses on only one trait; a dihybrid cross focuses on two traits.
10. Both are kinds of genotypes. Heterozygous genotypes have two different alleles of a gene, one on each chromosome of a homologous pair. Homozygous genotypes have two of the same alleles of a gene, one on each chromosome of a homologous pair.
11. Genotype refers to the underlying alleles, or genetic makeup; phenotype refers to how those alleles are expressed.

6 Review

INTERACTIVE Review
HMHScience.com
GO ONLINE
Review Games • Concept Map • Section Self-Checks

CHAPTER VOCABULARY

6.1 somatic cell, gamete, homologous chromosome, autosome, sex chromosome, sexual reproduction, fertilization, diploid, haploid, meiosis

6.2 gametogenesis, sperm, egg, polar body

6.3 trait, genetics, purebred, cross, law of segregation

6.4 gene, allele, homozygous, heterozygous, genome, genotype, phenotype, dominant, recessive

6.5 Punnett square, monohybrid cross, testcross, dihybrid cross, law of independent assortment, probability

6.6 crossing over, genetic linkage

Reviewing Vocabulary

Visualize Vocabulary

For each term below, use simple shapes, lines, or arrows to illustrate its meaning. Below each picture, write a short caption. Here's an example for the term *diploid*:

1. gene
2. fertilization
3. crossing over
4. genetic linkage
5. haploid

Diploid cells have two copies of each chromosome.

READING TOOLBOX GREEK WORD ORIGINS

6. The word *meiosis* comes from a Greek word meaning "to diminish," or make less. How does this word's origin relate to its meaning?
7. The word *haploid* comes from the Greek word *haplous*, which means "single." The word *diploid* comes from the Greek word *diplous*, which means "double." Explain how these two terms' meanings relate to their origins.
8. The Greek prefix *homo-* means "one and the same." How does this relate to the words *homologous* and *homozygous*?

Compare and Contrast

Describe one similarity and one difference between the two terms in each of the following pairs.

9. monohybrid cross, dihybrid cross
10. heterozygous, homozygous
11. genotype, phenotype

Reviewing MAIN IDEAS

12. Each of your cells has a set of chromosomes, including autosomes and sex chromosomes. Explain the main differences between these two types of chromosomes.
13. A fruit fly has diploid cells with 8 chromosomes. Explain how many chromosomes are in its haploid gametes.
14. Meiosis is a continuous process, but we can think of it as taking place in two stages, meiosis I and meiosis II. How do the products of meiosis I differ from those of meiosis II?
15. The foundation for our modern study of genetics began with Gregor Mendel, who studied pea plants. What were Mendel's two main conclusions about how traits are passed between generations?
16. How did Mendel's use of purebred plants—for example, purebred white- and purebred purple-flowered peas—contribute to his understanding of inheritance?
17. How does the homozygous condition differ from the heterozygous condition? In your answer, use the terms *gene*, *homologous chromosome*, and *allele*.
18. What does each of the following parts of a Punnett square represent: (a) the entries on each axis of the grid and (b) the entries in the four squares within the grid?
19. How did the results of Mendel's dihybrid crosses lead him to formulate the law of independent assortment?
20. How does crossing over during meiosis I increase genetic diversity?

Reviewing Main Ideas

12. Sex chromosomes directly control the development of sexual characteristics. Autosomes control the development of characteristics that are not directly sex related.
13. four chromosomes, because meiosis results in haploid gamete cells with only one set of chromosomes
14. Meiosis I separates homologous pairs of chromosomes and results in haploid cells with duplicated chromosomes. Meiosis II separates sister chromatids and results in haploid cells with chromosomes that are not duplicated.
15. Mendel concluded that traits are inherited from parents and that organisms receive two copies of hereditary units, now called genes, one from the mother and one from the father. The two copies segregate during gamete formation.
16. When Mendel crossed two different purebred lines, for example, purple-flowered and white-flowered peas, he saw that there were no white-flowered offspring, but that if F_1 plants were crossed, the white flowers reappeared. This showed that the white flower trait had not disappeared; it was just masked. Additionally, this suggested that offspring received two forms of each gene, one from each parent.
17. The homozygous condition occurs when an organism has two of the same alleles for a particular gene—one on each chromosome of a homologous pair—for example, an allele for white flower color at the locus for the flower color gene on the maternal chromosome, and also an allele for white color at the flower color locus on the paternal chromosome. The heterozygous condition occurs when there are two different alleles of a gene. For example, one chromosome has the purple allele, and its homologous chromosome has the white allele.
18. (a) the possible gamete genotypes for each parent; (b) the possible offspring genotypes
19. Mendel learned from his dihybrid crosses that traits are inherited independently of each other. For example, a white-flowered pea plant could be either short or tall, and a purple-flowered pea plant also could be either short or tall. Flower color and height were not inherited together.
20. Chromatids from homologous chromosomes (maternal and paternal chromosomes) exchange segments during meiosis I, which alters and recombines the genetic makeup of the chromosomes.

CHAPTER REVIEW

Critical Thinking

21. No, because somatic cells do not turn into gametes. Mutations in germ cells can affect offspring.
22. The chromosome number of the offspring would double each generation. In the first generation, the two gametes with 4 chromosomes would join to make an organism with 8 chromosomes. This organism would make 8-chromosome gametes, which would join to make a 16-chromosome organism, and so on.
23. Before duplication, the pair of homologous chromosomes should be shown as two single chromosomes of the same size and shape. Although the homologous chromosomes carry the same genes, they may have different alleles for those genes. After duplication, each homologous chromosome consists of two identical sister chromatids held together by a centromere.
24. Mendel's law of independent assortment does not apply to two genes that are close together on the same chromosome, because they tend to be linked, or inherited together. Genes that are far apart on a chromosome are more likely to assort independently, because crossing over occurs frequently between them.
25. Smooth petals are likely dominant over wrinkled, and the parents were likely both heterozygous. If smooth = *S* and wrinkled = *s*, the parents were *Ss*.
26. The law of independent assortment does not apply, because the two genes are on the same chromosome. The genes move together, not independently. In other words, the alleles for antenna shape and antenna color are inherited together from the same parent.

Critical Thinking

21. Hypothesize Could a mutation in one of an individual's somatic cells be passed on to the individual's offspring? Explain your answer.

22. Predict Consider a species with a 2*n*, or diploid, chromosome number of 4. If gametes were formed by mitosis, rather than meiosis, what would happen to the chromosome number of the offspring of these organisms over generations? Explain.

23. Contrast Draw a pair of homologous chromosomes before and after duplication. Use your drawings to explain how homologous chromosomes and sister chromatids differ.

24. Synthesize Mendel's law of independent assortment states that allele pairs separate independently of each other during meiosis. How does this law relate to crossing over and genetic linkage?

25. Infer Imagine that you are studying the trait of flower petal shape in a species of plant. Petal shape is determined by a single gene with two alleles. You make a cross of two plants with unknown genotypes, both with smooth petals, and get the following F_1 offspring phenotypes: 23 wrinkled and 77 smooth. What conclusions can you draw about the inheritance of this trait? In your answer, include the probable genotypes of each parent, and indicate which allele is likely dominant.

26. Analyze In a particular species of butterfly, the genes for two different traits, antenna shape and antenna color, are located on the same chromosome. As a result, crosses between these butterflies do not obey one of Mendel's laws. Which law does not apply, and why?

Interpreting Visuals

The drawing to the right shows a cell at a certain point during meiosis. Use the drawing to answer the next two questions.

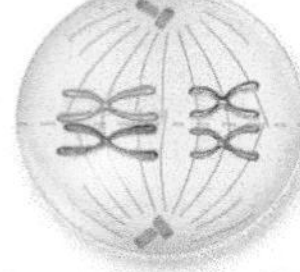

27. Identify What stage of meiosis is shown above? Defend your answer.

28. Apply Is the above cell diploid or haploid? Explain.

Analyzing Data Interpret a Bar Graph

During meiosis, pairs of homologous chromosomes separate independently of the others, and gametes receive one of the two chromosomes from each pair. The number of possible chromosome combinations for a species is 2^n, where n = the number of homologous pairs. The graph below shows the number of possible chromosome combinations for a variety of species. Use it to answer the next two questions.

POSSIBLE CHROMOSOME COMBINATIONS

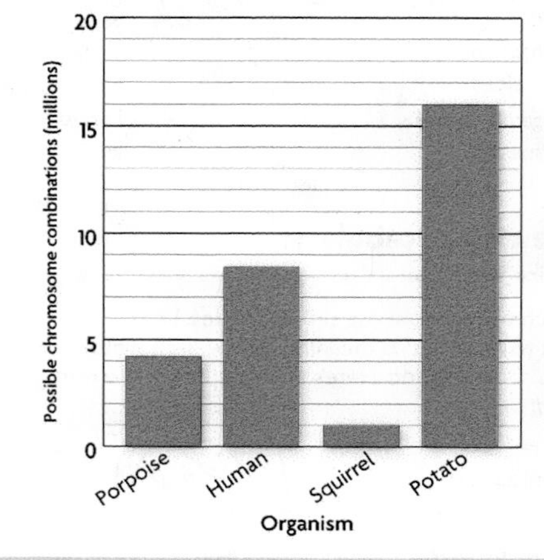

Source: Rutgers University

29. Summarize List the organisms in the above graph, in order, from least to most possible chromosome combinations.

30. Infer What can you infer from the graph about the number of homologous chromosomes in squirrels compared with potatoes?

Making Connections

31. Write a Diary Entry Put yourself in Mendel's shoes. It is the mid-1800s. DNA and genes have not been identified, and the mechanisms of heritability are not understood. Write a diary entry (or letter) about one of Mendel's crosses from his perspective. Describe the results of the cross and ideas that may have come from the results.

32. Synthesize Look again at the picture of the egg and sperm cells on the chapter opener. Each of these sperm cells is genetically unique. What are the sources of variation that make each one different from the others?

Interpreting Visuals

27. Metaphase I, pairs of homologous chromosomes, each consisting of two sister chromatids, are lined up together at the equator.
28. The cell is still diploid because it has two sets of chromosomes.

Analyzing Data

29. squirrel, porpoise, human, potato
30. Squirrels have fewer homologous chromosomes. (Students may correctly determine that the potato has 24 (2^{24} = ~16 million) and the squirrel has 20 (2^{20} = ~1 million) chromosomes.

188 Unit 3: Genetics

Standards-Based Assessment

Record your answers on a separate piece of paper.

MULTIPLE CHOICE

1 Researchers crossed two types of mice together, type A and type B. In the resulting offspring, half of the DNA for specifying traits comes from type A and half comes from type B. Why?

A X-inactivation occurs with a 50/50 chance in each cell.

B The offspring get their DNA from the sperm and their cytoplasm from the egg.

C Each parent contributes one set of chromosomes to each offspring.

D The offspring make binary divisions during development.

2 Unlike cells that divide by mitosis, the gametes formed during meiosis undergo two cell divisions. What is the significance of this second cell division to sexual reproduction?

A It ensures that offspring develop from cells that are identical to the parent cell.

B It ensures that all gametes formed are genetically identical to each other.

C It reduces the number of chromosomes in each resulting gamete by half.

D It provides a fertilized egg with twice as many chromosomes as were present in the parent organisms.

3

A mutation occurs in a gene on chromosome 3, which is shown above. This mutation could be passed along to offspring if it occurs —

A in any cell except sex cells

B after fertilization but before the zygote develops

C during development of the zygote

D in a sex cell that undergoes fertilization

4 In peas, the gene for green pod color (*G*) is dominant to the gene for yellow pod color (*g*). The gene for round shaped peas (*R*) is dominant to wrinkled-shaped peas (*r*). If a plant that is homozygous dominant for both genes is crossed with a plant that is heterozygous for both genes, what is the probability that the offspring will have yellow pods and round peas?

A 0

B ¼

C ½

D ¾

THINK THROUGH THE QUESTION

If necessary, take the time to draw out a Punnett square to answer this question. The *Gg* and *Rr* genotypes are the same as the *gG* and *rR* genotypes.

5

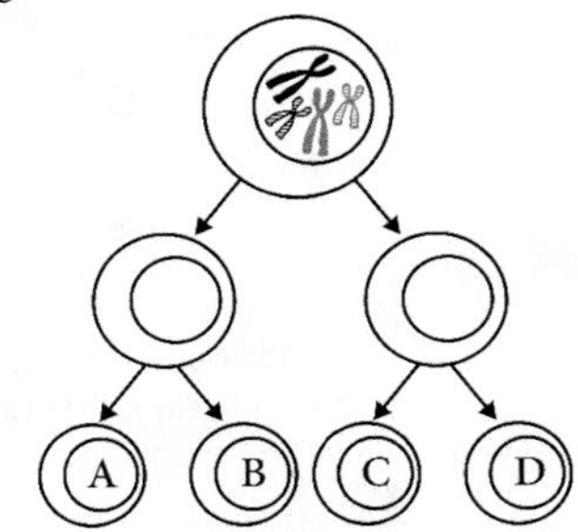

If the process of meiosis shown here proceeds normally, how many chromosomes will cells A, B, C, and D have?

A 2 each

B 4 each

C 6 each

D 8 each

Standards-Based Assessment

The Standards-Based Assessment questions will help students prepare for their final examination in the course. If you wish to give students practice in coding their answers, look for the Standards-Based Assessment Answer Sheet at **HMHScience.com**. To give students practice under timed testing conditions, allow them five minutes per question.

Question	Answer	Depth of Knowledge	Cognitive Complexity
1	C	I	L
2	C	II	M
3	D	II	L
4	A	IV	H
5	A	II	M

KEY

Depth of Knowledge		Cognitive Complexity	
I	Recall	L	Low
II	Skill/Concept	M	Moderate
III	Strategic Thinking	H	High
IV	Extended Thinking		

Making Connections

31. Students' responses should summarize the particular monohybrid or dihybrid cross selected. Students should then explain, from Mendel's perspective, what possible conclusions could be made based on the results of the cross.

32. The independent assortment and crossing over of chromosomes during meiosis result in unique gametes, such as sperm.

CHAPTER 7

Instruction and Intervention Support

Extending Mendelian Genetics

① Core Instruction

The **Core Instruction** resources below can be used for all students. Core instruction should be followed by ongoing assessment to determine which students need further help.

Available in both English and Spanish

Available Online

Section	Instruction	PRINT	ONLINE	Labs
7.1	Textbook **Chromosomes and Phenotype**	■	●	**QuickLab** Sex-Linked Inheritance
	PowerPresentation and Notes 7.1		●	
7.2	Textbook **Complex Patterns of Inheritance**	■	●	Codominance Incomplete Dominance **Video Lab** Plant Genetics
	PowerPresentation and Notes 7.2		●	
7.3	Textbook **Gene Linkage and Mapping**	■	●	Examining Banding Patterns in Polytene Chromosomes (Challenge Lab)
	Teaching Visuals Interpreting Pedigree Charts		●	
	PowerPresentation and Notes 7.3		●	
7.4	Textbook **Human Genetics and Pedigrees**	■	●	Pedigree Analysis Human Heredity
	Animated Biology Human Chromosomes		●	
	Teaching Visuals Tracing Autosomal Genes (Fig. 4.3), Tracing Sex-Linked Genes (Fig. 4.3)		●	
	PowerPresentation and Notes 7.4		●	

Additional online resources available for this chapter include **Interactive Whiteboard resources.**

2 Support and Intervention

Support and Intervention resources are useful for students who need targeted help beyond the Core Instruction

Resources	PRINT	ONLINE
Assess and Reteach (TE wrap)	■	⊙
Concept Map		⊙
Interactive Reader	■	⊙
Interactive Review Games		⊙
Section Self-Checks		⊙
Study Guide B		⊙
Virtual Investigation Experiments and Models of Heredity		⊙
Vocabulary Practice Worksheets		⊙

3 Specialized Support

Students who need more intensive personalized intervention benefit from **Specialized Support** resources.

Resources	PRINT	ONLINE
Chapter Audio Files		⊙
Differentiated Instruction Inclusion, Below Level, and English Learners (TE wrap)	■	⊙
ELL Strategies	■	⊙
Modified Lesson Plans for English Learners		⊙
Reinforcement Worksheets		⊙
Study Guide A		⊙

Extension and Assessment

Enrichment and Challenge

Resources	PRINT	ONLINE
Active Reading Worksheets		⊙
Data Analysis Practice Worksheet		⊙
Differentiated Instruction Pre-AP (TE wrap)	■	⊙
Pre-AP Activity Incomplete Dominance in Four O'Clocks		⊙
Smart Grapher Activity		⊙
The Inside Story and **Take It Further** (TE wrap)	■	⊙
Unit Project		⊙
WebLinks		⊙
WebQuest Genetic Heritage (7.4)		⊙

Assessment

Resources	PRINT	ONLINE
Alternative Assessment		⊙
Chapter Tests A and B		⊙
Diagnostic Test		⊙
ExamView Banks		⊙
Extended Response Test		⊙
Online Assessment System		⊙
Section Quizzes		⊙
Standards-Based Assessment	■	⊙

CHAPTER 7

Chapter Overview

- **Section 1** provides coverage of autosomal genes, which affect phenotype and sex-linked traits.
- **Section 2** explains the non-Mendelian patterns of inheritance.
- **Section 3** describes the discovery of gene linkage and how linkage maps can be used to estimate distances between genes.
- **Section 4** explains inheritance patterns in humans and describes how pedigrees and chromosome mapping are used in genetics.

▼ Focus and Motivate

Why are there so many variations among people?

Have students think back to the work of Mendel. **Ask,** What were some of the traits that Mendel studied in pea plants? pea shape and color, pod shape and color, plant height, flower color and position **Ask,** How many varieties did each trait have? two; for example, tall or short plants Remind students that Mendel specifically chose those traits because they had either-or characteristics and no intermediate forms.

Have students examine the people in the photos. **Ask,** Do you think hair color is an either-or characteristic? No, there are more than two hair colors shown. **Ask,** What other observable traits show intermediate forms? skin and eye color Tell students that some traits, such as skin, hair, and eye color, are determined by many genes, allowing for greater variation.

BIOZINE
HMHScience.com

Students can access BioZine at **HMHScience.com** to learn about the variety of careers open to biologists.

CHAPTER 7

Extending Mendelian Genetics

BIG IDEA Mendel's laws of inheritance do not account for the expression of all traits, which may be influenced by the number of genes involved, linkages with other genes, or the environment in which the organism lives.

ONLINE BIOLOGY HMHScience.com

ONLINE Labs
- **QuickLab** Sex-Linked Inheritance
- Codominance
- Pedigree Analysis
- Incomplete Dominance
- Human Heredity
- Examining Banding Patterns in Polytene Chromosomes
- **Video Lab** Plant Genetics

Teacher Demo

Eye Opener **To give students a personal example of non-Mendelian genetics, demonstrate variation in student height.**

Prepare Reserve a large open area, such as a gym or hallway, for this demonstration.

Introduce Explain to students that most human phenotypes are not directly observable as following Mendel's principles. One of these traits is height. Tell students that they are going to make a living histogram showing variation in height in the class.

Demonstrate Have students arrange themselves in order according to their height, with the shortest student on the left and the tallest on the right. Each height forms a column, and students of the same height should stand one behind the other in the column. A student who is unable to stand can help to organize the others in the correct order. When all students have been arranged, number the columns or measure the actual heights of students. Then record the number of students in each column.

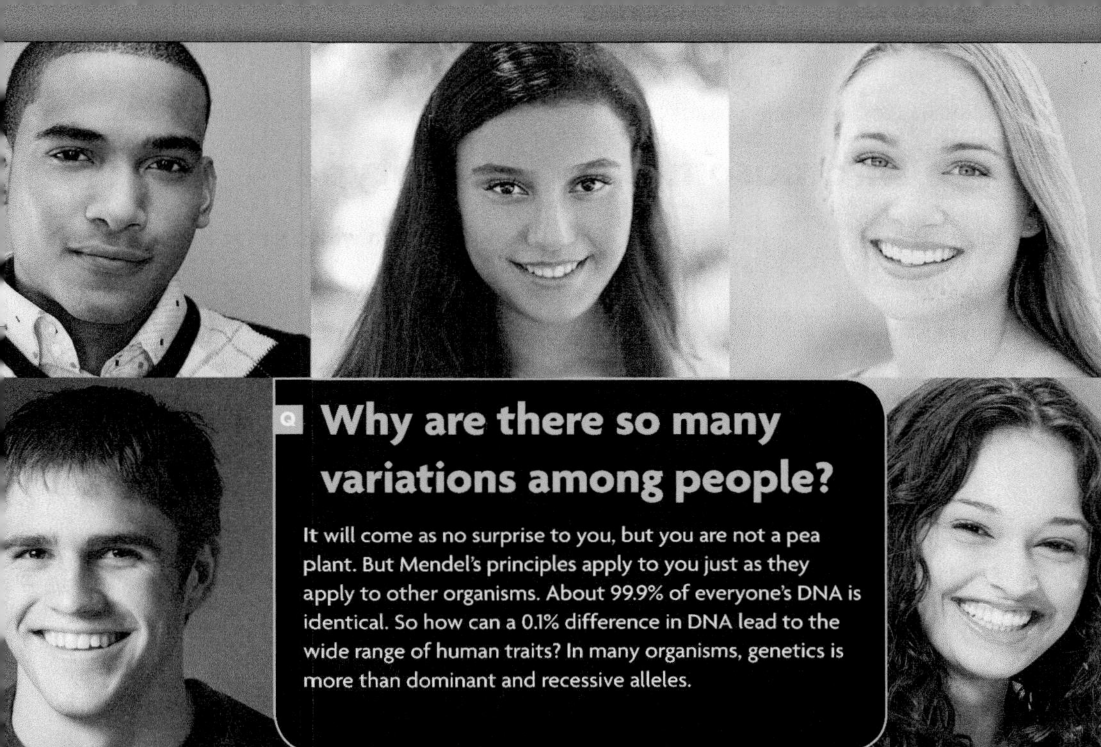

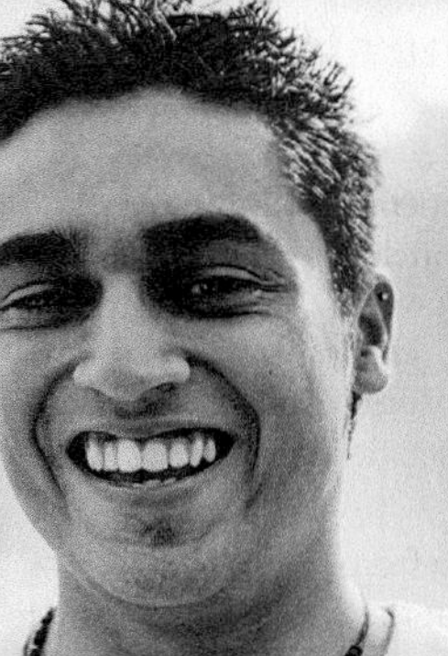

Why are there so many variations among people?

It will come as no surprise to you, but you are not a pea plant. But Mendel's principles apply to you just as they apply to other organisms. About 99.9% of everyone's DNA is identical. So how can a 0.1% difference in DNA lead to the wide range of human traits? In many organisms, genetics is more than dominant and recessive alleles.

READING TOOLBOX **This reading tool can help you learn the material in the following pages.**

USING LANGUAGE

Analogies An analogy question asks you to analyze the relationship between two words in one pair and to identify a second pair of words that have the same relationship. Colons are used to express the analogy for this type of question. For example, the analogy "up is to down as top is to bottom" is written "up : down :: top : bottom." In this example, the relationship between the words in each pair is the same.

YOUR TURN

Use information in the chapter to complete this analogy.

allele : gene :: trait: __________

(Hint: Finding out how alleles and genes are related will help you figure out which word to use to fill in the blank.)

Once back in the classroom, draw a histogram on the board with height or column number labeled on the *x*-axis and number of students on the *y*-axis. The graph will probably be bell-shaped.

Discuss Discuss the results. **Ask**

- How is the distribution of height that you observed different from that of Mendelian inheritance? There is a wide range of phenotypes (heights), not just two.
- What would the results have been if human height were inherited by an either-or gene according to Mendel's principles? Only two heights would have been observed in the class.

Explain that human height is influenced by several genes that, in turn, can be affected by the environment. **Ask,** What relationship would you expect between the amount of variation in height and the number of genes involved? The more genes involved, the greater the variability. Point out that most human traits are controlled by more than one gene. Students will learn about different kinds of gene interactions in this chapter.

Activate Prior Knowledge

Tell students that Mendel's laws of inheritance do not account for the expression of all traits. For example, if you cross a red-flowered snapdragon with a white one, the next generation of plants will have pink flowers. Direct students' attention to the chapter title and the photographs. **Ask,** When you look at the photos, why do you think **Mendelian genetics** needs to be extended? It doesn't explain the variation in hair, eye, and skin color.

Preview Vocabulary

Academic Vocabulary Two words commonly used in science are *law* and *principle.* Students may think of them as being synonymous.

law, a statement of what occurs under certain conditions

principle, a basic rule or quality that explains how something works

Use this chapter as a way to help students appreciate the difference. While patterns of inheritance must conform to the principles of genetics, Mendel's laws do not apply in all circumstances, which leads to "non-Mendelian" genetics.

English Learners Students will see the words *map* and *mapping* applied to genes and chromosomes in this chapter. Typically maps involve a two-dimensional coordinate system applied to a surface area. Tell students that chromosome maps are linear and indicate where along a chromosome a gene can be found.

Integrating Chemistry

The color of a baby's eyes at birth does not necessarily represent their true color. Coloration is due to the pigment melanin: the more melanin present, the darker the eyes. Many newborns with blue or gray eyes will develop darker coloration as their bodies begin to produce melanin, usually within the first six months.

Answers

characteristic

▼ Plan and Prepare

Activate Prior Knowledge Hold up a pair of dice. **Ask,** If each die only had one number, how many different combinations could you roll? 1 Have students imagine other possible combinations, not counting a number reversal such as 2/1 for 1/2. **Ask,** How many combinations are possible with two different numbers on each die? 3 with 6? 21 Compare the increasing number of combinations to phenotype variations that can occur when multiple alleles are involved in determining traits.

▼ Teach

Take It Further

Mendel did not study sex-linked genes. In fact, pea plants do not have **sex chromosomes.** Only certain plant species that have male and female sex organs on separate plants have sex cells, a characteristic called **dioecious.** Most flowering plants have both male and female parts. Thus, most plants are **hermaphroditic,** or of both sexes.

7.1 Chromosomes and Phenotype

VOCABULARY

carrier
sex-linked gene
X chromosome inactivation

KEY CONCEPT **The chromosomes on which genes are located can affect the expression of traits.**

MAIN IDEAS

- Two copies of each autosomal gene affect phenotype.
- Males and females can differ in sex-linked traits.

Connect to Your World

The next time you are in a crowd of people, take a moment to look at the variety of traits around you. Hair color and texture, eye color and shape, height, and weight are all influenced by genetics. Can dominant and recessive alleles of one gene produce so many subtle differences in any of those traits? In most cases, the answer is no. But the dominant and recessive relationship among alleles is a good place to start when learning about the complexities of genetics.

MAIN IDEA

Two copies of each autosomal gene affect phenotype.

You have already learned how some genetic traits depend on dominant and recessive alleles. But many factors affect phenotype, including the specific chromosome upon which a gene is located. Gene expression is often related to whether a gene is located on an autosome or on a sex chromosome. Recall that sex chromosomes determine an organism's sex. Autosomes are all of the other chromosomes, and they do not play a direct role in sex determination.

You also know that sexually reproducing organisms have two of each chromosome. Each pair consists of one chromosome from each of two parents. Both chromosomes have the same genes, but the chromosomes might have different alleles for those genes. And, as Mendel observed, different alleles can produce different phenotypes, such as white flowers or purple flowers.

All of the traits that Mendel studied are determined by genes on autosomes. In fact, most traits in sexually reproducing organisms, including humans, are the result of autosomal genes. Look at **FIGURE 1.1.** Is your hair curly or straight? What about your parents' hair? The genes that affect your hair texture—curly hair or straight hair—are autosomal genes.

Many human genetic disorders are also caused by autosomal genes. The chance of a person having one of these disorders can be predicted, just as Mendel could predict the phenotypes that would appear in his pea plants. Why? Because there are two copies of each gene on autosomes—one on each homologous chromosome—and each copy can influence phenotype.

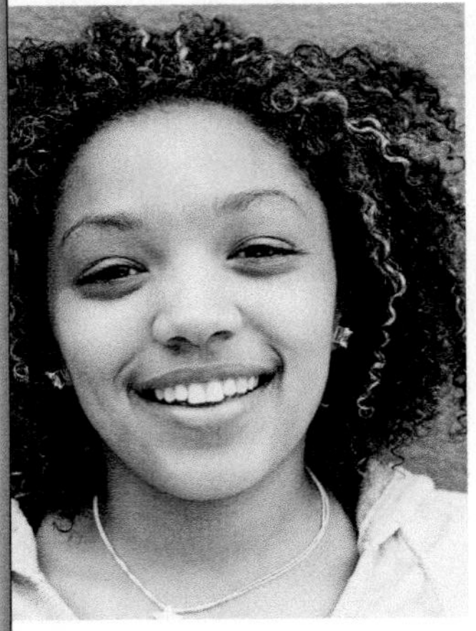

FIGURE 1.1 Hair texture is just one example of a trait that is controlled by autosomal genes.

Differentiated Instruction

ENGLISH LEARNERS

Have students recall the following review terms: *dominant, recessive, allele, gene,* and *trait.* Have small groups of students do a word splash activity that includes these review terms, the new section vocabulary, and the terms *phenotype* and *Punnett square.* Show the words as a cluster on the board. Have students skim the section, work together to arrange the vocabulary in categories, and then explain their choices.

Teacher Toolkit, Section D, Word Splash

BELOW LEVEL

Work with students to prepare a cluster diagram that relates review vocabulary (*dominant, recessive, allele, gene,* and *trait*) to the new vocabulary in the section.

Teacher Toolkit, Section C, Cluster Diagram

Disorders Caused by Recessive Alleles

Some human genetic disorders are caused by recessive alleles on autosomes. Two copies of the recessive allele must be present for a person to have the disorder. These disorders often appear in offspring of parents who are both heterozygotes. That is, each parent has one dominant, "normal" allele that masks the one disease-causing recessive allele.

For example, cystic fibrosis is a severe recessive disorder that mainly affects the sweat glands and the mucus glands. A person who is homozygous for the recessive allele will have the disease. Someone who is heterozygous for the alleles will not have the disease but is a carrier. A **carrier** does not show disease symptoms but can pass on the disease-causing allele to offspring. In this way, alleles that are lethal, or deadly, in a homozygous recessive individual can remain in a population's gene pool. This inheritance pattern is shown in **FIGURE 1.2.**

FIGURE 1.2 AUTOSOME INHERITANCE

Some genetic disorders, such as cystic fibrosis, are inherited according to Mendel's principles.

heterozygous parent (*Cc*), carrier	*C*	*c*
C	*CC* homozygous dominant	*Cc* heterozygous, carrier
c	*Cc* heterozygous, carrier	*cc* homozygous recessive, affected

heterozygous parent (*Cc*), carrier

C = Normal allele (dominant)
c = Cystic fibrosis allele (recessive)

Disorders Caused by Dominant Alleles

Dominant genetic disorders are far less common than recessive disorders. One example is Huntington's disease. Huntington's disease damages the nervous system and usually appears during adulthood. Because the disease is caused by a dominant allele, there is a 50% chance that a child will have it even if only one parent has one of the alleles. If both parents are heterozygous for the disease, there is a 75% chance that any of their children will inherit the disease. Because Huntington's disease strikes later in life, a person with the allele can have children before the disease appears. In that way, the allele is passed on in the population even though the disease is fatal.

A Connect **How are Mendel's observations related to genes on autosomes?**

MAIN IDEA

Males and females can differ in sex-linked traits.

Mendel figured out much about heredity, but he did not know about chromosomes. As it turns out, he only studied traits produced by genes on autosomes. Now we know about sex chromosomes, and we know that the expression of genes on the sex chromosomes differs from the expression of autosomal genes.

Sex-Linked Genes

Genes that are located on the sex chromosomes are called **sex-linked genes.** Recall that many species have specialized sex chromosomes called the X and Y chromosomes. In mammals and some other animals, individuals with two X chromosomes—an XX genotype—are female. Individuals with one X and one Y—an XY genotype—are male. As **FIGURE 1.3** shows, a female can pass on only an X chromosome to offspring, but a male can pass on an X or a Y chromosome.

FIGURE 1.3 SEX CHROMOSOME INHERITANCE

The gametes from an XY male determine the sex of the offspring.

female parent (XX)	X	X
X	XX female	XX female
Y	XY male	XY male

male parent (XY)

INCLUSION

To help students who are visually impaired work with Punnett squares, glue a yarn outline of a blank Punnett square to a piece of cardboard. Cut out letters from sandpaper to represent alleles or X and Y chromosomes.

TEACH FROM VISUALS

FIGURE 1.2 Have students work through the Punnett square. Review the definitions of *homozygous* and *heterozygous*.

Ask

- Is a carrier homozygous or heterozygous? heterozygous
- What percentage of the offspring is expected to be a carrier? 50 percent
- Is it possible for a *CC* individual to have offspring with cystic fibrosis? No, offspring must inherit two recessive alleles, one from each parent. A *CC* parent has no recessive allele.

History of Science

George Huntington, an American physician, first documented Huntington's disease in 1872. At the time, he called it Huntington's chorea. This name was taken from the Greek word *chorea,* meaning "dance." Individuals with Huntington's disease often had involuntary, erratic movements suggestive of a dance. After 1963, the disorder became known as **Huntington's disease** in order to represent all forms of the disorder.

The dominant allele that causes Huntington's disease was brought to the United States in 1630 by three men whose families had been persecuted for witchcraft in England because of their strange behavior and mental disturbances. At that time, these symptoms were believed to be caused by consorting with the devil.

Answers

A **Connect** The traits Mendel studied were due to the expression of two copies of autosomal genes.

▼ Teach *continued*

QUICKLAB

Time 20 minutes TEACHER TESTED

Purpose Model the inheritance of a sex-linked trait.

LAB MANAGEMENT

- Give each group an index card with a different monohybrid cross to model so that all possibilities are covered.
- Explain the notation used for sex-linked genes: sex chromosome is shown as a capital *X* or *Y*; allele is shown as a superscript.
- Students should record both the sex and the genotype of each offspring.

EXPECTED RESULTS

After 50 tosses, calculated frequencies should approach those listed below:

- $X^AX^a \times X^AY$: 25% homozygous dominant females, 25% carrier females, 25% recessive males, 25% males with dominant allele
- $X^AX^A \times X^aY$: 50% carrier females, 50% males with dominant allele
- $X^aX^a \times X^AY$: 50% carrier females, 50% recessive males
- $X^AX^a \times X^aY$: 25% recessive females, 25% carrier females, 25% recessive males, 25% dominant males
- $X^aX^a \times X^aY$: 50% recessive females, 50% recessive males
- $X^AX^A \times X^AY$: 50% homozygous dominant females, 50% males with dominant allele

Answers

Analyze and Conclude

1. Answers will depend on the cross, but should follow the expected results. Females are recessive only if they inherit two recessive alleles; males are recessive if they inherit one.
2. Results should be close to those predicted by the Punnett squares.

READING TOOLBOX

TAKING NOTES

Use a two-column chart to compare and contrast the expression of autosomal and sex-linked genes.

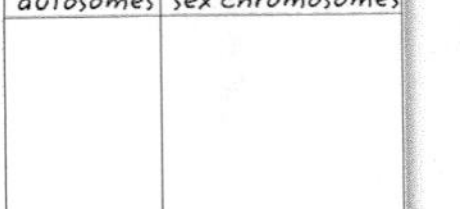

Genes on the Y chromosome are responsible for the development of male offspring, but the X chromosome actually has much more influence over phenotype. The X chromosome has many genes that affect many traits. Scientists hypothesize that the Y chromosome may have genes for more than sex determination, but there is little evidence to support this idea.

In many organisms, including humans, the Y chromosome is much smaller and has many fewer genes than the X chromosome. Evidence suggests that over millions of years of evolution, the joining of the X and Y chromosomes during meiosis has resulted in segments of the Y chromosome being transferred to the X. You will read more about specific sex-linked genes and their locations on the human X and Y chromosomes in Section 4.

Expression of Sex-Linked Genes

Because the X and Y chromosomes have different genes, sex-linked genes have a pattern of expression that is different from autosomal genes. Remember, two copies of an autosomal gene affect a trait. What happens when there is only one copy of a gene, as is the case in an XY male? Because males have only one copy of each type of sex chromosome, they express all of the alleles on both chromosomes. In males, there are no second copies of sex-linked genes to mask the effects of another allele. This means that even if all of the alleles of sex-linked genes in a male are recessive, they will be expressed.

QUICKLAB PREDICTING

Sex-Linked Inheritance

The relationship between genotype and phenotype in sex-linked genes differs from that in autosomal genes. A female must have two recessive alleles of a sex-linked gene to express a recessive sex-linked trait. Just one recessive allele is needed for the same trait to be expressed in a male. In this lab, you will model the inheritance pattern of sex-linked genes.

PROBLEM How does probability explain sex-linked inheritance?

PROCEDURE

1. Use the tape and marker to label two coins with the genetic cross shown on your group's index card. One coin represents the egg cell, and the other coin represents the sperm cell.
2. Flip the two coins and record the genotype of the "offspring."
3. Repeat Step 2 until you have modeled 50 genetic crosses. Make a data table to record each genetic cross that you model.
4. Calculate the genotype and phenotype probabilities for both males and females. Calculate the frequency of male offspring and female offspring.

MATERIALS

- 2 coins
- masking tape
- marker
- index card with genetic cross

ANALYZE AND CONCLUDE

1. **Analyze** Do all of the females from the genetic cross show the recessive trait? Do all of the males show the recessive trait? Why or why not?
2. **Apply** Make a Punnett square that shows the genetic cross. Do the results from your Punnett square agree with those from your experiment? Why or why not?

Differentiated Instruction

PRE-AP

Have students compare the inheritance of a gene on an autosome with the inheritance of a gene on each kind of sex chromosome. Have them consider these questions:

- How is a male offspring's phenotype affected if he inherits a recessive autosomal allele? a recessive sex-linked allele?
- How is autosomal and sex-linked inheritance similar in heterozygous female offspring?

Teacher Toolkit, Section C, Compare/Contrast Chart

TEACH WITH TECHNOLOGY

If students have access to a spreadsheet program, they can use it to record and organize their coin-toss data and do their calculations for the QuickLab. Students can also make a bar graph using different colors to show male and female offspring of each genotype.

FIGURE 1.4 The female calico cats have two X chromosomes with different alleles for fur color. Both alleles are expressed in a random pattern. The male cat has only one X chromosome, and its allele for fur color is expressed across the entire body.

X^O = Orange fur allele
X^o = Black fur allele

In mammals, the expression of sex-linked genes in females is also different from the way in which genes on other chromosomes are expressed. In each cell of female mammals, one of the two X chromosomes is randomly "turned off" by a process called **X chromosome inactivation.** Because of X chromosome inactivation, females are a patchwork of two types of cells—one type with an active X chromosome that came from the mother, and a second type with an active X chromosome that came from the father.

Colorful examples of X chromosome inactivation are seen in female tortoiseshell cats and female calico cats. The female calico cats shown in **FIGURE 1.4** have white fur, as well as alleles for black or orange fur on their X chromosomes. Those alleles are expressed randomly in cells across the cat's body. As a result, its coat is a mixture of color splotches. It is truly a patchwork of cells. Because male calico cats only have one X chromosome, they have white fur and one sex-linked gene for either orange or black fur.

Infer **Why are males more likely than females to have sex-linked genetic disorders?**

CONNECT TO

MITOSIS

Recall from the chapter **Cell Growth and Division** that DNA coils to form chromosomes. In XX females, one of the two X chromosomes in each cell is "inactivated" by becoming even more tightly coiled.

SELF-CHECK Online
HMHScience.com
GO ONLINE

7.1 Formative Assessment

REVIEWING MAIN IDEAS

1. How are autosomal traits, including recessive genetic disorders that are carried in a population, related to Mendel's observations of heredity?
2. Describe how **sex-linked genes** are expressed differently in males and in females.

CRITICAL THINKING

3. **Apply** How might a scientist determine whether a trait is sex-linked by observing the offspring of several genetic crosses?
4. **Compare and Contrast** How is the expression of sex-linked genes both similar to and different from the expression of autosomal genes?

CONNECT TO

MEIOSIS

5. Scientists hypothesize that over millions of years, the Y chromosome has lost genes to the X chromosome. During what stages of meiosis might the Y chromosome have transferred genes to the X chromosome? Explain.

7.1 FORMATIVE ASSESSMENT

1. Two copies of autosomal genes affect phenotype, as observed in all of Mendel's crosses.
2. In males, all sex-linked genes are expressed. In females, two copies of genes on the X chromosomes affect phenotype, although one X in each cell is randomly inactivated.
3. If more males than females have a particular phenotype, the trait is probably sex-linked.
4. In males, all sex-linked genes are expressed because there is only one copy of each sex-linked gene. In females, sex-linked genes are expressed similarly to autosomal genes in terms of dominance and recessiveness.
5. prophase of meiosis I, because that is when homologous chromosomes pair and crossovers occur

Take It Further

Tell students that the size of the colored splotches in female **calico cats** is determined by the period of time in embryonic development that the X chromosome is inactivated. If inactivation occurs early in development, more skin cells with the expressed color will be formed, and the splotch will be large. If inactivation occurs later in development, most of the skin cells will have already been formed with white fur, and the colored splotch will be small.

Science Trivia

- The human X chromosome carries more than 1000 known genes.
- The human Y chromosome was once thought to hold only a few genes, but it is now known to hold many more. Estimates vary on the number of genes on the Y chromosome, ranging from about 70 to almost 400. Of the known 78 genes, 27 are shared with the X chromosome.
- The X and Y chromosomes are thought to have been the same size at one time. Scientists have calculated that the Y chromosome has lost an average of five genes every million years.

Answers

A **Infer** because all sex-linked genes, even recessive alleles, are expressed in males

Assess and Reteach

Assess Use the Section Self-Check or Section Quiz, both available at **HMHScience.com**.

Reteach Have students make a Punnett square showing the offspring that would be expected from a cross between an X^RX^r female and an X^RY male, where *R* is a dominant allele for round eyes, and *r* is a recessive allele for oval eyes. Have students list the genotypes and phenotypes for both male and female offspring. Check them for accuracy.

SECTION 7.2

▼ Plan and Prepare

Activate Prior Knowledge Have students think of a human trait, such as eye color or height, that has many phenotypes. **Ask,** How might this trait be inherited so that more than two phenotypes are possible? More than two alleles of a gene or more than one gene may be involved. **Ask,** Is this pattern of inheritance Mendelian? It is not Mendelian, because Mendel's traits were either-or traits; that is, each trait had only two possible phenotypes.

▼ Teach

Vocabulary

Academic Vocabulary Mendel realized that genes are inherited as **discrete** units, separate and self-contained. However, the phenotype produced can sometimes show **continuous** variation, especially when multiple genes are involved. The word *continuous* suggests an uninterrupted range of expression.

7.2 Complex Patterns of Inheritance

KEY CONCEPT **Phenotype is affected by many different factors.**

MAIN IDEAS
- Phenotype can depend on interactions of alleles.
- Many genes may interact to produce one trait.
- The environment interacts with genotype.

VOCABULARY
incomplete dominance
codominance
polygenic trait

Connect to Your World

Suppose you have blue and yellow paints to paint a room. You paint the walls yellow, let them dry, then paint the walls blue. The blue paint masks the yellow paint, so you could say that the blue paint is "dominant." You could also combine the paints in other ways. You could paint the room in blue and yellow stripes, or you could mix the colors and paint the room green. You can think of different alleles as different paint colors, but in genetics there are many more paint colors—alleles—and many more ways that they are combined.

CONNECT TO
PRINCIPLES OF GENETICS
Recall from the chapter **Meiosis and Mendel** that a homozygote has two identical alleles of a gene, and a heterozygote has two different alleles of a gene.

GO ONLINE
Experiments and Models of Heredity

MAIN IDEA
Phenotype can depend on interactions of alleles.

Although Mendel's basic theory of heredity was correct, his research could not have explained all of the continuous variations for many traits. For example, many traits result from alleles with a range of dominance, rather than a strict dominant and recessive relationship.

The pea flowers that Mendel observed were either white or purple. One allele was dominant, but dominance does not mean that one allele "defeats" the other. Usually, it means that the dominant allele codes for a certain protein, and the recessive allele codes for a variation of the protein that has little or no effect. In Mendel's pea flowers, a heterozygous plant makes enough of the purple color that only one dominant allele is needed to give the flowers a purple color. But in many cases, a phenotype comes from more than just one gene, and many genes in a population have more than just two alleles.

Incomplete Dominance

Sometimes, alleles show **incomplete dominance,** in which a heterozygous phenotype is somewhere between the two homozygous phenotypes. Neither allele is completely dominant nor completely recessive. One example of incomplete dominance is the four-o'clock plant. When plants that are homozygous for red flowers are crossed with plants that are homozygous for white flowers, the offspring have pink flowers. The pink color is a third, distinct phenotype. Neither of the original phenotypes of the plants in the parent's generation can be seen separately in the F_1 generation offspring.

Differentiated Instruction

ENGLISH LEARNERS

After reading the section, show students how to create a compare/contrast chart to study incomplete dominance and codominance. Write the terms in two large boxes at the top. Draw arrows down from these to a single box for shared characteristics. Draw arrows from this box down again to a series of smaller boxes that align with one of the two at the top and detail how the two types of interactions are different.

Teacher Toolkit, Section C, Compare/Contrast Chart

FIGURE 2.1 Incomplete Dominance

PHENOTYPE	GENOTYPE	PHENOTYPE	GENOTYPE	PHENOTYPE	GENOTYPE
green	B_1B_1	steel blue	B_2B_2	royal blue	B_1B_2

The green betta fish is homozygous for the green color allele.

The steel blue betta fish is homozygous for the blue color allele.

The royal blue betta fish is heterozygous for the two color alleles.

Another example of incomplete dominance is the color of betta fish shown in **FIGURE 2.1.** When a green fish (B_1B_1) is crossed with a steel blue fish (B_2B_2), all of the offspring have the heterozygous genotype (B_1B_2). These offspring will be a royal blue color that comes from the phenotypes from both alleles. The alleles of this gene follow a pattern of incomplete dominance. What happens when two royal blue betta fish are crossed? Some offspring (25%) will be green (B_1B_1), some (50%) will be royal blue (B_1B_2), and some (25%) will be steel blue (B_2B_2).

READING TOOLBOX

VOCABULARY

When alleles are neither dominant nor recessive, such as with incomplete dominance, uppercase letters with either subscripts or superscripts are used to represent the different alleles.

Codominance

Sometimes, both alleles of a gene are expressed completely—neither allele is dominant nor recessive. In this case, alleles show **codominance,** in which both traits are fully and separately expressed. Suppose a plant that is homozygous for red flowers is crossed with a plant that is homozygous for white flowers. In incomplete dominance, the offspring have pink flowers. Codominant alleles are different. Instead of what looks like an intermediate phenotype, both traits are expressed. The flowers will have some red areas and some white areas.

One trait that you likely know about—human ABO blood types—is an example of codominance. And, because the blood types come from three different alleles in the human population, this trait is also considered a multiple-allele trait. The multiple alleles, shown in **FIGURE 2.2,** are called I^A, I^B, and i. Both I^A and I^B result in a protein, called an antigen, on the surface of red blood cells. Allele i is recessive and does not result in an antigen. Someone with a genotype of I^Ai will have type A blood, and someone with a genotype of I^Bi will have type B blood. But remember that the I^A and I^B alleles are codominant.

FIGURE 2.2 CODOMINANCE

PHENOTYPE (BLOOD TYPE)		GENOTYPES
A	antigen A 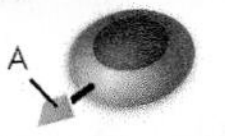	I^AI^A or I^Ai
B	antigen B 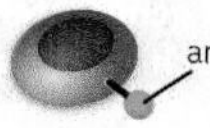	I^BI^B or I^Bi
AB	both antigens 	I^AI^B
O	no antigens 	ii

TEACH FROM VISUALS

FIGURE 2.1 Have students study the phenotypes and genotypes of the betta fish. **Ask,** How can you tell that the two color alleles show incomplete dominance? The color of the heterozygote (royal blue) is a combination of blue and green.

History of Science

Experiments involving **blood transfusions** took place as early as the 1600s; however the first documented instance of human-to-human blood transfusion didn't occur until the early 1800s. While transfusing blood was seen as a great medical advance, mixing blood could lead to blood clumping or other toxic reactions that were fatal. A physician, **Karl Landsteiner,** recognized the adverse reaction as an immune response. His work led to the development of the **ABO system** of blood typing in 1901, for which he was awarded a Nobel Prize in 1930.

Integrating Chemistry

The **antigens** that determine human blood groups are complex molecules found on the surface of red blood cells. The protein base of each molecule is embedded in the cell membrane. Attached to the base is a chain of sugar molecules, called antigen H, which sticks out from the membrane. The alleles for the A and B blood groups do not actually code for A and B antigens. Instead, they code for different enzymes that complete the A and B antigens by attaching a specific molecule to the sugar chain to make it functional.

PRE-AP

Have students create their own example of a trait to compare Mendelian inheritance patterns to patterns of codominance and incomplete dominance. Suggest that they format this comparison as a table that shows patterns of inheritance in ratio form, across several generations.

Teacher Toolkit, Section D, Semantic Feature Analysis

ENGLISH LEARNERS

Students may have a difficult time differentiating between incomplete dominance and codominance. Explain that *in-* can mean "into." Tell students that when red four o'clock flowers are crossed with white four o'clock flowers, the red "goes into" the white, forming pink. Tell students that *co-* means "together." If type A blood is crossed with type B blood, they are expressed together as type AB.

▼ Teach *continued*

Vocabulary

epistasis The prefix *epi-* can mean "at," and *stasis* means "a standstill." Because an epistatic gene can prevent the expression of other genes, it could be said that epistasis causes the expression of other genes to be at a standstill. Students may also be familiar with the word **epicenter,** referring to the center of an earthquake or sometimes the center of a controversy.

Take It Further

Geneticists have identified as many as ten genes in humans that affect **eye color.** Three of these genes are called GEY, BEY1, and BEY2. The GEY gene is located on chromosome 19 and has a green and a blue allele. The green allele is dominant. The BEY1 gene is on chromosome 15 and is the central brown eye color gene. The BEY2 gene is also on chromosome 15 and has a brown and a blue allele. The brown allele is dominant. Geneticists have designed a model using the BEY2 and GEY gene pairs to explain the inheritance of blue, green, and brown eyes. However, the model cannot explain other eye colors such as hazel and gray, nor can it explain why eye color can change over time. Geneticists have acknowledged that eye color exists on a much more complicated gradient than the color categories usually discussed.

Answers

A Apply If two people are heterozygotes (I^Bi), they can each pass the recessive allele (i) to their offspring.

People with both codominant alleles (I^AI^B) have both antigens, so they have type AB blood. People with an *ii* genotype have red blood cells without either antigen, and they have type O blood. Two heterozygous people, one with type A blood (I^Ai) and one with type B blood (I^Bi), can have offspring with any of the four blood types, depending on the alleles that are passed on.

A Apply How can two people with type B blood have a child with type O blood?

MAIN IDEA

Many genes may interact to produce one trait.

As you have seen, some variations in phenotype are related to incomplete dominance, codominance, and multiple alleles. But most traits in plants and animals, including humans, are the result of several genes that interact.

Polygenic Traits

Traits produced by two or more genes are called **polygenic traits.** Human skin color, for example, is the result of four genes that interact to produce a continuous range of colors. Similarly, human eye color, which is often thought of as a single gene trait, is polygenic. As **FIGURE 2.3** shows, at least three genes with complicated patterns of expression play roles in determining eye color. For example, the green allele is dominant to blue alleles, but it is recessive to all brown alleles. These genes do not account for all eye color variations, such as changes in eye color over time, the continuous range of eye colors, and patterns of colors in eyes. As a result, scientists hypothesize that still undiscovered genes affect eye color.

VISUAL VOCAB

Traits that are produced by two or more genes are called **polygenic traits.**

many — poly; genes — genic

Epistasis

Another polygenic trait is fur color in mice and in other mammals. In mice, at least five different genes interact to produce the phenotype. Two genes give the mouse its general color, one gene affects the shading of the color, and one gene determines whether the mouse will have spots. But the fifth gene involved in mouse fur color can overshadow all of the others. In cases such as this, one gene, called an epistatic gene, can interfere with the expression of other genes.

FIGURE 2.3 Eye Color

At least three different genes interact to produce the range of human eye colors, such as in the examples on the right.

GENE NAME	DOMINANT ALLELE	RECESSIVE ALLELE
BEY1	brown	blue
BEY2	brown	blue
GEY	green	blue

Order of dominance: brown > green > blue.

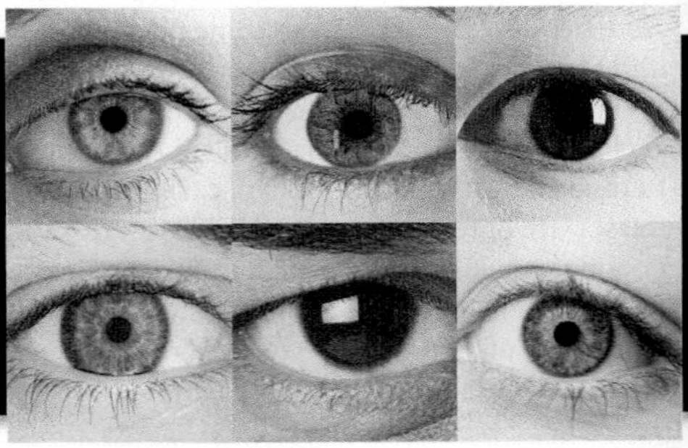

Differentiated Instruction

BELOW LEVEL

The ABO blood group system is a difficult example of codominance because multiple alleles complicate the picture. For a simpler example, describe to students the inheritance of hair color in shorthorn cattle. If a red-haired cow is bred with a white-haired bull, all the offspring are roan, a light red. Examination of the offspring's hairs with a hand lens reveals that some hairs are red and some are white. The allele for red hair and the allele for white hair are expressed equally in codominance.

TEACH WITH TECHNOLOGY

If students have access to graphing calculators, have them enter the data from the Eye Opener Demonstration on the chapter opener to produce a graph. The graph will show a bell-shaped distribution of phenotypes. Explain to students that polygenic inheritance is quantitative; each dominant allele adds a certain amount of height to the phenotype.

In albinism, a single epistatic gene interferes with the expression of other genes. Albinism, as you can see in **FIGURE 2.4**, is characterized by a lack of pigment in skin, hair, and eyes. A mouse that is homozygous for the alleles that prevent the coloration of fur will be white, regardless of the phenotypes that would normally come from the other four genes. A person with the alleles for albinism will have very light skin, hair, and eyes, regardless of the other genes he or she has inherited.

Contrast **How do multiple-allele traits differ from polygenic traits?**

FIGURE 2.4 Albinism in mammals, such as this hedgehog, is caused by an epistatic gene that blocks the production of pigments.

MAIN IDEA

The environment interacts with genotype.

Phenotype is more than the sum of gene expression. For example, the sex of sea turtles depends both on genes and on environment. Female turtles make nests on beaches and bury their eggs in the sand. Eggs that mature in warmer temperatures develop into female turtles. Eggs that mature in cooler temperatures develop into male turtles.

Genes and environment also interact to determine human traits. Think about height. Genes give someone a tendency to be either short or tall, but they do not control everything. An interesting question for the interaction between genes and environment is "Are identical twins always identical?" Studies of identical twins have shown that the environment during early development can have long-lasting effects. One twin might get more nutrients than the other because of its position in the mother's uterus. This difference can result in height and size differences that last throughout the twins' lives. Also, twins raised in environments with different nutrition and health care often differ in height and other physical traits. In the end, phenotype is usually a mixture of genes and environment.

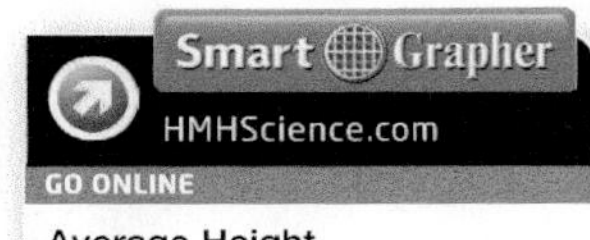

Average Height

Connect **Sunlight can cause a person's hair to become lighter in color. Is this an example of an interaction between genes and the environment? Why or why not?**

7.2 Formative Assessment

REVIEWING MAIN IDEAS

1. How is **incomplete dominance** expressed in a phenotype?
2. Why might **polygenic traits** vary more in phenotype than do single-gene traits?
3. Explain how interactions between genes and the environment can affect phenotype.

CRITICAL THINKING

4. **Synthesize** How is **codominance** the same as having no dominant and recessive relationship at all between two alleles?
5. **Compare and Contrast** How are codominant alleles and incompletely dominant alleles similar? How are they different?

CONNECT TO

PRINCIPLES OF GENETICS

6. Why can parents who are heterozygous for type A and type B blood have children with any of the four human blood types? Use a Punnett square to support your answer.

7.2 FORMATIVE ASSESSMENT

1. Neither parental phenotype is expressed. Instead, a third, intermediate phenotype is expressed.
2. because many genes are interacting
3. Genes provide a tendency toward a phenotype that the environment can alter.
4. Both alleles are completely expressed in the phenotype; neither is masked.
5. Both are neither completely dominant nor completely recessive. Incomplete dominance produces an intermediate phenotype; codominance produces both traits in a phenotype.
6. A Punnett square will demonstrate that there is a 25 percent chance of any of the four phenotypes because each parent has an allele for either A or B blood as well as the recessive *i* allele.

ONLINE Biology
HMHScience.com

Students can study the height distribution of men and women in the United States over the past 150 years. Go to Data Analysis Smart Grapher activity for this chapter, available at **HMHScience.com**.

Take It Further

The distinctive patterns of an individual's **fingerprints** are controlled by polygenic inheritance, but they are also influenced by the fetal environment. The ridge pattern of a fingerprint can be altered during weeks 6 through 13 of fetal development, as the fetus touches the wall of the amniotic sac with its finger pads. This explains why identical twins, who have identical genes, have slightly different fingerprints.

Answers

A **Contrast** Multiple-allele traits are influenced by several different versions of one gene; polygenic traits are influenced by multiple genes.

B **Connect** yes, because phenotype can be altered by environment

Assess and Reteach

Assess Use the Section Self-Check or Section Quiz, both available at **HMHScience.com**.

Reteach Have students make two Punnett squares showing crosses between two homozygotes that have different alleles of a gene. One Punnett square should show an incomplete dominance pattern and the other a codominance pattern. The traits shown in the Punnett squares can be fictitious, but the inheritance pattern should be accurately shown. Make sure students label the phenotypes and genotypes.

Introduce

Students may know or be related to someone with ASD. Tell students that not only is there a wide range of expressions of ASD, but that child prodigies can share some of the same genetic differences as people with ASD on chromosome 1. People with ASD can become fixated on or obsessed with certain things they find interesting, which can lead to expertise in that area. **Ask,** What benefits might there be to having a different way of thinking or looking at the world around us?

Discuss

The researchers compared parent DNA with child DNA and found that if the parents had one child with ASD, the child had a 10% chance of having extra or missing DNA (CNVs) when compared with their parental DNA. If the parents had no children with ASD, only 1% of the children had CNVs. However, if the parents had more than one child with ASD, 3% of the children had CNVs. **Ask,** Why test families with no children with ASD? (as a controlled group, for comparison) What might explain the result that families with two or more children with ASD have children with fewer CNVs (compared with their parents' DNA) than families with one autistic child? (The CNVs could have been passed on from the parents and expressed in their children. In other words, there could be CNVs as compared with the children's grandparents' DNA rather than their parents' DNA).

Answers

1. It suggests there is a genetic basis to ASD.
2. No, because identical twins are likely to have been raised in the same environment.
3. There is a wide range of possible effects and perhaps the number of genes involved may correlate with the severity of the symptoms ASD patients exhibit.

The Genetics of Autism

S.T.E.M. Interactions

Autism affects an estimated 1 in 68 people in the United States. The incidence has been rising since autism was first recognized as a disorder, in part because of better awareness and diagnosis, but perhaps also because of changes in the environment. In addition, researchers are certain there is a genetic component to autism, but determining exactly what genes are involved is complicated.

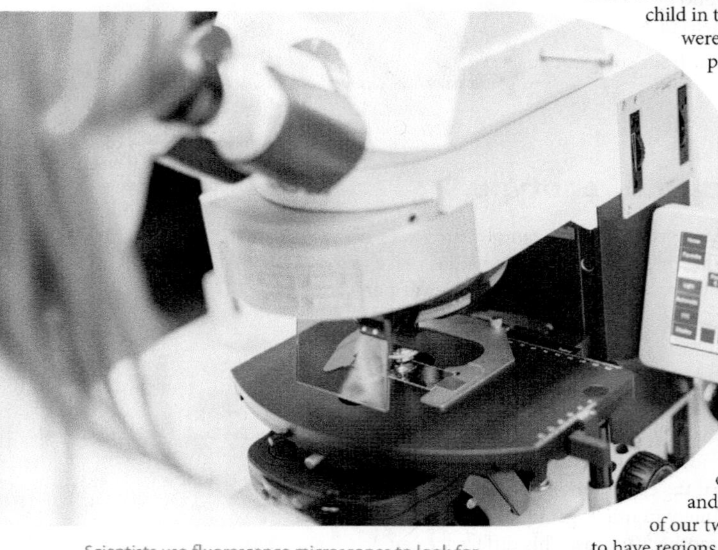

Scientists use fluorescence microscopes to look for copy number variants on fragments of DNA.

Part of the difficulty in determining the causes of autism comes from the wide range of symptoms displayed by those with the disorder. Autism is more accurately called Autism Spectrum Disorder (ASD), which reflects that there is a wide range of effects, from barely detectable to severely disabling. To varying degrees, people who have been diagnosed with ASD have problems with communicating and relating to others. The disorder is often characterized by restrictive, repetitive patterns of behavior and interests. Early signs in young children include not making eye contact, not returning smiles, not asking to be picked up, and not playing games such as peek-a-boo. Sometimes, toddlers with ASD start developing these skills but then seem to lose them. Boys have a three to four times greater chance of being diagnosed with ASD than girls do.

Scientific interest in what causes ASD has been so great that large databases of DNA samples have been collected from families where at least one member has been diagnosed with ASD. Researchers who used one such database determined that if one child in a family has ASD, there is a two to six percent chance of a second child in that family having the disorder. If ASD were due to a mutation on a single gene, the probability of siblings having ASD would be close to either 25% or 50%. While most research has looked at small changes in genes, these researchers found that either duplications or deletions of entire sections of DNA are common in many ASD patients. Called copy number variants (CNVs), these differences were discovered using comparative genomic hybridization (CGH) arrays. Fragments of DNA, both from a person with ASD and a person without ASD, are separated into single strands and labeled with a fluorescent tag. The strands are then allowed to bind, and any differences can be observed with computer software and a fluorescence microscope. Twenty out of our twenty-three pairs of chromosomes appear to have regions that influence the onset of ASD, suggesting that there may be many different ways for this disorder to arise.

Questions

1. Researchers have found that identical twins are much more likely to have ASD than are fraternal twins. Identical twins share the same genes, whereas fraternal twins are no more genetically related than any two siblings. What does this suggest about ASD?
2. Does the fact that identical twins share a likelihood of having ASD rule out environmental factors as a cause or trigger of the disorder? Explain.
3. How does the wide range of possible symptoms of ASD support the finding that multiple genes and biological pathways are involved in the disorder?

7.3 Gene Linkage and Mapping

KEY CONCEPT **Genes can be mapped to specific locations on chromosomes.**

VOCABULARY

linkage map

MAIN IDEAS

- Gene linkage was explained through fruit flies.
- Linkage maps estimate distances between genes.

Connect to Your World

If you leave a banana out on a table until it is very ripe, you might see some of the most useful organisms for genetic research—fruit flies—buzzing around it. In your kitchen, fruit flies are pests. In the laboratory, early experiments with fruit flies showed not only that genes are on chromosomes, but also that genes are found at specific places on chromosomes.

MAIN IDEA

Gene linkage was explained through fruit flies.

Gene linkage, which you read about previously, was first described by William Bateson and R. C. Punnett, who invented the Punnett square. Punnett and Bateson, like Mendel, studied dihybrid crosses of pea plants. But their results differed from the 9:3:3:1 phenotype ratios that Mendel observed. The results suggested that some genes were linked together. But how could genes be linked and still follow Mendel's law of independent assortment?

American scientist Thomas Hunt Morgan, who worked with fruit flies (*Drosophila melanogaster*), found the answer. At first, Morgan was just looking for an organism to use in genetic research. He found fruit flies very useful because he could quickly and cheaply grow new generations of flies. He observed among fruit flies easily identifiable variations in eye color, body color, and wing shape. Knowing these variations, Morgan and his students set up experiments similar to Mendel's dihybrid crosses. They chose one type of fly with traits associated with the wild type, or most common phenotype. They crossed the wild type flies with mutant flies, or flies with a different, less common phenotype. You can see examples of fruit flies in **FIGURE 3.1.**

Wild type

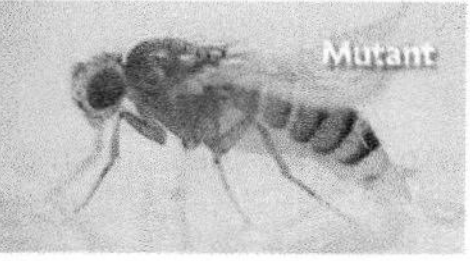

FIGURE 3.1 The wild type fruit fly (top) shows the most common phenotype. The mutant fruit fly (bottom) has a yellow body and curly wings.

Morgan's results, like those of Punnett and Bateson, did not always follow the 9:3:3:1 ratio predicted by Mendel. But the results did differ in a noticeable pattern. Some traits appeared to be inherited together. Morgan called these traits linked traits, and they appeared to fall into four groups. As it turns out, fruit flies have four pairs of chromosomes. Each of the four groups of linked traits identified by Morgan matches one of the chromosome pairs. Morgan concluded that linked genes were on the same chromosome. The chromosomes, not the genes, assort independently during meiosis. Because the linked genes were not inherited together every time, Morgan also concluded that chromosomes must exchange homologous genes during meiosis.

Ⓐ Synthesize **How did Morgan's research build upon Mendel's observations?**

Differentiated Instruction

ENGLISH LEARNERS

Have students study **FIGURE 3.2** as an example of a linkage map. Have students describe what they see in the picture. Keep asking questions as you help them see the details of the fly. Use words such as *size, color, shape,* and *texture* in your questions and clarify the meanings of these words as needed.

Teacher Toolkit, Section C, Connect to Content through Visuals

BELOW LEVEL

Have students work in pairs to develop a model of gene linkage, using differently colored beads to represent alleles and doubled-up pipe cleaners to represent chromosomes. Students should model how linkage of two traits to a particular chromosome can cause the genes to sort out together during meiosis. Have students address the question of why Mendel did not discover this in his work with garden peas.

Teacher Toolkit, Section C, Think-Pair-Share

SECTION 7.3

Plan and Prepare

Activate Prior Knowledge Ask students if they have ever waited in line with a group of friends to see a movie or to get on an amusement park ride. **Ask,** When it came time to be seated, who did you sit next to—the friend who was standing next to you or the friend at the front of the line? friend next to you Describe how this is similar to gene linkage.

Teach

Take It Further

In *Drosophila,* the most frequent allele in a natural population is designated the **wild type.** All other alleles are considered **mutant** by default. Typically the symbol for an allele comes from the mutant form, not the wild type.

Answers

Ⓐ **Synthesize** Morgan used dihybrid crosses in fruit flies to study a new pattern of inheritance that revealed gene linkage in phenotypes.

▼ Teach *continued*

DATA ANALYSIS

Discuss

Bar graphs can be used to compare data that are not related. Multiple sets of data can be compared by drawing several bars next to each other.

Answers

1.

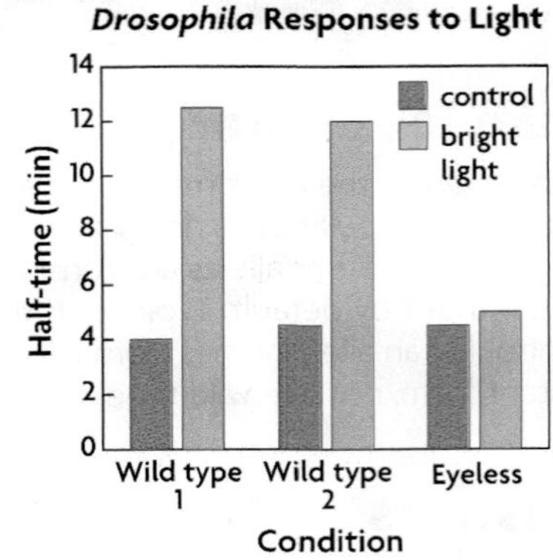

2. The eyeless strain was unaffected due to the mutation, but the other two strains reacted by increasing the amount of time it took half the flies to reach food.

Online Student Resources, Data Analysis Practice

History of Science

A white-eyed male in the wild population of fruit flies in **Thomas Hunt Morgan's** "fly room" led to his **chromosomal theory of heredity.** He discovered that chromosomes are cellular structures that house small units of heredity called genes and that each gene has a specific location on a specific chromosome. In 1933, Morgan was awarded a Nobel Prize for his work.

DATA ANALYSIS

CONSTRUCTING BAR GRAPHS

Scientists tested the reaction of fruit flies to stress by exposing them to bright light—a source of stress for *Drosophila.* The scientists recorded the time it took for half of the flies in each group to reach food, which they called a "half-time." Three strains of flies were tested—wild type 1, wild type 2, and a mutant eyeless type—under a controlled condition and with bright light. The data are shown in Table 1.

1. **Graph Data** Construct a bar graph that shows the data in the table. Recall that the independent variable is on the *x*-axis and the dependent variable is on the *y*-axis.
2. **Analyze** How did the condition of bright light affect the flies? Were all strains affected to the same degree? Why or why not?

TABLE 1. *DROSOPHILA* RESPONSES TO LIGHT

Strain	Condition	Half-Time (min)
Wild type 1	control	4.0
Wild type 1	bright light	12.5
Wild type 2	control	4.5
Wild type 2	bright light	12.0
Eyeless	control	4.5
Eyeless	bright light	5.0

Source: V. Min, B. Condron, *Journal of Neuroscience Methods*, 145.

MAIN IDEA

Linkage maps estimate distances between genes.

The probability that two genes on a chromosome will be inherited together is related to the distance between them. The closer together two genes are, the more likely it is that they will be inherited together. The farther apart two genes are, the more likely it is that they will be separated during meiosis.

One of Morgan's students, Alfred Sturtevant, hypothesized that the frequency of cross-overs during meiosis was related to the distance between genes. This meant that the closer together two genes were, the more likely they were to stay together when cross-overs took place. Sturtevant identified three linked traits in fruit flies—body color, eye color, and wing size—and then crossed the fruit flies. He recorded the percentage of times that the phenotypes did not appear together in the offspring. This percentage represented the frequency of cross-overs between chromosomes.

From the cross-over frequencies, Sturtevant made **linkage maps,** which are maps of the relative locations, or loci, of genes on a chromosome. On a linkage map, one map unit is equal to one cross-over for each 100 offspring, or one percentage point. You can see an example of a linkage map in **FIGURE 3.2.**

Making a linkage map is fairly easy if all of the cross-over frequencies for the genes being studied are known. Suppose the following data were collected.

- Gene A and gene B cross over 6.0% of the time.
- Gene B and gene C cross over 12.5% of the time.
- Gene A and gene C cross over 18.5% of the time.

According to Sturtevant's conclusions, genes A and B are 6 map units apart because they cross over 6% of the time. Similarly, genes B and C are 12.5 map units apart because they cross over 12.5% of the time. But where are the genes located in relation to each other on the chromosome?

CONNECT TO

CROSSING OVER

Recall from the chapter **Meiosis and Mendel** that segments of non-sister chromatids can be exchanged during meiosis.

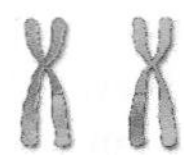

Differentiated Instruction

PRE-AP

Tell students that the crossover frequency between linked genes A and B is 40%; between B and C, 20%; between C and D, 10%; between C and A, 20%; and between D and B, 10%. Have students determine the sequence of the genes on the chromosome. A–C–D–B Upon completion, have students write a brief paragraph explaining how they can determine which genes are more likely to be inherited together.

Teacher Toolkit, Section C, Quick-Write

FIGURE 3.2 Gene Linkage in *Drosophila*

Linkage maps show the relative locations of genes.

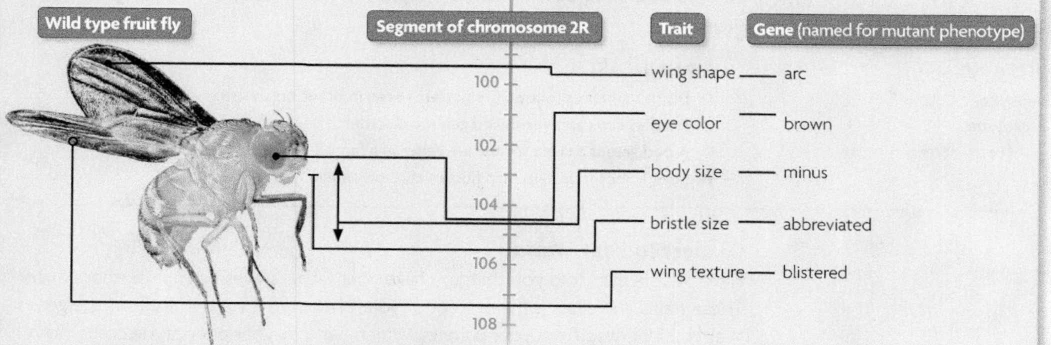

Wild type fruit fly | Segment of chromosome 2R | Trait | Gene (named for mutant phenotype)

100 — wing shape — arc
102 — eye color — brown
body size — minus
104 — bristle size — abbreviated
106 — wing texture — blistered
108

A Apply **Which genes are most likely to cross over? least likely? Why?**

Think about gene A as a point on a line. Gene B is either to the left or to the right of gene A. The same is true of the relationship between genes B and C. But if you only know the distances between genes A and B, and between genes B and C, you cannot determine the order of all three genes. You must also know the distance between genes A and C. As shown in **FIGURE 3.3**, the map distances between genes A and B and between genes B and C equal the map distance between genes A and C. Therefore, gene B must be located between genes A and C. If the map distance between genes A and C were 6.5 map units instead of 18.5 map units, then gene A would be between genes B and C.

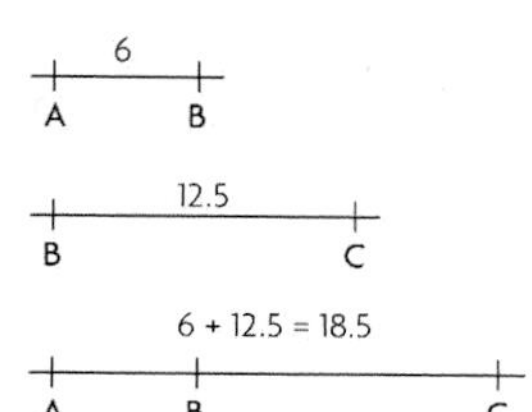

FIGURE 3.3 The order of genes on a chromosome can be determined if all of their cross-over frequencies are known.

Although linkage maps show the relative locations of linked genes, the maps do not show actual physical distances between genes. Linkage maps can give you a general idea about distances between genes, but many factors affect gene linkage. As a result, two pairs of genes may be the same number of map units apart, but they may not have the same physical distance between them.

B Summarize **How can a linkage map be used to analyze chromosomes?**

7.3 Formative Assessment

SELF-CHECK Online HMHScience.com GO ONLINE

REVIEWING MAIN IDEAS

1. Summarize the importance of comparing wild type and mutant fruit flies in genetic research.
2. How is a **linkage map** related to cross-overs that take place during meiosis?

CRITICAL THINKING

3. **Compare and Contrast** How are linked genes similar to sex-linked genes? How are they different?
4. **Apply** Draw a linkage map based on the following cross-over percentages for three gene pairs: A – B = 8%, B – C = 10%, and A – C = 2%.

CONNECT TO SCIENTIFIC PROCESS

5. Punnett, Bateson, and Morgan found phenotype ratios that differed from Mendel's results. Explain how these differences led to new hypotheses and new investigations in genetics.

7.3 FORMATIVE ASSESSMENT

1. The different types of flies were important in determining gene linkage because the different phenotypes were easily observed.
2. The higher the frequency of two genes crossing over separately, the farther they are from each other on a chromosome.
3. similar because both show a pattern of linkage in inheritance; different because linked genes are linked to each other on the same chromosome whereas sex-linked genes are linked to either the X or Y chromosome
4. 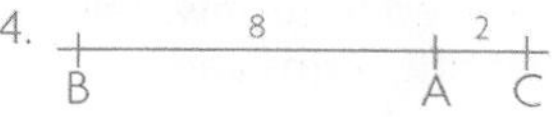

5. In order to explain the differences in results, the scientists proposed an explanation and then tested it.

Science Trivia

The common fruit fly, *Drosophila melanogaster*, is one of about 900 fruit fly species. It is the favorite of geneticists because it lives and breeds so quickly. It takes about 11 days for eggs to hatch and develop into a new generation of adults capable of laying more eggs or contributing sperm. The speed with which geneticists can produce new generations of fruit flies has allowed them to catalogue—and, in some cases, manipulate—as many as 3000 different mutations, including:

- hairy and bald exoskeletons
- red, pink, purple, and maroon eye colors
- antennae with functional eyes
- two sets of wings

Answers

A Apply blistered and arc, farthest apart; brown and minus, closest together

B Summarize by calculating the percentage of times phenotypes do not appear together in offspring of parents with known genotypes

Assess and Reteach

Assess Use the Section Self-Check or Section Quiz, both available at **HMHScience.com**.

Reteach Project on the board the images from **FIGURE 3.2** from this page and **FIGURE 6.3** in Meiosis and Mendel, both available on Media Gallery. Relate the numbers on the gene map to genes shown as bands on the chromosome. Gene B could be the wing shape, with C and D being the genes for eye color and body size, respectively. Have students describe how phenotype and gene linkage could enable these traits to be mapped to the chromosome.

SECTION 7.4

▼ Plan and Prepare

Activate Prior Knowledge Discuss with students the general nature of a genealogy. **Ask,** Have you ever seen a genealogy of your family? How could it be used to trace patterns of inheritance? Students should recognize that a genealogy just traces descendants through a family tree. To be useful for discerning patterns of inheritance, one would need to know about traits of the individuals.

▼ Teach

Vocabulary

Academic Vocabulary Tell students that the words **genealogy** and **pedigree** are defined in the same way: a record of ancestors, a family tree. However, a pedigree chart is typically associated with establishing a blood line or tracing particular traits through descendants.

Answers

A Apply Mendel's principles rely on independent assortment, a process that occurs during meiosis in all sexually reproducing organisms.

7.4 Human Genetics and Pedigrees

KEY CONCEPT **A combination of methods is used to study human genetics.**

VOCABULARY
pedigree
karyotype

MAIN IDEAS
- Human genetics follows the patterns seen in other organisms.
- Females can carry sex-linked genetic disorders.
- A pedigree is a chart for tracing genes in a family.
- Several methods help map human chromosomes.

Connect to Your World

Have people ever told you that you have your father's eyes or your mother's nose? These traits, and every other aspect of your phenotype, are the result of the genes that you inherited from your parents. Which parts of your phenotype come from which parent? In some cases, such as hair color or eye color, it may be very easy to tell. Often, however, it is not so obvious.

MAIN IDEA

Human genetics follows the patterns seen in other organisms.

Fruit flies and pea plants may seem boring and simple, but the basic principles of genetics were worked out using those organisms. Humans follow the same patterns of heredity. First, meiosis independently assorts chromosomes when gametes are made for sexual reproduction. Second, human heredity involves the same relationships between alleles—dominant and recessive interactions, polygenic traits, and sex-linked genes, among others.

The inheritance of many traits is very complex. A single trait may be controlled by several genes that interact. As you read in Section 2, eye color is controlled by at least three different genes. And, although several genes affect height, a person's environment during growth and development plays a large role in his or her adult height. What might seem like an obvious phenotype is rarely as simple as it looks.

Nonetheless, single-gene traits are very helpful in understanding human genetics. One such trait is the shape of a person's hairline. A hairline with a downward point, such as a widow's peak shown in **FIGURE 4.1**, is a dominant trait. A straight hairline is a recessive trait. The inheritance of this trait follows the same dominant and recessive pattern as the traits in Mendel's pea plants. Many genetic disorders, such as Huntington's disease, hemophilia, and Duchenne's muscular dystrophy, are also caused by single genes that follow a dominant and recessive pattern. In fact, much of what is known about human genetics comes from studying genetic disorders.

FIGURE 4.1 The widow's peak, or pointed hairline, is a phenotype produced by a dominant autosomal gene.

A Apply Why can the genetics of pea plants and fruit flies be applied to humans?

Differentiated Instruction

ENGLISH LEARNERS

Have students scan the pages for terms they may not know or may need to review. Tell them to focus on scientific terms and combinations of terms, such as *homozygous recessive genotype,* but allow them to include unfamiliar general terms as well. Encourage students to use context to create their own definitions, consult the dictionary for expert definitions, and draw visuals to reinforce meaning.

Teacher Toolkit, Section D, Student Vocabulary

MAIN IDEA

Females can carry sex-linked genetic disorders.

Recall from Section 1 that some genetic disorders are caused by autosomal genes. A carrier of an autosomal disorder does not show the disease but can pass on the disease-causing allele. Both males and females can be carriers of an autosomal disorder.

In contrast, only females can be carriers of sex-linked disorders. Several genetic disorders are caused by genes on the X chromosome, as you can see in **FIGURE 4.2.** Recall that males have an XY genotype. A male who has a gene for a disorder located on the X chromosome will not have a second, normal allele to mask it. One copy of the allele is enough for males to have the disorder. There are no male carriers of sex-linked disorders because any male who has the gene displays the phenotype. Females can be carriers because they may have a normal allele that gives them a normal phenotype. The likelihood of inheriting a sex-linked disorder depends both on the sex of the child and on which parent carries the disorder-causing allele. If only the mother has the allele and is a carrier, a child has a 50% chance of inheriting the allele. A daughter who inherits it will not show the phenotype, but a son will.

The British royal family provides a historical example of a sex-linked disorder. Queen Victoria (1819–1901) was a carrier of a recessive sex-linked allele for a disorder called hemophilia, which is a lack of proteins needed for blood to clot. People with hemophilia do not stop bleeding easily. Queen Victoria passed the allele to her son, who had hemophilia. He passed it to his daughter, who was a carrier, and so on. Members of royal families tended to marry into royal families in other countries, and by the early 1900s the royal families of several countries, including Russia and Spain, also had the allele for hemophilia. The allele in all of these people is traced back to Queen Victoria.

Contrast **How can carriers differ between autosomal and sex-linked disorders?**

READING TOOLBOX

VOCABULARY

The term *carrier* means "a person who transports something." In genetics, a carrier is a person who "transports" a recessive allele but does not express the recessive phenotype.

FIGURE 4.2 Comparing the X and Y Chromosomes

The X chromosome has about 1100 known genes, including many that cause genetic disorders. The Y chromosome is about one-third the size of the X and has only about 250 known genes.

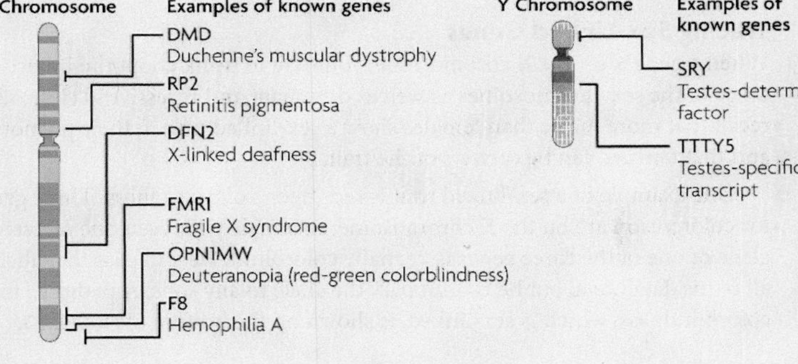

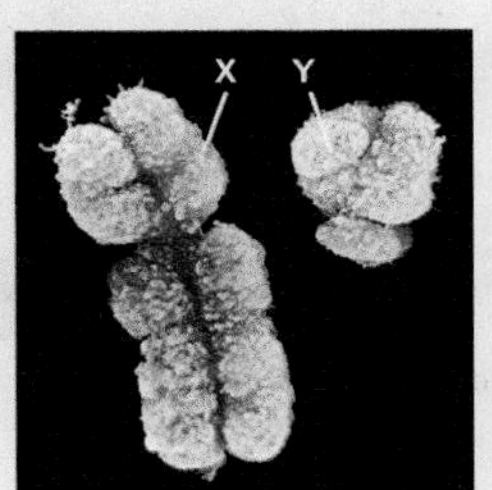

These X and Y chromosomes are duplicated and condensed. (colored SEM; magnification about 15,000×)

BELOW LEVEL

To have students become more familiar with the patterns of inheritance, have students make an ongoing chart of human traits and genetic disorders as they read this section. They should write the name of each trait or disorder and its pattern of inheritance. At the end of the section, they should briefly summarize the key differences among the different patterns of inheritance. Students can also add information on other human traits or disorders from earlier sections.

Teacher Toolkit, Section C, Content Frame

Vocabulary

Academic Vocabulary Tell students that they may see the words **disease** and **disorder** used to describe the same medical condition.

disease, a pathological condition resulting from various causes, including infection, genetic defect, or environmental stress

disorder, an ailment that affects the function of the body or mind

Today, many researchers apply the word *disorder* specifically to those conditions that are caused by genes.

Take It Further

Very few genes have been linked to the **human Y chromosome** through pedigree analysis. A mutation on the Y chromosome should be easy to track because the gene would have an immediate effect on the male who possesses it and would be passed on to all of his sons and none of his daughters. Instead, understanding the male-specific genes of the Y chromosome has become the goal of genomic researchers. The Y chromosome was fully sequenced in 2003, but researchers currently have an incomplete picture of the functions it controls. Students will learn more about genomic research in Frontiers of Biotechnology.

Answers

A **Contrast** Only females can be carriers of sex-linked disorders.

▼ Teach *continued*

CONNECT TO

Genetic Screening Although genetic tests are available for many disorders, people who might be at risk do not always want to be tested. When a test for Huntington's disease became available, many at-risk people refused to be tested. They did not want to live with the knowledge that they would develop a debilitating, fatal disorder later in their lives.

The Inside Story

Huntington's disease (HD) has been described as a genetic time bomb. The allele for the disorder is dominant, so the child of a carrier has a 50-50 chance of inheriting the gene. But since the disorder does not present itself until well into adulthood—between the ages of 30 and 50—a parent may unwittingly pass the gene onto a child long before the parent's symptoms appear.

As a young woman, **Nancy Wexler** watched as HD slowly and painfully claimed her mother's life. In 1978, at risk for the disorder herself, she began a search for the underlying cause. That search took her to a small village in Venezuela, where a relatively large number of the villagers were afflicted with HD. Wexler eventually compiled a massive pedigree of the villagers, which included almost 10,000 people. She also took 2000 blood samples that enabled her to locate the HD gene in 1993, at the tip of chromosome 4. Wexler is today still active in HD research and free of the disorder.

ONLINE Biology
HMHScience.com

Have students trace family history, using DNA from mitochondria and the Y chromosome. Go to the WebQuest on genetic heritage, available at **HMHScience.com**.

CONNECT TO

GENETIC SCREENING

DNA testing is a direct method of studying genetic disorders. You will learn more about DNA tests and genetic screening in the chapter **Frontiers of Biotechnology.**

MAIN IDEA

A pedigree is a chart for tracing genes in a family.

If two people want to know their child's chances of having a certain genetic disorder, they cannot rely upon their phenotypes. The parents also need to know their genotypes. A **pedigree** chart can help trace the phenotypes and genotypes in a family to determine whether people carry recessive alleles. When enough family phenotypes are known, genotypes can often be inferred.

A human pedigree shows several types of information. Boxes represent males and circles represent females. A shaded shape means that a person shows the trait, a white shape means that the person does not, and a shape that is half-shaded and half-white means that a person is a carrier. Lines connect a person to his or her mate, and to their children.

Using phenotypes to figure out the possible genotypes in a family is like putting pieces of a puzzle together. You have to use clues and logic to narrow the possibilities for each person's genotype. One particular clue, for example, can tell you whether the gene is on an autosome or on a sex chromosome. If approximately the same number of males and females have the phenotype, then the gene is most likely on an autosome. If, however, the phenotype is much more common in males, then the gene is likely on the X chromosome.

Tracing Autosomal Genes

It is fairly easy to trace genotypes through a pedigree when you know that you are dealing with a trait controlled by an autosomal gene. Why? A person who does not show the phenotype must have a homozygous recessive genotype. Any other genotype—either heterozygous or homozygous dominant—would produce the phenotype. Use the following steps to work your way through a pedigree for a gene on an autosome. The inheritance of an autosomal trait, such as the widow's peak described earlier, is shown on the top of **FIGURE 4.3.**

- People with a widow's peak have either homozygous dominant (*WW*) or heterozygous (*Ww*) genotypes.
- Two parents without a widow's peak are both homozygous recessive (*ww*) and cannot have children who have a widow's peak.
- Two parents who both have a widow's peak can have a child who does not (*ww*) if both parents are heterozygous for the dominant and recessive alleles (*Ww*).

Genetic Heritage

Tracing Sex-Linked Genes

When a gene is on the X chromosome, you have to think about the inheritance of the sex chromosomes as well as dominant and recessive alleles. Also, recall that more males than females show a sex-linked trait in their phenotype and that females can be carriers of the trait.

One example of a sex-linked trait is red-green colorblindness. Three genes for color vision are on the X chromosome, so a male with even one recessive allele of one of the three genes is partially colorblind. He will pass that allele to all of his daughters, but he cannot pass the allele to any sons. A pedigree for colorblindness, which is sex-linked, is shown on the bottom of **FIGURE 4.3.**

Differentiated Instruction

PRE-AP

Have students make a Venn diagram with two overlapping circles to compare and contrast the inheritance pattern of autosomal genes and sex-linked genes. Students should note that autosomal genes are expressed equally in males and females and that sex-linked genes are expressed mostly in males. Heterozygotes can be carriers only if the trait is autosomal and recessive. Only females can be carriers for a sex-linked recessive trait.

Teacher Toolkit, Section C, Venn Diagram

FIGURE 4.3 Interpreting Pedigree Charts

Figuring out genotypes from phenotypes requires you to use a process of elimination. You can often determine which genotypes are possible, and which ones are not.

- Male without phenotype
- Male with phenotype
- Male carrier
- Female without phenotype
- Female with phenotype
- Female carrier

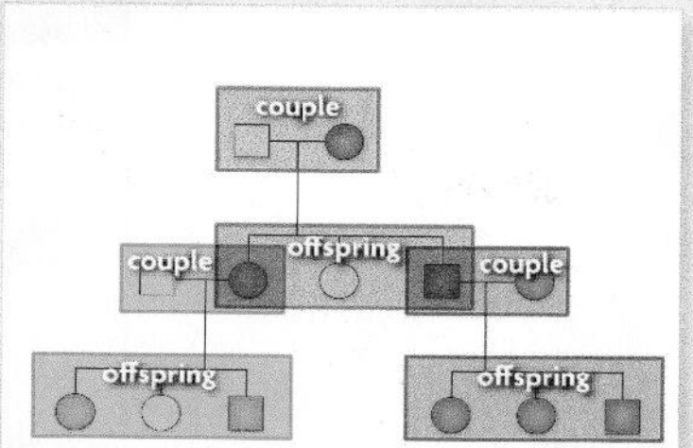

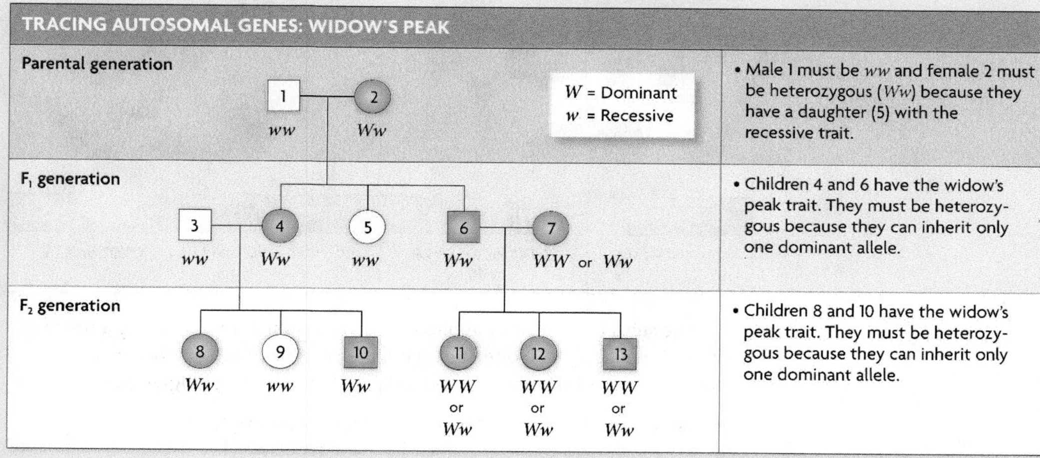

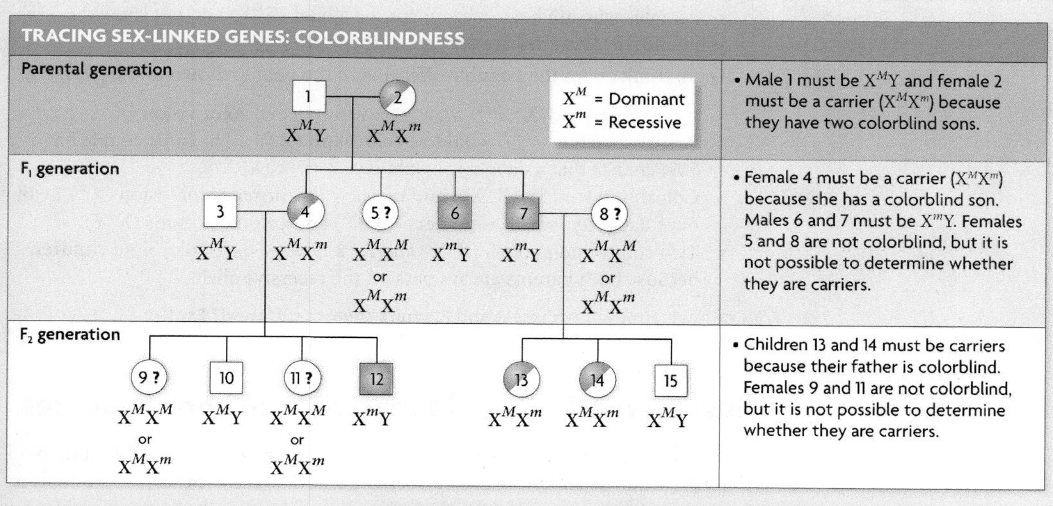

CRITICAL VIEWING **Explain why it is not possible to identify all of the genotypes in the pedigree charts above. What information would you need to identify the genotypes of those people?**

BELOW LEVEL

Tell students that when they analyze a pedigree chart, they should start by asking two questions: Are there patterns in the pedigree that are consistent with a particular type of inheritance? Are there patterns in the pedigree that are inconsistent with a particular pattern of inheritance? Working in pairs, have students analyze the pedigree charts in **FIGURE 4.3.**

Teacher Toolkit, Section C, Think-Pair-Share

TEACH FROM VISUALS

FIGURE 4.3 Have students examine the widow's peak pedigree chart. **Ask**

- Why can't you tell the genotype of individual 7? You do not know her family history, so all you know for sure is that she has at least one dominant W allele, because she has a widow's peak.
- What is individual 7's most likely genotype? There is a good chance that she is *WW*, because all her children have a widow's peak.
- Have students study the colorblindness pedigree chart. What predictions could you make about future daughters of individuals 7 and 8 if individual 8 were X^MX^m? There is a 50 percent chance that the daughters will be colorblind.

Vocabulary

Word Origins The word **pedigree** is based on the Old French phrase *pied de gru,* which means "foot of a crane." When family members were placed on a genealogical chart, the branching lines that connected them resembled the imprint of a crane's foot.

The term **widow's peak** comes from English folklore. The word *peak* refers to the appearance of a widow's mourning cap, which had a point extending down at the center of the forehead. The story was that a woman with such a hairline would outlive her husband.

Answers

A Critical Viewing Additional family information is necessary when there is more than one possible genotype.

▼ Teach *continued*

Address Misconceptions

Common Misconception Students may think that someone who is colorblind only sees black and white.

Correcting the Misconception With the exception of monochromasy (a form of colorblindness with complete absence of color detection), people who are colorblind see some degree of color.

Take It Further

Three types of **cone cells** in the retina of the eye determine **color vision.** Each type contains a different photopigment that captures a particular range of wavelengths of light. A photopigment molecule consists of a vitamin A–derived portion called retinal and a protein portion called opsin. Production of three types of opsins is controlled by three genes.

The gene for short-wavelength opsin, which determines blue vision, is located on chromosome 7. Blue colorblindness is called **tritanopia.** The genes for middle-wavelength (yellow-green vision) and long-wavelength (yellow-red vision) opsins are on the X chromosome. Yellow-green colorblindness is called **deuteranopia;** yellow-red colorblindness is called **protanopia.** Both deuteranopia and protanopia are commonly referred to as red-green colorblindness.

Answers

A Contrast Punnett squares predict offspring phenotypes from known genotypes; pedigrees predict genotypes from phenotypes. Punnett squares show predicted outcomes, whereas pedigrees show actual outcomes.

FIGURE 4.4 RED-GREEN COLORBLINDNESS

A person with normal color vision can easily distinguish between different colors. A person who is red-green colorblind cannot.

PHENOTYPE	GENOTYPES	PHENOTYPE	GENOTYPES
normal vision	X^MX^m *or* X^MX^M *or* X^MY	red-green colorblind	X^mX^m *or* X^mY

The steps below can be applied to any sex-linked trait. By using a process of elimination, you can often figure out the possible genotypes for a given phenotype. First, think about the individuals shown in the pedigree chart.

- Colorblind females must be homozygous recessive (X^mX^m).
- Males who are colorblind must have the recessive allele (X^mY).
- Females who are heterozygous for the alleles (X^MX^m) do not show the phenotype, but they are carriers of the trait.

Then, think about the possible offspring of the people shown in the pedigree.

- A female carrier (X^MX^m) and a male with normal color vision (X^MY) have a 50% chance that a son would be colorblind (X^mY). The same couple has a 50% chance that a daughter would be a carrier (X^MX^m).
- Colorblind females (X^mX^m) and males with normal color vision (X^MY) will have daughters who are carriers (X^MX^m) and colorblind sons (X^mY).
- Two colorblind parents (X^mX^m and X^mY) always have colorblind children because both parents always pass on the recessive allele.

A Contrast How are pedigrees and Punnett squares different? Explain.

MAIN IDEA

Several methods help map human chromosomes.

The human genome, or all of the DNA in a human cell, is so large that mapping human genes is difficult. As a result, a combination of several methods is used. Pedigrees are useful for studying genetics in a family. Scientists can even gather a large number of pedigrees from people who are not related to look for inheritance patterns.

Differentiated Instruction

HANDS-ON ACTIVITY

Provide students with charts that are used to test for various color-vision defects. Many of them can be found in reference books and on the Internet. Have students examine the charts to determine what colors a person must be able to see if he or she is to interpret each chart correctly.

Other methods more directly study human chromosomes. A **karyotype** (KAR-ee-uh-TYP), for example, is a picture of all of the chromosomes in a cell. In order to study the chromosomes, chemicals are used to stain them. The chemical stains produce a pattern of bands on the chromosomes, as shown in **FIGURE 4.5.** The sizes and locations of the bands are very consistent for each chromosome, but the bands differ greatly among different chromosomes. Therefore, different chromosomes can be easily identified in a karyotype.

Karyotypes can show changes in chromosomes. Chromosome changes can be dramatic, such as when a person has too many chromosomes. In Down syndrome, for example, a person has an extra copy of at least part of chromosome 21. In XYY syndrome, a male has an extra Y chromosome. Other times, a karyotype reveals the loss of part of a chromosome. In the figure, you can see a deletion of a large part of chromosome 1. Scientists also use karyotypes to estimate the distances between genes on a chromosome. A karyotype can help show the possible location of a gene on a chromosome.

Chromosome mapping can be done directly by searching for a particular gene. All of the chromosomes are cut apart into smaller pieces. Then this library of chromosome parts is searched to find the gene. Although many genes and their locations have been identified through this process, it is a slow and inefficient method. The large-scale mapping of all of the genes on human chromosomes truly began with the Human Genome Project, an international effort to map, sequence, and identify all of the genes in the human genome.

Animated Biology HMHScience.com
GO ONLINE
Human Chromosomes

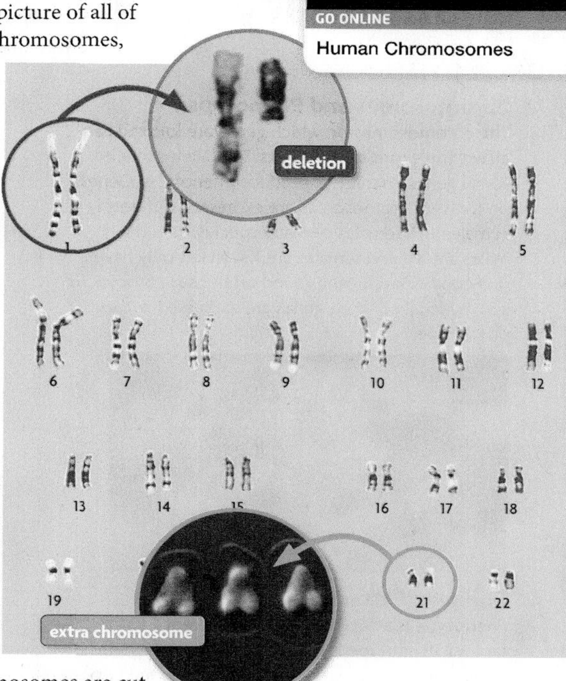

FIGURE 4.5 A karyotype can help show chromosomal disorders, such as the deletion in chromosome 1 (top inset) and the extra chromosome 21 in Down syndrome (bottom inset). (LM; magnifications: deletion 8000×; colored LM, extra chromosome 11,000×)

A Apply Why must a combination of methods be used to study human genetics?

7.4 Formative Assessment

SELF-CHECK Online HMHScience.com
GO ONLINE

REVIEWING MAIN IDEAS

1. How can Mendel's principles be used to study human traits?
2. Is a person who is homozygous recessive for a recessive genetic disease a carrier? Explain.
3. Describe how phenotypes can be used to predict genotypes in a **pedigree**.
4. How can a **karyotype** be used to study human chromosomes?

CRITICAL THINKING

5. **Apply** Suppose a colorblind male and a female with no recessive alleles for colorblindness have children. What is the probability they will have a colorblind son or daughter?
6. **Contrast** How do pedigrees for autosomal genes differ from pedigrees for sex-linked genes?

CONNECT TO PRINCIPLES OF GENETICS

7. Explain why Mendel's principles of inheritance can be applied to all sexually reproducing species.

Take It Further

About 95 percent of **Down syndrome** results from **trisomy 21,** having an extra copy of chromosome 21. However, Down syndrome can also result when an individual has a portion of chromosome 21 in triplicate. In this case, the total number of chromosomes is normal, but there are three copies of critical genes on chromosome 21. This occurs when a piece of chromosome 21 gets stuck onto another chromosome (usually chromosome 14) in the egg or sperm. When such an egg or sperm is involved in fertilization, the resulting individual has **translocation trisomy 21.** This form of Down syndrome is the only form that can be inherited from a parent.

Answers

A Apply because of the size of the human genome

Assess and Reteach

Assess Use the Section Self-Check or Section Quiz, both available at **HMHScience.com**.

Reteach Have students make a pedigree chart of a fictitious family in which cystic fibrosis occurs. The chart should show four generations and include some family members who are carriers and others who have the disease. Check the pedigree charts to be sure students have shown the inheritance pattern correctly.

7.4 FORMATIVE ASSESSMENT

1. They apply to autosomal single-gene traits with dominant and recessive patterns in all sexually reproducing organisms.
2. No, a carrier is someone who has a gene for the disorder but does not display the phenotype.
3. From a known phenotype, possible genotypes can be inferred.
4. A karyotype is an arrangement of pictures of all chromosomes in a cell that can be used to study their structure.
5. Zero; any son will inherit the normal allele from his mother. Any daughter will have a normal phenotype but will be a carrier.
6. Pedigrees for sex-linked genes will show more males with a recessive trait.
7. because offspring receive one copy of each gene from each parent

Chapter 7: Extending Mendelian Genetics 209

CHAPTER REVIEW

GO ONLINE

Encourage students to go to **HMHScience.com** for a detailed review of each section, including visuals and vocabulary practice.

Online Student Resources, Vocabulary Practice Worksheet

CHAPTER

7 Summary

BIG IDEA Mendel's laws of inheritance do not account for the expression of all traits, which may be influenced by the number of genes involved, linkages with other genes, or the environment in which the organism lives.

KEY CONCEPTS

7.1 Chromosomes and Phenotype

The chromosomes on which genes are located can affect the expression of traits. Two alleles of autosomal genes interact to produce phenotype. Genes on the sex chromosomes are expressed differently in males and females of many species. In humans, males are XY and females are XX. Males only have one copy of each gene found on the sex chromosomes, so all of those genes are expressed in their phenotype.

7.2 Complex Patterns of Inheritance

Phenotype is affected by many different factors. Phenotype is rarely the result of a simple dominant and recessive relationship between two alleles of a gene. Often, there are more than two possible alleles of a gene. Incomplete dominance produces an intermediate phenotype. Codominance results in both alleles being fully and separately expressed. Many traits are polygenic, or controlled by several genes. Interactions between genes and the environment also affect phenotype.

7.3 Gene Linkage and Mapping

Genes can be mapped to specific locations on chromosomes. Studies of wild type and mutant fruit flies led to a new understanding of genetics. Linked genes are often inherited together. During meiosis, linked genes can be separated from each other when parts of chromosomes are exchanged. By studying the frequency of cross-overs between chromosomes, it is possible to create a linkage map that shows the relative order of genes on a chromosome.

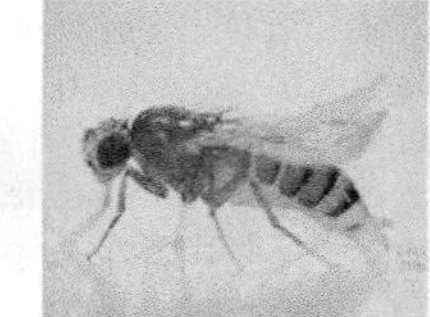

7.4 Human Genetics and Pedigrees

A combination of methods is used to study human genetics. Although most traits do not follow a simple dominant and recessive pattern, single-gene traits are important in the study of human genetics. Several genetic disorders are caused by a single gene with dominant and recessive alleles. Carriers are people who have an allele for a genetic disorder but do not express the allele in their phenotype. The patterns of genetic inheritance can be studied in families by pedigree analysis. Pedigree analysis is an indirect method of investigating human genotypes. Karyotypes can show large changes in chromosomes.

READING TOOLBOX SYNTHESIZE YOUR NOTES

Main Idea Web Use a main idea web like the one shown below to organize your notes. Make connections among the genetics concepts in the chapter, such as chromosomes and gene expression.

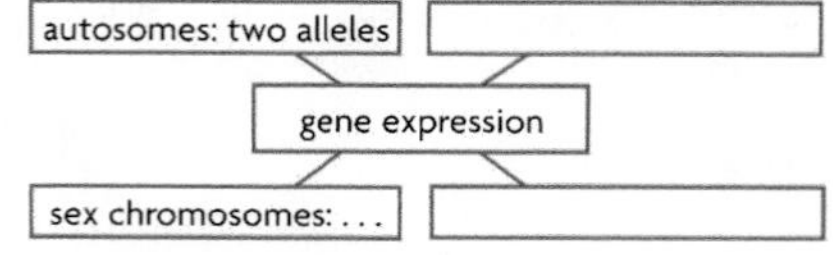

Concept Map Make a concept map like the one shown below to synthesize your knowledge of Mendelian genetics with more complex patterns of inheritance.

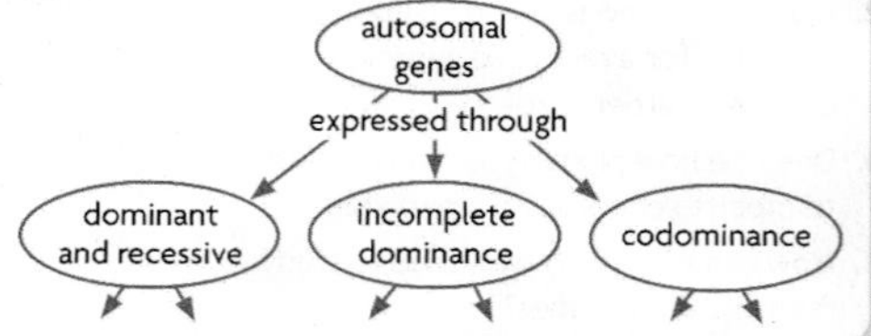

210 Unit 3: Genetics

Reviewing Vocabulary

1. Both can be related to genes on the X chromosome. A sex-linked gene is a gene on a sex chromosome. A carrier has one gene for a disorder but does not show the disorder, and many disorders are sex-linked.
2. Both are types of gene expression in which the phenotype of the heterozygote is different from either homozygote. In incomplete dominance, neither allele is completely dominant nor completely recessive. In codominance, both alleles are fully and equally expressed.
3. Both are maps of chromosomes. A linkage map shows the relative order of genes on a chromosome, based on observations of phenotypes. A karyotype is a picture that shows overall chromosome structure.
4. Polygenic trait: Answers should indicate a trait produced by two or more genes.
5. Pedigree: Answers could show an example of a pedigree chart.
6. X chromosome inactivation: Answers could show two XX cells, one cell with one X chromosome active and the other cell with the other X chromosome active.
7. A polygenic trait is the result of the interaction of many *(poly-)* genes *(genic)*.
8. Codominant alleles each express "the same amount" of dominance.

7 Review

INTERACTIVE Review
HMHScience.com
GO ONLINE
Review Games • Concept Map • Section Self-Checks

CHAPTER VOCABULARY

7.1	carrier sex-linked gene X chromosome inactivation	7.2	incomplete dominance codominance polygenic trait	7.3 7.4	linkage map pedigree karyotype

Reviewing Vocabulary

Compare and Contrast

Describe one similarity and one difference between the two terms in each of the following pairs.

1. sex-linked gene, carrier
2. incomplete dominance, codominance
3. linkage map, karyotype

Visualize Vocabulary

For each term below, use simple shapes, lines, or arrows to illustrate the meaning. Below each picture, write a short caption. Here's an example for the term *linkage map*.

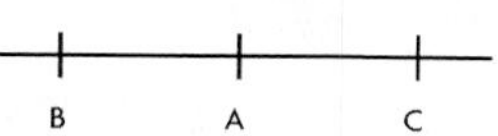

A linkage map shows the order of genes on a chromosome.

4. polygenic trait
5. pedigree
6. X chromosome inactivation

READING TOOLBOX WORD ORIGINS

Use the definitions of the word parts to answer the next two questions.

Word Part	Meaning
poly-	many
co-	together; the same amount
genic	produced by genes

7. How are the word parts *poly-* and *genic* related to the meaning of the term *polygenic trait*?

8. How is the prefix *co-* related to the meaning of the term *codominant*?

Reviewing MAIN IDEAS

9. Explain why disorders caused by dominant alleles on autosomes are less common than those caused by recessive alleles on autosomes.

10. Describe how the expression of sex-linked genes can differ between males and females.

11. How do codominance and incomplete dominance differ from a simple dominant and recessive relationship between alleles?

12. Humans have a tremendous range of hair, eye, and skin color. How does the polygenic nature of these traits explain the wide range of phenotypes?

13. Give two examples that demonstrate how the environment can interact with genotype to affect an organism's phenotype.

14. How did Morgan's research with fruit flies help to explain Punnett's and Bateson's observations of pea plants?

15. Explain how linked genes and cross-over frequencies are used to make linkage maps.

16. What are two main ways in which human genetics follows the genetic patterns seen in other organisms?

17. Under what circumstances could two individuals with no symptoms of a recessive genetic disease have children that do have the disease?

18. What are one similarity and one difference between patterns for autosomal and sex-linked genes on a pedigree chart?

19. What is a karyotype, and how can it be used to study human chromosomes and to map human genes?

CHAPTER REVIEW

Reviewing Main Ideas

9. because dominant disorders are frequently fatal, with no offspring produced
10. A female must have two recessive alleles to show a recessive phenotype, whereas a male needs only one recessive allele.
11. A dominant trait is one that is fully expressed in heterozygotes, so there are only two possible phenotypes. In codominance and incomplete dominance, both alleles are expressed in heterozygotes and interact to make a third phenotype, different from either homozygote.
12. These phenotypes are the result of the interaction of more than two genes, so there is a great variety of genetic expression of alleles and, hence, phenotypes.
13. Environmental factors such as nutrition and fetal development can affect height and size. Temperature can affect the sex of offspring in some animals, such as turtles.
14. Morgan's results showed that linked genes are on the same chromosome.
15. Genes on the same chromosome tend to be inherited together, but they can be separated by crossing over during meiosis. The frequency of crossing over can be used to determine the relative locations of genes on a chromosome and distances between them. Crossover frequencies are directly proportional to the distance between genes (in map units).
16. (1) Chromosomes independently assort during meiosis in all sexually reproducing organisms, and (2) the interaction of alleles (such as dominance and codominance) is the same across sexually reproducing species.
17. If the disorder is autosomal, both parents must be carriers (heterozygotes). If the disorder is sex-linked, the mother must be a carrier.
18. In both cases, the symbols represent the same thing. If the gene is autosomal, both males and females will show the phenotype with equal frequency. If the gene is sex-linked, mostly males will be affected.
19. A karyotype is a picture of stained chromosomes that shows differences between chromosomes, which can be used to detect chromosomal mutations.

Critical Thinking

20. No, if a person has just one allele for a dominant trait, that trait will be expressed. A carrier is someone who has an allele for a trait that is not expressed (recessive).

21. If a male has a recessive allele of a sex-linked gene, such as for colorblindness, the allele is always expressed because males have only one X chromosome. In contrast, females have two X chromosomes and therefore must have two copies of a recessive allele to express the trait.

22. Both codominance and incomplete dominance can explain these results. White-flowered and purple-flowered plants would be homozygotes, and the lavender-flowered plants would be heterozygotes. This fits with the 1:2:1 ratio of offspring. We cannot necessarily distinguish whether the lavender color is a result of codominance or incomplete dominance. Multiple alleles is not a good explanation, because it does not fit with the 1:2:1 ratio. With multiple alleles, there would likely be more than just the three phenotypes.

23.

Alleles:	Possible genotypes:
3 (A, B, C)	6 (AA, AB, AC, BB, BC, CC)
4 (A, B, C, D)	10 (AA, AB, AC, AD, BB, BC, BD, CC, CD, DD)

24. David and his unaffected siblings are either heterozygotes *(Dd)* or homozygous dominant *(DD)*. David's parents are heterozygotes *(Dd)*, because they are both unaffected but have an affected offspring. The affected grandparents and David's affected sister are homozygous recessive *(dd)*. The unspecified grandparents are either homozygous dominant *(DD)* or heterozygous *(Dd)*.

25. Because identical twins have the same genotypes, phenotype differences between them can be studied in connection with environmental differences.

Critical Thinking

20. Analyze Can a person be a carrier for a dominant genetic disorder? Explain.

21. Apply Both men and women can be colorblind, but there are approximately 100 times as many colorblind men as women in the world. Explain why men are more likely to be colorblind than women.

22. Apply Suppose two plants with light purple, or lavender, flowers are crossed. About 25% of the offspring have white flowers, 25% have purple flowers, and 50% have lavender flowers. Which of the following could explain these results: codominance, incomplete dominance, or multiple alleles? Explain.

23. Apply Copy the chart below into your science notebook. Following the provided example, fill in the chart to show the number of possible genotypes given 2, 3, or 4 alleles.

Number of Alleles	Number of Possible Genotypes
2 (A, B)	3 (AA, AB, BB)
3 (A, B, C)	
4 (A, B, C, D)	

24. Apply Some members of David's family have an autosomal recessive disease. David does not have the disease; neither do his parents, nor his two brothers. His maternal grandfather has the disease, his paternal grandmother has the disease, and his sister has the disease. Draw a pedigree chart to represent the genotypes of all grandparents, parents, and children. Next to each person, write his or her possible genotype.

25. Synthesize Why are studies of identical twins important in helping understand interactions between environment and genotype? Explain.

Interpreting Visuals

Copy into your science notebook the pedigree chart on the right to answer the next two questions. Use *A* as the dominant allele, and use *a* as the recessive allele.

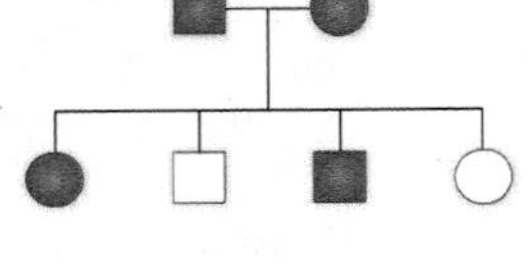

26. Analyze Is this trait most likely recessive or dominant? Explain.

27. Analyze What is the genotype of each individual in the pedigree chart? Explain your answers.

Analyzing Data Construct a Bar Graph

A scientist studies four linked traits in fruit flies and observes the frequency with which the traits cross over. The bar graph below shows the cross-over frequencies among genes A, B, C, and D. Use the graph to answer the next three questions.

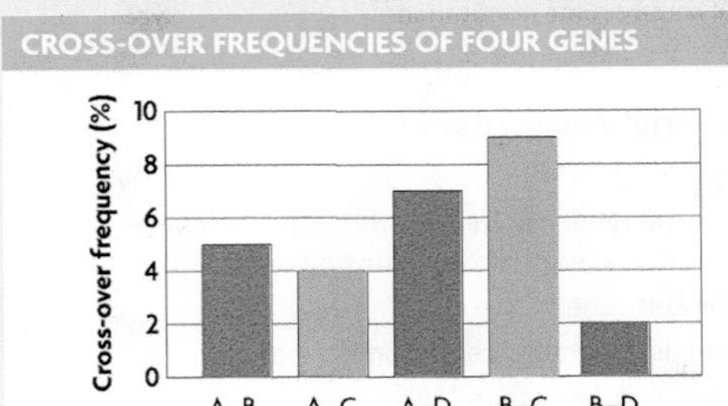

28. Evaluate Which two genes are least likely to be inherited together? How do you know?

29. Evaluate Which two genes are most likely to be inherited together? How do you know?

30. Apply Explain why a bar graph is an appropriate type of graph for displaying these data.

Making Connections

31. Write an Ad Imagine that you are starting a business that will make pedigree charts for people who want to map particular family traits. Write an ad in simple language that all readers will understand. Your ad should demonstrate that you have the necessary understanding of human genetics for a successful pedigree chart-making business.

32. Synthesize Look again at the tremendous range of human phenotypes in the photographs on the chapter opener. How is human genetics similar to and different from the genetics of Mendel's pea plants?

Interpreting Visuals

26. The trait is probably dominant because it is relatively common.

27. The parents must both be heterozygous for the dominant allele; the offspring without the trait must be homozygous recessive. The offspring with the trait can be either homozygous dominant or heterozygous.

Analyzing Data

28. B and C, because they are the farthest apart; they could be separated by cross-overs that occur anywhere between them.

29. B and D, because they are so close together; for them to be separated, a cross-over would have to occur in the very short distance between them.

30. because the percentages are not dependent on one other

Standards-Based Assessment

Record your answers on a separate piece of paper.

MULTIPLE CHOICE

1 A genotyped pedigree of 239 people shows evidence of an inheritable recessive disease. One female, however, doesn't fit the pattern of inheritance demonstrated by all of the other family members. What is ***most likely*** true of this individual?

A She had been treated for the disease.

B She accumulated additional mutations.

C She is immune to the disorder.

D She was genotyped incorrectly.

THINK THROUGH THE QUESTION

Consider both what a pedigree chart shows and what it doesn't show. Phenotypes are shown on a pedigree, but genotypes are inferred from the phenotypes.

2 Many animals, including humans, have sex chromosomes. Which of the following shows the sex chromosome genotype a normal human male would inherit from his parents?

A XX

B YY

C XY

D Y

3 A scientist studying two traits in mice knows that each trait is determined by one gene and that both genes are on the same chromosome. If the two traits are not always inherited together by the offspring of the mice, what is ***most likely*** true?

A The genes are not on the same chromosome.

B The genes are far enough apart to allow crossing over.

C The inheritance of these genes leads to codominance.

D One of the genes has a high rate of mutation.

4 Genes on a pair of chromosomes often cross over during meiosis, as shown in the diagram below.

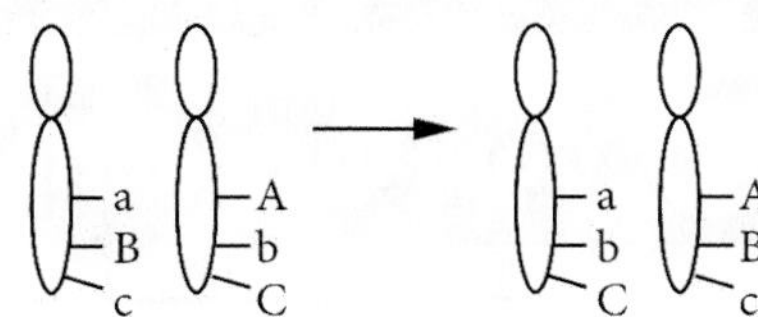

The discovery of crossing over added to Mendel's law of independent assortment, which states that genes assort independently of one another. What do crossovers indicate?

A Crossing over allows for more than two alleles of a gene.

B Independent assortment between genes depends on their locations.

C Genes do not assort independently of one another.

D Crossing over decreases genetic variation in populations.

5

Fruit Fly Dihybrid Cross

Eeww\eeWw	eW	ew	eW	ew
Ew				
Ew				
ew				
ew				

Red eyes is dominant (*E*); white eyes is recessive (*e*).
Normal wings is dominant (*W*); short wings is recessive (*w*).

A fruit fly with red eyes and short wings is crossed with a fruit fly with white eyes and normal wings. According to the cross shown in the diagram above, what is the expected phenotype of fruit flies in the shaded box?

A white eyes and normal wings

B white eyes and short wings

C red eyes and normal wings

D red eyes and short wings

Standards-Based Assessment

The Standards-Based Assessment questions will help students prepare for their final examination in the course. If you wish to give students practice in coding their answers, look for the Standards-Based Assessment Answer Sheet at **HMHScience.com**. To give students practice under timed testing conditions, allow them five minutes per question.

Question	Answer	Depth of Knowledge	Cognitive Complexity
1	D	II	H
2	C	I	L
3	B	III	M
4	B	III	H
5	A	III	H

KEY

Depth of Knowledge		Cognitive Complexity	
I	Recall	L	Low
II	Skill/Concept	M	Moderate
III	Strategic Thinking	H	High
IV	Extended Thinking		

Making Connections

31. Responses should define sex-linked and autosomal genes and explain how chromosomes are inherited, including a comparison between sex-linked and autosomal inheritance.

32. Both are the result of the same processes: gamete formation by way of meiosis, and interaction of alleles. However, all of the traits Mendel studied were autosomal, dominant/recessive, two-allele traits. The human phenotypes on the chapter opener pages are the result of both autosomal and sex-linked genes, multiple alleles and genes, and many types of allelic interactions, in addition to simple dominant/recessive genetics.

CHAPTER 8

Instruction and Intervention Support

From DNA to Proteins

① Core Instruction

The **Core Instruction** resources below can be used for all students. Core instruction should be followed by ongoing assessment to determine which students need further help.

Available in both English and Spanish

Available Online

Section	Instruction	PRINT	ONLINE	Labs
8.1	Textbook **Identifying DNA as the Genetic Material**	■	●	Extracting DNA **Video Lab** DNA Extraction from Wheat Germ
	Animated Biology Hershey-Chase Experiment		●	
	PowerPresentation and Notes 8.1		●	
8.2	Textbook **Structure of DNA**	■	●	
	PowerPresentation and Notes 8.2		●	
8.3	Textbook **DNA Replication**	■	●	**QuickLab** Replication
	Animated Biology Replicating DNA		●	
	PowerPresentation and Notes 8.3		●	
8.4	Textbook **Transcription**	■	●	Modeling Transcription
	Animated Biology Transcription		●	
	PowerPresentation and Notes 8.4		●	
8.5	Textbook **Translation**	■	●	
	Animated Biology Build a Protein		●	
	PowerPresentation and Notes 8.5		●	
8.6	Textbook **Gene Expression and Regulation**	■	●	
	PowerPresentation and Notes 8.6		●	
8.7	Textbook **Mutations**	■	●	UV Light and Skin Cancer (Design Your Own) Observing *Drosophila* Mutations Exploring Protein Crystallization (Challenge Lab)
	PowerPresentation and Notes 8.7		●	

Additional online resources available for this chapter include **Interactive Whiteboard Resources.**

GO ONLINE! for all your teacher resources at HMHScience.com

② Support and Intervention

Support and Intervention resources are useful for students who need targeted help beyond the Core Instruction

Resources	PRINT	ONLINE
Assess and Reteach (TE wrap)	■	●
Concept Map		●
Interactive Reader	■	●
Interactive Review Games		●
Section Self-Checks		●
Study Guide B		●
Virtual Investigation Gene Regulation		●
Vocabulary Practice Worksheets		●

③ Specialized Support

Students who need more intensive personalized intervention benefit from **Specialized Support** resources.

Resources	PRINT	ONLINE
Chapter Audio Files		●
Differentiated Instruction Inclusion, Below Level, and English Learners (TE wrap)	■	●
ELL Strategies	■	●
Modified Lesson Plans for English Learners		●
Reinforcement Worksheets		●
Study Guide A		●

Extension and Assessment

Enrichment and Challenge

Resources	PRINT	ONLINE
Active Reading Worksheets		●
Data Analysis Practice Worksheet		●
Differentiated Instruction Pre-AP (TE wrap)	■	●
Pre-AP Activity Modeling DNA Structure		●
Smart Grapher Activity		●
The Inside Story and **Take It Further** (TE wrap)	■	●
Unit Project		●
WebLinks		●
WebQuest Transgenic Organisms (8.5)		●

Assessment

Resources	PRINT	ONLINE
Alternative Assessment		●
Chapter Tests A and B		●
Diagnostic Test		●
ExamView Banks		●
Extended Response Test		●
Online Assessment System		●
Section Quizzes		●
Standards-Based Assessment	■	●

CHAPTER 8

Chapter Overview

- **Section 1** outlines the history behind the identification of DNA as the genetic material in living organisms.
- **Section 2** identifies the components of DNA and it's structure.
- **Section 3** explains the purpose and process of DNA replication.
- **Section 4** explains the purpose and process of transcription.
- **Section 5** explains the purpose and process of translation.
- **Section 6** discusses the roles of DNA, RNA, and environmental factors in gene expression and cell differentiation.
- **Section 7** discusses and illustrates mutations.

▼ Focus and Motivate

Why is this mouse glowing?

Have students read the boxed text that explains the mouse's genetic modification. **Ask,** Why would someone want to make a mouse glow? to demonstrate the effectiveness of GFP as a marker

Tell students that mice are important test subjects because they have many of the same or similar genes as humans have. Researchers can now use GFP to track cancer cells or to map the activity of neurons in the brain.

BIOZINE
HMHScience.com

Students can access BioZine at **HMHScience.com** to take a poll about current issues in biology.

CHAPTER 8 From DNA to Proteins

BIG IDEA DNA and RNA are the genetic material in all living things and provide the molecular basis for reproduction and development.

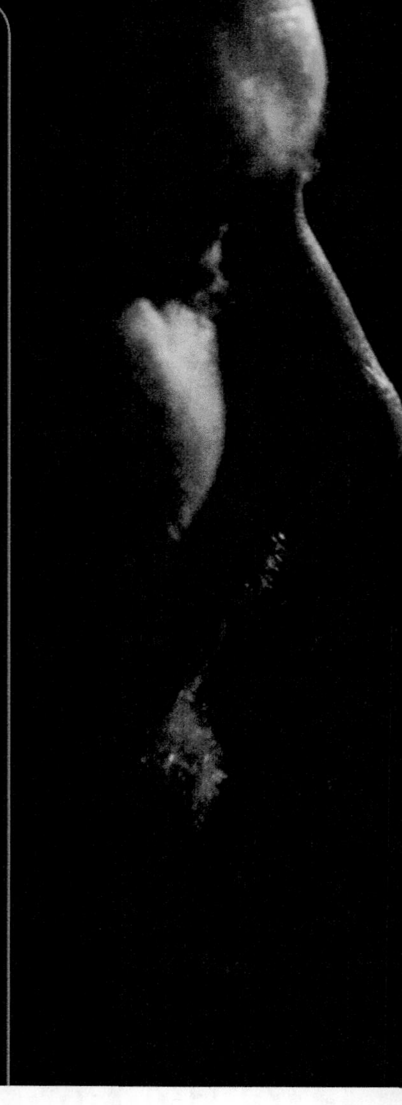

ONLINE BIOLOGY HMHScience.com

ONLINE Labs
- Extracting DNA
- **QuickLab** Replication
- UV Light and Skin Cancer
- Modeling Transcription
- Observing *Drosophila* Mutations
- Exploring Protein Crystallization
- **Video Lab** DNA Extraction from Wheat Germ

Student Activity

Purpose **Model replication by using a template and complementary forms.**

Prepare Draw two complementary strands on the board, using two sets of paired symbols, for example +/− and ○/□. Then redraw each strand to the right of the original, separated and labeled *Template 1* and *Template 2.*

Note: A student worksheet for this activity is provided in Teacher Resources at **HMHScience.com.** If you choose to use the Replication worksheet, you will need a copy and a pair of scissors for each group of three students.

Why is this mouse glowing?

This mouse's eerie green glow comes from green fluorescent protein (GFP), which glows under ultraviolet light. Scientists put a GFP gene from a glowing jellyfish into a virus that was then used to infect a mouse egg. The jellyfish gene became part of the mouse's genes. As a result, the mouse's cells produce the same jellyfish protein and make the mouse glow. Researchers hope to use GFP to track cancer cells.

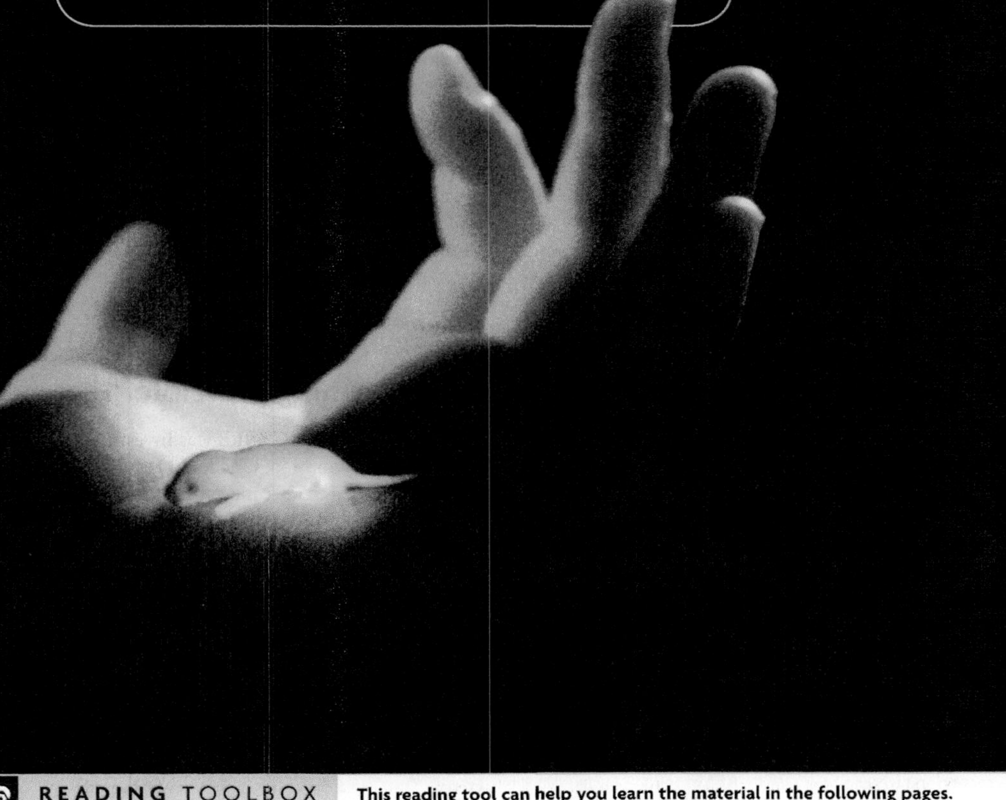

READING TOOLBOX **This reading tool can help you learn the material in the following pages.**

USING LANGUAGE

Finding Examples When you are reading scientific explanations, finding examples can help you put a concept into practical terms. Thinking of your own examples will help you remember what you read.

YOUR TURN

For each category of items below, brainstorm as many examples as you can think of that could fit into the category.

1. hereditary traits
2. words that include the word part *–her–*

Introduce Point out that *replication* is the term used for DNA synthesis, which occurs before mitosis. Each strand of the DNA molecule acts as a template, or pattern, for making a complementary strand. The word *complement* refers to a corresponding form that completes a whole, for example, DNA base pairs.

Have two volunteers complete the single strands on the board. Point out that the complementary strand for Template 1 goes below the original and the strand for Template 2 goes above.

Discuss Have students compare the replicated strands with the original. **Ask**

- How does a template work? It serves as a pattern or gauge for that which is to be made.
- Is the resulting strand a mirror image? No, the complementary strand is made up of different shapes.
- What has happened to the original DNA molecule? It has been divided between the two new strands. You may want to discuss this in terms of what is conserved.

Activate Prior Knowledge

Direct students' attention to the chapter title. **Ask**

- What is the relationship between DNA and proteins? DNA contains the information a cell needs to make proteins.
- Why are proteins important? Proteins make up the structural components of a cell and direct most of its chemical activity.
- How do Mendel's experiments with pea plants compare to the experiment with the glowing mouse? Both examine the effects of DNA. Mendel crossbred plants of the same species; the mouse experiment used biotechnology to transfer DNA between species.

Preview Vocabulary

Academic Vocabulary

Tell students that understanding that DNA is a code is critical to this chapter. The word *code* has different applications:

- a systematic collection of laws or regulations
- a system of signals or symbols used to transmit a message
- a system of symbols and rules used to program a computer

Ask, What idea is central to each definition? information is transmitted in a systematic way

English Learners Ask students if they are familiar with the word *code*. Lead them to the idea that a code carries a message and that DNA is a code. Point out the titles in **Sections 4** and **5.** Discuss that *transcription* involves copying the code and *translation* involves converting it into its final form.

Answers

1. Students will likely offer physical features of themselves, animals, or plants. Traits may include hair color, eye color, height, flower color, etc.
2. inherit, inheritable, inheritance, inherent, inherence, heritage, or heredity

SECTION 8.1

▼ Plan and Prepare

Activate Prior Knowledge In 1866, Mendel reported that the transferal of pollen between different types of true-breeding pea plants caused a noticeable transformation in some of the offspring. **Ask,** What do you think Mendel's observations have to do with the transforming principle mentioned in this section? Mendel studied specific traits related to genes that are made up of DNA, the transforming principle.

▼ Teach

TEACH FROM VISUALS

FIGURE 1.1 Review Griffith's experiments. **Ask**

- What were the variables in Griffith's experiment? dead and alive S bacteria, and live R bacteria
- Based on the first three results, what should have happened in the fourth experiment? The mice should have lived because the S bacteria, along with whatever caused the bacteria to be deadly, had been killed by heat.

8.1 Identifying DNA as the Genetic Material

KEY CONCEPT **DNA was identified as the genetic material through a series of experiments.**

VOCABULARY

bacteriophage

MAIN IDEAS

- Griffith finds a "transforming principle."
- Avery identifies DNA as the transforming principle.
- Hershey and Chase confirm that DNA is the genetic material.

Connect to Your World

Some people think that a complicated answer is better than a simple one. In the early 1900's, for example, most scientists thought that DNA's chemical composition was too repetitive for it to be the genetic material. Proteins, which are more variable in structure, appeared to be a better candidate. Starting in the 1920s, experiments provided data that did not support this idea. By the 1950s, sufficient evidence showed that DNA—the same molecule that codes for GFP in the glowing mouse—carries genetic information.

MAIN IDEA

Griffith finds a "transforming principle."

In 1928 the British microbiologist Frederick Griffith was investigating two forms of the bacterium that causes pneumonia. One form is surrounded by a coating made of carbohydrates. This form is called the S form because its colonies look smooth. The second form of bacteria does not have a smooth coating and is called the R, or rough, form. As you can see in **FIGURE 1.1**, when Griffith injected the two types of bacteria into mice, only the S type killed the mice. When the S bacteria were killed with heat before injection, the mice were unaffected. Therefore, only live S bacteria would cause the mice to die.

READING TOOLBOX

TAKING NOTES

Make a table to keep track of the experiments discussed in this section and to note how they contributed to our understanding of DNA.

Experiment	Results
Griffith's mice	A transferable material changed harmless bacteria into disease-causing bacteria.

FIGURE 1.1 Griffith's Experiments

The S form of the bacterium is deadly; the R form is not.

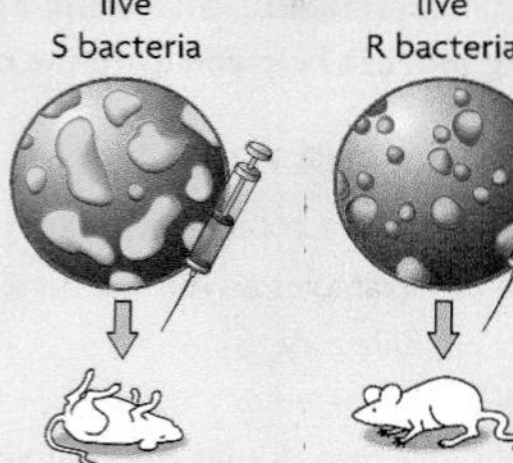

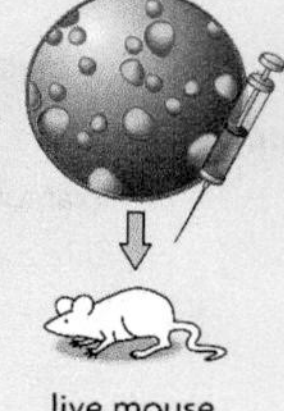

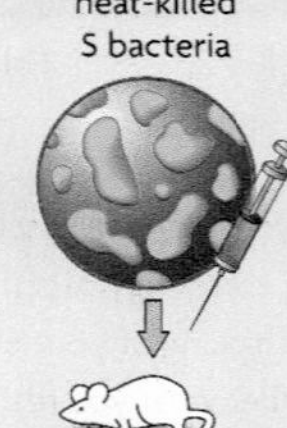

Differentiated Instruction

BELOW LEVEL

Suggest that students use the PLAN strategy while reading this chapter:

Predict what a section is about using the key concept and main ideas.

Locate key vocabulary and important concepts.

Add definitions and details to their notes while reading.

Note in a paragraph or two a summary of the section.

Teacher Toolkit, Section C, PLAN

PRE-AP

Explain to students that Griffith was working on a vaccine for pneumonia when he noticed the transformation bacteria. He was hoping to use heat-killed S bacteria to stimulate an immune response. Have students prepare a sequence diagram of the experiments shown in **FIGURE 1.1,** indicating what each demonstrated. Have students change the result of the fourth experiment to reflect a healthy mouse. Ask them to speculate what Griffith's next steps would have been in testing for a vaccine.

Teacher Toolkit, Section C, Sequence Diagram

Griffith next injected mice with a combination of heat-killed S bacteria and live R bacteria. To his surprise, the mice died. Even more surprising, he found live S bacteria in blood samples from the dead mice. Griffith concluded that some material must have been transferred from the heat-killed S bacteria to the live R bacteria. Whatever that material was, it contained information that changed harmless R bacteria into disease-causing S bacteria. Griffith called this mystery material the "transforming principle."

Infer **What evidence suggested that there was a transforming principle?**

CONNECT TO

MICROBIOLOGY

Much of our knowledge of the chemical basis of genetics has come from the study of bacteria. You will learn much more about bacteria in the chapter **Viruses and Prokaryotes.**

MAIN IDEA

Avery identifies DNA as the transforming principle.

What exactly is the transforming principle that Griffith discovered? That question puzzled Oswald Avery and his fellow biologists. They worked for more than ten years to find the answer. Avery's team began by combining living R bacteria with an extract made from S bacteria. This procedure allowed them to directly observe the transformation of R bacteria into S bacteria in a petri dish.

Avery's group next developed a process to purify their extract. They then performed a series of tests to find out if the transforming principle was DNA or protein.

- **Qualitative tests** Standard chemical tests showed that no protein was present. In contrast, tests revealed that DNA was present.
- **Chemical analysis** As you can see in **FIGURE 1.2**, the proportions of elements in the extract closely matched those found in DNA. Proteins contain almost no phosphorus.
- **Enzyme tests** When the team added to the extract enzymes known to break down proteins, the extract still transformed the R bacteria to the S form. Also, transformation occurred when researchers added an enzyme that breaks down RNA (another nucleic acid). Transformation failed to occur only when they added an enzyme that specifically destroys DNA.

FIGURE 1.2 Avery's Discoveries

CHEMICAL ANALYSIS OF TRANSFORMING PRINCIPLE

	% Nitrogen (N)	% Phosphorus (P)	Ratio of N to P
Sample A	14.21	8.57	1.66
Sample B	15.93	9.09	1.75
Sample C	15.36	9.04	1.69
Sample D	13.40	8.45	1.58
Known value for DNA	15.32	9.05	1.69

Source: Avery, O. T. et al., *The Journal of Experimental Medicine* 79:2.

B Analyze **How do the data support the hypothesis that DNA, not protein, is the transforming principle?**

Oswald Avery

In 1944 Avery and his group presented this and other evidence to support their conclusion that DNA must be the transforming principle, or genetic material. The results created great interest. However, some scientists questioned whether the genetic material in bacteria was the same as that in other organisms. Despite Avery's evidence, some scientists insisted that his extract must have contained protein.

Summarize **List the key steps in the process that Avery's team used to identify the transforming principle.**

ENGLISH LEARNERS

After students read the section, have them form three groups. Set up three pieces of chart paper, one each for the experiments of Griffith, Avery, and Hershey and Chase. Label the charts and include this question on each: "What did the experiments show and how did they show it?" Assign a group to each chart and have students answer the question, adding as much information as they can. Then rotate the groups. Discuss the answers with the class.

Teacher Toolkit, Section C, Carousel Review

The Inside Story

Following World War I, **Frederick Griffith** and **Oswald Avery** were both engaged in the effort to stop a global epidemic of **influenza.** Griffith was in London, working on a vaccine to protect against bacterial infection. Avery was in New York, developing serums to control bacterial growth. Neither was thinking about DNA.

Vaccines use either dead or weakened bacteria to stimulate an immune response. In setting up a negative control for his experiments, Griffith accidentally discovered the transforming principle that could change a population of bacteria from one type to another. When Avery first learned of Griffith's discovery, he refused to accept the results. This was no small issue for Avery. He was working on developing **serums** specific to known types of bacteria. What good would a serum be if bacteria could change from one type to another?

Ironically it was Avery, not Griffith, who eventually isolated and identified DNA as the transforming principle. And, equally ironic, Avery's results would also be met with skepticism—until Hershey and Chase came along.

Integrating Microbiology

Heating bacteria to 60°C (140°F) can kill the bacteria without denaturing their DNA. DNA can remain unchanged up to 90°C (194°F). Therefore, the S bacteria in Griffith's experiment died, but their DNA remained intact.

Answers

A **Infer** R bacteria in the presence of dead S bacteria became pathogenic.

B **Analyze** The transforming principle contained about the same relative amount of phosphorus as DNA. Proteins contain almost no phosphorus.

C **Summarize** Avery and his team purified the transforming factor and then performed three tests: for the presence of DNA versus protein, for the relative proportion of nitrogen to phosphorus, and for interaction with specific enzymes.

Teach *continued*

TEACH FROM VISUALS

FIGURE 1.3 Point out that the phage functions almost like a hypodermic syringe. The DNA stored in the head is injected through the tail into the bacterium. **Ask,** What happens to the phage after it injects its DNA? It is just an empty shell and can no longer cause disease.

Answers

A Apply Avery's data strongly suggested that DNA was the transforming principle. Hershey and Chase confirmed this by directly labeling the DNA and proteins of bacteriophages growing in culture. The presence of radioactive phosphorus inside the bacteria clearly showed that it was the DNA, not protein, that was transmitted between the viruses and the bacteria.

Assess and Reteach

Assess Use the Section Self-Check or Section Quiz, both available at **HMHScience.com**.

Reteach Have students connect Griffith's experiments to those of Hershey and Chase. Then have them speculate about what was happening within the bacterial population in Griffith's fourth experiment.

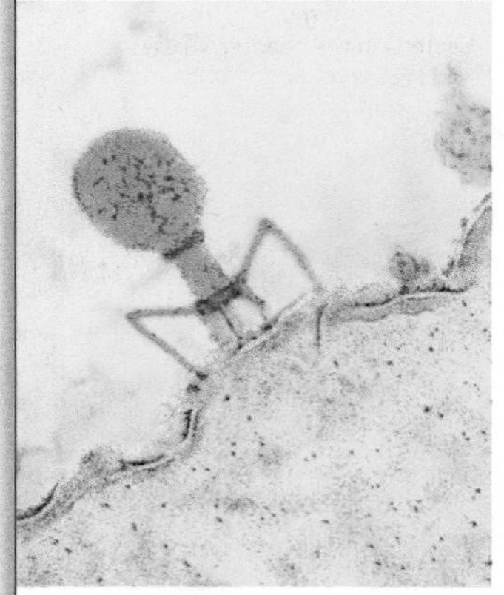

FIGURE 1.3 This micrograph shows the protein coat of a bacteriophage (orange) after it has injected its DNA into an *E. coli* bacterium (blue). (colored TEM; magnification 115,000×)

MAIN IDEA

Hershey and Chase confirm that DNA is the genetic material.

Conclusive evidence for DNA as the genetic material came in 1952 from two American biologists, Alfred Hershey and Martha Chase. Hershey and Chase were studying viruses that infect bacteria. This type of virus, called a **bacteriophage** (bak-TIR-ee-uh-FAYJ), or "phage" for short, takes over a bacterium's genetic machinery and directs it to make more viruses.

Phages such as the ones Hershey and Chase studied are relatively simple—little more than a DNA molecule surrounded by a protein coat. This two-part structure of phages offered a perfect opportunity to answer the question, Is the genetic material made of DNA or protein? By discovering which part of a phage (DNA or protein) actually entered a bacterium, as shown in **FIGURE 1.3**, they could answer this question once and for all.

Hershey and Chase thought up a clever procedure that made use of the chemical elements found in protein and DNA. Protein contains sulfur but very little phosphorus, while DNA contains phosphorus but no sulfur. The researchers grew phages in cultures that contained radioactive isotopes of sulfur or phosphorus. Hershey and Chase then used these radioactively tagged phages in two experiments.

- **Experiment 1** In the first experiment, bacteria were infected with phages that had radioactive sulfur atoms in their protein molecules. Hershey and Chase then used a kitchen blender and a centrifuge to separate the bacteria from the parts of the phages that remained outside the bacteria. When they examined the bacteria, they found no significant radioactivity.
- **Experiment 2** Next, Hershey and Chase repeated the procedure with phages that had DNA tagged with radioactive phosphorus. This time, radioactivity was clearly present inside the bacteria.

From their results, Hershey and Chase concluded that the phages' DNA had entered the bacteria, but the protein had not. Their findings finally convinced scientists that the genetic material is DNA and not protein.

A Apply How did Hershey and Chase build upon Avery's chemical analysis results?

8.1 Formative Assessment

SELF-CHECK Online
HMHScience.com
GO ONLINE

REVIEWING MAIN IDEAS

1. What was "transformed" in Griffith's experiment?
2. How did Avery and his team identify the transforming principle?
3. Summarize how Hershey and Chase confirmed that DNA is the genetic material.

CRITICAL THINKING

4. **Summarize** Why was the **bacteriophage** an excellent choice for research to determine whether genes are made of DNA or proteins?
5. **Analyze** Choose one experiment from this section and explain how the results support the conclusion.

CONNECT TO

MENDELIAN GENETICS

6. Describe how Mendel's studies relate to the experiments discussed in this section.

8.1 FORMATIVE ASSESSMENT

1. Harmless R bacteria were transformed into pathogenic S bacteria.
2. They purified the component of S bacteria that caused R bacteria to transform into S bacteria. This extract was tested for the presence of DNA or protein, its chemical composition, and its reaction to enzymes.
3. They labeled the protein of bacteriophages with radioactive sulfur and their DNA with radioactive phosphorus. The bacteriophages were allowed to infect bacteria. Hershey and Chase separated the phages from the infected bacteria and showed that phosphorus, a component of DNA, not sulfur, had entered the bacteria.
4. A bacteriophage consists of little more than a protein coat surrounding DNA. The protein coat is left behind when the viral DNA enters a bacterium.
5. Answers will vary depending on the experiment chosen.
6. Both Mendel's experiments and this series of experiments demonstrate how ideas build on each other, and how data from one experiment can raise new questions and lead to more experiments and data. Mendel's observations and ideas about heredity helped lead to questions about the physical nature of what was being transmitted from parent to offspring.

Epigenetics

S.T.E.M. Interactions

Inheritance through the passing on of genes is well understood, but it is becoming increasingly clear that it is not the whole story when it comes to our DNA. Even if DNA is completely unchanged, how it is expressed can be controlled by "tags" on our genes, and those tags just might pass through to future generations. The branch of science that investigates how these tags affect genes is called epigenetics (*epi-* means "over, above"), and it can have implications for disease, nutrition, and many lifestyle choices people make.

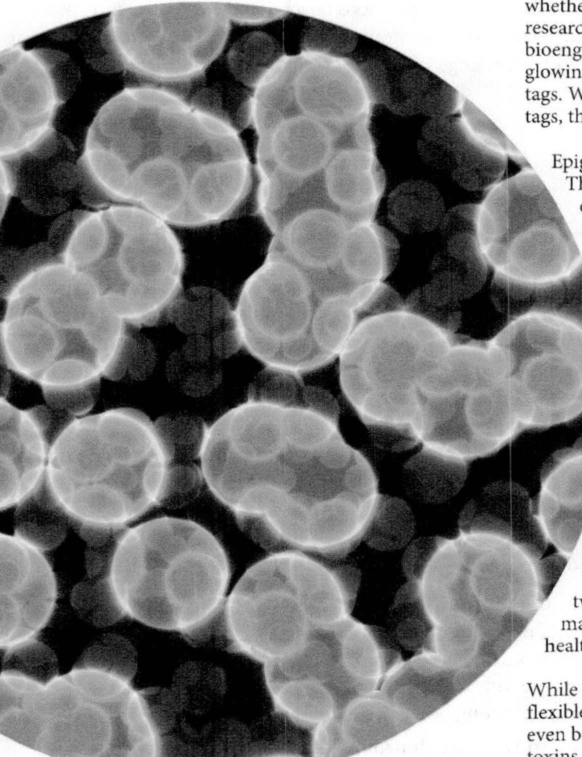

Researchers have demonstrated the effects of epigenetic tags on cells by using bioengineered cells that express the GFP protein—the same protein that can be used to make mice glow—when the gene is switched on. Researchers then added a chemical that causes methyl ($-CH_3$) group tags to attach to genes. Methyl group tags are one of the ways that genes are controlled in living organisms. They attach to cytosine on DNA without disrupting the DNA double helix itself. Methyl and acetyl ($-COCH_3$) groups also can attach to histone proteins, controlling how tightly the DNA is wound around the histone spools and thereby controlling whether the segments of DNA are copied. The researchers found that methyl group tags added to the bioengineered cell culture prevented the cells from glowing, indicating that the genes were "silenced" by the tags. When another chemical was added to remove the tags, the cells began to glow brightly again.

Epigenetic tags are critical for our cell processes. They are responsible for much of how our cells differentiated—changing from stem cells into eye, liver, bone, or any other specialized cell type that organisms have. Epigenetic tags also are responsible for genetic imprinting, determining whether a father's or mother's copy of a gene is expressed.

Epigenetic tags play a role in more unlikely processes as well. Researchers have made the surprising discovery that high or low maternal care in mice may affect the number of methyl group epigenetic tags in offspring that is then passed down through generations and affects how the offspring handle stress. In Sweden, scientists looked at 200 years' worth of harvest records to determine that the amount of food that boys had when they were between the ages of nine and twelve, when immature sperm cells were first maturing in their bodies, may have affected the health of their future children and grandchildren.

While DNA remains fixed for a lifetime, epigenomes are flexible and able to respond to the environment, and can even be formed through food choices and exposure to toxins. This discovery has changed the way scientists are looking at how genes affect phenotypes and at the influence of our lifestyle choices on not only our health but also the health of generations to come.

Introduce

Ask students to open their textbook to a random page, place a bookmark there, and then close the book. **Ask,** what is the purpose of the bookmark? a shortcut to the page Could you find that page easily a month from now? (yes) Explain that the bookmark essentially tags the page. Epigenetic tags are similar in that they mark a gene, reminding it to act in a certain way (produce certain proteins) even when the signal is long gone. The signal may result from stress hormones, nutrients from diet, or other body cells.

Discuss

Many cancers are the result of epigenetic tags, as the tags can promote the uncontrolled cell growth that forms tumors or silence the suppressor genes that stop tumors from forming. Epigenomic drug therapies have been developed for several types of cancers. Ask students how they think these therapies might work and what challenges must be overcome to be successful. The challenge for all cancer medicines is to target certain cells and not others. In the case of epigenetic tags, the goal is to target specific methylated genes and not cells for which methyl group tags may be beneficial.

Other diseases and disorders, including mental health disorders and immune diseases, also have epigenetic influence. Discuss obstacles to epigenetic research on humans. Guide students to understand that research on humans is constrained by the following factors:

1. Our long life spans: it takes four generations to demonstrate epigenetic inheritance because three generations—a pregnant mother, the fetus, and the reproductive cells of the fetus—might be directly influenced by another factor all at once
2. Our wide range of genetic diversity, especially compared with animals bred for laboratory use
3. The transient nature of epigenetic tags: they can be switched on and off by environmental triggers
4. Ethical considerations: human experimentation is rightfully under strict regulation

SECTION 8.2

B.1.2 Analyze how the shape of a molecule determines its role in the many different types of cellular processes (e.g., metabolism, homeostasis, growth and development, and heredity) and understand that the majority of these processes involve proteins that act as enzymes.

B.4.2 Construct an explanation for how the structure of DNA determines the structure of proteins which carry out the essential functions of life through systems of specialized cells.

▼ Plan and Prepare

Activate Prior Knowledge Tell students that scientists found it hard to accept DNA as the genetic material because of its structural simplicity. **Ask**

- What are some examples of simple units that can be used to produce great complexity? letters of an alphabet, 0s and 1s of computer code, building blocks
- Which of these examples offer the best analogy to DNA? alphabet and computer code, because both are informational units

▼ Teach

TEACH FROM VISUALS

Have students compare the structure of the nucleotide monomer in **VISUAL VOCAB** to the DNA polymer shown in CONNECT TO. **Ask**

- What part of the monomer serves to connect the two DNA strands? connection between bases
- What is the pattern of that connection? single ring bonding to double ring

8.2 Structure of DNA

KEY CONCEPT **DNA structure is the same in all organisms.**

VOCABULARY

nucleotide
double helix
base pairing rules

MAIN IDEAS

- DNA is composed of four types of nucleotides.
- Watson and Crick developed an accurate model of DNA's three-dimensional structure.
- Nucleotides always pair in the same way.

Connect to Your World

The experiments of Hershey and Chase confirmed that DNA carries the genetic information, but they left other big questions unanswered: What exactly is this genetic information? How does DNA store this information? Scientists in the early 1950s still had a limited knowledge of the structure of DNA, but that was about to change dramatically.

MAIN IDEA

DNA is composed of four types of nucleotides.

Since the 1920s, scientists have known that the DNA molecule is a very long polymer, or chain of repeating units. The small units, or monomers, that make up DNA are called **nucleotides** (NOO-klee-uh-TYDZ). Each nucleotide has three parts.

- A phosphate group (one phosphorus with four oxygens)
- A ring-shaped sugar called deoxyribose
- A nitrogen-containing base (a single or double ring built around nitrogen and carbon atoms)

VISUAL VOCAB

The small units, or monomers, that make up a strand of DNA are called **nucleotides.** Nucleotides have three parts.

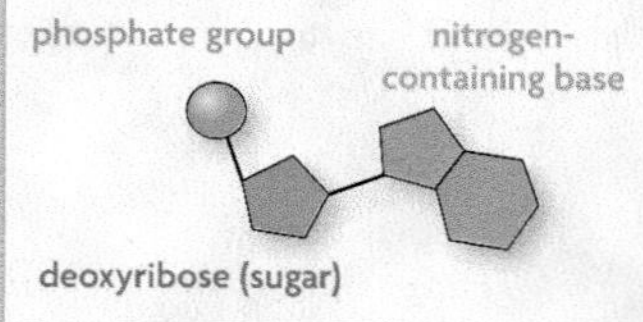

One molecule of human DNA contains billions of nucleotides, but there are only four types of nucleotides in DNA. These nucleotides differ only in their nitrogen-containing bases.

The four bases in DNA are shown in **FIGURE 2.1.** Notice that the bases cytosine (C) and thymine (T) have a single-ring structure. Adenine (A) and guanine (G) have a larger, double-ring structure. The letter abbreviations refer both to the bases and to the nucleotides that contain the bases.

For a long time, scientists hypothesized that DNA was made up of equal amounts of the four nucleotides, and so the DNA in all organisms was exactly the same. That hypothesis was a key reason that it was so hard to convince scientists that DNA was the genetic material. They reasoned that identical molecules could not carry different instructions across all organisms.

CONNECT TO

BIOCHEMISTRY

The nucleotides in a strand of DNA all line up in the same direction. As a result, DNA has chemical polarity, which means that the two ends of the DNA strand are different. The 5′ carbon is located at one end of the DNA strand, and the 3′ carbon is located at the other end. When the two strands of DNA pair together, the 5′ end of one strand aligns with the 3′ end of the other strand.

5′ A T G C T A 3′ 3′ 5′

Differentiated Instruction

BELOW LEVEL

Prepare a series of short-answer questions or true/false statements to check students' knowledge of DNA structure. This will help students focus on the critical information in the section. Students should answer the questions before reading and then check and correct their responses as they read.

Teacher Toolkit, Section C, Anticipation Guide

PRE-AP

Have students prepare a timeline of the discoveries detailed in **Sections 2** and **3.** Have them identify each critical discovery about the genetic makeup of a cell, the point in time when each was revealed, and the scientist(s) responsible for each discovery.

Teacher Toolkit, Section C, Timeline

FIGURE 2.1 The Four Nitrogen-Containing Bases of DNA

PYRIMIDINES = SINGLE RING			PURINES = DOUBLE RING		
Name of Base	Structural Formula	Model	Name of Base	Structural Formula	Model
thymine	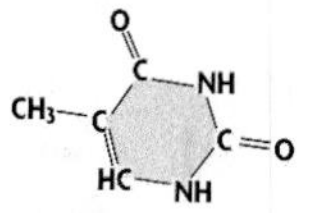	 T	adenine	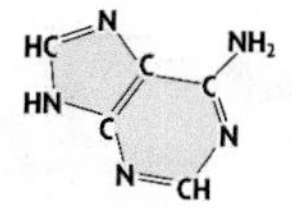	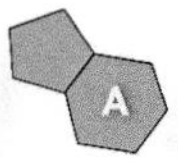 A
cytosine	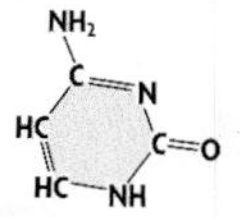	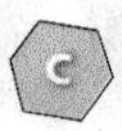 C	guanine	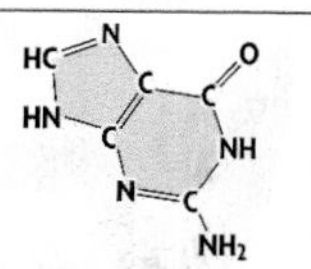	 G

A Compare Which base is most similar in structure to thymine?

By 1950 Erwin Chargaff changed the thinking about DNA by analyzing the DNA of several organisms. Chargaff found that the same four bases are found in the DNA of all organisms, but the proportion of the four bases differs somewhat from organism to organism. In the DNA of each organism, the amount of adenine approximately equals the amount of thymine. Similarly, the amount of cytosine roughly equals the amount of guanine. These A = T and C = G relationships became known as Chargaff's rules.

B Summarize How do the four DNA nucleotides differ in structure?

READING TOOLBOX

VOCABULARY

An amine is a molecule that contains nitrogen. Notice that the four DNA bases end in *-ine* and all contain nitrogen.

MAIN IDEA

Watson and Crick developed an accurate model of DNA's three-dimensional structure.

The breakthrough in understanding the structure of DNA came in the early 1950s through the teamwork of American geneticist James Watson and British physicist Francis Crick. Watson and Crick were supposed to be studying the structure of proteins. Both men, however, were more fascinated by the challenge of figuring out DNA's structure. Their interest was sparked not only by the findings of Hershey, Chase, and Chargaff but also by the work of the biochemist Linus Pauling. Pauling had found that the structure of some proteins was a helix, or spiral. Watson and Crick hypothesized that DNA might also be a helix.

X-Ray Evidence

At the same time, Rosalind Franklin, shown in **FIGURE 2.2**, and Maurice Wilkins were studying DNA using a technique called x-ray crystallography. When DNA is bombarded with x-rays, the atoms in DNA diffract the x-rays in a pattern that can be captured on film. Franklin's x-ray photographs of DNA showed an X surrounded by a circle. Franklin's data gave Watson and Crick the clues they needed. The patterns and angle of the X suggested that DNA is a helix consisting of two strands that are a regular, consistent width apart.

FIGURE 2.2 Rosalind Franklin (above) produced x-ray photographs of DNA that indicated it was a helix. Her coworker, Maurice Wilkins, showed the data without Franklin's consent to Watson and Crick, which helped them discover DNA's structure.

INCLUSION

For students who have difficulty sorting out the relationship between different aspects of the text, use DNA's base pairs as a point of reference. Show students where the base pairs are found in various diagrams and photos in the section. Suggest a mnemonic to help students remember the pairs: C-G: Cars need gas; A-T: Acorns grow on trees. Or point out that the letters *C* and *G* are both round, whereas the letters *A* and *T* are made of straight lines.

ONLINE Biology
HMHScience.com

Have students evaluate the genomes of four different species in terms of Chargaff's rules by completing the Data Analysis Smart Grapher activity at **HMHScience.com**.

The Inside Story

In 1951, **Rosalind Franklin** was invited to King's College London to be part of a team working on DNA analysis. Franklin used x-rays to study DNA's crystalline structure. Meanwhile, at Cambridge University, **James Watson** and **Francis Crick** were feverishly working to be the first to accurately describe DNA's structure. They knew DNA's components, as did many others, but no one could figure out how the pieces fit together.

In 1953, **Maurice Wilkins,** Franklin's coworker, showed Watson one of Franklin's x-rays, which provided an all-important clue—a DNA molecule was a two-stranded helix of a constant width. Within weeks, Watson and Crick had figured out the structure of DNA.

In 1962, Watson, Crick, and Wilkins shared the Nobel Prize for Physiology or Medicine for this work. Franklin had died of cancer four years earlier, at the age of 37. Some attribute her cancer to exposure to x-rays. While the Nobel Prize is never awarded posthumously, no mention of Franklin's contribution was made at that time. Her work and its oversight have now ensured her a place in history.

Answers

A Compare cytosine, because it has a single ring

B Summarize Their nitrogen-containing bases differ from one another.

▼ Teach *continued*

Vocabulary

Greek and Latin Word Origins The words **spiral** and **helix** are synonymous. The word *spiral* comes from a Latin root meaning "coil." The word *helix* comes from a Greek root meaning "to wrap around." A single molecule of DNA molecule has two helixes, or strands, making it a double helix.

Science Trivia

Interpretation of Rosalind Franklin's x-ray image showed the following:

- DNA has a width of about 2 nanometers (10^{-9} m).
- One complete turn of the helix occurs every 3.4 nanometers.
- There are ten base pairs in each turn of the helix, so the base pairs are stacked 0.34 nanometers apart.
- There are approximately 3 billion base pairs in human DNA.

CONNECT TO

Chemical Bonds Helping students understand the relative strengths of covalent bonds and hydrogen bonds lays the groundwork for understanding DNA replication in **Section 3.** Because hydrogen bonds between the bases are easily broken, the two strands of DNA can be readily separated, while the strong covalent bonds between nucleotides keep the individual strands intact.

Answers

Ⓐ Apply Because A pairs only with T, and C pairs only with G, DNA will always have approximately the same proportion of A and T and the same proportion of C and G.

FIGURE 2.3 James Watson (left) and Francis Crick (right) used a model to figure out DNA's structure. Their model was influenced by data from other researchers, including an x-ray image (far right) taken by Rosalind Franklin. When x-rays bounce through a sample of DNA, they form this characteristic x-shaped pattern.

James Watson and Francis Crick

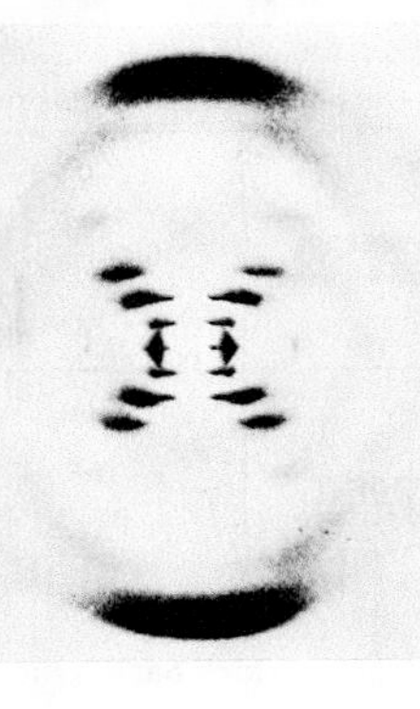

The Double Helix

Back in their own laboratory, Watson and Crick made models of metal and wood to figure out the structure of DNA. Their models placed the sugar-phosphate backbones on the outside and the bases on the inside. At first, Watson reasoned that A might pair with A, T with T, and so on. But the bases A and G are about twice as wide as C and T, so this produced a helix that varied in width. Finally, Watson and Crick found that if they paired double-ringed nucleotides with single-ringed nucleotides, the bases fit like a puzzle.

In April 1953 Watson and Crick published their DNA model in a paper in the journal *Nature*. **FIGURE 2.3** shows their **double helix** (DUB-uhl HEE-liks) model, in which two strands of DNA wind around each other like a twisted ladder. The strands are complementary—they fit together and are the opposite of each other. That is, if one strand is ACACAC, the other strand is TGTGTG. The pairing of bases in their model finally explained Chargaff's rules.

Ⓐ Apply **How did the Watson and Crick model explain Chargaff's rules?**

MAIN IDEA

Nucleotides always pair in the same way.

CONNECT TO

CHEMICAL BONDS

Recall from the chapter **Chemistry of Life** that a covalent bond is a strong bond in which two atoms share one or more pairs of electrons. Hydrogen bonds are much weaker than covalent bonds and can easily be broken.

The DNA nucleotides of a single strand are joined together by covalent bonds that connect the sugar of one nucleotide to the phosphate of the next nucleotide. The alternating sugars and phosphates form the sides of a double helix, sort of like a twisted ladder. The DNA double helix is held together by hydrogen bonds between the bases in the middle. Individually, each hydrogen bond is weak, but together, they maintain DNA structure.

As shown in **FIGURE 2.4**, the bases of the two DNA strands always pair up in the same way. This is summarized in the **base pairing rules:** thymine (T) always pairs with adenine (A), and cytosine (C) always pairs with guanine (G). These pairings occur because of the sizes of the bases and the ability of the

Differentiated Instruction

ENGLISH LEARNERS

Use the Assessment questions in this section to go over question-answer relationships. Explain that the best way to look for an answer depends on the type of question asked. Tell students that there are two basic categories: "in the book" and "in my head."

Tell students that the review questions at the end of a section are "in the book" questions. The answers can be found either "right there" (in the text), as with question 1, or the question may require students to "think and search," as with question 2.

For "in my head" questions, the answers are not directly stated in the text. With critical-thinking questions, students use information from the text to work out the answer. Such questions are categorized as "author and you." Other questions, such as those labeled *Connect To*, require students to answer "on my own." The answer may rely on something the student learned earlier or gained from personal experience.

Teacher Toolkit, Section C, QAR

FIGURE 2.4 Base Pairing Rules

The base pairing rules describe how nucleotides form pairs in DNA. T always pairs with A, and G always pairs with C.

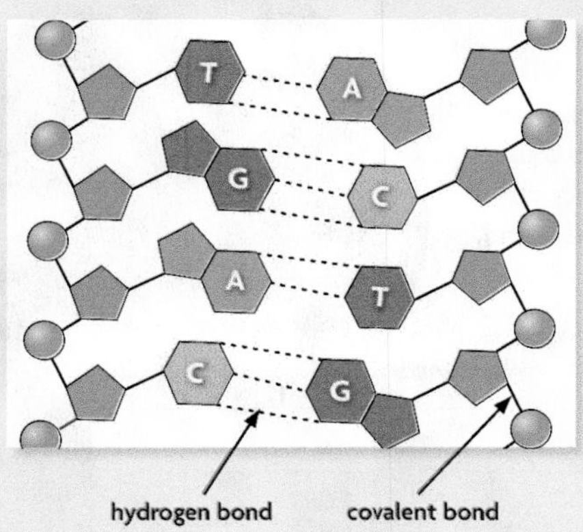

hydrogen bond

covalent bond

This ribbonlike part represents the phosphate groups and deoxyribose sugar molecules that make up DNA's "backbone."

The nitrogen-containing bases form hydrogen bonds in the middle to form the rungs of the DNA ladder.

T A
G C
A T
C G

A Synthesize **Which base pairs do you think are held more tightly together? Why?**

bases to form hydrogen bonds with each other. Due to the arrangement of their molecules, A can form unique hydrogen bonds with T, and C with G. Notice that A and T form two hydrogen bonds, whereas C and G form three.

You can remember the rules of base pairing by noticing that the letters C and G have a similar shape. Once you know that C and G pair together, you know that A and T pair together by default. If a sequence of bases on one strand of DNA is CTGCTA, you know the other DNA strand will be GACGAT.

B Apply **What sequence of bases would pair with the sequence TGACTA?**

SELF-CHECK Online
HMHScience.com
GO ONLINE

8.2 Formative Assessment

REVIEWING MAIN IDEAS

1. How many types of **nucleotides** are in DNA, and how do they differ?
2. How are the **base pairing rules** related to Chargaff's research on DNA?
3. Explain how the **double helix** model of DNA built on the research of Rosalind Franklin.

CRITICAL THINKING

4. **Infer** Which part of a DNA molecule carries the genetic instructions that are unique for each individual: the sugar-phosphate backbone or the nitrogen-containing bases? Explain.
5. **Predict** In a sample of yeast DNA, 31.5% of the bases are adenine (A). Predict the approximate percentages of C, G, and T. Explain.

CONNECT TO EVOLUTION

6. The DNA of all organisms contains the same four bases (adenine, thymine, cytosine, and guanine). What might this similarity indicate about the origins of life on Earth?

TEACH FROM VISUALS

FIGURE 2.4 Help students decode the figure. **Ask**

- How many rings are there in each base pair? three
- Why is DNA's shape called a double helix? It is made of two spirals that are twisted around each other.
- How are the two diagrams related to each other? The left diagram can be superimposed onto the right diagram, with the sugar-phosphate backbones on the spiral strands and the bases on the rungs connecting the strands.

Answers

A **Synthesize** C and G because they are connected by three hydrogen bonds, whereas A and T are held by only two

B **Apply** ACTGAT

Assess and Reteach ▼

Assess Use the Section Self-Check or Section Quiz, both available at **HMHScience.com**.

Reteach Have students make models of DNA by cutting out and arranging cardboard shapes representing deoxyribose, phosphate groups, and the four bases. Encourage students to make their model at least four nucleotides long.

8.2 FORMATIVE ASSESSMENT

1. four; their nitrogen-containing bases differ
2. Because A pairs only with T, and C pairs only with G, DNA will always have approximately the same proportion of A and T and the same proportion of C and G.
3. Franklin's data suggested that DNA was a helix made of two strands an even width apart. From this, Watson and Crick realized that a base with one ring would bond with a base with two rings.
4. The backbone is the same in all DNA. The nitrogen-containing bases provide the unique instructions.
5. Matching A, T is approximately 31.5 percent. Thus, C and G together make up 37 percent of the bases, so each makes up approximately 18.5 percent of the bases.
6. It suggests that the wide diversity of life that we see might have stemmed from a common ancestor.

DATA ANALYSIS

Introduce

Histograms differ from bar graphs in that a histogram shows data intervals that are continuous. **Ask**

- How are the data intervals continuous in Graph 1? The ages are divided into continuous 10-year intervals from age 30 to age 89.
- What trend is shown in Graph 1? The most common age of the Nobel laureates is 50–59. Very young and very old winners are less common.

Science Trivia

- The youngest person to receive a Nobel Prize was Sir William Lawrence Bragg, at age 25. He won the prize in physics jointly with his father in 1915 for work in x-ray diffraction, which later paved the way for Rosalind Franklin's work with DNA.
- Leonid Hurwicz was the oldest Nobel Prize laureate. He was 90 when he won the Nobel Prize for Economic Sciences in 2007.

Discuss

It is estimated that humans have between 20,000 and 25,000 genes. **Ask,** In which bar in Graph 2 would humans be included? the sixth bar, on the far right

Online Student Resources, Data Analysis Practice

DATA ANALYSIS

Interpreting Histograms

Smart Grapher
HMHScience.com
GO ONLINE
Nucleotide Bases

A histogram is a graph that shows the frequency distribution of a data set. First, a scientist collects data. Then, she groups the data values into equal intervals. The number of data values in each interval is the frequency of the interval. The intervals are shown along the *x*-axis of the histogram, and the frequencies are shown on the *y*-axis.

Model

The histogram at right shows the frequency distribution of the ages of winners of the Nobel Prize in Medicine at the time of winning. Francis Crick was 46 and James Watson was 34 when they were jointly awarded a Nobel Prize in Medicine in 1962.

According to the histogram, the most winners have been between 50 and 59 years old at the time of winning. Only five scientists have been between the ages of 80 and 89 at the time of winning a Nobel Prize in Medicine.

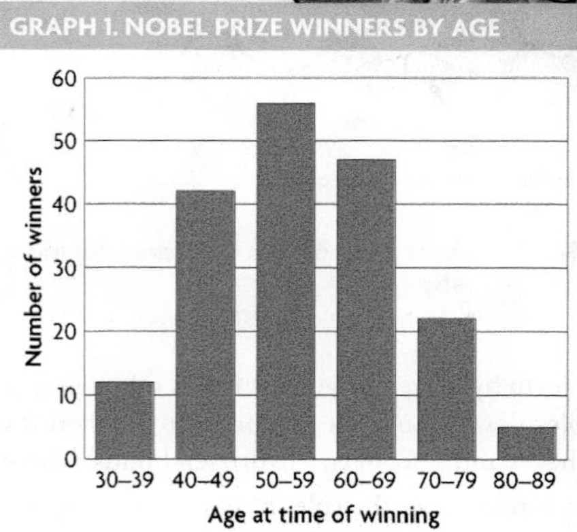

GRAPH 1. NOBEL PRIZE WINNERS BY AGE

Practice **Interpret a Histogram**

The histogram to the right categorizes data collected based on the number of genes in 11 species.

1. **Identify** How many species had between 10,001 and 15,000 genes?
2. **Analyze** Are the data in graph 2 sufficient to reveal a trend in the number of genes per species? Explain your reasoning.

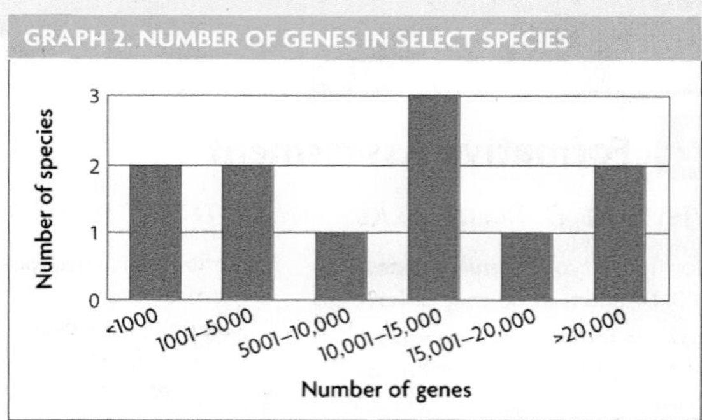

GRAPH 2. NUMBER OF GENES IN SELECT SPECIES

Answers

1. three
2. No, there is no obvious correlation. The highest number of species (3) and the lowest number of species (1) differ by only two. This difference is not significant. Data from 11 species are inadequate to reveal a trend for species in general.

224 Unit 3: Genetics

8.3 DNA Replication

KEY CONCEPT **DNA replication copies the genetic information of a cell.**

VOCABULARY

replication
DNA polymerase

MAIN IDEAS

- Replication copies the genetic information.
- Proteins carry out the process of replication.
- Replication is fast and accurate.

Connect to Your World

Do you know that some of your cells are dying right now? You may live to be 100 years old, but most of your cells will have been replaced thousands of times before you blow out the candles on that birthday cake. Every time that cells divide to produce new cells, DNA must first be copied in a remarkable process of unzipping and zipping by enzymes and other proteins. The next few pages will take you through that process.

MAIN IDEA

Replication copies the genetic information.

One of the powerful features of the Watson and Crick model was that it suggested a way that DNA could be copied. In fact, Watson and Crick ended the journal article announcing their discovery with this sentence: "It has not escaped our notice that the specific pairing we have postulated immediately suggests a possible copying mechanism for the genetic material."

Recall that the bases that connect the strands of DNA will pair only in one way, according to the rules of base pairing. An A must bind with a T, and a C must bind with a G. If the base sequence of one strand of the DNA double helix is known, the sequence of the other strand is also known. Watson and Crick realized that a single DNA strand can serve as a template, or pattern, for a new strand. This process by which DNA is copied during the cell cycle is called **replication.**

Suppose all of your classmates took off their shoes, placed their left shoe in a line, and tossed their right shoe into a pile. You could easily pick out the right shoes from the pile and place them with the matching left shoes. The order of the shoes would be preserved. Similarly, a new strand of DNA can be synthesized when the other strand is a template to guide the process. Every time, the order of the bases is preserved, and DNA can be accurately replicated over and over again.

Replication assures that every cell has a complete set of identical genetic information. Recall that your DNA is divided into 46 chromosomes that are replicated during the S phase of the cell cycle. So your DNA is copied once in each round of the cell cycle. As a result, every cell has a complete set of DNA.

CONNECT TO

CELL BIOLOGY

In the chapter **Cell Structure and Function** you learned that the cell cycle has four main stages. DNA is replicated during the S (synthesis) stage.

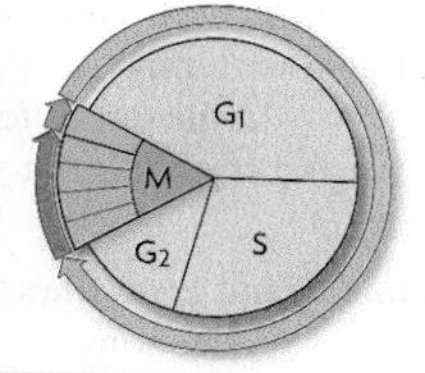

Differentiated Instruction

ENGLISH LEARNERS

Have students divide into groups of three. Ask each group to summarize one of the three parts of the section. Encourage students to identify the main points and restate them in concise language. Then one or more students from each group can present the group summary to the class. You may wish to have each of the other groups write questions as they listen to the summaries and ask their questions following the presentations.

Teacher Toolkit, Section C, Summarizing

SECTION 8.3

B.1.2 Analyze how the shape of a molecule determines its role in the many different types of cellular processes (e.g., metabolism, homeostasis, growth and development, and heredity) and understand that the majority of these processes involve proteins that act as enzymes.

Plan and Prepare

Activate Prior Knowledge Make sure students understand the complementary nature of a template and what it produces. **Ask,** What are some everyday uses of a template? Word-processing templates give text a particular format; carpenters use templates to reproduce shapes; stencils have openings for creating specific shapes.

Teach

Vocabulary

Academic Vocabulary A **copy** is a **duplicate** of what already exists. A **template** provides a pattern that someone can use to make a copy; it is not the same as a copy. **Ask,** How is a DNA sequence used as a template? The sequence of bases in one strand is a template that reproduces the sequence of bases in the other strand. Point out that the sequence of bases makes a copy of the second strand.

▼ Teach *continued*

Vocabulary

Academic Vocabulary Help students distinguish between the words **complement** and **compliment.**

complement = either of two parts that completes a whole

compliment = expression of praise

Point out that the word *complement* has as its root the word *complete.* To remember the meaning of *compliment,* students can use the mnemonic that both *praise* and *compliment* have the letter *i.* Tell students that the word *complimentary* can also refer to something given freely, as in a gift.

Take It Further

DNA polymerase adds nucleotides only to the 3′ end of a strand, so a new DNA strand can elongate only in a 5′ to 3′ direction. Along one template strand, a new strand is made in one continuous piece toward the Y-shaped junction of the strands. This new strand is called the **leading strand.** To make the second new strand, DNA polymerase must work along the other template strand in the direction away from the Y-shaped junction of the strands. This new strand of DNA is called the **lagging strand.** The process is similar to backstitching in sewing, and the new strand is made in short fragments. Another enzyme bonds these fragments together to form a continuous strand.

Answers

A Apply It doubles the amount of DNA so that both of the daughter cells resulting from mitosis have their own complete set of DNA.

B Infer Each strand of the DNA molecule dictates what the other strand must be according to the rules of base pairing. That is, because A bonds with T, and C with G, the nucleotides arrange themselves in a complementary pattern. Each replicated molecule consists of one original (template) strand and one new strand.

The fact that cells throughout the body have complete sets of DNA is very useful for forensic scientists. They can identify someone from nearly any cell in the body. A few cells from a drop of blood or from saliva on a cigarette butt are all detectives need to produce a DNA "fingerprint" of a criminal suspect.

A Apply How does replication ensure each cell has a complete set of DNA?

MAIN IDEA

Proteins carry out the process of replication.

> CONNECT TO
> **BIOCHEMISTRY**
> You read in the chapter **Chemistry of Life** that many proteins are enzymes that function as catalysts. Enzymes decrease the activation energy and increase the rate of chemical reactions. DNA polymerase catalyzes the reaction that bonds two nucleotides together.

Although people may say that DNA copies itself, the DNA itself does nothing more than store information. Enzymes and other proteins do the actual work of replication. For example, some enzymes start the process by unzipping the double helix to separate the strands of DNA. Other proteins hold the strands apart while the strands serve as templates. Nucleotides that are floating free in the nucleus can then pair up with the nucleotides of the existing DNA strands. A group of enzymes called **DNA polymerases** (puh-LIM-muh-rays) bond the new nucleotides together. When the process is finished, the result is two complete molecules of DNA, each exactly like the original double strand.

> **VISUAL VOCAB**
> **DNA polymerases** are enzymes that form bonds between nucleotides during replication.
> The ending *-ase* signals that this is an enzyme.
> 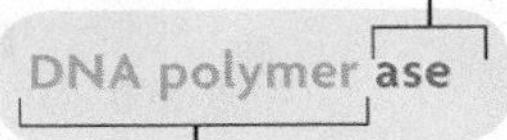
>
> This part of the name tells what the enzyme does—makes DNA polymers.

The Replication Process

The following information describes the process of DNA replication in eukaryotes, which is similar in prokaryotes. As you read, follow along with each step illustrated in **FIGURE 3.1.**

1. Enzymes begin to unzip the double helix at numerous places along the chromosome, called origins of replication. That is, the hydrogen bonds connecting base pairs are broken, the original molecule separates, and the bases on each strand are exposed. Like unzipping a suitcase, the process of unzipping DNA proceeds in two directions at the same time.
2. One by one, free nucleotides pair with the bases exposed as the template strands unzip. DNA polymerases bond the nucleotides together and form new strands complementary to each template. On one template, DNA replication occurs in a smooth, continuous way in one direction. This continuous strand is called the leading strand. On the other template, replication occurs in a discontinuous, piece-by-piece way in the opposite direction. Replication of this strand, known as the lagging strand, is not shown or described in detail here.
3. Two identical molecules of DNA result, each with one strand from the original molecule and one new strand. As a result, DNA replication is called semiconservative because one old strand is conserved, and one new strand is made.

> **READING TOOLBOX**
> TAKING NOTES
> Use a cycle diagram to take notes about processes such as replication.
> existing molecule → unzipping → nucleotides added → two DNA molecules formed → existing molecule

B Infer How does step 3 of replication show that DNA acts as a template?

Differentiated Instruction

BELOW LEVEL

Have students relate what they see in **FIGURE 3.1** to **FIGURE 2.4** from the previous section. Have them visualize the replication process. Tell students that they can be creative and describe not just what they see, but also what they hear and feel. Have them write continuously for five minutes.

Teacher Toolkit, Section C, Connect to Content through Visuals and Quick-Write

INCLUSION

Have students practice base pairing to reinforce the concept of complementary strands. Write base sequences on the board and have students produce the complementary strand. For students who are visually impaired, make a cardboard cutout of a single-stranded base sequence, using different-shaped notches for the bases. For example, A could have a V-shaped notch. T would then have a pointed tab that would fit into the notch to base pair. The nucleotides should be T-shaped and include a fragment of backbone and the base.

FIGURE 3.1 REPLICATION

When a cell's DNA is copied, or replicated, two complete and identical sets of genetic information are produced. Then cell division can occur.

1 A DNA molecule unzips as nucleotide base pairs separate. Replication begins on both strands of the molecule at the same time.

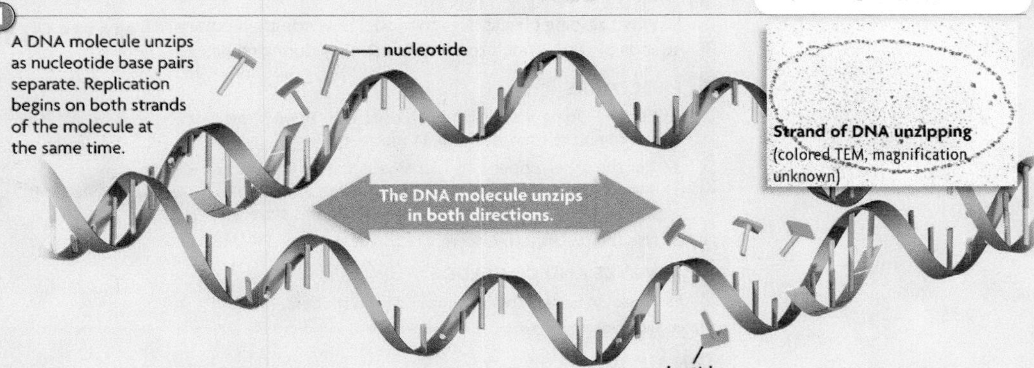

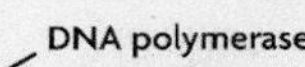

2 Each existing strand of the DNA molecule is a template for a new strand. Free-floating nucleotides pair up with the exposed bases on each template strand. DNA polymerases bond these nucleotides together to form the new strands. The arrows show the directions in which new strands form.

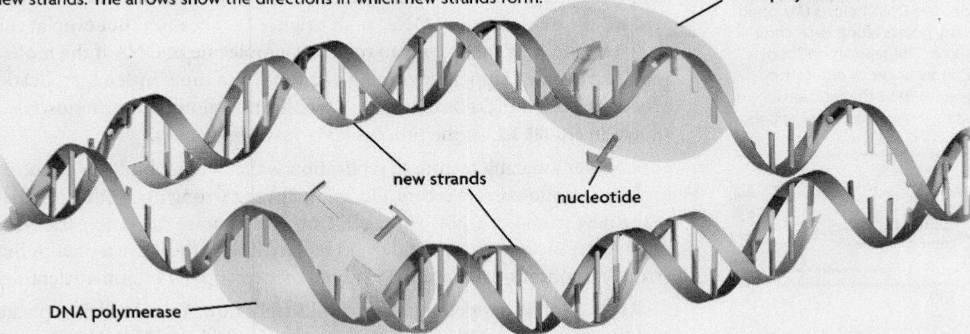

3 Two identical double-stranded DNA molecules result from replication. DNA replication is semiconservative. That is, each DNA molecule contains an original strand and one new strand.

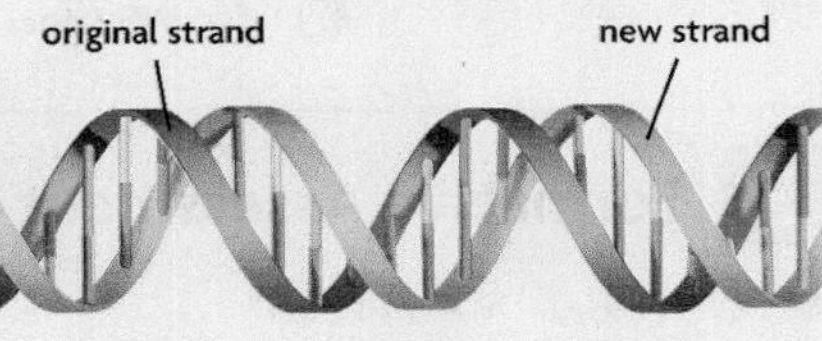

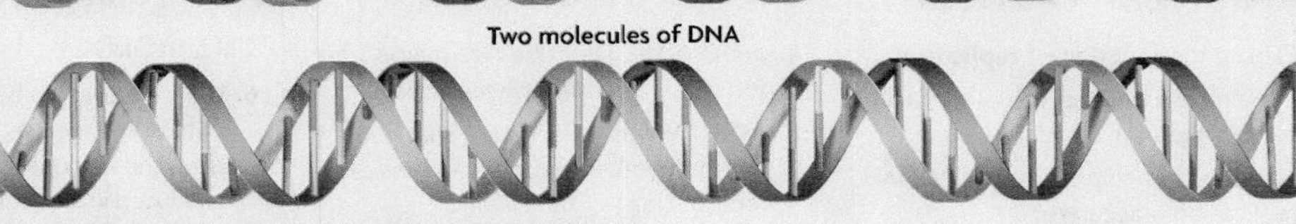

CRITICAL VIEWING **How is each new molecule of DNA related to the original molecule?**

TEACH FROM VISUALS

FIGURE 3.1 Discuss each step in the figure separately. **Ask**

- In step 1, how does the DNA unzip? The hydrogen bonds between the base pairs break.
- In step 2, how do the new strands compare with the template strands? Each new strand is the complement of its template strand.
- What enzyme is important in step 2? DNA polymerase
- What is the result of DNA replication? two identical DNA molecules
- Why is it important for the cell to correct any errors that occur during replication? If errors were not corrected, one of the new cells that form during cell division would have DNA with incorrect genetic information.

History of Science

The Watson-Crick model of DNA predicted that **DNA replication** is **semiconservative;** that is, each new molecule contains one original strand and one new strand. However, there were two other possible hypotheses. In the **conservative model,** the template molecule remained intact and a new molecule, consisting of two new strands, formed. In the **dispersive model,** the two original strands broke up and dispersed throughout the two new molecules that formed.

Matthew Meselson and **Franklin Stahl** demonstrated that the semiconservative model is correct. They used radioactive nitrogen to label the bases in bacterial DNA and then followed the path of the label through several generations of growth in an unlabeled medium. Their data showed that at first, the radioactivity was all in the parent DNA. After the first generation, all the cells had DNA that was half-labeled. After two generations, half the cells had DNA that was half-labeled, and half the cells had DNA that had no label.

HANDS-ON ACTIVITY

Give students two strands of red yarn and six strands of blue yarn—all of similar length. Have them make a model of DNA from the two red strands. Then have students go through two generations of replication, using the red yarn as template strands and the blue yarn as new strands.

Describe for students the conservative, dispersive, and semiconservative models of replication. (See History of Science.) **Ask**

- If the conservative model were correct, what would the model DNA look like after one generation? One molecule would be all red, and the other would be all blue.
- If the dispersive model were correct, what would the model DNA look like after one generation? Each molecule would consist of segments of red and blue.
- After two divisions, how many molecules have a strand from the original DNA? only two of four

Answers

A Critical Viewing It is identical to the original DNA molecule.

▼ Teach *continued*

QUICKLAB

Time 5 minutes — TEACHER TESTED

Purpose Model the replication of DNA.

LAB MANAGEMENT

- Have students compare what they are doing to **FIGURE 3.1.**
- The lab can be extended to model complementary base pairing by drawing dots of four different colors on the template strands and dots of matching colors on the pieces representing free nucleotides.

Answers

Analyze and Conclude

The pairing of the free nucleotides in the model is not specific. Pieces of a zipper can pair anywhere on the template strand, whereas free nucleotides can pair only with specific bases in DNA replication.

Take It Further

DNA replication takes about eight hours in human cells. If there were only one origin, the process would take about a hundred times longer.

Answers

A Infer Our cells have a large amount of DNA. It must be copied quickly enough to keep up with the demand for cell division and to enable the cell to carry out its normal functions.

▼ Assess and Reteach

Assess Use the Section Self-Check or Section Quiz, both available at **HMHScience.com**.

Reteach Have students review **FIGURE 3.1** and make a flow chart that lists the steps in the process of DNA replication.

QUICKLAB MODELING

Replication

Use two zipping plastic bags to model how complementary strands of DNA attach to template strands during replication.

MATERIALS
- 2 zipping bags
- scissors

PROCEDURE

1. Cut the sliding zippers off both bags. One zipper represents the template strands of a DNA molecule.
2. Cut the other zipper into four smaller pieces and unzip each of them. These represent free nucleotides. Don't worry about which nucleotide is which in this activity.
3. Use the pieces to model replication as shown in **FIGURE 3.1**.

ANALYZE AND CONCLUDE

Evaluate What are the limitations of this model?

MAIN IDEA

Replication is fast and accurate.

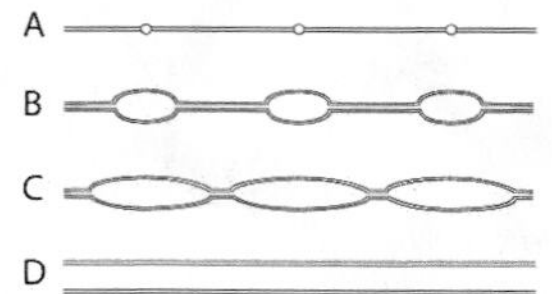

FIGURE 3.2 Eukaryotic chromosomes have many origins of replication. The DNA helix is unzipped at many points along each chromosome. The replication "bubbles" grow larger as replication progresses in both directions, resulting in two complete copies.

In every living thing, DNA replication happens over and over again, and it happens remarkably fast. In human cells, about 50 nucleotides are added every second to a new strand of DNA at an origin of replication. But even at this rate, it would take many days to replicate a molecule of DNA if the molecule were like a jacket zipper, unzipping one tooth at a time. Instead, replication proceeds from hundreds of origins of replication along the chromosome, as shown in **FIGURE 3.2**, so the process takes just a few hours.

Another amazing feature of replication is that it has a built-in "proofreading" function to correct errors. Occasionally, the wrong nucleotide is added to the new strand of DNA. However, DNA polymerase can detect the error, remove the incorrect nucleotide, and replace it with the correct one. In this way errors in replication are limited to about one error per 1 billion nucleotides.

Replication is happening in your cells right now. Your DNA is replicated every time your cells turn over, or replicate themselves. Your DNA has replicated trillions of times since you grew from a single cell.

A Infer Why does a cell need to replicate its DNA quickly?

8.3 Formative Assessment

REVIEWING MAIN IDEAS

1. Explain the function of **replication**.
2. Explain how DNA serves as its own template during replication.
3. How do cells help ensure that DNA replication is accurate?

CRITICAL THINKING

4. **Summarize** Describe two major functions of **DNA polymerases.**
5. **Infer** Why is it important that human chromosomes have many origins of replication?

CONNECT TO

CELL BIOLOGY

6. DNA is replicated before both mitosis and meiosis. How does the amount of DNA produced in a cell during mitosis compare with that produced during meiosis?

8.3 FORMATIVE ASSESSMENT

1. to make a copy of all the DNA in a cell so that it can be passed on to a new cell
2. Both strands act as a template. Because base pairing is specific, the sequence of one strand dictates what the sequence of the other strand has to be.
3. Certain types of DNA polymerase have a built-in proofreading function that corrects most mispaired nucleotides.
4. DNA polymerases bond nucleotides together and "proofread" to ensure accuracy.
5. Each chromosome in a eukaryotic cell is very long. If replication started at only one place, it would take a very long time to finish. Multiple origins of replication let the process happen more quickly.
6. Cells produced by mitosis typically have twice the amount of DNA as cells produced by meiosis.

8.4 Transcription

KEY CONCEPT **Transcription converts a gene into a single-stranded RNA molecule.**

MAIN IDEAS

- RNA carries DNA's instructions.
- Transcription makes three main types of RNA.
- The transcription process is similar to replication.

VOCABULARY

central dogma
RNA
transcription
RNA polymerase
messenger RNA (mRNA)
ribosomal RNA (rRNA)
transfer RNA (tRNA)

Connect to Your World

Suppose you want to play Skee-Ball® at a game center, but the Skee-Ball lane takes tokens and you only have quarters. Do you go home in defeat? Do you stand idly by as someone else becomes high scorer? No, you exchange your quarters for tokens and then proceed to show the other players how it's done. In a similar way, your cells cannot make proteins directly from DNA. They must convert the DNA into an intermediate molecule called RNA, or ribonucleic acid. That conversion process, called transcription, is the focus of this section.

MAIN IDEA

RNA carries DNA's instructions.

Soon after his discovery of DNA structure, Francis Crick defined the **central dogma** of molecular biology, which states that information flows in one direction, from DNA to RNA to proteins. The central dogma involves three processes, as shown in **FIGURE 4.1.**

- Replication, as you just learned, copies DNA (blue arrow).
- Transcription converts a DNA message into an intermediate molecule, called RNA (red arrow).
- Translation interprets an RNA message into a string of amino acids, called a polypeptide. Either a single polypeptide or many polypeptides working together make up a protein (green arrow).

In prokaryotic cells, replication, transcription, and translation all occur in the cytoplasm at approximately the same time. In eukaryotic cells, where DNA is located inside the nuclear membrane, these processes are separated both in location and time. Replication and transcription occur in the nucleus, whereas translation occurs in the cytoplasm. In addition, the RNA in eukaryotic cells goes through a processing step before it can be transported out of the nucleus. Unless otherwise stated, the rest of this chapter describes how these processes work in eukaryotic cells.

RNA acts as an intermediate link between DNA in the nucleus and protein synthesis in the cytoplasm. Like DNA, **RNA,** or ribonucleic acid, is a chain of nucleotides, each made of a sugar, a phosphate group, and a nitrogen-containing base. You can think of RNA as a temporary copy of DNA that is used and then destroyed.

FIGURE 4.1 The central dogma describes the flow of information from DNA to RNA to proteins. It involves three major processes, shown in a eukaryotic cell below.

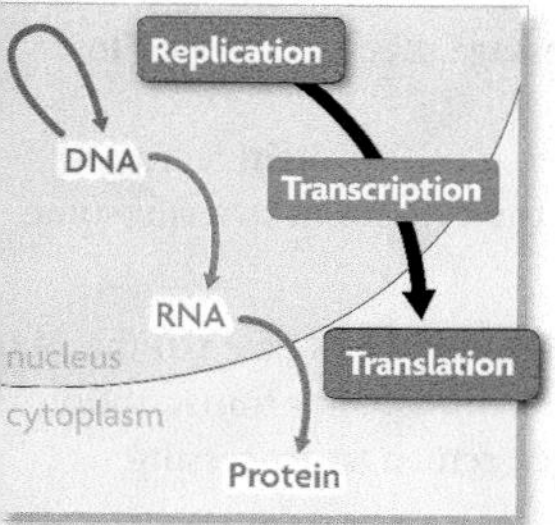

Differentiated Instruction

BELOW LEVEL

Tell students that after reading the section, they will pair up to compare the process of DNA replication with DNA transcription. Have students answer the following questions: How are the processes alike? How are they different?

Teacher Toolkit, Section C, Think-Pair-Share

SECTION 8.4

B.1.2 Analyze how the shape of a molecule determines its role in the many different types of cellular processes (e.g., metabolism, homeostasis, growth and development, and heredity) and understand that the majority of these processes involve proteins that act as enzymes.

B.4.2 Construct an explanation for how the structure of DNA determines the structure of proteins which carry out the essential functions of life through systems of specialized cells.

Plan and Prepare

Activate Prior Knowledge Tell students there are many types of transcriptions. **Ask,** How is the word *transcription* used in music? Typically a piece of music written for one instrument or group is reworked for another. Point out that the music, or message, is the same, but that the medium has changed. Tell students that a similar process happens when DNA is transcribed.

Teach

Take It Further

The central dogma is true for all organisms, from bacteria to humans. However, the dogma does not hold for a type of virus known as a **retrovirus.** In a retrovirus, RNA is the genetic material. When a retrovirus enters a host cell, a single-stranded DNA copy of the RNA is made. The host then adds a complementary strand of DNA to make double-stranded DNA, which directs protein synthesis. HIV is a retrovirus.

▼ Teach *continued*

The Inside Story

According to **Francis Crick,** in his book *What Mad Pursuit,* it was he who came up with the term **central dogma** to describe the sequence DNA-to-RNA-to-protein. He thought that *dogma,* rather than *hypothesis,* was more appropriate for a powerful new idea that could act as a guide in directing further research. Not everyone was happy with his choice of terminology, because a dogma is a belief that cannot be doubted. It is in the nature of science to foster doubt, not suppress it. From Crick's point of view, he was thinking of the central dogma as an organizing principle, which if demonstrated to be false, could be replaced by another.

Vocabulary

Academic Vocabulary The word **dogma** is not really a comfortable fit for the world of science.

dogma, an authoritative principle, belief, or statement of ideas or opinion, especially one considered to be absolutely true

theory, a set of statements or principles devised to explain a group of facts or phenomena, especially one that has been repeatedly tested or is widely accepted and can be used to make predictions about natural phenomena

Answers

A Contrast DNA and RNA have different sugar molecules. Also, DNA is typically double-stranded and is made up of nucleotides with bases C, G, A, and T. RNA is single-stranded and is made up of nucleotides with bases C, G, A, and U.

B Analyze DNA is located in the nucleus of eukaryotes, so processes involving DNA, such as transcription, must occur there as well.

CONNECT TO

DNA STRUCTURE

As you learned in **Section 2,** nucleotides are made of a phosphate group, a sugar, and a nitrogen-containing base. In DNA, the four bases are adenine, thymine, guanine, and cytocine. In RNA, uracil (below) replaces thymine and pairs with adenine.

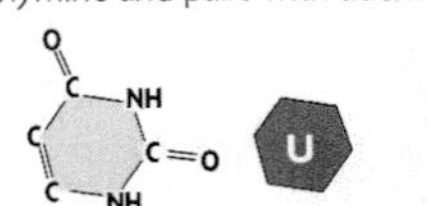

RNA differs from DNA in three significant ways. First, the sugar in RNA is ribose, which has one additional oxygen atom not present in DNA's sugar (deoxyribose). Second, RNA has the base uracil in place of thymine. Uracil, like thymine, forms base pairs with adenine. Third, RNA is a single strand of nucleotides, in contrast to the double-stranded structure of DNA. This single-stranded structure allows some types of RNA to form complex three-dimensional shapes. As a result, some RNA molecules can catalyze reactions much as enzymes do.

A Contrast How do DNA and RNA differ?

MAIN IDEA

Transcription makes three main types of RNA.

Transcription is the process of copying a sequence of DNA to produce a complementary strand of RNA. During the process of transcription, a gene—not an entire chromosome—is transferred into an RNA message. Just as replication is catalyzed by DNA polymerase, transcription is catalyzed by **RNA polymerases,** enzymes that bond nucleotides together in a chain to make a new RNA molecule. RNA polymerases are very large enzymes composed of many proteins that play a variety of roles in the transcription process. **FIGURE 4.2** shows the basic steps of transcription in eukaryotic cells.

1. With the help of other proteins and DNA sequences, RNA polymerase recognizes the transcription start site of a gene. A large transcription complex consisting of RNA polymerase and other proteins assembles on the DNA strand and begins to unwind a segment of the DNA molecule, until the two strands separate from each other.
2. RNA polymerase, using only one strand of DNA as a template, strings together a complementary strand of RNA nucleotides. RNA base pairing follows the same rules as DNA base pairing, except that uracil, not thymine, pairs with adenine. The growing RNA strand hangs freely as it is transcribed, and the DNA helix zips back together.
3. Once the entire gene has been transcribed, the RNA strand detaches completely from the DNA. Exactly how RNA polymerase recognizes the end of a transcription unit is complicated. It varies with the type of RNA.

Transcription produces three major types of RNA molecules. Not all RNA molecules code for proteins, but most play a role in the translation process. Each type of RNA molecule has a unique function.

- **Messenger RNA (mRNA)** is an intermediate message that is translated to form a protein.
- **Ribosomal RNA (rRNA)** forms part of ribosomes, a cell's protein factories.
- **Transfer RNA (tRNA)** brings amino acids from the cytoplasm to a ribosome to help make the growing protein.

Remember that the RNA strand must be processed before it can exit the nucleus of a eukaryotic cell. This step occurs during or just after transcription. However, we will next examine translation and then return to processing.

B Analyze Explain why transcription occurs in the nucleus of eukaryotes.

READING TOOLBOX

VOCABULARY

The word *transcribe* means "to make a written copy of." *Transcription* is the process of transcribing. A *transcript* is the copy produced by transcription.

Differentiated Instruction

ENGLISH LEARNERS

To understand the process of transcription, have students use a sequence diagram to detail the information provided on this page and in **FIGURE 4.2** on the next page. Help students use the information in the diagram to make statements about the relationships between the different parts of the process.

Teacher Toolkit, Section C, Sequence Diagram

PRE-AP

Have students read through the steps of transcription described on this page and shown in **FIGURE 4.2.** With their books closed, have them create a comic strip recounting the process. Suggest that students think of transcription as an assembly line in which molecules of RNA are manufactured by large transcription complexes. Suggest they use the dialogue balloon typically found in a comic strip to provide short summaries.

FIGURE 4.2 Transcription

Transcription produces an RNA molecule from a DNA template. Like DNA replication, this process takes place in the nucleus in eukaryotic cells and involves both DNA unwinding and nucleotide base pairing.

1 A large transcription complex made of RNA polymerase and other proteins recognizes the start of a gene and begins to unwind the segment of DNA.

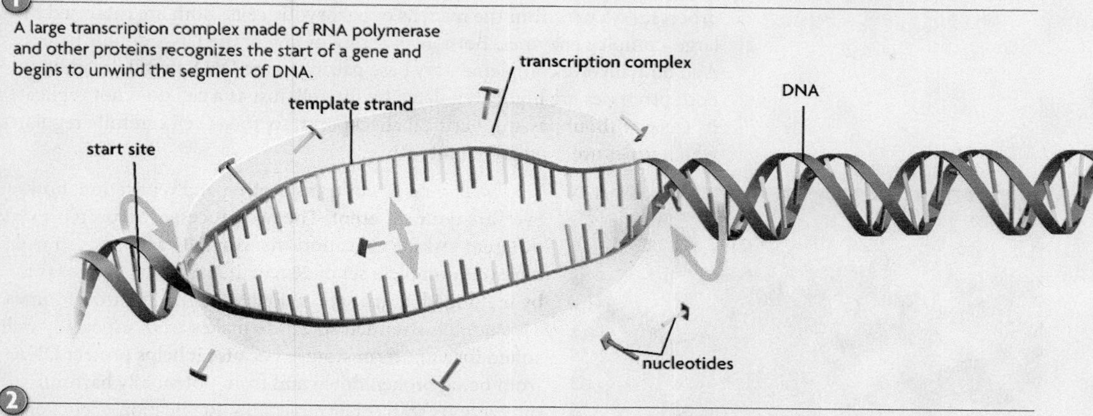

2 RNA polymerase uses one strand of the DNA as a template. RNA nucleotides form complementary base pairs with the DNA template. G pairs with C, and A pairs with U. The growing RNA strand hangs freely as it is transcribed. Then the DNA strand closes back together.

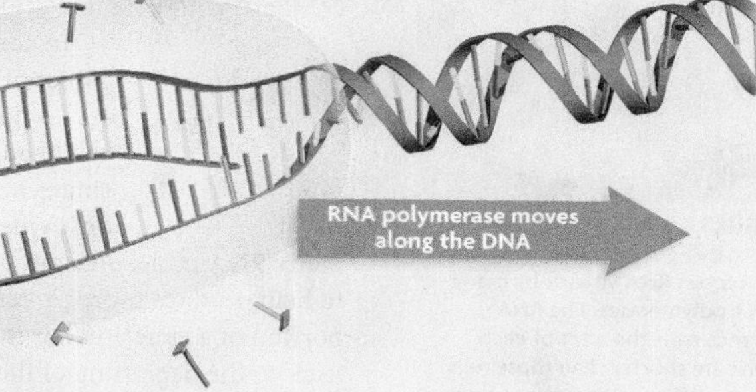

3 The completed RNA strand separates from the DNA template, and the transcription complex falls apart.

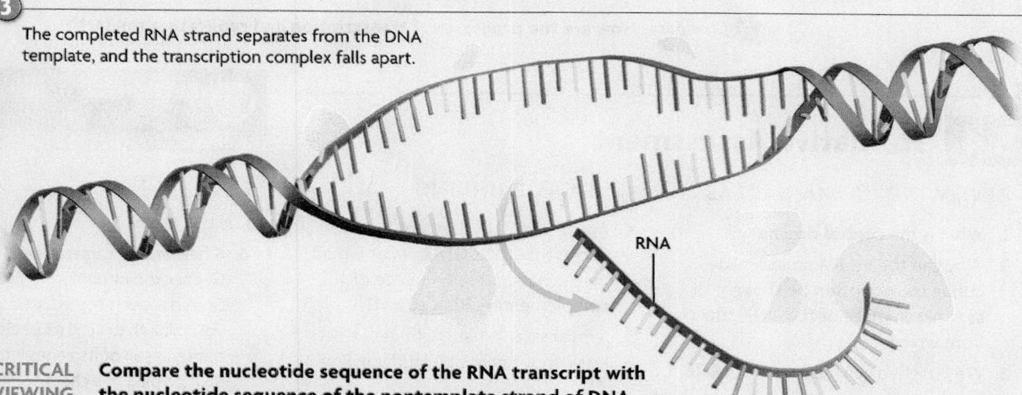

CRITICAL VIEWING **Compare the nucleotide sequence of the RNA transcript with the nucleotide sequence of the nontemplate strand of DNA.**

HANDS-ON ACTIVITY

Use a video camera or digital camera to record the steps of transcription. Assign students to come to the front of the room, holding cards labeled with a base. Students should arrange themselves into double-stranded DNA with the correct base pairing. Assign other students holding cards to represent free RNA nucleotides. When the DNA strands unwind, the RNA nucleotides can base pair with the template strand of the DNA.

INCLUSION

Have students extend the mnemonic suggested on second page of Section 2. For example, "Don't you know, Acorns grow on Trees, but to Reproduce, Acorns must go Underground."

TEACH FROM VISUALS

FIGURE 4.2 Discuss each step in the figure separately. **Ask**

- Why must the DNA strands unwind and separate before transcription can take place? The bases must be exposed so that free nucleotides can pair with them.
- In step 2, how does the base sequence of the RNA transcript being formed compare with the sequence on the template strand? It is complementary.
- What happens to the double-stranded DNA as the RNA polymerase moves to the right, following the arrow? The DNA unwinds to expose more of the gene.
- What happens to the RNA transcript after it separates from the DNA in step 3? It is processed and leaves the nucleus.

Take It Further

Unlike DNA polymerase, **RNA polymerase** cannot proofread the transcript being formed. Consequently, transcription produces more errors than replication does. Because most genes are transcribed many times, a few defective copies of mRNA, and thus protein, usually cause no harmful effects. These errors are not transmitted to the next generation because they affect only the mRNA and protein sequences, not the DNA.

Answers

A Critical Viewing It is the same except that T is replaced by U.

▼ Teach *continued*

TEACH FROM VISUALS

FIGURE 4.3 Have students notice the different sizes of the growing RNA transcripts. **Ask,** How can you tell where transcription of the genes begins? It will be that point where the mRNA strands are the shortest.

Answers

A Compare Both processes occur within the nucleus of eukaryotic cells, are catalyzed by complex enzymes, involve unwinding of the double helix, involve complementary base pairing to the DNA strand, and are highly regulated by the cell.

▼ Assess and Reteach

Assess Use the Section Self-Check or Section Quiz, both available at **HMHScience.com**.

Reteach Group students into pairs. Have one student in each pair write a ten-base-long DNA sequence and identify the template strand. Have the other student in the pair then write the RNA transcript that will be formed during transcription from that template.

MAIN IDEA

The transcription process is similar to replication.

The processes of transcription and replication share many similarities. Both processes occur within the nucleus of eukaryotic cells. Both are catalyzed by large, complex enzymes. Both involve unwinding of the DNA double helix. And both involve complementary base pairing to the DNA strand. In addition, both processes are highly regulated by the cell. Just as a cell does not replicate its DNA without passing a critical checkpoint, so, too, a cell carefully regulates which genes are transcribed into RNA.

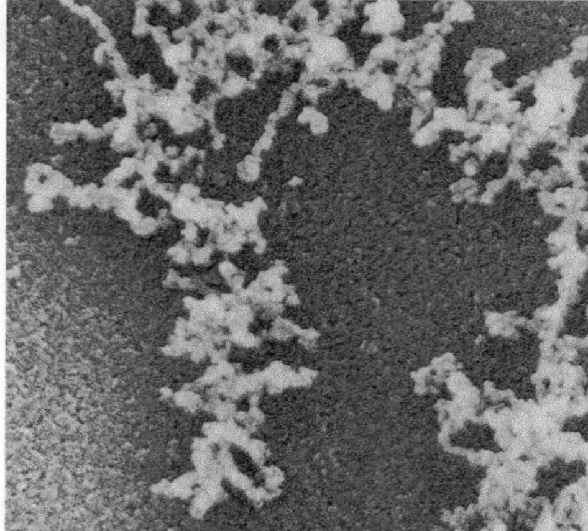

FIGURE 4.3 This TEM shows DNA being transcribed into numerous RNA strands by many RNA polymerases. The RNA strands near the start of each gene are shorter than those near the end. (TEM; magnification unknown)

The end results of transcription and replication, however, are quite different. The two processes accomplish very different tasks. Replication ensures that each new cell will have one complete set of genetic instructions. It does this by making identical sets of double-stranded chromosomes. This double-stranded structure makes DNA especially well suited for long-term storage because it helps protect DNA from being broken down and from potentially harmful interactions with other molecules. Replication occurs only once during each round of the cell cycle because each cell needs to make only one copy of its DNA.

In contrast, a cell may need hundreds or thousands of copies of certain proteins, or the rRNA and tRNA molecules needed to make proteins. Transcription enables a cell to adjust to changing demands. It does so by making a single-stranded complement of only a segment of DNA and only when that particular segment is needed. In addition, many RNA molecules can be transcribed from a single gene at the same time to help produce more protein. Once RNA polymerase has transcribed one portion of a gene and has moved on, another RNA polymerase can attach itself to the beginning of the gene and start the transcription process again. This process can occur over and over again, as shown in **FIGURE 4.3**.

A Compare How are the processes of transcription and replication similar?

8.4 Formative Assessment

SELF-CHECK Online
HMHScience.com
GO ONLINE

REVIEWING MAIN IDEAS

1. What is the **central dogma**?
2. Why can the **mRNA** strand made during **transcription** be thought of as a mirror image of the DNA strand from which it was made?
3. Why might a cell make lots of **rRNA** but only one copy of DNA?

CRITICAL THINKING

4. **Apply** If a DNA segment has the nucleotides AGCCTAA, what would be the nucleotide sequence of the complementary **RNA** strand?
5. **Synthesize** What might geneticists learn about genes by studying RNA?

CONNECT TO CELL CYCLE

6. A healthy cell cannot pass the G_2 checkpoint until all of its DNA has been copied. Do you think that a cell must also transcribe all of its genes into RNA to pass this checkpoint? Explain.

8.4 FORMATIVE ASSESSMENT

1. It is a statement that summarizes how information flows in one direction from DNA to RNA to proteins.
2. The mRNA chain is complementary to the DNA molecule. Like a mirror image, the mRNA chain has a distinct relationship to the DNA molecule, but is not identical to it.
3. rRNA is a component of ribosomes, and many ribosomes are needed to keep up with the level of protein synthesis needed by a cell. In contrast, each cell needs only one set of DNA, so it is copied only in preparation for cell division.
4. UCGGAUU
5. Because mRNA encode for only a single gene, studying mRNA can help researchers learn where genes begin and end on a chromosome. It could also indicate what genes are active in specific types of cells.
6. No, every cell has a complete set of DNA, but every cell does not need to use every gene. Therefore, only those genes that are needed by a cell are expressed, and the cell can still pass G_2.

8.5 Translation

KEY CONCEPT **Translation converts an mRNA message into a polypeptide, or protein.**

VOCABULARY

translation
codon
stop codon
start codon
anticodon

MAIN IDEAS

- Amino acids are coded by mRNA base sequences.
- Amino acids are linked to become a protein.

Connect to Your World

As you know, translation is a process that converts a message from one language into another. For example, English words can be translated into Spanish words, into Chinese characters, or into the hand shapes and gestures of sign language. Translation occurs in cells too. Cells translate an RNA message into amino acids, the building blocks of proteins. But unlike people who use many different languages, all cells use the same genetic code.

MAIN IDEA

Amino acids are coded by mRNA base sequences.

Translation is the process that converts, or translates, an mRNA message into a polypeptide. One or more polypeptides make up a protein. The "language" of nucleic acids uses four nucleotides—A, G, C, and T in DNA; or A, G, C, and U in RNA. The "language" of proteins, on the other hand, uses 20 amino acids. How can four nucleotides code for 20 amino acids? Just as letters are strung together in the English language to make words, nucleotides are strung together to code for amino acids.

CONNECT TO

BIOCHEMISTRY

Recall from the chapter **Chemistry of Life** that amino acids are the building blocks of proteins. Although there are many types of amino acids, only the same 20 types make up the proteins of almost all organisms.

Triplet Code

Different words have different numbers of letters. In the genetic code, however, all of the "words," called codons, are made up of three letters. A **codon** is a three-nucleotide sequence that codes for an amino acid. Why is the genetic code read in units of three nucleotides? Well, we can't entirely answer that question, but consider the possibilities. If one nucleotide coded for one amino acid, RNA could code for only four amino acids. If two nucleotides coded for one amino acid, RNA could code for 16 (4^2) amino acids—still not enough. But if three nucleotides coded for one amino acid, RNA could code for 64 (4^3) amino acids, plenty to cover the 20 amino acids used to build proteins in the human body and most other organisms.

VISUAL VOCAB

A **codon** is a sequence of three nucleotides that codes for an amino acid.

codon for methionine (Met)

codon for leucine (Leu)

A U G C U U

Segment of mRNA

Differentiated Instruction

ENGLISH LEARNERS

Have students create a concept definition map for some key vocabulary from **Sections 3–5:** *replication, transcription,* and *translation.* Students should prepare a graphic organizer that starts with the word and its *Category* (what type of thing it is). From this, students should branch out boxes for its *Properties* (what it is like, what it does) and *Examples.* You may wish to include *Comparisons* (some other things like it).

Teacher Toolkit, Section D, Concept Definition Map

SECTION 8.5

B.1.2 Analyze how the shape of a molecule determines its role in the many different types of cellular processes (e.g., metabolism, homeostasis, growth and development, and heredity) and understand that the majority of these processes involve proteins that act as enzymes.

B.4.2 Construct an explanation for how the structure of DNA determines the structure of proteins which carry out the essential functions of life through systems of specialized cells.

B.4.3 Construct a model to explain that the unique shape and function of each protein is determined by the sequence of its amino acids, and thus is determined by the sequence of the DNA that codes for this protein.

Plan and Prepare

Activate Prior Knowledge Discuss with students the nature of a code. Have them compare a coded message to a computer code. **Ask,** How are these codes the same, and how are they different? Both require translation of information. However, the coded message reproduces the same information, whereas computer code produces actions—operational commands. Tell students that the translation of RNA into protein is more like what happens with a computer code. The information encoded in nucleic acids becomes functioning proteins.

Teach

Vocabulary

Word Origins Tell students that **transcription** is not synonymous with **translation.** The root of *transcribe* is "to write," whereas the root of *translate* is "to transfer."

▼ Teach *continued*

TEACH FROM VISUALS

FIGURE 5.1 Go over the steps for reading the code. **Ask**

- What amino acid is coded by GGA? glycine by UGG? tryptophan by ACU, ACC, ACA, ACG? threonine
- What happens when a ribosome reads the codon AUG? Methionine (the start codon) is produced. UGA? Translation stops.

Addressing Misconceptions

Common Misconception Students may think that there are only 20 different amino acids.

Correcting the Misconception Remind students that the structure of an amino acid consists of a central carbon atom bonded to an amino group (–NH_2), a carboxyl group (–COOH), a hydrogen atom (–H), and a side group. Draw the structure on the board. Tell students that an infinite number of side groups are possible, so there is an infinite number of amino acids. Only 20 are commonly found in proteins, however.

History of Science

In 1961, **Francis Crick** and a group of colleagues performed an ingenious series of experiments to demonstrate that the **genetic code** is a **triplet code,** consisting of three consecutive nucleotides. They used a chemical to delete one, two, and three nucleotides from the DNA of a bacteriophage and then looked at a gene "downstream" from the deletions to see if it was transcribed correctly. They found that when one or two nucleotides were deleted, the reading frame of the gene was shifted, and the downstream gene was misread. When three nucleotides were deleted, the downstream gene was read correctly. This finding also suggested that the reading of the code was continuous, without "punctuation" interrupting the reading.

Answers

Ⓐ **Apply** arginine (Arg)

FIGURE 5.1 Genetic Code: mRNA Codons

The genetic code matches each mRNA codon with its amino acid or function.

Suppose you want to determine which amino acid is encoded by the CAU codon.

1. Find the first base, C, in the left column.
2. Find the second base, A, in the top row. Find the box where these two intersect.
3. Find the third base, U, in the right column. CAU codes for histidine, abbreviated as His.

First base	Second base U		Second base C		Second base A		Second base G		Third base
U	UUU	phenylalanine (Phe)	UCU	serine (Ser)	UAU	tyrosine (Tyr)	UGU	cysteine (Cys)	U
U	UUC		UCC		UAC		UGC		C
U	UUA	leucine (Leu)	UCA		UAA	STOP	UGA	STOP	A
U	UUG		UCG		UAG	STOP	UGG	tryptophan (Trp)	G
C	CUU	leucine (Leu)	CCU	proline (Pro)	CAU	histidine (His)	CGU	arginine (Arg)	U
C	CUC		CCC		CAC		CGC		C
C	CUA		CCA		CAA	glutamine (Gln)	CGA		A
C	CUG		CCG		CAG		CGG		G
A	AUU	isoleucine (Ile)	ACU	threonine (Thr)	AAU	asparagine (Asn)	AGU	serine (Ser)	U
A	AUC		ACC		AAC		AGC		C
A	AUA		ACA		AAA	lysine (Lys)	AGA	arginine (Arg)	A
A	AUG	methionine (Met)	ACG		AAG		AGG		G
G	GUU	valine (Val)	GCU	alanine (Ala)	GAU	aspartic acid (Asp)	GGU	glycine (Gly)	U
G	GUC		GCC		GAC		GGC		C
G	GUA		GCA		GAA	glutamic acid (Glu)	GGA		A
G	GUG		GCG		GAG		GGG		G

Ⓐ **Apply Which amino acid would be encoded by the mRNA codon CGA?**

As you can see in **FIGURE 5.1**, many amino acids are coded for by more than one codon. The amino acid leucine, for example, is represented by six different codons: CUU, CUC, CUA, CUG, UUA, and UUG. There is a pattern to the codons. In most cases, codons that represent the same amino acid share the same first two nucleotides. For example, the four codons that code for alanine each begin with the nucleotides GC. Therefore, the first two nucleotides are generally the most important in coding for an amino acid. As you will learn in Section 7, this feature makes DNA more tolerant of many point mutations.

In addition to codons that code for amino acids, three **stop codons** signal the end of the amino acid chain. There is also one **start codon,** which signals the start of translation and the amino acid methionine. This means that translation always begins with methionine. However, in many cases, this methionine is removed from the protein later in the process.

For the mRNA code to be translated correctly, codons must be read in the right order. Codons are read, without spaces, as a series of three nonoverlapping nucleotides. This order is called the reading frame. Changing the reading frame completely changes the resulting protein. It may even keep a protein from being made if a stop codon turns up early in the translation process. Therefore, punctuation—such as a clear start codon—plays an important role in the genetic code. **FIGURE 5.2** shows how a change in reading frame changes

FIGURE 5.2 Codons are read as a series of three nonoverlapping nucleotides. A change in the reading frame changes the resulting protein.

Reading frame 1

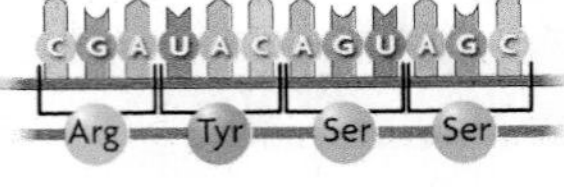

Reading frame 2

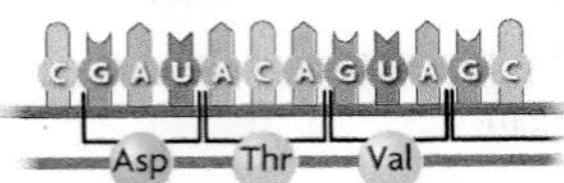

Differentiated Instruction

BELOW LEVEL

Group students into pairs to practice translating codons. One member of each pair should write a 15-base mRNA sequence starting with AUG. Remind students that RNA sequences do not contain T. The other member of each pair should use **FIGURE 5.1** to translate the sequence into amino acids.

PRE-AP

As mentioned in the text on this page, most amino acids are coded by more than one codon, a feature called redundancy. Have students write for five minutes on this question: Why might redundancy in the genetic code be an advantage to a cell?

Teacher Toolkit, Section C, Quick-Write

the resulting protein. When the mRNA strand is read starting from the first nucleotide, the resulting protein includes the amino acids arginine, tyrosine, and two serines. When the strand is read starting from the second nucleotide, the resulting protein includes aspartic acid, threonine, and valine.

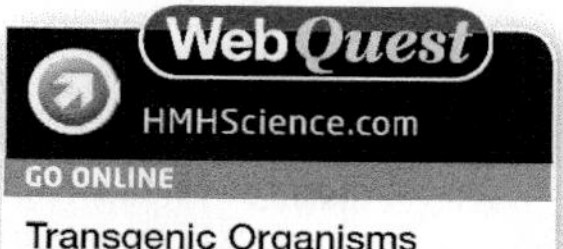

Common Language

The genetic code is shared by almost all organisms—and even viruses. That means, for example, that the codon UUU codes for phenylalanine when that codon occurs in an armadillo, a cactus, a yeast, or a human. With a few minor exceptions, almost all organisms follow this genetic code. As a result, the code is often called universal. The common nature of the genetic code suggests that almost all organisms arose from a common ancestor. It also means that scientists can insert a gene from one organism into another organism to make a functional protein.

Calculate **Suppose an mRNA molecule in the cytoplasm had 300 nucleotides. How many amino acids would be in the resulting protein?**

MAIN IDEA

Amino acids are linked to become a protein.

Let's take a step back to look at where we are in the process of making proteins. You know mRNA is a short-lived molecule that carries instructions from DNA in the nucleus to the cytoplasm. And you know that this mRNA message is read in sets of three nucleotides, or codons. But how does a cell actually translate a codon into an amino acid? It uses two important tools: ribosomes and tRNA molecules, as illustrated in **FIGURE 5.3.**

Recall that ribosomes are the site of protein synthesis. Ribosomes are made of a combination of rRNA and proteins, and they catalyze the reaction that forms the bonds between amino acids. Ribosomes have a large and small subunit that fit together and pull the mRNA strand through. The small subunit holds onto the mRNA strand, and the large subunit holds onto the growing protein.

The tRNA acts as a sort of adaptor between mRNA and amino acids. You would need an adaptor to plug an appliance with a three-prong plug into an outlet with only two-prong openings. Similarly, cells need tRNA to carry free-floating amino acids from the cytoplasm to the ribosome. The tRNA molecules fold up in a characteristic L shape. One end of the L is attached to a specific amino acid. The other end of the L, called the anticodon, recognizes a specific codon. An **anticodon** is a set of three nucleotides that is complementary to an mRNA codon. For example, the anticodon CCC pairs with the mRNA codon GGG.

FIGURE 5.3 TRANSLATION MACHINERY

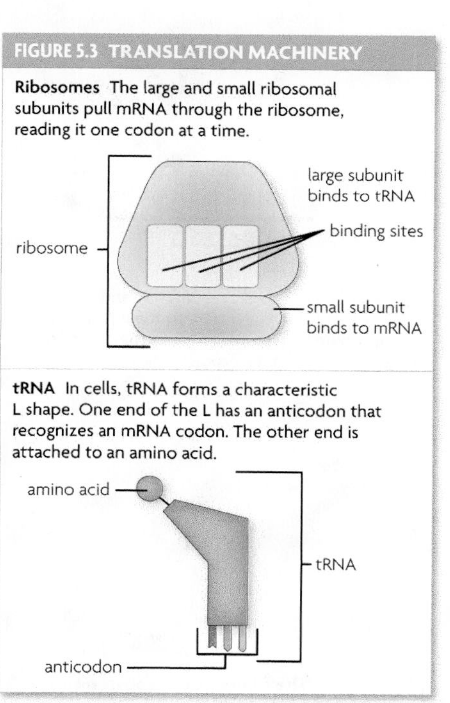

Ribosomes The large and small ribosomal subunits pull mRNA through the ribosome, reading it one codon at a time.
large subunit binds to tRNA
binding sites
ribosome
small subunit binds to mRNA
tRNA In cells, tRNA forms a characteristic L shape. One end of the L has an anticodon that recognizes an mRNA codon. The other end is attached to an amino acid.
amino acid
tRNA
anticodon

ENGLISH LEARNERS

Have students prepare word squares for *codon, stop codon, start codon,* and *anticodon.* Students' word squares should include the word and its translation, a symbol or picture, their own definition plus the Glossary definition, and a sentence using the word.

Teacher Toolkit, Section D, Word Squares

Use the WebQuest to explore the potential benefits and risks of transgenic organisms at **HMHScience.com**.

Vocabulary

Academic Vocabulary Students may find it odd to describe the genetic code as having the **punctuation** of stop and start codes. The Latin word *punctum* means "point," and is derived from an older form meaning "to pierce" or "puncture." Punctuation, in a general sense, signifies an interruption. The word *punctuate* can also be used to describe the act of placing stress or emphasis on a point.

Take It Further

Although most DNA is found in the nucleus, a small amount is located in mitochondria and chloroplasts. Scientists were shocked in the early 1980s when they determined the base sequences of **mitochondrial DNA** and found a somewhat different genetic code than in nuclear DNA. Since then, the genetic code of some protists, such as *Paramecium,* has been found to differ. Thus, the genetic code is not quite universal.

TEACH FROM VISUALS

FIGURE 5.3 Point out that the process of translation requires the transfer of information from one chemical form (nitrogen-containing bases) to another (amino acids); that is, from the language of nucleic acids to the language of proteins. The transition is facilitated by an intermediate—tRNA. In contrast, the language of complementary base pairing of nucleotides used to copy information in both replication (DNA to DNA) and transcription (DNA to RNA) occurs directly. The language does not change.

Answers

 100

▼ Teach *continued*

TEACH FROM VISUALS

FIGURE 5.4 Use the figure with the text on the following page to summarize the section. Point out the three binding sites in the ribosome and the complementarity of the codon and anticodon. **Ask**

- What is the function of mRNA? provides a copy of the genetic code
- What is the function of tRNA? brings amino acids to the ribosome, in the proper order
- What is the function of ribosomes? The ribosome positions mRNA so that it can be read by tRNA. It breaks the bonds between the tRNAs and their attached amino acids, and forms peptide bonds between amino acids, assembling the protein coded for in a gene.

Integrating Biochemistry

The end of a tRNA molecule opposite the anticodon binds to a specific amino acid with the help of the enzyme **aminoacyl tRNA synthetase.** There are 20 kinds of these enzymes in a cell, one for each kind of amino acid. Each enzyme ensures that the correct amino acid is attached to a tRNA having the anticodon corresponding to that amino acid. The enzymes have two specific binding sites, one for a particular amino acid and the other for a particular tRNA. This specificity is sometimes referred to as the second DNA code.

Answers

A Critical Viewing Students' sketches should look very similar to panels 1–3 in Figure 5.4. Amino acid 3 should be bonded to amino acid 2, and the bond between amino acid 2 and tRNA 2 broken. Then tRNA 2 will move to the next position, where it exits. This places tRNA 3 in the middle position and leaves the first position open for tRNA 4 to come in and bond. Amino acid 4 should be bonded to amino acid 3.

FIGURE 5.4 Translation

Translation converts an mRNA transcript into a polypeptide. The process consists of three repeating steps.

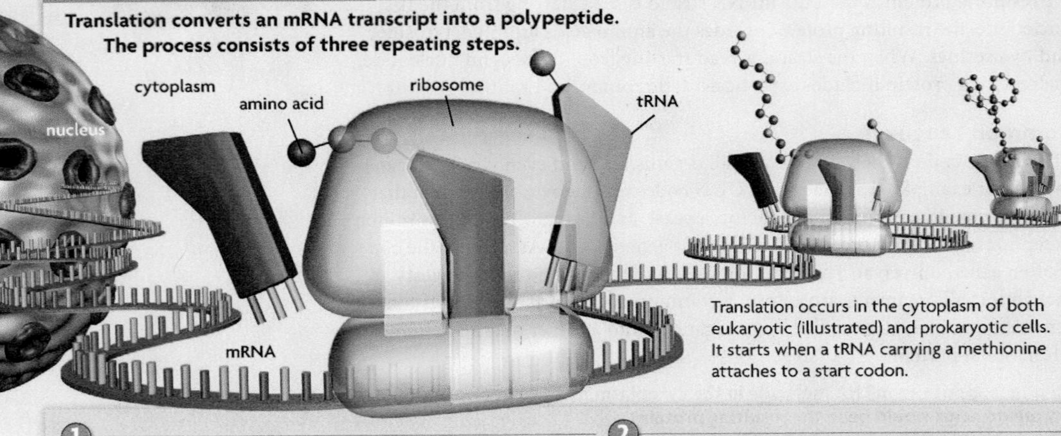

Translation occurs in the cytoplasm of both eukaryotic (illustrated) and prokaryotic cells. It starts when a tRNA carrying a methionine attaches to a start codon.

1 The exposed codon in the first site attracts a complementary tRNA bearing an amino acid. The tRNA anticodon pairs with the mRNA codon, bringing it very close to the other tRNA molecule.

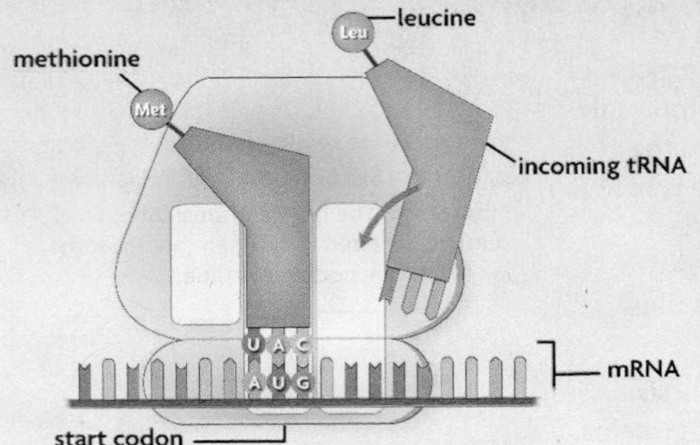

2 The ribosome forms a peptide bond between the two amino acids and breaks the bond between the first tRNA and its amino acid.

3 The ribosome pulls the mRNA strand the length of one codon. The first tRNA is shifted into the exit site, where it leaves the ribosome and returns to the cytoplasm to recharge. The first site is again empty, exposing the next mRNA codon.

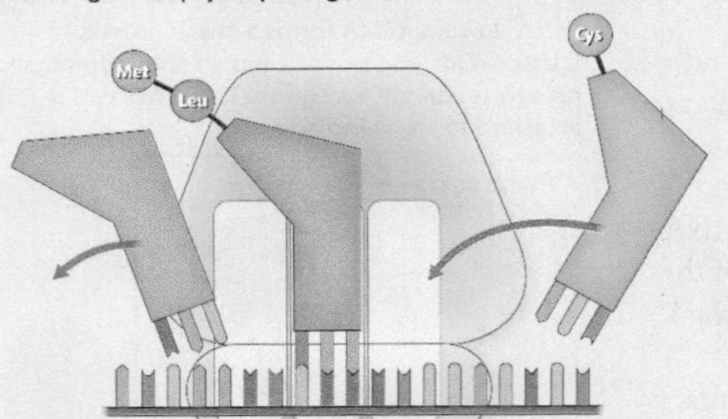

The ribosome continues to translate the mRNA strand until it reaches a stop codon. Then it releases the new protein and disassembles.

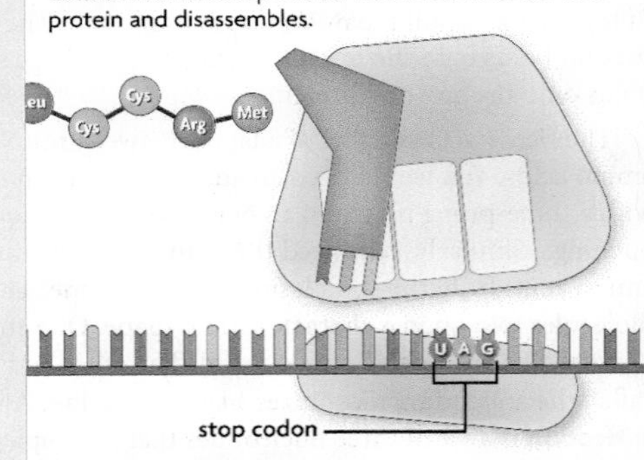

A CRITICAL VIEWING **The figure above shows how the first two amino acids are added to a growing protein. Draw a series of sketches to show how the next two amino acids are added.**

Differentiated Instruction

BELOW LEVEL

Have students make a flow chart sequencing the events of translation. Suggest that they include drawings.

Teacher Toolkit, Section C, Sequence Diagram

PRE-AP

Have students make a four-column table comparing mRNA, rRNA, and tRNA. They should list the three kinds of RNA in the first column. The second column should indicate where each is found during translation. The third column should give the function of each. Finally, students should write in the fourth column how the molecule's structure makes it suitable for its function.

Teacher Toolkit, Section C, Content Frame

GO ONLINE

Build a Protein

Translation, shown in **FIGURE 5.4**, has many steps and takes a lot of energy from a cell. It happens in the cytoplasm of both prokaryotic and eukaryotic cells. Before translation can begin, a small ribosomal subunit must bind to an mRNA strand in the cytoplasm. Next, a tRNA with methionine attached binds to the AUG start codon. This binding signals a large ribosomal subunit—which has three binding sites for tRNA molecules—to join. The ribosome pulls the mRNA strand through itself one codon at a time. As the strand moves, the start codon and its complementary tRNA molecule shift into the second site inside the large subunit. This shift leaves the first site empty, which exposes the next mRNA codon. The illustration shows the process in one ribosome, but in a cell many ribosomes may translate many mRNA molecules from the same gene at the same time.

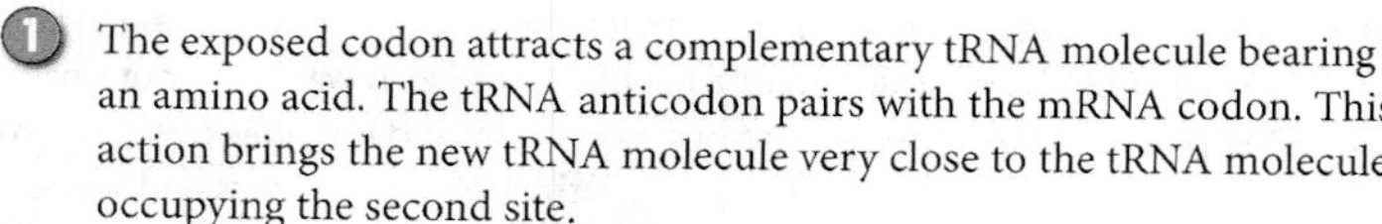

1. The exposed codon attracts a complementary tRNA molecule bearing an amino acid. The tRNA anticodon pairs with the mRNA codon. This action brings the new tRNA molecule very close to the tRNA molecule occupying the second site.
2. Next, the ribosome helps form a peptide bond between the two amino acids. The ribosome then breaks the bond between the tRNA molecule in the second site and its amino acid.
3. The ribosome pulls the mRNA strand the length of one codon. The tRNA molecule in the second site is shifted into the third site, which is the exit site. The tRNA leaves the ribosome and returns to the cytoplasm to be charged with another amino acid. The tRNA molecule that was in the first site shifts into the second site. The first site is again empty, exposing the next mRNA codon.

Another complementary tRNA molecule is attracted to the exposed mRNA codon, and the process continues. The ribosome moves down the mRNA strand, attaching new amino acids to the growing protein, until it reaches a stop codon. Then the ribosome lets go of the new protein and falls apart.

(A) Summarize **Explain the different roles of the large and small ribosomal subunits.**

8.5 Formative Assessment

SELF-CHECK Online
HMHScience.com
GO ONLINE

REVIEWING MAIN IDEAS

1. Explain the connection between a **codon** and an amino acid.
2. Briefly describe how the process of **translation** is started.

CRITICAL THINKING

3. **Synthesize** Suppose a tRNA molecule had the **anticodon** AGU. What amino acid would it carry?
4. **Hypothesize** The DNA of eukaryotic cells has many copies of genes that code for rRNA molecules. Suggest a hypothesis to explain why a cell needs so many copies of these genes.

CONNECT TO BIOCHEMICAL REACTIONS

5. Enzymes have shapes that allow them to bind to a substrate. Some types of RNA also form specific three-dimensional shapes. Why do you think RNA, but not DNA, catalyzes biochemical reactions?

HMHScience.com

Simulate building a protein from a DNA code in the Animated Biology at **HMHScience.com**.

Integrating Biochemistry

An rRNA molecule in the large subunit of the ribosome catalyzes the formation of peptide bonds between amino acids. In this role, it acts as an enzyme. This type of molecule is called a ribozyme.

Answers

(A) **Summarize** The small subunit holds onto the mRNA transcript. The large subunit has three sites where the tRNA molecules can dock; it helps form the peptide bond between the amino acids and helps break the bond between the amino acid and its carrier tRNA molecule.

Assess and Reteach ▼

Assess Use the Section Self-Check or Section Quiz, both available at **HMHScience.com**.

Reteach Write on the board a DNA sequence three bases long and tell students that it comes from the template strand. (Make sure not to write ATT, ATC, or ACT, as they all code for stop codons.) Have students determine the mRNA codon transcribed from this triplet, the sequence of the tRNA anticodon, and the amino acid that is translated.

8.5 FORMATIVE ASSESSMENT

1. A codon is a sequence of three nucleotides that specifies a particular amino acid. Students may describe the physical connection between these two as the tRNA molecule. Each tRNA molecule binds to a specific amino acid and has an anticodon that binds to a specific codon.
2. The small ribosomal subunit binds to the mRNA strand at the start codon, which binds the first tRNA molecule. This complex signals the large ribosomal subunit to bind, forming a functional ribosome, which can then continue accepting tRNA molecules and forming bonds between amino acids.
3. That tRNA molecule would recognize the mRNA codon UCA, so it would carry the amino acid serine.
4. rRNA is critical for making ribosomes to carry out protein synthesis. rRNA must be made in sufficient quantities to keep up with a cell's demands for various proteins.
5. DNA is usually in double-stranded form, wrapped up and condensed to make it compact, not in a catalytic form. In contrast, hydrogen bonds can form between the nucleotides of a single strand of RNA, causing it to form a catalytic structure.

Chapter 8: From DNA to Proteins 237

▼ Plan and Prepare

Activate Prior Knowledge Tell students that humans have an estimated 30,000 genes. **Ask,** Why wouldn't you expect all these genes to be transcribed and translated at the same time? The cell would run out of energy and raw materials (amino acids and nucleotides). Proteins would accumulate in the cell if they were not needed. **Ask,** What might be an analogy to this in your own life? eating all the food in the house at one time, everyone in class speaking at once, spending savings all at once

▼ Teach

Vocabulary

Academic Vocabulary The word **expression** has different applications, but most involve conveying a message or an idea in some form. In genetics, a gene that is expressed is one that is or has been transcribed and translated and thus produces an effect on an organism's phenotype.

8.6 Gene Expression and Regulation

KEY CONCEPT **Gene expression is carefully regulated in both prokaryotic and eukaryotic cells.**

MAIN IDEAS
- Prokaryotic cells turn genes on and off by controlling transcription.
- Eukaryotic cells regulate gene expression at many points.
- Environmental factors influence gene expression, resulting in different cell types.

VOCABULARY
promoter
operon
exon
intron
RNA interference

Connect to Your World

Ours is a world of marvels. So many, in fact, that we may overlook what seem like little ones, such as plumbing. The turn of a handle sends clean water to your sink or shower. One twist and the water trickles out; two twists and it gushes forth. Another turn of the handle and the water is off again. But think about the mess and waste that would result if you couldn't control its flow. In a similar way, your cells have ways to control gene expression. Depending on an organism's needs, a gene can make a lot of protein, a little protein, or none at all.

MAIN IDEA

Prokaryotic cells turn genes on and off by controlling transcription.

The regulation of gene expression allows prokaryotic cells, such as bacteria, to better respond to stimuli and to conserve energy and materials. In general, this regulation is simpler in prokaryotic cells than in eukaryotic cells, such as those that make up your body. DNA in a prokaryotic cell is in the cytoplasm. Transcription and translation can happen at the same time. As a result, gene expression in prokaryotic cells is mainly regulated at the start of transcription.

A gene includes more than just a protein-coding sequence. It may have many other nucleotide sequences that play a part in controlling its expression. The start of transcription is largely controlled by these sequences, including promoters and operators. A **promoter** is a DNA segment that allows a gene to be transcribed. It helps RNA polymerase find where a gene starts. An operator is a DNA segment that turns a gene "on" or "off." It interacts with proteins that increase the rate of transcription or block transcription from occurring.

READING TOOLBOX

VOCABULARY
The word *promote* comes from the Latin prefix *pro-*, meaning "forward," and the Latin word *movere*, meaning "to move."

Bacteria have much less DNA than do eukaryotes, and their genes tend to be organized into operons. An **operon** is a region of DNA that includes a promoter, an operator, and one or more structural genes that code for all the proteins needed to do a specific task. Operons are most often found in prokaryotes and roundworms. The *lac* operon was one of the earliest examples of gene regulation discovered in bacteria. It will serve as our example. The *lac* operon has three genes, which all code for enzymes that play a role in breaking down the sugar lactose. These genes are transcribed as a single mRNA transcript and are all under the control of a single promoter and

Differentiated Instruction

ENGLISH LEARNERS

Have students use a Y diagram to compare and contrast gene expression and regulation in prokaryotic and eukaryotic cells. At the top of each arm of the Y, they should list the characteristics of each as they read. Once students have finished the section, they should move down to the stem of the Y, and list all those characteristics shared by both types of cells.

Teacher Toolkit, Section C, Y Diagram

INCLUSION

Have students who are visually impaired work with a partner to go through the process of gene regulation and expression in prokaryotic and eukaryotic cells. Provide yarn, scissors, and construction paper so students can make physical representations of all the components. Have students consider this question: How will the DNA strand containing the genes differ from the RNA transcript?

Teacher Toolkit, Section C, Think-Pair-Share

operator. This means that although we're dealing with several genes, they act together as a unit.

The *lac* operon is turned on and off like a switch. When lactose is absent from the environment, the *lac* operon is switched off to prevent transcription of the *lac* genes and save the cell's resources. When lactose is present, the *lac* operon is switched on to allow transcription. How does this happen?

Bacteria have a protein that can bind specifically to the operator. When lactose is absent, this protein binds to the operator, which blocks RNA polymerase from transcribing the genes. Because the protein blocks—or represses—transcription, it is called a repressor protein.

Without lactose (switched off)

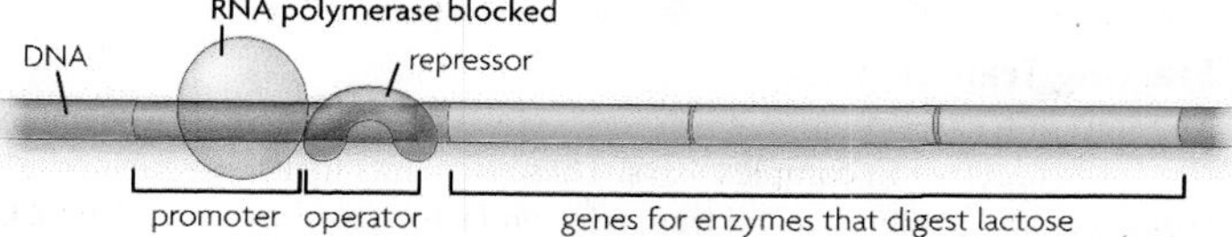

When lactose is present it binds to the repressor, which makes the repressor change shape and fall off the *lac* operon. RNA polymerase can then transcribe the genes in the *lac* operon. The resulting transcript is translated and forms three enzymes that work together to break down the lactose.

With lactose (switched on)

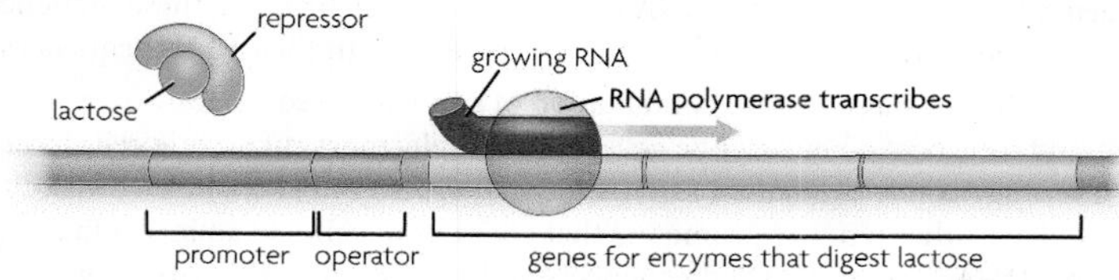

Analyze **Explain how the *lac* operon is turned on or off like a switch.**

MAIN IDEA

Eukaryotic cells regulate gene expression at many points.

You have already learned that every body cell in an organism has the same set of DNA. But your cells are not all the same. Cells differ from each other because different sets of genes are expressed in different types of cells. Eukaryotic cells can control the process of gene expression at many different points because of their internal compartments and chromosomal organization. As in prokaryotic cells, however, one of the most highly regulated steps is the start of transcription. In both cell types, RNA processing is a part of the transcription process. In eukaryotic cells, however, RNA processing also includes the removal of extra nucleotide segments from an mRNA transcript.

PRE-AP

Have students write an operational definition of a prokaryotic operon. They should include all the parts that make up a switched-off operon in their definitions, such as promoter, operator, genes, and repressor.

Teacher Toolkit, Section C, Quick-Write

TEACH FROM VISUALS

Have students look at **FIGURE 4.2** (transcription) from this chapter, and compare it to the diagrams on this page. Point out that the DNA strand is much simplified here; the bases are no longer shown. Point out that the color coding for DNA (blue) and RNA (brown) has been carried over. **Ask**

- In the diagrams on this page, are you looking at one DNA strand or two? one How do you know? Genes consist of a sequence of bases that are read by mRNA when the DNA helix opens up.
- Why is the *lac* operon an advantage to a bacterial cell? The cell does not waste energy making enzymes to digest lactose when lactose is not present.

Answers

A Analyze When lactose is absent, a repressor protein binds to the operon and blocks RNA polymerase from transcribing genes ("off"). When lactose is present, it binds to the repressor protein, which blocks the repressor from binding to the operon. RNA polymerase can then transcribe the genes ("on").

Take It Further

Eukaryotic cells have several different ways to control **gene expression.** In addition to RNA processing, other points of regulation include the following:

- relative tightness or looseness of the chromatin structure
- RNA transport out of the nucleus
- stability of mRNA molecule
- initiation of translation
- protein processing, stability, and transport

For example, some mRNA molecules have sequences that label them for rapid breakdown; others remain in the cytoplasm much longer. Similarly, some proteins are rapidly degraded or are not fully active until they reach their site of action.

▼ Teach *continued*

TEACH FROM VISUALS

FIGURE 6.1 Tell students that several regulatory sequences are clustered together in the DNA and that protein transcription factors bind to them. **Ask**

- What regulatory sequences are shown in the figure? TATA box, enhancer, promoter
- How do transcription factors function? They guide the RNA polymerase to the start of the gene.

Addressing Misconceptions

Common Misconception Students often think that every gene in a eukaryotic genome is expressed in every cell. Alternatively, they may think that a cell has only the genes that are needed for that type of cell.

Correcting the Misconception Explain that almost all cells in multicellular organisms contain the same full set of genes. Because the cells are specialized for particular functions, however, they have no use for most of the proteins coded by the genome. Thus, most of the genes they carry are not expressed. For example, a white blood cell has no use for digestive enzymes. If it made them, it would waste energy and raw materials in the process. Tell students that some genes code for proteins that are so specialized that those genes have never been expressed in most cells.

Answers

A Predict No, the DNA can bend, bringing an enhancer that is far away close to the start site of a gene.

FIGURE 6.1 Starting Transcription

Transcription factors that bind to promoters and other DNA sequences help RNA polymerase recognize the start of a gene in a eukaryotic cell.

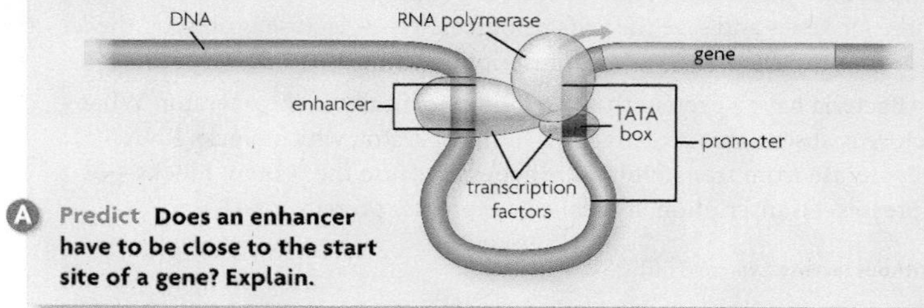

A Predict Does an enhancer have to be close to the start site of a gene? Explain.

Starting Transcription

The start of transcription in eukaryotic cells is controlled by many elements that work together in complex ways. These elements include regulatory DNA sequences and proteins called transcription factors, as shown in **FIGURE 6.1.** They occur in different combinations in different types of cells. The interplay between these elements results in specialized cells and cell responses.

Eukaryotes have many types of regulatory DNA sequences. These sequences are recognized by transcription factors that bind to the DNA strand and help RNA polymerase know where a gene starts. Some DNA sequences, such as promoters, are close to the start of a gene. Others are far away from the genes they affect. However, DNA can loop and bend, bringing these sequences with their transcription factors into close contact with their target sequences.

Each gene has a unique combination of regulatory sequences. Some are found in almost all eukaryotic cells. For example, most eukaryotic cells have a seven-nucleotide promoter (TATAAAA) called the TATA box. Eukaryotic cells also have other types of promoters that are more specific to an individual gene. DNA sequences called enhancers and silencers also play a role by speeding up or slowing down, respectively, the rate of transcription of a gene.

Some genes control the expression of many other genes. Regulation of these genes is very important because they can have a large effect on development. One such gene codes for a protein called sonic hedgehog. This protein was first found in fruit flies, but many other organisms have very similar proteins that serve a similar function. Sonic hedgehog helps establish body pattern. When sonic hedgehog is missing in fruit flies, the embryos are covered with little prickles and fail to form normal body segments.

mRNA Processing

Another important part of gene regulation in eukaryotic cells is RNA processing, which is shown in **FIGURE 6.2.** The mRNA produced by transcription is similar to a rough cut of a film that needs a bit of editing. A specialized nucleotide is added to the beginning of each mRNA molecule, which forms a cap. It helps the mRNA strand bind to a ribosome and prevents the strand from being broken down too fast. The end of the mRNA molecule gets a string of nucleotides, called the tail, that helps the mRNA molecule exit the nucleus.

CONNECT TO

ANIMALS

As you will learn in the chapter **Invertebrate Diversity,** most animals have homeobox genes. These genes are among the earliest that are expressed and play a key role in development. The illustration below shows the expression of homeobox genes in fruit fly and human embryos.

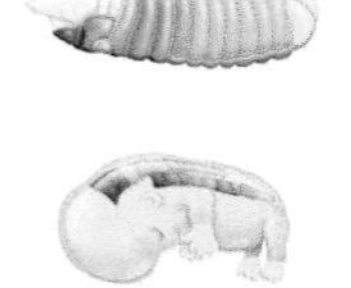

Differentiated Instruction

BELOW LEVEL

Have students compare gene regulation in prokaryotes to gene regulation in eukaryotes. Ask students to write for five minutes on the question of what the advantage might be for a eukaryotic organism to have such a complicated system of gene regulation. Have them think in terms of a unicellular organism versus a multicellular one, as well as the relative number of genes in each.

Teacher Toolkit, Section C, Quick-Write

FIGURE 6.2 mRNA Processing

An mRNA molecule typically undergoes processing during or immediately after DNA transcription.

In eukaryotic cells, DNA contains noncoding stretches called introns and coding stretches called exons.

Protein-coding DNA is transcribed into mRNA.

mRNA goes through three major processing steps: the removal of introns and the addition of a cap and tail.

The exons are spliced together, and the mRNA molecule enters the cytoplasm, where it can be translated.

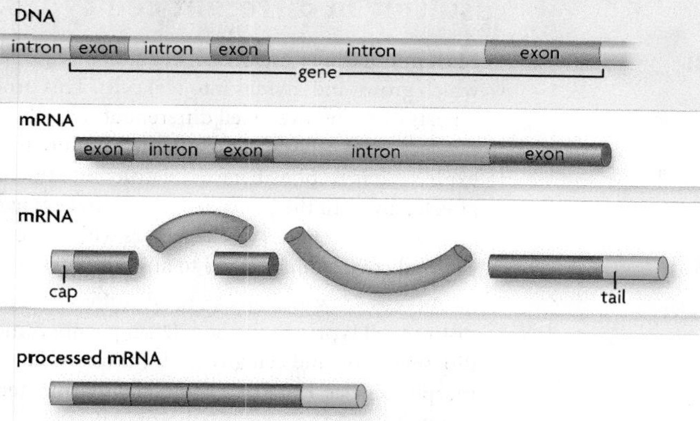

A Connect Where does mRNA processing take place in a eukaryotic cell?

The "extra footage" takes the form of nucleotide segments that are not included in the final protein. In eukaryotes, **exons** are nucleotide segments that code for parts of the protein. **Introns** are nucleotide segments that intervene, or occur, between exons. Introns are rare in prokaryotes. Introns are removed from mRNA before it leaves the nucleus. The cut ends of the exons are then joined together by a variety of molecular mechanisms.

The role of introns is not fully understood. They may regulate gene expression. In addition, some mRNA strands can be cut at various points, resulting in different proteins. As a result, introns increase genetic diversity without increasing the size of the genome.

RNA Interference

RNA can also be stopped from translating the amino acids that build a protein. One way to interrupt the process is by cleaving a protein-coding mRNA transcript so that it cannot translate a full protein. Surprisingly, the molecules that perform this cleaving are other RNA molecules. These special types of RNA function not to code for proteins but instead to regulate mRNA in a process called **RNA interference** (RNAi).

RNAi is performed by naturally occurring small RNA molecules, known as small interfering RNAs (siRNAs) or microRNAs (miRNAs) depending on their cellular origin. miRNAs are formed from regions of RNA transcripts that fold back on themselves to form short hairpin loops, while siRNAs derive from longer regions of double-stranded RNA. In each case, an enzyme called Dicer chops up the larger molecules into either miRNA or siRNA. These small RNAs, spanning about 20 nucleotides, match part of the target mRNA sequence and, with the help of catalytic proteins, cause the mRNA molecules to be cleaved. By degrading mRNA and preventing translation, the expression of specific genes can be increased, decreased, or even silenced.

INCLUSION

For students who have difficulty following a multistep process, use **FIGURE 6.2** to show how transcription of the blue DNA strand leads to the red mRNA strand. Explain and show that processing the mRNA happens between transcription and translation.

PRE-AP

Developing diabetes and other autoimmune diseases appears to be caused both by a genetic predisposition and environmental factors that affect gene expression. Ask students to conduct Internet research about the environmental factors that may trigger type 1 or type 2 diabetes in people who are genetically predisposed to the disease. Students should write a single paragraph summary of their findings, and include sources.

Vocabulary

intron, exon Given the prefixes *in-* and *ex-*, students may automatically think of introns as those portions of the genetic code left in and exons as those portions taken out. Tell students that geneticists think of genes with extra noncoding nucleotides as **interrupted genes.** Thus, the segments that do the interrupting are referred to as introns. Tell students to think of them as sequences that interrupt or interfere with the genetic message. Exons are sequences that exit the nucleus and are expressed.

Take It Further

Small RNA-and-protein particles in the nucleus recognize short nucleotide sequences at the ends of introns and cut out the introns. These particles are called small nuclear ribonucleoproteins (snRNPs), or **snurps.**

Addressing Misconceptions

Common Misconception Students may think that all traits are either genetic or acquired, such as learned behavior. Students may not realize the role that environmental factors play on the expression of genes and, ultimately, genetic traits.

Correcting the Misconception Explain that genetic traits are the result of proteins. Translation, or the synthesis of proteins, is the third of three highly regulated processes: gene expression, transcription, and translation. While translation is limited to proteins that are coded for by DNA, the different factors, or triggers, that regulate expression, transcription, and translation are related to the environment inside and outside the cell and organism.

Answers

A Connect in the nucleus

B Apply exons

▼ Teach *continued*

Vocabulary

The formation of the structure of an organism is called *morphogenesis*. The term uses the prefix *morpho-* which means shape or structure and the stem *genesis* which means creation. Morphogenesis results from cell differentiation and growth to form tissues and organs.

Take It Further

Some of the signal molecules that regulate gene expression are hormones. Male-pattern baldness, the loss of hair on the top of the head, is controlled by an autosomal gene. The allele for baldness is affected by high levels of two male hormones. Because females have much lower levels of these two hormones, they rarely express male-pattern baldness. When some females are stressed, their bodies increase the production of male hormones. Loss of hair can result.

Science Trivia

Nine-banded armadillos (*Dasypus novemcinctus*) are mammals with many unusual characteristics. Nine-banded armadillos are the only species of the order Xenarthra to be found outside of Central and South America. The animal's unusual appearance includes a bony external carapace which serves as armor. Armadillos are not buoyant in water, and they walk across the bottoms of narrow streams or bodies of water instead of swimming across. Finally, nine-banded armadillos give birth to identical quadruplets. This unusual characteristic allows researchers to observe how the environment influences gene expression and phenotypic differences among armadillos who are genetically identical.

MAIN IDEA

Environmental factors influence gene expression, resulting in different cell types.

Most multicellular organisms begin as a single fertilized egg cell, or zygote, which grows and divides into two cells. This process of growth and division repeats over and over. Cell differentiation is the process by which unspecialized cells develop into their mature forms and functions. Gene expression is responsible for the differentiation of cells. Gene expression is affected by both the internal and external environment. An organism's internal environment includes all the factors within the organism and its cells. The external environment refers to any factors outside the organism.

As cells grow and divide, subtle differences become more evident as distinct cell types are formed. During embryonic development, cell differentiation and cell growth form tissues and organs in a process called morphogenesis. **FIGURE 6.3** shows the morphogenesis of embryonic eyes through the differentiation of cells.

Internal Factors

The differentiation of embryonic cells is based on several internal factors. First, the genetic make-up of the zygote provides the organism with many instructions for differentiation. A zygote's genetic make-up includes all the genes that can be expressed within any cell of the organism, even after the organism has grown and developed. Genes that are expressed in the cells of a developing organism initiate cell differentiation.

Even before an egg cell is fertilized, the internal environment of the egg cell promotes differentiation. Proteins, mRNA, organelles, and other substances in the egg cell cytoplasm are not spread evenly throughout the egg cell. After fertilization, as the zygote divides, the molecules in the cytoplasm are distributed unevenly among the different cells of the developing embryo. These molecules regulate gene expression in each cell and help determine what type of cell it will become.

FIGURE 6.3 DIFFERENTIATING EMBRYONIC EYES

The eyes of human embryos begin to develop about 32 days after the egg cell is fertilized to become a zygote. The cells that form eye tissue differentiate due to chemical signals from nearby cells.

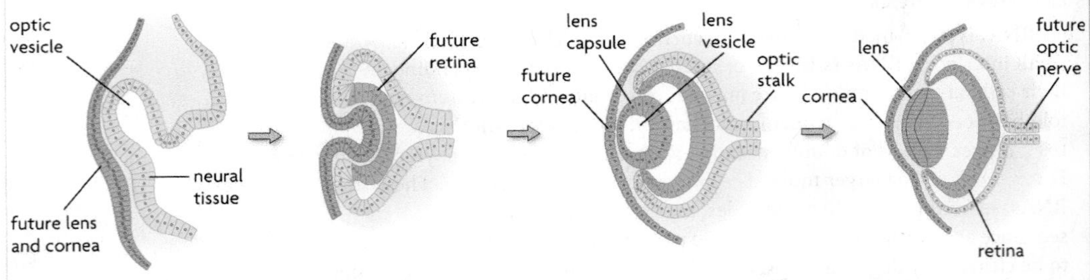

Differentiated Instruction

HANDS-ON ACTIVITY

Demonstrate how splitting egg cell cytoplasm leads to two cells with different molecular makeup. First, pour a large dollop of clear dish soap into a shallow pan. Add a smaller dollop of colored dish soap to represent the nucleus. Then, unevenly sprinkle small objects, such as beads, dried beans, or small pieces of colored paper, throughout the clear dish soap (the cytoplasm). Students should see that some areas of cytoplasm contain more of a substance than other areas. Lay two pipe cleaners side by side through the "cell," making sure to bisect the "nucleus." Pull the pipe cleaners apart to separate the "cells."

TEACH WITH TECHNOLOGY

There are many videos and images of embryonic development available on the Internet. Find a scholarly source to show to the class and lead a discussion of how cellular differentiation leads to the development of different tissues and organs.

Each cell in a developing embryo is influenced by other cells around it. In the developing eyes, for example, cells close to the optic vesicle are influenced to thicken and fold inward. These changes eventually lead to the development of the lens and cornea. Cells influence and communicate with each other by sending and receiving molecules that act as signals. Signals may also come from molecules embedded in the cell membrane. Signal molecules are proteins that induce a cell to follow a specific developmental path by causing a change in its gene expression. Signal molecules cause the expression of certain genes to be turned on or off. Some signal molecules can affect genes by preventing a gene from transcribing genetic information to mRNA. Gene expression also can be controlled after translation has occurred. For example, a protein may be produced by translation and then broken down by enzymes.

External Factors

Factors in an organism's external environment also can affect gene expression. For example, temperature can influence gene expression in some organisms. The *C* gene in Himalayan rabbits is involved in development of the black color of fur, skin, and eyes. When the external temperature is above 35°C, the central parts of the rabbit's body are over 30°C, and the gene is inactive. No pigments are produced, and the fur color is white. Below 20°C, the outer parts of the rabbit—such as the ears, tail, feet, and tip of the nose—are cooler, and the gene is expressed. These body parts are black.

The presence of drugs and chemicals in an organism's external environment can also affect gene expression and cell differentiation. When magnesium chloride is present in the environment of certain fish embryos, they develop one eye instead of two. In the 1960s, the drug thalidomide was found to cause severe arm and leg deformities in human embryos. Children born from mothers who took this drug often had shortened and malformed limbs.

Light affects gene expression in *Vanessa* butterflies. If the immature caterpillars are placed in red light, the wings that develop in the adult butterflies are brightly colored. When the caterpillars are placed in green light, the adults have dark wings. Under blue light or in darkness, the wings are a pale color.

Identify **Name two internal and two external factors that affect gene expression.**

8.6 Formative Assessment

REVIEWING MAIN IDEAS

1. What is a **promoter**?
2. In eukaryotic cells, genes each have a specific combination of regulatory DNA sequences. How do these combinations help cells carry out specialized jobs?

CRITICAL THINKING

3. **Predict** Suppose a bacterium had a mutated repressor protein that could not bind to the *lac* operator. How might this affect regulation of the **operon**?
4. **Summarize** What are the three major steps involved in mRNA processing?

CONNECT TO

DNA

5. DNA is loosely organized in areas where RNA polymerase is transcribing genes. What might you infer about a region of DNA that was loosely organized in muscle cells but tightly coiled in lung cells?

8.6 FORMATIVE ASSESSMENT

1. A promoter is a DNA sequence that allows a gene to be transcribed by helping RNA polymerase recognize the start of a gene.
2. These combinations help a cell turn on only specific genes. Based on the different genes that are turned on or off, a cell has a unique set of proteins that enables it to carry out certain functions.
3. The operon could never be turned off. The genes would be continually transcribed.
4. addition of the cap, addition of the tail, and removal of introns with the splicing together of exons
5. The genes in that region of DNA must be used by muscle cells but not by lung cells.

Connect to Ecology

The gender of some reptiles is determined by environmental temperatures around the developing eggs. For example, painted turtle eggs that mature in cooler temperatures develop into male turtles, whereas painted turtle eggs that mature in warmer temperatures develop into female turtles. With normal fluctuations in annual temperature, an appropriate balance of genders will result. However, studies conducted in the 1990s found that there were seasons in which clutches of painted turtles contained all females and others that were all males. These clutches correlated to warmer and cooler July weather respectively, and suggest that the trend toward warmer global climate conditions could eventually result in the elimination of painted turtles. Ecologists warn that painted turtles may have to find ways to adapt, such as laying eggs earlier in the season, or face extinction.

Answers

A Identify answers should include two of the following internal factors: genetics, internal environment of the egg cell, communication from nearby cells; and two of the following external factors: amount of oxygen available, temperature, presence of drugs or chemicals, light

Assess and Reteach

Assess Use the Section Self-Check or Section Quiz, both available at **HMHScience.com**.

Reteach Work with the class to prepare a concept map that details gene regulation in both prokaryotic and eukaryotic cells.

SECTION 8.7

B.4.5 Make and defend a claim based on evidence that inheritable genetic variations may result from: (1) new genetic combinations through meiosis, (2) viable errors occurring during replication, and (3) mutations caused by environmental factors.

Plan and Prepare

Activate Prior Knowledge Tell students that sometimes a small mistake can have a big effect. **Ask,** What happens if, in recording your grade, a teacher transposes the numbers of your 3.1 GPA? My B grade becomes an F. Tell students that in this section, they will learn about the effects of mistakes incorporated into the genetic code.

Teach

Take It Further

Cystic fibrosis is caused by a defective CFTR protein, a channel protein in the cell membrane that transports chloride ions in and out of the cell. Although more than 1000 mutations have been found in the gene that encodes this protein, the most common one is a DNA deletion of a TTT sequence. When the defective DNA is transcribed, the mRNA lacks a UUU codon, and thus a phenylalanine is missing from position 508 of the 1480-amino-acid protein. Loss of this single amino acid causes the protein to fold incorrectly, and as a result, it cannot function.

8.7 Mutations

KEY CONCEPT **Mutations are changes in DNA that may or may not affect phenotype.**

VOCABULARY

mutation
point mutation
frameshift mutation
mutagen

MAIN IDEAS

- Some mutations affect a single gene, while others affect an entire chromosome.
- Mutations may or may not affect phenotype.
- Mutations can be caused by several factors.

Connect to Your World

We all make mistakes. Some may be a bit embarrassing. Others become funny stories we tell our friends later. Still others, however, have far-reaching effects that we failed to see in our moment of decision. Cells make mistakes too. These mistakes, like our own, can have a range of effects. When they occur in DNA, they are called mutations, and cells have evolved a variety of methods for dealing with them.

MAIN IDEA

Some mutations affect a single gene, while others affect an entire chromosome.

You may already know the term *mutation* from popular culture, but it has a specific meaning in biology. A **mutation** is a change in an organism's DNA. Many types of mutations can occur, as shown in **FIGURE 7.2.** Typically, mutations that affect a single gene happen during replication, whereas mutations that affect a group of genes or an entire chromosome happen during meiosis.

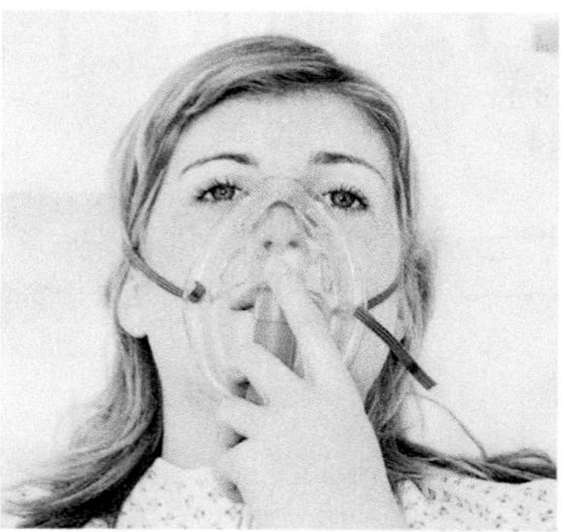

FIGURE 7.1 Cystic fibrosis (CF) is a genetic disease that is most commonly caused by a specific deletion. It causes the overproduction of thick, sticky mucus. Although CF cannot be cured, it is treated in a number of ways, including oxygen therapy (above).

Gene Mutations

A **point mutation** is a mutation in which one nucleotide is substituted for another. That is, an incorrect nucleotide is put in the place of the correct nucleotide. Very often, such a mistake is caught and fixed by DNA polymerase. If it is not, the substitution may permanently change an organism's DNA.

A **frameshift mutation** involves the insertion or deletion of a nucleotide in the DNA sequence. It usually affects a polypeptide much more than does a substitution. Frameshift mutations are so named because they shift the entire sequence following them by one or more nucleotides. To understand how this affects an mRNA strand, imagine a short sentence of three-letter "codons":

THE CAT ATE THE RAT

If the letter *E* is removed, or deleted, from the first "THE," all the letters that follow shift to the left. The sentence now reads:

THC ATA TET HER AT . . .

Differentiated Instruction

ENGLISH LEARNERS

Point out to students that an outline would be a good way to preview and summarize this section. Have students use the standard format: Roman numerals, capital letters, Arabic numerals, and lowercase letters organized under the section title. Remind students to use the same grammatical form for each level, for example, single words or sentences, and present tense verbs or infinitives. You may want to go over different students' outlines to discuss the decisions they made.

Teacher Toolkit, Section C, Outline

PRE-AP

Challenge students to answer and explain the following question: When does a deletion or an insertion not result in a frame shift? If three nucleotides—an entire codon—are either deleted or inserted, one amino acid will be affected, but a frame shift will not occur. Have students write the answer to the question, exchange papers with a partner, and discuss their responses.

Teacher Toolkit, Section C, Think-Pair-Share

FIGURE 7.2 Types of Mutations

A mutation is a change in an organism's DNA.

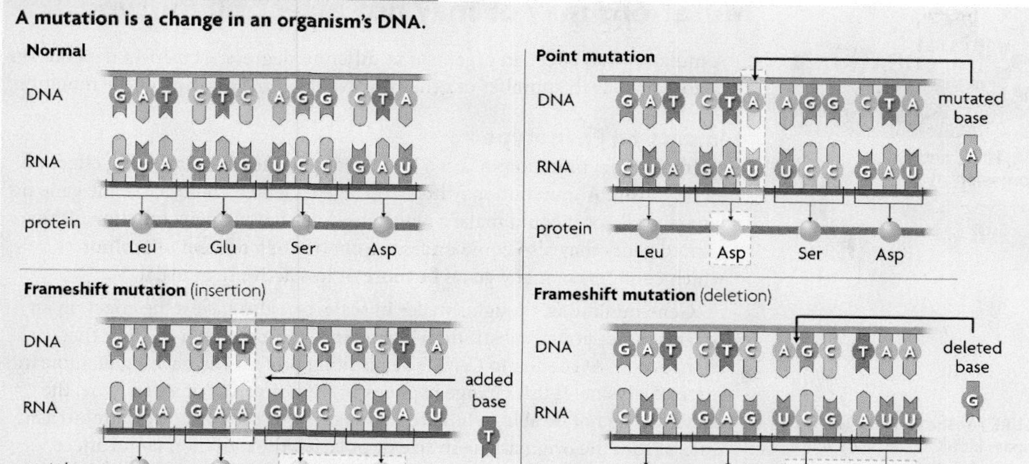

A Evaluate Explain which mutation you think would have the greatest effect.

The sentence no longer makes sense. The same would be true if a nucleotide was added, or inserted, and all the letters shifted to the right. In the same way, a nucleotide sequence loses its meaning when an insertion or deletion shifts all the codons by one nucleotide. This change throws off the reading frame, which results in codons that code for different amino acids.

Chromosomal Mutations

Recall that during meiosis, homologous chromosomes exchange DNA segments through crossing over. If the chromosomes do not align with each other, these segments may be different in size. As a result, one chromosome may have two copies of a gene or genes, which is called gene duplication. The other chromosome may have no copy of the gene or genes. Gene duplication has happened again and again throughout eukaryotic evolution.

Translocation is another type of chromosomal mutation. In translocation, a piece of one chromosome moves to a nonhomologous chromosome. Translocations are often reciprocal, which means that the two nonhomologous chromosomes exchange segments with each other.

Gene duplication

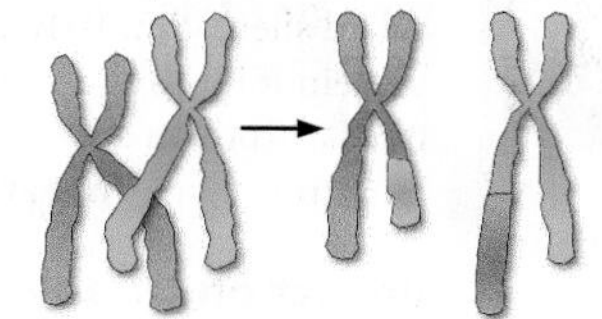

Gene translocation

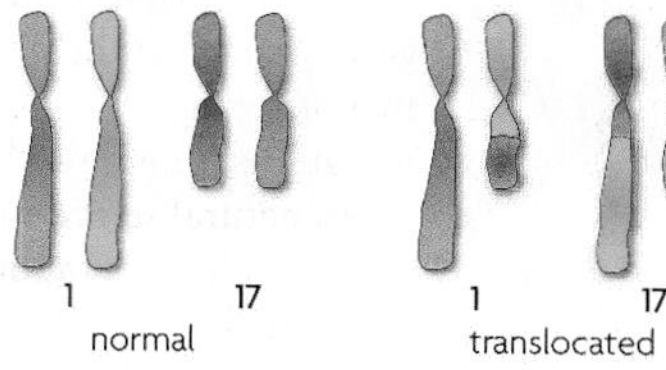

B Explain How does a frameshift mutation affect reading frame?

Vocabulary

Academic Vocabulary The word **frame** originates from a word in Old English that means "forward" or "to further." A **reading frame** is a point of departure, a **frame of reference.** The DNA code is a triplet code; the frame establishes which triplets are created. Have students consider three ways to frame this repeating sequence: CGACGACGA . . .

CGA CGA CGA CGA

GAC GAC GAC GAC

ACG ACG ACG ACG

TEACH FROM VISUALS

FIGURE 7.2 Have students study the details of each diagram. **Ask**

- Would a frameshift mutation have a greater effect if it occurred near the promoter or near the end of the gene? The promoter is located at the very beginning of the gene, so a frameshift mutation occurring there would affect the entire polypeptide. The same mutation occurring at the end of the gene would affect only the final few amino acids.
- Does a point mutation always change the amino acid sequence of the encoded polypeptide? No, if the codon with the substituted nucleotide coded for the same amino acid as the original codon, the amino acid sequence would not change.

Take It Further

Point out that **gene duplications** and **translocations** usually occur in germ cells during prophase I of meiosis. This is when homologous chromosomes pair tightly and cross over.

BELOW LEVEL

Refer students to **FIGURE 7.2.** Have them write a caption for each type of mutation shown, describing the mutation and its consequence.

HANDS-ON ACTIVITY

Provide plastic snap-together beads so students can make models of a pair of homologous chromosomes. The chromosomes should be of different colors if possible. If not, mark the beads on one chromosome with stickers or pieces of masking tape. Have students exchange segments between chromosomes to model gene duplication and translocation. After students have demonstrated these mutations, have them summarize how each kind of mutation occurs.

Answers

A Evaluate Many students may select one of the frameshift mutations as having the greatest effect because they are more likely to affect a greater number of codons.

B Explain The insertion or deletion of a nucleotide throws off the reading frame because genes are read as a series of three nonoverlapping nucleotides.

▼ Teach *continued*

Integrating Evolution

Mutant alleles are not always removed from a population by **natural selection.** In the case of **heterozygote superiority,** a mutant allele persists because the heterozygote has an adaptive advantage. Neither of the alleles involved can be eliminated from a population because, in each generation, heterozygotes produce more offspring than homozygotes do.

For example, many people who have **sickle cell disease** (homozygote recessive) die before they can reproduce, so they do not transmit the recessive allele to the next generation. However, people who are heterozygous for the gene have an advantage. They are less likely to contract **malaria,** possibly because the parasite cannot reproduce in their sickled red blood cells. These people, who are said to have the sickle cell trait, do not die of malaria, and they do not die of sickle cell disease. When they reproduce, there is a 50 percent chance that they will transmit the recessive allele to their offspring.

Answers

Ⓐ **Apply** because body cells are not passed from one generation to another

MAIN IDEA

Mutations may or may not affect phenotype.

A mutation can affect an organism to different degrees. The effect depends on factors such as the number of genes involved and the location of the mutation.

Impact on Phenotype

Chromosomal mutations affect a lot of genes and tend to have a big effect on an organism. A mutation may break up a gene, which could make the gene no longer work, or it could make a new hybrid gene with a new function. Translocated genes may also come under the control of a new set of promoters, which could make many genes be more or less active than usual.

Gene mutations, though smaller in scale, can also have a big effect on an organism. Suppose a substitution occurs in a coding region of DNA that changes an AAG codon to CAG. The resulting protein will have a glutamine in place of a lysine. If this change happens in the active site of an enzyme, the enzyme may not be able to bind to its substrate. If the substituted amino acid differs from the original one in size or polarity, the mutation could affect protein folding and thus possibly destroy the protein's function. A substitution could also result in a premature stop codon.

Even a mutation that occurs in a noncoding region can cause problems. For example, such a mutation could disrupt an mRNA splice site and prevent an intron from being removed. A mutation in a noncoding region could also interfere with the regulation of gene expression, keeping a protein from being produced or causing it to be produced all the time.

FIGURE 7.3 The coronary artery supplies blood to the heart. If it becomes blocked (top), a heart attack may result. Some people have a mutation that appears to help protect against coronary artery disease (bottom) by increasing their "good" cholesterol levels and decreasing their triglyceride levels. (colored LMs; magnifications: 15×)

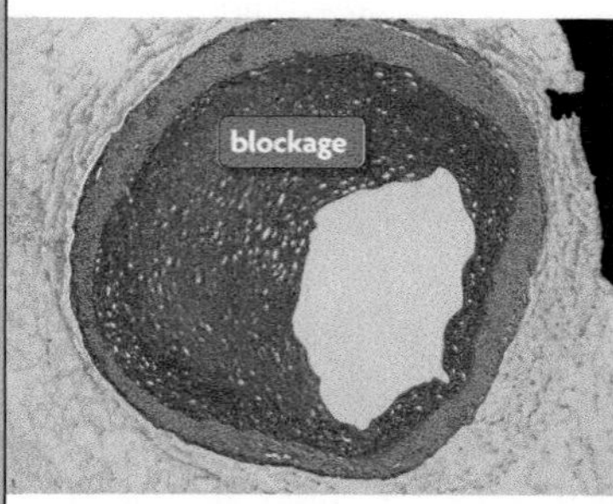

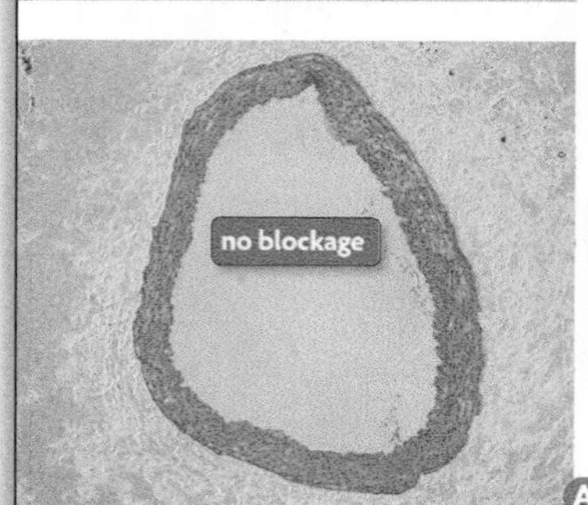

Many gene mutations, however, do not affect an organism's phenotype. Remember that many codons code for the same amino acid. Therefore, some substitutions have no effect, especially those occurring in the third nucleotide of a codon. If AAG changes to AAA, the resulting protein still has the correct amino acid, lysine. A mutation that does not affect the resulting protein is called silent. Similarly, an incorrect amino acid might have little effect on a protein if it has about the same size or polarity as the original amino acid or if it is far from an active site. If a mutation occurs in a noncoding region, such as an intron, it may not affect the encoded protein at all.

Impact on Offspring

Mutations happen both in body cells and in germ cells. Mutations in body cells affect only the organism in which they occur. In contrast, mutations in germ cells may be passed to offspring. They are the underlying source of genetic variation, which is the basis of natural selection. Mutations in the germ line affect the phenotype of offspring. Often, this effect is so harmful that offspring do not develop properly or die before they can reproduce. Other mutations, though less severe, still result in less adaptive phenotypes. In such cases, natural selection removes these mutant alleles from the population. More rarely, a mutation results in a more beneficial phenotype. These mutations are favored by natural selection and increase in a population.

Ⓐ Apply **Why aren't mutations in body cells passed on to offspring?**

Differentiated Instruction

TEACH WITH TECHNOLOGY

Some biological supply companies sell kits containing root tips of onion plants that have been exposed to gamma radiation. The root tips are not radioactive and are safe for classroom use. Students can stain the root tips, prepare slides, and observe mitosis. Chromosome breakage and rearrangements can be observed. In addition, a PC microscope can be used to transfer the images from the microscope to class computers.

MAIN IDEA

Mutations can be caused by several factors.

Mutations are not uncommon, and organisms have many tools to repair them. However, events and substances can make mutations happen faster than the body's repair system can handle.

Replication Errors

As you have learned, DNA polymerase has a built-in proofreading function. Nevertheless, a small number of replication errors are not fixed. They build up over time, and eventually affect how the cell works. For example, many studies suggest that mutations are a significant cause of aging.

Mutagens

Mutagens are agents in the environment that can change DNA. They speed up the rate of replication errors and, in some cases, even break DNA strands. Some mutagens occur naturally, such as ultraviolet (UV) rays in sunshine. Many others are industrial chemicals. Ecologists such as Rachel Carson, shown in **FIGURE 7.4**, warned the public about mutagens.

The human body has DNA repair enzymes that help find and fix mutations. For instance, UV light can cause neighboring thymine nucleotides to break their hydrogen bonds to adenine and bond with each other instead. Typically, one enzyme removes the bonded thymines, another replaces the damaged section, and a third bonds the new segment in place. Sometimes, these enzymes do not work. If these mistakes interfere with regulatory sites and control mechanisms, they may result in cancer. In rare cases, people inherit mutations that make their DNA repair systems less active, which makes these people very vulnerable to the damaging effects of sunlight.

Some cancer drugs take advantage of mutagenic properties by causing similar damage to cancer cells. One type of drug wedges its way between nucleotides, causing so many mutations that cancer cells can no longer function.

FIGURE 7.4 Rachel Carson was one of the first ecologists to warn against the widespread use of pesticides and other potential mutagens and toxins.

A Summarize **Explain why mutagens can damage DNA in spite of repair enzymes.**

8.7 Formative Assessment

SELF-CHECK Online HMHScience.com GO ONLINE

REVIEWING MAIN IDEAS

1. Explain why **frameshift mutations** have a greater effect than do **point mutations**.
2. If GUA is changed to GUU, will the resulting protein be affected? Explain.
3. Explain how **mutagens** can cause genetic **mutations** in spite of your body's DNA repair enzymes.

CRITICAL THINKING

4. **Connect** Some genetic mutations are associated with increased risk for a particular disease. Tests exist for some of these genes. What might be the advantages and disadvantages of being tested?
5. **Illustrate** How could a mutated gene produce a shorter protein than that produced by the normal gene? Draw an example.

CONNECT TO ECOLOGY

6. How might the presence of a chemical mutagen in the environment affect the genetic makeup and size of a population over time?

Vocabulary

Academic Vocabulary Point out the similarity in the words **mutagen, carcinogen,** and **allergen.** The root *gen* means "to give birth to." The word **agent** can be applied in the definition of each, as in the agent that causes mutation, cancer, or allergic reactions. The root for agent is not the same, however. *Agere* means "to do."

Answers

A **Summarize** The mutagens can induce more mutations than the repair enzymes can fix.

Assess and Reteach

Assess Use the Section Self-Check or Section Quiz, both available at HMHScience.com.

Reteach Work with students to make a concept map summarizing the material in this section. Have them include the four vocabulary terms *mutation, point mutation, frameshift mutation,* and *mutagen,* as well as the terms *gene mutations, chromosomal mutations, gene duplication,* and *gene translocation.*

8.7 FORMATIVE ASSESSMENT

1. Point mutations typically affect only one codon (unless they create a premature stop codon). A frameshift mutation affects all the codons in a gene that follow it.
2. No, both GUA and GUU code for the amino acid valine.
3. Mutagens may cause so much damage that the repair enzymes cannot keep up with the repairs.
4. *Sample answer:* Advantage: A person would know to look for symptoms and would be able to prepare and seek possible treatment. Disadvantage: There may be no cure for the disease, or simply having the gene may not mean that getting the disease is inevitable.
5. Students may draw a frameshift or point mutation in a sequence of codons in which a codon in the sequence is changed to a stop codon (UAA or UAG).
6. Initially, the population size would likely decrease due to disease. But over time, individuals that had a resistance to the mutagenic effect would be more likely to pass on that trait, and it would become more common in the population. Or, if the trait were advantageous to some, the mutation could become more prevalent than the original allele.

CHAPTER REVIEW

GO ONLINE

Encourage students to go to **HMHScience.com** for a detailed review of each section, including visuals and vocabulary practice.

Online Student Resources, Vocabulary Practice Worksheet

CHAPTER

8 Summary

BIG IDEA DNA and RNA are the genetic material in all living things and provide the molecular basis for reproduction and development.

KEY CONCEPTS

8.1 Identifying DNA as the Genetic Material

DNA was identified as the genetic material through a series of experiments. Griffith discovered a "transforming principle," which Avery later identified as DNA. Hershey and Chase's experiments with bacteriophages conclusively demonstrated that DNA is the genetic material.

8.2 Structure of DNA

DNA structure is the same in all organisms. DNA is a polymer made up of four types of nucleotides. Watson and Crick discovered that DNA consists of two strands of nucleotides bonded together into a double helix structure. Nucleotides always pair in the same way— C with G, and A with T.

8.3 DNA Replication

DNA replication copies the genetic information of a cell. During replication, a DNA molecule separates into two strands. Each strand serves as a template for building a new complementary strand through a rapid, accurate process involving DNA polymerase and other enzymes.

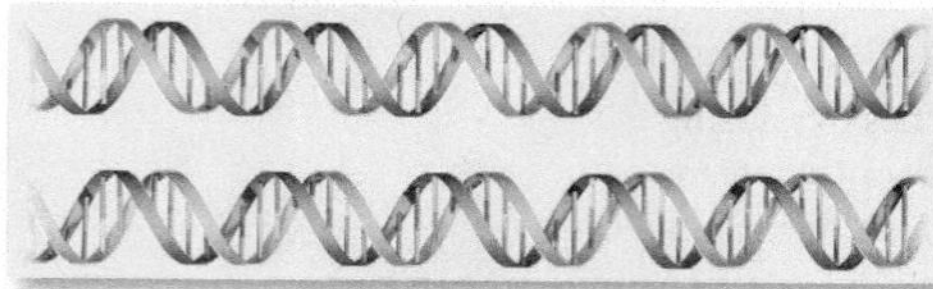

Two identical double-stranded DNA molecules result from replication.

8.4 Transcription

Transcription converts a gene into a single-stranded RNA molecule. The transcription process is similar to DNA replication and makes three types of RNA. Messenger RNA is an intermediate molecule that carries DNA's instructions to be translated.

8.5 Translation

Translation converts an mRNA message into a polypeptide, or protein. This process occurs on ribosomes, which are made of rRNA and proteins. Transfer RNA molecules bring amino acids to the growing protein by selectively pairing with mRNA codons.

8.6 Gene Expression and Regulation

Gene expression is carefully regulated in both prokaryotic and eukaryotic cells. In prokaryotes, transcription is the primary point of control. In eukaryotes, gene expression is controlled at many points, including RNA processing. Internal and external factors influence gene expression and cell differentiation.

8.7 Mutations

Mutations are changes in DNA that may or may not affect phenotype. Some mutations affect a single gene, and others affect an entire chromosome. Mutations may occur naturally, or they may be caused by mutagens. A mutation that does not affect phenotype is called a silent mutation. Mutations in sperm or egg cells can be passed to offspring.

READING TOOLBOX SYNTHESIZE YOUR NOTES

Summarize How can you summarize the process by which proteins are made? Use your notes to make a detailed version of the graphic organizer below. Include important details about the processes of transcription and translation. Mark important vocabulary terms.

From DNA to Proteins

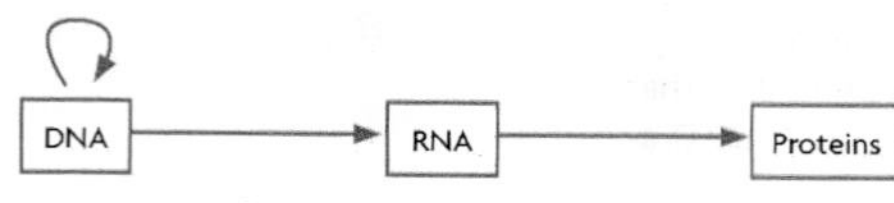

Concept Map Use a concept map like the one below to summarize what you know about mutations.

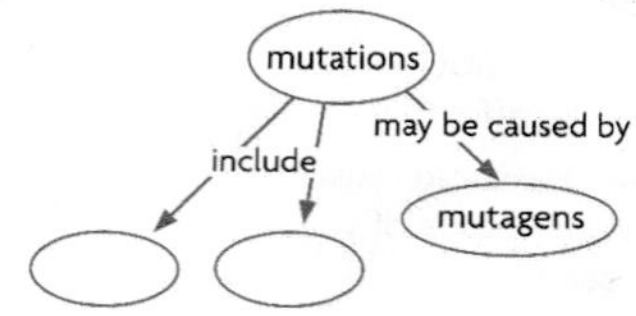

Reviewing Vocabulary

1. Both processes involve the conversion of one type of message into another type of message. Translation reads RNA to make proteins, whereas transcription reads DNA to make RNA.
2. Both types of mutations are changes in the DNA nucleotide sequence. A point mutation involves a change in only one nucleotide. A frameshift mutation involves the insertion or deletion of a nucleotide and throws off the entire reading frame.
3. Both types of RNA are involved in the making of proteins. mRNA makes a template of the code for the protein from DNA. tRNA is a carrier molecule that transfers amino acids to the ribosome.
4. Both are three-nucleotide sequences. A codon is on an mRNA molecule and indicates which amino acid is needed. The anticodon on a tRNA molecule is complementary to the mRNA codon and brings in the needed amino acid.
5. A codon is a three-nucleotide "unit" that "codes" for an amino acid. The nucleotide codons in DNA provide the information that cells need to develop and function, and are passed on from one generation to the next.
6. mutagen: a chemical that causes, or gives birth to, a change in DNA; bacteriophage: a virus that infects, or "eats" into, bacteria; polypeptide: a molecule that is constructed with many peptide bonds
7. polygenic: something that involves many genes; phagocyte: a cell that eats other cells

INTERACTIVE Review
HMHScience.com
GO ONLINE
Review Games • Concept Map • Section Self-Checks

8 Review

CHAPTER VOCABULARY

8.1 bacteriophage
8.2 nucleotide, double helix, base pairing rules
8.3 replication, DNA polymerase
8.4 central dogma, RNA, transcription, RNA polymerase, messenger RNA (mRNA), ribosomal RNA (rRNA), transfer RNA (tRNA)
8.5 translation, codon, stop codon, start codon, anticodon
8.6 promoter, operon, exon, intron
8.7 mutation, point mutation, frameshift mutation, mutagen

Reviewing Vocabulary

Compare and Contrast

Describe one similarity and one difference between the two terms in each of the following pairs.

1. translation, transcription
2. point mutation, frameshift mutation
3. messenger RNA (mRNA), transfer RNA (tRNA)
4. codon, anticodon

READING TOOLBOX WORD ORIGINS

5. The word *codon* was coined in 1962 by putting together the word *code* with the suffix *-on,* which means "a hereditary unit." How do these word parts relate to the meaning of the term *codon*?

Use the word parts in this table to answer the next two questions.

Part	Meaning
-gen	to give birth
muta-	to change
phago-	eating
poly-	many

6. Use the meaning of the word parts to write your own definitions for the following terms: *mutagen, bacteriophage, polypeptide.*
7. Suggest a likely definition for these biology terms: *polygenic, phagocyte.*

Reviewing MAIN IDEAS

8. How did qualitative, chemical, and enzyme tests help Avery identify DNA as the transforming principle?
9. Hershey and Chase confirmed that DNA, not protein, was the genetic material. How do the results of their two experiments support this conclusion?
10. Describe Watson and Crick's double helix DNA model. Include a labeled drawing of the model.
11. One DNA strand has the nucleotide sequence AACGTA. What is the sequence of the other strand?
12. How do the base pairing rules explain how a strand of DNA acts as a template during replication?
13. What are three main steps in DNA replication?
14. What does it mean to say that there is a "proofreading" function in DNA replication?
15. Describe two differences between DNA and RNA.
16. List the main types of RNA and their functions.
17. Explain the process of mRNA codons and tRNA anticodons coding for a specific amino acid.
18. What role do ribosomes play in translation?
19. Where in the eukaryotic cell do replication, transcription, RNA processing, and translation each occur?
20. How do the promoter and operator work together to control gene expression?
21. Describe mRNA processing in eukaryotic cells.
22. Describe three ways mutations can occur.

CHAPTER REVIEW

Reviewing Main Ideas

8. Qualitative tests identified DNA, not protein; chemical analyses identified elements found in DNA, but not in protein; and enzyme tests showed that when proteins were destroyed, the genetic information was still active.
9. When phage proteins were labeled, no radioactivity was found in the bacteria, but when DNA was tagged, radioactivity was found in the bacteria.
10. The double helix is two twisted strands of DNA, with sugar-phosphate backbones on the outside and base pairs matching up on the inside. A pairs with T, and C with G.
11. TTGCAT
12. During DNA replication, nucleotide T always pairs with A, and C with G. The nucleotides on one strand are complementary to those on the other.
13. (1) The double helix unzips. (2) DNA polymerase bonds complementary nucleotides in the growing strands. (3) The final product is two double helixes, each with one old strand and one new strand.
14. DNA polymerases identify mismatched nucleotides and replace them during replication so that the genetic codes "read" correctly.
15. *Sample answer:* DNA is double-stranded, whereas RNA is single-stranded. DNA is made up of A, T, C, and G, whereas RNA is made up of A, U, C, and G.
16. mRNA: transcribes genes in DNA into a complementary code; rRNA: part of a ribosome and active in putting together amino acids to form protein; tRNA: translates mRNA so that necessary amino acids brought in from cytoplasm add to a growing polypeptide
17. mRNA codons are the three-nucleotide sequences that code for specific amino acids. Anticodons are tRNA sequences complementary to the mRNA codons that bring the specific amino acid into the growing polypeptide.
18. A ribosome binds to the mRNA that is being translated, and to tRNA molecules, which bring in amino acids that attach to the growing polypeptide in the proper sequence.
19. Replication, transcription, and RNA processing occur in the nucleus. Translation occurs in the cytoplasm.
20. The promoter helps RNA polymerase recognize the start of a gene so that an mRNA strand can be made. The operator interacts with other proteins that either block RNA polymerase or allow the gene to be transcribed by mRNA, depending on conditions in the cell.
21. mRNA processing includes the removal of introns, the addition of the cap and tail, and the splicing together of exons.
22. Mutations can occur from mutagens, replication errors, or errors in the exchange of chromosome segments during meiosis.

Critical Thinking

23. A mutation may result in a premature stop codon and prevent a protein from being made. A different mutation may result in a codon still coding for the same amino acid, so there would be no change.
24. Replication copies DNA. A gene is transcribed from DNA to RNA. Translation interprets RNA into a polypeptide. Gene expression is regulated and influenced, usually during transcription, in response to internal and external environmental factors. Differences in gene expression influence cell differentiation, or the differences between cell types.
25. The rate of protein synthesis might be slowed because fewer RNA molecules could exit the nucleus.
26. AUGGUUCACUUUUAA; methionine, valine, histidine, phenylalanine, stop; *Sample answer:*

    AUGGUUCAAUUUUAA; methionine, valine, glutamine, phenylalanine, stop
27. No, because the gene has other sets of regulatory sequences and its own promoter; the presence of lactose and the operator would probably be insufficient to trigger RNA polymerase to begin transcribing.
28. Watson and Crick already knew DNA's composition, based on the accumulated work of other researchers. They applied this knowledge to piece together the three-dimensional structure of DNA. Griffith, Avery, and Hershey and Chase worked with living organisms. They systematically manipulated the possible components of DNA in ways that would enable them to identify DNA as the genetic material based on experimental results.
29. For a long time, scientists hypothesized that DNA was made up of equal amounts of the four nucleotides, and so the DNA in all organisms was exactly the same. They reasoned that identical molecules could not carry different instructions across all organisms. In 1950 Chargaff found that the proportion of the four bases differs somewhat among organisms.

Critical Thinking

23. Identify Give one example of how a mutation may affect an organism's traits, and one example of how a mutation may not affect an organism's traits.

24. Describe Explain the roles of DNA, RNA, and environmental factors in gene expression and cell differentiation.

25. Hypothesize If the nucleus were surrounded by a membrane that had fewer pores than usual, how might the rate of protein synthesis be affected, and why?

26. Illustrate For the DNA sequence TACCAAGTGAAAATT, write the sequence of its RNA transcript and the sequence of amino acids for which it codes. Write the sequence of its RNA transcript to illustrate an example of a point mutation.

27. Predict Suppose you genetically altered a gene in a line of eukaryotic cells by inserting only the operator from the bacterial *lac* operon. Would adding lactose to the cell culture cause the cells to start transcribing the altered gene? Explain your reasoning.

28. Contrast What process did Watson and Crick use to develop their model of DNA, and how did it differ from the controlled experiments used by Griffith, Avery, and Hershey and Chase?

29. Recognize Why was it difficult for scientists to be convinced that DNA was the genetic material common to all organisms?

30. Synthesize Watson and Crick learned from Franklin's x-ray crystallography that the distance between the backbones of the DNA molecule was the same for the length of the molecule. How did this information, combined with what they knew about the four base sizes, lead to their model of DNA structure?

Interpreting Visuals

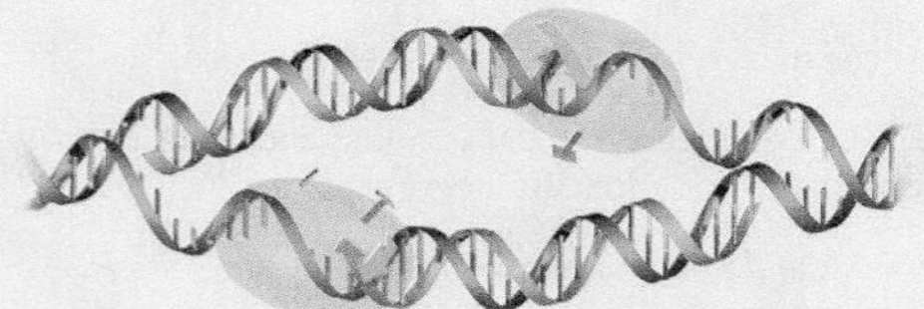

Use the diagram to answer the next three questions.

31. Apply What process is taking place in this diagram?

32. Apply What do the arrows on the yellow strands indicate?

33. Predict If you were to extend the diagram in both directions, what would you expect to see?

Analyzing Data Interpret a Histogram

Many factors contribute to breast cancer, including some that are genetic. For example, women with a mutation in the BRCA1 gene have an especially high risk of developing breast cancer. The histogram below shows the total estimated number of new breast cancer cases for women in the United States for 2003. Use the data in the histogram to answer the next two questions.

ESTIMATED NEW CASES OF BREAST CANCER

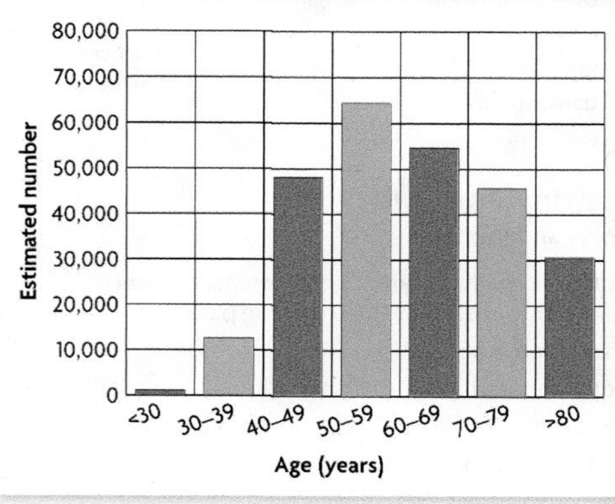

Source: American Cancer Society

34. Analyze In which age group was the incidence of new cases the lowest? the highest?

35. Hypothesize Using the data in this histogram, develop a hypothesis to explain why breast cancer genes are still present in the population.

Making Connections

36. Write an Analogy This chapter includes an analogy about exchanging quarters for tokens at a game center to represent the process of transcription. Think of your own analogy for one of the processes you learned about in this chapter. Write a paragraph using that analogy to explain the process. Also, note any limitations of your analogy. (That is, in what ways does it not "fit" the process you're explaining?)

37. Synthesize Look again at the picture of the glowing mouse on the chapter opener. The gene for the protein GFP was inserted into a mouse egg, and then expressed in the mouse. What genetic processes are involved in the expression of this gene?

30. They recognized that if a base with one ring paired with a base with two rings, the DNA molecule would have a uniform width. In conjunction with their understanding of Chargaff's rules, this information led Watson and Crick to conclude that A pairs with T, and C pairs with G.

Interpreting Visuals

31. DNA replication
32. the direction of replication
33. more replication "bubbles" where DNA is unzipping at numerous origins of replication

250 Unit 3: Genetics

Standards-Based Assessment

Record your answers on a separate piece of paper.

MULTIPLE CHOICE

1 Cell specialization results from interactions between regulatory DNA sequences and proteins called transcription factors. What is the role of DNA regulatory sequences in cells?

A They cause all of the genes in a cell to be expressed.

B They prevent transcription from taking place.

C They identify the start of a gene for RNA polymerase so transcription can occur.

D They prevent homeobox genes from being expressed.

2 Before the genetic code could be understood, scientists needed to know that a codon is composed of three nucleotides. This situation is an example of the —

A scientists making inferences based on data

B cumulative nature of scientific evidence

C way that theories can lead to scientific laws

D ability of scientists to make hypotheses

3

AAACACUAU

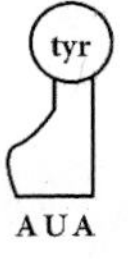

The illustration above shows a strand of mRNA and the complementary tRNA molecules that can base pair with the mRNA codons. What is the correct sequence of amino acids?

A lys-his-tyr

B his-tyr-lys

C tyr-lys-his

D lys-tyr-his

4 Less than 60% of the DNA sequence of the human GM-CSF gene and the mouse GM-CSF gene is the same. When scientists put the human gene into mice, however, it functions properly. Which statement ***best*** explains why this happens?

A The resulting proteins are similar enough.

B Each gene codes for a different protein.

C The human DNA sequence undergoes a mutation once placed into mice.

D Both DNA sequences must produce identical strands of RNA.

THINK THROUGH THE QUESTION

The name of the gene is not important in answering this question. Recognize that the question involves only one type of gene. Don't let a complicated name distract you from answering the real question.

5

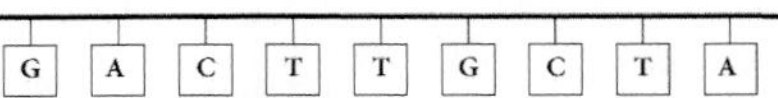

The diagram above shows the nucleotides making up a segment of DNA. Which diagram below illustrates the type of change in the DNA characterized as a frameshift insertion mutation?

A

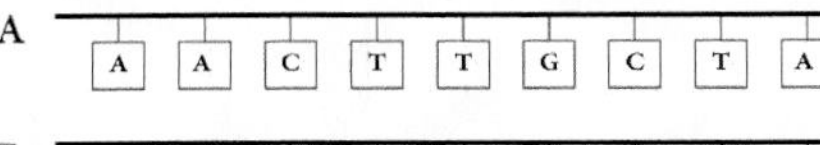

B

C

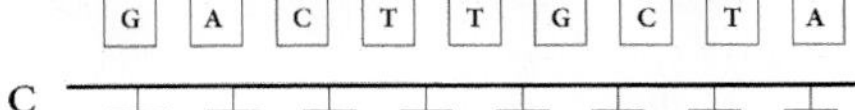

D

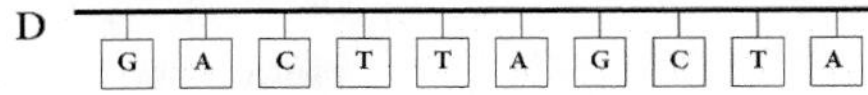

CHAPTER REVIEW

Standards-Based Assessment

The Standards-Based Assessment questions will help students prepare for their final examination in the course. If you wish to give students practice in coding their answers, look for the Standards-Based Assessment Answer Sheet at **HMHScience.com**. To give students practice under timed testing conditions, allow them five minutes per question.

Question	Answer	Depth of Knowledge	Cognitive Complexity
1	C	IV	M
2	B	I	L
3	A	II	M
4	A	IV	M
5	D	III	H

KEY

Depth of Knowledge
I Recall
II Skill/Concept
III Strategic Thinking
IV Extended Thinking

Cognitive Complexity
L Low
M Moderate
H High

Analyzing Data

34. under 30; 50–59

35. Breast cancer typically develops at a later age, after most women have had children. Therefore, the genes are passed from mother to children and remain in the population.

Making Connections

36. *Sample answer:* comparing DNA replication to making a photocopy, or comparing translation to translating a book from one language to another

37. The gene is on a chromosome that had to be replicated with each cell division. The gene is then expressed by way of transcription, RNA processing, and translation.

CHAPTER 9

Instruction and Intervention Support

Frontiers of Biotechnology

① Core Instruction

The **Core Instruction** resources below can be used for all students. Core instruction should be followed by ongoing assessment to determine which students need further help.

Available in both English and Spanish

Available Online

Section	Instruction	PRINT	ONLINE	Labs
9.1	Textbook **Manipulating DNA**	■	●	Modeling Forensics Analysis of DNA Restriction Fragment Size (Biotechnology Lab) **Video Lab** Protein Detection **Virtual Lab** Gel Electrophoresis
	Animated Biology Restriction Enzymes		●	
	Teaching Visuals Restriction Map (Fig. 1.3)		●	
	PowerPresentation and Notes 9.1		●	
9.2	Textbook **Copying DNA**	■	●	
	Animated Biology Polymerase Chain Reactions		●	
	Teaching Visuals Polymerase Chain Reaction (Fig. 2.2)		●	
	PowerPresentation and Notes 9.2		●	
9.3	Textbook **DNA Fingerprinting**	■	●	DNA Fingerprinting (Forensics Lab) **Video Lab** DNA Fingerprint Analysis
	PowerPresentation and Notes 9.3		●	
9.4	Textbook **Genetic Engineering**	■	●	Modeling Genetic Engineering Genetic Engineering **QuickLab** Modeling Plasmids and Restriction Enzymes **Virtual Lab** Bacterial Transformation
	Animated Biology Recombinant Cloning		●	
	PowerPresentation and Notes 9.4		●	
9.5	Textbook **Genomics and Bioinformatics**	■	●	
	That's Amazing! Video Inquiry Coral Colds		●	
	PowerPresentation and Notes 9.5		●	
9.6	Textbook **Genetic Screening and Gene Therapy**	■	●	Genetic Screening
	PowerPresentation and Notes 9.6		●	

Additional online resources available for this chapter include **Interactive Whiteboard Resources.**

GO ONLINE! for all your teacher resources at HMHScience.com

2 Support and Intervention

Support and Intervention resources are useful for students who need targeted help beyond the Core Instruction

Resources	PRINT	ONLINE
Assess and Reteach (TE wrap)	■	●
Concept Map		●
Interactive Reader	■	●
Interactive Review Games		●
Section Self-Checks		●
Study Guide B		●
Virtual Investigation Gene Technologies		●
Vocabulary Practice Worksheets		●

3 Specialized Support

Students who need more intensive personalized intervention benefit from **Specialized Support** resources.

Resources	PRINT	ONLINE
Chapter Audio Files		●
Differentiated Instruction Inclusion, Below Level, and English Learners (TE wrap)	■	●
ELL Strategies	■	●
Modified Lesson Plans for English Learners		●
Reinforcement Worksheets		●
Study Guide A		●

Extension and Assessment

Enrichment and Challenge

Resources	PRINT	ONLINE
Active Reading Worksheets		●
Data Analysis Practice Worksheet		●
Differentiated Instruction Pre-AP (TE wrap)	■	●
Pre-AP Activity DNA Forensics: Solving a Royal Mystery, Meet the Y Chromosome		●
The Inside Story and **Take It Further** (TE wrap)	■	●
Unit Project		●
WebLinks		●
WebQuest Animal Cloning (9.4)		●

Assessment

Resources	PRINT	ONLINE
Alternative Assessment		●
Chapter Tests A and B		●
Diagnostic Test		●
ExamView Banks		●
Extended Response Test		●
Online Assessment System		●
Section Quizzes		●
Standards-Based Assessment	■	●

CHAPTER 9

Chapter Overview

- **Section 1** introduces several DNA manipulation techniques used in biotechnology.
- **Section 2** summarizes the polymerase chain reaction technique used to copy DNA segments.
- **Section 3** describes DNA fingerprinting and details how it is used for identification.
- **Section 4** explains how genetic engineering produces organisms with new traits and how organisms can be cloned.
- **Section 5** describes genomics and details how genes and proteins are studied with the help of technology.
- **Section 6** explains genetic screening and gene therapy research.

Focus and Motivate

How can biotechnology reunite families?

Discuss the questions that can be answered by DNA testing. **Ask,** What are some situations or circumstances in which DNA testing could help identify someone or something? *Sample answer:* Human remains are found that cannot be identified by other means. People need to determine whether or not they are biologically related. DNA is left at a crime scene.

Students can access BioZine at **HMHScience.com** to learn about some of the latest research in the biological sciences.

CHAPTER 9 Frontiers of Biotechnology

BIG IDEA Advances in biotechnology and the study of genomes allow scientists to manipulate DNA and combine the genes of multiple organisms, and may provide new medical treatments in the future.

ONLINE BIOLOGY HMHScience.com

ONLINE Labs
- Modeling Forensics
- **QuickLab** Modeling Plasmids and Restriction Enzymes
- Modeling Genetic Engineering
- Genetic Screening
- Genetic Engineering
- DNA Fingerprinting
- Analysis of DNA Restriction Fragment Size
- **Virtual Lab** Gel Electrophoresis
- **Virtual Lab** Bacterial Transformation
- **Video Lab** Protein Detection
- **Video Lab** DNA Fingerprint Analysis

Student Activity

Purpose **Have students examine bar codes to develop a greater understanding of the banding patterns of DNA fingerprints. Students will treat bar code patterns as DNA fingerprints to identify a crime suspect.**

Materials (per team)
- enlarged photocopies of commercial bar codes: 5 unique and 2 identical
- envelope

Prepare To prepare bar codes, cut out or black out the numbers from commercial bar codes. Use an enlargement option, such as 220 percent, to create easy-to-read photocopies of each bar code. Remember to make double the number of copies of the bar code that will serve as the match between the DNA from the crime scene and that of a guilty suspect, but to put only one copy of this code in each "suspect" envelope.

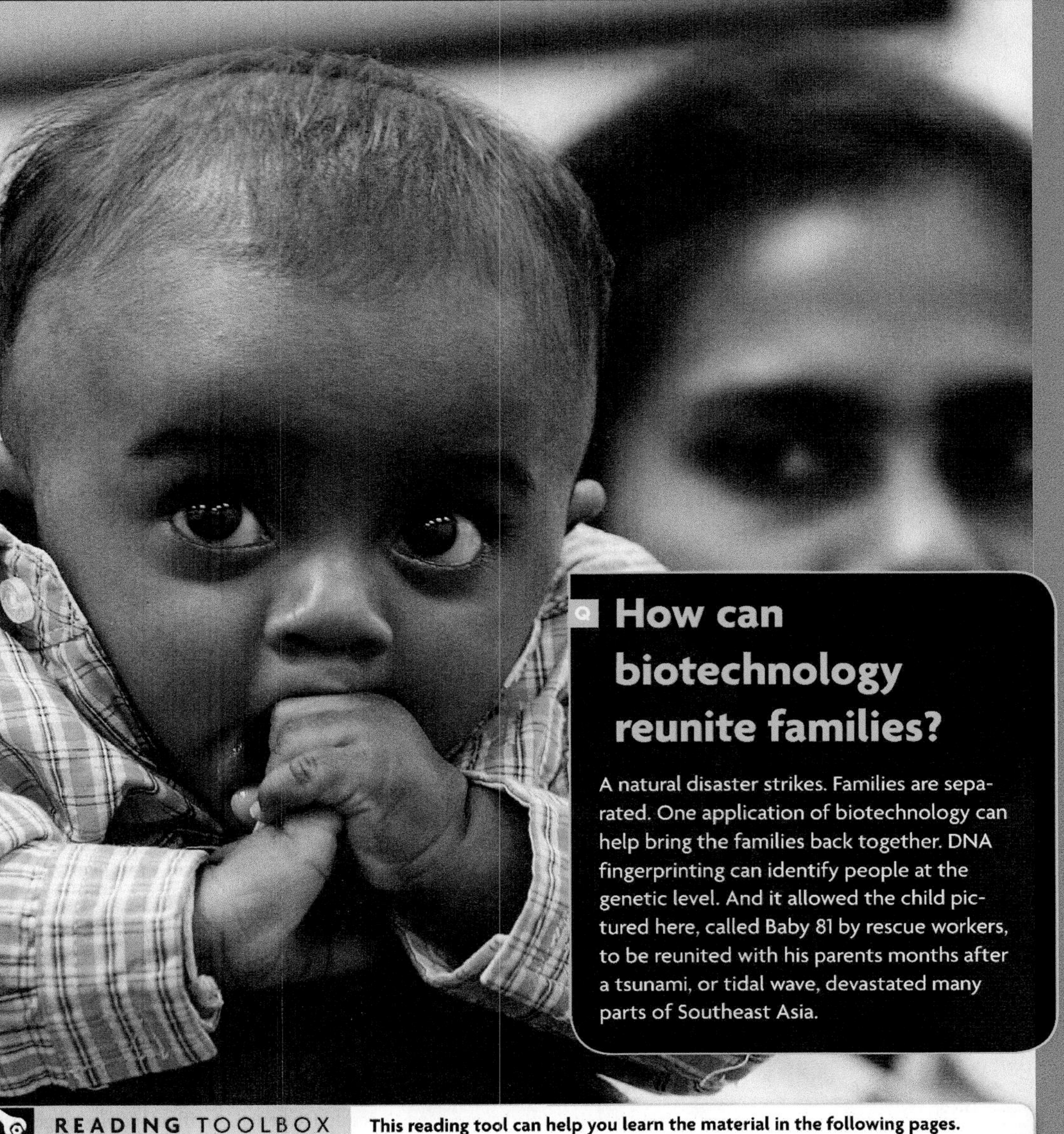

How can biotechnology reunite families?

A natural disaster strikes. Families are separated. One application of biotechnology can help bring the families back together. DNA fingerprinting can identify people at the genetic level. And it allowed the child pictured here, called Baby 81 by rescue workers, to be reunited with his parents months after a tsunami, or tidal wave, devastated many parts of Southeast Asia.

READING TOOLBOX **This reading tool can help you learn the material in the following pages.**

USING LANGUAGE

Analogies Analogies compare words with similar relationships. You can write analogies with words or with colons. For example, the analogy "*up* is related to *down* in the same way that *top* is to *bottom*" can be written "up : down :: top : bottom." To answer an analogy problem, you must figure out how the words are related. In this example, *up* is above *down*, and *top* is above *bottom*.

YOUR TURN

Use information found in prior chapters to complete the following analogy:

transcription : RNA :: translation : ___________

Activate Prior Knowledge

Remind students of the role of **meiosis** in sexual reproduction. **Ask**

- How does a child's DNA compare with the DNA of his or her parents? A child inherits half of his or her chromosomes from each parent, so half of the child's DNA will match the mother's DNA, and half will match the father's DNA.
- How is biotechnology involved in the story on this page? Students may suggest that molecular analysis of the child's DNA and parents' DNA was used to prove that they were related, and that these techniques are the product of advances in biotechnology.

Preview Vocabulary

Greek and Latin Word Origins
Tell students that they will see the words *manipulation* and *technique* used to describe DNA technology. Tell students they can think of *manipulation* as "what is being done" and *technique* as "how it is being done." The Latin root *manus* means "hand": *manipulation* is the product of "moving, arranging, or operating, often by hand." The Greek root *teknikos* refers to the "art" of doing something: *technique* means "the systematic procedure for accomplishing a complex task."

Academic Vocabulary Remind students that *technology* is the application of science to solving practical problems. Explain that *biotechnology* involves not only the application of scientific understanding of biological systems and processes to solve problems, but also uses living organisms to achieve the desired effect.

Introduce Explain that because it is very unlikely that two people have the same DNA fingerprint, DNA fingerprints can be used to identify a specific person. Bar codes are analogous to DNA fingerprints. Give each team an envelope labeled "DNA" that contains six different bar codes labeled *A–F*. Tell students that these represent the DNA fingerprints of six suspects. Pass out one more bar code that represents DNA found at the crime scene. Have students compare the "samples" to determine who should be charged with the crime.

Discuss Have students discuss how DNA fingerprinting assists in solving crimes and how it can influence a trial. Tell them that some people in prison who were convicted were later exonerated by DNA evidence.

Ask, How would an investigation be affected if the suspect whose DNA matched the evidence had an identical twin who was also in the area at the time of the crime? Because twins' DNA is identical, DNA fingerprinting alone would not be enough to prove beyond a reasonable doubt which of the twins committed the crime.

Answers

protein or amino acid chain

SECTION 9.1

Plan and Prepare

Activating Prior Knowledge Discuss how the ability to collect and interpret DNA has changed crime investigation—and television programming. **Ask,** How many of you watch a television show with the abbreviation *CSI* in its title? What does *CSI* stand for? Crime Scene Investigation Discuss how DNA figures into a crime investigation. Remind students that human DNA has about 3 billion base pairs, so it is difficult to isolate any one pair or sequence. Tell students that scientists have devised ways to cut DNA and differentiate various sequences from one another, so just a small portion of DNA is needed to make an identification.

Teach

Answer

A Infer because DNA is microscopic, very long and complex, and difficult to handle or manipulate

9.1 Manipulating DNA

KEY CONCEPT **Biotechnology relies on cutting DNA at specific places.**

VOCABULARY

restriction enzyme
gel electrophoresis
restriction map

MAIN IDEAS

- Scientists use several techniques to manipulate DNA.
- Restriction enzymes cut DNA.
- Restriction maps show the lengths of DNA fragments.

Connect to Your World

Many applications of genetics that are widely used today were unimaginable just 30 years ago. Our use of genetics to identify people is just one example. Biotechnology and genetics are used to produce transgenic organisms and clones. They are used to study diseases and evolution. They are used to produce medical treatments for people with life-threatening illnesses. Through many years of research and a combination of many kinds of methods, advances in biotechnology seem to happen on a daily basis.

MAIN IDEA

Scientists use several techniques to manipulate DNA.

By the middle of the 1950s, scientists had concluded that DNA was the genetic material. Watson and Crick had determined the structure of DNA. Yet the field of genetics as we know it today was just beginning. For example, even the genetic code that you just learned about was not fully understood until the early 1960s. Since that time, scientists have developed a combination of methods to study DNA and genes.

DNA is a very large molecule, but it is still just a molecule. It is far too small to see, and you cannot pick it up or rearrange it with your hands. Therefore, scientists must be able to work with DNA without being able to see or handle it directly. Chemicals, computers, and bacteria are just a few of the tools that have allowed advances in genetics research.

Artificial nucleotides are used to sequence genes. Artificial copies of genes are used to study gene expression. Chemical mutagens are used to change DNA sequences. Computers analyze and organize the vast amounts of data from genetics research. Enzymes, often from bacteria, are used to cut and copy DNA. Bacteria also provide one of the ways in which genes are transferred between different organisms. Throughout this chapter, you will learn about some of the techniques used in biotechnology, as well as some of its applications. You likely have heard of genetic engineering, DNA fingerprinting, and cloning, but how are they done? In many cases, one of the first steps in biotechnology and genetics research is to precisely cut DNA.

A Infer Why might so many different methods be needed to study DNA and genes?

READING TOOLBOX

TAKING NOTES

Use a supporting main ideas chart to organize your notes on ways in which DNA is manipulated.

Cutting DNA
- Restriction enzymes cut DNA.
- Gel electrophoresis . . . . . .

Differentiated Instruction

ENGLISH LEARNERS

To help students focus on "right there" questions whose answers can be found in the text, demonstrate the QAR (Question-Answer Relationships) strategy for the section headed "Restriction enzymes cut DNA." **Ask**

- How do bacteria protect themselves against viruses? They produce enzymes that cut up viral DNA.
- Where do restriction enzymes cut DNA molecules? at specific nucleotide sequences called restriction sites
- How do different restriction enzymes cut DNA differently? Some make cuts leaving blunt ends; some leave sticky ends.
- Which is more useful to scientists—DNA with blunt ends or DNA with sticky ends? DNA with sticky ends

Have students write more questions. Then, in small groups, have them prepare "right there" questions about restriction maps.

Teacher Toolkit, Section C, QAR

MAIN IDEA

Restriction enzymes cut DNA.

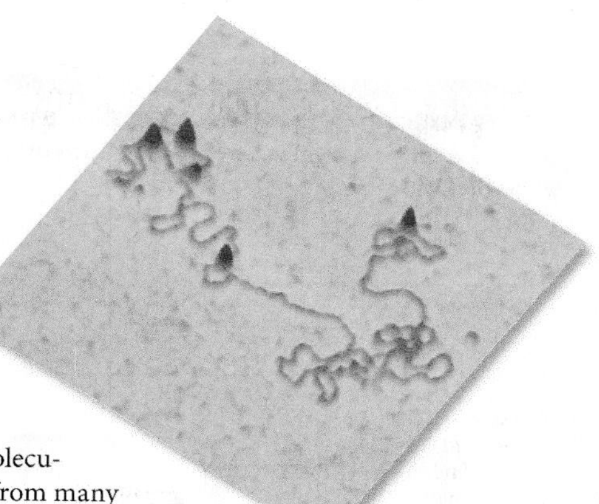

FIGURE 1.1 A restriction enzyme (blue peaks) from an *E. coli* bacterium helps protect against viruses by cutting DNA (red). This cutting "restricts" the effect of a virus on a bacterium. (colored 3D atomic force micrograph; magnification 63,000×)

Why would scientists want to cut DNA? To answer that question, you have to remember that a gene is a sequence of DNA nucleotides, and that a chromosome is one long DNA molecule. A whole chromosome is too large for scientists to study a particular gene easily, so they had to find a way to get much smaller pieces of DNA. Of course, slicing a chromosome into pieces is not as simple as picking up the molecule and cutting it with a pair of scissors. Instead, scientists use enzymes that act as molecular "scissors." These enzymes, which slice apart DNA, come from many types of bacteria.

Bacterial cells, like your cells, can be infected by viruses. As protection against these invaders, bacteria produce enzymes that cut up the DNA of the viruses. As **FIGURE 1.1** shows, a DNA molecule can be cut apart in several places at once by several molecules of a restriction enzyme, or endonuclease. **Restriction enzymes** are enzymes that cut DNA molecules when they identify specific nucleotide sequences. In fact, any time the enzyme finds that exact DNA sequence, it cuts the DNA molecule. The sequence of nucleotides that is identified and cut by a restriction enzyme is called a restriction site. These enzymes are called restriction enzymes because they restrict, or decrease, the effect of the virus on the bacterial cell.

There are hundreds of known restriction enzymes. Different restriction enzymes will cut the same DNA molecule in a variety of ways. For example, one restriction enzyme may find three of its restriction sites in a segment of DNA. Another restriction enzyme might find six of its restriction sites in the same segment. Different numbers of fragments with different lengths result. As you can see below, two different restriction enzymes can cut the same strand of DNA in very different ways.

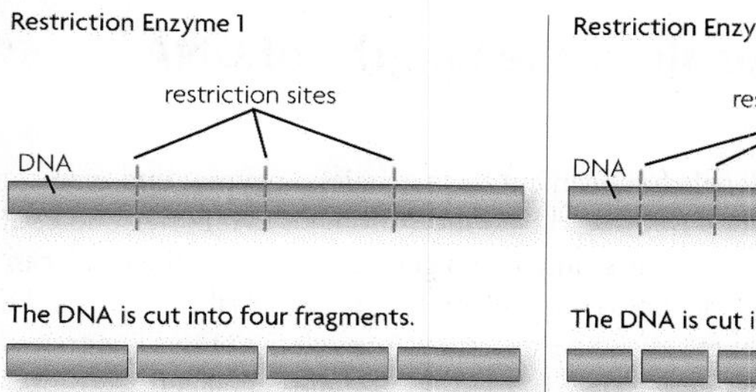

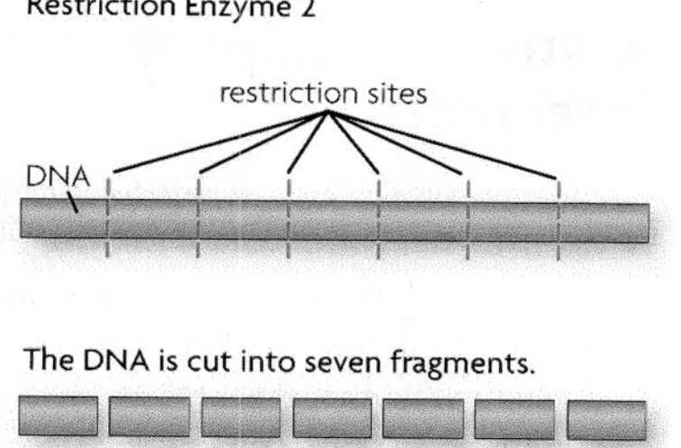

Restriction enzymes recognize nucleotide sequences that are between four and eight base pairs long, and then cut the DNA. Some enzymes make cuts straight across the two strands of a DNA molecule. These cuts leave behind fragments of DNA that end in what are called "blunt ends."

BELOW LEVEL

Have students outline the Main Idea "Restriction enzymes cut DNA" on this page and the following page. Remind them to use a system of Roman numerals, Arabic numerals, capital letters, and lowercase letters. Have students include information from **FIGURE 1.2** in their outlines as an example of how a restriction enzyme cuts DNA at a specific site.

Teacher Toolkit, Section C, Outline

Integrating Chemistry

Restriction enzymes are a bacterial defense mechanism that destroys the DNA of invading viruses. Students may wonder why the DNA of the host bacterium in **FIGURE 1.1** is not destroyed in the process, or how the bacterium's defensive enzymes recognize friend from foe. Explain that bacterial DNA is highly methylated, meaning methyl groups ($-CH_3$) are attached to some of the bases. The methyl groups protect the bacterium's DNA from the cutting effects of its restriction enzymes.

Take It Further

Restriction enzymes are named using a kind of code. The first letter of the name represents the genus of the bacterium from which the enzyme was isolated. The second two letters come from the first two letters of the bacterium's species descriptor. The first three letters are italicized because they are part of the bacterium's scientific name. If there is a fourth letter, it represents the particular strain of bacteria. A Roman numeral reveals the order in which an enzyme was discovered in the bacterium. So, *Taq*I, seen in **FIGURE 1.2,** was the first restriction enzyme isolated from the bacterium *Thermus aquaticus*. Two other commonly used restriction enzymes are *Eco*RI, isolated from *E. coli* strain RY13, and *Bam*HI, isolated from *Bacillus amyloliquefaciens* strain H.

▼ Teach *continued*

Students can complete a virtual lab in which gel electrophoresis is used to make a DNA fingerprint of someone who committed a crime. See the virtual lab on gel electrophoresis at **HMHScience.com**.

Take It Further

A **palindrome** is a word or phrase that reads the same backward or forward. *Radar, racecar,* and *Madam, I'm Adam* are palindromes. Palindromes in nucleic acids read the same backward or forward across the double strand. For example, the sequence GATC forms a palindrome with the complementary CTAG on the opposite strand; GACT does not make a palindrome with its complementary sequence, CTGA. Restriction enzymes usually recognize palindromic sequences and cut the DNA between the same two bases on the opposite strands at these locations. A restriction site must be a palindrome if sticky ends are to be produced. If the restriction site is not a palindrome, blunt ends form.

Answers

A Infer The ends of the segments would not have nucleotide tails available to bind to complementary base pairs.

B Summarize They recognize and cut different nucleotide sequences, or restriction sites, resulting in different fragments.

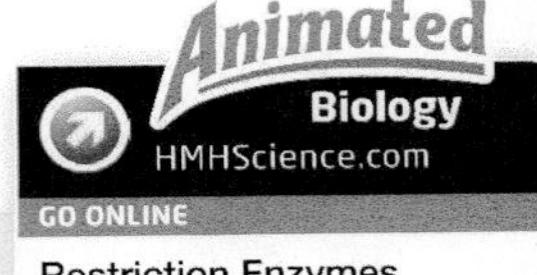

Restriction Enzymes

FIGURE 1.2 Restriction Enzymes Cut DNA

Some restriction enzymes leave behind nucleotide tails, or "sticky ends," when they cut DNA.

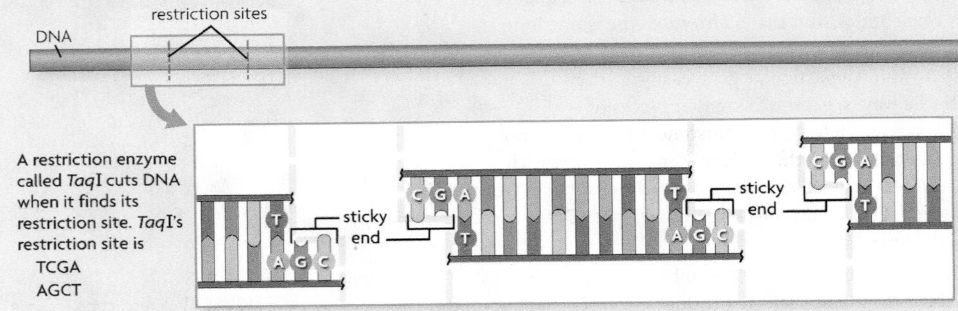

A restriction enzyme called *Taq*I cuts DNA when it finds its restriction site. *Taq*I's restriction site is
TCGA
AGCT

A Infer How would the above illustration change if *Taq*I left behind blunt ends rather than sticky ends when it cuts DNA?

CONNECT TO

DNA BASE PAIRS

In the chapter **From DNA to Proteins** you learned that DNA nucleotides match up by complementary base pairing. A always pairs with T, and C always pairs with G.

Other restriction enzymes, as shown in **FIGURE 1.2**, make staggered cuts that leave tails of free DNA bases on each side of the cut. These nucleotide tails of the cut DNA strands are called "sticky ends." Sticky ends are like tiny pieces of Velcro® that are ready to hook on to their opposite sides. If two pieces of DNA with sticky ends and complementary base pairs come close to each other, the two segments of DNA will join by hydrogen bonding. Because of this characteristic of DNA, restriction enzymes that leave sticky ends when they cut DNA are often used in biotechnology, as you will learn in Section 4.

B Summarize How do different restriction enzymes produce different DNA fragments from the same DNA molecule?

MAIN IDEA

Restriction maps show the lengths of DNA fragments.

After a long DNA molecule has been cut by restriction enzymes into many smaller fragments, several things can be done with the DNA. For example, the DNA sequence of a gene can be studied, or a gene cut out from the DNA can be placed into the DNA of another organism. But before anything else can be done, the DNA fragments have to be separated from one another. The fragments are sorted according to their sizes by a technique called gel electrophoresis (ih-LEHK-troh-fuh-REE-sihs).

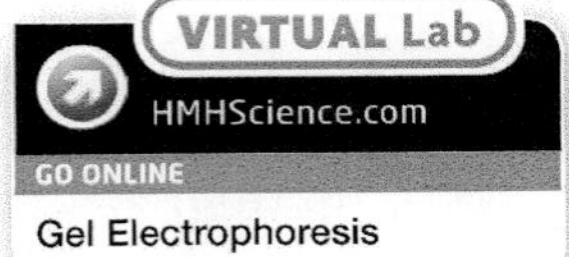

Gel Electrophoresis

In **gel electrophoresis,** an electrical current is used to separate a mixture of DNA fragments from each other. A sample of DNA is loaded into a gel, which is like a thin slab of hard gelatin. A positive electrode is at one end of the gel. At the other end is a negative electrode. Because DNA has a negative charge,

Differentiated Instruction

PRE-AP

Write the following sequence of numbers on the board:

2 9 5 8 2 7 2 1 0 3 9 7 8 2 2 5 4 1 8 2 2 6

Tell students that a certain restriction enzyme makes a cut between an 8 and a 2. Have students copy the sequence and mark the places where the enzyme would cut. **Ask,** How many fragments are produced? four **Ask,** Are all the fragments the same length? no **Ask,** Can you think of a basis or measure by which you could organize the fragments? size or mass (weight) the fragments move toward the positive electrode, or the positively charged pole. The gel also has tiny pores running through it. The pores allow small molecules to move quickly. Larger molecules cannot easily move through the gel and they travel more slowly. Therefore, the length of a DNA fragment can be estimated from the distance it travels through a gel in a certain period of time. As shown in **FIGURE 1.3**, DNA fragments of different sizes appear as different bands, or lines, on a gel. The pattern of bands on the gel can be thought of as a map of the original strand of DNA. **Restriction maps** show the lengths of DNA fragments between restriction sites in a strand of DNA.

The bands on a gel indicate only the lengths of DNA fragments. Alone, they do not give any information about the DNA sequences of the fragments. Even though restriction maps do not directly show the makeup of a fragment of DNA, the maps are very useful in genetic engineering, which you will read about in Section 4. They can also be used to study gene mutations. How? First, a mutation may add or delete bases between restriction sites, which would change the lengths of DNA fragments on a gel. Second, a mutation may change a restriction site, and the DNA would not be cut in the same places.

Suppose, for example, that when a normal allele of a gene is cut by a restriction enzyme, five DNA fragments appear as five different bands on a gel. Then, when a mutant allele of the same gene is cut with the same enzyme, only three bands appear. Comparisons of restriction maps can help diagnose genetic diseases, as you will see in Section 6. A restriction map from a person's DNA can be compared with a restriction map from DNA that is known to be normal. If the restriction maps differ, it is an indication that the person has inherited a disease-causing allele of the gene.

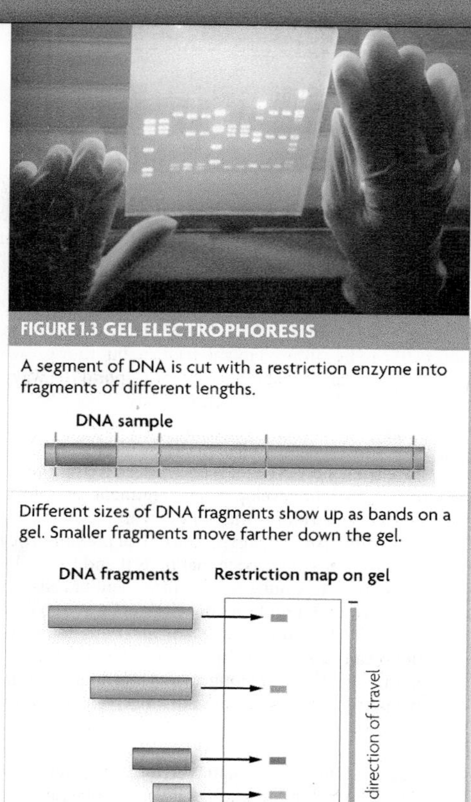

FIGURE 1.3 GEL ELECTROPHORESIS

A segment of DNA is cut with a restriction enzyme into fragments of different lengths.

DNA sample

Different sizes of DNA fragments show up as bands on a gel. Smaller fragments move farther down the gel.

A Synthesize **How are restriction enzymes used in making restriction maps?**

9.1 Formative Assessment

SELF-CHECK Online
HMHScience.com
GO ONLINE

REVIEWING MAIN IDEAS

1. List four ways in which scientists can manipulate DNA.
2. What determines how DNA will be cut by a **restriction enzyme**?
3. How does **gel electrophoresis** separate DNA fragments from each other?

CRITICAL THINKING

4. **Apply** Suppose you cut DNA. You know that you should find four DNA fragments on a gel, but only three appear, and one fragment is very large. Explain what happened.
5. **Synthesize** What is the relationship between restriction sites and a **restriction map**?

CONNECT TO MUTATIONS

6. Would a mutation in a gene always be detectable by using restriction maps? Why or why not?

9.1 FORMATIVE ASSESSMENT

1. DNA can be cut, copied, sequenced, and changed (mutated).
2. the number and location of restriction sites recognized by the restriction enzyme
3. The DNA sample is loaded into a gel through which an electrical current flows. The negatively charged DNA fragments are pulled toward the positive electrode. The largest molecules move slowest, and the smallest move quickest.
4. This might indicate a mutation. One of the restriction sites may have been deleted or changed by the mutation, resulting in one very large fragment where there should have been two fragments.
5. A restriction map reveals the lengths of DNA fragments between restriction sites. The more restriction sites there are, the more fragments there will be on the map.
6. No, a very small change in DNA would not be large enough to detect, even though a mutation occurred.

TEACH FROM VISUALS

FIGURE 1.3 Students may find it difficult to understand that the length of a DNA fragment is represented on the gel by how far it moves from the negative electrode to the positive electrode. **Ask,** If the purple fragment is farthest from the green in the original DNA strand, why is the yellow fragment farthest away from the green in the gel? because the yellow fragment is smaller, it traveled faster toward the positive electrode

History of Science

The 1978 Nobel Prize in Physiology or Medicine was awarded to **Werner Arber, Hamilton Smith,** and **Daniel Nathans** for their collaborative work on restriction enzymes. Arber discovered the first restriction enzyme and hypothesized that it bonded to DNA at specific sites. Smith verified this and showed how it cut DNA at a specific base sequence. Nathans used the enzyme to develop a genetic-mapping method, an application of restriction enzymes to genetics.

Answers

A Synthesize A restriction map is based on the sizes of the DNA fragments produced when restriction enzymes cut a strand of DNA.

Assess and Reteach

Assess Use the Section Self-Check or Section Quiz, both available at **HMHScience.com**.

Reteach Write a sequence diagram for the steps a scientist would take to make a restriction map from a sample of DNA.

Introduce

Use a small computer memory chip to show students the approximate size of the organ-on-a-chip technology. **Ask,** What benefits do you think there are to working on such a miniature scale? The article mentions several benefits, such as using fewer reagents and taking up less space. Tell students that some researchers have used the same technology to create "Labs-on-a-chip," which contain diagnostic tests that can be performed and taken anywhere in the world. **Ask,** How might that technology be especially useful in developing countries?

Discuss

Have students design their own "organ-on-a-chip." Which organ would they choose, and how would they mimic the organ on a three-dimensional chip? Have students consider what is on the inside and on the outside of the organ that cells of that organ might come in contact with. What diseases or disorders affect that organ, and how could you use the organ-on-a-chip to investigate treatment for that condition?

Answers

1. Testing on animals other than humans is not always effective, because the animal may have a different physiological response than a human has. Students may point out the ethical and economic benefits of replacing animal research.
2. Students should recognize that organ systems work together, and linking chips of different organs would better mimic the responses of the human body.

Organs-on-a-Chip

Researching human diseases and the drugs that could possibly treat these diseases can be tough to do. Ethics and regulations strictly limit using humans as subjects. Using other animals for testing is also not ideal, as the physiology of a rat or dog does not always react the same way that a human body does. Human cells can be cultured in a petri dish, but they grow into a flat layer that also may not respond the way they would as part of an entire body.

A new technology called an organ-on-a-chip may solve some of these issues and reduce the amount of time it takes to develop a new treatment for a disease. Cells are grown on a membrane within a small, three-dimensional plastic "chip." The membrane can be hooked up to a device that pulls it and then allows it to contract, simulating the movement of cells within the body. Different types of cells can be grown on each side of the membrane, and air or liquids such as blood can be sent flowing above and below the membrane. Cells live longer in this arrangement than in a petri dish culture, making longer-term studies possible.

Like DNA microarrays, in which many genes are placed on a chip for study, cellular microarrays miniaturize the scale of research. Fewer materials and less space are needed with chip biotechnology, and at a lower cost than similar research on a larger scale. Organs that have been studied using this method include the heart, kidneys, liver, and lungs.

Based on the lung-on-a-chip technology, scientists at Harvard University recently developed an airway-on-a-chip to study inflammation caused by common disorders such as asthma. Airway cells on one side of the membrane are exposed to air, and capillary cells on the other side are exposed to blood cells. Adding a factor that triggers asthma allows researchers to study how the cells become inflamed and what treatments are effective to reduce the inflammation. While many diseases can affect people as they age, asthma is a condition that affects millions of children as well as adults. Asthma is one of the most common causes of missed school days, and severe attacks can be life-threatening.

Because diseases such as asthma affect each individual differently, using one person's cells on a chip can potentially offer that individual personalized treatment in less time than it takes new pharmaceuticals to reach the market. While it may be too early to rely solely on this new biotechnology for disease and treatment research, it is a tool that someday might be available in a doctor's office near you.

Questions

1. How might organs-on-a-chip be able to replace animal testing in the future?
2. Some researchers are investigating a "human-on-a-chip" model that connects the various organ chips. What do you think would be the benefits of linking chips with different types of cells?

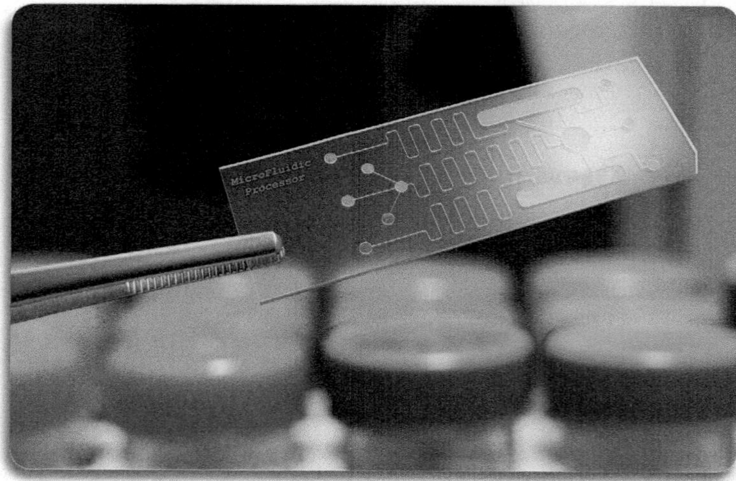

9.2 Copying DNA

KEY CONCEPT **The polymerase chain reaction rapidly copies segments of DNA.**

VOCABULARY

polymerase chain reaction (PCR)

primer

MAIN IDEAS

- PCR uses polymerases to copy DNA segments.
- PCR is a three-step process.

Connect to Your World

Forensic scientists use DNA from cells in a single hair at a crime scene to identify a criminal. Doctors test a patient's blood to quickly detect the presence of bacteria that cause Lyme disease. Scientists compare DNA from different species to determine how closely the species are related. However, the original amount of DNA from any of these sources is far too small to accurately study. Samples of DNA must be increased, or amplified, so that they can be analyzed.

MAIN IDEA

PCR uses polymerases to copy DNA segments.

How do scientists get an amount of DNA that is large enough to be studied and manipulated? They copy the same segment of DNA over and over again. **Polymerase chain reaction (PCR)** is a technique that produces millions—or even billions—of copies of a specific DNA sequence in just a few hours. As the name indicates, the DNA polymerase enzymes that help copy DNA play key roles in this process.

Kary Mullis, who invented PCR, is shown in **FIGURE 2.1.** While working for a California biotechnology company in 1983, Mullis had an insight about how to copy DNA segments. He adapted the process of DNA replication that occurs in every living cell into a method for copying DNA in a test tube. Under the right set of conditions, DNA polymerases copy DNA in a test tube just as they do inside cells. However, in cells several other enzymes are needed before the polymerases can do their job. For example, before a cell can begin to copy its DNA, enzymes called helicases unwind and separate DNA molecules. Instead of using these enzymes, Mullis used heat to separate the DNA strands.

FIGURE 2.1 Kary Mullis came up with the idea for PCR while on a surfing trip in 1983. He won the Nobel Prize in chemistry in 1993.

Unfortunately, heat also broke down the *E. coli* polymerases that Mullis first used. Then came Mullis's second stroke of genius: Why not use polymerases from a bacterium that lives in temperatures above 80°C (176°F)? By using this enzyme, Mullis was able to raise the temperature of the DNA to separate the strands without destroying the DNA polymerases. Here again, just as with restriction enzymes that you read about in Section 1, a major advance came from applying an adaptation found in nature to biotechnology. Mullis introduced PCR to the world in 1985, and in 1993 he won the Nobel Prize in chemistry for his revolutionary technique.

(A) Compare and Contrast **How are replication and PCR similar? different? Explain.**

Differentiated Instruction

ENGLISH LEARNERS

After students read the section, have them do a carousel review. On chart paper posted in different parts of the room, write questions such as "How do scientists get a large enough sample of DNA to manipulate?" and "What is PCR?" Assign a small group to each chart, and give each a different colored marker. Groups should review the question, discuss an answer, and write a response. Every three minutes, have groups rotate, put a check mark by answers they agree with, comment on answers they do not agree with, and add their own answers.

Teacher Toolkit, Section C, Carousel Review

SECTION 9.2

Plan and Prepare

Activating Prior Knowledge Remind students of the Copy and Paste functions common to word-processing programs. **Ask,** How do you use these functions? Students will probably mention isolating and moving material from one place to another. Explain that copying DNA through PCR is a somewhat analogous process.

Teach

Answers

(A) **Compare and Contrast** Both use polymerases to make copies of DNA. Replication occurs in cells, where other enzymes separate strands of DNA to be copied. PCR is the artificial copying of DNA in a laboratory, with heat used to separate the strands.

▼ Teach continued

TEACH FROM VISUALS

FIGURE 2.2 Discuss the information in this figure. **Ask**

- Why is a heat-stable polymerase needed? It must be able to withstand the high temperature needed to separate the DNA strands at the beginning of each cycle.
- Why are two primers needed for each DNA molecule? There must be a primer on each strand of DNA. DNA polymerase cannot make double-stranded DNA unless a primer starts the process.
- How do free nucleotides attach to the existing strand? hydrogen bonding Tell students that it is not until the third cycle of PCR that copies of DNA being produced by PCR actually match the target sequence that the original DNA strand contained.

Integrating Chemistry

Enzymes work best at an **optimum temperature,** usually one that is similar to the temperature of the environment of a cell or an organism. Up to the optimum temperature, the reaction rate increases geometrically because both the enzyme and the substrate have more kinetic energy, so they collide more often. Also, more molecules can overcome the activation energy. Above the optimum temperature, the reaction rate decreases as the thermal energy breaks hydrogen bonds holding the enzyme together. The enzyme's shape changes, and the substrate can no longer bind to the active site.

Answers

Ⓐ Critical Viewing 16; 64

FIGURE 2.2 Polymerase Chain Reaction (PCR)

PCR is a cyclical process that quickly makes many copies of a DNA segment.

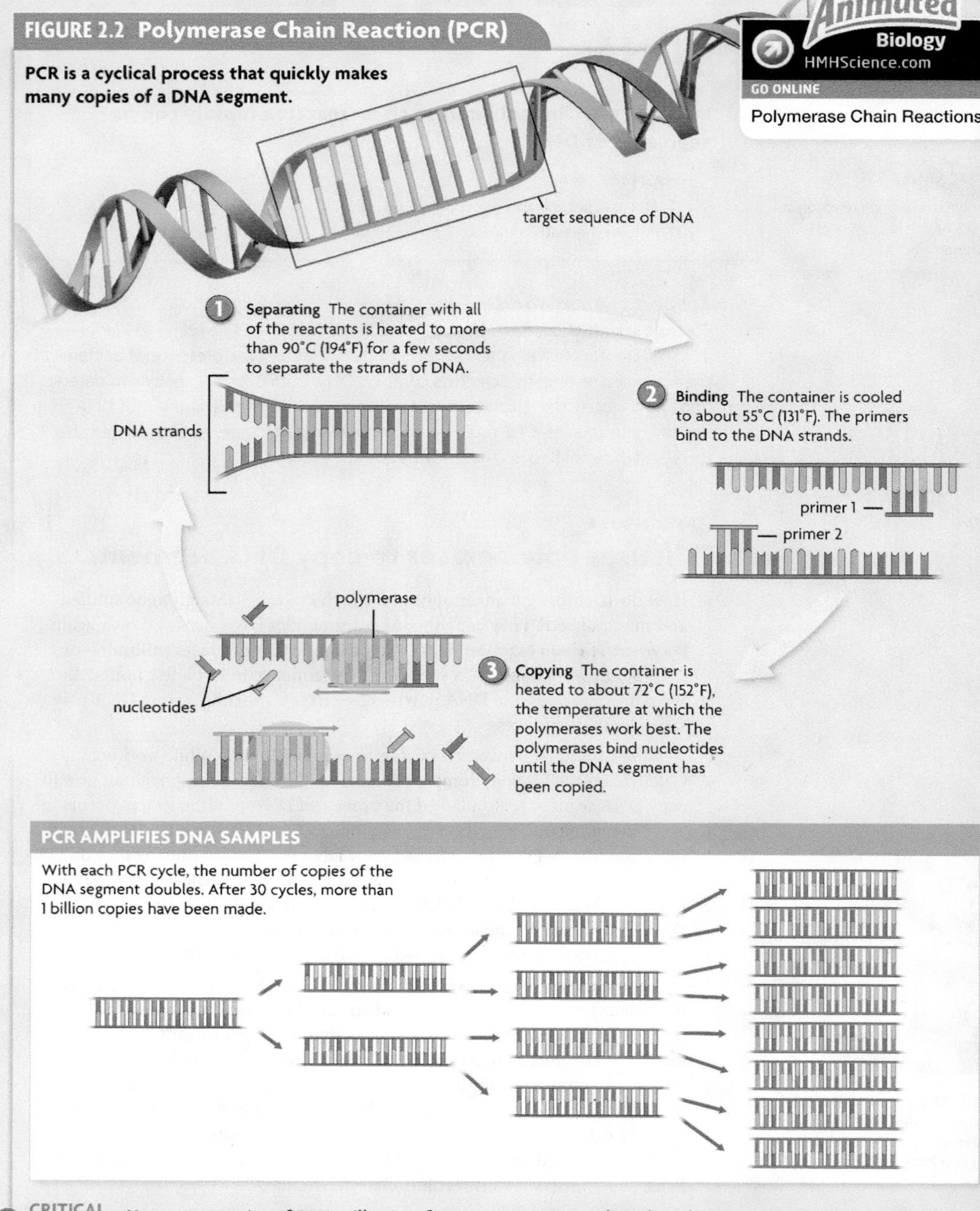

Animated Biology
HMHScience.com
GO ONLINE
Polymerase Chain Reactions
target sequence of DNA
1 Separating The container with all of the reactants is heated to more than 90°C (194°F) for a few seconds to separate the strands of DNA.
DNA strands
2 Binding The container is cooled to about 55°C (131°F). The primers bind to the DNA strands.
primer 1
primer 2
polymerase
nucleotides
3 Copying The container is heated to about 72°C (152°F), the temperature at which the polymerases work best. The polymerases bind nucleotides until the DNA segment has been copied.
PCR AMPLIFIES DNA SAMPLES
With each PCR cycle, the number of copies of the DNA segment doubles. After 30 cycles, more than 1 billion copies have been made.

Ⓐ CRITICAL VIEWING **How many copies of DNA will exist after one more PCR cycle? After three more cycles?**

Differentiated Instruction

PRE-AP

Tell students that primers are needed in both PCR and DNA replication. Have students compare **FIGURE 2.2** to **FIGURE 4.2** in the chapter From DNA to Proteins. Have students compare and contrast the process of PCR with that of DNA transcription, including the role of primers and enzymes.

Teacher Toolkit, Section C, Compare/Contrast Chart

INCLUSION

If you plan to go through the steps of PCR in detail, project **FIGURE 2.2** from the Media Gallery. Have hearing-impaired students use a set of signals, such as thumbs-up/thumbs-down, to indicate whether they are following your explanation or whether they need you to repeat information. Remember to face the students when speaking, so they can watch your lips.

Teacher Toolkit, Section C, Signals

MAIN IDEA

PCR is a three-step process.

PCR is a surprisingly simple process. It uses just four materials: the DNA to be copied, DNA polymerases, large amounts of each of the four DNA nucleotides (A, T, C, and G), and two primers. A **primer** is a short segment of DNA that acts as the starting point for a new strand. If DNA polymerases build new DNA strands, why are primers needed for PCR? DNA polymerases can add nucleotides to strands that have already been started, but they cannot start the strands. In PCR, two primers are used to start the copying of DNA close to the desired segment. The two primers are like bookends for the DNA strand. They limit the length of the copied DNA to one small segment of the strand.

PCR has three main steps, as shown in **FIGURE 2.2.** All of the steps of the cycle take place in the same container but at different temperatures. The main function of the first two PCR cycles is to produce the small segment of DNA that is desired. By making a copy of the desired segment, many copies of that tiny piece of DNA can be made, rather than copying an entire chromosome.

1. **Separating** The container with all of the reactants is heated to separate the double-stranded DNA into single strands.
2. **Binding** The container is cooled and the primers bind to their complementary DNA sequences. One primer binds to each DNA strand. The primers bind on opposite ends of the DNA segment being copied.
3. **Copying** The container is heated again and the polymerases begin to build new strands of DNA. Added nucleotides bind to the original DNA strands by complementary base pairing. The polymerases continue attaching nucleotides until the entire DNA segment has been copied.

Each PCR cycle doubles the number of DNA copies. The original piece of DNA becomes two copies. Those two copies become four copies. And the cycle is repeated over and over to quickly copy enough DNA for study. After only 30 cycles of PCR, for example, the original DNA sequence is copied more than 1 billion times. This doubling is why the process is called a chain reaction.

Infer **Why is it necessary to keep changing the temperature in the PCR process?**

READING TOOLBOX

VOCABULARY

The term *primer* comes from a Latin word that means "first." In PCR, a primer is the starting point for the DNA copying process.

CONNECT TO

REPLICATION

Look back at the process of DNA replication in the chapter **From DNA to Proteins** to compare PCR with replication.

9.2 Formative Assessment

REVIEWING MAIN IDEAS

1. Briefly describe the function of **polymerase chain reaction (PCR).**
2. Summarize the cycle involved in the PCR process.

CRITICAL THINKING

3. **Synthesize** Describe how heating double-stranded DNA separates the strands. Why does heating also inactivate DNA polymerases from many organisms?
4. **Analyze** Explain two reasons why **primers** are important in PCR.

SELF-CHECK Online
HMHScience.com
GO ONLINE

CONNECT TO

HUMAN GENETICS

5. Many human genetic diseases are caused by recessive alleles of genes. How might PCR be important in the diagnosis of these illnesses?

9.2 FORMATIVE ASSESSMENT

1. PCR is used to make many copies of a specific segment of DNA.
2. heat separates strands; primers bind; polymerase builds new strands
3. Heating breaks the hydrogen bonds between bases, causing the strands to separate. Heat also causes hydrogen bonds in proteins (enzymes) to break apart, which inactivates the enzymes.
4. Primers allow DNA polymerases to add nucleotides, and they limit the size of the DNA segment being copied.
5. PCR can be used to make many copies of different alleles so that they can be analyzed and isolated.

Take It Further

In each **PCR cycle,** the primers bind to their target binding site and allow polymerases to add nucleotides from that point on—in one direction only. This means that the portion of a DNA strand that is downstream from where the primer binds is left out of the PCR process. The same thing is true on the other strand, but on that one, the primer and polymerases are working in the opposite direction, and what was skipped on the other strand is copied. The DNA copies based on each strand are therefore a little bit closer to containing only the target segment than the original DNA. Once the DNA being produced is an exact match of the target sequence, the primers that bind to the separated strands are doing so right at the ends. From that point on, almost all of the DNA copies match the target DNA segment.

Vocabulary

Academic Vocabulary Tell students that the word **prime** is often used as a verb, meaning "to make ready" or "prepare." Walls are primed before painting, and wells are primed by pouring water into the pump.

Answers

A **Infer** High temperatures are needed to separate DNA strands, and both enzymes and primers function best at different specific temperatures.

Assess and Reteach ▼

Assess Use the Section Self-Check or Section Quiz, both available at **HMHScience.com**.

Reteach Have students close their books, then ask them to put the steps of PCR into a sequence diagram. They should include the words *primer, separate, bind,* and *copy.*

▼ Plan and Prepare

Activate Prior Knowledge Show students a blowup photo of a fingerprint, or have them look at their own. **Ask**

- What characteristics of a fingerprint make it useful for identification? the unique pattern of whorls and ridges in the skin
- What characteristic of DNA might make it useful for identification? the unique sequence of nucleotides

▼ Teach

TEACH FROM VISUALS

FIGURE 3.1 Have students compare the bands of the children with the bands of each parent. **Ask,** What is it about the DNA fingerprints that indicates each child is related to these parents? Each DNA band, or absence of a band, in a child's fingerprint matches that of one of the parent's fingerprints.

Answers

Ⓐ **Synthesize** No, it just indicates the number of repeat sequences. Most DNA fingerprinting uses DNA sequences outside of genes.

9.3 DNA Fingerprinting

VOCABULARY
DNA fingerprint

KEY CONCEPT **DNA fingerprints identify people at the molecular level.**

MAIN IDEAS
- A DNA fingerprint is a type of restriction map.
- DNA fingerprinting is used for identification.

Connect to Your World

You hear about it in the news all the time. DNA evidence is used to convict a criminal, release an innocent person from prison, or solve a mystery. A couple of decades ago, the lines and swirls of someone's fingertip were a detective's best hope for identifying someone. Now, investigators gather biological samples and analyze DNA for another kind of evidence: a DNA fingerprint.

MAIN IDEA
A DNA fingerprint is a type of restriction map.

Unless you have an identical twin, your complete set of DNA, or your genome, is unique. This variation in DNA among people is the basis of DNA fingerprinting. A **DNA fingerprint** is a representation of parts of an individual's DNA that can be used to identify a person at the molecular level.

A DNA fingerprint is a specific type of restriction map, which you learned about in Section 1. First, a DNA sample is cut with a restriction enzyme. Then the DNA fragments are run through a gel and the pattern of bands on the gel is analyzed. As you can see in **FIGURE 3.1**, a DNA fingerprint can show relationships among family members. The children (C) have similar DNA fingerprints to one another, but they are not identical. Also, their DNA fingerprints are combinations of the DNA fingerprints of the parents (M and F).

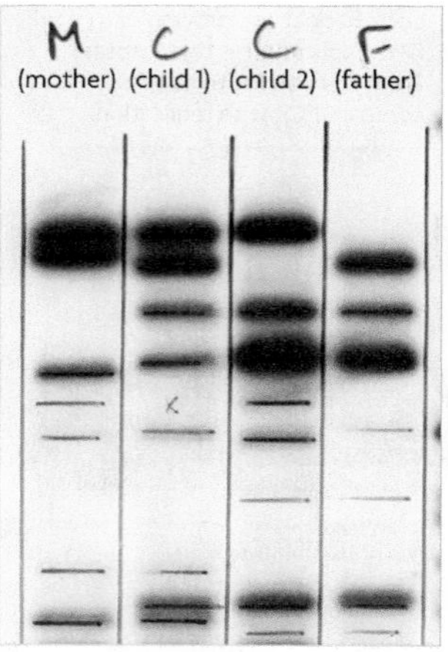

M (mother) C (child 1) C (child 2) F (father)

FIGURE 3.1 DNA fingerprints can be compared to identify people. Both children share some bands with each parent.

The greatest differences in DNA among people are found in regions of the genome that are not parts of genes. As a result, DNA fingerprinting focuses on noncoding regions of DNA, or DNA sequences outside genes. Noncoding DNA sequences often include stretches of nucleotides that repeat several times, one after another, as shown in **FIGURE 3.2.** Each person's DNA differs in the numbers of copies of the repeats. For example, one person may have seven repeats in one location, and another person may have three in the same place. To get to the specific regions of DNA that can be identified through DNA fingerprinting, the DNA is cut in known locations with restriction enzymes.

The differences in the number of repeats are found by separating the DNA fragments with gel electrophoresis. When there are more repeats, a DNA fragment is larger. The pattern of DNA fragments on a gel represents the uniqueness of a person's DNA. Individuals might have some of the fragments in common, but it is very unlikely that all of them would be the same.

Ⓐ Synthesize **Does a DNA fingerprint show a person's genotype? Why or why not?**

Differentiated Instruction

ENGLISH LEARNERS

Have students create a mind map, starting with the sentence "DNA fingerprinting is used for identification" in a large oval. On diagonals extending from the oval, they can write all of the uses described in the section. Review and assess their work by creating a mind map on the board and completing it with answers that students call out.

Teacher Toolkit, Section C, Mind Map

FIGURE 3.2 DNA Fingerprinting

A DNA fingerprint shows differences in the number of repeats of certain DNA sequences.

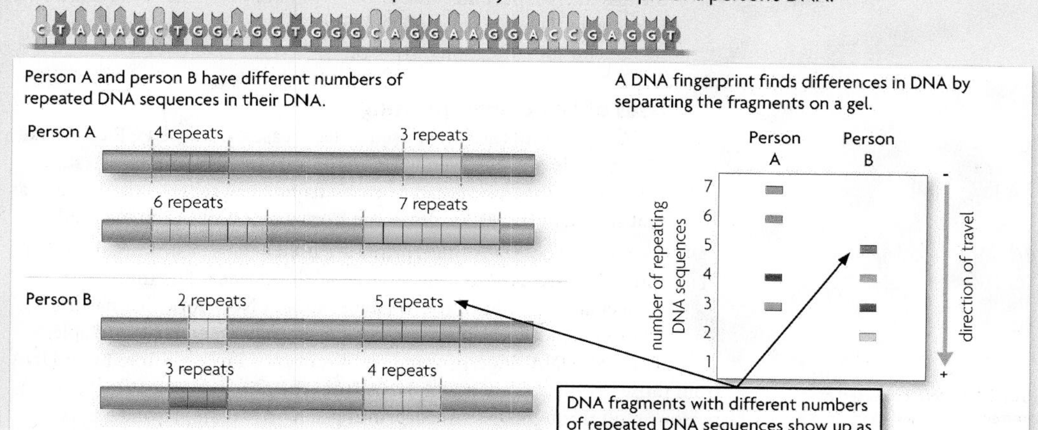

This DNA sequence of 33 bases can be repeated many times in a sample of a person's DNA.
Person A and person B have different numbers of repeated DNA sequences in their DNA.
Person A
4 repeats
3 repeats
6 repeats
7 repeats
Person B
2 repeats
5 repeats
3 repeats
4 repeats
A DNA fingerprint finds differences in DNA by separating the fragments on a gel.
Person A
Person B
number of repeating DNA sequences
7
6
5
4
3
2
1
direction of travel
DNA fragments with different numbers of repeated DNA sequences show up as different bands on a gel.

A Infer **How would the DNA fingerprints change if a different restriction enzyme cut the DNA in the middle of one of the repeated DNA sequences?**

MAIN IDEA

DNA fingerprinting is used for identification.

DNA fingerprinting to identify people has become a reliable and widely used process since the 1990s. Why? The specific nucleotide sequences that are repeated can be found in everyone. More importantly, from one person to another, the number of repeat sequences can differ greatly, even among brothers and sisters.

DNA Fingerprints and Probability

Identification with DNA fingerprinting depends on probability. Suppose that 1 in every 500 people has three copies of the repeat at location A. This means any person has a 1-in-500 chance of having a matching DNA fingerprint for that region of a chromosome. By itself, the number of repeats in one location cannot be used for identification, because too many people would match.

But then suppose that 1 in every 90 people has six copies of the repeat sequence at location B, and 1 in every 120 people has ten copies of the repeat sequence at location C. Individual probabilities are multiplied by each other to find the total probability. Therefore, when the three separate probabilities are multiplied, suddenly the chance that two people have the same DNA fingerprint is very small.

$$\frac{1}{500} \times \frac{1}{90} \times \frac{1}{120} = \frac{1}{5{,}400{,}000} = \text{1 chance in 5.4 million people}$$

CONNECT TO

GENOME

Recall from the chapter **Meiosis and Mendel** that a genome is the entire set of DNA in a cell. You will learn more about genome research in **Section 5.**

TEACH FROM VISUALS

FIGURE 3.2 Discuss the information in this figure. **Ask**

- Where were the DNA samples placed in the gel? at the end nearest to the negative electrode
- Why are the fragments with the fewest number of repeats at the bottom of the fingerprint? Fragments with the fewest number of repeats are smaller and move farther than fragments with more repeats.

The Inside Story

After DNA fragments are separated by gel electrophoresis, the bands are blotted onto a membrane and analyzed with dyes or radioactive probes to make them visible. This technique, the **Southern blot,** has nothing to do with direction. It was developed by **Edwin Southern,** a British biologist. As a play on his name, other blot methods have been named the Western blot, Northern blot, Southwestern blot, and Hawaiian blot. Who says scientists don't have a sense of humor?

Science Trivia

- In most forensic cases, at least five regions of DNA are analyzed.
- Depending on ethnic group, the probability of two people having identical DNA fingerprints ranges from 1 in 100,000 to 1 in 1 billion. The world population is about 6.5 billion.

BELOW LEVEL

Explain to students that probabilities are often written as fractions. A one-in-two chance of flipping the head side of a coin is written as 1/2. One chance in 5.4 million people is written as 1/5,400,000. Give students some probabilities of inheriting genetic disorders, such as cystic fibrosis (1 in 2500 Caucasians) and sickle cell disease (1 in 400 African Americans). Have students write the probabilities as fractions, and then pair up to compare answers.

Teacher Toolkit, Section C, Think-Pair-Share

Answers

A Infer A different pattern would appear in the gel because one of the larger fragments would be split in two.

▼ Teach *continued*

Take It Further

There is now at least one **Innocence Project** in every state. Most projects rely on volunteer attorneys and law students who review cases of prisoners who claim they were falsely convicted of violent crimes. Although the Cardozo project alone receives up to 200 requests a month, it accepts only those cases in which DNA testing of evidence is possible.

The Inside Story

DNA fingerprinting is helpful in identifying human remains that are otherwise unidentifiable. **The Tomb of the Unknowns** in Arlington National Cemetery contained the remains of one unidentified soldier each from World War I, World War II, the Korean War, and the Vietnam War. In 1998, DNA fingerprinting was used to identify the remains of the Vietnam War soldier. They were returned to his family and reburied in Missouri.

Answers

Ⓐ **Summarize** The more sites that are compared, the lower the probability that two people's DNA would share all of them.

▼ Assess and Reteach

Assess Use the Section Self-Check or Section Quiz, both available at **HMHScience.com**.

Reteach Review DNA fingerprinting by projecting **FIGURE 3.1** from the Media Gallery and asking students to point out how the band patterns of the children reflect their relatedness to the parents. Review why bands appear as they do.

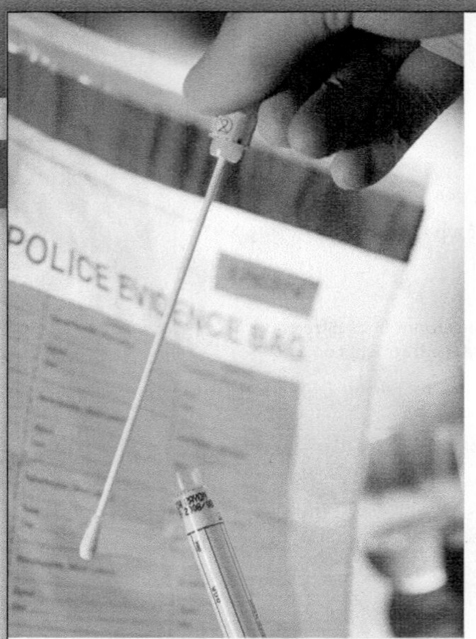

FIGURE 3.3 DNA collected at crime scenes is used as evidence in many legal cases.

Usually, DNA fingerprinting compares at least five regions of the genome. That way it is more certain that the pattern of DNA fragments in the fingerprint is unique. The more regions of DNA that are studied, the less likely it becomes that another person would have the same DNA fingerprint. For this reason, DNA fingerprinting is considered very reliable for identification purposes.

Uses of DNA Fingerprinting

DNA fingerprints are often used in legal cases. Because PCR can make a large sample of DNA even when there is a very small sample to start with, DNA fingerprints can be made from a few cells. Evidence, such as that shown in **FIGURE 3.3**, can come from just a single drop of blood.

Sometimes, DNA fingerprints are used against a suspect, but other times they are used to prove someone's innocence. The Innocence Project at Benjamin Cardozo Law School in New York City has used DNA evidence to help free nearly 300 wrongfully convicted people. Through DNA fingerprinting, the Innocence Project showed that DNA from those people did not match DNA from the crime scenes. Proving a person's guilt through DNA fingerprinting is harder than proving a person's innocence. For example, a DNA sample can become contaminated with other DNA if it is not handled carefully. Investigators must also consider the probability that another person has the same DNA fingerprint and what chance is low enough to be acceptable. In fact, there is no legal standard for this probability of a random DNA fingerprint match.

Outside of the courtroom, DNA fingerprints can prove family relationships, such as paternity and the kinship necessary for immigration requests. Small samples and bone fragments can be sequenced to identify victims of catastrophes or resolve historical debates. DNA fingerprinting may also be used to study human migration patterns and genealogy. Genetic comparisons through DNA fingerprinting are used to study biodiversity and to locate genetically engineered crops. And, as you saw at the beginning of the chapter, DNA fingerprinting has even been used in disasters to identify the parents of lost children.

Ⓐ Summarize **How does identification by DNA fingerprinting depend on probability?**

9.3 Formative Assessment

REVIEWING ⊙ MAIN IDEAS

1. On what, in a person's DNA, is a **DNA fingerprint** based?
2. Describe two ways in which DNA fingerprinting is used.

CRITICAL THINKING

3. **Compare and Contrast** How are DNA fingerprints and restriction maps similar? different? Explain.
4. **Synthesize** Briefly describe how restriction enzymes, gel electrophoresis, and PCR are used in DNA fingerprinting.

CONNECT TO

MUTATIONS

5. Why might noncoding regions of DNA outside of genes be more variable than coding regions of DNA?

9.3 FORMATIVE ASSESSMENT

1. the number of repeats of certain DNA sequences
2. *Sample answer:* establishing genetic relationships between people, tracking genetically modified crops, identifying different species, identifying specific people
3. Both are based on the lengths of fragments produced by the restriction enzymes. A DNA fingerprint is a restriction map of specific noncoding regions of an individual's DNA.
4. PCR produces multiple copies of a DNA sample, restriction enzymes cut the DNA into fragments to be analyzed, and gel electrophoresis separates the fragments so that their lengths can be compared.
5. Changes in DNA outside genes are less likely to be harmful to an organism or its chances of reproducing successfully. Therefore, mutations in these parts of DNA are more likely to accumulate over generations than are mutations of genes.

9.4 Genetic Engineering

KEY CONCEPT **DNA sequences of organisms can be changed.**

MAIN IDEAS
- Entire organisms can be cloned.
- New genes can be added to an organism's DNA.
- Genetic engineering produces organisms with new traits.

VOCABULARY
clone
genetic engineering
recombinant DNA
plasmid
transgenic
gene knockout

Connect to Your World

Glowing mice are used in cancer research. Glowing plants are used to track genetically modified crops. And, in 1999, British researchers introduced glowing yeast cells that locate water pollution. The scientists put a gene for a fluorescent protein into yeast. Under normal conditions, the yeast cells do not glow. But they do glow when certain chemicals are present. The glow identifies areas that need to be cleaned. New biotechnology applications seem to be developed on a daily basis. What advances will you see during your lifetime?

MAIN IDEA
Entire organisms can be cloned.

GO ONLINE
Animal Cloning

The term *cloning* might make you think of science fiction and horror movies, but the process is quite common in nature. A **clone** is a genetically identical copy of a gene or of an organism. For example, some plants clone themselves from their roots. Bacteria produce identical genetic copies of themselves through binary fission. And human identical twins are clones of each other.

People have cloned plants for centuries. The process is fairly easy because many plants naturally clone themselves and also because plants have stem cell tissues that can develop into many types of cells. Some simple animals, such as sea stars, can essentially clone themselves through a process called regeneration. Mammals, however, cannot clone themselves.

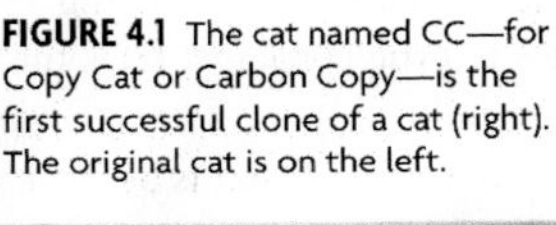

FIGURE 4.1 The cat named CC—for Copy Cat or Carbon Copy—is the first successful clone of a cat (right). The original cat is on the left.

To clone a mammal, scientists swap DNA between cells with a technique called nuclear transfer. First, an unfertilized egg is taken from an animal, and the egg's nucleus is removed. Then the nucleus of a cell from the animal to be cloned is implanted into the egg. The egg is stimulated and, if the procedure is successful, the egg will begin dividing. After the embryo grows for a few days, it is transplanted into a female. In 1996 a sheep named Dolly became the first clone of an adult mammal. The success of Dolly led to the cloning of adult cows, pigs, and mice. Now, a biotechnology company has even said that it can clone people's pets.

But pet owners who expect cloning to produce an exact copy of their furry friend will likely be disappointed. As you can see from the cat called CC in **FIGURE 4.1**, a clone may not look like the original, and it will probably not behave like the original, either. Why? Because, as you have learned, many factors, including environment, affect the expression of genes.

Differentiated Instruction

ENGLISH LEARNERS

Have students answer questions on slates so you can check their comprehension of genetic engineering. As you present the lesson, ask questions such as "Does cloning increase biodiversity?" (no) and "What do some bacteria have that allows for the production of recombinant DNA?" (plasmids). Students write their answers and hold up their slates. Scan the answers and use them to clarify.

Teacher Toolkit, Section C, Slates

SECTION 9.4

Plan and Prepare

Activating Prior Knowledge Have students think about whether there are traits they would change in themselves if they could. Tell them that in the near future it may be possible to modify DNA so that children have alleles not found in either parent's DNA. **Ask,** Do you think it is ethical to manipulate the DNA of a human being? Answers will vary, but most students may agree it is beneficial to correct genetic disorders.

Teach

Vocabulary

Greek and Latin Word Origins The word **clone** comes from the Greek *klōn,* meaning "twig," which conveys the idea of branching off. Cloning is a practice commonly used to produce new plants from old.

Have students complete the WebQuest on animal cloning to learn how scientists clone animals and weigh the risks and benefits.

▼ Teach continued

History of Science

In 1902, German embryologist **Hans Spemann** used a noose made of a hair from his baby boy's head to divide a two-celled salamander embryo. Each cell developed into a salamander. Spemann repeated his experiments with more-developed embryos, but found that cells teased apart from one another in these later stages of development did not develop into salamanders. He concluded that at a certain stage in development, the cells differentiate.

Later, in the late 1920s, Spemann transferred a nucleus from a 16-cell embryo to a single salamander embryo cell that had no nucleus. The cell developed normally, proving that nuclear transfer was possible. Spemann proposed that adult cell nuclei could be used to create clones. Spemann was awarded the Nobel Prize in 1935.

Integrating Microbiology

Plasmids carry only a small number of genes. These genes are not required for the survival and reproduction of the bacterium, but they often provide a benefit to the cell, such as antibiotic resistance. A single plasmid may have as many as ten genes for resistance to various antibiotics. Plasmids can be transferred from cell to cell by a process called **conjugation.**

Answers

A Apply Answers should address the risk of producing an unhealthy clone and the effort that would be needed to produce even one clone.

B Summarize A gene's DNA sequence is translated into the same amino acid sequence across different organisms.

Cloning brings with it some extraordinary opportunities. For example, scientists are studying how to use organs from cloned mammals for transplant into humans. This use of cloning could save an enormous number of lives each year and would not cause rejection problems in the organ recipient. Cloning could even help save endangered species. Cells from endangered species could be taken and used to produce clones that would increase the population of the species.

Cloning is also controversial. Many people think the success rate is too low to be attempted. The success rate in cloning mammals has improved substantially, but it varies widely by species. As cloning has become more common, ecological concerns have been raised. Cloned animals in a wild population would reduce biodiversity because the clones would be genetically identical.

Apply **Given the opportunity, would you have a pet cloned? Explain your answer based on your knowledge of genetics, biotechnology, and cloning.**

> CONNECT TO
> **BIODIVERSITY**
> In the chapter **Biology in the 21st Century,** you learned that biodiversity can be defined as the number of different species in an area. You will learn much more about genetic diversity within a species in the **Evolution** unit.

A MAIN IDEA

New genes can be added to an organism's DNA.

Genetic research relies on cloning, but not the cloning of organisms. Instead, it relies on the cloning of individual genes. A clone of a gene is a copy of that one segment of DNA. In some cases, scientists insert cloned genes from one organism into a different organism. This changing of an organism's DNA to give the organism new traits is called **genetic engineering.** Genetic engineering is possible because the genetic code is shared by all organisms.

Genetic engineering is based on the use of recombinant DNA technology. **Recombinant DNA** (ree-KAHM-buh-nuhnt) is DNA that contains genes from more than one organism. Scientists use recombinant DNA in several ways. For example, recombinant DNA is used to produce crop plants that make medicines and vitamins. Large amounts of medicines are made through this process, which has been called "pharming." Scientists are also studying ways of using recombinant DNA to make vaccines to protect against HIV, the virus that causes AIDS.

Bacteria are commonly used in genetic engineering. One reason is because bacteria have tiny rings of DNA called plasmids. **Plasmids,** as shown in **FIGURE 4.2,** are closed loops of DNA that are separate from the bacterial chromosome and that replicate on their own within the cell. Recombinant DNA is found naturally in bacteria that take in exogenous DNA (or DNA from a different organism) and add it to their own. Scientists adapted what happens in nature to make artificial recombinant DNA. First, a restriction enzyme is used to cut out the desired gene from a strand of DNA. Then plasmids are cut with the same enzyme. The plasmid opens, and when the gene is added to the plasmid, their complementary sticky ends are bonded together by a process called ligation. The resulting plasmid contains recombinant DNA, as shown in **FIGURE 4.3.**

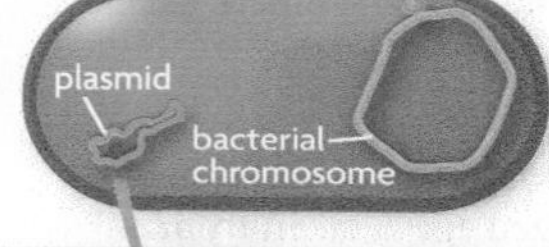

FIGURE 4.2 A plasmid is a closed loop of DNA in a bacterium that is separate from the bacterial chromosome. (colored TEM; magnification 48,000×)

B Summarize **How does genetic engineering rely on a shared genetic code?**

Differentiated Instruction

BELOW LEVEL

Have students make a three-column chart and label the columns *Know, Want to Know,* and *Learned.* Have them list in the first column several things they already know about genetic engineering, such as the use of PCR to clone segments of DNA. Have them list in the second column several things they want to know. Then have students read the section and list several things they have learned about genetic engineering.

Teacher Toolkit, Section C, KWL

FIGURE 4.3 Making Recombinant DNA

Foreign DNA can be inserted into a plasmid to make recombinant DNA.

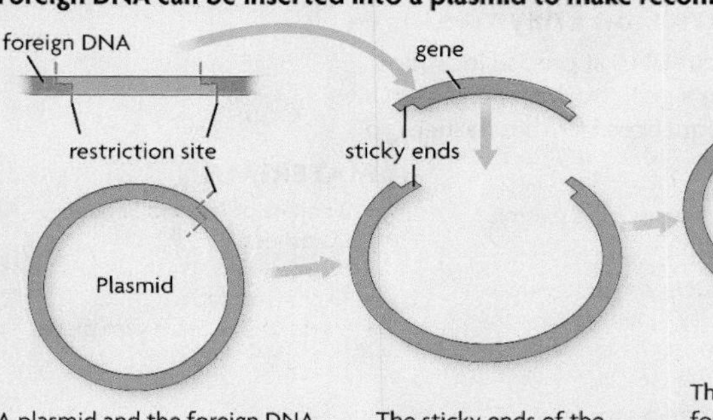

A plasmid and the foreign DNA with the gene are cut with the same restriction enzyme.

The sticky ends of the plasmid and the foreign gene match.

The plasmid and the foreign gene are bonded together to form recombinant DNA.

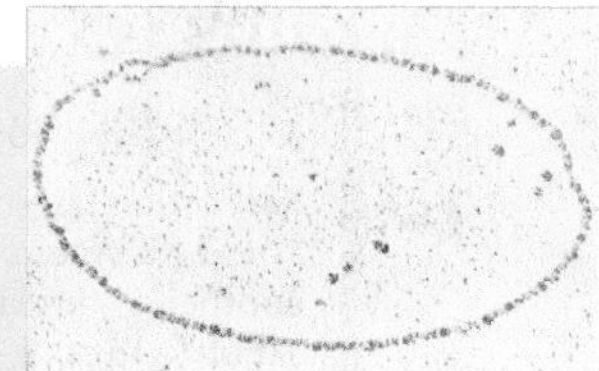

Plasmids are small rings of DNA used in genetic engineering. Foreign genes (various colors) can be inserted into plasmids. (colored TEM, magnification unknown).

Apply **Why are sticky ends important for making recombinant DNA?**

MAIN IDEA

Genetic engineering produces organisms with new traits.

After a gene is added to a plasmid, the genetically engineered plasmids can be put into bacteria. In a way, bacteria are turned into tiny gene factories that make copy after copy of the plasmid. As a result, the transformed bacteria make many copies of the new gene. The bacteria will express the new gene and make that gene's product. The bacteria with the recombinant plasmid are described as transgenic. A **transgenic** organism has one or more genes from another organism inserted into its genome. For example, the gene for human insulin can be put into plasmids. The plasmids are inserted into bacteria. The transgenic bacteria make human insulin that is collected and used to treat people with diabetes.

Bacterial Transformation

Genetic Engineering of Plants

Genetic engineering of plants is directly related to genetic engineering of bacteria. To change a plant's DNA, a gene is inserted into a plasmid and the plasmid is inserted into bacteria. After the bacteria infect the plant, the new gene becomes a part of the plant's DNA and is expressed like any other gene.

This technique has allowed scientists to give plants new traits, such as resistance to frost, diseases, and insects. For instance, certain bacteria, called *Bt*, produce a natural protein pesticide. Farmers used to spray their crops with *Bt* bacteria to prevent the crops from being attacked by insects. But by genetically engineering the crop plants, the plants can make the bacterial pesticide themselves. These genetically engineered crops, which are also called genetically modified (GM), are now common in the United States. They include *Bt* potatoes and corn. GM crops are even more important in developing countries because by increasing crop yields, more food is produced quickly and cheaply.

VOCABULARY

The prefix *trans-* means "across," and the root *genic* means "referring to genes." When genes are transferred across different organisms, transgenic organisms are produced.

Students can perform a virtual lab on bacterial transformation at **HMHScience.com**.

Take It Further

In biotechnology, a cell is **transformed** when foreign DNA is incorporated into its genome and it expresses the product of the new gene. Producing a **transgenic bacterium,** such as the one that makes human insulin, involves many more steps than those that are presented in the text. In addition to inserting a gene into a plasmid, an appropriate promoter must be present, the gene itself might have to be altered so that the protein can be made, and the protein has to be purified so that it can be used.

Answers

A **Apply** A desired gene can bind to a plasmid's DNA through complementary base pairing.

PRE-AP

After reading the section, tell students to think about a kind of plant that they would like to genetically modify. Give them five minutes to write how they would use restriction enzymes and bacteria plasmids to insert a gene from another species into the DNA of the plant they would like to modify.

Teacher Toolkit, Section C, Quick-Write

▼ Teach *continued*

QUICKLAB

Time 15 minutes

TEACHER TESTED

Purpose Model the formation of recombinant DNA using three restriction enzymes.

LAB PREPARATION

- Make and distribute three copies of the Plasmid Sequence datasheet, available at **HMHScience.com**.

LAB MANAGEMENT

- Explain to students that the vehicle that carries a gene from one organism into another is called a vector. Plasmids are one type of vector. Other vectors are viruses and tiny "bullets" containing the gene that are shot into cells.

Answers

Analyze and Conclude

1. You would get four fragments (4-inch, 6-inch, 12-inch, and 18-inch).
2. Because restriction enzymes act at different restriction sites, an enzyme that acts at the beginning and end of the desired gene must be used.

Vocabulary

Academic Vocabulary The word **vector** is used in a number of applications.

- In *physics,* it is a quantity, such as velocity, that has both magnitude and a direction.
- In *microbiology,* it refers to an organism, such as a mosquito or tick, that carries disease-causing micro-organisms from one host to another.
- In *genetics,* it refers to a bacteriophage, plasmid, or other agent that transfers genetic material from one cell to another.

QUICKLAB MODELING

Modeling Plasmids and Restriction Enzymes

Restriction enzymes are enzymes that cut DNA at precise locations. These enzymes allow scientists to move a gene from one organism into another. In this lab, you will use DNA sequences from a datasheet to simulate the use of restriction enzymes.

MATERIALS

- 3 copies of Plasmid Sequence Datasheet
- scissors
- 10 cm clear tape
- 3 sets of five 5-cm yarn pieces

PROBLEM How do different restriction enzymes cut a plasmid?

PROCEDURE

1. Make models of 3 plasmids. Cut out the DNA sequences from the copies of Figure 1 on the datasheet. Use tape to attach the appropriate piece of yarn to each end. The yarn represents the entire plasmid. The finished plasmid should be a circle.
2. Use the scissors to cut a plasmid at the correct sites for *EcoR*I.
3. Use the sequences for sites of *Hind*III and *Sma*I to repeat step 2 with the other two plasmids.

ANALYZE AND CONCLUDE

1. **Apply** How many DNA fragments would you get if you cut the same plasmid with both *EcoR*I and *Sma*I?
2. **Infer** Why might scientists use different restriction enzymes to cut out different genes from a strand of DNA?

FIGURE 4.4 This knockout mouse has been bioengineered so researchers can use it as a model to study obesity.

Genetic Engineering in Animals

In general, transgenic animals are much harder to produce than GM plants because animals are more resistant to genetic manipulation. To produce a transgenic animal, a researcher must first get a fertilized egg cell. Then the foreign DNA is inserted into the nucleus and the egg is implanted back into a female. However, only a small percentage of the genetically manipulated eggs mature normally. And only a portion of those that develop will be transgenic. That is, only a small number will have the foreign gene as a part of their DNA. But those animals that are transgenic will have the gene in all of their cells—including reproductive cells—and the transgenic trait will be passed on to their offspring.

Transgenic mice are often used as models of human development and disease. The first such animal was called the oncomouse. This mouse is more likely to develop cancer, because a gene that controls cell growth and differentiation was mutated. Researchers use the oncomouse to study both cancer and anti-cancer drugs. Other types of transgenic mice are used to study diabetes, brain function and development, and sex determination.

Some mice have genes that have been purposely "turned off." These mice, called **gene knockout** mice, are very useful for studying a gene's normal function because a researcher can observe specific changes in gene expression and traits. For example, scientists are using a gene knockout mouse to study obesity, as you can see in **FIGURE 4.4**. Other mice, called knockdown mice, are created using RNAi technology to decrease the expression of a specific gene or to silence the expression temporarily. Recall that RNAi technology shuts down expression of a gene by preventing a gene from making its protein. Scientists use knockdown technology to study metabolic pathways in animals.

Differentiated Instruction

TEACH WITH TECHNOLOGY

Assemble a digital slide show of images of cloned animals such as the domestic cat, pig, cattle, frog, carp, sheep, horse, mule, and deer, and transgenic animals such as fluorescent green pigs.

You might be surprised to learn that humans do not have the largest genome—the most DNA—among organisms. Scientists have determined the DNA sequences for the genomes of several species, including the ones listed in **FIGURE 5.1.** In some cases, the genomes are used to study basic questions about genes and genetics. In other cases, a genome is sequenced because that organism is used as a model in medical research. In all cases, the genomes of organisms that have been sequenced, including bacteria, insects, plants, and mammals, give us important clues toward finding out how genes function.

Yeast, for example, are very useful for scientists who study gene regulation. Genes that control development in the fruit fly are very similar to those genes in humans. The genomes of several plants have been sequenced so that scientists can learn ways to improve crop yields and to increase the resistance of those crops to disease and weather extremes. The genomes of rats and mice are quite similar to the human genome. As a result, both of these species are used as models for human diseases and gene function.

FIGURE 5.1 COMPARING GENOME SIZES

Organism	Approximate Total DNA (millions of base pairs)
E. coli	5
Yeast	12
Fruit fly	165
Banana	873
Chicken	1200
Human	3000
Vanilla	7672
Crested newt	18,600
Lungfish	139,000

Source: University of Nebraska

The Human Genome Project

The genomes of yeast and fruit flies are easier to sequence than the human genome. This difficulty is not due to the number of genes that humans have. In fact, while there is still a debate about the exact number of human genes, scientists agree it is surprisingly small. It is estimated that there are between 20,000 and 25,000 protein-coding genes in the human genome. But think about the amount of DNA that each of us has in our cells. The human genome has at least 3 billion base pairs. This means that there is an average of about one gene in each sequence of "120,000 to 150,000" bases. Now just try to imagine the huge task of finding out the exact order of all of those DNA bases. In 1990, an international effort began to do exactly that.

The two main goals of the **Human Genome Project** were (1) to map and sequence all of the DNA base pairs of the human chromosomes and (2) to identify all of the genes within the sequence. The first goal was accomplished in 2003 when scientists announced that they had sequenced the human genome. However, the Human Genome Project only analyzed the DNA from a few people. Knowing those few complete DNA sequences was only the first step in understanding the human genome.

Today scientists continue to work on determining the roles of genes and other functional elements. Some scientists are studying how DNA sequences vary among people in a project called HapMap. The goal of the HapMap is to develop a method that will quickly identify genetic differences that may play a part in human diseases. By identifying and studying the estimated 10 million single-base differences that occur in the human genome, scientists hope to learn what makes different populations of humans similar, and yet different, and use that knowledge to customize the treatment of diseases.

FIGURE 5.2 Computer analysis of DNA was necessary in sequencing the human genome.

Synthesize **How is genomics related to genes and DNA?**

PRE-AP

Ask students how the genomes of a human and a mouse can be so similar when the two organisms are so different. Give students five minutes to write everything they know that might answer this question. Students should recognize that both a mouse and a human have similar tissues, organs, and metabolic reactions. Both organisms need similar enzymes and structural proteins to perform biochemical reactions and build tissues.

Teacher Toolkit, Section C, Quick-Write

Take It Further

Any two humans have DNA sequences that are 99.9 percent identical. The variations, however, are important in determining an individual's risk for genetic disorders. These variations are single-base changes called **SNPs** (pronounced *snips*) that occur every few thousand bases. SNPs tend to be inherited together as blocks known as **haplotype blocks.** The goal of the HapMap project is to determine how the haplotype blocks, which are shared by many people, are arranged in the human genome. Once the haplotype blocks are mapped, the specific sequences can be linked to disorders such as diabetes and diseases such as heart disease.

Vocabulary

Word Origins The term **haplotype** is a contraction of the phrase *haploid genotype,* which is the genotype of a single chromosome or single set of chromosomes. For example, if an organism has a genotype of *AaBb,* two haplotypes are possible, depending on which alleles are found on each chromosome. One chromosome in a homologous pair may have the alleles *AB* and the other *ab*, or the homologs may have the alleles *Ab* and *aB*.

Take It Further

Two approaches were used to map the human genome. Some scientists first made **linkage maps** of known markers. They used the location of the markers to map the sequences between the markers. Finally, they assembled an overall sequence. Another method called the **shotgun approach** sequenced random fragments of DNA. Then powerful computer programs were used to find overlapping sequences that could be arranged relative to each other to produce a longer sequence.

Answers

A **Synthesize** Genomics is the study and comparison of genes and genomes within and across species.

Teach *continued*

DATA ANALYSIS

Introduce

When a scientist makes a **histogram,** he or she sorts data into categories that are related, such as variations in size or height. Histograms are often used to show frequency. In a bar graph, the categories show comparisons of data that are not related or interdependent.

Discuss

Write the students' heights on the board, then construct a histogram. To show how histograms can change based on the ranges within categories, compare a histogram based on 6-inch height intervals with one based on 3-inch intervals. **Ask,** In general, what trend do we see in our histograms of students' heights? More students should be of intermediate height. **Ask,** What kind of height data would be better illustrated by a line graph? the growth (annual height) of a student over a period of time

Answers

1. bar graph comparing the base pair lengths
2. 101–150 million base pairs
3. Most chromosomes are of intermediate size.

Online Student Resources, Data Analysis Practice

DATA ANALYSIS

CONSTRUCTING HISTOGRAMS

To construct a histogram a scientist will count the number of data points in each category and then graph the number of times that category occurs. The categories are shown on the *x*-axis and the frequencies are shown on the *y*-axis. The data table to the right shows the ranges of base pair lengths for the 24 human chromosomes (chromosomes 1–22, the X chromosome, and the Y chromosome). The data are organized by these ranges.

TABLE 1. HUMAN CHROMOSOME SIZES

Millions of Base Pairs	Number of Human Chromosomes
0–50	2
51–100	6
101–150	8
151–200	6
201–250	2

Source: U.S. Department of Energy Office of Science

1. **Graph Data** Construct a histogram that shows the frequency of base pair lengths for the 24 human chromosomes.
2. **Interpret** Which range of base pair length is most common for human chromosomes?
3. **Analyze** Summarize the overall trend for human chromosome length shown in the histogram.

MAIN IDEA

Technology allows the study and comparison of both genes and proteins.

You have learned about specific genes that produce specific traits. But you also know that genes act as more than simple, separate units. They interact and affect each other's expression. Most biological processes and physical traits are the result of the interactions among many different genes.

Bioinformatics

Genes are sequenced, genomes are compared, and proteins are analyzed. What happens to the huge amounts of data that are produced? These data can be analyzed only if they are organized and searchable. **Bioinformatics** is the use of computer databases to organize and analyze biological data. Powerful computer programs are needed to compare genomes that are billions of base pairs in length, especially if the genomes differ by only a small amount.

Bioinformatics gives scientists a way to store, share, and find data. It also lets researchers predict and model the functions of genes and proteins. A scientist can now search databases to find the gene that is the code for a known protein. Bioinformatics can help researchers find the genetic basis of some diseases and the causes of molecular diseases.

CONNECT TO

COMPUTER MODELS

Recall from **Biology in the 21st Century** how computer models are used to investigate biological systems that cannot be studied directly. Computer models are often used in genetics and genomics.

DNA Microarrays

DNA microarrays are tools that allow scientists to study many genes, and their expression, at once. A microarray is a small chip that is dotted with all of the genes being studied. The genes are laid out in a grid pattern. Each block of the grid is so small that a one-square-inch chip can hold thousands of genes.

Virtual INVESTIGATION

HMHScience.com

GO ONLINE

Gene Technologies

Differentiated Instruction

BELOW LEVEL

Use the following activity to show how short sequences can be overlapped to make a long sequence. Have students copy the following mixed-up word fragments onto a sheet of paper. Then have students arrange them to make a sentence:

seq tand how ce D I un dersta
quen nder e DNA ow to se
quence NA

Have students rewrite the fragments one under the other, overlapping common letters. The final sentence should read "I understand how to sequence DNA."

Complementary DNA (cDNA) labeled with a fluorescent dye is added to the microarray. A cDNA molecule is a single-stranded DNA molecule that is made from an mRNA molecule. The mRNA acts as a template for the cDNA. Therefore, a cDNA molecule is complementary to an mRNA molecule and is identical to a gene's DNA sequence. The cDNA binds to its complementary DNA strand in the microarray by the same base pairing that you learned about previously.

Anywhere cDNA binds to DNA in the microarray shows up as a glowing dot because of the dye. A glowing dot in the microarray is a match between a cDNA molecule and the DNA on the chip. Therefore, a glowing dot shows which genes are expressed and how much they are expressed. Microarrays, as shown in **FIGURE 5.3**, help researchers find which genes are expressed in which tissues, and under what conditions. For example, DNA microarrays can compare gene expression in cancer cells with gene expression in healthy cells. Scientists hope that this method will lead to cancer treatments that target the faulty genes.

FIGURE 5.3 Gene expression can be studied with microarrays. The red dots show genes that are expressed after exposure to a toxic chemical.

Proteomics

You have read how genomics is the study of genomes. **Proteomics** (PROH-tee-AH-mihks) is the study and comparison of all the proteins that result from an organism's genome. Proteomics also includes the study of the functions and interactions of proteins. Identifying and studying proteins is more difficult than identifying and studying genes. A single gene, depending on how its mRNA is edited, can code for more than one polypeptide. Different proteins are found in different tissues, depending on gene expression. And, often, the functions of proteins have to be studied within a biological system.

Proteomics has potential benefits for many areas of biology. Shared evolutionary histories among organisms are studied by comparing proteins across species. Proteomics allows scientists to learn about proteins involved in human diseases. By better understanding the proteins that might play a part in cancer, arthritis, or heart disease, scientists might be able to develop new treatments that target the proteins. Proteomics even has the potential to help doctors match medical treatments to a patient's unique body chemistry.

Apply **How is bioinformatics a form of data analysis?**

SELF-CHECK Online
HMHScience.com
GO ONLINE

9.5 Formative Assessment

REVIEWING MAIN IDEAS

1. Describe the goals of the **Human Genome Project.**
2. Why is **bioinformatics** important in genetic research?

CRITICAL THINKING

3. **Apply** Describe the difference between **gene sequencing** and DNA fingerprinting.
4. **Compare and Contrast** How is the study of specific genes different from the study of a genome?

CONNECT TO

CELL BIOLOGY

5. How might **genomics** and **proteomics** help researchers predict how a medical treatment might affect cells in different tissues?

9.5 FORMATIVE ASSESSMENT

1. to map and sequence the human genome and to identify all the genes within it
2. Genetic information consists of a very large, complex volume of data. Computer databases store and organize the data.
3. Gene sequencing finds the DNA sequence; a DNA fingerprint shows a number of repeated DNA sequences.
4. Genomics studies all genes.
5. By knowing about how genes and their products interact, researchers could be able to predict how one drug will affect many different areas of the body. They could tailor a treatment to target a specific gene or protein in order to avoid damaging others.

Take It Further

The mRNA molecule used to make complementary DNA (cDNA) for a **microarray** is isolated from the cells in a tissue sample. Single strands of cDNA, which bind to the mRNA, are made using fluorescently labeled nucleotides. The enzyme **reverse transcriptase** catalyzes the formation of the cDNA from the mRNA. The labeled mRNA–cDNA hybrid is applied to a microarray that contains spots of short, single-stranded DNA from each gene being tested. The excess cDNA is rinsed off the array, and the array is scanned for fluorescence. Each fluorescent spot represents a gene that is expressed in the original tissue sample.

Integrating Evolutionary Biology

Most proteins are identified by their functional sites, such as the active site of an enzyme. Nine out of ten functional sites found in human proteins have counterparts in enzymes of fruit flies and nematodes, and 60 percent of human proteins are similar to the proteins of fruit flies and worms. These data suggest that many metabolic processes were established early in evolutionary history.

Answers

Ⓐ **Apply** It is the organization and analysis of large amounts of data.

Assess and Reteach ▼

Assess Use the Section Self-Check or Section Quiz, both available at **HMHScience.com**.

Reteach Work with students to create a cluster diagram that includes bioinformatics, proteomics, DNA microarrays, the Human Genome Project, and DNA sequencing.

SECTION 9.6

▼ Plan and Prepare

Activate Prior Knowledge Tell students that 11 cousins chose to have their stomachs surgically removed after genetic screening revealed that they had inherited the rare CDH1 allele, giving them a 70 percent chance of developing a stomach cancer that had killed their relatives. **Ask,** Do you think some knowledge is not worth having? How would you react in such a situation? Answers will vary.

▼ Teach

TEACH FROM VISUALS

FIGURE 6.1 Tell students that the screening test for DMD is designed to detect deletions or duplications of a particular gene. **Ask,** Do deletions or duplications cause the disease in the three people tested? deletions How do you know? People with the disease have four, five, or six bands; people without it have seven.

Answers

A Infer Answers will vary but could include a discussion of genetic information being used to discriminate against a person in some way.

9.6 Genetic Screening and Gene Therapy

KEY CONCEPT **Genetics provides a basis for new medical treatments.**

VOCABULARY
genetic screening
gene therapy

MAIN IDEAS
- Genetic screening can detect genetic disorders.
- Gene therapy is the replacement of faulty genes.

Connect to Your World
Anyone could be a carrier of a genetic disorder. Genetic screening is used to help people figure out whether they are at risk for passing on that disorder. If they are at risk, what do they do? Do they not have children? Do they have children and hope that a child does not get the disorder? What would you do?

MAIN IDEA
Genetic screening can detect genetic disorders.

Every one of us carries alleles that produce defective proteins. Usually, these genes do not affect us in a significant way because we have other alleles that make up for the deficiency. But about 10 percent of people will find themselves dealing with an illness related to their genes at some point in their lives.

Genetic screening is the process of testing DNA to determine a person's risk of having or passing on a genetic disorder. Recall that genetic screening often involves both pedigree analysis and DNA tests. Because our knowledge of the human genome is still limited, it is not yet possible to test for every possible defect. Often, genetic screening is used to look for specific genes or proteins that indicate a particular disorder. Some tests can detect genes that are related to an increased risk of developing a disease, such as a gene called BRCA1 that has been linked to breast cancer. There are also tests for more than 1000 genetic disorders, including cystic fibrosis and Duchenne's muscular dystrophy (DMD). In DMD, it is quite easy to see differences in DNA tests between people with and without the disorder, as shown in **FIGURE 6.1.**

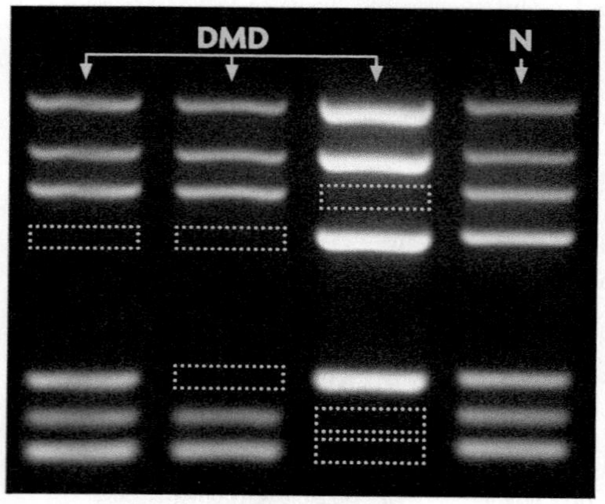

DMD
N

FIGURE 6.1 Genetic screening can be used to detect Duchenne's muscular dystrophy (DMD). Notice the missing bands on the gel (boxes) for three people with DMD as compared with a person without the disorder (N).

Genetic screening can help save lives. It can also lead to some difficult choices. Suppose a person has a family history of cancer and tests positive for a gene that may lead to an increased risk of cancer. Is that information helpful or harmful? If a person has a chance of being a carrier of a genetic disorder, should screening be required? As genetic screening becomes more common, more questions like these will need to be answered.

A Infer **Why might genetic screening raise ethical concerns about privacy?**

Differentiated Instruction

ENGLISH LEARNERS

Have students complete a concept definition map. Write the terms *genetic screening* and *gene therapy* down the left side of a table. Write the words *Category, Characteristics, Examples,* and *Comparison* across the top as column heads. Then have pairs of students complete the map. Under *Category,* for example, students might write *testing* for *genetic screening* and *treatment* for *gene therapy.*

Teacher Toolkit, Concept Definition Map

MAIN IDEA

Gene therapy is the replacement of faulty genes.

A defective part in a car or in a computer can be easily replaced. If someone has a faulty gene that causes a disorder, is it possible to replace the gene? The goal of gene therapy is to do exactly that. **Gene therapy** is the replacement of a defective or missing gene, or the addition of a new gene, into a person's genome to treat a disease. If the gene is replaced in a somatic cell, the change in the genome will affect only the individual and cannot be inherited by the patient's offspring. Scientists are trying to make the change in the patient's gametes as well so the change will be inherited.

For any type of gene therapy to work, researchers such as Dr. Betty Pace, shown in **FIGURE 6.2**, must first get the new gene into the correct cells of a patient's body. Once in the body, the gene has to become a part of the cells' DNA. One method of gene therapy that scientists have tried is to take a sample of bone marrow stem cells and "infect" them with a virus that has been genetically engineered with the new gene. Then the stem cells are put back into the patient's bone marrow. Because they are stem cells, they divide and make more blood cells with the normal gene.

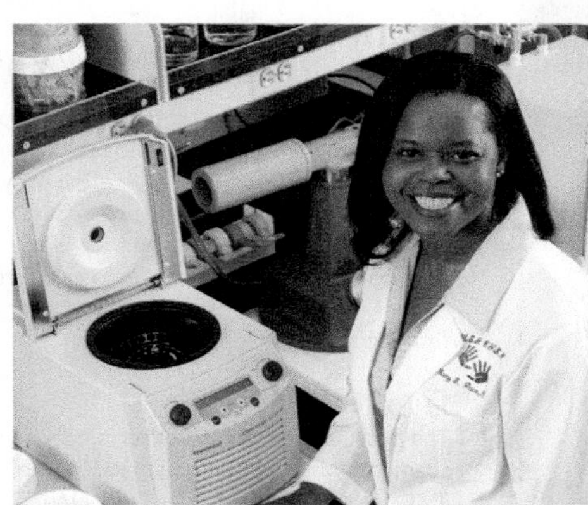

FIGURE 6.2 Dr. Betty Pace, a molecular and cell biologist is studying potential gene therapy treatments for sickle cell disease.

The first successful trial of gene therapy took place in 1990. The treatment was used on two children with a genetic autoimmune disorder, and the children are now adults leading normal lives. However, much of gene therapy is still experimental. For example, researchers are studying several methods to treat cancer with gene therapy. One experimental approach involves inserting a gene that stimulates a person's immune system to attack cancer cells. Another method is to insert "suicide" genes into cancer cells. These genes activate a drug inside those cells so that only the cancer cells are killed.

Gene therapy has many technical challenges. First, the correct gene has to be added to the correct cells. And even after researchers have figured out how to transfer the desired gene, the gene's expression has to be regulated so that it does not make too much or too little protein. Scientists must also determine if the new gene will affect other genes. The many trials have produced long-lasting positive results in only a few diseases. But because of its great potential, research on gene therapy continues.

Synthesize **How does gene therapy rely on genetic screening?**

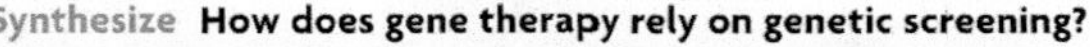

9.6 Formative Assessment

SELF-CHECK Online
HMHScience.com
GO ONLINE

REVIEWING MAIN IDEAS

1. How does **genetic screening** use both old and new methods of studying human genetics?
2. Briefly describe the goals and methods of **gene therapy.**

CRITICAL THINKING

3. **Compare and Contrast** How is gene therapy similar to, and different from, making a transgenic organism?
4. **Synthesize** How are restriction enzymes and recombinant DNA important for gene therapy?

CONNECT TO

CELL SPECIALIZATION

5. How is the type of cell into which a new gene is inserted important in gene therapy?

9.6 FORMATIVE ASSESSMENT

1. Genetic screening uses pedigrees and family histories as well as DNA testing.
2. The goal of gene therapy is to replace faulty or missing genes. In some cases, genetically engineered viruses are inserted into the patient's body to deliver functional genes. Another method is to insert genes into cancer cells that will render them vulnerable to specific drugs.
3. They both involve inserting a new gene into an organism, but gene therapy replaces a defective gene with a normal gene in an adult organism; a transgenic organism has genes from more than one species.
4. Restriction enzymes cut DNA to insert a gene into a virus, producing recombinant DNA.
5. Gene expression can depend on promoters, as well as on the particular cell type.

Integrating Medical Science

Many people worry that genetic screening will dramatically alter the way health care is given. One major concern is that **health insurance** companies will either deny coverage or raise health-care costs for people who have genes that cause disorders or other medical problems. Another concern is over who gets to decide what genetic screening tests are appropriate and who pays for them.

Take It Further

Gene editing is a new technology for therapy of genetic disorders. The CRISPR-Cas9 system uses an endonuclease enzyme to directly modify a defective gene without the intervention of a vector such as a virus to carry the normal gene into a patient's cells. The location at which the Cas9 "molecular scissors" cuts the DNA to be edited is determined by guide RNA, which is made up of two smaller RNA components. The guide RNA directs the molecular scissors to cut the DNA at the exact site of the mutation. Once the DNA is cut, the cell's mechanisms and exogenously added DNA use the cell's machinery to repair the damaged DNA.

Answers

A Synthesize Screening to identify which gene is faulty must be completed before gene therapy can be attempted.

Assess and Reteach

Assess Use the Section Self-Check or Section Quiz, both available at **HMHScience.com**.

Reteach Tell students that scientists now have the tools to test individuals for possible risks of developing illnesses in the future. Have students write a short essay in which they discuss some of the ethical problems that might arise from this technology, such as the possibility of genomic discrimination and loss of personal privacy.

GO ONLINE

Encourage students to go to **HMHScience.com** for a detailed review of each section, including visuals and vocabulary practice.

Online Student Resources, Vocabulary Practice Worksheet

CHAPTER 9 Summary

BIG IDEA Advances in biotechnology and the study of genomes allow scientists to manipulate DNA and combine the genes of multiple organisms, and may provide new medical treatments in the future.

KEY CONCEPTS

9.1 Manipulating DNA

Biotechnology relies on cutting DNA at specific places. Bacterial enzymes called restriction enzymes are used to cut DNA. Each restriction enzyme cuts DNA at a specific DNA sequence. After DNA is cut with a restriction enzyme, the fragments of DNA can be separated using gel electrophoresis. A restriction map of the DNA is made based on the lengths of the fragments.

9.2 Copying DNA

The polymerase chain reaction rapidly copies segments of DNA. The polymerase chain reaction (PCR) is based on the process of DNA replication. By combining the DNA to be copied, DNA nucleotides, primers, and specific polymerase enzymes, a desired segment of DNA can be copied in the laboratory.

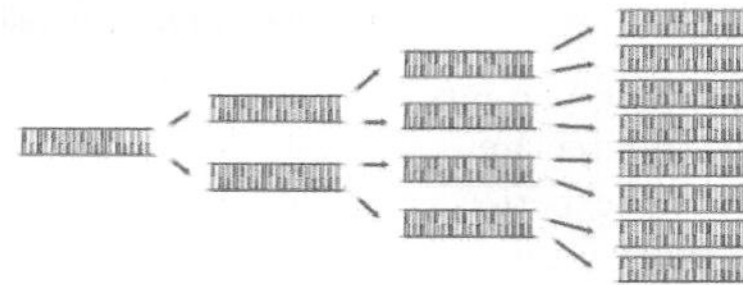

9.3 DNA Fingerprinting

DNA fingerprints identify people at the molecular level. DNA has many repeating base sequences. The number of repeats differs from person to person. DNA fingerprinting uses restriction enzymes and gel electrophoresis to detect these differences. By using DNA fingerprinting on several regions of DNA, one particular person can be identified.

9.4 Genetic Engineering

DNA sequences of organisms can be changed. Clones, or identical genetic copies, of many organisms can be made. Organisms can also be implanted with genes that give them new traits. Often, genes are inserted into plasmids to make recombinant DNA. Genetically engineered plasmids are inserted into bacteria, producing a transgenic organism. Transgenic bacteria, plants, and animals are used in many ways.

Recombinant DNA

9.5 Genomics and Bioinformatics

Entire genomes are sequenced, studied, and compared. Through DNA sequencing, the genomes of several organisms, including humans, have been found and studied. Genomic data are organized and analyzed through bioinformatics. DNA microarrays are used to study interactions among genes in a genome. In addition, genomics has led to the study and comparison of proteins through proteomics.

9.6 Genetic Screening and Gene Therapy

Genetics provides a basis for new medical treatments. Genetic screening is used to test people for genes that are linked to genetic disorders. One method to correct these faulty genes or to replace missing genes is gene therapy. Gene therapy is experimental, but has the potential to cure many diseases.

READING TOOLBOX SYNTHESIZE YOUR NOTES

Two-Column Chart Use your notes to make two-column charts for the processes described in the chapter. On one side of the chart, define and explain the process. On the other side, draw a sketch of the process

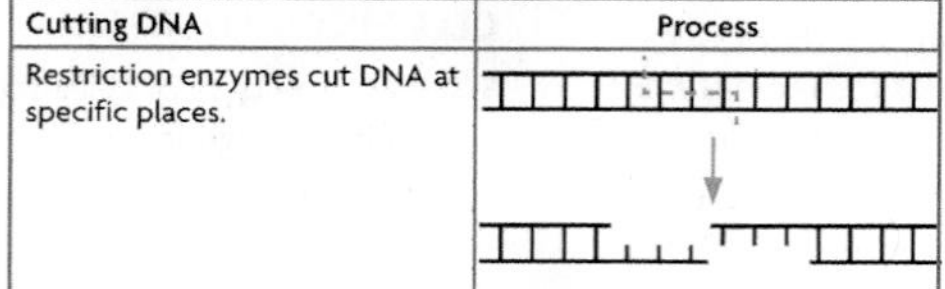

Cutting DNA	Process
Restriction enzymes cut DNA at specific places.	

Concept Map Use concept maps like the one below to visualize the relationships among different biotechnologies.

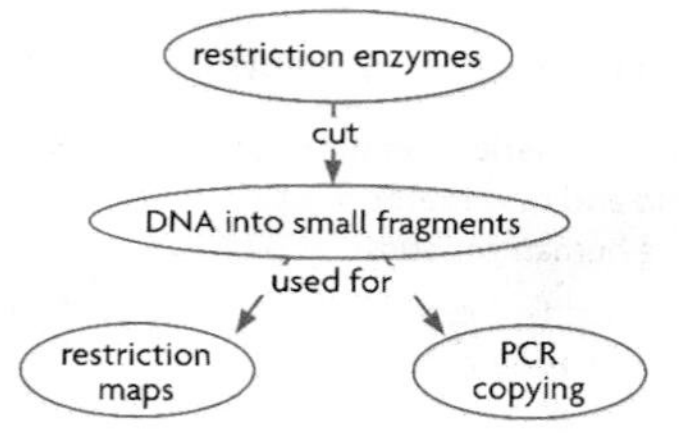

Reviewing Vocabulary

1. plasmid
2. recombinant DNA
3. transgenic organism
4. DNA testing for disorders
5. studying and comparing genomes
6. unique DNA pattern
7. identical genetic copy
8. Fragments of DNA are separated and carried by an electrical current.
9. genomes; proteins; biological information

9 Review

INTERACTIVE Review
HMHScience.com
GO ONLINE
Review Games • Concept Map • Section Self-Checks

CHAPTER VOCABULARY

9.1 restriction enzyme
gel electrophoresis
restriction map

9.2 polymerase chain reaction (PCR)
primer

9.3 DNA fingerprint

9.4 clone
genetic engineering
recombinant DNA
plasmid
transgenic
gene knockout

9.5 genomics
gene sequencing
Human Genome Project
bioinformatics
DNA microarray
proteomics

9.6 genetic screening
gene therapy

Reviewing Vocabulary

Label Diagrams

In your science notebook, write the vocabulary term that matches each item that is pointed out below.

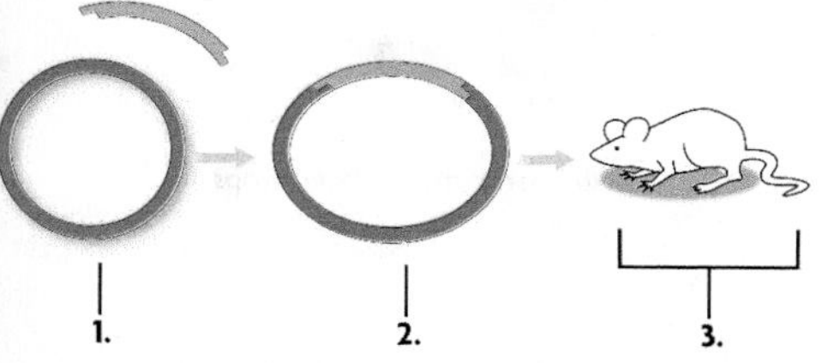

Keep It Short

For each vocabulary term below, write a short, precise phrase that describes its meaning. For example, a short phrase to describe *PCR* could be "DNA copying tool."

4. genetic screening
5. genomics
6. DNA fingerprint
7. clone

READING TOOLBOX WORD ORIGINS

8. The prefix *electro-* means "electricity." The suffix *-phoresis* means "transmission" or "carrying." How do these meanings relate to the meaning of the term *electrophoresis*?

9. The suffix *-ics* means "science or study of." What is studied in *genomics*? in *proteomics*? in *bioinformatics*?

Reviewing MAIN IDEAS

10. Why can restriction enzymes be thought of as molecular "scissors"?

11. Explain what gel electrophoresis shows about DNA, and how it is used to separate DNA.

12. PCR requires DNA polymerase from bacteria that live in hot springs. Why can't DNA polymerase from organisms that live in cooler temperatures be used in PCR?

13. Briefly describe the three main steps of PCR.

14. What parts of DNA molecules are the basis of the differences detected by DNA fingerprinting?

15. Why is probability important in DNA fingerprinting?

16. What is the role of nuclear transfer in the process of cloning an animal?

17. Describe the general process used to make bacteria that have recombinant DNA. Include the terms *restriction enzyme* and *plasmid* in your answer.

18. How are gene knockout mice useful in determining the function of genes?

19. How does genomics rely on DNA sequencing?

20. Explain why computer databases are important in genomics and proteomics.

21. How are pedigree analysis and DNA testing used together in genetic screening?

22. What is gene therapy, and how might it be used as a treatment for cancer or for genetic disorders?

CHAPTER REVIEW

Reviewing Main Ideas

10. Restriction enzymes cut DNA molecules.
11. Gel electrophoresis reveals the sizes of different DNA fragments. Fragments that are smaller are more easily pulled toward the positive electrode, while larger fragments are slower and remain closer to the negative electrode.
12. Heat is used to separate DNA strands in PCR. Enzymes from organisms that live in cooler temperatures would break down at these high temperatures.
13. Complementary strands of DNA are separated, primers bind to each strand, and DNA polymerase binds nucleotides together to form new copies of the DNA.
14. noncoding regions of DNA that contain repeated base sequences
15. The more regions that are compared, the less likely it is that two individuals will have the same DNA fingerprint.
16. The nucleus from a cell of the animal to be cloned is transferred to an egg cell.
17. A restriction enzyme is used to cut a desired gene from a DNA molecule. The same enzyme is used to cut open a plasmid. The gene is inserted into the plasmid to form recombinant DNA. The plasmid is then inserted into a bacterium.
18. They allow scientists to study how a gene affects a living organism.
19. In order to find genes and their locations, and to compare genomes across species, the sequence of DNA nucleotides must be determined.
20. Computer databases store a large amount of information that can be quickly and easily searched.
21. A pedigree analysis can indicate a family history of a genetic disorder, and DNA testing can determine whether a person has the disorder or is a carrier of the disorder.
22. Gene therapy is the replacement of a faulty gene or adding a missing gene to treat a disease. In genetic disorders, gene therapy can give the body a means of performing certain functions that its original genes do not code for. With cancer, gene therapy can make cancer cells vulnerable to drugs.

CHAPTER REVIEW

Critical Thinking

23. Microarrays allow gene expression and gene interactions to be studied.
24. Both use patterns of bands in a gel. A restriction map shows the sizes of DNA fragments between random restriction sites; DNA fingerprinting shows the sizes of fragments in known locations.
25. A clone of an animal is a genetically identical copy, but cloning is done artificially by implanting a cell's nucleus into an egg and then forcing the egg to develop.
26. The manipulations needed to produce transgenic organisms transfer only selected genes, whereas crossbreeding is a combination of two entire genomes. Both techniques involve two species.
27. Gene expression is affected by many different factors, including the environment both inside and outside the womb, and different mutations within the DNA of each twin.
28. The gene for insulin is added to a plasmid, which is then put into a bacterium. Because the genetic code is the same in all organisms, the transgenic bacteria will express the gene and produce the protein.

Critical Thinking

23. Analyze How are DNA microarrays related to genomics?

24. Compare and Contrast How are restriction maps and DNA fingerprints similar? How are they different? Explain your answers.

25. Compare and Contrast A plant can send out a runner that will sprout a new plant that is a clone of the "parent." Single-celled organisms divide in two, forming two clones. How is the cloning of an animal similar to and different from the cloning that happens in nature?

26. Synthesize Some fruits and vegetables are the result of crossing different species. A tangelo, for example, results from crossing a tangerine with a grapefruit. How are the genetic engineering processes of making transgenic organisms similar to and different from crossbreeding?

27. Apply Identical twins are technically clones of each other but can differ in both appearance and behavior. How is it possible that two people with the same genome could be different?

28. Synthesize Transgenic bacteria can be used to make human insulin. Explain how bacteria can produce a human protein.

Interpreting Visuals

The gel below shows two different restriction maps for the same segment of DNA. One of the maps is for a normal gene (N) and the other is for a disease gene (D). Use the information in the gel to answer the next two questions.

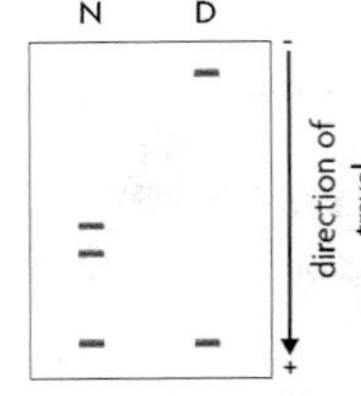

29. Analyze Which restriction map (N or D) has the smallest fragment of DNA? Which has the largest fragment? Explain your answers.

30. Interpret What do the restriction maps tell you about differences between a normal allele (N) and a disease (D) allele? Explain.

Analyzing Data Construct a Histogram

Ten of the most commonly modified crops include rice, potatoes, maize, papayas, tomatoes, corn, soybeans, wheat, alfalfa, and sugar cane. The histogram below shows how many times these crops have been modified. Among the 15 countries studied from 2001 through 2003, for example, different researchers modified rice a total of 37 times. Use the data to answer the next two questions.

FREQUENCY OF CROP MODIFICATION

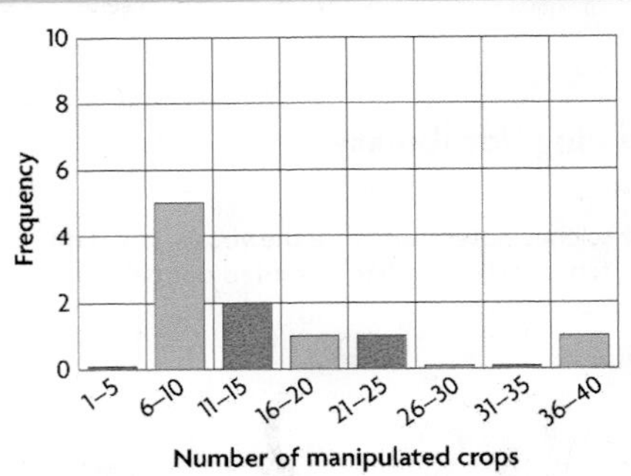

Source: Cohen, *Nature Biotechnology*, 23:1.

31. Analyze What is the most common range of genetic modifications for crop plants? The least common?

32. Calculate What percentage of crop types fall in the range of 11–15 genetic modifications?

Making Connections

33. Write an Informational Pamphlet Suppose that you work for a biotechnology company that specializes in DNA fingerprinting to help reunite families that have been separated. Write a pamphlet that describes how DNA fingerprinting works. Explain why the results of DNA fingerprinting can be trusted.

34. Synthesize Look again at the picture of Baby 81 on the chapter opener. After reading this chapter, you know that DNA fingerprinting is just one part of biotechnology. Choose a topic from the chapter, such as genetic engineering or PCR. Discuss how that topic is related to Mendel's work on heredity, and how it is related to the structure and function of DNA.

Interpreting Visuals

29. Both have the smallest fragment; D has the largest fragment. The fragment sizes are shown by the distance they travel through the gel.
30. The disease-causing allele has a mutation that changes a restriction site, so the disease-causing allele is cut only once, not twice.

Analyzing Data

31. 6–10: most common; 1–5, 26–30, 31–35: least common
32. 20 percent

Standards-Based Assessment

Record your answers on a separate piece of paper.

MULTIPLE CHOICE

1 The graph below shows the amount of DNA production over time during a polymerase chain reaction (PCR).

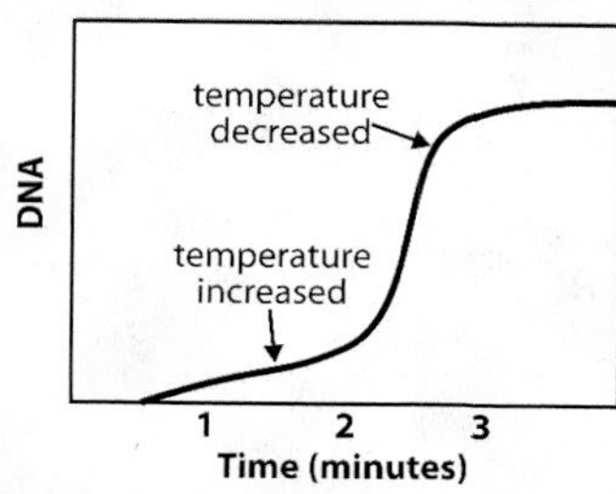

Changes that take place during PCR are shown with arrows. Based upon the graph, it can be inferred that —

A PCR doesn't function at high temperatures

B DNA production decreased after three minutes

C one PCR cycle takes about three minutes

D temperature does not affect DNA production

2 Some genetic diseases can be treated with medication or lifestyle changes. But the only way to cure genetic diseases is to —

A transplant the affected tissue

B change the affected DNA sequence

C induce additional mutations in the affected gene

D remove the affected gene

3 Some scientists want to genetically engineer apples to produce the insecticide pyrethrin. In order to ensure that all offspring from the original tree also produce apples with the chemical, they must be sure that the gene that produces pyrethrin is in the cells of what tissue?

A root

B leaf

C stem

D seed

THINK THROUGH THE QUESTION

To answer this question you don't need to know the details used in the example, such as insecticides and the names of chemicals. Instead, focus on the main point of the question, which addresses genetic engineering and reproduction.

4 A scientist wants to insert a gene into a plasmid as shown in the diagram at right. In order to open the plasmid to insert the gene, the scientist must use —

A restriction mapping

B PCR

C restriction enzymes

D restriction sites

5 *Bt* soybeans are transgenic. These soybean plants express a bacterial gene that codes for a natural pesticide. This is an example of —

A mutation

B gene sequencing

C proteomics

D genetic engineering

Standards-Based Assessment

The Standards-Based Assessment questions will help students prepare for their final examination in the course. If you wish to give students practice in coding their answers, look for the Standards-Based Assessment Answer Sheet at **HMHScience.com**. To give students practice under timed testing conditions, allow them five minutes per question.

Question	Answer	Depth of Knowledge	Cognitive Complexity
1	C	II	M
2	B	II	L
3	D	II	M
4	C	III	M
5	D	I	L

KEY

Depth of Knowledge		Cognitive Complexity	
I	Recall	L	Low
II	Skill/Concept	M	Moderate
III	Strategic Thinking	H	High
IV	Extended Thinking		

Making Connections

33. Students should explain the basis of DNA fingerprinting, the role of probability in DNA fingerprinting, and how DNA fingerprints are interpreted.

34. Students should synthesize information from the entire unit. Answers should include information on genes, alleles, gene expression, and DNA sequences and may include information on transcription and translation.

UNIT

3

Introduce

Tell students that technology includes the tools, machines, and processes that increase our ability to control or learn about our environment. Technology is often the application of science knowledge.

Technology began in the Stone Age with the use of hand axes that were used as tools for work or for making other tools. By the Bronze Age, tens of thousands of years later, people had learned to control fire and use it to work with metals.

In the 1800s and 1900s, technology increased rapidly and made huge changes in daily life. Homes and businesses now had indoor plumbing, electricity, and heating and cooling. Means of transportation went from horses to railroads, automobiles, and airplanes. Have students think about changes to modes of communication. Today, information can be communicated instantaneously, via television and radio, cellular phones, text messaging, and the Internet.

Medical technology also has advanced rapidly. New microscopes, diagnostic equipment, and medicines have improved the quality of life and increased the average life span. Many people who would have died from illnesses a century ago now survive.

Discuss with students technology in their lives. **Ask**

- What technology is used in your school that would not have been in a school 150 years ago? *Sample answers:* electrical lights, heating and cooling systems, computers, telephones, and running water
- What technology allows you to learn about advances in medical technology? Students might mention journals, magazines, newspapers, television news programs, radio broadcasts, and the Internet.

UNIT 3: GENETICS

BIOZINE at HMHSCIENCE.COM

INTERNET MAGAZINE

Go online for the latest biology news and updates on all BioZine articles.

Expanding the Textbook

News Feeds

Science Daily

CNN

BBC

Careers

Bio Bytes

Opinion Poll

Strange Biology

A patient is rushed to emergency care following an adverse drug reaction.

Medical Technology—The Genetic Forefront

A college student comes down with the flu. Worried about missing class, he goes to an emergency clinic and is given a prescription for an antiviral flu drug. Thirty minutes after taking the first pill, he is gasping for breath and his heart is racing. He is rushed to the hospital, where doctors tell him he has had an adverse reaction to his antiviral medication.

Current News

Using the Current News section of BioZine at **HMHScience.com**, have students look for stories about medical technology. **Ask**

- What medical technology is making headlines in the news?
- What effect will the technology have on genetics research?
- How is the technology changing testing, drugs, or other treatments people receive?
- How are people being affected by changes in medical technology?

Opinion Poll

Have students participate in the BioZine online poll. **Ask**

- Should polls be used to evaluate the public's level of acceptance of medical advances?
- Do you think that being aware of advances in medical research makes a person more willing to engage in risky behavior, such as smoking?
- Do advances in technology also bring with them the potential for new risks?

A Cure Worse than the Disease

Usually, medications cause only mild side effects, such as drowsiness, headaches, or nausea. Occasionally, patients are allergic to medicines and break out in hives or go into shock. But sometimes reactions to drugs are more serious. In the United States, about 2.2 million patients per year are hospitalized because of adverse drug reactions, and more than 100,000 die. No doctor intends for a drug's side effects to be worse than the disease it is meant to cure. Nonetheless, the current process of prescribing drugs based on medical and family history is one of trial and error.

Customized Drugs

An emerging field called pharmacogenomics is revolutionizing the prescription process. Pharmacogenomics is the study of how genetic variations can cause different people to react in different ways to the same drugs. In most cases, for example, genetics determines the way in which—and the speed at which—a person's body breaks down a medication. If a person's body metabolizes a drug too quickly, the drug may not be effective. If the drug is metabolized too slowly, a standard dose may be too much.

In the future, a patient in need of a prescription could have a blood test, and health care workers could run the blood test results through a computer using biochip, or microarray, technology. In hours, a doctor could have enough information about a patient's genetic background to predict how the person would respond to a certain drug and decide whether to adjust the dose. Individuals may even be able to have their genomes mapped and put onto cards to take to doctor visits. Biochip technology is not yet available in most doctors' offices, but many drugs are already being labeled with pharmacogenomic information advising doctors that patients with certain genetic variations may need a lower or higher dose of the medication.

Gene Therapy

While pharmacogenomics can provide doctors with more information about their patients, gene therapy may someday provide them with another tool. Some diseases, such as Alzheimer's or hemophilia, have a strong genetic basis. Doctors are beginning clinical trials in which they treat Alzheimer's by injecting

TECHNOLOGY S.T.E.M.

Biochips

Doctors can now analyze a patient's DNA by using biochip technology. A biochip is a solid surface to which tiny strands of DNA are attached. When this type of screening becomes clinically feasible, it will take several steps.

1. DNA will be extracted from the patient's blood.

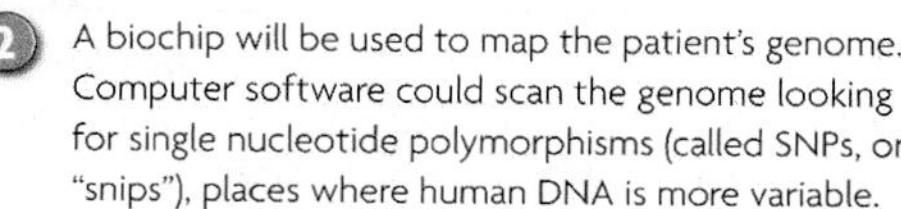

2. A biochip will be used to map the patient's genome. Computer software could scan the genome looking for single nucleotide polymorphisms (called SNPs, or "snips"), places where human DNA is more variable.

3. A doctor will then compare the patient's genomic results with the latest available medical research.

Ideally, the resulting prescription would be customized to the patient. If a patient has a variation that is found in a small percentage of the population, however, the doctor is unlikely to have enough data about possible reactions.

Read More >> at HMHScience.com

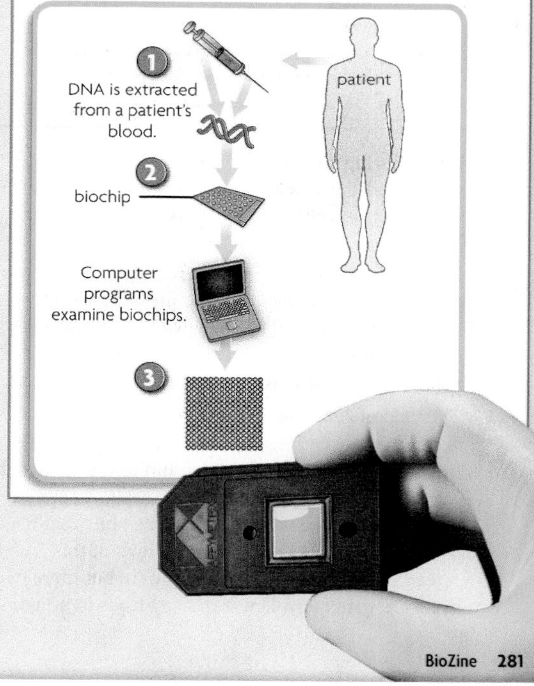
1
DNA is extracted from a patient's blood.
patient
2
biochip
Computer programs examine biochips.
3

Vocabulary of Medical Technology

Students may need clarification of some of the terms used in medical technology.

pharmacology—the science of drugs, including their origin, composition, and uses. A pharmacologist searches for and develops new medicine.

adverse drug reaction—abnormal, undesired, and potentially harmful effects of a medicine, ranging from mild to life-threatening.

genomics—the study of all the nucleotide sequences in the chromosomes of an organism. Using genomics, the Human Genome Project has identified, sequenced, and mapped human DNA. Genomic sequencing of pathogens may produce better targeted vaccines or drugs.

pharmacogenomics—the study of the way an individual's genetic makeup affects a drug's effects on the body. Depending on an individual's genes, a drug can be therapeutic, toxic, or ineffective.

therapeutic—exhibiting healing powers.

toxic—capable of causing injury or death, especially by chemical means.

genetic biochip—an orderly arrangement of genomic DNA on a small, solid surface. Genetic biochips, also known as DNA microarrays, enable researchers to identify specific genes and their level of activity.

gene therapy—a technique for correcting defective genes responsible for the development of diseases or disorders. The most common research in gene therapy involves replacing the defective gene with a normal gene.

transgenic animal—an animal whose genome has been altered to contain genes of another organism or species. Such animals can be used to produce protein-based drugs, such as insulin.

Expanding the Textbook

Have students go to BioZine at **HMHScience.com** to read more about the role of genetics in modern medicine. Have them take notes on different types of medical technologies, such as customized drugs and gene therapy. Suggest that they use a matrix to compare different technologies, including potential risks and benefits. Students should come to class prepared to discuss what they have learned.

You could extend the discussion to include students' understanding of the challenges or ethical issues surrounding technology.

- What are some ethical questions that can arise from technology?
- Who should fund medical research, and how does that affect who has access to its benefits?
- How can society ensure that everyone benefits from basic medical research?

Take It Further

Genetic disorders result when a gene that contains the instructions for making a specific protein is defective. The goal of gene therapy is to correct the defective gene. In most research, scientists try to replace the defective gene with a normal gene. But how can a gene, which is present in every cell in the body, be replaced? It doesn't have to be replaced in every cell. The gene needs to be replaced only in cells that will produce the needed protein. These cells are called target cells.

A vector, or molecule that carries the normal gene, is used to deliver the normal gene to the target cells. The most commonly used vector is a virus. Viruses can be used because they enter human cells and cause the cells to reproduce the DNA they contain. When viruses are modified to carry a normal human gene, they enter human cells, deliver the normal human gene, and cause the cells to produce the normal gene.

CAREERS

Cancer Geneticist in Action

DR. OLUFUNMILAYO OLOPADE

TITLE Director, Center for Clinical Cancer Genetics, University of Chicago

EDUCATION M.D., University of Ibadan, Nigeria

Breast cancer occurs in many different forms. It has been most widely studied in Caucasian women but takes a very different form in women of African ancestry. Breast cancer hits women of African ancestry earlier and more aggressively than it does Caucasian women. Dr. Olufunmilayo Olopade wants to learn why. Working with scientists in her native Nigeria, Dr. Olopade compared gene expression in samples of cancer tissue from African women with samples of cancer tissue from Caucasian women. She found that cancer cells from the African women often lacked estrogen receptors. This finding means that many of the standard treatments are not effective for this group of women.

Dr. Olopade's work will have a huge impact on breast cancer screening and treatment in women of African ancestry. "Cancer doesn't start overnight," she says. "We can develop strategies for preventing it."

Read More >> at HMHScience.com

genes, during surgery, into the area of the brain that has the most affected brain cells. The new genes will instruct brain cells to make more of a protein that keeps nerve cells alive longer.

Doctors are also beginning to treat hemophilia using gene therapy. One method is to inject genes into the liver. In other clinical trials, new DNA is inserted into a virus that can then be used to "infect" a patient's diseased cells.

The field of gene therapy is developing slowly because it requires researchers to accomplish several feats. First, they must engineer, and test, a gene that is safe to insert into humans. Then, they must find a way to get the gene to the part of the body that needs it—often using nanotechnology. Much of this research is still being done in animals, but there have been a few successful gene therapy trials in humans.

Other Uses

New uses for DNA technology offer both solutions and hard choices. Some of the more difficult questions involve the following kinds of projects:

- Researchers can alter the DNA of viruses to make them harmless and usable as vaccines.
- Scientists are developing transgenic animals that can make organs for human transplants.
- Researchers are engineering crops that contain vaccines that could be administered orally. These vaccines would be easier to grow and distribute in developing countries than are current vaccines.

A scientist examines different types of genetically modified rice plants.

Unanswered Questions

Some exciting new pharmacogenomic research is being done by the Human Genome Project. However, many challenges must be addressed before pharmacogenomics can have widespread clinical application.

- Many current studies of patients' drug responses have conflicting results, likely due to small sample sizes, different criteria for measuring a good response, and different population groups.
- Patients' responses to a drug may be caused by many genes. Scientists will need to study the effect of multiple genes to determine response.
- Genotype testing may increase short-term health-care costs, raising questions about who will pay and who will have access to the technology.

Read More >> at HMHScience.com

Careers

Have students go to this unit's BioZine at **HMHScience.com** to learn about careers in biology. Have students check out job listings in a metropolitan newspaper. **Ask**

- How has technology changed this job market?
- What careers did not exist 40 years ago?
- Do you think education must change to meet the needs of the current job market? Explain your thinking.

UNIT 4

Evolution

BIOZINE
HMHScience.com

Drug-Resistant Bacteria— A Global Health Issue

TECHNOLOGY **New Drug Delivery System**

CAREER **Evolutionary Biologist**

Unit Project

Purpose **Understand, compare, and contrast the historical achievements, lives, and time of Charles Darwin and Gregor Mendel.**

Overview Students research the lives of Charles Darwin and Gregor Mendel, comparing their lives and work. Students will

- research and take notes of the biographies of Darwin and Mendel
- prepare a timeline showing the significant dates in the lives of each scientist
- write a booklet that describes significant events on the timeline of each scientist and compares and contrasts their lives and work

Preparation Make a copy of the project description and rubric for each student. Encourage students to be innovative and creative in the preparation of the timelines and booklet.

Project Management Allow three weeks for the completion of the project. Check students' progress at the end of each week leading up to the completion date.

Online Student Resources, Unit 4 Project

CHAPTER 10 # Instruction and Intervention Support

Principles of Evolution

1 Core Instruction

The **Core Instruction** resources below can be used for all students. Core instruction should be followed by ongoing assessment to determine which students need further help.

Available in both English and Spanish

Available Online

Section	Instruction	PRINT	ONLINE	Labs
10.1	Textbook **Early Ideas About Evolution**	■	●	
	Animated Biology Principles of Natural Selection		●	
	PowerPresentation and Notes 10.1		●	
10.2	Textbook **Darwin's Observations**	■	●	Using Patterns to Make Predictions
	PowerPresentation and Notes 10.2		●	
10.3	Textbook **Theory of Natural Selection**	■	●	Adaptations in Beaks **Video Lab** Natural Selection Simulation
	Animated Biology Natural Selection, The Theory of Evolution by Natural Selection		●	
	PowerPresentation and Notes 10.3		●	
10.4	Textbook **Evidence of Evolution**	■	●	Predator-Prey Pursuit **QuickLab** Piecing Together Evidence
	PowerPresentation and Notes 10.4		●	
10.5	Textbook **Evolutionary Biology Today**	■	●	Biochemical Evidence for Evolution
	PowerPresentation and Notes 10.5		●	

Additional online resources available for this chapter include **Interactive Whiteboard Resources.**

GO ONLINE! for all your teacher resources at HMHScience.com

2 Support and Intervention

Support and Intervention resources are useful for students who need targeted help beyond the Core Instruction

Resources	PRINT	ONLINE
Assess and Reteach (TE wrap)	■	⊘
Concept Map		⊘
Interactive Reader	■	⊘
Interactive Review Games		⊘
Section Self-Checks		⊘
Study Guide B		⊘
Virtual Investigation Evolution by Natural Selection		⊘
Vocabulary Practice Worksheets		⊘

3 Specialized Support

Students who need more intensive personalized intervention benefit from **Specialized Support** resources.

Resources	PRINT	ONLINE
Chapter Audio Files		⊘
Differentiated Instruction Inclusion, Below Level, and English Learners (TE wrap)	■	⊘
ELL Strategies	■	⊘
Modified Lesson Plans for English Learners		⊘
Reinforcement Worksheets		⊘
Study Guide A		⊘

Extension and Assessment

Enrichment and Challenge

Resources	PRINT	ONLINE
Active Reading Worksheets		⊘
Data Analysis Practice Worksheet		⊘
Differentiated Instruction Pre-AP (TE wrap)	■	⊘
Pre-AP Activity Bioinformatics: Sequencing the Clock Gene		⊘
Smart Grapher Activity		
The Inside Story and **Take It Further** (TE wrap)	■	⊘
Unit Project		⊘
WebLinks		⊘
WebQuest Dinosaur Descendants		⊘

Assessment

Resources	PRINT	ONLINE
Alternative Assessment		⊘
Chapter Tests A and B		⊘
Diagnostic Test		⊘
ExamView Banks		⊘
Extended Response Test		⊘
Online Assessment System		⊘
Section Quizzes		⊘
Standards-Based Assessment	■	⊘

CHAPTER 10

Chapter Overview

- **Section 1** discusses early ideas about evolution.
- **Section 2** describes how Darwin arrived at his idea about species variation.
- **Section 3** summarizes the principles of natural selection and the factors Darwin considered when forming his theory.
- **Section 4** details the major sources of evidence for evolution and examines the patterns that give clues to a species' history.
- **Section 5** describes the different types of evidence that support evolution.

▼ Focus and Motivate

How could evolution lead to this?

Tell students that there are two parts to the evolution story: descent and modification. **Ask,** What sorts of modifications are obvious in the star-nosed mole? ray-like feelers extending from snout, poor eyesight, and prominent claws **Ask,** How do such traits arise in the first place? mutation **Ask,** What is the role of descent in evolution? Mutations can be passed from one generation to the next.

Discuss with students that mutation must occur for new or modified traits to appear. However, mutation does not explain how that trait becomes common in a species or why some traits disappear altogether.

BIOZINE
HMHScience.com

Students can access BioZine at **HMHScience.com** to check out articles featured in Strange Biology.

CHAPTER 10 Principles of Evolution

BIG IDEA Many different forms of evidence support the theory that Earth is ancient and that species can change over time.

ONLINE BIOLOGY HMHScience.com

ONLINE Labs
- **QuickLab** Piecing Together Evidence
- Predator-Prey Pursuit
- Using Patterns to Make Predictions
- Adaptations in Beaks
- Biochemical Evidence for Evolution
- **Video Lab** Natural Selection Simulation

Student Activity

Purpose **Have teams of students use photographs to group different organisms according to shared traits. Students should recognize that not only closely related species can share traits. Similar features can arise in distantly related organisms in response to similar environmental factors.**

Materials (per team)

Provide each group of students with the same images. Look for pictures of animals that share physical features (for example, wings, horns, claws) but are not necessarily closely related. For example:

cockatoo	hummingbird	ant
sparrow	bee	marlin
toucan	crab	lobster

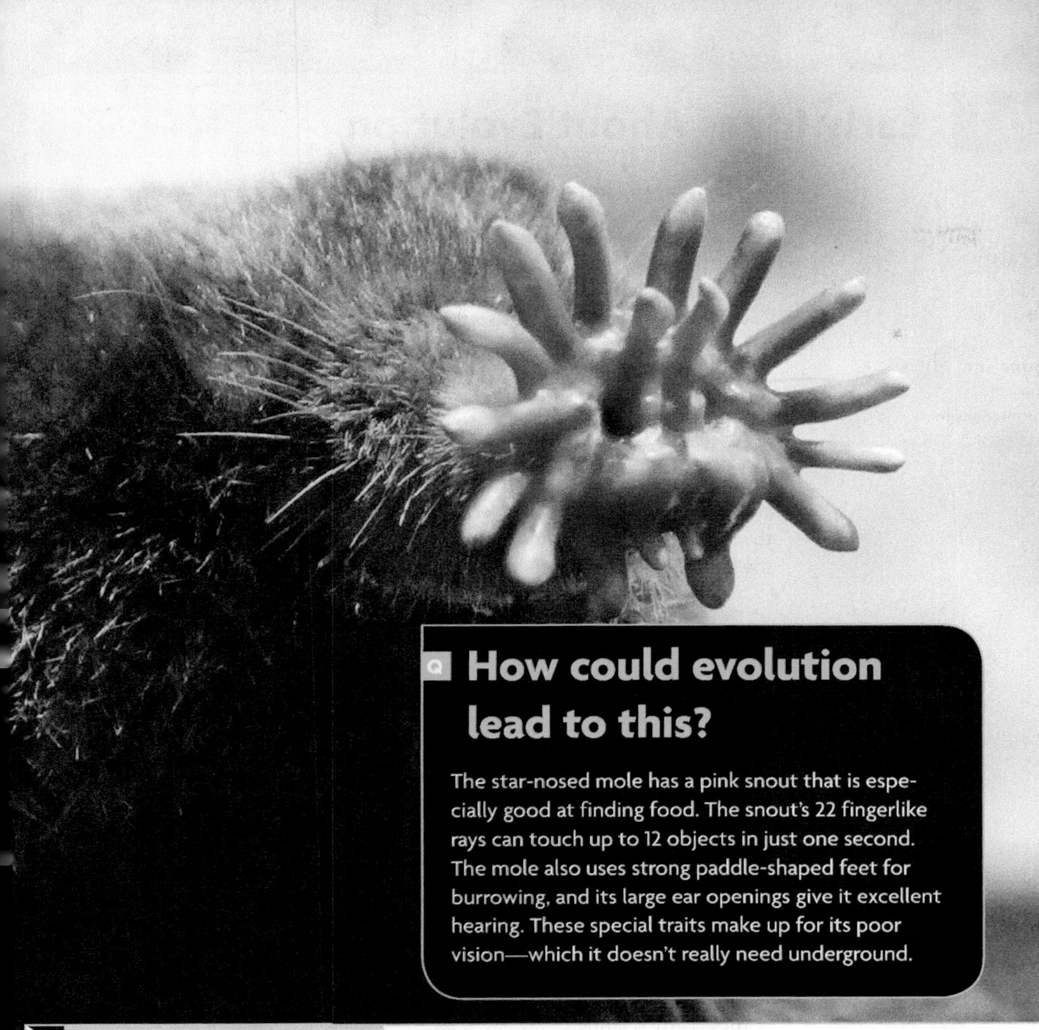

How could evolution lead to this?

The star-nosed mole has a pink snout that is especially good at finding food. The snout's 22 fingerlike rays can touch up to 12 objects in just one second. The mole also uses strong paddle-shaped feet for burrowing, and its large ear openings give it excellent hearing. These special traits make up for its poor vision—which it doesn't really need underground.

READING TOOLBOX **This reading tool can help you learn the material in the following pages.**

USING LANGUAGE

Hypothesis or Theory? In everyday language, there is little difference between a *hypothesis* and a *theory*. But in science, the meanings of these words are more distinct. A *hypothesis* is a specific, testable prediction for a limited set of conditions. A *theory* is a general explanation for a broad range of data. A theory can include hypotheses that have been tested and can also be used to generate new hypotheses. The strongest scientific theories explain the broadest range of data and incorporate many well-tested hypotheses.

YOUR TURN

Use what you have learned about a hypothesis and a theory to answer the following questions.

1. List some scientific theories that you have heard of.
2. Make a simple concept map or Venn diagram to show the relationship between hypotheses and theories.
3. The word *theory* may also be used to describe general trends and areas of active investigation in a scientific field. In this context, what does the term *evolutionary theory* mean?

Introduce Tell students to group the organisms according to shared traits. Discuss different options for grouping. For example, crabs, lobsters, and fish are all aquatic; however, crabs and lobsters are invertebrates, whereas fish are vertebrates. The goal is to establish groups of animals that are likely to be closely related. Have students look at the physical characteristics of organisms, just as Darwin did. Then have each group present its results to the class and give the reasons for the choices made.

Discuss Explain that similarities and differences in traits reflect evolutionary relationships. Talk about any differences in the choices made and point out shared traits students may have overlooked. For example, although ants, bees, crabs, and lobsters live in different habitats, they are all invertebrates.

Ask, What is the source of the shared characteristics in closely related species? shared genes **Ask,** Why do distantly related species share similar traits? They occupy similar environments and therefore may need similar features to move, feed, find shelter, and survive.

Activate Prior Knowledge

Direct students' attention to the chapter title. **Ask,** What does the word *evolution* mean to you in an everyday sense? Answers may include: evolution of character, physical development, personal growth, and changes in thinking or attitude. Tell students that in science, *evolution* refers not to change in individuals but rather to change in species over generations.

Preview Vocabulary

Greek and Latin Word Origins

The words **evolve** and **evolution** come from the Latin *evolvere,* which means "to unroll." Students may have heard the word **devolve** (Latin, "to roll down, fall to") in a way that suggests that it is the opposite of *evolve*. While *devolve* does mean "to degenerate or deteriorate gradually," this word is not used in biology as an antonym of *evolve*.

English Learners Students will see a number of common words transformed into "*-isms*." Explain that the suffix can refer to an action, as in *terrorism,* or a quality, as in *heroism*. In this chapter, *-ism* refers to a theory or set of principles, as in *gradualism*. Point out that the term *Darwinism* is not a scientific term.

Integrating Zoology

The rays on the star-nosed mole's snout enable it to forage at speeds so fast that the human eye can barely register them. Using high-speed video cameras, scientists have clocked moles detecting and engulfing prey—a worm or an insect larva—in one-fourth of a second. One hypothesis for the reason this animal eats so fast is that the fact that its prey is so tiny, the mole must eat twice as fast as animals that eat larger prey.

Answers

1. *Sample answer:* theory of gravity, cell theory
2. Answer should indicate that hypotheses are based on observations and theories explain observations.
3. Evolutionary theory describes the general trends of how species change over time.

SECTION 10.1

B.5.3 Apply concepts of statistics and probability to support a claim that organisms with an advantageous heritable trait tend to increase in proportion to organisms lacking this trait.

▼ Plan and Prepare

Activate Prior Knowledge Find out what misconceptions students may have about Darwin and the theory of natural selection. **Ask,** Have you ever heard the expression "survival of the fittest"? What does it suggest to you? Answers will probably focus on the idea that only the strong survive or that fitness is associated with physical strength. Point out that many of the most successful species—cockroaches and bacteria, for example—are small and have little physical strength. **Ask,** With evolution, what is it that survives? genes associated with specific traits

▼ Teach

Vocabulary

Greek and Latin Word Origins The word **species** comes from the Latin root meaning "kind" or "form." As with the word *series,* the spelling of *species* is the same for both its singular and plural forms. Point to the definition in the text. **Ask,** Why is the ability to produce fertile offspring important to the concept of species? Traits must be passed on.

10.1 Early Ideas About Evolution

KEY CONCEPT **There were theories of biological and geologic change before Darwin.**

MAIN IDEAS
- Early scientists proposed ideas about evolution.
- Theories of geologic change set the stage for Darwin's theory.

VOCABULARY

evolution
species
fossil
catastrophism
gradualism
uniformitarianism

Connect to Your World

Why are there so many kinds of living things, such as the strange looking star-nosed mole? Earth is home to millions of species, from bacteria to plants to ocean organisms that look like they came from science fiction. The search for reasons for Earth's great biological diversity was aided in the 1800s, when Charles Darwin proposed his theory of evolution by natural selection. But long before Darwin, evolution had been the focus of talk among scholars.

MAIN IDEA

Early scientists proposed ideas about evolution.

Although Darwin rightly deserves much of the credit for evolutionary theory as we know it today, he was not the first person to come up with the idea. **Evolution** is the process of biological change by which descendants come to differ from their ancestors. This concept had been discussed for more than 100 years when Darwin proposed his theory of the way evolution works. Today, evolution is a central theme in all fields of biology.

The 1700s were a time of great advances in intellectual thought. Many fields of science developed new ways of looking at the world during that century. Four scientists in particular are important. They not only made valuable contributions to biology in general, but they also laid the foundations upon which Darwin would later build his ideas. **FIGURE 1.1** highlights the work of some of these early scientists.

READING TOOLBOX

TAKING NOTES

Create a chart with a column for the scientists mentioned in this section and a second column for their contributions to evolutionary theory.

Scientist	Contribution
Linnaeus	
Buffon	

Carolus Linnaeus In the 1700s, the Swedish botanist Carolus Linnaeus developed a classification system for all types of organisms known at the time. Although Linnaeus used his system to group organisms by their similarities, the system also reflects evolutionary relationships. This system is still in use by scientists today. Years into his career, Linnaeus abandoned the common belief of the time that organisms were fixed and did not change. He proposed instead that some might have arisen through hybridization—a crossing that he could observe through experiments with varieties, or species, of plants. A **species** is a group of organisms that are closely related and can mate to reproduce fertile offspring.

Differentiated Instruction

ENGLISH LEARNERS

Help students set up a table to categorize the content in this section. Suggest an eight-row, five-column matrix. Explain that they may not need to use every column or row. For example, column 1 might identify early scientists and where they came from, column 2 the dates for their writing or research, column 3 their research, and column 4 their theories or findings.

Teacher Toolkit, Section C, Content Frame

BELOW LEVEL

Have students sort a stack of baseball cards by several criteria, such as league, teams, and positions. Help students understand that Linnaeus used a similar method to group species into categories based on trait similarities. Encourage students to come up with other categories. As a simpler alternative, you can do the same with a deck of playing cards, sorting by suit and number.

Georges-Louis Leclerc de Buffon Buffon, a French naturalist of the 1700s, challenged many of the accepted ideas of the day. Based on evidence of past life on Earth, he proposed that species shared ancestors instead of arising separately. Buffon also rejected the common idea of the time that Earth was only 6000 years old. He suggested that it was much older. This argument was similar to that of Charles Lyell, a geologist whose work helped inspire Darwin's writings. You will read more about Lyell later in this section.

Erasmus Darwin Born in 1731, Charles Darwin's grandfather was a respected English doctor and a poet. He proposed that all living things were descended from a common ancestor and that more-complex forms of life arose from less-complex forms. This idea was expanded upon 65 years later by his grandson.

Jean-Baptiste Lamarck In 1809, the year of Darwin's birth, a French naturalist named Lamarck proposed that all organisms evolved toward perfection and complexity. Like other scientists of the time, he did not think that species became extinct. Instead, he reasoned that they must have evolved into different forms.

Lamarck proposed that changes in an environment caused an organism's behavior to change, leading to greater use or disuse of a structure or organ. The structure would become larger or smaller as a result. The organism would pass on these changes to its offspring. For example, Lamarck thought that the long necks of giraffes evolved as generations of giraffes reached for leaves higher in the trees. Lamarck's idea is known as the inheritance of acquired characteristics.

CONNECT TO

SCIENTIFIC PROCESS

Recall from the chapter **Biology in the 21st Century** that in every scientific field, knowledge is built upon evidence gathered by earlier scientists.

FIGURE 1.1 Early Naturalists

Evolutionary thought, like all scientific inquiry, draws heavily upon its history. The published works of these scientists contributed important ideas prior to Darwin's theory.

1735 *Systema Naturae*	1749 *Histoire Naturelle*	1794–1796 *Zoonomia*	1809 *Philosophie Zoologique*
Carolus Linnaeus proposed a new system of organization for plants, animals, and minerals based upon their similarities. 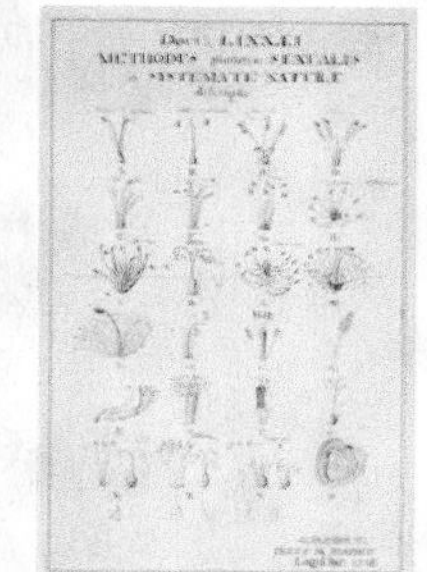	**Georges Buffon** discussed important ideas about relationships among organisms, sources of biological variation, and the possibility of evolution. 	**Erasmus Darwin** considered how organisms could evolve through mechanisms such as competition. 	**Jean-Baptiste Lamarck** presented evolution as occurring due to environmental change over long periods of time. 

Summarize **Explain why Darwin was not the first scientist to consider evolution.** Ⓐ

PRE-AP

Tell students that the 18th and 19th centuries were periods of great social, political, and scientific change. Have students create a timeline of this period, incorporating information from the text as well as other important dates such as these:

1776—Declaration of Independence (war over)

1789—French Revolution

1798—Malthus: massive human population growth

1848—Karl Marx and Freidrich Engels publish *Communist Manifesto.*

1859—Darwin publishes *On the Origin of Species.*

1866—Mendel publishes research on pea plants.

Teacher Toolkit, Section C, Timeline

History of Science

The ideas that Earth was ancient and that species could change over time represented radical thinking in the 1700s. The scientific community had for a long time accepted that life forms were ordered in a **Great Chain of Being**. This concept described a system in which species were positioned in a hierarchy of complexity or "perfection"—from lower organisms such as insects and worms to higher, more "perfect" beings such as mammals. The concept was founded on the idea that all species were created in their present form and, therefore, could not change.

Take It Further

Lamarck's idea of the inheritance of **acquired traits** is often presented as the flawed standard by which Darwin's theories are measured. What is sometimes overlooked is that Lamarck understood two things that are key to evolutionary theory—that new physical forms and traits have emerged in response to environmental changes and that these traits appeared in subsequent generations. Because he did not know the mechanism by which traits were passed on, Lamarck made the reasonable but incorrect conclusion that traits in individual animals arose in direct response to environmental changes.

Science Trivia

Many of the great naturalists involved in the early debates on evolution were famous in their day for other achievements.

- Cuvier served as the inspector general of public education for Napoleon.
- Erasmus Darwin was a well-known poet.
- Lamarck was the first naturalist to study insects and worms in depth. He coined the term *invertebrates* and thus established an entire branch of zoology.

Answers

Ⓐ **Summarize** Naturalists before Darwin considered evolution. Darwin built upon their ideas.

▼ Teach *continued*

Science Trivia

In 1822, the tiger shark, one of the ocean's largest predatory fish and one of its most dangerous, was given the scientific name *Galeocerdo cuvier* in honor of French zoologist Georges Cuvier, who introduced many marine fish species—such as the ruby snapper, black marlin, and wahoo—to science.

TEACH FROM VISUALS

FIGURE 1.2 Point out to students that the **VISUAL VOCAB** on the next page is based on the right-hand photograph on this page. **Ask**

- What were the rock layers originally? layers of sediment that were buried over time
- Make the comparison of rock strata to an archaeological dig or an excavation at a building site. How would the cultural artifacts you find change as you dig deeper? They would reflect older technology or practices.

Answers

A Compare that organisms can change from one generation to the next

B Compare and Contrast All the theories propose how landforms were created. Gradualism and uniformitarianism are based on the idea of slow change and an ancient Earth, with uniformitarianism adding the concept of uniform change. Catastrophism suggested that all extinctions and landform creations were caused by extreme sudden events.

Lamarck did not propose how traits were passed on to offspring, and his explanation of how organisms evolve was flawed. However, Darwin was influenced by Lamarck's ideas that changes in physical characteristics could be inherited and were driven by environmental changes over time.

A Compare What common idea about organisms did these scientists share?

MAIN IDEA

Theories of geologic change set the stage for Darwin's theory.

The age of Earth was a key issue in the early debates over evolution. The common view was that Earth was created about 6000 years earlier, and that since that time, neither Earth nor the species that lived on it had changed.

French zoologist Georges Cuvier did not think that species could change. However, he did think that they could become extinct, an idea considered radical by many of his peers. Cuvier had observed that each stratum, or rock layer, held its own specific type of fossils. **Fossils** are traces of organisms that existed in the past. He found that the fossils in the deepest layers were quite different from those in the upper layers, which were formed by more recent deposits of sediment. Cuvier explained his observations in the early 1800s with the theory now known as catastrophism, shown in **FIGURE 1.2.**

CONNECT TO

EARTH SCIENCE

Cuvier based his thinking on what we know as the law of superposition. It states that in a sequence of layered rocks, a given layer was deposited before any layer above it.

FIGURE 1.2 Principles of Geologic Change

Ideas from geology played a role in the development of Darwin's theory.

CATASTROPHISM	GRADUALISM	UNIFORMITARIANISM
Volcanoes, floods, and earthquakes are examples of catastrophic events that were once believed responsible for mass extinctions and the formation of all landforms.	Canyons carved by rivers show gradual change. Gradualism is the idea that changes on Earth occurred by small steps over long periods of time.	Rock strata demonstrate that geologic processes, which are still occurring today, add up over long periods of time to cause great change.

B Compare and Contrast How are these three theories similar, and what are their differences?

Differentiated Instruction

INCLUSION

To demonstrate the Law of Superposition, have students who are visually impaired create their own "rock" sequence, using layers sliced from a block of clay. Have students make the first layer the longest, with each subsequent layer trimmed to be slightly shorter at one end. This will produce a step effect. Have students use these "steps" to walk up the layers and indicate relative age as they do.

The theory of **catastrophism** (kuh-TAS-truh-FIHZ-uhm) states that natural disasters such as floods and volcanic eruptions have happened often during Earth's long history. These events shaped landforms and caused species to become extinct in the process. Cuvier argued that the appearance of new species in each rock layer resulted from other species moving into the area from elsewhere after each catastrophic event.

In the late 1700s, the Scottish geologist James Hutton proposed that the changes he observed in landforms resulted from slow changes over a long period of time, a principle that became known as **gradualism** (GRAJ-oo-uh-LIHZ-uhm). He argued that the laying down of soil or the creation of canyons by rivers cutting through rock was not the result of large-scale events. He believed, rather, that they resulted from slow processes that had happened in the past. This idea has become so important to evolution that today the term gradualism is often used to mean the gradual change of a species through evolution.

One of the leading supporters of the argument for an ancient Earth was the English geologist Charles Lyell. In *Principles of Geology*, published in the 1830s, Lyell expanded Hutton's theory of gradualism into the theory of **uniformitarianism** (YOO-nuh-FAWR-mih-TAIR-ee-uh-NIHZ-uhm). This theory states that the geologic processes that shape Earth are uniform through time. Lyell observed processes that made small changes in Earth's features. He inferred that similar changes had happened in the past. Uniformitarianism combines Hutton's idea of gradual change over time with Lyell's observations that such changes have occurred at a constant rate and are ongoing. Uniformitarianism soon replaced catastrophism as the favored theory of geologic change. Lyell's theory greatly affected the scientific community—particularly a young English naturalist named Charles Darwin.

VISUAL VOCAB

Uniformitarianism proposes that present geologic processes are the key to the past.

Every layer of rock was formed by the uniform laying down of sediment that still occurs today.

A Compare **What important concepts about Earth did Hutton and Lyell agree upon?**

READING TOOLBOX

VOCABULARY

The names of these geologic theories can be broken down into familiar words.

- *Catastrophe* means "sudden disaster."
- *Gradual* means "moving or changing slowly."
- *Uniform* means "always staying the same."

CONNECT TO

SCIENTIFIC PROCESS

Recall from the chapter **Biology in the 21st Century** that in science, the term theory describes a well-supported explanation that incorporates observations, inferences, and tested hypotheses.

The Inside Story

Before we had the means and understanding to accurately date the age of Earth, many scholars turned to the Bible as one of the earliest accounts of Earth's history. **Isaac Newton** tried to interpret the Bible scientifically, using the Book of Genesis as an accurate, historical account of Earth's creation. **James Ussher,** an archbishop of Ireland and noted religious scholar, went one step further. In 1650, he painstakingly added the ages of Adam and his descendants, as written in the Bible. From this, Ussher deduced the date and time of the day Earth was created—the evening of October 22, 4004 B.C. The result of this calculation is an Earth just a little over 6000 years young.

Answers

A **Compare** that changes to Earth's surface occur slowly and gradually over time

10.1 Formative Assessment

REVIEWING MAIN IDEAS

1. Briefly describe two ideas about **evolution** that were proposed by scientists in the 18th century.
2. What ideas in Lyell's theory of **uniformitarianism** were important for evolutionary theory?

CRITICAL THINKING

3. **Contrast** What are the key differences between the theories of **gradualism** and **catastrophism**?
4. **Apply** Why are the ideas that Earth undergoes change and is billions of years old important for evolutionary theory?

CONNECT TO

GENETICS

5. How can you use the concept of genetic inheritance to disprove Lamarck's idea of the inheritance of acquired characteristics?

SELF-CHECK Online
HMHScience.com
GO ONLINE

Assess and Reteach

Assess Use the Section Self-Check or Section Quiz, both available at **HMHscience.com**.

Reteach Have students present an oral summary that compares the three theories of geologic change with changes in thinking about evolution. Students can present this as a timeline that compares ideas about life changing over time with the idea that Earth has also changed.

10.1 FORMATIVE ASSESSMENT

1. They proposed that species could change, and that different species may have come from a common ancestor.
2. Lyell stated that observable geologic processes, such as the deposition of soil, occur over a long period of time at a uniform rate.
3. Gradualism emphasizes slow changes on Earth over long periods of time, while catastrophism emphasizes change through natural disasters.
4. Evolution often happens over long periods of time. The fact that Earth can change over time inspired the idea that organisms can also change. Earth's great age makes it possible for significant changes to have occurred.
5. For a trait to be passed on to offspring, it must be encoded in the genes. The genes must first be passed on for the trait to appear.

SECTION 10.2

B.5.3 Apply concepts of statistics and probability to support a claim that organisms with an advantageous heritable trait tend to increase in proportion to organisms lacking this trait.

▼ Plan and Prepare

Activate Prior Knowledge Tell students that Darwin's thoughts began to take shape while visiting the Galápagos Islands. **Ask,** Thinking in terms of genetics, what is it about a cluster of islands that makes it a good laboratory for studying variation? physical separation **Ask,** What is it that the islands keep separate? genes, meaning that the gene pool is isolated

▼ Teach

Vocabulary

Academic Vocabulary Discuss how the everyday meaning of **adaptation** differs from its scientific meaning. For example, a new student may adapt to an unfamiliar school by joining clubs. In that sense, *adapt* is something one does knowingly and with purpose. In nature, adaptations are traits or behaviors that are genetically determined. No finch can choose to grow its beak bigger.

Answers

A Connect The birds had beaks of different sizes and shapes that were suited to the available food in the particular ecosystem where each lived.

10.2 Darwin's Observations

KEY CONCEPT **Darwin's voyage provided insights into evolution.**

MAIN IDEAS
- Darwin observed differences in appearance among island species.
- Darwin observed fossil and geologic evidence supporting an ancient Earth.

VOCABULARY
variation
adaptation

Connect to Your World

Maybe you would love the chance to sail around the world. Or maybe just the thought of it makes you seasick! In 1831, the ship HMS *Beagle* set sail from England on a five-year journey to map the coast of South America and the Pacific islands. Hired at first to keep the captain company, Darwin was interested in observing the land and its inhabitants. During the voyage, he read Lyell's *Principles of Geology.* When the ship reached South America, Darwin spent most of his time ashore, where he found much evidence supporting Lyell's views.

MAIN IDEA

Darwin observed differences in appearance among island species.

Darwin, shown in **FIGURE 2.1**, was struck by the variation of traits among similar species that he observed in all his travels. In biology, **variation** is the difference in the physical traits of an individual from those of other individuals in the group to which it belongs. Variation can occur either among members of different species (*inter*specific variation) or among individuals of the same species (*intra*specific variation). Darwin noted that the species found on one island looked different from those on nearby islands and that many of the islands' species looked different from those on the nearest mainland.

FIGURE 2.1 Darwin spent more than 20 years compiling evidence before publishing in 1859 his ideas on how evolution works.

The differences between species on different islands was especially noticeable in the Galápagos Islands, an island chain off the coast of Ecuador in South America. Some differences seemed well suited to the animals' environments and diets, as shown in **FIGURE 2.2.** For example, saddle-backed tortoises, which have long necks and legs, lived in areas with a lot of tall plants. Domed tortoises, with their shorter necks and legs, lived in wet areas rich in mosses and short plants. Similarly, finches with strong, thick beaks lived in areas with a lot of large, hard-shelled nuts, while those species of finch with more delicate beaks were found where insects or fruits were widely available.

These observations led Darwin to realize that species may somehow be able to adapt to their surroundings. An **adaptation** is a feature that allows an organism to better survive and reproduce in its environment. Adaptations can lead to genetic change in a population over time.

A Connect What adaptations did Darwin see in the finches of the Galápagos Islands?

Differentiated Instruction

PRE-AP

Describe a scenario in which sea lions in the Galápagos suddenly lose their main food source when changes in sea temperature and currents keep anchovies away from the islands. The only food is a small species of crab that lives on the sea floor 100 feet below the surface. Discuss traits in the sea lion population that might be adaptive and how the population could change. Have students write a description of one possible outcome.

Teacher Toolkit, Section D, Cause-and-Effect Chain

TEACH WITH TECHNOLOGY

Have students use the Internet to put together a virtual tour of the Galápagos Islands as a digital slideshow.

Teacher Toolkit, Section G, Presentation Software

FIGURE 2.2 Adaptations Within Species

Galápagos tortoises (*Geochelone elephantopus*) are evidence that species can adapt to their environments.

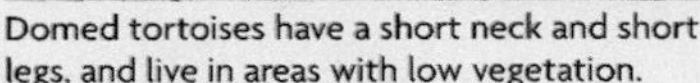

Domed tortoises have a short neck and short legs, and live in areas with low vegetation.

Saddle-backed tortoises have a high shell edge, allowing them to stretch their long necks.

N
W E
S
70°W
VENEZUELA
PANAMA
COLOMBIA
0°
Equator
Galápagos Islands
ECUADOR
PACIFIC OCEAN
BRAZIL
PERU
10°S
0 500 miles
0 500 kilometers
90°W
80°W
BOLIVIA

Galápagos Islands

A Explain **Why do these tortoises of the same species look different?**

MAIN IDEA

Darwin observed fossil and geologic evidence supporting an ancient Earth.

On his voyage, Darwin found fossil evidence of species changing over time. In Argentina, he found fossils of huge animals, such as *Glyptodon,* a giant armadillo. The fact that these fossils looked like living species suggested that modern animals might have some relationship to fossil forms. These fossils suggested that, in order for such changes to occur, Earth must be much more than 6000 years old.

During his voyage, Darwin also found fossil shells of marine organisms high up in the Andes mountains. Darwin later experienced an earthquake during his voyage and saw firsthand the result: land that had been underwater was moved above sea level. This experience explained what he saw in the Andes. Darwin's observations on his voyage supported Lyell's theory that daily geologic processes can add up to great change over a long period of time. Darwin later extended the ideas of an old Earth and slow, gradual change to the evolution of organisms. This became known as evolutionary gradualism.

B Infer **What could account for fossils of marine organisms being found on top of modern-day mountain ranges?**

10.2 Formative Assessment

SELF-CHECK Online
HMHScience.com
GO ONLINE

REVIEWING MAIN IDEAS

1. What accounts for the **variation** Darwin observed among island species?
2. What did Darwin learn from the fossils that he observed on his voyage?

CRITICAL THINKING

3. **Apply** Explain how wings are an **adaptation** for birds.
4. **Synthesize** How did Darwin's observations support Lyell's theory of an ancient Earth undergoing continual geologic change?

CONNECT TO ECOLOGY

5. Some birds in the Galápagos Islands build nests in trees, while others hide eggs in rock crevices. What could account for this difference in nesting behaviors?

The Inside Story

The world's oldest living animal—Harriet, a **Galápagos tortoise**—was once Charles Darwin's shipmate. She was one of three Galápagos tortoises captured by Darwin during his expedition. Darwin took the animals back to England and, thinking all three were males, named them Tom, Dick, and Harry. Because they were poorly adapted to the cool English climate, the animals were moved to Australia around 1840. In the 1960s, scientists realized that Harry, the last remaining member of the trio, was actually female. In 1992, DNA testing suggested that Harriet was born around 1830. Harriet lived at the Australia Zoo outside Brisbane until her death in 2006.

Answers

A Explain Genetic variation within the population enabled particular variations in traits to be expressed. Some of these variations proved beneficial within certain environments or conditions.

B Infer Land that was once a marine environment could be uplifted by Earth processes and become terrestrial.

Assess and Reteach

Assess Use the Section Self-Check or Section Quiz, both available at **HMHScience.com**.

Reteach Have students write a news bulletin on Darwin's remarkable voyage on the *Beagle* and the amazing things he saw on his trip. Students should incorporate the terms *variation* and *adaptation* into their report.

10.2 FORMATIVE ASSESSMENT

1. The islands had different environments, and the organisms had adaptations (such as distinctively shaped beaks among birds) that enabled the organisms to live in those environments.
2. Modern animals might be related to fossil forms; Earth is older than was thought at the time; and geologic processes can add up to great change.
3. *Sample answer:* Wings enable birds to escape prey and hunt for food, helping the birds survive and reproduce.
4. Darwin observed marine fossils in the mountains and the uplift of land by an earthquake.
5. One can speculate that the birds nesting in rock crevices may have predators that can climb trees or cannot reach into a crevice. Similarly, birds nesting in trees suggests that the eggs are safer above ground.

SECTION 10.3

B.5.3 Apply concepts of statistics and probability to support a claim that organisms with an advantageous heritable trait tend to increase in proportion to organisms lacking this trait.

B.5.4 Evaluate evidence to explain the role of natural selection as an evolutionary mechanism that leads to the adaptation of species, and to support claims that changes in environmental conditions may result in: (1) increases in the number of individuals of some species, (2) the emergence of new species over time, and/or (3) the extinction of other species.

B.5.5 Construct an explanation based on evidence that the process of evolution primarily results from four factors: (1) the potential for a species to increase in number, (2) the heritable genetic variation of individuals in a species due to mutation and sexual reproduction, (3) competition for limited resources, and (4) the proliferation of those organisms that are better able to survive and reproduce in the environment.

▼ Plan and Prepare

Activate Prior Knowledge Tell students that one idea that Darwin brought home from his voyage on the *Beagle* was that life forms were infinitely variable. He wanted to study species variation in real time. **Ask,** Why would Darwin turn to animal and plant breeders as a source of information in studying variation? Breeders actively manipulate traits—a form of variation—by pairing mates rather than by letting reproduction occur naturally.

▼ Teach

Science Trivia

- The archaeological record suggests that humans began to domesticate dogs, probably from wolves, about 15,000 years ago.
- There are more than 400 breeds of domestic dogs in the world today, but all of them are the same species (*Canis familiaris*).

10.3 Theory of Natural Selection

KEY CONCEPT **Darwin proposed natural selection as a mechanism for evolution.**

VOCABULARY

artificial selection
heritability
natural selection
population
fitness

MAIN IDEAS

- Several key insights led to Darwin's idea for natural selection.
- Natural selection explains how evolution can occur.
- Natural selection acts on existing variation.

Connect to Your World

Have you ever had an experience that changed your outlook or your opinion about an issue? Darwin began his voyage thinking that species could not change. However, his experiences during the five-year journey changed the way he thought about life and evolution. He became convinced that evolution occurs. But he had yet to determine how it could happen.

MAIN IDEA

Several key insights led to Darwin's idea for natural selection.

After his voyage, Darwin spent more than 20 years conducting research while thinking about the way evolution occurs. Although he had traveled the world, Darwin also found great insight in his home country of England. One important influence on Darwin's research was the work of farmers and breeders.

Artificial Selection

Darwin noticed a lot of variation in domesticated plants and animals. The populations of domesticated species seemed to show variation in traits that were not shown in their wild relatives. Through selection of certain traits, breeders could produce a great amount of diversity. The process by which humans change a species by breeding it for certain traits is called **artificial selection.** In this process, humans make use of the genetic variation in plants and animals by acting as the selective agent. That is, humans determine which traits are favorable and then breed individuals that show those traits.

To explore this idea, Darwin turned to the hobby of breeding pigeons. Although Darwin had no knowledge of genetics, he had noticed certain traits being selected in animals such as livestock and pets. For thousands of years, humans had been breeding pigeons that showed many different traits, such as those in **FIGURE 3.1.** In order for artificial—or natural—selection to occur, the trait must be heritable. **Heritability** (HER-ih-tuh-BIHL-uh-tee) is the ability of a trait to be passed down from one generation to the next.

Differentiated Instruction

ENGLISH LEARNERS

Have students use Cornell Notes to outline this lesson. They can record key terms and definitions in a left-hand column across from the appropriate point in the outline. Then they can add a summary in the bottom section. Encourage students to be concise but still try to include all key information.

Teacher Toolkit, Section C, Cornell Notes

TEACH WITH TECHNOLOGY

There are many organizations associated with domesticated breeding of ornamental plants and animals. Others are involved with heirloom breeds. Choose a selection of images from the Internet to project in class. Discuss how, breeders can, in the process of amplifying a particular trait, amplify other traits as well.

Darwin compared what he learned about breeding to his ideas on adaptation. In artificial selection, features such as reversed neck feathers, large crops, or extra tail feathers are favored over generations only if these traits are liked by breeders. However, breeders might also select against features that are not desirable or "useful." During artificial selection, humans act as the selective agent. In nature, however, the environment creates the selective pressure that determines if a trait is passed on or not.

Darwin used this line of thinking for his theory of natural selection. **Natural selection** is a mechanism by which individuals that have inherited beneficial adaptations show differential reproductive success. In other words—they tend to produce more offspring on average than do other individuals. In nature, the environment is the selective agent. Therefore, in nature, characteristics are selected only if they give advantages to individuals in the environment as it is right now. Furthermore, Darwin reasoned, desirable breeds are not produced immediately. He knew that it sometimes took many generations for breeders to produce the varieties he had observed.

Struggle for Survival

Another important idea came from English economist Thomas Malthus. Malthus had proposed that resources such as food, water, and shelter were natural limits to population growth. That is, human populations would grow geometrically if resources were unlimited. Instead, disease and a limited food

FIGURE 3.1 Artificial Selection of Pigeon Traits

For thousands of years, new varieties of organisms, such as pigeons, have resulted from selective breeding for particular traits.

Jacobins are bred for their reversed neck feathers.

Croppers are bred for their inflatable crop.

Fantails are bred to have many tail feathers.

Connect **What other species of organisms are often subjects of artificial selection?**

Vocabulary

Academic Vocabulary As students learn about natural **selection** and see the word **select** used in an evolutionary context, it is important that they do not confuse these words with *choice* or *choose,* or ascribe to them any kind of deliberate, goal-oriented sense of purpose. Students will benefit if they think of *selection* as something that occurs for very specific reasons yet isn't chosen or planned.

Integrating Agricultural Science

Using traditional methods, scientists could crossbreed only closely related species or individual plants of the same species. Today, many scientists take advantage of **genetic engineering** techniques to produce plants that incorporate genes from widely different species. For example, **golden rice** is a genetically engineered rice that contains a large amount of beta carotene, a precursor of vitamin A.

Vitamin A deficiency is a leading cause of blindness in the developing world. Golden rice was developed by taking genes that code for beta carotene in daffodils and inserting them into rice. This type of artificial selection would have been almost impossible to accomplish with traditional breeding methods.

See the BioZine feature in the Plants unit for more on golden rice and genetically modified crops.

Answers

A Connect Answers will vary but may include plants, pets, or livestock.

BELOW LEVEL

Have students use a Venn diagram to compare artificial selection to natural selection. Have them consider the selective agent and whether species or breeds are involved. Also, have students consider a benefit that is derived from the process.

Teacher Toolkit, Section C, Venn Diagram

Teach *continued*

Vocabulary

Greek and Latin Word Origins The root *popu* in the word **population** comes from the Latin word *populus,* meaning "people." Other words or expressions that use this root include *popular* and *populist.* The important distinction made about members of a population in science is that they are part of the same gene pool.

Answers

A Explain The competition for resources that Malthus saw among humans was applied by Darwin to all living organisms.

The Inside Story

In 1858, after years of quietly tinkering with his ideas about evolution, **Charles Darwin** received an unpublished paper in the mail, from **Alfred Russel Wallace** (1823–1913). Wallace was a naturalist who, like Darwin, sought the mechanism for evolution. He had also spent a lot of time in the tropics, observing interactions between environments and species. Wallace was going to publish his paper *(On the Tendency of Varieties to Depart Indefinitely from the Original Type),* but he first wanted feedback from Darwin, who was a well-respected member of the scientific community.

As Darwin read Wallace's paper, he realized that this stranger had somehow come to conclusions about evolution that were nearly identical to his own. Fearing that his life's work was about to be preempted, Darwin sought advice from **Charles Lyell,** who arranged for the two naturalists' ideas to be featured concurrently at a meeting of the Linnean Society of London. A year later, in 1859, Darwin's book *On the Origin of Species* was published. It had been 28 years since he first set sail on the *Beagle.*

READING TOOLBOX

VOCABULARY

The term *descent* is used in evolution to mean the passing of genetic information from generation to generation.

supply kept the population smaller. Darwin reasoned that a similar struggle took place in nature. If resources are limited and organisms have more offspring than could survive, why do some individuals, and not others, survive?

Darwin found his answer in the variation he had seen within populations. A **population** is all the individuals of a species that live in an area. Darwin had noticed in the Galápagos Islands that in any population, such as the tortoises or the finches, some individuals had variations that were particularly well-suited to their environment. He proposed that these adaptations arose over many generations. Darwin called this process of evolution "descent with modification."

A Explain How did Malthus's economic theory influence Darwin?

MAIN IDEA

Natural selection explains how evolution can occur.

Charles Darwin was not the only person to develop a theory to explain how evolution may take place. An English naturalist named Alfred Russel Wallace independently developed a theory very similar to Darwin's. Both Darwin and Wallace had studied the huge diversity of plants and animals in the tropics, and both had studied the fossil record. In 1858, the ideas of Darwin and Wallace were presented to an important group of scientists in London. The next year, Darwin published his ideas in the book *On the Origin of Species by Means of Natural Selection.*

READING TOOLBOX

TAKING NOTES

Write a sentence in your own words that summarizes each of the four principles of natural selection.

variation
overproduction
adaptation
descent with modification

There are four main principles to the theory of natural selection: variation, overproduction, adaptation, and descent with modification.

- **Variation** The heritable differences, or variations, that exist in every population are the basis for natural selection. The differences among individuals result from differences in the genetic material of the organisms, whether inherited from a parent or resulting from a genetic mutation.
- **Overproduction** While having many offspring raises the chance that some will survive, it also results in competition between offspring for resources.
- **Adaptation** Sometimes a certain variation allows an individual to survive better than other individuals it competes against in its environment. More successful individuals are "naturally selected" to live longer and to produce more offspring that share those adaptations for their environment.
- **Descent with modification** Over time, natural selection will result in species with adaptations that are well suited for survival and reproduction in an environment. More individuals will have the trait in every following generation, as long as the environmental conditions continue to remain beneficial for that trait.

A well-studied example of natural selection in jaguars is shown in **FIGURE 3.2.** About 11,000 years ago, many species faced extinction. Large cats, including jaguars, faced a shortage of food due to the changing climate of that time. There were fewer mammals to eat, so the jaguars had to eat reptiles. In

Differentiated Instruction

PRE-AP

Tell students that the influence of Darwin's evolutionary theories has extended beyond science. His concept of "fitness" was transformed into the idea of "survival of the fittest," which has been incorporated into literature, philosophy, psychology, religion, politics, and economics. Have students write for five minutes on a particular way in which the concept of "survival of the fittest" has been used in popular culture. Have them compare their example to what Darwin meant by "fitness."

Teacher Toolkit, Section C, Quick-Write

the jaguar population, there were variations of jaw and tooth size that became important for survival. Like many other species, jaguars can produce more offspring than can be supported by the environment. Jaguars with the biggest jaws and teeth could prey more easily on the shelled reptiles. Because jaw size and tooth size are heritable traits and were beneficial, large jaws and teeth became adaptations for this population. The jaguars' descendants showed modifications, or changes, over time.

In biology, the term **fitness** is a measure of the ability to survive and produce more offspring relative to other members of the population in a given environment. After the change in climate, jaguars that had larger teeth and jaws had a higher fitness than other jaguars in the population. Jaguars that ate less didn't necessarily all die or stop producing altogether; they just reproduced a little less. Today, large teeth and jaws are considered typical traits of jaguars.

READING TOOLBOX

VOCABULARY

In everyday language, *fitness* means "physically fit." In biology, however, fitness is related to reproductive success.

A Compare and Contrast **What are the similarities and differences between natural selection and artificial selection?**

GO ONLINE

Principles of Natural Selection

FIGURE 3.2 The Principles of Natural Selection

Certain traits become more common in a population through the process of natural selection.

jaguar 1

jaguar 2

OVERPRODUCTION

A jaguar may produce many offspring, but not all will survive due to competition for resources.

VARIATION

Some jaguars, such as jaguar 1 shown here, may be born with slightly larger jaws and teeth due to natural variation in the population. Some variations are heritable.

jaguar skull 1

jaguar skull 2

ADAPTATION

Jaguars with larger jaws and teeth are able to eat shelled reptiles. These jaguars are more likely to survive and to have more offspring than jaguars that can eat only mammals.

DESCENT WITH MODIFICATION

Because large teeth and jaws are heritable traits, they become more common characteristics in the population.

B Summarize **How did large jaws and teeth become typical characteristics of jaguars?**

ONLINE Biology

HMHScience.com

To see natural selection in action, have students use the Animated Biology simulation.

TEACH FROM VISUALS

FIGURE 3.2 Use the figure to discuss the four principles of natural selection. **Ask,** What traits are being selected for in this figure? jaw size and teeth size

Relate the diagram to the bulleted list on the previous page. Explain that the figure can be read as a cycle diagram, an ongoing series of events that cause the traits in a population to change over time. **Ask,** How might changes in the jaguar population affect the population of reptiles? It's possible for a prey population to develop a certain defensive mechanism, such as a stronger shell or perhaps a toxin in the skin, to counter the jaguar's adaptation.

Answers

A Compare and Contrast In natural selection, the environment determines which traits will be favored; in artificial selection, however, humans do the selecting.

B Summarize Natural variation in the population meant that some jaguars had larger jaws and teeth, and these jaguars were better able to survive in the environment and reproduce. Over many generations, these heritable traits became common in the jaguar population.

INCLUSION

Students who have difficulty focusing on details will need to decode **FIGURE 3.2.** Have students work in pairs to isolate each principle depicted. Then ask them to consider how the phenomenon described affects the population as a whole. Have students put the parts back together to describe the cycle of change that causes populations to change.

Teacher Toolkit, Section C, Think-Pair-Share

▼ **Teach** *continued*

DATA ANALYSIS

Discussion

Ask, What does the variation in the trend line for the experimental group suggest? Wheel-running ability generally increases but still varies until Generation 8. By Generation 9, alleles for the ability have a much higher frequency in the experimental group than in the control group. The researchers hypothesized a recessive allele for the trait. Explain that the trend for improved wheel-running ability cannot continue indefinitely. There are limitations to the physical capabilities of all living things.

Address Misconceptions

Common Misconception Once a pattern in a graph line is established, the pattern will continue indefinitely.

Correcting the Misconception Have students look at the trend line for the experimental group. **Ask,** What do you think the line will look like by Generation 15? It will become flatter as the mice near their physical limitations

Tell students that data must be considered in the context of the animals themselves.

Answers

1. The mice in the experimental group show an increase in wheel-running ability as the generation number increases. The mice in the control group show little change in wheel-running ability.
2. The trend suggests that the number of revolutions may be even greater in Generation 10.

Online Student Resources, Data Analysis Practice

DATA ANALYSIS

INTERPRETING LINE GRAPHS

Scientists used mice to study whether exercise ability can improve in animals over several generations. In this experiment, mice were artificially selected for increased wheel-running behavior. The mice that were able to do the most wheel running were selected to breed the next generation. The control group represents generations of mice that were allowed to breed randomly.

- The *x*-axis shows different generations of mice, from Generation 1 to Generation 9.
- The *y*-axis shows the number of revolutions the mice ran on the wheel per day.
- The solid blue line represents the control group, in which generations of mice were allowed to breed randomly.
- The dotted orange line represents the generations of mice that were artificially selected based on their wheel-running ability. This is the experimental group.

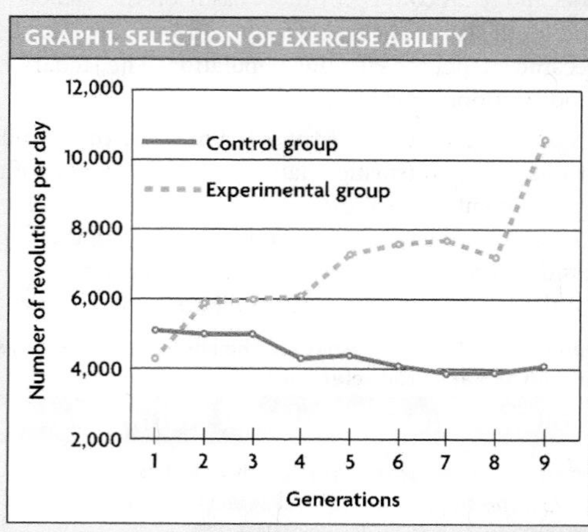

Source: Swallow et. al, *Behavior Genetics* 28:3.

1. **Interpret** What is the difference in results between the mice in the control group and the mice in the experimental group?
2. **Predict** Use the trend in the data to make a general prediction about the number of revolutions on the wheel per day for mice in Generation 10 of the experimental group.

Natural Selection

MAIN IDEA

Natural selection acts on existing variation.

Natural selection acts on phenotypes, or physical traits, rather than on genetic material itself. New alleles are not made by natural selection—they occur by genetic mutations. Natural selection can act only on traits that already exist.

Changing Environments

Ecologists Peter and Rosemary Grant observed an example of natural selection acting on existing traits within a population of medium ground finches on one of the Galápagos Islands. A drought in 1977 suddenly reduced the amount of small, soft seeds that the finches preferred. However, there were still plenty of large, tough-shelled seeds. Because the large-beaked finches in the population were able to crack the large, tough seeds, they did not starve. The next year, the Grants noted a big increase of large-beaked hatchlings. In contrast, most of the finches with small beaks had died.

Differentiated Instruction

INCLUSION

Photocopy the graph above at twice its size to help students with visual impairments follow the graph lines in the Data Analysis example. Or, using a copy made at the same size, push a pin through the data points to help students to distinguish the trend in each graph line. Have students describe the trends as they move their fingers across the graph.

Darwin's theory predicted exactly what the Grants observed. A trait that was already in the population became favorable for survival because of a change in the environment, and thus was passed on to future generations.

As an environment changes, different traits will become beneficial. The numbers of large-beaked finches on this Galápagos Island kept rising until 1984, when the supply of large seeds went down after an unusually wet period. These conditions favored production of small, soft seeds and small-beaked birds. With evolution, a trait that is an advantage today may be a disadvantage in the future.

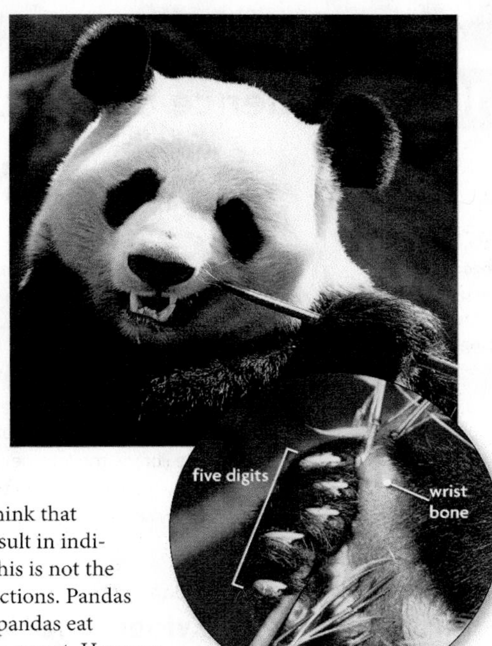

FIGURE 3.3 A panda's wrist bone also functions like a thumb.

Adaptations as Compromises

One mistake people make about natural selection is to think that adaptive characteristics passed down over a long time result in individuals that are perfectly suited to their surroundings. This is not the case. For example, some structures may take on new functions. Pandas have a structure in their wrist that acts like a thumb. As pandas eat bamboo shoots, they hold the shoots as you would hold a carrot. However, a close look at the paw reveals that it has six digits: five digits that resemble your fingers, plus a small thumblike structure. The panda's "thumb," shown in **FIGURE 3.3**, is actually an enlarged wrist bone. The ancestors of today's pandas had five full digits like today's bears, but those early pandas with bigger wrist bones had an advantage in eating bamboo. Because of its size and position, this bone functions like a human thumb. It is not considered a true thumb, because it does not have separate bones and joints as a human thumb does. It is also not a typical wrist bone, as the bone is clearly longer than needed to function for the wrist. Instead, it functions both as a wrist bone and a thumb.

Explain **Why is the panda's "thumb" considered an adaptive compromise?**

ONLINE Biology
HMHScience.com

Have students complete the Data Analysis Smart Grapher activity for this chapter to work with some of the Grants' data on Galápagos finches.

Integrating Anatomy

The enlarged wrist bone that is often mistaken as the **panda's "thumb"** is technically a sesamoid bone. Sesamoids are small, round bones that grow in connective tissue, specifically, in the tendons that cross joints. The kneecap, or patella, also is a sesamoid. In the joints, sesamoids act like pulleys, increasing the leverage of the tendon as it moves across the joint. This modifies the pressure on the tissue as it moves, decreasing the incidence of tissue tears.

Answers

A **Explain** The panda's "thumb" was originally adapted for a different function, but the animals can use it the way humans use their thumbs.

10.3 Formative Assessment

SELF-CHECK Online
HMHScience.com
GO ONLINE

REVIEWING MAIN IDEAS

1. What did Darwin hope to learn about **artificial selection** by studying pigeons?
2. What are the four principles of **natural selection**?
3. Why must there be variation in the **population** in order for natural selection to occur?

CRITICAL THINKING

4. **Evaluate** Explain why there was an increase in large-beaked finch hatchlings following a drought that left a finite amount of the small, soft seeds the birds preferred.
5. **Synthesize** Why is it said that natural selection acts on phenotypes rather than on the genetic material of organisms?

CONNECT TO

ECOLOGY

6. You have learned that the environment affects how organisms change over generations. How would you explain a species that remains the same for millions of years?

Assess and Reteach

Assess Use the Section Self-Check or Section Quiz, both available at **HMHScience.com**.

Reteach Work with students to create a concept map that describes the four principles of natural selection.

10.3 FORMATIVE ASSESSMENT

1. how certain traits can be selected and emphasized
2. The four principles of natural selection are overproduction, variation, adaptation, and descent with modification.
3. Because natural selection acts on phenotypes, there must be variations so that one phenotype offers a better chance of survival than another.
4. Nature selected for the large-beaked finches, which could eat the large, tough seeds. These finches were better able to survive and pass the trait for large beaks to their offspring.
5. The environment selects the expression of traits, or phenotypes, that are best suited for survival and reproductive fitness. These traits may be coded for by the organism's genotype, but the environment does not affect or change the genes themselves.
6. The environment may not have changed enough to favor new variations in the population, or the organism may not be very sensitive to changes.

SECTION 10.4

B.5.2 Communicate scientific information that common ancestry and biological evolution are supported by multiple lines of empirical evidence including both anatomical and molecular evidence.

▼ Plan and Prepare

Activate Prior Knowledge Most students have probably seen fossil displays in museums. **Ask,** Why are the fossil organisms so different from the animals on Earth today? Fossils take millions of years to form, and Earth's surface has changed significantly over time. In that time, evolution has been introducing new species and rendering some extinct.

▼ Teach

Take It Further

Trilobites, shown in **FIGURE 4.1** in fossilized form, were once among the most numerous marine invertebrates in the world. By the end of the Permian period, about 248 million years ago, all trilobite species were extinct, possibly due to a change in the depths of their coastal habitats. A different hypothesis suggests that the way in which a trilobite molted (shed its exoskeleton as a new one grew) may have contributed to the extinction of this species.

10.4 Evidence of Evolution

KEY CONCEPT **Evidence of common ancestry among species comes from many sources.**

VOCABULARY

biogeography
homologous structure
analogous structure
vestigial structure

MAIN IDEAS

- Evidence for evolution in Darwin's time came from several sources.
- Structural patterns are clues to the history of a species.

Connect to Your World

Whenever you need to complete an assignment on an unfamiliar topic, you first need to gather information. The different pieces of information might come from the library, the Internet, your teachers, or maybe even your friends. Together, all these pieces help you to understand the topic. Darwin also drew information from many sources, all of which helped to strengthen his understanding of evolution.

MAIN IDEA

Evidence for evolution in Darwin's time came from several sources.

Darwin found evidence from a wide range of sources to support his argument for evolution. The most important and convincing support came from fossils, geography, developmental similarities, and anatomy.

Fossils

Even before Darwin, scholars studying fossils knew that organisms changed over time. Scientists who study fossils focus on more than just the fossil itself. They also think about its age, its location, and what the environment was like when the organism it came from was alive.

In the late 1700s, geologists wondered why certain types of fossils were found in some layers of rock and not others. Later studies suggested that the fossil organisms in the bottom, or older, layers were more primitive than those in the upper, or newer, layers. Geologists during this time were mostly interested in the order in which fossils were found within rock strata as a record of natural events such as earthquakes, not as proof of evolution. However, the sequential nature of fossil groups and other findings in the fossil record supported Darwin's concept of descent with modification.

Geography

Recall that during the *Beagle* expedition Darwin saw that island plants and animals looked like, but were not identical to, species on the South American continent. He extended this observation, proposing that island species most closely resemble species on the nearest mainland.

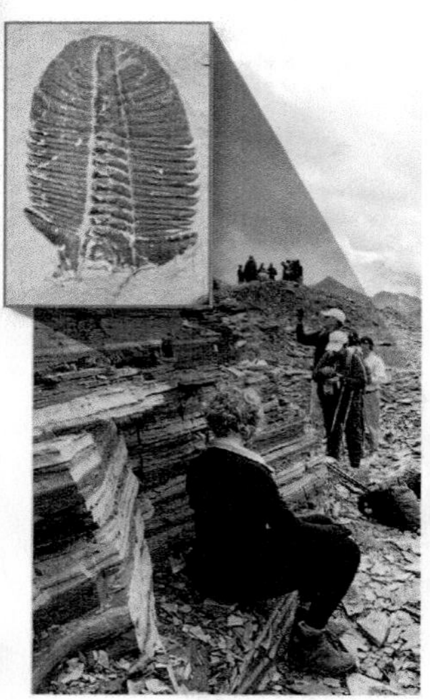

FIGURE 4.1 This trilobite, an early marine invertebrate that is now extinct, was found in this national park in British Columbia, Canada. Although far from modern-day oceans, this site is actually the floor of an ancient sea.

Differentiated Instruction

ENGLISH LEARNERS

Have students form into home groups of four, and ask each group to count off from 1 to 4. Assign a number to each category of evidence for evolution discussed in this section. Then have students regroup by their corresponding number to prepare a lesson plan for each category. Reconvene the home groups, and have students take turns presenting evidence to their group.

Teacher Toolkit, Section C, Jigsaw Reading

PRE-AP

Have students state the theory of evolution as a hypothesis, writing it as an if-then statement about life forms having changed over time. Then have students write the hypothesis at the center of a circle and, on lines extending from the central circle, have them record the evidence that supports the hypothesis.

Teacher Toolkit, Section C, Mind Map

FIGURE 4.2 Variation in Galápagos Finches

Finches on certain Galápagos Islands live in different environments and have beaks of different sizes and shapes.

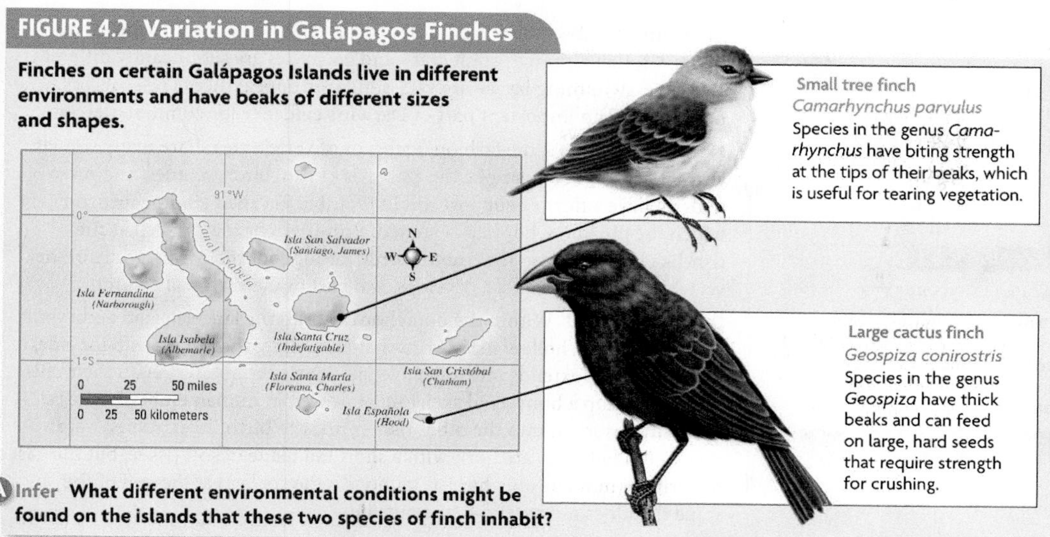

A Infer What different environmental conditions might be found on the islands that these two species of finch inhabit?

Darwin hypothesized that at some point in the past, some individuals from the South American mainland had migrated to the islands. This relationship between island and mainland species is today an important principle of **biogeography**, the study of the distribution of organisms around the world.

Different ecosystems on each island—with different plants, climates, and predators—had favored different traits in these migrants. Over time, these new traits became well established in the separate island populations, since the islands were too far apart for mating to occur.

One clear example of local adaptation is found in what are now known as Darwin's finches. The finches from the Galápagos Islands, shown in **FIGURE 4.2**, have distinct-looking beaks, as well as different habits, diets, and behaviors that evolved after generations of adaptation to specific island habitats. However, they all share a common ancestor from the South American mainland.

Since Darwin's time, the same pattern of evolution on islands has been studied in many living things, such as fruit flies and honeycreepers found among the Hawaiian Islands. A 2011 study analyzing DNA from all living species of Hawaiian honeycreepers indicated that they are all likely descended from a population of rosefinches that arrived in Hawaii from Asia sometime between 7.2 million and 5.8 million years ago. The evidence from this study also indicated that nearly all species of honeycreepers likely diverged between 5.8 million and 2.4 million years ago, the same period during which the island of Oahu first appeared. Like the honeycreepers, most species of plants and animals on the Hawaiian Islands are not found anywhere else on Earth, and the age of these species is close to the age of the islands on which they live.

Developmental Similarities

A study proposing a relationship between barnacles, which are fixed in place as adults, and crabs, which are mobile at all stages in their life cycles, fascinated Darwin. Darwin collected specimens of barnacles over many years of research.

Answers

A Infer The small tree finch might be found in areas with more moisture and softer foods such as fruit; the large cactus finch might be found in drier areas in which seeds are hard.

Integrating Earth Science

The major islands of Hawaii formed over millions of years as the Pacific plate moved over a volcanic **hotspot** in Earth's crust. The islands are currently home to 18 species of **Hawaiian honeycreeper,** a small finchlike bird, although many are now endangered. All these species are descended from an ancestral species of a rosefinch that arrived in Hawaii between 7.2 and 5.8 million years ago. At that time, most of the archipelago had not yet formed. Over millions of years, the number of honeycreeper species grew as more islands formed in the chain. At one time, there were as many as 50 species. **Ask,** What factors might have led to the dramatic spread of the honeycreepers? lack of competition; new niches as new islands formed

BELOW LEVEL

Have students use context clues to help understand the meaning of key vocabulary in this section. Students should look for examples that help reinforce meaning.

Teacher Toolkit, Section D, Context Clues

▼ Teach *continued*

Integrating Anatomy

Those organisms, such as the lancelet, that retain the notochord throughout their lives, are generally aquatic, with water providing their main support. The notochord serves as a brace for their muscles to pull against in order to move. In the higher chordates, like humans, a bony spiny column and skeleton provide the support needed to be mobile on land.

Vocabulary

Greek and Latin Word Origins The root of **notochord** is the Greek word *noton*, which means "back" and the Latin word, *chorda*, or "cord".

CONNECT TO

ANIMAL DIVERSITY

Refer to sections 1 and 2 of the chapter **Invertebrate Diversity** to find out more about how members of the animal kingdom are alike and different.

In making his observations of these crustaceans, he noticed, as shown in **FIGURE 4.3**, that although adult crabs and barnacles are significantly different, their free-swimming larvae are very similar in appearance. These observations formed an important part of Darwin's evidence for common descent.

Notochord In the same fashion, embryos of vertebrates share many similar characteristics. For example, the embryos of fish, birds, reptiles, and mammals all have a flexible support rod in their backs called a notochord, for which the phylum Chordata is named. Primitive chordates, such as the fish-like lancelet, keep their notochords throughout their lives, while in the vertebrates, the notochord develops into part of the vertebral column.

Dorsal nerve cord Within the notochord of both the lancelets and embryonic vertebrates lies a hollow nerve cord that runs along the dorsal, or back side, of the animal and extends into a flexible tail. Many vertebrates retain their tails as they develop a bony axial skeleton. However, in human embryos, the tail is generally absorbed into the other tissues prior to birth. In extremely rare cases, human babies are born with a short tail made of soft tissue, but the vast majority of humans only have a "tailbone" (the coccyx) at the end of the spine that does not extend to the outside.

Pharyngeal arches All chordate embryos have six structures known as pharyngeal arches, separated by slits. The upper arches develop into structures of the face, ears, and jaws. In adult fish, the two lower arches become the gills. However, in humans, the fifth arch disappears and the third, fourth, and sixth arches develop into the nerves, bones, and other structures of the throat.

The similarity of features in vertebrate embryos, shown in **FIGURE 4.4**, has been the subject of controversy since the late 1800s, when *Natural History of Creation (Natürliche Schöpfungsgeschichte)* was published by German scientist Ernst Haeckel. A great follower of Darwin's theory, Haeckel maintained that

FIGURE 4.3 Although adult crabs and barnacles look and behave very differently, they can look very similar as larvae. This suggested to Darwin that they share a common ancestor.

Differentiated Instruction

BELOW LEVEL

Provide students with diagrams of the internal anatomy of a lancelet, both larval and adult forms, and of a vertebrate embryo and adult. Have students label the notochord, pharyngeal arches, and tail on each of the embryo diagrams. On the diagram of the adult lancelet, have students label the same three structures as on the larvae. Point out to students that the adult vertebrate no longer has those three structures. Ask them what happened to those structures as the vertebrates developed. Tail was reabsorbed into the tissues; pharyngeal arches became structures of the jaw and throat; notochord became part of the intervertebral disks If time permits, have students use colored pencils to color code the homologous structures in each diagram.

the stages of development found in vertebrate embryos reflected the stages of evolution for each of those organisms. This became known as the recapitulation theory and was stated as "ontogeny recapitulates phylogeny."

His book and its accompanying drawings, which were borrowed and adapted from vertebrate anatomy experts of the time, immediately drew criticism from those who disputed evolutionary theory. Despite this, for many years, Haeckel's drawings commonly appeared in textbooks throughout the world. When photography became more widely used, some scientists pointed out discrepancies in size and scale between Haeckel's drawings and photographs. Other scientists argued that Haeckel openly stated in the captions of his drawings that he deliberately reduced them to similar sizes to enable observers to make comparisons. Although Haeckel revised and added new evidence with each of the five editions of his book, his reputation never recovered from the accusations of fraud. His recapitulation theory is no longer under serious consideration by scientists.

With today's technology, scientists have shown that all vertebrates have a set of very similar genes that direct the development of body structures from a basic body plan. These genes, the *Hox* genes, are discussed in more detail in the chapter Invertebrate Diversity. Evidence such as this suggests that vertebrates and other organisms evolved from distant common ancestors.

Evaluate **What aspects of Ernst Haeckel's book led to criticism by his peers?**

FIGURE 4.4 Developmental Homologies

Although humans, pigs, and chickens appear different from each other as adults, several of the same structures can be seen at various stages in their developing embryos.

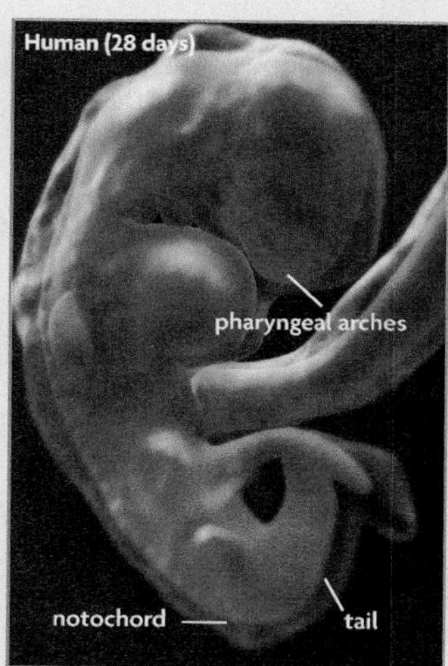

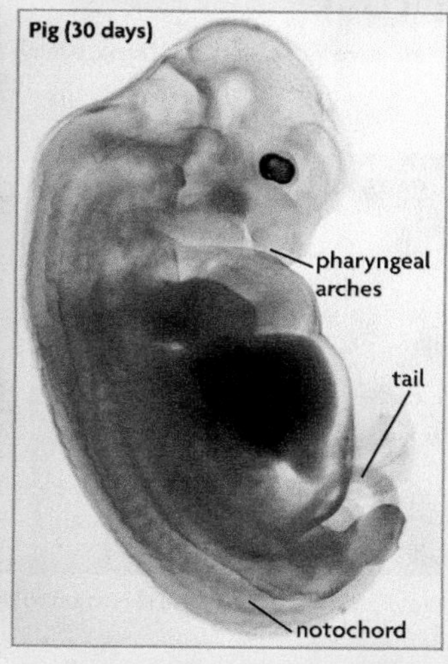

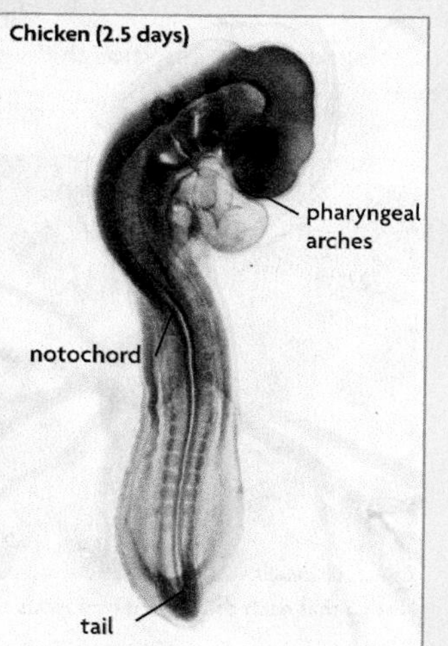

Analyze **How would these similar structures provide evidence of a common vertebrate ancestor?**

Science Trivia

Originally studying medicine, Ernst Haeckel soon became caught up in the study of comparative anatomy and its relationship to Darwin's theories regarding evolution. Haeckel is best known for his highly-disputed views on evolution and his habit of mixing speculation with verifiable research. However, many terms that biologists still use today, such as phylum, phylogeny, and ecology, were all coined by Haeckel in the course of his research.

TEACH FROM VISUALS

Have students compare the three photographs in **FIGURE 4.4.** Ask: What might account for the larval forms of the three vertebrates appearing to be very similar, while their adult forms are so different? Vertebrates start from similar body plans, but as they develop into adults, their DNA gives instructions for adaptations specific to their needs.

Answers

A Evaluate Scientists objected to the fact that the size and scale of Haeckel's drawings were not consistent.

B Analyze The similar features of embryos in very different organisms suggest evolution from a distant common ancestor.

INCLUSION

Have students create a two-column chart. Instruct them to label the top of the first column with the heading, "Homologous Structures" and the top of the second column with "Vestigial Structures". Under each heading, have students write the appropriate definition. Have students use internet or library resources to find as many examples of each structure as they can. Have students list the examples of each type of structure in the column beneath the appropriate definition.

▼ Teach *continued*

Vocabulary

Greek and Latin Word Origins Some students find it difficult to keep the definitions of **homologous** and **analogous** straight. The difference suggested by each prefix is subtle.

homo- = same, like
ana- = proportionate

Here are two mnemonics that may help students distinguish these terms:

- Homologous structures share a common origin but may not be adapted for similar functions.
- Analogous structures are adapted for similar functions but do not have a common origin.

Take It Further

Although the hind limbs of horses, humans, and dogs are homologous structures, the relative sizes of the bones are quite different in each group. As a result, these organisms walk differently.

- Humans, bears, raccoons, and many other animals are **plantigrades.** They walk on the whole foot, from toes to heel.
- Dogs and cats are **digitigrades.** They walk only on their toes.
- Most hoofed animals, including horses, cows, and deer, are **unguligrades.** They walk on hardened tissue at the very tips of their toes.

The bone of a horse's lower leg that seems equivalent to the human shin is actually made up of a metatarsal—a foot bone that usually makes up the lower half of a vertebrate's ankle. The hoof, which bears so much of the great weight of these animals, is equivalent to a fingernail.

Answers

A Apply A dolphin's flipper is homologous to the forelimbs of other mammals.

Dinosaur Descendants

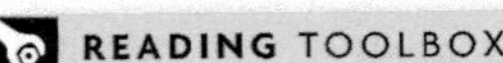

VOCABULARY
A tetrapod is a four-limbed animal. *Tetra-* means "four," and *-pod* means "foot."

Anatomy

Some of Darwin's best evidence came from comparing the body parts of different species. Chief among such evidence were homologous structures. **Homologous structures** (huh-MAHL-uh-guhs) are features that are similar in structure but appear in different organisms and have different functions. Their appearance across different species offers strong evidence for common descent. It would be unlikely for many species to have such similar anatomy if each species evolved independently.

The most common examples of homologous structures are the forelimbs of tetrapod vertebrates. The forelimbs of humans, bats, and moles are compared in **FIGURE 4.5.** In all of these animals, and indeed in every tetrapod, the forelimbs have several bones that are very similar to each other despite their different functions. Notice also how the same bones vary in different animals. In addition to this, all tetrapods, including birds, will have five digits on their limbs at some point in their development. Homologous structures are different in detail but similar in structure and relation to each other.

In using homologous structures as evidence of evolution, Darwin posed a logical question: If each of these groups descended from a different ancestor, why would they share these homologous structures? A simple answer is that they share a common ancestor.

The idea of common descent provides a logical explanation for how homologous structures appeared in diverse groups. Having similar structures doesn't always mean two species are closely related, however. Some structures found in different species have the same functions but did not evolve from a common ancestor.

FIGURE 4.5 Homologous Structures

Homologous structures, though they often have differing functions, are the result of a common ancestor.

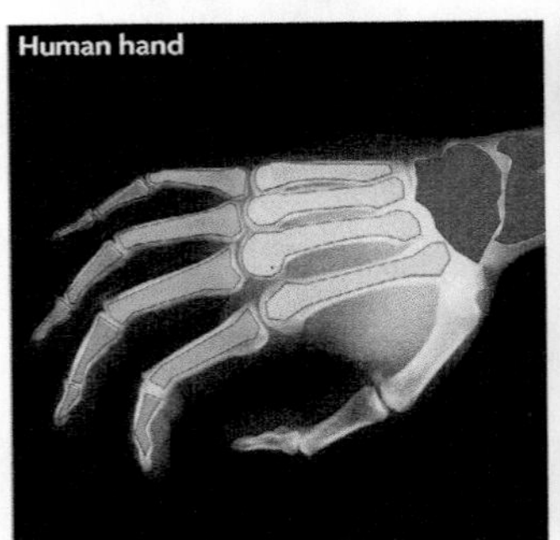

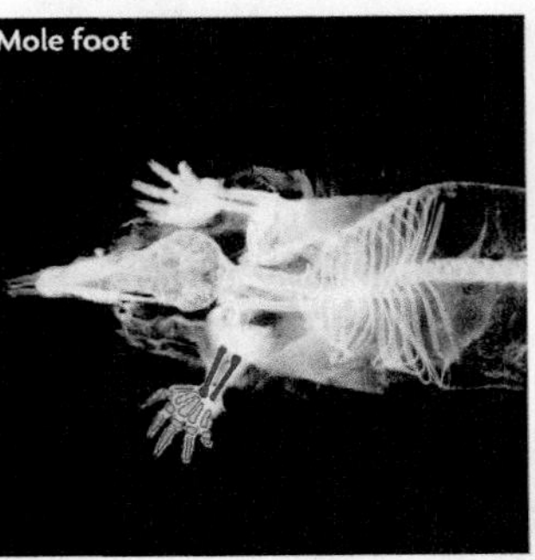

Notice that each of these homologous structures uses the same bones in relation to the others.

A Apply **What body part of a dolphin is homologous to the structures shown above?**

Differentiated Instruction

HANDS-ON ACTIVITY

Magnify the drawings included here and have students compare homologous structures in the human forearm and the flipper of a whale. Even though the vertebrates evolved in different ways, the limbs are formed from similar bone elements. The diagrams are included in Teacher Resources at **HMHScience.com.**

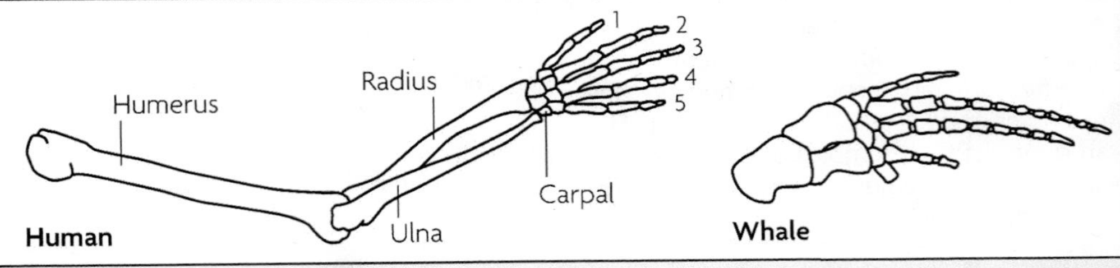

Suppose two organisms have similar needs caused by the environment. For example, two different organisms benefit from the ability to fly. Both can develop similar adaptations using different body parts. Think about the wings of bats and the wings of flying insects. Clearly these organisms differ in more ways than they are similar. Insects are arthropods, while bats are mammals. The wings of bats and insects are called analogous structures, as shown in **FIGURE 4.6.** **Analogous structures** (uh-NAL-uh-guhs) are structures that perform a similar function—in this case, flight—but are not similar in origin. This means that in each of the organisms, the analogous structures did not derive from the same original structure. Bat wings, when examined closely, have the same bone structure as an elongated hand, connected by thin skin. In contrast, insect wings do not have bones, only membranes that are supported by a series of long veins with cross-connections for strength. The similar function of wings in bats and flying insects evolved separately. Their ancestors faced similar environmental challenges and evolved similar adaptations to overcome those challenges.

FIGURE 4.6 ANALOGOUS STRUCTURES

Analogous structures evolved separately and are not evidence of a common ancestor. Bat wings and insect wings are derived from different structures.

A Analyze **Using the terms *homologous* and *analogous*, identify which group of structures provides evidence for a common ancestor. Explain.**

QUICKLAB INFERRING

Piecing Together Evidence

Evolutionary biologists and paleontologists rarely get all of the pieces of what they are studying. In this activity, you will receive pieces of "evidence" about a picture in order to make observations, inferences, and predictions about it.

PROBLEM How are inferences modified when new information is obtained?

MATERIALS
picture cut into strips

PROCEDURE

1. Using the three strips that your teacher has provided, write down all observations and inferences that you can make about this picture.
2. Make a prediction about the picture's topic, using your observations as supporting evidence for your prediction.
3. Record observations, inferences, and a prediction for each remaining strip of "evidence" that you receive from your teacher.

ANALYZE AND CONCLUDE

1. **Analyze** What inferences did you modify as you gathered more evidence from your teacher?
2. **Provide Examples** What type of evidence might paleontologists find that would allow them to see the big picture of a species' evolutionary past?

ENGLISH LEARNERS

Have students practice saying the vocabulary terms *homologous*, *analogous*, and *vestigial* by offering examples of each and asking students to call out an answer. While English learners may be reluctant to speak in class, these are words that will be a challenge for most students.

ONLINE Biology
HMHScience.com

Explore evidence suggesting that *T. rex* may have ancestors living on Earth today by completing the WebQuest for this chapter at **HMHScience.com**.

Answers

A **Analyze** Homologous structures provide evidence for a common ancestor because, despite differing in appearance or function, they are composed of the same structures; for example, bones. The two species probably had an ancestor in common. Analogous structures are structurally different and therefore do not suggest common ancestry.

QUICKLAB

Time 10 minutes

Purpose Form inferences and make predictions from incomplete evidence.

LAB MANAGEMENT

- Choose a picture that fills the entire frame, rather than one with a lot of background.
- Cut the picture into strips no wider than an inch for a 13 cm × 18 cm-(5 in. × 7 in.) sized picture. Give each student three non-adjoining strips to start with, then one strip at a time until they have determined the subject of the picture.

Answers

Analyze and Conclude

1. Answers will vary.
2. Answers might include a complete skeleton or fossil remains that give information about the environment or other species existing at the same time.

▼ Teach continued

Science Trivia

- The ostrich *(Struthio camelus)* is the largest living bird species. Males can approach 3 meters (9 ft) in height and weigh 155 kilograms (340 lbs).
- Female ostriches lay the largest eggs on Earth. At 15 centimeters (6 in.) long and nearly 13 centimeters (5 in.) wide, the ostrich egg is equivalent in volume to two dozen chicken eggs.
- Although flightless, ostriches can reach running speeds of 72 kilometers per hour (45 mph), making it the fastest-moving land bird.

Answers

Ⓐ **Summarize** Vestigial structures are remnants of an organ or a structure that still served a useful function or served a different function in an ancestor. Because a vestigial structure still exists, we can infer that the modern organism is a descendant of a species for which the structure served a useful or different purpose.

▼ Assess and Reteach

Assess Use the Section Self-Check or Section Quiz, both available at **HMHScience.com**.

Reteach Have students summarize the evidence for evolution (fossil, developmental, anatomical). Ask them to explain what homologous, analogous, and vestigial structures indicate about evolutionary relationships.

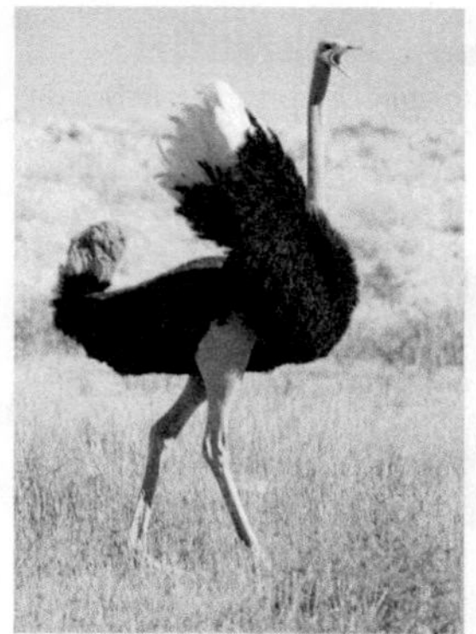

FIGURE 4.7 Vestigial structures, such as the wings of an ostrich, are organs or structures that are greatly reduced from the original ancestral form and have little or no current use.

MAIN IDEA

Structural patterns are clues to the history of a species.

Some organisms have structures or organs that seem to lack any useful function, or at least are no longer used for their original purpose. For example, snakes have tiny pelvic bones and stumplike limbs, even though snakes don't walk. Underdeveloped or unused features are called vestigial structures. **Vestigial structures** (veh-STIHJ-ee-uhl) are remnants of organs or structures found in an early ancestor that no longer serve a useful function or may now serve a different function. As vertebrates, snakes share a common ancestor with tetrapods such as lizards and dogs. The tiny pelvic bones and hind limbs in many snakes are homologous to the pelvic bones of tetrapods.

The wings of ostriches are another example of vestigial structures. Ostriches use wings for balance but not to fly, as shown in **FIGURE 4.7.** Over generations, their increasingly large bodies and powerful long legs may have been enough to avoid predators. If ancient ostriches could escape by running or by kicking viciously, their large wings would no longer have been useful. Thus, the genes coding for large wings were not preserved over generations.

Examples of vestigial structures are found in many organisms. In humans, the appendix is often cited as an example of a vestigial structure. The appendix is a remnant of the cecum, a major part of the large intestine in plant-eating mammals. It helps to digest the cellulose in plants. As omnivores, humans do not eat much cellulose and the appendix cannot digest cellulose. Whether or not the appendix retains any function is still not certain.

Vestigial structures did not get smaller in one individual organism. It took many generations for those organs to shrink. Today, biologists consider vestigial structures among the most important examples demonstrating how evolution works.

Ⓐ Summarize **What are vestigial structures, and how do they demonstrate common ancestry?**

10.4 Formative Assessment

SELF-CHECK Online
HMHScience.com
GO ONLINE

REVIEWING MAIN IDEAS

1. Describe the four sources of evidence for evolution upon which Darwin based his ideas on common ancestry.
2. Why are **vestigial structures** considered critical evidence of evolution?

CRITICAL THINKING

3. **Evaluate** How would you assess the biogeographic evidence used to explain the divergence of Hawaiian honeycreeper species?
4. **Apply** How can a bat's wing be considered both a **homologous structure** and an **analogous structure**?

CONNECT TO HUMAN BIOLOGY

5. Wisdom teeth are a third set of molars that usually appear in humans between the ages of 17 and 25, and often need removing because they crowd out other teeth. Explain why wisdom teeth are vestigial structures.

10.4 FORMATIVE ASSESSMENT

1. Fossils found in deeper and therefore older rock layers were more primitive. Geography also affects the evolution of species. For example: islands with different habitats support species that evolved with adaptations for that environment. Similar features found in the earliest stage of embryonic development provide evidence of a common ancestor. The fourth source comes from studying the anatomy of different organisms, revealing homologous structures in some species and analogous structures in others. Vestigial structures also provide evidence of evolutionary relationships.
2. They are homologous to functional features found in ancestors and show evidence of common ancestry among organisms that share them.
3. *Sample answer:* The biogeographic evidence is strong because all these species of honeycreepers are found only in Hawaii and are close in age to that of the islands on which they live. This evidence is further strengthened by DNA evidence that indicates all honeycreeper species have a common ancestor that arrived from Asia millions of years ago.
4. A bat wing is homologous to the forelimbs of other vertebrates. It is analogous to the wing of an insect because the wings are structurally different even though they perform the same function.
5. Wisdom teeth are vestigial structures because they serve no useful purpose. The human diet and jaw have changed over many generations. The wisdom teeth are no longer necessary.

The Uses of Stable Isotopes

S.T.E.M. Interactions

You may have heard about radiometric dating, in which radioactive isotopes are used to determine the age of objects such as fossils and rocks. Radioactive isotopes, or radioisotopes, are naturally occurring elements that have unstable nuclei, and so they decay. As a radioisotope's neutrons change into protons and electrons, it emits radiation and eventually becomes another element. Because radioisotopes decay at a constant rate, they are useful for determining the age of rocks and fossils. But not all isotopes are radioactive.

Stable isotopes are isotopes that do not decay over time. Because the ratios of stable isotopes typical for a certain environment remain constant, stable isotopes are useful for tracking objects and organisms. Analysis of stable isotopes can be used for a variety of purposes, such as authenticating that a cheese labeled as Parmesan was truly produced in Parma, Italy.

Stable isotopes of four elements are commonly used to authenticate a biological product, such as a type of food. Hydrogen exists as the isotopes ^{1}H and ^{2}H. Oxygen exists as ^{16}O, ^{17}O, and ^{18}O. Carbon exists as ^{12}C and ^{13}C (^{14}C is a radioactive isotope). Nitrogen exists as ^{14}N and ^{15}N.

Stable isotope analysis can tell scientists whether this wedge of cheese was made in Parma, Italy, or Hoboken, New Jersey.

Stable isotopes can be used to identify the geographic origins of water and test whether the bottled water you're drinking is from Fiji, a spring in France, or the local municipal water supply. How is this possible? Oceans show only small variations in isotopic abundance. Therefore, ocean water is typically used as a standard, where both the H and O isotope ratios are deemed to be 0 percent. However, as water evaporates from the ocean and condenses into clouds, the isotopic ratios differ significantly, depending on cloud temperature and the amount of leftover moisture in the cloud mass. Bodies of water, such as lakes and rivers, reflect these isotopic ratios from the input of precipitation. These isotopic abundances can further change as evaporation occurs over these bodies of water. Through the water and oxygen cycles, plants and animals incorporate hydrogen and oxygen isotopes from local water sources into their bodies. The isotopic analysis of water samples collected from locations all across the United States, as well as from locations around the world, has allowed scientists to create a map that indicates the expected isotopic ratios in a substance from a given area. Thus, when testing a bottled water sample, scientists can determine if the water's source is correctly labeled.

Measuring Stable Isotopes

To determine the stable isotope ratio in a sample, whether it is a drop of water or a piece of meat, the sample is placed into a machine called a mass spectrometer. The sample is converted to a gaseous form and then bombarded with ions to scatter the sample's atoms. A strong magnet is used to pull the sample's atoms through a flight tube. Because the different isotopes vary in mass, it takes longer for the more massive atoms to travel through the flight tube, thereby separating the different isotopes in flight. A detector at the end of the flight tube counts the number of atoms for each specific atomic mass. The counts of each isotope are added and calculated as a ratio. It is the ratios of heavy to light isotopes that convey the important information to scientists.

Question
Stable isotopes are also used from ice cores, tree rings, or ocean sediments as evidence about past climate conditions. Why could this information be beneficial to future generations?

Introduce

Check for student understanding of radioactive decay and its use in dating fossils and rock strata. **Ask,** How do scientists determine the age of rocks and fossils? Students may know that fossils can be used to date certain layers or rock and vice versa. Students also may know that in undisturbed layers of rock, like those of the Grand Canyon, primitive one-celled organisms similar to bacteria seen today are found in the oldest, deepest layers. As one examines rock layers progressively closer to the top, more complex fossilized organisms can be found. Reinforce the concept that one way scientists age rock is though *relative dating,* based on what is above and below particular rock strata.

Explore

Students could quickly get an idea of half-life by turning a handful of pennies all heads up, then turning half of them to tails, then half again to tails, and then half again to tails. At any point in the turning, someone could figure out how many turns they did by looking at the ratio of heads to tails of the pennies. The tails in this activity would represent the daughter product and the heads the parent material.

Chapter 10: Principles of Evolution 305

SECTION 10.5

B.5.2 Communicate scientific information that common ancestry and biological evolution are supported by multiple lines of empirical evidence including both anatomical and molecular evidence.

▼ Plan and Prepare

Activate Prior Knowledge Tell students that in this section, the work of Darwin and Mendel come together. **Ask,** What was Darwin's mechanism for explaining the diversity of life? natural selection Mendel's mechanism? mixing of genes transmitted from parents to offspring

▼ Teach

Take It Further

Many missing links are no longer missing. Scientists have found transitional fossils that link dinosaurs and birds; four-legged terrestrial vertebrates (tetrapods) and fish; our species and our apelike ancestors. Based on the fossil evidence of the dinosaur-bird link *(Archaeopteryx lithographica)*, some scientists think that birds should be classified as dinosaurs.

Answers

A Infer They are intermediates between a modern species and an ancient ancestor, in this case, a modern whale and a terrestrial mammal.

10.5 Evolutionary Biology Today

VOCABULARY

paleontology

KEY CONCEPT **New technology is furthering our understanding of evolution.**

MAIN IDEAS

- Fossils provide a record of evolution.
- Molecular and genetic evidence support fossil and anatomical evidence.
- Evolution unites all fields of biology.

Connect to Your World

Darwin had spent many years collecting evidence of evolution from different fields of science before publishing his results. Since that time, technology has advanced greatly. Scientists can now share information and examine evidence that was only dreamed about in the 1800s. In particular, the relatively new fields of genetics and molecular biology have added strong support to Darwin's theory of natural selection. They have shown how hereditary variation occurs.

MAIN IDEA

Fossils provide a record of evolution.

READING TOOLBOX

VOCABULARY

Paleontology is the study of prehistoric life forms. *Paleo-* means "ancient," and *-ology* means "the study of."

Paleontology (PAY-lee-ahn-TAHL-uh-jee), the study of fossils or extinct organisms, continues to provide new information and support current hypotheses about how evolution occurs. The fossil record is not complete, because most living things do not form into fossils after they die, and because fossils have not been looked for in many areas of the world. However, no fossil evidence that contradicts evolution has ever been found.

In Darwin's time, paleontology was still a new science. Darwin worried about the lack of transitional fossils between groups of organisms. Since Darwin's time, however, many transitional forms between species have been discovered, filling in large gaps in the fossil record. The fossil record today includes many thousands of species that show the change in forms over time that Darwin outlined in his theory. These "missing links" demonstrate the evolution of traits within groups as well as the common ancestors between groups.

Although scientists classify organisms into groups, the mix of traits in transitional species often makes it difficult to tell where one group ends and another begins. One example of transitional species in the evolution of whales is shown in **FIGURE 5.1.** *Basilosaurus isis* had a whalelike body, but it still had the limbs of land animals.

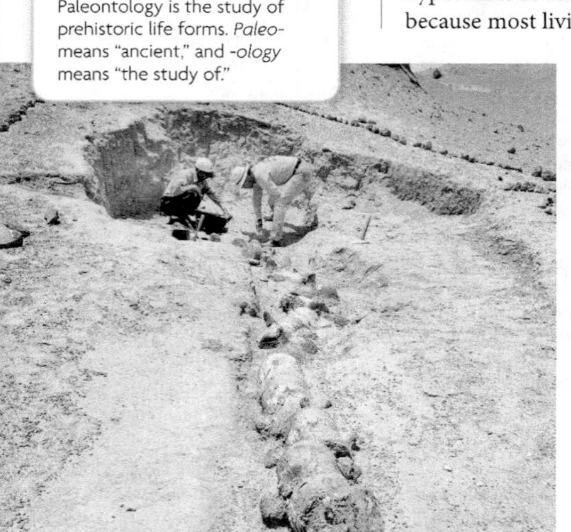

FIGURE 5.1 This spinal column of a 40-million-year-old whale was found in a desert in Egypt.

A Infer Why are fossils such as *Basilosaurus isis* considered transitional fossils?

Differentiated Instruction

ENGLISH LEARNERS

Have pairs of students work together to provide support for the statement "Much evidence exists today to support the theory of evolution." Students can choose a graphic organizer they have used before. For example, have them place the statement in the center of a circle. Then have students extend four lines from the circle, and at the end of each line, write a statement that addresses molecular, genetic, fossil, and anatomical evidence.

Teacher Toolkit, Section C, Mind Map

BELOW-LEVEL

To ensure that students understand the difference between the theory of evolution and Darwin's theory of natural selection, have them write a paragraph or two on the subject.

Teacher Toolkit, Section C, Quick-Write

MAIN IDEA

Molecular and genetic evidence support fossil and anatomical evidence.

As with homologous traits, very different species have similar molecular and genetic mechanisms. Because all living things have DNA, they share the same genetic code and make most of the same proteins from the same 20 amino acids. DNA or protein sequence comparisons can be used to show probable evolutionary relationships between species.

DNA sequence analysis Recall that the sequences of nucleotides in a gene change over time due to mutations. DNA sequence analysis depends on the fact that the more related two organisms are, the more similar their DNA will be. Because there are thousands of genes in most organisms, DNA contains a huge amount of information on evolutionary history.

Because all living organisms share the same genetic code and use the same 20 amino acids, it has been possible to determine that organisms share a remarkable number of proteins that are similar to one another. Due to mutations, the sequences of nucleotides change over time. Thus, comparing the sequences of DNA in organisms can show evolutionary relationships among the organisms. Scientists hope to eventually be able to correlate changes in DNA sequences with past geological events.

Pseudogenes Sequences of DNA nucleotides known as pseudogenes also provide evidence of evolution. Pseudogenes are like vestigial structures. They no longer function but are still carried along with functional DNA. They can also change as they are passed on through generations, so they provide another way to figure out evolutionary relationships. Functioning genes may be similar in organisms with similar lifestyles, such as a wolf and a coyote, due to natural selection. Similarities between pseudogenes, however, must reflect a common ancestor.

Protein comparisons Similarities among cell types across organisms can be revealed by comparing their proteins, a technique called molecular fingerprinting. A unique set of proteins are found in specific types of cells, such as liver or muscle cells. Computers are used to search databases of protein sequences and look for homologous sequences in different species. Cells from different species that have the same proteins most likely come from a common ancestor. For example, the proteins of light-sensitive cells in the brainlike structure of an ancient marine worm, as shown in **FIGURE 5.2**, were found to closely resemble those of cells found in the vertebrate eye. This resemblance shows a shared ancestry between worms and vertebrates. It also shows that the cells of the vertebrate eye originally came from cells in the brain.

Homeobox genes As you will learn in the chapter Invertebrate Diversity, homeobox genes control the development of specific structures. These sequences of genes are found in many organisms, from fruit flies to humans. They also indicate a very distant common ancestor. Evidence of homeobox gene clusters are found in organisms that lived as far back as 600 million years ago.

Explain **How have protein comparisons helped determine ancestral relationships between organisms?**

READING TOOLBOX

VOCABULARY

A pseudogene is a DNA sequence that resembles a gene but seems to have no function. *Pseudo-* means "false" or "deceptive."

FIGURE 5.2 The eye spots of this ragworm have light-sensitive cells with a molecular fingerprint similar to that of a vertebrate eye.

Take It Further

Much of the molecular evidence used to support evolution and evolutionary relationships among organisms comes from comparisons of **mitochondrial DNA.** Unlike nuclear DNA, mitochondrial DNA ordinarily does not undergo recombination. Therefore, any differences between two sequences of mitochrondrial DNA are the result of mutations that occurred after the two species diverged from their common lineage.

Vocabulary

Academic Vocabulary The prefix **pseudo-** has been affixed to a number of nouns to suggest a fake, or counterfeit.

pseudointellectual, someone who pretends to be more intelligent than he or she really is

pseudonym, a fictional name, or alias; the writer Stephen King wrote several books under the *pseudonym* Richard Bachman

pseudoscience, theories or methods that have no real scientific basis

Science Trivia

The photosensitive eyespots such as those found in marine and freshwater worms are called *ocelli.* Although the eyespots give these organisms a cross-eyed appearance, the difference between "whites" and "pupils" is merely a difference in pigment colors.

PRE-AP

On the board, use colored chalk or markers to represent chromosomes and colored sticky notes for genes to create this diagram comparing homeobox genes. Have students discuss what can be inferred from the similarities and differences between the gene clusters in the three species. The two insects are closely related. The mouse's genes are laid out in a similar fashion, but on different chromosomes. Similarities suggest common ancestry; differences suggest evolution. The diagram is included in Teacher Resources at **HMHScience.com**.

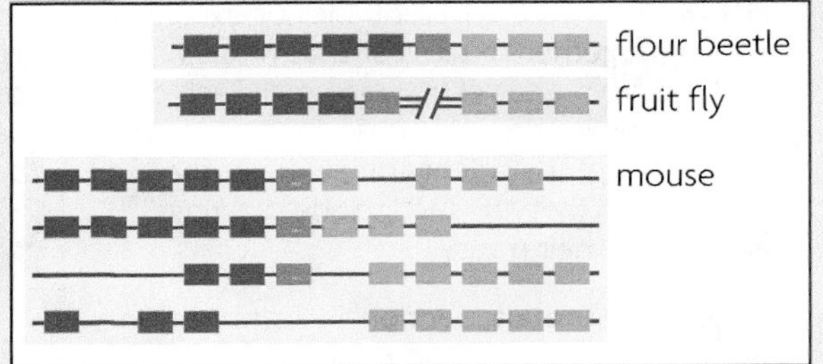

Answers

A **Explain** Cells from different species that have similar types of proteins are likely to be descended from a common ancestor.

▼ Teach *continued*

TEACH FROM VISUALS

FIGURE 5.3 Tell students that the term *ungulates,* which refers to hoofed mammals, is not a particularly useful term anymore. It makes sense for ungulates such as the horse, elephant, hippopotamus, and antelope. However, recent fossil and molecular evidence has brought sea cows and aardvarks into the group, and possibly whales and dolphins. All of these animals appear to share a common ancestor that dates back about 90 million years. The object of this diagram is to show the various lines of evidence suggesting that whales are part of the ungulate family.

Ask, Looking at the fossil evidence, which features show clear homology among the three fossil species? Answers may include features such as jaws, teeth, and vertebrae, but certainly forelimbs. Ask students to relate the diagram of the vestigial pelvic and leg bones to the three fossils shown.

Take It Further

Whales are among the most distinctive groups of organisms on Earth. There are nearly 80 species of whales living today. They include the blue whale, which is the largest animal that ever lived, and the humpback whale, which courts mates by "singing." The Gray whale undertakes a remarkable journey each year, swimming from Baja California to the southern edge of the Arctic Ocean in spring and then returning to the Baja coast in the fall. This journey is 12,000 miles roundtrip, making it one of the longest known animal migrations.

Answers

A **Critical Viewing** Toothed whales are more closely related to *Dorudon* because both species have teeth.

FIGURE 5.3 Evidence of Whale Evolution

The evidence that whales descended from hoofed mammals is supported by scientific research in several different fields of biology.

Modern-day whale

Vestigial Evidence

Many modern whale species have vestigial pelvic and leg bones. They also have vestigial nerves for the sense of smell, and small muscles devoted to external ears that no longer exist.

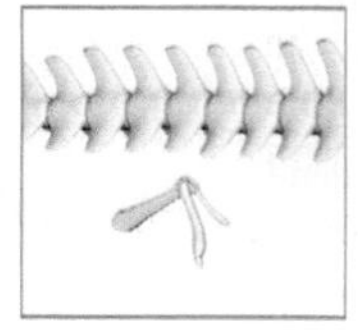

Embryological Evidence

Whale embryos have features such as hind leg buds and nostrils that resemble those of land animals. Nostrils are at the end of the whale's snout early in development but travel to the top of the head to form one or more blowholes before birth.

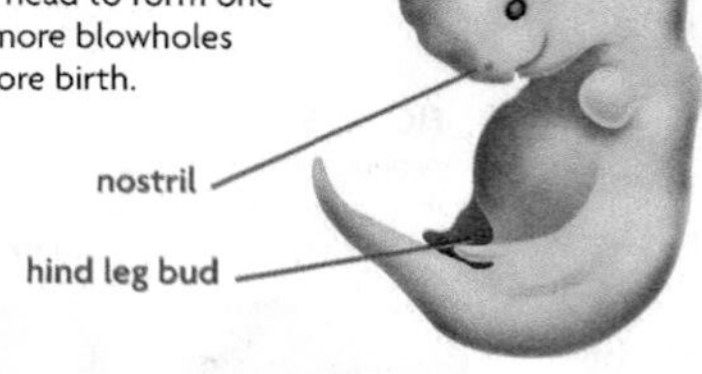

Molecular Evidence

The DNA sequences of milk protein genes in whales and hoofed mammals are very similar, as demonstrated by the DNA fragments below.

Hippopotamus	TCC TGGCA GTCCA GTGGT
Humpback whale	CCC TGGCA GTGCA GTGCT

Fossil Evidence

There are many transitional fossils that have characteristics of both land mammals and whales. These are a few examples.

Dorudon about 40 million years ago

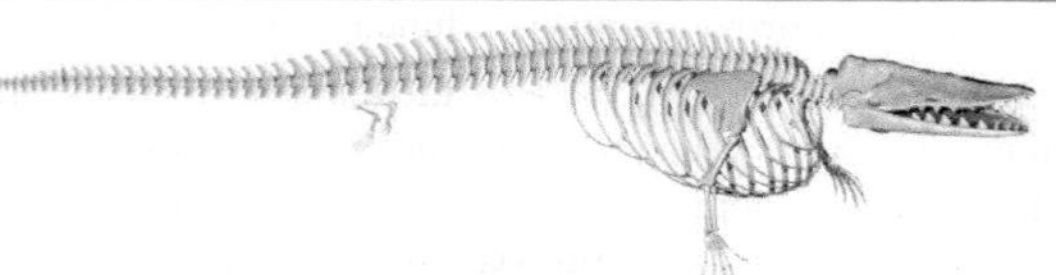

Tiny hind legs were useless on land, and a shorter neck and longer tail makes *Dorudon* similar to modern-day whales. Its ankle joints closely resemble those of modern ungulates.

Ambulocetus natans about 50 million years ago

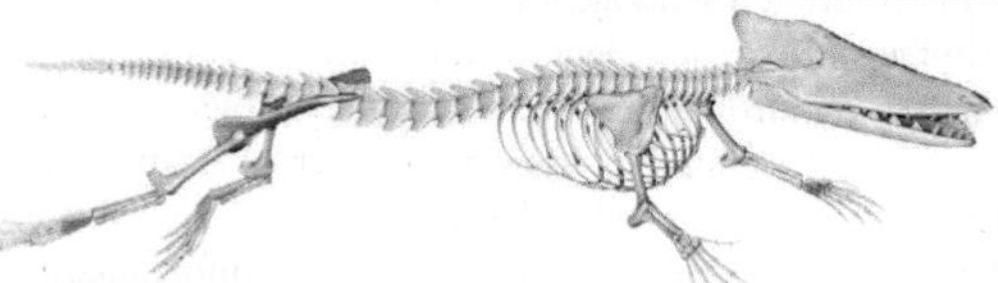

With a name that means "the walking whale that swims," *Ambulocetus natans* was an amphibious fish eater the size of a sea lion.

Pakicetus about 50 million years ago

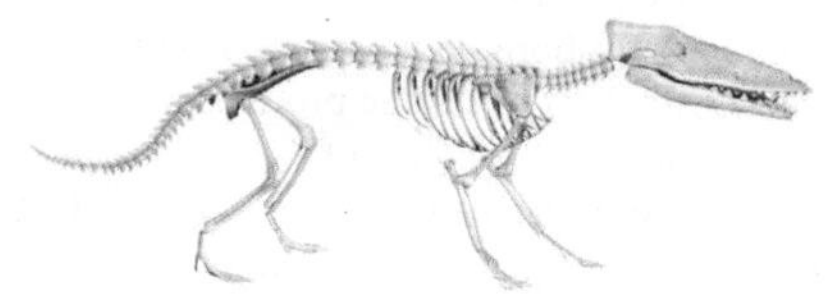

Pakicetus had a whale-shaped skull and teeth adapted for hunting fish. However, with ear bones that are in between those of land and aquatic mammals, it could not hear well underwater or make deep dives.

A CRITICAL VIEWING **Whales are divided into two groups: toothed whales, such as the orca pictured above, and baleen whales, such as the humpback whale pictured on the next page. Which would you predict is most closely related to *Dorudon*? Explain.**

Differentiated Instruction

INCLUSION

For students who have difficulty processing complex visual information, describe how **FIGURE 5.3** shows different lines of evidence coming together to suggest that whales evolved from a terrestrial mammal. Each of the four boxes provides one piece of the puzzle. Suggest students break down the information by type and include drawings along with their notes.

Teacher Toolkit, Section C, Combination Notes

PRE-AP

Using the three fossil skeletons shown in **FIGURE 5.3,** have students prepare a sequence diagram. Tell them to start with the oldest organism and describe a series of events that could lead to the evolution of a sea mammal, the whale, from a land mammal, the *Pakicetus.*

Teacher Toolkit, Section C, Sequence Diagram

MAIN IDEA

Evolution unites all fields of biology.

Scientists are still actively studying evolution through natural selection. The 21st century is an exciting time to study evolutionary biology. New tools are providing more data than ever before. Considering the number of proteins in a single organism, the amount of data gathered through molecular evidence alone is overwhelming.

Scientists from many fields of science are shedding new light on the mechanisms and patterns of evolution. In some cases, the use of modern technology has supported fossil evidence. For example, you have read that fossil evidence suggests that early ancestors of whales were hoofed land mammals. Comparing the examples from the fossil record shown in **FIGURE 5.3** highlights the transitional characteristics between land mammals and whales. Shifts in skull shape, modified limb structures, and changes in tail length provide evidence for the descent of modern whales from a common ancestor with the group of hoofed mammals that includes deer, antelope, and hippopotamuses. Comparisons of milk protein genes confirm this relationship and even provide evidence that the hippopotamus is the closest living land animal related to whales.

FIGURE 5.4 Baleen whales, such as this humpback whale, have evolved a highly specialized adaptation for catching microscopic food. Molecular techniques have allowed scientists to discover the whale's relationship with hoofed animals.

The basic principles of evolution are used in fields such as medicine, geology, geography, chemistry, and ecology. The idea of common descent helps biologists understand where new diseases come from, as well as how to best manage endangered species. There is so much more waiting to be discovered about life on Earth. As the great geneticist Theodosius Dobzhansky (1900–1975) once noted, "Nothing in biology makes sense except in the light of evolution."

Evaluate How would you rate the strength of the support provided by fossil evidence for common ancestry among groups such as land mammals and whales? Explain.

10.5 Formative Assessment

SELF-CHECK Online
HMHScience.com
GO ONLINE

REVIEWING MAIN IDEAS

1. How has our knowledge of the fossil record changed since Darwin proposed his theory of natural selection?
2. How has molecular genetics, combined with **paleontology**, added to our understanding of evolution?
3. What are some of the fields of science to which evolutionary biology contributes?

CRITICAL THINKING

4. **Apply** Describe how similar protein comparisons of cells in two species can suggest a close evolutionary relationship.
5. **Synthesize** You have discovered the fossil remains of three organisms. One is mammalian, one is reptilian, and the third has both mammalian and reptilian features. What techniques could you apply to determine possible relationships among these organisms?

CONNECT TO GENETICS

6. Researchers have found that a gene controlling reproduction is linked to the gene for the number of digits an organism has. How does this help explain why many vertebrates have five digits per limb, despite the fact that there is no fitness benefit in having five rather than six or four?

10.5 FORMATIVE ASSESSMENT

1. Many more fossils have been found, and many gaps in the fossil record, such as the gap between humans and our apelike ancestors, are being filled.
2. Genetics has provided the understanding of the way traits can be inherited; paleontology adds supporting data about events that have been inferred from the fossil record.
3. *Sample answers:* medicine, geology, geography, chemistry, and ecology
4. Proteins are encoded by an organism's DNA, which transmits heritable traits. If cells from different species have similar or identical proteins, this suggests an evolutionary relationship.
5. comparative anatomy, DNA sequence analysis, and protein comparisons
6. The gene that controls reproduction is important and likely to be conserved. Because this gene is linked to (close to) the gene affecting the digit number on limbs, this trait is likely to be conserved as well.

History of Science

At the age of 15, **Theodosius Dobzhansky** read Darwin's *On the Origin of Species.* He went on to study biology at the University of Kiev. In 1927, he immigrated to the United States, where he worked on fruit fly genetics with Thomas Hunt Morgan. By that point, Darwin's theory of natural selection had lost momentum because many scientists found it difficult to reconcile the new understanding of genes with Darwin's ideas on species origins.

In his 1937 book *Genetics and the Origin of Species,* Dobzhansky defined species in terms of gene compatibility: organisms whose genomes are too different cannot successfully produce offspring. He also proposed that most mutations were neutral in their immediate effect, neither harmful nor helpful to an individual, but the variation they introduced could prove adaptive at some future point. His ideas helped lead to development of the **modern synthesis,** which proposed how mutations and natural selection could produce large-scale evolutionary changes.

Answers

A Evaluate Answers will vary. Accept any answer that the student can support with a logical argument based on evidence. Students who find the evidence to be weak may say that they want to see additional fossil evidence.

Assess and Reteach

Assess Use the Section Self-Check or Section Quiz, both available at **HMHScience.com.**

Reteach Have students work in groups to present an oral summary of the major lines of evidence (molecular, genetic, fossil, comparative anatomy, comparative embryology) supporting evolution.

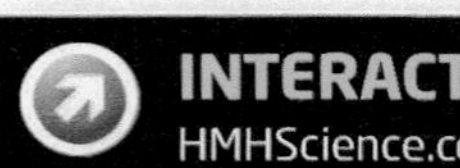

INTERACTIVE Review
HMHScience.com

GO ONLINE

Encourage students to go to **HMHScience.com** for a detailed review of each section, including visuals and vocabulary practice.

Online Student Resources, Vocabulary Practice Worksheet

CHAPTER 10 Summary

BIG IDEA Many different forms of evidence support the theory that Earth is ancient and that species can change over time.

KEY CONCEPTS

10.1 Early Ideas About Evolution

There were theories of biological and geologic change before Darwin. Early biologists suggested that different species might have shared ancestors, and geologists observed that new species appeared in the fossil record. Charles Lyell proposed the theory of uniformitarianism to explain how present-day observations explain past events.

10.2 Darwin's Observations

Darwin's voyage provided insights into evolution. Darwin observed variations between island species on his voyage, such as with the Galápagos tortoises. He noticed that species have adaptations that allow them to better survive in their environments. He also observed fossil evidence of species changing over time.

10.3 Theory of Natural Selection

Darwin proposed natural selection as a mechanism for evolution. Natural selection is a mechanism by which individuals that have inherited beneficial adaptations produce more offspring on average than do other individuals. Natural selection is based upon four principles: overproduction, variation, adaptation, and descent with modification.

10.4 Evidence of Evolution

Evidence of common ancestry among species comes from many sources. Fossil evidence is a record of change in a species over time. The study of biogeography showed that species could adapt to different environments. Two species that exhibit similar traits during development likely have a common ancestor. Vestigial and homologous structures also point to a shared ancestry.

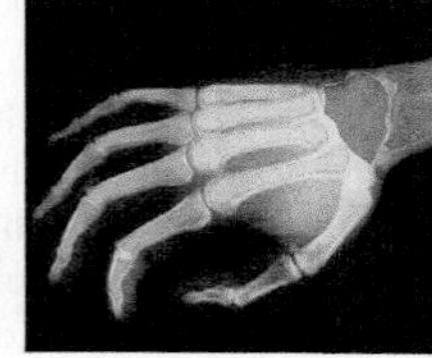

10.5 Evolutionary Biology Today

New technology is furthering our understanding of evolution. Modern techniques, such as DNA sequence analysis and molecular fingerprinting, continue to provide new information about the way evolution occurs. Evolution is a unifying theme of all the fields of biology today.

READING TOOLBOX SYNTHESIZE YOUR NOTES

Main Idea Web Use a main idea web to summarize the four principles of natural selection.

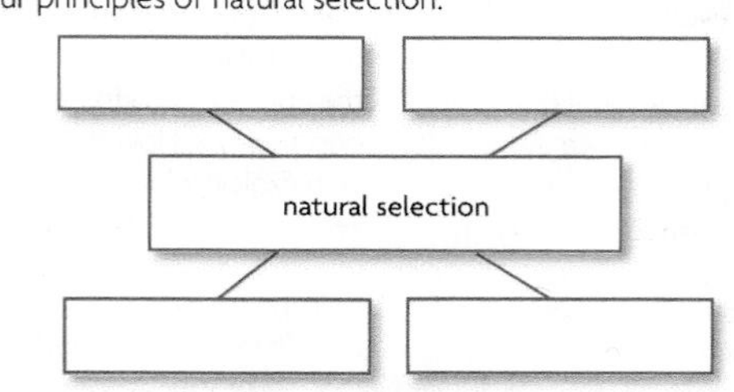

Concept Map Use a concept map like the one below to summarize what you know about evolutionary evidence.

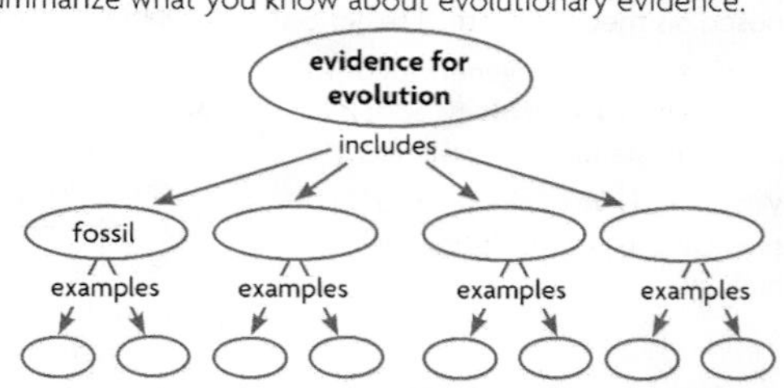

Reviewing Vocabulary

1. **Catastrophism** is the theory that geologic change happened because of sudden large-scale events, while **gradualism** states that geologic change occurred slowly over a long span of time.
2. Within every **population,** there is natural **variation.**
3. **Evolution** occurs through natural selection as changes in the environment make different **adaptations** more or less beneficial for the survival of the species.
4. **Analogous structures** have similar functions but different structures. **Vestigial structures** have little or no function but are homologous to functional structures possessed by an ancestor.
5. **Fossils** are remains of past organisms that are studied by scientists in the field of **paleontology.**
6. The meaning of the prefix *homo-*, "same," refers to the way homologous structures exhibit a similar structure and origin.
7. The meaning of the word *vestigium*, "track" or "footprint," refers to the way a vestigial structure is like a footprint from the past, offering clues about an organism's evolution.

Reviewing Main Ideas

8. Possible answers may include the following ideas: species could change over time, species shared common ancestors, more complex forms of life arose from less complex forms, or the environment affected organisms and could cause them to change over time.

10 Review

INTERACTIVE Review
HMHScience.com
GO ONLINE
Review Games • Concept Map • Section Self-Checks

CHAPTER VOCABULARY

10.1 evolution, species, fossil, catastrophism, gradualism, uniformitarianism

10.2 variation, adaptation

10.3 artificial selection, heritability, natural selection, population, fitness

10.4 biogeography, homologous structure, analogous structure, vestigial structure

10.5 paleontology

Reviewing Vocabulary

Vocabulary Connections

The vocabulary terms in this chapter are related to each other in various ways. For each group of words below, write a sentence or two to clearly explain how the terms are connected. For example, for the terms *variation* and *natural selection*, you could write "Natural selection depends on heritable variations."

1. catastrophism, gradualism
2. population, variation
3. adaptation, evolution
4. vestigial structure, analogous structure
5. fossil, paleontology

READING TOOLBOX GREEK AND LATIN WORD ORIGINS

6. The term *homologous* comes from the Greek word *homos*, which means "the same". Explain how this meaning relates to *homologous* structures.
7. The term *vestigial* comes from the Latin word *vestigium*, which means "track or footprint". Explain how this meaning relates to *vestigial* structures.

Reviewing MAIN IDEAS

8. Describe one idea about evolution that was proposed before Darwin published his theory of natural selection.
9. Briefly explain how the geologist Charles Lyell influenced Darwin's ideas about how evolution works.
10. What insights did Darwin gain from observing island organisms such as the Galápagos tortoises and finches?
11. On his voyage, Darwin found fossils of extinct organisms that resembled living organisms and shells of marine organisms high up in the mountains. How did these observations provide evidence that Earth is very old?
12. Thomas Malthus was an economist who proposed that resources such as food, water, and shelter are natural limits to human population growth. Explain how Darwin extended this idea in his theory of natural selection.
13. Why is heritability important for both natural and artificial selection?
14. Natural selection is based on four main principles: variation, overproduction, adaptation, and descent with modification. Briefly explain how each of these principles is necessary for natural selection to occur.
15. Explain how the sequential nature of fossil groups found in rock strata supports Darwin's principle of "descent with modification".
16. Embryology provides evidence of evolution by revealing developmental homologies among species. Analyze and evaluate one example of such embryological evidence.
17. Give an example of a vestigial structure and explain how vestigial structures are significant to evolution.
18. Paleontology is the study of fossils or extinct organisms. Explain how this field is important to evolutionary biology.
19. How are genes and proteins similar to homologous structures when determining evolutionary relationships among species?
20. Explain what the following quote by Theodosius Dobzhansky means: "Nothing in biology makes sense except in the light of evolution."

9. Lyell proposed the theory of uniformitarianism, which states that the geologic processes that shape Earth are uniform through time. He concluded, from observed changes, that Earth must be very old. Darwin thought that species might also change through time, but that this, too, could only be possible if Earth were much older than commonly believed at the time.

10. Similar organisms on different islands have slight differences called variations.

11. The fact that fossils look like living species suggested that modern animals might have some relationship to fossil forms. For such changes to occur, Earth must be very old. Fossil shells of marine organisms high in the mountains also indicated change occurs over long periods of time.

12. Resources are limited in nature, and organisms have more offspring than can survive. Variation in a population makes it more likely that some individuals will survive and produce offspring with beneficial adaptations.

13. Only if traits are heritable can they be selected by either natural or artificial selection and passed on to offspring.

14. **Variation** in a population ensures that some traits will be beneficial in a given environment. **Overproduction** increases competition for resources and decreases chances that all individuals will survive to reproduce. **Adaptations** give an individual a survival advantage over competitors. **Descent with modification** occurs as environments "select" certain adaptations through differential reproductive success.

15. Rock strata provide a record of some of the adaptations of different organisms living in a location over time. Fossil organisms found in the bottom, or older, layers are more primitive than those in the upper, or newer, layers. The addition of complexity and new adaptations over time supports descent with modification.

16. *Sample answers:* The embryos of chordates all have a dorsal nerve cord that extends into a flexible tail. Many vertebrates retain their tails throughout their lives. Humans retain only a shortened remnant called the coccyx, or tailbone, at the end of the spine. The presence of similar embryological structures provides evidence of a common ancestor.

17. *Sample Answers:* A snake's pelvic bones and hind limbs, an ostrich's wings, and the human appendix are examples of vestigial structures and show evidence of common ancestry with other species possessing those structures.

18. Paleontology provides a record of past life forms and the way they have changed over time, which illuminates relationships between species.

19. If very different species share a similar set of genes or proteins, they probably share a common ancestor.

20. Students should communicate that all fields of biology are based on evolutionary principles.

Critical Thinking

21. Both Darwin and Lamarck thought that traits that helped an organism survive were passed on to offspring, but neither of them knew how.
22. Answers will vary. Accept any answer that the student can support with a logical argument.
23. *Sample answer:* Carrion eaters with fewer head feathers may have been less susceptible to disease because fewer feathers meant fewer ways for germs to collect. They survived longer or in greater numbers, allowing them to reproduce more than heavily feathered birds. If the number of head feathers was a heritable trait, then over generations, the carrion eaters with the highest fitness may have been those with no feathers on their head.
24. *Sample answer:* A shift in the position of nostrils from the front of the muzzle to a blowhole on the top of the skull. A reduction in limb size, with an increase in size and strength of the tail. Changes in the bone structure of the ear.

Interpreting Visuals

25. The flower was emphasized to produce the cauliflower, and the leaves were emphasized to produce the cabbage.
26. Students should mention that plants with the desirable traits would have to be selected to reproduce for many generations to finally obtain broccoli with small flowers and thick stems.
27. A protein comparison of broccoli, cabbage, and cauliflower would confirm that they all share a common ancestor.

Critical Thinking

21. Compare Jean-Baptiste Lamarck hypothesized that changes in an environment led to an organism's greater or lesser use of a body part. Although his hypothesis was incomplete, what ideas related to evolution did Lamarck and Charles Darwin share?

22. Evaluate What types of scientific evidence provide support for common ancestry among groups such as land mammals and whales? How would you assess the relative strength of these different types of evidence?

23. Analyze The turkey vulture and the California condor both feed upon dead animals, known as carrion. Neither species of bird has feathers on its head. Explain how natural selection may have played a role in the featherless heads of these carrion eaters.

24. Analyze What are three trends that biologists have identified in the transitional characteristics of different groups in the whale fossil record?

Interpreting Visuals

Use the following diagram, which shows the evolution of the wild mustard plant, to answer the next three questions.

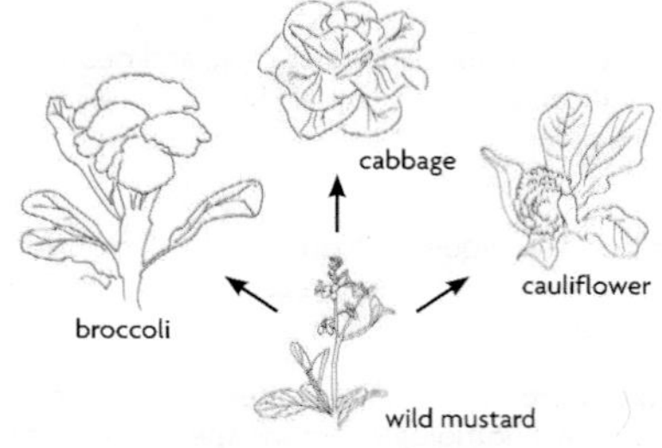

25. Infer Traits of the wild mustard plant have been emphasized by artificial selection to produce different vegetables. In some varieties, the flower heads were emphasized. In other vegetables, it was the leaves or the stems that were to be eaten. Which traits were emphasized to produce cauliflower? Cabbage?

26. Apply Describe a procedure humans may have used to produce broccoli, which has small flowers and thick stems.

27. Predict What would a protein comparison of broccoli, cabbage, and cauliflower confirm about their relationships to each other?

Analyzing Data Interpret Line Graphs

One hundred million seabirds use the island of Gaugh, in the South Atlantic Ocean, as a critical nesting ground. Non-native carnivorous mice eat the helpless seabird chicks at a rate of about 1 million per year. Prior to the arrival of the mice, no natural predators existed on the island, so the birds did not evolve any defense mechanisms. Scientists estimate the current population of the mice at 700,000. The graph below displays a projection of seabird casualties and changes in the size of the mouse population.

SEABIRD CASUALTIES AND MOUSE POPULATION

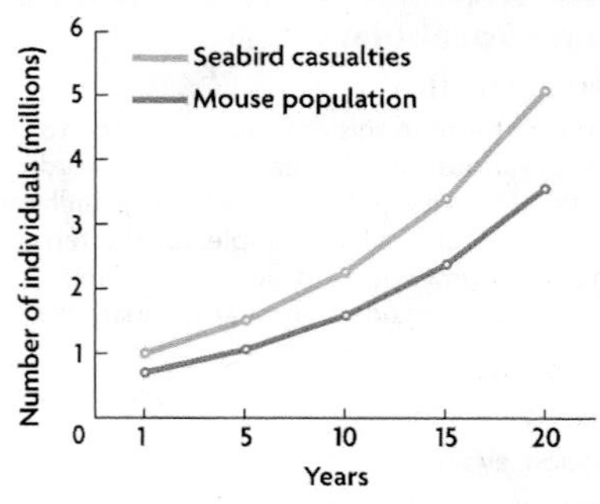

28. Interpret What does the graph show about seabird casualties and the mouse population over a 20-year period?

29. Predict Imagine that some seabirds began defending their nests from the mice, and that this behavior is heritable. What changes might such a graph show over the next 20 years? Explain.

Making Connections

30. Write a Scenario Imagine a way in which seabirds could adapt to the mouse population and avoid predation of their chicks. Then consider how, after many generations, the mouse population could counter this defense and again limit the seabird population. What are possible adaptations that could lead to this co-evolution of mice and seabirds?

31. Synthesize Look again at the picture of the star-nosed mole. Its claws are well adapted for breaking through soil. How could natural selection have played a role in this trait becoming common among star-nosed moles?

Analyzing Data

28. As the mouse population increased, the seabird casualties increased.

29. Accept all reasonable answers. *Sample answer:* As seabirds began defending their nests and this became a common behavior in the population, the seabird casualty line would level off and then drop. The mouse population would also drop, possibly at a very similar rate and time span.

Standards-Based Assessment

Record your answers on a separate piece of paper.

MULTIPLE CHOICE

1 As developing embryos, some organisms appear to have features that are similar in structure. As these organisms continue their development, features that were similar in the embryonic stage develop into different structures that have different functions. What type of evidence of common ancestry do these features represent?

A vestigial structures

B homologous structures

C analogous structures

D fossil structures

2 Although the fossil record is incomplete, paleontologists continue to search for fossils that are commonly referred to as "missing links." What evidence of evolution do discoveries of fossil evidence known as "missing links" provide to scientists?

A Discoveries of "missing links" provide fossil evidence that contradicts the theory of evolution.

B Discoveries of "missing links" show that organisms once thought to be related are not.

C Discoveries of "missing links" serve as transitional species that show the evolution within and between related groups.

D Discoveries of "missing links" serve as additional evidence that organisms do not change or evolve.

3 All vertebrates have very similar *Hox* genes. How does this provide evidence suggesting vertebrates evolved from a common ancestor?

A Greater similarity of genes indicates closer evolutionary relationships among species.

B Species with major differences in *Hox* genes would have gone extinct.

C The greater the number of *Hox* genes present, the greater the relationship among species.

D *Hox* genes control the same genes in all species of vertebrates.

4 The diagram below represents several sedimentary rock layers in which fossils of different organisms have been found. The rock layers show no evidence of having been disturbed since their formation.

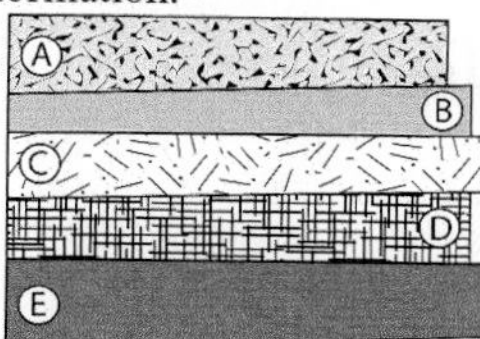

What information about the ages of the fossils relative to each other can be explained by their positions in these rock layers?

A The rock layers do not provide any information about the ages of the fossils relative to each other.

B The rock layers suggest that the fossils in layer A are much older than those in layers B, C, D, and E.

C The rock layers suggest that the oldest fossils are in layer E and the youngest are in layer A.

D The rock layers suggest that all of the fossils found in the rocks will be of the same age regardless of the type of organism the fossil represents.

5 An herbicide killed 99% of a weed population. Which of the following is the ***best*** biological explanation for some weeds being able to survive?

A Some individuals were able to evolve before the spraying.

B The spray caused some individuals to mutate, and they were able to survive and reproduce.

C Each individual occupied a different ecological niche and so some were unaffected.

D Genetic variation in the population allowed some weeds to survive.

THINK THROUGH THE QUESTION

Consider what conditions must be present for natural selection to occur.

Standards-Based Assessment

The Standards-Based Assessment questions will help students prepare for their final examination in the course. If you wish to give students practice in coding their answers, look for the Standards-Based Assessment Answer Sheet at **HMHScience.com**. To give students practice under timed testing conditions, allow them five minutes per question.

Question	Answer	Depth of Knowledge	Cognitive Complexity
1	B	II	L
2	C	III	M
3	A	I	M
4	C	II	M
5	D	II	M

KEY

Depth of Knowledge		Cognitive Complexity	
I	Recall	L	Low
II	Skill/Concept	M	Moderate
III	Strategic Thinking	H	High
IV	Extended Thinking		

Making Connections

30. *Sample answer:* The seabirds might use aggressive behavior, actively defending their nests. The mice start eating the eggs when the nests are not being watched rather than waiting for chicks to hatch. Possible seabird adaptations might be behavioral, such as loud squawking, wing-flapping, pecking. Mouse adaptations might include larger jaws or sharper teeth to pierce eggshells.

31. *Sample answer:* Moles that had longer, stronger claws may have been able to find food faster and thus have better nutrition and reach reproductive age more frequently than moles with shorter claws. Or, better nutrition meant they had larger numbers of offspring. If longer, stronger claws were heritable traits and continued to be beneficial to the moles, over generations, they would become common throughout the star-nosed mole population.

CHAPTER 11

Instruction and Intervention Support

The Evolution of Populations

① Core Instruction

The **Core Instruction** resources below can be used for all students. Core instruction should be followed by ongoing assessment to determine which students need further help.

Available in both English and Spanish | Available Online

Section	Instruction	PRINT	ONLINE	Labs
11.1	Textbook **Genetic Variation Within Populations**	■	◉	
	That's Amazing! Video Inquiry Shark Trails		◉	
	PowerPresentation and Notes 11.1		◉	
11.2	Textbook **Natural Selection in Populations**	■	◉	Natural Selection in African Swallowtails
	PowerPresentation and Notes 11.2		◉	
11.3	Textbook **Other Mechanisms in Evolution**	■	◉	Modeling Alleles (Challenge Lab) **QuickLab** Genetic Drift **Video Lab** Genetic Drift
	Animated Biology Founder Effect, Population Size and Genetic Drift		◉	
	PowerPresentation and Notes 11.3		◉	
11.4	Textbook **Hardy-Weinberg Equilibrium**	■	◉	Investigating an Anole Lizard Population Population Genetics S.T.E.M. Lab Hardy-Weinberg Equation
	Animated Biology Mechanisms of Evolution		◉	
	PowerPresentation and Notes 11.4		◉	
11.5	Textbook **Speciation Through Isolation**	■	◉	Exploring Dog Genetics and Evolution
	PowerPresentation and Notes 11.5		◉	
11.6	Textbook **Patterns in Evolution**	■	◉	Exploring Adaptations Microevolution and Antibiotic-Resistant Bacteria (Biotechnology Lab) Investigating Plant Adaptations (Challenge Lab)
	PowerPresentation and Notes 11.6		◉	

Additional online resources available for this chapter include **Interactive Whiteboard Resources.**

GO ONLINE! for all your teacher resources at HMHScience.com

2 Support and Intervention

Support and Intervention resources are useful for students who need targeted help beyond the Core Instruction

Resources	PRINT	ONLINE
Assess and Reteach (TE wrap)	■	●
Concept Map		●
Interactive Reader	■	●
Interactive Review Games		●
Section Self-Checks		●
Study Guide B		●
Virtual Investigation Population Genetics		●
Vocabulary Practice Worksheets		●

3 Specialized Support

Students who need more intensive personalized intervention benefit from **Specialized Support** resources.

Resources	PRINT	ONLINE
Chapter Audio Files		●
Differentiated Instruction Inclusion, Below Level, and English Learners (TE wrap)	■	●
ELL Strategies	■	●
Modified Lesson Plans for English Learners		●
Reinforcement Worksheets		●
Study Guide A		●

Extension and Assessment

Enrichment and Challenge

Resources	PRINT	ONLINE
Active Reading Worksheets		●
Data Analysis Practice Worksheet		●
Differentiated Instruction Pre-AP (TE wrap)	■	●
Pre-AP Activity Calculating Gene Frequencies		●
Smart Grapher Activity		●
The Inside Story and **Take It Further** (TE wrap)	■	●
Unit Project		●
WebLinks		●
WebQuest Speciation in Action (11.5)		●

Assessment

Resources	PRINT	ONLINE
Alternative Assessment		●
Chapter Tests A and B		●
Diagnostic Test		●
ExamView Banks		●
Extended Response Test		●
Online Assessment System		●
Section Quizzes		●
Standards-Based Assessment	■	●

CHAPTER 11

Chapter Overview

- **Section 1** describes the sources and significance of genetic variation within populations.
- **Section 2** describes how natural selection affects the distribution of traits within a population.
- **Section 3** explains how populations can evolve due to gene flow, genetic drift, and sexual selection.
- **Section 4** describes the use of the Hardy-Weinberg equilibrium equation as a framework for understanding the evolution of populations.
- **Section 5** explains how the isolation of populations can lead to speciation.
- **Section 6** describes different types and rates of evolution.

Focus and Motivate

How does a population of penguins evolve?

Have students discuss ways in which the penguin population could be evolving. **Ask**

- What traits of penguins are adaptive to the Antarctic environment? insulating layer of blubber, feathers, brood pouch
- What factors would result in changes to the genetic variation of penguins in a colony? mutation, recombination of alleles

BIOZINE HMHScience.com

Students can access BioZine at **HMHScience.com** to find topics suitable for research reports, writing assignments, or classroom debates.

CHAPTER 11 The Evolution of Populations

BIG IDEA The genetic composition of populations evolves through natural selection as species adapt to changes in their environment.

ONLINE BIOLOGY HMHScience.com

ONLINE Labs

- Natural Selection in African Swallowtails
- **QuickLab** Genetic Drift
- Investigating an Anole Lizard Population
- Exploring Adaptations
- S.T.E.M. Lab Population Genetics
- Microevolution and Antibiotic-Resistant Bacteria
- Exploring Dog Genetics and Evolution
- Modeling Alleles
- Investigating Plant Adaptations
- **Video Lab** Genetic Drift
- S.T.E.M. Lab Hardy-Weinberg Equation

Student Activity

Purpose **Introduce students to phenotypic variation by showing two traits: hitchhiker's thumb and tongue-rolling ability. Students will calculate the frequency of each trait within the classroom population. Students should understand that frequency of a phenotype depends on the frequency of the genotype that codes for the trait.**

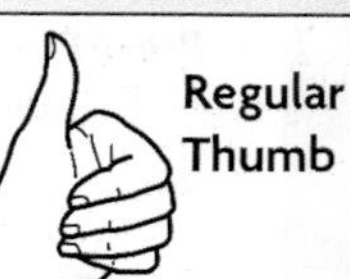

Prepare On the board, create a table similar to the example shown below.

	Hitchhiker's Thumb	Tongue Rolling
Yes	8	16
No	18	10
Total pop.	26	26

How does a population of penguins evolve?

Every year, king penguins return to breed in the same colony in which they were born. These colonies help penguins to guard, protect, and defend their young. By ensuring the success of their young, penguins pass on their genes to future generations. Variation in these genes is the basis for the evolution of populations.

READING TOOLBOX **This reading tool can help you learn the material in the following pages.**

USING LANGUAGE

General Statements A general statement often summarizes the features of a group or describes an average or typical feature of members of the group. But if many features are summarized, some individual members in the group probably do not share all of those features. And if an average feature is described, some members of the group will not match the average. So, general statements may be true most of the time, but not always.

YOUR TURN

Use what you know about general statements to complete the following tasks.

1. Write a general statement about apples, bananas, tomatoes, and peanuts.
2. List exceptions to the statement "Humans are bigger than monkeys."

Introduce Tell students that the ability to roll one's tongue or to flex a thumb tip backward into hitchhiker's thumb are traits that are coded for by genes. Have students work in small groups to determine which classmates have these traits. Compile the data on the board. Ask students to calculate the frequency of each phenotype and express it as a percentage.

Discuss Explain that tongue rolling and hitchhiker's thumb are examples of phenotypic variation within a population. Discuss how this phenotypic variation is the result of different combinations of alleles on multiple genes.

Ask, What would happen to the genetic variation of the population if, for example, all the tongue-rolling students left the class or if ten hitchhiker-thumbed students were added to the class? Frequencies would change. Perhaps some traits would disappear completely.

Remind students that genetic variation is the basis for the evolution of populations.

Activate Prior Knowledge

Have students look at the picture of the penguins. **Ask,** Do you see any variation in this population of penguins? very hard to see **Ask,** How would you describe variation in a human population? tends to be much more obvious

Point out that one reason for phenotypic variation in humans is that our ancestors lived in very different environments over tens of thousands of years. Over many generations, certain traits were selected for in response to conditions in those environments.

Ask, How might this population of penguins change if Antarctica suddenly got much warmer? Over time the penguins might develop less blubber or fewer feathers.

Preview Vocabulary

Academic Vocabulary The concept of *variation* is important in this unit, particularly as it relates to differences in populations—both genotypic and phenotypic. Ask students to identify other words that share the Latin root *varius,* meaning "of different kinds."

vary	*variable*
variability	*variation*
variety	*various*
variance	*variant*

Have students write down these words in their science notebook, define them, and then use the words in sentences.

Answers

1. *Sample answer:* Apples, bananas, tomatoes, and peanuts are fruits.
2. *Sample answers:* Some baby humans are shorter than some adult monkeys. Most monkey arms are proportionally longer than human arms.

SECTION 11.1

▼ Plan and Prepare

Activate Prior Knowledge Have students think about putting together a basketball team. **Ask,** What are the chances that you can put together a good team if just ten players try out? okay, but not great What about 30 players? much better Discuss with students that the larger group represents a larger pool of talent and skills. Tell them that the same applies to gene pools.

▼ Teach

Vocabulary

Word Origins Students will be familiar with the word **pool** in the context of swimming or billiards. Tell them that when applied to evolution and genetics, the word refers to the available supply, or pool, of alleles found in a population. This *pool* comes from the Old French *poule,* or "chicken," which goes back to the Latin *pullus,* "the young of an animal."

Answers

A Analyze Allele frequencies measure how common certain alleles are in a gene pool.

11.1 Genetic Variation Within Populations

KEY CONCEPT **A population shares a common gene pool.**

MAIN IDEAS
- Genetic variation in a population increases the chance that some individuals will survive.
- Genetic variation comes from several sources.

VOCABULARY
gene pool
allele frequency

Connect to Your World
You may think that if you've seen one penguin, you've seen them all. However, penguins can differ in body size, feather patterns, and many other traits. Just like humans, penguins are genetically different from one another. What causes genetic variation in populations of organisms? And what methods do biologists use to measure this variation?

GO ONLINE
Shark Trails

READING TOOLBOX

TAKING NOTES
Use mind maps to show relationships among related terms and concepts.

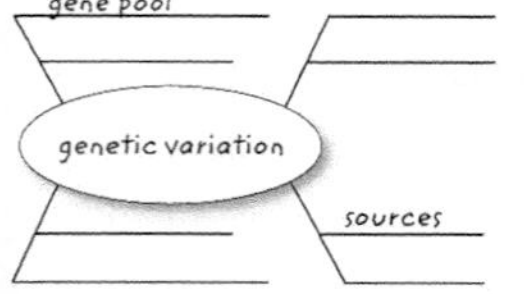

MAIN IDEA

Genetic variation in a population increases the chance that some individuals will survive.

Body size and feather patterns in penguins are each examples of phenotypes. A phenotype is a trait produced by one or more genes. In a population, there may be a wide range of phenotypes. For example, some penguins may be short and rounded. Others could be tall and slim.

Natural selection acts on different phenotypes in a population. The expression of different phenotypes, however, depends on genetic variation in a population. A population with a lot of genetic variation likely has a wide range of phenotypes. The greater the variation in phenotypes, the more likely it is that some individuals can survive in a changing environment. For example, in an unusually cold winter, short, rounded penguins might be better able to stay warm than tall, slim penguins. But if there is a shortage of food, tall, slim penguins might be better divers, allowing them to catch more fish.

Genetic variation is stored in a population's **gene pool**—the combined alleles of all of the individuals in a population. Different combinations of alleles in a gene pool can be formed when organisms mate and have offspring. Each allele exists at a certain rate, or frequency. An **allele frequency** is a measure of how common a certain allele is in the population. As shown in **FIGURE 1.1**, you can calculate allele frequencies. First, count the number of times an allele occurs in a gene pool. Then, divide by the total number of alleles for that gene in the gene pool.

A Analyze What is the relationship between allele frequencies and a gene pool?

Differentiated Instruction

ENGLISH LEARNERS

Help students recall the meanings of words *phenotype, gene, allele, meiosis,* and *gametes* by modeling the strategy Connect to Content Through Visuals: Picture Imaging. Choose one of the terms, and share with students what you visualize when you see that word. Ask them to tell you what they "see" related to it. After studying the new vocabulary in context on this page, do the same with those words.

Teacher Toolkit, Section C, Connect to Content Through Visuals

PRE-AP

Have students relate the concept of a gene pool to Mendel's work with garden peas. Ask students to write a paragraph or two about the way Mendel manipulated the gene pool in his experiments with pure-bred peas.

Teacher Toolkit, Section C, Quick-Write

FIGURE 1.1 Allele Frequency

An allele frequency is the ratio of one allele to the total number of the alleles for that gene in the gene pool.

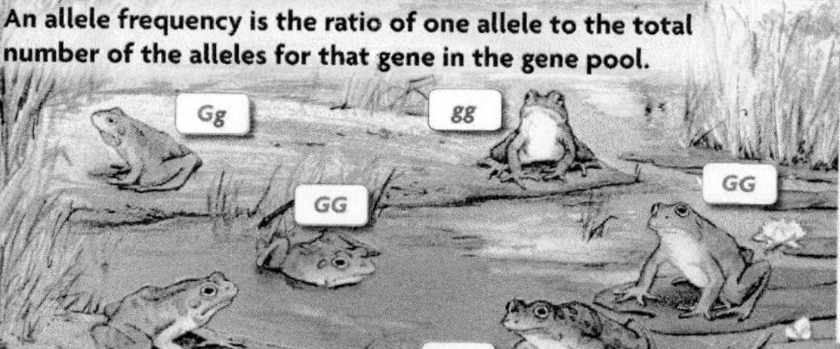

CALCULATING ALLELE FREQUENCIES

G codes for green	*g* codes for brown
7 *G*s in gene pool	5 *g*s in gene pool

12 total alleles for skin color trait in gene pool

Frequency of allele $G = \frac{7}{12} = 0.583 \approx 58.3\%$

Frequency of allele $g = \frac{5}{12} = 0.417 \approx 41.7\%$

A Predict If brown skin color became advantageous, what would likely happen to the frequencies of alleles *G* and *g* in this gene pool?

MAIN IDEA

Genetic variation comes from several sources.

Genetic variation comes from two main sources: mutation and recombination.

- **Mutation** A mutation is a random change in the DNA of a gene. This change can form a new allele. Mutations in reproductive cells can be passed on to offspring. This increases the genetic variation in the gene pool. Because there are many genes in each individual and many individuals in a population, new mutations form frequently in gene pools.
- **Recombination** New allele combinations form in offspring through a process called recombination. Most recombination occurs during meiosis—the type of cell division needed for sexual reproduction. When gametes are made, each parent's alleles are arranged in new ways. This shuffling of alleles results in many different genetic combinations.

Some biologists are studying hybridization as another source of genetic variation. Hybridization is the crossing of two different species that share common genes. Research suggests that this process occurs within many groups of animals, including birds and mammals, when similar species live in the same area and individuals cannot easily find mates of their own species.

B Infer Why aren't mutations in nonreproductive cells sources of genetic variation?

CONNECT TO

GENETICS

As you learned in the chapter **From DNA to Proteins,** mutations on noncoding regions of DNA do not affect phenotypes. Only mutations on coding regions of DNA can affect an organism's phenotype.

11.1 Formative Assessment

SELF-CHECK Online
HMHScience.com
GO ONLINE

REVIEWING MAIN IDEAS

1. Why does genetic variation increase the chance that some individuals in a population will survive?
2. Describe two main sources of genetic variation.

CRITICAL THINKING

3. **Analyze** In what way is a **gene pool** representative of a population?
4. **Apply** If a certain trait's **allele frequency** is 100%, describe the genetic variation for that trait in the population.

CONNECT TO

GENETICS

5. How does crossing over during meiosis provide a source of genetic variation? Draw a diagram to show this process.

11.1 FORMATIVE ASSESSMENT

1. Genetically diverse populations display high phenotypic variation. If changing environmental conditions favor a particular phenotype—for example, resistance to a certain disease—there is a good chance that a genetically diverse population will have some individuals who have that advantageous phenotype.
2. Mutation is a random change in DNA that can result in a new allele. Recombination rearranges allele combinations on a chromosome, possibly resulting in a new phenotype.
3. The gene pool contains all the alleles found within a population.
4. If an allele frequency for a trait is 100 percent, there is no genetic variation for that trait within the population (assuming the trait is a single-gene trait).
5. Diagrams should accurately illustrate prophase I of meiosis with homologous chromosomes crossing over, resulting in the exchange of alleles between the chromosomes and new combinations of alleles on the offspring's chromosomes.

Vocabulary

Academic Vocabulary In the word **inheritable,** the prefix *in-* does not mean "cannot" or "is not," as in *incomplete* or *incorrect*. Therefore, it is not the antonym, or opposite, of **heritable.** Rather it is a synonym that is used primarily in the context of inheriting money or property from a relative. In biology, the word *heritable* is more commonly used for the inheritance of traits. Here is a way to help students remember the distinction:

obtain the *inheritable* upon death
obtain the *heritable* upon birth

Ask, What are the antonyms? noninheritable, nonheritable

TEACH FROM VISUALS

FIGURE 1.1 The diagram shows a hypothetical population of frogs. **Ask,** What does *advantageous* mean in this example? It refers to fitness, meaning that the trait improves the chances of an individual passing on its genes to offspring. Remind students that this advantage applies to this specific environment. An advantage in one environment could be a disadvantage in a different environment.

Answers

A Predict The *G* allele would decrease in frequency, and the *g* allele would increase in frequency.

B Infer A source of genetic variation for a population must be heritable. Mutations in nonreproductive cells are not heritable.

Assess and Reteach

Assess Use the Section Self-Check or Section Quiz, both available at **HMHScience.com**.

Reteach Use the graphic organizer shown on the previous page to reteach the material. Work with students to incorporate review vocabulary words into this mind map: *phenotype, gene, allele, meiosis, gametes.*

SECTION 11.2

▼ Plan and Prepare

Activate Prior Knowledge Tell students that natural selection helps to determine not only which traits are found in a population, but also the range of a particular trait. Remind students of the Grants' study of Darwin's finches. **Ask,** When a drought resulted in the survival of more large-beaked ground finches than small-beaked ground finches, both of the same species, what was natural selection acting upon? alleles affecting beak size

▼ Teach

Vocabulary

Academic Vocabulary In everyday use, **normal** means common or average. When applied to a set of data, as in a *normal distribution* or *normal curve,* it is understood that most of the values tend to be near the average, while relatively few values are at or near the extremes.

Answers

Ⓐ **Synthesize** body weight, average income, batting averages in baseball

11.2 Natural Selection in Populations

KEY CONCEPT **Populations, not individuals, evolve.**

MAIN IDEAS
- Natural selection acts on distributions of traits.
- Natural selection can change the distribution of a trait in one of three ways.

VOCABULARY
normal distribution
microevolution
directional selection
stabilizing selection
disruptive selection

Connect to Your World

How do you describe a person's appearance? Perhaps you use height, hair color, ar eye color. These traits are often used in descriptions because these traits vary wid among humans. In this section, you will learn about the way natural selection can a on such variation.

MAIN IDEA

Natural selection acts on distributions of traits.

CONNECT TO

GENETICS

As you learned in the chapter **Extending Mendelian Genetics,** single-gene traits are expressed in either one distinct form or another. However, the range of phenotypes common for most traits is the result of polygenic traits, which are controlled by multiple genes.

Any time you stand in a large crowd of people, you are likely to observe a w range of heights. Imagine organizing this crowd across a football field accor ing to each individual's height, with very short people at one end, people of average height in the middle, and very tall people at the other end. You wou soon notice a pattern in distribution of the human height trait. Relatively fe people would be at each extreme height, very short or very tall. A majority people of medium height would be in the middle.

This type of distribution, in which the frequency is highest near the mean value and decreases toward each extreme end of the range, is called a **normal distribution.** When these frequency values are graphed, the result is bell-shaped curve like the one you see in **FIGURE 2.1.**

FIGURE 2.1 NORMAL DISTRIBUTION

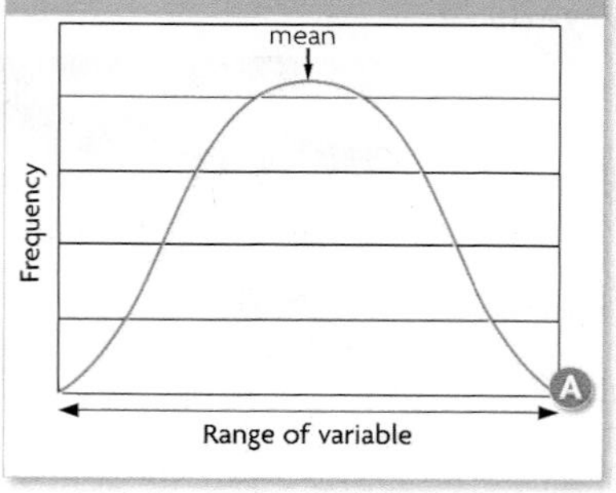

mean
Frequency
Range of variable
Ⓐ

For some traits, all phenotypes provide an equal chance of survival. The distribution for these traits generally shows a norma distribution. Phenotypes near the middle of the range tend to be most common, while the extremes are less common. However, environmental conditions can change, and a certain phenotype may become an advantage. Natural selection favors individuals wi this phenotype. These individuals are able to survive and reproduc at higher rates than individuals with less favorable phenotypes. Therefore, alleles associated with favorable phenotypes increase in frequency through differential reproductive success.

Synthesize **What other types of data might follow a normal distribution?**

Differentiated Instruction

ENGLISH LEARNERS

Plan for a round-table activity. Tell students upon finishing this section to close their books and divide into groups. Each group will be given a sheet of paper labeled with one of the three types of natural selection: *Directional, Stabilizing,* or *Disruptive.* Each student in the group will write something he or she knows about the topic, then pass the sheet to the next person. Everyone has to write something different. Allow five minutes, then compile the information for the class.

Teacher Toolkit, Section C, Round Table

HANDS-ON ACTIVITY

To demonstrate a normal distribution, pass out sticky notes, using different colors for male and female. Ask each student to write his or her height on the note. Then collect the data. Make the analogy that these are two populations and you want to find the distributions of a specific trait. Plot the two data sets on the same graph. Have students compare both the distribution and the range of sizes in the two populations. Point out that the mean is a useful statistic, but that it is possible for it to not actually appear in the population.

MAIN IDEA

Natural selection can change the distribution of a trait in one of three ways.

Microevolution is the observable change in the allele frequencies of a population over time. Microevolution occurs on a small scale—within a single population. One process that can lead to microevolution is natural selection. Natural selection can change the distribution of a trait along one of three paths: directional, stabilizing, or disruptive selection. Such changes can have major effects on how a population looks and behaves.

Directional Selection

A type of selection that favors phenotypes at one extreme of a trait's range is called **directional selection.** Directional selection causes a shift in a population's phenotypic distribution. An extreme phenotype that was once rare in a population becomes more common. As shown in **FIGURE 2.2**, during directional selection, the mean value of a trait shifts in the direction of the more advantageous phenotype.

The rise of drug-resistant bacteria provides a classic example of this type of selection. Before antibiotics were developed in the 1940s, a trait for varying levels of drug resistance existed among bacteria. At the time, there was no advantage to having drug resistance. But once antibiotics came into use, the resistant bacteria had a great advantage.

The early success of antibiotics in controlling infectious diseases led to overuse of these drugs. This overuse favored even more resistant phenotypes. New drugs were then developed to fight the resistant bacteria. This resulted in the evolution of "superbugs" that are highly resistant to many drugs. Today, over 200 types of bacteria show some degree of antibiotic resistance.

CONNECT TO

BACTERIA

Although many bacteria are helpful to other organisms, some do cause disease. You will learn more about how bacteria can evolve and become resistant to antibiotics in the chapter **Viruses and Prokaryotes.**

FIGURE 2.2 Directional Selection

Directional selection occurs when one extreme phenotype is favored by natural selection.

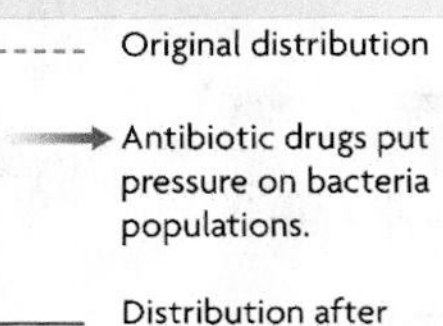

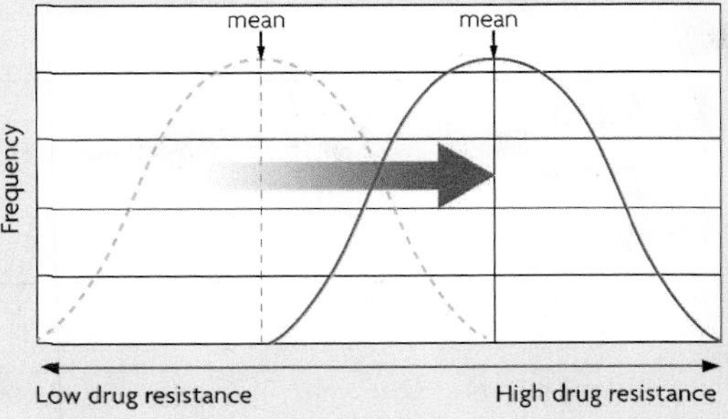

Today, scientists continue to research new drugs developed to treat infection-causing bacteria such as *Enterococcus faecalis*, which is resistant to many antibiotics.

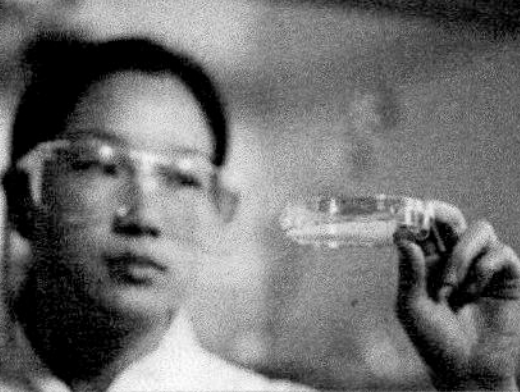

Vocabulary

Academic Vocabulary What follows are some terms commonly used in statistical analysis.

Frequency refers to the number of times a specific thing occurs or is found within a given interval or space.

Mean is the average. In a *normal distribution,* the *mean* is also the point at which the *frequency* is highest.

Range is the difference or interval between the smallest and largest values in a frequency distribution. For example, the *range* of heights is from the shortest to the tallest.

Median is the middle value in a distribution, with an equal number of values above and below. For example, in a range of integers from 0 to 10, the *median* is 5. There are five integers above and five integers below the median. In a normal distribution, the median is equal to the mean.

Mode is the value occurring most frequently in a set of data. For example, if there are five flowers in a bunch, and three of them are red, one is white, and one is pink, the *mode* is red because it is the most common color. In a normal distribution, the mode is equal to the median and the mean.

Take It Further

One of the most threatening types of **antibiotic-resistant bacteria** is *Staphylococcus aureus*, or "Staph," a major cause of infections in hospitals. Mutations in these bacteria have resulted in antibiotic-resistant strains. The bacteria's resistance to penicillin began to show up in hospitals in the 1950s. By the 1980s, *Staphylococcus aureus* had become 100 percent resistant to penicillin. Since then, different strains have evolved to become resistant to methicillin and vancomycin, which are the drugs typically used as a last resort against infection.

PRE-AP

Provide the following hypothetical data sets on Coho salmon reproduction and have students plot both on the same graph, using different colors for each data set.

# of eggs in 15 Coho salmon nests, 1985
813, 830, 830, 837, 839, 839, 839, 842, 843, 845, 847, 860, 881, 890, 893

# of eggs in 15 Coho salmon nests, 2005
853, 871, 876, 883, 883, 888, 889, 897, 899, 899, 905, 905, 905, 908, 912

Have students determine the mean, median (middle value), and mode (most common value) of each set.

1985: mean = 848.5; median = 842; mode = 839

2005: mean = 891.5; median = 897; mode = 905

Ask, Which phenotype does directional selection seem to be favoring? more eggs per nest

▼ Teach continued

TEACH FROM VISUALS

FIGURE 2.4 To help students understand the difference between stabilizing and directional selection, have them compare **FIGURE 2.4** to **FIGURE 2.2. Ask**

- What type of selection would occur if only the woodpeckers were putting pressure on the gall fly population? directional selection
- What would the resulting graph look like? The graph would resemble Figure 2.2 but shifted to the left.
- How is the dashed line being used in the graph? It represents the distribution of gall fly phenotypes that produce various gall sizes in the absence of predators.

Integrating Earth Science

Many factors that put pressure on populations are the result of changes in the physical environment. For example, changes in sea level caused by melting or freezing of polar ice, changes in land surface caused by earthquakes or volcanic eruptions, and glaciation or drought would force populations to adapt to the new conditions or migrate. Such changes might also lead to extinction for some populations.

Recent research and modeling in **climatology,** the study of the Earth's weather and climate, suggest that the huge extinction that marked the end of the Permian period may have been triggered by an increase in atmospheric carbon dioxide. Such an increase would have warmed the oceans, effectively shutting down the currents and upwelling that distribute oxygen and nutrients throughout the seas.

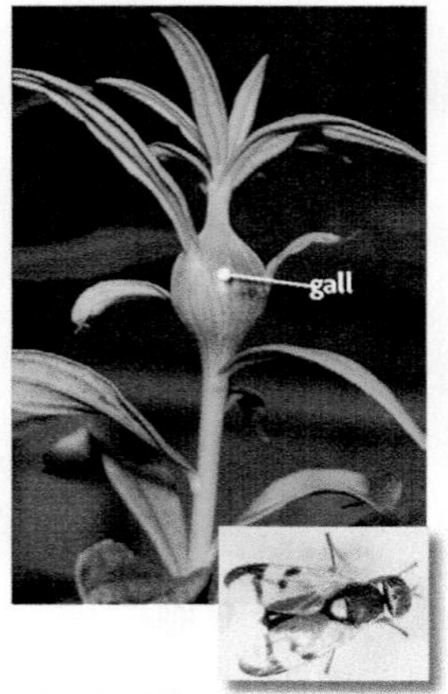

FIGURE 2.3 The gall fly and the goldenrod plant have a parasitic relationship. The fly benefits by receiving shelter and food during its larval stage, while the goldenrod is harmed, growing more slowly than a gall-free goldenrod.

Stabilizing Selection

The gall fly and its predators provide an excellent example of stabilizing selection. During **stabilizing selection,** the intermediate phenotype is favored and becomes more common in the population. That is, the distribution becomes stable at the intermediate phenotype rather than shifting toward one of the extremes. In the case of gall flies, something in nature selects against phenotypes at both extremes of the trait's range.

Gall flies lay their eggs in developing shoots of the tall goldenrod plant. The fly larvae produce a chemical that causes the plant tissue to swell around them. **FIGURE 2.3** shows the resulting mass of plant tissue, called a gall. The gall serves as a home where the larvae can develop. There is a range of phenotypes for body size in gall-fly larvae. Each body size causes a certain size gall to form, and each of the two main predators of gall flies specializes on a specific gall size.

- Downy woodpeckers attack larger galls and feed on the larvae inside.
- The parasitic wasp lays its own eggs inside small galls. After the wasp larvae emerge from the eggs, they eat the gall-fly larvae.

In this situation, selective pressure from predators works against fly phenotypes that produce galls at both extremes, large and small. As a result, flies that produce middle-sized galls become more common. As you can see in **FIGURE 2.4**, over time, stabilizing selection results in a higher frequency of flies that produce middle-sized galls.

Stabilizing selection increases the number of individuals with intermediate phenotypes. Notice, however, that selection against both extremes decreases the genetic diversity of the gall-fly population. Flies that produce small and large galls become less common. In some populations, these extreme phenotypes may be lost altogether.

FIGURE 2.4 Stabilizing Selection

Stabilizing selection occurs when intermediate phenotypes are favored by natural selection.

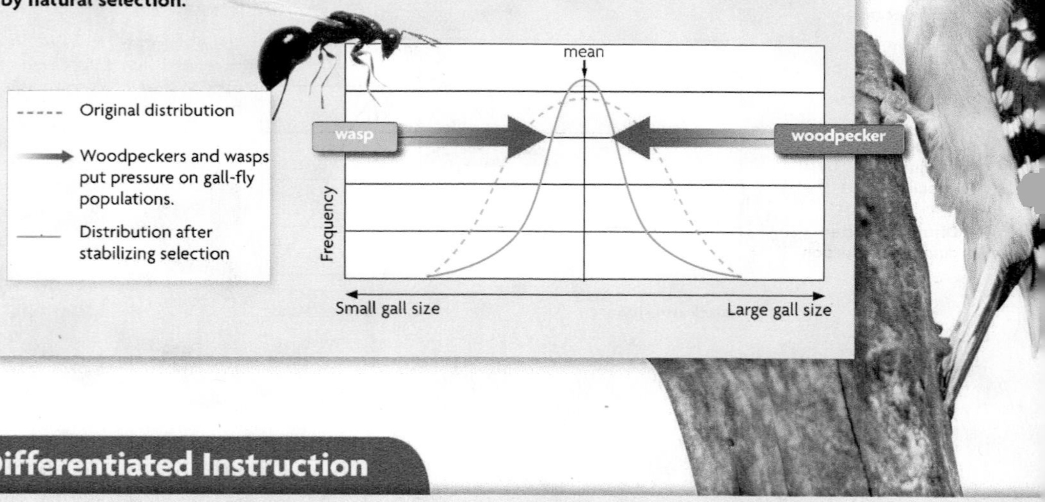

Differentiated Instruction

INCLUSION

For students who are literal thinkers, the graphs shown in **FIGURES 2.2, 2.4,** and **2.5** can be recreated by using a distribution of colored beads to represent different phenotypes. Using a horizontal line on a sheet of paper to represent the *x*-axis, align each set of phenotypic beads on a vertical, the uppermost bead representing a point on a graph. The resulting pattern of bead lines will suggest the shape of a distribution curve. Change the number of beads in response to "selection pressures" to model disruptive, directional, and stabilizing selection.

BELOW LEVEL

Make sure students see the connection between the gall fly and goldenrod plant pictured in **FIGURE 2.3** and the wasp and woodpecker pictured in **FIGURE 2.4.** Have students reinterpret the interaction of the four populations in a cause-and-effect diagram. Have them start with a goldenrod population with only gall flies present (the dashed curve of **FIGURE 2.4**), then add the wasp and woodpecker.

Teacher Toolkit, Section C, Cause-and-Effect Diagram

Disruptive Selection

Disruptive selection occurs when both extreme phenotypes are favored, while individuals with intermediate phenotypes are selected against by something in nature. As you can see in **FIGURE 2.5**, the middle of the distribution is disrupted. One example of this type of selection involves feather color in male lazuli buntings, a bird species native to North America.

Young male lazuli buntings vary widely in the brightness of their feathers, ranging from dull brown to bright blue. Dominant adult males are those with the brightest blue feathers on their heads and backs. These birds have their pick of the best territories. They also are most successful at attracting females. However, for young buntings, the brightest blue and dullest brown males are more likely to win mates than males with bluish brown feathers.

Research suggests that dominant adult males are aggressive toward young buntings that they see as a threat, including bright blue and bluish brown males. The dullest brown birds can therefore win a mate because the adult males leave them alone. Meanwhile, the bright blue birds attract mates simply because of their color.

FIGURE 2.5 Disruptive Selection

Disruptive selection occurs when both extreme phenotypes are favored by selection.

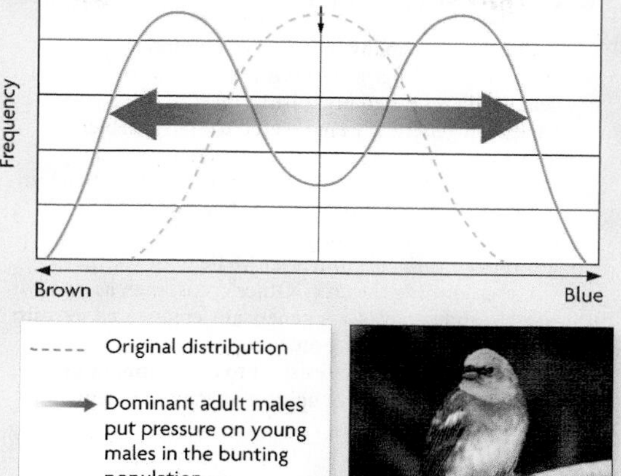
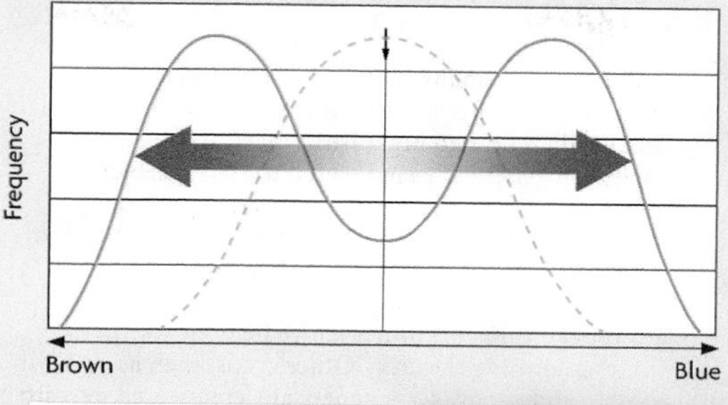

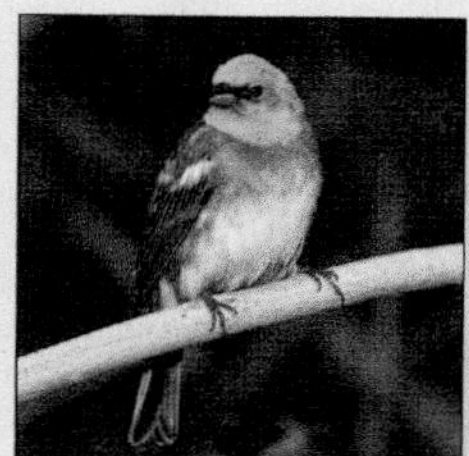

Adult male lazuli bunting

Both extreme phenotypes are favored in this situation, while intermediate forms are selected against. The bluish brown males are not as well adapted to compete for mates because they are too blue to be left alone by adult males, but not blue enough to win a mate based on color alone. By favoring both extreme phenotypes, disruptive selection can lead to the formation of new species.

A Apply If bluish brown coloring became advantageous for young males, what type of selection would likely occur in a lazuli bunting population?

SELF-CHECK Online
HMHScience.com
GO ONLINE

11.2 Formative Assessment

REVIEWING MAIN IDEAS

1. In terms of phenotypes, describe what is meant by the phrase "distribution of traits."
2. What are the three ways in which natural selection can change a distribution of traits?

CRITICAL THINKING

3. **Analyze** How might the extinction of downy woodpeckers affect the phenotypic distribution within a population of gall flies?
4. **Analyze** How might overfishing of large pink salmon select for smaller body size in subsequent generations?

CONNECT TO GENETICS

5. For polygenic traits, a smooth curve results when the range of phenotypes is plotted against frequency. If you were to plot the frequencies of two phenotypes of a single-gene trait, you would end up with a double bar graph. Explain why.

Answers

A Apply stabilizing selection toward bluish-brown coloring in males

Assess and Reteach ▼

Assess Use the Section Self-Check or Section Quiz, both available at **HMHScience.com**.

Reteach Have students draw graphs to illustrate directional, stabilizing, and disruptive selection. They should be able to explain how populations change as a result of the three types of natural selection.

11.2 FORMATIVE ASSESSMENT

1. The phrase "distribution of traits" refers to the frequencies of the different phenotypes of a particular trait within a population.
2. Directional selection: natural selection favors phenotypes at one extreme; stabilizing selection: natural selection favors intermediate phenotypes; and disruptive selection: natural selection favors phenotypes at both extremes.
3. Selection could become directional in favor of medium-sized to large-sized galls.
4. Smaller fish may be able to survive longer and reproduce more often than larger fish that are being fished. Alleles for small body size could then become more common in the population, and, over generations, smaller adult salmon could become more and more common in the population. This is natural selection.
5. Only two phenotypes are being plotted, not a continuous range of phenotypes.

Introduce

Students may not realize how many agricultural crops are now genetically engineered to help increase yield. Worldwide, almost 150 million hectares (370 acres) of GE crops are planted. Crops are most commonly genetically engineered to be herbicide resistant or to resist insect pests. Almost 90 percent of the corn, soybeans, canola, and cotton sold in the United States is genetically engineered. At least one genetically engineered animal product may be reaching consumers soon—salmon. GE salmon have genes from Atlantic salmon, Chinook salmon, and other fish that all increase the growth rate of the fish. GE salmon grow twice as fast as non-GE salmon. Some scientists have concerns about GE salmon mating with wild Atlantic salmon to produce a hybrid with increased fitness that could outcompete native species. The company that raises GE salmon has answered those concerns by growing GE salmon in land-based tanks. Also, all of the GE salmon are sterile females, so if one were to escape into the wild, it would likely be unable to reproduce.

Discuss

Have students discuss the results of their research on possible methods to prevent viable hybrids produced by crossbreeding GE plants and native plants. Discuss how the use of technology can have advantages and disadvantages.

Crossbreeding: Genetically Modified Organisms

S.T.E.M. Interactions

Today there are many types of agricultural crops that are genetically engineered (GE), often referred to as genetically modified organisms (GMOs). The crops have been genetically engineered to resist herbicides, insect pests, viruses, and cold temperatures, among other harmful conditions. These traits are beneficial to both the plants and the growers. If a crop is herbicide resistant, such as GE cotton or soybeans, it means a grower can spray his or her entire field for weeds without harming the crop. Other crops, such as corn, squash, and papayas, are genetically engineered to resist insect pests or viruses. Some crops, such as GE strawberries, are more resistant to cold temperatures. All of these genetically engineered traits can help increase crop yields.

Scientists who study plants and ecosystems have investigated what effects, if any, the introduction of GE plants into human-made ecosystems (agricultural operations) would have on natural ecosystems. Over the last decade, research in both laboratory and natural settings has shown that GE plants can successfully crossbreed with related wild plants and that the GE traits are passed on to the hybrid offspring. In a laboratory experiment, rice genetically engineered to be resistant to a common herbicide easily crossbred with a weed relative. The resulting hybrid did contain the GE trait and had higher rates of photosynthesis and produced more flowers and seeds than non-GE hybrids. Another study, conducted under controlled conditions, found that sunflowers that were genetically engineered to be resistant to a moth pest crossbred with wild sunflowers. The hybrid offspring had the GE trait. As a result, the hybrids were more fit and produced 50 percent more seeds than nonhybrid wild sunflowers. The hybrids also showed less physical damage due to insects.

In a natural setting, genetically engineered creeping bentgrass, a grass commonly planted on golf courses, crossbred with related wild grasses through wind pollination. The hybrid offspring contained the GE trait, resistance to a common herbicide. A similar situation occurred with GE rapeseed (canola), which naturally crossbred with wild relatives, producing hybrids that contained the GE trait of herbicide resistance.

Some scientists are concerned that transgenic hybrids may be able to outcompete native plants in natural ecosystems. In the case of the weedy rice, scientists are concerned that the transgenic hybrid could even outcompete the cultivated rice that is its parent. With creeping bentgrass, scientists are concerned that the transgenic bentgrass could outcompete native grasses. Also, if the hybrid grass grew in an area where it needed to be controlled, such as a waterway, it could not be eradicated through the traditional method of spraying with a common herbicide that is safe to use in a water environment. The general concern of some scientists is that in any natural setting, a hybrid with increased fitness due to inheriting a GE trait could cause an imbalance in an ecosystem.

S.T.E.M. Activity

Research more about proposed methods to prevent GE plants from producing viable hybrids if they were to crossbreed with related native plants. How are scientists using the technology behind genetic engineering to help prevent such occurrences?

Genetically engineered creeping bentgrass can crossbreed with wild grasses through wind pollination.

322 Unit 4: Evolution

Answers

Students may find that scientists are working to create GM crops that, if they were to crossbreed, the second generation of hybrid seeds would be sterile or would not be able to reproduce without a specific chemical. In some cases, scientists have recoded the genes of bacteria (used in part of the process of creating GM plants) so that the bacteria produce a synthetic amino acid. The resulting GM plants would be dependent on the synthetic amino acid for survival. If they were to crossbreed with non-GM plants, the "new" DNA would not be able to be transferred.

11.3 Other Mechanisms of Evolution

KEY CONCEPT **Natural selection is not the only mechanism through which populations evolve.**

MAIN IDEAS
- Gene flow is the movement of alleles between populations.
- Genetic drift is a change in allele frequencies due to chance.
- Sexual selection occurs when certain traits increase mating success.

OCABULARY
ene flow
enetic drift
ottleneck effect
ounder effect
exual selection

Connect to Your World

Have you ever wondered why many male birds, such as cardinals, are brightly colored while females of the same species are dull brown? Such bright coloring may not make sense in terms of natural selection, since the male birds are more likely to be seen by predators. However, natural selection is not the whole story. There are other factors that can lead to the evolution of populations.

MAIN IDEA

Gene flow is the movement of alleles between populations.

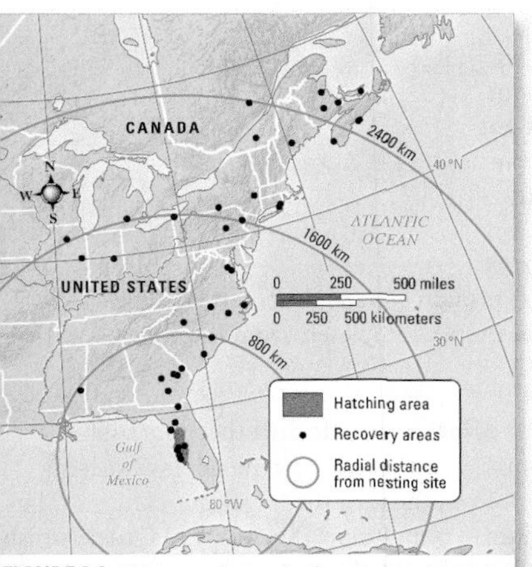

FIGURE 3.1 This map shows the locations where banded bald eagles were found during the first summer after hatching.

Bird-banding studies have shown that certain birds leave their nesting areas once they are able to fly. As shown in **FIGURE 3.1**, bald eagles that were banded as nestlings have been tracked during the same summer more than 2500 kilometers away. These eagles have possibly joined a new population.

When an organism joins a new population and reproduces, its alleles become part of that population's gene pool. At the same time, these alleles are removed from the gene pool of its former population. The movement of alleles from one population to another is called **gene flow.** For many animals, gene flow occurs when individuals move between populations. Gene flow can occur in fungi and plant populations when spores or seeds are spread to new areas.

Gene flow increases the genetic variation of the receiving population. Gene flow between neighboring populations keeps their gene pools similar. However, the less gene flow that occurs between two populations, the more genetically different the two populations can become. A lack of gene flow also increases the chance that the two populations will evolve into different species.

A Evaluate **How does gene flow affect neighboring populations?**

Differentiated Instruction

ENGLISH LEARNERS

Have students use the technique of reciprocal teaching for this section. Assign students to small groups, with different members of each group taking responsibility to guide the discussion of different topics. Each topic leader first predicts what a selection is about by previewing the text, and then uses questions to draw out information about the topic and identify any problems in understanding the material. Different members of the group alternate as topic leaders. Bring everyone back together to summarize.

Teacher Toolkit, Section C, Reciprocal Teaching

BELOW LEVEL

Have students set up a chart to compare and contrast different mechanisms of evolution. They should include natural selection, as well as gene flow, genetic drift, and sexual selection. Have them think about what causes the selection of certain genes and how that affects the gene pool of a population.

Teacher Toolkit, Section C, Compare/Contrast Chart

Plan and Prepare

Activate Prior Knowledge Have students think about the way the human population in the United States has changed since 1776, when most settlers were of European origin. **Ask,** What effect has immigration had on the genetic variation of the U.S. population? Immigration from many different continents has increased the population's genetic variation by introducing new alleles to the gene pool.

Teach

TEACH FROM VISUALS

FIGURE 3.1 Direct students' attention to the map. **Ask,** With recovery areas in Maine, Michigan, Indiana, and Mississippi, which of these populations would you expect to have the most gene flow with the bald-eagle populations in Florida? Mississippi's populations

Answers

A **Evaluate** Gene flow between neighboring populations keeps their gene pools similar.

▼ Teach *continued*

Vocabulary

Academic Vocabulary The word **founder** comes from the verb *found,* which means "to establish or set up." Remind students that the individuals who drafted the Constitution of the United States are referred to as the Founding Fathers.

Differentiate between the meaning of *found* and the past tense of *find* by using these examples:

My grandmother *founded* an organization that funds medical research.

I lost my watch last week but later *found* it under my bed.

Encourage students to think of the *founder effect* as the building of a new foundation for a population, in this case from relatively few genetic resources.

Address Misconceptions

Common Misconception Genetic drift causes the bottleneck effect and founder effect.

Correcting the Misconception Genetic drift commonly occurs after processes such as bottleneck or founder effects have resulted in a small population.

Take It Further

The **African cheetah** (*Acinonyx jubatus*) is endangered, in part because of the population's extremely low **genetic variation.** A drastic reduction in the cheetah population about 10,000 years ago resulted in a bottleneck effect. The cause of this reduction is thought to have been human beings widening their range and hunting the cheetahs. Because of low genetic variation, the cheetah population is not well equipped to resist disease or adapt to environmental changes.

MAIN IDEA

Genetic drift is a change in allele frequencies due to chance.

Imagine a patch of 100 flowers growing in a field. Fifty are white, and fifty are purple. If you randomly pick flowers from this patch to create a bouquet, you would expect about half white and half purple flowers. The more flowers you randomly pick, the more likely you are to get these proportions. However, the fewer flowers you pick, the more likely you are to have a bouquet that is not representative of the patch. It might even be all one color.

A similar situation can occur in small populations. Small populations, like small sample sizes, are more likely to be affected by chance. Due to chance alone, some alleles are likely to decrease in frequency and become eliminated. Other alleles are likely to increase in frequency and become fixed. These changes in allele frequencies that are due to chance are called **genetic drift.** Genetic drift causes a loss of genetic diversity in a population.

READING TOOLBOX

VOCABULARY

The word *fixed* means "not subject to change." If an allele increases to a frequency of 1.0 (100%), it is said to be fixed in the population.

Two processes commonly cause populations to become small enough for genetic drift to occur. Each of these processes results in a population with different allele frequencies than existed in the original population.

Bottleneck Effect

The **bottleneck effect** is genetic drift that occurs after an event greatly reduces the size of a population. One example of the bottleneck effect is the overhunting of northern elephant seals during the 1800s. By the 1890s, the population was reduced to about 20 individuals. These 20 seals did not represent the genetic diversity of the original population. Since hunting has ended, the population has grown to over 100,000 individuals. However, it has very little genetic variation. Through genetic drift, certain alleles have become fixed, while others have been lost completely from the gene pool.

VISUAL VOCAB

The **bottleneck effect** describes the effect of a destructive event that leaves only a few survivors in a population.

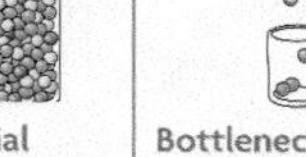

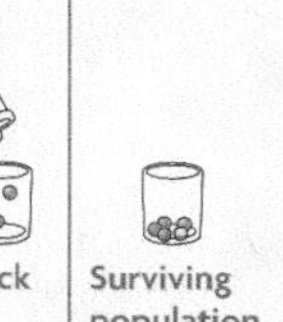

Founder Effect

As shown in **FIGURE 3.2**, the **founder effect** is genetic drift that occurs after a small number of individuals colonize a new area. The gene pools of these populations are often very different from those of the larger populations. The founder effect can be studied in human populations, such as Old Order Amish communities. These communities were founded in North America by small numbers of migrants from Europe. For example, the Amish of Lancaster County, Pennsylvania, have a high rate of Ellis–van Creveld syndrome. Although this form of dwarfism is rare in other human populations, it has become common in this Amish population through genetic drift. Geneticists have traced this syndrome back to one of the community's founding couples.

Differentiated Instruction

HANDS-ON ACTIVITY

Have students model genetic drift in a small population by doing coin tosses. Working in pairs, have students state the results of their coin tosses for three flips of a coin. Some groups may see skewed ratios. Then continue on and record the results after ten flips of the coin. The results will probably show that the more coin flips that are performed, the closer the ratio will be to 1:1. Use the early skewed ratios as an analogy to genetic drift occurring in a small population.

FIGURE 3.2 The Founder Effect

The founder effect can occur if a small number of individuals colonize a new area.

Animated Biology HMHScience.com
GO ONLINE
Founder Effect

The gene pool for a population of flowers has genetic diversity that results in red, yellow, and blue phenotypes.

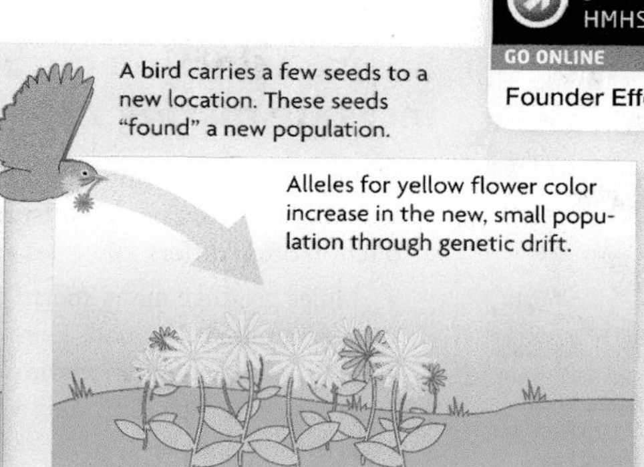

A bird carries a few seeds to a new location. These seeds "found" a new population.

Alleles for yellow flower color increase in the new, small population through genetic drift.

Effects of Genetic Drift

Genetic drift can cause several problems for populations. One problem is that the population loses genetic variation. With little genetic variation, a population is less likely to have some individuals that will be able to adapt to a changing environment. Another problem is that alleles that are lethal in homozygous individuals may be carried by heterozygous individuals and become more common in the gene pool due to chance alone.

Apply **Why is genetic drift more likely to occur in smaller populations?**

QUICKLAB MODELING

Genetic Drift

Use a deck of cards to represent a population of island birds. The four suits represent different alleles for tail shape. The allele frequencies in the original population are 25% spade, 25% heart, 25% club, and 25% diamond tail shapes.

PROBLEM How does genetic drift occur?

MATERIALS
- deck of cards

PROCEDURE

1. Shuffle the cards, and hold the deck face down. Turn over 40 cards to represent the alleles of 20 offspring produced by random matings in the initial population.
2. Separate the 40 cards by suit. Find the allele frequencies for the offspring by calculating the percentage of each suit.
3. Suppose a storm blows a few birds to another island. They are isolated on this island and start a new population. Reshuffle the deck, and draw 10 cards to represent the alleles of five offspring produced in the smaller population.
4. Repeat Step 2 to calculate the resulting allele frequencies.

ANALYZE AND CONCLUDE

1. **Analyze** Compare the original allele frequencies to those calculated in Steps 2 and 4. How did they change?
2. **Analyze** Did Step 1 or 3 demonstrate genetic drift?
3. **Evaluate** Does this activity demonstrate evolution? Why or why not? Does it demonstrate natural selection? Explain.

PRE-AP

Have students use the examples of overhunting of elephant seals and the occurrence of Ellis–van Creveld syndrome in the Amish population to produce a concept map that shows how the bottleneck and founder effects yield a small population in which genetic drift can occur.

Teacher Toolkit, Section C, Concept Map

Answers

A Apply Chance events are more likely to affect smaller populations. In larger populations, the effects of chance events tend to become "averaged out."

QUICKLAB

Time 15 minutes

Purpose Model how isolation of a small population can affect allele frequency.

LAB MANAGEMENT

Realize that students may not see the purpose of what they are doing right away. **Ask,** In step 3, what effect are you modeling? founder effect

Inclusion Pair students who have visual impairments with partners. Have the partners call out the suit of the cards as they are drawn so that the students with visual impairments can complete the lab.

Sample Data

Trial 1

Diamond	Heart	Club	Spade
10	13	9	8
25%	32.5%	22.5%	20%

Trial 2

Diamond	Heart	Club	Spade
3	3	2	2
30%	30%	20%	20%

Analyze and Conclude

1. Answers will vary.
2. After either step 1 or 3, if the allele frequencies differ from the original distribution of 25 percent each, then genetic drift has occurred. It is more likely in step 3 because the population is smaller.
3. The activity demonstrates evolution because it shows how the allele frequencies in a population can change. The activity does not demonstrate natural selection, because changes in allele frequencies were due to chance alone.

▼ Teach *continued*

Vocabulary

Academic Vocabulary Point out the word **investment** used in the context of reproduction. Typically, an *investment* is a commitment of money in hope of a future return. In biology, the sperm and eggs of sexually reproducing organisms also represent an investment. In many species, males produce millions of sperm, while females produce a far smaller number of eggs. The male's investment in mating is far less than the female's. The difference helps to explain why competitive courtship behaviors are more common in males than in females, even when females are more numerous: sperm still vastly outnumber eggs.

Answers

A Apply An exaggerated trait in a male would be advantageous if females associated the trait with "quality" and preferentially mated with such males. This trait and the female's response trait would be passed on to offspring.

▼ Assess and Reteach

Assess Use the Section Self-Check or Section Quiz, both available at **HMHScience.com**.

Reteach Start with a population of imaginary animals and have students use the vocabulary in this section to describe different scenarios that cause the population to evolve.

FIGURE 3.3 Male frigate birds inflate an air sac in their chest to attract females. This trait has evolved through sexual selection.

READING TOOLBOX

VOCABULARY

The prefix *intra-* is Latin for "within." Intrasexual selection occurs within one sex.
The prefix *inter-* is Latin for "between." Intersexual selection occurs between both sexes.

MAIN IDEA

Sexual selection occurs when certain traits increase mating success.

Mating can have an important effect on the evolution of populations. Both sexes benefit from having offspring that survive. However, the cost of reproduction often differs for males and females.

- Males produce many sperm continuously, making the value of each sperm relatively small. They can make many investments at little cost.
- Females are much more limited in the number of offspring they can produce in each reproductive cycle. Therefore, each investment they make is more valuable.

In many species, this difference in reproductive cost makes females more choosy than males about mates. **Sexual selection** occurs when certain traits increase reproductive success. There are two types of sexual selection.

- Intrasexual selection involves competition among males, such as the head-butting of bighorn sheep. The winner of the competition mates with the female.
- Intersexual selection occurs when males display certain traits that attract the female, such as peacocks fanning out their tails.

Traits that increase mating success are not always adaptive for the survival of the individual. As shown in **FIGURE 3.3**, bright red air sacs likely make male frigate birds very easy to spot by predators. How could such an exaggerated trait evolve?

Research has shown that some showy traits may be linked with genes for good health and fertility. Other traits are present in males that can offer better care for offspring or defense from predators. Therefore, females may use showy traits as signs of quality and health in males. These traits, such as the red air sacs of male frigate birds, can become very exaggerated over time through sexual selection.

A Apply Male Irish elks, now extinct, had 12-foot-wide antlers. Describe how sexual selection could have caused such an exaggerated trait to evolve.

SELF-CHECK Online
HMHScience.com
GO ONLINE

11.3 Formative Assessment

REVIEWING MAIN IDEAS

1. How are neighboring populations affected by **gene flow**?
2. Name two processes through which **genetic drift** can occur.
3. How does **sexual selection** occur?

CRITICAL THINKING

4. **Analyze** Would a population of 10 individuals or 100 individuals be more vulnerable to genetic drift? Why?
5. **Infer** What impact can the **bottleneck effect** have on populations that have rebounded after near extinction?

CONNECT TO

GENETICS

6. Ellis–van Creveld syndrome is a recessive trait. Explain why it has become common in the Amish of Lancaster County but is very rare in other human populations.

11.3 FORMATIVE ASSESSMENT

1. Gene flow decreases genetic diversity between neighboring populations.
2. bottleneck effect and founder effect
3. Certain male traits are favored by females when choosing a mate. Over time, the alleles associated with the preferred phenotype increase in the population.
4. A smaller population is more vulnerable to genetic drift because it has a smaller gene pool and is therefore more likely to be affected by chance events.
5. The bottleneck effect occurs after an event that greatly reduces the size of a population, sometimes to only a few individuals. As a result, the population has little genetic variation. Even if that population rebounds, genetic diversity will likely still be low. Thus the bottleneck effect impacts the genetic diversity of a population that has rebounded after near extinction.
6. Among the Amish founders, one couple carried the recessive allele for Ellis–van Creveld syndrome. Because marriages occurred primarily within the small Amish community, the frequency of the recessive allele increased within the gene pool over many generations. This increased the likelihood of a child getting two recessive alleles. Ellis–van Creveld syndrome is relatively rare in other populations because of the high frequency of dominant alleles in the larger gene pools.

Identifying Patterns

Smart Grapher
HMHScience.com
GO ONLINE
Genetic Drift

Identifying patterns in data from graphs and charts is essential for formulating hypotheses and making predictions.

Model

The data in Graph 1 were collected during an experiment involving widowbirds in Kenya. The biologist was trying to determine the relationship between tail feather length and reproductive success in males of this species. The average number of nesting sites was used to measure reproductive success and was recorded for four groups of birds. Tail feathers were artificially shortened in one group, two groups were used as control groups, and tail feathers were artificially lengthened in the fourth group.

- Look at the bar representing the group with shortened tail feathers. Notice that this group averaged less than 0.5 nesting sites.
- Next, notice that the bars for the two control groups show that these groups both averaged less than one nesting site.
- Now look at the bar representing lengthened tail feathers. Notice that birds in this group averaged almost two nesting sites.
- Finally, look for trends and patterns. The data show a trend that males with longer tail feathers have greater reproductive success: on average, they had more nesting sites.

GRAPH 1. TAIL FEATHER LENGTH AND REPRODUCTIVE SUCCESS

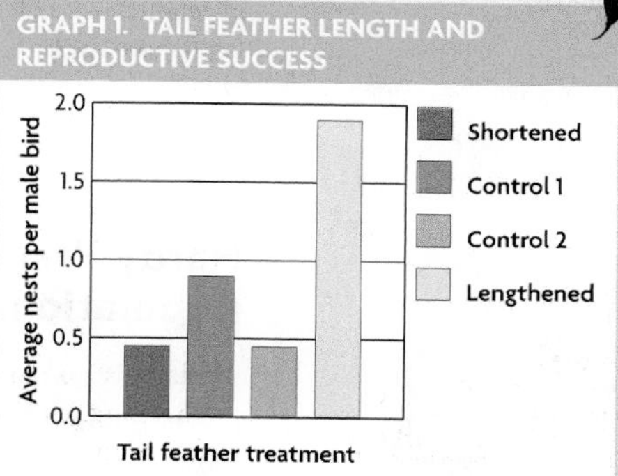

Source: Anderson, *Nature* 299-5886

Practice Identify Patterns

The graph at the right shows sexual selection patterns in guppies. Three experiments were run to determine if female guppies prefer males with specific tail sizes. In each experiment, female guppies were given the choice of two males to mate with, each having a different tail size: large versus small, large versus medium, and medium versus small.

1. **Analyze** What tail sizes were compared in each experiment?
2. **Analyze** What is the relationship between tail size in male guppies and female preference for mates?
3. **Infer** Why might the difference in preference be larger in Experiment 1 than in Experiment 2?

GRAPH 2. SEXUAL SELECTION IN GUPPIES

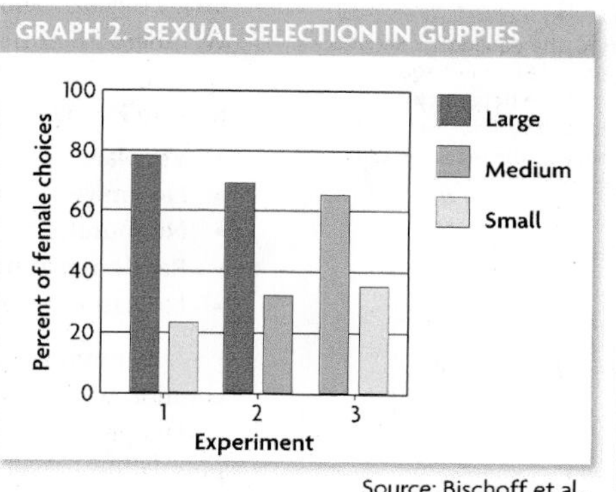

Source: Bischoff et al., *Behavioral Ecology and Sociobiology* 17:3

DATA ANALYSIS

Introduce

Point out that, in the widowbird experiment, the researchers made sure that the birds in the test groups had noticeably different tail lengths. **Ask,** Why didn't researchers simply choose birds with somewhat longer or shorter tails? By using birds that looked identical and then changing the tail length of some of them, researchers were able to control conditions to ensure that selection was in response to tail length.

Discuss

Make sure students focus on the trends in the data as displayed by the graphs. **Ask,** According to the data, what gives a male widowbird greater reproductive success? longer tail feathers What about the male guppy? larger tail

Take It Further

There is a communication element in sexual selection. The female response and the male display had to have coevolved for these traits to mean anything or be selected for. An Irish elk's huge antlers or a widowbird's long tail only mean something to potential mates if the females inherited the trait that makes them differentiate and value the male trait.

Sexual selection can arise because of a correlation between a display characteristic and a reproductive advantage. For example, a large-antlered elk might produce stronger, healthier offspring.

Online Student Resources, Data Analysis Practice

Answers

1. Experiment 1: large and small; Experiment 2: large and medium; Experiment 3: medium and small
2. Female guppies prefer to mate with males that have larger tails.
3. The difference in the two tail sizes was greater in Experiment 1 (large vs. small) than in Experiment 2 (large vs. medium), meaning that the female could more easily differentiate between her two choices in the first experiment.

▼ Plan and Prepare

Activate Prior Knowledge Discuss the idea of equilibrium. **Ask,** What does it mean to be in a state of equilibrium? Students may suggest that it means a steady, unchanging state. Discuss equilibrium as being similar to an equation in which values can be added or subtracted, but the result maintains equivalence.

▼ Teach

Vocabulary

Academic Vocabulary Students will associate **immigration** and **emigration** with people who change citizenship and move to or from a country. In the study of populations and evolution, *immigration* refers to the flow of genes into a population, and *emigration* refers to the flow of genes out of a population. Here is a good way to distinguish between the two: immigration begins with *i*, like *in;* emigration begins with *e*, like *exit.*

Answers

A Summarize Population biologists compare real population data to a model to study how the population may be changing.

11.4 Hardy-Weinberg Equilibrium

VOCABULARY

Hardy-Weinberg equilibrium

KEY CONCEPT **Hardy-Weinberg equilibrium provides a framework for understanding how populations evolve.**

MAIN IDEAS

- Hardy-Weinberg equilibrium describes populations that are not evolving.
- The Hardy-Weinberg equation is used to predict genotype frequencies in a population.
- There are five factors that can lead to evolution.

Connect to Your World

Have you ever heard people talk about "the good old days"? Maybe they're remembering a time when music and clothes were different from today. Long-term trends in society's music and fashion tastes are difficult to anticipate. In some ways, changes in genetics are a bit more predictable. Scientists can use models and equations to learn more about how populations change over time.

MAIN IDEA

Hardy-Weinberg equilibrium describes populations that are not evolving.

Biologists often compare their data to a model to study how a population is changing. One important model is based on the research of a British mathematician named Godfrey Hardy and a German physician named Wilhelm Weinberg. In 1908, Hardy and Weinberg showed that genotype frequencies in a population stay the same over time as long as certain conditions are met. They also showed that these frequencies can be predicted. Hardy and Weinberg identified five conditions needed for a population to stay in equilibrium. Populations that meet these conditions are not evolving. They are said to be in **Hardy-Weinberg equilibrium.**

- **Very large population** No genetic drift can occur.
- **No emigration or immigration** No gene flow can occur.
- **No mutations** No new alleles can be added to the gene pool.
- **Random mating** No sexual selection can occur.
- **No natural selection** All traits must equally aid in survival.

Real populations rarely meet all five conditions. However, Hardy-Weinberg equilibrium is still a very important concept. Biologists can compare real data to data predicted by the model. Then they can learn more about the way the population is evolving. The model also gives a framework for testing the factors that can lead to evolution.

Summarize **How are models used by population biologists?**

CONNECT TO

GENETICS

The Hardy-Weinberg model and its equation are based on Mendelian genetics, which you learned about in the chapter **Meiosis and Mendel.** As you will soon see, the equation is derived from a simple Punnett square in which p is the frequency of the dominant allele, and q is the frequency of the recessive allele.

	p	q
p	p^2	pq
q	pq	q^2

Differentiated Instruction

ENGLISH LEARNERS

Given the technical nature of the Hardy-Weinberg equilibrium, you might want to check students' comprehension as you discuss the material with the class. You can use signals such as thumbs-up or thumbs-down for comprehension, or a hand behind the ear to have students signal that they need to hear you repeat an explanation. Remember to periodically ask for feedback and to scan the group for signals.

Teacher Toolkit, Section C, Signals

MAIN IDEA

The Hardy-Weinberg equation is used to predict genotype frequencies in a population.

For traits in simple dominant-recessive systems, biologists can predict genotype frequencies by using the Hardy-Weinberg equation, as seen in **FIGURE 4.1**. Values predicted by the equation are those that would be present if the population were in equilibrium. If p equals the frequency of the dominant allele, and q equals the frequency of the recessive allele, the equation can be written as follows:

$$p^2 + 2pq + q^2 = 1$$

Population biologists compare predicted genotype frequencies with actual frequencies. If they are the same, the population is in Hardy-Weinberg equilibrium for that trait. If the genetic data do not match the equation, the population is not in equilibrium; it is evolving.

FIGURE 4.1 Using the Hardy-Weinberg Equation

Use the Hardy-Weinberg equation to calculate predicted genotype frequencies for this population.

In a population of 1000 fish, 640 have forked tail fins and 360 have smooth tail fins. Tail fin shape is determined by two alleles: T is dominant for forked, and t is recessive for smooth.

tt

TT or Tt

VARIABLES

p = frequency of allele T (dominant allele)

q = frequency of allele t (recessive allele)

p^2 = frequency of fish with TT (homozygous dominant genotype)

$2pq$ = frequency of fish with Tt (heterozygous genotype)

q^2 = frequency of fish with tt (homozygous recessive genotype)

1. Find q^2, the frequency of smooth-finned fish (recessive homozygotes).

$$q^2 = \frac{\text{360 smooth-finned fish}}{\text{1000 fish in population}} = 0.36$$

2. To find the predicted value of q, take the square root of q^2.

$$q = \sqrt{0.36} = 0.6$$

3. Use the equation $p + q = 1$ to find the predicted value of p. Rearrange the equation to solve for p.

$p = 1 - q$

$p = 1 - 0.6 = 0.4$

These are the predicted allele frequencies: $p = 0.4$ and $q = 0.6$.

4. Calculate the predicted genotype frequencies from the predicted allele frequencies.

$p^2 = 0.4^2 = 0.16$ → 16% of fish have forked fins (TT)

$2pq = 2 \times (0.4) \times (0.6) = 0.48$ → 48% of fish have forked fins (Tt)

$q^2 = 0.6^2 = 0.36$ → 36% of fish have smooth fins (tt)

A Analyze Through genetic analysis, scientists have found the genotype frequencies of the same fish population to be $TT = 0.50$, $Tt = 0.14$, and $tt = 0.36$. What can you infer by comparing these data with the values predicted by the Hardy-Weinberg equation?

BELOW LEVEL

Draw a Punnett square on the board to show how the two alleles for tail-fin shape in fish (T and t) result in two phenotypes (forked tail and smooth tail) but three genotypes (TT, Tt, and tt). Have students look at the Punnett square and discuss which genotype should be labeled with the following terms: *heterozygous dominant, homozygous dominant, homozygous recessive*. If students have difficulty distinguishing among these terms, point out the prefixes *homo-* and *hetero-*, and discuss what they mean.

PRE-AP

Provide students with a chance to work in pairs using the Hardy-Weinberg equation to predict genotype frequencies of a simple dominant-recessive system. Tell students that an earlier study of a population showed frequencies of 0.66, 0.31, and 0.03. Have students determine if the current population, with $p = 0.8$, has evolved. They should first get $q = 0.2$ by subtracting p from 1. The Hardy-Weinberg equation will show the population has evolved: 0.64, 0.32, 0.04.

Teacher Toolkit, Section C, Think-Pair-Share

Students can study genetic drift in a population of fruit flies, using the Hardy-Weinberg equation. See the Smart Grapher activity for this chapter at **HMHScience.com**.

Integrating Medical Science

The **Hardy-Weinberg equation** may seem like something whose purpose is to prove the obvious: that evolution is occurring in most populations. However, the principles have practical value in population genetics and medicine. For example, researchers can apply the Hardy-Weinberg equation to a population to determine the prevalence of a recessive disease gene, such as **cystic fibrosis,** within a population. If scientists determine that 1 out of every 1700 Caucasian newborns is born with the disease, then they can calculate that approximately 1 out of 21 Caucasians in the population is a carrier. It is important to stress that results of applying the Hardy-Weinberg equation to an evolving population (one that has genetic drift, sexual selection, and so on) are at best approximations.

TEACH FROM VISUALS

FIGURE 4.1 Before students follow the steps in solving the Hardy-Weinberg equation, have them review the variables listed in the chart. **Ask,** Why can't the frequency of fork-tailed fish be used to calculate p? Some fork-tailed fish have the heterozygous genotype. They carry both the dominant, forked-tail allele and the recessive, smooth-tail allele.

Answers

A Analyze Because its genotype frequencies do not match those predicted by the Hardy-Weinberg equation, the fish population must be evolving.

▼ Teach *continued*

TEACH FROM VISUALS

FIGURE 4.2 Point out that the circle graphs show the relative frequencies of the different body-color alleles in the population, while each colored ball represents one allele. **Ask**

- What are the frequencies of the four different alleles in the initial population? 0.25 or 25% each
- Which of the factors led to a decrease in body-color variation in the population? genetic drift
- Which of the factors led to an increase in body-color variation in the population? mutation
- Which of the factors led to a change in the frequencies of different body colors in the population? all five factors

Take It Further

The fiber nylon was first synthesized in 1937. A type of bacterium has since evolved that feeds exclusively on nylon byproducts. The bacterium evolved as a result of a **frame-shift mutation** in a single gene, which produced a new protein that reacts with nylon products. The invention of nylon provided a niche for the new species of bacterium, but it was the mutation that enabled this species to diverge from the original species in the first place, similar to the way bacteria evolve to be resistant to antibiotics. Heavy use of antibiotics may pave the way for new strains or species of bacteria to arise, but without mutation, speciation and evolution cannot occur.

Answers

A Critical Viewing Accept any well-explained answer. For example, while sexual selection may increase blue alleles, natural selection may increase white alleles. This type of scenario can be seen in nature in many bird species. Brightly colored males attract female mates, while female birds of the same species blend in with their surroundings, thereby avoiding predation and preserving their reproductive potential.

FIGURE 4.2 Factors That Can Lead to Evolution

There are five factors that can lead to evolution at the population level.

Mechanisms of Evolution

INITIAL POPULATION

Here are the alleles associated with body color in a hypothetical population.

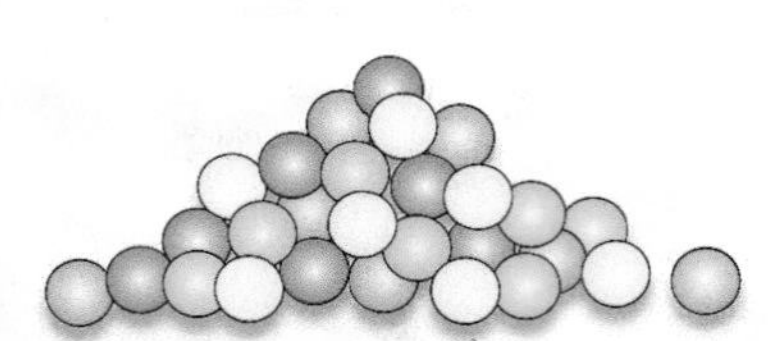

GENETIC DRIFT

After a bottleneck event, only orange and blue alleles remained in the small population. Through genetic drift, orange alleles increase in frequency.

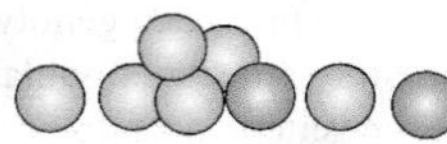

GENE FLOW

Green alleles increase in frequency because of immigration; orange alleles decrease in frequency because of emigration.

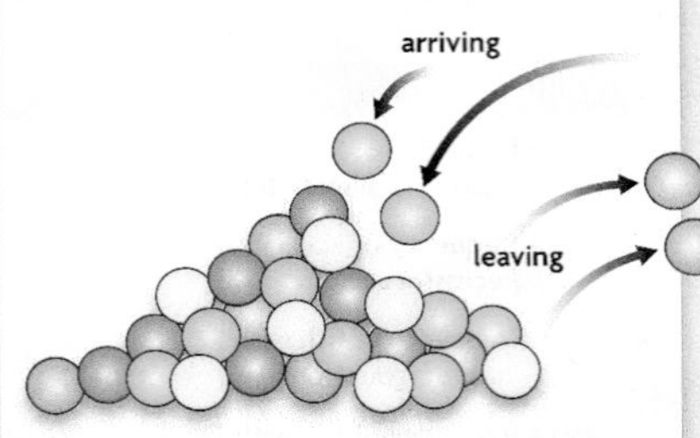

MUTATION

A new allele, associated with red body color, is formed through mutation. This could affect sexual selection if red body color improves mating success. It could affect natural selection if red body color increases the chance for survival.

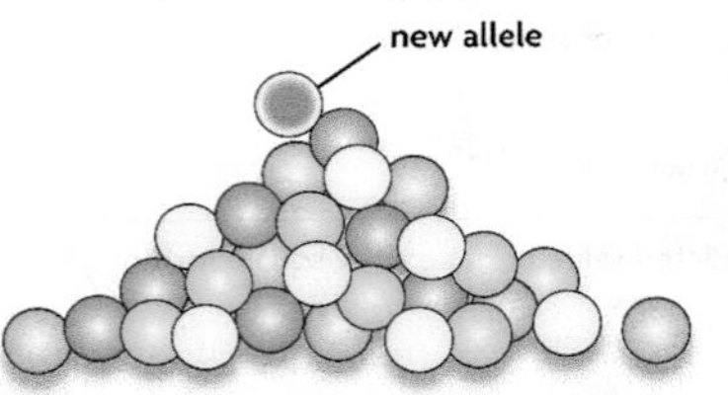

SEXUAL SELECTION

Blue alleles are associated with blue body color, which improves mating success. Blue alleles, therefore, increase in frequency.

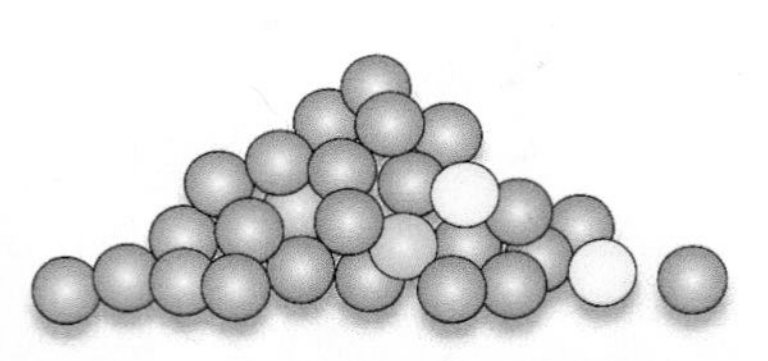

NATURAL SELECTION

White alleles are associated with white body color, which allows individuals to blend in with their environment and avoid predation. White alleles, therefore, increase in frequency.

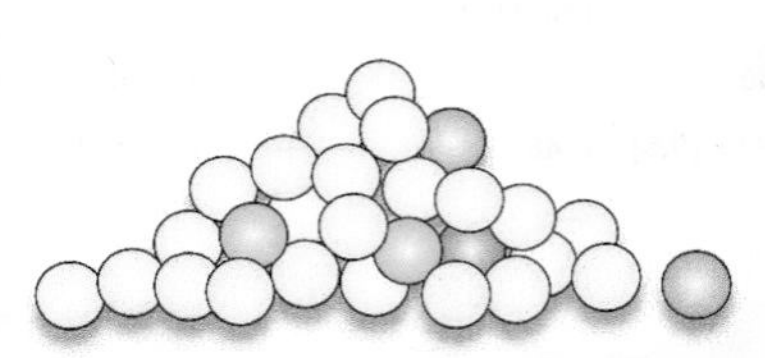

A CRITICAL VIEWING **Describe a scenario in which more than one factor could influence this population at the same time.**

Differentiated Instruction

HANDS-ON ACTIVITY

Have students work in groups with two sets of differently colored beads (about 50 of each color per group) to compare random changes in frequency to those brought about by natural (nonrandom) selection. Mix the beads together in a bowl, and have students randomly select ten beads to represent the initial population. One color will represent the value *p*, the other the value *q*. Have students create a data table for five rounds of selection, in which they record values for *p* and *q*. With the initial population of ten established, have some groups remove three beads from this initial population at random (eyes covered). The other groups should, when possible, remove beads of just one color to model natural selection. The students should randomly select three replacements from the bowl and record the *p* and *q* values for the second round. Conduct at least five rounds before having students compare their results. You can have students compute the frequencies of each round and compare them to the Hardy-Weinberg equilibrium.

MAIN IDEA

There are five factors that can lead to evolution.

The conditions needed for Hardy-Weinberg equilibrium are not common in nature. Some parts of a population's environment may stay the same over time. However, other things are likely to change. Perhaps a flood carries part of a population to a new place. This population may then go through genetic drift. A mutation may create a new allele that allows some individuals to run faster and get away from predators. The frequency of this allele may then increase in the gene pool as it is passed on to future generations.

In nature, populations evolve, or change, in response to their environments. Populations that are not in Hardy-Weinberg equilibrium are evolving. In their studies, Hardy and Weinberg concluded that evolution should be expected in all populations almost all of the time. Their model shows that there are five factors that can lead to evolution. These factors are illustrated in **FIGURE 4.2.**

- **Genetic drift** Allele frequencies can change due to chance alone.
- **Gene flow** The movement of alleles from one population to another changes the allele frequencies in each population.
- **Mutation** New alleles can form through mutation. Mutations create the genetic variation needed for evolution.
- **Sexual selection** Certain traits may improve mating success. Alleles for these traits increase in frequency.
- **Natural selection** Certain traits may be an advantage for survival. Alleles for these traits increase in frequency.

Evolution is continuous. Environments are always changing, though often very slowly relative to a human's lifetime. Evolution is a response to these changes. As environments change, populations either adapt or go extinct. When a population becomes extinct, a different species can take its place, and the cycle continues.

A Infer **Why do real populations rarely reach Hardy-Weinberg equilibrium?**

Answers

A Infer Real populations rarely reach the Hardy-Weinberg equilibrium because environments are constantly changing, which changes what traits are adaptive. Sexual selection in some species indicates that mating is not random. Mutations and gene flow can occur, and not all populations are large enough to reach equilibrium.

Assess and Reteach ▼

Assess Use the Section Self-Check or Section Quiz, both available at **HMHScience.com**.

Reteach Use **FIGURE 4.2** to review the different factors that can lead to evolution in a population.

11.4 Formative Assessment

SELF-CHECK Online
HMHScience.com
GO ONLINE

REVIEWING MAIN IDEAS

1. What conditions are necessary for populations to remain in **Hardy-Weinberg equilibrium**?
2. What can be predicted by using the Hardy-Weinberg equation?
3. What are the five factors that can lead to evolution?

CRITICAL THINKING

4. **Analyze** Why is phenotypic variation necessary for natural selection and sexual selection?
5. **Evaluate** Based on what you read in Section 3, is it likely that a population of peacocks would be in Hardy-Weinberg equilibrium? Why or why not?

CONNECT TO GENETICS

6. How are the concepts of dominant, recessive, heterozygous, and homozygous related to the Hardy-Weinberg equation?

11.4 FORMATIVE ASSESSMENT

1. very large population; no emigration or immigration; no mutations; random mating; no natural selection
2. genotype frequencies for a trait in a simple dominant-recessive system that is in equilibrium
3. genetic drift, gene flow, mutation, sexual selection, and natural selection
4. Individuals with advantageous phenotypes are better able to survive and/or reproduce. The alleles associated with these phenotypes may then become more common in the population.
5. No, because females select males as mates based on the size of their tails, indicating that sexual selection is occurring.
6. In a simple dominant-recessive system, there are two homozygous genotypes (dominant-dominant; recessive-recessive) and one heterozygous genotype (dominant-recessive). One can calculate the frequency of these genotypes by using the Hardy-Weinberg equation.

SECTION 11.5

▼ Plan and Prepare

Activate Prior Knowledge Have students think about the potential for speciation in dog breeds. **Ask**

- How do we know that a three-foot-tall Irish wolfhound and a six-inch-high Chihuahua are the same species? They are capable of mating and producing fertile offspring.
- At what point would the two breeds become separate species? unable to mate or produce fertile offspring Tell students that at that point, speciation has occurred.

▼ Teach

Science Trivia

- The common fruit fly, *Drosophila melanogaster,* is one of 900 fruit fly species.
- This fly has an estimated 13,600 genes on four chromosomes and over 3000 known mutations.
- It takes 11 days for the fly's fertilized egg to develop into an adult that is capable of reproducing.

11.5 Speciation Through Isolation

KEY CONCEPT **New species can arise when populations are isolated.**

VOCABULARY

reproductive isolation
speciation
behavioral isolation
geographic isolation
temporal isolation

MAIN IDEAS

- The isolation of populations can lead to speciation.
- Populations can become isolated in several ways.

Connect to Your World

If you travel through two different cities, towns, or even neighborhoods, you'll notice differences in the way people live. When groups of people are separated, ideas and resources are not shared, and so these groups of people may become more different. Similarly, genes cannot flow between populations that are isolated from each other, and they are more likely to become different. What happens if no gene flow occurs between two populations? This is one way that new species can arise.

MAIN IDEA

The isolation of populations can lead to speciation.

If gene flow between two populations stops for any reason, the populations are said to be isolated. As these populations adapt to their environments, their gene pools may change. Random processes such as mutation and genetic drift can also change gene pools. All of these changes add up over many generations. With time, the two isolated populations become more and more genetically different. Individuals in one population may also begin to look and behave differently from individuals in the other population.

Reproductive isolation occurs when members of different populations can no longer mate successfully. Sometimes members of the two populations are not physically able to mate with each other. In other cases, they cannot produce offspring that survive and reproduce. Reproductive isolation between populations is the final step of becoming separate species. The rise of two or more species from one existing species is called **speciation.**

FIGURE 5.1 illustrates a recent experiment that shows how one mutation can result in reproductive isolation. Scientists studied the *ds2* gene of fruit flies. This gene affects how well fruit flies can deal with cold temperatures. Fruit flies living in tropical areas, where competition for food is high, have a tropical allele. Fruit flies living in cooler regions, where there is less competition for food, have a temperate allele. The *ds2* gene also affects chemical scents called pheromones. Fruit flies use these scents to attract mates of their own species.

CONNECT TO

GENETICS

Fruit flies *(Drosophila melanogaster)* are very common in genetic research, as you may recall from the **Genetics** unit. Their popularity is based on several factors: they are easy to obtain, they reproduce easily and quickly, and they have well-understood genetic structures.

Differentiated Instruction

ENGLISH LEARNERS

Have students form into home groups of three and number off. Make all 1s responsible for the concept of behavioral isolation, 2s for geographic isolation, and 3s for temporal isolation. Ask each student to start a cluster diagram with the key concept of the section. Have students form into "expert" groups to complete their part of the cluster diagram and then return to the home group to construct a complete version.

Teacher Toolkit, Section C, Jigsaw Reading; Cluster Diagram

FIGURE 5.1 Reproductive Isolation

Reproductive isolation occurs when members of isolated populations are no longer able to mate with each other successfully.

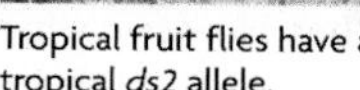

Tropical fruit flies have a tropical *ds2* allele.

Temperate fruit flies have a temperate *ds2* allele.

1 Scientists used lab fruit flies that are genetically similar. They developed a technique that allowed them to replace the *ds2* gene in each lab fruit fly with either the tropical or temperate allele.

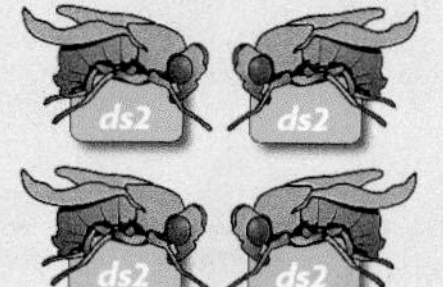

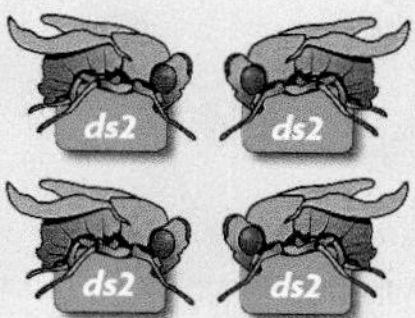

2 Laboratory males that received the tropical allele were attracted to females that received the tropical allele. Males that received the temperate allele were attracted to females that received the temperate allele.

A Synthesize **Explain why fruit flies with a specific *ds2* allele prefer to mate with fruit flies that have the same allele.**

This experiment shows how speciation may have occurred in natural fruit fly populations. Fruit flies migrating north from Africa to areas where there is less competition for food faced colder temperatures. A mutation in the *ds2* gene may have produced the temperate allele. This allele allows fruit flies to survive in cooler climates. Because the *ds2* gene also affects pheromones, mating behaviors changed. Fruit flies with the temperate allele and fruit flies with the tropical allele mated together less and less often. Eventually, these populations became reproductively isolated.

B Summarize **Why is reproductive isolation considered to be the final stage in speciation?**

C MAIN IDEA

Populations can become isolated in several ways.

Several kinds of barriers can prevent mating between populations, leading to reproductive isolation. These include behavioral, geographic, and temporal barriers.

Behavioral Barriers

Chemical scents, courtship dances of birds, and courtship songs of frogs are examples of sexual signals used to attract mates. Changes in these signals can prevent mating between populations. **Behavioral isolation** is isolation caused by differences in courtship or mating behaviors. Over 2000 species of fireflies are isolated in this way. Male and female fireflies produce patterns of flashes that attract mates of their own species. For example, *Photuris frontalis* emits one flash every second, *P. hebes* emits one flash every 2 seconds, and *P. fairchildi* produces a double flash every 5.5 seconds.

BELOW LEVEL

Have students use sequence diagrams to summarize how behavioral, geographic, and temporal isolation can lead to reproductive isolation and speciation.

Teacher Toolkit, Section C, Sequence Diagram

PRE-AP

Tell students that when the Isthmus of Panama formed about three million years ago, it separated the Pacific Ocean and Caribbean Sea. The Panama Canal has reestablished a connection. Have students write a few paragraphs addressing the question of whether long-isolated marine species could possibly interbreed if they were to migrate from one body of water to the other.

Teacher Toolkit, Section C, Quick-Write

TEACH FROM VISUALS

FIGURE 5.1 Have students read the captions. **Ask**

- Why didn't the scientists bring together flies from the original locations? They wanted to be sure the flies would mate.
- What type of isolation produced populations of tropical and temperate flies? geographic
- What type of isolation kept lab flies from mating? behavioral

Take It Further

When the two different *ds2* alleles became selected for in the different climates, mating behaviors were also affected. This is because the *ds2* gene codes for both temperature tolerance and mating behaviors. The two populations of fruit flies were first isolated geographically. Then, because of how the allele mutation affected mating behaviors, the populations also became isolated reproductively.

Vocabulary

Word Origins A **pheromone** is a chemical that is secreted by an organism and affects others of the same species, often for the purpose of attracting a mate. The Greek root is *pherein,* meaning "to carry." Students may better remember the meaning *pheromone* if they think of the word **ferry,** which also means "to carry" and is derived from the Middle English word *ferein*—probably derived from the same Greek root.

Answers

A **Synthesize** Fruit flies with the temperate *ds2* allele produce a specific pheromone that only attracts mates that have the same *ds2* allele. The same is true for the tropical *ds2* allele.

B **Summarize** When populations can no longer mate successfully with each other, they are considered to be separate species. Until this occurs, other forms of isolation can be overcome as long as the two populations can still interbreed and have healthy, fertile offspring.

▼ Teach *continued*

TEACH FROM VISUALS

FIGURE 5.2 Have students find the Isthmus of Panama on the map. Tell them that the isthmus formed about three million years ago from the shifting of Earth's tectonic plates. **Ask**

- How did the formation of the isthmus affect marine species? They became geographically isolated
- How did the formation of the isthmus affect the land species of North and South America? Land populations were no longer geographically isolated.
- What might it mean for marine species that there is now a canal connecting the Caribbean Sea and the Pacific Ocean? Some species may be able to migrate.

Answers

Ⓐ **Compare and Contrast** Behavioral isolation involves differences in courtship or mating behaviors; temporal isolation involves differences in the *timing* of courtship or mating behaviors.

▼ Assess and Reteach

Assess Use the Section Self-Check or Section Quiz, both available at **HMHScience.com**.

Reteach Give students hypothetical examples of populations becoming isolated. Have them identify the type of isolation each example illustrates.

FIGURE 5.2 GEOGRAPHIC BARRIER

Although snapping shrimp in the Atlantic and Pacific Oceans look similar, they are distinct species that have evolved through geographic isolation.

Geographic Barriers

The most commonly studied type of isolation is geographic isolation. **Geographic isolation** involves physical barriers that divide a population into two or more groups. These barriers can include rivers, mountains, and dried lakebeds. As shown in **FIGURE 5.2**, the formation of the Isthmus of Panama created a barrier for many marine species. Marine organisms could no longer easily cross between the Atlantic and Pacific Oceans. Over time, the isolated populations became genetically different. Several species of snapping shrimp have evolved through geographic isolation. These species appear almost identical to one another. However, when males and females from opposite sides of the isthmus are placed together, they snap at each other instead of courting. Because they will no longer mate, these shrimp are classified as different species.

READING TOOLBOX

VOCABULARY

The word *temporal* comes from the Latin word *tempus*, meaning "time."

Temporal Barriers

Barriers can also involve timing. **Temporal isolation** exists when timing prevents reproduction between populations. Some members of a population may show signs of courtship at different times if there is a lot of competition for mates. Reproductive periods may change to a different time of the year or a different part of the day. These differences in timing can lead to speciation. For example, two tree species that grow on the Monterey Peninsula in California are very closely related. However, they have different pollination periods. The Monterey pine sheds its pollen in February, while the Bishop pine sheds its pollen in April. These pine species have likely evolved through temporal isolation.

Ⓐ **Compare and Contrast What are the differences and similarities between behavioral isolation and temporal isolation?**

11.5 Formative Assessment

REVIEWING MAIN IDEAS

1. How can **reproductive isolation** lead to **speciation**?
2. What are three types of barriers that can lead to reproductive isolation?

CRITICAL THINKING

3. **Apply** Why are the flash patterns of fireflies considered to be **behavioral isolation**?
4. **Analyze** How did **geographic isolation** affect the diversity Darwin observed in Galápagos finches?

CONNECT TO SCIENTIFIC PROCESS

5. What could have been used as a control group in the fruit fly experiment described in Figure 5.1?

11.5 FORMATIVE ASSESSMENT

1. If populations cannot mate successfully, genetic differences may accumulate in the populations. Over time, the populations may change so much that they become different species.
2. behavioral barriers, geographic barriers, and temporal barriers
3. The flash-pattern mating behaviors of fireflies are not related to the timing of mating, so this is considered behavioral isolation rather than temporal isolation.
4. The geographic isolation of the finches on different islands meant that each island's environment selected for traits that were beneficial on that particular island. Over time, genetic differences accumulated in the isolated populations, leading to many distinct finch species.
5. Flies bred in the laboratory with their original *ds2* genes could have been used as a control group, because they would not have received any kind of treatment. The effects of *ds2* insertions on the two treatment groups could have been compared against this group.

11.6 Patterns in Evolution

KEY CONCEPT **Evolution occurs in patterns.**

MAIN IDEAS

- Evolution through natural selection is not random.
- Species can shape each other over time.
- Species can become extinct.
- Speciation often occurs in patterns.

VOCABULARY

convergent evolution
divergent evolution
coevolution
extinction
punctuated equilibrium
adaptive radiation

Connect to Your World

People adapt their behavior to their situation. As you go through school, you are likely to change how you dress, talk, and study. When you learn something that makes your life better, you hold on to that new skill. On a genetic level and over multiple generations, species hold onto traits that benefit them in their environment. Natural selection is the process that preserves these adaptive traits in a population. However, sudden changes in an environment can wipe out a species quickly. The rise and fall of species over time reveal clear evolutionary patterns.

MAIN IDEA

Evolution through natural selection is not random.

In science, the terms *chance* and *random* relate to how easily an outcome can be predicted. Because mutations and genetic drift cannot be predicted, they are called random events. These random events are sources of genetic diversity. However, natural selection, which acts on this diversity, is not random. Individuals with traits that are better adapted for their environment have a better chance of surviving and reproducing than do individuals without these traits.

You have learned about directional, stabilizing, and disruptive selection. In each of these modes of selection, the effects of natural selection add up over many generations. In other words, natural selection pushes a population's traits in an advantageous direction. As you can see in **FIGURE 6.1**, alleles associated with these traits add up in the population's gene pool.

Remember, however, that having direction is not the same as having purpose or intent. The environment controls the direction of natural selection. When the environment changes, different traits may become advantageous. The response of species to environmental challenges and opportunities is not random.

FIGURE 6.1 PATTERNS IN NATURAL SELECTION

In this hypothetical population, green body color is favored by natural selection. With each generation, alleles associated with green body color increase in frequency. Over time, more and more individuals in the population will have the advantageous phenotype.

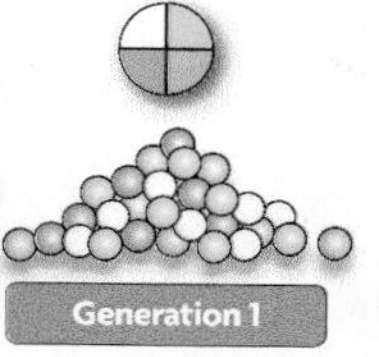

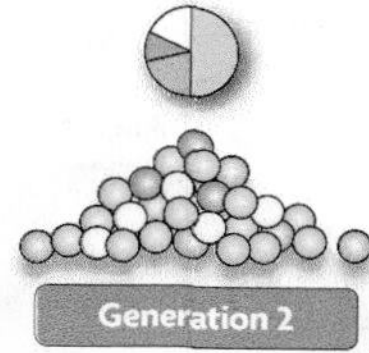

Differentiated Instruction

ENGLISH LEARNERS

Have students preview this section using the PLAN strategy: Predict, Locate, Add, and Note. Have them read the Connect to Your World paragraph at the beginning of the section. Ask them to make a prediction about each main idea and the way it relates to the vocabulary and the black headings in the text (locate). They can then read the section, adding details and noting descriptions of patterns in both types and rates of evolution.

Teacher Toolkit, Section C, PLAN

BELOW LEVEL

Have a brainstorming session in which students develop a cluster diagram for the central idea that evolution occurs in patterns. Focus on patterns of evolution, including adaptive radiation. Have students include what happens at the genetic level.

Teacher Toolkit, Section C, Brainstorming; Cluster Diagram

SECTION 11.6

B.5.4 Evaluate evidence to explain the role of natural selection as an evolutionary mechanism that leads to the adaptation of species, and to support claims that changes in environmental conditions may result in: (1) increases in the number of individuals of some species, (2) the emergence of new species over time, and/or (3) the extinction of other species.

Plan and Prepare

Activate Prior Knowledge Make a list of organisms and their adaptations. **Ask,** What are some different adaptations in plants and animals that seem to relate directly to features of their environment? *Sample answers:* heavy fur and layers of fat for warmth, camouflage for protection, food-pollen exchange between birds or insects and particular flowers Encourage students to distinguish between examples of divergent and convergent evolution, based on whether the plants or animals are likely to share genes. Also discuss coevolution.

Teach

TEACH FROM VISUALS

FIGURE 6.1 Use the diagram to distinguish between the random and selective aspects of evolution. **Ask**

- What aspect of the initial population is random? different alleles, resulting from mutation
- What aspect of the initial population is not random? natural selection, in this case for the green allele

▼ Teach *continued*

Vocabulary

Greek and Latin Word Origins The terms **convergent** and **divergent** share the Latin root *vergere,* which means "to bend."

The prefixes in the words provide a sense of the direction, with *convergent* meaning "to bend or come together" and *divergent* meaning "to bend away or separate."

It is important for students to remember that in coming together in **convergent evolution,** populations had to start far apart. Have students associate *con-* with "come together." Populations come to have similar characteristics despite the lack of a close common ancestor: similar characteristics, dissimilar genes.

The opposite is true in **divergent evolution.** Have students associate *divergent* with *divide.* These populations start close together, but move apart: dissimilar characteristics, similar genes.

Answers

A Infer The shells of turtles and snails are examples of convergent evolution. Turtles and snails do not share a recent common ancestor. (Turtles are vertebrate reptiles, and snails are invertebrate mollusks.) The shells evolved as a means of protection from predators.

B Analyze In convergent evolution, a similar trait in unrelated species is selected for because of a common benefit the trait provides in a given environment. In divergent evolution, closely related species that are in different environments increasingly adapt to those differences with traits that are advantageous for survival in their different environments.

Convergent Evolution

Different species often must adapt to similar environments. Evolution toward similar characteristics in unrelated species is called **convergent evolution.** Analogous structures, such as wings on birds and insects, are common examples of convergent evolution. Another example is the tail fin of fish and marine mammals, as shown in **FIGURE 6.2.** Sharks, which are fish, and dolphins, which are mammals, are separated by about 300 million years of evolution. Separately, they have both evolved similar tail fins to propel themselves through the water. However, the tail fins of sharks and other fish are vertical, while those of dolphins are horizontal.

Divergent Evolution

When closely related species evolve in different directions, they become increasingly different through **divergent evolution.** The evolution of the red fox and the kit fox is an example of this trend. Though closely related, the two species have different appearances that are the result of adapting to different environments. The red fox lives in temperate regions, usually in forests. Its dark reddish coat helps it to hide from predators. The sandy-colored coat of the kit fox allows it to blend in with its desert surroundings. Kit foxes also have large ears relative to their body size. This adaptation helps them to keep cool in the desert heat.

A Infer Are the shells of turtles and snails examples of convergent or divergent evolution? Explain.

FIGURE 6.2 Convergent and Divergent Evolution

Natural selection is not random. It can have direction, and its effects are cumulative through generations.

CONVERGENT EVOLUTION

Dolphins, which are mammals, and sharks, which are fish, have evolved similar tail fins, as each has adapted to similar environmental conditions.

Dolphin

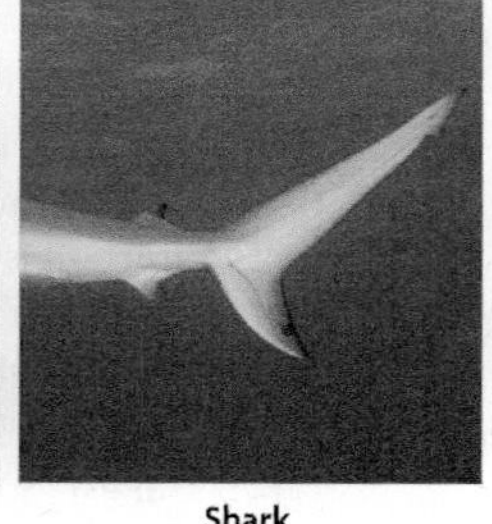

Shark

DIVERGENT EVOLUTION

The kit fox and the red fox evolved from a common ancestor while adapting to different environments.

Kit fox

Red fox

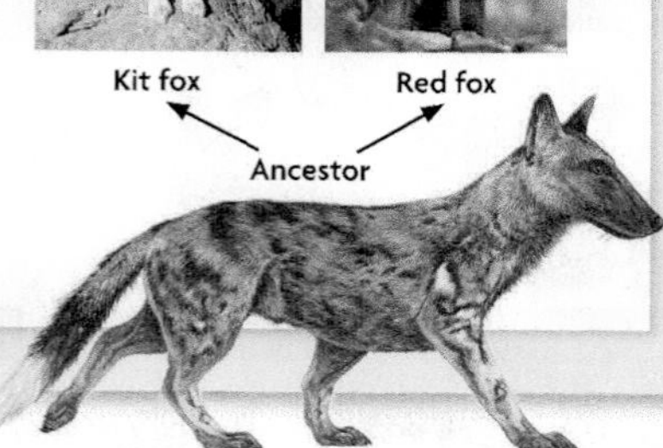

Ancestor

B Analyze How do convergent and divergent evolution illustrate the directional nature of natural selection?

Differentiated Instruction

TEACH WITH TECHNOLOGY

Create a PowerPoint presentation of images that convey different patterns in evolution. Build on the examples used in **FIGURE 6.2.**

Tail Fins Compare the various tail fins that have evolved through convergence and divergence in marine species. Thresher sharks have long, scythelike tails that are quite unlike those of their relatives, such as the mako or great white shark. In fact, the tails of mako and great white sharks are more similar to those of tunas and billfishes—which are more distantly related than the thresher sharks.

Fur Color, Ear Size Compare the fur coloration and relative ear size in different species of fox, such as the kit fox, red fox, arctic fox, and fennec. Discuss how traits in these closely related species have diverged in response to different environments. The light brown fur of the fennec enables it to blend in with the sands of its desert environment, while its large ears provide a large surface area to release body heat. The arctic fox has a white winter coat that allows it to blend in with the snow, and small ears to limit heat loss.

MAIN IDEA

Species can shape each other over time.

Species interact with each other in many different ways. For example, they may compete for the same food source or be involved in a predator-prey relationship. Most of these interactions do not involve evolutionary changes. However, sometimes the evolutionary paths of two species become connected.

Beneficial Relationships Through Coevolution

The bull-thorn acacia is a plant species with branches covered in hollow thorns. Although the thorns protect the plant from being eaten by large animals, small herbivores such as caterpillars can fit between them. To the rescue comes *Pseudomyrmex ferrugineus*, a species of stinging ants. As shown in **FIGURE 6.3,** these ants live inside the thorns and feed on the plant's nectar. The ants protect the plant by stinging animals that try to eat the leaves.

This relationship is much more than a simple cooperation between two species. The acacia and the ants share an evolutionary history. The hollow thorns and nectar-producing leaves of the acacia and the stinging of the ants have evolved due to the relationship between the two species. Relatives of these species that are not involved in this type of relationship do not have these traits. Such relationships form through **coevolution,** the process in which two or more species evolve in response to changes in each other.

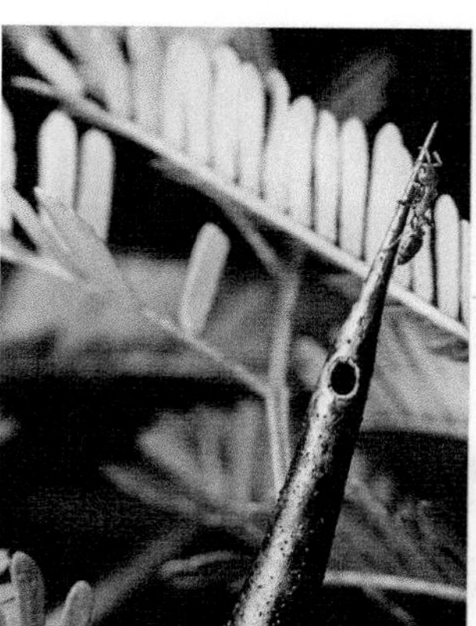

FIGURE 6.3 The relationship between this ant and the acacia plant has developed through coevolution. The ant lives inside the hollow thorn and protects the acacia by stinging any potential predators.

Evolutionary Arms Races

Coevolution can also occur in competitive relationships. These interactions can lead to "evolutionary arms races," in which each species responds to pressure from the other through better adaptations over many generations.

For example, many plants produce defense chemicals in the soil to discourage other plants from growing nearby and competing for resources. Natural selection then favors competing plants that can overcome the effects of the chemicals. After many generations, most competitors have some level of resistance and are again able to grow near the defensive plant. Natural selection then favors plants that have evolved even more potent chemicals. In another case, the thick shells and spines of murex snails are an adaptive response to predation by crabs. In turn, crabs have evolved powerful claws that are strong enough to crack the snails' shells.

A Predict **What do you think will happen in future generations of crabs and snails?**

The crab is the natural predator of the snail.

Natural selection favors snails with thicker shells and spines.

Through natural selection, crabs evolve more powerful claws that can pierce the snails' thick, spiny shells.

In response, natural selection favors snails with even thicker shells and spines.

BELOW LEVEL

Have students trace the coevolution between crab and snail populations by having them prepare a series of drawings similar to the photographs at the bottom of this page. Students should alternate the crab and snail drawings, following the sequence of events described in the captions. Have students draw the crab claws noticeably bigger as they move through the sequence.

Teacher Toolkit, Section C, Sequence Diagram

PRE-AP

Have students recast the evolutionary arms race between the crab and snail species shown at the bottom of this page in terms of genes. Ask them to write one or two paragraphs describing the real winners and losers in this race: the alleles selected for in each species.

Teacher Toolkit, Section C, Quick-Write

Integrating Chemistry

Many plant species have evolved to produce chemicals whose sole purpose seems to be to make plants unpalatable to grazing herbivores. Some of these substances have, in fact, made the plants attractive to humans. These include **nicotine** from tobacco plants and **caffeine** from coffee plants.

Plants that belong to the mustard family produce **chemical deterrents** that keep most plant-eaters from feeding on their leaves. Among these substances are the oils used to make the condiments mustard and horseradish. In an evolutionary sense, these plants represent a ready source of food for any animal that could digest the oils. Certain species of bugs, beetles, and moths did evolve to take advantage of this unused food source.

ONLINE Biology
HMHScience.com

Students can examine how populations of *Mycobacterium tuberculosis* have changed in response to antibiotics. In this case, the arms race is between the bacteria that cause tuberculosis and the scientists who develop new drugs. See the Animated Biology at **HMHScience.com**.

Answers

A Predict The history of competitive evolution between snails and crabs suggests that the shells of snails could continue to become thicker and spinier in response to the evolution of stronger claws in crabs. It is also possible that different mechanisms for protection and feeding could coevolve.

▼ Teach continued

Science Trivia

The five largest mass-extinction events occurred at the ends of the Ordovician, Devonian, Permian, Triassic, and Cretaceous periods. One unit of measurement for extinctions is how many genera go extinct. (*Genera* is the plural form of *genus*, the taxonomic group just above species.)

- Terminal Ordovician event: ~ 443 million years ago, 57 percent of marine genera became extinct.
- Terminal Devonian event: ~ 359 million years ago, 50 percent of marine invertebrates became extinct.
- Terminal Permian event: ~ 251 million years ago, 57 percent of marine genera and 70 percent of land species became extinct.
- Terminal Triassic event: ~ 199 million years ago, 52 percent of marine invertebrates became extinct.
- Terminal Cretaceous event: ~ 65 million years ago, 47 percent of marine genera and 18 percent of land vertebrate families became extinct.

TEACH FROM VISUALS

FIGURE 6.5 Have students identify the mass extinction events on the graph and compare the scale of extinction. **Ask**

- What was the extinction rate 400 million years ago? about ten families per million years
- What does the blue area represent? number of families that were going extinct per million years

Answers

A **Compare and Contrast** Background extinctions occur continuously, sometimes in a particular ecosystem or location, and they occur at low rates relative to those of mass extinctions. Mass extinctions, while rare, occur relatively suddenly and affect many species, often on a global level. Both processes result in the elimination of a species from Earth.

MAIN IDEA

Species can become extinct.

Just as birth and death are natural events in the life of an individual, the rise and fall of species are natural processes of evolution. The elimination of a species from Earth is called **extinction.** Extinction often occurs when a specie as a whole is unable to adapt to a change in its environment. Biologists divide extinction events into two categories—background extinctions and mass extinctions. Although they differ in degree, the effect of both is the same: the permanent loss of species from Earth.

FIGURE 6.4 Native to Portugal and Spain, the Iberian lynx is the world's most endangered feline. The World Wildlife Federation estimates that there are only 84 to 143 adult individuals remaining in the wild.

Background Extinctions

Extinctions that occur continuously but at a very low rate are called background extinctions. They are part of the cycle of life on Earth. Background extinctions occur at roughly the same rate as speciation. Unlike catastrophic mass extinctions, background extinction events usually affect only one or a few species in a relatively small area, such as a rain forest or a mountain range. They can be caused by local changes in the environment, such as the introduction of a new predator species or a decrease in food supply. From a human perspective, such extinctions seem to occur randomly but at a fairly constant rate.

Mass Extinctions

Mass extinctions are much more rare than background extinctions. However, as illustrated in **FIGURE 6.5**, they are much more intense. These events often occur at the global level. Therefore, they destroy many species—even entire orders or families. Mass extinctions are thought to occur suddenly in geologic time, usually because of a catastrophic event such as an ice age or asteroid impact. The fossil record confirms that there have been at least five mass extinctions in the past 600 million years. Some scientists also think that we are in the midst of a sixth mass extinction that has been caused by human impact on the biosphere

A Compare and Contrast **What are the differences and similarities between background extinctions and mass extinctions?**

FIGURE 6.5 EXTINCTION RATES THROUGH TIME

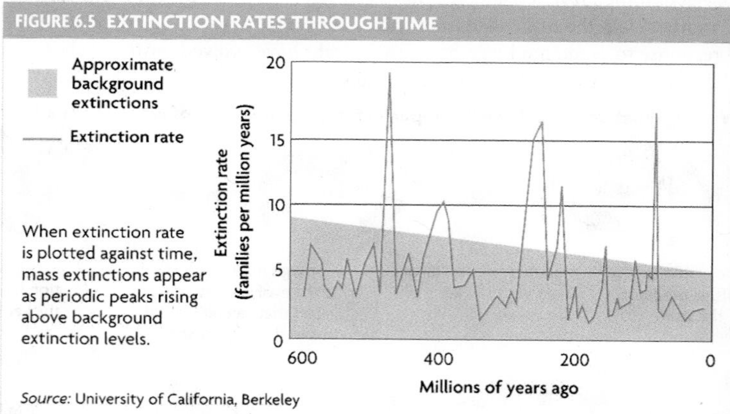

Source: University of California, Berkeley

Differentiated Instruction

HANDS-ON ACTIVITY

Put together an extinction timeline with the class, using **Figure 6.5** as a starting point. Ask students to identify the time of extinction for an animal or a plant of their choice. Encourage students to find not only examples from the distant past, but also recent examples. These might include the passenger pigeon, dodo bird, mastodon, woolly mammoth, or Irish elk.

Teacher Toolkit, Section C, Timeline

MAIN IDEA

Speciation often occurs in patterns.

Paleontologists have long noticed repeating patterns in the history of life, reflected in the fossil record. Among these patterns, two stand out from the rest. In evolutionary gradualism, discussed in Section 2 of the chapter Principles of Evolution, evolutionary changes are thought to occur over long periods of time. For many years, advocates of evolution adhered to this idea.

In the second of the two patterns, bursts of evolutionary activity are followed by long periods of stability. This pattern is described by the theory of **punctuated equilibrium,** which states that episodes of speciation occur suddenly in geologic time and are followed by long periods of little evolutionary change, or stasis. Paleontologist Niles Eldredge, a curator at The American Museum of Natural History in New York, and evolutionary biologist Stephen Jay Gould originally proposed the theory of punctuated equilbrium in 1972. Both men were graduate students at Columbia University, studying fossils of four closely related species of trilobite. The fossils showed evidence of the sudden appearance of a new form of eye. This new trilobite eye appears to be linked to an increased ability to roll into a protective ball, allowing for better defense against predators.

The theory of punctuated equilibrium was written as a revision of Darwin's idea that new species arise through gradual transformations of ancestral species. It must be noted that in the sixth edition of his book *On the Origin of Species,* Darwin wrote that "the periods, during which species have undergone modification, though long as measured by years, have probably been short in comparison with the periods during which they retained the same form."

CONNECT TO

GEOLOGY

Refer back to Section 1 of the chapter **Principles of Evolution** to review James Hutton's theory that led to the concept of evolutionary gradualism.

FIGURE 6.6 Evolutionary Gradualism and Punctuated Equilibrium

The concept that species evolve slowly, over long periods of time, is known as evolutionary gradualism.

Punctuated equilibrium proposes that species show little evolutionary change for millions of years, followed by periods of rapid speciation.

TEACH FROM VISUALS

FIGURE 6.6 Have students examine the illustrations of two types of evolution closely. **Ask**

- After comparing the two illustrations, what do you think is the main visual clue that describes gradual change? Which other clue describes abrupt changes after long periods of stasis? The gradual curves and slight changes from stage to stage in the butterflies' appearance in the illustration on the left give clues that the changes occurred gradually. The straight vertical lines followed by abrupt branching of lines and sudden, significant changes in butterfly appearance give clues about punctuated equilibrium in the illustration on the right side.

INCLUSION

Project an image of **Figure 6.6** onto the board where students can see it clearly. Use an analogy of doing laundry to help students understand the concepts of evolutionary gradualism and punctuated equilibrium. Ask students to think about a favorite item of clothing that has slowly faded with many washings. Explain to them that this is how evolutionary gradualism occurs, with changes occurring slowly over a long period of time. Then, ask them to picture washing a brand new garment and accidentally adding a cup of bleach. This sort of "catastrophic event" will cause a sudden change in the appearance of the garment, such as described by the theory of punctuated equilibrium.

Teacher Toolkit, Section C, Connect to Content Through Visuals

▼ Teach *continued*

TEACH FROM VISUALS

FIGURE 6.7 Have students study the image of *Leptictidium*. Explain that this is a model of the animal that was created for display in a museum. All that was actually found of the organism was a handful of fossilized bones. **Ask:** What methods do scientists use to recreate a facsimile of what an ancient animal might have looked like? Scientists can combine information from other partial skeletons and from living organisms with similar structures to recreate the appearance of ancient animals.

Vocabulary

Academic Vocabulary Students may first think of the word **radiation** as it relates to nuclear power, x-ray machines, or science fiction. In terms of evolution, *radiation* refers to organisms *radiating* out into new habitats and niches. As a result, new and distinct species evolve from a shared ancestor **(VISUAL VOCAB).** The roots of these words are Latin: *radius*, or "ray" and *radiät-*, or "to emit beams." Students may better remember the meaning of **adaptive radiation** if they think of the way a radio emits signals that radiate outward.

Modern studies show us that in stable ecosystems, most species are well adapted and generally resistant to change, unless some outside force causes disruption. In the case of punctuated equilibrium, this is believed to occur because a portion of a population becomes isolated and undergoes a speciation event. This isolation may be due to some sort of catastrophe, after which those organisms able to evolve quickly are more likely to survive. Isolation may also occur as a result of long-term environmental changes, like the formation of mountains or deserts, or due to a mutation that gives the organism a significant survival advantage over competitors.

When an ecosystem is greatly damaged, such as after the 1980 volcanic eruption of Mt. Saint Helens, in Washington state, other organisms will rapidly move into the area to fill empty niches. Although rapid evolutionary bursts can be compared in some ways to what is seen when such modern ecosystems are seriously disturbed, there is a distinct difference between the two. Rather than existing species moving in to fill vacancies in a changed ecosystem, in punctuated equilibrium, new speciation occurs suddenly following a long interval of stasis. Both evolutionary gradualism and punctuated equilibrium are viable scientific theories, and both are supported by evidence found in the fossil record. Although scientists still debate which of these two ideas best accounts for observed patterns of evolutionary change, most accept that it is likely that evolution occurs by a combination of these two major theories.

VISUAL VOCAB

Adaptive radiation is the rapid evolution of many diverse species from ancestral species.

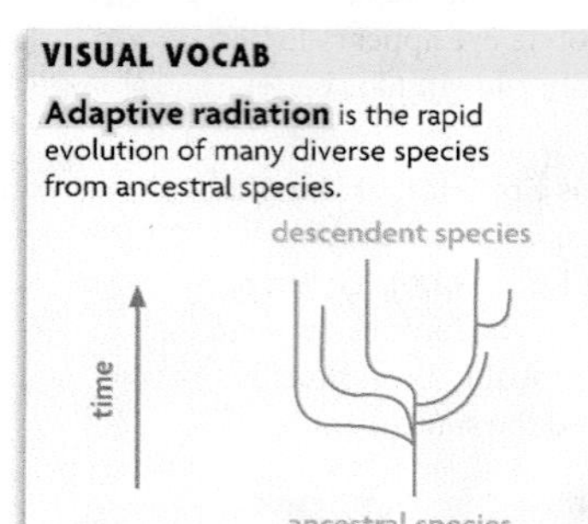

The process involving the diversification of one ancestral species into many descendent species is referred to as **adaptive radiation.** These descendent species are usually adapted to a wide range of environments. One example of adaptive radiation is the variation found in Galápagos finches, which were discussed in the chapter Principles of Evolution. Another rather dramatic example is seen in the radiation of mammals following the mass extinction at the end of the Cretaceous period about 65 million years ago.

According to the fossils that have been found thus far, the earliest mammals were tiny, mostly nocturnal, and probably insect eaters, such as the shrew-like *Leptictidium*, seen in **FIGURE 6.7**, allowing them to coexist with the dinosaurs for about 150 million years.

FIGURE 6.7 LEPTICTIDIUM

This model of *Leptictidium* was made based on the bone structures found in fossil specimens.

Differentiated Instruction

TEACH WITH TECHNOLOGY

Have students use library and internet resources to research paleontological explorations that have been done in their country of origin. They should focus their research on a particular fossil discovery. Using posters, digital slide shows, or web-based presentation programs, have students create a presentation on the results of their research.

Teacher Toolkit, Section G, Presentation Software

FIGURE 6.8 The K-T Boundary

The K-T boundary layer is marked clearly in rock layers in many places around the world. It is linked to the collision of an asteroid with Earth around 65 million years ago. The layer contains high concentrations of the element Iridium. Iridium is very rare on Earth, but is found in much greater abundance in objects from space.

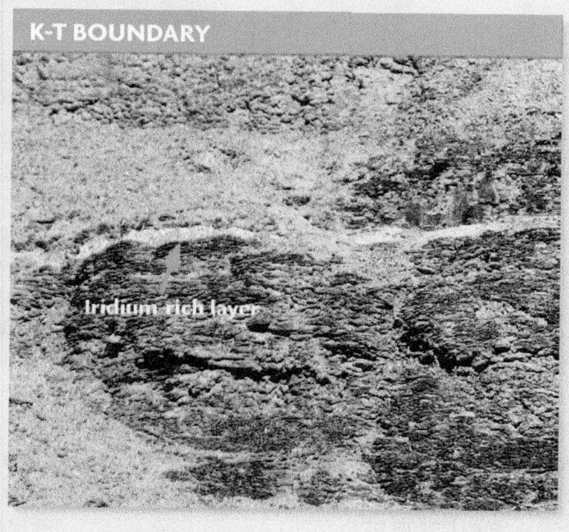

The extinction of the dinosaurs about 65 million years ago left environments full of open niches for other types of animals. In the first 10 million years of the Tertiary period following the mass extinction event, more than 4000 mammal species had evolved, including the ancestors of modern whales, bats, rodents, and primates. Evidence of this mass extinction, known as the Cretaceous-Tertiary (K-T) boundary, can be seen in **FIGURE 6.8.**

The fossil record indicates that there have been at least five mass extinctions in the past 600 million years, where large percentages of global populations were decimated. Studying these extinctions reveals that following each was a period of rapid evolutionary changes and the appearance of new species.

A Synthesize The adaptive radiation of mammals followed the extinction of the dinosaurs. How do these events support the theory of punctuated equilibrium?

Answers

A Synthesize When dinosaurs were dominant, most mammals were small, nocturnal insect-eaters. After the extinction of the dinosaurs, which left many niches empty, there was a period of sudden and rapid evolution of mammals, during which thousands of new and diverse species evolved and filled some of those niches.

Assess and Reteach ▼

Assess Use the Section Self-Check or Section Quiz, both available at **HMHScience.com**.

Reteach Have students present an oral summary of the section content. Students should use the section heads to organize the content.

11.6 Formative Assessment

SELF-CHECK Online
HMHScience.com
GO ONLINE

REVIEWING ▶ MAIN IDEAS

1. Explain what it means to say that natural selection is not random.
2. How does **coevolution** shape two species over time?
3. How can mass **extinctions** lead to the sudden appearance of new species?
4. What pattern is described by the theory of **punctuated equilibrium**?

CRITICAL THINKING

5. **Synthesize** Defensive chemicals are usually found in unripe fruit, but not in ripe fruit. In terms of coevolution, why might this be?
6. **Infer** Analogous structures are often examples of **convergent evolution.** What types of structures would likely be examples of **divergent evolution**?

CONNECT TO HUMAN BIOLOGY

7. Through mutation, HIV can accumulate resistance to drugs developed for treatment. Describe the relationship between HIV and the humans who develop these drugs in terms of an evolutionary arms race.

11.6 FORMATIVE ASSESSMENT

1. Natural selection pushes a population's traits in an advantageous direction. There is nothing random about certain environmental conditions determining that some traits are beneficial, causing those traits to become more common over time.
2. If two species share an evolutionary history, changes in one species can lead to changes in the other species, causing a continuous dynamic pattern.
3. Following a mass extinction, many ecological niches are left vacant. Surviving organisms may rapidly evolve into new species that fill those vacant niches.
4. long periods of relatively little evolutionary change interspersed with sudden, rapid periods of speciation
5. Some fruit-eating animals act as seed dispersers for various plants. If the seeds are not ready for germination, it does the plant no good to have them dispersed by an animal. If the fruit is only edible when the seeds are ready to be dispersed, this greatly improves the chances of that plant having its genes passed on to offspring.
6. homologous structures
7. As humans develop new and improved drugs, some HIV strains that are resistant to these drugs will have an advantage and will therefore become more common. Humans then must develop even more drugs, to which HIV will evolve greater resistance, and so on.

CHAPTER REVIEW

Encourage students to go to **HMHScience.com** for a detailed review of each section, including visuals and vocabulary practice.

Online Student Resources, Vocabulary Practice Worksheet

CHAPTER 11 Summary

BIG IDEA The genetic composition of populations evolves through natural selection as species adapt to changes in their environment.

KEY CONCEPTS

11.1 Genetic Variation Within Populations

A population shares a common gene pool. Genetic variation in a gene pool can be measured through allele frequencies. Genetic variation increases the chance that some members of a population will be able to adapt to their environment.

11.2 Natural Selection in Populations

Populations, not individuals, evolve. Natural selection acts on distributions of traits in a population. Directional selection occurs when one extreme phenotype is advantageous for survival. If intermediate phenotypes are advantageous, they become more common through stabilizing selection. In the process of disruptive selection, extreme phenotypes are selected.

11.3 Other Mechanisms of Evolution

Natural selection is not the only mechanism through which populations evolve. Gene flow is the movement of alleles between populations. Changes in allele frequencies due to chance alone can occur through genetic drift. If certain traits increase mating success, those traits can become more common through sexual selection.

11.4 Hardy-Weinberg Equilibrium

Hardy-Weinberg equilibrium provides a framework for understanding how populations evolve. A population in Hardy-Weinberg equilibrium is not evolving. The conditions required for this equilibrium are rarely met in nature. However, Hardy-Weinberg equilibrium provides a framework for understanding the factors that can lead to evolution. It is therefore very useful to population biologists.

11.5 Speciation Through Isolation

New species can arise when populations are isolated. Reproductive isolation occurs when members of two populations are no longer able to mate successfully. It is the final stage in speciation—the rise of two or more species from one existing species. Behavioral, geographic, or temporal barriers can lead to isolation.

11.6 Patterns in Evolution

Evolution occurs in patterns. Evolution through natural selection can have direction, and its effects add up over many generations. The evolutionary paths of two or more species can become connected through the process of coevolution. Extinction and speciation events also appear in patterns in the fossil record.

READING TOOLBOX SYNTHESIZE YOUR NOTES

Two-Column Chart Make a two-column chart to synthesize your notes about the three modes of natural selection.

Type of Selection	Graph
Directional Selection Cause: Result:	Frequency / Range of phenotypes

Concept Map Use a concept map to summarize factors that can lead to evolution.

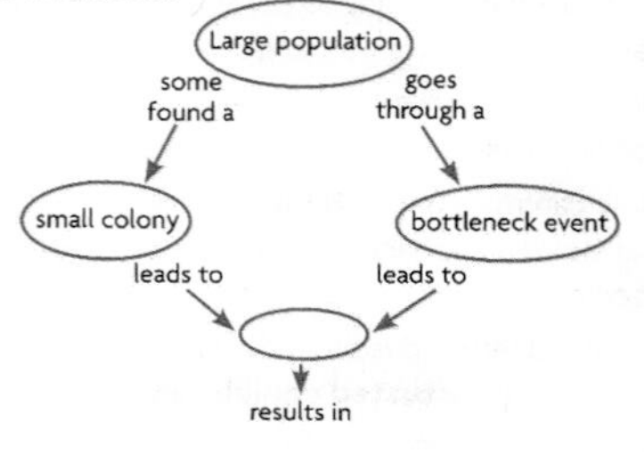

Reviewing Vocabulary

1. Picture could show a population of triangles and a population of squares with arrows pointing in both directions between them. Possible caption: Gene flow is the movement of alleles between populations.
2. Picture could show one population of circles separated from a mixed population of squares and Xs by a mountain range. Possible caption: Mountains can geographically isolate the populations.
3. Picture could show a triangle with diverging arrows above it, one leading to a triangle with rounded corners and the other to a triangle with wavy edges. Possible caption: The two closely related species are evolving with different characteristics.
4. It is likely that students will draw a line graph that shows spikes in the rate of speciation over time. Possible caption: Long periods of little evolutionary change are separated by bursts of rapid speciation.
5. all the alleles in a population
6. inability to mate with each other
7. formation of new species
8. evolving toward similar characteristics
9. species evolving in response to each other
10. many species evolving from one species

11 Review

INTERACTIVE Review
HMHScience.com
GO ONLINE
Review Games • Concept Map • Section Self-Checks

CHAPTER VOCABULARY

11.1 gene pool
allele frequency

11.2 normal distribution
microevolution
directional selection
stabilizing selection
disruptive selection

11.3 gene flow
genetic drift
bottleneck effect
founder effect
sexual selection

11.4 Hardy-Weinberg equilibrium

11.5 reproductive isolation
speciation
behavioral isolation
geographic isolation
temporal isolation

11.6 convergent evolution
divergent evolution
coevolution
extinction
punctuated equilibrium
adaptive radiation

Reviewing Vocabulary

READING TOOLBOX VISUALIZING VOCABULARY

For each term below, use simple shapes, lines, or arrows to illustrate their meaning. Below each picture, write a short caption. Here's an example for the term *founder effect*.

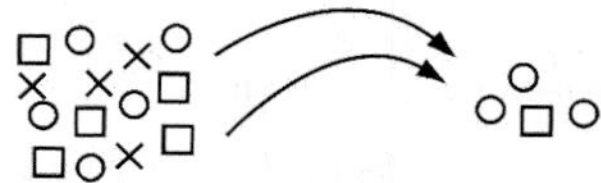

A small group of individuals starts a population that is subject to genetic drift.

1. gene flow
2. geographic isolation
3. divergent evolution
4. punctuated equilibrium

Keep It Short

For each vocabulary word below, write a short, precise phrase that describes its meaning. For example, a short phrase to describe the word *extinction* could be "gone forever."

5. gene pool
6. reproductive isolation
7. speciation
8. convergent evolution
9. coevolution
10. adaptive radiation

Reviewing MAIN IDEAS

11. Would a population with a lot of genetic variation or little genetic variation be more likely to have individuals that can adapt to a changing environment? Explain your answer.
12. Describe two major sources of genetic variation.
13. A certain trait in a population is not under any selective pressure. Draw a curve showing the likely phenotypic distribution for this trait.
14. Over many generations, certain insect species have become more and more resistant to insecticides. What type of natural selection does this show, and how does it differ from the other types?
15. Describe how gene flow can increase genetic variation within two neighboring populations.
16. How are the effects of genetic drift similar to the effects of having a small sample size in a scientific experiment?
17. Give an example of the way sexual selection can cause extreme phenotypes in a population.
18. What are the conditions necessary for a population to stay in Hardy-Weinberg equilibrium?
19. How can a lack of gene flow between populations lead to speciation?
20. Describe three types of barriers that can cause populations to become reproductively isolated from each other.
21. Explain why mutation and genetic drift are random events, while natural selection is not.
22. Speciation is the rise of two or more species from one existing species. What process keeps the number of total species on Earth from growing exponentially through speciation?
23. What is the relationship between speciation and the theory of punctuated equilibrium?

Reviewing Main Ideas

11. A population with a lot of genetic variation is likely to have more phenotypic variation; such a population would be more likely to have individuals that can adapt to a changing environment.
12. Mutation can result in new alleles on chromosomes. Recombination rearranges alleles and produces new allele combinations on chromosomes.
13. The curve should show a normal distribution (bell-shaped curve).
14. This shows directional selection; it differs from stabilizing and disruptive selection in that one extreme phenotype is favored by natural selection.
15. New alleles can enter a population when an individual from a neighboring population mates with an individual from the original population.

CHAPTER REVIEW

16. A small sample size in an experiment can skew the results, because out-of-the-ordinary data will not be averaged out. This is the same effect that genetic drift can have on small populations. By chance, certain alleles may increase or decrease in frequency because of the small population size.
17. *Sample Answer:* Female widowbirds prefer to mate with male widowbirds that have longer tail feathers. Thus, alleles associated with longer tail feathers in males get passed on to future generations. Over time, males have longer and longer tail feathers.
18. very large population, no emigration or immigration, no mutations, random mating, and no natural selection
19. Without gene flow, the populations may begin to become more and more genetically different. They may become so genetically different that individuals from one population are no longer able to mate successfully with individuals from the other population. At this point, the two populations are different species.
20. Behavioral barriers are differences in courtship or mating behaviors, such as courtship dances and songs, between populations. Geographic barriers are physical barriers, such as mountains and rivers, that divide a population. Temporal barriers are differences in the timing of two populations' reproduction.
21. Mutation and genetic drift are random because they cannot be predicted and they are due to chance alone. Natural selection is not random because there is a cause-and-effect relationship: changes or new conditions in the environment result in the selection of traits that are adaptive to those changes.
22. extinction
23. The theory of punctuated equilibrium states that speciation occurs suddenly in geologic time and is followed by long periods of little evolutionary change or speciation.

Critical Thinking

24. *Sample answer:* Descendants of the common ancestor of honeycreepers became geographically isolated when they colonized different islands. Each population adapted to its island's environment, remaining reproductively isolated. In time, these populations evolved into distinct species.
25. Gene flow can introduce new alleles to a small population, and because the population is small to begin with, this flow can result in substantial changes in allele frequency.
26. disruptive selection; In disruptive selection, the intermediate phenotype is selected against, whereas in stabilizing selection, the intermediate phenotype is selected for.
27. Genetic drift cannot be predicted. Certain alleles in small populations may increase or decrease by chance alone, since there are so few individuals reproducing.
28. The allele frequencies in a gene pool always add up to 100 percent because a gene pool is the combined alleles of all the individuals in a population. It is the sum of its parts.
29. Natural selection favors individuals that are best adapted to survive and reproduce in a given environment. Sexual selection favors individuals that are best adapted to win mates. Both types of selection are involved in reproductive success; however, traits that increase chances of winning a mate may sometimes be less advantageous for survival of that individual.

Interpreting Visuals

30. disruptive selection; Intermediate beak size has the lowest frequency, indicating it is selected against, while extreme phenotypes are selected for.
31. small beaks and large beaks
32. *Sample answer:* Two main types of food are available: tiny insects and large, dry seeds. Small-beaked birds can pluck tiny insects from nooks and crannies; large-beaked birds have the ability to crack open the large seeds; medium-beaked birds are not good at either task.

Critical Thinking

24. Evaluate Biogeographic and genetic evidence indicates that more than 50 species of Hawaiian honeycreeper birds have likely descended from a common ancestor. The 18 surviving species occupy many different niches and exhibit a variety of beak types, songs, and nesting behaviors. What role do the concepts of reproductive isolation and adaptive radiation play in interpreting the evidence for the speciation of Hawaiian honeycreepers?

25. Apply How could gene flow affect a population that was founded by a small number of individuals?

26. Analyze What type of selection produces a distribution of phenotypes opposite to that produced by stabilizing selection? Explain your answer.

27. Analyze Explain how the process of genetic drift occurs completely by chance.

28. Analyze Why must allele frequencies in a gene pool always add up to 100%?

29. Compare and Contrast What are the differences and similarities between natural selection and sexual selection?

Interpreting Visuals

Below is a frequency distribution for beak size in a hypothetical population of birds. Use this graph to answer the next three questions.

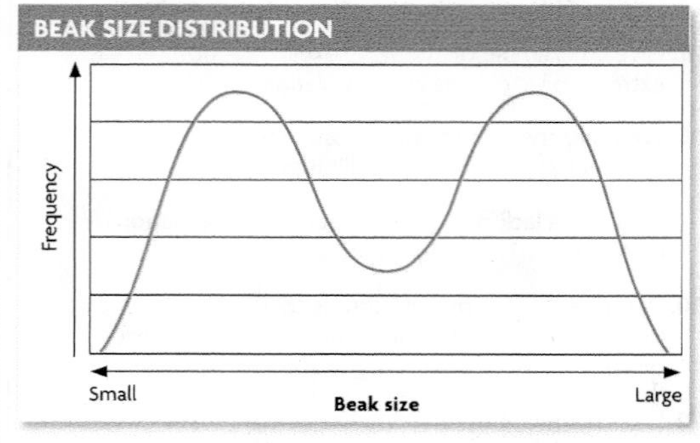

30. Analyze What type of selection is demonstrated by the data in this graph? Explain your answer.

31. Analyze Which phenotypes are the most common in this population?

32. Synthesize Describe a scenario that could realistically lead to this pattern of selection in a bird population.

Analyzing Data Identify Patterns

Below is a graph showing the relationship between female chimpanzee rank and the survival of offspring. Use the graph to answer the next three questions.

SURVIVAL OF CHIMPANZEE OFFSPRING

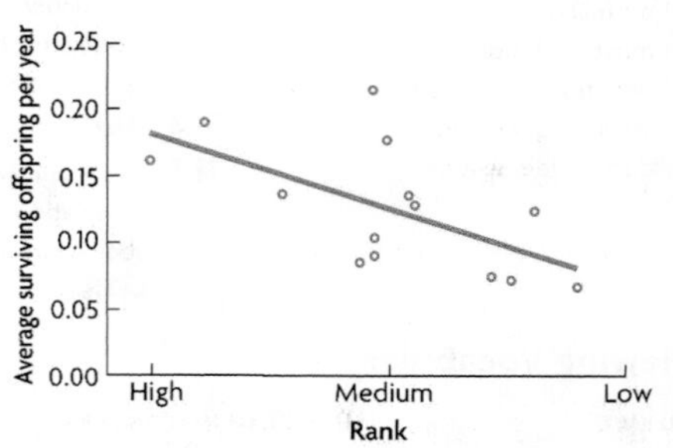

Source: Jane Goodall Institute

33. Analyze What is the relationship between female rank and the survival of her offspring?

34. Analyze Is there a level of rank that prevents a female chimp from reproducing? Explain.

35. Infer What can you infer by studying the scale of the y-axis on this graph?

Making Connections

36. Write a Proposal The explosive growth of nonnative species is a major global issue. A few individuals from one area act as founders of new populations on other continents or in other oceans. This is causing many native populations to decline. Human activities such as global commerce and travel are directly causing these destructive founding populations. Write a proposal to an international committee on the environment regarding this issue. Include in your proposal the significance of the changes to native populations, using terms and concepts from the chapter.

37. Infer Hemoglobin, an oxygen-carrying protein found in the red blood cells of vertebrates, helps to circulate oxygen from the lungs to all parts of the body. In penguins, the blood has a very high concentration of hemoglobin. Penguin muscles have a high concentration of myoglobin, which also stores oxygen. What might be a reason for these adaptations?

Analyzing Data

33. In general, higher female rank means improved survival rate of offspring.
34. No, the lowest value on the graph is greater than zero (approximately 7 percent), so it would appear that every female is able to reproduce.
35. The survival rate of chimpanzee offspring is low. Even among the highest-ranked females, less than 20 percent of their offspring survive each year.

Standards-Based Assessment

Record your answers on a separate piece of paper.

MULTIPLE CHOICE

1 Which explanation describes how natural selection produces changes in organisms?
  A Natural selection enables a trait of an individual to be expressed.
  B Natural selection occurs when a favorable phenotype allows for differential reproductive success in a population of organisms.
  C Natural selection occurs when individuals that develop disease die.
  D Natural selection occurs when neutral phenotypes become common in a population.

2 A drought occurs in an environment with a large plant population. Which element of natural selection is ***most likely*** to enable part of the population to survive and reproduce?
  A the potential for the plant population to produce more offspring than can survive
  B a change in climate conditions
  C competition with other plant and animal populations for finite water resources
  D some individual plants inherited traits that enable them to survive a drought

THINK THROUGH THE QUESTION

Read each of the answer choices carefully. Which of these choices would make a population more likely to survive in a changing environment?

3 In the 1800s, Georges Cuvier proposed the theory of catastrophism to explain how some species disappear from the fossil record by going extinct and new species appear in the fossil record through immigration. How could Cuvier's theory be used to explain periods of stasis?
  A Periods of stasis would result when organisms were not subject to the effects of natural disasters for extended periods of time.
  B Periods of stasis would appear in the fossil record when regions of Earth were subject to frequent natural disasters.
  C Periods of stasis would result only if an area was completely destroyed by a natural disaster.
  D Periods of stasis would result from slow and steady changes that were constantly occurring on Earth.

4 Scientists often use the relative positions of fossils in sedimentary rock layers to draw conclusions about the sequential nature of groups of organisms in the fossil record. Why are scientists able to use such observations as a key to the relative ages of fossils?
  A Sedimentary rocks are laid down in layers, so the oldest layers in an undisturbed rock bed will be located beneath upper layers.
  B Even when sedimentary rock layers are disturbed, the oldest layer is always deposited on top of the youngest rock layer.
  C Younger rock layers are always deposited under older layers.
  D Weathering and erosion expose fossils making them easier to examine.

5

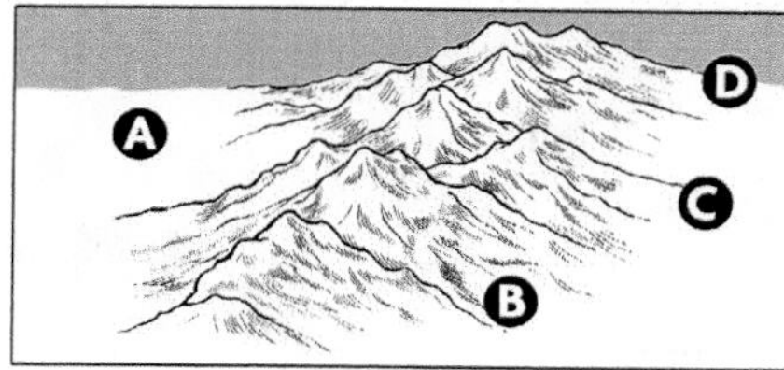

The map above shows the location of four populations of a bee species. Over time, Population A is ***most likely*** to evolve into a new species due to—
  A geographic isolation
  B temporal isolation
  C convergent evolution
  D adaptive radiation

Standards-Based Assessment

The Standards-Based Assessment questions will help students prepare for their final examination in the course. If you wish to give students practice in coding their answers, look for the Standards-Based Assessment Answer Sheet at **HMHScience.com**. To give students practice under timed testing conditions, allow them five minutes per question.

Question	Answer	Depth of Knowledge	Cognitive Complexity
1	B	I	L
2	D	II	M
3	A	IV	H
4	A	III	H
5	A	II	M

KEY

Depth of Knowledge
I Recall
II Skill/Concept
III Strategic Thinking
IV Extended Thinking

Cognitive Complexity
L Low
M Moderate
H High

Making Connections

36. Students' answers should incorporate chapter concepts such as natural selection, gene flow, genetic drift, and extinction. Students could also incorporate concepts from ecology, including the fact that foreign founding populations are likely to affect multiple species, such as those in a common food web and those that coevolved with the native species that are now in jeopardy.

37. These adaptations allow penguins to search for food underwater for long periods of time, without needing to come up to the surface for oxygen.

CHAPTER 12

Instruction and Intervention Support

The History of Life

1 Core Instruction

The **Core Instruction** resources below can be used for all students. Core instruction should be followed by ongoing assessment to determine which students need further help.

Available in both English and Spanish

Available Online

Section	Instruction	PRINT	ONLINE	Labs
12.1	Textbook **The Fossil Record**	■	●	Radioactive Decay Stride Inferences (Design Your Own) **Video Lab** Model of Rock Strata
	Teaching Visuals Permineralization (Fig. 1.2), Radiometric Dating (Fig. 1.4)		●	
	PowerPresentation and Notes 12.1		●	
12.2	Textbook **The Geologic Time Scale**	■	●	Understanding Geologic Time
	Animated Biology Geologic Time Scale		●	
	Teaching Visuals Geologic Time Scale (Fig. 2.2)		●	
	PowerPresentation and Notes 12.2		●	
12.3	Textbook **Origin of Life**	■	●	
	Teaching Visuals Miller-Urey Experiment (Fig. 3.2)		●	
	PowerPresentation and Notes 12.3		●	
12.4	Textbook **Early Single-Celled Organisms**	■	●	
	Animated Biology Endosymbiosis, Endosymbiotic Theory		●	
	Teaching Visuals Endosymbiosis (Fig. 4.2)		●	
	PowerPresentation and Notes 12.4		●	
12.5	Textbook **Radiation of Multicellular Life**	■	●	
	PowerPresentation and Notes 12.5		●	
12.6	Textbook **Primate Evolution**	■	●	Comparing Indexes Among Primates **QuickLab** Geologic Clock **Virtual Lab** Comparing Hominoid Skulls
	That's Amazing! Video Inquiry Crafty Cavemen		●	
	Teaching Visuals Phylogeny of Primates (Fig. 6.2), Hominid Skulls (Fig. 6.6)		●	
	PowerPresentation and Notes 12.6		●	

Additional online resources available for this chapter include **Interactive Whiteboard Resources.**

GO ONLINE! for all your teacher resources at HMHScience.com

2 Support and Intervention

Support and Intervention resources are useful for students who need targeted help beyond the Core Instruction

Resources	PRINT	ONLINE
Assess and Reteach (TE wrap)	■	●
Concept Map		●
Interactive Reader	■	●
Interactive Review Games		●
Section Self-Checks		●
Study Guide B		●
Vocabulary Practice Worksheets		●

3 Specialized Support

Students who need more intensive personalized intervention benefit from **Specialized Support** resources.

Resources	PRINT	ONLINE
Chapter Audio Files		●
Differentiated Instruction Inclusion, Below Level, and English Learners (TE wrap)	■	●
ELL Strategies	■	●
Modified Lesson Plans for English Learners		●
Reinforcement Worksheets		●
Study Guide A		●

Extension and Assessment

Enrichment and Challenge

Resources	PRINT	ONLINE
Active Reading Worksheets		●
Data Analysis Practice Worksheet		●
Differentiated Instruction Pre-AP (TE wrap)	■	●
Pre-AP Activity Geologic Time Puzzle, The Flores Hobbit Controversy		●
The Inside Story and **Take It Further** (TE wrap)	■	●
Unit Project		●
WebLinks		●
WebQuest Geologic Dating (12.1)		●

Assessment

Resources	PRINT	ONLINE
Alternative Assessment		●
Chapter Tests A and B		●
Diagnostic Test		●
ExamView Banks		●
Extended Response Test		●
Online Assessment System		●
Section Quizzes		●
Standards-Based Assessment	■	●

CHAPTER 12

Chapter Overview

- **Sections 1, 2,** and **6** provide coverage of the history of life on Earth.
- **Section 3** summarizes the main hypotheses about how life on Earth began.
- **Section 4** describes the role of microbes in shaping life on Earth and the major theories about how eukaryotic cells evolved.
- **Section 5** summarizes the key events in the radiation of multicellular life.

▼ Focus and Motivate

What can fossils teach us about the past?

Have students think about fossils they may have seen in museums or what they may have learned about ancient life from popular media. **Ask**

- What are some things we can learn about fossils simply by looking at them? what they looked like (size, shape), how they moved and ate, where they lived (habitats)
- In an evolutionary sense, relating fossils to the history of life on Earth, what else do they offer us? direct evidence of extinct organisms, insight into evolutionary relationships of both extinct and living organisms, evidence of climate change and continental drift

BIOZINE
HMHScience.com

Students can access BioZine at **HMHScience.com** to take a poll about current issues in biology.

CHAPTER 12

The History of Life

BIG IDEA Scientists use many types of data collection and experimentation to form hypotheses and theories about how life formed on Earth.

ONLINE BIOLOGY HMHScience.com

ONLINE Labs
- Radioactive Decay
- **QuickLab** Geologic Clock
- Stride Inferences
- Understanding Geologic Time
- Comparing Indexes Among Primates
- **Virtual Lab** Comparing Hominoid Skulls
- **Video Lab** Model of Rock Strata

Student Activity

Purpose **Students will gain an appreciation for the information that can be obtained from trace fossils.**

Materials
- plaster of Paris
- petri dishes, jar lids, or other flat-bottomed containers
- petroleum jelly
- objects with distinct textures or shapes, such as shells, leaves, feathers, fern fronds, toy animals with feet or hands that will leave prints

What can fossils teach us about the past?

This man, known only as Tollund Man, died about 2200 years ago in what is now Denmark. Details such as his skin and hair were preserved by the acid of the bog in which he was found. A bog is a type of wetland that accumulates peat, the deposits of dead plant material. Older remains from bogs can add information to the fossil record, which tends to consist mostly of hard shells, teeth, and bones.

READING TOOLBOX **This reading tool can help you learn the material in the following pages.**

USING LANGUAGE

Describing Time Certain words and phrases can help you get an idea of a past event's time frame (when it happened) and duration (for how long it happened). These phrases are called *specific time markers*. Specific time markers include phrases such as 1 hour, yesterday, the 20th century, and 30 years later.

YOUR TURN

Read the sentences below, and write the specific time markers.

1. Jennifer celebrated her 16th birthday on Saturday two weeks ago.
2. Dinosaurs became extinct about 65 million years ago, at the end of the Cretaceous Period.

Introduce Have students work in pairs or small groups. The petroleum jelly will make it easier to remove the specimens from the plaster. Each group should take one specimen and proceed as follows:

1. Pour some plaster of Paris into a petri dish.
2. Cover each specimen with a very thin layer of petroleum jelly.
3. When the plaster begins to set, press a specimen into the surface of the plaster.
4. When the plaster hardens, carefully remove the specimen.

Have students examine their fossil imprint and make notes and sketches of its characteristics. You can have the groups exchange fossils to see if other students make different inferences or observations.

Discuss When many students hear the word *fossil*, they think immediately of a fossilized bone or other mineralized body part. **Ask,** What types of information can be gathered from examining trace fossils? shape, general form, size, surface patterns (leaves and feathers), gait (footprints)

Activate Prior Knowledge

Point out the photograph of the Tollund Man and explain that he represents a rare type of preserved remains because his soft tissues are still present. **Ask,** What can we learn about Tollund Man that we can't from most fossils? features of his skin and muscles, hair, clothing **Ask,** What are some famous examples of preserved or fossilized remains? King Tut and other mummies, dinosaur bones and footprints, shark teeth, Lucy and other hominid bones, Pompeii

Preview Vocabulary

Academic Vocabulary The word *interval* is used frequently in this chapter. Remind students of the meaning of the prefix *inter-* as "between, among, or within." Furthermore, on the axes of a graph, intervals are uniform in length or value; in evolution, intervals are defined by characteristics and events that distinguish them from the ones they follow and precede, not by their length. In evolution, intervals are about the ways Earth and life have changed.

Integrating Earth Science

In Media Gallery, show students the image of the fossil of an extinct lobster-like arthropod, discovered at a site where some of the world's oldest fossils are found—the Burgess Shale, in British Columbia, Canada. Some of the Burgess Shale fossils are *trace fossils*, meaning that they appear as dark carbon and clay imprints on shale. The area that includes the Burgess Shale was a huge reef in a warm, shallow sea. Frequent mud slumps carried the organisms down into deeper water. Over time, the mud was compacted into shale. This muddy burial preserved the fossils, allowing for both hard and soft body parts to leave their impressions.

Answers

1. 16th, Saturday, two weeks ago
2. 65 million years ago, end of the Cretaceous period

SECTION 12.1

▼ Plan and Prepare

Activate Prior Knowledge Poll students to see how many have been to a natural history museum. **Ask,** What are some of the ancient life forms you remember? woolly mammoths, dinosaurs, armored fish, insects in amber Introduce them to the idea that not all species that have lived on Earth are represented in the fossil record and that we may never know of all the other kinds of life that have occupied the planet.

▼ Teach

Science Trivia

The dung or scat of an animal can reveal a great deal about its diet and habits. Even a piece of fossilized scat, or **coprolite,** can be very helpful to scientists. The largest dinosaur coprolite was uncovered in 1995 in Saskatchewan, Canada. It came from a *Tyrannosaurus rex.* The dung measured about 44 × 16 × 13 centimeters, weighed 7 kilograms (15 lb), had an estimated volume of 2.4 liters (0.6 gal.), and contained bone fragments of herbivorous dinosaurs.

12.1 The Fossil Record

VOCABULARY
relative dating
radiometric dating
isotope
half-life

KEY CONCEPT **Fossils are a record of life that existed in the past.**

MAIN IDEAS
- Fossils can form in several ways.
- Radiometric dating provides a close estimate of a fossil's age.

Connect to Your World

Do you ever consider how much the world and its inhabitants have changed in the past 15, 50, or 100 years? Have you studied ancient civilizations that existed thousands of years ago? These time frames are tiny blips on the scale of time revealed by the fossil record. Some of the world's oldest fossils, found at the Burgess Shale site in Canada, offer a glimpse of what life was like 500 million years before Tollund Man lived. These specimens are keys to understanding the history of life on Earth.

MAIN IDEA

Fossils can form in several ways.

Fossils are far more diverse than the giant dinosaur skeletons we see in museums. The following processes are some of the ways fossils form. **FIGURE 1.1** shows examples of fossils produced in these different ways.

- **Permineralization** occurs when minerals carried by water are deposited around a hard structure. They may also replace the hard structure itself.
- **Natural casts** form when flowing water removes all of the original bone or tissue, leaving just an impression in sediment. Minerals fill in the mold, recreating the original shape of the organism.
- **Trace fossils** record the activity of an organism. They include nests, burrows, imprints of leaves, and footprints.
- **Amber-preserved fossils** are organisms that become trapped in tree resin that hardens into amber after the tree gets buried underground.
- **Preserved remains** form when an entire organism becomes encased in material such as ice or volcanic ash or immersed in bogs.

FIGURE 1.1 The fossil record includes fossils that formed in many different ways.

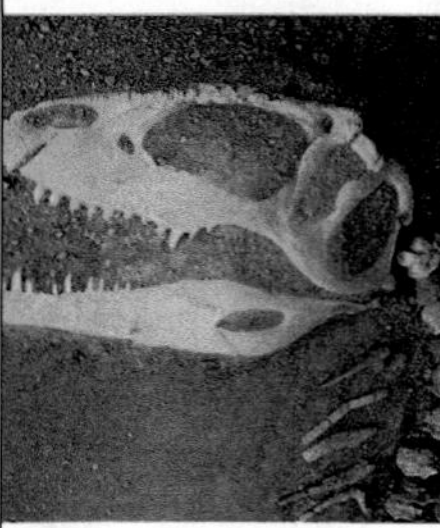

Permineralized skeleton of a *Velociraptor* dinosaur

Natural cast of a crinoid, a marine animal

Trace fossils of footprints from a *Dimetrodon* dinosaur

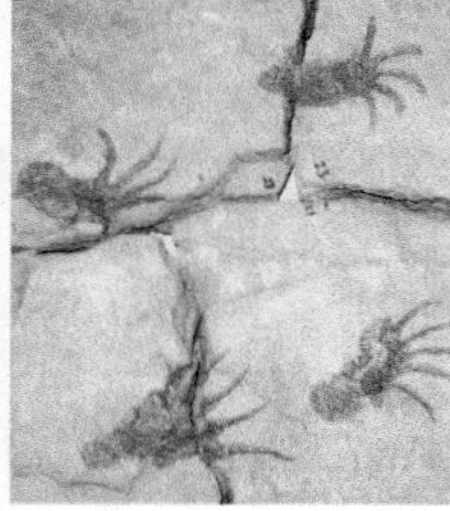

Amber-preserved spider

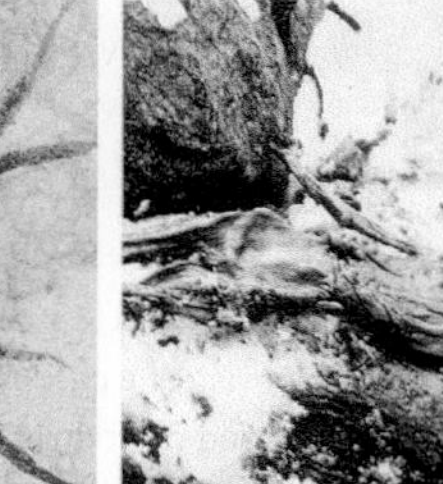

Ice-preserved 5000-year-old remains of a man found in the Italian Alps

Differentiated Instruction

ENGLISH LEARNERS

Have students create a compare-contrast chart to differentiate among the five fossil types shown on this page. In one column, have them record the fossil types in which the actual form or structures of an organism are preserved. In the other column, have them list the fossil types that do not preserve the structures. Students can look for specific words, such as *impression* or *encased,* to help them identify the appropriate category for each fossil type.

Teacher Toolkit, Section C, Compare/Contrast Chart

FIGURE 1.2 The Process of Permineralization

The process of permineralization requires rapid burial in an area with water and continuous sedimentation.

An organism dies in a location, such as a riverbed, where sediments can rapidly cover its body.

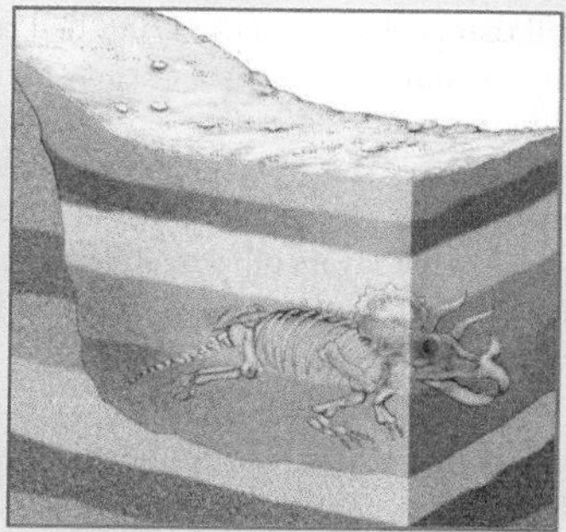

Over time, pressure from additional sediment compresses the body, and minerals slowly replace all hard structures, such as bone.

Earthquakes or erosion may expose the fossil millions of years after formation, or it may be uncovered by paleontologists, hikers, or road-building crews.

A Infer **What conditions could occur that would prevent an organism from being preserved through permineralization?**

Most fossils form in sedimentary rock, which is made by many layers of sediment or small rock particles. The best environments for any type of fossilization include wetlands, bogs, and areas where sediment is continuously deposited, such as river mouths, lakebeds, and floodplains.

The most common fossils result from permineralization. Several circumstances are critical for this process, as shown in **FIGURE 1.2.** The organism must be buried or encased in some type of material—such as sand, sediment, mud, or tar—very soon after death, while the organism's features are still intact. After burial, groundwater trickles into tiny pores and spaces in plants, bones, and shells. During this process, the excess minerals in the water are deposited on the remaining cells and tissues. Many layers of mineral deposits are left behind, creating a fossilized record by replacing organic tissues with hard minerals. The resulting fossil has the same shape as the original structure and may contain some original tissue.

With such specific conditions needed for fossilization, it is easy to see why only a tiny percentage of living things that ever existed became fossils. Most remains decompose or are destroyed before they can be preserved. Even successful fossilization is no guarantee that an organism's remains will be added to the fossil record. Natural events such as earthquakes and the recycling of rock into magma can destroy fossils that took thousands of years to form.

B Summarize **Why are so few complete fossils discovered?**

READING TOOLBOX

TAKING NOTES

Make a cause-and-effect chain of the conditions required for fossilization. Fill in important details.

An organism dies and is encased in mud.
Cause

Effect
Cause

Effect
Cause

TEACH WITH TECHNOLOGY

When re-creations or models of extinct organisms are featured in movies or museum displays, their creators often take liberties when it comes to representing certain features, such as hair color, feathers, and, of course, behavior. Show a PowerPoint presentation of actual fossil remains alongside their re-creations, such as a *T. rex* skeleton next to a screen shot from a recent film. Discuss which features may be based on the fossil evidence and which are wholly assumed or invented by the model's creators.

Teacher Toolkit, Section G, Presentation Software

TEACH FROM VISUALS

FIGURE 1.2 Use the figure to review conditions necessary for fossilization.
Ask

- Why are fossils commonly found near ancient or modern lakebeds and floodplains? These environments experience continuous sediment deposition, a necessary condition for fossilization.
- What role does groundwater play in the middle figure? Groundwater brings in dissolved minerals, which replace hard tissues such as bone and enamel.

Take It Further

Some of the world's best-preserved fossils come from the **Gobi** in central Asia. For many years, scientists thought that these animals had been buried by sandstorms that frequently occur in the region. Later studies revealed that the exquisite condition of many Gobi fossils is the result of the animals being buried alive when sand dunes collapsed suddenly during severe rainstorms. This rapid burial not only preserved the animals, but also preserved them while they were engaged in activities, such as fighting. One such amazing Gobi specimen consists of two dinosaurs—a *Velociraptor* and its prey, a *Protoceratops*—locked in combat. The *Velociraptor*'s foot claw is embedded in the neck of the *Protoceratops*, which, in turn, appears to have bitten and broken the *Velociraptor*'s right forelimb.

Answers

A Infer It may decompose before it is buried, be buried where there is no water, or get destroyed by geological processes.

B Summarize Because of the specific conditions and events that are required for fossilization to occur, only a tiny fraction of organisms are preserved. Also, rock recycling destroys many fossils.

▼ Teach continued

Vocabulary

Greek and Latin Word Origins The term **isotope** relates to the fact that all isotopes of an element are located at the same place on the periodic table.

isos = same or equal
topos = place

Integrating Molecular Biology

Scientists use **molecular clocks** to support evidence from the fossil record and to establish the date of evolutionary events. A molecular clock is a technique based on the assumption that mutations in DNA occur at a particular rate over time. After two species diverge from their ancestral lineage, each species continues to accumulate mutations in its DNA. The greater the number of differences in the DNA sequences of two species, the longer it has been since they shared a common ancestor.

Address Misconceptions

Common Misconception Students often think that fossils are rare and can be found only in certain areas.

Correcting the Misconception Fossils can be found almost anywhere that sedimentary rock has formed, and sedimentary rock is found all over the world. In places where conditions for fossilization were favorable, enormous numbers of fossils have been found.

Students can do a WebQuest on geological dating methods.

CONNECT TO

CHEMISTRY OF LIFE

Recall from the chapter **Chemistry of Life** that all atoms of a given element have the same number of protons. Isotopes are named for the total number of protons and neutrons in their nuclei.

○ neutrons ○ protons

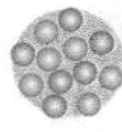
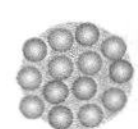

CARBON-12 NUCLEUS
6 protons
6 neutrons

CARBON-14 NUCLEUS
6 protons
8 neutrons

MAIN IDEA

Radiometric dating provides a close estimate of a fossil's age.

Recall that geologists in the 1700s had realized that rock layers at the bottom of an undisturbed sequence of rocks were deposited before those at the top, and therefore are older. The same logic holds true for the fossils found in rock layers. **Relative dating** estimates the time during which an organism lived by comparing the placement of fossils of that organism with the placement of fossils in other layers of rock. Relative dating allows scientists to infer the order in which groups of species existed, although it does not provide the actual ages of fossils.

To estimate a fossil's actual, or absolute, age, scientists use **radiometric dating**—a technique that uses the natural decay rate of unstable isotopes found in materials in order to calculate the age of that material. **Isotopes** are atoms of an element that have the same number of protons but a different number of neutrons. Most elements have several isotopes. For example, the element carbon (C) has three naturally occurring isotopes. All carbon isotopes have six protons. Isotopes are named, however, by their number of protons plus their number of neutrons. Thus, carbon-12 (^{12}C) has six neutrons, carbon-13 (^{13}C) has seven neutrons, and carbon-14 (^{14}C) has eight neutrons. More than 98 percent of the carbon in a living organism is ^{12}C.

Some isotopes have unstable nuclei. As a result, their nuclei undergo radioactive decay—they break down—over time. This releases radiation in the form of particles and energy. As an isotope decays, it can transform into a different element. The decay rate of many radioactive isotopes has been measured and is expressed as the isotope's half-life, as shown in **FIGURE 1.3.** A **half-life** is the amount of time it takes for half of the isotope in a sample to decay into a different element, or its product isotope. An element's half-life is not affected by environmental conditions such as temperature or pressure. Both ^{12}C and ^{13}C are stable, but ^{14}C decays into nitrogen-14 (^{14}N), with a half-life of roughly 5700 years.

Radiocarbon Dating

The isotope ^{14}C is used commonly for radiometric dating of recent remains, such as those of Tollund Man shown at the beginning of this chapter. Organisms absorb carbon through eating and breathing, so ^{14}C is constantly being resupplied. When an organism dies, its intake of carbon stops, but the decay of ^{14}C continues. The fossil's age can be estimated by comparing the ratio of a stable isotope, such as ^{12}C, to ^{14}C. The longer the organism has been dead, the larger the difference between the amounts of ^{12}C and ^{14}C there will be. The half-life of carbon-14 is roughly 5700 years, which means that after 5700 years, half of the ^{14}C in a fossil will have decayed into ^{14}N, its decay product. The other half remains as ^{14}C. After 11,400 years, or two half-lives, 75 percent of the ^{14}C will have decayed.

FIGURE 1.3 DECAY OF ISOTOPES

Isotope (parent)	Product (daughter)	Half-life (years)
rubidium-87	strontium-87	48.8 billion
uranium-238	lead-206	4.5 billion
chlorine-36	argon-36	300,000
carbon-14	nitrogen-14	5730

Differentiated Instruction

PRE-AP

Give students the following scenario: On a research expedition, scientists uncover two different fossils in two different places. The first appears to be a humanlike skull in a stratum associated with a time period of approximately 4 million years ago; the second is a mummified human found in a crypt. Have students write proposals for determining the age of each set of remains and the reasons their methods are the appropriate ones to use.

Teacher Toolkit, Section C, Quick-Write

INCLUSION

Have students create a matrix to compare different types of dating and their uses. Students should compare relative and absolute dating, and, within radiometric techniques, they should compare how isotopes with different half-lives can be used to date things that are as "young" as a few thousand years and as "old" as billions of years.

Teacher Toolkit, Section C, Content Frame

FIGURE 1.4 Radiometric Dating Using Carbon-14

Radiometric dating uses the natural decay rate of unstable isotopes to calculate the age of a fossil.

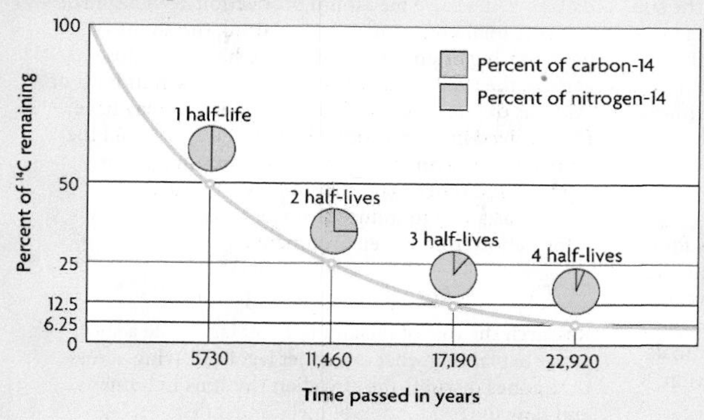

One-quarter of the original ^{14}C remains. Radioactive decay of ^{14}C is shown in **FIGURE 1.4.** Carbon-14 dating can be used to date objects only up to about 45,000 years old. If the objects are older than that, the fraction of ^{14}C will be too small to measure accurately. Older objects can be dated by using an isotope that has a longer half-life, such as uranium.

Determining Earth's Age

Scientists have used radiometric dating to determine the age of Earth. Because Earth constantly undergoes erosion and rock recycling, rocks on Earth do not remain in their original state. Unlike Earth's rocks, meteorites—which are mostly pieces of rock and iron that have fallen to Earth's surface from space—do not get recycled or undergo erosion. Meteorites are thought to have formed at about the same time as Earth. Therefore, meteorites provide an unspoiled sample for radiometric dating. Uranium-to-lead isotope ratios in many meteorite samples consistently estimate Earth's age at about 4.5 billion years.

Summarize **Why are meteorites helpful for determining the age of Earth?**

12.1 Formative Assessment

REVIEWING MAIN IDEAS

1. What types of evidence of ancient life can be preserved as fossils?
2. In **radiometric dating,** why is a uranium **isotope** often used instead of ^{14}C to determine the age of Earth?

CRITICAL THINKING

3. **Apply** Considering that millions of species have lived on Earth, why are there relatively few fossils?
4. **Contrast** Explain the difference between **relative dating** and absolute dating.

SELF-CHECK Online
HMHScience.com
GO ONLINE

CONNECT TO

EARTH SCIENCE

5. When mountains form, the order of rock layers can be disturbed. How could radiometric dating be used to sort out the relative ages of such rock layers?

Chapter 12: The History of Life 351

TEACH FROM VISUALS

FIGURE 1.4 Have students examine the axes and other features of the graph. **Ask**

- Why do the intervals between the horizontal lines that intersect the points on the graph get smaller as time passes? The intervals really represent that percentage of decay relative to the initial sample, so even though it is being cut in half with each half-life, the number of carbon-14 atoms decaying into nitrogen-14 is getting smaller and smaller.
- What do the green portions of each circle graph represent? portion of the sample that has decayed from carbon-14 into nitrogen-14
- If you plotted the rate of formation of nitrogen-14 on the same graph, using the right-hand *y*-axis for nitrogen, what would the curve look like? horizontal mirror image of the carbon decay curve

Assess and Reteach ▼

Assess Use the Section Self-Check or Section Quiz, both available at **HMHScience.com**.

Reteach Have students add to or multiply their cause-and-effect chains from earlier in this section by creating sequences that end in each type of fossil shown in **FIGURE 1.1**.

Answers

A Summarize They are thought to have formed at the same time as Earth. Because they have fallen to Earth from space relatively recently, they have not been spoiled by erosion or rock recycling.

12.1 FORMATIVE ASSESSMENT

1. An organism itself, its shape, or some sense of its activities can be preserved.
2. It has a longer half-life than ^{14}C, and so it is a better gauge for determining Earth's age.
3. Specific environmental conditions are required for a fossil to form, and many organisms have only soft body parts that do not preserve well. Also, rock cycling, erosion, and other geological processes destroy many fossils before they are found.
4. Both relative dating and absolute dating are used to find how old a site or fossil is. Relative dating does not give specific dates, but places the time of a sample in context with other samples. Absolute dating gives a specific age of a sample within a margin of error.
5. Disturbed rock strata may not be ordered sequentially. Radiometric dating of different layers can sort out the absolute ages of the rocks and determine the correct sequence of the strata.

Introduce

Remind students that evolution does not occur unless environmental pressure drives it. An organism with a change must be more "fit" in its environment if that change is to be inherited by future generations. **Ask,** What environmental pressure might have driven marine worm larvae to produce melatonin? Students may conclude that moving to deep water may protect the larvae from damaging UV radiation during daylight.

Discuss

Discuss possible environmental pressures that might have driven vertebrates to produce melatonin. Explain to students that the hormone has several functions besides inducing sleep. It functions in cell-to-cell communication, which may enhance cell survival. It also triggers the expression of genes that prevent biological compounds in the cell from oxidizing, thus enhancing homeostasis.

Effects of Melatonin

Until recently in evolutionary history, humans went to sleep when the sun went down and awoke when the sun rose. This daily light-induced sleeping and waking cycle is known as a circadian rhythm or biological clock and is regulated by the hormone melatonin. These days, with artificial lighting and airplane travel across time zones, our daily activities are no longer tied to our biological clocks.

Scientists have recently discovered that the same melatonin that regulates the human sleep cycle is found in microscopic marine worm larvae, organisms that are part of the huge mass of plankton living in the ocean. Plankton are composed of drifting microscopic algae, protozoans, and larvae that fish and marine mammals feed on. Worm larvae do not sleep, so what function could their melatonin possibly have? Why did melatonin production evolve in these animals?

Worm larvae make a daily vertical migration. Organisms deep in the ocean swim upward during daytime by beating their cilia, microscopic hairlike projections on their outer surface. The larvae arrive at the surface as the sun goes down. Then, during the night, they gradually drift back down to deeper water. The cycle is repeated every day.

When scientists studied the larvae's simple brains, they discovered a group of nerve cells that were light-sensitive. These brain cells produce melatonin at night. Other nerve cells connected to the larvae's cilia respond to the melatonin by causing the cilia to beat less often. During the pauses between beats, the larvae slowly sink into deeper water. No melatonin is produced during the day. The cilia begin to beat without pauses, causing the organisms to swim upward. When the scientists exposed worm larvae to melatonin in the lab during daytime hours, the cilia beat in their typical paused nighttime pattern.

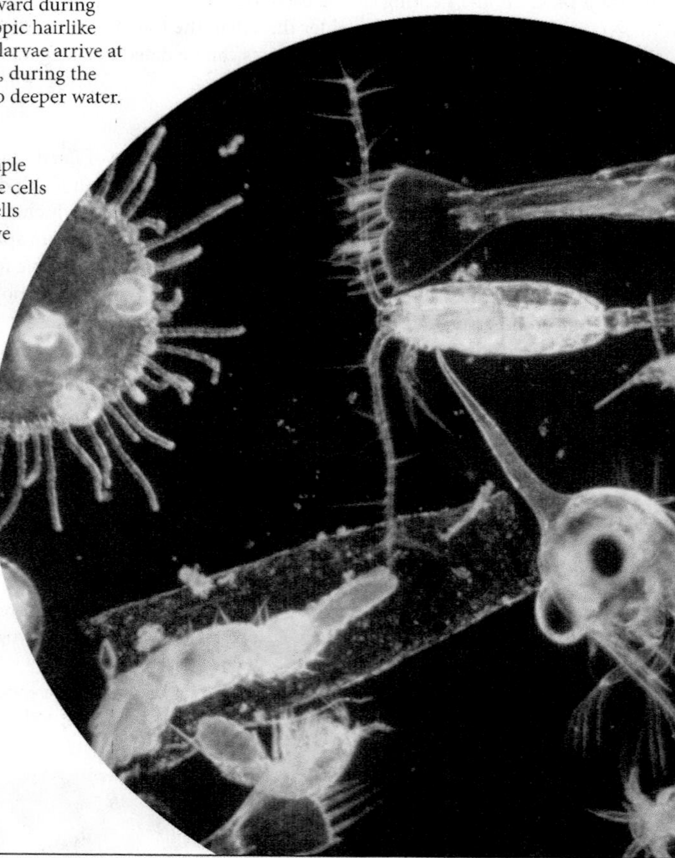

Marine zooplankton, including copepods, cladocerans, barnacle nauplius larvae, and a zoea larva of a crab

Almost all animals make melatonin, the "hormone of darkness." Because melatonin production is widespread in the animal kingdom, scientists think the ability of light-sensing brain cells to make the hormone arose early in the evolutionary history of animals, hundreds of millions of years ago. Melatonin production may have first evolved in marine organisms as a way to avoid the damaging ultraviolet (UV) radiation in sunlight. In humans and other mammals, it may have further evolved as a way to induce sleep by blocking sensory information from the environment.

S.T.E.M. Activity

Research the role of melatonin in jet lag. Write a short paper explaining what causes jet lag, how flying across time zones disrupts the circadian rhythms in humans, and how the production of melatonin affects jet lag. Does the direction in which a person travels affect the symptoms of jet lag? Why might that happen?

12.2 The Geologic Time Scale

VOCABULARY

index fossil
geologic time scale
era
period
epoch

KEY CONCEPT **The geologic time scale divides Earth's history based on major past events.**

MAIN IDEAS

- Index fossils are another tool to determine the age of rock layers.
- The geologic time scale organizes Earth's history.

Connect to Your World

Life is marked by increments of progress. From your first year of school through high school graduation, each new year is a step in your life development. Earth's life spans about 4.5 billion years. Scientists have divided the Earth's progress into manageable units based on the occurrence of major geologic changes.

MAIN IDEA

Index fossils are another tool to determine the age of rock layers.

You have learned that both relative dating and radiometric dating can help scientists determine the age of rock layers. Scientists who are trying to determine the age of a rock layer almost always use two or more methods to confirm results. Index fossils provide an additional tool for determining the age of fossils or the strata in which they are found. **Index fossils** are fossils of organisms that existed only during specific spans of time over large geographic areas.

Using index fossils for age estimates of rock layers is not a new idea. In the late 1700s, English geologist William Smith discovered that certain rock layers contained fossils unlike those in other layers. Using these key fossils as markers, Smith could identify a particular layer of rock wherever it was exposed.

The shorter the life span of a species, the more precisely the different strata can be correlated. The best index fossils are common, easy to identify, found widely around the world, and existed only for a relatively brief time. The extinct marine invertebrates known as ammonites, shown in **FIGURE 2.1**, are one example of an index fossil. They were at one time very common, but disappeared after a mass extinction event about 251 million years ago. The presence of ammonites indicates that a rock layer must be between 251 million and 359 million years old. Ammonite fossils are useful for dating fossils of other organisms in strata, because the presence of both organisms in one layer shows that they lived during the same time period.

FIGURE 2.1 Ammonites, marine fossils that range from 1 millimeter to 1 meter in size, are good index fossils. They are abundant in marine sediment, widely distributed, and representative of a specific period of time.

Apply **Could a rock layer with ammonite fossils be 100 million years old? Explain.**

A

SECTION 12.2

B.5.6 Analyze and interpret data for patterns in the fossil record and molecular data that document the existence, diversity, extinction, and change of life forms throughout the history of life on Earth under the assumption that natural laws operate today as in the past.

Plan and Prepare

Activate Prior Knowledge Scientists have identified five mass extinctions that have occurred since Earth formed. Many scientists have suggested that today we are in the midst of another mass extinction event because the extinction rate is so high. **Ask,** What are some reasons that species become extinct? habitat loss, climate change, increased predation, competition for resources, pollution, overfishing

Teach

Vocabulary

Academic Vocabulary The term **index** is used for fossils that serve as points of reference for different time periods. *Index* is a Latin word that means "indicator." The first finger, or pointer finger, is also called the index finger. Students can think of an index fossil as one that points, like a finger, to the time period that another fossil came from.

Answers

A Apply No, fusulinids lived between 359 and 251 million years ago, so the rock layers in which they are found must have formed in that time.

Differentiated Instruction

PRE-AP

Provide small groups of students with a stack of four colored index cards, ordered as shown. (Enlarged images are included in the Teacher Resources at **HMHScience.com**.) Students are to infer the time period for each stratum and for species 1 and 2. Tell students that if a species existed within the time period represented by a stratum, a well-defined rock layer, its fossil will appear there. Stratum 4 dates to 280–210 mya, stratum 3 dates to 210–150 mya, stratum 2 dates to 150-110 mya; species 1 existed 150–35 mya, species 2 existed 210–150 mya.

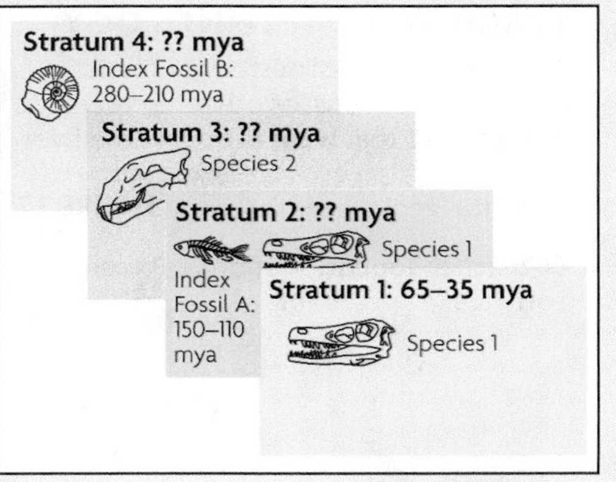

▼ Teach *continued*

TEACH FROM VISUALS

FIGURE 2.2 Have students review the geologic time scale. **Ask**

- What was significant about the Cambrian period? All existing animal phyla evolved during the Cambrian period.
- Did humans and dinosaurs coexist? Explain. No, dinosaurs became extinct at the end of the Cretaceous period, whereas the first primates did not evolve until well into the Tertiary period.
- In what period and era are we living today? Quaternary period, Cenozoic era

Science Trivia

The concept of one billion of anything is often difficult to grasp. Ask students to consider the following:

- If one billion children stood on each others' shoulders, they would reach past the Moon.
- If you laid one billion $1 bills end to end, they would encircle Earth nearly four times.
- If you stacked the bills on top of each other, the pile would be more than 47 miles high.
- If you wanted to count one billion $1 bills, it would take about 5787 days (almost 16 years) of counting without taking a break.

GO ONLINE

Geologic Time Scale

FIGURE 2.2 Geologic Time Scale

Millions of years ago (mya): 100, 250, 550, 1000, 2000

X = Major extinction

CENOZOIC ERA

QUATERNARY PERIOD

1.8 mya–present This period continues today and includes all modern forms of life.

TERTIARY PERIOD (PALEOGENE AND NEOGENE)

65–1.8 mya Mammals, flowering plants, grasslands, insects, fish, and birds diversified. Primates evolved.

Primate

MESOZOIC ERA

CRETACEOUS PERIOD

145–65 mya Dinosaur populations peaked and then went extinct. Birds survived to radiate in the Tertiary period. Flowering plants arose.

JURASSIC PERIOD

200–145 mya Dinosaurs diversified, as did early trees that are common today. Oceans were full of fish and squid. First birds arose.

Mononykus

TRIASSIC PERIOD

251–200 mya Following the largest mass extinction to date, dinosaurs evolved, as did plants such as ferns and cycads. Mammals and flying reptiles (pterosaurs) arose.

PALEOZOIC ERA

PERMIAN PERIOD

299–251 mya Modern pine trees first appeared, and Pangaea supercontinent was formed as major landmasses joined together.

Pine tree

CARBONIFEROUS PERIOD

359–299 mya Coal-forming sediments were laid down in vast swamps. Fish continued to diversify. Life forms included amphibians, winged insects, early conifers, and small reptiles.

DEVONIAN PERIOD

416–359 mya Fish diversified. First sharks, amphibians, and insects appeared. First ferns, trees, and forests arose.

SILURIAN PERIOD

444–416 mya Earliest land plants arose. Melting of glaciers allowed seas to form. Jawless and freshwater fishes evolved.

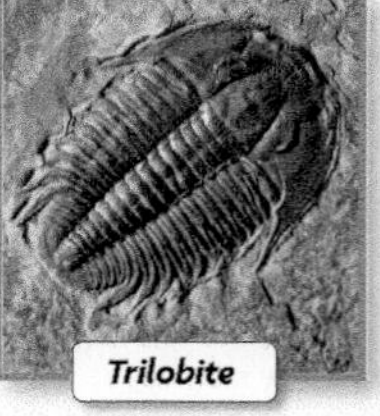

Jawless fish

ORDOVICIAN PERIOD

488–444 mya Diverse marine invertebrates evolved, as did the earliest vertebrates. Massive glaciers formed, causing sea levels to drop and a mass extinction of marine life to occur.

CAMBRIAN PERIOD

542–488 mya All existing animal phyla developed over a relatively short period of time known as the Cambrian Explosion.

Trilobite

PRECAMBRIAN TIME

This time span makes up the vast majority of Earth's history. It includes the oldest known rocks and fossils, the origin of eukaryotes, and the oldest animal fossils. (colored SEM; magnification 50×)

Cyanobacteria

Differentiated Instruction

TEACH WITH TECHNOLOGY

Assemble a digital slideshow of fossils, models, illustrations, or other representations of organisms that went extinct in the five major extinction events marked with an X along the geologic time scale in **FIGURE 2.2.**

Teacher Toolkit, Section G, Presentation Software

ENGLISH LEARNERS

Have students organize the geologic time scale in **FIGURE 2.2** into a content frame with these column heads: Years, Era, Period, Life Forms, Other Characteristics. Students may prefer to start with the oldest first. Make sure they realize that, if they do, they will need to read the diagram from bottom to top.

Teacher Toolkit, Section C, Content Frame

MAIN IDEA

The geologic time scale organizes Earth's history.

The **geologic time scale,** shown in **FIGURE 2.2,** is a representation of the history of Earth. It organizes Earth's development by major changes or events that have occurred, using evidence from the fossil and geologic records. Scientists worked out the entire geologic time scale during the 1800s and early 1900s. Although the scale is still being changed a little bit here and there, the main divisions of geologic time have stayed the same for over a hundred years.

The time scale is divided into a series of units based on the order in which different groups of rocks and fossils were formed. The geologic time scale consists of three basic units of time.

- **Eras** last tens to hundreds of millions of years and consist of two or more periods.
- **Periods** are the most commonly used units of time on the geologic time scale, lasting tens of millions of years. Each period is associated with a particular type of rock system.
- **Epochs** (EHP-uhks) are the smallest units of geologic time and last several million years.

The names of the eras came from early ideas about life forms preserved as fossils. *Paleozoic* means "ancient life," *Mesozoic* means "middle life," and *Cenozoic* means "recent life." Within the eras, the boundaries between many of the geologic periods are defined by mass extinction events. These events help to define when one period ends and another begins. The largest adaptive radiations tend to follow large mass extinctions. Recall that adaptive radiation happens when a group of organisms diversifies into several species. Those species adapt to different ecological niches because mass extinctions make many niches available. Over generations, the adaptive traits favored within these newly opened niches may become common for that population of organisms, and speciation may occur.

Summarize **Why do adaptive radiations often occur after mass extinctions?**

CONNECT TO

ADAPTIVE RADIATION

Recall from the chapter **The Evolution of Populations** that *adaptive radiation* refers to the change of a single species into several forms that are each adapted to a specific environmental niche.

SELF-CHECK Online
HMHScience.com
GO ONLINE

12.2 Formative Assessment

REVIEWING MAIN IDEAS

1. How are **index fossils** used to date rock layers?
2. What is the usefulness of categorizing Earth's history into the **geologic time scale**?

CRITICAL THINKING

3. **Infer** The most common index fossils are shells of invertebrates. Give two reasons why this is so.
4. **Analyze** Scientists have inferred that there have been at least five mass extinctions in Earth's history. How would fossil evidence support this inference?

CONNECT TO

SCIENTIFIC PROCESS

5. French physicist Henri Becquerel discovered radioactivity in 1896, after geologists had developed the geologic time scale. How did Becquerel's discovery help later geologists as they refined the time scale?

Vocabulary

Academic Vocabulary Make the analogy between **period** in the geologic sense and a school period. Geologists identify periods not by uniform intervals of time but by their characteristics, such as what kinds of organisms were prevalent or dominant. Students have school periods that are defined not so much by their length or sequence as by their subject, such as math or science.

Assess and Reteach ▼

Assess Use the Section Self-Check or Section Quiz, both available at **HMHScience.com**.

Reteach Choose 11 students to represent the 11 periods. Students should describe the period without naming it. The rest of the class should identify the periods and direct the 11 students to stand in a line in the correct chronological sequence.

Answers

A **Summarize** Mass extinctions create the opportunity for organisms to disperse across a wider range of habitats or environments. Over generations, populations evolve adaptations to the conditions of these environments.

12.2 FORMATIVE ASSESSMENT

1. Index fossils are remains of organisms that are known to have lived during a specific span of time. They can be used to date other fossils by comparing their positions in strata.
2. The geologic time scale helps us organize Earth's history into periods that are characterized by conditions at Earth's surface and the forms of life found there.
3. Invertebrates have been abundant throughout much of Earth's history, and some had shells that are more easily fossilized than soft parts. Many shelled invertebrates lived in the ocean, where the conditions for preservation are better.
4. Abrupt changes in the fossil record support this inference, because species found in older (deeper) rock layers are not found in younger (upper) rock layers. Less species diversity in a younger layer suggests a mass extinction. Boundary layers of changed sedimentation may also indicate a catastrophic event.
5. Prior to Becquerel's discovery, geologists relied exclusively on the relative dating of rock layers. Discovering radioactivity led to the development of radiometric dating, which offers absolute ages, rather than just relative ages, of rock layers.

SECTION 12.3

▼ Plan and Prepare

Activate Prior Knowledge Gauge students' familiarity with theories of Earth's origins. **Ask,** What scientific theories or ideas about the formation of Earth and the solar system have you heard? "big bang," collapsing and expanding universe (matter squeezed into a grapefruit-sized mass) Discuss the role of the Hubble Space Telescope—direct observation of astronomical phenomena—in shaping or revising cosmological theories.

▼ Teach

Vocabulary

Greek and Latin Word Origins
Nebula is a Latin word meaning "cloud." Like many Latin words ending in *a,* the plural of *nebula* is *nebulae.* **Ask,** What other words ending in *a* are made plural by adding *e*? amoeba(e), antenna(e), nova(e), seta(e)

12.3 Origin of Life

KEY CONCEPT **The origin of life on Earth remains a puzzle.**

MAIN IDEAS
- Earth was very different billions of years ago.
- Several sets of hypotheses propose how life began on Earth.

VOCABULARY
nebula
ribozyme

Connect to Your World
By studying the geologic time scale, it is clear that the farther back in Earth's history we go, the tougher it is to piece together what life was like at that time. Hypotheses about the way Earth formed and life began have been proposed and researched. But as with any branch of science, questions still remain.

MAIN IDEA
Earth was very different billions of years ago.

For centuries, many of history's greatest minds have wondered about the origin of Earth and its living things. Despite differences over the details of Earth's origins, most scientists agree on two key points: (1) Earth is billions of years old, and (2) the conditions of the early planet and its atmosphere were very different from those of today.

Today, the most widely accepted hypothesis of Earth's origins suggests that the solar system was formed by a condensing **nebula,** a cloud of gas and dust in space, as shown in **FIGURE 3.1.** This hypothesis is supported by computer models and observations made with the Hubble Space Telescope. It suggests that about 4.6 billion years ago, the sun formed from a nebula. Over time, most of the material in the nebula pulled together because of gravity. Materials that remained in the nebula's disk circled the newly formed sun. Over millions of years, repeated collisions of this space debris built up into the planets of our solar system.

FIGURE 3.1 One hypothesis proposes that the Sun and planets formed from a rotating disk of gas and dust about 4.6 billion years ago.

Earth was most likely violent and very hot for its first 700 million years, a time now called the Hadean eon. Many asteroids, meteorites, and comets struck the planet, releasing enormous amounts of heat. Meanwhile, the radioactive decay of elements trapped deep within Earth released heat as well. This intense heat kept the materials making up Earth in a molten state. Over time, these materials separated into Earth's layers. Hydrogen, carbon monoxide, and nitrogen gas were released from the interior. They combined to form an atmosphere containing compounds such as ammonia, water vapor, methane, and carbon dioxide. Most scientists agree that free oxygen was not abundant until about 2 billion years ago, after the first forms of life had begun to evolve.

Toward the end of the Hadean eon, between 4 and 3.8 billion years ago, impacts became less frequent. That allowed Earth to cool down. Solar radiation and lightning produced energy for reactions on Earth and in the early atmosphere. The continents began to form. Water vapor condensed and fell as rain that collected in pools and larger bodies of water.

Differentiated Instruction

ENGLISH LEARNERS

Help students connect to content through visuals. They can use different-colored squares of paper to represent each sentence of the paragraphs on this page where the formation of the solar system is described. Have a student read a sentence and ask others to describe what they "see." Summarize each sentence description on a card, and post them all on the board until the paragraph is complete. Then ask for a picture summary of each square/sentence.

Teacher Toolkit, Section C, Connect to Content Through Visuals

BELOW LEVEL

Have students do sequence diagrams for the nebular hypothesis of Earth's formation and the Miller-Urey experiment. Suggest that students connect the two ideas.

Teacher Toolkit, Section C, Sequence Diagram

Once liquid water was present, organic compounds could be formed from inorganic materials. All living matter is organic, as are the building blocks of life, such as sugars and amino acids. However, you'll see below that the leap that resulted in life on Earth required conditions other than just the presence of water.

READING TOOLBOX

VOCABULARY

Organic compounds are carbon based and contain carbon–carbon bonds.

A Summarize **Describe the nebular hypothesis of Earth's origin.**

MAIN IDEA

Several sets of hypotheses propose how life began on Earth.

Since the 1950s, scientists have proposed several hypotheses to explain how life began on Earth. These hypotheses have taken into consideration early organic molecules, the formation of organic polymers from these organic building blocks, the evolution of cell structures, and early genetic material.

Organic Molecule Hypotheses

There are two general hypotheses about the way life-supporting molecules appeared on early Earth.

Miller-Urey experiment In 1953 Stanley Miller and Harold Urey designed an experiment to test a hypothesis first proposed by Alexander Oparin in the 1920s. Earlier scientists had proposed that an input of energy from lightning led to the formation of organic molecules from inorganic molecules present in the atmosphere of early Earth. Miller and Urey built a system to model conditions they thought existed on early Earth, as shown in **FIGURE 3.2.** They demonstrated that organic compounds could be made by heating and passing an electrical current, to simulate lightning, through a mixture of gases. These gases—methane (CH_4), ammonia (NH_3), hydrogen (H_2), and water vapor (H_2O)—were thought to be present in the early atmosphere. The Miller-Urey experiment produced a variety of organic compounds, such as amino acids.

After Miller's death in 2007, scientists found sealed vials from his early experiments that when tested, proved that more than 20 different amino acids had been formed. Since Miller's experiments occurred, it has been suggested by some scientists that due to volcanic eruptions more than 4 billion years ago, different compounds were present in the early atmosphere. Experiments using more recent estimates of conditions on early Earth have also produced organic molecules, including amino acids and nucleotides.

FIGURE 3.2 Miller-Urey Experiment

A laboratory model was used to represent the conditions of early Earth. This experiment demonstrated that organic molecules can be made from inorganic molecules.

A boiling chamber was used to heat "ocean" water to produce water vapor. The vapor traveled through a tube to the "atmosphere."

An electric spark in a mixture of gases simulated lightning.

electrodes

"atmosphere"

water

"ocean"

heat source

The experiment produced simple organic molecules such as amino acids.

amino acids

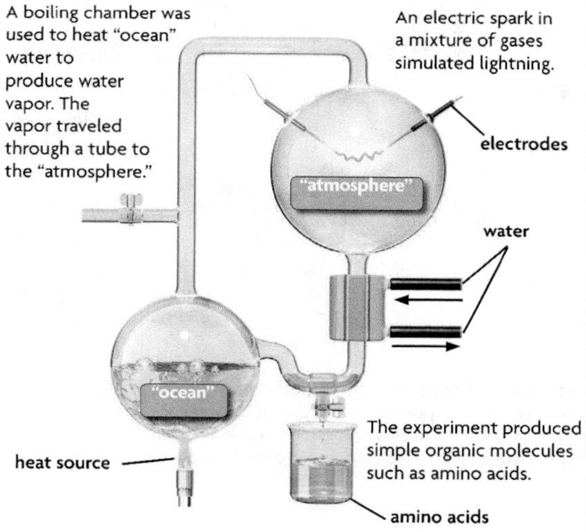

Integrating Chemistry

Chemists divide all chemical compounds into two major groups—**organic** and **inorganic.** Organic compounds contain both carbon and hydrogen atoms; inorganic compounds lack hydrocarbons. **Ask,** What inorganic compounds might be found in a living organism? water, carbon dioxide, sodium chloride, other salts

History of Science

The **Miller-Urey experiment** was one of the most famous scientific experiments of the 20th century. It was the first experiment to demonstrate that Earth's organic compounds, which are the building blocks of life, could have been synthesized from inorganic compounds already present on Earth. The results of the experiment stimulated many further inquiries in the scientific community. Later studies incorporated Miller's techniques to show how components of nucleic acids, such as adenine, could have been synthesized from atmospheric gases. The Miller-Urey experiment also laid the foundation for a new branch of science—**exobiology**—that is concerned with life outside Earth. A meteorite that landed in Australia in 1969 contained many organic compounds, some of which were similar to those produced in the Miller-Urey experiment, that are not found in living systems on Earth.

PRE-AP

Using the description of the Miller-Urey experiment in **FIGURE 3.2,** have students translate the information into an illustration of early Earth. They should include active volcanoes, which were a likely source of carbon and nitrogen compounds as well as water vapor.

Teacher Toolkit, Section C, Connect to Content Through Visuals.

Answers

A Summarize Earth and the other planets in our solar system were formed through space debris collisions in a cloud of gas and dust, called a nebula, which circled the sun.

▼ Teach *continued*

Integrating Bioastronomy

On August 6, 2012, the Mars Science Laboratory mission set down inside a deep Martian crater in a textbook perfect landing. The mobile laboratory, or rover, known as Curiosity will spend 23 months on the surface of the planet collecting samples of dirt and rocks, photographing the landscape, and performing a variety of scientific tests. The goals of Curiosity's mission are to investigate whether conditions on Mars have ever favored the existence of microbial life and to collect information that is necessary for planning future human explorations of the planet.

The Inside Story

In 1996, the world was astounded when a team of NASA scientists, led by Dr. David McKay, announced that a meteorite identified as having come from Mars showed possible evidence of microbial life forms. In a real-life example of the scientific research process, researchers across the globe sought to offer explanations both supporting and debating the validity of the original claims. While acknowledging that each piece of evidence can also be caused by non-biological processes, the team has continued their research, stating that when all of the evidence is regarded as a whole, the implications are overwhelming.

Meteorite hypothesis Analysis of a meteorite that fell near Murchison, Australia, in 1969 revealed that organic molecules can be found in space. More than 90 amino acids have been identified from this meteorite. Nineteen of these amino acids are found on Earth, and many others have been made in experiments similar to the Miller-Urey study. This evidence suggests that amino acids could have been present when Earth formed, or that these organic molecules may have arrived on Earth through meteorite or asteroid impacts.

Organic Polymer Hypotheses

Once amino acids and other organic building blocks existed on early Earth, certain requirements would have to have been met in order for more complex organic polymers to form. Planetary conditions were still extreme, ranging from ice sheets to areas having high temperatures and extensive volcanic activity. Since there was no ozone layer at that time, high levels of ultraviolet radiation would have permeated the atmosphere. All of these factors would have contributed to breaking apart the chemical bonds of organic molecules unless they were protected in some way. The survival of organic molecules would have depended on them either dissolving in water or adsorbing to some type of mineral.

Frozen seawater hypothesis If you fill a container to the top and place it into your freezer, the ice that forms will expand beyond the rim of the container. This occurs as water molecules form into rigid crystals. Because of this, a solution that is water-based will push any dissolved materials into the spaces between the crystals as it freezes. Recent research has shown that when solutions containing nucleotides are frozen, the nucleotides are pushed into the spaces between the water crystals. As **FIGURE 3.3** illustrates, when nucleotides are concentrated into a tiny area, they can bind together and form long, complex molecules that can carry information. On the basis of these experiments, Scripps Oceanographic scientist Jeffrey Bada proposed in 2004 that biological polymers may have formed in sea ice on the early planet.

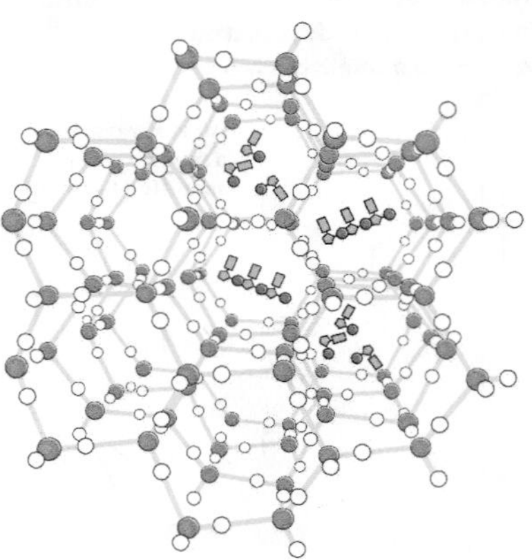

FIGURE 3.3 Frozen Seawater Hypothesis
Nucleotides trapped within the spaces between ice crystals and kept in close proximity to one another may have combined to form more-complex polymers.

Clay adsorption hypothesis In the late 1950s and early 1960s, Florida State University scientist Sidney Fox found that when dilute solutions of amino acids and cyanide were dripped onto hot, dry sand, rock, or clay, polymers that he called "proteinoids" were formed spontaneously. The metallic ions on the particles of clay acted as catalysts, binding to the monomers and concentrating them closely enough for the molecules to join together, forming more-complex organic polymers similar to proteins.

Differentiated Instruction

HANDS-ON ACTIVITY

Prepare three batches of samples for students to examine. Place equal amounts of sand into each of three containers. Add a small amount of table sugar to each container. Grind two effervescent antacid tablets into a fine powder and mix with the sand and sugar in one container. Mix two packets of baker's yeast into the second container. Do not add anything to the mixture in the third container.

Divide the class into groups of 3–4 students. Without identifying the contents, provide groups with samples of the sand mixtures labeled A, B, or C. Have students examine the samples for signs of life using hand lenses. Explain that living organisms require liquid water. Have them add 10 mL of warm water to their samples and record their observations. Ask if any of their samples showed signs of activity. Discuss their observations. The sand/antacid and sand/yeast mixtures will generate gas bubbles. Students should recognize that some changes are caused by non-biological chemical reactions.

Implications of polymer formation Many hypotheses describing the origin of life on Earth rely on the formation of self-replicating polymers—made from either amino acid or nucleic acid monomers—on early Earth. Once a molecule capable of replication formed, the sequence information contained in the molecule, as well as any variation introduced during replication, would have been inherited by each new generation of molecules. In successive generations, molecules with variations that improved replication efficiency or added other advantageous functions may have been selected, leading to more-complex molecules that carried more information.

Early Cell Formation Hypotheses

There are several hypotheses about the formation of the first cells. One focuses on the way organic molecules could have been brought together, and others addresses the way cell membranes may have formed.

Iron-sulfide bubbles hypothesis In the 1990s, biologists William Martin and Michael Russell noted that hot iron sulfide rising from below the ocean floor reacts with the cooler ocean water to form chimneylike structures with many compartments, such as those shown in **FIGURE 3.4**. Russell modeled this in the laboratory by injecting warm sodium sulfide into a cool, iron-rich solution. Iron sulfide bubbles quickly formed, making a chimney structure within minutes. Russell proposed that, around 4 billion years ago, biological molecules combined in the compartments of these chimneys. The compartment walls concentrated the basic organic molecules in a small space. The walls of the compartments, Russell proposed, acted as the first cell membranes. Once the right ingredients combined, the first organic cell membranes could form. These membranes would have let early microbes leave their rocky compartments and spread out into other environments.

CONNECT TO

CELLS

Recall from the chapter **Cell Structure and Function** that most cell membranes are composed of two layers of lipids, or fats. The cell membrane maintains a boundary between the environments inside and outside the cell.

FIGURE 3.4 Iron–Sulfide Bubbles Hypothesis

Hydrothermal vents produce sulfur that mixes with ocean water to make compartments of rock. These structures may have created conditions necessary for early life to form.

TEACH WITH TECHNOLOGY

Arrange students in five groups and assign each group one of the hypotheses discussed in this section. Have each group present a digital slideshow or multimedia presentation on its assigned hypothesis, using visuals and other materials gathered from online resources.

Teacher Toolkit, Section G, Presentation Software

Science Trivia

- The water surrounding hydrothermal vents can reach temperatures as high as 380°C (716°F).
- Common inhabitants of hydrothermal vents include tube worms *(Riftia pachyptila)* that grow as long as 2–3 meters (7–10 ft), giant mussels *(Bathymodiolus thermophilus)* 20 centimeters (8 in.) in length, and giant clams *(Calyptogena magnifica)* 25 centimeters (10 in.) in length.

Integrating Ecology

A "black smoker" is a type of hydrothermal vent found deep within the abyssal zones of the sea. Fields of black chimney-like structures hundreds of meters wide spread across the ocean floor, giving off clouds of black, sulfur-bearing minerals. "White smokers" are also hydrothermal vents, but tend to have plumes at lower temperatures that emit clouds of lighter-colored minerals. One of the most unique characteristics of both of these vents is that deep in the ocean, far from any access to sunlight, both support thriving ecological communities. Hydrothermal vent communities include prokaryotes, mollusks, crustaceans, and worms. Tube worms surrounding the vents can grow to over 2 meters (about 7 ft.) tall. At the base of the food chain are archaea and bacteria that feed directly on the minerals given off by the vent plumes. These microorganisms use chemosynthesis, the process by which ATP is synthesized by using chemicals as an energy source instead of light.

▼ Teach *continued*

Integrating Medical Science

The structure and biochemistry of the liposome make it an excellent vehicle for delivering drugs directly to cancerous tumors. In the laboratory, scientists produce **artificial liposomes** that contain a particular drug (for example, a chemotherapy agent) enclosed in a phospholipid sac. Sequestering the drug inside the lipid membrane protects the drug from being degraded by the patient's body. In studies with cancer patients, researchers have found that liposome-containing drugs accumulate at the target site (such as a tumor or site of infection) in higher numbers than at nontarget sites. This allows for greater delivery of the drug to its intended target and a lowered concentration of the drug at nontarget sites, where it could cause undesirable side effects.

Vocabulary

Word Origins The word **Ribozyme** has an interesting origin. *Ribo-* comes from part of the chemical structure that includes a 5-carbon sugar called "ribose." The second half of the word, *-zyme,* comes from the Greek word *zyme* meaning "a leaven." Leavens are substances that cause fermentation. An example would be baker's yeast, which is used to make bread rise.

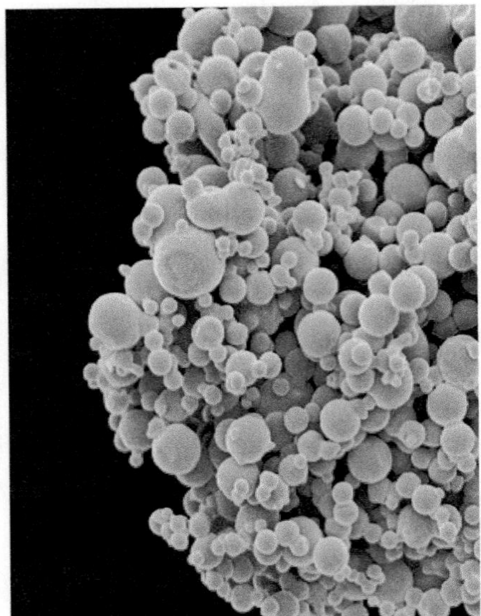

FIGURE 3.5 Liposomes have a lipid membrane that is similar to the membrane of a living cell. (colored SEM; magnification 1500×)

Lipid membrane hypothesis Several scientists have proposed that the evolution of lipid membranes was a crucial step for the origin of life. Lipid molecules spontaneously form membrane-enclosed spheres, called liposomes, shown in **FIGURE 3.5.** In 1992 biochemist Harold Morowitz tested the idea that at some point liposomes were formed with a double, or bilayer, lipid membrane. These liposomes could then form around a variety of organic molecules, such as amino acids, fatty acids, sugars, and nucleotides. The liposomes would act as membranes that separated these organic molecules from the environment. These cell-like structures may have later given rise to the first true cells.

Coacervate hypothesis In the 1930s, long before Morowitz proposed that cell-like structures formed from liposomes, Alexander Oparin found that by adding a substance called gum arabic into a water-based solution of gelatin, then cooling it down, tiny capsules that he called "coacervates" were produced. These coacervates, when surrounded by water, could absorb and release some compounds in a way that was similar to how bacteria feed and then excrete wastes.

Proteinoid microsphere hypothesis In the late 1950s, Sydney Fox, working with Kaoru Harada, took his previous work with the clay adsorption hypotheses a step further. The two scientists discovered that when the proteinoids, produced in hot conditions, were cooled by dropping them into water, they spontaneously formed into microspheres. The proteinoids had a water-soluble chemical group attached to a water-insoluble group. The parts that were water-soluble turned inwards and the insoluble group outwards, forming a bilayer similar to the structure of cell membranes. Under certain laboratory conditions, these proteinoid microspheres would slowly grow larger and eventually bud, forming new spheres.

Liposomes, coacervates, and microspheres were not capable of genetic coding or true replication. In other words—none of them were alive. However, the research of these scientists into how cells originally formed provided the foundations upon which current research is based.

RNA as Early Genetic Material

A hypothesis that has gained much support in recent years proposes that RNA, rather than DNA, was the genetic material that stored information in living things on early Earth. In the 1980s, Thomas Cech from the University of Colorado and Sidney Altman from Yale University independently discovered that RNA can catalyze reactions. **Ribozymes** are RNA molecules that can catalyze specific chemical reactions. As **FIGURE 3.6** shows, ribozymes can catalyze their own replication and synthesis. RNA can copy itself, chop itself into pieces, and from these pieces make even more RNA. Unlike RNA, DNA needs enzymes to replicate itself.

Differentiated Instruction

ENGLISH LEARNERS

This section contains a number of familiar terms used in a new context. Have students use the Multilanguage Glossary to review the following terms: *replication, lipid, catalyst, prokaryotic cell, eukaryotic cell.*

Teacher Toolkit, Section D, Student Vocabulary

FIGURE 3.6 RNA AND DNA

RNA, in the form of a ribozyme, is able to replicate itself without the help of additional enzymes.

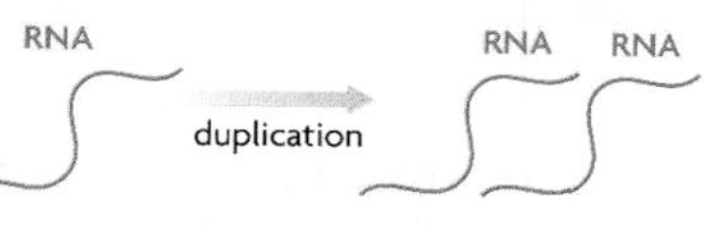

DNA requires many enzymes to replicate. Helicase enzymes separate the DNA strands and polymerase enzymes add nucleotides to the DNA strands.

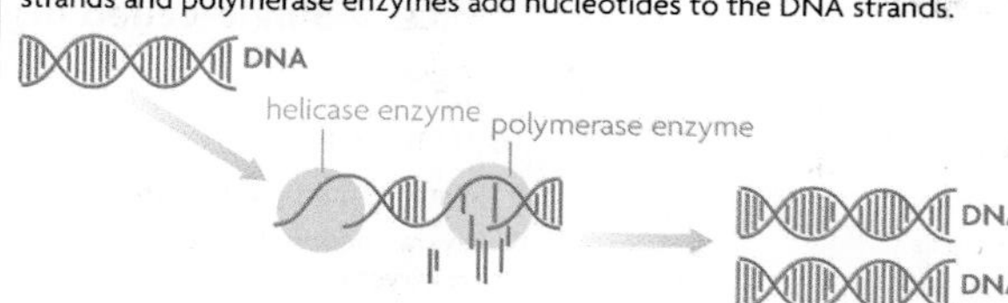

Along with the discovery of ribozymes, several other types of evidence support the RNA hypothesis. Short chains of RNA will form from inorganic materials in a test tube. If zinc is added as a catalyst, longer chains will grow. Also, RNA will fold into different shapes depending upon its sequence of nucleotides. Thus, it can perform more functions than DNA. But RNA does not catalyze chemical reactions as well as proteins do, nor does it store genetic information as well as DNA does. Over time, RNA may have become less important for these functions.

Perhaps the earliest replicating RNA molecule gained simple membranes over many generations through natural selection. Membranes might protect chemical reactions and make them work more efficiently. RNA molecules that made copies of themselves in a double-stranded form, similar to DNA, might eventually have been selected because fewer mutations would occur. Because DNA is more stable than RNA, it could reliably store more sequence information for a longer period of time. This may have led to DNA replacing RNA as the primary genetic material. Currently, there are several hypotheses about how RNA could have led to life as we know it today. Laboratory experiments in which RNA molecules survive and self-replicate support the idea of early cells being based on RNA. This model of the origins of life on Earth is sometimes called the RNA world.

Synthesize Could cell structures or RNA have been present before organic molecules existed on Earth? Explain.

12.3 Formative Assessment

REVIEWING MAIN IDEAS

1. Describe the environmental conditions that are thought to have existed during the Hadean eon.
2. What evidence do the two organic molecule hypotheses provide regarding the formation of simple organic molecules?

CRITICAL THINKING

3. **Analyze** What factors do the two organic polymer hypotheses have in common regarding how more-complex organic polymers originated?
4. **Compare and Contrast** Choose two of the early cell formation hypotheses and discuss their differences.

SELF-CHECK Online
HMHScience.com
GO ONLINE

CONNECT TO

PROTEIN SYNTHESIS

5. RNA is hypothesized to be the earliest form of genetic material because it can store information, catalyze its own replication, and catalyze other reactions. Which two of these functions can DNA not do? Which two can proteins not do?

TEACH FROM VISUALS

FIGURE 3.6 Have students review the two parts of the figure. **Ask**

- What are ribozymes? RNA molecules that function as enzymes
- What is the primary difference between the replication of ribozymes and DNA as demonstrated in this figure? Ribozymes can replicate without the help of additional enzymes, whereas DNA requires several enzymes for replication.

Discuss the use of the word part *-zyme* as indicative of a chemical that promotes chemical activity.

Assess and Reteach

Assess Use the Section Self-Check or Section Quiz, both available at **HMHScience.com**.

Reteach Work with students to map out a scenario that starts with the formation of Earth and leads to the creation of the first self-replicating "cell."

Answers

A Synthesize No, cell structures and RNA both require organic molecules in their synthesis.

12.3 FORMATIVE ASSESSMENT

1. The environment was very hot and Earth was bombarded by asteroids, meteorites, and comets; there was no liquid water; ammonia, water vapor, methane, and carbon dioxide existed in the atmosphere.
2. The Miller-Urey hypothesis proposes that organic molecules were formed from inorganic molecules present in the atmosphere of early Earth. The Miller-Urey experiment produced a variety of organic compounds including amino acids. The meteorite hypothesis proposes that the first organic molecules fell to Earth on meteorites or asteroids, or were present when Earth formed. Analysis of a meteorite that fell to Earth in 1969 identified 19 amino acids found on Earth.
3. The survival of complex polymers required them to be protected from extreme conditions and be concentrated into a tiny space to form bonds.
4. The iron-sulfide bubbles hypothesis proposes that cells first formed in rocky compartments as organic materials were concentrated in a small space. The walls acted as the first cell membranes. The lipid membrane hypothesis proposes that a bilayer lipid membrane formed around organic molecules, isolating them as cell structures.
5. DNA cannot catalyze other reactions or its own replication. Proteins cannot store information or catalyze their own replication.

▼ Plan and Prepare

Activate Prior Knowledge When scientists look for signs of life, they often look for evidence of water. **Ask,** If you put photosynthetic organisms together with water, what do you get? oxygen as a product Discuss how oxygen first entered Earth's atmosphere.

▼ Teach

Vocabulary

cyanobacteria The prefix *cyano-* comes from *cyan,* a greenish blue color. These bacteria used to be called **blue-green algae.** Tell students that they may see *blue-green algae* in some books and references.

Answers

A Apply Stromatolite fossils can be as old as 3.5 billion years, which means that we know of at least one life form (cyanobacteria) that was alive at that time. Also, cyanobacteria, being photosynthetic, may have helped pave the way for aerobic life forms.

12.4 Early Single-Celled Organisms

KEY CONCEPT **Single-celled organisms existed 3.8 billion years ago.**

VOCABULARY
cyanobacteria
endosymbiosis

MAIN IDEAS
- Microbes have changed the physical and chemical composition of Earth.
- Several theories have been proposed for how eukaryotic cells evolved from prokaryotic cells.
- The evolution of sexual reproduction led to increased diversity.

Connect to Your World

If you have ever assembled a complicated model or worked on a car, you know that putting the parts together to get a working result can be very difficult. Billions of years ago, organic molecules were everywhere. However, they didn't yet fully work together. Once the first cells arose from these molecules, the steps toward even more complicated organisms, such as humans, truly began.

MAIN IDEA

Microbes have changed the physical and chemical composition of Earth.

Single-celled organisms changed Earth's surface by depositing minerals. These organisms changed the atmosphere by giving off oxygen as a byproduct of photosynthesis. Before photosynthesis evolved, however, the first prokaryotes would have been anaerobic, or living without oxygen. Many of these early prokaryotes probably got their energy from organic molecules.

Scientists have found evidence that photosynthetic life evolved around 3.5 billion years ago, since that is the age of the oldest known fossils. These fossils are of a group of marine **cyanobacteria** (SY-ah-noh-bak-TEER-ee-uh), which are bacteria that can carry out photosynthesis. Like all early life forms, each cyanobacterium was a single prokaryotic cell. Recall that prokaryotic cells have no membrane-bound organelles.

Some cyanobacteria live in colonies and form stromatolites (stroh-MAT-l-YTS). Stromatolites are domed, rocky structures made of layers of cyanobacteria and sediment. There are many stromatolite fossils, but some are living communities, as shown in **FIGURE 4.1.** Fossils of stromatolites as old as 3.5 billion years have been found. Communities of photosynthesizing cyanobacteria in stromatolites released oxygen as a byproduct. Higher oxygen levels in the atmosphere and the ocean allowed the evolution of aerobic prokaryotes, which need oxygen to live.

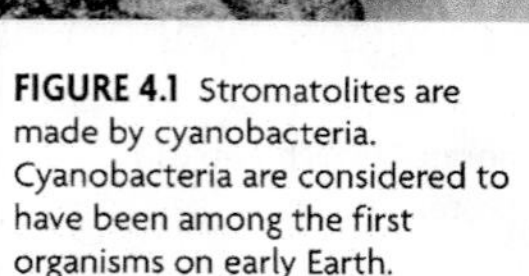

FIGURE 4.1 Stromatolites are made by cyanobacteria. Cyanobacteria are considered to have been among the first organisms on early Earth.

A Apply **How are stromatolites evidence of Earth's early life?**

Differentiated Instruction

ENGLISH LEARNERS

Students can get more out of this section if you incorporate a comprehensive vocabulary review. To the two new vocabulary words at the beginning of the chapter, add *stromatolite.* To the list of review vocabulary, add *photosynthesis (photosynthetic), organelle, chloroplast, mitochondria,* and *ribosome.* Have students work in pairs to create word squares, assigning one or two terms to each pair. When students finish, collect or review their squares.

Teacher Toolkit, Section D, Word Squares

INCLUSION

If there are students who have difficulty accessing the material, pair them with other students for a think-pair-share with a KWL focus. They will share what they know about the early Earth, what they want to know, and what they learn from the section.

Teacher Toolkit, Section C, KWL; Think-Pair-Share

MAIN IDEA

Several theories have been proposed for how eukaryotic cells evolved from prokaryotic cells.

The fossil record shows that eukaryotic organisms had evolved by 1.5 billion years ago. A eukaryote is more complex than a prokaryote, having a nucleus and other membrane-bound organelles. While the first eukaryotes were made of only one cell, later eukaryotic organisms became multicellular. Bacterial, plant, and animal cells share certain complex traits, including specific enzymes, metabolic pathways, ribosomes, cell membranes, and the genetic code carried in DNA. While these traits originated in prokaryotes, other eukaryotic traits such as organelles arose through the processes of evolution.

Endosymbiont theory One hypothesis of eukaryote evolution did not get much attention until the 1970s. Biologist Lynn Margulis found evidence to support the endosymbiont theory. **Endosymbiosis** (EHN-doh-SIHM-bee-OH-sihs) is a relationship in which one organism lives within the body of another—with both organisms benefitting.

The endosymbiont theory suggests that mitochondria and chloroplasts were once simple prokaryotic cells that were engulfed by larger prokaryotes around 1.5 billion years ago. Instead of being digested, some of the smaller prokaryotes may have survived inside the larger ones as illustrated in **FIGURE 4.2.** If it took in a prokaryote that acted as a mitochondrion, the larger cell got energy in the form of ATP. If it took in a prokaryote that acted as a chloroplast, the larger cell could use photosynthesis to make sugars. In exchange, the mitochondria and the chloroplasts found a stable environment and nutrients.

Margulis based her theory on several factors. Unlike other organelles, mitochondria and chloroplasts have their own DNA and ribosomes. They can copy themselves within the cell in which they are found. Mitochondria and chloroplasts are also about the same size as prokaryotes, their DNA forms a circle, and their gene structures are similar to those of prokaryotes.

A Analyze **What evidence supports the theory of endosymbiosis?**

READING TOOLBOX

VOCABULARY

Endosymbiosis can be broken down into *endo-*, meaning "within," *sym-*, meaning "together," and *biosis*, meaning "way of life."

GO ONLINE
Endosymbiosis

FIGURE 4.2 Endosymbiosis

The theory of endosymbiosis proposes that the mitochondria found in eukaryotic cells descended from ancestors of infection-causing bacteria. Likewise, chloroplasts are considered descendants of cyanobacteria.

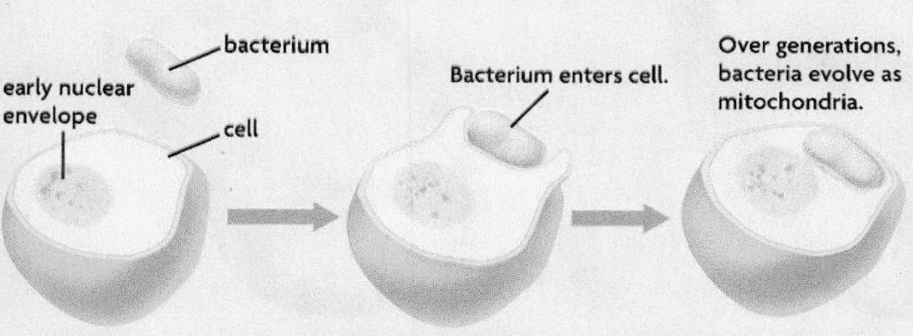

HOST CELL

Infection-causing bacteria entering a host cell

colored SEM; magnification 13,000×

TEACH FROM VISUALS

FIGURE 4.2 Use the figure to review the theory of endosymbiosis. **Ask**

- What selective advantage did the host prokaryotes gain from taking in and maintaining the mitochondria-like prokaryotes? ability to process energy more efficiently And for taking in chloroplast-like prokaryotes? ability to make their own sugars via photosynthesis
- What advantages did the mitochondria-like and chloroplast-like prokaryotes get? stable environment, nutrients

Vocabulary

Greek and Latin Word Origins The roots of **endosymbiosis** can be found in many other words used in biology.

- *Endocytosis* is the process *(-osis)* of taking something into a cell *(cyto-)*.
- *Endotherm* describes an organism that maintains a constant internal temperature *(-therm)*.
- *Endoskeleton* is an internal skeleton.
- *Symbiosis* is a process *(-osis)* or relationship in which two organisms function together, in some cases for their mutual benefit.

Answers

A Analyze Mitochondria and chloroplasts copy themselves within the cell instead of relying on the cell's replication apparatus, indicating that these organelles were once distinct organisms, probably ancestors of early prokaryotes. They are about the same size as prokaryotes, their DNA forms a circle like that of prokaryotes, and their gene structures also resemble those of prokaryotes.

PRE-AP

Have students spend five minutes creating cause-and-effect chains describing how life evolved, beginning with cyanobacteria, then aerobic prokaryotes, and finally eukaryotes. Have students incorporate key terms—*cyanobacterium, photosynthesis,* and *chloroplast*—in a way that defines each through context.

Teacher Toolkit, Section C, Cause-and-Effect Chain

BELOW LEVEL

Have students use a combination of descriptive sentences and diagrams to help them understand the theory of endosymbiosis. Encourage them to highlight the selective advantages to both host and infecting cells.

Teacher Toolkit, Section C, Combination Notes

▼ Teach *continued*

TEACH FROM VISUALS

FIGURE 4.3 Use the figure to review the structures of mitochondria and chloroplasts. Remind students that the endoplasmic reticulum and the Golgi apparatus are also made up of many folds and pockets that make, process, sort, and deliver proteins. **Ask**

Does the structure of eukaryotic organelles tend to support or oppose the autogenous theory? Answers will vary.

Answers

Ⓐ **Analyze** Since prokaryotes do not have membrane-bound organelles, all of their metabolic reactions take place in the cytoplasm. Membrane-bound organelles in eukaryotes enable chemical reactions for metabolic processes to be isolated from the others, which is much more efficient.

Autogenous theory In 1976 botanist F.J.R. Taylor proposed an alternative to the endosymbiont theory. Taylor's theory, known as autogeny, is based upon the extensive folding of the internal membranes found within chloroplasts and mitochondria, as seen in **FIGURE 4.3.**

You may recall that one of the major differences between prokaryotes and eukaryotes is that eukaryotes have membrane-bound organelles and prokaryotes do not. This provides eukaryotes with a distinct adaptive advantage. Since prokaryotic metabolic reactions all occur in the cytoplasm, it is possible for them to interfere with one another. Eukaryotes, on the other hand, have the specialized chemical reactions involved in metabolism separated by the membranes surrounding each organelle.

The autogenous theory proposes that eukaryotic organelles evolved from infoldings of the plasma membrane, creating pockets that eventually pinched off. When they pinched off into separate structures, small sections of nucleic acids and ribosomes were trapped inside. These new structures became specialized in performing different metabolic processes. Having these reactions isolated from one another is much more efficient, allowing eukaryotic cells to evolve even greater complexity. According to the autogenous theory, those organelles that performed photosynthesis eventually developed into chloroplasts. The theory also proposes that those new structures that specialized in providing energy to the other organelles through cellular respiration evolved into mitochondria.

Ⓐ Analyze **Why do membrane-bound organelles give eukaryotes an adaptive advantage over prokaryotes?**

FIGURE 4.3 Autogenous Theory

According to the autogenous theory, eukaryotes arose directly from a single prokaryotic ancestor through isolation of metabolic functions by infoldings of the plasma membrane. Such infoldings and pockets can be seen in chloroplasts and in mitochondria.

CHLOROPLAST

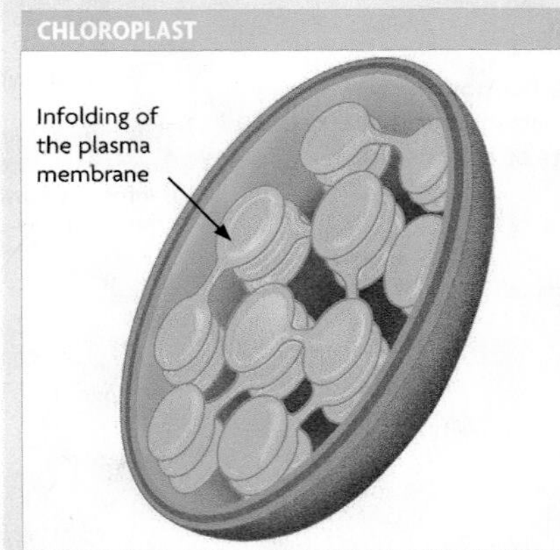

MITOCHONDRIA

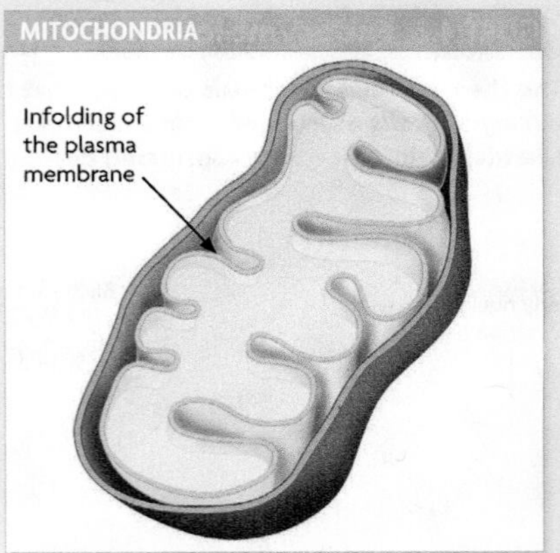

Differentiated Instruction

TEACH WITH TECHNOLOGY

Divide the class into groups of 3–4 students. Challenge the groups to use the drawing and animation functions of whatever presentation software is available to them and make simple animations of one of the three theories regarding the evolution of eukaryotes from prokaryotes. Have each group present their animation to the class.

Teacher Toolkit, Section G, Building Animations Using Presentation Software

FIGURE 4.4 Horizontal Gene Transfer

Horizontal gene transfer occurs commonly among bacteria. The donor cell forms a cytoplasmic bridge called a pilus, connecting to the recipient cell. A strand of DNA separates from a plasmid within the donor and moves into the recipient. Each cell then replicates a new, complementary strand of DNA and forms a new plasmid. In time, the new DNA may be incorporated into the genetic material of the recipient cell.

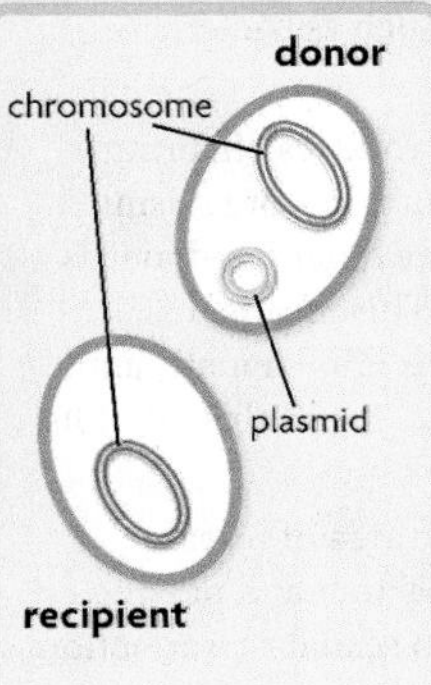

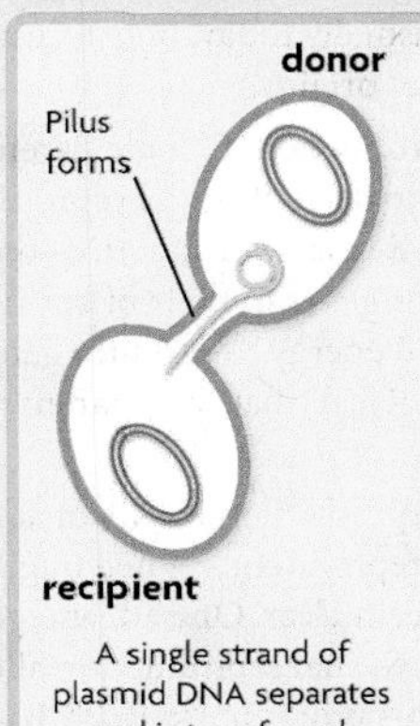

A single strand of plasmid DNA separates and is transferred.

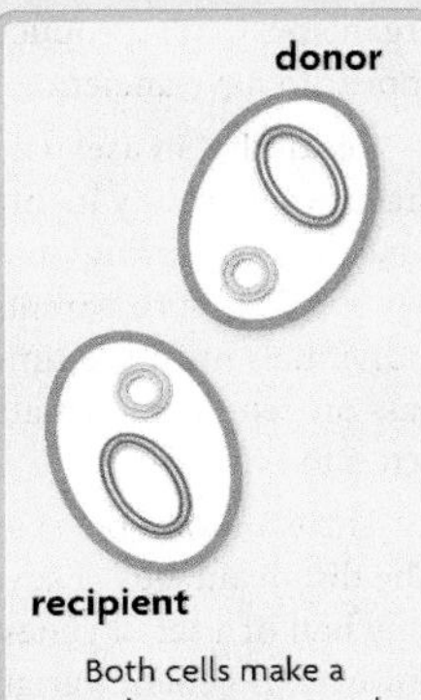

Both cells make a complementary strand of DNA to produce a new plasmid.

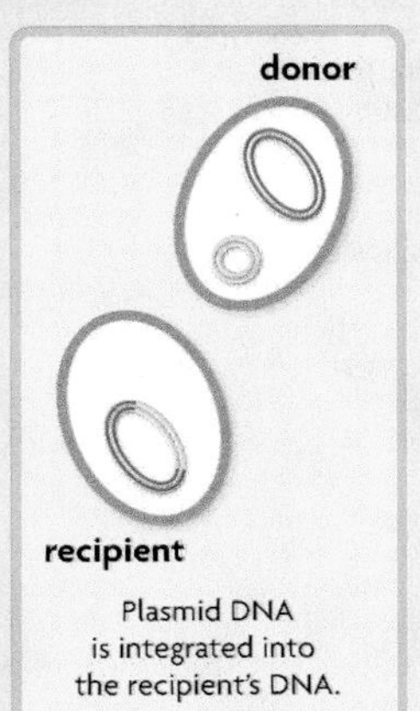

Plasmid DNA is integrated into the recipient's DNA.

Horizontal gene transfer theory In 2002 biologist Carl Woese proposed a third theory of how the complexity of eukaryotes evolved. Woese's earlier research into the genetic differences among prokaryotes led to the establishment of the currently accepted classification of all living things into three domains: eukaryotes and two groups of prokaryotes, bacteria and archaea.

Woese pointed out that the endosymbiont theory posits that eukaryotes arose when fully evolved prokaryotic cells engulfed and incorporated other prokaryotes. Based on his genetic research, Woese proposed instead that the genetic makeup of early cells was highly fluid and that eukaryotes, bacteria, and archaea evolved more or less in parallel. Woese further hypothesized that extensive exchange of genetic information took place among these evolving cell types through a process of horizontal gene transfer (HGT). This type of gene transfer continues to take place today when modern prokaryotes reproduce by a process called conjugation, as illustrated in **FIGURE 4.4.**

According to Woese's theory, horizontal gene transfer enabled the appearance of more complex cell structures. Distinct cell types emerged only when each of the cell organizations we know today reached a degree of complexity and interconnectedness that made it impossible for HGT to further change the organization in a fundamental way. Woese called this critical point the "Darwinian threshold," because this was the point in the evolution of life when natural selection on distinctly separated gene pools could begin to act.

Evaluate **Some scientists propose that a combination of theories may best describe the evolution of eukaryotes. What information would you use to support this view?**

TEACH FROM VISUALS

FIGURE 4.4 Have students examine the figure. Emphasize that prokaryotes commonly form cytoplasmic bridges between individuals and exchange packets of genetic material across the bridges. **Ask**

Why do prokaryotes need to successfully merge the new genetic material into their own genetic code and internal functions before they are considered to be a new species?

Vocabulary

Latin Word Origins The root of **pili** comes from the modern Latin word *pilus*, meaning "hair." This refers to the structure of pili, which is that of narrow, hollow, strands that extend out from the cell. The root word, *pilus*, is still used as the singular form of the term.

Answers

A Evaluate The endosymbiont theory is supported by the fact that unlike other organelles, chloroplasts and mitochondria both have their own DNA and ribosomes. Evidence supporting the theory of horizontal gene transfer is provided by the common prokaryotic activity of exchanging genes across cytoplasmic bridges.

Differentiated Instruction

BELOW LEVEL

Project an image of the figure onto the board where students can see it. Go over the process with students a step at a time. Remind students that bacteria transfer genetic data from one to another by this process constantly. **Ask** What other adaptation advantage might bacteria be able to gain by the process of gene transfer? antibiotic resistance

ENGLISH LEARNERS

Have students create a three-column chart to help them to understand the differences between the three theories regarding how eukaryotic cells evolved. Direct students to label the top of each column with the name of one of the theories. Under each column, students should give a brief description in their own words, of the basic concepts involved in each theory. Have them share their charts with other students to make sure that they have interpreted the theories correctly.

▼ Teach *continued*

Address Misconceptions

Common Misconception Because sexual reproduction and genetic diversity are stressed as adaptive advantages, students may think that organisms that reproduce asexually are less successful.

Correcting the Misconception Genetic variation through sexual reproduction can be a selective advantage, but some asexual species have survived for millions of years. One example is the bdelloid rotifers, a group of microscopic aquatic animals found around the world. All bdelloids are females that reproduce asexually. Not only has this group endured for more than 80 million years, it also includes more than 360 species. One advantage of asexual reproduction is that the rate of mutations is greater, which is another way of achieving genetic variation in a population. Echinoderms and sponges have species that reproduce both asexually and sexually.

▼ Assess and Reteach

Assess Use the Section Self-Check or Section Quiz, both available at **HMHScience.com**.

Reteach Arrange students in three groups. Have each group prepare an oral summary based on a section heading.

Answers

A Infer Mutations can provide a trait that is useful in the environment in which the organism exists.

CONNECT TO

GENETICS

Recall from the chapter **Meiosis and Mendel** that recombination is an important source of genetic variation. Sexual reproduction results in many phenotypes through the processes of producing gametes and crossing over in meiosis.

MAIN IDEA

The evolution of sexual reproduction led to increased diversity.

The first prokaryotes and eukaryotes could only reproduce asexually. Some time later, eukaryotic cells began to reproduce sexually. Of the groups of organisms that reproduce asexually today, only a few—such as bacteria—appear to have ancient asexual origins.

Recall that in asexual reproduction, a single parent produces offspring that are genetically identical to itself. Asexual reproduction lets organisms have many offspring quickly. Sexual reproduction, on the other hand, needs two parents. Both parents give genes to their offspring. This means that individuals must use time and energy to produce gametes, find a mate, and pass on genetic information. Recall that each parent passes on only half of its genes to offspring.

The evolution of sexual reproduction is still an active area of research. The disadvantages of sexual reproduction—needing a partner and passing on only half of a set of genes—seem clear. One advantage to sexual reproduction, however, is genetic variation. Sexual reproduction allows new combinations of genes to come together. This process may mask harmful mutations, and in some cases it may also bring beneficial mutations together.

Sexual reproduction may also have resulted in an increase in the rate of evolution by natural selection. Sexual reproduction creates more genetic variation, which lets a population adapt quickly to new conditions. Over a long time, early eukaryotes may have gained variations that made living closely together, and eventually cooperating, beneficial. Thus, sexual reproduction may have been the first step in the evolution of multicellular life.

Infer How can mutations be beneficial to organisms?

SELF-CHECK Online
HMHScience.com
GO ONLINE

12.4 Formative Assessment

REVIEWING MAIN IDEAS

1. How did early **cyanobacteria** affect the physical and chemical conditions on Earth?
2. How does the theory of **endosymbiosis** differ from the autogenous and horizontal gene transfer theories in explaining the evolution of eukaryotes?
3. How does sexual reproduction increase diversity among living things?

CRITICAL THINKING

4. **Apply** How does sexual reproduction increase the chances that some individuals will survive in changed environmental conditions?
5. **Infer** For photosynthetic organisms to become more common than those that get energy from eating organic molecules, what environmental conditions must have changed?

CONNECT TO

SCIENTIFIC PROCESS

6. According to the theory of endosymbiosis, mitochondria were once independent organisms. Is it possible that mitochondria might now be able to exist independently if removed from a cell? Describe how you could investigate this question.

12.4 FORMATIVE ASSESSMENT

1. Cyanobacteria created mineral structures and supported aerobic life through the production of oxygen.
2. The endosymbiont theory proposes that larger prokaryotes engulfed smaller prokaryotes. This differs from the other theories in that it resulted in a symbiotic relationship between multiple organisms that was an adaptive advantage for all.
3. Through gamete production and crossing-over, sexual reproduction provides genetic variation.
4. A population can adapt to new environmental conditions more rapidly when new advantageous traits are introduced to its individuals. An asexually reproducing population depends on mutation alone to develop new traits. In a sexually reproducing population, recombination of alleles can yield new traits relatively quickly, increasing the chances that individuals will survive changed environmental conditions.
5. In order for photosynthetic organisms to evolve and thrive, there must have been increased levels of sunlight and plenty of carbon dioxide in the atmosphere and oceans.
6. Mitochondria might be able to survive on their own if they were in a nutrient-rich environment. One test would be to try to raise excised mitochondria in a cell culture, with normal eukaryotic cells as a control.

Calculating Axes Intervals

Smart Grapher
HMHScience.com
GO ONLINE
Create animated charts and graphs using Smart Grapher.

Determining the correct scales of axes on graphs is important so that all data points can be plotted. The scale can also influence the reader's perception of the results. If the intervals are too far apart, the slope of the graph will seem steep—indicating a fast rate or a large change in the data. If the intervals are too small, the graph will be flatter, with change that seems small or nonexistent.

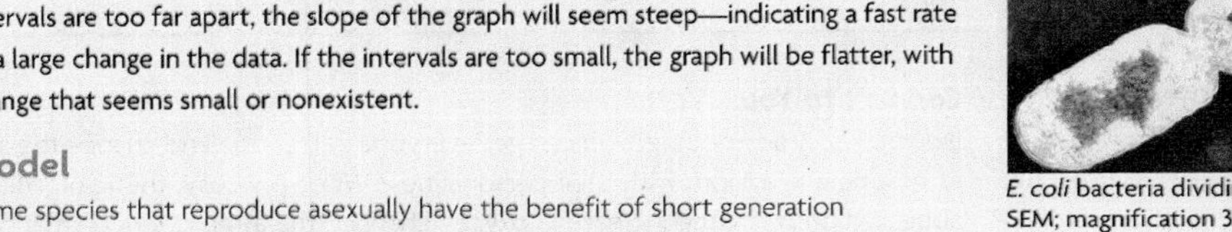

E. coli bacteria dividing (colored SEM; magnification 32,000+)

Model

Some species that reproduce asexually have the benefit of short generation times. They may be able to adapt more quickly to changing environmental conditions. Bacteria populations, for instance, can quickly become resistant to antibiotics. Individual bacteria that survive antibiotic treatment will pass the gene for resistance to their offspring when they reproduce.

The population of bacteria doubles with each generation. The following are the steps used to determine axis intervals of the line graph of the growth of *Escherichia coli* over 5 generations:

- Calculate the difference between the smallest and largest values of the variable and divide the difference by the number of data points. For the *E. coli* data, 85 – 17 = 68. Divided by 5, this equals 13.6.
- Round the result to the nearest convenient number, such as 2, 5, or 10. For *E. coli*, the interval was rounded down to 12.
- Use the rounded number as the interval.
- Begin the scale on the axis at zero (or at one interval lower than the lowest value if the values to be graphed are much larger than the interval).
- End the scale above the highest value. For *E. coli*, the scale ranges from 0 to 96.

GRAPH 1. GENERATION TIME IN *E. COLI*

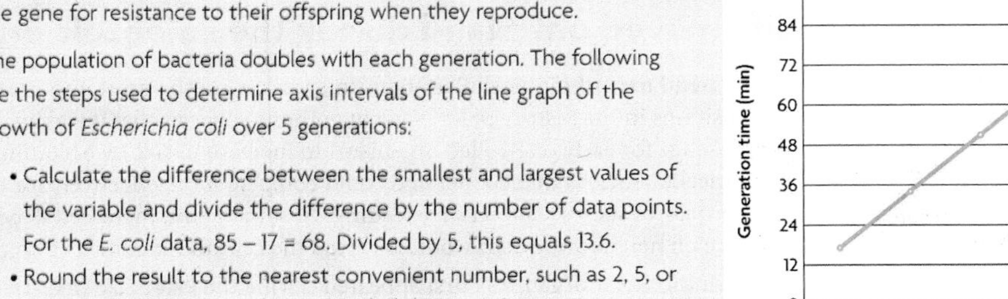

Practice Calculate Axes Intervals

1. **Graph Data** Calculate the intervals for the *y*-axis and *x*-axis for a graph that compares the generation times of all three of the bacteria species listed below. Draw the axes, plot the data, and label each of the three plotted lines. Be sure to title your graph and label your axes.
2. **Analyze** Using your graph for *E. coli* as an example, explain how changing the axes of a graph can influence how data are interpreted.

TABLE 1. GENERATION TIMES FOR COMMON BACTERIA

Bacteria	Generation 1 Time (min)	Generation 2 Time (min)	Generation 3 Time (min)	Generation 4 Time (min)	Generation 5 Time (min)
	10 bacteria	20 bacteria	40 bacteria	80 bacteria	160 bacteria
E. coli	17	34	51	68	85
B. megaterium	25	50	75	100	125
S. lactis	48	96	144	192	240

Answers

1. Graphs will vary depending on how students calculate the intervals, but all should show three different linear curves of varying slopes and a *y*-axis that goes to approximately 250. See samples to the right.
2. The rate of change can be emphasized or minimized by changing the scales, thereby influencing the reader's interpretation of the results. For *E. coli*, the slope of the line is reduced if the intervals are set to suit the *S. lactis* data, making it appear as though *E. coli* population growth is relatively slow.

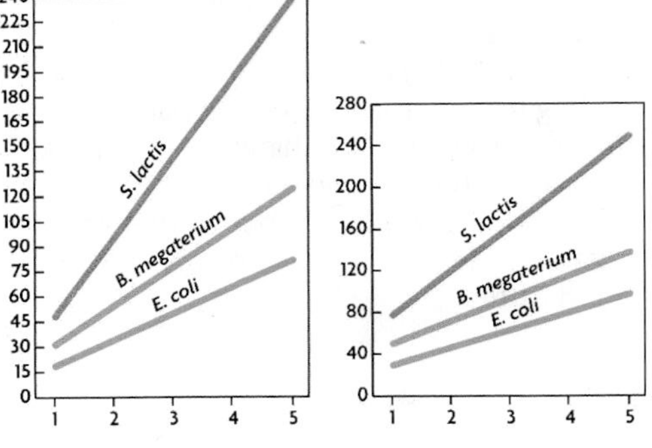

DATA ANALYSIS

Introduce

Graphs are powerful tools for communicating data, but if created incorrectly, they may steer one's interpretations in an incorrect direction. **Ask**

- What would the slope of the *E. coli* graph look like if the *y*-axis scale had a range of 0 to 540 minutes? It would appear much flatter.
- What does the slope of the line on the graph represent? the rate at which the population doubles

Discuss

After the students have completed their graphs, have them consider what changes would need to be made if data from other species were added. **Ask**

- What is the value of placing all three curves on the same graph? The generation time of the different bacteria can be compared directly.
- What would three existing curves look like if data of a fourth bacterium—with generation times of 150, 300, 600, 1200, and 2400 minutes—were added? The other curves would become flat and hard to differentiate from one another.
- Imagine that you also have the data of generation times for three species of mammal. What kind of graph would you create to compare the generation times of the mammals with those of the bacteria? Graph all six species' data on the same graph.
- What would be difficult to see in such a graph? Explain. The data of the three bacteria would look like a single horizontal line on the bottom of the graph, because the intervals needed for the mammal generation times (years) would be enormous compared to what would be appropriate for bacteria.

Online Student Resources, Data Analysis Practice

SECTION 12.5

Plan and Prepare

Activate Prior Knowledge Students likely will have some prior knowledge of dinosaurs and the Mesozoic era. **Ask,** To what kinds of habitats were dinosaurs and reptiles of the Mesozoic era adapted? tropical and temperate terrain, desert, oceans **Ask,** Assuming that those habitats are similar to today's, why aren't there dinosaurs on Earth anymore? They were wiped out, possibly by a meteorite, climate change, or disease.

Teach

Take It Further

An important development during the Paleozoic era was the **amniotic egg.** The amniotic egg is surrounded by a hard shell that prevents the interior structures from drying out. Inside the eggs, fluid-filled membranes help the developing embryos survive. Both traits allowed for these eggs to be laid in non-aquatic habitats—a crucial step in the transition of animals from aquatic habitats to terrestrial ones.

12.5 Radiation of Multicellular Life

KEY CONCEPT **Multicellular life evolved in distinct phases.**

MAIN IDEAS

- Life moved onto land during the Paleozoic era.
- Reptiles radiated during the Mesozoic era.
- Mammals radiated during the Cenozoic era.

VOCABULARY

Paleozoic
Cambrian explosion
Mesozoic
Cenozoic

Connect to Your World

Do you know any people who can get everyone's attention and change the social atmosphere in a room with their personalities? When photosynthetic organisms appeared on Earth, the increase in oxygen changed the atmosphere dramatically. New ecological opportunities arose, and multicellular organisms began to evolve.

MAIN IDEA

Life moved onto land during the Paleozoic era.

The trend toward multicellular organisms was one of the most important transitions in the history of life. One hypothesis suggests that it was an advantage for early one-celled organisms to increase in size by becoming multicellular. Cells that cooperated could compete more effectively for energy, by processes such as cooperative feeding. At some point, increased dependence on neighboring cells would have led the cells to function as a colony.

Multicellular organisms first appeared during the **Paleozoic** (PAY-lee-uh-ZOH-ihk) era, which began 542 million years ago. Members of every major animal group evolved within only a few million years. The era ended 251 million years ago with a mass extinction. More than 90 percent of marine species and 70 percent of land species of that time became extinct. In between these remarkable events, multicellular animals radiated, the first vertebrates evolved, and early plants moved onto land.

FIGURE 5.1 This illustration depicts a scene from the Carboniferous period of the Paleozoic era. Note the diversity of animals and plants represented.

The earliest part of the Paleozoic era is often called the **Cambrian explosion.** During the Cambrian explosion, a huge diversity of animal species evolved. At the start of the Paleozoic era, all life was found in the ocean. Among the earliest vertebrates was a group of jawless fishes. The only species of jawless fish still remaining are the Agnathan fish, which you will read about in the chapter Vertebrate Diversity. Marine invertebrates, such as the trilobites, were especially abundant. This highly diverse group of arthropods had thousands of species, though almost half of these species died in the mass extinction event at the end of the Cambrian period. Many other animals from this time period are also extinct. The best known of these are found at the Burgess Shale site in British Columbia, where many fossils were well preserved.

Differentiated Instruction

ENGLISH LEARNERS

Point out to students that although the word *explosion* is commonly associated with bombs, *explosion* can mean the flowing or bursting forth in many directions of virtually anything, from physical things to emotions. The Cambrian explosion refers not to a violent physical explosion but to the rapid radiation of species within a relatively short period of time.

The middle of the Paleozoic era was a time of great diversity as life moved onto land. The number and variety of plant groups greatly increased. Four-legged vertebrates, such as amphibians, became common. Most of the coal used in the United States formed during the Carboniferous period of this era, illustrated in **FIGURE 5.1.** The decomposed remains of millions of organisms were buried in sediment. Over time they changed into coal and the petroleum that fuels our cars today.

Summarize **Why is part of the Cambrian period also called the Cambrian explosion?**

MAIN IDEA

Reptiles radiated during the Mesozoic era.

The **Mesozoic** (MEHZ-uh-ZOH-ihk) era began 251 million years ago and ended 65 million years ago. Called the Age of Reptiles because the dinosaurs roamed Earth during this era, the Mesozoic also featured birds and flowering plants. The oldest direct ancestor of mammals first appeared during this era. By the era's end, mammals—particularly marsupials, whose young develop in a pouch—had evolved numerous key traits that improved their chances of survival during the mass extinction at the end of the era.

The Mesozoic era is divided into three periods: the Triassic, the Jurassic, and the Cretaceous. Life took off slowly in the early Triassic. On land, the earliest crocodiles and dinosaurs arose. The fossil record shows that the first mammals also evolved during this time. An extinction event near the end of the Triassic destroyed many types of animals. This mass extinction allowed the radiation of the dinosaurs in the Jurassic period, illustrated in **FIGURE 5.2.**

Although life had moved onto land, it was still abundant underwater. Ichthyosaurs (IK-thee-uh-SAWRZ), a group of predatory marine reptiles, dominated the oceans. Sharks and bony fishes continued to evolve more complex forms.

The Cretaceous period also ended in a mass extinction—the cause of which is still debated. Evidence shows that a massive asteroid struck Earth. The most accepted hypothesis is that this impact sent enormous amounts of dust and debris into the atmosphere, blocking much of the Sun's light. As a result, the climate changed, and plants were unable to perform photosynthesis. Without sufficient plants to eat, herbivorous dinosaurs and many other animal species became extinct. The loss of these herbivorous animals reduced the food supply of meat-eating dinosaurs, contributing to the meat eaters' extinction.

Analyze **How did life on Earth change from the beginning of the Paleozoic era to the end of the Mesozoic?**

FIGURE 5.2 The illustration below depicts a scene from the Jurassic period of the Mesozoic era. Fossils of pterosaurs (above) have been found in groups, suggesting that they may have lived in colonies.

Vocabulary

Greek and Latin Word Origins The eras of the geologic time scale are named for when they occurred relative to the present time. The suffix *-zoic* comes from the Greek root *zöikos,* meaning "of animals." The prefixes refer to each era's relative age:

paleo = ancient
meso = middle
ceno = new

Science Trivia

When it was first discovered by paleontologists, the slender dinosaur *Oviraptor* was immediately labeled a thief. During a desert expedition to the Gobi in 1924, paleontologists uncovered a small fossilized theropod dinosaur on top of a clutch of broken dinosaur eggs. To paleontologists, the case seemed clear. The dinosaur, a biped with the powerful hind limbs and strong, clawed fingers of a predator, obviously had been preying on the eggs of another dinosaur—most likely a *Protoceratops,* because several fossils of that species lay nearby. So the newly discovered dinosaur was named *Oviraptor,* from the Latin words for *egg* and *robber.*

Then in the mid-1990s, scientists once again found a nest of dinosaur eggs underneath an *Oviraptor* skeleton. This skeleton, however, had the posture of a chicken or other animal that incubates its own eggs. Later the scientists found that one egg contained a tiny *Oviraptor* embryo. Far from being an egg predator, the *Oviraptor* was being a good mother.

BELOW LEVEL

Have students form groups of three and then number off and form expert groups, one for each era discussed in this section. After each expert group discusses and writes down the major characteristics and developments of its assigned era, have the original groups come back together and share what they have learned.

Teacher Toolkit, Section C, Jigsaw Reading

Answers

A **Summarize** There was a tremendous diversification of life forms and radiation of species during this time.

B **Analyze** There were relatively few types of organisms at the beginning of the Paleozoic era, and most were quite small. By the end of the Mesozoic era, many organisms had roamed Earth and the seas.

▼ Teach *continued*

Integrating Ecology

Why did mammals become so successful and undergo such a dramatic radiation in the early Cenozoic era? The sudden availability of many **niches** may have been a factor. A *niche* is the role that an organism plays in its environment. As the dominant land animals during the Mesozoic, dinosaurs occupied many varied niches. As the dinosaurs decreased in number, the niches they had occupied opened up. Mammals that had key adaptations (traits that allowed them to evolve to fill the niches) were better able to compete for and occupy these niches. Thus, the demise of the dinosaurs and many other animals at the close of the Cretaceous opened up new opportunities for mammals of the Cenozoic. Students will learn more about niches in **Interactions in Ecosystems**.

Answers

A Infer Placental mammals and monotremes, or egg-laying mammals, both diversified during this era.

MAIN IDEA

Mammals radiated during the Cenozoic era.

HORSE ANCESTOR (55 MYA)

FIGURE 5.3 The illustration below depicts a scene from the Tertiary period of the Cenozoic era. This ancestor of modern-day horses (above) was the size of a small dog.

The **Cenozoic** era (SEH-nuh-ZOH-ihk) began 65 million years ago and continues today. It is divided into two periods, the Tertiary (65–1.8 million years ago), illustrated in **FIGURE 5.3**, and the Quaternary (1.8 million years ago until today). During the Tertiary, placental mammals and monotremes—a small group of mammals that lay eggs—evolved and diversified. Their adaptive radiation rivaled that of the marsupials in the Mesozoic. The most dramatic radiation of the mammals, however, occurred with the placentals. Today, this group numbers roughly 4000 species. During the Tertiary period, birds, ray-finned fishes, and flowering plants also underwent dramatic radiations.

CONNECT TO

MAMMALS

Placental mammals include all mammals except monotremes, which lay eggs, and marsupials, which rear their underdeveloped young in a pouch. You will learn more about animal classification in the chapter **The Tree of Life.**

The earliest ancestors of modern humans evolved near the end of the Tertiary. However, anatomically modern humans did not appear until very recently in Earth's history, nearly 200,000 years ago. The evolution of primates is covered in the next section.

A Infer Why is the Cenozoic era sometimes referred to as the Age of Mammals?

12.5 Formative Assessment

REVIEWING MAIN IDEAS

1. What important events occurred during the **Paleozoic** era?
2. What were some of the key appearances and radiations in the **Mesozoic** era?
3. What two groups of mammals evolved during the **Cenozoic** era?

CRITICAL THINKING

4. **Evaluate** Explain how natural selection related to the development of diversity in and among species during the **Mesozoic** era.
5. **Infer** How does a great diversity of organisms increase the chances that some will survive a major change in the environment?

CONNECT TO

ECOLOGY

6. How do you think the evolution of flowering plants affected the evolution and radiation of birds?

▼ Assess and Reteach

Assess Use the Section Self-Check or Section Quiz, both available at **HMHScience.com**.

Reteach Have students work in groups to summarize the major events of each era discussed in this section.

12.5 FORMATIVE ASSESSMENT

1. Multicellular organisms arose, life moved from sea to land, and there were both the rapid diversification of the Cambrian explosion and a mass extinction event.
2. *Sample answer:* dinosaurs, marsupial mammals, flowering plants, birds, predatory marine reptiles, bony fishes
3. placentals and monotremes
4. Due to mass extinction events during the Mesozoic era, many new niches would have opened up. Species that were able to survive the catastrophe would have radiated out to fill the niches, evolving many diverse traits to adapt to new conditions
5. If there is a wide diversity among organisms, it is more likely that at least some will have characteristics that will be beneficial, or at least good enough, when environmental conditions change.
6. The evolution of flowering plants gave birds a greater diversity of habitats and foods.

12.6 Primate Evolution

VOCABULARY
primate
prosimian
anthropoid
hominid
bipedal

KEY CONCEPT **Humans appeared late in Earth's history.**

MAIN IDEAS
- Humans share a common ancestor with other primates.
- There are many fossils of extinct hominins.
- Modern humans arose nearly 200,000 years ago.

Connect to Your World

In terms of the geologic time scale, the evolution of humans has occurred only very recently. Many fossils of our early ancestors consist of partial skeletons from which details must be inferred through careful study. Though far from complete, this fossil record offers a fascinating glimpse of our past.

MAIN IDEA

Humans share a common ancestor with other primates.

The common ancestor of all primates probably arose before the mass extinction that closed the Cretaceous period 65 million years ago. **Primates** make up a category of mammals with flexible hands and feet, forward-looking eyes—which allow for excellent three-dimensional vision—and enlarged brains relative to body size. Primates also have arms that can rotate in a circle around their shoulder joint, and many primates have thumbs that can move against their fingers. Primates include lemurs, monkeys, apes, and humans. In addition to sharing similar physical traits, primates share strong molecular similarities.

Primate Evolution

Similar to other groups of related organisms, the relationship among the primate groups forms a many-branched tree. At the tree's base is the common ancestor of all primates. Just above this base, the tree splits into two main subgroups: the prosimians and the anthropoids.

Prosimians (proh-SIHM-ee-uhnz) are the oldest living primate group, and most are small and active at night. This group of nocturnal animals includes the lemurs, the lorises, and the tarsiers, like the ones shown in **FIGURE 6.1.** Prosimians are differentiated from anthropoids by smaller size and skull plates that are not fused together when mature.

FIGURE 6.1 Prosimians, such as these tarsiers, are the oldest living primate group. They are active at night and have large eyes and ears.

READING TOOLBOX

TAKING NOTES

Make a concept map of primate classification. Add more shapes as needed.

primates
include
prosimians — such as
anthropoids — such as
such as

Differentiated Instruction

ENGLISH LEARNERS

In groups of approximately four, have students number off. Ask several questions about each of the section's three parts. Have students discuss for a few minutes to find and agree on an answer. Decide whether they can or cannot consult the text. Choose one number, and have group members with that number say the answer or write it on the board. Provide feedback on their answers.

Teacher Toolkit, Section C, Numbered Heads Together

SECTION 12.6

Plan and Prepare

Activate Prior Knowledge Students may have heard that chimp and human DNA is about 99 percent identical. **Explain** that this percentage is a measure of the similarity of base sequences in the functional genes shared by chimps and humans. Ongoing research indicates a lower percentage of similarity in non-coding regions of DNA, which may play a role in regulatory or other functions.

Teach

Vocabulary

Greek and Latin Word Origins Students may become confused by the similarity between **hominoid** and **hominid.** Explain that the suffixes *-oid* and *-id* are from the Greek words meaning "resembles" and "belonging to." *Hominoid* is a more general group of primates that includes gibbons, orangutans, humans, chimpanzees, and gorillas. In contrast, *hominid* refers specifically to the great apes and species in the human lineage.

▼ Teach *continued*

Science Trivia

For a long time, it was thought that only humans had the ability to use tools. It was finally expanded to include all primates, when chimpanzees were observed using sticks to extract termites from cement-like mounds in order to eat the insects. Finally, scientists found that a number of animals have managed to use simple tools, even without having opposable thumbs. Crows and their relatives have been seen to drop rocks into containers to raise the water level, allowing them to reach tasty, floating worms. Elephants break sticks to just the right length to swat insects that bother them. They have also been known to use chewed-up bark to plug up water holes, keeping the water from being drained by other animals.

Vocabulary

Latin Word Origins The root word for the terms **hominoid**, **hominid**, and **hominin** comes from the Latin word *homo*, meaning "human" as well as the Greek word, *homoios*, meaning "like."

Answers

A Interpret Being able to manipulate objects and adapt them to use as tools or weapons allowed hominids to make better use of available resources, hunt more efficiently, and defend themselves.

READING TOOLBOX

VOCABULARY

The term *anthropoid* comes from the word root *anthropo*, which means "human."

Further distinguishing the prosimians is a single, long grooming claw on the second toe of their hind feet and a unique type of horizontal tooth structure known as a grooming comb. Tarsiers have been called living fossils, as their physical traits have changed little since their appearance in the fossil record more than 40 million years ago.

Anthropoids (AN-thruh-POYDZ), the humanlike primates, are further subdivided into the New World monkeys, Old World monkeys, and hominoids, as shown in **FIGURE 6.2.** New World monkeys, which are native to the Americas, all live in trees. Many species have prehensile, or grasping, tails, an adaptation that allows them to hang by their tails from tree branches while feeding. Some Old World monkeys also spend time in trees, but most travel and forage on the ground as well. They have larger brains than do New World monkeys and a greater ability to manipulate objects.

Classification of organisms will be covered in much more detail in the Tree of Life chapter. You will then learn more about how scientists determine how to categorize and name an organism. However, to reduce confusion, it is necessary to show the difference between some of the terms used to classify anthropoids. The terms *hominoid, hominid*, and a third term, *hominin*, all sound very similar because they all originate from the same Latin root word, *homo*, meaning "man."

Hominoids include gibbons and the great apes (orangutans, chimpanzees, and gorillas) as well as humans. **Hominids** include orangutans, chimpanzees, gorillas, and humans, but not gibbons. The term *hominin* refers only to modern humans and their immediate ancestors.

Among primates, hominids are particularly known for using opposable thumbs to their advantage. Because their thumbs are placed in opposition to the four fingers, hominids are able to manipulate objects and adapt them. This trait enables hominids not only to pick up and grasp an object but also to use it for multiple purposes. For example, wild chimpanzees in Tanzania have been observed adapting grass and sticks to remove honey from beehives, as well as to dig up roots to eat, and to pry open boxes of bananas left for them by scientists. The chimpanzees also use leaves for collecting water and for wiping mud and sticky fruit from their bodies. Young chimps in Gombe learn how to "fish" for termites by observing adults as they demonstrate the steps involved. Without these observations, it is unlikely that the youngsters would become successful at obtaining termites for food.

FIGURE 6.3 Opposable thumbs gave hominids the ability to grasp, manipulate, and adapt objects for use as tools or weapons.

A Interpret How did the ability to manipulate objects, as well as adapt them for use as tools or weapons, give hominids an evolutionary advantage over other primates?

Differentiated Instruction

HANDS-ON ACTIVITY

Have students choose a partner from among their classmates. Instruct them to take turns folding their thumbs down to touch their palms and having their partner tape the thumbs in place using masking tape. Challenge them to try using only the four fingers on their hands to perform tasks that normally require the use of fingers and thumbs. An example would be holding a pen to write their name, tying their shoe laces, or picking up a dime from the desktop.

Teacher Toolkit, Section B, Making Qualitative Observations

FIGURE 6.2 Evolutionary Relationships of Primates

Phylogenetic trees, or cladograms, that depict evolutionary relationships between primate groups can be constructed by scientists using karyotype analysis of chromosomes.

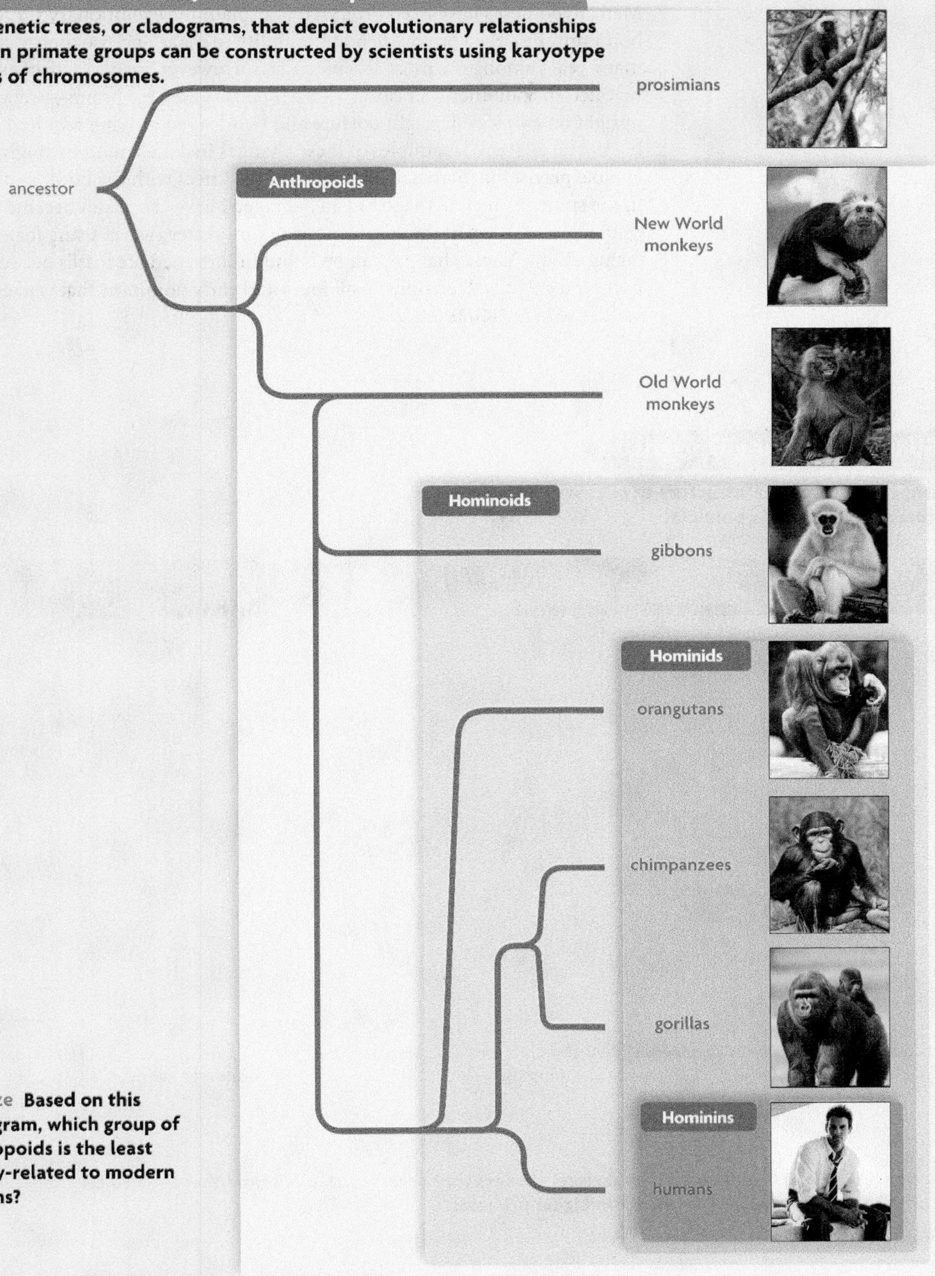

ancestor
prosimians
Anthropoids
New World monkeys
Old World monkeys
Hominoids
gibbons
Hominids
orangutans
chimpanzees
gorillas
Hominins
humans

Analyze **Based on this cladogram, which group of anthropoids is the least closely-related to modern humans?**

Differentiated Instruction

PRE-AP

Have students write for five minutes describing the points of divergence in primate evolution and what they suggest about the genomes of the species that represent these groups today. For example, what can we infer about the similarities between the human genome and the genomes of the orangutan and Old World monkeys?

Teacher Toolkit, Section C, Quick-Write

Take It Further

Anthropoid primates are divided into two main groups: the **platyrrhines** and the **catarrhines.**

- The New World, or Neotropical, monkeys are *platyrrhines* (plat-ih-RINES). They are so named because they have flattened *(platy-)* noses *(rhin-)* with nostrils that point to the side.
- The *catarrhines* (cat-ih-REENS) include the Old World monkeys, apes, and humans. Catarrhines have straight noses with nostrils that point downward *(cata-)*.

TEACH FROM VISUALS

FIGURE 6.2 is structured like a family tree. At each point of separation, two distinct groups of organisms evolved from a common ancestor. **Ask,** Is a gorilla more closely related to a gibbon or an orangutan, and how can you tell? orangutan, because point of divergence for orangutans and hominids is about 8 million years after divergence of hominid/orangutan and gibbon group

Science Trivia

- Howler monkeys (of the genus *Alouatta*) are the largest monkeys and loudest animals in the Americas. They can grow up to 1.2 meters (4 ft) tall and may weigh up to 9 kilograms (20 lb). Their howl can be heard as far away as 4.8 kilometers (3 mi).
- The world's tiniest monkeys are the pygmy marmosets. Native to South American rain forests, these animals measure about 13 centimeters (5 in.) long (not including their tails) and weigh 113–199 grams (4–7 oz).

Answers

A Analyze New World Monkeys are the group of anthropoids that are least closely-related to modern humans.

▼ Teach *continued*

History of Science

During a 1976 expedition to Laetoli in Tanzania, paleoanthropologist **Andrew Hill** accidentally discovered a trail of footprints that radically altered the timeline of human evolution. The footprints were made by bipedal hominids about 3.6 million years ago. The trail, which measured approximately 24 meters (80 ft) long, was preserved in a deposit of volcanic ash. Further study suggested that the footprints were made by several *Australopithecus afarensis* individuals. The discovery of the Laetoli footprints startled the scientific community. Before then, the oldest known evidence of hominid bipedalism was only tens of thousands of years old.

Science Trivia

Most people have seen images of primates that walk more-or-less upright, but supporting part of their weight on the knuckles of their hands. Known as knuckle-walking, this form of locomotion is only found among the primates in a handful of African species. Examples include chimpanzees and gorillas. However, African primates do not hold a monopoly on this method of locomotion. For very different anatomical reasons, knuckle-walking is also seen among anteaters, whose long claws interfere with walking and in the platypus. In the platypus, the characteristic type of locomotion developed due to the animals' webbed feet, used for swimming. Since the webs extend beyond the ends of the animals' toes, when on land, they walk on their knuckles to avoid stumbling on the webbed membranes.

Answers

A Analyze Through time, the pelvis became less flat and more cup-shaped, the knees moved to be more aligned with the upright trunk of the body, the spine became less arched and more s-shaped, and the skull became more centered at the top of the spine.

Walking Upright

Many hypotheses have been proposed to explain the evolutionary success of the hominins. Enlarged brain size and the ability to make and use tools were for many years among the most accepted ideas. However, fossil discoveries have revealed that another trait came before tool use and large brains—walking upright on two legs. Upright posture and two-legged walking required changes in skeletal anatomy. Examples of these changes include a more strongly curved, cuplike pelvis, the increased alignment of the knees with the body, and a change in the spine from arch-shaped to an S-shaped curve. The skull became more centered on the top of the spine, allowing for greater ease in using forward-facing vision. These changes can be found in intermediate fossils between hominoids that walked only on all fours and early hominins that walked on two legs, as seen in **FIGURE 6.4.**

FIGURE 6.4 Walking Upright

Changes in the skeletal structure of primates were necessary before bipedalism was possible.

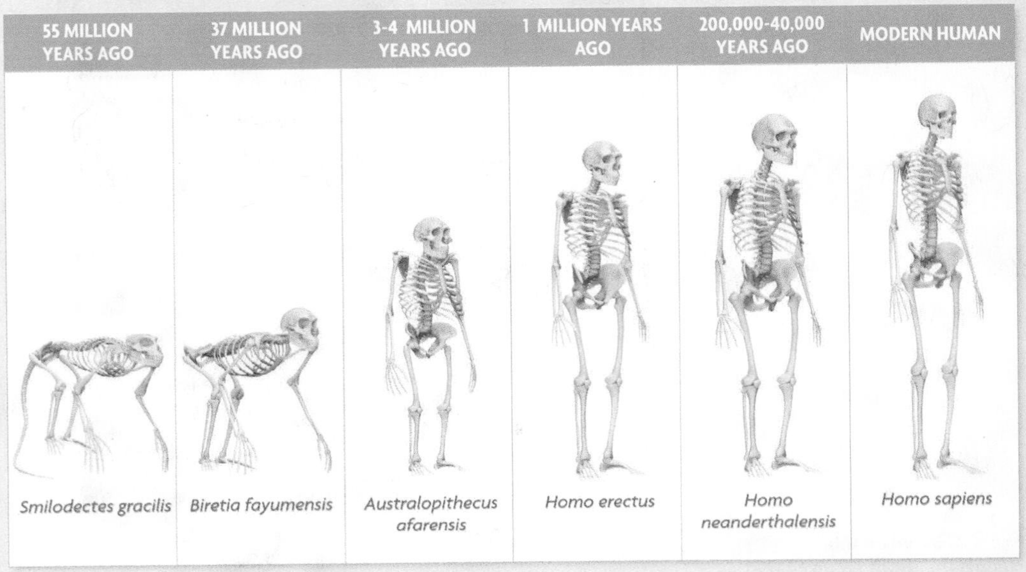

55 MILLION YEARS AGO	37 MILLION YEARS AGO	3-4 MILLION YEARS AGO	1 MILLION YEARS AGO	200,000-40,000 YEARS AGO	MODERN HUMAN
Smilodectes gracilis	*Biretia fayumensis*	*Australopithecus afarensis*	*Homo erectus*	*Homo neanderthalensis*	*Homo sapiens*

A Analyze **Give a brief summary of the skeletal changes that occurred through time that allowed for an upright posture and bipedal stance in higher primates.**

Differentiated Instruction

ENGLISH LEARNERS

Give students copies of the skeletal images found in **FIGURE 6.4** and a piece of poster paper. Have each student set up a chart on the poster paper. Instruct students to use a ruler or meter stick to draw six vertical columns on the paper. Then, using glue or tape, students should attach the images to the poster in a straight row across the top of the paper. Under each picture, students should write brief descriptions of the skeletal characteristics, noting how they change through time.

BELOW LEVEL

Have students add distinguishing characteristics or more groups to their concept maps from the Reading Toolbox at the beginning of this section. From "anthropoids," they can draw diverging arrows to "hominid" and "hominoid" circles. As they proceed through the remaining sections, they can add more groups and species, including the extinct hominins discussed later in this section.

Teacher Toolkit, Section C, Concept Map

Animals that can walk on two legs are called **bipedal** (BY-PEHD-l). This trait has important adaptive advantages for higher primates. It allows higher reach into tree branches while foraging, and perhaps most importantly, it frees the hands for foraging, carrying infants and food, and using tools. As the landscapes where ancestral humans evolved gradually shifted from heavily forested areas to vast grasslands, food would have become more scarce. Hunter-gatherers would have had to travel farther in order to find enough sources of nutrition for survival. The ability to travel upright on two feet would have enabled them to travel farther while expending less energy than animals that walked on their hind feet and their front knuckles.

VISUAL VOCAB

Bipedal is an adjective that describes two-legged or upright walking. *Bi-* means "two," and *ped-* means "foot."

In addition to tool usage, bipedal hominins would have been able to fashion weapons to kill prey or to protect themselves, their mates, and their offspring. The higher vantage point provided by their upright posture would have enabled them to better see over obstacles to observe approaching threats.

Connect **What is another common animal that is bipedal? Why did this organism need its forelimbs to be free from providing support for its body?**

QUICKLAB MODELING

Geologic Clock

One way to understand the relative length of time in Earth's history is to compare its age to a clock face. Precambrian time goes from 12 noon to about 10:30 P.M. The time span from early human ancestors—more than 5 million years ago—to *Homo sapiens* covers less than a second on our 12-hour clock!

12
4600 MYA
9–?
?–3
?
6

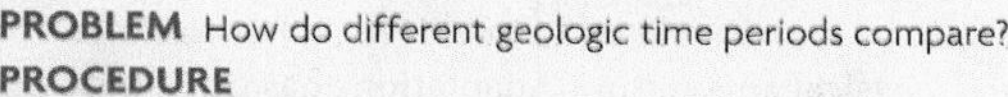

PROBLEM How do different geologic time periods compare?

PROCEDURE

1. Draw a large circle and mark the 12, 3, 6, and 9 positions of a clock face. Use the scale 1 hour = 400 million years ago, and label the four positions with the appropriate number of years, starting with 12 o'clock = 4800 million years ago. (Example: the three o'clock position = 3600 million years ago.)
2. Using the geological time scale, label Precambrian time and the three eras on your clock, along with the approximate time frames in which they occurred.
3. Label the following events on your clock in the appropriate positions, also filling in the approximate time frames they occurred: formation of Earth, oldest rocks, first stromatolites, first aerobic prokaryotes, first eukaryotes, first fishes, first flowering plants, first dinosaurs, first birds, and earliest hominids.

MATERIALS

- paper
- pencil

ANALYZE AND CONCLUDE

1. **Synthesize** How are eras and periods related? Where would the periods fit in this diagram?
2. **Calculate** Using your scale of 1 hour = 400 million years, how many millions of years in Earth's history would 1 minute represent?

TEACH WITH TECHNOLOGY

Encourage students to use the Internet to learn more about primate phylogeny. Invite them to expand one branch of the cladogram in **FIGURE 6.2** (for example, Old World monkeys). Students should use a computer graphics program to construct their cladograms, or they can create multimedia presentations to be shared with the class.

Teacher Toolkit, Section G, Presentation Software

Answers

A Connect birds

QUICKLAB

Time 20 minutes

Purpose Model relative interval lengths of the geologic time scale.

LAB MANAGEMENT

- If students are confusing time of day with time period, have them make marks without time labels.
- Have students first create a table of the ages and then label the circle.

Teacher Note "If a pie chart is referenced in the first step to assist students in picturing the final product, students will understand the step better."

Answers

Sample Data

For a sample clock, go to the online Teacher Resources at **HMHScience.com.**

Analyze and Conclude

1. Periods are the units within an era, as hours are the units within a day. On the diagram, periods would fit between the hours of the clock.
2. 6.7 million years (400 million years/hour divided by 60 minutes/hour)

▼ Teach *continued*

The Inside Story

In one of the all-time greatest hoaxes in science, a British amateur archaeologist, **Charles Dawson,** announced in 1912 that he had discovered a species of hominid that had lived a million years ago. His findings were two skulls that displayed the primitive jaws of an ape and the brow of a human. The remains were given the common name **Piltdown Man,** named for the region in which the bones were allegedly found, while Dawson used his own name in formulating the scientific name, *Eoanthropus dawsoni.*

Here, surely, was the missing link in the ancestry of both humans and apes. Some scientists, however, were skeptical. Details of the actual discovery of the skull and of subsequent Piltdown Man finds were murky, and there were obvious differences between the jaw and brow bones, suggesting that they were from different individuals.

During a meeting of paleontologists in London in 1953, the teeth and other parts of the Piltdown Man were examined by several scientists, who confirmed that the skulls were a deliberate fraud. They consisted of bones from a 500-year-old human and a modern orangutan.

Address Misconceptions

Common Misconception Humans are descended from modern apes.

Correcting the Misconception Humans did not descend from modern apes. Humans and the African apes (gorillas and chimpanzees) descended from a common ape ancestor that lived approximately 6–8 million years ago. The ancestor's descendants diverged into two lineages: one gradually evolved into gorillas; the other diverged into two lines, again about 5 million years ago, one giving rise to the ancestors of modern chimpanzees and the other leading to the early hominins.

Answers

A Hypothesize fossil specimens found in the same strata dated to the same time period

MAIN IDEA

There are many fossils of extinct hominins.

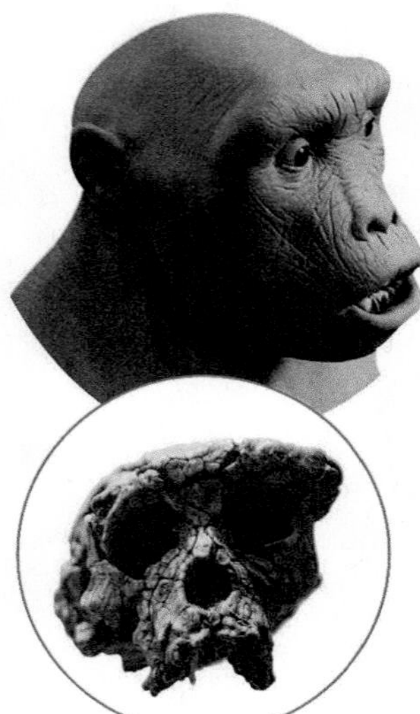

FIGURE 6.5 Computer technology allowed scientists to piece together 7-million-year-old skull fragments found in Africa. The three-dimensional reconstruction suggests that this may be the oldest known hominin ancestor of *Homo sapiens;* it has been named *Sahelanthropus tchadensis.*

Hominins are classified into several groups. Two important groups are the genus *Homo* and the older genus *Australopithecus* (aw-STRAY-loh-PIHTH-ih-kuhs). *Australopithecus* was a long-lived and successful genus. *Australopithecus afarensis* (AF-uh-REHN-sihs), which lived 3 to 4 million years ago in Africa, is one of the better known species of early hominins. Although its brain was much smaller than that of a modern human—about the size of a modern-day chimpanzee's brain—*A. afarensis* had very humanlike limbs.

The earliest member of the genus *Homo* was *Homo habilis.* Nicknamed "handy man" because of the crude stone tools associated with its skeletons, *H. habilis* lived 2.4–1.5 million years ago in what are now Kenya and Tanzania. This species may have lived alongside the australopithecine species for about 1 million years. *H. habilis* is the earliest known hominin to make stone tools. The brain of *H. habilis* was much larger than that of any of the australopithecines, and it more closely resembled the modern human brain in shape.

Another hominin species was *H. neanderthalensis,* commonly called Neanderthals for the Neander Valley in Germany, where their fossils were first found. This group lived from 200,000 to around 40,000 years ago in Europe and the Middle East. Evidence suggests that *H. neanderthalensis* coexisted with modern *Homo sapiens* for approximately 5,000 years, possibly even exchanging ideas and culture. The extinction of *H. neanderthalensis* was most likely caused by a period of extreme cold, inbreeding due to low numbers, and economic competition with *H. sapiens.*

Observations from the fossil record, such as the fossil seen in **FIGURE 6.5**, demonstrate a trend toward increased brain size in the human lineage. Although brain size can only be loosely related to intelligence, the combination of modern-day humans' physical and cultural adaptations has no doubt contributed to our success as a species.

A Hypothesize **What type of evidence could indicate that *H. sapiens* and *H. neanderthalensis* coexisted?**

Crafty Cavemen

MAIN IDEA

Modern humans arose nearly 200,000 years ago.

Fossil evidence reveals that *Homo sapiens* evolved nearly 200,000 years ago in what is now Ethiopia. However, many of their features were different than those of humans today. After becoming a distinct species, *H. sapiens* clearly did not stop evolving.

The Role of Culture

Human evolution is influenced by culture. Tools are among key markers of culture in human evolution, although they are used by some other animals as well. A comparison of tools from their first appearance some 2.5 million years ago, through their association with later *Homo* fossil sites, shows a steady trend of increasing sophistication and usefulness.

Differentiated Instruction

BELOW LEVEL

Have students make flash cards to help them keep track of the various species discussed in this section. They may wish to use some special method, such as color coding, to identify the evolutionary relationships of groups. For example, they could draw a blue border on hominin cards, red on nonhuman anthropoid cards, and green on prosimian cards.

Teacher Toolkit, Section C, Connect to Content Through Visuals

FIGURE 6.6 Examples of Hominin Skulls

Hominin evolution shows changes in brain size.

4–3 MILLION YEARS AGO	2.4–1.5 MILLION YEARS AGO	200,000–40,000 YEARS AGO	200,000 YEARS AGO–PRESENT
Australopithecus afarensis	*Homo habilis*	*Homo neanderthalensis*	*Homo sapiens*
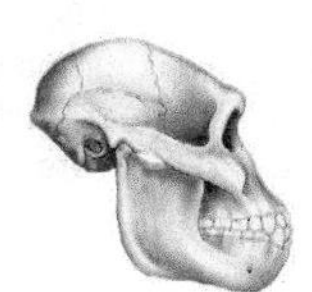	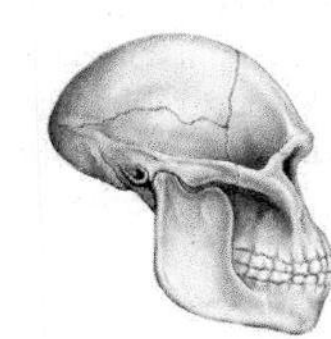	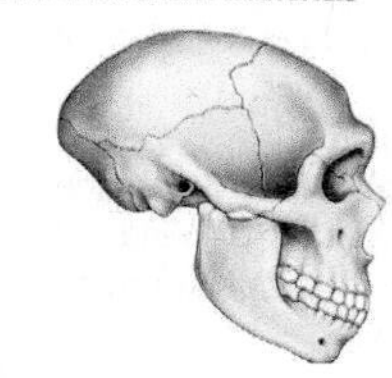	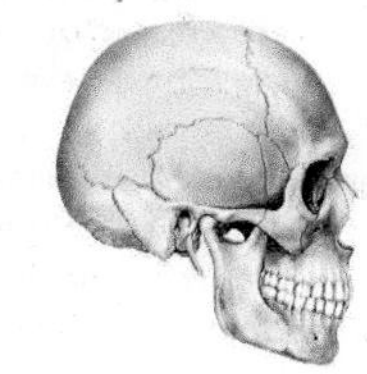
Australopithecus afarensis had a brain volume of 430 cm^3.	*Homo habilis* had a brain volume of about 700 cm^3.	*Homo neanderthalensis'* brain volume may have reached 1500 cm^3.	Modern *Homo sapiens* have a brain volume average of about 1350 cm^3.

A Contrast **What characteristics besides brain size differ among the species shown?**

The Evolution of the Human Brain

Human evolution would not have advanced as it did without an enlarging skull and brain size, as shown in **FIGURE 6.6.** One recent study has demonstrated that genes controlling the size and complexity of the human brain evolved faster than analogous genes in nonhuman primates. Researchers compared the DNA sequences for more than 200 genes affecting brain development in humans, Old World monkeys, rats, and mice. They found that these genes evolved at a much faster rate in the two primates than in the two rodents and that brain-related genes in humans evolved faster than did those in the monkeys. The results of the study support the hypothesis that the rapid evolution of large brain size posed an especially strong selective advantage among the hominids.

B Synthesize **When might having an increasingly larger brain size no longer be a selective advantage?**

VIRTUAL Lab
HMHScience.com
GO ONLINE
Comparing Hominoid Skulls

CONNECT TO
CLASSIFICATION
A genus is a closely related group of species. You will learn more about categories for classification in **The Tree of Life.**

12.6 Formative Assessment

SELF-CHECK Online
HMHScience.com
GO ONLINE

REVIEWING MAIN IDEAS

1. What characteristics shared by humans and other **primates** suggest that they have a common ancestor?
2. According to the fossil record, what other *Homo* species was present when modern humans arose?
3. From the hominin fossils described, what common trends can be found?

CRITICAL THINKING

4. **Apply** Explain why, according to the fossil record, it is not correct to say that humans evolved from chimpanzees.
5. **Infer** Scientists can often identify whether a fossil skull was from a **bipedal** primate. What characteristics of a skull might help them make this determination?

CONNECT TO
ANATOMY

6. Consider the skull illustrations above. Besides size, how did skull structure change as hominins evolved? What features are considered more apelike than humanlike?

12.6 FORMATIVE ASSESSMENT

1. *Sample answer:* flexible hands and feet, forward-looking eyes, enlarged brains relative to body size
2. *H. neanderthalensis*
3. Trends include larger skull size and greater sophistication of tools found near the fossils.
4. According to the fossil record, both chimps and humans diverged from a common ancestor at approximately the same time.
5. Accept all reasonable answers. *Sample Answer:* the location of the opening at the base of the skull, which shows how cervical vertebrae may have attached and therefore how the spine may have been positioned
6. *Sample answer:* jaw size, teeth size, brow position. A low brow, protruding mouth, and sloping forehead are three features considered more apelike than humanlike.

ONLINE Biology
HMHScience.com

Have students compare the features of different hominoid skulls in a virtual lab. at **HMHScience.com.**

Integrating Anthropology

In 2004, on the Indonesian island of Flores, scientists discovered bones, including a near complete skeleton, of a tiny bipedal human whose brain was the size of a chimpanzee's. The skeleton was of a 30-year-old female, and nearby were stone tools and bones of other individuals of the same species, which the scientists named *Homo floresiensis* and jokingly referred to as "hobbits." Also associated with these bones were those of an extinct, tiny elephant called Stegodon, which the Flores may have hunted.

What really caught scientists off guard was the age of the hominin: 18,000 years. Scientists speculate that the Flores human could have evolved from *Homo erectus,* which is known to have reached Java 1.6 million years ago, and that its small size is the result of inbreeding among a relatively small gene pool—a not uncommon evolutionary trend on isolated islands. Other scientists think that the Flores fossil may simply be a *Homo sapiens* that had microcephaly, a condition that causes the brain to be very small.

Assess and Reteach ▼

Assess Use the Section Self-Check or Section Quiz, both available at **HMHScience.com.**

Reteach Use **FIGURE 6.2** to review the material in this section. Have students identify distinguishing characteristics of each group.

Answers

A Contrast *Sample answer:* the jaw size and position relative to eyes and nose, teeth size, brow position

B Synthesize *Sample answer:* if the cranium becomes so large that it is too hard to carry around, or the larger brain does not confer reproductive success

CHAPTER REVIEW

GO ONLINE

Encourage students to go to **HMHScience.com** for a detailed review of each section, including visuals and vocabulary practice.

Online Student Resources, Vocabulary Practice Worksheet

CHAPTER 12 Summary

BIG IDEA Scientists use many types of data collection and experimentation to form hypotheses and theories about how life formed on Earth..

KEY CONCEPTS

12.1 The Fossil Record

Fossils are a record of life that existed in the past. Fossils can form in several different ways. The age of a fossil or rock can be determined by radiometric dating, which uses radioactive isotopes to determine the age of a fossil or the rock in which it is found. Through radiometric dating, scientists estimate that Earth is about 4.5 billion years old.

12.2 The Geologic Time Scale

The geologic time scale divides Earth's history based on major past events. Index fossils can be used along with radiometric dating to determine the age of a fossil or rock.

12.3 Origin of Life

The origin of life on Earth remains a puzzle. There are several hypotheses about the way early organic molecules appeared on Earth and about the way early cells may have formed. The discovery of ribozymes, RNA molecules that can catalyze reactions without the help of proteins, led to the hypothesis that RNA arose before DNA as the first genetic material on Earth.

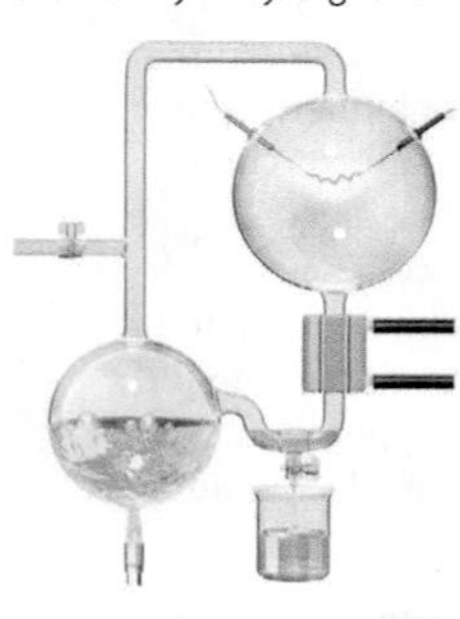

12.4 Early Single-Celled Organisms

Single-celled organisms existed 3.8 billion years ago. The first organisms on Earth were most likely anaerobic prokaryotes. The theory of endosymbiosis proposes that the first eukaryotic cells arose from a large prokaryote engulfing a smaller prokaryote.

The theories of autogeny and horizontal gene transfer provide alternate ideas of how more complex cell structure arose.

12.5 Radiation of Multicellular Life

Multicellular life evolved in distinct phases. During the Paleozoic era, members of every major animal group evolved within only a few million years. During the Mesozoic era, dinosaurs, flowering plants, birds, and mammals inhabited Earth. During the Cenozoic era, mammals, birds, fishes, and flowering plants diversified and flourished. Modern humans did not appear until 200,000 years ago.

12.6 Primate Evolution

Humans appeared late in Earth's history. Humans share a common ancestor with other primates. Primates include all mammals with flexible hands and feet, forward-looking eyes, and enlarged brains relative to their body size. The hominins include all species in the human lineage, both modern and extinct.

READING TOOLBOX SYNTHESIZE YOUR NOTES

Timeline Make a timeline noting the history of hominid evolution. Add details about characteristics of each hominid that is on your diagram.

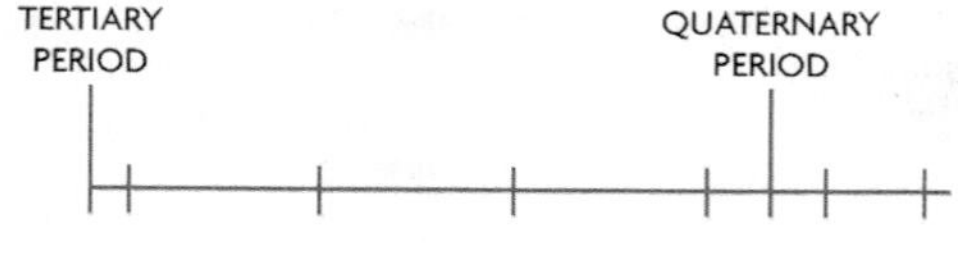

Concept Map Use a concept map to summarize hypotheses about the origin of life on Earth.

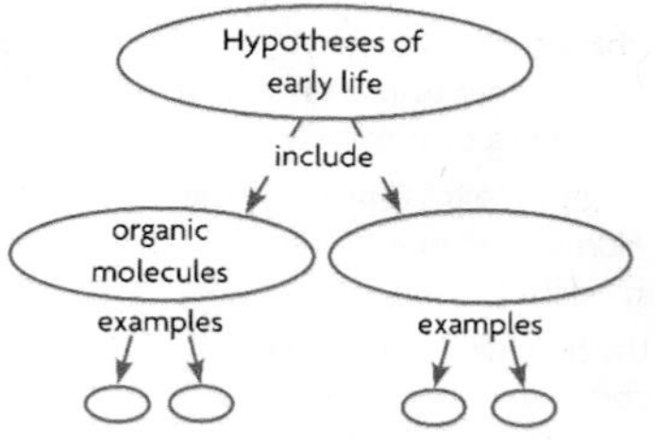

Reviewing Vocabulary

1. *Sample Answer:* Both relative dating and radiometric dating are methods of determining the age of artifacts or rock layer samples. Relative dating does this by comparing a sample's position in strata to that of other objects whose ages are known, while radiometric dating determines the absolute age of a sample based upon the decay of radioactive elements.
2. *Sample Answer:* Both an isotope and half-life are used in radiometric dating, but only radioactive isotopes can be used in radiometric dating. The half-life of an isotope is the time it takes for half of the isotope to decay to another element.
3. *Sample Answer:* Both eras and periods are units of time used to organize the geologic time scale. Eras consist of two or more periods. Periods are the most common time unit used in the geologic time scale.
4. *Sample Answer:* Cyanobacteria are prokaryotes. Endosymbiosis is a theory that suggests that prokaryotes may have absorbed other prokaryotes, such as precursors of mitochondria and chloroplasts, and evolved into eukaryotes.
5. *Sample Answer:* The Paleozoic was an era, the Cambrian a period within the Paleozoic. Both are units of the geologic time scale. In the Cambrian, life was limited to the ocean environment. By the middle of the Paleozoic, life had also moved onto land.
6. *Sample Answer:* Hominids are a subgroup of primates that can walk upright on two feet. Primates are an order of mammals with flexible hands and feet, forward-looking eyes, and large brains relative to body size. Primates also have arms that can rotate in a circle around their shoulder joint, and many primates have opposable thumbs.
7. reference point to date other fossils
8. shortest unit of time in the geologic time scale
9. RNA that acts like an enzyme
10. walks on two feet
11. Astronomers observed what appeared to be a "cloud" of gas and dust.
12. Isotopes are forms of the same element, differing only by the number of neutrons.

INTERACTIVE Review
HMHScience.com
GO ONLINE
Review Games • Concept Map • Section Self-Checks

12 Review

CHAPTER VOCABULARY

12.1 relative dating, radiometric dating, isotope, half-life
12.2 index fossil, geologic time scale, era, period, epoch
12.3 nebula, ribozyme
12.4 cyanobacteria, endosymbiosis
12.5 Paleozoic, Cambrian explosion, Mesozoic, Cenozoic
12.6 primate, prosimian, anthropoid, hominid, bipedal

Reviewing Vocabulary

Compare and Contrast

Describe one similarity and one difference between the two terms in each of the following pairs.

1. relative dating, radiometric dating
2. isotope, half-life
3. era, period
4. cyanobacteria, endosymbiosis
5. Paleozoic, Cambrian explosion
6. primate, hominid

Keep It Short

Write a short, precise phrase that describes the meaning of each vocabulary term below. For example, a short phrase to describe *geologic time scale* could be "organizes life's history."

7. index fossil
8. epoch
9. ribozyme
10. bipedal

READING TOOLBOX GREEK AND LATIN WORD ORIGINS

11. *Nebula* is a Latin word that means "cloud." Why do you think astronomers chose this word as a name for what they were observing in outer space?
12. The prefix *iso-* means "the same." How does this meaning relate to the definition of *isotope*?

Reviewing MAIN IDEAS

13. Fossils can form in several ways, one of which is by permineralization. Describe the process of permineralization and give an example of the type of fossil that may result.
14. Give an example of the way the concept of half-life is used in radiometric dating.
15. How are index fossils used in relative dating?
16. The geologic time scale organizes the history of Earth into eras, periods, and epochs. How are these units of time related to one another?
17. Compare and contrast the evidence that supports the two hypotheses describing how long, complex molecules that carry information, such as DNA, might have formed on early Earth.
18. What are two ways that cyanobacteria have changed the physical or chemical composition of Earth?
19. Summarize the evidence supporting each of the theories describing the origins of eukaryotic cells.
20. One evolutionary advantage of sexual reproduction is that it creates more genetic variation in a population than asexual reproduction. Why might this be an advantage?.
21. What are some criteria by which we can evaluate the relative complexity of a cell?
22. In which era did mammals, dinosaurs, and birds appear on Earth? What happened to these groups in the following era?
23. Humans, apes, monkeys, and lemurs are all examples of primates. What characteristics do all primates share?

Reviewing Main Ideas

13. Permineralization can occur if an organism is buried quickly after death. Additional layers of sediment add pressure, and water flows through over time to distribute minerals that replace those present in the organism's hard parts, such as bone. This process maintains the shape of the organism. The resulting fossil is rocklike, or petrified.
14. *Sample Answer:* By measuring the ratio of an unstable isotope such as carbon-14 with a stable one such as carbon-12, one can determine how much the carbon-14 has decayed. This information can then be applied the known half-life value to calculate how long this decay has been occurring, in other words, how old the substance is.
15. Because the approximate age of an index fossil is already known, other fossils found within the same or nearby strata can be dated on a relative time scale.
16. Eras (between ten million and hundreds of millions of years) are subdivided into periods (up to tens of millions of years), which are further subdivided into epochs (several million years).
17. In support of both hypotheses, scientists promoted polymerization by concentrating organic monomers. In frozen seawater experiments, this was achieved at very low temperatures with ice crystal formation, whereas Sidney Fox used high temperatures and particular substrates, such as clay.
18. Cyanobacteria, being photosynthetic, have produced oxygen for Earth's atmosphere and oceans, and have also deposited minerals.
19. The endosymbiotic theory is based on mitochondria and chloroplasts, which have characteristics (such as their own DNA and the ability to self-replicate) of independent prokaryotes. The autogenous theory is also based on these two structures, but refers to the infolding of membranes that occurs within them. The theory of horizontal gene transfer is based on the common exchange of genetic material between prokaryotes.
20. Genetic variation is advantageous because it increases the chances that some individuals will have genes that are beneficial for survival in a certain environment. Without genetic variation, the entire population is vulnerable to environmental change.
21. *Sample answer:* specific enzymes, metabolic pathways, ribosomes, cell membranes, the genetic code in DNA
22. Mammals, dinosaurs, and birds all appeared on Earth during the Mesozoic era. During this time, dinosaurs were first dominant, then became extinct. In the Cenozoic era, many mammals evolved, using the resources that became available once the dinosaurs were gone. Birds diversified during the Cenozoic era.
23. Primates make up a category of mammals with flexible hands and feet, forward-looking eyes, large brains relative to body size, and opposable thumbs.

Critical Thinking

24. Answers may vary. *Sample answer:* The horizontal transfer of genes is a proven phenomenon and may have increased cell complexity in addition to either of the other explanations.
25. There wasn't enough oxygen to support aerobes until after autotrophs had produced enough through photosynthesis.
26. Accept all reasonable answers. *Sample Answer:* Complex molecules could have formed by smaller molecules being dissolved in water and concentrated within a small space inside crystals of sea ice. Both the water and the ice would have protected the newly-formed complex molecules from extreme environmental conditions.
27. Yes. The fact that their brief simulation yielded more than half of the amino acids used by modern-day cells makes it reasonable to infer that reactions occurring on early Earth for billions of years could have worked in a similar way to produce the amino acids.

Interpreting Visuals

28. Accept all reasonable answers. *Sample Answer:* Within the past 7 million years, hominins have evolved from having small brains and large teeth to having larger brains and smaller teeth.
29. Only one representative of this species has been found, and in that case it was skull fragments (no jaw), which were pieced together by computer animation. It may have been impossible to tell how the spine was arranged beneath the base of the skull. One incomplete specimen is not enough to describe a species.
30. *Homo habilis* had many of the traits attributed to the members of the *Australopithecus* genus, such as a small brain, large teeth, and occasional bipedalism.

Critical Thinking

24. Analyze Some scientists propose that more than one of the theories given in Section 4 may be involved in the evolution of the eukaryotic cell. Explain how this might be possible.

25. Apply Why is it likely that autotrophs appeared on Earth before any aerobes, organisms that depended on oxygen?

26. Evaluate How does the frozen seawater hypothesis suggest that complex molecules that contain information, such as DNA, could have formed in spite of conditions on early Earth that would have inhibited their formation? How persuasive do you find the evidence supporting this hypothesis?

27. Evaluate Thirteen of the 20 amino acids used to make proteins in modern-day cells were made by Miller-Urey's simulation of early Earth's conditions. Do the results support Miller and Urey's hypothesis? Why or Why not?

Interpreting Visuals

The chart below shows when some human ancestors lived and traits that they had. Use the chart to answer the next three questions.

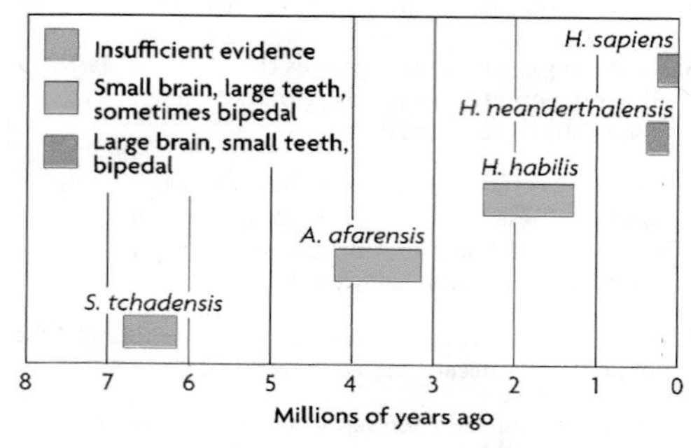

28. Summarize In one or two sentences, summarize the information in the chart.

29. Infer *Sahelanthropus tchadensis* was pictured in **FIGURE 6.5** of Section 6 as a three-dimensional computer reconstruction. Although skull fragments of this species have been found, the chart above shows that there is not enough evidence to describe the traits of *S. tchadensis.* Explain why this might be so. Consider the scientific process in your explanation.

30. Analyze Some scientists suggest that *Homo habilis* should be classified as *Australopithecus habilis.* Based upon the information in the chart, explain why this might be the case.

Analyzing Data Calculate Intervals

Both graphs show the rate of decay of chlorine-36, which changes into argon-36. Use the graphs to answer the next two questions.

GRAPH 1 OF CHLORINE-36 DECAY

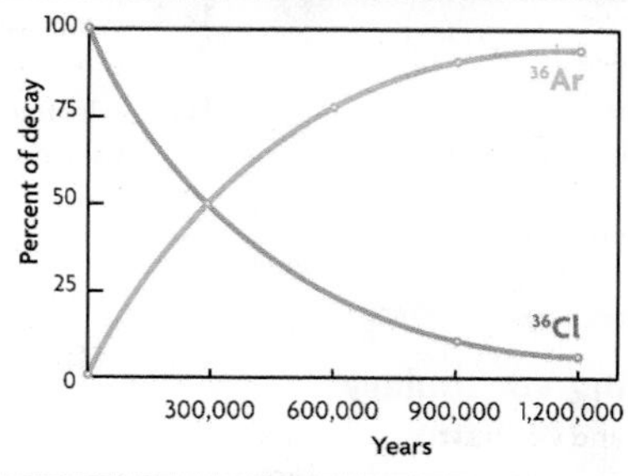

GRAPH 2 OF CHLORINE-36 DECAY

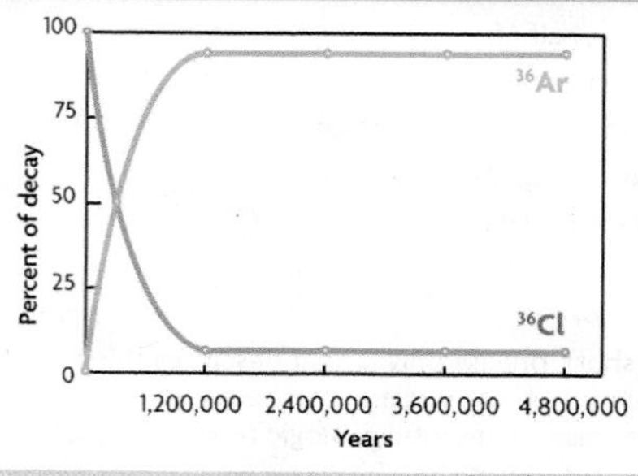

31. Analyze Which graph better shows the concept that the percentage change of ^{36}Cl and ^{36}Ar slows down dramatically over time? Explain.

32. Analyze From which graph can you more accurately determine the half-life in years of ^{36}Cl? Explain.

Making Connections

33. Write a Detailed Description Choose one of the periods in geological time and describe it in detail. Be sure to include vivid details about the organisms of the period.

34. Connect The time that the Tollund Man on the chapter opener lived was determined by radiocarbon dating. Why can't ^{14}C be used to date Burgess Shale fossils from the Cambrian period?

Analyzing Data

31. The second graph shows that the rates of decay of these isotopes slow down to an almost imperceptible rate after 1.2 million years because the *x*-axis scale goes beyond that time. The first graph's time scale is too short to show this dramatic change.
32. The first graph is easier to use for determining half-life. Because the *x*-axis features a narrower span of time, the point at which the isotopes are at 50 percent is much more precisely represented.

Standards-Based Assessment

Record your answers on a separate piece of paper.

MULTIPLE CHOICE

1 Sexual reproduction and mutation provides means for genetic variation in a population. Why is genetic variation an important element of natural selection?

A It ensures that all members of a population receive only traits that provide them with a survival advantage in their environment.

B It may provide an individual with traits that do not provide any survival advantage.

C It increases the chances that some individuals in a population will gain genes for traits that provide a survival advantage in a changing environment, enabling them to pass these genes to future generations.

D It increases the likelihood that a population will go extinct, providing more resources for other, stronger populations.

2

Percent of Native Bird Fossils in Hawaii

Excavated Section	^{14}C Dating (years before present)	% Bones from Non-native Species	% Bones from Native Species
I	390	100.0	0.0
II	770	98.8	1.2
III	4340	9.2	90.8
IV	7750	0.0	100.0

The table above shows the fossil evidence of birds in a section of cave wall in Hawaii. What can be determined from the data presented?

A A catastrophic event occurred between 770 and 4340 years ago.

B Native species out-competed non-native species.

C Most native species died out over 800 years ago.

D The disappearance of non-native species is a function of time.

3 In the evolution of eukaryotes, cells that contained mitochondria-like organelles had an advantage because they—

A could make use of photosynthesis

B could make use of more available energy

C had more DNA

D were protected from bacterial invasion

THINK THROUGH THE QUESTION

This question is really just asking about the way mitochondria can help a cell.

4 Many scientists believe that the cell parts that are now known as mitochondria and chloroplasts were early types of prokaryote cells. The theory of endosymbiosis suggests that early eukaryote cells formed when large prokaryote cells took in mitochondria or chloroplasts, enabling them to live inside the larger cell without harm. What advantage would the larger host prokaryote cell provide to the chloroplast?

A a stable, protected environment

B the ability to carry out photosynthesis

C access to sunlight

D ability to reproduce

5 The theory of endosymbiosis proposes that the chloroplasts present in some of today's eukaryotic cells descended from ancient cyanobacteria. Which piece of evidence supports this theory?

A Cyanobacteria are single-celled heterotrophs.

B Chloroplasts are much larger than today's prokaryotes.

C Chloroplasts are able to copy themselves independently of the cell.

D Chloroplasts help eukaryotic cells process energy more efficiently.

Standards-Based Assessment

The Standards-Based Assessment questions will help students prepare for their final examination in the course. If you wish to give students practice in coding their answers, look for the Standards-Based Assessment Answer Sheet at **HMHScience.com**. To give students practice under timed testing conditions, allow them five minutes per question.

Question	Answer	Depth of Knowledge	Cognitive Complexity
1	C	II	M
2	C	II	M
3	B	II	M
4	A	III	H
5	C	IV	H

KEY

Depth of Knowledge		Cognitive Complexity	
I	Recall	L	Low
II	Skill/Concept	M	Moderate
III	Strategic Thinking	H	High
IV	Extended Thinking		

Making Connections

33. Descriptions should include organisms that existed in the period, as well as overall trends such as extinctions and radiation.

34. Carbon-14 dating can only be used to age relatively recent fossils or remains because its half-life is only 5730 years. The amount of carbon-14 in a 500-million-year-old Burgess Shale fossil will be so minuscule that it will be imperceptible compared to the amount of carbon-12. An isotope with a much longer half-life must be used.

UNIT
4

Introduce

Tell students that people may be tempted to think of evolution as a theory about what happened in the past, and that it has no effect on them today. However, evolution involves the genetic changes in populations that occur over many generations.

Evolutionary change occurs most rapidly in organisms that reproduce quickly and in large numbers. For example, a mutation forms in a population of bacteria, and this mutation allows individuals to survive exposure to a certain drug. Through natural selection, that entire population of bacteria may become resistant to the drug. This change can occur within a time scale easily observable by humans, because bacteria produce several generations per day.

Viruses can also evolve quickly. The exchange of genetic material between different viral types results in constantly changing viruses. A virus that causes disease in a bird could mutate and infect a human. It could mutate again, evolving the ability to spread from one person to another. Ask

- How might people be affected by evolving populations of bacteria, insects, and viruses?
- How might human populations evolve in response to a changing world?

Drug-Resistant Bacteria—A Global Health Issue

A bicyclist falls, scrapes his knees, and within a few days is unable to walk. Soccer players with turf burns suddenly find themselves in the hospital with skin infections that require intravenous antibiotics. Why are these young, healthy athletes developing such serious infections?

Current News

Arrange for students to have Internet access so that they can look for stories involving modern-day evolution featured in the Current News section of BioZine at **HMHScience.com**. Have students consider these questions:

- What organisms are mentioned as being recently evolved?
- What evolutionary pressures are causing these changes?
- What is the nature of the adaptation involved?
- How long did it take for the evolutionary change to be noticed by scientists?
- What impact might these changes have on humans or the environment?

Staph Infections

These athletes were infected by *Staphylococcus aureus*, or "staph." Staph is a common bacteria that most people carry on the surface of their skin and in their nose. To cause an infection, staph bacteria must get inside your body. The scrapes athletes commonly get provide an ideal entrance.

Serious problems due to staph infections used to be rare. Doctors would prescribe antibiotics, such as penicillin, to kill the staph bacteria. Ordinary staph infections can still be treated this way. The athletes in our examples did not have ordinary infections. These athletes' scrapes were infected by methicillin-resistant *Staphylococcus aureus* (MRSA). This bacteria strain is one of many that has evolved resistance to antibiotics.

MRSA on the Rise

Percent of infections that are resistant

0, 10, 20, 30, 40, 50, 60, 70, 80, 90, 100

1987, 1991, 1995, 1999, 2003

Source: NNIS System and Centers for Disease Control and Prevention

Drug-Resistant Bacteria

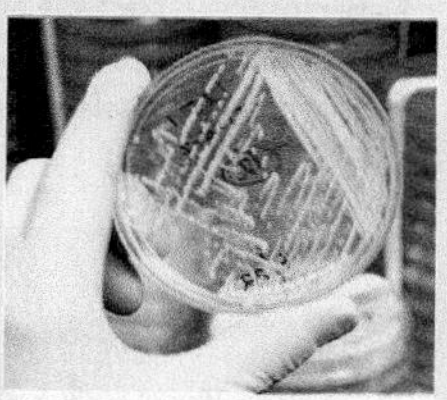

This petri dish contains *Staphylococcus aureus* bacteria.

Bacteria that can survive antibiotic treatment are called drug-resistant bacteria. Some bacteria have resistance for one particular antibiotic, some have resistance for several, and a few cannot be treated with any known antibiotic.

MRSA can resist an entire class of antibiotics. Patients with an MRSA infection must often be treated with what doctors call "the drug of last resort," vancomycin. Vancomycin is a drug that must be given intravenously. Not surprisingly, doctors began to see cases of vancomycin-resistant *Staphylococcus aureus* (VRSA) in 1997. By 2010, vancomycin-resistant bacteria were being discovered in the droppings of one out of ten seagulls, leading scientists to postulate that migrating birds may play a role in spreading drug-resistant "superbugs."

Staph isn't the only type of bacteria that is making a comeback with drug-resistant strains. In the mid-twentieth century, antibiotics nearly wiped out tuberculosis (TB). But in the 1990s, TB began to approach epidemic numbers again, and now it kills more than 2 million people every year. Drug-resistant TB kills thousands. Drug-resistant strains of cholera and bubonic plague also have been reported.

How Does Drug Resistance Evolve?

When you take antibiotics for a bacterial infection, most bacteria may be killed right away, but a few will likely survive. Antibiotics leave behind the more resistant bacteria to survive and reproduce. When they reproduce, the genes that make them resistant are passed on to their offspring. Some bacteria reproduce rapidly—*E. coli*, for example, doubles its population every 20 minutes.

In addition to their ability to reproduce quickly, populations of bacteria evolve rapidly. Bacteria use plasmids—small loops of DNA—to transfer genetic material between individual cells. This process is called conjugation. Some plasmids pass on resistance for one particular antibiotic. Others can transfer resistance for several antibiotics at once.

What characteristics do resistant bacteria pass on to their offspring? Some have cell membranes through which antibiotics cannot easily pass. Others have pumps that remove antibiotics once they enter the cell. Some can even produce enzymes that attack the antibiotic drugs themselves.

Expanding the Textbook

Have students go to BioZine at **HMHScience.com** to read more about infections caused by drug-resistant bacteria and how they have become a global health issue. Students should take notes on the information and come to class prepared to discuss drug resistance as a global problem. Have students identify diseases that are becoming more difficult to treat because of drug resistance and where outbreaks have occurred.

You could extend the discussion to include the role that people play in the development of drug resistance. **Ask**

- How has the use of antibiotics in farm animals contributed to drug resistance?
- How common are antibiotics in everyday products?
- What is the appropriate use of antibiotics?

Students can research how the use of antibiotics in humans, pets, and farm animals is changing.

Vocabulary of Drug-Resistant Bacteria

Students may not be familiar with all of the terms used to discuss drug-resistant bacteria.

bacteria—tiny, single-celled prokaryotic organisms. Many bacteria are helpful, but some cause serious infectious diseases.

selective pressure—the influence of some factor on natural selection, resulting in one group of organisms being favored over another. Antibiotics cause a selective pressure by killing susceptible bacteria, allowing antibiotic-resistant bacteria to survive and reproduce.

conjugation—a type of bacterial recombination in which organisms exchange genetic material through cell-to-cell contact. Bacteria can pass antibiotic resistance to other bacteria through conjugation.

antibiotic—a substance that destroys or inhibits bacterial growth and is used to treat diseases caused by bacteria.

penicillin—an antibiotic drug that is derived from penicillium molds or produced synthetically and used to treat various infections and diseases. It affects bacterial enzymes, inhibiting cell wall synthesis and causing the cell wall of the bacteria to break down.

methicillin—a synthetic antibiotic that is related to penicillin and is used to treat infections caused by staphylococci.

antibiotic resistance—a trait in microorganisms, especially bacteria, that enables them to survive in the presence of antibiotics.

plasmid—circular DNA that replicates within a cell independently of chromosomal DNA and is found in many bacterial strains. Plasmids are used in genetic engineering, gene cloning, gene therapy, and recombinant protein and DNA production research.

bacteriophage—a virus that infects a bacterium by attaching to it and inserting its genetic material into the bacterial cell. The bacteriophage may then destroy, or lyse, the bacterial cell.

Take It Further

According to the Centers for Disease Control and Prevention (CDC), over the last decade almost every type of bacteria has become stronger and less responsive to antibiotic treatment. Diseases such as gonorrhea, head lice, malaria, streptococcus pneumonia, and typhoid fever are connected to antibiotic resistance and threaten public health. As a result, antibiotic resistance is among the CDC's top concerns.

Antibiotic-resistant bacteria can be spread throughout a population in various ways. Some bacteria are dispersed to new locations by wind or water. Modern transportation enables bacteria to travel great distances quickly. People, especially those in an enclosed space such as an airplane, can spread the bacteria when they cough or sneeze or when they touch a person or object without first washing their hands.

Using proper sanitary practices, such as thorough hand washing with soap and water, can reduce the spread of bacteria. In hospitals, isolation is used to help keep antibiotic-resistant bacteria from spreading from one person to another. People visiting isolation rooms wear gowns and sometimes gloves and masks. An antibacterial cleanser may be provided in hospital rooms for use by visitors.

Point out that, to help reduce the speed with which antibiotic resistance develops, the overall use of antibiotics needs to be decreased. Antibiotics should be used only when necessary for bacterial infections and not for viral infections. All of an antibiotic prescription should be taken as directed and never shared.

Fighting Back

Some scientists are trying to develop ways to treat patients without killing the bacteria that are making them sick. Instead, they target the toxins produced by bacteria. If the bacteria are not harmed by the treatment, no selective pressure is produced. Scientists hope that by using this approach, bacteria will be slower to evolve defense mechanisms against the antibiotics. Other scientists hope to fight back by using bacteria's ancient rival, bacteriophages, which are viruses that infect bacteria.

CAREERS

Evolutionary Biologist in Action

DR. RICHARD LENSKI

TITLE Professor, Microbial Ecology, Michigan State University

EDUCATION Ph.D., Zoology, University of North Carolina, Chapel Hill

If you want to observe evolution in action, you must find populations that reproduce quickly. Dr. Richard Lenski, a professor at Michigan State University, has done just that. Dr. Lenski studies populations of *E. coli* bacteria, which he grows in flasks filled with a sugary broth. These bacteria produce about seven generations each day. Dr. Lenski has now observed more than 30,000 generations of *E. coli*.

The rapid rate of *E. coli* reproduction allows Dr. Lenski to watch evolution take place. Dr. Lenski can subject each generation of bacteria to the same environmental stresses, such as food shortages or antibiotics. He then can compare individuals from more recent generations with their ancestors, which he keeps in his laboratory freezer. By comparing generations in this way, Dr. Lenski can study how the population has evolved.

When Dr. Lenski began his research in 1988, watching evolution in action was still new. Now, many evolutionary biologists are following in his footsteps.

Read More >> at HMHScience.com

TECHNOLOGY STEM

New Drug Delivery System

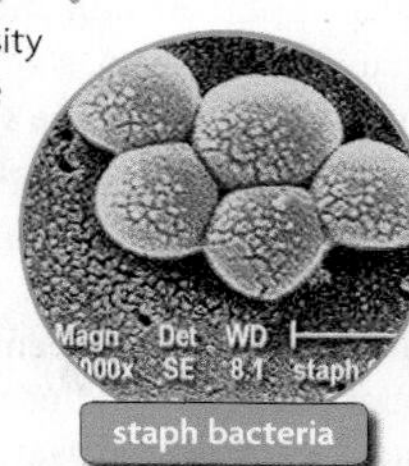
staph bacteria

Researchers at Yeshiva University decided to take on one of the most difficult bacterial infections of all, methicillin-resistant staph. They have developed a treatment using nanoparticles that can be delivered directly to a wound on the skin.

- Tiny nanoparticles carry nitric oxide (NO), which helps the immune system respond to infection.
- The nanoparticles are applied topically, to deep, infected skin abscesses.
- The nanoparticles absorb water, swell, and release NO. NO kills bacteria and dilates blood vessels, to speed healing.

Because the bacteria are "eating" the nanoballs, cell wall adaptations that once kept antibiotics out are no longer an obstacle.

Read More >> at HMHScience.com

Unanswered Questions

Some important research questions involving drug-resistant bacteria include the following:

- Can plasmids or bacteriophages be used in vaccines to fight bacteria?
- Are bacteria being exposed to antibiotics in sewage systems and evolving resistant strains there?
- How do antibacterial soaps and household cleaners contribute to the evolution of drug-resistant bacteria?
- Can drug-resistant bacteria be transferred from domestic animals to humans through food?

Read More >> at HMHScience.com

Bio Bytes

Have students go to BioZine at **HMHScience.com** to read Bio Bytes. Have them write a brief paragraph that addresses the following: Using information and examples from this unit, explain how the information in Bio Bytes can be viewed from an evolutionary perspective.

UNIT 5 Ecology

BIOZINE
HMHScience.com

Climate Change— Changing the Planet
TECHNOLOGY **Deep Sea Sediment Coring**
CAREER **Oceanographer**

Unit Project

Purpose **Consider an endangered species in the context of its benefit to biodiversity and describe conservation or recovery plans for the endangered species.**

Overview Students investigate an endangered species in their state and learn what measures are being taken to help the species survive. Students will

- search Internet, textbook, and/or library resources about an endangered species in their state
- analyze an existing recovery plan for the endangered species
- formulate a plan for improvement or support of the existing recovery plan, including how it would best be implemented
- prepare a report in an illustrated magazine-style article about their findings

Preparation Make a copy of the project description and rubric for each student. Tell students that their article will be scored for organization and completeness.

Project Management Allow three weeks for the completion of the project. Have students check in weekly for progress monitoring.

Online Student Resources Unit 5 Project

CHAPTER 13 Instruction and Intervention Support

Principles of Ecology

① Core Instruction

The **Core Instruction** resources below can be used for all students. Core instruction should be followed by ongoing assessment to determine which students need further help.

Available in both English and Spanish

Available Online

Section	Instruction	PRINT	ONLINE	Labs
13.1	Textbook **Ecologists Study Relationships**	■	●	Random Sampling **QuickLab** Quadrat Sampling **Virtual Lab** Estimating Population Size
	PowerPresentation and Notes 13.1		●	
13.2	Textbook **Biotic and Abiotic Factors**	■	●	Abiotic Factors and Plant Growth (Design Your Own)
	PowerPresentation and Notes 13.2		●	
13.3	Textbook **Energy in Ecosystems**	■	●	Build a Terrarium
	PowerPresentation and Notes 13.3		●	
13.4	Textbook **Food Chains and Food Webs**	■	●	**Video Lab** Ecosystem Change
	Animated Biology Build a Food Web		●	
	PowerPresentation and Notes 13.4		●	
13.5	Textbook **Cycling of Matter**	■	●	Nitrogen Fixation Interdependence of Plants and Animals (Probeware Lab)
	Animated Biology Water Cycle		●	
	PowerPresentation and Notes 13.5		●	
13.6	Textbook **Pyramid Models**	■	●	
	That's Amazing! Video Inquiry Vegetarian Alligators		●	
	Teaching Visuals Biomass Pyramid and Pyramid of Numbers (Fig. 6.2, 6.3)		●	
	PowerPresentation and Notes 13.6		●	

Additional online resources available for this chapter include **Interactive Whiteboard Resources.**

GO ONLINE! for all your teacher resources at HMHScience.com

2 Support and Intervention

Support and Intervention resources are useful for students who need targeted help beyond the Core Instruction

Resources	PRINT	ONLINE
Assess and Reteach (TE wrap)	■	●
Concept Map		●
Interactive Reader	■	●
Interactive Review Games		●
Section Self-Checks		●
Study Guide B		●
Vocabulary Practice Worksheets		●

3 Specialized Support

Students who need more intensive personalized intervention benefit from **Specialized Support** resources.

Resources	PRINT	ONLINE
Chapter Audio Files		●
Differentiated Instruction Inclusion, Below Level, and English Learners (TE wrap)	■	●
ELL Strategies	■	●
Modified Lesson Plans for English Learners		●
Reinforcement Worksheets		●
Study Guide A		●

Extension and Assessment

Enrichment and Challenge

Resources	PRINT	ONLINE
Active Reading Worksheets		●
Data Analysis Practice Worksheet		●
Differentiated Instruction Pre-AP (TE Wrap)	■	●
Pre-AP Activity Design a Mark-Recapture Study, Biomass in Coral Reef Ecosystems		●
The Inside Story and **Take It Further** (TE wrap)	■	●
Unit Project		●
WebLinks		●
WebQuest Keystone Species (13.2)		●

Assessment

Resources	PRINT	ONLINE
Alternative Assessment		●
Chapter Tests A and B		●
Diagnostic Test		●
ExamView Banks		●
Extended Response Test		●
Online Assessment System		●
Section Quizzes		●
Standards-Based Assessment	■	●

CHAPTER 13

Chapter Overview

- **Section 1** introduces ecology, the levels of organization in an ecosystem, and ecological research methods.
- **Section 2** discusses biotic and abiotic factors in ecosystems.
- **Section 3** describes the flow of energy in ecosystems.
- **Section 4** describes the flow of matter and energy within ecosystems using the food chain and food web models.
- **Section 5** summarizes Earth's biogeochemical cycles and their relationship to ecosystems.
- **Section 6** explains the distribution of energy and matter in an ecosystem using pyramid models.

▼ Focus and Motivate

How does this bird interact with its ecosystem?

Students may state the obvious answer, the bird gets food. **Ask,** In what other ways does the anhinga (an-HING-guh) interact with its environment? The environment provides water, shelter, oxygen, and other materials needed to support life and reproduction.

BIOZINE
HMHScience.com

Students can access BioZine at **HMHScience.com** to receive updates to featured topics in the book.

CHAPTER 13 Principles of Ecology

BIG IDEA Living things interact with other organisms and with their environment.

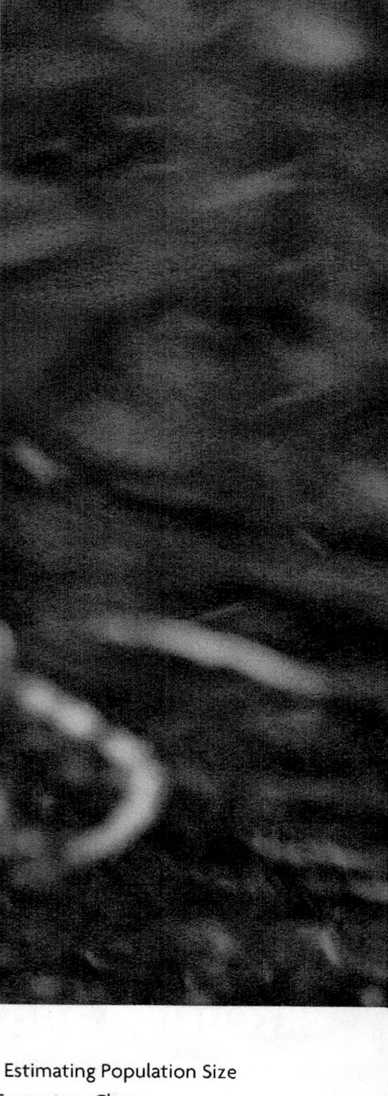

ONLINE BIOLOGY HMHScience.com

ONLINE Labs
- **QuickLab** Quadrat Sampling
- Abiotic Factors and Plant Growth
- Random Sampling
- Build a Terrarium
- Nitrogen Fixation
- Interdependence of Plants and Animals
- **Virtual Lab** Estimating Population Size
- **Video Lab** Ecosystem Change

Student Activity

Purpose **Have teams of students model the flow of energy through food chains. Each team makes a food chain using pictures of organisms provided.**

Materials (per team)

Each team will need pictures of various producers and consumers. Examples:

- **Marine food chain** phytoplankton (for example, diatoms), zooplankton (for example, crustacean larvae), seaweed (green or brown algae), fish, sea turtle, heron, dolphin, shark
- **Woodland food chain** grass, fern, tree, insect, insect larva (for example, caterpillar), snail, spider, mouse, rabbit, weasel, sparrow, owl, fox

Introduce Describe how to make a food chain with the pictures, emphasizing that a food chain is a one-to-one linking of a producer and a series of consumers. Tell students that there are several different food chains possible with the organisms you provided, but that all food chains start with a producer.

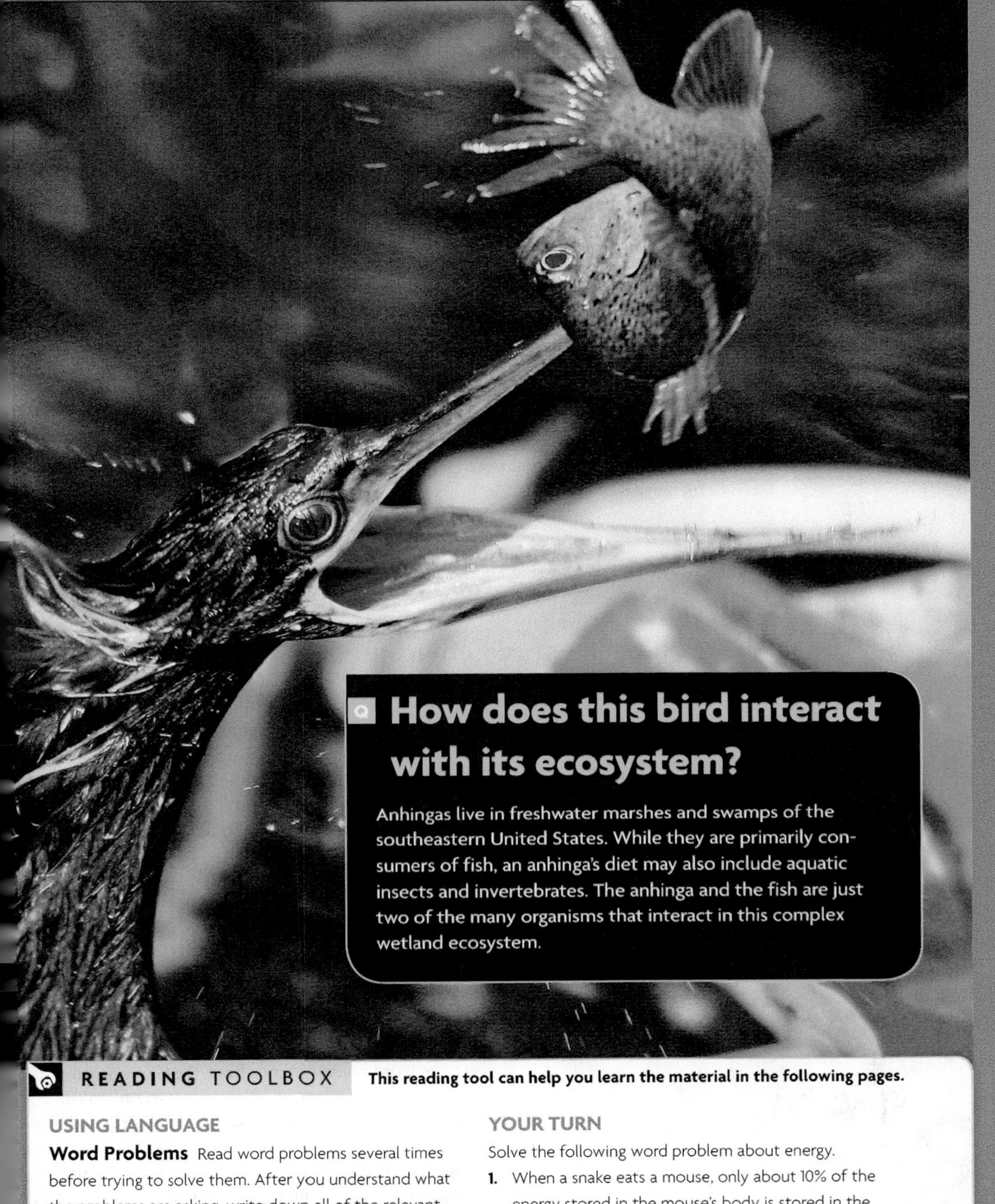

How does this bird interact with its ecosystem?

Anhingas live in freshwater marshes and swamps of the southeastern United States. While they are primarily consumers of fish, an anhinga's diet may also include aquatic insects and invertebrates. The anhinga and the fish are just two of the many organisms that interact in this complex wetland ecosystem.

READING TOOLBOX **This reading tool can help you learn the material in the following pages.**

USING LANGUAGE

Word Problems Read word problems several times before trying to solve them. After you understand what the problems are asking, write down all of the relevant information on a piece of paper. Then, use the mathematical processes that apply to the situation.

YOUR TURN

Solve the following word problem about energy.

1. When a snake eats a mouse, only about 10% of the energy stored in the mouse's body is stored in the snake. If the body of a mouse contains 2000 kcal of energy, how much energy is stored in the snake?

Discuss Have teams critique one another's food chain. Make sure food chains are realistic. If time allows, arrange the food chains into a food web, showing how one food chain overlaps another.

Ask, How does energy flow in a food chain? Energy is first captured by a producer and then flows from each organism that is eaten to the organism that eats it.

Ask, Is all the energy captured by the producers kept within a food chain? No, at each step of the way, energy is lost as heat or as other waste material.

Activate Prior Knowledge

Students were introduced to the idea of systems as a unifying theme in biology. Ecologists study ecosystems. **Ask**

- What is a system? smaller parts working together, organized into a larger whole
- What systems are you a part of? Students will probably think in terms of social constructs, such as a school system.

Focus on the idea that, as animals, humans are part of an ecosystem. We interact with the environment to get energy and materials.

Preview Vocabulary

Greek and Latin Word Origins

Two word roots are important to the vocabulary in this chapter.

The Latin root *vorare* means "to swallow or devour." The emphasis is on the act of eating and what is eaten:

herbivore *omnivore*
carnivore *detritivore*

The word *trophic* comes from the Greek root *trephein,* "to nourish." Point out that the emphasis is different. For example, the words

autotroph *heterotroph*

are broader in scope. The term *trophic level* refers to the source of nutrition for a whole group of organisms.

English Learners Students will see vocabulary words from everyday language that are used as scientific terminology:

producer *consumer*
community *specialist*
generalist

Give students a few minutes to check the words in the *Multilanguage Glossary.* Discuss how the meaning in this context differs from everyday use.

Answers

1. 10% x 2000 kcal = 200 kcal

Chapter 13: Principles of Ecology 387

▼ Plan and Prepare

Activate Prior Knowledge **Ask,** What does the word *relationship* mean to you? family, friends, team, job In each instance, the word suggests a connection, an *interaction,* typically with other human beings. An ecologist studies the close connection all organisms have with their natural environment. This is not just how the environment affects the organism, but also how the organism affects the environment as well as other organisms in that environment.

▼ Teach

Vocabulary

Word Origins The root of **environment** is from the French *environner,* meaning "to encircle." **Environmental science** considers not just the natural world but also the effects of human activity, including social institutions, cultural attitudes, agricultural practices, and industrial conditions. **Ecology** focuses specifically on the interdependent relationship between living things and their environment.

13.1 Ecologists Study Relationships

KEY CONCEPT **Ecology is the study of the relationships among organisms and their environment.**

VOCABULARY
- ecology
- community
- ecosystem
- biome

MAIN IDEAS
- Ecologists study environments at different levels of organization.
- Ecological research methods include observation, experimentation, and modeling.

Connect to Your World

Water birds such as anhingas, along with a variety of other plants and animals, rely on the presence of wetlands for their survival. How might the loss of wetland areas affect these aquatic species? Learning about organisms and how they interact with one another, with other species, and with their environment is what the study of ecology is all about.

MAIN IDEA

Ecologists study environments at different levels of organization.

Over their life cycle, Pacific salmon are the main food source for more than 140 species of wildlife, including grizzly bears, as shown in **FIGURE 1.1.** If they are not eaten, their bodies return vital nutrients back into the river system, some of which are used by plants to grow. In addition to their role in the health of river systems, salmon are also important to the Pacific Northwest's economy. Today, many species of wild Pacific salmon are threatened with extinction due to competition from hatchery fish, blocked river paths, and loss of spawning grounds. As salmon populations decline, how are other species affected? What effect would the loss of salmon have on a local and a global scale? These are the types of questions ecologists are trying to answer.

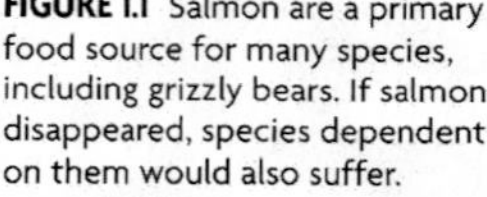

FIGURE 1.1 Salmon are a primary food source for many species, including grizzly bears. If salmon disappeared, species dependent on them would also suffer.

What Is Ecology?

Ecology is the study of the interactions among living things, and between living things and their surroundings. The word *ecology* comes from the Greek word *oikos,* which means "house." This word origin makes sense if you think of Earth as home and all organisms as members of Earth's household. Ernst Haeckel, a German biologist, coined the term *ecology* in 1866 to encourage biologists to consider the ways organisms interact. Until that time, most scientists studied a plant or an animal as though it existed in isolation—as if it did not affect its surroundings, and its surroundings did not affect it.

Differentiated Instruction

ENGLISH LEARNERS

Offer students a few questions to guide their reading of the section. For example:

- What is ecology?
- What types of relationships and interactions does an ecologist study?
- What are some ways an ecologist can get information about an ecosystem?

Have them study the section, close their books, and write answers to the questions.

Teacher Toolkit, Section C, Questions to Guide Reading

BELOW LEVEL

Students can preview each section, using this strategy:

- Predict what the section is about, using the headings.
- Locate key terms.
- Add details and definitions as they read.
- Note how the text supports the section's main ideas, summarizing the main ideas in their own words.

Teacher Toolkit, Section C, PLAN

Levels of Organization

Ecologists study nature on different levels, from a local to a global scale. These levels, shown in **FIGURE 1.2**, reveal the complex relationships found in nature.

- **Organism** An organism is an individual living thing, such as an alligator.
- **Population** A population is a group of the same species that lives in one area, such as all the alligators that live in a swamp.
- **Community** A **community** is a group of different species that live together in one area, such as groups of alligators, turtles, birds, fish, and plants that live together in the Florida Everglades.
- **Ecosystem** An **ecosystem** includes all of the organisms as well as the climate, soil, water, rocks, and other nonliving things in a given area. Ecosystems can vary in size. An entire ecosystem may exist within a decaying log, which in turn may be part of a larger wetland ecosystem.
- **Biome** A **biome** (BY-OHM) is a major regional or global community of organisms. Biomes are usually characterized by the climate conditions and plant communities that thrive there.

Ecologists study relationships within each level of organization and also between levels. For example, researchers may study the relationships within a population of alligators, as well as the relationships between alligators and turtles in a community.

Apply **What level of organization describes a flock of pigeons in a park?**

READING TOOLBOX

TAKING NOTES

Use a diagram to take notes on the levels of organization.

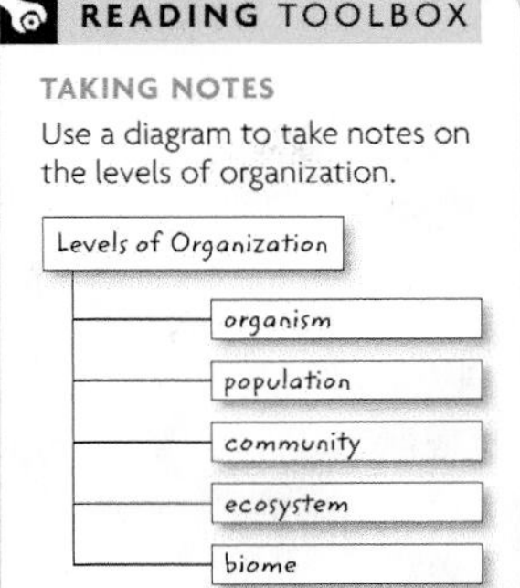

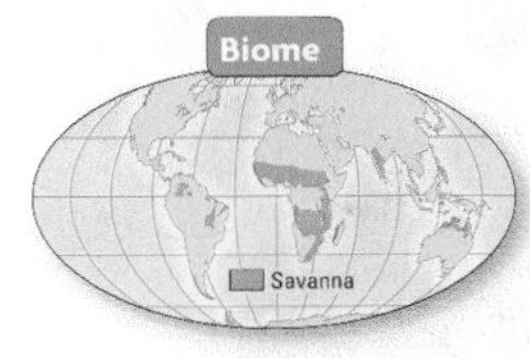

FIGURE 1.2 Levels of Organization

The Florida Everglades is an example of the subtropical savanna biome. Many organisms live in this aquatic ecosystem.

Integrating Earth Science

Wetlands play important roles that go beyond just supporting diverse biological communities. Wetlands act as nature's sponge. They purify water by removing silt and filtering toxins. Wetlands also hold floodwaters. In coastal areas, they help stabilize shorelines and can reduce storm damage. The significant loss of wetlands along the U.S. Gulf Coast exacerbated the effects of Hurricane Katrina in 2005.

TEACH FROM VISUALS

FIGURE 1.2 Use the illustration to walk through the different levels of organization that ecologists study. The organism is one individual and represents a single species. The population also represents a single species but includes more than one individual. **Ask**

- What populations besides alligators could you find in this ecosystem? grasses, mangroves, osprey, herons, egrets, turtles, fish
- What do these different populations taken together represent? a community
- What does the ecosystem include in addition to the living things you see here? physical conditions; nonliving components, such as water, soil, sunlight

Answers

A Apply population

BELOW LEVEL

Remind students that mnemonic devices, or memory aids, can help with recall. For example, to remember the levels of organization, ask students to come up with a sentence that uses the first letter of each level. Example: Overpopulation crowds everybody. To help students interpret the relationship between levels, discuss the significance of the nested circles in **FIGURE 1.2.**

ENGLISH LEARNERS

Have students extend the note-taking diagram shown in their textbook to include a word square for each of the levels of organization. The first square includes the term accompanied by the word's translation in the student's native language. All of these terms appear in the *Multilanguage Glossary*. In the remaining squares, students draw a picture, rewrite the definition in their own words, and then write the English definition (also found in the *Multilanguage Glossary*).

Teacher Toolkit, Section C, Word Squares

▼ Teach *continued*

History of Science

During the 1700s and 1800s, many scientists, including **Charles Darwin** and **Alfred Russell Wallace,** traveled to different parts of the world to catalog new species. The work of Darwin and Wallace made clear the connection between the physical characteristics of a place and the types of species found there—**biogeography.** The British botanist **Arthur Tansley** coined the word **ecosystem** in 1935 to describe the interactive system that exists *between* the living and nonliving components of an environment. From 1903 to 1907, Tansley had coordinated field studies that surveyed and mapped the types of vegetation found across the British Isles. As an educator, he strongly advocated fieldwork as being necessary to the education of any good ecologist.

Take It Further

Prairie dogs are not only an important food source for the black-footed ferret but also a critical part of the **prairie ecosystem.** Prairie ecosystems that have healthy prairie-dog populations support a greater number of animals overall and have greater species diversity than prairies without them. **Ask,** In what ways, other than as a food source, might prairie dogs support other species? Their burrows provide shelter for other animals. In digging burrows, prairie dogs increase the nitrogen content in the soil and open up more area for oxygen and water absorption, all of which aid plant growth.

Answers

A Apply A scientist might directly survey mountain goats by using binoculars or might indirectly survey them by looking for signs of feces (commonly called *scat*). A scientist could also use radio telemetry to track the goats.

MAIN IDEA

Ecological research methods include observation, experimentation, and modeling.

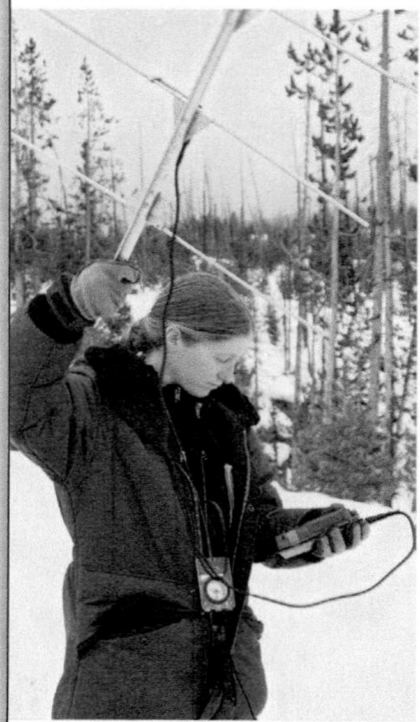

FIGURE 1.3 Much of the data gathered by ecologists results from long hours of observation in the field. This ecologist is using radio telemetry to track gray wolves.

Scientists rely on a variety of methods and tools to conduct research. Tools can range from a simple tape measure used to find an organism's size to a sophisticated computer system used to create a model of an entire ecosystem.

Observation

Observation is the act of carefully watching something over time. Such observations may occur over short or long periods of time. Long-term studies are a key part of a scientist's toolkit because most environmental changes happen over a long period of time. For example, studies of prairie-dog populations are helping scientists to determine which locations are most appropriate for the reintroduction of the black-footed ferret. The black-footed ferret is an endangered species that relies on the prairie dog as its main food source.

One way that scientists monitor and observe populations is by conducting surveys. Visual surveys may be direct or indirect.

- Direct surveys are used for species that are easy to follow. In these surveys, scientists watch animals either with the naked eye or with tools such as binoculars or scopes.
- Indirect surveys are used for species that are difficult to track. In these surveys, scientists search for other signs of its presence, such as feces or a recent kill.

Radio telemetry is another method used by scientists to monitor populations. Scientists fit an animal with a radio collar that emits a signal and then use the signal to track the animal's movement, as shown in **FIGURE 1.3.** This practice is especially useful when studying a species that has a broad range, such as the gray wolf.

In addition to observing the activities of a species, scientists often determine the species' population size. Rather than count every individual organism in a large study area, scientists can sample the population instead. Mark-recapture is a method used by scientists to estimate the population size of mobile organisms. For example, to monitor prairie-dog populations, scientists capture and mark prairie dogs with ear tags and then release them back into the wild. When scientists later repeat the survey, the captured prairie dogs will include both marked and unmarked animals. Scientists calculate the ratio of marked to unmarked animals and use this value to estimate the total population size.

To monitor plant populations, scientists use a method called quadrat sampling. In this method, quadrats, or rectangular frames, are randomly placed on the study site. To determine plant population numbers, scientists identify and count the number of plants within each randomly selected plot. The total number of counted plants is then plugged into a mathematical formula to determine the plant population of the entire study site.

A Apply **How might a scientist use observation to study a population of mountain goats? Explain your answer.**

Differentiated Instruction

PRE-AP

Have students use a graphic organizer to compare the advantages and disadvantages of direct animal surveys with those of indirect surveys. To get students started, have them consider these questions:

- How invasive is the technique to the animal?
- How easy is it to identify individuals?
- Is there the possibility of counting individuals more than once?
- How might weather conditions affect observations?

Teacher Toolkit, Section C, T-Chart

TEACH WITH TECHNOLOGY

Using a mapping database such as Google Earth or NASA's Visible Earth, print out images of natural areas in your vicinity. Ask students to identify ecosystems from these images. Have students suggest strategies for mapping the vegetation in an area.

QUICKLAB SAMPLING

Quadrat Sampling

Ecologists often use quadrats—square or rectangular grids—to collect data about population numbers in an ecosystem. In this lab, you will use a quadrat to collect accurate and precise data on three "species."

PROBLEM What is the population size of each species?

PROCEDURE

1. Obtain a quadrat frame. Measure, calculate, and record the area of the quadrat.
2. Stand at the edge of the area you will sample and randomly throw your quadrat.
3. Move your quadrat so that it does not overlap with any other quadrat. Each different object represents a different species. Count how many individuals of each species are in your quadrat and record your data in a data table. Repeat this procedure three times.
4. Combine your data with that of your classmates. Find the average number of each species for all of the samples. Obtain the area of the sampling plot from your teacher. Calculate how many quadrats would fit in the area of the sampling plot. Multiply this by the average number of each species found in one quadrat to estimate the population of each species.

MATERIALS

- quadrat
- meter stick
- calculator
- objects to count

ANALYZE AND CONCLUDE

1. **Analyze** Compare your population estimate for each species to the actual number that your teacher provides. Is the estimate accurate? Why or why not?
2. **Evaluate** How can you ensure that your estimate of population size will be as accurate as possible?

Experimentation

Scientists may perform experiments in the lab or in the field. There are benefits and drawbacks to each type of experiment. While a lab experiment gives the researcher more control, the artificial setting does not reflect the complex interactions that occur in nature. A field experiment, on the other hand, gives a more accurate picture of how organisms interact in a natural setting. However, in a field study, it is more difficult to determine cause and effect due to the large number of factors at work in nature.

A lab experiment is conducted in a controlled, indoor environment. This isolation helps scientists to focus each experiment on a very specific part of an ecosystem, such as a single organism. For example, to find out how climate change affects the growth rates of plants, scientists can grow plants in a lab and adjust temperature settings. Working in a lab allows scientists to control variables in a way that would not be possible in the field.

A field experiment is performed where the organisms live. Like lab experiments, field experiments also have controls and manipulated variables. For example, to determine how browsing by deer affects plant and small-animal communities, scientists might fence off large study plots to keep out the deer. By monitoring the fenced and unfenced plots over a period of time, scientists can determine whether deer significantly change the areas in which they browse for food.

Contrast **What is the difference between a lab experiment and a field experiment?**

CONNECT TO

SCIENTIFIC METHOD

As you learned in the chapter **Biology in the 21st Century**, all fields of science, including ecology, use scientific methods to investigate and answer scientific questions. Applied ecology uses the principles of ecology along with scientific methods to solve environmental problems.

BELOW LEVEL

To illustrate the importance of a random sample, draw a square on a sheet of acetate and scatter paper dots across the square. Use a second sheet of acetate to cover the dots. Place on an overhead projector. With a small cardboard quadrat, show how different placements of the quadrat can affect the estimate. Discuss what would happen to the estimate if the quadrat were placed only where there were lots of dots to count. **Ask,** What is it called if a person's own preferences influence a choice? bias

PRE-AP

Calculations of population density will be covered in **Interactions in Ecosystems**. **Ask,** Knowing the size of a population for a given area, how could you predict the size of a population for a similar but much larger area? Calculate the average number of individuals per unit of area and apply to the larger area.

QUICKLAB

Time 15 minutes

Purpose Estimate population sizes by quadrat sampling.

LAB MANAGEMENT

- Conduct the lab indoors using common objects, such as paper clips, pencils, and erasers, placed randomly in a location whose area you have measured ahead of time.
- Count and record the objects before distributing them.
- Have students count any object within or touched by the quadrat.
- It is possible a very small population might not be sampled, depending on the placement of the quadrats.

Safety Avoid quadrats made from wire hangers.

Teacher Note "I used to make quadrats out of hangers and had a couple of accidents with overzealous students. Surprisingly, a Hula-Hoop® is almost a perfect square meter."

Answers

Analyze and Conclude

1. Accept all reasonable answers. If the estimate is inaccurate, it could be because of inaccurate counting, miscalculation of averages, nonrandom sampling, or nonrandom distribution of species in a population.
2. *Sample answer:* Increase the number of samples taken, be sure quadrat size is appropriate for the size of the area sampled, obtain random samples, count accurately, and calculate averages accurately.

Answers

A Contrast A lab experiment is conducted in the controlled setting of a laboratory; a field experiment is conducted in a less controlled natural setting.

▼ Teach continued

TEACH FROM VISUALS

FIGURE 1.4 Discuss the challenges involved in developing and deploying transmitters on wild animals. **Ask,** What concerns must scientists address in developing transmitters to be placed on animals in their natural environments? safety in placing the unit; remote control of the unit; battery life; adequate storage space for data; size of unit (small, lightweight); durability; ability to access data without disturbing the animal; data retention if animal moves out of study area

Answers

A Evaluate Modeling is computer-based or math-based and relies on large amounts of data to make predictions. Experimentation involves the direct study of organisms, either in the lab or in the field.

▼ Assess and Reteach

Assess Use the Section Self-Check or Section Quiz, both available at HMHScience.com.

Reteach Project on the board the image of **FIGURE 1.2** from the Media Gallery. Have students take turns writing the types of research methods that would be appropriate at each level of the ecosystem. Have students explain their choices.

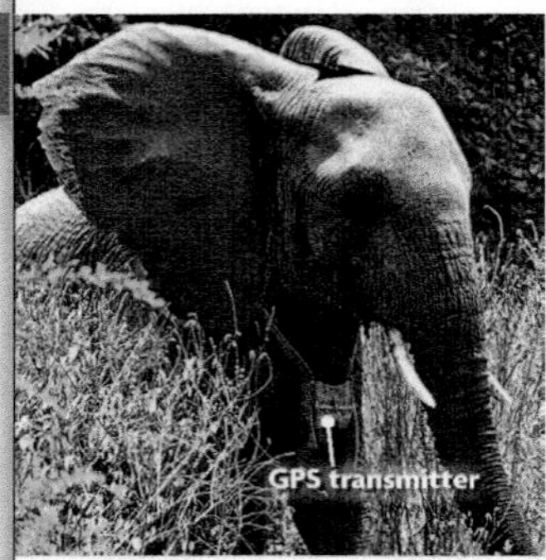

FIGURE 1.4 Ecologists use data transmitted by GPS receivers worn by elephants to develop computer models of the animals' movements.

Modeling

Sometimes the questions scientists wish to ask cannot be easily answered through observation or experimentation. Instead, scientists use computer and mathematical models to describe and model nature. Scientists can manipulate different model variables to learn about organisms or whole ecosystems in ways that would not be possible in a natural setting.

Although they are used to test hypothetical situations, models are created with the use of real data. For example, in Kenya, scientists are using satellite technology to track the movement of elephants, as shown in **FIGURE 1.4.** These data, in turn, can be used to create a model to study how changes to the ecosystem might affect elephant movement patterns. Before putting the model to use, scientists can test it by inserting actual data values. Such testing allows scientists to make sure that the values predicted by the model are similar to actual observations in the field.

In the United States, scientists developed a computer software program to create a virtual model of the Greater Yellowstone ecosystem. A variety of data were used to create this model, including

- the movements of elk, bison, bear, and wolf populations
- the location of different vegetation, such as meadows and forests
- the amount of snow
- the activities of geysers and other geothermal landforms

The combination of these data together with computer-generated maps creates a virtual ecosystem that scientists can use to model how one variable affects another. This type of modeling program sometimes plays a role in the development of wildlife conservation plans. Computer programs modeled population dynamics with and without the presence of the gray wolf. These programs were used to study how the reintroduction of gray wolves into Yellowstone might affect other species within the park and the surrounding area. By understanding how different organisms and factors within an ecosystem interact, wildlife managers are able to make well-informed decisions.

A Evaluate How is modeling limited in representing ecosystems and the organisms within them?

13.1 Formative Assessment

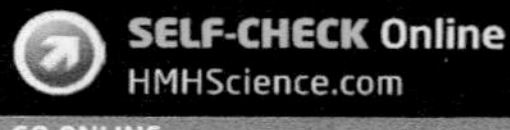
SELF-CHECK Online
HMHScience.com
GO ONLINE

REVIEWING MAIN IDEAS

1. What are the five different levels of organization studied by ecologists?
2. Describe the three general methods used by ecologists to study organisms.

CRITICAL THINKING

3. **Apply** What ecological research methods would you use to study bird migration? Explain your choices.
4. **Apply** How might an ecologist use modeling to study fire in a forest **ecosystem**? What are the limitations of such a model?

CONNECT TO EVOLUTION

5. Ernst Haeckel was greatly influenced by the writings of Charles Darwin. How do the principles of **ecology** relate to understanding how adaptations occur?

13.1 FORMATIVE ASSESSMENT

1. organism, population, community, ecosystem, biome
2. Observation is the act of watching something over time, such as a population of birds; experimentation can occur in the lab or in the field and involves testing a hypothesis; modeling is a computer-based or math-based method used to predict how changes in one variable may affect another.
3. observation—band birds and capture them at each end of their migratory route to record their movement; experimentation—devise an experiment to test what triggers migration; modeling—develop a computer model that includes different variables that might predict the time and path of migration
4. *Sample answer:* Ecologists could use models to determine movement of fire, locations where prescribed burns should take place, and areas with the potential for fire outbreaks. Limitations might include forest density, types of trees, plant and animal populations, wind patterns, and weather conditions.
5. Species are adapted to their environments. This concept is directly related to the study of ecology, in which the interactions between organisms and the environment are studied. By understanding the interactions within an ecosystem, scientists can develop an understanding of how populations evolve in response to their environments.

Populations and Samples

Create animated charts and graphs using Smart Grapher.

DATA ANALYSIS

One part of studying a population is to record its size. Often, it is possible to count all of the individuals in a population of organisms, such as large mammals or trees. With smaller organisms or more numerous populations, the population must be estimated based on representative samples. A **sample** is a portion of the population that is defined and counted.

Quadrat sampling is most often used to survey plant populations. This method can be used to identify species, calculate species' frequency, and monitor changes in plant communities over time.

Model

One method used to estimate populations is to count the number of individuals within a known sample area. To sample plants, quadrats are randomly placed over a large area and the number of individuals of the same species within the quadrat is counted. The number of quadrats sampled depends on the size of the entire area under study. In the example shown here, a scientist used quadrats to estimate the population of shrubs in a field. A simple equation can be used to find the population estimate: $T = NA$

$T = NA$

T = Total population estimate

$$N = \frac{\text{Total number of individuals counted}}{\text{Number of quadrats}}$$

$$A = \frac{\text{Total area}}{\text{Area of quadrat}}$$

In the example, each darkly shaded area represents a quadrat. Six shrubs were counted in five quadrats. The area of each quadrat is 1 m^2. The total area of the sampling plot is 200 m^2.

$T = NA$

$T = \frac{6}{5} \bullet \frac{200\ m^2}{1\ m^2}$

$T = 1.20 \bullet 200 = 240$

T = 240 individuals = estimated population of shrubs in the field

Practice Estimate Population Size

For each example, calculate the estimated population. Use the formula and show all of your work.

1. **Calculate** A scientist uses a quadrat of 2 m^2 to estimate the population of daisies in a field. She counts 173 individuals in 15 quadrats. The total area of the field is 250 m^2.
2. **Calculate** A scientist uses a 0.25 m^2 quadrat to sample a population of dandelions in a garden that is 500 m^2. The number of dandelions counted in 10 quadrats is 63.

Answers

1. 1442 individuals (173/15 = 11.53 = N; 250/2 = 125 = A; 11.53 • 125 = 1441.67)
2. 12,600 individuals (63/10 = 6.3 = N; 500/0.25 = 2000 = A; 6.3 • 2000 = 12,600)

DATA ANALYSIS

Introduce

Scientists use very carefully calculated sampling techniques and statistical analysis to estimate population sizes with a high degree of confidence. **Ask**

- Why is sampling important to the study of ecology? No scientist can count every member of a wild population or all members of all the interacting populations within a community.
- What does the sample represent? population as a whole
- What does a different count for each sample suggest? Individuals in the sampling areas are not spaced uniformly.
- What does the expression *level of confidence* mean when discussing data? It describes the degree to which a scientist trusts the data to be accurate, typically expressed as a percentage. The higher the percentage, the greater is the confidence.

Discuss

Have students look at the population shown in the diagram. **Ask**

- If the quadrats were placed in very sparse areas or very dense areas, how would that affect the estimate of the population's size? low estimates for sparse areas, high estimates for dense areas
- What might a biased choice look like in this example? *Sample answer:* choosing quadrats that have at least one shrub in them.

Online Student Resources, Data Analysis Practice

SECTION 13.2

B.3.1 Use mathematical and/or computational representation to explain why the carrying capacity ecosystems can support is limited by the available energy, water, oxygen, and minerals and by the ability of ecosystems to recycle the remains of dead organisms.

B.3.2 Design, evaluate, and refine a model which shows how human activities and natural phenomena can change the flow of matter and energy in an ecosystem and how those changes impact the environment and biodiversity of populations in ecosystems of different scales, as well as, how these human impacts can be reduced.

B.3.3 Evaluate the claims, evidence, and reasoning that the complex interactions in ecosystems maintain relatively consistent numbers and types of organisms in stable conditions, and identify the impact of changing conditions or introducing non-native species into that ecosystem.

▼ Plan and Prepare

Activate Prior Knowledge Have students imagine themselves in a woodland and then a desert. **Ask,** If you picked up a handful of soil in each place, what differences would you find? Woodland soil is rich with organic matter and holds water well. Sandy soil has little organic matter and won't hold water. Discuss the effect of soil type on plant type.

▼ Teach

Take It Further

Mangrove forests, which are typically home to biting insects, crocodiles, and snakes, are often cut back to make room for hotels and housing along the coast. However, the very tropical fish and coral reefs that attract tourists may be threatened if some portion of the forest is not preserved.

Answers

A Contrast Biotic factors are living components; abiotic factors are nonliving.

13.2 Biotic and Abiotic Factors

KEY CONCEPT **Every ecosystem includes both living and nonliving factors.**

VOCABULARY
biotic
abiotic
biodiversity
keystone species

MAIN IDEAS
- An ecosystem includes both biotic and abiotic factors.
- Changing one factor in an ecosystem can affect many other factors.

Connect to Your World

A vegetable garden is a small ecosystem, and its success depends on many factors. You can probably list several without too much thought. You might think of sunlight, fertilizer, or insects to pollinate the plants' flowers. Gardeners usually don't think of themselves as scientists, but they must take into account how these factors affect their plants in order for the plants to flourish.

MAIN IDEA

An ecosystem includes both biotic and abiotic factors.

All ecosystems are made up of living and nonliving components. These parts are referred to as biotic and abiotic factors.

- **Biotic** (by-AHT-ihk) factors are living things, such as plants, animals, fungi, and bacteria. Each organism plays a particular role in the ecosystem. For example, earthworms play a key role in enriching the soil.
- **Abiotic** (ay-by-AHT-ihk) factors are nonliving things such as moisture, temperature, wind, sunlight, and soil. The balance of these factors determines which living things can survive in a particular environment.

FIGURE 2.1 The underwater roots of mangrove trees camouflage young coral-reef fish from predators.

In the Caribbean Sea, scientists found that coral reefs located near saltwater marshes have more fish than do reefs farther out at sea. As shown in **FIGURE 2.1**, the key biotic factor is the mangrove trees that live in the marshes. The trees provide food and shelter for newly hatched fish, protecting them from predators. After the fish mature, they swim to the reefs. Abiotic factors that affect the growth of mangrove trees include low levels of oxygen in the mud where they grow and changing levels of salinity, or saltiness, due to daily tidal changes.

An ecosystem may look similar from one year to the next, with similar numbers of animals and plants. However, an ecosystem is always undergoing some changes. For example, a long period of increased precipitation might allow one plant species to grow better than others. As the plant continues to grow, it may crowd out other plant species, changing the community's composition. Though the total number of plants in the community may remain the same, the species have changed. As these cyclic changes occur, an ecosystem falls into a balance, or an approximate equilibrium.

A Contrast **What is the difference between biotic and abiotic factors?**

Differentiated Instruction

BELOW LEVEL

Make use of a terrarium or an aquarium to help students identify biotic and abiotic factors. Encourage them to go beyond the obvious plants and animals, water, and soil. Ask about unseen factors, such as microorganisms, oxygen, pH, and temperature. A similar activity can be done with matter cycles in **Section 5.**

MAIN IDEA

Changing one factor in an ecosystem can affect many other factors.

An ecosystem is a complex web of connected biotic and abiotic factors. You may not always think of yourself as part of the ecosystem, but humans, like other species, rely on the environment for survival. All species are affected by changes to the biotic and abiotic factors in an ecosystem.

Biodiversity

The relationships within an ecosystem are very complicated. If you attached a separate string between a forest tree and each of the living and nonliving things in the ecosystem that influenced it, and did the same for each of those living and nonliving things, the forest would quickly become a huge web of strings. The web would also reveal the biodiversity in the forest. **Biodiversity** (BY-oh-dih-VUR-sih-tee) is the assortment, or variety, of living things in an ecosystem. An area with a high level of biodiversity, such as a rain forest, has a large assortment of species living near one another. The amount of biodiversity found in an area depends on many factors, including moisture and temperature.

Some areas of the world have an unusually large amount of biodiversity in comparison to other locations. For example, tropical rain forests, which are moist and warm environments, cover less than 7 percent of Earth's ground surface. However, they account for over 50 percent of the planet's plant and animal species. This large amount of biodiversity emphasizes the importance of conserving such areas. Tropical rain forests and coral reefs are two of several areas referred to as hot spots. These hot spots, located across the globe, are areas that are rich in biodiversity, but are threatened by human activities.

CONNECT TO

BIODIVERSITY

The discovery of potential medicines and new species are two reasons why it is important to maintain biodiversity. In the chapter **Human Impact on Ecosystems,** you will learn how human activities impact biodiversity and how the loss of biodiversity affects us all.

Keystone Species

The complex relationships in ecosystems mean that a change in a single biotic or abiotic factor—a few broken strings in the web—can have a variety of effects. The change may barely be noticed, or it may have a deep impact. In some cases, the loss of a single species may cause a ripple effect felt across an entire ecosystem. Such an organism is called a keystone species. A **keystone species** is a species that has an unusually large effect on its ecosystem.

One example of a keystone species is the beaver. By felling trees to construct dams, beavers change free-flowing stream habitats into ponds, wetlands, and meadows. This modification leads to a cascade of changes within their ecosystem.

VISUAL VOCAB

Like a keystone that holds up an arch, a **keystone species** holds together a dynamic ecosystem.

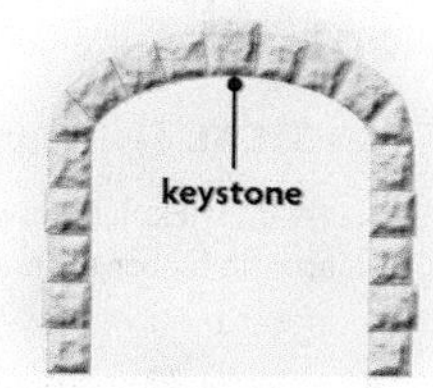

Have students learn more about keystone species by taking a look at the story of California's sea otter in the WebQuest for this chapter at **HMHScience.com.**

Vocabulary

Academic Vocabulary The word **diversity,** in a general sense, encompasses the idea of differences. In biology, *diversity* becomes **biodiversity,** the measure of the number of species in a given area or system or even the world. **Genetic diversity** refers to the range of different alleles within a species. Just as populations with greater genetic diversity are more stable, so too are ecosystems with greater biodiversity more stable.

Take It Further

Neither precious minerals nor exotic spices drew explorers into the vast expanses of the North American wilderness during the late 17th and early 18th centuries. It was a rodent—a rather exotic one though, with webbed feet, self-sharpening teeth, and a flat rudder-like tail. The **North American beaver** was prized for its pelt and the waterproof fur that could be compressed into a felt to be used for coats and hats.

The beaver, or at least its skin, found itself adorning the heads of royalty, captains of industry, and statesmen alike. The stovepipe hat of President Abraham Lincoln was made from beaver pelt. The beaver's image adorned coats of arms, a newspaper masthead, coinage, and stamps. The Iroquois Wars were fought, in part, over control of the beaver trade.

So highly valued was the beaver pelt that the animal was on the brink of extinction by the mid-19th century. The emergence of the silk top hat, which, unlike the beaver top hat, could be collapsed for easy handling, helped to save the animal. Such are the vagaries of fashion.

PRE-AP

Have students map out a possible sequence of events to predict what would happen if a population of fast-growing trees took root in a meadow. As they plot the transformation of the ecosystem, students should indicate whether each successive step results from a change in a biotic factor, an abiotic factor, or both.

Teacher Toolkit, Section C, Sequence Diagram

BELOW LEVEL

Build on the metaphor of the arch. Tell students that with the keystone in place, more rows of stone can be placed above. The choice of the word *keystone* signals the importance of a keystone species to an ecosystem. To underscore the point, give students playing cards to construct a house of cards. **Ask,** What happens if the keystone species is removed?

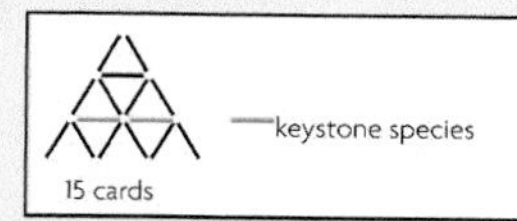

Teach *continued*

TEACH FROM VISUALS

FIGURE 2.2 Beavers are considered a keystone species partly because of their dam-building behavior. **Ask**

- How does dam building affect fish populations? The dam creates a pond from free-flowing water, which allows a greater number and variety of fish to live and reproduce in the water.
- What effect does the increase in fish populations have on the pond? Fish attract species to the pond that feed on them.
- What is the overall effect of damming? increase in biodiversity

Answers

A Connect Salmon are the main food source for more than 140 species. They return vital nutrients to the river system when they die and decompose. Many species would suffer without their presence.

Assess and Reteach

Assess Use the Section Self-Check or Section Quiz, both available at **HMHScience.com**.

Reteach Have pairs of students take turns quizzing each other on the main ideas and terms in this section. Let one student write a question and the other student answer it. Have partners switch roles and repeat the activity until they have covered all the main ideas and terms.

FIGURE 2.2 Keystone Species

Beavers are a keystone species. By constructing dams, beavers create an ecosystem used by a wide variety of species.

Keystone Species

As **FIGURE 2.2** shows, beavers cause changes that create an ecosystem used by a variety of species, leading to an overall increase in biodiversity.

- A greater number and wider variety of fish are able to live in the still waters of the pond.
- The fish attract fish-eating birds, such as herons and kingfishers.
- Insects inhabit the pond and the dead trees along the shore, attracting insect-eating birds, such as great-crested flycatchers, that nest in the tree cavities.
- Waterfowl nest among the shrubs and grasses along the pond's edge.
- Animals that prey on birds or their eggs are also attracted to the pond.

Keystone species form and maintain a complex web of life. Whatever happens to that species affects all the other species connected to it.

A Connect **Explain why the Pacific salmon, introduced in Section 1, could be considered a keystone species.**

13.2 Formative Assessment

REVIEWING MAIN IDEAS

1. Select an ecosystem that is familiar to you and describe the biotic and abiotic factors that exist there.
2. How would the removal of a keystone species affect an ecosystem's biodiversity?

CRITICAL THINKING

3. **Predict** Explain how a change in an abiotic factor such as sunlight would affect biodiversity.
4. **Analyze** Humans are sometimes described as being a keystone species. Does this label fit? Why or why not?

CONNECT TO EVOLUTION

5. What role might an abiotic factor such as temperature play in the evolution of a species?

13.2 FORMATIVE ASSESSMENT

1. Answers should show that students understand that biotic factors are living things and abiotic factors are nonliving.
2. The removal of a keystone species would decrease the ecosystem's biodiversity.
3. Changes in amount of sunlight might affect local temperatures, leading to a change in the numbers and types of species in the ecosystem. New species may move into the area, taking the place of those that cannot survive.
4. Keystone species are those that help to establish and maintain a complex web of life. Humans do not fit this label because human activities often decrease, rather than increase, biodiversity.
5. A long-term temperature change could result in selective pressure that selects for individuals better adapted to the temperature, causing populations to evolve. It could alter the types of food available, again creating selective pressure toward individuals that can take advantage of different food sources.

Algae Farms—Producing a Fuel of the Future?

S.T.E.M. Interactions

When you think of farms, you probably picture fields of wheat, corn, or other agricultural crops, or perhaps cattle, chickens, or hogs grazing. But can you imagine a farm that grows microscopic algae to be used as a biofuel? Compared with other sources of biofuels, such as corn, algae can produce more fuel in a smaller amount of space.

A biofuel is any fuel that contains energy from recently living organisms, such as peanut oil from peanuts and ethanol from corn. Biofuels are produced by subjecting biomass (plant or animal material) to heat, chemicals, or bacteria to break down the material. Dwindling petroleum resources, the unstable prices of fossil fuel resources, and the inability to exploit potential new resources have steadily increased the demand for alternative fuel sources such as those derived from plant and animal materials. One of those potential sources is algae, which produce oil that can be used as biodiesel in cars, trucks, and airplanes.

Some scientists are working with businesses to determine the best ways to grow and process algae. At one type of algae farm, microscopic green algae are grown in large open ponds, called raceways. Each raceway has a specially designed paddle wheel that continuously moves the water, mixing the algae so that it does not settle on the bottom of the pond.

After the algae are collected and processed, the cell walls of the algae must be broken down to extract the oil. One way to do this is through the use of ultrasound, sound waves with frequencies too high for humans to hear.

When algae cells are exposed to ultrasound, the cell wall breaks apart. Then the oil is extracted and processed at a biorefinery, in much the same way that petroleum is processed in a traditional oil refinery.

Scientists are researching different ways of growing algae, such as vertically in large plastic sheets like the ones below. The clear plastic exposes the algae to sunlight while the algae are provided the carbon dioxide, oxygen, and nutrients they need. Other studies are being conducted to modify plant cells genetically to make it easier to extract the oil from algae.

As with any fuel source, there are advantages and disadvantages to the production of biofuel from algae. Algae use carbon dioxide as they carry out photosynthesis, so most algae farms could be carbon-neutral operations. Also, algae can produce up to 60 times the amount of oil as land-based plants used to produce biofuels do.

Disadvantages to using algae as a biofuel include the expense of production and the use of water. Current processes use about 350 gallons of water to produce one barrel of algae oil. It costs more to produce oil from algae than it does to produce petroleum. As with most innovations, however, continued research and improved methods of production will lower costs.

S.T.E.M. Activity

Research more about new designs and technologies being developed for algae farms. What are the latest designs for different types of algae farms? What are some of the advantages and disadvantages of each design?

Introduce

Algae are only one source of biofuel. Ethanol, derived from corn, sugarcane, or cellulose, is already being used in vehicles as a blended mix of gasoline and ethanol. Many innovators are looking for other sources as well. For example, Professor Jon Veramendi of the Instituto de Agrobiotecnología in Navarre, Spain, thinks one potential source of a new biofuel might be found in the tobacco plant. Tobacco is a surprisingly fast-growing, high-yielding plant and, if cultivated correctly, could contain higher levels of starches and sugars necessary to produce ethanol.

Another interesting project is the use of human waste as a biofuel. The Bill and Melinda Gates Foundation supports research that would place science-fiction-like toilets in some of the world's poorest countries. These toilets wouldn't simply dispose of human waste in an environmentally friendly way. They would also transform it into resources such as charcoal, salt, and even drinking water. It's all part of an initiative to "Reinvent the Toilet" without the need for a substantial infrastructure of pipes and other sanitation systems. To date, several models have been proposed. Some even extract hydrogen waste from human waste—hydrogen that could one day fuel hydrogen-powered cars.

Discuss

Have students present the results of their research on new designs and technology involved in growing algae for biofuel. Encourage students to ask questions about the advantages and disadvantages of each idea.

Answers

Students may find that some companies are working on improving photobioreactors, bioreactors that use a light source to grow algae, in order to increase algal yields and lower costs. Other innovations include growing algae in closed containers to ensure control over variables that open, outdoor facilities do not provide, such as contamination by pathogens. Some companies have patented systems that produce algae consistently and sustainably. These systems may focus on improving aspects of the strains of algae used; growing, harvesting, or processing the algae; or extracting the oil from the algae.

SECTION 13.3

B.2.3 Use mathematical and/or computational representations to support claims for the cycling of matter and flow of energy among organisms in an ecosystem.

B.2.4 Develop a model to illustrate the role of photosynthesis and cellular respiration in the cycling of carbon among the biosphere, atmosphere, hydrosphere, and geosphere.

B.3.2 Design, evaluate, and refine a model which shows how human activities and natural phenomena can change the flow of matter and energy in an ecosystem and how those changes impact the environment and biodiversity of populations in ecosystems of different scales, as well as, how these human impacts can be reduced.

Plan and Prepare

Activate Prior Knowledge Write on the board the equation for photosynthesis:

$$6H_2O + 6CO_2 \xrightarrow{\text{light energy}} C_6H_{12}O_6 + 6O_2$$

Ask, Why does life as you know it depend upon this formula? Photosynthesis captures the sun's energy and transforms it to chemical energy; then it can be used by other organisms. Discuss the products.

Teach

TEACH FROM VISUALS

FIGURE 3.1 Remind students that chlorophyll is a pigment found in the cells of most producers. **Ask,** What does chlorophyll have to do with energy? Excitation of chlorophyll molecules by sunlight sets up a series of chemical reactions that end with glucose, which stores energy.

Answers

A Predict Many producers would die. Fewer plant-eating consumers would survive and reproduce, affecting food available to other consumers.

13.3 Energy in Ecosystems

KEY CONCEPT **Life in an ecosystem requires a source of energy.**

MAIN IDEAS

- Producers provide energy for other organisms in an ecosystem.
- Almost all producers obtain energy from sunlight.

VOCABULARY

producer
autotroph
consumer
heterotroph
chemosynthesis

Connect to Your World

You play an important role in the cycling of energy on Earth, as do the plants and animals you eat. This energy that cycles through Earth's ecosystems is needed to fuel your life processes, such as breathing and growing. Where does this energy come from, and what role does it play in an ecosystem?

MAIN IDEA

Producers provide energy for other organisms in an ecosystem.

All organisms must have a source of energy in order to survive. However, not all organisms obtain their energy by eating other organisms.

- **Producers** are organisms that get their energy from nonliving resources, meaning they make their own food. Their distribution is shown in **FIGURE 3.1.** Producers are also called **autotrophs** (AW-tuh-TRAHFS). In the word *autotroph,* the suffix *-troph* comes from a Greek word meaning "nourishment." The prefix *auto-* means "self."
- **Consumers** are organisms that get their energy by eating other living or once-living resources, such as plants and animals. Consumers are also called **heterotrophs** (HEHT-uhr-uh-TRAHFS). In the word *heterotroph,* the prefix *hetero-* means "different."

All ecosystems depend on producers, because they provide the basis for the ecosystem's energy. Even animals that eat only meat rely on producers. One such species is the gray wolf. Gray wolves are consumers that eat elk and moose. Elk and moose are consumers that eat plants, such as grasses and shrubs. Plants are producers that make their own food. If the grasses and shrubs disappeared, the elk and moose would either have to find some other producer to eat or they would starve. The wolves would also be affected because they eat elk and moose. Although the wolves do not eat plants, their lives are tied to the grasses and shrubs that feed their prey. Likewise, all consumers are connected in some way to producers.

FIGURE 3.1 This satellite image uses chlorophyll abundance to show the distribution of producers in the Western Hemisphere. Dark green areas are heavily forested, while yellow areas have limited vegetation.

Most producers need sunlight to make food. These producers depend directly on the sun as their source of energy. For this reason, all the consumers connected to these producers depend indirectly on the sun for their energy.

A Predict **How would a long-term drought affect producers and consumers?**

Differentiated Instruction

BELOW LEVEL

To test student understanding, write a series of declarative statements about the main points of the section. Focus on the word pairs *producer-consumer* and *autotroph-heterotroph.* Connect the word pairs to the process words *photosynthesis* and *chemosynthesis.* Have students react to the statements as being true or false before reading the section and then again after reading.

Teacher Toolkit, Section C, Anticipation Guide

PRE-AP

Write on the board the equation for chemosynthesis just below that of photosynthesis:

$$6CO_2 + 6H_2O + 3H_2S \longrightarrow C_6H_{12}O_6 + 3H_2SO_4$$

Have students compare and contrast the two equations, considering both reactants and products. You may want to label hydrogen sulfide and sulfuric acid. Chemosynthesis occurs in extreme environments.

MAIN IDEA

Almost all producers obtain energy from sunlight.

Most producers on Earth use sunlight as their energy source. Photosynthesis is the two-stage process that green plants, cyanobacteria, and some protists use to produce energy. Chemical reactions form carbohydrates from carbon dioxide and water. Oxygen is released as a waste product.

Photosynthesis in plants begins when energy from the sun hits chloroplasts and is absorbed by chlorophyll. In the first stage of photosynthesis, energy from sunlight is converted to chemical energy. In the second stage, this chemical energy is used to change carbon dioxide into carbohydrates, such as glucose. Plants use these carbohydrates as an energy source to fuel cellular respiration.

Not all producers depend on sunlight for their energy. Scientists were stunned in 1977 when they first visited deep-sea vents on the bottom of the ocean. There they found thriving ecosystems in places where super-heated water shoots up from the ocean floor. Studies showed that tiny prokaryotes were making their own food from minerals in the water. They had no need for sunlight. **Chemosynthesis** (KEE-moh-SIHN-thih-sihs) is the process by which an organism forms carbohydrates using chemicals, rather than light, as an energy source. A series of reactions changes the chemicals into a usable energy form. Different reactions occur depending on which chemicals are present.

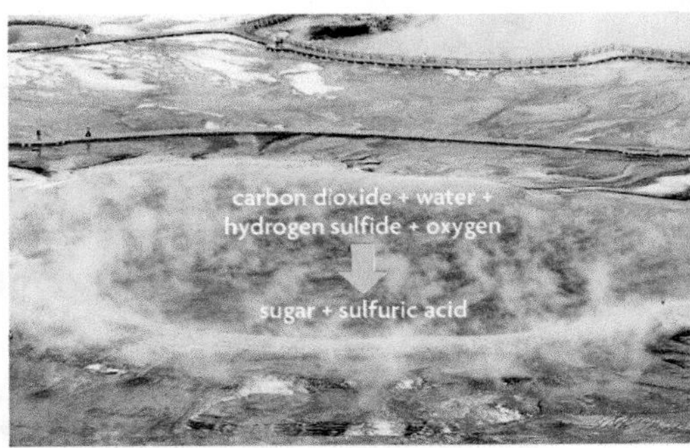

FIGURE 3.2 Chemosynthetic bacteria thrive in many of Yellowstone National Park's hydrothermal pools.

In addition to deep-sea vents, chemosynthetic organisms are also found in sulfur-rich salt marsh flats and in hydrothermal pools, such as those in Yellowstone National Park, shown in **FIGURE 3.2.** In this case, chemical energy is used to change carbon dioxide (CO_2), water (H_2O), hydrogen sulfide (H_2S), and oxygen (O_2) into an energy-rich sugar molecule. Sulfuric acid (H_2SO_4) is released as a waste product.

Contrast **How do photosynthesis and chemosynthesis differ?**

13.3 Formative Assessment

SELF-CHECK Online
HMHScience.com
GO ONLINE

REVIEWING MAIN IDEAS

1. How does the stability of an ecosystem depend on its **producers**?
2. What are the two processes used by producers to obtain energy?

CRITICAL THINKING

3. **Hypothesize** Few producers live deep below a lake's surface. Suggest an explanation for this pattern.
4. **Infer** Could producers survive without **consumers**? Explain why or why not.

CONNECT TO

HISTORY OF LIFE

5. How might chemosynthetic organisms help scientists to understand how life developed on Earth?

13.3 FORMATIVE ASSESSMENT

1. Producers bring energy into an ecosystem.
2. photosynthesis and chemosynthesis
3. Sunlight cannot penetrate the water to a great depth, so photosynthesizing organisms are more common near the surface.
4. Producers do not require consumers to fill material needs as a food source. So in that sense, producers do not need consumers to survive.
5. Chemosynthetic organisms live in environments that may be similar to those that existed on Earth billions of years ago, when life was beginning to develop. Studying these organisms enables scientists to infer how different life forms may have evolved as Earth changed.

Vocabulary

Academic Vocabulary Review the definition of the word **synthesis** in the context of **photosynthesis** and **chemosynthesis.**

synthesis, combining of separate elements or substances to form a complex whole

Students may have a general sense of the word as meaning "to make or produce" and so might be tempted, for example, to interpret *photosynthesis* as producing light. The root of synthesis actually means

"to put together with"

A carbohydrate, a complex whole, is put together *(synthesized)* using light *(photo-)* or chemicals *(chemo-)* as the initial source of energy.

Answers

A Contrast Both photosynthesis and chemosynthesis are processes by which producers capture energy. In photosynthesis, sunlight is the energy source. In chemosynthesis, chemicals are the energy source.

Assess and Reteach

Assess Use the Section Self-Check or Section Quiz, both available at **HMHScience.com.**

Reteach Work with the class to put the following terms into a concept map: *producer, consumer, autotroph, heterotroph, photosynthesis,* and *chemosynthesis.* Have students supply details and tell you which terms to connect as you write them on the board. Then have students write a paragraph using the terms in context.

SECTION 13.4

B.2.3 Use mathematical and/or computational representations to support claims for the cycling of matter and flow of energy among organisms in an ecosystem.

B.2.4 Develop a model to illustrate the role of photosynthesis and cellular respiration in the cycling of carbon among the biosphere, atmosphere, hydrosphere, and geosphere.

B.3.2 Design, evaluate, and refine a model which shows how human activities and natural phenomena can change the flow of matter and energy in an ecosystem and how those changes impact the environment and biodiversity of populations in ecosystems of different scales, as well as, how these human impacts can be reduced.

▼ Plan and Prepare

Activate Prior Knowledge Have students describe a typical meal. **Ask**

- What do you get from these foods? matter, energy
- How does energy and matter come to be in these foods? Help students trace back to a producer.
- What other way could you obtain energy for your body? There is none.

▼ Teach

TEACH FROM VISUALS

FIGURE 4.1 Point out the yellow arrows used to depict energy flow. They are used here and in other diagrams. **Ask**

- What is the original source of energy? sunlight
- How do the cottontail and hawk differ as consumers? Cottontail feeds on producer; hawk feeds on another consumer.

13.4 Food Chains and Food Webs

KEY CONCEPT **Food chains and food webs model the flow of energy in an ecosystem.**

VOCABULARY

food chain	herbivore
carnivore	omnivore
detritivore	decomposer
specialist	generalist
trophic level	food web

MAIN IDEAS

- A food chain is a model that shows a sequence of feeding relationships.
- A food web shows a complex network of feeding relationships.

Connect to Your World

What if you were to write down the names of ten people you know, and then each of them wrote down ten more people, and so on? Very quickly a complex web of relationships would form. Like those in human communities, relationships among organisms in an ecosystem are very complex. These relationships are often described as chains or webs, connecting many species together.

MAIN IDEA

A food chain is a model that shows a sequence of feeding relationships.

The simplest way to look at energy flow in an ecosystem is through a food chain. A **food chain** is a sequence that links species by their feeding relationships. Rather than describe every potential relationship, this model chain only follows the connection between one producer and a single chain of consumers within an ecosystem. For example, in a desert ecosystem, a desert cottontail eats grass. The food chain is, therefore, grass–desert cottontail. If another consumer such as a Harris's hawk eats a desert cottontail, the food chain gets longer: grass–desert cottontail–Harris's hawk, as shown in **FIGURE 4.1.**

FIGURE 4.1 Food Chain

Energy flows through a food chain.

GRAMA GRASS

Grama grass, a producer, obtains its energy through photosynthesis.

DESERT COTTONTAIL

The desert cottontail, a consumer, obtains its energy by eating the seeds of plants, such as grama grass.

HARRIS'S HAWK

The Harris's hawk, a consumer, obtains its energy by eating other animals, such as desert cottontails.

Differentiated Instruction

ENGLISH LEARNERS

Use analogies to help students remember the meanings of new vocabulary words. Ask them to make a three-column chart with the heads *Key Concept*, *Definition*, and *Analogy*. Have them complete the first two columns on their own by writing the ten new vocabulary words in the first and finding definitions in context to complete the second. Help them create analogies for the third column, such as "an herbivore is to a carnivore as a plant is to meat."

Teacher Toolkit, Section D, Analogies

PRE-AP

Have students list and then group keywords in this section:

consumer-producer-decomposer
herbivore-carnivore-omnivore-detritivore

Have students differentiate between the groups by describing the type of information each set of terms provides.

Teacher Toolkit, Section D, List-Group-Label.

Types of Consumers

As you read in Section 3, consumers are organisms that eat other organisms. All consumers, however, are not alike.

- **Herbivores,** such as desert cottontails, are organisms that eat only plants.
- **Carnivores** are organisms that eat only animals. Harris's hawks are carnivores that eat desert cottontails.
- **Omnivores** are organisms that eat both plants and animals. Kangaroo rats are omnivores that eat both seeds and insects.
- **Detritivores** (dih-TRY-tuh-VOHRZ) are organisms that eat detritus, or dead organic matter. A millipede is a detritivore that feeds on particles of detritus on the ground.
- **Decomposers** are detritivores that break down organic matter into simpler compounds. Microorganisms and fungi, for example, are decomposers. Decomposers are important to the stability of an ecosystem because they return vital nutrients back into the environment.

Food chains are especially helpful in describing feeding relationships among extremely selective eaters, known as specialists. A **specialist** is a consumer that primarily eats one specific organism or feeds on a very small variety of organisms.

Specialists are very sensitive to changes in the availability of prey. For example, the Florida snail kite, shown in **FIGURE 4.2**, is a specialist that depends on the apple snail as its main source of food. In the early 1900s, apple snails became less common in Florida as a result of land development. Florida snail kite populations declined suddenly, and in 1967, the bird was listed as an endangered species. Currently, the snails and the birds continue to survive in lower numbers in protected areas, such as the Everglades.

Most species do not rely on a single source of food. These species are called generalists. **Generalists** are consumers that have a varying diet. For example, the diet of a gray wolf may include a number of animals, including elk, moose, white-tailed deer, beavers, and even mice.

READING TOOLBOX

VOCABULARY

Most words for consumers come from Latin words.

- *Vorāe* means "to swallow or devour."
- *Herba* means "vegetation."
- *Carnus* means "flesh."
- *Omnis* means "all."
- *Détrere* means "to wear away."

FIGURE 4.2 Florida snail kites are specialists that rely on apple snails as their primary food source.

Trophic Levels

Trophic levels are the levels of nourishment in a food chain. For example, the producer–herbivore–carnivore chain has three trophic levels. Carnivores are at the highest trophic level. Herbivores are at the second trophic level. Producers are at the first, or bottom, trophic level. Energy flows up the food chain from the lowest trophic level to the highest.

- Primary consumers are herbivores because they are the first consumer above the producer trophic level.
- Secondary consumers are carnivores that eat herbivores.
- Tertiary consumers are carnivores that eat secondary consumers.

Omnivores, such as humans that eat both plants and animals, may be listed at different trophic levels in different food chains. When a person eats a salad, the trophic levels in the food chain are producer–omnivore. When a person eats a steak, the trophic levels are producer–herbivore–omnivore.

A Connect What is the connection between food chains and trophic levels?

HANDS-ON ACTIVITY

Unlike snail kites, owls are generalists. They often feed on small animals, which they swallow whole. Because an owl cannot digest bones, fur, or feathers, these remains are pressed into a tight mass and regurgitated some hours after eating. The result is an owl pellet.

With enough owl pellets, identification keys, and needle tools or tweezers for every two students, have students form pairs. Each pair will need gloves and a paper towel or tray. Have students pull apart the pellet and identify the remains. Remind students to wash their hands after the materials are discarded and the tools cleaned.

At the end of the activity, **ask**

- Why doesn't a consumer digest all the food it consumes? Not all food matter can be digested—for example bones and seeds.
- What happens to the waste material left behind by consumers? It can become a source of nutrition for detritivores and decomposers.

Take It Further

What was a beneficial adaptation for the **Florida snail kite** has now become a serious liability. The kite beak evolved a hook that enabled it to feed on a once-plentiful food supply: **apple snails.** The beak is so deeply hooked that the population's survival is now linked to this single food source.

The Florida snail kite is endangered in part because of a reduced habitat but also because of changes to water levels throughout the Florida Everglades. Water height affects the behavior and availability of apple snails. Water that is too shallow restricts the snails' breeding and movement. Water that is too high covers the vegetation where the kite can prey upon the snails.

Address Misconceptions

Common Misconception A number of misconceptions about food chains and food webs are based on an association of higher trophic levels with higher numbers. **Ask,** Are the following statements true or false?

- Organisms higher in a food chain eat everything that is lower. F
- Populations higher in a food chain increase in number because they deplete those lower in the chain. F
- The top of the food chain has the most energy because it accumulates up the chain. F

Correcting the Misconception Remind students of the specialization that occurs as populations adapt to the conditions of their environment and of the patterns of evolution described in **The Evolution of Populations**. **Section 6** will address the loss of energy as matter moves from producer to consumers, but students may already be familiar with the concept of entropy.

Answers

A Connect Food chains illustrate the flow of energy from one trophic level to the next.

▼ Teach *continued*

TEACH FROM VISUALS

FIGURE 4.3 Point out that all food webs require an initial source of energy, usually from sunlight. Have students use the color key of the diagram to identify different trophic levels. **Ask**

- What do the yellow arrows represent? the flow of energy
- Which organisms bring energy into this ecosystem? the producers phytoplankton and algae
- Starting with a producer, identify three food chains in this food web. *Sample answer:* algae-parrotfish-reef shark; phytoplankton-sea sponge; phytoplankton-shrimp-triggerfish-reef shark
- Which organism is a tertiary consumer? reef shark

Answers

A Critical Viewing The removal of phytoplankton or algae would have the most impact because they are producers, and many consumers rely on them as a food source, either directly or indirectly.

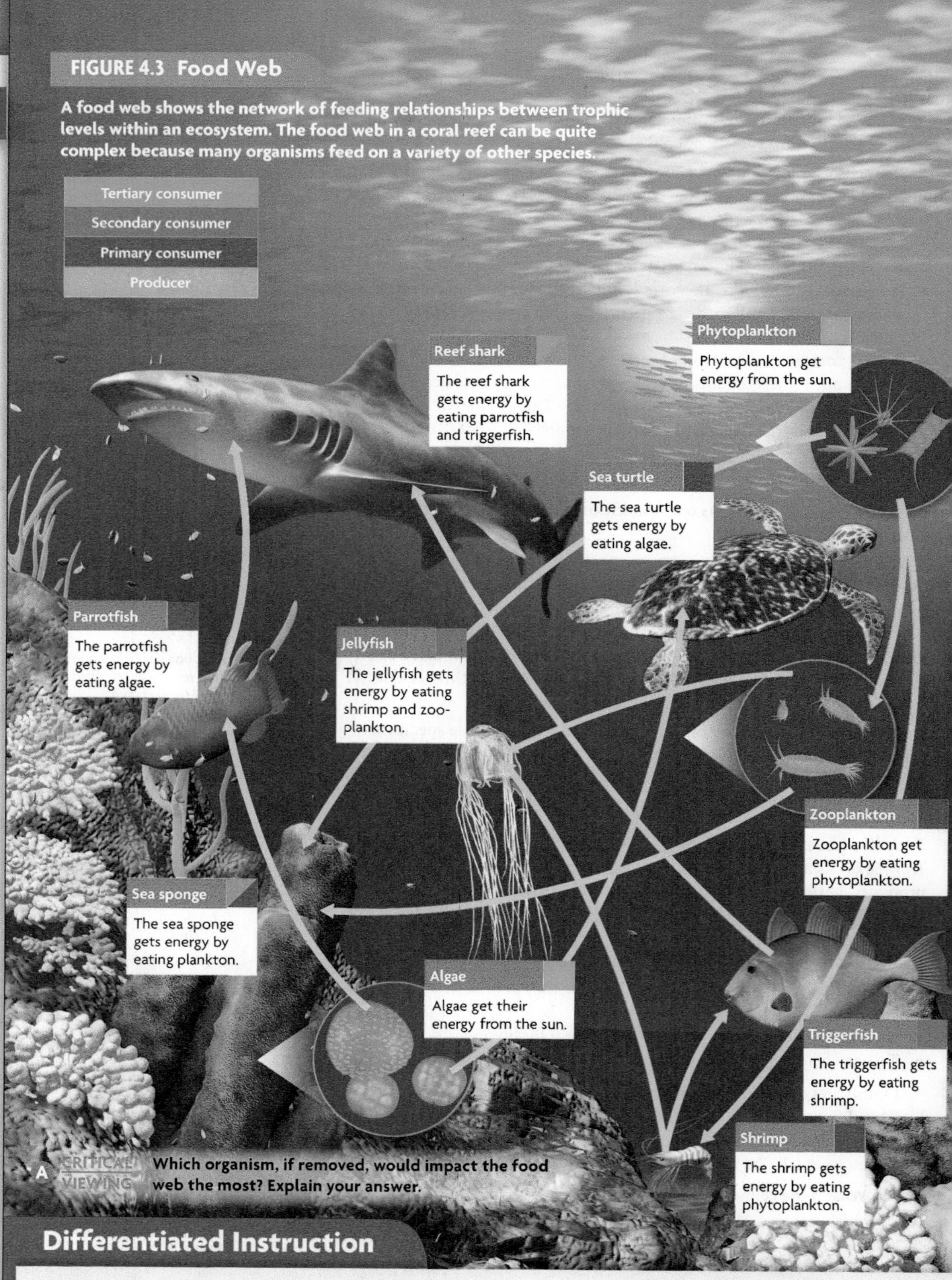

Tertiary consumer
Secondary consumer
Primary consumer
Producer
Reef shark
The reef shark gets energy by eating parrotfish and triggerfish.
Phytoplankton
Phytoplankton get energy from the sun.
Sea turtle
The sea turtle gets energy by eating algae.
Parrotfish
The parrotfish gets energy by eating algae.
Jellyfish
The jellyfish gets energy by eating shrimp and zooplankton.
Zooplankton
Zooplankton get energy by eating phytoplankton.
Sea sponge
The sea sponge gets energy by eating plankton.
Algae
Algae get their energy from the sun.
Triggerfish
The triggerfish gets energy by eating shrimp.
Shrimp
The shrimp gets energy by eating phytoplankton.
A CRITICAL VIEWING Which organism, if removed, would impact the food web the most? Explain your answer.

FIGURE 4.3 Food Web

A food web shows the network of feeding relationships between trophic levels within an ecosystem. The food web in a coral reef can be quite complex because many organisms feed on a variety of other species.

Differentiated Instruction

BELOW LEVEL

Have students who will have difficulty following the arrows use their fingers to trace the arrows. Tell them that an arrow pointing toward an organism indicates what that organism eats. Have them identify individual food chains by drawing sequence diagrams. Show them that when more than one arrow leads from an organism, they have a choice of which arrow to follow.

Teacher Toolkit, Section C, Sequence Diagram

MAIN IDEA

A food web shows a complex network of feeding relationships.

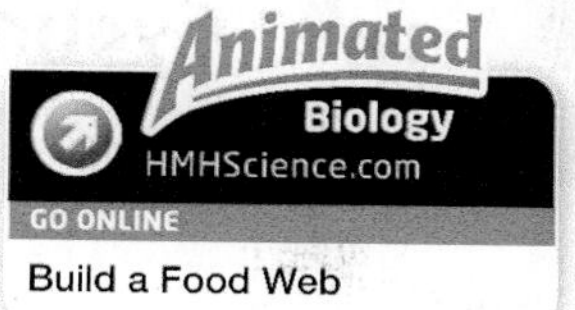

Generalists may be involved in many food chains, depending on which links are in the chain. Each of the organisms in those links, in turn, may be part of many other food chains. As a result, scientists use food webs to describe these interconnections. A **food web** is a model that shows the complex network of feeding relationships and the flow of energy within and sometimes beyond an ecosystem. At each link in a food web, some energy is stored within an organism, and some energy is dissipated into the environment.

Coral reefs are often referred to as rain forests of the sea, due to the abundance and diversity of species found there. The complex connections in a coral reef ecosystem, illustrated in **FIGURE 4.3**, are created by the feeding relationships within the food web.

The stability of any food web depends on the presence of producers, as they form the base of the food web. In the case of a marine ecosystem such as a coral reef, algae and phytoplankton are two of the producers that play this important role.

An organism may have multiple feeding relationships within a food web. For example, reef sharks are generalists that eat several kinds of food items. When a reef shark eats a parrotfish, it is a secondary consumer, because a parrotfish is a primary consumer that eats algae. However, a reef shark is a tertiary consumer when it eats a triggerfish. This difference in trophic levels occurs because a triggerfish is a secondary consumer that feeds on shrimp. The shrimp, in turn, is a primary consumer that eats phytoplankton. Food webs like this one emphasize both the complicated nature of feeding relationships and the flow of energy within an ecosystem.

CONNECT TO

MARINE ECOSYSTEMS

Coral reefs are ecosystems that are rich in diversity. In the chapter **The Biosphere** you will learn about the complex relationships found in these underwater ecosystems.

A Analyze **How might the introduction of a new predator affect the flow of energy through a food web?**

Answers

A **Analyze** A new predator might cause other populations in the food web to decrease in size, thus decreasing the amount of energy available.

Assess and Reteach ▼

Assess Use the Section Self-Check or Section Quiz, both available at **HMHScience.com**.

Reteach Have students prepare a list of the vocabulary in this section. Have them use each term as they describe what they see in **FIGURE 4.3.**

13.4 Formative Assessment

SELF-CHECK Online
HMHScience.com
GO ONLINE

REVIEWING MAIN IDEAS

1. Why are **food chains** especially useful for describing the relationships of **specialists**?
2. What happens to energy as it flows through a **food web**?

CRITICAL THINKING

3. **Compare and Contrast** Only a small percentage of all consumers are specialists. What danger does a specialist face that a **generalist** does not?
4. **Predict** How might the stability of an ecosystem be affected if all of the **decomposers** were suddenly removed?

CONNECT TO

POLLUTION

5. How might an oil spill in the ocean affect an aquatic food web? What might happen to the food web on land located near the spill? Explain your answers.

13.4 FORMATIVE ASSESSMENT

1. Specialists have specific diets that include only one type of organism, which produces a simple food chain.
2. Some energy is stored in the organism, but much energy is dissipated into the environment.
3. If a specialist's food source becomes scarce or disappears, the population may die out. A generalist facing the loss of one of its food sources can shift to a different food source.
4. The stability of the ecosystem would be negatively affected, because without decomposers, vital nutrients would not be returned to the environment.
5. The entire food web would be affected by an oil spill. Oily water may kill off phytoplankton. The loss of smaller fish would affect the larger fish, which would, in turn, affect tertiary consumers. Plants and animals that live along the coast would also be affected as the oil seeped onto the shore. The overall effect would be a decline in the availability of food sources both within and outside the ocean.

SECTION 13.5

B.2.4 Develop a model to illustrate the role of photosynthesis and cellular respiration in the cycling of carbon among the biosphere, atmosphere, hydrosphere, and geosphere.

B.3.2 Design, evaluate, and refine a model which shows how human activities and natural phenomena can change the flow of matter and energy in an ecosystem and how those changes impact the environment and biodiversity of populations in ecosystems of different scales, as well as, how these human impacts can be reduced.

▼ Plan and Prepare

Activate Prior Knowledge Remind students that a human being that begins life as a single cell ends up with anywhere from 10 trillion to 100 trillion cells as an adult. **Ask,** Where does all that material come from? It cycles from Earth into the living parts of an ecosystem. Humans absorb most through food. **Ask,** What would you include on a shopping list for elements that are critical to a human? The list should include oxygen, carbon, hydrogen, and nitrogen.

▼ Teach

Science Trivia

- The total volume of water on Earth is about 326 million trillion gallons.
- If Earth's water could fit into a gallon container, only about 3 tablespoons would be usable. The rest would be either frozen or salty.

Answers

A Analyze So little of Earth's water is fresh water. Increasing population puts a strain on available supply.

13.5 Cycling of Matter

KEY CONCEPT **Matter cycles in and out of an ecosystem.**

MAIN IDEAS

- Water cycles through the environment.
- Elements essential for life also cycle through ecosystems.
- Natural and human activities can disrupt biogeochemical cycles and ecosystems.

VOCABULARY

hydrologic cycle
biogeochemical cycle
nitrogen fixation

Connect to Your World

Since life in most ecosystems requires a constant inflow of energy from the Sun, Earth is an open system in terms of energy. However, in terms of matter, such as oxygen and carbon, Earth is a closed system. Today's Earth has roughly the same amount of carbon as it had billions of years ago, meaning that the same carbon atoms that make up your body may once have been part of a tree, or gases spewed by a volcano, or even part of a dinosaur.

MAIN IDEA

Water cycles through the environment.

Matter changes form, but it does not disappear. It can be used over and over again in a continuous cycle. If you crush a rock, for example, it does not vanish. Instead, it turns into sand and other bits of minerals. Although matter may change form over time, the total amount of matter remains the same.

As you learned earlier, a major part of life on Earth is water, which has a cycle of its own. The **hydrologic cycle** (HY-druh-LAHJ-ihk), also known as the water cycle, is the circular pathway of water on Earth from the atmosphere, to the surface, below ground, and back. Part of that pathway involves humans and other organisms, which all have bodies made mostly of water.

As shown in **FIGURE 5.1**, precipitation, such as rain or snow, falls to Earth. Some of this precipitation seeps into the ground, some drops into ponds, streams, lakes, or other waterways, and some forms puddles or other temporary pools. Depending on the type of soil and rocks surrounding it and also on its location, groundwater may empty directly into oceans. Sometimes water flows first into lakes, swamps, or wetlands, but these—along with rivers, streams, and other freshwater sources—also feed into oceans.

In addition, some droplets of water quickly reenter the atmosphere through evaporation. Since oceans cover over 70 percent of Earth's surface, about 85 percent of Earth's evaporation occurs between the oceans and the atmosphere. On land, water vapor is released by plants during transpiration, which is evaporation that occurs between plant leaves and the atmosphere. The cycle is completed as water vapor in the atmosphere condenses and forms clouds, returning water to the surface once again in the form of precipitation.

CONNECT TO

PROPERTIES OF WATER

The presence of water is necessary for life on Earth. All organisms depend on the simple structure of the water molecule. As you learned in the chapter **Chemistry of Life**, water has several unique properties. Water's high specific heat helps keep cells at the right temperature to carry out life processes.

A Analyze **If the total amount of water on Earth does not change, why are there concerns about global freshwater shortages?**

Differentiated Instruction

ENGLISH LEARNERS

Have students form five small groups, and ask questions about one of five cycles described in this section. Students can use the strategy Survey/Question/Read/Recite/Review to monitor learning as they read. They gather information by surveying headings, vocabulary, visuals, and end-of-section questions. They develop questions and read to fill in information. Then students stop to recall the questions, answer them, and then review if needed.

Teacher Toolkit, Section C, SQ3R

BELOW LEVEL

To organize the notes for this section, have students draw each cycle as a diagram (like the one shown in **FIGURE 5.3**) and then annotate it with notes, including:

- the role of the substance in supporting life
- how the substance cycles into and out of the living parts of an ecosystem
- where the cycles overlap

Teacher Toolkit, Section C, Combination Notes

FIGURE 5.1 Hydrologic Cycle

The hydrologic cycle is the circular pathway of water on Earth.

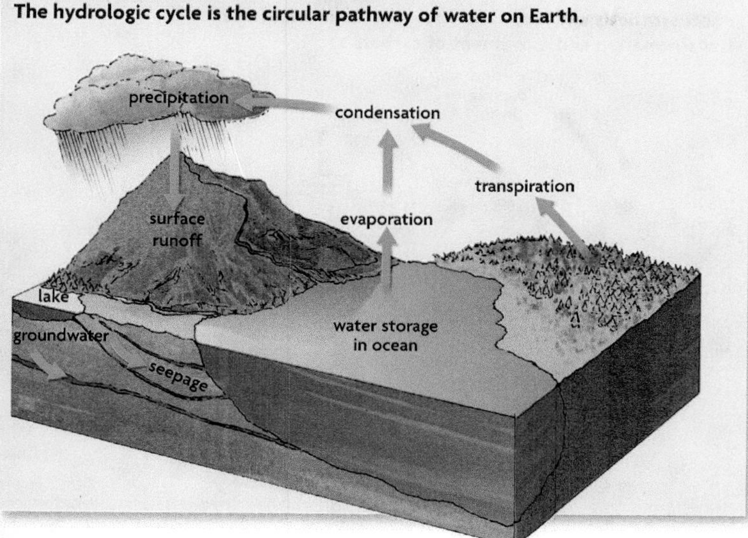

MAIN IDEA

Elements essential for life also cycle through ecosystems.

Many elements are essential to the structure and function of organisms. Elements are basic chemical substances, such as the oxygen and hydrogen found in the chemical compound of water. Additional elements important to life include carbon, nitrogen, phosphorus, and sulfur. As you learned in Chemistry of Life, oxygen, carbon, nitrogen, and hydrogen make up 96 percent of the mass of the human body. This is just one reason why the cycling of these elements is important. All of these elements cycle through ecosystems, as water does.

A **biogeochemical cycle** (BY-oh-JEE-oh-KEHM-ih-kuhl) is the movement of a particular chemical through the biological and geological, or living and nonliving, parts of an ecosystem. Just as water changes from solid form (ice or snow) to liquid form (rain) or gaseous form (water vapor), other substances may also change state as they move through their cycles.

The Oxygen Cycle

Plants, animals, and most other organisms need oxygen for cellular respiration. As shown in **FIGURE 5.2**, plants release oxygen as a waste product during photosynthesis. In turn, humans and other organisms take in this oxygen and release it as carbon dioxide through respiration. Oxygen is also indirectly transferred through an ecosystem by the cycling of other nutrients, including carbon, nitrogen, and phosphorus.

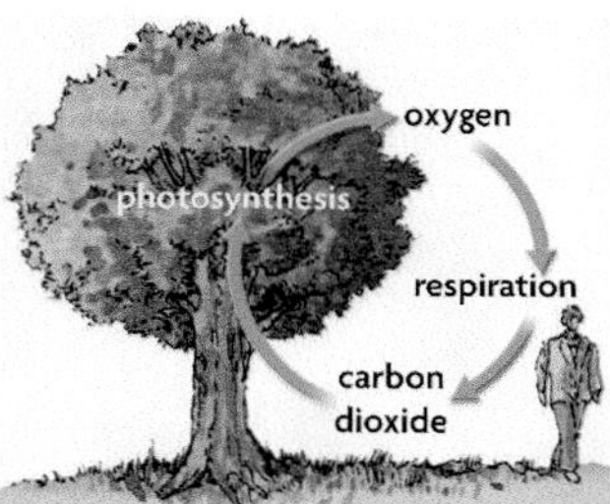

FIGURE 5.2 In the oxygen cycle, oxygen flows into the atmosphere as a byproduct of photosynthesis. Organisms take in this oxygen and release it as carbon dioxide through respiration.

Apply **Explain how deforestation might affect the oxygen cycle.**

INCLUSION

Have a student who is visually impaired work with a small group of students, each of whom will walk through one of the cycles described in the section as if relating a journey. Each student should give a brief description of how one atom or molecule makes its way through a cycle. All the participants should ask questions to clarify.

BELOW LEVEL

Working in pairs, have students address the question of why the cycles shown in this section are referred to as *biogeochemical*. Each pair should think through and answer the question and then share it with the class.

Teacher Toolkit, Section C, Think-Pair-Share

TEACH FROM VISUALS

FIGURE 5.1 During the water cycle, water changes states, alternating between solid, liquid, and vapor. **Ask**

- In which parts of the water cycle is water in the liquid state? precipitation, runoff, ground water, ocean water, lakes, seepage
- What sources of water are used for drinking water and by plants for their life processes? lake, ground water, runoff, precipitation
- What processes return water vapor to the atmosphere? transpiration, evaporation
- What process transforms water vapor to liquid water? condensation
- Which state of water is not shown in the diagram but is still an important reservoir of water? solid: ice, snow

Vocabulary

Academic Vocabulary Students will be familiar with the word **cycle,** which, in a literal sense, means "to move in a circle." However, the word often refers to a sequence of events—for example, a life cycle. Matter in a cycle doesn't literally move in circles, but it does repeatedly move from Earth's physical environment, into living matter, and then back in the environment again.

TEACH FROM VISUALS

FIGURE 5.2 Remind students that both plants and animals respire. Cellular respiration is the process by which eukaryotic cells release energy. Plants, like animals, need oxygen to break down carbohydrates for energy. **Ask,** What organelles use oxygen to release energy? mitochondria

Answers

A **Apply** The loss of trees would result in less oxygen being released into the atmosphere.

Chapter 13: Principles of Ecology **405**

▼ Teach *continued*

Integrating Earth Science

As the theory of **uniformitarianism** states, the same processes that shaped Earth's past are at work in the world today. **Ask,** Does that mean that new supplies of fossil fuels are being generated today? The tectonic processes by which these fuels were generated still occur. Carbon-rich organic matter still returns to the Earth. The difficulty is that to generate more fuel, that organic matter must fall undisturbed into a layer of sediment, get covered by still more layers of sediment or sand, and be compressed into rock under great pressure over millions of years to produce a deposit of coal, oil, or natural gas.

Science Trivia

- The total amount of carbon on Earth is estimated to be 450 quadrillion kilograms.
- There is 50 times as much carbon dissolved in the ocean as exists in the atmosphere, but the majority of carbon is stored in Earth's crust.

FIGURE 5.3 Carbon Cycle

Photosynthesis and respiration account for much of the transformation and movement of carbon.

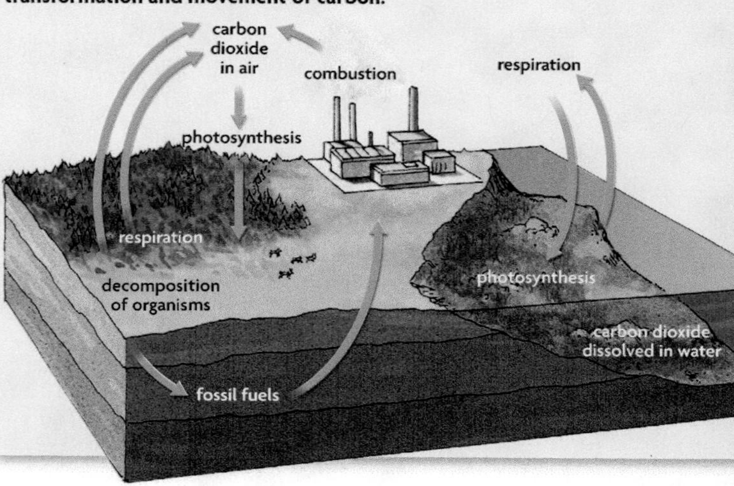

READING TOOLBOX

TAKING NOTES

For each cycle, draw and label a simple diagram in your notes.

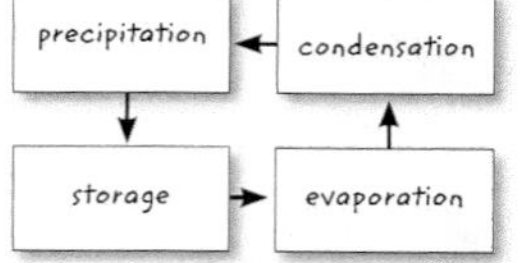

The Carbon Cycle

Carbon is the building block of life—it is key to the structure of all organisms on our planet. It is an essential component of carbohydrates, proteins, fats, and all the other organic molecules that make up your body. Carbon continually flows from the environment to living organisms and back again in the carbon cycle, shown in **FIGURE 5.3.**

Carbon exists in the abiotic world in several forms. Carbon can be found in solid, liquid, and gaseous states. Sources of carbon include

- carbon dioxide (CO_2) gas in the atmosphere
- bicarbonate (HCO_3^-) dissolved in water
- fossil fuels, which are underground deposits of oil, natural gas, and coal
- carbonate rocks, such as limestone
- dead organic matter, such as humus, in the soil

The simplest transfer of carbon occurs between plants and animals. Plants use energy from the sun to convert carbon dioxide from the air into organic material that becomes a part of the plant's structure. The carbon then moves through the biotic world as one organism eats another.

Carbon is returned to the atmosphere as carbon dioxide by respiration or through the decomposition of dead organisms. The burning of fossil fuels and wood, as well as emissions from factories and automobiles, adds to carbon dioxide in the atmosphere. Another source of atmospheric carbon is methane, which is emitted from wetlands, landfills, and livestock.

Not all carbon molecules move freely through the cycle. Areas that store carbon over a long period of time are called carbon sinks. One example is forest land, where large amounts of carbon are stored in the cellulose of wood.

Differentiated Instruction

TEACH WITH TECHNOLOGY

If you have pressure sensors available and the appropriate probeware or CBL technology, you can demonstrate the participation of organisms in biogeochemical cycles. Introducing hydrogen peroxide to a suspension of yeast and glucose in skim milk or antacid will cause hydrogen peroxide to break down into water and oxygen gas. Students can measure the pressure of the oxygen gas released.

PRE-AP

Point out to students that matter that makes up organisms—such as oxygen, carbon, nitrogen, and phosphorus—can cycle through the atmosphere or through sediments at Earth's surface. Have students write a brief analysis of which nutrients cycle through the atmosphere and which cycle through sediments. Have them consider which cycle is more likely to return materials more quickly into an ecosystem.

Teacher Toolkit, Section C, Quick-Write

The Nitrogen Cycle

About 78 percent of Earth's atmosphere is made of nitrogen gas. However, most organisms can use nitrogen only in the form of ions such as ammonium (NH_4^+) or nitrate (NO_3^-). As shown in **FIGURE 5.4**, much of the nitrogen cycle takes place underground.

Certain types of bacteria convert gaseous nitrogen into ammonia (NH_3) through a process called **nitrogen fixation.** A few types of cyanobacteria fix nitrogen in aquatic ecosystems. On land, some nitrogen-fixing bacteria live in small outgrowths, called nodules, on the roots of plants such as beans and peas. Other nitrogen-fixing bacteria live freely in the soil. The ammonia released by these bacteria is transformed into ammonium by the addition of hydrogen ions found in acidic soil. Some ammonium is taken up by plants, but most is used by nitrifying bacteria as an energy source. Through the process called nitrification, these bacteria change ammonium into nitrate.

Nitrates released by soil bacteria are taken up by plants, which convert them into organic compounds such as amino acids and proteins. Nitrogen continues along the cycle as animals eat plant or animal matter. When decomposers break down animal excretions or dead animal and plant matter, nitrogen is returned to the soil as ammonium, in a process called ammonification.

Denitrifying bacteria use nitrate as an oxygen source, releasing nitrogen gas into the atmosphere as a waste product. Some nitrogen also enters the soil as a result of atmospheric fixation by lightning. Lightning's energy breaks apart nitrogen molecules in the atmosphere. Nitrogen recombines with oxygen in the air, forming nitrogen oxide. The combination of nitrogen oxide with rainwater forms nitrates, which are absorbed by the soil.

FIGURE 5.4 Nitrogen Cycle

Much of the nitrogen cycle occurs underground, where bacteria transform ammonium into nitrates, which are used by plants to make amino acids.

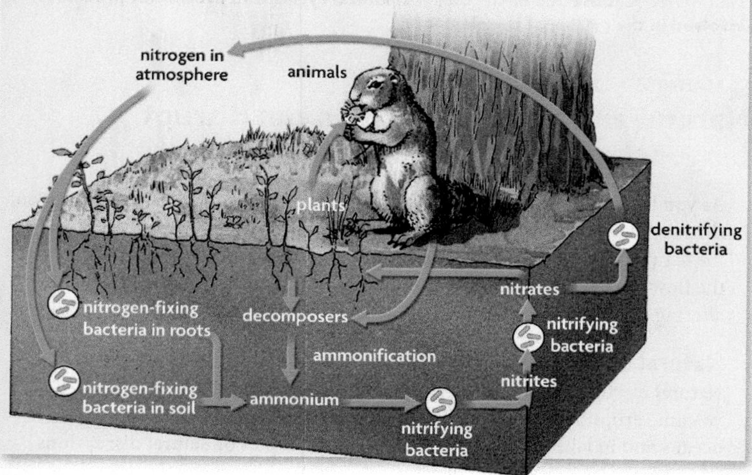

ENGLISH LEARNERS

It might be helpful to students if you model your own analysis of the nitrogen cycle by reading aloud from the text. Show students how to use the text and **FIGURE 5.4** together to clarify the details of what is happening. Once you have demonstrated how to decode the text for meaning, model for students how to summarize the main points.

Integrating Chemistry

Nitrogen makes up nearly 80% of Earth's atmosphere. As a component of DNA and the amino acids that make up proteins, nitrogen is an element essential to all life. However, nitrogen gas, N_2, is very unreactive because of the strong bonds between the nitrogen atoms. To make nitrogen chemically reactive and available to enter into biochemical reactions, the nitrogen must go through **nitrogen fixation,** which in essence means to convert atmospheric nitrogen into usable nitrogen.

Vocabulary

Word Origins Students will probably be most familiar with the sense of fixing as a process of repair. The root of **fix** actually means "to fasten," which is how it is used in this context. Nitrogen gas must be "fastened" into a compound that can then be taken up by plants, bacteria, and ultimately all other living things. Students might be familiar with another derivative of *fix* that has a similar meaning: *affix.*

TEACH FROM VISUALS

FIGURE 5.4 Suggest that students think of the nitrogen cycle diagram as divided into two spheres: atmosphere and lithosphere as represented by the soil. Have students look carefully at the figure. **Ask**

- What is the source of nitrogen for the animal? plant matter
- What is the source of nitrogen for plants? decomposers, bacteria
- What is the source of nitrogen for decomposers? once-living matter
- Which organisms act as a bridge between the nitrogen in the atmosphere and the organisms of the biosphere? bacteria

▼ Teach *continued*

TEACH FROM VISUALS

FIGURE 5.5 Have students note the two smaller cycles that make up the phosphorus cycle. **Ask,** What are the sources of phosphates in the soil? weathering of rocks and decomposition

Answers

A Summarize *Sample answer:* Phosphate is released by the weathering of rocks; plants and fungi take up the phosphate; it is then transferred via the food chain from producers to consumers; phosphate reenters soil or water through decomposition.

Integrating Botany

Phosphorus is an important soil nutrient for plant growth. Commercial fertilizers list a ratio of three numbers on packaging materials. The numbers stand for ratio of nitrogen to phosphorus (delivered as phosphate) to potassium (delivered as potash). Signs of phosphorus deficiency in plants include reddening of leaves and slow or no growth. Signs of too much phosphorus from fertilizers in soil include pale leaves. Before adding fertilizers, home gardeners should test the soil and determine what, if any, nutrients are deficient.

The Phosphorus Cycle

Unlike the other cycles, the phosphorus cycle does not include an atmospheric portion. Instead, most of the cycle takes place at and below ground level, as shown in **FIGURE 5.5.**

FIGURE 5.5 Phosphorus Cycle

The phosphorus cycle occurs on a local, rather than global, scale. Its cycle is limited to water, soil, and ocean sediment.

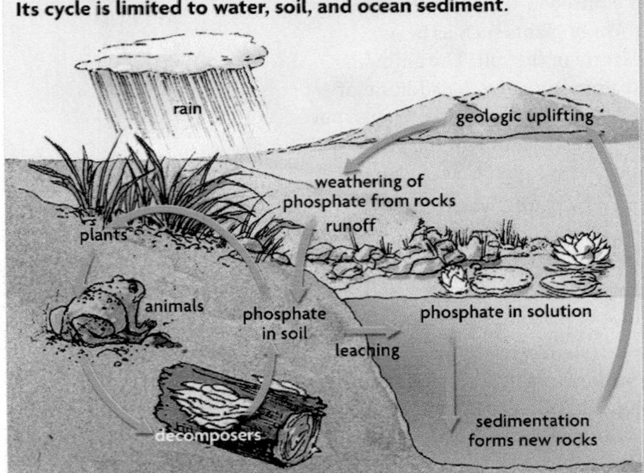

The phosphorus cycle begins when phosphate is released by the weathering of rocks. Plants and some fungi found near plant roots are able to take up phosphate. Phosphorus moves from producers to consumers through the food web. When the producers and consumers die, decomposers break down the organisms. This process releases phosphorus back into the soil or water for use by producers. Some phosphorus may leach into groundwater from the soil. This groundwater may flow into a lake or other body of water, where the phosphorus becomes locked in sediments at the bottom. Over many thousands of years, these sediments eventually become rock again, and the cycle starts again as phosphate is released by the weathering of these newly formed rocks.

Mining and agricultural runoff also add to the overall amount of phosphorus in the environment. The excessive flow of phosphorus into an aquatic ecosystem from sewage and agricultural runoff can cause significant problems. Phosphorus is a limiting factor for the growth of plants. Large amounts of phosphorus within an aquatic environment can lead to algal blooms. These blooms crowd out other plant species and negatively impact wildlife populations as well.

A Summarize **Choose one of the biogeochemical cycles, and list the key processes involved in the cycling of the element.**

MAIN IDEA

Natural and human activities can disrupt biogeochemical cycles and ecosystems.

As you have learned, matter moves through biogeochemical cycles throughout the Earth's ecosystems. But disruptions can occur due to natural events and the actions of humans. The consequences of disruptions include interrupting the flow of elements that serve as chemical building blocks for living systems, altering the balance of nutrients available for organisms, and climate change.

Natural Disruptions

Natural disruptions occur without direct human causation. Earthquakes, volcanic eruptions, variations in weather, and changes to water movement in oceans and in lakes, rivers, and streams are examples of natural disruptions.

Differentiated Instruction

ENGLISH LEARNERS

Students can develop language skills while explaining the movements of phosphorus. In small groups of 2-3, students use their fingers to trace each arrow from the phosphorus cycle in **FIGURE 5.5.** Students should describe each arrow using a complete sentence.

Teacher Toolkit, Section C Sequence Diagram

FIGURE 5.6 Natural Disruptions to Biogeochemical Cycles

Natural disruptions have occurred throughout the history of Earth and will continue.

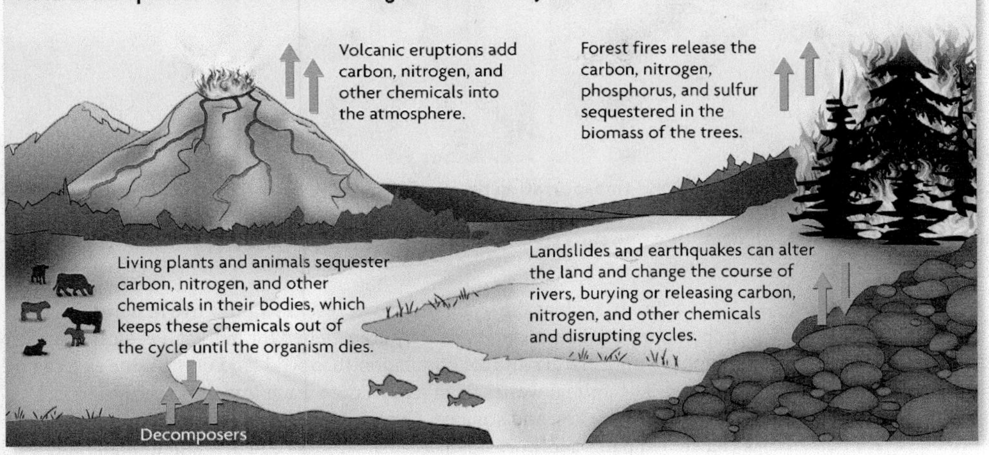

Volcanic eruptions add carbon, nitrogen, and other chemicals into the atmosphere.

Forest fires release the carbon, nitrogen, phosphorus, and sulfur sequestered in the biomass of the trees.

Living plants and animals sequester carbon, nitrogen, and other chemicals in their bodies, which keeps these chemicals out of the cycle until the organism dies.

Landslides and earthquakes can alter the land and change the course of rivers, burying or releasing carbon, nitrogen, and other chemicals and disrupting cycles.

Decomposers

The history of Earth includes many examples of significant natural disruptions, such as a series of volcanic eruptions about 250 million years ago. The consequences of the eruptions and other natural disruptions included the Permian mass extinction and the end of the Paleozoic Era. As shown in **FIGURE 5.6**, volcanic eruptions release gases, ash, and other substances into the atmosphere. The carbon dioxide and nitrogen gases released may overload normal cycles. Also, particles released can block and reduce the amount of sunlight that reaches Earth for several years. When less sunlight reaches Earth, the process of photosynthesis is adversely affected, which in turn, disrupts biogeochemical cycles.

Natural disruptions take place all the time, and most do not lead to mass extinctions. Variations in conditions are normal and disruptions of biogeochemical cycles are compensated for by other events. For example, the growth of forested areas sequesters carbon by taking it out of the carbon cycle and locking it into organisms. However, forest fires, another natural disruption, release the carbon tied up in forest plants back into the atmosphere.

Other natural disruptions include earthquakes, landslides, and changes in water movement. Such disruptions may bury or release materials used in biogeochemical cycles and ecosystems. For example, when a river changes course, the flowing water causes erosion to the land in the river's new path. Phosphorus within the eroded land is released and enters the water phase of the phosphorus cycle.

Disruptions Caused by Humans

Human actions disrupt both biogeochemical cycles and ecosystems. As the human population grows, so do our needs. Agriculture is responsible for growing most of the foods that humans eat and many products needed for many industries. But poor farming practices cause disruptions to the cycles.

BELOW LEVEL

Discuss that a disruption to a cycle does not mean the cycle is stopped. Rather, it means the normal rates and amounts of substance are increased or decreased. Use a cycle diagram from previous pages to discuss how significantly increasing or decreasing a substance in one step of the cycle must be addressed by subsequent steps.

PRE-AP

Have students spend five minutes creating cause-and-effect chains describing how a natural disruption or a disruption caused by humans affects multiple biogeochemical cycles.

Teacher Toolkit, Section C, Cause-and-Effect Chain

Science Trivia

Mount St. Helen's is an active volcano in the state of Washington.

- The last major eruption began in 1980, followed by smaller eruptions occurring on and off from 1986-2006.
- The volume of ash deposited after the largest eruption in 1980 was 1.4 billion cubic yards or 0.26 cubic miles.

TEACH FROM VISUALS

FIGURE 5.6 Have students use the diagram of natural disruptions to identify one disruption in the image. **Ask,** How does this disruption affect the water, carbon, nitrogen, and phosphorus cycles? How will the cycles rebalance and recover over time? Answers will vary depending on the disruption chosen. Students should recognize that disruptions are compensated for by other events.

Integrating Climatology

The concentration of carbon dioxide today has increased 30 percent since preindustrial times. If the present amount of carbon dioxide emission continues, this concentration will double by 2080. Many scientists speculate that as a result, Earth's temperature may rise by 3°C.

Vocabulary

Word Origins Remind students that breaking a word into word parts can help to identify relationships with other words. The prefix *eu-* means "true" or "good" and the stem *troph* means "nourishment." Eutrophication literally means a condition of good nourishment. Other words that use *eu-* include *euphemism*, the use of a good or pleasant term instead of a harsh one, and *euphoria*, a feeling of great goodness or elation. Other words that use *troph* include *autotroph*, an organism that makes its own food, and *heterotroph*, an organism that gets food from other organisms.

Answers

A Describe *Sample answer:* Poor farming practices can lead to phosphorus runoff in water sources. The consequences of too much phosphorus in water sources include the overgrowth of algae populations and eutrophication.

▼ Assess and Reteach

Assess Use the Section Self-Check or Section Quiz, both available at **HMHScience.com**.

Reteach Have student groups summarize the different cycles. Suggest that they use the figures in the section and trace the movement of water or an element through the ecosystem. Assign each student a different cycle to summarize for the group, or have students divide up the work among themselves.

FIGURE 5.7 Disruptions Caused by Humans

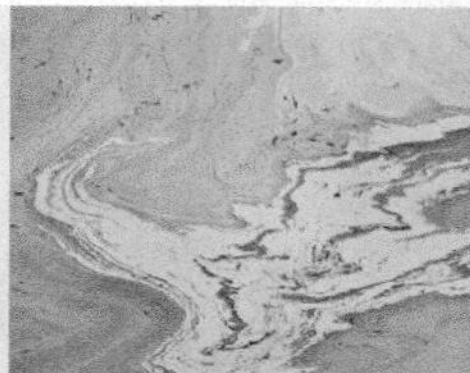

Some of the methods used to meet food and transportation needs of humans, such as raising herds of livestock and driving vehicles, have consequences for biogeochemical cycles and ecosystems. Algal blooms, which crowd out aquatic plants and cause fish death, are one such consequence.

Herd animals, such as the water buffalo in **FIGURE 5.7**, may live in dense populations or in feedlots where they are fattened for market. Feedlots can support a much larger animal population than wild land of the same size can support. The animal wastes from feedlots can leach into groundwater or run off into rivers, lakes, and streams. Contamination of water with fecal matter can spread pathogenic organisms, causing illness and death in humans and other organisms.

Poor farming practices can also lead to depletion of soil nutrients, such as nitrogen and phosphorus. Replacing these nutrients through man-made fertilizers can lead to contaminated runoff. When fertilizer-contaminated runoff enters bodies of water, the nutrients promote the overgrowth of algae populations and can cause algal blooms . The algae crowd out aquatic plants and may release harmful toxins. As the algae die and decay, the decomposition process uses up oxygen in the water, causing fish and other organisms to die.

Agricultural practices are not the only ways that humans disrupt biogeochemical cycles and ecosystems. Cars, factories, and power plants burn fossil fuels and release carbon into the atmosphere as carbon dioxide. As a result, the amount of carbon dioxide in the atmosphere has steadily increased, which in turn contributes to climate change. Climate change is an overall increase in the temperature of the Earth, which further disrupts cycles and ecosystems.

Describe **Choose one way that humans disrupt biogeochemical cycles and describe the consequences of the disruption.**

13.5 Formative Assessment

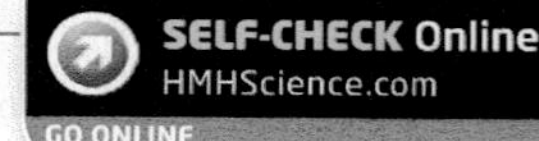

REVIEWING MAIN IDEAS

1. How does the **hydrologic cycle** move water through the environment?
2. Describe a human activity that disrupts the carbon cycle and the consequences of that disruption.

CRITICAL THINKING

3. **Summarize** How can microorganisms, such as some green algae, affect the health of organisms in aquatic ecosystems?
4. **Synthesize** Explain the importance of decomposers to the overall **biogeochemical cycle**.

CONNECT TO EVOLUTION

5. How might Earth's biogeochemical cycles help scientists to understand the early history of life on Earth?

13.5 FORMATIVE ASSESSMENT

1. Precipitation falls to Earth, and transpiration and evaporation transfer water back into the atmosphere as water vapor.
2. *Sample answer:* Humans drive vehicles that burn fossil fuels and release carbon dioxide into the atmosphere. Carbon dioxide is a greenhouse gas that contributes to climate change.
3. Microorganisms can crowd out and use the resources needed by other organisms in an ecosystem. Algae may harm or kill other organisms by releasing toxins. Decomposition of dead algae uses up dissolved oxygen and promotes eutrophication.
4. Decomposers break down organisms and release various elements, including nitrogen and phosphorus, which other organisms can then use.
5. Studies of the biogeochemical cycles and how they interact may help scientists reconstruct the sequence of events that led to changes at Earth's surface that would enable different types of organisms to evolve.

13.6 Pyramid Models

KEY CONCEPT **Pyramids model the distribution of energy and matter in an ecosystem.**

VOCABULARY

biomass
energy pyramid

MAIN IDEAS

- An energy pyramid shows the distribution of energy among trophic levels.
- Other pyramid models illustrate an ecosystem's biomass and distribution of organisms.

Connect to Your World

You have likely seen pictures of the pyramids of Ancient Egypt. Each level of a pyramid requires a larger level below it for support. Similarly, each trophic level requires a larger level beneath it to support its energy needs. Ecologists use the structure of a pyramid as a model to describe trophic levels in ecosystems. Pyramids can represent the general flow of energy in an ecosystem or the mass or number of organisms at each trophic level.

MAIN IDEA

An energy pyramid shows the distribution of energy among trophic levels.

Nearly all ecosystems get their energy from sunlight. Sunlight provides the energy for photosynthesis, and that energy flows up the food chain. However, along the way, some of the energy is dissipated, or lost. Recall that when energy changes form, the total amount of energy is conserved, but some of the energy is no longer useful for doing work. For instance, producers use energy from sunlight to make food. Herbivores eat the plants, but in the process, some energy is given off as heat. Carnivores then eat the herbivores, but again lose energy as heat. In other words, each level in the food chain contains much less useful energy than the level below it.

Loss of Available Energy

Each meal that you consume is packed with energy in the form of proteins, fats, and carbohydrates. Your body uses this energy for many purposes such as movement and growth. The majority of the food you consume is used to keep your body at its normal temperature. Your body is very inefficient at converting what you consume into useful energy, so there will always be some material that is not used. Unused material is simply excreted as waste.

Energy in an ecosystem works in much the same way, only on a larger scale. **Biomass** is a measure of the total dry mass of organisms in a given area. When a consumer incorporates the biomass of a producer into its own biomass, a great deal of energy is lost in the process as heat and waste. The conversion of biomass from a producer into biomass of the consumer is inefficient.

Consider the simple producer-to-consumer food chain of grass–prairie dog. Photosynthesis stores energy as carbohydrates, which can be thought of as a high-quality form of energy. A hungry prairie dog then eats the grass.

CONNECT TO

CELLULAR RESPIRATION

As you learned in the chapter **Cells and Energy**, the processes of cellular respiration use ATP to maintain your body's functions. While the chemical reactions of metabolism are relatively efficient, there will always be some loss of available energy.

Differentiated Instruction

ENGLISH LEARNERS

Students will see a series of pyramid models in this section that appear almost identical. Have students copy the diagrams into their notebooks and then look carefully at the captions and labels. Have students summarize for you the differences between these models.

Teacher Toolkit, Section D, Context Clues

SECTION 13.6

B.2.3 Use mathematical and/or computational representations to support claims for the cycling of matter and flow of energy among organisms in an ecosystem.

Plan and Prepare

Activate Prior Knowledge Tell students that the unit of measure of energy in an ecosystem is one they can readily find by looking on just about any package of the food they buy. **Ask**

- How is food energy measured? in Calories
- What do Calories measure? the amount of energy needed to produce a certain amount of heat

Teach

Vocabulary

Academic Vocabulary The word **efficiency** is often associated with business, describing the least wasteful use of time, materials, and energy. In ecology, *efficiency* is a measure of how much of the energy stored in producers as biomass is available to support the consumers of an ecosystem.

Teach *continued*

TEACH FROM VISUALS

FIGURE 6.1 Make sure students understand that the shape of an energy pyramid represents the amount of energy available at each trophic level. The pyramid shape works because each succeeding trophic level typically supports fewer individuals.

Ask, Why are there fewer owls than prairie dogs in a prairie ecosystem? Less energy is available to support the owl population because energy is lost at each trophic level.

Vocabulary

kilocalorie A kilocalorie (kcal) is equal to 1000 calories, also referred to as a gram or small calorie, written with a lowercase c. The Calories (capital C) listed on food labels are each equivalent to 1 kilocalorie, or 1000 small calories.

Answers

A Connect Pyramids should show grass in the bottom level, cottontails in the middle level, and hawks in the top level. Arrows should point from the bottom level to the middle level and from the middle level to the top level. Each level should also include outward-pointing arrows to show energy loss.

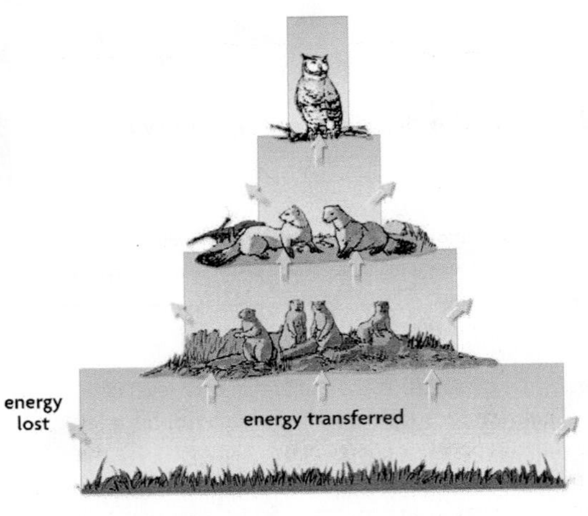

FIGURE 6.1 An energy pyramid illustrates the energy flow between trophic levels in an ecosystem. Between each tier, up to 90 percent of the energy is lost as heat into the atmosphere.

Some of the energy is used by the animal to grow. The remaining energy may be used to fuel cellular respiration or remains undigested. The dissipation, or loss, of energy between trophic levels may be as much as 90 percent, meaning that only 10 percent of the available energy is left to transfer from one trophic level to another.

Energy Pyramids

Because energy is lost at each stage of a food chain, the longer the chain is, the more energy is lost overall. The total energy used by producers far exceeds the energy used by the consumers they support. This concept can be illustrated with an energy pyramid. An **energy pyramid** is a diagram that compares energy used by producers, primary consumers, and other trophic levels. The pyramid, therefore, illustrates how available energy is distributed among trophic levels in an ecosystem. The unit of measurement used to describe the amount of energy at each trophic level in an energy pyramid is the kilocalorie (kcal).

A typical energy pyramid has a very large section at the base for the producers, and sections that become progressively smaller above. For example, in a prairie ecosystem, as illustrated in **FIGURE 6.1**, energy flows from grass at the producer level, to prairie dogs at the primary consumer level, to black-footed ferrets at the secondary consumer level, to a great horned owl at the tertiary consumer level.

A Connect Draw an energy pyramid for the desert food chain introduced in Section 4. Use arrows to illustrate the flow of energy.

MAIN IDEA

Other pyramid models illustrate an ecosystem's biomass and distribution of organisms.

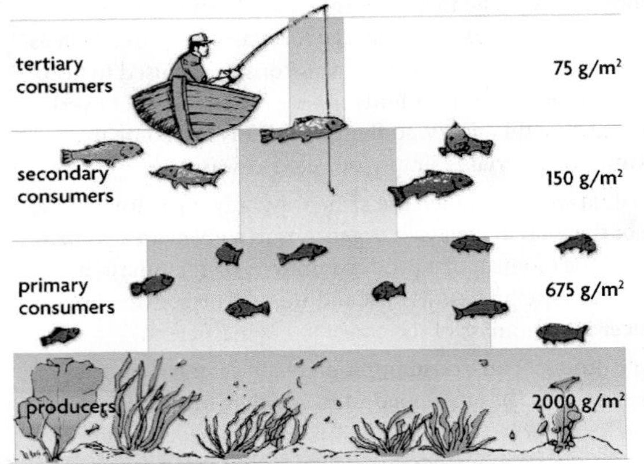

FIGURE 6.2 The biomass pyramid depicts the total dry mass of organisms found at each trophic level.

A biomass pyramid is a diagram that compares the biomass of different trophic levels within an ecosystem. Unlike an energy pyramid, which represents energy use, a biomass pyramid provides a picture of the mass of producers needed to support primary consumers, the mass of primary consumers required to support secondary consumers, and so on.

In a pond ecosystem, such as the one illustrated in **FIGURE 6.2**, a biomass pyramid shows that the total dry mass (given in grams per square meter, or g/m^2) of algae within the pond is far greater than the dry mass of fish. This example illustrates yet again the important role producers play in maintaining a stable ecosystem.

Differentiated Instruction

BELOW LEVEL

Have students use a chart to compare all the pyramids shown in this section. Tell them to identify at least two features common to all the pyramids. Tell them not to use shape as one of the features. Have them note the key difference that makes each pyramid distinctive.

Teacher Toolkit, Section C, Content Frame

PRE-AP

For students to see how quickly energy flows from an ecosystem, have them calculate the loss of energy in a sample ecosystem, using percents. Students should start with a pyramid that has 15,000 energy units. Remind them that 90 percent of available energy is lost from one trophic level to the next. Have them continue to make the calculation until they reach a value less than one. Have them do a calculation for a system twice the size of the first to see if there is an appreciable difference.

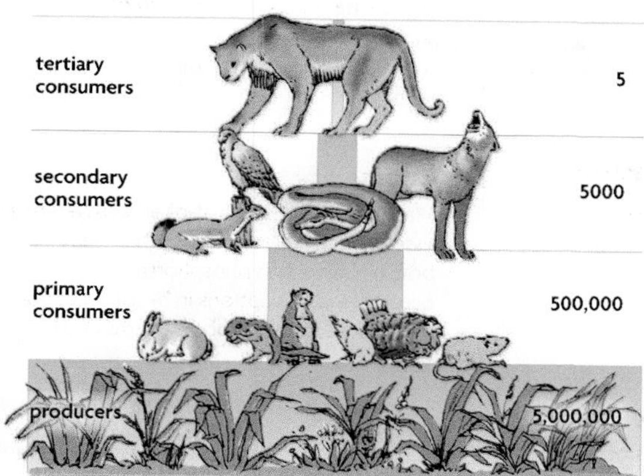

FIGURE 6.3 In a pyramid of numbers, each tier represents the actual number of individual organisms present in each trophic level.

A pyramid of numbers shows the number of individual organisms at each trophic level in an ecosystem. For example, a pyramid of numbers depicting a mountainous habitat, as shown in **FIGURE 6.3**, might include organisms such as grasses, snowshoe hares, gophers, coyotes, snakes, and mountain lions. This type of pyramid is particularly effective in showing the vast number of producers required to support even a few top level consumers.

In certain situations, both biomass pyramids and pyramids of numbers may occur in an inverted, or upside down, formation. Consider, for example, a pyramid of numbers based on a single tree. This single tree would be greatly outnumbered by the primary and secondary consumers, such as insects and birds, that live within it. In this case, the upper tiers of the pyramid of numbers would be much larger than the bottom tier representing the single tree.

A Apply If a scientist wanted to compare the exact number of organisms at each trophic level within a desert ecosystem, which pyramid model would he or she use?

Vegetarian Alligators

Vocabulary

Academic Vocabulary The word **distribution** is used to describe the pyramid models shown in this section. The word is also used in business, as in the distribution of goods, and in law, as in the distribution of property. The concept that is common to these two uses is the idea of an *allotment,* a share or portion of a larger whole that is divided among different groups or individuals. The distribution shown in ecological pyramids is somewhat different. The word refers to the *arrangement* of organisms through which energy flows.

Answers

A Apply pyramid of numbers

13.6 Formative Assessment

REVIEWING MAIN IDEAS

1. How does an **energy pyramid** help to describe energy flow in a food web?
2. What is the difference between a **biomass** pyramid and a pyramid of numbers?

CRITICAL THINKING

3. **Apply** How would you draw a pyramid of numbers for a dog with fleas? What shape would the pyramid take?
4. **Calculate** If each level in a food chain typically loses 90 percent of the energy it takes in, and the producer level uses 1000 kcal of energy, how much of that energy is left after the third trophic level?

CONNECT TO

NUTRITION

5. Why is an herbivorous diet more energy efficient than a carnivorous diet? Explain your answer.

Assess and Reteach ▼

Assess Use the Section Self-Check or Section Quiz, both available at **HMHScience.com**.

Reteach Draw on the board a pyramid with three levels. Pointing to each trophic level, ask students what each level represents and what units are used for each pyramid type: energy, biomass, and numbers.

13.6 FORMATIVE ASSESSMENT

1. An energy pyramid shows the relative contribution to energy flow made by each trophic level in an ecosystem.
2. A biomass pyramid compares the mass of organisms that make up each trophic level in an ecosystem; a pyramid of numbers compares the number of individual organisms that make up each trophic level.
3. The bottom level of the pyramid would be the dog, and the fleas would be the top level. This would be an inverted pyramid because there are many fleas to just one dog.
4. The first trophic level uses 1000 kcal; the second trophic level uses 100 kcal; the third trophic level uses 10 kcal, leaving 1 kcal.
5. A herbivorous diet is more energy efficient because it is the closest trophic level to the producers, meaning there is more available energy to use.

CHAPTER REVIEW

GO ONLINE

Encourage students to go to **HMHScience.com** for a detailed review of each section, including visuals and vocabulary practice.

Online Student Resources, Vocabulary Practice Worksheet

CHAPTER 13 **Summary**

BIG IDEA Living things interact with other organisms and with their environment.

KEY CONCEPTS

13.1 Ecologists Study Relationships

Ecology is the study of the relationships among organisms and their environment. Ecologists study environments at different levels of organization. Ecologists use methods such as observation, experimentation, and modeling to study ecological principles.

13.2 Biotic and Abiotic Factors

Every ecosystem includes both living and nonliving factors. Changing one factor in an ecosystem can affect many other factors. The removal of a keystone species may lead to changes in an ecosystem's biodiversity.

13.3 Energy in Ecosystems

Life in an ecosystem requires a source of energy. Producers provide energy for other organisms in an ecosystem. Most producers obtain their energy from sunlight through photosynthesis. Other producers obtain their energy through a process called chemosynthesis.

13.4 Food Chains and Food Webs

Food chains and food webs model the flow of energy in an ecosystem. A food chain is a simple model that shows a sequence of feeding relationships. A food web provides a more complex picture of the network of feeding relationships among organisms in an ecosystem.

13.5 Cycling of Matter

Matter cycles in and out of an ecosystem. Elements essential for life on Earth, such as water, oxygen, carbon, nitrogen, and phosphorus, also cycle through ecosystems. Disruptions in biogeochemical cycles have consequences for organisms and ecosystems.

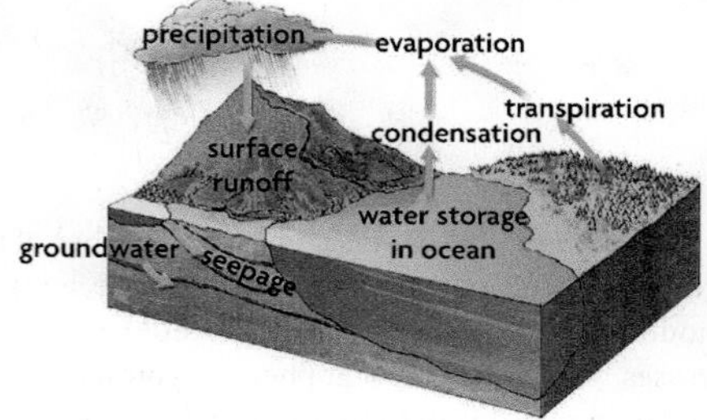

13.6 Pyramid Models

Pyramids model the distribution of energy and matter in an ecosystem. An energy pyramid shows the distribution of energy in a food chain. Energy flows upward from producers to consumers. Between each tier of the energy pyramid, energy is lost as heat. Sometimes only 10 percent of the original energy is transferred to the next trophic level. A biomass pyramid shows the total mass of organisms at each trophic level, while a pyramid of numbers shows the actual number of organisms present in each trophic level.

energy lost

energy transferred

READING TOOLBOX SYNTHESIZE YOUR NOTES

Energy Pyramid Add labels and organisms that belong in each trophic level to this energy pyramid.

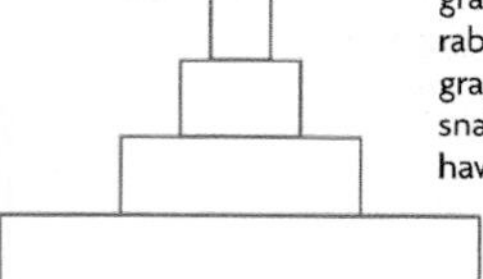

Concept Map Use a concept map to summarize what you know about food webs.

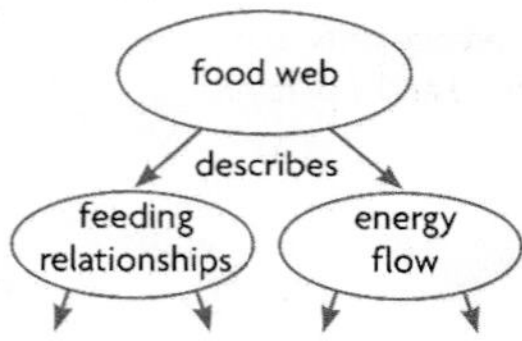

Reviewing Vocabulary

1. Biotic factor—both are parts of an ecosystem. Biotic factors are living things; abiotic factors are nonliving things.
2. Consumer—both get energy from food. Consumers obtain food from producers; producers make their own food.
3. Autotroph—both get energy from food. Heterotrophs obtain food from producers; autotrophs make their own food.
4. Herbivore—both are types of consumers. Carnivores eat only animals; herbivores eat only plants.
5. Generalist—both are types of consumers. Specialists eat only one or a few types of food; generalists eat many types of food.
6. The root *vore* means "to eat." It is used in the names of consumers, which eat other organisms.
7. All but one of the terms refers to the living components of ecosystems, describing different aspects. The exception is "abiotic," which refers to the nonliving components.
8. An ecosystem is a home to both living and nonliving things in an area.
9. Both processes are involved in making carbohydrates by chemically combining other substances.

3 Review

INTERACTIVE Review
HMHScience.com
GO ONLINE
Review Games • Concept Map • Section Self-Checks

:HAPTER VOCABULARY

3.1 ecology
community
ecosystem
biome

3.2 biotic
abiotic
biodiversity
keystone species

3.3 producer
autotroph
consumer
heterotroph
chemosynthesis

13.4 food chain
herbivore
carnivore
omnivore
detritivore
decomposer
specialist
generalist
trophic level
food web

13.5 hydrologic cycle
biogeochemical cycle
nitrogen fixation

13.6 biomass
energy pyramid

؛eviewing Vocabulary

ind an Opposite

air each of the words listed below with a different ocabulary term that has an opposing definition. Then, rite one sentence describing a difference.

1. abiotic factor
2. producer
3. heterotroph
4. carnivore
5. specialist

EADING TOOLBOX GREEK AND LATIN WORD ORIGINS

Jse the definitions of the word parts to answer the ollowing questions.

Part	Meaning
bio-	life
eco-	home
syn-	together, joined
vore	eat

6. Explain why the root *vore* is used in the appropriate vocabulary terms.

7. Six vocabulary terms include the prefix *bio-*. Describe how they are all related.

8. Use the meaning of *eco-* to write your own definition of *ecosystem*.

9. *Photo-* means "light," and *chemo-* means "chemical." Explain why *photosynthesis* and *chemosynthesis* both include the prefix *syn-*.

Reviewing MAIN IDEAS

10. How can an individual organism simultaneously be part of a population, community, ecosystem, and biome?

11. What are the major differences between observation, experimentation, and modeling?

12. A biomass pyramid and a pyramid of numbers are two ways of modeling the flow of matter in an ecosystem. What is the main difference between the two?

13. What is a keystone species and how might the removal of it affect the stability of and biodiversity within its ecosystem?

14. What would happen to a forest ecosystem if a fire killed most of its producers?

15. Describe one similarity and one difference between photosynthesis and chemosynthesis.

16. An acorn is eaten by a squirrel, which is eaten by an owl. What model best describes this simple relationship, and how does it show energy flow?

17. How is a food web related to energy flow within an ecosystem?

18. Describe the main processes involved in the hydrologic cycle.

19. Give an example of one biogeochemical cycle and explain how it is important to living things.

20. How does a biomass pyramid show the flow of matter in an ecosystem?

Reviewing Main Ideas

10. An individual organism is involved in many interactions within its environment. It interacts with others of the same species in a population, with different species in a community, and with abiotic factors in an ecosystem, which is part of a biome.

11. Observation involves watching and recording what is occurring naturally, experimentation is a controlled procedure designed to answer a question, and modeling is used to determine what might happen in the future.

12. Energy pyramids compare the energy used by organisms at different tropic levels and biomass pyramids show the biomass needed at each tropic level.

13. A keystone species has an unusually large effect on shaping an ecosystem. Its removal may change an ecosystem by decreasing its stability and amount of biodiversity.

14. Primary consumers might die out or move to a new location because their food source is gone. Secondary consumers might die out or move to a new location because of the lack of primary consumers to eat.

15. Similarity: both form carbohydrates. Difference: photosynthesis uses sunlight as an energy source; chemosynthesis uses chemicals.

16. A food chain would best describe this relationship. Energy flows from the acorn to the squirrel to the owl.

17. A food web is made up of many interconnected food chains. At each trophic level in a food chain, some energy is stored in new structures within organisms, but most energy is dissipated into the environment.

18. Precipitation moves water from the atmosphere to Earth's surface, evaporation and transpiration return water to the atmosphere as water vapor, and condensation leads to cloud formation and precipitation.

19. Answers should describe how an element or compound cycles between the environment and living matter. *Sample answer:* Carbon, an element found in all living matter, is brought into an ecosystem through producers by photosynthesis. Producers are the source of carbon compounds for consumers. Some carbon returns to the atmosphere through respiration. The rest returns to the environment as organisms die and their remains are broken down by decomposers.

20. An biomass pyramid compares the biomass at different trophic levels in an ecosystem. The pyramid shows the mass of producers needed to support primary consumers, the mass of primary consumers needed to support secondary consumers, and so on.

Chapter 13: Principles of Ecology **415**

Critical Thinking

21. Apply At what level of organization would a scientist study the interaction between seals and polar bears in the Arctic? Explain your answer.

22. Apply Explain which biotic factors used by the beaver are related to its role as a keystone species.

23. Evaluate Scientists used to say that all living things depend on the sun. Explain why this statement is no longer valid.

24. Analyze How might a drought affect a grassland food web? Which trophic level would the drought affect the most? Explain your answer.

25. Synthesize Humans have changed many ecosystems on Earth. Compare different types of consumers, and predict which types would be more likely to adapt to these changes and which would not. Explain your answers.

26. Synthesize Use the information you learned about carbon-based molecules to explain a human's need to participate in the biogeochemical cycles.

27. Connect What role do decomposers play in the nitrogen cycle?

28. Predict In a pyramid of numbers, the highest organism has the smallest number of individuals in a community. What might happen if this organism increased its numbers significantly? Explain the effect this increase would have on the other members of the community.

Interpreting Visuals

Use the energy pyramid below to answer the following questions.

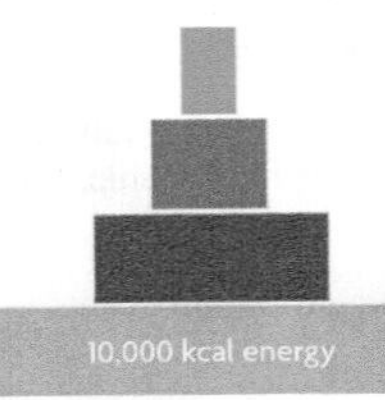

29. Apply Use the energy pyramid to describe the flow of energy within an ecosystem. Identify which tier represents producers, primary consumers, and so on.

30. Calculate If 90 percent of the energy is lost as heat between trophic levels, approximately how much energy is available to the secondary consumers in this energy pyramid? Show your calculations.

Analyzing Data Estimate Population Size

Use the equation $T = N \times A$ to estimate the population size in questions 31–32. Show all of your work.

31. Calculate A scientist wants to estimate the population of mushrooms on a forest floor with an area of 300 m^2. Each quadrat is 2 m^2. She counts 13 mushrooms in 20 quadrats. What is the population of mushrooms in the forest?

32. Calculate A scientist uses quadrats to sample the population of strawberry cactus plants in a section of the Chihuahuan desert that is 150 m^2. He counts 5 cacti in 10 quadrats. Each quadrat is 2 m^2. What is the population of strawberry cacti in the desert?

33. Analyze What are the advantages and disadvantages of using random sampling to obtain an estimate of the population size?

34. Evaluate A scientist uses quadrats to determine the population size of lupines in a field 500 m^2 in size. She uses ten 1 m^2 quadrats. Is this an adequate sample size? Explain your answer.

35. Apply Scientists often use tables of random numbers to determine where to place quadrats on their study site. Why might they do this? Why can't they choose where to place the quadrats?

36. Apply A scientist wants to determine the population size of whiptail lizards within a 15-acre area. What sampling method should she use? How can she ensure that she obtains an accurate estimate of the lizard population? Explain your answer.

Making Connections

37. Write About Your Own Ecosystem Imagine you built a large greenhouse in your home to create your own ecosystem. What types of organisms would you include? How would you ensure that the biogeochemical cycles were in place? Describe in detail an ecosystem you would like to have in your home. Be sure to include the biotic and abiotic factors in your explanation of how the ecosystem would sustain itself.

38. Make a Food Web Read the description of anhingas on the chapter opener and draw a partial food web of a freshwater marsh ecosystem. Include producers and consumers in your web.

Critical Thinking

21. Scientists would study the interactions between seals and polar bears at the community level of organization.
22. Beavers use trees to block moving water, which in turn changes the habitat and allows for more types of organisms to populate the ecosystem.
23. Chemosynthetic organisms use chemicals instead of sunlight as an energy source to make food.
24. Producers might die out because of water loss, which might reduce the number of herbivores who have less food available. Carnivores would also be affected by loss of prey. The producer populations might be most affected because they cannot move from the drought area.
25. Omnivores and generalists would be the most likely to adapt to changes in their environments because they eat a wide variety of foods. Specialists and carnivores would have the most difficult time adapting to changes in the environment because their diets are more restricted.
26. Carbon is the central element in organic molecules that make up all organisms. Carbon compounds incorporate different elements such as oxygen, nitrogen, phosphorous—all of which are needed for carbohydrates, nucleic acids, lipids, and proteins. The source of these materials for humans are biogeochemical cycles that make carbon compounds available as food.
27. Decomposers release nitrogen into the soil as ammonia as they break down dead organic matter.
28. Consumers at the top of a pyramid are often larger carnivores. If their number increases, this may reduce the number of prey animals at the middle levels of the pyramid. Producers might increase in number as a result of fewer herbivores.

Interpreting Visuals

29. As you move up the energy pyramid, less energy is available for organisms at each trophic level to use. Typically 90 percent of the energy is lost between trophic levels, so only 10 percent is transferred from one trophic level to the next. The bottom level is producers, then primary consumers, secondary consumers, and tertiary consumers.
30. 100 kcal ($10{,}000 - 9000 = 1000$; $1000 - 900 = 100$)

Analyzing Data

31. 98 mushrooms
32. 38 cacti
33. Random sampling lets scientists estimate population size without having to count every single organism within the population. However, there is a chance that the sample is not representative of the group as a whole, so the estimate may be too high or too low.
34. This would not be an adequate sample size, because for such a large area, more quadrats should be used.
35. Scientists use random number tables to avoid introducing bias into the sampling process. Avoiding bias is also why they cannot choose the plot sites themselves.

Standards-Based Assessment

Record your answers on a separate piece of paper.

MULTIPLE CHOICE

1 The nitrogen cycle relies on various organisms carrying out very specific functions. One vital group is that of nitrogen-fixing bacteria. Which of the following explains how the nitrogen cycle would be disrupted if there was a sudden population explosion of nitrogen-fixing bacteria in an aquatic ecosystem?

A A population explosion of nitrogen-fixing bacteria would lead to a decrease in ammonium levels in the water, which will cause the water to become very acidic.

B A population explosion of nitrogen-fixing bacteria will cause dissolved nitrogen levels in the water to increase.

C A population explosion of nitrogen-fixing bacteria will cause dissolved oxygen and dissolved carbon dioxide levels to decrease.

D A population explosion of nitrogen-fixing bacteria will cause ammonia levels to rise, which can be detected by testing the ammonia levels in the water.

2

hawk
coyote
snakes
lizards
squirrel
insects
sheep
sagebrush
cacti

The food web above shows the relationships between organisms in an ecosystem. Which type of organism not shown in this food web is important to the stability of the ecosystem?

A producer

B consumer

C herbivore

D decomposer

3 Several types of plant species grew in an empty lot. The city council decided to turn the lot into a park and planted grass alone to create a playing field. The ecological factor that was ***most likely*** affected by the change was the lot's —

A biomass

B carbon cycle

C biodiversity

D hydrologic cycle

4 In the carbon cycle, through what process does carbon move from an abiotic resource into organic matter?

A deforestation

B combustion

C respiration

D photosynthesis

5

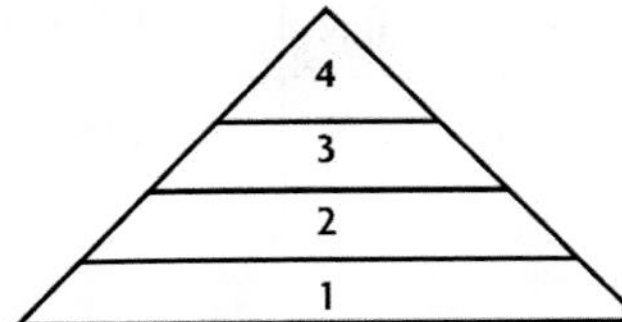

In which direction does energy flow through the energy pyramid shown above?

A 4, 3, 2, 1

B 1, 2, 3, 4

C 2, 1, 3, 4

D 3, 4, 2, 1

THINK THROUGH THE QUESTION

Remember that an energy pyramid shows the amount of energy in each trophic level, with producers at the bottom of the pyramid, and consumers at the top.

36. The scientist could use the mark-recapture method to determine the population size. She should set out a number of traps that evenly cover the entire study site area to be sure that all the lizards within the area have an equal chance of being caught.

Making Connections

37. Students should include plants, bacteria, soil, and water at a minimum to maintain an ecosystem. Any animals would need to have continuing food sources and adequate space.

38. *Sample answers:* Producers include algae and aquatic plants. Primary consumers include insects, secondary consumers include fish, and tertiary consumers include anhingas. Other animals in the ecosystem might include alligators (tertiary consumers) and other aquatic birds, such as herons or cormorants (both tertiary consumers).

Standards-Based Assessment

The Standards-Based Assessment questions will help students prepare for their final examination in the course. If you wish to give students practice in coding their answers, look for the Standards-Based Assessment Answer Sheet at **HMHScience.com**. To give students practice under timed testing conditions, allow them five minutes per question.

Question	Answer	Depth of Knowledge	Cognitive Complexity
1	A	IV	H
2	D	I	L
3	C	I	L
4	D	II	M
5	B	II	M

KEY

Depth of Knowledge
- I Recall
- II Skill/Concept
- III Strategic Thinking
- IV Extended Thinking

Cognitive Complexity
- L Low
- M Moderate
- H High

CHAPTER 14

Instruction and Intervention Support

Interactions in Ecosystems

① Core Instruction

The **Core Instruction** resources below can be used for all students. Core instruction should be followed by ongoing assessment to determine which students need further help.

Available in both English and Spanish

Available Online

Section	Instruction	PRINT	ONLINE	Labs	
14.1	Textbook **Habitat and Niche**	■	●	Making a Local Field Guide Monitoring Bird Populations (Design Your Own)	
	Animated Biology Survive within a Niche		●		
	PowerPresentation and Notes 14.1		●		
14.2	Textbook **Community Interactions**	■	●	Modeling Predation	
	PowerPresentation and Notes 14.2		●		
14.3	Textbook **Population Density and Distribution**	■	●	**QuickLab** Survivorship Curves	
	PowerPresentation and Notes 14.3		●		
14.4	Textbook **Population Growth Patterns**	■	●	Population Dynamics (Probeware Lab) Limiting Nutrients for Algae Predator-Prey Interactions **Video Lab** Yeast Population Growth	
	Animated Biology What Limits Population Growth?, Exponential Growth		●		
	Teaching Visuals Population Graphs (Fig. 4.1, 4.3)		●		
	PowerPresentation and Notes 14.4		●		
14.5	Textbook **Ecological Succession**	■	●	Using GPS in Ecological Surveys (Challenge Lab)	
	Teaching Visuals Primary Succession (Fig. 5.2), Secondary Succession (Fig. 5.3)		●		
	PowerPresentation and Notes 14.5		●		

Additional online resources available for this chapter include **Interactive Whiteboard Resources.**

2 Support and Intervention

Support and Intervention resources are useful for students who need targeted help beyond the Core Instruction

Resources	PRINT	ONLINE
Assess and Reteach (TE wrap)	■	●
Concept Map		●
Interactive Reader	■	●
Interactive Review Games		●
Section Self-Checks		●
Study Guide B		●
Virtual Investigation Population Niches and Competition		●
Vocabulary Practice Worksheets		●

3 Specialized Support

Students who need more intensive personalized intervention benefit from **Specialized Support** resources.

Resources	PRINT	ONLINE
Chapter Audio Files		●
Differentiated Instruction Inclusion, Below Level, and English Learners (TE wrap)	■	●
ELL Strategies	■	●
Modified Lesson Plans for English Learners		●
Reinforcement Worksheets		●
Study Guide A		●

Extension and Assessment

Enrichment and Challenge

Resources	PRINT	ONLINE
Active Reading Worksheets		●
Data Analysis Practice Worksheet		●
Differentiated Instruction Pre-AP (TE wrap)	■	●
Pre-AP Activity Brood Parasitism		●
Smart Grapher Activity		●
The Inside Story and **Take It Further** (TE wrap)	■	●
Unit Project		●
WebLinks		
WebQuest Environmental Stress (14.4)		●

Assessment

Resources	PRINT	ONLINE
Alternative Assessment		●
Chapter Tests A and B		●
Diagnostic Test		●
ExamView Banks		●
Extended Response Test		●
Online Assessment System		●
Section Quizzes		●
Standards-Based Assessment	■	●

CHAPTER 14

Chapter Review

- **Section 1** differentiates between habitat and niche and details the importance of resource availability.
- **Section 2** describes the ways in which organisms interact within ecosystems.
- **Section 3** details the effects of geography and density on populations and the relationship of reproductive strategies to survivorship curves.
- **Section 4** identifies and describes factors that affect population growth.
- **Section 5** describes the characteristics of primary and secondary succession.

▼ Focus and Motivate

Why are these zebras fighting?

Have students speculate on reasons why the zebras are fighting. two males fighting over a mate **Ask**

- Is *fighting* really the right word? Can you think of a better one? competing
- What do organisms in an ecosystem compete for? resources such as food, water, shelter, and a mate

Point out that the competition in the picture is between males of the same species. In general, most competition for mates does not result in significant harm to either animal. The fights are rituals.

BIOZINE
HMHScience.com

Students can access BioZine at **HMHScience.com** to check the daily science news feeds.

CHAPTER 14 Interactions in Ecosystems

BIG IDEA Individual organisms and populations of organisms interact with each other and with the environment.

ONLINE BIOLOGY HMHScience.com

ONLINE Labs
- Modeling Predation
- **QuickLab** Survivorship Curves
- Limiting Nutrients for Algae
- Making a Local Field Guide
- Predator-Prey Interactions
- Monitoring Bird Populations
- Using GPS in Ecological Surveys
- Population Dynamics
- **Video Lab** Yeast Population Growth

Teacher Demo

Eye Opener Introduce students to the idea of an ecological niche by using the classic study of the feeding habits of North American warblers by ecologist Robert MacArthur. The five species of warblers are about the same size and eat insects commonly found in fir and pine trees. MacArthur discovered that each bird fed in different parts of the tree, dividing up the resources of their shared habitat.

Demonstrate Reproduce on individual acetates the diagrams shown on the next page, and also prepare a simple outline of the tree and its feeding zones. Place the tree outline on an overhead projector, then layer on the acetate for each warbler. (Diagrams available in Media Gallery.)

Point out how little overlap there is. Make sure students don't jump to the conclusion that a niche is simply a feeding location. Each bird feeds on different insects, at different times of the day, and has a different feeding behavior.

Why are these zebras fighting?

For the zebra, life on the African savannah is about survival. Whether escaping the ambush of a pride of lions, walking vast distances to drink fresh water, or competing for the right to mate with females, only the best adapted zebras will survive and pass on their genes. The interactions among organisms, and between organisms and their environment, make ecosystems function.

READING TOOLBOX

This reading tool can help you learn the material in the following pages.

USING LANGUAGE

Predictions Some predictions are conditional: Something might happen, but only if something else happens first. For example, if the temperature drops below freezing, snow might fall. The prediction is that snow might fall tonight. But snow might fall under one condition. First, the temperature has to drop below freezing.

YOUR TURN

In the following sentences, identify the condition and the prediction.

1. After the deer population reaches 600 individuals on the island, the deer will eat most of the vegetation, and the number of deer will decrease.
2. If the otters are removed from the ecosystem, the sea urchins will eat all of the kelp.

Warbler Feeding Zones Enlarge as needed.

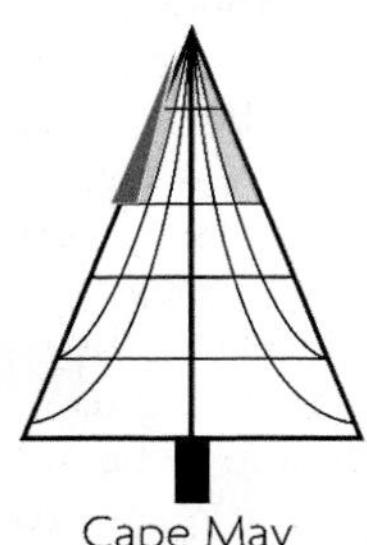
Cape May warbler

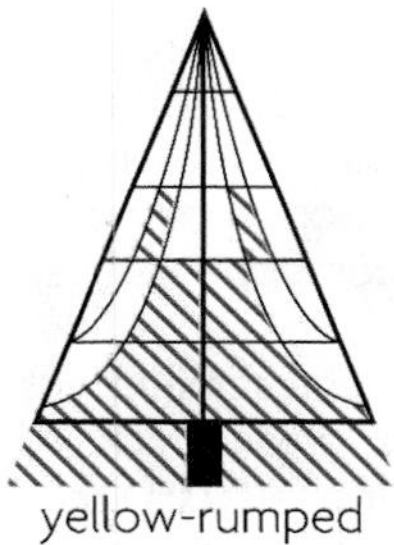
yellow-rumped warbler

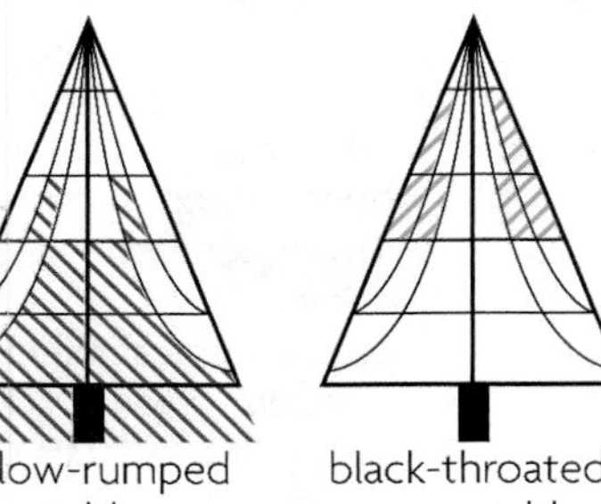
black-throated green warbler

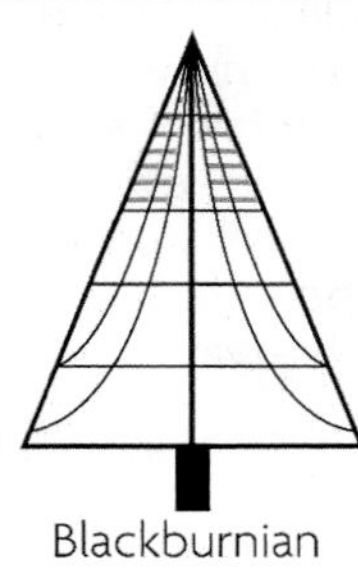
Blackburnian warbler

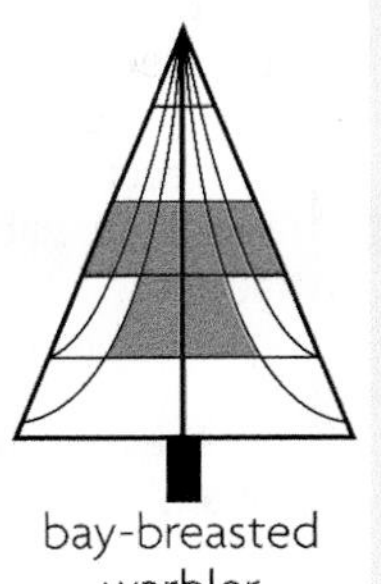
bay-breasted warbler

Activate Prior Knowledge

Direct students' attention to the word *interaction* in the chapter title and references to *population* in the Key Concepts on each section opener. **Ask,** What are some interactions common to human population? How do you interact with others? Students might mention family interactions that involve cooperation in maintaining shelter, preparing food, or caring for family members, or competition for parents' attention or household resources. In school, students cooperate in learning activities but also compete for school resources and in sports.

Remind students that living things must obtain matter and energy to survive. In an ecosystem, different populations live in the same environment and share or compete for resources.

Preview Vocabulary

English Learners Prepare an anticipation guide to test students' understanding of the way that terms describing behavior are applied in ecology. Students are probably familiar with the words *competition* and *parasitic,* but may not see how they relate to resources.

Integrating Earth Science

Because of the climate in Africa and the zebras' need for food and water, large herds of plains zebras migrate more than 480 kilometers (300 mi) every year. When one area becomes dry, they move to another that has rain and fresh grass.

Answers

1. Condition: the deer population reaching 600 individuals; Prediction: Most of the vegetation will be eaten and the number of deer will decrease.
2. Condition: removal of the otters; Prediction: All the sea urchins will eat all the kelp.

SECTION 14.1

B.3.1 Use mathematical and/or computational representation to explain why the carrying capacity ecosystems can support is limited by the available energy, water, oxygen, and minerals and by the ability of ecosystems to recycle the remains of dead organisms.

▼ Plan and Prepare

Activate Prior Knowledge Students will probably be familiar with the word **niche** as a marketing term. **Ask,** How would you define the word *niche*? highly specialized taste, function People are also said to fill a niche in the functions they perform. **Ask,** What are some niches found in a school community? teacher, coach, counselor, student, janitor Discuss that while all schools have these niches, different people in different schools fill the niches.

▼ Teach

Vocabulary

Academic Vocabulary Sometimes a word that has a general meaning in everyday language takes on a specialized meaning in science. For example, **niche** comes from the Latin "to nest." An **ecological niche** describes the role an organism plays in an ecosystem as well as its living conditions. Another example is the word **habitat,** from the Latin root "to dwell." In ecology, *habitat* refers to the place where the niche conditions are found.

14.1 Habitat and Niche

KEY CONCEPT **Every organism has a habitat and a niche.**

MAIN IDEAS

- A habitat differs from a niche.
- Resource availability gives structure to a community.

VOCABULARY

habitat
ecological niche
competitive exclusion
ecological equivalent

Connect to Your World

The ways in which a zebra or a lion interacts with its environment and other organisms are only a small part of the ecology of the African plains. To understand what individuals, populations, and communities need to survive, ecologists study the interactions among species and between species and their environment. Why does a lion fit so well into the African savannah?

MAIN IDEA

A habitat differs from a niche.

On the vast plains of Africa, tall grasses grow among trees and shrubs, and small pools of water surrounded by thirsty animals dot the landscape. This challenging environment is the home of the African lion, shown in **FIGURE 1.1**. Here, lions stalk through tall grass to hunt zebras and antelope, find places to rest in the shade of trees, and never stray far from valuable pools of water. These are just a few of the environmental features that make up the lion's habitat. A **habitat** can be described as all of the biotic and abiotic factors in the area where an organism lives. These factors include all aspects of the environment, including the grass, the trees, and the watering holes.

FIGURE 1.1 A lion must hunt and kill its prey in order to survive on the African savannah. Its role as a top predator is part of the lion's niche.

Each species interacts with its environment in a different way. Within an ecosystem, each species has an ecological niche. An **ecological niche** (nihch) is composed of all of the physical, chemical, and biological factors that a species needs to survive, stay healthy, and reproduce.

You can think of a habitat as *where* a species lives and a niche as *how* it lives within its habitat. A niche includes

- **Food** The type of food a species eats, how a species competes with others for food, and where it fits in the food web are all part of its niche.
- **Abiotic conditions** A niche includes the range of conditions, such as air temperature and amount of water, that a species can tolerate.
- **Behavior** The time of day a species is active as well as where and when it reproduces are factors in the niche of a species.

Differentiated Instruction

BELOW LEVEL

Help students understand the difference between *habitat* and *niche* by reinforcing the sentence "You can think of a habitat as *where* a species lives and a niche as *how* it lives within its habitat." Have students pair up and apply this to a food web. Students should then share their observations with the class.

Teacher Toolkit, Section C, Think-Pair-Share

HANDS-ON ACTIVITY

To model the concept of niches found in similar habitats, bring in two similar mechanical or electronic objects that can be safely taken apart. For example, disassemble two nonfunctioning hair dryers. Students will see similar components in each. Even though the components are not exactly the same, they produce the same effect. Compare this to different organisms filling the same niche in different habitats. Discuss how this relates to ecological structure.

Looking closely at all of these factors, we can see that while an antelope may use the tall grasses of the African plains as a food resource, a lion may use the same grasses as camouflage for hunting. A lion uses the antelope as a food resource and hunts primarily during low-light times, such as dawn or dusk. In order to avoid the intense heat of the savannah, lions often spend afternoons in the shade. These examples are only a few parts of the lion's ecological niche, but they help to give a picture of how a lion fits into the African savannah.

Connect **What are some of the abiotic and biotic factors of your habitat?**

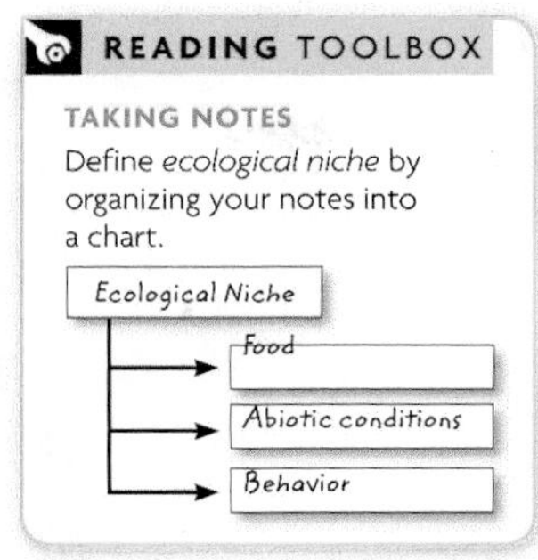

MAIN IDEA

Resource availability gives structure to a community.

You have learned that the ability of an individual to survive and reproduce is the driving force behind natural selection. A species needs resources such as food, water, and shelter to be successful in its habitat. The organism that is best suited to obtain these resources is most likely to survive and reproduce. But what if two species are competing over limited resources?

Competitive Exclusion

We have already seen that many species can share similar habitats and that they may use some of the same resources, as shown in **FIGURE 1.2**. But when two species use the same resources in the same ways, one species will always be better adapted to the environment. The principle of **competitive exclusion** states that when two species are competing for the same resources, one species will be better suited to the niche, and the other species will be pushed into another niche or become extinct.

The North American gray squirrel was introduced to Great Britain in the late 1800s. The native European red squirrel was forced to compete with the newcomer for the same food resources, habitat, and space. In this case the gray squirrel was better adapted to the niche and pushed out its smaller competitor. Currently, the red squirrel population is declining due to competition with its larger, more aggressive cousin. But competitive exclusion can also result in other outcomes.

FIGURE 1.2 Even though bees and butterflies both use these flowers for food, they occupy different niches. Many species with similar niches can coexist.

- **Niche partitioning** The two squirrel species could have naturally divided different resources based on competitive advantages. If one type of squirrel ate nuts from the tops of trees while others ate nuts from the ground, the niche would have been divided.
- **Evolutionary response** The two species of squirrel could have experienced divergent evolution. Selection for larger teeth might have allowed one type of squirrel to become better at cracking large nuts, while selection for smaller teeth might have allowed the other to eat small seeds.

PRE-AP

Remind students that selective pressures can result in divergent evolution occurring between related populations in a shared habitat or can result in convergent evolution occurring with unrelated populations in separate but similar habitats. Work with students to develop a concept map that links these ideas about patterns in evolution to the discussion of structure in an ecological community, as described in this section.

Teacher Toolkit, Section C, Brainstorming

ENGLISH LEARNERS

Use the example of competition between the American gray squirrel and European red squirrel described on this page to help students understand the concepts of ecological niches and competitive exclusion. Use a cluster diagram to explore possible outcomes of this competition.

Teacher Toolkit, Section C, Cluster Diagram

Answers

A Connect Abiotic factors might include air, temperature, buildings, roads, and water. Biotic factors might include animals, plants, and people.

History of Science

The principles of **competitive exclusion** and **niche partitioning** apply to organisms of all sizes and types in an ecosystem. Yet they were discovered by a scientist observing tiny protists, single-cell organisms, interacting in a laboratory. In 1934, **G. F. Gause,** a Russian ecologist, observed two cultures of closely related species of protists in the genus *Paramecium*. The paramecia fed on bacteria in culture flasks. Both species grew well when they were in separate flasks, but when placed in the same flask, *Paramecium aurelia* grew well and *Paramecium caudatum* died. Gause inferred that one species was better adapted to take advantage of limited resources and prevented the other from doing the same. Ecologists call this the competitive exclusion principle.

Gause also grew two other species of protists in the same flask and observed these species separating from each other. One species lived exclusively in the medium while the other species lived on the flask's walls. He had observed niche partitioning.

Vocabulary

niche partitioning Have students notice the roots *part* and *partition* in the word *partitioning*. A part is a "portion, piece, or segment of a whole." *Partition* is "the act or process of dividing something into parts." **Ask,** How would niche partitioning be described using the word roots? Two organisms use or divide up different parts of the same niche.

▼ Teach *continued*

TEACH FROM VISUALS

FIGURE 1.3 Use a globe or map to locate the frog habitats. **Ask**

- Where is each frog found? mantella frog on Madagascar, off southeastern coast of Africa; poison dart frog in northern part of South America
- How are the frogs similar? similar insect prey, defense mechanisms, bright coloration, and poisonous toxin
- In what ways are these frogs ecological equivalents? similar niches in geographically separate areas

Answers

A Synthesize *Sample answer:* Two species in similar niches were exposed to similar adaptive pressures, resulting in similar adaptations. This is known as convergent evolution.

B Apply This is not an example of competitive exclusion because the frogs are not in the same community, competing for the same limited resources.

▼ Assess and Reteach

Assess Use the Section Self-Check or Section Quiz, both available at **HMHScience.com**.

Reteach Have students summarize the section's content by comparing and contrasting the examples in **FIGURES 1.2** and **1.3,** using the section vocabulary.

GO ONLINE
Survive within a Niche

FIGURE 1.3 Ecological Equivalents

Ecological equivalents are two species that occupy similar niches in geographically separate areas.

The mantella frog (left) and the poison dart frog (right) have evolved similar defense mechanisms. The bright coloration of each is a warning to predators. Each frog secretes a highly poisonous toxin through its skin that makes it an unpleasant meal for a predator.

A Synthesize **Explain how natural selection resulted in the evolution of two similar frog species in two similar niches.**

> CONNECT TO
> **AMPHIBIANS**
> Amphibians were the first vertebrates to move out of the water and onto land. In the chapter **Vertebrate Diversity,** you will learn more about amphibians.

Ecological Equivalents

The competitive exclusion principle involves species competing for resources in the same community. In different communities, ecological equivalents occur in very similar niches. In mathematics, numbers that are equal are called equivalents. Similarly, **ecological equivalents** are species that occupy similar niches but live in different geographical regions. Pictured in **FIGURE 1.3,** the mantella frog of Madagascar and the poison dart frog of South America have similar niches in similar habitats. They both have brightly colored skin that secretes a highly poisonous toxin to ward off predators. Both prey on similar insects and live in a similar habitat, but because they live in different regions of the world, they never compete for the same resources.

B Apply **Are these frogs experiencing competitive exclusion? Explain.**

14.1 Formative Assessment

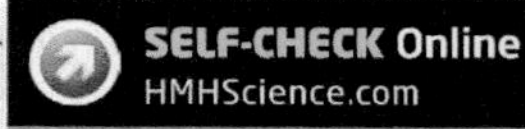

REVIEWING ▶ MAIN IDEAS

1. What are the three parts of an organism's **ecological niche**?
2. What does the principle of **competitive exclusion** say will happen when two species compete for the same resource?

CRITICAL THINKING

3. **Predict** If a group of mantella frogs were transported to the ecosystem of the poison dart frogs, what might happen to the two species' populations?
4. **Analyze** A bison and an elk live in the same **habitat** and feed on the same grasses. Does this mean that the competitive exclusion principle does not apply? Explain.

CONNECT TO
EXOTIC SPECIES

5. Considering the competitive exclusion principle, why may it be harmful to transport a species, such as a rabbit, to another habitat where it currently does not exist?

14.1 FORMATIVE ASSESSMENT

1. Three parts of a niche include food type, abiotic conditions, and behavior.
2. One species will be better suited to the niche and the other species will either be pushed into another niche or become extinct.
3. As ecological equivalents, they share a similar niche. The population better suited to the niche might deprive the other of resources, causing the other to die off. Or one population might respond to limited resources by altering its niche.
4. *Sample answer:* The competitive exclusion principle only applies if the two species occupy the same niche and habitat. These two species use the same food resource but occupy different niches.
5. *Sample answer:* If a new species is introduced to an area, it may occupy a similar niche as a native species and be better adapted for the niche or have no natural predators. This could drive the native species to extinction.

14.2 Community Interactions

KEY CONCEPT **Organisms interact as individuals and as populations.**

MAIN IDEAS
- Competition and predation are two important ways in which organisms interact.
- Symbiosis is a close relationship between species.

VOCABULARY
ompetition
redation
ymbiosis
nutualism
ommensalism
arasitism

Connect to Your World

Each day, two hot dog vendors sell virtually identical products to anyone who is hungry. They may be on different sides of the street, but they are still trying to sell hot dogs to the same hungry consumers. A vendor selling hot pretzels may also be trying to sell to the same customers, but with a slightly varied product. Just like these vendors, organisms constantly compete with one another.

MAIN IDEA

Competition and predation are two important ways in which organisms interact.

Two birds may fight over territories. A fish may prey on insects floating on the water. These are just two examples of the many interactions within and between species in an ecosystem.

Competition

Competition occurs when two organisms fight for the same limited resources. There are two different types of competition: interspecific competition and intraspecific competition.

Even though they may have different niches, two species may still use similar resources. Interspecific competition occurs when two different species compete for a limited resource, such as space. In a lawn, for example, grass, dandelions, and many other plants all compete for nutrients and water.

Competition also occurs among members of the same species. This is known as intraspecific competition. Individuals of a particular species struggle against one another for limited resources. You can observe intraspecific competition during the spring breeding season of birds. A typical male will share a particular territory with males of different bird species but will not tolerate another male of its own species in the same area.

FIGURE 2.1 Snakes are predators that swallow their prey whole. The hollow fangs of this timber rattlesnake inject venom to paralyze and kill its prey.

Predation

Another way species interact with one another is through predation. **Predation** is the process by which one organism captures and feeds upon another organism. Many organisms, such as the snake in **FIGURE 2.1**, have become highly adapted to hunting and killing their prey.

Differentiated Instruction

INCLUSION

Students who are literal thinkers may assume that all competition for resources results in an actual battle between organisms. Use the analogy of a habitat as a market with limited supplies. A shopper's business is with the market, not with other shoppers. The shopper who buys all of a particular product deprives others who shop for the same thing even though there is no direct interaction. Have students work on analogies for other terms in the section.

Teacher Toolkit, Section C, Analogies

SECTION 14.2

B.3.1 Use mathematical and/or computational representation to explain why the carrying capacity ecosystems can support is limited by the available energy, water, oxygen, and minerals and by the ability of ecosystems to recycle the remains of dead organisms.

B.3.2 Design, evaluate, and refine a model which shows how human activities and natural phenomena can change the flow of matter and energy in an ecosystem and how those changes impact the environment and biodiversity of populations in ecosystems of different scales, as well as, how these human impacts can be reduced.

B.3.3 Evaluate the claims, evidence, and reasoning that the complex interactions in ecosystems maintain relatively consistent numbers and types of organisms in stable conditions, and identify the impact of changing conditions or introducing non-native species into that ecosystem.

Plan and Prepare

Activate Prior Knowledge Mention that competition and cooperation occur in ecosystems just as they do in human interactions. **Ask,** What are some ways that you compete or cooperate with others? *Sample answers:* compete in grades, cooperate in learning; compete in sports, cooperate on teams

Ask, How does cooperation and competition among organisms differ from human cooperation and competition? Cooperation and competition in nature relate to survival. Organisms are not making a conscious choice.

Teach

Vocabulary

Latin Word Origins Point out that prefixes can help students remember the difference between *interspecific* and *intraspecific competition.*

inter- = between *intra-* = within

Ask, How does an international competition differ from an intramural competition? (Hint: *Mural* derives from a Latin root meaning "wall.") International occurs between nations; intramural occurs within the same school.

▼ Teach *continued*

Answers

A Evaluate Predators that are better adapted to catching and consuming prey and prey that are better adapted to avoiding and escaping from predators are more likely to survive and reproduce.

Take It Further

The Brazil nuts we buy at the store result from a complex **symbiotic relationship** among four species in the tropical forests of South America. The flower of the Brazil nut tree is pollinated by a species of orchid bee that feeds on the flower's nectar (relationship #1). Once pollinated, the Brazil nut flower produces a large, hard seed pod that contains up to 24 seeds—the Brazil nuts.

The seed pod falls to the ground where the agouti, a small mammal with chisel-like teeth, breaks into the seed pod. No other animal does this. The agouti feeds on some of the nuts, then carries off the rest to bury for later (relationship #2). Some seeds may germinate before the agoutis can retrieve them, and thus new trees grow.

Another part of the story is that of male orchid bees. To attract a mate, the bees gather a fragrant chemical from orchids also growing in the forest. The bees pollinate the orchids in the process (relationship #3).

Ask, How would you describe the complex interactions between Brazil nut trees, orchid bees, orchids, and agoutis? mutualism

These complex interactions make it difficult to cultivate Brazil nut trees away from the forest.

The timber rattlesnake, for example, is a predator that preys on small animals such as mice, voles, rabbits, and squirrels. Lying silently, hidden among leaf litter on the forest floor, the rattlesnake has found a niche as an ambush predator. A swift bite from the snake's fangs injects its venom. The venom attacks the nervous system and eventually paralyzes the prey. The snake swallows the paralyzed animal whole.

Herbivores can also be considered predators. The deer that eats grass in fields and leaves from trees is preying on the plants.

A Evaluate How does natural selection shape predator–prey relationships?

MAIN IDEA

Symbiosis is a close relationship between species.

READING TOOLBOX

VOCABULARY

The word *symbiosis* comes from the Greek word *sumbios*, which means "living together."

A honeybee buzzes away from a flower with its reward of nectar. Small pollen grains have become attached to the bee's back. When the bee arrives at the next flower, the pollen fertilizes the egg of the next plant. In this way, a relationship, or symbiosis, between the bee and the flower has evolved. **Symbiosis** is a close ecological relationship between two or more organisms of different species that live in direct contact with one another. There are three major types of symbiosis: mutualism, commensalism, and parasitism.

READING TOOLBOX

TAKING NOTES

Mutualism, commensalism, and parasitism are distinct types of symbiosis. Add details with examples of your own.

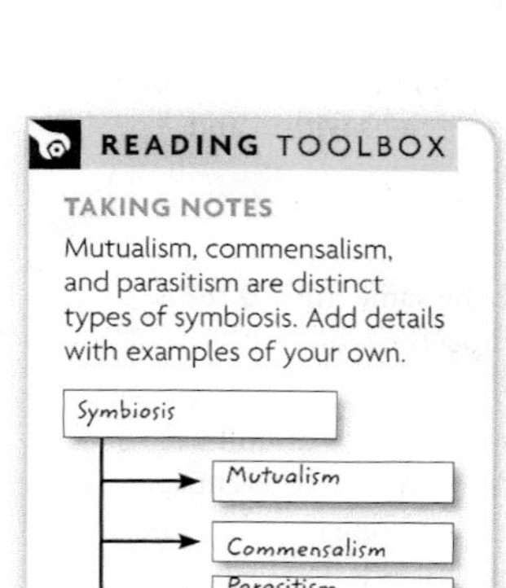

Mutualism

Mutualism is an interspecies interaction in which both organisms benefit from one another. The relationship between the lesser long-nosed bat and the saguaro cactus is an example of mutualism. During the spring, the bats help pollinate the cacti through the indirect transfer of pollen as they fly from one cactus to another to feed on flower nectar. When the fruit ripens in the summer, the bats become fruit eaters, as shown in **FIGURE 2.2.** The cactus benefits when the bat spreads its indigestible seeds across the desert.

Commensalism

Another type of symbiotic relationship is commensalism. **Commensalism** is a relationship between two organisms in which one receives an ecological benefit from another, while the other neither benefits nor is harmed. Right now you may be a part of a commensal relationship. Buried deep in the hair follicles of your eyelashes are microscopic mites that feed on the secretions and dead skin cells of your body. These harmless organisms are called demodicids, and they have found their highly specialized niche in your hair follicles.

Parasitism

Parasitism is a symbiotic relationship involving a species that directly harms its host. **Parasitism** is a relationship similar to predation in that one organism benefits while the other is harmed. But unlike a predator, which quickly kills and eats its prey, a parasite benefits by keeping its host alive for days or years. For example, the braconid wasp lays its eggs inside a caterpillar. When the larvae hatch, they eat the caterpillar from the inside out, consuming the nutrients they need to grow into adults.

Differentiated Instruction

BELOW LEVEL

To help students remember the different terms introduced in the section, have them draw a 2-by-2 matrix, with a circle at the center. Students place the term in the circle and then fill in the surrounding cells with the following information:

- definition
- characteristics
- examples
- nonexamples

Teacher Toolkit, Section D, Frayer model

ENGLISH LEARNERS

Work with students to analyze the interactions of organisms described in this section by listing the characteristics of those given as examples. Features to have students consider are whether the relationships are interspecific or intraspecific; whether they are symbiotic and if so, of what type; and what resources are involved in the interaction.

Teacher Toolkit, Section D, Semantic Feature Analysis

FIGURE 2.2 Symbiotic Relationships

The interactions between species in an ecosystem can take many forms. A symbiotic relationship involves interactions between organisms of different species that live in direct contact.

− Organism is harmed

Ø Organism is not affected

\+ Organism benefits

Parasitism

− **Hornworm caterpillar** The host hornworm will eventually die as its organs are consumed by wasp larvae.

\+ **Braconid wasp** Braconid larvae feed on their host and release themselves shortly before reaching the pupae stage of development.

Commensalism

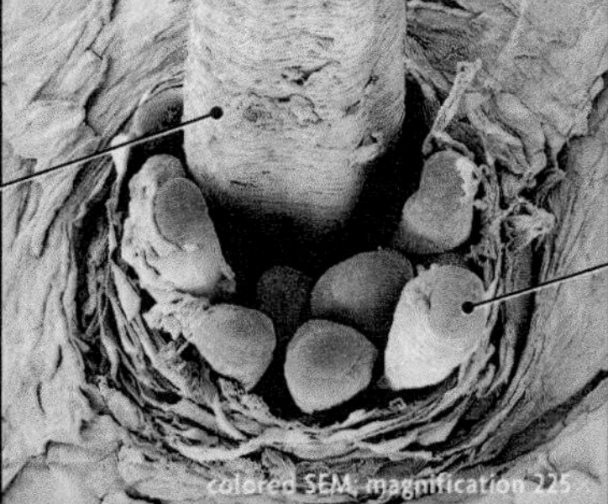

Ø **Human** Our eyelashes are home to tiny mites that feast on oil secretions and dead skin. Without harming us, up to 20 mites may be living in one eyelash follicle.

\+ **Demodicids** Eyelash mites find all they need to survive in the tiny follicles of eyelashes. Magnified here 225 times, these creatures measure 0.4 mm in length and can be seen only with a microscope.

Mutualism

\+ **Lesser long-nosed bat** The bat depends on night-blooming cacti as its primary source of food. Cacti are a rich source of fruit and nectar, staples of the bat's diet.

\+ **Saguaro cactus** As the bat feeds on the cactus' fruit, it also ingests the seeds. These indigestible seeds are dispersed to new locations as the bat flies across the desert.

CRITICAL VIEWING How might the symbiotic relationship change if eyelash mites destroyed hair follicles?

PRE-AP

Have students write for five minutes on the question: In what ways are symbiotic relationships distinct from other interactions such as predator-prey interactions? Have them consider the role coevolution plays in symbiotic relationships, and whether coevolution is a factor in nonsymbiotic relationships.

Teacher Toolkit, Section C, Quick-Write

TEACH FROM VISUALS

FIGURE 2.2 Point out the symbols in the key and have students use them as a memory aid. **Ask**

- What symbols are used for parasitism, and what do they mean? − and +; one organism is harmed, the other benefits
- What symbols are used for commensalism, and what do they mean? Ø and +; one organism is not affected, the other benefits
- Why are two of the same symbols needed for mutualism? Both organisms benefit.

Science Trivia

- Mites are arachnids, as are spiders.
- Most people have follicle mites. A human head has about 100,000 follicles.
- The mite's elongated body enables it to fit into a hair follicle.

Take It Further

The human body is home to billions of microorganisms, not just mites. Most are different species of bacteria that colonize the body upon birth. They inhabit the skin, as well as the respiratory, digestive, and urinary tracts. Referred to as the **normal flora** of the human body, they perform important physiological, nutritional, and protective functions. It is possible that there are more bacterial cells at work in the human body than there are body cells. Though some flora cause illness, scientists think that most such relationships are mutually beneficial to both the host and its unseen guests.

Answers

Ⓐ **Critical Viewing** The relationship would be classified as parasitic.

▼ Teach *continued*

Integrating Medical Science

Leeches, once used by doctors to remove the "bad" blood that caused illness, are back. A species of freshwater leech, raised in laboratories, is being used as a medical device for some **skin grafts** and **reattachment surgeries.** Two or three leeches attach to the injured site of the body and remove blood that the body is unable to circulate. After about 40 minutes, the leeches drop off and new leeches are applied. The used leeches are treated as infectious waste material and destroyed. **Ask,** How does this change the natural type of symbiosis between these two organisms? The person benefits instead of being harmed by the parasite. Although the leech initially benefits, it is eventually harmed as a result of the relationship. The parasitic relationship is reversed.

Answers

A Hypothesize Hosts remove ectoparasites if they detect them.

B Connect mutualism

▼ Assess and Reteach

Assess Use the Section Self-Check or Section Quiz, both available at **HMHScience.com**.

Reteach Make sure students complete their note-taking graphic organizer about types of symbiosis. Have them work together to add examples of their own for each type of symbiosis.

FIGURE 2.3 Human Parasites: Inside and Out

Humans can get parasites in many ways. Leeches attach to the exposed skin of humans. By penetrating human skin, hookworms find their home in the digestive tract.

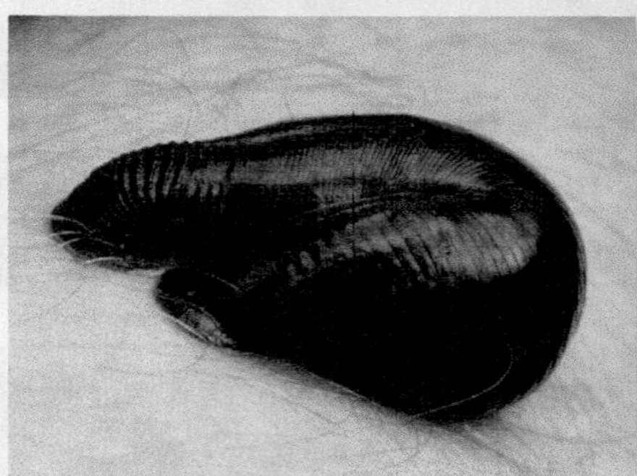

Many leeches feed on the blood of a host organism. Freshwater leeches such as this one can grow to lengths of 12 cm or more.

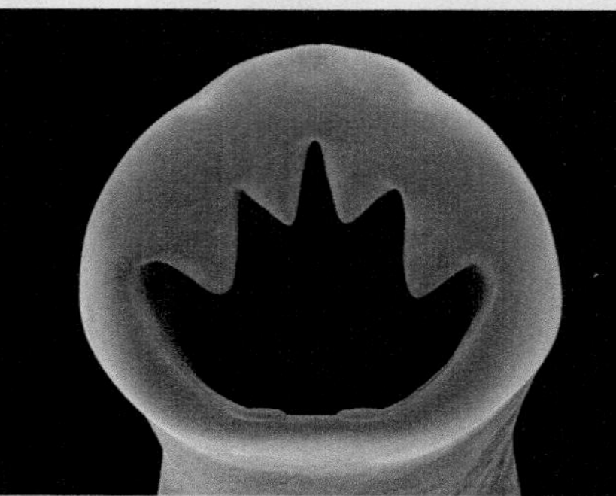

Hookworms are endoparasites with sharp teeth that attach to the intestinal wall of a host organism and absorb nutrients for food.

A Hypothesize **Why is it important for ectoparasites to stay undetected by their hosts?**

CONNECT TO

INVERTEBRATES

Leeches and hookworms are classified as invertebrates. In the chapter **Invertebrate Diversity,** you will learn more about the diversity of invertebrates.

The needs of a parasite are met by a host—the victim of the parasite. There are two ways that parasites can use their host. An ectoparasite makes its home on the exterior of an organism, attaching itself to the outside of the host and usually feeding on its fluids. Common ectoparasites include fleas, ticks, and leeches, such as the one seen in **FIGURE 2.3.** Many types of ectoparasites are also known to carry a wide variety of diseases that can affect their host. Parasites can also be found inside of living organisms. Endoparasites live in the tissues and organs of a host where, safely hidden, they feed on the nutrients ingested by their host. Large endoparasites, such as tapeworms and hookworms, and smaller protozoan endoparasites can kill their host if not treated.

B Connect **What type of symbiosis is the relationship between a dog and its owner?**

14.2 Formative Assessment

SELF-CHECK Online
HMHScience.com
GO ONLINE

REVIEWING MAIN IDEAS

1. During the fall spawning of salmon, grizzly bears fight over space on the banks of a river. What type of **competition** is this?
2. Describe and give examples of the three types of **symbiosis**.

CRITICAL THINKING

3. **Compare and Contrast** How are **predation** and **parasitism** similar? How do they differ?
4. **Synthesize** After a lion has made a kill, birds will sometimes arrive to pick at the leftover carcass. Which are the predators: the birds, the lion, or both? Why?

CONNECT TO

ANIMAL BEHAVIOR

5. You have probably heard the saying "There is safety in numbers." Why might traveling in a large group be beneficial to prey species?

14.2 FORMATIVE ASSESSMENT

1. The bears are fighting among themselves, so it is considered intraspecific competition.
2. Mutualism, commensalism, and parasitism; examples may vary.
3. Predation and parasitism are both relationships in which one organism benefits while the other is harmed. In predation, the predator needs to kill its prey in order to benefit. In parasitism, the parasite benefits by keeping the host alive.
4. The term *predator* is restricted to an organism that finds and eats another living organism. The lion is the predator; the birds are scavengers.
5. *Sample answer:* A predator may become overwhelmed when facing a large number of prey. Although a predator may have the speed to chase down and kill a single prey animal, it may switch from chasing one individual to another when faced with a large group of prey and tire before it is successful.

Sharks and Increased CO_2

S.T.E.M. Interactions

The ocean and the atmosphere naturally interact. Gases, including oxygen and carbon dioxide (CO_2), are exchanged because of wind and wave action, evaporation, and biological processes. Over the last century, the concentration of CO_2 in the atmosphere has increased, leading to increased surface temperatures, melting ice sheets and glaciers, and rising sea levels. The increase in CO_2 in the atmosphere has also led to an increase in CO_2 in ocean water. Carbon dioxide is a normal part of ocean processes and the chemical reactions that occur in seawater. However, an excess of CO_2 has thrown off the balance of certain reactions, resulting in more acid being produced in the ocean, lowering the pH. The acidity of ocean water has increased by about 30 percent over the last 250 years. Scientists predict that the acidity of ocean water will increase even more by the year 2100, with pH lowering by 0.3 units.

The effects of increased acidity of ocean water are already evident in some organisms, including certain species of sharks. Researchers from the University of Adelaide in Australia tested the effects of increased carbon dioxide in ocean water on the ability of Port Jackson sharks to hunt for prey. The increased carbon dioxide may interfere with the sharks' ability to smell, one of the main senses sharks use to locate prey.

In a laboratory setting, the researchers kept the sharks in tanks of ocean water with normal levels of CO_2 and in tanks with increased levels of CO_2. After keeping the sharks an average of 56 days in each tank (the control tank and the experimental tank), the researchers tested the sharks' hunting ability. The test was conducted by hiding the same food in the same way in each tank. The researchers measured how long it took sharks in both tanks to find the food. The graph on the left below shows the results of the experiment. Sharks in the tank with increased CO_2 took about 4 times longer to find food than the control group did.

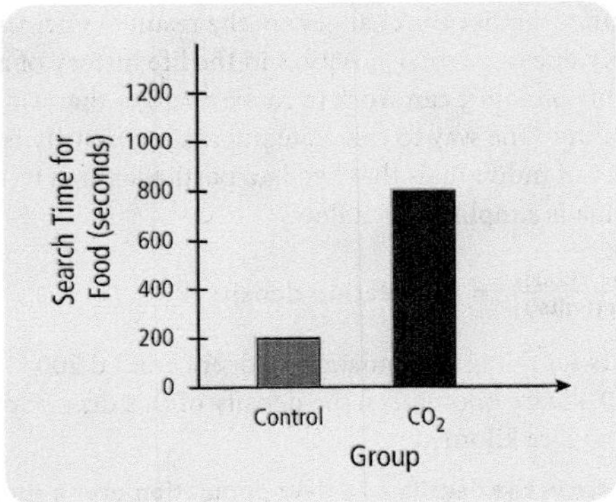

Other studies have found that increased levels of CO_2 in ocean water can interfere with the smooth dogfish's sense of smell. The smooth dogfish is another type of shark. Similar results have been found in experiments conducted on bony fish, such as damselfish and clownfish. Scientists have determined that the increased levels of CO_2 in the water interfere with the fishes' nervous system, causing the impairment of nerves involved in the senses of smell and hearing. Scientists are concerned about the broader effects of this discovery on a fish's ability to detect predators and escape. There also may be changes to the food web as a result of changes in predator-prey interactions.

S.T.E.M. Activity

The researchers from the University of Adelaide also measured the effect of increased CO_2 on the growth rate of the Port Jackson sharks. This graph shows their results.

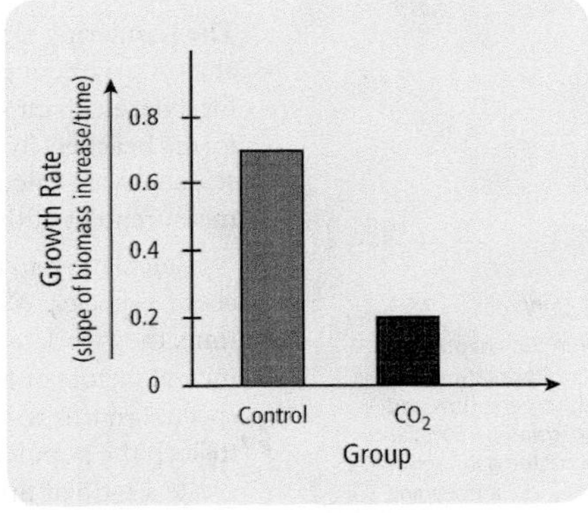

1. What is the relationship between increased CO_2 and growth rate in the sharks that were tested?
2. How is the growth rate under increased CO_2 conditions likely related to the sharks' ability to find prey in those conditions?
3. How could increased CO_2 affect an ocean food web overall?

Introduce

Remind students of the effects of increased carbon dioxide in the atmosphere by starting a discussion of climate change. The changes do not only affect ecosystems on land; ocean ecosystems are also affected. Increases in sea surface temperatures have led to an increase in coral bleaching and disease in coral reefs. An increase in the strength and frequency of tropical storms or hurricanes could also affect ocean ecosystems in terms of erosion and weathering.

Discuss

Make sure students have analyzed the graphs thoroughly. Have students answer the questions as a class. Encourage them to make connections between an increase in CO_2 in ocean water and possible effects on an ocean food web. Show students a food web that includes Port Jackson sharks. Have them explain what could happen in the food web if the size of Port Jackson sharks decreases as a result of increased CO_2. How would it affect organisms that prey on Port Jackson sharks as well as organisms that are the prey of Port Jackson sharks? How would these changes affect other organisms in the food web?

Answers

1. Exposure to increased carbon dioxide resulted in decreased growth rates in the sharks.
2. Under conditions of increased carbon dioxide, the sharks took four times longer to find food. If the sharks' ability to hunt for and find prey is significantly affected by increased levels of carbon dioxide, they may not get enough food, which would likely result in decreased growth rates.
3. If fish growth rates decrease, the fish that prey on them may not get enough food, or they may have to consume more prey to get enough food. This could affect the numbers of both populations. If predators cannot find prey, they may not be able to get enough food. This could cause an increase in the prey population and a decrease in predator population. Both of these changes could affect organisms that are higher or lower on the food chain. If fish cannot escape from predators, it could lead to dwindling prey populations.

SECTION 14.3

B.3.1 Use mathematical and/or computational representation to explain why the carrying capacity ecosystems can support is limited by the available energy, water, oxygen, and minerals and by the ability of ecosystems to recycle the remains of dead organisms.

B.3.3 Evaluate the claims, evidence, and reasoning that the complex interactions in ecosystems maintain relatively consistent numbers and types of organisms in stable conditions, and identify the impact of changing conditions or introducing non-native species into that ecosystem.

Plan and Prepare

Activate Prior Knowledge Describe density as the number of objects in an area. Suggest students think of this as a measure of how crowded the area is. **Ask,** Which parking lot has a higher density of cars—a 40-car lot with 40 cars parked in it or a 1000-car lot with 40 cars parked in it? 40-car lot

Teach

Integrating Mathematics

Density is expressed as a **ratio,** a mathematical expression that describes a direct relationship between two quantities. With **population density,** the relationship is between the number of individuals and the size of the area they occupy.

Answers

A Connect Resources may be depleted or the community may have changed due to, for example, the arrival of a new predator.

14.3 Population Density and Distribution

KEY CONCEPT **Each population has a density, a dispersion, and a reproductive strategy.**

VOCABULARY

population density
population dispersion
survivorship curve

MAIN IDEAS

- Population density is the number of individuals that live in a defined area.
- Geographic dispersion of a population shows how individuals in a population are spaced.
- Survivorship curves help to describe the reproductive strategy of a species.

Connect to Your World

If you have ever traveled from a rural area into a city, you may have noticed a change in population density. Cities have more dense populations, while rural areas have more widely dispersed populations. Scientists measure species populations in a similar way. What can we learn from population data?

MAIN IDEA

Population density is the number of individuals that live in a defined area.

The wandering albatross may fly over open ocean waters for days or weeks at a time without ever encountering another bird. In contrast to this solitary lifestyle, elephant seals may gather in groups of a thousand or more on California beaches. By collecting data about a population in a particular area, scientists can calculate the density of a population. **Population density** is a measurement of the number of individuals living in a defined space.

Calculating an accurate population density can tell scientists a great deal about a species. When scientists notice changes in population densities over time, they work to determine whether the changes are the result of environmental factors or are simply due to normal variation in the life history of a species. In this way a wildlife biologist can work to make changes that will help to keep the population healthy. One way to calculate population density is to create a ratio of the number of individuals that live in a particular area to the size of the area. This formula is simplified as follows:

$$\frac{\text{\# of individuals}}{\text{area (units}^2\text{)}} = \text{population density}$$

For example, if scientists sampling a population of deer counted 200 individuals in an area of 10 square kilometers, the density of this deer population would be 20 deer per square kilometer.

CONNECT TO

GENE FLOW

Recall that in the chapter **The Evolution of Populations** you learned about gene flow and geographic isolation. Population dispersion patterns influence the rate of gene flow among and between species.

A Connect **What might a decrease in the density of a deer population over a specific time period tell scientists about the habitat in the area?**

Differentiated Instruction

ENGLISH LEARNERS

Have students form into home groups of three, numbering off one to three. By the number, have them re-form into "expert" groups to study the key concepts of dispersion patterns, population density, and survivorship curves. Have them return to the home groups to share what they have learned.

Teacher Toolkit, Section C, Jigsaw Reading

BELOW LEVEL

Discuss population density in terms of a school. Different areas of a school will have different population densities. The same area may have different densities at different times. **Ask**

- What areas of your school have the most students at lunch? cafeteria before the bell rings? hallway after the bell rings? classroom, gym
- What factors affect the population density of a school? time of day, day of the week, time of the year

FIGURE 3.1 Dispersion Patterns

Dispersion patterns help us understand species interactions by showing how populations group together.

CLUMPED DISPERSION

Many species of fish swim together in large groups called schools. By moving as a large mass, individuals have an advantage in avoiding predators.

UNIFORM DISPERSION

Nesting sites of the gannet show uniform distances for protection of eggs from other males. Territorial organisms generally display uniform dispersion.

RANDOM DISPERSION

The three-toed tree sloth, a solitary animal, spends most of its life in the canopy of tropical forests. The sloth has almost no competitors and has few natural predators.

MAIN IDEA

Geographic dispersion of a population shows how individuals in a population are spaced.

Other information can be gained from population density measurements. Patterns of geographical dispersion give us ideas of how individuals of the same species interact and how different species interact with one another. **Population dispersion** is the way in which individuals of a population are spread in an area or a volume. **FIGURE 3.1** shows the three types of population dispersion.

- **Clumped dispersion** Individuals may live close together in groups in order to facilitate mating, gain protection, or access food resources.
- **Uniform dispersion** Territoriality and intraspecies competition for limited resources lead to individuals living at specific distances from one another.
- **Random dispersion** Individuals are spread randomly within an area or a volume.

VISUAL VOCAB

Population dispersion is the way in which individuals of a population are spread in an area or a volume.

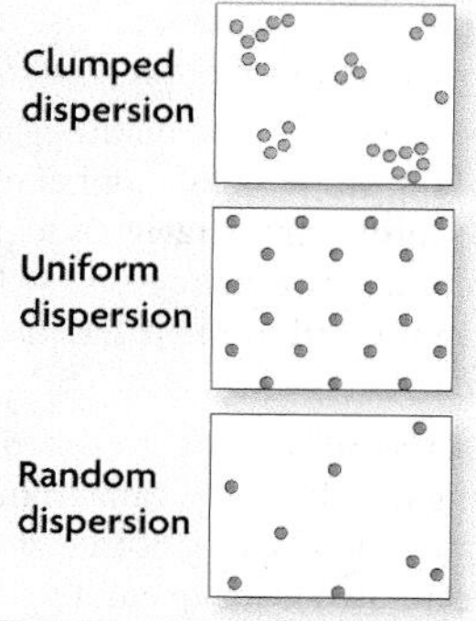

Infer **What type of intraspecies interaction might cause uniform dispersion?**

INCLUSION

For students who are visually impaired, look for ways to incorporate concrete representations into the lesson. For example, in the QuickLab, a pile of 35 pennies can be subdivided to represent age groups. For the survivorship curves on the last page of this section, overlay string or yarn on the curves to emphasize the characteristic shapes of each.

TEACH FROM VISUALS

FIGURE 3.1 Have students observe the animals in each photograph and then match each pattern to the corresponding pattern in the **VISUAL VOCAB. Ask**

- In what type of dispersion pattern can the distance between individual organisms be predicted accurately? uniform dispersion
- What type of dispersion would a herd of wild horses have? clumped dispersion

Take It Further

Plants also exhibit the same dispersion patterns as those of animals. A clumped dispersion pattern is most common. Different **plant populations** tend to grow in clumps where the soil type and amounts of water, nutrients, and sunlight are what they are best adapted to. Some species of plants have populations with a uniform dispersion pattern. This pattern results when plants growing closely together would compete for the same resources. In other cases, some plants add a toxic substance to the soil that keeps plants of the same species equally distant from each other. A random dispersion pattern is less common in plants, but can occur with plants that are adapted to a variety of conditions and have windblown seeds.

Vocabulary

Academic Vocabulary Have students consider the difference between the term **density** and the terms **distribution** and **dispersion.** The words all relate to the same physical quality but describe different aspects of it. *Density* provides the number of objects or organisms to be found in a given unit of measure. *Distribution* and *dispersion* describe the manner in which those objects or organisms are placed relative to one another.

Answers

A **Infer** competition for limited resources

▼ Teach *continued*

QUICKLAB

Time 15 minutes — TEACHER TESTED

Purpose Model a survivorship curve, using obituary data.

LAB MANAGEMENT

- Students record the number of deaths by age group, using 35 obituary notices from a newspaper, and use the data to suggest the proportion of survivors within each age group. Note that the data collected is number of deaths, not number of survivors.
- To get a large sampling, check online for death notices published in a large metropolitan newspaper.
- Tell students that the lines in the "Death" column of the table represent hatch marks, not numerals.

Answers

Sample Data

For a sample of student data and a chart of precalculated percentages, go to **HMHScience.com**.

Analyze and Conclude

1. The graph should show few or no deaths through middle age, with a downward trend as age increases. Note the graph might rise at the end because the model assumes an equivalent population size for each group, including people in their 90s.
2. *Sample answer:* The data showed few deaths before age 50. Most people live until old age.

Vocabulary

Word Origins The origin of the word **strategy** is a military one. It refers to the "office of general," the commander who prepares and executes a plan. Ecologists consider patterns of survivorship as characteristics of species and refer to them as **reproductive strategies.** In this case, the strategy does not result from planning but rather from response to evolutionary pressures.

QUICKLAB INTERPRETING DATA

Survivorship Curves

In this lab, you will make a type 1 survivorship curve using data from the obituary section of a newspaper.

MATERIALS
- obituary section of a newspaper
- graph paper

PROBLEM What is the trend in data for type 1 survivorship curves?

PROCEDURE

1. Obtain the obituary section of the newspaper.
2. Create a data table like the one at right that extends to include five-year age groups up to 91–95 years.
3. For 35 obituaries, place a tally next to the age group in which the individual died.
4. Subtract the number of individuals that died from the number of remaining survivors, and record the answer in the third column of your data table. Calculate the percent surviving in each age group by dividing the number of survivors by 35 and multiplying by 100. Repeat this step for all age groups.

TABLE 1. SURVIVORSHIP DATA

Age (years)	Deaths	Survivors	% Surviving
0–5	I	35 – 1 = 34	97
6–10	I	34 – 1 = 33	94
11–15	0	33 – 0 = 33	94
16–20	IIII	33 – 4 = 29	83
21–25	I	29 – 1 = 28	80

ANALYZE AND CONCLUDE

1. **Graph Data** Draw a survivorship curve by plotting the age group on the *x*-axis, and the percent survivors on the *y*-axis.
2. **Analyze** Explain the trend in the data.

MAIN IDEA

Survivorship curves help to describe the reproductive strategy of a species.

The California red-legged frog of the western United States is an amphibian that reproduces by laying 2000 to 5000 eggs in late winter and early spring. In one to two weeks, these eggs hatch, and over the next four to seven months, the tadpoles grow into frogs. If so many eggs are laid, why is this frog a threatened species in much of the western United States?

Many predators feed on the eggs of the red-legged frog, so of the thousands of eggs laid, only a small number of offspring will survive to adulthood. This type of reproductive strategy is to produce a lot of offspring. Species use many other reproductive strategies as well. Survivorship curves illustrate how offspring survival from birth to death fits in with the survival strategies of a particular species.

A **survivorship curve** is a generalized diagram showing the number of surviving members over time from a measured set of births. By measuring the number of offspring born in a year and following those offspring through until death, survivorship curves give information about the life history of a species. For example, we will begin with 100 coyotes born in year zero. After one year, 10 of those baby coyotes died from disease or predation. Of the original 100, 90 are left. During year two, 4 more coyotes die, leaving 86 of

Differentiated Instruction

PRE-AP

Ask students to write a paragraph or two on what a reproductive strategy characterized by a high number of births might suggest about conditions in a habitat. It could suggest unlimited resources, as with an insect population, or a slim chance of survival for offspring, as with fish or frog eggs.

Teacher Toolkit, Section C, Quick-Write

the original 100. In year three, 3 more die, leaving 83 of the original 100. The number of individuals surviving from year to year decreases, but a substantial portion of the group will live a full life and reproduce. In **FIGURE 3.2**, you can see the three basic patterns of animal survivorship curves.

FIGURE 3.2 SURVIVORSHIP CURVES

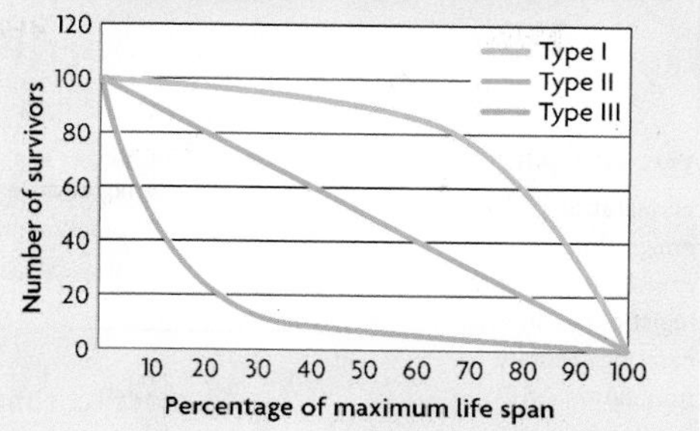

Type I
Type II
Type III
Number of survivors
Percentage of maximum life span

Type I The graph shows a type I survivorship curve in orange. Type I survivorship represents a life history that is common among large mammals, including humans. The curve shows a low level of infant mortality and a population that generally will survive until old age. A behavior that most organisms showing type I survivorship share is parental care for the young. Most infant organisms are unable to care for themselves. By protecting their young, parents are better able to ensure that their offspring stay alive until they can survive on their own.

Type II Organisms such as birds, small mammals, and some reptiles show a survivorship rate that is roughly equal at all ages of an organism's life. At all times, these species have equal chances of living and dying, whether from disease or as a result of predation. A type II survivorship curve is shown in green on the graph.

Type III Organisms with type III survivorship (shown in blue) have a very high birth rate and also a very high infant mortality rate. Species with type III survivorship are generally invertebrates, fish, amphibians, and plants. Many of their offspring will die from predation, but inevitably a few will survive to adulthood and be able to pass their genes on to the next generation. Though the California red-legged frogs are threatened largely because of habitat loss and pollution, the frogs are also targets of high levels of predation at an early age, making recovery for this species especially difficult.

Synthesize Is there any connection between survivorship curves and reproductive strategies? Explain.

14.3 Formative Assessment

SELF-CHECK Online
HMHScience.com
GO ONLINE

REVIEWING MAIN IDEAS

1. A shoreline mussel species has a **population density** of one organism per square meter. Will all mussels be found one meter apart? Explain.
2. Draw and label a diagram showing the three **population dispersion** patterns.
3. How do **survivorship curves** show three types of reproductive strategies?

CRITICAL THINKING

4. **Analyze** What might be the advantages of having a clumped dispersal pattern?
5. **Infer** An organism has ten offspring. Two of these offspring die each year over a five-year period. Is the organism more likely to be a bird or an insect? Explain.

CONNECT TO ABIOTIC FACTORS

6. On the African savannah, what types of abiotic factors may lead to high population density and clumped dispersion patterns?

TEACH FROM VISUALS

FIGURE 3.2 Help students interpret the graph. **Ask**

- In any of the curves, what do the 100 individuals have in common? They are from the same population and were born in the same year.
- How many of the individuals in the type I curve live 10 percent of their maximum life span? about 97 How many in the type II curve? about 90 How many in the type III curve? about 50
- How many of the individuals in the type I curve live 70 percent of their maximum life span? about 80 How many in the type II curve? about 30 How many in the type III curve? about 5

Answers

A Synthesize There is a connection. Type I organisms tend to produce fewer offspring. Type III individuals produce a large number of offspring but provide little or no parental care.

Assess and Reteach

Assess Use the Section Self-Check or Section Quiz, both available at **HMHScience.com**.

Reteach Choose a particular organism, such as a bird, and discuss its individual characteristics. Then extend the discussion to a population of birds and the types of characteristics an ecologist uses to describe that population.

14.3 FORMATIVE ASSESSMENT

1. No, population density simply describes the number of individuals per unit area, not the dispersion pattern.
2. Student diagrams should include three dispersion patterns: clumped, uniform, and random. Diagrams should be similar to those in the Visual Vocab on the second page of this section.
3. *Sample answer:* If the curve shows a low level of infant mortality, the parents probably care for their young. If the curve shows a very high infant mortality rate, the organisms probably have a high birth rate and provide little or no parental care.
4. *Sample answer:* Individuals do not have to move very much to find mates, organisms have better protection from predators, and there is more access to food resources from other population members.
5. The organism is a bird because the mortality pattern described is closest to type II. Insects tend to be type III, with many offspring and high mortality in early life stages.
6. Answers may include limited water supplies, high temperature, and little or no precipitation.

SECTION 14.4

B.3.1 Use mathematical and/or computational representation to explain why the carrying capacity ecosystems can support is limited by the available energy, water, oxygen, and minerals and by the ability of ecosystems to recycle the remains of dead organisms.

B.3.2 Design, evaluate, and refine a model which shows how human activities and natural phenomena can change the flow of matter and energy in an ecosystem and how those changes impact the environment and biodiversity of populations in ecosystems of different scales, as well as, how these human impacts can be reduced.

B.3.3 Evaluate the claims, evidence, and reasoning that the complex interactions in ecosystems maintain relatively consistent numbers and types of organisms in stable conditions, and identify the impact of changing conditions or introducing non-native species into that ecosystem.

▼ Plan and Prepare

Activate Prior Knowledge Discuss the population size of your town or city. **Ask,** What are some of the factors that affect the size of a population? immigration, emigration, jobs, housing, availability of resources, births, deaths

▼ Teach

Take It Further

Charles Darwin realized that species have the capacity to increase in number beyond what is needed to replace existing members of a population. Yet populations tend to remain constant in size, given limits on available resources. **Ask,** How does Darwin's observation connect to natural selection? Competition for limited resources causes a struggle for survival between individuals. Individuals with advantages over others are more likely to survive and have offspring.

Answers

A Apply Deaths and emigration are outpacing births and immigration.

14.4 Population Growth Patterns

KEY CONCEPT **Populations grow in predictable patterns.**

MAIN IDEAS

- Changes in a population's size are determined by immigration, births, emigration, and deaths.
- Population growth is based on available resources.
- Ecological factors limit population growth.

VOCABULARY

immigration
emigration
exponential growth
logistic growth
carrying capacity
population crash
limiting factor
density-dependent limiting factor
density-independent limiting factor

Connect to Your World

That banana you left in your backpack did not go unnoticed. After one week, you open your bag and dozens of tiny insects swarm out. The smell of rotting fruit follows close behind. Only a week ago, the population of fruit flies in your backpack was zero. Just before you opened it, the population had grown to several dozen. How did this population grow so quickly?

MAIN IDEA

Changes in a population's size are determined by immigration, births, emigration, and deaths.

The size of a population is usually changing. If resources such as food and water are abundant, or plentiful, a population may grow. On the other hand, if resources are in short supply, the population may decrease in size. Hopefully, the normal fruit fly population in your backpack is zero. But if an abundance of resources, such as an overripe banana, becomes available, the population will increase dramatically. However, when the resources are removed, the fruit fly population in your backpack will once again return to zero. Four factors affect the size of a population.

- **Immigration** When one or two fruit flies found the banana, they immigrated into your backpack. **Immigration** is the movement of individuals into a population from another population.
- **Births** Additional fruit flies were born in your backpack. Births increase the number of individuals in a population.
- **Emigration** After you opened your backpack, some fruit flies flew out and left to find other rotting fruit. **Emigration** is the movement of individuals out of a population and into another population.
- **Deaths** You might have squashed a couple of unlucky fruit flies as you were opening your backpack. The size of a population decreases when individuals die.

READING TOOLBOX

VOCABULARY

The word *immigrate* comes from the Latin word *immigrare*, meaning "to go into," and the word *emigrate* comes from the Latin word *emigrare*, meaning "to move."

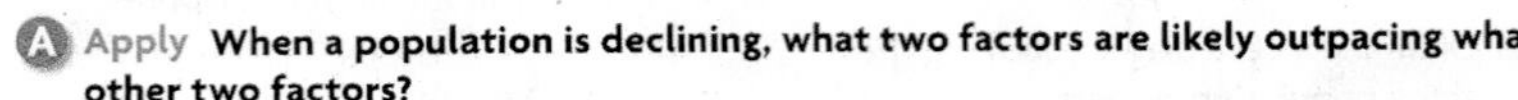

A Apply When a population is declining, what two factors are likely outpacing what other two factors?

Differentiated Instruction

BELOW LEVEL

Have students use a two-column format to take notes on new terms. In the first column, they should include their notes and definitions. In the second column, they should draw a diagram that illustrates the concept.

Teacher Toolkit, Section C, Combination Notes

ENGLISH LEARNERS

When students have read the section, reinforce vocabulary by asking them to write for three minutes on each of these pairs of contrasting concepts: immigration/emigration; exponential growth/logistic growth; density-dependent limiting factor/density-independent limiting factor.

Teacher Toolkit, Section C, Quick-Write

MAIN IDEA

Population growth is based on available resources.

Population growth is a function of the environment. The rate of growth for a population is directly determined by the amount of resources available. A population may grow very rapidly, or it may take a bit of time to grow. There are two distinct types of population growth.

Exponential Growth

When resources are abundant, a population has the opportunity to grow rapidly. This type of growth, called **exponential growth,** occurs when a population size increases dramatically over a period of time. In **FIGURE 4.1,** you can see that exponential growth appears as a J-shaped curve.

FIGURE 4.1 EXPONENTIAL GROWTH

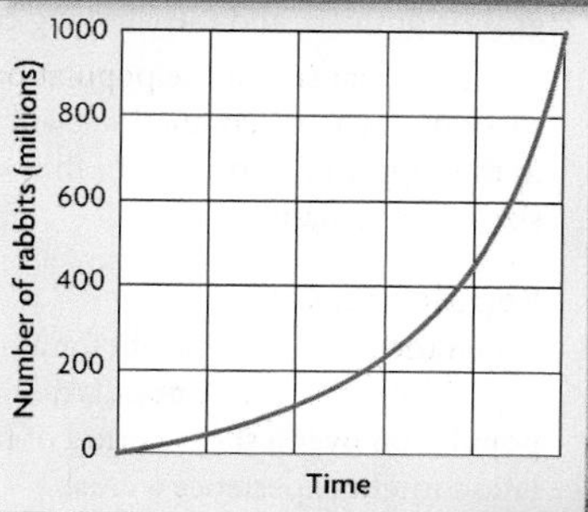

Number of rabbits (millions): 0, 200, 400, 600, 800, 1000

Time

Exponential growth may occur when a species moves to a previously uninhabited area. For example, in 1859 an Australian landowner returning home from England brought 24 European rabbits to the country for the purpose of sport hunting. The rabbits were introduced into an environment that had abundant space and food and no predators fast enough to catch them. The initial population of 24 rabbits grew exponentially and spread across the country. After many attempts to control the population, today there are between 200 million and 300 million rabbits in Australia.

FIGURE 4.2 In Australia during the early 1900s, the introduced European rabbit population exhibited exponential growth.

Logistic Growth

Most populations face limited resources and thus show a logistic growth rate. During **logistic growth,** a population begins with a period of slow growth followed by a brief period of exponential growth before leveling off at a stable size. A graph of logistic growth takes the form of an S-shaped curve and can be seen in **FIGURE 4.3,** which models a population's change in size over time. During initial growth, resources are abundant, and the population is able to grow. Over time, resources begin to deplete, and growth starts to slow. As resources become limited, the population levels off at a size the environment can support.

FIGURE 4.3 LOGISTIC GROWTH

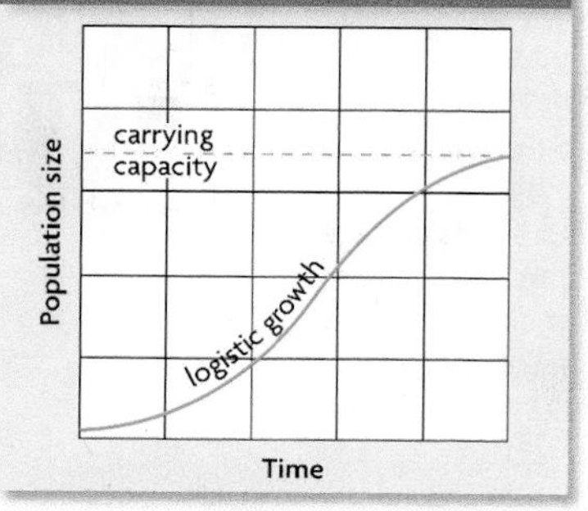

carrying capacity

logistic growth

Population size

Time

HANDS-ON ACTIVITY

To model exponential growth, use the story of the king who receives the gift of a beautiful chessboard. He offers to reward the giver and is surprised by what seems to be so insignificant a request: 1 grain of rice on the first square, 2 on the second, 4 on the third, and so on, doubling the amount for each of the 64 squares. The king soon realizes he doesn't have enough rice in the kingdom to honor the request. To establish the pattern, use sticky notes to mark the amount on the first two rows of a chessboard.

ONLINE Biology
HMHScience.com

Have students complete the Data Analysis Smart Grapher activity for this chapter to plot the logistic growth curve of a bison population.

TEACH FROM VISUALS

FIGURES 4.1 AND 4.3 Point out that both the J-shaped and S-shaped curves are models that approximate patterns of growth seen in actual populations. **Ask,** Do you see any similarities between the two models? Both show a pattern of exponential growth at the beginning.

Explain that the exponential growth model represents a situation that cannot be sustained in the real world. No population can grow unchecked because the resources available are finite; they have a limit. The logistic growth model can be described as what happens to a growing population when the effects of those limits are felt. **Ask**

- Looking at the dotted line in the logistic growth model, what do you infer the *carrying capacity* to be? the maximum number of organisms in a population that the resources can support
- Which of the two models relates population growth to population density? Logistic growth; population growth decreases as population density increases.

Take It Further

Biotic potential is the rate that a population increases under ideal circumstances, including unlimited resources. It is the maximum rate at which a species can reproduce and results in exponential growth. The giant puffball mushroom has a very impressive biotic potential. It is capable of producing 7 trillion offspring in a single generation. If all offspring survived and reproduced, then together all descendants would weigh more than Earth in just two generations.

The same environmental factors, such as food, water, shelter, and low predation, that affect biotic potential also combine to determine the carrying capacity of an environment. There are limits.

▼ Teach *continued*

DATA ANALYSIS

Discuss

A fish kill event is reported when dead or dying fish are observed in a body of water. It can involve a small number of fish or thousands of fish. The combination graph shows data from 1991 to 2001. The bars represent the total number of fish kill events for each month. The line graph represents the average rainfall for each month. **Ask,** What is the advantage of graphing 10 years of data? more reliable comparison and to see long-term trends

Address Misconceptions

Common Misconception Most fish kill events are caused by human activities.

Correcting the Misconception In Florida, most fish kill events have natural causes. The most common cause is low dissolved oxygen levels in water. Rainfall, number of cloudy days, temperature, and number of organisms living in the water affect oxygen levels in water. However, fertilizers and herbicides can contribute to low dissolved oxygen levels.

Answers

1. July, November, and December
2. *Sample answer:* The number of fish kill events rises slowly from January through May, are the most numerous from June through August, decrease in September and October, and then begin to rise again in November. The most fish kill events occur during the summer months. The amount of rainfall is low from January through April, increases in May and June, decreases in July, rises in August, levels off in September, and decreases from October through December.
3. *Sample answer:* Increased rainfall may lead to more fish kills, at least until another factor or set of factors comes into play and the correlation between rainfall and fish kill events becomes less evident.

Online Student Resources, Data Analysis Practice

What Limits Population Growth?

Carrying Capacity

The environment determines how many individuals of the species can be supported based on natural cycles and species diversity. An environment, therefore, has a carrying capacity for each species living in it. The **carrying capacity** of an environment is the maximum number of individuals of a particular species that the environment can normally and consistently support.

In nature, a carrying capacity can change when the environment changes. Consider a population of grasshoppers that feed on meadow grasses. If a fire burns part of the meadow, the insects' food resources diminish, and the carrying capacity declines. But during years with plentiful rain, the meadow grasses flourish, and the carrying capacity rises.

The actual size of the population usually is higher or lower than the carrying capacity. Populations will rise and fall as a result of natural changes in the supply of resources. In this way, the environment naturally controls the size of a population.

Population Crash

When the carrying capacity for a population suddenly drops, the population experiences a crash. A **population crash** is a dramatic decline in the size of a population over a short period of time. There are many reasons why a population might experience a crash.

DATA ANALYSIS

READING COMBINATION GRAPHS

Combination graphs show two sets of data on the same graph. One set of data may be shown as a bar graph, while the other set may be shown as a line graph. The two data sets must share the same independent variable on the *x*-axis. Scientists can then interpret the data to determine if a relationship exists between the variables.

This combination graph displays data about fish kill events, during which many fish died at once, and average monthly rainfall in Florida from 1991–2001.

- The *y*-axis on the left side represents the total number of fish kill events.
- The *y*-axis on the right side represents average monthly rainfall during that time.
- The *x*-axis shows the month of data collection.

The graph shows that in January there were four fish kill events and an average of 2.7 inches of rain.

GRAPH 1. FLORIDA FISH KILLS 1991–2001

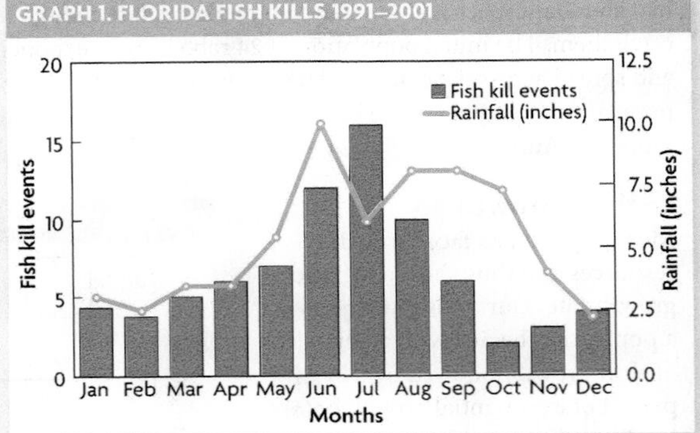

Source: The University of Florida Extension Information Circular 107. Used by permission.

1. **Analyze** An increase in fish kills and a decrease in rainfall occurs in what months?
2. **Analyze** Describe the trend in the fish kill events throughout the year. Describe the trend in rainfall data throughout the year.
3. **Hypothesize** What relationship might exist between fish kill events and rainfall?

Differentiated Instruction

BELOW LEVEL

Go over the structure of the Fish Kill graph in the Data Analysis activity. Point out that the two *y*-axes enable two sets of data to be graphed on the same *x*-axis. Point out that a similar setup is used in **FIGURE 4.5.**

PRE-AP

Prepare a list of 6–10 statements about limiting factors—some true, some false. Give students the list before discussing the topic in class. Have students react to the statements, indicating whether the statements are true or false based on their understanding of population dynamics. Then have them correct any mistakes following class.

Teacher Toolkit, Section C, Anticipation Guide

For example, in 1944, 29 reindeer were introduced to St. Matthew Island off the coast of Alaska. At the time of the introduction, the entire island was covered with a rich mat of lichens. Plenty of good food allowed the reindeer herd to grow at an exponential rate. By the summer of 1963, the island population had grown to 6000 reindeer. However, over the winter, large amounts of snow fell on food resources that had already become greatly depleted by the large herd. By the spring of 1964, only 50 reindeer remained. The population crash on St. Matthew Island came as the result of two factors that limited resources: the harsh winter and the scarcity of food.

Predict What would have eventually happened to the reindeer herd if the winter had not made foraging so difficult? Explain.

MAIN IDEA

Ecological factors limit population growth.

Many factors can affect the carrying capacity of an environment for a population of organisms. The factor that has the greatest effect in keeping down the size of a population is called the **limiting factor.** There are two categories of limiting factors—density dependent and density independent.

Density-Dependent Limiting Factors

Density-dependent limiting factors are limiting factors that are affected by the number of individuals in a given area. Density-dependent limiting factors include many types of species interactions.

Competition Members of populations compete with one another for resources such as food and shelter. As a population becomes denser, the resources are used up, limiting how large the population can grow.

Predation The population of a predator can be limited by the available prey, and the population of prey can be limited by being caught for food. On Isle Royale in Michigan, changes in wolf and moose populations, shown in **FIGURE 4.5**, provide an example. As the moose population grows, so does the wolf population. But at a certain point, the wolves eat so many moose that there are not enough left to feed all the wolves. The result is a decrease in the wolf population. Over time, the two populations rise and fall in a pattern, shown in **FIGURE 4.5**.

Parasitism and disease Parasites and diseases can spread more quickly through dense populations. The more crowded an area becomes, the easier it is for parasites or diseases to spread. The parasites or diseases can then cause the size of the population to decrease.

Analyze How does the wolf population on Isle Royale affect the carrying capacity of the moose population?

FIGURE 4.4 Taking down prey as large as a moose requires that the members of a pack work together. As many as ten wolves may take hours or even days to wear down this moose.

FIGURE 4.5 DENSITY-DEPENDENT LIMITING FACTORS

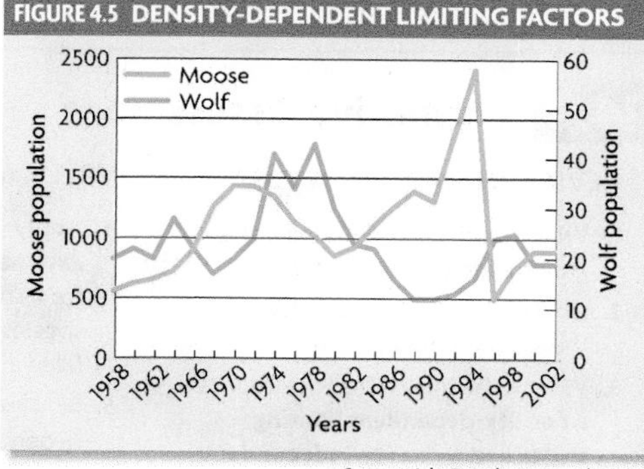

Source: Isle Royale Research Data

TEACH WITH TECHNOLOGY

Use the Internet to gather data on prey/predator populations, for example, the Hudson Bay Company data on hare/lynx populations or Isle Royal data on moose/wolf populations. Place the data into a spreadsheet program and use an interactive white board to demonstrate different ways to format the data.

TEACH FROM VISUALS

FIGURE 4.5 Point out the inverse relationship between the size of each population shown in the two graphs.

Ask

- What happens to the moose population as the wolf population increases? It decreases.
- What happens to the moose population as the wolf population decreases? It increases.
- Is there something in the data to suggest that the wolf population crashed? a dramatic drop in the wolf population starting about 1978
- In what way does the data suggest that something other than availability of prey caused the wolf population to crash? The wolf population continued to fall even though the moose population rebounded dramatically and plenty of prey was available. What might have caused the crash? The initial decrease in prey may have caused the birth rate of the wolf population to decrease.
- Is there something in the data to suggest that the moose population crashed? a dramatic drop in the moose population starting about the year 1994
- What might have caused the moose population to crash? With few predators to control their numbers, the moose exceeded the carrying capacity of their environment.

Answers

A Predict Because of the limited quantity of food on the island, the population would have stopped growing and then leveled off and eventually decreased as food became scarce.

B Analyze Wolves keep the population of moose at a level that the environment can support.

▼ Teach continued

Have students explore density-independent factors by completing the WebQuest for this chapter at **HMHScience.com**.

Answers

A Apply It is density-independent unless the algae population becomes large enough to block sunlight.

▼ Assess and Reteach

Assess Use the Section Self-Check or Section Quiz, both available at **HMHScience.com**.

Reteach Collect from the Media Gallery all the graphs presented in this section. Use the graphs to review the patterns of population growth. Have students refer to the vocabulary listed on the first page of this section.

FIGURE 4.6 The storm surge accompanying a hurricane can cause dangerous flooding.

Density-Independent Limiting Factors

Density-independent limiting factors are the aspects of the environment that limit a population's growth regardless of the density of the population.

Unusual weather Weather can affect the size of a population regardless of its density. For example, along the western coast of the United States, a lack of southerly winds can prevent nutrient-poor warm water from being replaced, as it normally is, with nutrient-rich cold water. The lack of nutrients in the water along the coast can prevent phytoplankton, which form the base of the marine ecosystem, from growing in their usual large numbers. In turn, zooplankton, tiny organisms that feed on phytoplankton, have smaller populations. The effects are felt all the way up the food chain, with smaller populations of fish and birds.

Natural disasters Volcanoes, tsunamis, tornados, and hurricanes, shown in **FIGURE 4.6**, can wipe out populations regardless of density. For example, the large wave of a tsunami can damage fragile coral reefs, knock down entire mangrove forests, and destroy sea turtle nesting beaches.

Human activities Destruction of a wetland habitat along the Platte River in Nebraska has threatened an important feeding ground for the sandhill crane. Urbanization in this area is depleting the resources these migratory birds need during their trek to nesting grounds in northern Canada and in Alaska. By clearing forests, filling wetlands, and polluting the air, land, and water, humans threaten habitats and the organisms that live in them. As we will discuss in Human Impact on Ecosystems, human influence as a limiting factor has had a profound effect on populations. For example, the introduction of nonnative species has caused population crashes in many parts of the world where biodiversity is an important part of the ecosystem's functioning.

A Apply A population of algae in a pond is limited in size by the amount of sunlight that strikes the pond's surface. Is sunlight a density-dependent or density-independent limiting factor for the algae population?

14.4 Formative Assessment

REVIEWING MAIN IDEAS

1. What four factors determine the growth rate of a population?
2. How does **carrying capacity** affect the size of a population?
3. What is the main difference between a **density-dependent limiting factor** and a **density-independent limiting factor**? Give examples of each.

CRITICAL THINKING

4. **Apply** What might cause **exponential growth** to occur only for a short period when a new species is introduced to a resource-filled environment?
5. **Synthesize** How might density-dependent limiting factors be affected by a flood or some other natural disaster?

CONNECT TO

SYMBIOSIS

6. Give an example of how a symbiotic relationship could cause a population crash.

14.4 FORMATIVE ASSESSMENT

1. immigration, births, deaths, emigration
2. Carrying capacity limits the size of a population.
3. A density-dependent limiting factor is affected by the number of individuals in a given area, but a density-independent limiting factor is not affected by population size. Examples of density-dependent limiting factors include predation, competition, and disease. Examples of density-independent limiting factors include weather, natural disasters, and human activities.
4. Eventually, the growing population will consume all available resources, and the species may experience a population crash.
5. Answers might include effects such as a flood or other natural disaster destroying resources, predators, or prey in an area, which are density-dependent factors.
6. If a parasite or disease spreads in a dense population, it could cause a population to decline dramatically over a short period of time.

14.5 Ecological Succession

KEY CONCEPT **Ecological succession is a process of change in the species that make up a community.**

MAIN IDEAS

- Succession occurs following a disturbance in an ecosystem.

VOCABULARY

succession
primary succession
pioneer species
secondary succession

Connect to Your World

It begins with a dirty sock. Then a discarded homework assignment. But this is only the start. If you have ever spent a Saturday afternoon cleaning your bedroom, you may have wondered how a perfectly clean room could manage to become such a cluttered mess. A clean room becoming cluttered is a gradual process much like the process that rebuilds damaged ecosystems.

MAIN IDEA

Succession occurs following a disturbance in an ecosystem.

After an ecosystem experiences a devastating catastrophe and begins to regrow, the space re-forms itself through a process known as succession. **Succession** is the sequence of biotic changes that regenerate a damaged community or create a community in a previously uninhabited area.

The Hawaiian Islands began to form more than 70 million years ago. Over time, volcanic eruptions such as the one shown in **FIGURE 5.1** created these islands in the middle of the Pacific Ocean. Eventually, the bare volcanic rock began to break down into soil, which provided a place for plants to grow. As time passed, the process of succession created unique tropical ecosystems. Succession from bare rock to such highly diverse vegetation takes a great deal of time.

FIGURE 5.1 The path of a lava flow, such as this one on the island of Hawaii (left), leaves behind nothing but solid rock. Over time, primary succession will turn this harsh landscape into a fertile ecosystem (right).

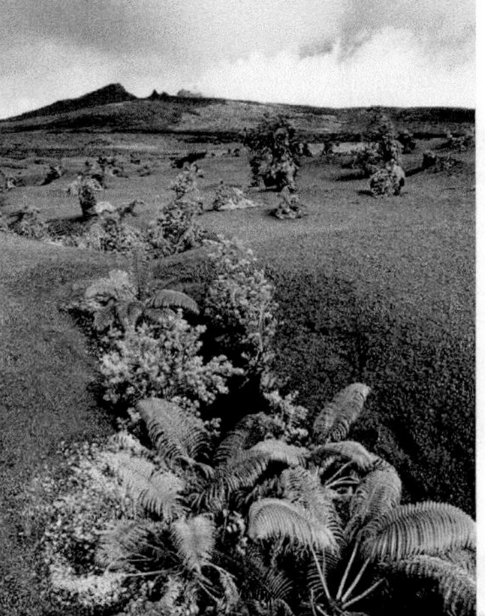

437

Differentiated Instruction

BELOW LEVEL

Make sure the sequence of events shown by the two photographs in **FIGURE 5.1** is clear. The lava flow in the first photograph hardens to form a surface layer of rock. The plants in the second photograph take root much later, after pioneer species, such as moss or lichen, have begun to break down the rock into soil.

SECTION 14.5

B.3.3 Evaluate the claims, evidence, and reasoning that the complex interactions in ecosystems maintain relatively consistent numbers and types of organisms in stable conditions, and identify the impact of changing conditions or introducing non-native species into that ecosystem.

Plan and Prepare

Activate Prior Knowledge Most students will have observed some form of secondary succession. Remind students that an ecosystem can be a large forest or a small, empty lot and that a disturbance is a change to the existing ecological community. **Ask,** What happens to a garden or field when plants are removed in the fall and not replanted in spring? Seeds or roots from the original plants may regrow, or weeds, grasses, wildflowers, or saplings might take root. **Ask,** What term is used to describe the arrival of new plants? immigration

Teach

Vocabulary

succession The shared root of the words *succeed* and *succession* refers to a sequence of events, not to success or victory. A team can have a succession of wins, or a prince can succeed his father to the throne. **Ask,** How are these uses similar to its use in ecology? Succession in an ecosystem follows a sequence of events that enable new species to colonize a habitat.

▼ Teach *continued*

TEACH FROM VISUALS

FIGURE 5.2 Point out how the cross section of soil changes during the process of primary succession. The land goes from having large rocks to soil with smaller and smaller rocks. Changes in the soil correspond to changes in surface vegetation as plant roots break down the rock and add organic matter. **Ask**

- What are the first organisms to break down rock? lichens and mosses
- What types of trees or large plants are the first to appear in primary succession? alders, cottonwoods, shrubs

Integrating Earth Science

The process of breaking down rock into smaller and smaller pieces is called **weathering.** Plants and other organisms help break down rocks, but most weathering is caused by water and wind. Over a long period of time, most weathered rock eventually becomes soil.

Answers

A Apply Mosses and lichens help break up the rock and add organic matter; they aid in soil formation.

FIGURE 5.2 Primary Succession

Melting glaciers, volcanic eruptions, landslides, and strip mines can all begin the process of primary succession.

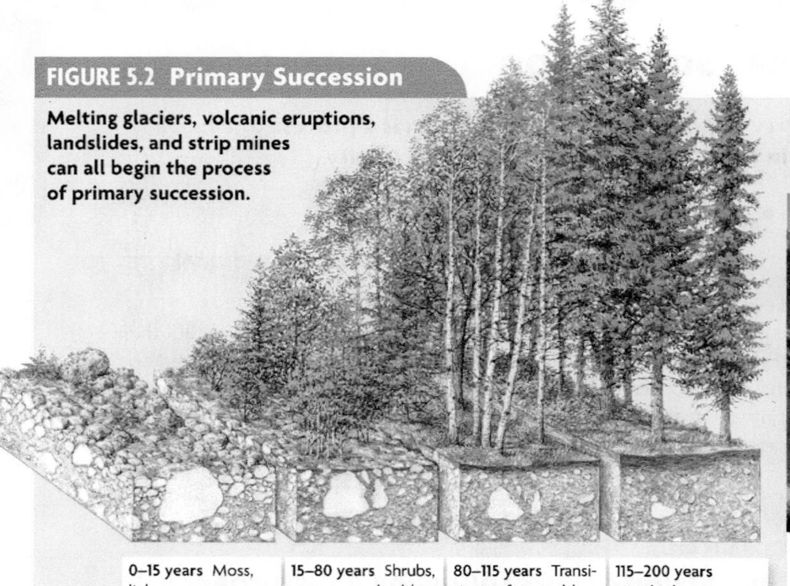

0–15 years Moss, lichens, grasses

15–80 years Shrubs, cottonwoods, alder thicket

80–115 years Transition to forest, alder, spruce

115–200 years Hemlock-spruce forest

Glacier Bay National Park in Alaska has given scientists an opportunity to witness primary succession as the glacier recedes.

A Apply **What function might the mosses and lichens serve in primary succession?**

Primary Succession

One of the best ways to understand succession is to watch it progress. **Primary succession** is the establishment and development of an ecosystem in an area that was previously uninhabited. The first organisms that live in a previously uninhabited area are called **pioneer species.** Typical examples of pioneer species are lichens and some mosses, which can break down solid rock into smaller pieces. The process of primary succession, which is illustrated in **FIGURE 5.2**, follows this basic pattern:

- Bare rock is exposed by a retreating glacier or is created when lava cools. Wind, rain, and ice begin to break down the surface of the rock, forming cracks and breaking the rock into smaller pieces.
- Lichen and moss spores are blown in by wind. As they grow, they break up the rock further. When they die, their remains mix with the rock pieces to form a thin layer of soil.
- Over time, seeds are blown into the area or are dropped by birds. Small flowers and hardy shrubs grow from these seeds. These new plants provide a habitat for small animals, break up the rock with their roots, and add material to the soil when they die.
- As the soil continues to grow thicker, small trees take root, and different animals move into the area. These trees provide shade.
- Different tree species take root in the shade and eventually replace the original trees, which need direct sunlight to thrive.

CONNECT TO

SYMBIOSIS

A lichen is actually two completely different species. Fungi and algae form a symbiotic relationship in which the fungi collect water, while the algae use chlorophyll to conduct photosynthesis and synthesize food for the lichen community.

Differentiated Instruction

PRE-AP

Have students prepare sequence diagrams of primary and secondary succession. Tell them to pay attention not only to descriptions in the text but to the details of the diagrams. For example, have students look carefully at how the community of trees changes over the course of secondary succession.

Teacher Toolkit, Section C, Sequence Diagram

HANDS-ON ACTIVITY

Collect some historical pictures of your area and share these with students. Have them look for changes in the natural landscape that point to ecological succession.

FIGURE 5.3 Secondary Succession

Following a flood or a fire, a community is given a chance for new life. Plants remaining after the disturbance reestablish the ecosystem.

A Analyze **Why does secondary succession take less time than primary succession?**

Secondary Succession

Succession does not always begin from bare rock. More often, a disturbance, such as a fire or hurricane, halts the progress of succession or destroys an established community. **Secondary succession,** which is illustrated in **FIGURE 5.3,** is the reestablishment of a damaged ecosystem in an area where the soil was left intact. Plants and other organisms that remain start the process of regrowth. There is no end to secondary succession. Small disturbances, such as a tree falling, start the process again and again. The dynamic processes of succession are always changing the face of an ecosystem.

B Connect **Where might succession occur in the ocean?**

14.5 Formative Assessment

SELF-CHECK Online HMHScience.com GO ONLINE

REVIEWING MAIN IDEAS

1. How is **primary succession** different from **secondary succession**?
2. Why are **pioneer species** so important for primary succession?

CRITICAL THINKING

3. **Infer** Does the process of primary succession take longer in tropical or arctic areas? Explain.
4. **Predict** During **succession,** what might become the limiting factor for sun-loving mosses as taller plants begin to grow?

CONNECT TO

BIOLOGICAL NICHE

5. At what point during primary succession does an ecosystem provide the fewest habitats for organisms? Explain your reasoning.

TEACH FROM VISUALS

FIGURE 5.3 Point out to students the passage of time noted in the labels and compare it to the passage of time shown in **FIGURE 5.2. Ask**

- Which process takes longer? primary succession
- Why are shrubs and grasses able to take root so quickly with secondary succession? The ecosystem already has soil, so these plants can grow in the first stage of the process. They may have been growing there before the fire.
- What part of the ecosystem undergoes very little change with secondary succession? the quality of the soil

Answers

A **Analyze** Secondary succession starts with soil instead of bare rock.

B **Connect** in a coral reef

Assess and Reteach ▼

Assess Use the Section Self-Check or Section Quiz, both available at **HMHScience.com.**

Reteach Have students summarize the section's content by explaining the meaning of each vocabulary term listed on the first page of this section.

14.5 FORMATIVE ASSESSMENT

1. Primary succession begins with bare rock, worn down and colonized by pioneer species. Secondary succession begins with established soil in which many different plants can grow.
2. Pioneer species, such as mosses and lichens, can break down rock into smaller pieces. When they die, their remains mix with tiny pieces of rock to form a thin layer of soil. They change the ecosystem in ways that enable the support of more diverse species.
3. *Sample answer:* Primary succession takes longer in arctic areas because rock is covered with snow part of the year, the growing season is shorter, and cold temperatures slow growth and decomposition. Soil takes much longer to form in arctic areas.
4. the amount of sunlight that reaches them
5. *Sample answer:* There are no habitable areas in the earliest stages of succession because there is no soil to support producers. Land becomes habitable once rock has weathered enough to support mosses and lichens. Over time, the mosses and lichens will provide the resources needed to support other organisms.

CHAPTER REVIEW

GO ONLINE

Encourage students to go to **HMHScience.com** for a detailed review of each section, including visuals and vocabulary practice.

Online Student Resources, Vocabulary Practice Worksheet

BIG IDEA Individual organisms and populations of organisms interact with each other and with the environment.

CHAPTER 14 Summary

KEY CONCEPTS

14.1 Habitat and Niche

Every organism has a habitat and a niche. Each organism in an ecosystem has an ecological niche, which includes the type of food it consumes, its behavior, and its habitat—the place where it lives. Competitive exclusion prevents two species from sharing the same niche. In different geographical regions, ecological equivalents may have similar ecological niches.

14.2 Community Interactions

Organisms interact as individuals and as populations. Interactions between species include competition and predation. Interactions shape ecosystem dynamics. Parasitism, commensalism, and mutualism are symbiotic relationships involving two species living in direct contact with one another.

14.3 Population Density and Distribution

Each population has a density, a dispersion, and a reproductive strategy. The distribution of a population can be measured by population density. Species can have clumped, uniform, or random dispersion patterns. Survivorship curves describe the reproductive strategies of different species.

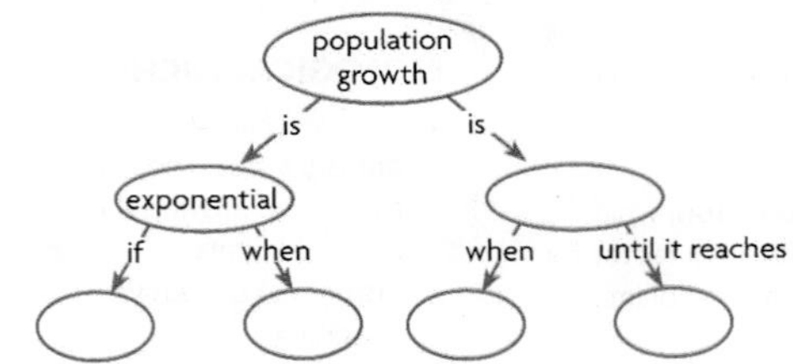

14.4 Population Growth Patterns

Populations grow in predictable patterns. Population growth accommodates changes in population size due to births and deaths as well as immigration and emigration. Populations experiencing exponential growth increase dramatically over time. When resources become a limiting factor, a population will grow logistically until it reaches the environmental carrying capacity, or the maximum population size the environment can support. Density-dependent limiting factors affect dense populations, but density-independent limiting factors affect populations regardless of density.

14.5 Ecological Succession

Ecological succession is a process of change in the species that make up a community. Succession refers to the progression of plants and animals that repopulate a region after an ecological disturbance. Primary succession begins in a previously uninhabited area, such as bare rock exposed by the receding of a glacier or created by a volcanic eruption. Secondary succession occurs in a previously inhabited area that is damaged by an ecological disturbance, such as a fire or a flood.

READING TOOLBOX SYNTHESIZE YOUR NOTES

Concept Map Use a concept map to display the differences between exponential and logistic growth.

population growth — is → exponential (if → ___; when → ___); is → ___ (when → ___; until it reaches → ___)

Main Idea Chart Use the main idea chart to explain and give examples of density-independent and density-dependent limiting factors.

Density-Independent	Density-Dependent

Reviewing Vocabulary

1. mutualism
2. parasitism
3. commensalism
4. clumped
5. random
6. uniform
7. exponential
8. population crash
9. carrying capacity
10. *Sample answer:* A niche is a unique set of characteristics that describe how a species lives in its environment. Therefore, it can be considered special because a niche is unique to a species.
11. *Sample answer:* The place a person inhabits includes all the living and nonliving things surrounding him or her. Likewise, a habitat of an organism includes all of the biotic and abiotic factors in its surroundings.

14 Review

GO ONLINE

Review Games • Concept Map • Section Self-Checks

CHAPTER VOCABULARY

14.1 habitat
ecological niche
competitive exclusion
ecological equivalent

14.2 competition
predation
symbiosis
mutualism
commensalism
parasitism

14.3 population density
population dispersion
survivorship curve

14.4 immigration
emigration
exponential growth
logistic growth
carrying capacity
population crash
limiting factor
density-dependent limiting factor
density-independent limiting factor

14.5 succession
primary succession
pioneer species
secondary succession

Reviewing Vocabulary

Category Clues

For each clue in the category group, list the appropriate vocabulary words from the chapter.

Category: Types of Symbiosis

1. two-way benefit
2. host is harmed
3. no effect on host

Category: Types of Dispersion

4. a herd
5. no pattern
6. territories

Category: Population Growth

7. quick growth
8. sudden decrease in size
9. number environment can sustain

READING TOOLBOX WORD ORIGINS

10. *Niche* is an English word with a French origin. In general, it means "a special place." How does this meaning relate to the ecological definition of the word?

11. *Habitat* comes from a Latin word meaning "it inhabits." Connect this meaning with the definition in Section 1.

Reviewing MAIN IDEAS

12. A deer is a large herbivore that usually lives in a forest. What is the deer's habitat, and what is its niche?

13. How does competitive exclusion differ from ecological equivalents?

14. A brown bear is an omnivore. Explain how a brown bear and a squirrel can be in interspecific competition and have a predatory–prey relationship.

15. The remora fish has an adaptation that allows it to attach to a shark, and it feeds on scraps of food left over from the shark's meal. What type of symbiotic relationship is this? Explain.

16. If you were to add two goldfish into a fish tank that already contains three goldfish, explain what happens to the population density of the fish tank.

17. Explain how the three types of survivorship curves align with different reproductive strategies.

18. If a large number of individuals immigrated into a population of bison, what two things could happen to return the population to its original size?

19. Why does a population that experiences exponential growth have a high chance of having a population crash?

20. How might the carrying capacity of an environment for a particular species change in response to an unusually long and harsh winter? Why?

21. Describe and give examples of two limiting factors that affect a dense population.

22. Why is succession considered an ongoing process?

Reviewing Main Ideas

12. The deer's habitat is the forest. Its niche is an herbivore that lives in the forest.
13. Competitive exclusion occurs between two species competing for the same resources in the same environment. These two species would be considered ecological equivalents if they lived in different geographical regions.
14. A brown bear and a squirrel are in interspecific competition when they both eat the same resources, such as acorns. They have a predator-prey relationship when the bear eats the squirrel.
15. It is commensalism because the remora fish benefits by getting food, and the shark apparently is not harmed and does not benefit.
16. The population density increases.
17. A type I survivorship curve shows a low level of infant mortality and a population that generally will survive until old age. This curve is associated with organisms that take care of their young until the young can care for themselves. A type II survivorship curve shows a survivorship rate that is roughly equal at all ages of an organism's life. A type III survivorship curve shows a very high birth rate and a very high infant mortality rate. There is generally little or no parental care in organisms showing a type III curve.
18. Answers should include deaths and emigration.
19. *Sample answer:* A population experiencing exponential growth is likely to exceed the carrying capacity of the ecosystem and consequently run out of resources such as food.
20. The carrying capacity for a species could decline because an unusually long and harsh winter could reduce the food resources for the species.
21. Answers should describe and give examples of two of the following density-dependent limiting factors: competition, predation, and parasitism and disease.
22. Succession is an ongoing, dynamic, and long-term process. Even small disturbances, such as a tree falling, restart the process.

CHAPTER REVIEW

Critical Thinking

23. mutualism
24. The prairie dogs could experience a population crash, or growth could slow down and level off to a level the environment can support.
25. This is a density-dependent factor because it is the high numbers of beetles that make the population more susceptible to competition.
26. The crash was caused by a density-dependent limiting factor because disease can spread more easily in a dense population.
27. Different species have certain conditions under which they thrive, including the availability of water and specific sources of nutrients, as well as access to sunlight. Ecological succession can change the conditions within an ecosystem, which may not support or favor the organisms living under the previous conditions.
28. The stability of an ecosytem could be impacted if environmental conditions such as temperature, rainfall, deforestation, or the introduction of chemical pollutants or exotic species cause existing organisms to leave the area or to die.

Analyzing a Diagram

29. The left side of the diagram depicts pioneer species because it shows mosses and lichens growing on bare rock. These species are pioneer species because they are often the first species to grow in a previously uninhabited area.
30. *Sample answer:* Any disturbance, such as a fire, hurricane, or volcano, that destroys or damages the ecosystem could make it revert to an earlier stage of succession. Human activity could also cause the ecosystem to regress.

Critical Thinking

23. Apply A bee gathers nectar from a flower by using a strawlike appendage called a proboscis. While on the flower, grains of pollen attach to the bee's back. When the bee travels to another flower, the pollen fertilizes the new plant. What type of symbiosis is this?

24. Predict A population of prairie dogs is experiencing high immigration and birthrates, but resources are beginning to deplete. What could eventually happen to this population? Give two possibilities.

25. Synthesize A species of beetle is in a period of exponential growth, but a competing species has started sharing the same space. Is the competing species an example of a density-dependent or a density-independent limiting factor? Explain.

26. Evaluate Imagine that scientists introduced a disease into the rabbit population of Australia, and the rabbit population crashed. Was the crash caused by a density-dependent or density-independent limiting factor? Justify your answer.

27. Describe How can the process of ecological succession change populations and affect species diversity within an ecosystem?

28. Describe How can environmental change impact ecosystem stability?

Analyzing a Diagram

Use the diagram below to answer the next two questions.

29. Apply What part of the diagram depicts pioneer species? Explain your answer.

30. Infer What could happen in the ecosystem shown that could make it revert to an earlier stage of succession?

Analyzing Data Read a Combination Graph

Use the graph to answer the next three questions.

The combination graph below shows changes in the sizes of bee and mite populations in one area of the Midwest. The mites live as parasites on the bees.

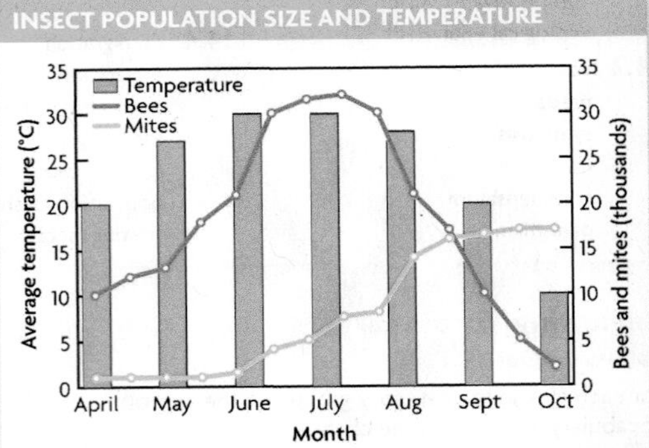

31. Interpret A decrease in the number of bees occurs during which months?

32. Analyze Describe the trends in the bee and mite populations from April through October.

33. Hypothesize What might explain the relationship between the bee and mite population numbers?

Making Connections

34. Write Ad Copy Imagine that you are an advertising agent trying to encourage a new species to move into an environment. Design an advertisement using the concepts from the chapter. Keep in mind that a population will not want to move to a new area without abundant resources. Choose a target species and make sure that your advertisement answers the following questions: What resources and environmental factors would make this species want to move? What abiotic and biotic factors does it need? Include several vocabulary terms from the chapter.

35. Apply The two zebras on the chapter opener are competing for the right to mate with females. Are they engaging in intraspecific or interspecific competition? Explain your answer.

Analyzing Data

31. A decrease in the number of bees occurs during August, September, and October.
32. The bee population slowly and steadily increases from early spring through mid-summer. After this point, the bee population steadily declines through the fall. The mite population starts very low in the spring and then starts increasing significantly as the bee population begins to fall in mid-summer. It continues its increase inversely to the bee decline.
33. *Sample Answer:* As the bee population grows, so can the mite population. Then, as temperatures fall and bees begin to die, the mites continue to reproduce because there are still enough bees for them to live on, though their rate of population growth is slowed.

442 Unit 5: Ecology

Standards-Based Assessment

Record your answers on a separate piece of paper.

MULTIPLE CHOICE

1 How do lichens and mosses make an ecosystem suitable for colonization by plant populations?

A They serve as a food source to new plant populations that colonize an ecosystem.

B They provide a suitable shelter for plant populations.

C They break down rock to help form organically rich soil that can support plant growth.

D They filter pollutants from air and water to make them suitable for use by plants.

2 A lava flow from a volcanic eruption destroys a forest and leaves behind a layer of rock. Before plants can begin to grow again, what event must occur as a part of primary succession?

A Large trees that provide shade must take root.

B Animals must return to the area.

C Lichens and mosses must be blown into the environment.

D Heavy rain must wash pollutants from the area.

3

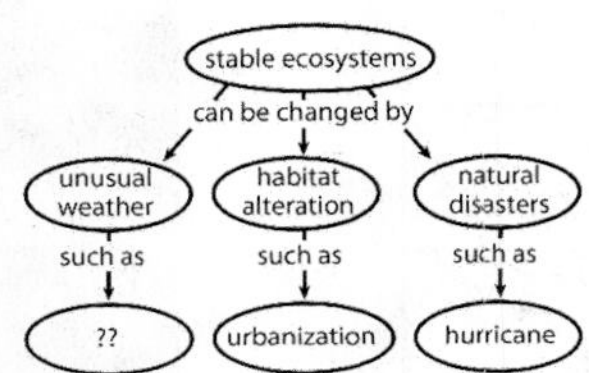

Which of the following ***best*** completes the concept map shown above?

A volcanic eruption

B toxic spill

C earthquake

D extended drought

THINK THROUGH THE QUESTION

Keep in mind that unusual weather is a natural part of ecosystem function.

4 Over many years, a diverse hardwood tree population formed a dense forest ecosystem in a region that was previously a meadow. As the population of hardwood trees increased, the species diversity of the grasses and other plants decreased. What event led to the decrease in diversity of the meadow plants as the populations of hardwood trees increased?

A As more trees began growing, animals ate all of the grasses and small plants.

B Many species of low-growing plants died out as the hardwood trees prevented them from getting enough sunlight, water, and soil nutrients to sustain their growth.

C A change in the species diversity of the animal populations corresponded with a change in the diversity of the tree population.

D Decomposition improved soil fertility for tree growth.

5

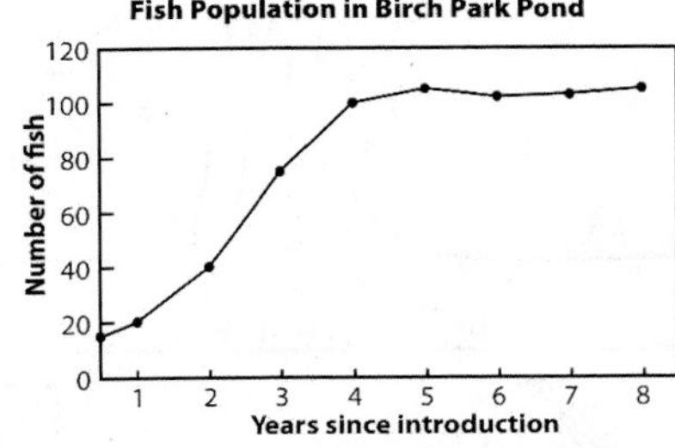

A fish species is introduced to a park pond. Which statement ***best*** describes the population growth of these fish shown in the graph?

A The population stopped growing because the fish stopped reproducing.

B The population stopped growing because this species of fish lives less than one year.

C The population grew until disease caused the population to level off.

D The population grew until it reached the pond's carrying capacity.

CHAPTER REVIEW

Standards-Based Assessment

The Standards-Based Assessment questions will help students prepare for their final examination in the course. If you wish to give students practice in coding their answers, look for the Standards-Based Assessment Answer Sheet at **HMHScience.com**. To give students practice under timed testing conditions, allow them five minutes per question.

Question	Answer	Depth of Knowledge	Cognitive Complexity
1	C	II	M
2	C	II	M
3	D	I	L
4	B	IV	H
5	D	II	M

KEY

Depth of Knowledge
I Recall
II Skill/Concept
III Strategic Thinking
IV Extended Thinking

Cognitive Complexity
L Low
M Moderate
H High

Making Connections

34. The ad copy should be directed at a target species and include resources and environmental factors that would make the species want to move, abiotic and biotic factors it needs, and several vocabulary terms from the chapter.

35. The two zebras are engaging in intraspecific competition because the competition is between members of the same species.

Chapter 14: Interactions in Ecosystems **443**

THING EXPLAINER BY RANDALL MUNROE

RANDALL MUNROE
XKCD.COM

TREE

A tree and the living and not living things around it

You know that a tree is a complex living thing. Trees also provide important habitats for a large variety of other living things, a biotic community. These symbiotic components make up the ecosystem in a tree. Here's an overview in simple terms.

GROWING UP
Trees grow taller only by making the ends of their branches longer. The spot where a branch joins the main part of the tree is never lifted higher.

LEAVES
Trees make power from the Sun's light using leaves. The green stuff in leaves eats light (and the kind of air we breathe out) and turns it into power (and the kind of air we breathe in).

POINTY CAT
This animal walks around slowly, climbing trees and eating leaves and sticks. It's covered in sharp points that can stick in your skin, so most animals don't bother it.

GRAY TREE-JUMPER
These little animals sleep in big round houses made of sticks and leaves high up in the branches.

QUIET NIGHT CATCHER
These birds fly very quietly and have big eyes to catch animals on the ground in the dark.

People think of them as knowing a lot of things, although that may just be because they're quiet and have big eyes.

BIRD HOLES
Some birds make holes, but a lot of them just use holes other birds make.

DRINK HOLES
These were made by a head-hitting bird looking for tree blood to drink.

TREE-EATING FLOWERS
This flower makes holes in trees and steals food and water from inside them. If the flowers get big, they can kill the branches they're growing on, or even kill the whole tree.

When people stand under this flower at a party, other people tell them to kiss.

LOUD JUMPERS
These two kinds of tiny animals make loud noises and are known for jumping. One has bones.

HEAD-HITTING BIRD
This kind of bird hits trees with its head, making holes in the wood with its sharp mouth. They make holes to find things to eat, and some also make holes to live in.

STORM BURN
When flashes of power from storms hit a tree, they can burn a line in the wood.

TREE

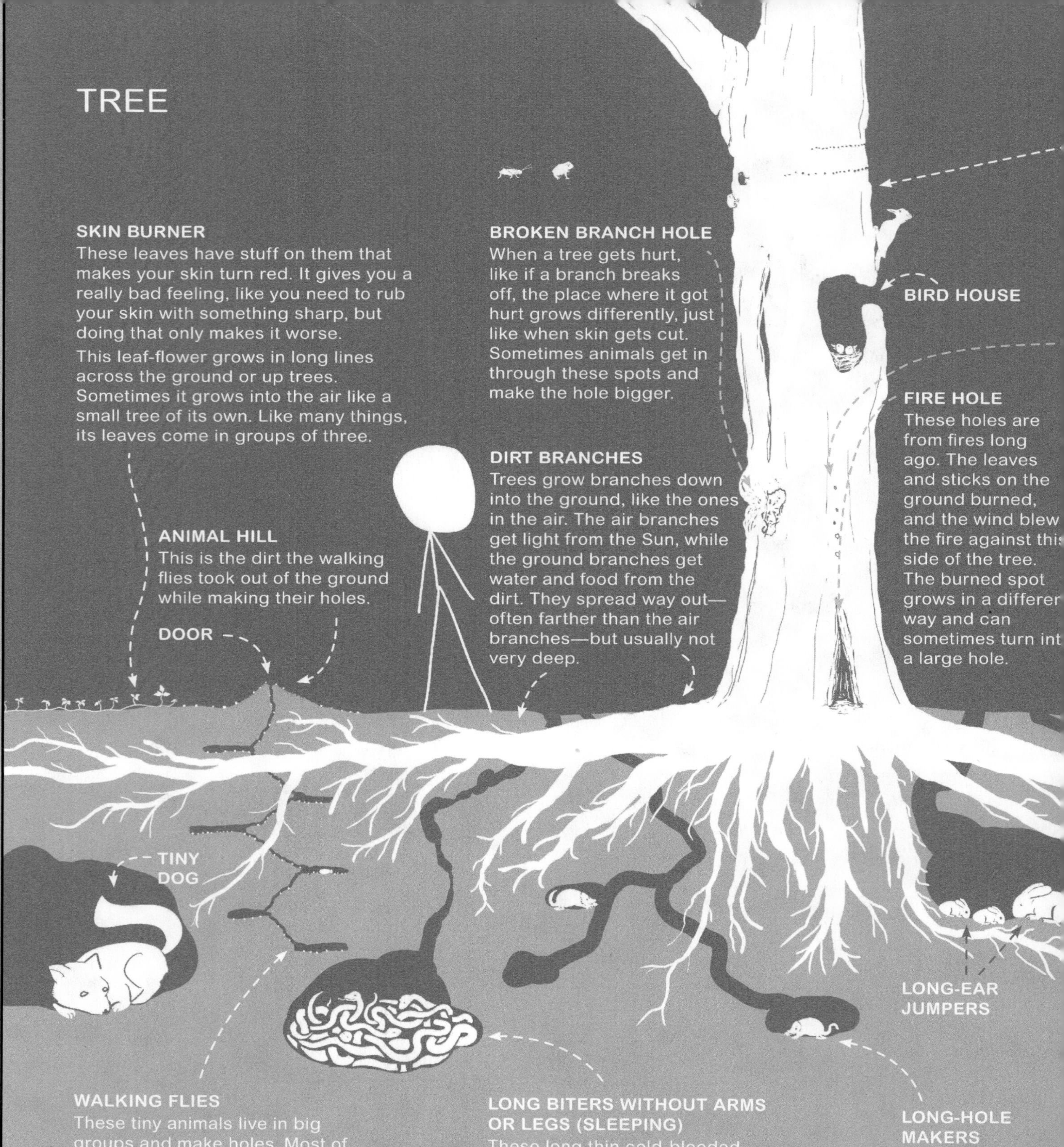

SKIN BURNER

These leaves have stuff on them that makes your skin turn red. It gives you a really bad feeling, like you need to rub your skin with something sharp, but doing that only makes it worse.

This leaf-flower grows in long lines across the ground or up trees. Sometimes it grows into the air like a small tree of its own. Like many things, its leaves come in groups of three.

ANIMAL HILL

This is the dirt the walking flies took out of the ground while making their holes.

DOOR

TINY DOG

WALKING FLIES

These tiny animals live in big groups and make holes. Most of them don't have babies; each family has one mother who makes all the new animals for the house.

They usually don't fly, and they're not much like house flies. They're in the same group with the kinds of flies whose back end has a sharp point that can hurt you.

BROKEN BRANCH HOLE

When a tree gets hurt, like if a branch breaks off, the place where it got hurt grows differently, just like when skin gets cut. Sometimes animals get in through these spots and make the hole bigger.

DIRT BRANCHES

Trees grow branches down into the ground, like the ones in the air. The air branches get light from the Sun, while the ground branches get water and food from the dirt. They spread way out—often farther than the air branches—but usually not very deep.

LONG BITERS WITHOUT ARMS OR LEGS (SLEEPING)

These long thin cold-blooded animals don't usually hang out together, and sometimes eat each other.

During the winter, though, lots of different kinds come together and sleep all wrapped up together in big holes under the ground where it's warmer.

BIRD HOUSE

FIRE HOLE

These holes are from fires long ago. The leaves and sticks on the ground burned, and the wind blew the fire against thi side of the tree. The burned spot grows in a differer way and can sometimes turn int a large hole.

LONG-EAR JUMPERS

LONG-HOLE MAKERS

SKIN

The outer skin of trees is where growing happens and where they carry food up and down. Cutting off a ring of skin all the way around a tree will kill it.

Trees grow by adding new layers, and grow differently in different parts of the year. If you cut open a tree, you can see old layers, and count them to tell how many years old the tree is.

OLD METAL

When people use metal to stick signs to trees, sometimes the tree grows around the metal and eats it up.

Then, many years later, if someone needs to cut down the tree, their saw can hit the metal and send tiny sharp pieces flying everywhere.

TREE-FOOD STEALER

Instead of growing dirt branches of their own, these flowers grow onto the dirt branches of other trees and steal food from them.

Some of these little flowers don't even have green leaves and can't make their own food from light.

TALL AND WIDE TREES

The same kind of tree can grow tall or wide. If there are other trees around, they'll grow mostly up, each one trying to get above the others to reach the Sun's light. If a tree is growing alone in a field, it will spread branches out to the sides so it can catch more light.

FIELD TURNING INTO FOREST

When people cut down a forest, sometimes they leave a few trees—to make a cool shadow area, or because the tree looks nice—and those trees will grow out into the new space.

If the forest grows back, the new trees—fighting with each other as they grow—will be tall and thin.

If you find a forest of tall thin trees with one wide tree with low branches in the middle, it might mean the forest you're in was someone's field a hundred years ago.

LITTLE HOLE-MAKERS

BIG HOLE-MAKERS

DIRT-BRANCH LIFE

Most trees and flowers have life growing on their dirt branches. This life helps them talk to the other trees and flowers around them. They can even use this life to share food or attack each other.

If something tries to eat one tree, it can tell other trees through messages carried by this ground life, and the other trees can start making bad water and other things to make themselves harder to eat.

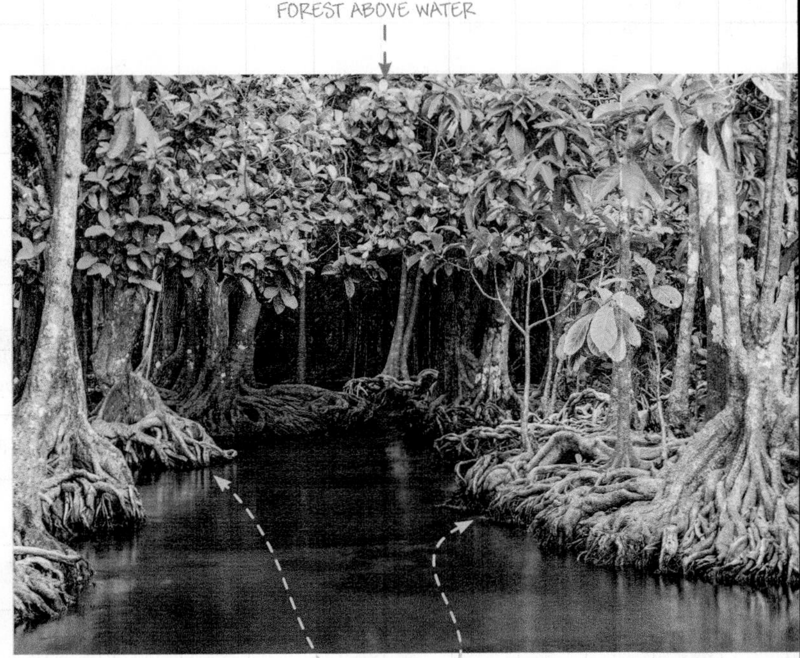

CHAPTER 15

Instruction and Intervention Support

The Biosphere

① Core Instruction

The **Core Instruction** resources below can be used for all students. Core instruction should be followed by ongoing assessment to determine which students need further help.

Available in both English and Spanish

Available Online

Section	Instruction	PRINT	ONLINE	Labs
15.1	Textbook **Life in the Earth System**	■	●	
	PowerPresentation and Notes 15.1		●	
15.2	Textbook **Climate**	■	●	Heating and Cooling Rates of Water and Soil **QuickLab** Microclimates
	Teaching Visuals Climate Zones (Fig. 2.2)		●	
	PowerPresentation and Notes 15.2		●	
15.3	Textbook **Biomes**	■	●	Modeling Biomes (Design Your Own)
	Teaching Visuals Biomes (Fig. 3.1)		●	
	PowerPresentation and Notes 15.3		●	
15.4	Textbook **Marine Ecosystems**	■	●	
	Animated Biology Where Do They Live?		●	
	Teaching Visuals Ocean Zones (Fig. 4.2)		●	
	PowerPresentation and Notes 15.4		●	
15.5	Textbook **Estuaries and Freshwater Ecosystems**	■	●	Winter Water Chemistry (Design Your Own) Modeling the Water Cycle Aquatic Primary Productivity (Open Inquiry)
	Animated Biology Lake Turnover		●	
	PowerPresentation and Notes 15.5		●	

Additional online resources available for this chapter include **Interactive Whiteboard Resources.**

GO ONLINE! for all your teacher resources at HMHScience.com

2 Support and Intervention

Support and Intervention resources are useful for students who need targeted help beyond the Core Instruction

Resources	PRINT	ONLINE
Assess and Reteach (TE wrap)	■	●
Concept Map		●
Interactive Reader	■	●
Interactive Review Games		●
Section Self-Checks		●
Study Guide B		●
Virtual Investigation Ecosystems and Energy Pyramids		●
Vocabulary Practice Worksheets		●

3 Specialized Support

Students who need more intensive personalized intervention benefit from **Specialized Support** resources.

Resources	PRINT	ONLINE
Chapter Audio Files		●
Differentiated Instruction Inclusion, Below Level, and English Learners (TE wrap)	■	●
ELL Strategies	■	●
Modified Lesson Plans for English Learners		●
Reinforcement Worksheets		●
Study Guide A		●

Extension and Assessment

Enrichment and Challenge

Resources	PRINT	ONLINE
Active Reading Worksheets		●
Data Analysis Practice Worksheet		●
Differentiated Instruction Pre-AP (TE wrap)	■	●
Pre-AP Activity Climate Change Controversy		●
Smart Grapher Activity		●
The Inside Story and **Take It Further** (TE wrap)	■	●
Unit Project		●
WebLinks		
WebQuest Explore an Ecosystem		●

Assessment

Resources	PRINT	ONLINE
Alternative Assessment		●
Chapter Tests A and B		●
Diagnostic Test		●
ExamView Banks		●
Extended Response Test		●
Online Assessment System		●
Section Quizzes		●
Standards-Based Assessment	■	●

CHAPTER 15

Chapter Overview

- **Section 1** explains how biotic and abiotic factors interact within the biosphere, one of Earth's four interconnected systems.
- **Section 2** provides coverage of Earth's three main climate zones.
- **Section 3** describes Earth's six major biomes and their characteristics.
- **Section 4** describes the major zones of Earth's oceans and their characteristics.
- **Section 5** describes and differentiates the characteristics of estuarine and freshwater ecosystems.

▼ Focus and Motivate

What species would you expect to find in a rain forest?

Have students read the caption for the photograph of the temperate rain forest. **Ask,** How does a temperate rain forest differ from a tropical rain forest? The temperate rain forest is cooler and has seasons, and the tropical forest is full of monkeys and colorful birds.

Although both types of rain forest receive abundant rainfall, temperate rain forests are farther from the equator and therefore have a cooler climate. **Ask,** What adaptations might you expect in the mammal species in each rain forest? Temperate mammals might have more fur or seasonal hibernation or migration behaviors to avoid cold temperatures. Tropical mammals might be short-haired.

BIOZINE
HMHScience.com

Students can access BioZine at **HMHScience.com** to receive updates to topics featured in the book.

CHAPTER 15 The Biosphere

BIG IDEA Climate and the distribution of land and water play a role in shaping ecosystems and influencing the distribution of organisms on Earth.

ONLINE BIOLOGY HMHScience.com

ONLINE Labs
- **QuickLab** Microclimates
- Winter Water Chemistry
- Modeling Biomes
- Heating and Cooling Rates of Water and Soil
- Modeling the Water Cycle
- **Open Inquiry Lab** Aquatic Primary Productivity

Student Activity

Purpose **Observe enclosed ecosystems to visualize the concepts of biosphere and biome.**

Materials (per class)
- a self-contained terrarium (terrestrial ecosystem) or photos of such a terrarium
- a self-contained aquarium (aquatic ecosystem) or photos of such an aquarium

What species would you expect to find in a rain forest?

Not all rain forests are teeming with monkeys and macaws. The temperate rain forest of the Pacific Northwest is inhabited by an entirely different community of plants and animals than is found in tropical rain forests. Location, climatic conditions, and other abiotic factors determine what species you will find in a particular area.

READING TOOLBOX **This reading tool can help you learn the material in the following pages.**

USING LANGUAGE

Hypothesis or Theory? To scientists, a theory is a well-supported scientific explanation that makes useful predictions. The main difference between a theory and hypothesis is that a hypothesis has not been tested, and a theory has been tested repeatedly and seems to correctly explain all the available data.

YOUR TURN

Use information from the chapter to complete the following tasks.

1. Is the greenhouse effect a hypothesis? Explain.
2. Write your own hypothesis that explains the increase in global temperatures.

Introduce Display the two environments so students can examine them. Tell students that each represents an ecosystem that has boundaries, just as Earth does. **Ask**

- What is Earth's boundary? The upper reaches of the atmosphere. The atmosphere marks the boundary of the biosphere—where all living things on Earth live.
- What abiotic factors may be affecting these systems from the inside? oxygen, carbon dioxide levels, humidity from the outside? the sun
- What areas within the ecosystem might some of the living things prefer? any spaces in which to hide, areas of different height or temperature or light exposure

Discuss Have students observe different areas within each ecosystem. Discuss how these different areas might support different organisms, relating back to what they learned about evolution, habitats, and niches. For example, there may be organisms in the soil that are adapted to its conditions, or organisms adapted to different zones within the water column.

Activate Prior Knowledge

Encourage students to think about Earth's regions and climates. **Ask,** What types of environments might you go through if you get in a car and travel from coast to coast in the United States? forest, prairie, desert, wetland, swamp Discuss the conditions that exist in these different environments, such as the humidity, temperature, air quality, and winds. **Ask,** What are some ways in which we organize or categorize Earth's regions? continents, oceans, seas, hemispheres, time zones, countries Tell students that some of these environments and major features of Earth are known as biomes, and that all of them are in the biosphere.

Preview Vocabulary

English Learners Tell students that in the context of biology, *sphere* rarely refers to an actual shape. *Hydrosphere, biosphere, atmosphere,* and *geosphere* are terms that organize the contents of the spherical Earth—liquid, solid, gas, and what is alive in all three. However, these spheres have no particular shape, and their boundaries are often unclear. Have students think of a seashore, where the atmosphere, hydrosphere, and geosphere are mixing and colliding, and among all three are living things such as bacteria, fish, crabs, birds, humans, and much more. Point out that all four spheres are present, but their shapes are constantly shifting.

Answers

1. The greenhouse effect is a theory. Scientific tests provide data that show that certain atmospheric gases, such as carbon dioxide, can absorb heat. Tests also show that the amount of carbon dioxide in Earth's atmosphere is increasing.
2. Accept all reasonable answers.

SECTION 15.1

B.2.4 Develop a model to illustrate the role of photosynthesis and cellular respiration in the cycling of carbon among the biosphere, atmosphere, hydrosphere, and geosphere.

▼ Plan and Prepare

Activate Prior Knowledge Students deal with many boundaries in their everyday lives. **Ask,** In an average day, how many boundaries do you cross, and what are they? *Sample answers:* doorways, yards, sidelines (sports) Discuss the difficulty of identifying the boundaries of the biosphere.

▼ Teach

Vocabulary

Greek and Latin Word Origins

Flora, which is Latin for "flower," refers to the plant life of a given area. **Fauna,** or "animals," refers to all of the animals in a given area. Once bacteria and archaea were discovered, the scientific community was not sure whether to group them in with the flora or the fauna. The word **biota,** which comes from the Greek *bios,* meaning "life," functions as a catchall word for the flora, fauna, bacteria, and archaea of our world.

Answers

A Connect The air is part of the biosphere. It contains living things such as bacteria, but air itself is not alive.

15.1 Life in the Earth System

KEY CONCEPT The biosphere is one of Earth's four interconnected systems.

MAIN IDEAS

- The biosphere is the portion of Earth that is inhabited by life.
- Biotic and abiotic factors interact in the biosphere.

VOCABULARY

biosphere
biota
hydrosphere
atmosphere
geosphere

Connect to Your World

You've probably seen many photos of tropical rain forests, complete with monkeys and brightly colored frogs. But did you know that there are also temperate rain forests? They get just as much rain but have cooler temperatures and different types of plants and animals. These are just two of the biomes found within the biosphere.

MAIN IDEA

The biosphere is the portion of Earth that is inhabited by life.

The **biosphere** is the part of Earth where life exists. All of Earth's ecosystems, taken together, form the biosphere. If you could remove all the nonliving parts of the biosphere—all the water, air, rocks, and so on—you would be left with the biota. The **biota** are the living things within the biosphere.

VISUAL VOCAB

The **biosphere** includes living organisms and the land, air, and water on Earth where living things reside.

biosphere
biota

The collection of living things in the biosphere may also be called the **biota.**

The biosphere is one of Earth's four major interconnected systems. The other three Earth systems are

- the **hydrosphere,** all of Earth's water, ice, and water vapor
- the **atmosphere,** the air blanketing Earth's solid and liquid surface
- the **geosphere,** the features of Earth's surface—such as the continents, rocks, and the sea floor—and everything below Earth's surface

You need to look at how all four Earth systems interact to really understand how an ecosystem works. For example, a plant growing in a swamp depends on the soil in which it grows just as much as on the water in the swamp. It uses carbon dioxide from the atmosphere to make sugars, and it gives off excess oxygen, slightly changing the air around it. One plant growing in one swamp has a small effect on the Earth system as a whole. But all living things together throughout the planet's history have had a vast effect.

READING TOOLBOX

TAKING NOTES

Use a diagram to take notes on the biosphere.

Biosphere
→ biota
→ land
→ air
→ water

 Connect **Is the air in your classroom part of the biosphere or the biota? Explain.**

Differentiated Instruction

ENGLISH LEARNERS

Have students study the parts of the words *biosphere, atmosphere, hydrosphere,* and *geosphere.* For each prefix, have students write a list of any other words they know in which it appears. To reinforce the meaning of the prefixes and the whole terms, have students use the *Multilanguage Glossary* and practice writing sentences that use these terms in a way that clarifies their meanings through context.

Teacher Toolkit, Section D, New Word Analysis

PRE-AP

Draw this figure on the board:

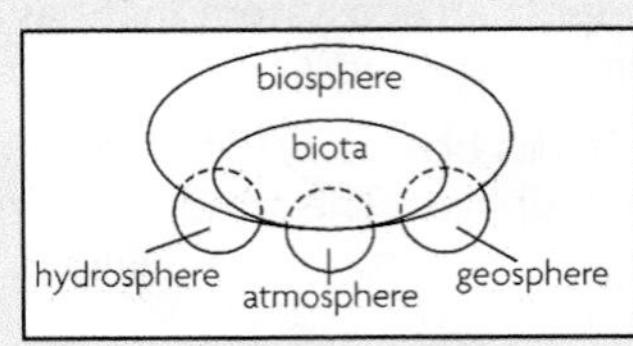

Have students look at this figure and write a paragraph on the interactions and overlaps between the five circles.

Teacher Toolkit, Section C, Quick-Write

MAIN IDEA

Biotic and abiotic factors interact in the biosphere.

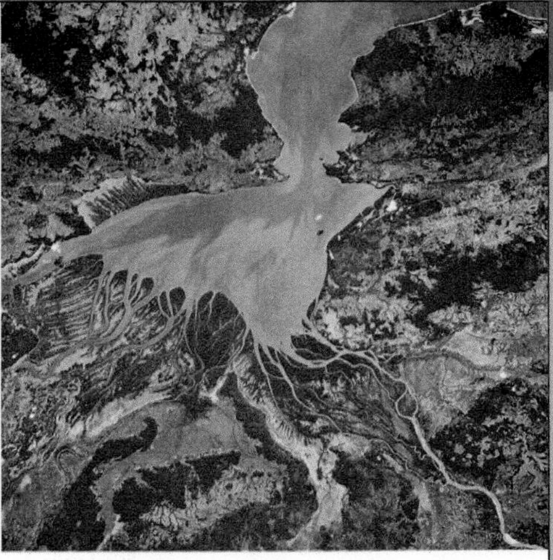

FIGURE 1.1 Deforestation, or the removal of forests, along the Mahajamba Bay in Madagascar has led to erosion along the waterway, clogging the water with silt and soil.

Just as one ecosystem is connected to another, all four Earth systems are also connected. A change in one sphere can affect the others. If plants are removed from a riverbank, for example, rain may flow more easily from the land to the water. This increased flow would likely carry more sediment and therefore make the river water murkier, as shown in **FIGURE 1.1.** The murky water might block sunlight, affecting the growth of aquatic plants. This change might in turn prevent these plants from taking up carbon dioxide and releasing oxygen.

James Lovelock, an atmospheric scientist from the United Kingdom, proposed the Gaia hypothesis to explain how biotic and abiotic factors interact in the biosphere. This hypothesis considers Earth itself a kind of living organism. Its atmosphere, geosphere, and hydrosphere are cooperating systems that yield a biosphere full of life. He called this living planet Gaia after the Greek goddess of Earth. In the early 1970s, Lynn Margulis, a microbiologist from the United States, added to the hypothesis, specifically noting the ties between the biosphere and other Earth systems. For example, when carbon dioxide levels increase in the atmosphere, plants grow more quickly. As their growth continues, they remove more and more carbon dioxide from the atmosphere. The atmospheric carbon dioxide level drops, and plant growth slows. This give-and-take, known as a feedback loop, helps maintain a fairly constant level of carbon dioxide in the atmosphere.

Sometimes, people mistakenly believe that the Gaia hypothesis suggests that Earth is a thinking being that regulates the geosphere, the atmosphere, and the hydrosphere. This is obviously not the case. Rather, the Gaia hypothesis recognizes the extensive connections and feedback loops between the living and nonliving parts of the planet. Many scientists are now devoting their careers to organizing new fields of study, such as geobiology and geomicrobiology, to examine these intriguing relationships.

Summarize **Explain the Gaia hypothesis in your own words.**

SELF-CHECK Online
HMHScience.com
GO ONLINE

15.1 Formative Assessment

REVIEWING MAIN IDEAS

1. What is the relationship between the **biota** and the **biosphere**?
2. How does the Gaia hypothesis explain the interaction between biotic and abiotic factors in the biosphere?

CRITICAL THINKING

3. **Apply** A frog jumps into a pond and its skin absorbs water. What spheres has the water moved through?
4. **Predict** How might a rise in global temperatures affect the biosphere?

CONNECT TO

PREDATOR-PREY

5. Explain how feedback loops, such as those described in the Gaia hypothesis, might apply to predator-prey relationships.

15.1 FORMATIVE ASSESSMENT

1. The biosphere contains the biota—all the living things on Earth—as well as portions of the hydrosphere, atmosphere, and geosphere.
2. According to the Gaia hypothesis, Earth itself is analogous to a living organism. The interactions between the atmosphere, geosphere, biosphere, and hydrosphere are like the interactions of an organism's vital organs.
3. hydrosphere and biosphere
4. A rise in global temperatures might affect the distribution of living things in the biosphere. Some species might increase in number; others could decrease or become extinct.
5. When a prey population increases in size, the predator population has more food to eat. As a result, the predator population increases in size. When the predators become so plentiful that the prey population decreases, the predators have less food to eat. As a result, the predator population decreases in size.

Integrating Chemistry

Carbon dioxide constitutes only about 0.035 percent of the atmosphere. Carbon dioxide, along with methane, nitrous oxide, and water vapor, is a major **greenhouse gas.** These gases inside Earth's atmosphere absorb heat, keeping Earth's average temperature at about 16°C (60°F). Without these gases, Earth's average temperature would be about −18°C (0°F). Excess greenhouse gases in the atmosphere, however, can lead to an increase in average temperature. Most scientists think that the increase in greenhouse gases, especially carbon dioxide emissions, in the atmosphere is leading to an overall increase in global temperatures.

Answers

A **Summarize** Answers will vary but should include that the Gaia hypothesis proposes that Earth is a kind of living organism in which the hydrosphere, geosphere, biosphere, and atmosphere are interacting systems that maintain one another's balance.

Assess and Reteach ▼

Assess Use the Section Self-Check or Section Quiz, both available at **HMHScience.com.**

Reteach Have students draw a graphic, such as a series of nested circles, that summarizes the hierarchy of the organization of life within the biosphere as follows: organisms, populations, communities, ecosystems, biomes, biosphere.

▼ Plan and Prepare

Activate Prior Knowledge Have students describe different types of climates they are familiar with. **Ask**

- Why are there different climates on Earth? The main factor is the angle at which sunlight hits Earth's surface.
- If you were on the equator and wanted to take a trip on which you would experience each climate type, would you travel in a north-south direction or east-west? north-south, because climate change is most pronounced as you move into different latitudes

▼ Teach

Vocabulary

Greek and Latin Word Origins Remind students of the Greek prefixes *micro-* and *macro-*, and relate them to climate.

micro- = exceptionally small
macro- = large

Answers

A Analyze *Sample answer:* forest canopy, (more sunlight) or the forest floor (less sunlight)

15.2 Climate

KEY CONCEPT **Climate is a key abiotic factor that affects the biosphere.**

VOCABULARY
climate
microclimate

MAIN IDEAS
- Climate is the prevailing weather of a region.
- Earth has three main climate zones.

Connect to Your World

Although you might sometimes check the local weather report to see if you'll need an umbrella, you are already familiar with the general climate where you live. If you live in the Midwest, you know that winter means cold temperatures, while in the Southwest, winter temperatures are much milder. The long-term weather patterns of an area help determine which plants and animals you will find living there.

MAIN IDEA

Climate is the prevailing weather of a region.

The weather of an area may change from day to day, and even from hour to hour. In contrast, the **climate** is the long-term pattern of weather conditions in a region. Climate includes factors such as average temperature and precipitation and relative humidity. It also includes the seasonal variations an area experiences, such as rainy or dry seasons, cold winters, or hot summers.

The key factors that shape an area's climate include temperature, sunlight, water, and wind. Among these abiotic factors, temperature and moisture play a large role in the shaping of ecosystems. Descriptions of a specific region's climate take these abiotic factors into consideration. For example, a specific region such as a desert may be described as hot and dry, while a rain forest may be described as warm and moist.

Even within a specific region, climate conditions may vary dramatically. A **microclimate** is the climate of a small specific place within a larger area. A microclimate may be as small as a hole in a decaying log where mushrooms grow, as pictured in **FIGURE 2.1**, or as large as a city neighborhood. San Francisco, for example, is characterized by frequent fog and cool temperatures. However, not far beyond the city limits, and even within other sections of the city itself, the weather may be quite different.

Microclimates can be very important to living things. The same grassy meadow, for example, may be home to both frogs and grasshoppers. The frogs may tend toward areas that are moist, often at the base of the grasses, while the grasshoppers may prefer drier sites and cling to the tops of the grass blades. Each of these locations is a microclimate.

FIGURE 2.1 The cavity in this log provides a humid microclimate that supports the growth of mushrooms.

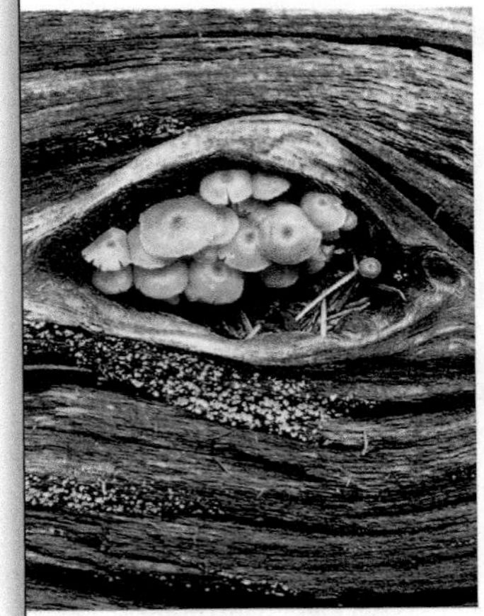

A Analyze **Where in a forest might you find different microclimates?**

Differentiated Instruction

ENGLISH LEARNERS

Have students work in small groups to create a content frame that lists the three different climates, the range of latitudes associated with each, the characteristics of each climate, and some examples of real places within each climate.

Teacher Toolkit, Section C, Content Frame

TEACH WITH TECHNOLOGY

Prepare a digital slide show depicting habitats in which there could be microclimates very different from the general climate. Ask students to identify the likely areas of microclimates and explain why conditions there might differ from those of the general area. Mix natural examples with human ones such as a tall apartment building (air conditioners in some windows) or a standard refrigerator-freezer appliance.

MAIN IDEA

Earth has three main climate zones.

Scientists use average temperature and precipitation levels to categorize a region's climate. Using this system, Earth can be divided into three main climate zones, as shown in **FIGURE 2.2.** These three zones are the polar, tropical, and temperate climates. The polar climate is found at the far northern and southern regions of Earth. The tropical zone surrounds the equator. The temperate zone is the wide area in between the polar and tropical zones.

Influence of Sunlight

What determines an area's climate? The answer begins with the sun. The sun's rays are most intense, and therefore hottest, on the portion of the planet that sunlight strikes most directly. Earth's surface is heated unevenly due to its curved shape. The area of Earth that receives the most direct radiation from the sun all year is the region at and around the equator, where the tropical climate zone is found. Near the North and South poles, or polar climate zones, the sun's rays strike Earth's surface at a lower angle, diffusing their heat over a larger area.

Earth's tilt on its axis also plays a role in seasonal change. As Earth orbits the sun, different regions of the planet receive higher or lower amounts of sunlight. When the North Pole is at its maximum tilt away from the sun, it is winter in the Northern Hemisphere and summer in the Southern Hemisphere. When the North Pole reaches its maximum tilt toward the sun, the opposite is true.

CONNECT TO

SEASONS

At the March and September equinoxes, both hemispheres receive equal amounts of sunlight. At the June solstice, the Northern Hemisphere enters summer and the Southern Hemisphere enters winter. The opposite is true at the December solstice.

FIGURE 2.2 Climate Zones

The uneven heating of Earth by the sun results in three different climate zones.

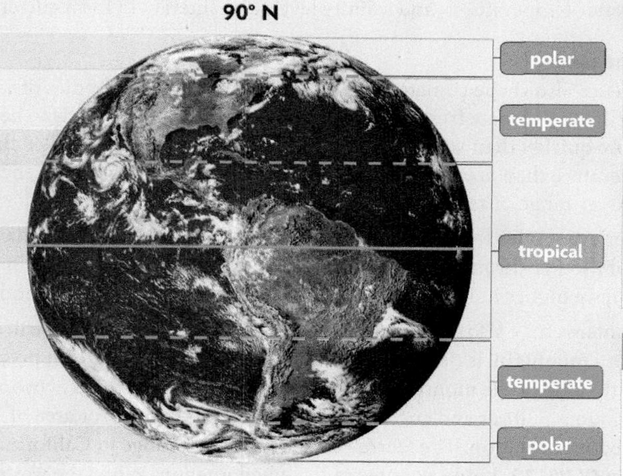

POLAR CLIMATE

The polar climate zone is located in far northern and far southern reaches of the planet, where the temperature is typically cold and often below freezing.

TROPICAL CLIMATE

The tropical climate zone, which surrounds the equator, runs from the Tropic of Cancer to the Tropic of Capricorn and is characterized by warm, moist conditions.

TEMPERATE CLIMATE

The temperate climate zone is located in the broad area lying between the polar and tropical climate zones. This zone experiences summer and winter seasons of about equal length.

A Apply **What is the relationship between sunlight and climate zone?**

BELOW LEVEL

Have students write for five minutes about the climate in which they live, including descriptions of any seasonal variations in temperature and precipitation. Have students address the effect of their region's position on Earth's surface in terms of the angle of sunlight and the hours of daylight.

Teacher Toolkit, Section C, Quick-Write

CONNECT TO

Seasons Remind students that an **equinox** is the day of a year when the sun's rays hit corresponding latitudes in both hemispheres equally, meaning the day is precisely as long in Philadelphia (40°N) as it is in the north island of New Zealand (40°S), though one is in spring and the other is in fall.

A **solstice** occurs when the sun's rays are at their most direct in one hemisphere while at their most indirect in the other. The summer solstice is the longest day of the year, with the most hours of daylight; the winter solstice has the longest night. At the poles, things are especially extreme during a solstice: 24 hours of the sun at the same height in the sky, or 24 hours of extreme cold and darkness.

TEACH FROM VISUALS

FIGURE 2.2 Tell students that the yellow bars running horizontally into the left side of Earth represent rays of sunlight. **Ask**

- At which latitude or area is the sunlight striking Earth most directly? 0° (equator, tropical zone)
- Where is sunlight striking at the steepest angle? highest latitudes (polar)
- Where is sunlight striking at a slight angle? temperate latitudes (halfway between the equator and either pole)

Vocabulary

Academic Vocabulary Lines of **longitude** run north-south and indicate east-west positions on Earth, whereas lines of **latitude** indicate north-south positions.

Answers

A Apply Intense sunlight indicates tropical climates, less intense sunlight indicates temperate climates, and weak sunlight indicates polar climates.

▼ Teach *continued*

QUICKLAB

Time 15 minutes — TEACHER TESTED ✓

Purpose Identify microclimates in and around school grounds.

LAB MANAGEMENT

- Group students for this activity and assign one student in each group to be in charge of handling the thermometer.
- Assist students in choosing their locations.
- Have students prepare their data tables prior to the investigation.

Safety Avoid mercury thermometers.

Answers

Analyze and Conclude

Sunlit locations with low wind will register higher temperatures than nearby shaded locations or windy areas.

Integrating Earth Science

Climate change may be causing a slowdown of one of the Atlantic Ocean's most powerful currents. The **Gulf Stream** works like a conveyor belt. Cold, dense seawater in the Arctic sinks and flows to the south as water in the tropics warms, rises to the surface, and flows northward to take the place of the sinking cold water. This warm surface current gives off heat as it travels north, keeping western Europe's winters relatively mild. As the ice sheets of the Arctic melt into the sea and atmospheric temperatures are not chilling the waters of the Arctic as quickly, the conveyor is slowing down, meaning colder winters for Europe.

QUICKLAB — OBSERVING

Microclimates

Determine the temperature of inside and outside areas of your school to identify different microclimates.

PROBLEM Where are different microclimates in and around your school grounds?

PROCEDURE

1. Identify one place inside and one place outside your school where microclimates may exist.
2. Place a thermometer at each location. Wait at least five minutes before recording the temperature.

MATERIALS

- thermometer
- stopwatch

ANALYZE AND CONCLUDE

Compare the temperatures you collected with those recorded by your classmates at different locations.

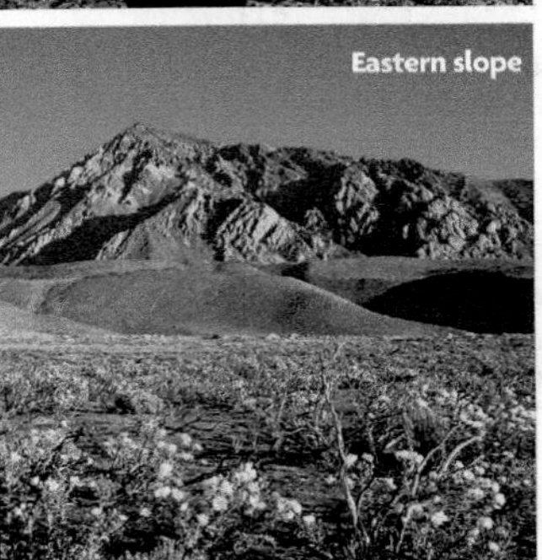

FIGURE 2.3 The western slope of the Sierra Nevada, which faces the prevailing winds, receives precipitation throughout the year. Due to the rain shadow, the eastern slope of the Sierras is much drier.

Air and Water Movement

When the sun heats Earth, it warms not only the land and the rocks but also the water and the air. This heating causes movements in both water and air. Warm air and warm water are less dense than cooler air and water, and therefore they rise. Because the tropics near the equator are especially warm, the warm air here rises and the cooler air from areas to the north or south moves in to take its place. As the warm air rises, it cools. Since cold air holds less moisture than warm air does, a large amount of precipitation drops as rain. This large amount of precipitation, along with warm temperatures, defines the tropical rain forest regions found near the equator. The movement of air also leads to movement in water, forming currents. The rotation of Earth, water temperatures, and salinity levels also interact to form currents.

Landmasses

Landmasses also shape climates. For example, areas closer to bodies of water have a different climate from areas farther away because land tends to heat and cool more quickly than water. Thus, coastal areas tend to have smaller changes in temperature than areas farther inland. Farther inland, areas experience a much larger range of seasonal high and low temperatures.

Water evaporates from open bodies such as lakes or oceans faster than it does from soil or through plant transpiration. As a result, coastal sites in general have higher humidity and receive more precipitation than inland areas.

Mountains may also have a large effect on an area's climate. As warm, moist air nears a mountain, it rises and cools. This cooling of air results in precipitation on the side of the mountain range facing the wind. On the downwind side of the mountain, drier and cooler air produces a rain shadow, or area of decreased precipitation. The Sierra Nevada mountain range in California, shown in **FIGURE 2.3**, is one example of this phenomenon. While the western slope receives a large amount of precipitation, the Great Basin to the east of the mountains is dry.

Differentiated Instruction

HANDS-ON ACTIVITY

Have students bring in weather maps from newspapers or online sources and analyze the movement or development of weather fronts in relation to mountains, bodies of water, and other features of Earth's surface. Are there signs of rain shadow effect? What are the sources of the water that is coming down as rain or snow?

DATA ANALYSIS

CONSTRUCTING COMBINATION GRAPHS

Climatograms are combination graphs that represent weather data for a specific location or biome over a period of time. Refer to the Data Analysis Feature in **Section 4** of the chapter **Interactions in Ecosystems**.

1. **Graph Data** Plot the average precipitation as a bar graph, and plot the average temperature as a line graph.
2. **Analyze** How would you describe the temperature change throughout the year in this location?
3. **Identify** During which month is the precipitation level lowest for this location?
4. **Analyze** Is there a relationship between temperature and precipitation in Albuquerque, New Mexico? If so, explain how they are related.
5. **Explain** What is the benefit of using a combination graph to illustrate an area's climate?

TABLE 1. AVERAGE CLIMATE IN ALBUQUERQUE, NM

Month	Precipitation (mm)	Temperature (°C)
January	12.4	2.1
February	11.2	5.2
March	15.5	8.9
April	12.7	13.1
May	15.2	18.2
June	16.5	23.8
July	32.3	25.8
August	43.9	24.5
September	27.2	20.6
October	25.4	14.1
November	15.7	6.9
December	12.4	2.3

Source: National Oceanic and Atmospheric Administration

Adaptations to Climate

Many organisms have adaptations that allow them to survive in a specific climate. The water-holding frog shown in **FIGURE 2.4** is a dramatic example. It lives in the dry grasslands and deserts of inland Australia, where the rainy season comes only once a year. Dry periods can last 10 months or more. The frog survives the dry season by burrowing underground, where water evaporates more slowly. Moisture loss is further reduced by a cocoonlike structure formed from the frog's shed skin. When rains soak the ground, the frogs crawl out of their burrows to mate, and the females lay eggs in water puddles that form in depressions along the ground. Within a matter of weeks, the eggs hatch into tadpoles, and the tadpoles develop into frogs. This frog must move through its life cycle very quickly because the water evaporates quickly once the rains end. If the tadpoles are not ready to leave the ponds, they will die.

FIGURE 2.4 Water-holding frogs crawl out of their burrows to mate during the rainy season.

Connect **Describe the climate where you live.**

15.2 Formative Assessment

SELF-CHECK Online HMHScience.com GO ONLINE

REVIEWING MAIN IDEAS

1. What is the difference between **climate** and weather?
2. What are the three different climate zones, and where are they located?

CRITICAL THINKING

3. **Connect** Where might there be **microclimates** in your area?
4. **Infer** Would areas along the shores of the Great Lakes have warmer summers and colder winters than other inland areas? Explain.

CONNECT TO NICHES

5. Would you expect an area with several microclimates to have more or fewer ecological niches? Explain your answer.

15.2 FORMATIVE ASSESSMENT

1. Weather is the day-to-day temperature, precipitation, and wind conditions in a region. Climate is the long-term pattern of weather.
2. The polar climate is found at the North and South poles. The tropical climate is located near the equator. The temperate climate is found between the tropical and polar climates.
3. Answers will vary and may include forests, gardens, alleys, and open lots.
4. No, because of the buffering effects of the water, shoreline areas have moderate seasonal temperature changes compared to inland areas.
5. An area with several microclimates would have more ecological niches, allowing for a wider variety of organisms to find suitable habitats.

DATA ANALYSIS

Discuss

Climatograms are usually constructed with precipitation on one y-axis and temperature on the other. **Ask**

- What is the benefit of using a climatogram instead of simply studying the data? Trends in the data are easier to see in a graph.
- On many climatograms, temperature on the y-axis begins at −30°C. What is the benefit of having the temperature scale run so low if temperatures do not get that low? It sets the temperature curve well above that of precipitation, so the curves are more easily seen and compared.

Answers

1. Accept all reasonable graphs.
2. Temperatures are lowest in winter, rise in spring, peak in summer, and decrease in autumn.
3. February
4. Precipitation increases slightly as temperatures rise in spring. The highest amounts of precipitation occur with the summer peak in temperature. Precipitation decreases as temperatures decrease throughout autumn and winter.
5. It illustrates relationships between temperature and precipitation, two main factors in characterizing a climate.

Online Student Resources, Data Analysis Practice

Answers

A Connect Descriptions should include temperature, precipitation, wind conditions, and other climatic factors.

Assess and Reteach ▼

Assess Use the Section Self-Check or Section Quiz, both available at **HMHScience.com**.

Reteach Have students use a globe to describe Earth's three climate zones, identify their locations, and indicate how the angle of sunlight is involved.

SECTION 15.3

Plan and Prepare

Activate Prior Knowledge Because the United States has several biomes, students should be familiar with them without necessarily knowing them as biomes. **Ask,** Thinking in terms of both climate and terrain, what kinds of general environments can we see in the United States? hardwood forests, desert, prairie (grassland), mountain, beach, tundra (Alaska)

Teach

TEACH FROM VISUALS

FIGURE 3.1 Remind students that a biome is a classification based on abiotic factors, not a location. **Ask,** Which continents have all six biomes? Asia, North America Remind students that biomes often do not have well-defined borders as shown on the map. There are often transition zones, including non-biome areas, between biomes.

Answers

A Identify all six biomes

15.3 Biomes

KEY CONCEPT **Biomes are land-based, global communities of organisms.**

MAIN IDEAS
- Earth has six major biomes.
- Polar ice caps and mountains are not considered biomes.

VOCABULARY
canopy
grassland
desert
deciduous
coniferous
taiga
tundra
chaparral

Connect to Your World
Have you ever seen a cactus in a tropical rain forest or a penguin in a desert? Individual plant and animal species have adaptations that let them thrive only in certain biomes. In this section, you will learn about the major biomes of the world and the characteristics of each.

MAIN IDEA
Earth has six major biomes.

The global distribution of biomes is shown in **FIGURE 3.1.** Characteristics of each biome are given in **FIGURE 3.2.** As you will see, these broad biome types can be divided into even more specific zones. For example, the grassland biome can be further separated into zones of temperate and tropical grassland.

A variety of ecosystems are found within a biome. However, because a biome is characterized by a certain set of abiotic factors, ecosystems located across the globe in the same biome—the tropical rain forest of Brazil or Madagascar, for example—tend to have similar plant and animal species.

CONNECT TO
LEVELS OF ORGANIZATION
Recall from the chapter **Principles of Ecology** that a biome is a major community of organisms, usually characterized by the climate conditions and plant communities that live there.

FIGURE 3.1 World Biomes

A biome is defined by its climate and by the plant communities that live there.

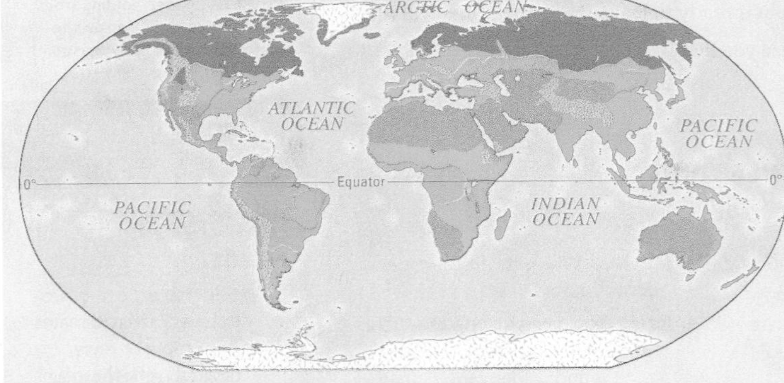

A Identify **Which biomes are found in North America?**

Differentiated Instruction

PRE-AP

Though they are so small that they are scarcely represented in maps such as **FIGURE 3.1,** the Pacific Islands are home to millions of people, dozens of languages, and a diversity of organisms both on land and in the water. Have students write a paragraph speculating what kinds of biomes may exist in the Pacific Islands, the majority of which are between 20°N and 20°S. Students should think about how the ocean, latitude, and elevations of the islands are involved in affecting climates.

Teacher Toolkit, Section C, Quick-Write

TEACH WITH TECHNOLOGY

Show the class a digital slide show of labeled photographs of the six biomes. After you have run through a number of photographs of each biome type, test students' ability to recognize biomes by showing them unfamiliar photographs that have telltale characteristics or species. You could also show them climatograms and give them a few minutes to infer in what biome or biomes the data could have been recorded. Go to **HMHScience.com** for visual resources.

FIGURE 3.2 Biomes

Biome	Characteristics
TROPICAL	
Tropical rain forest	• Warm temperatures and abundant rainfall occur all year. • Vegetation includes lush thick forests. • Animals that live within the thick cover of the uppermost branches of rain forest trees use loud vocalizations to defend their territory and attract mates.
GRASSLAND	
Tropical grassland	• Temperatures are warm throughout the year, with definite dry and rainy seasons. • Vegetation includes tall grasses with scattered trees and shrubs. • Hoofed animals, such as gazelles and other herbivores, dominate this biome.
Temperate grassland	• This biome is dry and warm during the summer; most precipitation falls as snow during the winter. • Vegetation includes short or tall grasses, depending on the amount of precipitation. • Many animals live below ground to survive the dry and windy conditions in this biome.
DESERT	
Desert	• This biome has a very dry climate. • Plants, such as cacti, store water or have deep root systems. • Many animals are nocturnal; they limit their activities during the day.
TEMPERATE	
Temperate deciduous forest	• Temperatures are hot in the summer and cold in the winter; precipitation is spaced evenly over the year. • Broadleaf forest dominates this biome, and deciduous trees lose their leaves in the winter.
Temperate rain forest	• This biome has one long wet season and a relatively dry summer. • Evergreen conifers, which retain their leaves (needles) year-round, dominate this biome. • While some species remain active in the winter, others migrate to warmer climates or hibernate.
TAIGA	
Taiga	• This biome has long, cold winters and short, warm, humid summers. • Coniferous trees dominate this biome. • Mammals have heavy fur coats to withstand the cold winters.
TUNDRA	
Tundra	• Subzero temperatures are the norm during the long winter, and there is little precipitation. • The ground is permanently frozen; only mosses and other low-lying plants survive. • Animal diversity is low.

BELOW LEVEL

Have students create a content frame that lists the six biomes and their characteristics such as temperature, precipitation, plants, and animals. If content frames are made for climates, as suggested in **Section 2** (English Learners), students can study both to reinforce the differences between a climate and a biome.

Teacher Toolkit, Section C, Content Frame

Address Misconceptions

Common Misconception All deserts are hot and dry.

Correcting the Misconception It is the amount of rainfall an area receives that defines a desert, not the temperature range. **FIGURE 3.1** illustrates the wide range of latitudes in which deserts exist.

Take It Further

Biodiversity tends to decrease the farther an ecosystem is located from the equator. As one moves from the tropics to the poles, the tendency is to find larger and larger populations of fewer and fewer species. This is one reason much of the current loss of species is occurring most swiftly in the tropics. Populations there are smaller and more vulnerable to habitat loss, overfishing, and other factors.

Vocabulary

Greek and Latin Word Origins

- **Temperate** comes from the Latin *temperatus,* "to temper." To temper something, whether it is a material (glass, metal) or an emotion (anger), means to moderate or adjust it into a milder or more moderate state. Students can think of temperate climates and biomes as the mild middle ground between polar and tropical biomes and climates.
- **Pole,** from the Greek *polos,* refers to either extremity of an axis through a sphere, in this case, Earth.
- **Tropical** comes from Greek and Latin roots meaning "turning." If students think of Earth turning on its axis, it is at the equator that a given point on Earth is "turning" the fastest. Relative to Earth's axis, a person in Ecuador is traveling about 1000 miles an hour, while someone at one of the poles is barely moving.

▼ Teach *continued*

For an exercise in analyzing the distribution of amphibians in the world's biomes, see the Data Analysis Smart Grapher activity for this chapter at **HMHScience.com**.

Integrating Pharmacology

Because a tropical rain forest is the most biologically diverse biome, it offers medical scientists abundant opportunities to find compounds that can function as anesthetics and treatments for diseases. For example, **poison-dart frogs** of Central and South American rain forests have been studied closely for their medical and pharmaceutical potential.

Scientists observed native forest hunters dipping their blowgun darts in the **alkaloids** secreted by three species of these colorful amphibians. Epibatidine, which is an alkaloid in the skin secretion of the South America poison-dart frog, *Epipedobates tricolor,* is a painkiller 200 times more powerful than morphine. The alkaloids of another species, *Dendrobates auratus,* have been shown to stimulate heart activity. Unfortunately, much of the rain forest is now threatened by slash-and-burn agriculture and the timber industry.

Vocabulary

Greek and Latin Word Origins Plants that have evolved strategies that enable them to survive the hot, dry climate of a desert are called **xerophytes.** The prefix *xero-* comes from the Greek word *xeros,* meaning "dry." The suffix *-phyte* is from the Greek phyton, meaning "plant." *Xerophyte* ("dry plant") adaptations include reduced leaf surface area, stems that collect and hold water, and very short reproductive cycles so that they can bloom and make seeds during brief periods of rain.

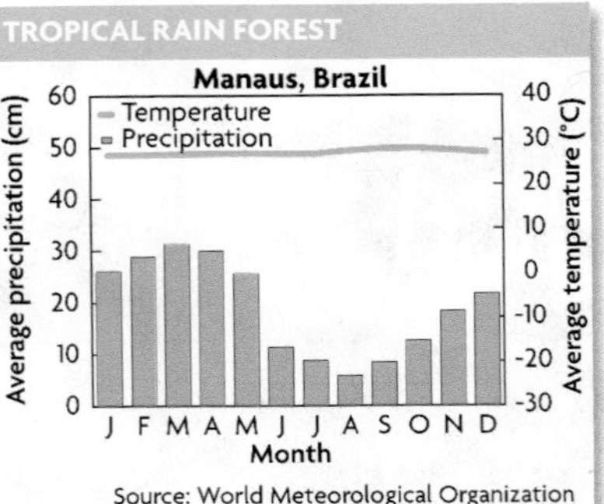

Tropical Rain Forest Biome

A tropical rain forest has warm temperatures and abundant precipitation throughout most, if not all, of the year. This climate typically produces lush, thick forests that can completely shade the forest floor. The limiting factor for plants that live on the forest floor is sunlight. In fact, as little as 1 percent of the sunlight that strikes the uppermost branches of the trees, called the **canopy,** may make it through to the ground. The soil is very thin and low in nutrients. Most organisms that live in this biome inhabit branches of the upper canopy. Some plants, called epiphytes, grow above the ground on the branches of trees. A few of these, such as some figs, sprout and develop on branches and then send down long lengths of roots that grow into the ground below.

Grassland Biomes

Grassland biomes occur in a variety of climates. A **grassland** is an area where the primary plant life is grass. Tropical grasslands are found in the tropical climate zones of South America, Africa, and Australia. Temperate grasslands are found in the temperate climate zones of South Africa, eastern Europe, and central North America.

Tropical grasslands, also called savannas, are covered with grass plants that may stand 1–2 meters (3–7 ft) in height. Some grasslands have scattered trees or shrubs, but the trees are never as thick and lush as in the tropical rain forests. The limiting factor in the savanna is rainfall. For five months or more each year, precipitation averages at most 10 centimeters (4 in.) a month; often there is much less. During the rainy season, however, water can replenish lakes, rivers, streams, and wetlands and form temporary ponds. This biome is home to plants and animals that have adapted to the extreme shifts in moisture.

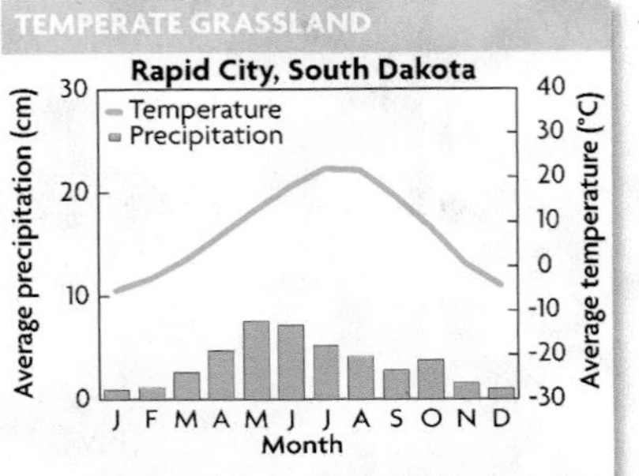

Temperate grasslands receive 50–90 centimeters (20–35 in.) of annual precipitation, most occurring as rain in the late spring and early summer. Summers may be warm or quite hot, depending on the latitude of the grassland. Under such arid conditions, fast-spreading fires are common. Some plants in temperate grasslands have adapted to fire by producing fire-resistant seeds that require the fire's heat to start germination.

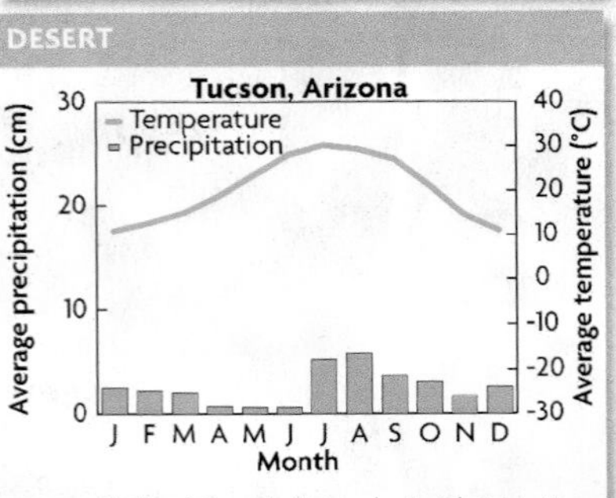

Desert Biome

Desert biomes receive less than 25 centimeters (10 in.) of precipitation annually, and are always characterized by a very dry, or arid, climate. There are four types of deserts: hot, semiarid, coastal, and cold.

In hot deserts, such as the Sonoran Desert in Arizona, the daily summer temperature may easily top 38°C (100°F). At night, however, the temperature can drop by 10 degrees Celsius or more. During the winter, the temperature may be as low as 0°C (32°F). The precipitation falls as rain in hot deserts.

Differentiated Instruction

ENGLISH LEARNERS

After students have read and reviewed this section, organize students into six groups. Around the classroom, place six stations, each featuring a large sheet of paper displaying the name of one of the major biomes along with several questions about its characteristics. Have the groups rotate through the six stations and answer the questions by working together. Afterwards, regroup as a class to review and discuss.

Teacher Toolkit, Section C, Carousel Review

Semiarid deserts, like hot deserts, have long and dry summers and low amounts of rain in the winter. In comparison with hot deserts, however, temperatures are cooler and rarely exceed 38°C. Coastal deserts are characterized by cool winters followed by relatively long, warm summers. Temperatures range from a maximum of 35°C (95°F) in the summer to −4°C (25°F) in the winter. In cold deserts, such as the Great Basin of the western United States, precipitation falls evenly throughout the year and often occurs as snow in the winter. Summer temperatures range between 10°C (50°F) at night to 24°C (75°F) during the day, and winter temperatures can drop below freezing.

Plants use a variety of strategies to survive a desert's heat and lack of moisture. The reduced surface area of a cactus's spines helps it to retain more water by avoiding moisture loss from transpiration. Many desert plants have the ability to conserve or store water over a long period of time. Some desert plants, such as mesquite, have extremely long root systems that absorb water by reaching down to the water table. Desert plants also have heat- and drought-resistant seeds.

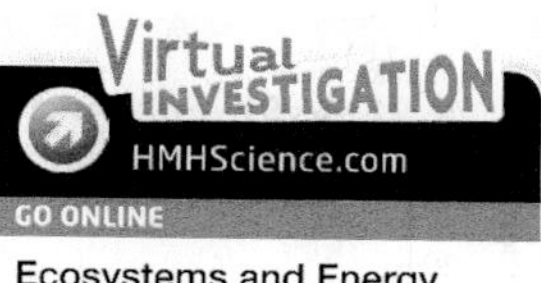

GO ONLINE
Ecosystems and Energy Pyramids

CONNECT TO
LOCAL ECOSYSTEMS
See **Appendix D** for information about local ecosystems and guidelines for analyzing an ecosystem.

A Contrast **How do rainfall amounts differ in deserts and in tropical rain forests?**

Temperate Forest Biomes

A key feature of temperate biomes is their distinguishable seasons. The growing season occurs during the warmer temperatures from mid-spring to mid-fall and depends upon the availability of water.

The **temperate deciduous forest** typically receives about 75–150 centimeters (30–59 in.) of precipitation spread over the entire year as rain or snow. This biome is characterized by hot summers and cold winters. **Deciduous** trees have adapted to winter temperatures by dropping their leaves and going dormant during the cold season. Trees, such as oaks, beeches, and maples, along with shrubs, lichens, and mosses, make up the main vegetation.

The **temperate rain forest** does not receive precipitation evenly spaced across the year. Instead, it has one long wet season and a relatively dry summer, during which fog and low-lying clouds provide the needed moisture. Precipitation in the temperate rain forest averages over 250 centimeters (98 in.) per year. Evergreen conifers, such as spruces, Douglas firs, and redwoods, dominate this biome. **Coniferous** trees retain their needles all year. Mosses, lichens, and ferns are plant species found on the forest floor.

TEMPERATE FOREST

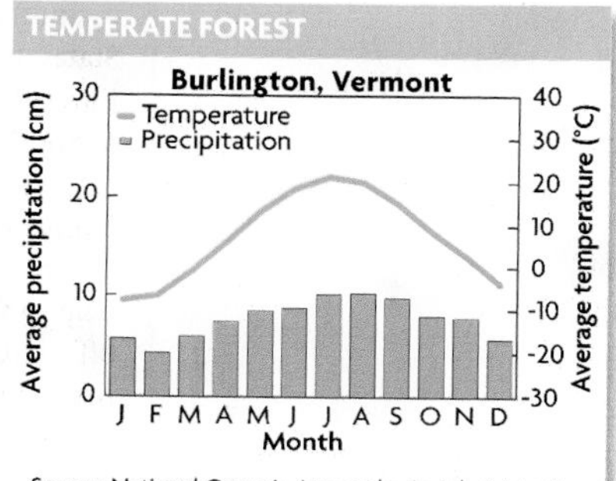

Source: National Oceanic Atmospheric Administration

TAIGA

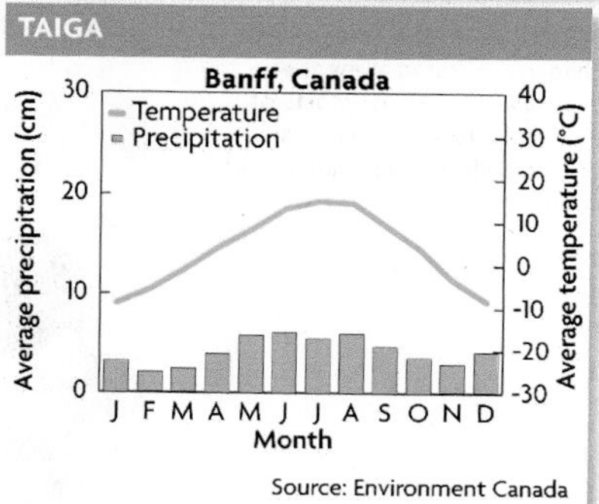

Source: Environment Canada

Taiga Biome

The **taiga** (TY-guh), also known as the boreal forest, is located in cooler climates. Winters are long and cold, often lasting six months or more. The average winter temperature is below freezing. Summers are short, typically with only two to three months of frost-free days. However, they may be quite humid and warm, sometimes reaching 21°C (70°F). Precipitation in the taiga is 30–85 centimeters (12–33 in.) per year, which is similar to that in the arid temperate grasslands. Coniferous forest is dominant in the taiga.

Answers

A **Contrast** Deserts receive less than 25 centimeters (10 in.) of rain a year, while tropical rain forests are characterized by abundant levels of rainfall throughout the year, as shown in the climatogram on the previous page.

Take It Further

Giant sequoias, also known as Sierra redwoods, are the largest trees in the world. Sequoias depend on fire as an abiotic factor to clear away competing saplings from the forest floor and to dry out their cones so that seeds will fall and germinate. For years the U.S. Forest Service used fire suppression to protect the trees. With a better understanding of the ecosystem, the Forest Service recently began a program of **prescribed burning.** Prescribed burns help maintain and promote the growth of redwood forests, as well as other plant communities, such as prairies, that depend on fire for long-term stability.

Science Trivia

- Giant sequoias can approach 90 meters (300 feet) in height and 11 meters (37 feet) in trunk diameter.
- Probably the largest single organism on Earth is a giant sequoia named General Sherman.
- The General Sherman sequoia is estimated to weigh more than 1000 tons, equivalent to about 10 blue whales—the largest animals on Earth.
- Some giant sequoias are ancient, having lived as long as 3200 years.

INCLUSION

The differences between the leaves and seed pods of deciduous and coniferous trees can be appreciated visually, but also through touch. Give students who are visually impaired a chance to handle various pinecones, pine branches, deciduous leaves, and deciduous seed pods so they can better understand how these groups are adapted to life in the temperate forests or taiga. Be sure to ask students about plant allergies and have them wash their hands after handling the plants.

▼ Teach *continued*

Vocabulary

Tundra comes from the Finnish word *tunturia,* meaning "barren land" or "treeless plain." While trees cannot grow in the tundra because permafrost prevents root growth, there are shrubs, sedges, mosses, lichens, and grasses, some of which provide food for migrating herds of caribou.

Take It Further

Plants of the chaparral are adapted to fire in several different ways. Plants known as **obligate resprouters** cope with fire by resprouting from root systems in the ground. **Obligate seeders** depend on their offspring (seedlings) to maintain the population. Seeds of these plants often will germinate only if some fire-related cue, such as smoke or heat, is abundant in the soil. The Tecate cypress, a conifer, has cones that open only when there is a fire.

This is not to say that these plants are dependent on fire. These adaptations simply mean that when fires do occur, the plants can survive or at least pass on their genes to their offspring.

Answers

A Connect Answers will vary according to students' geographic location.

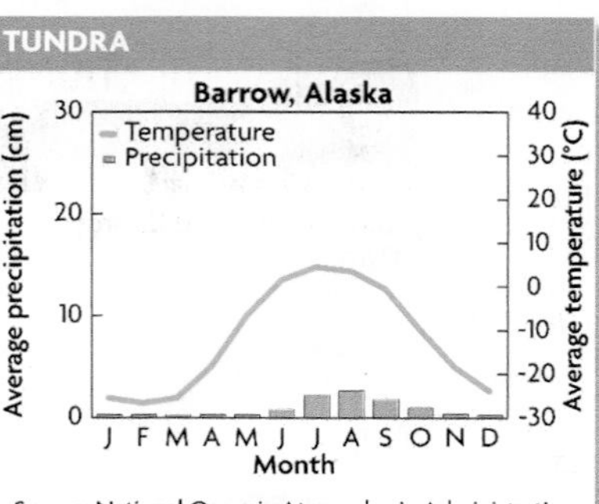

Tundra Biome

Often described as bleak, the **tundra** is located beyond the taiga in far northern latitudes. Winter lasts as long as 10 months a year. The average winter temperature is below freezing. The ground below the surface is always frozen. This frozen ground is known as permafrost. Summers last just 6 to 10 weeks. Precipitation is meager, averaging less than 13 centimeters (5 in.) annually.

In addition to limited precipitation, permafrost captures and holds moisture, making very little available to plants. Therefore, the tundra is quite barren. Only mosses, other tiny, low-lying plants, and a few scattered shrubs are able to survive. Trees and most flowering plants do not grow here.

Minor Biomes

In addition to the six major biomes, there are also some other biomes that occur globally, but on a smaller scale. One example is chaparral, shown in **FIGURE 3.3. Chaparral** (SHAP-uh-RAL), also called Mediterranean shrubland, is characterized by its hot, dry summers and cool, moist winters. Over the year, temperatures in the chaparral range from 10°C (50°F) to 40°C (104°F). Annual precipitation ranges from 38–102 centimeters (15–40 in.), and occurs mostly during the winter as rain. The dominant plants in the chaparral are small-leaved evergreen shrubs. This biome is found in small areas across the globe, including the central and southern coast of California in the western United States, the coast of Chile in South America, the Mediterranean Sea coast in Europe, the southern and western coasts of Australia, and the southwestern tip of South Africa. Because of the fairly hot climate, the plants in this biome exhibit some of the same adaptations to heat as those found in the desert biome. Many plants have shallow root systems that let them take in as much water as possible when it rains. The leaves of shrubs have thick cuticles that help in water retention. Many plant species, such as sage and rosemary, give off a strong smell. These aromatic oils are also highly flammable, and promote fire. As in temperate grasslands, chaparral plants have adapted to the presence of fire, and some plants need fire in order for their seeds to germinate.

A Connect What biome includes the area where you live?

FIGURE 3.3 In the United States, chaparral is found along the central and southern coasts of California. This biome is characterized by hot, dry summers and cool, moist winters.

Differentiated Instruction

PRE-AP

It may be difficult for students to understand how fire could be anything but a disaster for any system. Have them think of reasons why some chaparral plants have evolved to withstand or depend on fire. What would be the selective advantage of reproducing after a fire has devastated the standing plants in a community? Why would plants secrete oils that are flammable?

Teacher Toolkit, Section C, Quick-Write

MAIN IDEA

Polar ice caps and mountains are not considered biomes.

Polar ice caps are ice-covered areas that have no soil and do not have a specific plant community. In mountains, the climate and the animal and plant communities change depending on elevation. Because of these characteristics, polar caps and mountains are not categorized as biomes.

Polar ice caps occur around the poles at the top and bottom of Earth. In the Northern Hemisphere, the polar ice cap includes parts of Greenland and permanently frozen portions of the Arctic Ocean and surrounding islands. In the Southern Hemisphere, the polar ice cap includes the glacier-covered continent of Antarctica. At the ice caps, ice and snow cover the surface all year. Very few plants or fungi are able to survive the harsh conditions found in the polar regions. Some species found in Antarctica include mosses and lichens. Most animals in this region depend on the sea for their food. Animals such as polar bears, shown in **FIGURE 3.4**, have layers of fat that keep them warm in the cold polar conditions. Different animals are found in the northern and southern polar regions. For example, polar bears are found only in the north, while penguins are found only in the south.

FIGURE 3.4 A polar bear's thick layer of fat, or blubber, keeps it well insulated from the cold as it rests on an ice floe or swims in Arctic waters to catch food.

Mountains are often rich with life. Different communities of species have adapted to the variety of ecosystems found at different mountain elevations. As you move up a mountain, the different communities that you see are similar to the biomes found in different latitudes across the globe. For example, you may begin a hike in a grassland at the base of the mountain, continue upward through a coniferous forest, and finally reach a desolate tundralike zone at the mountain's top. While the life zones found on mountains are similar across biomes, their species of plants and animals differ as a result of the different abiotic factors that shape each biome.

Summarize **Explain why neither polar ice caps nor mountains are considered biomes.**

15.3 Formative Assessment

SELF-CHECK Online
HMHScience.com
GO ONLINE

REVIEWING MAIN IDEAS

1. List and describe the six major biome types.
2. What are some characteristics of mountains and polar ice caps?
3. Compare variations and adaptations of desert organisms with organisms in the tundra.

CRITICAL THINKING

4. **Predict** How might stopping fires change a temperate **grassland**?
5. **Infer** Polar bears have white fur but black skin underneath. Consider the climate in which the bears live. What might be the adaptive advantage of the bears' black skin?

CONNECT TO

ANIMAL BEHAVIOR

6. Male birds that migrate the earliest to their summer nesting sites can usually secure the best territories. What limiting factor keeps birds from arriving too early in the **taiga**?

Take It Further

The current warming trend in the Arctic has spelled trouble for the **polar bear.** These carnivores hunt seals for food, but they do so from the stability of the ice shelf or an ice floe. Because the ice pack is breaking up and retreating northward earlier and farther than it used to, bears now have to swim great distances—sometimes between 50 and 100 miles—to get to hunting grounds. Some bears that attempt these exhausting swims end up drowning; others end up starving.

Answers

A **Summarize** Polar ice caps have no characteristic plant life. Mountains may exhibit the characteristics of several biomes in sequence from top to bottom, because an increase in elevation is analogous to an increase in latitude.

Assess and Reteach

Assess Use the Section Self-Check or Section Quiz, both available at **HMHScience.com**.

Reteach Print out copies of **FIGURE 3.1** from the Media Gallery and distribute to students. Have students create an expanded map key that includes the characteristics of each biome type.

15.3 FORMATIVE ASSESSMENT

1. tropical rain forest: warm temperatures and abundant precipitation; grassland: varied climates with distinct dry and rainy seasons; desert: very dry, temperatures can be very high in daytime and cold at night; temperate forest: distinguishable seasons; taiga: long, cold winters and short, humid summers; tundra: long, cold winters and little precipitation
2. Different communities that are analogous to biomes are found at different elevations of mountains. Polar ice caps are ice-covered, have no soil, and lack plant communities.
3. Tundra organisms have adaptations for living in extreme cold most of the time. For example, plants are low growing, with shallow roots due to the permafrost and many animals have white fur in the winter. Desert organisms have adaptations such as being nocturnal, to avoid the heat, or narrow leaves to reduce water loss.
4. Stopping fires would change the grassland landscape, as some plants that grow there need fire to germinate, and other plants that are suppressed by fire could thrive and dominate. In time, the grassland could become a forest.
5 The black skin on a polar bear absorbs heat from the sun.
6. temperature, because it dictates how much water is available for drinking and also the growth of food that birds rely on

SECTION 15.4

B.3.2 Design, evaluate, and refine a model which shows how human activities and natural phenomena can change the flow of matter and energy in an ecosystem and how those changes impact the environment and biodiversity of populations in ecosystems of different scales, as well as, how these human impacts can be reduced.

▼ Plan and Prepare

Activate Prior Knowledge Name some marine ecosystems that students may be familiar with: coral reefs, estuaries or salt marshes, kelp forests, deep-sea thermal vents, abyssal plain, and open ocean. **Ask,** What abiotic conditions define, affect, and distinguish these systems? sunlight, temperature, salinity, turbidity, depth, water chemistry

▼ Teach

Take It Further

Intertidal zones can be found in sandy bays, estuaries, mud flats, rocky shorelines, and even a piling, seawall, or jetty. Intertidal zones offer various niches in which different species and adaptations have evolved. **Ask,** In intertidal zones where there is periodic battering by waves, what kinds of adaptations might be seen in animals that live there? features that allow the animals to attach to rocks and withstand the force of the waves

15.4 Marine Ecosystems

KEY CONCEPT **Marine ecosystems are global.**

MAIN IDEAS

- The ocean can be divided into zones.
- Coastal waters contain unique habitats.

VOCABULARY

intertidal zone
neritic zone
bathyal zone
abyssal zone
plankton
zooplankton
phytoplankton
coral reef
kelp forest

Connect to Your World

If you've ever been to the ocean, you are already familiar with some ocean zones. If you walked on the beach at the edge of the surf, you were in the intertidal zone. If you went into the water, you were swimming in the neritic zone. In this section, you will learn about these and other zones that divide the ocean. You will also read about the unique habitats found along the ocean's coasts.

MAIN IDEA

The ocean can be divided into zones.

The oceans are a global expanse of water containing a large variety of living things that dwell from coastal shallows to the great depths of the deep-sea vents.

Ocean Zones

Scientists use several systems to divide the ocean into different zones. The simplest division of the ocean separates the water of the open sea, or pelagic zone, from the ocean floor, which is called the benthic zone.

The presence of light is also used to differentiate between areas of the ocean. The photic zone is the portion of the ocean that receives plentiful sunlight. In contrast, the aphotic zone refers to the depths of the ocean where sunlight does not reach.

In a third system, as shown in **FIGURE 4.2,** the ocean is separated into zones using distance from the shoreline and water depth as dividing factors.

The **intertidal zone** is the strip of land between the high and low tide lines. Organisms in this zone, such as those that inhabit tidal pools, must tolerate a variety of conditions that result from changing water levels. Organisms must contend with changes in temperature, amount of moisture, and salinity. The sea anemone, for example, opens up when underwater during high tide. It avoids drying out during low tide by closing up.

The **neritic zone** (nuh-RIHT-ihk) extends from the intertidal zone out to the edge of the continental shelf. The depth of the neritic zone may range from a few centimeters at low tide to more than 200 meters deep.

FIGURE 4.1 Organisms that live in tidal pools, such as this one off the Washington coast, are adapted to habitats with constantly changing salt and moisture levels.

Differentiated Instruction

HANDS-ON ACTIVITY

Display an assortment of once-living marine organisms, such as dried sea stars, shells of bivalves and snails, crab and lobster carapaces, dried plants, and pieces of coral. Have students speculate on the kinds of habitats or zones these organisms may have lived in. Even if students know the answer already, they should explain why the characteristics and adaptations of the organism are well suited to a specific habitat or zone.

ENGLISH LEARNERS

Students may wonder why the word *zone* is used to define parts of a marine ecosystem. Point out that the word suggests subdivisions of a whole.

FIGURE 4.2 Ocean Zones

The ocean is divided into four major zones.

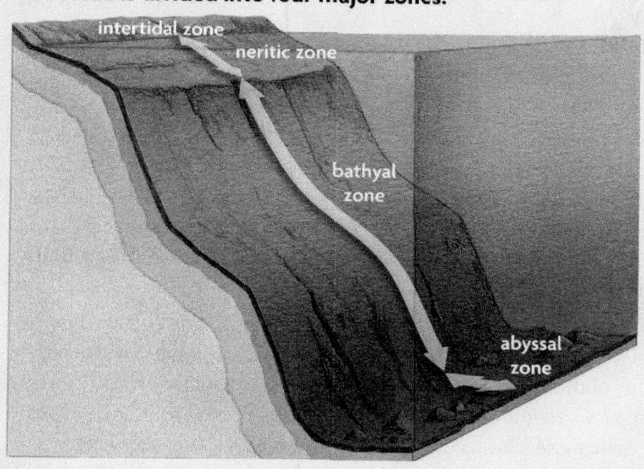

The **bathyal zone** (BATH-ee-uhl) extends from the edge of the neritic zone to the base of the continental shelf. The bathyal zone lies between the depths of 200 and 2000 meters. This zone is characterized by water that is turbid, or murky, due to the accumulation of silt. Fish that have adapted to living in areas of high pressure live in the bathyal zone. Burrowing animals thrive in this zone.

The **abyssal zone** (uh-BIHS-uhl) lies below 2000 meters and is in complete darkness. While deep-sea vents support a large number of organisms, the total number of species found in this zone is much smaller than the number found in the neritic zone. Because there is no light, photosynthetic organisms do not exist. Chemosynthetic organisms are the base of the food webs at the deep-sea vents. Many organisms that live in the abyssal zone make their own light, much as a firefly produces its glow. This light is often used to attract mates and prey.

READING TOOLBOX

VOCABULARY

In the word *bathyal*, the prefix *bathy-* comes from a Greek word meaning "deep." In the word *abyssal*, the word part *abyss* comes from a Greek word meaning "bottomless."

Life in the Neritic Zone

Although the neritic zone represents less than one-tenth of the total ocean area, it contains 40 times more biomass than the rest of the ocean. Much of the biomass consists of organisms called plankton. **Plankton** are tiny free-floating organisms that live in the water. These organisms include both animals and protists. **Zooplankton** is another term for animal plankton. **Phytoplankton** are photosynthetic plankton, which include microscopic protists such as algae.

Marine phytoplankton, especially blue-green algae and other types of algae, are critical to life on the planet. These organisms carry out the bulk of photosynthesis on Earth, and therefore provide most of the oxygen. According to many estimates, 70 percent or more of the oxygen in every breath you take can be traced back to marine phytoplankton. In addition to their role in oxygen production, phytoplankton also form the base of the oceanic food web.

CONNECT TO

INVERTEBRATES

Some invertebrates, such as sea stars and lobsters, are plankton during their larval stage. You will learn more about the life stages of invertebrates in the chapter **Invertebrate Diversity.**

Hypothesize **What other adaptations might organisms have in the abyssal zone?**

ONLINE Biology
HMHScience.com

Have students view an interactive animation on ocean zones. See the Animated Biology called Where Do They Live? at **HMHScience.com**.

TEACH FROM VISUALS

FIGURE 4.2 Have students locate each of the major ocean zones. **Ask,** What are some abiotic factors that affect organisms in each zone? intertidal zone: wave action, exposure to air, temperature fluctuations; neritic zone: sunlight, surface currents; bathyal zone: little or no sunlight, high pressure; abyssal zone: no light, cold temperatures, high pressure, thermal vents

Vocabulary

Greek and Latin Word Origins The prefix *zoo-* in **zooplankton** (ZOH-oh-playng tuhn) comes from the Greek *zöion,* meaning "animals." **Zoology,** meaning "the study of animals," has the same prefix.

Science Trivia

- Zooplankton is one food source of whales, the world's largest animals.
- A typical humpback whale may eat up to 1800 kilograms (4000 lb) of plankton per day.

Answers

A **Hypothesize** ability to withstand high pressure, light organs, large eyes for light detection

BELOW LEVEL

Have students make a drawing similar to **FIGURE 4.2** and label each zone with its characteristics and depth profile.

Teacher Toolkit, Section C, Combination Notes

PRE-AP

Have students imagine that they are equipped with special diving suits or submersibles that allow them to dive down through the different ocean zones. Give them five minutes to describe in writing what they see and feel as they descend through the zones.

Teacher Toolkit, Section C, Quick-Write

▼ Teach *continued*

The Inside Story

Jacques-Yves Cousteau was famous for his explorations of the underwater world and his influence on generations of marine enthusiasts. Perhaps his greatest contribution to science was the invention of **scuba** (self-contained underwater breathing apparatus). This invention allowed divers to go deeper under water and explore for longer periods without being tethered to the ship by a breathing tube.

Science Trivia

- The Great Barrier Reef (GBR) is the largest tropical coral reef system on Earth.
- It is roughly the length of Japan, stretching 2300 kilometers (1429 mi) along the northeastern coast of Australia.
- The GBR is not a single reef, but a chain of over 3000 reefs and 900 small islands.

Answers

A Compare Both are highly productive and support enormous biological diversity.

▼ Assess and Reteach

Assess Use the Section Self-Check or Section Quiz, both available at **HMHScience.com**.

Reteach Have students study **FIGURE 4.2** for a few minutes. Then ask them to close their books and make a diagram of the ocean zones that shows their relative locations from the shore and their approximate depths.

MAIN IDEA

Coastal waters contain unique habitats.

FIGURE 4.3 Ecologists are working to rebuild coral reef ecosystems by building artificial reefs like this one.

The shallow, coastal waters that make up the neritic zone contain much more than plankton. Two highly diverse habitats found within these coastal waters are coral reefs and kelp forests.

Coral reefs are found within the tropical climate zone. In this area, water temperatures remain warm all year. A single coral reef may be home to 50 to 400 species of corals, along with hundreds of other species, including fishes, sponges, and sea urchins. Studies indicate that the biomass in coral reefs may be up to 1000 times greater than the biomass in a similar area of ocean that does not contain a reef.

Corals are animals that have a mutualistic relationship with algae. The coral provides a home for the algae, and algae provide nutrients for the coral as a byproduct of photosynthesis. Coral reefs are made mostly of coral skeletal material, which packs together over thousands of years into solid structures. Coral reefs are delicate. A change in conditions, such as increased water temperature or pollution, can kill the algae, which then starves the coral. With global ocean temperatures on the rise, coral reefs are in decline around the world.

Ecologists are trying to reintroduce these diverse communities in some areas by making artificial reefs, shown in **FIGURE 4.3**, where organisms can find shelter. In addition, some shipwrecks and sunken oil rigs have become artificial reefs that can support fishes and other species associated with coral reefs.

In contrast to coral reefs, **kelp forests** exist in cold, nutrient-rich waters, such as those found in California's Monterey Bay. These forests are composed of large communities of kelp, a seaweed. Kelp grows from the ocean floor up to the water's surface, sometimes extending up to a height of over 30 meters (about 100 ft). Kelp forests are areas of high productivity that provide habitat and food sources to many marine species ranging from tiny invertebrates to large mammals, such as sea lions.

A Compare What are the similarities between coral reefs and kelp forests?

15.4 Formative Assessment

SELF-CHECK Online HMHScience.com GO ONLINE

REVIEWING MAIN IDEAS

1. What criteria do scientists use to divide the ocean into different zones?
2. What conditions account for the development of highly diverse habitats in coastal waters?

CRITICAL THINKING

3. **Connect** A red tide occurs when a bloom of **plankton** causes discoloration of ocean waters. What causes this increase in plankton populations?
4. **Predict** What might organisms that inhabit the **abyssal zone** eat?

CONNECT TO FOOD WEBS

5. How might the disappearance of coastal habitats affect an oceanic food web?

15.4 FORMATIVE ASSESSMENT

1. open sea and ocean floor; presence of light; distance from shoreline and water depth
2. sunlight, upwelling of nutrients, temperature variations, currents, wind, waves, tides
3. Answers may include increased amounts of nutrients in the water and temperature that is conducive to these types of plankton.
4. Organisms in the abyssal zone might eat other organisms that inhabit the zone or organic matter that sinks from the bathyal zone. This organic matter may be bits of dead plants or animals or the feces of living animals.
5. Because many fish species spend an early stage of their lives in coastal habitats and many marine organisms feed on these and other coastal organisms, the disappearance of these habitats would be devastating to oceanic food webs.

15.5 Estuaries and Freshwater Ecosystems

KEY CONCEPT **Freshwater ecosystems include estuaries as well as flowing and standing water.**

MAIN IDEAS
- Estuaries are dynamic environments where rivers flow into the ocean.
- Freshwater ecosystems include moving and standing water.
- Ponds and lakes share common features.

OCABULARY
tuary
atershed
toral zone
nnetic zone
enthic zone

Connect to Your World

You rely on aquatic ecosystems more than you might realize. Many of the fish and shellfish that you might eat depend, at least for a part of their lives, on estuaries. But more importantly for you, freshwater ecosystems provide the water that you need to survive.

MAIN IDEA

Estuaries are dynamic environments where rivers flow into the ocean.

An **estuary** is a partially enclosed body of water formed where a river flows into an ocean. The San Francisco and Chesapeake bays are estuaries. So are the Louisiana bayous, Florida Bay in the Everglades, and many other harbors, sounds, and inlets around the world.

The distinctive feature of an estuary is the mixture of fresh water from a river with salt water from the ocean. The river carries high levels of nutrients from inland areas. The tidal movements of water in the ocean also bring in large volumes of organic matter and a variety of marine species from the ocean. Large numbers of species thrive in this rich mixture of fresh water and salt water.

Estuaries are highly productive ecosystems, on a level comparable to tropical rain forests and coral reefs. Photosynthetic organisms thrive in estuaries throughout the year, providing the basis for the aquatic food web. Estuaries also have thriving detritivore communities that decompose the enormous amounts of dead plant and animal matter that build up in the estuary's waters. These decomposers return vital nutrients back to the ecosystem. Estuaries also provide the necessary habitat for a number of endangered and threatened species. For example, the brown pelican, the Morro Bay kangaroo rat, and a plant called the Morro manzanita are all threatened or endangered species that depend on the Morro Bay estuary in California, shown in **FIGURE 5.1.**

GURE 5.1 An estuary occurs here a river flows into the ocean. stuaries are high in biodiversity nd provide habitat for a number f species.

Differentiated Instruction

ENGLISH LEARNERS

Have students draw an estuarine system and label its features and characteristics, such as the flow of fresh water and salt water, the presence of larval and juvenile fish, and the role of reefs, sandbars, and barrier islands.

Teacher Toolkit, Section C, Combination Notes

SECTION 15.5

B.2.4 Develop a model to illustrate the role of photosynthesis and cellular respiration in the cycling of carbon among the biosphere, atmosphere, hydrosphere, and geosphere.

B.3.1 Use mathematical and/or computational representation to explain why the carrying capacity ecosystems can support is limited by the available energy, water, oxygen, and minerals and by the ability of ecosystems to recycle the remains of dead organisms.

B.3.2 Design, evaluate, and refine a model which shows how human activities and natural phenomena can change the flow of matter and energy in an ecosystem and how those changes impact the environment and biodiversity of populations in ecosystems of different scales, as well as, how these human impacts can be reduced.

Plan and Prepare

Activate Prior Knowledge Have students share experiences they have had near an estuary or a freshwater ecosystem, such as a lake or river. Tell them to describe any organisms they remember seeing. **Ask,** What kinds of abiotic factors influence organisms in an estuary or a freshwater ecosystem? climate, salinity, water movements, sunlight, sedimentation

Teach

Vocabulary

Academic Vocabulary Tell students the word **dynamic** relates to objects or energy in motion, often continuously. This word is often applied to systems, such as an estuary, where various factors and forces are interacting in a dynamic way. The often-used idea of a "balance of nature" is more accurately termed "dynamic equilibria," as this refers to the cyclical nature of many natural systems and to the fact that few systems ever arrive at some kind of final phase.

▼ Teach continued

Take It Further

The **San Francisco Bay** is the largest estuary on the west coast of the United States. The San Joaquin and Sacramento rivers flow into the bay, and salt water from the Pacific comes in on the high tide. In the last century, the bay's estuarine system has been changed by the introduction of as many as 250 exotic or non-native species. The striped bass, *Morone saxatilis,* arrived by way of boxcars from the east coast in 1879 so that San Franciscans would have another fish to dine on. Since then, it has become a rival of the indigenous salmon, competing for food and eating young salmon. The Asian clam, *Corbula amurensis,* arrived to the bay in the ballast water released from large trans-Pacific ships. It is a small bivalve, but it is now the dominant invertebrate in the bay.

Answers

A Analyze The area is rich in nutrients carried by the river(s) from inland areas. Tidal movements bring in nutrients from the ocean. Reefs and barrier islands provide protection to species within an estuary, particularly those who spend their larval or juvenile stages there.

FIGURE 5.2 The Tejo Estuary in Portugal is an important stop-over point for migratory birds such as these greater flamingos.

CONNECT TO

KEYSTONE SPECIES

Recall from the chapter **Principles of Ecology** that a keystone species is a species that has a large effect on its ecosystem. Migratory birds in the Delaware Bay depend on horseshoe crab eggs as a main food source. This dependence illustrates the importance of the horseshoe crab in its estuarine ecosystem.

Estuary Characteristics

The large number of phytoplankton and zooplankton in an estuary support a variety of species. Populations of fish and crustaceans depend on plankton as their primary food source. In turn, birds and other secondary consumers eat fish and crustaceans. Humans also rely on estuaries as a food source. In fact, 75 percent of the fish we eat depend on estuary ecosystems, making estuaries an important resource for the commercial fishing industry.

Estuaries provide a protected refuge for many species. Reefs and barrier islands along an estuary's boundary with the ocean protect estuary species from storms and the ocean's strong currents and waves. In an estuary's calm waters, many aquatic species lay eggs, and their young mature there before venturing into the ocean. The use of estuaries as spawning grounds explains why these areas are often called nurseries of the sea. Estuaries are also a key part of the migration paths of many bird species, as shown in **FIGURE 5.2.** Birds rely on estuaries as a refuge from the cold weather that occurs in the northern parts of their range during certain parts of the year.

Changing conditions in estuaries present challenges for species that live there. For example, in order to withstand changing salinities, some organisms have glands that remove the excess salt that builds up in their bodies. This adaptation helps organisms cope with an estuary's changing salinity level. Salt levels may lower with the tide and during periods of drought or heavy rainfall.

Threats to Estuary Ecosystems

Estuaries are made up of a variety of ecosystems, including salt marshes, mud flats, open water, mangrove forests, and tidal pools. When estuaries are lost to land development and other human activities, these ecosystems and the organisms that live within them are also lost.

The removal of estuaries also makes coastal areas more vulnerable to flood damage from catastrophic storms such as hurricanes. Estuaries act as a buffer between the ocean and coastal land. In some coastal areas of the United States, over 80 percent of the original estuary habitat has been lost to land development.

A Analyze **What characteristics make an estuary such a productive ecosystem?**

Differentiated Instruction

HANDS-ON

Have students work in pairs or small groups to create a guided tour of a freshwater or marine ecosystem in the area. The tour should include all parts and depths of the ecosystem and point out biotic and abiotic factors through the use of digital images. Have the groups use a digital slide show, poster, or other medium to serve as the virtual ecosystem for their tour.

BELOW LEVEL

Have students make a compare/contrast chart for the zones of marine and freshwater ecosystems. They can set up a table in which the systems are in the rows and their zones' characteristics are compared within columns. For example, littoral zone should be matched up with intertidal, and limnetic with neritic.

Teacher Toolkit, Section C, Compare/Contrast

MAIN IDEA

Freshwater ecosystems include moving and standing water.

Rivers and streams are the flowing bodies of fresh water that serve as paths through many kinds of ecosystems. Rivers and streams, along with lakes and ponds, originate from watersheds. A **watershed** is a region of land that drains into a river, a river system, or another body of water.

Freshwater Ecosystems

If you have ever paddled down a river in a canoe, you have probably witnessed the change in shoreline ecosystems, perhaps with a forest along one stretch and sand dunes along another. Along its course, a river may vary in many ways. For example, the speed of its flow is greater in narrow areas than in wide ones. The river bottom may be alternately sandy, gravel-covered, or rock-strewn. The water level may differ across seasons. In some areas, spring brings about the melting of snow and causes river water levels to rise. Humans also affect water levels by damming rivers or by draining water for irrigation or drinking water.

Unlike rivers and streams, wetlands have very little water flowing through them. A wetland is an area of land that is saturated by ground or surface water for at least part of the year. Bogs, marshes, and swamps are different types of wetlands that are identified by their plant communities. Common wetland plants include cattails, duckweed, and sedges.

Like estuaries, wetlands are among the most productive ecosystems on Earth. They provide a home for a large number of species, some of which are only found in wetlands. Wetlands also help maintain a clean water supply. A wetland filters dirty water and renews underground stores of water.

FIGURE 5.3 As the Colorado River travels southward from Colorado to Mexico, it flows through different ecosystems, including forests and deserts.

Adaptations of Freshwater Organisms

The particular variety of freshwater organisms found in a body of water depends on a number of factors. These factors include water temperature, oxygen levels, pH, and the water flow rate. Each type of freshwater ecosystem is home to species with adaptations suited to its conditions. In fast-moving rivers, for example, trout are adapted to swim against the current. They have streamlined bodies that can slice through the water easily. Some aquatic insects, such as the stonefly, have hooks on their bodies. The stonefly uses the hooks to attach itself to a solid surface in fast-running water to avoid being swept away. Similarly, tadpoles that live in fast-running water often have sucker mouths that they use to attach to a surface while feeding. These tadpoles also have streamlined bodies with long tails and low fins that help them to move in the fast water. Tadpoles that live in pools or in slower moving water often lack sucker mouths and have more rounded bodies and higher fins.

Predict **What effect would the construction of a dam have on a river ecosystem?**

Integrating Earth Science

Pollution resulting from urban buildup along the margins of estuaries and the rivers that feed them presents a series of challenges to the health of estuary systems and the species that live there. Discharge of sewage, runoff from paved roads, and fertilizers that leach into the system from upriver are all sources of pollution. **Soil erosion** is another problem, as it contributes to turbidity of the water, loss of tree cover, and warmer temperatures of the estuary.

Science Trivia

The Great Salt Lake in Utah is the largest lake west of the Mississippi River. It is three to five times saltier than the ocean. Runoff flows into the lake from the surrounding area, carrying dissolved salts from rocks. Because the lake has no outlet, water can escape only by evaporation, leaving the salts behind to accumulate over time. The Great Salt Lake has no fish but is teeming with brine shrimp.

Answers

A **Predict** Water would no longer flow at the same speed, water temperature might change, and erosion would occur at a slower rate. Species that depend on fast-flowing water might be threatened.

PRE-AP

Have students consult a map to determine the biomes, ecosystems, ocean zones, and other systems through which the waters of the Colorado River flow as they descend from the western United States to the Gulf of California. Students can draw their own map or diagram that illustrates this flow through these systems, and can use arrows to show how water from the ocean then is recycled back to the river through evaporation and precipitation.

▼ Teach *continued*

ONLINE Biology
HMHScience.com

Have students explore different ecosystems in the WebQuest for this chapter at **HMHScience.com**.

Vocabulary

Greek and Latin Word Origins The prefix *thermo-*, as in **thermocline,** comes from the Greek word *thermē,* meaning "heat." The suffix *-cline* comes from the Greek word *klīnein,* meaning "to lean." As in *decline* and *recline, -cline* means "a gradual change." Thus, *thermocline* means "a gradual change in heat."

Answers

A Analyze Lake turnover brings nutrients from the bottom of the lake to the top, where they are used by organisms.

▼ Assess and Reteach

Assess Use the Section Self-Check or Section Quiz, both available at **HMHScience.com**.

Reteach Ask students to call out answers and provide details by creating a cluster diagram to contrast estuaries, rivers, streams, wetlands, lakes, and ponds. You might include the terms *fresh water, salt water, moving water, standing water, productive ecosystem,* and *zones.*

Animated Biology
HMHScience.com
GO ONLINE
Lake Turnover

FIGURE 5.4 In the spring and fall, the water in a lake turns over, bringing nutrients from the bottom of the lake to the top.

WebQuest
HMHScience.com
GO ONLINE
Explore an Ecosystem

MAIN IDEA

Ponds and lakes share common features.

Although they are much smaller in size than oceans, freshwater ponds and lakes are also divided into zones. Scientists use the terms *littoral, limnetic,* and *benthic* to identify and separate these zones.

- The freshwater **littoral zone** is similar to the oceanic intertidal zone, and it is located between the high and low water marks along the shoreline. The waters of the littoral zone are well-lit, warm, and shallow. A diverse set of organisms, including water lilies, dragonflies, and snails, live in this zone.
- The **limnetic zone** (also called the pelagic zone) refers to the open water located farther out from shore. This zone is characterized by an abundance of plankton communities, which support populations of fish.
- The **benthic zone** is the lake or pond bottom, where less sunlight reaches. Decomposers, such as bacteria, live in the mud and sand of the benthic zone.

During the summer and the winter, the water temperature within a lake is stratified, which means that different layers of the lake have different temperatures. In the summer, water is warmer near the surface and colder at the bottom of the lake. These warm and cold regions are separated by a thin zone called the thermocline.

All of the water within a lake "turns over" periodically. This happens because water is most dense at 4°C (39°F). When water reaches this temperature, it will sink beneath water that is either warmer or cooler. In autumn, colder air temperatures cool the surface layer of water to 4°C, causing it to sink and mix with the water underneath. During the winter, the surface layer of water cools to less than 4°C. In the spring, when the surface water warms to 4°C, it sinks and mixes with the layers of water below. In both autumn and spring, the underlying water flows upward and switches places with the surface water. This upwelling brings nutrients such as bits of decaying plants and animals from the benthic zone to the surface, where they are eaten by surface-dwelling organisms.

A Analyze What is the significance of lake turnover to the lake ecosystem?

15.5 Formative Assessment

SELF-CHECK Online
HMHScience.com
GO ONLINE

REVIEWING MAIN IDEAS

1. What are the characteristics of an **estuary** ecosystem?
2. What abiotic factors might affect a river ecosystem?
3. How is a lake different from the ocean? How is it the same?

CRITICAL THINKING

4. **Compare and Contrast** How are coastal wetlands different from and similar to estuaries?
5. **Connect** What adaptation do some organisms living in estuaries have in order to survive the changing water conditions?

CONNECT TO
ADAPTATION

6. Many fish species and other aquatic animals have colorations that closely resemble the rocks or silt found on the bottom of their aquatic habitat. What types of ecological advantages might such an adaptation give an aquatic species?

15.5 FORMATIVE ASSESSMENT

1. An estuary is a partially enclosed body of fresh water and salt water mixing together. Estuaries have a large amount of biodiversity and are important breeding grounds for a variety of species.
2. seasonal changes in water level, geology of the water bed, siltation, erosion
3. A lake is smaller than an ocean and has seasonal water turnover that is similar to downwelling and upwelling in oceans. Like an ocean, a lake can be divided into zones based on depth.
4. An estuary is a shallow area with a mix of fresh water and salt water. A coastal wetland also is a shallow area, but it is fresh water.
5. In order to withstand changing salinities, some organisms have glands that remove the excess salt that builds up in their bodies.
6. Such colorations provide aquatic animals protection from predators, as the colors help camouflage the animals.

New Designs for Artificial Coral Reefs

S.T.E.M. Interactions

According to the International Maritime Organization, an artificial reef refers to any "submerged structure deliberately constructed or placed on the seabed to emulate some functions of a natural reef such as protecting, regenerating, concentrating, and/or enhancing populations of living marine resources." Some marine scientists also consider structures that are designed for other purposes—such as bridges, piers, and docks—to have the potential to be artificial reefs as well.

In past years, artificial reefs were constructed of concrete slabs, sunken ships, and old aircraft, subway cars, and tanks. Recent artificial reefs are not made up of these repurposed materials but are instead constructed especially for use as an artificial reef. Several companies make specialized structures for use as an artificial reef. These structures vary in shape and size.

A worker drops concrete pieces into the Gulf of Mexico off the coast of Marco Island, Florida, where 36 artificial reef habitats were installed in 2015.

New designs and innovations for artificial coral reefs are helping to solve some of the problems associated with past artificial reefs. For example, using large, hollow concrete mounds that have holes throughout has been very successful. The concrete is mixed with a silicon powder, which both strengthens the concrete and increases the pH of the material, making the chemical composition more attractive to organisms. In the past designers of artificial reefs encountered problems because corals cannot settle on certain metals. Materials that are made of or contain paint, plastic, and rubber have also discouraged organisms from settling on an artificial reef. The holes in the concrete mounds help prevent the concrete from moving during strong wave motion from heavy storms, another problem faced by designers of previous artificial reefs. In addition, the mounds can be strategically placed to increase the chances of organisms settling on the concrete and creating a natural habitat.

A large artificial reef is being constructed in Puerto Morelos, in Mexico's Yucatán Peninsula. The reef will be made of concrete as described above, except it will be made up of pyramid shapes. More than 1,000 hollow concrete pyramids containing silicon powder will be lowered by a crane onto a concrete base to create almost 2 kilometers of habitat along the Yucatán coastline.

Another new design for artificial reefs involves using electricity to hold a frame in place on the ocean floor. The frame is made from steel bars. When electricity runs through the metal, minerals in saltwater crystallize on the metal. As a result, the metal thickens a few centimeters every year. The material formed is stronger than concrete. More than 400 reefs have been successfully constructed using this method. Nearby buoys can generate electricity from wave action, while solar panels or a wind turbine can be mounted on a raft to produce electricity—all from renewable energy sources. The electricity does not harm the organisms that settle on the reef because it is weak.

Another intriguing development in the creation of artificial reefs is the use of 3D printers to print out pieces of reefs made from a sandstone material that is not toxic to living organisms. The designers add bumps to the normally smooth surface of the sandstone material to encourage corals and fish to use the reef as a habitat. Producing reefs with a 3D printer is faster than other methods of creating artificial reefs.

S.T.E.M. Activity

Design an artificial coral reef, including a labeled diagram. Explain the problem your reef solves, how you might test your design, the criteria you can use to evaluate it, and how you might refine it.

Introduce

Explain some of the advantages and disadvantages of artificial reefs to students. Artificial reefs not only increase habitat for fish and other marine species but also boost the local economy. Unusual artificial reefs, such as sunken subway cars or ships, are popular destinations for recreational divers. Artificial reefs also become excellent locations for sport fishing. However, not everyone is convinced that artificial reefs are successful. Some marine scientists are concerned that not all items pushed into the sea, even though thoroughly cleaned of grease and other potential contaminants beforehand, are suitable to become an artificial reef and may even contribute to ocean pollution. New technologies, such as those described in the feature, have helped to allay these fears. Some conservationists are still concerned that instead of protecting marine species, artificial reefs simply serve to draw populations away from their natural habitats, concentrating them around the artificial reef. This makes them easy targets for sport fishers.

Discuss

Hold a class discussion about artificial coral reefs. Have students conduct any additional research needed to answer the following questions. **Ask:** Do you think artificial reefs are a good idea or a bad idea? Do the benefits of artificial reefs to a marine ecosystem and to the local economy outweigh their costs? Do you think technology should be used to improve the design of artificial reefs? In general, where do you stand on the topic of artificial reefs?

Chapter 15: The Biosphere **465**

CHAPTER REVIEW

GO ONLINE

Encourage students to go to **HMHScience.com** for a detailed review of each section, including visuals and vocabulary practice.

Online Student Resources, Vocabulary Practice Worksheet

CHAPTER 15 Summary

BIG IDEA Climate and the distribution of land and water play a role in shaping ecosystems and influencing the distribution of organisms on Earth.

KEY CONCEPTS

15.1 Life in the Earth System

The biosphere is one of Earth's four interconnected systems. The biosphere includes living organisms, called the biota, and the land, air, and water on Earth where the biota live. Biotic and abiotic factors interact in the biosphere, and a change in one Earth system can affect the others.

biosphere

biota

15.2 Climate

Climate is a key abiotic factor that affects the biosphere. Factors that influence an area's climate include temperature, sunlight, water, and wind. The three main climate zones on Earth are polar, tropical, and temperate. The polar zone is located at the far northern and far southern reaches of the planet. The tropical zone surrounds the equator. The temperate zone is located in the broad area between the polar and tropical zones.

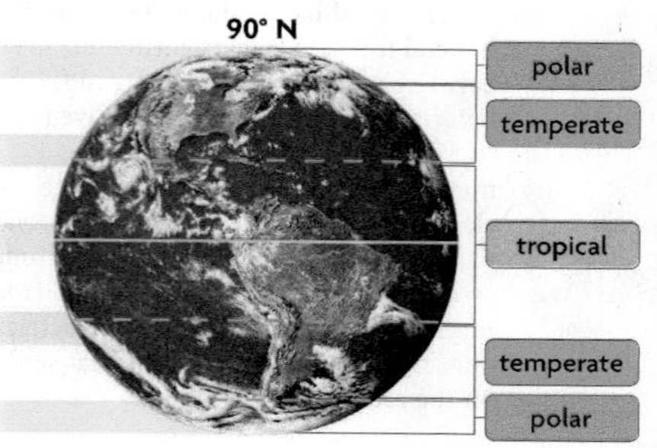

15.3 Biomes

Biomes are land-based, global communities of organisms. Earth has six major biomes. These biomes include tropical rain forest, grassland, desert, temperate forest, taiga, and tundra. Polar ice caps and mountains are not considered biomes.

15.4 Marine Ecosystems

Marine ecosystems are global. Scientists use different criteria to separate the ocean into different zones. One system separates the ocean into zones using distance from the shoreline and water depth as dividing factors. The neritic zone contains 40 times more biomass than the open ocean. Coral reefs are found in the warm, shallow waters of the tropical climate zone. Kelp forests thrive in cold, nutrient-rich waters.

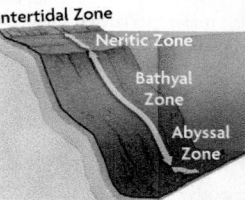

Intertidal Zone
Neritic Zone
Bathyal Zone
Abyssal Zone

15.5 Estuaries and Freshwater Ecosystems

Freshwater ecosystems include estuaries as well as flowing and standing water. An estuary is a partially enclosed body of water that exists where a river flows into an ocean. A variety of organisms are adapted to the constant change in salinity found in an estuarine ecosystem. Freshwater ecosystems include rivers and streams, wetlands, and lakes and ponds.

READING TOOLBOX SYNTHESIZE YOUR NOTES

Concept Map Use a concept map to summarize what you know about climate zones.

Climate Zones
include
located located located

Supporting Main Ideas Use a diagram like the one below to summarize what you know about biomes.

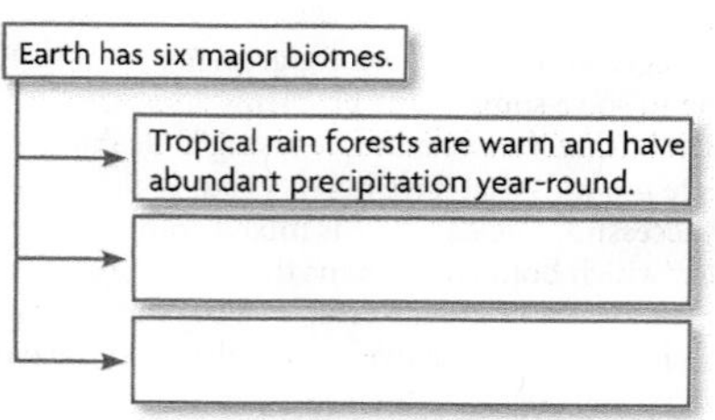

Reviewing Vocabulary

1. Both include living things, but the biosphere also includes nonliving things.
2. Both are tiny free-floating organisms that live in water. Zooplankton is animal plankton. Phytoplankton is photosynthetic plankton.
3. Both are Earth systems. The atmosphere is the air blanketing Earth's solid and liquid surface. The hydrosphere is all of Earth's water.
4. Both refer to the long-term pattern of weather conditions in a specific area. Microclimate is the climate of a small specific place within a larger area and climate.
5. Both are biomes. The taiga is located in cool climates, and coniferous forests are dominant. The tundra is located beyond the taiga in far northern latitudes, and few plants grow there.
6. Both are ocean zones. The intertidal zone is in the range between high and low tides. The neritic zone extends from the intertidal zone to the edge of the continental shelf.
7. Both are diverse habitats found in shallow coastal waters of the ocean. Kelp forests are found in cold waters. Coral reefs are found in warm tropical waters.
8. Plankton are organisms that drift in water, as though wandering. Their primary mode of movement is being carried by currents.
9. Climate is the long-term weather pattern of a specific region on Earth's solid and liquid surface.
10. An estuary is a body of water that forms where ocean and river water meet. This ecosystem is affected by both tidal movement and river flow.
11. The littoral zone is the area of a lake or pond nearest the shore.
12. Every year, in autumn, the leaves of deciduous trees fall off.

15 Review

INTERACTIVE Review
HMHScience.com

GO ONLINE

Review Games • Concept Map • Section Self-Checks

CHAPTER VOCABULARY

15.1 biosphere, biota, hydrosphere, atmosphere, geosphere

15.2 climate, microclimate

15.3 canopy, grassland, desert, deciduous, coniferous, taiga, tundra, chaparral

15.4 intertidal zone, neritic zone, bathyal zone, abyssal zone, plankton, zooplankton, phytoplankton, coral reef, kelp forest

15.5 estuary, watershed, littoral zone, limnetic zone, benthic zone

Reviewing Vocabulary

Compare and Contrast

Describe one similarity and one difference between the two terms in each of the following pairs.

1. biosphere, biota
2. zooplankton, phytoplankton
3. hydrosphere, atmosphere
4. climate, microclimate
5. taiga, tundra
6. neritic, intertidal
7. kelp forest, coral reef

READING TOOLBOX GREEK AND LATIN WORD ORIGINS

8. The term *plankton* comes from the Greek word *planktos*, which means "wandering." Explain how this meaning relates to plankton.
9. The term *climate* comes from the Greek word *klima*, which means "surface of the earth." Explain how this meaning relates to the definition of *climate*.
10. The term *estuary* comes from the Latin word *æstus*, which means "tide" or "surges." Using this meaning, explain how it relates to what an estuary is.
11. The term *littoral* comes from the Latin word *litoralis*, meaning "shore." Explain how this meaning relates to the definition of *littoral zone*.
12. The term *deciduous* comes from the Latin word *decidere*, which means "to fall off." How is this meaning related to the definition of *deciduous*?

Reviewing MAIN IDEAS

13. Explain the difference between the terms *biota*, *biosphere*, and *biome*.
14. After a forest fire wipes out plants growing on a hill, rainwater washes soil down into a stream, and the stream fills with silt. In this example, what are the interactions between biotic and abiotic factors?
15. If the temperature in an area drops five degrees between one day and the next, has the climate of the area changed? Explain.
16. What is the connection between sunlight, the curved shape of Earth, and Earth's three main climate zones?
17. Why are two different deserts, each on a separate continent, considered to be the same biome?
18. Why are polar caps and mountains not considered biomes?
19. Briefly compare the four ocean zones—intertidal, neritic, bathyal, and abyssal—based on their distance from the shoreline and their water depth.
20. Where, in terms of water depth, would you expect to find a coral reef? a kelp forest?
21. Estuaries occur where rivers flow into the ocean. What conditions in estuaries make them suitable as nurseries for organisms that live out in the open ocean as adults?
22. The ecosystem of a river upstream in the mountains and downstream in a valley can be very different. Describe the adaptations of an upstream organism and an organism that lives downstream in the same river.

Reviewing Main Ideas

13. The biosphere is the part of Earth where life exists. The biota is the collection of living things in the biosphere. A biome includes living things, meaning it overlaps with both the biosphere and the biota.
14. The forest fire (abiotic factor) interacts with the plants (biotic factor) when it kills the plants. Rainwater, soil, the hill, and the stream (all abiotic factors) interact when rainwater washes soil down the hill and into the stream. When silt (abiotic factor) accumulates in the stream, it may harm the organisms (biotic factor) living in the stream.
15. The climate has not changed; the weather has. Climate characteristics are long-term.
16. Because of Earth's curved shape, there is variability in how sunlight strikes and warms Earth's surface. It is most indirect and seasonally variable in the polar zone (temperature is low, daylight varies greatly), most direct and less seasonally variable in the tropical zone (high temperatures, little or no variability in daylight), and generally moderate in the temperate zone (temperature and daylight vary but within a smaller range).
17. They have the same climate and plant communities.
18. polar ice caps: no soil, no characteristic plant community; mountains: a range of climates and plant communities
19. intertidal zone: between the high and low tide extremes; neritic zone: from the intertidal zone to 200 m deep; bathyal zone: edge of the neritic zone to the base of the continental shelf (2000 m); abyssal zone: below 2000 m
20. Both are found in the neritic zone, where they receive sunlight.
21. Estuaries are rich in nutrients, and many feature outer reefs, sandbars, and barrier islands, which offer small organisms shelter.
22. Organisms living in the swift, cool waters of a mountain stream will be streamlined and may have ways (such as suckers) to grasp rocks or burrow into gravelly substrate. Organisms downstream, where the water may move more slowly and be more turbid, might be wider, slower, and capable of burrowing or hiding in the softer substrata.

Critical Thinking

23. hydrosphere, biosphere, atmosphere
24. The polar climate zone and the temperate climate zone would not have extreme seasonal changes of temperature or daylight.
25. A change in climate could cause a biome to change into another type of biome. For example, if a grassland receives very little rainfall over the course of many years, it could become a desert.
26. Algae provide the nutrients needed for coral to survive. Algae are at the base of a coral reef food web.
27. *Sample answer:* Estuaries support a large variety of species, especially fishes in their early life stages. They are a major stopover location for migratory birds, and they are among the most productive ecosystems on Earth.

Interpreting Visuals

28. The organisms get water from precipitation and the ocean spray during high tide.
29. Species in the spray zone must be able to retain moisture and protect themselves from terrestrial consumers. Species in the low-tide zone must be able to withstand tidal movements, surf, and fluctuations of temperature.
30. Some fish commute to the intertidal zone (especially on the high tide), but most need to go out with the tide in order to have enough water to respire and enough room to maneuver. They may divide their time between the neritic and intertidal zones.

Critical Thinking

23. Apply A deer drinks water from a stream, and then later it breathes out some of the water as vapor into the air. Through which three Earth spheres has this water moved?

24. Infer How would Earth's three main climate zones be different if Earth's axis were not tilted in relation to the Sun? (Hint: The tropical climate zone would likely be the most similar to how it is now.)

25. Infer Do you think it is possible for a biome to change from one type into another? Explain a situation in which this might happen.

26. Connect Why does the health of an entire coral reef ecosystem depend on algae?

27. Analyze Describe two reasons why it is critical to protect estuary ecosystems.

Interpreting Visuals

Use the diagram of a rocky intertidal zone to answer the next three questions.

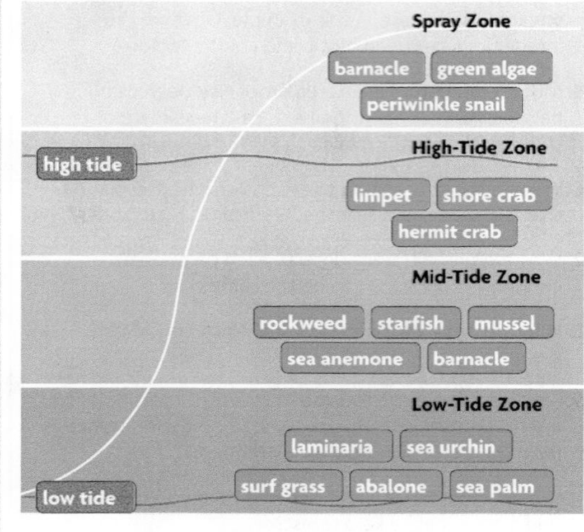

28. Predict How do you think the organisms above the high-tide mark are able to obtain the water they need to survive?

29. Compare What adaptations are necessary for a species to survive in the spray zone compared with a species in the low-tide zone?

30. Hypothesize Why do you think there aren't any fish shown in the diagram? Why wouldn't fish be a major part of the rocky intertidal zone?

Analyzing Data Construct a Combination Graph

Below is a climatogram for the city of Portland, Oregon. Use the graph to answer the next four questions.

AVERAGE CLIMATE OF PORTLAND, OREGON

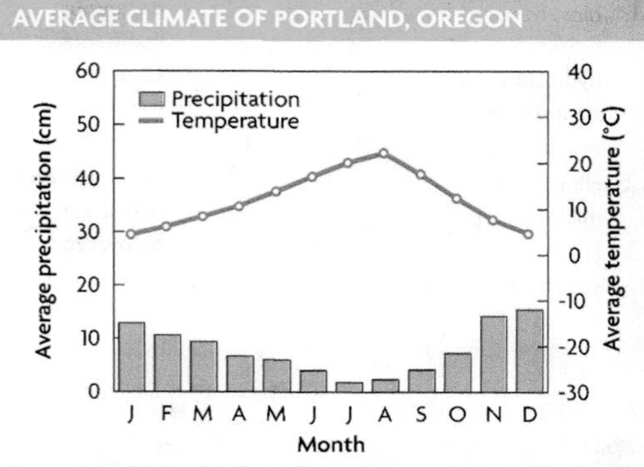

Source: National Oceanic Atmospheric Administration

31. Analyze Which month receives the highest amount of rain? the highest temperature?

32. Summarize Describe in one or two sentences the climate of Portland throughout the year.

33. Analyze A family is planning to vacation in Portland. Many of their planned activities occur outdoors. If they wish to avoid rain, in which month should they travel?

34. Connect Based on the data in the graph, which biome is Portland a part of? Explain your choice.

Making Connections

35. Write a Policy The majority of the wetlands in the United States have been drained and used for development. A company has submitted a proposal to purchase an area of 100 acres of wetland that it plans to develop. If you were an official in the area, how would you respond to this proposal? What would you say to a local environmental group that opposes the proposal? What might be a possible compromise? Use information from the chapter to convince your fellow elected officials to take your position.

36. Synthesize Reread the information about the temperate rain forest at the beginning of the chapter. Using your knowledge of climate, biomes, and evolution, explain why different species are found in temperate and tropical rain forests.

Analyzing Data

31. December, August
32. Portland is rainy and cool from fall through spring, but dry and warm in summer.
33. July
34. temperate rain forest: long wet season, dry summer

Standards-Based Assessment

Record your answers on a separate piece of paper.

MULTIPLE CHOICE

1 *Sylvilagus auduboni* is a rabbit species that lives in dry desert regions, while the species *Sylvilagus palustris* lives in marshes. Which variation in behavior would ***most*** likely benefit *S. palustris*, but not *S. auduboni*?

A an ability to swim

B being active at night

C building a nest immediately after mating

D burrowing to avoid predators

2

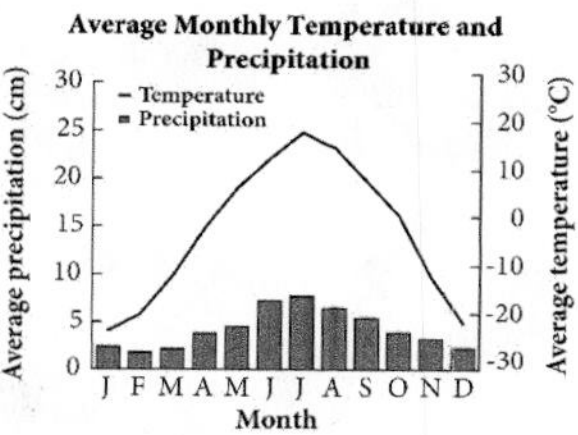

The graph above shows how the average temperature and precipitation for a given environment change over the course of a year. Which of these ***most likely*** describes an organism that is adapted to living in this environment?

A low growing mosses

B epiphytes that grow on tree branches

C a cactus that is able to store water

D a teak tree that blocks out most of the sunlight from reaching the ground

3 Over thousands of years, the plants in a region change from plants with lush foliage to deep-rooted plants adapted to dry conditions. This shift is ***most likely*** the result of a change in —

A predators

B climate

C sunlight

D weather

4 Tropical rain forests have the greatest number of species of any biome. However, the alteration of rain forest habitats into farmland threatens to ***most likely*** —

A increase biomass

B increase species diversity

C cause a mass extinction

D decrease biodiversity

5

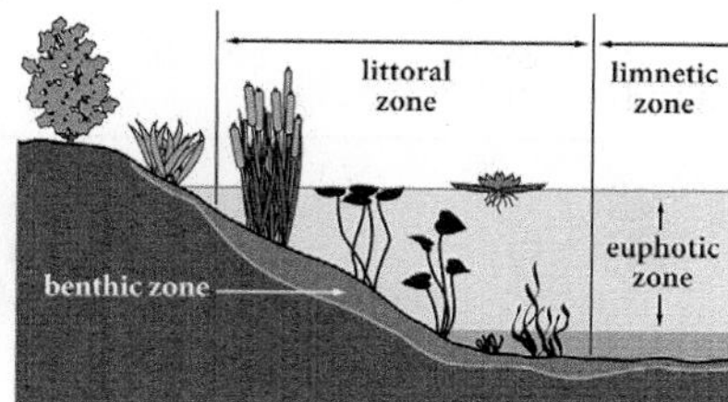

The diagram above shows the zones that exist in freshwater lakes. In the benthic zone, dead organic material is converted into nutrients that can be used by other organisms. What type of organisms carry out this conversion?

A decomposers

B consumers

C carnivores

D producers

6 High concentrations of sediment in the water can block out sunlight needed by aquatic plants for photosynthesis. This condition will ***most likely*** result in —

A increased concentrations of nitrogen

B decreased concentrations of nitrogen

C increased concentrations of oxygen

D decreased concentrations of oxygen

THINK THROUGH THE QUESTION

Think about what is produced and what is consumed during photosynthesis. If rates of photosynthesis decrease, the products of photosynthesis will decrease in the ecosystem.

Standards-Based Assessment

The Standards-Based Assessment questions will help students prepare for their final examination in the course. If you wish to give students practice in coding their answers, look for the Standards-Based Assessment Answer Sheet at **HMHScience.com**. To give students practice under timed testing conditions, allow them five minutes per question.

Question	Answer	Depth of Knowledge	Cognitive Complexity
1	A	II	M
2	A	IV	H
3	B	II	M
4	D	I	L
5	A	I	L
6	D	III	M

KEY

Depth of Knowledge		Cognitive Complexity	
I	Recall	L	Low
II	Skill/Concept	M	Moderate
III	Strategic Thinking	H	High
IV	Extended Thinking		

Making Connections

35. Answers will vary. A negative response to the proposal should include a discussion of the importance of wetlands in maintaining biodiversity and a clean water supply. A positive response to the proposal should include a discussion of the economic benefits of the proposed development to the local community. A possible compromise might be not developing the entire 100 acres or setting aside other wetland areas for protection.

36. While both types of rain forest are characterized by abundant rainfall, there are climatic differences between these two biomes that have necessitated the evolution of adaptations suited to the specifics of the two climates. For example, the cooler temperate zone may require that an organism be able to build or find shelter, or migrate elsewhere.

CHAPTER 16 Instruction and Intervention Support

Human Impact on Ecosystems

① Core Instruction

The **Core Instruction** resources below can be used for all students. Core instruction should be followed by ongoing assessment to determine which students need further help.

Available in both English and Spanish

Available Online

Section	Instruction	PRINT	ONLINE	Labs
16.1	Textbook **Human Population Growth and Natural Resources**	■	●	
	PowerPresentation and Notes 16.1		●	
16.2	Textbook **Air Quality**	■	●	Acid Rain (Design Your Own) **Video Lab** Effects of Acid Rain on Seeds
	Teaching Visuals Global Warming (Fig. 2.3, 2.4)		●	
	PowerPresentation and Notes 16.2		●	
16.3	Textbook **Water Quality**	■	●	Water Quality (Open Inquiry) Contamination of Groundwater Caffeine and Seed Germination Investigating How Pollution Affects Plant Life (Biotechnology Lab, Design Your Own) **QuickLab** Modeling Biomagnification
	Animated Biology Human Effects on a Food Web, Water Pollution		●	
	Teaching Visuals Biomagnification (Fig. 3.2)		●	
	PowerPresentation and Notes 16.3		●	
16.4	Textbook **Threats to Biodiversity**	■	●	Modeling the Effects of Habitat Fragmentation (Challenge Lab) Biodiversity and Ecosystems (Probeware Lab)
	That's Amazing! Video Inquiry Killer Kitties		●	
	PowerPresentation and Notes 16.4		●	
16.5	Textbook **Conservation**	■	●	
	PowerPresentation and Notes 16.5		●	

Additional online resources available for this chapter include **Interactive Whiteboard Resources.**

2 Support and Intervention

Support and Intervention resources are useful for students who need targeted help beyond the Core Instruction

Resources	PRINT	ONLINE
Assess and Reteach (TE wrap)	■	⊙
Concept Map		⊙
Interactive Reader	■	⊙
Interactive Review Games		⊙
Section Self-Checks		⊙
Study Guide B		⊙
Virtual Investigation Carbon Dioxide and Global Warming		⊙
Vocabulary Practice Worksheets		⊙

3 Specialized Support

Students who need more intensive personalized intervention benefit from **Specialized Support** resources.

Resources	PRINT	ONLINE
Chapter Audio Files		⊙
Differentiated Instruction Inclusion, Below Level, and English Learners (TE wrap)	■	⊙
ELL Strategies	■	⊙
Modified Lesson Plans for English Learners		⊙
Reinforcement Worksheets		⊙
Study Guide A		⊙

Extension and Assessment

Enrichment and Challenge

Resources	PRINT	ONLINE
Active Reading Worksheets		⊙
Data Analysis Practice Worksheet		⊙
Differentiated Instruction Pre-AP (TE wrap)	■	⊙
Pre-AP Activity Biomagnification of Fluorine in Penguins		⊙
Smart Grapher Activity		⊙
The Inside Story and **Take It Further** (TE wrap)	■	⊙
Unit Project		⊙
WebLinks		⊙
WebQuest Invasive Species (16.4)		⊙

Assessment

Resources	PRINT	ONLINE
Alternative Assessment		⊙
Chapter Tests A and B		⊙
Diagnostic Test		⊙
ExamView Banks		⊙
Extended Response Test		⊙
Online Assessment System		⊙
Section Quizzes		⊙
Standards-Based Assessment	■	⊙

CHAPTER 16

Chapter Overview

- **Section 1** describes the impact of human overpopulation on natural resources and the importance of resource management.
- **Section 2** identifies the major sources of air pollution and their effects on air quality.
- **Section 3** discusses the impact of water pollution and biomagnification on ecosystems.
- **Section 4** details the importance of and the threats to biodiversity.
- **Section 5** discusses the importance of conservation methods to help protect natural resources and ecosystems.

Focus and Motivate

What happened to this forest?

Discuss the fact that there is very little green in what is left of this forest. **Ask**, What other organisms, other than plants, are likely to be indirectly impacted by acid rain? Organisms that feed on the plants or rely on them for shelter or nesting will die or emigrate, as will secondary and tertiary consumers.

Tell students that rain water is naturally slightly acidic (typically a pH of 5.6). Acid rain has a lower pH, usually starting at 4.6. To put this in perspective, tell students that their bodies can tolerate liquids with low pH values. Cola, for example, has a pH of 3, as does vinegar.

BIOZINE HMHScience.com

Students can access BioZine at **HMHScience.com** to receive updates to featured topics in the book.

CHAPTER 16 Human Impact on Ecosystems

BIG IDEA Human population growth threatens environmental quality and biodiversity, so conservation methods are necessary to protect Earth's natural resources.

- **16.1** Human Population Growth and Natural Resources
- **16.2** Air Quality
- **16.3** Water Quality
  - Data Analysis: DISCRETE AND CONTINUOUS DATA
- **16.4** Threats to Biodiversity
- **16.5** Conservation

ONLINE BIOLOGY HMHScience.com

ONLINE Labs
- Acid Rain
- **QuickLab** Modeling Biomagnification
- **Open Inquiry Lab** Water Quality
- Water Quality Testing
- Contamination of Groundwater
- Caffeine and Seed Germination
- Investigating How Pollution Affects Plant Life
- Biodiversity and Ecosystems
- Modeling the Effects of Habitat Fragmentation
- **Video Lab** Effects of Acid Rain on Seeds

Teacher Demo

Eye Opener **Demonstrate the change in acidity represented by a difference of one pH unit.**

Materials
- 100-mL graduated cylinder
- 100-mL beaker
- water sample adjusted to pH 6 (use vinegar or baking soda)
- pH strips
- distilled water

What happened to this forest?

This once lush hillside has been destroyed by acid rain. Emissions from a nearby steel plant release chemical compounds that change the natural pH of rain, forming acid rain. Not only does acid rain damage leaves and branches, but because it lowers soil pH, it can damage plant root systems and kill useful microorganisms that release nutrients from dead organic material.

READING TOOLBOX

This reading tool can help you learn the material in the following pages.

USING LANGUAGE

Finding Examples Concrete examples often help clarify new information. Certain words and phrases can help you recognize examples. These words include *for example*, *such as*, *like*, and *including*.

YOUR TURN

Use what you have learned about examples to answer the following questions.

1. Find the examples in the following sentence: The Burmese python feeds on small animals such as rats, birds, raccoons, and even dogs.
2. Find the examples in the introductory paragraph of this reading tool.

Demonstrate Ask a volunteer to measure the pH of a water sample that you have adjusted to pH 6, which is close to the pH of normal rainwater (≈pH 5.6). Tell students that pure water has a neutral pH of 7. Then pour 10 mL of the water into a beaker and add 90 mL of distilled water to it. Have the volunteer measure the pH of the second water sample. This ten-fold dilution should result in a one-unit change in pH, to pH 7.

Discuss Students often have difficulty conceptualizing the actual difference in acidity between two solutions that differ by only one pH unit. Lead students to recognize from the demonstration that a difference of one pH unit is equivalent to a ten-fold difference in acid concentration. **Ask,** If unpolluted rain has a pH of 5.6, and acid rain has a pH of 4.6, how many times more acidic is acid rain than normal rain? 10 times **Ask,** If distilled water has a neutral pH of 7, how much more acidic is acid rain? about 240 times

Activate Prior Knowledge

Discuss how manufacturing, agriculture, mining, and transportation have improved people's lives. **Ask,** How have these improvements created problems for Earth's ecosystems? Students should mention air and water pollution, buildup of solid waste, depletion of resources, and habitat loss. **Ask,** What steps can people take to help address these problems? *Sample answer:* reducing activities that produce pollution, reducing waste by recycling, conserving resources, protecting habitats

Preview Vocabulary

Word Origins The words *conserve* and *preserve* share the same Indo-European root, which is related to the Greek *seros*, "protector," and the Latin *sera*, "a locking bolt."

conserve, to protect from loss or harm

preserve, to keep in unaltered condition

Discuss with students the difference between the two words. For example, compare the terms *nature preserve* and *habitat conservation*.

English Learners This chapter features a number of nouns that have specific meanings in the contexts of biology and conservation, but their verb forms are often applied in many other contexts. As students read and learn these terms (*sustainable, renewable, fragmentation, biomagnification, pollution*), discuss the meanings of the verbs *sustain, renew, fragment, magnify,* and *pollute*, and have students use them in sentences relating both to the material in the text and to everyday contexts.

Answers

1. rats, birds, raccoons, dogs
2. for example, such as, like, including

Chapter 16: Human Impact on Ecosystems 471

▼ Plan and Prepare

Activate Prior Knowledge Tell students that in 1963 Buckminster Fuller published his *Operating Manual for Spaceship Earth.* **Ask,** Have you ever heard the expression "Spaceship Earth"? What does it suggest to you? Earth is a closed system, like a spaceship, moving through space. Tell students that Earth has also been likened to an island. **Ask,** What do both of these images convey about Earth resources? a limit, a carrying capacity Remind students that many of Earth's resources are finite. How long they last depends largely on how many people inhabit Earth and the amount of resources used.

▼ Teach

TEACH FROM VISUALS

FIGURE 1.1 Have students study the graph. **Ask,** What kind of growth does the human population show? exponential **Ask,** In approximately what year does the graph predict that human population growth will begin to slow? 2050

16.1 Human Population Growth and Natural Resources

VOCABULARY

nonrenewable resource
renewable resource
ecological footprint

KEY CONCEPT **As the human population grows, the demand for Earth's resources increases.**

MAIN IDEAS

- Earth's human population continues to grow.
- The growing human population exerts pressure on Earth's natural resources.
- Effective management of Earth's resources will help meet the needs of the future.

Connect to Your World

Humans depend upon Earth's nutrient and energy cycles. We harness Earth's energy to power our televisions, radios, streetlights, automobiles, airplanes—and everythin else in our homes and cities. Your cotton T-shirt and this paper page came from plants that depend on Earth's nutrient cycles. The water you drink comes from wat sources replenished by the hydrologic cycle. We do not just use Earth's cycles, we a a part of Earth's cycles. Everything we eat, drink, and use comes from Earth. But the overuse of resources and the production of waste can cause disruptions in the energy and nutrient cycles of Earth.

MAIN IDEA

Earth's human population continues to grow.

How many people can Earth support? In other words, what is the carrying capacity for humans on Earth? Recall that carrying capacity refers to the maximum population size that an environment can consistently support.

FIGURE 1.1 WORLD POPULATION

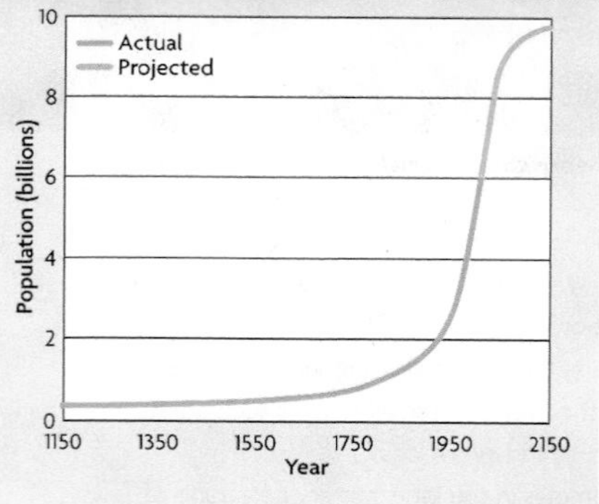

Source: United Nations, World Population Prospects, Population Reference Bureau

Earth's Carrying Capacity

Our predictions of Earth's human carrying capacity have change over time. In the late 1700s, a young economist named Thomas Malthus wrote a controversial essay in which he claimed that the human population was growing faster than Earth's resources could support. Today, scientists use his observations and predictions when they are describing the concept of an ecosystem's carrying capacity. In Malthus's lifetime, the world population wa around 1 billion. The graph in **FIGURE 1.1** shows how population size has changed over time. Today's human population of more than 7 billion has exceeded many earlier predictions. In the future, will Earth support 10 billion people, 20 billion, or even 50 billion people? Although we do not know of a fixed limit to th number of people that Earth can support, some limit must exist-Earth cannot support an infinite number of people.

Differentiated Instruction

ENGLISH LEARNERS

Have students write each of the main ideas in this section in a central box, each on a separate sheet of paper. From each central box, have them draw several lines that connect to other boxes. Within each of these boxes, have students write details that support the main idea. For example, "ecological footprint" would be in a box branching off from "resource management."

Teacher Toolkit, Section C, Main Idea Web

BELOW LEVEL

Suggest that students take notes using the Cornell method. Tell students to take abbreviated notes in outline form in the second column of a T-chart, with key points in the column on the left. Students can then create a large box beneath both columns that puts the terms and notes into a summary paragraph.

Teacher Toolkit, Section C, Cornell Notes

Technology and Human Population

Recall that the carrying capacity of an environment can change as the environment changes. As humans have modified their environment through agriculture, transportation, medical advances, and sanitation, the carrying capacity of Earth has greatly increased.

Technologies developed by humans have allowed Earth to support more people than Malthus could ever have imagined. Motorized farm equipment made possible the production of much more food than could be produced by human and animal power. Medical advances have also contributed to population growth. For example, infant mortality rates in the United States have dropped steadily over the last 70 years. In 1940, more than 40 infants died for every 1000 births. In 2002, only 7 infants died per 1000 births. Antibiotics and antiseptics have lowered infant mortality and the spread of diseases.

For a moment, think about how much we depend on technology. How have human lives changed with the help of plumbing to bring fresh water into homes and to take human waste out of homes? What if there were no transportation to move food and materials around the globe? What if there were no medicines? How many people could Earth support without electricity or gas, or if all construction had to be done by hand? Technological advances have allowed for continued human population growth.

READING TOOLBOX

TAKING NOTES
Use a diagram to summarize how technology has helped the human population grow.

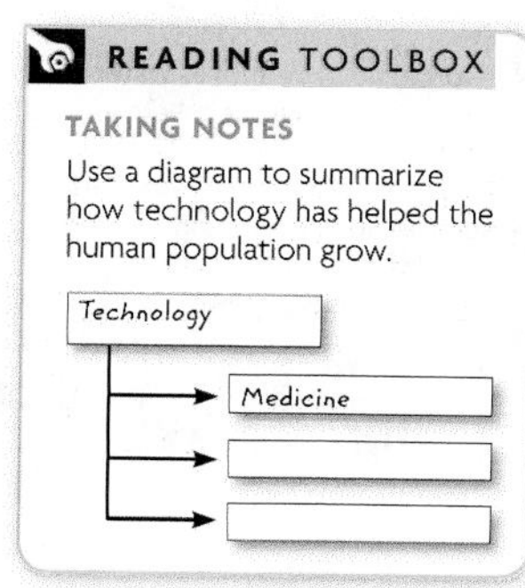

A Connect **What technologies do you depend on each day?**

MAIN IDEA

The growing human population exerts pressure on Earth's natural resources.

Two resources, oil and coal, currently support the majority of our country's energy use. Oil and coal are the result of natural processes. Over millions of years, natural processes transformed dead organisms into the concentrated carbon substances we use today as oil and coal. Oil and coal are **nonrenewable resources** because they are used faster than the rate at which they form. In 2006, the human population was using oil at a rate of about 77 million barrels per day, and world oil use continues to rise. The growing use of this limited resource will lead to energy crises in the decades ahead unless technologies are developed to use other forms of energy.

Not all resources are nonrenewable. A natural resource that can be replaced at the same rate at which it is used is called a **renewable resource.** For example, wind energy—captured by wind turbines such as those shown in **FIGURE 1.2**—and solar energy are renewable resources because they cannot be used up by humans. Other resources, such as those that come from plants and animals, can be used up, but because they could last indefinitely through regrowth and reproduction, they are renewable. As long as these resources are replenished faster than they are used, they are considered renewable. But if renewable resources are not used carefully, they can become nonrenewable.

FIGURE 1.2 Giant wind turbines such as these capture renewable energy from Earth's natural processes.

Take It Further

The use of oil and other limited resources is rising in part because of the growth of the human population, but it is also a function of modern technologies becoming more accessible and common in places where they were once rare. Things that used to be the luxury items, such as cars, air conditioners, and computers, are now commonplace in many countries.

China, for example, currently generates about half of the electricity that the United States does, despite having a population that is four times bigger. As China's economy grows, however, and more of its citizens are able to tap into electrical power, its consumption of electricity is expected to triple over the next 20 years, equivalent to a 4.3 percent increase per year.

Integrating Physics

Tell students that wind turbines convert the **kinetic energy** of the wind into **mechanical energy.** A generator converts this mechanical energy into electricity. A wind farm contains dozens or hundreds of wind turbines. The Nysted wind farm, located in the Baltic Sea off the coast of Denmark, has 72 turbines that provide about 20 percent of Denmark's electricity.

Answers

A **Connect** *Sample answer:* automobiles, microwave ovens, computers, digital music players, wireless phones

PRE-AP

Tell students that the metaphor of "Spaceship Earth" popularized in the mid–20th century may have come from a once-popular book *Progress and Poverty,* self-published in 1879 by Henry George. He wrote:

> *It is a well-provisioned ship, this on which we sail through space. If the bread and beef above decks seem to grow scarce, we but open a hatch and there is a new supply, of which before we never dreamed.*

Have students write for five minutes on how our view of Earth's resources has changed since the 19th century.

Teacher Toolkit, Section C, Quick-Write

Chapter 16: Human Impact on Ecosystems 473

Teach continued

Science Trivia

Americans produce a lot of solid waste. In 2013, according to the Environmental Protection Agency, Americans produced 254 million tons of household garbage. The composition was as follows:

- 27% paper
- 28.1% food scraps and yard trimmings
- 12.8% plastics
- 9.1% metals
- 9% rubber, leather, and textiles
- 6.2% wood
- 4.5% glass
- 3.3% other

Of this, about 34 percent was recycled or composted.

Per capita generation of garbage rose from 2.7 pounds per day in 1960 to 4.5 pounds in 1990. From 1990 to 2013, however, this number stayed about the same, suggesting that some people are finding ways to reduce the amount of garbage they produce.

Answers

A Analyze If water becomes contaminated with toxic chemicals, or if it continues to be extracted from aquifers faster than it is replaced, it will become a nonrenewable resource.

CONNECT TO

HYDROLOGIC CYCLE

In the chapter **Principles of Ecology,** you learned how the hydrologic cycle moves water through Earth's atmosphere and back to Earth's surface. This cycling of water from resources such as lakes, rivers, and aquifers sustains the needs of the surrounding ecosystem.

Drinking water is a renewable resource, but pollution and overuse threaten its supply. Pesticides, industrial waste, and other contaminants have been found in water sources that supply tens of millions of people across the United States with fresh water. Groundwater is also being extracted from aquifers faster than it is replaced.

As Earth's human population continues to grow, the management of renewable and nonrenewable resources will become increasingly important. Today, the United States uses more resources and produces more waste than any other country on Earth. Each year, the United States generates about 254 million tons of garbage. That is about 4.3 pounds per day per person, or almost 1 ton per year. What would happen if each of Earth's 7 billion humans generated 1 ton of garbage each year?

A Analyze **Explain how a renewable resource such as water could become a nonrenewable resource.**

MAIN IDEA

Effective management of Earth's resources will help meet the needs of the future.

Management of Earth's resources affects both current and future generations. The responsible use of Earth's resources can help to maintain these resources for future generations.

The story of Easter Island is a cautionary tale of destruction caused by careless use of resources. When humans first landed on Easter Island between 400 CE and 700 CE, it was thickly forested on rich soil, with many bird species. The human colony grew quickly over the next 1000 years, building the stone monuments for which the island is now famous. The inhabitants cut down the forests for lumber and for building boats. The trees were cut down faster than they could grow back. Eventually, Easter Island was left with no trees, as shown in **FIGURE 1.3.** Without trees, there was no wood for shelter or boats, the rich soil washed away, and habitat for the island's animal populations was lost. Without boats, there was no offshore fishing. Without food and island resources nearly gone, the Easter Island human population crashed and the Easter Islanders disappeared.

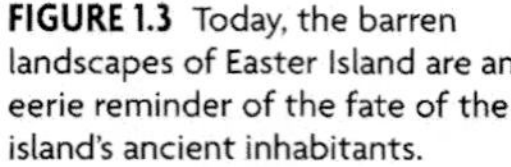

FIGURE 1.3 Today, the barren landscapes of Easter Island are an eerie reminder of the fate of the island's ancient inhabitants.

The Easter Islanders' use of trees was unsustainable. In other words, the islanders used trees to meet their short-term needs. But this resource could not be maintained into the future, and its use had negative long-term effects. In contrast, sustainable use of resources means using resources in such a way that they will be available for future generations.

Differentiated Instruction

HANDS-ON ACTIVITY

Tell students that between 10 and 50 percent of the cost of most products bought in supermarkets goes into packaging and that such packaging is one of the major sources of solid waste in landfills. Ask students to look at the packaged products in their homes and in stores. Have each of them bring in an example of an overpackaged product.

Students can then compare the actual volume, weight, or surface area of the product with the volume, weight, or surface area of the packaging.

Ecological Footprint

Humans need natural resources to survive, but the way resources are used threatens the welfare of the human population. Earth's carrying capacity depends on how much land is needed to support each person on Earth. The amount of land necessary to produce and maintain enough food and water, shelter, energy, and waste is called an **ecological footprint.** The size of an ecological footprint depends on a number of factors. These include the amount and efficiency of resource use, and the amount and toxicity of waste produced.

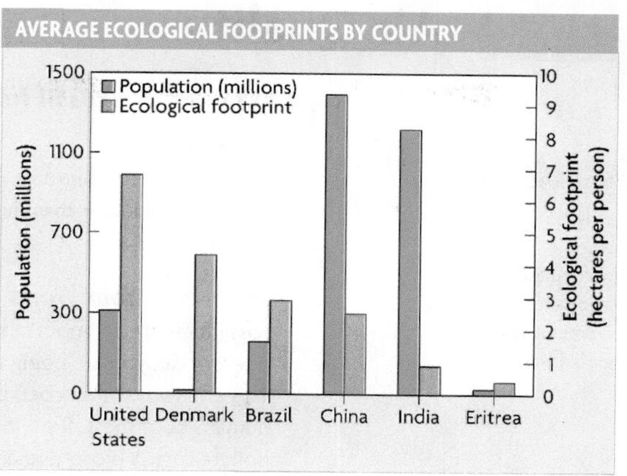

Source: Global Footprint Network

FIGURE 1.4 Different countries of the world have varying levels of impact on their environment. This graph shows the average ecological footprint of individuals around the world.

As shown in **FIGURE 1.4**, individuals and populations vary in their use of resources and production of waste, and therefore in the size of their ecological footprints. The average U.S. citizen's ecological footprint covers an area larger than 15 football fields (6.8 hectares) and is one of the largest in the world. But the ecological footprint of individuals in developing nations is growing, and nations such as China and India have populations that are more than three times the size of the U.S. population. Individuals in the United States may have a large footprint, but other nations have a lot more "feet."

As the world population continues to grow, we face many challenging decisions. Waste production and management is an issue that will become more important as we move into the future. Should we have rules to regulate resource use and waste production? If so, how much resource use and waste production should individuals and populations be allowed? How much land needs to be maintained for agriculture, how much for living space, and how much for other uses? How much fresh water should be used for crop irrigation and how much reserved for humans to drink? Our welfare, and the welfare of future generations, depends on sustainable management of Earth's resources.

A Analyze Why is our ecological footprint related to an area of land?

TEACH FROM VISUALS

FIGURE 1.4 Have students compare the population size with the size of the ecological footprint of each country shown on the graph. **Ask**

- Which country has the highest ratio of ecological footprint size to population size? United States
- Which country has the lowest ratio? Denmark
- How might you calculate the overall ecological footprint of each country? Multiply the average footprint by the population.
- If you use these overall footprints to assess environmental degradation and use of resources, how do the United States and India compare? The United States is about double the overall ecological footprint of India.
- In terms of Earth's resources, what is missing from the ecological footprint? oceans

Answers

A Analyze The production of all the material goods we use each day, including our homes, food, and clothing, at some point required use of or access to land. Also, our waste products are returned to the land.

SELF-CHECK Online
HMHScience.com
GO ONLINE

16.1 Formative Assessment

REVIEWING MAIN IDEAS

1. Give three examples of how technology has influenced human population growth.
2. What is the difference between **renewable** and **nonrenewable resources**?
3. Describe how a population can use resources in a sustainable way.

CRITICAL THINKING

4. **Connect** What factors can limit the growth of the human population?
5. **Synthesize** How could the Easter Islanders have prevented their population crash?

CONNECT TO CARRYING CAPACITY

6. The progressive increase in Earth's human carrying capacity came from advances in technology. What density-independent and density-dependent limiting factors may prevent the human population from continued growth?

Assess and Reteach

Assess Use the Section Self-Check or Section Quiz, both available at **HMHScience.com**.

Reteach On the board, make a T-chart in which students list renewable resources and nonrenewable resources in separate columns. Ask students to give their reasons for categorizing the resources as they did.

16.1 FORMATIVE ASSESSMENT

1. Advances in medicine have reduced infant mortality and prolonged life spans. Industrial technologies have made transportation and agriculture much easier, allowing for increased food production and distribution. Plumbing and sewage treatment have improved sanitation, reducing incidence of waterborne illness.
2. Renewable resources can be replenished by Earth's natural processes at the same rate at which they are used, whereas nonrenewable resources are used up faster than they can be replenished.
3. Humans can use recyclable goods, renewable energy sources such as wind and solar power, support only sustainable fisheries and agriculture, and minimize their use of products that contain toxins.
4. *Sample answer:* disease, drought, overuse of limited resources, crop pests, war
5. They could have limited their use of the island's forests.
6. density-dependent factors: disease, lack of food, limited water supplies; density-independent factors: exhaustion of nonrenewable resources, medical and cultural practices

▼ Plan and Prepare

Activate Prior Knowledge Initiate a class discussion of pollution problems that students have heard about. Encourage students to identify the pollutant and its effect on people and other organisms. **Ask,** In general, why is pollution a problem for Earth? It harms ecosystems. Discuss what steps are being taken to solve the problems students have discussed.

▼ Teach

Vocabulary

Academic Vocabulary New technologies, processes, and discoveries sometimes require new words. **Smog** is one of these. It comes from the combination of **smoke** and **fog.**

smoke, a suspension of fine solid or liquid particles in a gaseous medium

fog, condensed water vapor in cloudlike masses lying close to the ground

smog, fog that has become mixed and polluted with smoke

16.2 Air Quality

KEY CONCEPT **Fossil fuel emissions affect the biosphere.**

MAIN IDEAS
- Pollutants accumulate in the air.
- Air pollution is changing Earth's biosphere.

VOCABULARY
pollution
smog
particulate
acid rain
greenhouse effect
global warming

Connect to Your World
Fossil fuels are an important part of modern society. Consider that every time you ride in a car, you are being transported by energy that originally came from the sun. This energy was absorbed by ancient organisms and stored in their biomass. Today, as humans burn these fuels in the form of gas and oil, we are creating compounds that pollute Earth's biosphere. Without this energy our lives would be very different, but how does air pollution from fossil fuels affect the biosphere?

MAIN IDEA
Pollutants accumulate in the air.

Although it is sometimes easy to forget, humans are an important part of the biosphere. Our actions have direct and indirect effects on Earth's natural cycles. Each year humans add synthetic chemicals and materials to the Earth. Many of them cannot be integrated into normal ecosystem functions. The addition of these materials to the environment is called pollution. **Pollution** describes any undesirable factor, or pollutant, that is added to the air, water, or soil. Pollution can take the form of microscopic air particles, or waste products from factories and sewers, or household chemicals that are poured down the kitchen sink. The harmful effects of pollutants can be immediate or delayed, but these effects may add up over time and can disrupt the function of ecosystems.

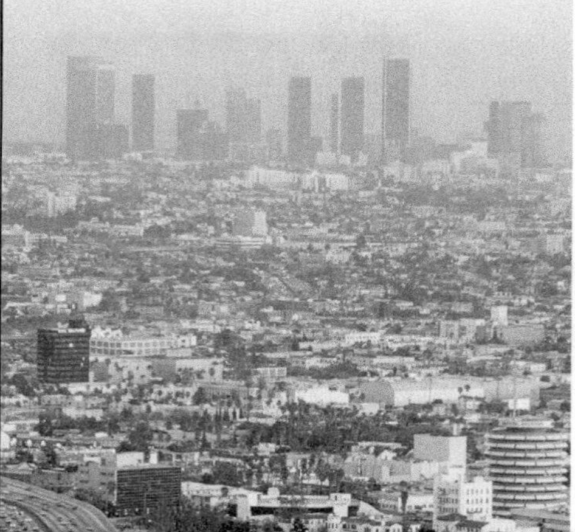

FIGURE 2.1 The hazy fog over the city of Los Angeles is largely produced by automobile emissions and industrial processes. Smog is a growing problem in many areas of the United States.

Smog and Ozone

The most common air pollution comes from the waste products produced by burning fossil fuels such as gas and oil. Chemical compounds released through this process can combine to form a haze of matter called smog, shown in **FIGURE 2.1. Smog** is a type of air pollution caused by the interaction of sunlight with pollutants produced by fossil fuel emissions. There are several components of smog, including particulate matter and ground-level ozone. **Particulates** are microscopic bits of dust, metal, and unburned fuel, 1–10 microns in size, that are produced by many industrial processes. Once in the air, some particulates may stay in the atmosphere for weeks before they settle to the ground. Fine particulates can be inhaled and can cause many types of health problems.

Differentiated Instruction

ENGLISH LEARNERS

Write on the board the six vocabulary terms listed at the top of the page. Before reading the section, have students discuss the relationships between the words. Then have them read the section. Next, have them write sentences that include two or more of the terms. Students should be able to include all the terms and the proper context in two sentences. Then have students format their sentences into a concept map.

Teacher Toolkit, Section C, Concept Map

TEACH WITH TECHNOLOGY

Assemble images of air pollution, such as smog, into a digital slide show. Show images taken by satellites as well as from the ground. See the PowerPresentation for this section for links to sources of online images, such as NASA's Earth Observatory.

The second component of smog is ground-level ozone. In the presence of sunlight, two types of chemicals react to produce ground-level ozone (O_3). Nitrogen oxides are produced during fossil fuel combustion, and these chemicals give smog a yellowish color. Ozone is formed when nitrogen dioxide (NO_2) reacts with oxygen (O_2) present in the atmosphere. In this reaction, one oxygen from an NO_2 molecule is transferred to an O_2 molecule, forming ozone (O_3). The ozone produced by reactions of nitrogen oxide and oxygen tends to stay close to the ground, where it can be harmful to human health and ecosystem functions. Although ozone is harmful to organisms, it also plays an important, protective role in the Earth's upper atmosphere. High concentrations of ozone in the stratosphere, also known as the ozonosphere or ozone layer, act as a shield protecting Earth's biosphere against harmful ultraviolet rays found in sunlight.

Acid Rain

The chemicals produced by the burning of fossil fuels become part of the ecosystem and can change the products of natural cycles. For example, nitrogen oxides and sulfur oxides from fossil fuel emissions can lead to the formation of acid rain. **Acid rain** is a type of precipitation produced when pollutants in the water cycle cause rain pH to drop below normal levels.

VISUAL VOCAB

Acid rain is a type of precipitation produced when pollutants in the water cycle cause rain pH to drop below normal levels.

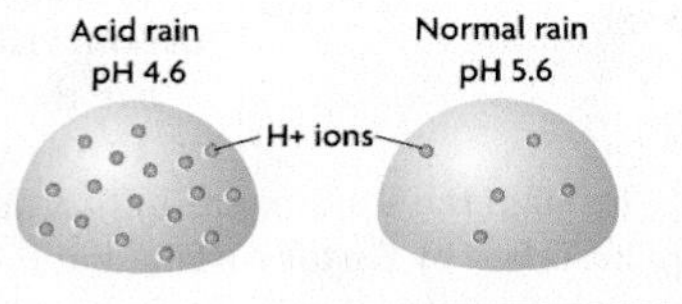

During the water cycle, rain falls through Earth's atmosphere and interacts with carbon dioxide molecules. As it falls, water molecules react with carbon dioxide molecules to form a weak carbonic acid, which then breaks apart, leaving lone hydrogen ions. This is normal. All rain that falls is slightly acidic, with a pH around 5.6. When pollutants such as nitrogen oxides and sulfur oxides become a part of the water cycle, acid rain is the result. Reactions between these chemicals and the oxygen and water normally present in the atmosphere create sulfuric and nitric acids that can cause pH levels to fall below 5.6.

CONNECT TO

pH

Recall from the chapter **Chemistry of Life** that pH is a measure of the concentration of H^+ ions in a solution. The concentrations of H^+ ions in acid rain are very high, giving the rain a lower pH level.

Acid rain falls in many areas of the United States and has a major effect on ecosystems. By decreasing pH levels in lakes and streams, acid rain threatens water supplies and species habitat. Acid rain can cause a decline in growth rates, as shown in **FIGURE 2.2.** It can also cause leaves and bark to break down more quickly and make trees more vulnerable to disease and weather.

FIGURE 2.2 The wide growth rings of this tree indicate a healthy environment. The smaller growth rings illustrate how acid rain directly impacts plant growth.

Synthesize **As the human population continues to increase and use more fossil fuels, why might acid rain become a bigger problem?**

BELOW LEVEL

Have students create cause-and-effect diagrams for acid rain, smog, and global warming. Diagrams should include chemical reactions and the elements and energy sources that are involved.

Teacher Toolkit, Section C, Cornell Notes

The Inside Story

The word *smog* first appeared in print in 1905, in a London newspaper's account of a meeting of the Public Health Congress at which **Dr. Harold Antoine des Voeux** presented his paper "Fog and Smoke." In his paper, Dr. des Voeux reported "something produced in great cities which was not found in the country, and that was **smoky fog,** or what was known as *smog*." Dr. des Voeux's coinage of *smog* occurred a half-century after smog first appeared in the atmosphere as a byproduct of England's Industrial Revolution.

Take It Further

Acid rain refers to all types of precipitation (rain, snow, sleet, and hail) that is acidic in nature. Acid rain does not just affect forests. It kills aquatic life, crops, and other vegetation; damages buildings and monuments; corrodes copper and lead pipes; damages automobiles; reduces soil fertility; and can cause toxic metals to leach into groundwater. In lakes, as acidity increases, aquatic plants die off and waterfowl lose their food source.

TEACH FROM VISUALS

FIGURE 2.2 Explain that the photo shows a cross section of a tree trunk. The rings consist of vascular tissue that carries water up the tree from the roots. When the drier, colder season occurs, growth of this tissue is very limited and the vessels are very narrow, creating the darker concentric lines shown in the figure. Each ring represents one year of growth, or one year in the life of the tree. The rings to the left are the innermost rings, and the rings on the right are nearer the outside of the tree trunk, or the younger part of the tree. **Ask,** For approximately how many years has acid rain inhibited the growth of the tree? 20

Answers

A Synthesize There is a positive correlation between fossil fuel emissions and acid rain. More fossil fuel combustion means more acid rain.

▼ Teach *continued*

TEACH FROM VISUALS

FIGURE 2.3 Review the graph with students. Tell them to note the pattern of a high in both temperature and carbon dioxide followed by a decline to a low point and then a relatively sudden rise back up. Describe this as a climate cycle. **Ask**

- According to the graph, about how long does it take for Earth to complete one climate cycle? 100,000 years
- From the graph, what can you infer about Earth's temperature and Earth's carbon dioxide level? There is a direct positive correlation between the two; as one goes up or down, so does the other.

History of Science

Researchers working at Vostok Station at Lake Vostok in Antarctica produced one of the **world's longest ice cores** in 1998. A joint Russian, French, and U.S. team drilled and analyzed the core, which is 3623 meters (11,886 ft) long. The tip of the ice core is estimated to be as old as 420,000 years. The data in **FIGURE 2.3** came from the analysis of the chemical composition of this ice core and air bubbles trapped in the ice.

Integrating Physics

The **type of surface** that sunlight first encounters is an important factor in the greenhouse effect. Forests, ocean surfaces, grasslands, ice caps, cities, and deserts all reflect sunlight to different degrees. For example, a white glacier strongly reflects sunlight, resulting in very little heating of the surface. Dark desert soil and concrete strongly absorb sunlight, resulting in high surface temperatures, as anyone who has walked across a parking lot on a hot day knows.

MAIN IDEA

Air pollution is changing Earth's biosphere.

Earth's atmosphere naturally includes molecules of carbon dioxide that play an important part in keeping the biosphere at a temperature that can support life. The levels of atmospheric carbon dioxide rise and fall over time as a normal part of the climate cycles of Earth. Collections of data from arctic ice cores allow scientists to look deep into Earth's atmospheric history. They have discovered that cycles of rising and falling carbon dioxide levels follow known patterns of periodic warming and cooling. The relationship between changes in global average temperatures and carbon dioxide levels is shown in **FIGURE 2.3.** We know that high levels of carbon dioxide are typical of Earth's warmer periods, while low levels are associated with cool climates, eventually leading to periods of extreme cold called ice ages.

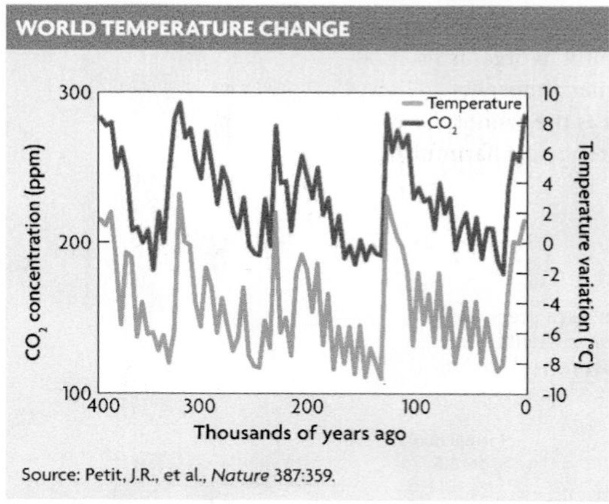

FIGURE 2.3 Scientists have found that changes in Earth's temperature correspond with fluctuations in global carbon dioxide levels.

The Greenhouse Effect

Earth gets nearly all of its energy from the wavelengths of both visible and invisible light emitted by the sun. When the sun's waves reach Earth, some are absorbed by Earth's atmosphere, but many of these rays pass through the atmosphere and reach Earth's surface. Some of this energy is absorbed by Earth's surface, but it is later reradiated as invisible infrared radiation—energy in the form of heat. After being reradiated from Earth's surface, this energy could travel away from Earth, be lost into space, and leave an extremely cold Earth that could never sustain life. But Earth is not cold and does have life. So what keeps Earth's temperature from dropping to extreme freezing conditions?

To answer this question, think about the greenhouses that scientists and gardeners use to grow plants. Greenhouses use glass that allows light and radiation from sunlight to pass through and provide energy for plant growth. The glass also prevents infrared radiation from escaping. This infrared radiation keeps the inside of the greenhouse warm. This same phenomenon occurs in a car, causing the inside to warm when the windows are closed.

In the same way that greenhouse glass creates an environment for plants to grow, the chemical composition of Earth's atmosphere plays an important role in maintaining an environment that is suitable for life. Earth's atmosphere contains gases called greenhouse gases that act as insulators and slow the loss of heat through the atmosphere. Water vapor, carbon dioxide, and methane are three of the most common greenhouse gases found in the atmosphere. Greenhouse gases absorb wavelengths of infrared radiation. This process is called the greenhouse effect and is illustrated in **FIGURE 2.4.** The **greenhouse effect** occurs when carbon dioxide, water, and methane molecules absorb energy reradiated by Earth's surface and slow the release of this energy from Earth's atmosphere.

Differentiated Instruction

HANDS-ON ACTIVITY

To demonstrate the greenhouse effect, have students work in pairs to make greenhouse models. Provide each pair with a clear-plastic 2-liter bottle with its cap on and its bottom cut out, two thermometers, cellophane tape, and graph paper. Tell students to punch a small hole near the top of the bottle and insert the thermometer into the hole, bulb end first. Have them use tape to secure the thermometer in place so that it can be easily read. Have students record the temperature on both thermometers before placing the bottle in a sunny area. The second thermometer should be placed near the bottle, but not in direct sunlight. Have students record both thermometers' temperature readings every five minutes for half an hour, then graph their data and write conclusions. Students should find that the temperatures in the greenhouse bottle were higher than those of the other thermometer.

IGURE 2.4 Greenhouse Effect

Vater vapor, carbon dioxide, and methane can be found all through arth's atmosphere. These greenhouse gases act as a blanket that lows the release of energy and helps to keep Earth at a temperature nat can support life.

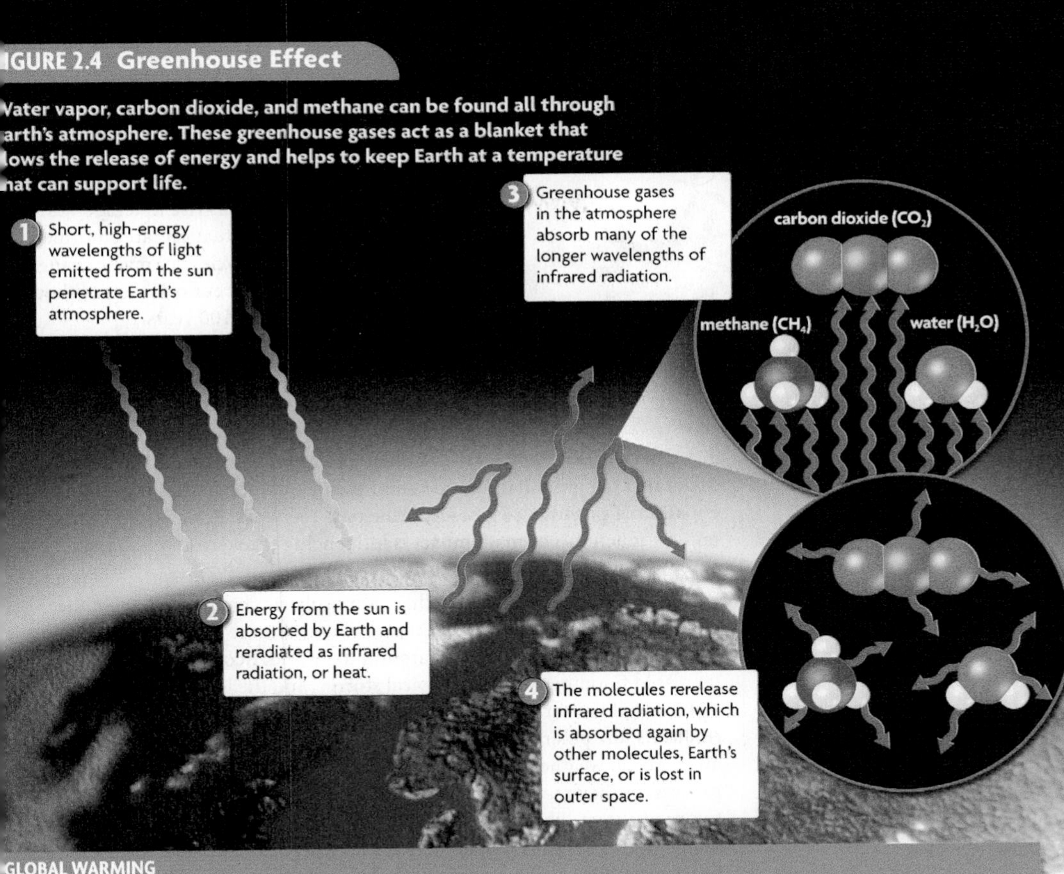

1 Short, high-energy wavelengths of light emitted from the sun penetrate Earth's atmosphere.
2 Energy from the sun is absorbed by Earth and reradiated as infrared radiation, or heat.
3 Greenhouse gases in the atmosphere absorb many of the longer wavelengths of infrared radiation.
carbon dioxide (CO_2)
methane (CH_4)
water (H_2O)
4 The molecules rerelease infrared radiation, which is absorbed again by other molecules, Earth's surface, or is lost in outer space.

GLOBAL WARMING

As automobile use and industry have grown, so have the levels of carbon dioxide and other greenhouse gases in the atmosphere. This graph shows average global temperature changes (blue) against atmospheric carbon dioxide levels (green) measured at Mauna Loa Observatory in Hawaii.

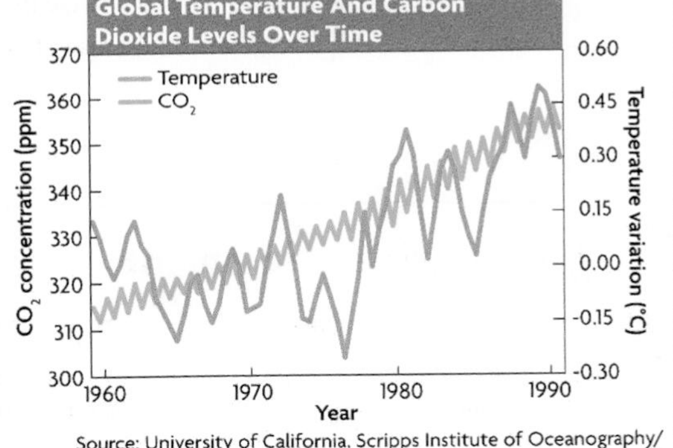

Source: University of California, Scripps Institute of Oceanography/ Hadley Centre for Climate Prediction and Research

CRITICAL VIEWING **How would an increase in atmospheric greenhouse gases contribute to an increase in average global temperatures?**

479

TEACH FROM VISUALS

FIGURE 2.4 Discuss each step of the figure with students. **Ask,** What would happen to the infrared radiation produced in step 2 if there were no greenhouse gases? Much of it would be released from the atmosphere. Point out the regular sawtooth appearance in the CO_2 curve. Explain that in many locations, such as the Mauna Loa Observatory in Hawaii, CO_2 levels fluctuate with the seasons. During the winter, trees do not take up CO_2 at as high a rate as they do in the summer, so there is more atmospheric CO_2. **Ask,** What is the general trend in both temperature and CO_2 concentration? increasing

Address Misconceptions

Common Misconception The greenhouse effect and global warming are the same thing.

Correcting the Misconception The greenhouse effect is essential for keeping the atmosphere warm enough for living things to survive. This is the natural greenhouse effect. Human activities, especially the burning of fossil fuels, can enhance the natural greenhouse effect by increasing the level of greenhouse gases, causing a general warming trend that is called global warming.

Answers

A Critical Viewing The gases in the atmosphere would absorb more heat.

PRE-AP

Suggest students use the fishbone graphic organizer to sort out all the factors that impact air quality. The head of the "fish" would be Air Quality, with the "bones" coming from the central backbone being Smog/Ozone, Acid Rain, and Greenhouse Effect. Students may also want a separate "bone" for Global Warming. Attached to each of these contributing factors would be the attributes or effects of each.

Teacher Toolkit, Section C, Fishbone Diagram

▼ Teach *continued*

TEACH FROM VISUALS

FIGURE 2.5 Have students trace the red line, indicating where the North Pole ice boundary used to be. Explain that Arctic ice is thinning, melting, and rupturing. The largest single block of ice in the Arctic, the Ward Hunt Ice Shelf, started cracking in 2000. By 2002, it had split all the way through and is now breaking into pieces. **Ask,** What effect will the melting of Arctic ice have on global warming? There will be less white surface to reflect solar radiation, so there will be more infrared radiation. Increased absorption of solar radiation will lead to more infrared radiation in the atmosphere. Tell students that wildlife also is being affected. Polar bears have to swim as far as 97 kilometers (60 mi) between ice floes to find food, and some are drowning in the process.

Answers

A Connect Seasonal temperature changes could be less pronounced.

▼ Assess and Reteach

Assess Use the Section Self-Check or Section Quiz, both available at **HMHScience.com**.

Reteach Create cause-and-effect diagrams for global warming, acid rain, and smog. Leave blanks in the diagrams and ask students to complete them.

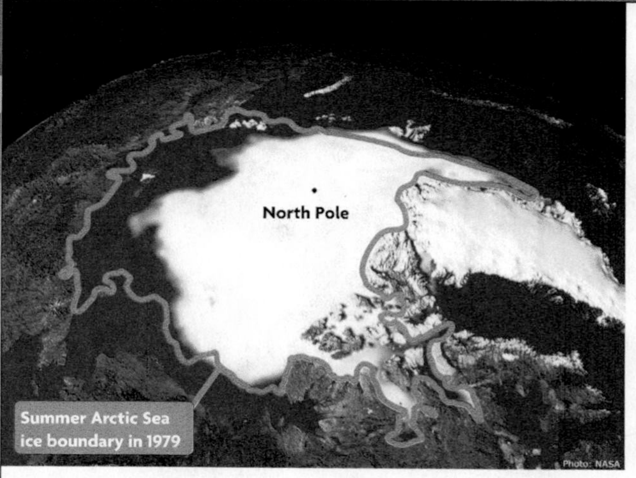

FIGURE 2.5 Over the past 20 years, increasing global temperatures have decreased summer ice pack around the North Pole by about 20 percent.

Carbon Dioxide and Global Warming

Climate Change

Over the past 100 years, the average global temperature has risen 0.74°C (1.3°F), with the most dramatic change occurring over the past 50 years. What is causing this rise in temperature? Global temperature fluctuations are a normal part of Earth's climate cycle. But major changes in temperature generally occur over tens of thousands of years, not over 100 years.

The trend of increasing global temperatures is known as **global warming.** From a variety of evidence, scientists can infer that the changes in temperature are the result of increased levels of greenhouse gases such as carbon dioxide, water, and methane. There is no doubt that the growth of industry and use of automobiles has increased the emission of greenhouse gases over the past 100 years. Scientists may disagree on how much this human impact is influencing the warming trend, but most agree that we must take steps to slow the process.

Scientists do not know how these atmospheric changes will affect the global biosphere. What they do know is that evidence shows climate change is already threatening ecosystems around the world. Ecological disasters, such as increased flooding, stronger tropical storms, and the loss of biodiversity, are just a few of the threats that may be caused by climate change. As shown in **FIGURE 2.5**, the polar ice pack is melting at a rapid pace, which may eventually affect global weather patterns. These changes may be part of a slow warming process, or they may be the beginning of a rapid global climate change. The future of climate change is uncertain, but scientists predict that average temperatures on Earth could increase anywhere from 1.1 to 6.4°C (2 to 11.5°F) by the year 2100, a change that could have dramatic effects on Earth's biosphere, and change the planet that we call home.

 Connect **How might climate change affect seasonal temperature changes?**

16.2 Formative Assessment

REVIEWING ▶ MAIN IDEAS

1. Name and describe two ways in which **pollution** affects ecosystems.
2. How does the **greenhouse effect** keep Earth warm?
3. Explain how a build-up of carbon dioxide in the atmosphere could increase Earth's global temperature.

CRITICAL THINKING

4. **Predict** Describe how **acid rain** falling in a forest could disrupt the trophic structure of the ecosystem.
5. **Connect** Name two important functions of greenhouse gases at Earth's surface.

CONNECT TO FOOD WEBS

6. Ocean producers such as phytoplankton are an important part of food webs, but they need a specific temperature to survive. How might increased water temperatures affect these ocean food webs?

16.2 FORMATIVE ASSESSMENT

1. Pollution can result in smog and acid rain. Smog is caused by the interaction of sunlight with pollutants produced by fossil fuel emissions. Acid rain results from the mixture of these emissions with water vapor.
2. Infrared energy reradiated from Earth's surface is absorbed by greenhouse gases such as water, carbon dioxide, and methane. This energy, also called heat, is then released and absorbed by other molecules in the atmosphere, Earth's surface, or lost in outer space.
3. With more greenhouse gases in the atmosphere, less heat would escape the atmosphere, causing Earth to become warmer.
4. The destruction of leaves in the forest canopy would let more sunlight reach the forest floor. Here plants adapted for less sunlight might be excluded by plants that thrive on more light. Herbivorous animals that feed on any of these plants could starve, as could the carnivores they sustain.
5. At Earth's surface, water vapor condenses to form precipitation that is part of the hydrologic cycle. Carbon dioxide is essential for photosynthesis.
6. If increased water temperatures kill the phytoplankton, the lowest trophic level of ocean ecosystems will be gone, and the food webs will probably collapse.

Digitizing Life on Earth

S.T.E.M. Interactions

How do biologists study biosphere-level concerns such as climate change, the spread of disease, the resiliency of crops, and patterns of extinction? Researching questions on a global scale is complicated. It usually can't be done in a laboratory, and developing computer models takes an enormous amount of data on past events to make accurate predictions of future changes. Increasingly, scientists are turning to natural history collections.

If you have ever been to a museum or botanic garden, you know there are not only many specimens or artifacts on display but also detailed information about each one. A plaque may state where or how long ago that organism was found, along with facts about its diet, method of reproduction, or requirements for survival. Usually the specimens on display at a museum represent only a portion of the museum's collection. It's likely that hundreds, thousands, or even millions of other specimens are in storage.

Where do all these specimens come from? Natural history collections can come from museum researchers for whom collecting is their job, from other scientists, or from donations by amateur collectors. Some collections are well documented and well preserved, while others may have lost information or are slowly deteriorating. Taken together, the collections reach back for centuries, providing a treasure trove of data on billions of animals, plants, fungi, and even bacteria. Using the specimens and other historical artifacts of the time, such as diaries, ship logs, photographs, and paintings, researchers are piecing together often fragmented information from multiple sources into a comprehensive look at Earth's past.

Among the world's biggest natural history museums are the Smithsonian in Washington, D.C., the Natural History Museum in London, England, and the Muséum National d'Histoire Naturelle in Paris, France. There are also thousands of smaller museums with collections, including in the world's most biodiverse and remote areas. It would take a lot of time and money to visit all the locations. Instead, researchers are calling for a digitization of all the information that these museums hold, making the information easily accessible to anyone who wants it. Taking digital photographs, transcribing handwritten field notes into computer programs, and recording entire collections as video makes the information searchable and machine-readable and provides billions of potential data points for scientists. The increasing collaboration between museums, botanic gardens, and researchers studying the biosphere is promising to provide new insights into the future of life on Earth.

A collection of beetles from around the world (Oxford University Museum of Natural History)

Introduce

Some students may not have visited a natural history museum or botanic garden, and most of them likely have not seen collections that are not on display. Show students images from collections, particularly the many drawers of catalogued specimens. **Ask,** Where do you think all these specimens came from? Why were they collected, and how old might they be? Do they represent all living things? Some specimens may be three hundred years old or more. Many specimens were collected on expeditions, for cataloging and taxonomic purposes. Even though there are millions of collected specimens from public and private collectors, they represent only a small fraction of species that exist or existed in the past.

Discuss

Ask students if they would like to assist with biosphere-level research and if they think such opportunities exist. Explain that there are many ways for students to become involved as citizen scientists. Managers of databases are often looking for students as well as professional scientists to post images and information about organisms in their own backyard (or schoolyard) to help maintain a record of biodiversity and biogeographical range information on species. Monitoring programs often seek help with gathering migration data on songbirds and butterflies. Natural history museums such as the one at the Smithsonian rely on citizens to assist with digitization of their collections, which can be done from remote locations. After a short online tutorial, students can transcribe text from photos of pages taken from historical field notebooks, thereby making the content freely accessible to anyone who may find it useful.

SECTION 16.3

B.3.2 Design, evaluate, and refine a model which shows how human activities and natural phenomena can change the flow of matter and energy in an ecosystem and how those changes impact the environment and biodiversity of populations in ecosystems of different scales, as well as, how these human impacts can be reduced.

▼ Plan and Prepare

Activate Prior Knowledge Many people assume that water pollution is the deliberate dumping of hazardous chemicals or wastes into bodies of water, but actually it is any pollution that ends up in water. **Ask,** What is it about water that allows so much pollution to be dispersed across thousands of miles of ocean? It is a powerful solvent, and it flows.

▼ Teach

Vocabulary

Greek and Latin Word Origins The word **eutrophication** comes from the Greek *eutrophos,* which means "well-nourished."

16.3 Water Quality

KEY CONCEPT **Pollution of Earth's freshwater supply threatens habitat and health.**

VOCABULARY
indicator species
biomagnification

MAIN IDEAS
- Water pollution affects ecosystems.
- Biomagnification causes accumulation of toxins in the food chain.

Connect to Your World

When you swallow a pill, your body only uses a part of the medicine in the pill and gets rid of the rest as waste, which is flushed away. Scientists have detected traces of many prescription drugs in freshwater supplies. Several fish species that live in fresh waters have been exposed to the female hormone estrogen. Some of the male fish have begun showing female characteristics. These "gender-bending" fish are only one effect of water pollution. What other pollutants can be found in our water?

MAIN IDEA

Water pollution affects ecosystems.

Pollution can have a major impact on water ecosystems. Chemical contaminants, raw sewage, trash, and other waste products are only a few pollutants that make their way into rivers, lakes, and aquifers all over the world.

Runoff from farms and cities may contain toxic chemicals and debris that can disrupt the chemical balance of freshwater lakes and streams and put entire freshwater ecosystems at risk. For example, detergents and fertilizers used in fields can affect a lake ecosystem by stimulating plant and algae overgrowth. A buildup of algae, such as the one shown in **FIGURE 3.1,** can drastically lower the levels of dissolved oxygen, leading to the dying off of fish populations. A lack of oxygen can also keep detritivores from breaking down waste materials. Over time, lakes and ponds slowly begin to fill in through a process called eutrophication.

FIGURE 3.1 A buildup of algae in lakes such as this one is the direct result of pollution. Eventually, the process of eutrophication will lead to the disappearance of the lake.

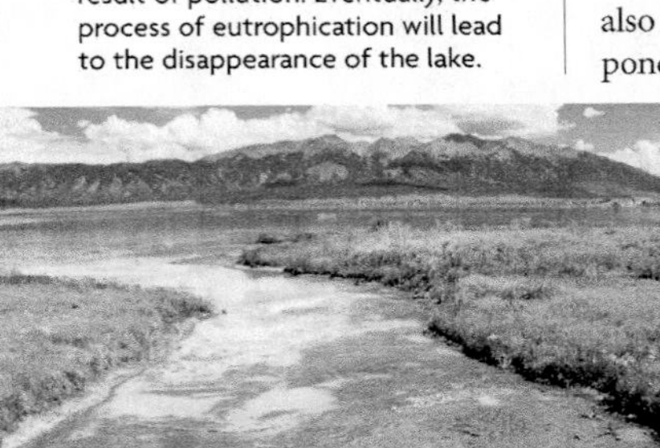

One way in which scientists can determine the health of an ecosystem is through the study of natural indicator species. An **indicator species,** also known as a bioindicator, is a species that provides a sign, or indication, of the quality of the ecosystem's environmental conditions. The gender-bending fish discussed above is an example of an aquatic indicator species. Frogs are sometimes considered an indicator species for water quality. Because the skin of tadpoles and adults is water-permeable, they come into direct contact with pollutants that can cause deformities such as extra arms and legs, as well as body tumors. Terrestrial ecosystems have indicator species as well, but the environmental impacts on these species are shown in different ways. Aquatic indicator species show the direct effects of pollution.

Differentiated Instruction

TEACH WITH TECHNOLOGY

Collect a water sample from a nearby pond, lake, or stream, using appropriate water-collection protocol, for students to test for pH by using a pH meter. Samples from several sites would provide a good opportunity for comparison. Prepare the buffer solutions and calibrate the pH meters before class. If you have samples from several sites, group students according to the number of site samples you have. Provide each group with five 50-mL portions of a sample. Demonstrate the proper use of the pH meter. Have groups measure and record the pH of each 50-mL portion and determine the average pH.

If the entire class is testing water from a single site, determine a class average for the water's pH. If groups are testing water from different sites, have them compare the pHs. Ask each group to write a summary of their procedure, present their data, and form conclusions about the quality of the body of water from which their water sample was taken.

The Forster's tern, a bird species native to coastal regions of the United States, has provided scientists with clues about pollution in the San Francisco Bay. This indicator species occupies a niche at the top of this ecosystem's food web. An important part of the tern's diet is fish it catches in the San Francisco Bay. By studying the tissues of dead tern chicks, scientists are finding large amounts of chemical contaminants such as mercury and PCBs, or polychlorinated biphenyls. These chemicals can harm developing eggs and can cause problems in the nervous system of adult birds. The high levels of these pollutants found in birds could lead to a decrease in the tern population and disrupt the balance of this aquatic ecosystem.

Apply If the population of an indicator species is increasing, what might you infer about the conditions of the ecosystem?

MAIN IDEA

Biomagnification causes accumulation of toxins in the food chain.

The high death rates in young Forster's terns are due to high levels of toxic compounds found in the parents. How did these chemicals get into the adult birds?

Some pollutants are water-soluble, which means that they dissolve in water and will exit an organism through its wastes. Other pollutants are fat-soluble and stay in the body fat of an organism. Fat-soluble pollutants can also move from one organism to another in a process known as biomagnification. In **biomagnification,** a pollutant moves up the food chain as predators eat prey, accumulating in higher concentrations in the bodies of predators. Scientists measure pollutants in parts per million (ppm). The illustration in **FIGURE 3.2** shows how biomagnification moves small traces of a pollutant to higher concentrations further up the food chain.

FIGURE 3.2 Biomagnification

The movement of fat-soluble pollutants through a food chain results in higher concentrations in the top consumer.

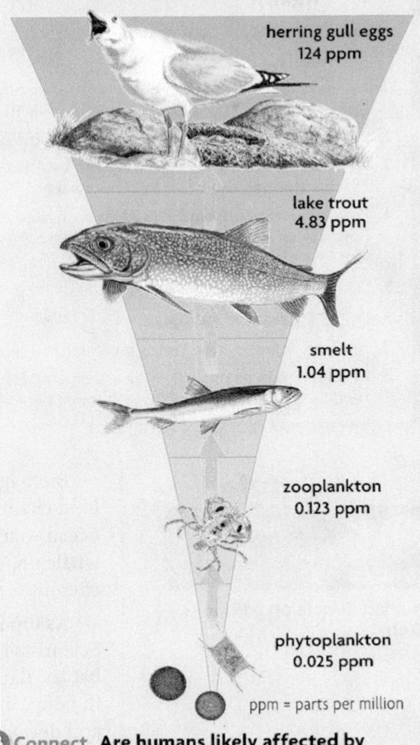

B Connect Are humans likely affected by biomagnification? If so, what foods might be dangerous?

After a pesticide is sprayed onto fields, large amounts of the chemical are washed into ponds and lakes, where phytoplankton pick up the chemical from their environment. The phytoplankton contain very small concentrations of the chemical, but when zooplankton feed on phytoplankton, they are also eating the chemical. Because the zooplankton eat many phytoplankton, higher levels of the chemical build up in the zooplankton. Secondary consumers such as small fish eat zooplankton and collect larger concentrations in their own body fat. Larger fish eat the chemical-laden fish, and the amount of the chemical in their fat builds up as they eat more and more. The increase in contamination is dramatic and causes the tertiary consumer at the top of the food chain, often a large predator such as an eagle or hawk, to receive the most concentrated dose of the pollutant.

CONNECT TO

ENERGY PYRAMID

In the chapter **Principles of Ecology,** you learned how energy is lost as it moves up through trophic levels. In comparison, the process of biomagnification increases toxic material as it moves up the trophic structure.

BELOW LEVEL

Help students make a diagram of the hydrologic cycle. Diagrams should include evaporation, precipitation, runoff, transpiration, and root uptake. Have students note in their diagrams the points in the water cycle where pollution can occur and what kind of pollution is likely. They can also trace this pollution from the water up through a food chain, such as the one shown in **FIGURE 3.2.**

Teacher Toolkit, Section C, Cycle Diagram

Take It Further

In the 1950s, eating fish contaminated with methylmercury resulted in death, illness, or birth defects for thousands of people living around Minamata Bay in Japan. The cause of the contamination was mercury-containing wastes that had been dumped into the bay by a manufacturing company. **Minamata disease** is now the name given to the disorder caused by methylmercury poisoning.

Besides being dumped into waterways, mercury can be discharged into the air by such sources as coal-burning power plants, incinerators, and mining. It eventually contaminates waterways, where it is converted by bacteria into methylmercury, which becomes concentrated in the bodies of fish through biomagnification.

Address Misconceptions

Common Misconception Industry is the biggest water polluter in the United States.

Correcting the Misconception The runoff of silt, pesticides, and fertilizers from agricultural land is the largest single source of water pollution.

Answers

A Apply It is likely that the ecosystem is healthy and resources are abundant.

B Connect Yes, fish that are high in marine food chains could be dangerous.

▼ Teach *continued*

QUICKLAB

Time 20 minutes TEACHER TESTED

Purpose Model the way fat-soluble toxic chemicals are biomagnified up a food chain.

LAB MANAGEMENT

- Fine, dry sand can substitute for salt.
- Dried pinto or kidney beans can substitute for beads.
- Make the holes in the cups large enough for the salt to pass through but small enough to prevent the beads from passing through.

Safety Caution students to handle sharp objects carefully. Remind them to wash their hands before leaving the lab.

Answers

Analyze and Conclude

1. The beads represent fat-soluble water pollutants.
2. Large carnivores end up accumulating the pollutants that are within their prey.

Answers

A Compare Because they occupy a higher trophic level, tertiary consumers accumulate more toxins than primary consumers do.

▼ Assess and Reteach

Assess Use the Section Self-Check or Section Quiz, both available at **HMHScience.com**.

Reteach Make a chain-of-events diagram that traces a pollutant released from the smokestack of an industrial complex to the eggs of a sea bird thousands of miles away.

QUICKLAB MODELING

Modeling Biomagnification

In this lab, you will model biomagnification. Small cups represent smelt, a fish that feeds on zooplankton. Medium-sized cups represent trout, which feed on smelt. The large cup represents an eagle, which feeds on trout.

PROBLEM How are contaminants magnified up the food chain?

PROCEDURE

1. Label the cups as smelt, trout, and eagle according to size. Punch holes in the bottom of each cup with the pencil. Cover the holes with masking tape.
2. Fill each of the cups halfway with salt. Add 4 beads to each small cup.
3. Hold each of the small cups over the beaker and remove the tape. Allow the salt to flow through the holes into the beaker.
4. Pour the remaining contents of two small cups into one medium cup. Pour the contents of the other two small cups into the second medium cup. Repeat step 3 with the medium-sized cups.
5. Pour the remaining contents of both of the medium cups into the large cup.

MATERIALS

- 4 small paper cups
- 2 medium paper cups
- 1 large paper cup
- marker
- sharpened pencil
- 10 cm masking tape
- 400 mL salt
- 16 beads
- 500-mL beaker

ANALYZE AND CONCLUDE

1. **Analyze** What do the beads represent in this model of biomagnification?
2. **Evaluate** Why is the following statement true: "Carnivores at the top of the food chain tend to be most affected by pollutants released into the environment"?

Biomagnification has the most serious effect on species near the top of the food chain. For example, the beluga whale is a top predator that lives in cold ocean waters and feeds on a wide variety of fish species. Studies of a beluga whale population in eastern Canada have shown such extreme levels of toxic chemicals that some whale carcasses have been treated as hazardous waste.

As top level consumers, humans can also be affected by biomagnification. Scientists have recently found small amounts of PCBs in the blood of newborn babies. Exposure to fat-soluble toxins such as PCBs during pregnancy and nursing can be dangerous to the developing fetus, and may also affect growth and development in young children.

A Compare **Why would tertiary consumers have higher concentrations of toxins than primary consumers?**

16.3 Formative Assessment

SELF-CHECK Online HMHScience.com GO ONLINE

REVIEWING MAIN IDEAS

1. What does an **indicator species** tell us about the health of an ecosystem?
2. How do PCBs affect bird populations through **biomagnification**?

CRITICAL THINKING

3. **Compare** How are the concepts of carrying capacity and indicator species related?
4. **Synthesize** Would a buffalo or a mountain lion be more affected by biomagnification? Why?

CONNECT TO ENERGY PYRAMID

5. How does the biomagnification "pyramid" compare with the energy pyramid?

16.3 FORMATIVE ASSESSMENT

1. It reveals what types of pollutants are in the ecosystem. A decrease in an indicator species population is probably the result of high levels of pollutants in the environment.
2. PCBs travel up through the trophic structure of an ecosystem and accumulate in large amounts in the eggs of large birds. PCBs can negatively impact growth and development within the egg, causing genetic mutations, deformities, and death. The population of birds may crash as a result.
3. If the population of an indicator species is far below an ecosystem's carrying capacity for that species, it may indicate the presence of toxins or another pollutant that is causing a decline in the species' population.
4. A mountain lion would be more affected because it is higher on the food chain and would ingest more contaminants from its food supply.
5. They are opposite. Energy decreases as you move up the food chain, but pollutants increase.

Discrete and Continuous Data

Collecting data is a fundamental part of the scientific process. Before you design and carry out an experiment, it is important to understand the two types of quantitative data: discrete and continuous.

Discrete data Data that cannot be broken down into smaller units and have meaning, such as the number of frogs in a pond, are called discrete data. Bar graphs are usually used for discrete data.

Continuous data Data that have fractional values—not whole numbers—are called continuous data. The length and mass of a frog are continuous data. Continuous data are usually shown on a line graph. The values of points that were not actually measured in an experiment can be inferred from the graph.

GRAPH 1. HATCHED TADPOLES (DISCRETE DATA)

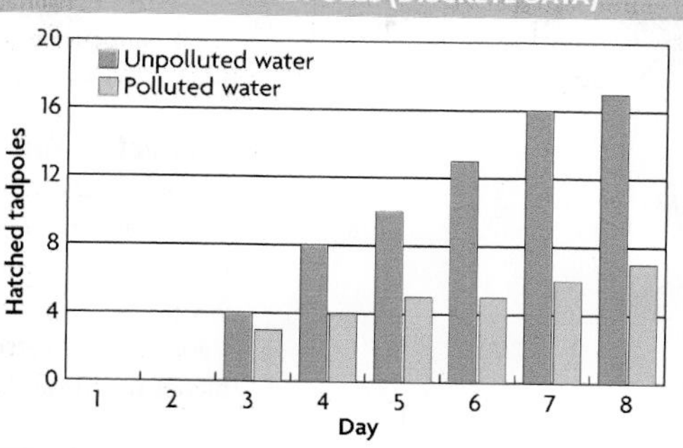

GRAPH 2. AVERAGE TADPOLE LENGTH (CONTINUOUS DATA)

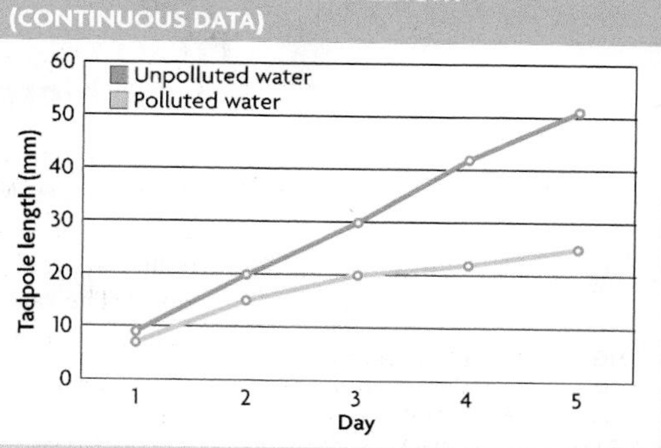

Model

Frogs are commonly used as a biological indicator for water quality. A classroom of students wishes to test how water quality affects growth rates in frogs. Frogs hatch from eggs into tadpoles and then slowly mature into adult frogs.

Students compared hatching rates in frog eggs over an eight-day period. Eggs were raised in one of two water samples, a sample from a known polluted pond, and a sample from an unpolluted pond. These data are discrete because a certain number of eggs hatched. There were no half or quarter tadpoles.

After hatching, students measured tadpole growth in both polluted and unpolluted water over the next five days. These data are continuous because they can be broken down further and data points between measurements can be inferred.

Practice **Identify Discrete and Continuous Data**

For each example, identify whether the data are discrete or continuous.

1. **Apply** A student collects data each spring and summer for five years about populations of endangered frogs in a wetland by counting the number of individual frogs in quadrats.
2. **Classify** The EPA compiles data about the mass of recycled aluminum (millions of tons) for every year since 1990.
3. **Analyze** Since 1860, the National Oceanic and Atmospheric Administration has collected data about the change in Earth's surface temperature and the concentration of carbon dioxide in the atmosphere.

Answers

1. discrete
2. continuous
3. continuous

DATA ANALYSIS

Introduce

There are generally two types of quantitative data—discrete and continuous. The type of data you have will determine the kind of graph you prepare to display your data.

Discuss

Tell students that sometimes it is difficult to determine whether data are discrete or continuous. One way to think about the difference between the two types of data is that discrete data involve counting, and continuous data involve measurement. For example, if you are surveying the number of children each family on a certain street has, you are counting and therefore collecting discrete data. If you are surveying the number of children on a certain street over the course of 30 years, you are collecting continuous data.

Another way to tell discrete data from continuous data is to ask yourself "When I plot the data on a graph, does it make sense to connect the dots on the graph?" **Ask**

- Which type of data should you plot and then connect the dots? continuous data
- What kind of graph will you produce? line graph
- Which type of data should you plot without connecting the dots? discrete data
- What kind of graph will you produce? bar graph

Point out to students that they can also differentiate discrete data from continuous data by asking themselves "Are these data whole numbers (discrete), or are there possible fractional quantities (continuous)?"

Online Student Resources, Data Analysis Practice

SECTION 16.4

B.3.2 Design, evaluate, and refine a model which shows how human activities and natural phenomena can change the flow of matter and energy in an ecosystem and how those changes impact the environment and biodiversity of populations in ecosystems of different scales, as well as, how these human impacts can be reduced.

▼ Plan and Prepare

Activate Prior Knowledge Discuss with students the meaning of biodiversity. **Ask,** How would you describe the species diversity locally? Answers will depend on how urban the area is, the climate, and how observant students are.

▼ Teach

Science Trivia

Many of the most biologically diverse ecosystems, including coral reefs, are found in the tropics. A recent survey of the reefs of the Raja Ampats, a cluster of islands in Indonesia, found

- 450 species of hard coral
- more than 600 mollusk species
- over 1000 species of fish.

One fish expert counted 283 different fish species during a single one-hour dive.

16.4 Threats to Biodiversity

KEY CONCEPT **The impact of a growing human population threatens biodiversity.**

VOCABULARY

habitat fragmentation
introduced species

MAIN IDEAS

- Preserving biodiversity is important to the future of the biosphere.
- Loss of habitat eliminates species.
- Introduced species can disrupt stable relationships in an ecosystem.

Connect to Your World

Imagine yourself taking a walk down your favorite street. But instead of bright colors and interesting sights, you see only one type of everything. There is one type of tree, one type of flower, and one type of car. At school all of your friends look exactly like you, lunch is the same every day, and everyone listens to the same music. We rarely think of the diversity we experience each day. The diversity of Earth makes our planet unique and maintains the stability of ecosystems.

MAIN IDEA

Preserving biodiversity is important to the future of the biosphere.

Ecosystems are constantly changing, and populations are always adjusting to these changes. Many times, human actions alter ecosystems in ways that harm a population and threaten biodiversity. The loss of habitat and the growing pollution problem are affecting animal and plant populations around the world. The value of biodiversity is not just measured in dollars. Biodiversity ensures the future of Earth.

Biodiversity is the diverse world of living things—the wide array and assortment of species that are found in any ecosystem. A decrease in an ecosystem's biodiversity will have a ripple effect through the entire ecosystem, affecting all species. Biodiversity is the foundation of much of our world.

Many medical and technological advancements come from nature. Nearly half of prescribed medicines are derived from plants. On the technological front, scientists in many fields continue to get inspiration from nature. For example, an adhesive from a mussel is being used as the pattern for a new coating for medical implants.

The loss of biodiversity has long-term effects. When a species goes extinct, it is gone forever. In many cases, all that remains of extinct species is a few dead specimens in a museum that can give little information other than where they were discovered. A loss of biodiversity can reduce an ecosystem's stability and make it more difficult for the ecosystem to handle future change.

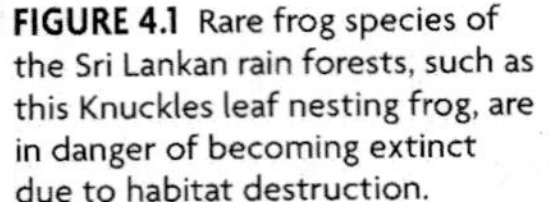

FIGURE 4.1 Rare frog species of the Sri Lankan rain forests, such as this Knuckles leaf nesting frog, are in danger of becoming extinct due to habitat destruction.

Differentiated Instruction

ENGLISH LEARNERS

Have students create a four-column chart to help them learn vocabulary. The columns should include: (1) the word; (2) a personal definition; (3) a definition from a dictionary or the *Multilanguage Glossary;* and (4) a visual interpretation. For example, from this page students might select *mussel, adhesive, array,* and *biodiversity.* Students' word lists should be of their own choosing, based on their own level of familiarity with the terms.

Teacher Toolkit, Section D, Student Vocabulary

PRE-AP

Obtain a list of the endangered species per state from Internet Department of Natural Resource sites. Have students look for correlations between each state's human population density, total area, climate type, and diversity of habitats, and its number of endangered species. Have students infer why a small, remote state, such as Hawaii, has more than 300 endangered species, while larger states, such as Montana, have barely more than a dozen. Tell students to note how many species listed are aquatic or marine, and what might be threatening these species.

For example, as the nation of Sri Lanka has modernized, the natural resources of the island have become increasingly depleted. Ninety-five percent of the island's rain forests have been lost, and with them more than 19 different frog species have gone extinct. In addition, numerous other species, such as the rare frog species shown in **FIGURE 4.1**, are endangered. The loss of even a single species can harm the overall stability of an ecosystem.

Biodiversity is highest in the rain forest biomes of the world, and these are the areas that are most threatened. Currently, about 1 percent of this biome is lost each year to logging or to clearing for agricultural use. Preserving the rain forests of the world will do a great deal to protect and preserve the biodiversity of our planet.

CONNECT TO

CARBON CYCLE

Rain forests around the world play an integral role in Earth's carbon cycle, storing large amounts of carbon in their structures.

A Connect **Why is biodiversity highest in tropical rain forests?**

MAIN IDEA

Loss of habitat eliminates species.

One way to protect species is to monitor and manage their numbers, and to ensure they have adequate habitat for survival. Governments and organizations around the world are developing programs to protect species that are threatened by overhunting, overcollecting, and habitat loss.

As the human population moves into what was formerly wilderness, people are moving into the territory of many species of wildlife. In many parts of the world, the loss of habitat can put species in danger of becoming extinct. Historically, for example, wetland habitats were viewed as breeding grounds for disease and as "wasted land." Between the 1780s and the 1980s, more than 53 percent of wetland habitat in the United States was eliminated. This destruction displaced large numbers of wildlife and disrupted migration patterns for many species of water birds.

Efforts to ensure adequate habitat must take into account the life history of the organism, including mating habits and migration patterns. Ecologists have become particularly worried about habitat fragmentation. **Habitat fragmentation** occurs when a barrier forms that prevents an organism from accessing its entire home range. Often, habitat fragmentation is caused by the building of roadways or the harvesting of forests. Bears, deer, raccoons, and opossums are just a few of the animals that find their home ranges fragmented as urban sprawl increases. To try to fix this growing problem, some states are building underpasses and overpasses so that wildlife can avoid busy roadways. Corridors such as the one shown in **FIGURE 4.2** help to maintain continuous tracts of habitat for those species that move between different areas.

B Connect **Why is wetland habitat important for migrating birds?**

FIGURE 4.2 By providing a safe way to cross barriers such as roads and highways, land bridges such as this one in Canada allow animals to move safely from one part of their habitat to the next.

BELOW LEVEL

Tell students that salmon are anadromous. They are born upriver in fresh water, live most of their lives in the oceans, and then return to their birthplace to reproduce. Have students write about how the construction of a dam on a large river could result in the habitat fragmentation of salmon species' home ranges. Have them also write a proposal for how the dam could be constructed or modified to eliminate or lessen this problem.

Teacher Toolkit, Section C, Quick-Write

TEACH FROM VISUALS

FIGURE 4.2 Tell students that animals often use "islands" of habitat—one for watering, one for hunting, one for nesting, and so on. When obstructions, such as the highway in the photo, get between these areas, the animal's habitat is fragmented. **Ask**

- How is the problem of habitat fragmentation dealt with in this photo? The bridge allows animals to cross the highway safely.
- In order to ensure that animals cross the highway only at these bridges, what must be constructed on either side? fences running the entire length of the roadway, with openings only at the corridors

Take It Further

In 1968, a massive oil field was discovered on the north coast of Alaska near **Prudhoe Bay,** but the ice-packed waters were inaccessible to oil tankers. Plans were made to begin construction of a pipeline more than 1200 kilometers (800 mi) long that would carry oil to the ice-free port at Valdez, Alaska. Conservation groups argued that the pipeline would fragment the caribou habitats of the Arctic, so 50 percent of the pipeline was built high enough above the ground to permit passage of caribou herds underneath. As of 2006, more than 550,000 gallons of crude oil have been spilled from the pipeline onto the land.

Answers

A Connect Tropical rain forests are found in areas where both temperature and precipitation are high, which are key to the survival of many species.

B Connect Wetlands provide all the essentials that birds need for a long journey: a variety of fish and plants for food, and abundant water to drink.

Chapter 16: Human Impact on Ecosystems **487**

▼ Teach *continued*

ONLINE Biology HMHScience.com

Students can learn about an invasive species in their local area and find out what can be done to control its damage. Go to the WebQuest for this chapter at **HMHScience.com**.

Vocabulary

Academic Vocabulary Any species that is brought by humans into a new ecosystem is **introduced,** but only those that prove highly successful in their new homes are referred to as **invasive.** If someone releases a carp from Asia into a pond ecosystem in Wisconsin, the carp is an introduced species. But if the carp dies or does not reproduce, it will not be considered invasive.

Take It Further

Tiny Macquarie Island lies about 1500 kilometers (932 mi) southeast of Tasmania in the Southern Ocean about halfway between Australia and Antarctica. Millions of sea birds go there to breed each year. The island was also home to **feral cats,** the wild descendants of cats brought there as pets by seal-hunters in 1820. Feral cat numbers reached about 500 at one time, and they were killing up to 60,000 sea birds a year. The Tasmanian government began a trapping program to eradicate cats from the island. Between 1974 and 2000, a total of 2450 cats were caught on the island. No feral cats have been seen since 2000. Today, mice and rats are being targeted through baiting programs to prevent population explosions of these animals.

FIGURE 4.3 Rodent plagues in India, Australia, and China can cost farmers millions of dollars in lost crops.

MAIN IDEA

Introduced species can disrupt stable relationships in an ecosystem.

Introduced species have a direct impact on the biodiversity and natural flow of energy in an ecosystem. An **introduced species** is any organism that was brought to an ecosystem as the result of human actions. Introduced species can pose a great threat to the stability of an ecosystem if they prey on or crowd out native species. In some instances, introduced species can cause economic damage. Just as native species interact with one another and their habitat, nonnative or introduced species are active and sometimes disruptive in their new ecosystems. Invasive species are successful in environments under many circumstances. If an environment has a niche that the invasive species can exploit, or if the invasive species is a better competitor in a particular niche, native species may be pushed out. Invasive species are also successful if there is a lack of predators to keep the population stable.

Invasive Species

Effect on Native Species

The Florida Everglades is a dynamic ecosystem where unique plants and animals have evolved for tens of thousands of years. The climate is similar to that of a tropical jungle, and the Everglades can support a great diversity of organisms. One species that has been introduced to this region originally came from the tropical jungles of Southeastern Asia. The Burmese python, shown in **FIGURE 4.4,** came to the United States as a pet species. Growing more than 6 meters (20 ft) in length, this massive snake can be difficult to care for. Irresponsible owners have released many of the snakes back into the wild. A large number of Burmese pythons have been captured and removed from Everglades National Park, and officials say that there is a good chance that a breeding population is present. As a constrictor species, the Burmese python feeds on small animals such as rats, birds, raccoons, and even dogs. Threats to endangered bird species in the park worry officials. As the python population begins to grow, endangered species protected in the Everglades could be affected.

FIGURE 4.4 Introduced species such as the Burmese python are growing in numbers in places like the Florida Everglades.

Differentiated Instruction

TEACH WITH TECHNOLOGY

The National Park Service has a list of alien plant species that are invading natural areas of the United States. Visit their Weeds Gone Wild website to look at different species on the list, where they can be found, and what they look like. Check for invasive plant species in your area.

Introduced animals are not the only problem. Plant species such as kudzu, another native of southeastern Asia, are invasive in the United States and are choking out native species of plants across the southeastern United States. The kudzu plant, shown in **FIGURE 4.5,** was introduced in 1876 as an ornamental tropical houseplant enjoyed for its fragrant flowers and large leaves. It was planted as field cover to prevent soil loss from erosion, but it rapidly began to spread out of the fields. Currently, kudzu is a classified as a problematic weed species in much of the eastern United States. Kudzu is a hardy plant, at home in virtually any soil, and it can grow up to 18 meters (60 ft) in a single growing season. This growth rate makes it difficult to control. Very few plant species can survive in an environment once kudzu is introduced. By blanketing trees and shrubs with its large leaves, kudzu deprives other plants of the sunlight they need to survive. The plant is resistant to most types of herbicides and can live for many years.

FIGURE 4.5 After a few months of being left in a single place, these cars have become covered with kudzu. Fast-growing kudzu can destroy natural habitats in just a few years.

Economic Damage

Invasive species can have a major impact on humans as well as ecosystems. The common house mouse is an introduced species to the Australian continent. During the late 1700s, mice came from Europe as stowaways on British cargo ships. Today, mice are considered a major pest species in Australia and have caused widespread economic damage. Every four or five years, mice populations increase exponentially. Seasons of heavy rainfall lead to bumper crops of corn and grain, causing a dramatic rise in mouse populations and leading to huge numbers of mice moving from one food source to another. It was estimated that during the 1993–1994 season, the mouse population in Australia cost farmers about $65 million in lost revenue. Mice continue to be a problem throughout the region.

Killer Kitties

A Predict **How might a species of carnivorous fish introduced into a lake have a negative impact on the lake ecosystem?**

16.4 Formative Assessment

REVIEWING MAIN IDEAS

1. Give two reasons why biodiversity is important to humans.
2. How does **habitat fragmentation** affect migrating bird populations?
3. What types of damage can **introduced species** cause?

CRITICAL THINKING

4. **Analyze** How could continued habitat fragmentation reduce biodiversity?
5. **Connect** How might the introduction of a mouse predator help with the mouse problem in Australia? What problems might it cause?

CONNECT TO

POPULATION GROWTH

6. Using your knowledge of populations, describe what will eventually happen to mouse populations in Australia as they run out of food.

16.4 FORMATIVE ASSESSMENT

1. Numerous medicines and technological advances have come from wild plant and animal species. We depend on ecosystems for food. A loss of diversity could mean a loss of food, medicine, and economic activity.
2. Birds need large areas of land or water on which to rest and feed during long migrations. If these habitats are not available, the birds may not be able to complete a migration.
3. Introduced species can disrupt ecosystems, threaten human health, and physically dominate or overtake waterways and humanmade structures.
4. If species are cut off from habitats they need for survival or reproduction, they could become extinct, thereby reducing biodiversity.
5. The mouse predator might keep the mouse populations in check, but it could also prey on other species and affect their populations.
6. It is likely that the mouse populations will eventually experience a population crash when they exceed their ecosystem's carrying capacity.

ONLINE Biology
HMHScience.com

Have students determine how the introduction of trout to lakes affects the lakes' frog population. Go to Data Analysis Smart Grapher for this chapter at **HMHScience.com**.

Take It Further

One of the more disastrous introductions of a non-native species to a new habitat occurred around 1950 in Guam, a Micronesian island in the western Pacific Ocean. The **brown tree snake,** *Boiga irregularis,* a venomous species native to Australia, Papua New Guinea, and other islands of Melanesia, established a population on Guam after individuals had stowed away on cargo ships and airplanes. Because Guam's forests offered plenty of prey species and no natural predators, the brown tree snake population exploded to a density of 13,000 per square mile.

Over the course of 50 years, this species has killed off much of Guam's native forest vertebrate species, caused thousands of power outages by biting electric cables, killed domestic pets, and delivered venomous bites to humans. Despite various controls aimed at ridding Guam of this species and preventing it from making its way to other Pacific islands, the brown tree snake has been found in Hawaii and Saipan.

Answers

A **Predict** The fish might increase pressure on prey species beyond what their populations can withstand. The introduced fish could also compete with other predators and drive them out of the lake ecosystem.

Assess and Reteach

Assess Use the Section Self-Check or Section Quiz, both available at **HMHScience.com**.

Reteach On the board, create a concept map. Begin with the word *Biodiversity,* and then form two branches with the connecting phrases *is important because* and *is threatened by.* Encourage students to include as many examples as they can.

SECTION 16.5

▼ Plan and Prepare

Activate Prior Knowledge Discuss with students the conservation practices or movements with which they are familiar. **Ask,** What are some species you know of that are endangered? *Sample answer:* giant pandas, whales, rhinos, elephants, gorillas **Ask,** What might be an added benefit of passing a law that protects a single species that lives in a specific forest ecosystem? The whole forest, including other species that live in it, could also be protected.

▼ Teach

Take It Further

DDT, which **Rachel Carson** wrote about in *Silent Spring,* is another chemical that accumulates up food chains through biomagnification. It has been banned in many countries, but it is still used to kill mosquitoes in countries where malaria is a severe public health problem. DDT's potential for eradicating malaria was so celebrated that in 1948, the Swiss chemist **Paul Müller,** who had discovered DDT's insecticidal properties, was awarded a Nobel Prize for his work.

16.5 Conservation

KEY CONCEPT **Conservation methods can help protect and restore ecosystems.**

VOCABULARY

sustainable development
umbrella species

MAIN IDEAS

- Sustainable development manages resources for present and future generations.
- Conservation practices focus on a few species but benefit entire ecosystems.
- Protecting Earth's resources helps protect our future.

Connect to Your World

When Rachel Carson's book *Silent Spring* was published in 1962, the wheels were set in motion for the creation of the modern environmental movement. The book, which described how the pesticide DDT was affecting wildlife, brought about a public uproar and helped lead to a ban on the use of DDT in the United States. Since then, a variety of measures have been put into place, both to restore Earth's biosphere and to protect it from further degradation.

MAIN IDEA

Sustainable development manages resources for present and future generations.

To ensure that Earth can continue to support, or sustain, a growing human population, it is important to secure the future of the Earth's ecosystems. This way of thinking is known as sustainable development. **Sustainable development** is a practice in which natural resources are used and managed in a way that meets current needs without hurting future generations.

Sustainable development covers a wide range of resource management methods. Concerns about the condition of the environment have led to changes in methods of harvesting natural resources. In the timber industry, for example, old growth forests are being lost at a fast rate due to a method called clear cutting. By cutting down large sections of wooded areas and removing entire forest ecosystems, lumber companies serve a growing need for building supplies. Today, with the raised awareness of forest ecosystem

FIGURE 5.1 Forests of bamboo in China grow quickly and can provide an abundant supply of wood to support the growing demand for building materials.

Differentiated Instruction

PRE-AP

Write the following quotation on the board:

> *The raging monster upon the land is population growth. In its presence, sustainability is but a fragile theoretical construct.*
>
> —E. O. Wilson (1992)

Have students write a five-minute essay about what they think the quotation means. When they are finished, they can form small groups for discussion. (Wilson means that talk of conservation and sustainability for the future has limited value unless we control population growth first.)

Teacher Toolkit, Section C, Quick-Write

safety, several companies are choosing to cut selected trees rather than clear-cutting forests. This practice encourages rapid regrowth of trees, and makes sure there is only minimal impact to the forest ecosystem. When choosing where and when to harvest trees, foresters must consider how the soil, water, and wildlife of the area will be affected and change their harvest strategy accordingly to protect them.

Global fisheries are also in need of sustainable development practices. Overfishing has depleted fish populations worldwide. Fish stocks are not as hardy as they once were. One reason for this is that the fish that are caught represent the healthy, reproducing age groups of the fish population. By removing the reproducing individuals from the population, the fishing industry is actually hurting itself. Without fish to reproduce now, there will be no fish for the future. In addition, unsustainable fishing techniques damage marine and coastal environments. A number of techniques can be adopted by fisheries to make the industry sustainable:

- **Rotation** Rotating catches between different species gives the "off" species time to recover their numbers following a harvest.
- **Fishing gear review** The gear used to catch fish can damage the sea floor and often unintentionally catches other species. Reviewing and possibly banning certain fishing gear could help avoid damaging the sea floor and prevent ecologically important organisms from being killed.
- **Harvest reduction** Slowing the harvests of deep-water species that grow very slowly allows them more time to recover their populations.
- **Fishing bans** Creating and enforcing fishing bans in certain areas helps to replenish populations within that area, which may lead to greater fish numbers in nearby locations.

CONNECT TO

NATURAL SELECTION

Recall from the chapter **The Evolution of Populations** that in natural selection the environment favors certain traits over others. In a fish's environment, nets used by humans catch fish that are large and slow. Fish that may be smaller and faster have a distinct advantage, thus leading to a genetic shift in the population.

A Connect **What important services do forests provide? How might their destruction have an effect on humans?**

MAIN IDEA

Conservation practices focus on a few species but benefit entire ecosystems.

Laws written to protect individual species also help to protect their habitats. The Endangered Species Act in the United States, for example, is designed to protect individual species that are near extinction by establishing protection for the organism and its environment. When a single species within an ecosystem is placed on a list of endangered species, many other species within the ecosystem also benefit. The listed species is often called an **umbrella species** because its protection means a wide range of other species will also be protected. Such is the case with the West Indian manatee. These aquatic mammals, shown in **FIGURE 5.2**, live in the waters of the Gulf of Mexico and Atlantic Ocean along the coast of the southeastern United States. Their range extends as far west as Texas and as far north as Virginia.

FIGURE 5.2 The West Indian manatee is an umbrella species whose protection helps to re-establish marine habitats.

Address Misconceptions

Common Misconception Planting trees after clear-cutting a forest restores the ecosystem.

Correcting the Misconception When a forest or part of one is clear-cut, every tree is removed. All the living things that depend on those trees die out or are pushed into new territory for which they may not be adapted. Simply replanting trees does not re-create a fully interacting ecosystem that took decades, hundreds of years, or thousands of years to develop. Replanting trees is only the first step in a process that nature must complete.

Take It Further

The growing human population, coupled with highly effective fishing techniques and technologies, has meant that numerous fish populations are being harvested beyond what is known as their **maximum sustainable yield,** the maximum amount of fish that can be caught without destroying the population's ability to replenish itself. Whether or not populations are overfished is due in part to the demand for them in world markets, but it is also a matter of the species' reproductive biology. Some fish species take years to reach maturity, and produce a relatively small number of offspring after a long pregnancy. These species are especially vulnerable to overfishing because the few individuals who avoid being caught will only produce a few young at a time. Species that reproduce at an early age and yield large numbers of offspring can recover much more quickly from overfishing.

Answers

A **Connect** Forests help to convert CO_2 to oxygen, purify water, and prevent the erosion of soil. Their destruction could lead to degradation and erosion of land, the increased pollution of water, and an increase in atmospheric CO_2.

BELOW LEVEL

To illustrate the concept of an umbrella species, provide students with the following scenario: Commercial longline fishing for swordfish sometimes results in the death or injury of endangered sea turtles. Other species caught by the longline fleets include yellowfin, bigeye, albacore, and skipjack tunas, blue and mako sharks, pelagic stingrays, and mahi mahi. Because the turtles are endangered, these fisheries have been shut down several times. Have students draw umbrella figures that illustrate how the protection of the sea turtles ends up protecting populations of other species as well. Point out that if regulations were aimed at protecting the swordfish instead of the turtles, it is likely that the same species would still be protected.

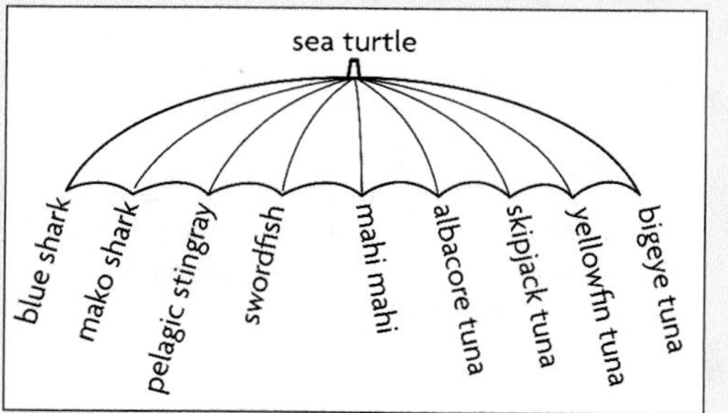

▼ Teach *continued*

Science Trivia

The bald eagle, *Haliaeetus leucocephalus*, has been the emblem of the United States since 1782.

- Their wingspans can reach up to 2.5 m (8 ft), and they can live for at least 28 years in the wild.
- The pesticide DDT was largely responsible for the bald eagle population crash that only recently has abated. DDT weakened the shells of bald eagle eggs to the point where they would collapse under the weight of the mother eagle.
- Bald eagles mate for life and will reuse nests over and over again, adding new building materials, such as mosses, twigs, and branches, each year. Nests can eventually weigh as much as 2 tons and be 2 m wide.

Take It Further

In June 1969, the Cuyahoga River in Cleveland, Ohio, caught fire. Debris and pollutants in the river were ignited by a worker's blowtorch. Though the actual blaze was relatively short-lived, the fire gained the attention of the nation, creating a national concern for our waterways, which eventually led to both the **Great Lakes Water Quality Act** and the **Clean Water Act** in the 1970s.

Answers

A Apply They might consider what other species and habitats might be affected by the recovery plan, and how the plan could affect economies and cultures.

The manatee was placed on the endangered species list in 1967. Its listing resulted from a variety of factors including loss of habitat, overhunting, and deaths due to collisions with powerboats. Today, the situation for manatees is difficult, and fewer than 3000 manatees remain in the United States. To promote their survival, local, state, and federal agencies are working to develop policies to protect their habitat. When developing recovery plans for an endangered species, scientists must consider many factors. For example, because manatees rely on seagrass as their main food source, areas rich in this resource must also be protected. By protecting waterways from pollution, restoring damaged areas, and limiting boating, the marine ecosystem that is the natural habitat for manatees is also protected. As a result, entire ecosystems can benefit from efforts to save a single species from extinction.

A Apply **What factors might scientists consider when developing a recovery plan for the endangered grizzly bear of western North America?**

MAIN IDEA

Protecting Earth's resources helps protect our future.

All living things, including humans, share Earth and its resources, and the value of the services our planet provides is priceless. The cycling of nutrients and the regulation of water provide essential resources that are almost impossible for humans to manufacture. If we were to put a human economic value on it, the total value of the services Earth's natural ecosystems provide has been estimated to be over $30 trillion a year.

Climate change, pollution, and the loss of biodiversity are only a few of the direct threats our planet is facing. To prevent further loss of the valuable resources of Earth, public actions are helping to preserve and protect the future of our planet.

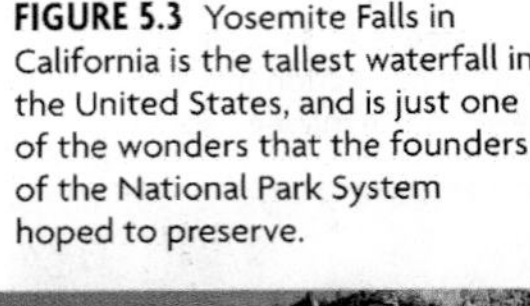

FIGURE 5.3 Yosemite Falls in California is the tallest waterfall in the United States, and is just one of the wonders that the founders of the National Park System hoped to preserve.

Protecting Natural Resources

The Environmental Protection Agency was created as part of the National Environmental Policy Act in 1970. Its creation paved the way for the development of policies and regulations to protect the environment across the United States. Laws such as the Clean Air Act, Clean Water Act, and Endangered Species Act have had a major impact on the environment. The Clean Air Act, signed into law in 1970, has helped to increase air quality across the nation. It regulates emissions from industrial factories and automobiles. In 1970, only 36 percent of the lakes and waterways in the United States were considered safe for swimming. Since the Clean Water Act was signed in 1972, regulations against pollution and an increased public awareness have helped to double the number of waterways that are safe today. Since 1973, when the Endangered Species Act was signed, breeding pairs of the bald eagle, once in danger of extinction, grew from 791 pairs to almost 6500 pairs in 2000.

Differentiated Instruction

HANDS-ON ACTIVITY

Ask students to make a list of all the energy-using devices they have in their homes. Remind them that any device that needs any kind of fuel, such as electricity from a wall outlet, batteries, or gasoline, should be listed. Have students highlight the items that are essential, to distinguish them from luxury items. Finally, have them organize a complete list on the board and then consider how location and climate might affect how an item is categorized.

PRE-AP

Have students bring in articles on conservation and other ecological issues from newspapers, magazines, and online sources. Set aside class time to discuss articles and students' views.

Setting aside areas as public land is another way that governments can protect ecosystems. The Yosemite Grant of 1864 was the United States' first step to protect nature from development. This grant established what would eventually become Yosemite National Park, part of which is shown in **FIGURE 5.3.** The success of this grant eventually led to the formation of the National Park Service. The management of multiple-use areas and wilderness areas balances recreation for visitors with protection of the natural ecosystem. Today, grassroots environmental organizations are working with local governments and private citizens to purchase and restore areas of land across the country to increase the amount of suitable habitat for wildlife.

A Sustainable Earth

Humans represent an integral part of Earth's ecosystems and are subject to the same limitations as other species living on the planet. However, unlike other organisms, we have a much larger impact on our environment because of our population size and the fact that we are found over the entire globe. At the same time, we have the ability and technology to change the extent of our impact on Earth's biosphere and ultimately control our destiny.

- We have the ability to control how fast our population grows by controlling birth rates.
- We can develop technology to produce more food and produce less waste.
- We have the ability to change our practices and take action to protect and maintain ecosystems. In some cases, we can reduce or even eliminate the pressures we place on the planet's biogeochemical processes.

FIGURE 5.4 Each year on Arbor Day, people around the world plant trees and play an important role in rebuilding ecosystems for future generations.

No places on Earth are untouched by humans. While we may not have directly visited each square inch of the planet, human-caused pollutants, invasive species, or ecosystem alterations have reached the world over. Yet our economies, and our very lives, depend on a healthy, thriving, sustainable Earth.

Connect **How could you reduce the amount of waste produced by your school?**

16.5 Formative Assessment

REVIEWING MAIN IDEAS

1. Give two examples of **sustainable development**.
2. Describe how the protection of an **umbrella species** can be beneficial to an ecosystem.
3. How do governmental actions help to preserve natural habitats and protect resources?

CRITICAL THINKING

4. **Connect** What can humans do to minimize the impact of urban sprawl on wildlife?
5. **Evaluate** Could the West Indian manatee be considered a keystone species? Justify your answer.

CONNECT TO

NUTRIENT CYCLING

6. Natural ecosystems provide important cleansing and recycling functions to humans. What specific products do Earth's natural cycles provide for humans?

16.5 FORMATIVE ASSESSMENT

1. *Sample answer:* selective cutting of trees from a forest, fishing-gear modification to target certain species and exclude others
2. Actions taken to protect a certain species may result in protection for other species, or even whole habitats or ecosystems.
3. The development of legislation can create consequences for harming the environment. The establishment of parks sets aside wilderness so that it will not be used by industry.
4. reduce or eliminate pollution in urban areas, construct corridors so animals can migrate through urban areas, limit the growth or sprawl of the urban area
5. *Sample answer:* yes, if it plays an integral role in maintaining the marine ecosystem it lives in, such as controlling the growth of eelgrass
6. oxygen, carbon, nitrogen, water, all of which are needed by us for respiration or for the production of foods

Take It Further

Since the 1960s, many companies that once packaged their products in paper, which is biodegradable, have switched to **plastic packaging.** Plastic does not leak like paper does and is lightweight and economical to ship. Most plastics are not biodegradable and therefore their disposal contributes to the solid waste problem. However, plastics are recyclable. Plastic packaging, such as plastic milk jugs and polystyrene food containers, is marked with a number that indicates the type of plastic, allowing for easy sorting of recyclables.

Some plastics are biodegradable. For example, polylactide (PLA) is a biodegradable plastic made from starch fermented by microorganisms.

Answers

A Connect *Sample answer:* Use less packaging material, participate in or start a recycling program, campaign for more natural foods in the lunchroom, and urge students and teachers to limit paper use.

Assess and Reteach

Assess Use the Section Self-Check or Section Quiz, both available at **HMHScience.com**.

Reteach Have students list five ways in which they can personally become involved in conservation and then write these suggestions on the board. For each idea, ask students to discuss how sustainable development and umbrella species could be targeted in order to ensure and maximize conservation.

CHAPTER REVIEW

GO ONLINE

Encourage students to go to **HMHScience.com** for a detailed review of each section, including visuals and vocabulary practice.

Online Student Resources, Vocabulary Practice Worksheet

CHAPTER **16** Summary

BIG IDEA Human population growth threatens environmental quality and biodiversity, so conservation methods are necessary to preserve Earth's natural resources.

KEY CONCEPTS

16.1 Human Population Growth and Natural Resources

As the human population grows, the demand for Earth's resources increases. The human population has grown tremendously due to advancements in technology. But a large population puts pressure on nonrenewable resources such as fossil fuels as well as on renewable resources such as water. Balancing the needs of our population with the resources of our environments will help to reduce our ecological footprint to sustainable levels.

16.2 Air Quality

Fossil fuel emissions affect the biosphere. Pollution is the addition of undesirable factors to the air, water, and soil. Fossil fuel emissions from industrial processes are causing an increase in smog and acid rain, which both threaten Earth's ecosystems. Carbon dioxide, methane, and other greenhouse gases slow the release of energy from Earth's atmosphere. But increased fossil fuel emissions appear to be contributing to rapid climate change, increasing global warming.

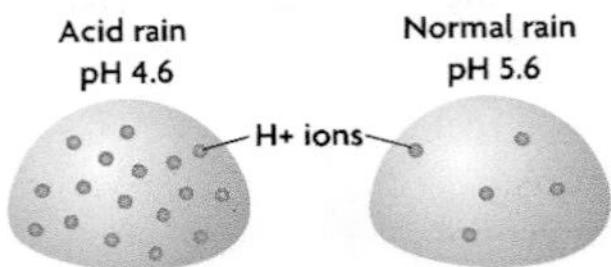

16.3 Water Quality

Pollution of Earth's freshwater supply threatens habitat and health. Indicator species help us understand the effects of pollution on an ecosystem. The process of biomagnification is a threat to both humans and ecosystems, as toxins accumulate at the top of food chains.

16.4 Threats to Biodiversity

The impact of a growing human population threatens biodiversity. The biodiversity of a region helps keep ecosystems stable. Habitat fragmentation and destruction are threatening biodiversity. Nonnative species can have a negative effect on ecosystems by pushing out native species and using up resources.

16.5 Conservation

Conservation methods can help protect and restore ecosystems. To protect Earth's natural resources for future generations, we need to plan for sustainable development. In addition, the protection of umbrella species and the positive support of government and industry can help to ensure Earth is protected for future generations.

READING TOOLBOX SYNTHESIZE YOUR NOTES

Concept Map Use a concept map like the one below to display the effects of pollution.

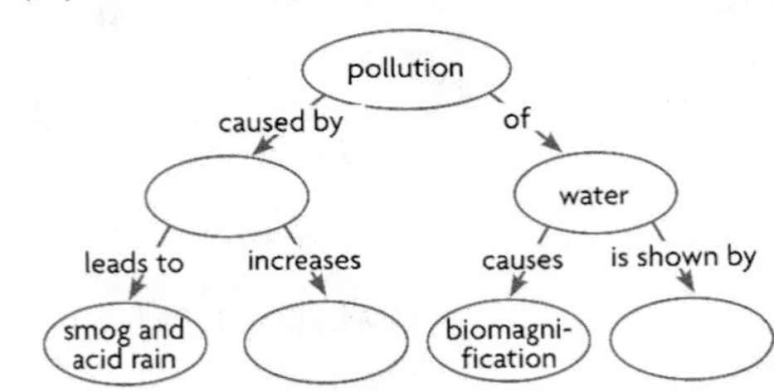

Process Diagram Use a process diagram like the one below to explain the greenhouse effect.

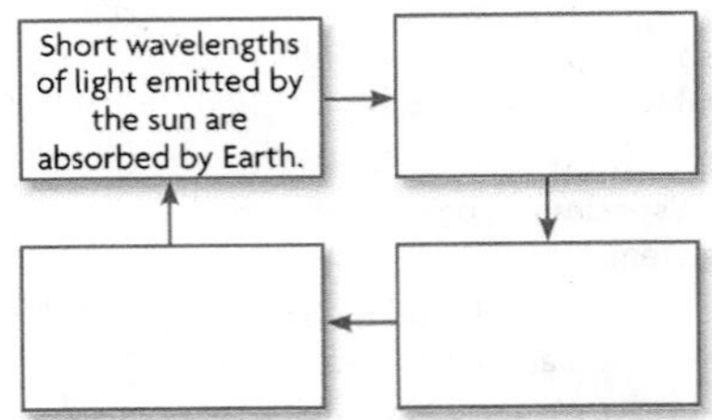

Reviewing Vocabulary

1. Both are things that humans use for energy and materials. Nonrenewable resources are used faster than they can be replenished, whereas renewable resources cannot be used up or are replenished as they are used.
2. Both are products of air pollution that comes from the combustion of fossil fuels. Smog involves particulates and ground-level ozone; acid rain involves sulfuric and nitric acids that cause the pH of rain to become more acidic.
3. The greenhouse effect is a natural phenomenon, whereas global warming is the consequence of human activities enhancing the greenhouse effect. Both terms describe processes that relate to heat in the atmosphere.
4. Both are used in conservation science. An indicator species is one that provides information about the health of an ecosystem, whereas an umbrella species is one whose conservation benefits other species or the ecosystem it lives in.
5. Sustainable development is development that holds or maintains the use of resources at or below the level that allows them to replenish or survive.
6. Biomagnification occurs when the concentration of a toxin in animals becomes greater, or is magnified, up through a food chain.
7. Anything within the shadow of an umbrella is protected from rain. An umbrella species is one whose protection affords protection to other organisms of its habitat or ecosystem.
8. Drawings will vary, but may compare the amount of resources required to support the life and lifestyle of humans from different countries.
9. Drawings will vary, but should relate fossil fuel emissions with increasing atmospheric temperatures.
10. Drawings will vary, but should show a species in an ecosystem or a habitat in which it has not lived before, and should show the effects of its introduction.

INTERACTIVE Review
HMHScience.com
GO ONLINE
Review Games • Concept Map • Section Self-Checks

16 Review

CHAPTER VOCABULARY

16.1	nonrenewable resource renewable resource ecological footprint	16.2	pollution smog particulate acid rain greenhouse effect global warming	16.3	indicator species biomagnification
				16.4	habitat fragmentation introduced species
				16.5	sustainable development umbrella species

Reviewing Vocabulary

Compare and Contrast

Describe one similarity and one difference between the two terms in each of the following pairs.

1. renewable resource, nonrenewable resource
2. smog, acid rain
3. greenhouse effect, global warming
4. indicator species, umbrella species

READING TOOLBOX WORD ORIGINS

5. The word *sustain* comes from the Latin words *sub-*, which means "below," and *tenere*, which means "to hold." Explain how these meanings relate to the term *sustainable development*.
6. The term *biomagnification* is comprised of the prefix *bio-*, which means "life," and the word *magnify*, which comes from a Latin word meaning "great" or "large." Explain how the meanings of the word parts make up the meaning of the term.
7. The word *umbrella* comes from the Latin word *umbra*, which means "shadow." How does the everyday meaning of the word *umbrella* relate to the ecological meaning of the term *umbrella species*?

Draw Cartoons

For each vocabulary term below, draw a cartoon that will best summarize the definition.

8. ecological footprint
9. global warming
10. introduced species

Reviewing MAIN IDEAS

11. Earth's human carrying capacity has exceeded many earlier predictions. How has technology affected human population growth?
12. The United States uses more resources and produces more waste than any other country. How is this resource use reflected in the ecological footprint of the United States?
13. What are the major causes of smog and acid rain? What are the effects of each type of pollution?
14. Since the 1970s, human activity has released approximately 150 billion tons of carbon dioxide into the atmosphere. How could the increase in atmospheric carbon dioxide impact the greenhouse effect?
15. Which organism is most likely to have accumulated toxins through biomagnification: plankton, a small plankton-eating fish, or a large fish that eats smaller fish? Explain.
16. How could the extinction of a single species, such as a predatory bird, affect an entire ecosystem?
17. In what ways can an introduced species impact an ecosystem it has colonized?
18. The North American grizzly bear is considered an umbrella species. Explain how the protection of the grizzly bear may affect the larger ecosystem to which the bear belongs.

CHAPTER REVIEW

Reviewing Main Ideas

11. Technology has improved human health and survival; made agriculture more intensive and productive; increased the speed of construction of living spaces, production of tools, equipment, and clothing; and has provided heating, air conditioning, plumbing, sanitation, water purification, transportation, and many other things that have allowed the human population to grow at an exponential rate.
12. The United States' ecological footprint is the largest in the world.
13. Smog forms from particulates and ozone produced by fossil fuel emissions. Acid rain forms from nitrogen oxides and sulfuric oxides in fossil fuel emissions. Smog is a hazy air pollution that can cause human health problems. Acid rain increases the acidity of water systems and can damage plants, soil, and other things.
14. The high carbon dioxide emissions could enhance the greenhouse effect, because each carbon dioxide molecule can absorb infrared radiation.
15. The large fish, because the toxins accumulate as they are passed up through the food chain. The plankton may have a small amount of the toxin in its system, and then the plankton-eating fish eats a lot of plankton, so the toxins in the plankton accumulate in the small fish. Then the larger fish eats a lot of the smaller fish, and the toxins from all of the smaller fish accumulate in the larger fish.
16. Each organism is part of a complex web of life, and the extinction of any part or strand of that web will affect the others. If a predatory bird, for example, becomes extinct, the population of its prey species, such as mice and other rodents, could increase greatly. These larger populations would, in turn, reduce the populations of the organisms they feed on. Also, the populations of species that competed with the extinct bird could now increase due to reduced competition for resources.
17. Introduced species can disrupt a stable ecosystem, for example, by preying on, crowding out, or competing with native species.
18. Protection of the grizzly bear would involve protecting the grizzly bear's habitat. Therefore, all the other organisms that lived in that habitat would be protected. If populations of grizzly bears rebound, populations of their prey could be reduced.

Critical Thinking

19. Cattle, chicken, and other meat sources are higher up on the food chain than vegetables (which are autotrophs), so the land required to raise these animals includes the land required to raise all of the things that go into their feed as well as the land required to dispose of their waste.
20. *Sample answer:* ride the bus, walk, ride a bike, carpool
21. Everything that is used to produce the carton of milk contributes to a person's ecological footprint. Land was used to produce the tree that yielded pulp to be made into the carton and also to feed the cow that made the milk.
22. Larger predators can be used as indicator species because their presence, and a healthy population of them, suggests that the ecosystem is functioning and the lower levels of the food chain are present. If a large carnivore population is dwindling, this may mean that there are few prey items and there may be a loss of producers. In addition, if an individual carnivore has high levels of toxins in its body, this may be an indication of a pollutant that has infiltrated the environment and is being magnified as it moves up through the food chain.
23. The predator insect may feed on or otherwise affect species other than the pest.

Critical Thinking

19. Analyze Assuming all other factors are the same, the more meat in a person's diet, the larger that person's ecological footprint. Why might this be the case?

20. Connect Nationwide, automobiles are the major source of carbon monoxide, carbon dioxide, nitrogen oxides, particulate matter, and cancer-causing toxins. What can you do to decrease your fossil fuel use?

21. Evaluate An ecological footprint is a measure of the impact of the resources we use on the environment. Explain how buying a carton of milk relates to your ecological footprint.

22. Infer Frogs are commonly used as an indicator species in aquatic habitats. Could a large predator such as a bear or an eagle be used as an indicator species? Explain.

23. Synthesize Explain how a predator insect species, introduced to help control insect pests, could become a threat to an ecosystem.

Interpreting Visuals

Use the simple food web outlined below to answer the next three questions.

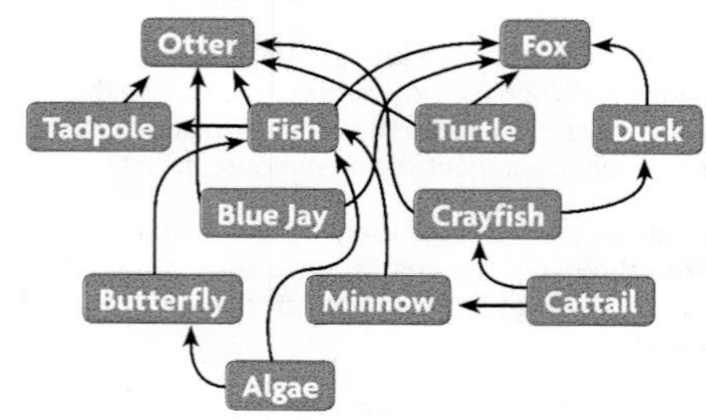

24. Apply Which of these organisms is likely to be most affected by biomagnification of toxins? Explain your answer.

25. Predict This food web includes both aquatic and terrestrial organisms. Imagine that a new road separates the aquatic environment from the nearby terrestrial environment. Do you think the turtle or the duck would be more affected by this habitat fragmentation? Explain.

26. Predict Imagine that an introduced species results in the local extermination of crayfish. How might this change affect the larger ecosystem?

Analyzing Data Identify Discrete and Continuous Data

This circle graph shows the components of the ecological footprint for a resident of a North American city. Use the graph to answer the next two questions.

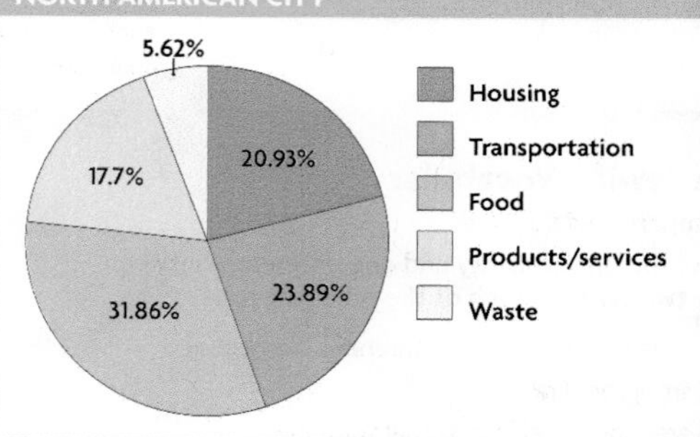

27. Apply Does the circle graph show discrete or continuous data? Explain.

28. Analyze In order of biggest to smallest impact, list the components of human activity that make up the average ecological footprint, according to this graph.

Making Connections

29. Write a Scenario Imagine that successful efforts in sustainable development have made global resource use and waste production fully sustainable by the year 2099. Write a few paragraphs that describe what a sustainable world might look like in 2099. Include information about resource use, waste production, pollution, biodiversity, and conservation.

30. Connect Look again at the damaged forest ecosystem on the chapter opener. The emissions produced in this region have led to the rapid decline in the biodiversity of this area. How might this decline affect the resources of local animal populations?

Interpreting Visuals

24. The fox or otter, because both are at the top of the food chain and will absorb the toxins in their prey.
25. The turtle would be more affected. The duck can fly, so it could more easily cross over the barrier that the road represents; the turtle runs the risk of being hit by cars or spotted by foxes if it walks across the road.
26. *Sample answer:* Otters and ducks may become less common because they have less food to eat. This may result in fewer foxes. Reduced consumption of cattails will allow minnows to flourish, which could lead to more fish and tadpoles. Fish could exert pressure on algae and butterfly populations, which are related.

Analyzing Data

27. discrete, because the data are specific to the footprint of someone in a city at a given time
28. food, transportation, housing, products/services, waste

Standards-Based Assessment

Record your answers on a separate piece of paper.

MULTIPLE CHOICE

1

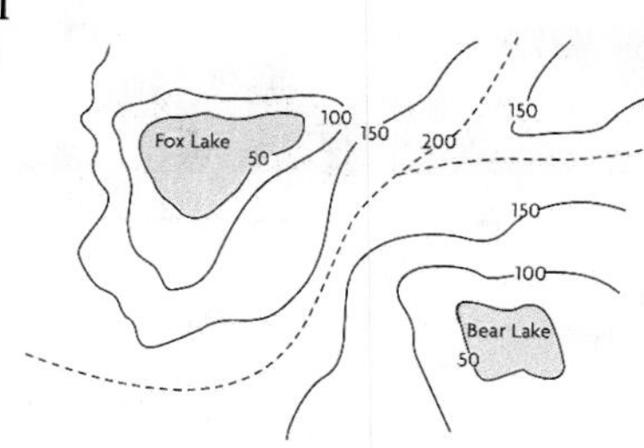

The topographic map above shows the watersheds, or regions that drain into Fox Lake and Bear Lake. The watershed boundary, shown with a dashed line, determines which lake water will flow into. According to the map above, this boundary follows —

A the highest elevation points between the lakes
B the lowest elevation points between the lakes
C a river that likely flows between the lakes
D a path exactly halfway between the two lakes

2

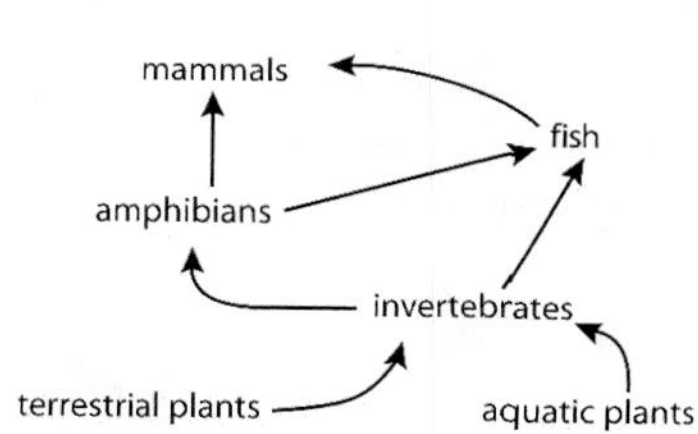

A farmer sprays his crops with pesticide. The runoff enters a nearby lake. Based on the food web above, in which of the following organisms would the pesticide concentration be the highest?

A cattail
B largemouth bass
C water striders
D river otters

3 Which situation would ***most efficiently*** decrease the size of a field mouse population?

A decreased death rates and emigration
B decreased birth rates and immigration
C increased death rates and immigration
D increased death rates and emigration

THINK THROUGH THE QUESTION

As you look at the answer choices, think carefully about how each factor—birth rates, death rates, immigration, and emigration—affect population size.

4 CO_2 is important in our atmosphere because it is required for photosynthesis and it traps some heat, keeping Earth warm. However, scientists speculate that excessive CO_2 production is a problem because it —

A leads to higher global temperatures
B disrupts the natural cycling of other greenhouse gases
C adds too much CO_2 to the oceans
D leads to uncontrolled photosynthesis

5 The nonnative zebra mussel was first found in a lake near Detroit in 1988. By 1989, it had colonized all Great Lakes waterways. Which scenario is ***most likely*** true regarding the introduction of this species?

A Native fish naturally eat zebra mussels.
B The higher biodiversity leads to healthier lakes.
C They compete with native mussels for food and other resources.
D Native mussel populations are growing rapidly.

Standards-Based Assessment

The Standards-Based Assessment questions will help students prepare for their final examination in the course. If you wish to give students practice in coding their answers, look for the Standards-Based Assessment Answer Sheet at **HMHScience.com**. To give students practice under timed testing conditions, allow them five minutes per question.

Question	Answer	Depth of Knowledge	Cognitive Complexity
1	A	III	M
2	D	III	M
3	D	II	M
4	A	II	L
5	C	II	M

KEY

Depth of Knowledge
I Recall
II Skill/Concept
III Strategic Thinking
IV Extended Thinking

Cognitive Complexity
L Low
M Moderate
H High

Making Connections

29. Answers will vary, but should include a description of nonrenewable resources being the primary sources of energy and materials, little or no pollution occurring, preservation of biodiversity, recycling, and production of very little non-biodegradable solid waste.

30. Acid rain would lead to a decline in the resources of the area and in turn will decrease animal populations.

CHAPTER 17 Instruction and Intervention Support

Animal Behavior

① Core Instruction

The **Core Instruction** resources below can be used for all students. Core instruction should be followed by ongoing assessment to determine which students need further help.

Available in both English and Spanish

Available Online

Section	Instruction	PRINT	ONLINE	Labs
17.1	Textbook **Adaptive Value of Behavior**	■	●	Pill Bug Behavior (Design Your Own) **Virtual Lab** Interpreting Bird Response
	PowerPresentation and Notes 17.1		●	
17.2	Textbook **Instinct and Learning**	■	●	**QuickLab** Human Behavior Investigating Behavior (Design Your Own)
	Animated Biology Pavlov's Dog		●	
	PowerPresentation and Notes 17.2		●	
17.3	Textbook **Evolution of Behavior**	■	●	Using an Ethogram to Describe Animal Behavior **Video Lab** Territorial Behavior
	That's Amazing! Video Inquiry Sharks Vs. Dolphins		●	
	Animated Biology Behavioral Costs and Benefits		●	
	PowerPresentation and Notes 17.3		●	
17.4	Textbook **Social Behavior**	■	●	
	PowerPresentation and Notes 17.4		●	
17.5	Textbook **Animal Cognition**	■	●	Animal Cognition
	PowerPresentation and Notes 17.5		●	

Additional online resources available for this chapter include **Interactive Whiteboard Resources.**

GO ONLINE! for all your teacher resources at HMHScience.com

2 Support and Intervention

Support and Intervention resources are useful for students who need targeted help beyond the Core Instruction

Resources	PRINT	ONLINE
Assess and Reteach (TE wrap)	■	●
Concept Map		●
Interactive Reader	■	●
Interactive Review Games		●
Section Self-Checks		●
Study Guide B		●
Vocabulary Practice Worksheets		●

3 Specialized Support

Students who need more intensive personalized intervention benefit from **Specialized Support** resources.

Resources	PRINT	ONLINE
Chapter Audio Files		●
Differentiated Instruction Inclusion, Below Level, and English Learners (TE wrap)	■	●
ELL Strategies	■	●
Modified Lesson Plans for English Learners		●
Reinforcement Worksheets		●
Study Guide A		●

Extension and Assessment

Enrichment and Challenge

Resources	PRINT	ONLINE
Active Reading Worksheets		●
Data Analysis Practice Worksheet		●
Differentiated Instruction Pre-AP (TE wrap)	■	●
Pre-AP Activity Navigation in Loggerhead Sea Turtle Hatchlings		●
The Inside Story and **Take It Further** (TE wrap)	■	●
Unit Project		●
WebLinks		●
WebQuest Animal Cognition (17.5)		●

Assessment

Resources	PRINT	ONLINE
Alternative Assessment		●
Chapter Tests A and B		●
Diagnostic Test		●
ExamView Banks		●
Extended Response Test		●
Online Assessment System		●
Section Quizzes		●
Standards-Based Assessment	■	●

CHAPTER 17

Chapter Overview

- **Section 1** discusses stimulus and response behaviors in animals.
- **Section 2** discusses innate and learned behaviors in animals.
- **Section 3** explains the costs and benefits of specific behaviors in animals.
- **Section 4** describes how social groups affect animal behavior.
- **Section 5** discusses animals that show problem-solving skills and other cognitive behaviors.

Focus and Motivate

What can be learned from this chimpanzee's behavior?

Students may come up with a variety of things that can be learned by observing the chimp's behavior. For example:

- Is the behavior learned or instinctive?
- How does the behavior contribute to the chimp's survival?
- Does the chimp exhibit similar behaviors in other contexts or with other kinds of tools?
- How did the behavior evolve?
- Do similar tool-using behaviors appear in other primates or other groups of animals?

Ask, What is the adaptive advantage of using a leaf to drink? The chimp can more easily scoop up water to drink.

Discuss the behavior in terms of efficiency and reducing energy spent.

BIOZINE
HMHScience.com

Students can access BioZine at **HMHScience.com** to receive updates to featured topics in the book.

CHAPTER 17 Animal Behavior

BIG IDEA Organisms use instinctive behaviors and learned behaviors to quickly adapt to their environment.

ONLINE BIOLOGY HMHScience.com

ONLINE Labs
- **QuickLab** Human Behavior
- Using an Ethogram to Describe Animal Behavior
- Pill Bug Behavior
- Animal Cognition
- Investigating Behavior
- **Virtual Lab** Interpreting Bird Response
- **Video Lab** Territorial Behavior

Student Activity

Purpose **Have students make careful observations and classify types of behavior visible with birds at a bird feeder.**

Materials (for the class)
- birdseed
- platform bird feeder

Place the feeder in an area where bird behavior can be observed from the classroom. You may want to do this a few days ahead to allow the birds to habituate to the circumstances.

What can be learned from this chimpanzee's behavior?

This chimpanzee is using a twig to dig safari ants out of their anthill. Chimpanzees use a variety of tools. Bunched up leaves might serve as a sponge to sop up water for drinking or for cleaning themselves. Some chimpanzees also use leaves to scoop up water to drink and rocks to crack open hard-shelled nuts or fruits. Tool use is considered an example of complex behavior.

READING TOOLBOX **This reading tool can help you learn the material in the following pages.**

USING LANGUAGE

Predictions You are probably familiar with the phrase "It might rain today." There are many words that are used to make predictions. In science, words such as *rarely, often,* and *always* can offer clues about the likelihood that an event will happen. Analyze the statement "Cats rarely enjoy getting a bath." The statement tells you that most cats, but maybe not all cats, dislike baths.

YOUR TURN

After reading your text, use *never, rarely, often,* or *always* to fill in the blank in the following sentences.

1. New male lions _____ kill all the young cubs in the pride.
2. Territorial behavior _____ results in serious injuries.

Introduce Remind students that scientists record observations and take measurements of natural phenomena. Behavior is a natural phenomenon, and animals display a wide variety of behaviors that are characteristic of their species.

Have students think about how to classify behaviors, for example, whether the behavior is submissive or aggressive. Does the size of a bird have an effect on its level of aggressiveness? What can be measured? Have them consider what stimuli the birds respond to. Tell students to distinguish between intraspecies behaviors and interspecies behaviors.

Discuss Have students discuss their observations. **Ask**

- What behaviors did you observe? vocalizing, flapping wings, ruffling feathers, thrusting beaks, chasing other birds
- How did the birds interact with each other? some species or individuals may be more aggressive than others, and there may be a hierarchy or pecking order

Activate Prior Knowledge

Remind students that they have many of the same physical traits as other members of their family. **Ask,** Are there also certain mannerisms or behavioral traits you share with members of your family? What sorts of things are they? Students will probably mention simple behaviors. **Ask,** Are the behaviors learned behaviors or instinctive? Most students will probably suggest that as young children they learned the behaviors by mimicking parents or older siblings. Tell students that they will be learning about complex behaviors in other animals in this chapter and that not all complex behaviors are learned.

Preview Vocabulary

Academic Vocabulary Have students think about the relationships among the following words and which ones can be applied to the behavior of animals:

perception, the act of becoming aware of something directly through a sensory experience

knowledge, familiarity, awareness, or understanding gained through experience or study

intelligence, the capacity to acquire and apply knowledge

learning, modification of behavior by experience

English Learners Have students prepare word squares for some of the words that appear in the section titles: *behavior, instinct, social, learning,* and *cognition.* Square 1: translate the word into their home language. Square 2: draw an image that captures the idea. Square 3: write their own definition, then preview the chapter and rewrite the definition to fit with how the word is used in the context of animal behavior. Square 4: use the word in a sentence.

Answers

1. often
2. rarely

SECTION 17.1

▼ Plan and Prepare

Activate Prior Knowledge Discuss with students some of the behaviors they have observed in common organisms such as cats, dogs, fish, birds, and people. Make a list on the board of some of their responses. **Ask,** Why do you think organisms have certain behaviors? *Sample answers:* to get attention from a potential mate, to obtain food, to play, or for defense and protection

▼ Teach

Vocabulary

Academic Vocabulary The word **stimulus** is used in contexts other than biology. A stimulus can be anything that incites activity. For example, an economic stimulus might be the lowering of interest rates to stimulate spending and thus economic growth. Ask students to give some other examples of stimuli in nonbiological contexts.

17.1 Adaptive Value of Behavior

VOCABULARY

stimulus
kinesis
taxis
circadian rhythm
biological clock

KEY CONCEPT **Behavior lets organisms respond rapidly and adaptively to their environment.**

MAIN IDEAS

- Behavioral responses to stimuli may be adaptive.
- Internal and external stimuli usually interact to trigger specific behaviors.
- Some behaviors occur in cycles.

Connect to Your World

Animal behavior can be simple, such as a moth flying toward a light, or it can be complex, such as a chimpanzee using a leaf as a tool to drink water from a stream. At its most basic level, however, every animal behavior demonstrates the adaptive advantage of an organism's ability to detect and respond to stimuli.

MAIN IDEA

Behavioral responses to stimuli may be adaptive.

READING TOOLBOX

TAKING NOTES

Use a cause-and-effect diagram to take notes on stimuli.

stimulus →

A houseplant bends its leaves toward a sunny window. A lizard moves into the shade on a hot day. A pufferfish inflates when threatened by a predator, as shown in **FIGURE 1.1.** Your cat comes running when it hears a can opener. What do these four observations have in common? They are all examples of organisms responding to stimuli in a beneficial way. A plant can only bend toward light by growing in its direction, but organisms such as the lizard, the pufferfish, or your cat have mechanisms that let them gather and actively respond to information. Behavior can be quite complex, especially in animals with complex nervous systems, but the adaptive nature of behavior can be seen in the relationship between a stimulus and a response.

Stimulus and Response

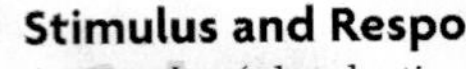

A **stimulus** (plural, *stimuli*) is a type of information that has the potential to make an organism change its behavior. Internal stimuli tell an animal what is occurring in its own body. For example,

- Hunger signals a need for more energy and causes an animal to search for food.
- Thirst signals a loss of internal fluid and causes an animal to look for water.
- Pain warns an animal that some part of its body may be subject to injury and causes it to take some action to avoid injury.

External stimuli give an animal information about its surroundings. For example,

- The sound of a predator can cause an animal to hide or run away to avoid being caught.
- The sight of a potential mate can trigger courtship behaviors.
- Changes in day length can trigger reproductive behaviors or migration.

FIGURE 1.1 When threatened, a pufferfish responds by inflating itself with water until its spines stick out from its rounded body.

Differentiated Instruction

ENGLISH LEARNERS

Tell students that once they've read the section, they will be asked to collect their thoughts on four questions:

- In what way are behavioral responses adaptive?
- What is the function of behavior?
- What are factors that contribute to behavioral responses?
- What function do cyclical behaviors serve?

Place chart paper at four stations around the room. Write one of the questions on the paper at each station. Divide students into four groups, and assign each group to a station. Give students five minutes to discuss and write answers to the question before rotating to the next station. As they rotate, tell them they can check off answers with which they agree, comment on answers with which they do not, and add new answers. When groups are finished, discuss the answers.

Teacher Toolkit, Section C, Carousel Review

Animals detect sensory information with specialized cells that are sensitive to changes in specific kinds of physical or chemical stimuli. These sensory cells may detect things such as light, sound, or chemicals. They transfer information to an animal's nervous system. The nervous system, in turn, may activate other systems in the animal's body that generate a response to the stimulus. For example, a stimulus may cause a gland to increase or decrease its production of a hormone. When you are startled or scared, your adrenal glands release a hormone called epinephrine that causes many other systems in your body to react in what is known as the "fight-or-flight" response. The most obvious organs activated in response to nervous activity are muscles. An animal's ability to move is what lets it behave in response to stimuli.

FIGURE 1.2 Being chased by a lioness activates the "flight" response in this zebra, helping it try to evade its predator.

The Function of Behavior

One way to look at an animal's behavior is to consider it as a kind of high-level homeostatic mechanism. Recall that homeostasis refers to the maintenance of constant internal conditions. Many animal behaviors are responses to stimuli—both internal and external—that affect an individual's well-being. For example, temperature receptors cause a lizard to move to a sunnier spot if it is too cold, or to a shadier spot if it becomes too warm. The lizard's body has an ideal temperature, and when its actual temperature differs from its ideal temperature, the lizard behaves in a way that returns its body to its ideal temperature.

Kinesis and taxis are two simple types of movement-related behaviors that illustrate behavior's adaptive nature. Both behaviors cause an animal to go from a less desirable location to a more desirable location. **Kinesis** is an increase in random movement that lasts until a favorable environment is reached. For example, when a pill bug begins to dry out, its activity increases until it happens upon a moist area, after which its activity decreases again. **Taxis** is a movement in a specific direction, either toward or away from a stimulus. For example, *Euglena* are light-sensitive and will move toward a light source.

VISUAL VOCAB

Kinesis is an increase in random movement.

Like a taxi that takes you directly from one location to another, **taxis** is a movement in a particular direction induced by a stimulus.

Like any trait, the way an animal behaves can vary from individual to individual. A zebra that waits too long to run may wind up being a lion's dinner, as shown in **FIGURE 1.2.** A male mockingbird with a weak repertoire of songs may not attract a mate. Animals with more successful behaviors tend to have more offspring. If the behaviors are heritable, their offspring will likely behave in similar ways. Just like any of an animal's characteristics, behaviors can evolve by natural selection.

CONNECT TO

NATURAL SELECTION

As you learned in the chapter **Principles of Evolution,** both physical and behavioral traits can be passed from an organism to its offspring. Favorable behaviors may increase an organism's chances of surviving and reproducing to pass on their traits to another generation.

A Analyze **How is taxis or kinesis an example of the adaptive nature of behavior?**

CONNECT TO

Plant Biology Tropic responses in plants include those to light, gravity, and touch. Some plants can make rapid responses to stimuli, as does a Venus flytrap to the presence of an insect. Tell students that plants also exhibit taxis. Remind them of the sperm cells that must "swim" or make their way to an egg cell to fertilize it. That response has direction.

Vocabulary

Greek and Latin Word Origins Mention to students that the word **kinesis** is derived from the Greek word *kinein,* meaning "to move." Students may be familiar with the term in the context of **kinetic energy,** which is the energy of motion. Remind students that atoms generally move in a random manner.

Taxis, based on the Greek word *tassein,* means "arrangement." Taxis can be thought of as movement in an arranged direction in response to a stimulus. **Taxonomy,** the arrangement of organisms, and **taxidermy,** the arrangement of animal skin, are also based on *tassein.*

Answers

A **Analyze** Both behaviors cause an animal to move from a less desirable location to a more desirable location, thus helping to maintain constant internal conditions. If such movements were not made, the animal might not survive.

BELOW LEVEL

Help students visualize the difference between kinesis and taxis. Tell them to imagine they are thirsty, but they are in a new school and do not know where the water fountains are located. Their search is similar to kinesis because they would follow a somewhat random path until they find the water fountain. Then tell students to imagine they are going to the refrigerator at home for a drink. Their movement is similar to taxis because they would move in a specific direction, toward the refrigerator.

PRE-AP

Have students address the question of whether behavior requires some form of nervous system to recognize a stimulus and produce a response. Ask students whether plants and sponges are capable of behavior.

Teacher Toolkit, Section C, Quick-Write

▼ Teach continued

To determine how male song sparrows respond to other males, use the Virtual Lab for this chapter, available at **HMHScience.com**.

Take It Further

Cyclic behavior is often complex and may involve the coordination of circadian rhythms with annual cycles. **White-crowned sparrows,** for example, migrate annually to their breeding grounds in the northern United States and Canada from their wintering grounds in the southern United States and Mexico. This migratory pattern is determined by the birds' sensitivity to day length.

The white-crowned sparrow's internal clock responds to photosensitive receptors in the brain, not in the eyes. Scientists learned this when blindfolding the birds did not disturb their circadian rhythm. By altering the birds' light and dark cycles, the scientists further discovered that the birds have a **photosensitive period,** during which the brain must receive light for hormones to be released and gonads to develop properly.

In birds, the energy needed to carry the extra weight of reproductive structures year-round is too costly, so gonad development starts when day length starts to change. At the same time the gonads are developing, the birds become increasingly restless and gain as much as one-third of their body weight in fat. All of these events depend on the release of hormones, which is in turn mediated by the hypothalamus.

Answers

A Connect internal: biological clock, hunger; external: alarm clock, awakened by parent or sibling, sunlight

MAIN IDEA

Internal and external stimuli usually interact to trigger specific behaviors.

VIRTUAL Lab HMHScience.com GO ONLINE Interpreting Bird Responses

Some behaviors can be triggered by a single stimulus, but most behaviors occur in response to a variety of internal and external stimuli. For example, an external signal, such as a change in day length, might cause an animal to secrete specific hormones. These hormones act as internal signals that cause other physiological changes. These changes, in turn, make the animal more likely to respond to another external stimulus, such as the mating display of an individual of the opposite sex. This kind of interaction can be seen in the reproductive behavior of green anoles.

Green anoles are small lizards that live in the woodlands of the southeastern United States. During most of the year, female anoles ignore males. However, their behavior changes each spring, when males begin to aggressively guard territories and court females. Two external stimuli trigger the females' change in behavior. First, females must be exposed to long days and short nights. Females must also see reproductively active males.

To court females, males that are ready to mate bob their bodies up and down while extending their dewlap. The dewlap, shown in **FIGURE 1.3,** is a flap of bright red skin under the lizard's chin. Seeing the red dewlap during the spring makes females release sex hormones into their bloodstream. Sex hormones are an internal signal that make females reproductively receptive.

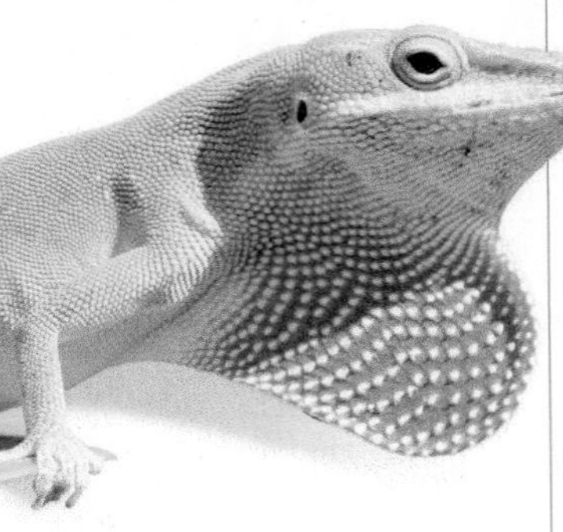

FIGURE 1.3 The extended red dewlap of this male green anole announces to females that it is ready to mate. The dewlap is also used in territorial defense as a "keep out" signal to other males.

Experiments with female anoles have shown that their reproductive behavior depends on the presence of both external and internal signals. Females that do not have sex hormones do not respond to courtship. And hormones are not released unless females are exposed to both external stimuli.

A Connect What might be internal and external stimuli that cause you to wake up in the morning?

MAIN IDEA

Some behaviors occur in cycles.

Many environmental changes are predictable, especially those that occur on a daily, monthly, or yearly basis. Animals often use cues such as differences in day length to keep track of these changes, triggering adaptive changes in their behavior. For example, in order to be active during the day, your body requires a period of sleep every night. This daily pattern of activity and sleep is an example of a circadian rhythm. A **circadian rhythm** (suhr-KAY-dee-uhn) is the daily cycle of activity that occurs over a 24-hour period of time.

READING TOOLBOX

VOCABULARY

The term *circadian* comes from a combination of the Latin words *circa*, meaning "around," and *dies*, meaning "day."

These activity patterns are controlled by an internal mechanism called a **biological clock.** Evidence indicates that an organism's biological clock is run by a combination of melatonin secretions by the pineal gland in the brain and proteins in the body that can detect changes in light.

Differentiated Instruction

TEACH WITH TECHNOLOGY

Students can use various online resources to follow the migrations of several species, such as monarch butterflies, sandhill cranes, Canada geese, and right whales.

HANDS-ON ACTIVITY

Ask students to monitor their own circadian rhythms for several days. Tell them to record the times they wake up and go to bed, and times when they are most energetic, least energetic, most hungry, and least hungry. Have students compile their observations to see if a particular pattern emerges. For example, is there a particular time of day when most people experience high energy levels?

Hibernation

Hibernation is a behavior in which an animal avoids cold winter temperatures by entering into a dormant state. During hibernation, an animal, such as the dormouse shown in **FIGURE 1.4**, has a lower body temperature, reduced heartbeat, and a slowed breathing rate. Hibernating animals prepare for the winter by eating large amounts of food and storing it as fat. This layer of fat not only provides a food source for the animal but also provides additional insulation from the cold.

External factors such as light intensity and temperature determine when an animal enters and leaves hibernation. Shorter days and cooler temperatures cause animals to enter hibernation in the fall. In the spring, increasing day length and warmer temperatures cause the secretion of hormones that awaken the animal out of its dormant state.

FIGURE 1.4 During hibernation, the dormouse's blood temperature drops from 36°C (97°F) to just above 0°C (32°F).

Migration

Many kinds of animals migrate, but you are probably most familiar with bird migration. If you've ever seen—or heard—a flock of geese flying southward during the fall, you've seen bird migration in action. Migratory Canada geese typically spend the spring and summer in Canada and the northern United States. They spend the winter in the southern United States and northern portions of Mexico. Like hibernation, migratory behavior allows animals to avoid harsh conditions in their home range for a part of the year.

Migration is set in motion by a variety of internal and external stimuli. A change in day length during the spring and fall stimulates a change in the portion of the bird's brain that controls hunger. This change causes birds to gain weight. An increase in fat storage is needed to fuel the bird's long-distance migration.

A Infer **How might climate change affect animal migration patterns?**

17.1 Formative Assessment

SELF-CHECK Online
HMHScience.com
GO ONLINE

REVIEWING ⊙ MAIN IDEAS

1. Why are behavioral responses to **stimuli** considered to be adaptive?
2. What internal and external stimuli might signal to Alaskan caribou that it is time to migrate?
3. What is the connection between a **circadian rhythm** and the **biological clock**?

CRITICAL THINKING

4. **Relate** What is the relationship between an animal's behavior and homeostasis?
5. **Analyze** Why is it important for animals to respond to external factors?

CONNECT TO

SEXUAL SELECTION

6. A peacock uses its colorful train of feathers to attract a mate. What factors might control how large a peacock's train of feathers may grow to be?

17.1 FORMATIVE ASSESSMENT

1. If a behavior necessary for survival does not result from a certain stimulus, the animal may not survive. Animals that do respond correctly to a stimulus have a greater chance of survival.
2. internal: hormonal changes; external: changes in day length or temperature
3. Circadian rhythms are the daily cycles of activity controlled by an internal mechanism, the biological clock.
4. An animal performs behaviors that maintain homeostasis.
5. External factors may require that an animal's body responds in a specific way to maintain homeostasis or that the animal's behavior changes in order to avoid danger.
6. Factors may include how the size of the tail affects the male bird's fitness or movement. The female's preference for tail size is another factor.

Take It Further

Bears such as the **American black bear** (*Ursus americanus*) hibernate through the winter. Bears can go without food or water for more than three months and do not defecate, urinate, or exercise during this time. Nutrients are supplied by the breaking down of fat tissue that releases water and up to 4000 calories per day, and by muscle and organ tissues that supply protein. Bears sleep rolled into a tight ball, with their heads under their paws, and their backs to the cold. This keeps their head and torso warm, which allows them to wake up easily when disturbed.

The **Arctic ground squirrel** (*Spermophilus parryii*) is the only known mammal that can lower its body temperature below freezing when hibernating. These squirrels hibernate between seven to eight months a year and can reduce their body temperature to as low as −3°C (27°F). With temperatures so low, they are said to be in a supercooled state. Every two to three weeks, however, without waking up, the squirrels shiver in order to raise their body temperature back up to 36°C (98°F).

Answers

A **Infer** Colder temperatures might cause migration to begin earlier in the year.

Assess and Reteach ▼

Assess Use the Section Self-Check or Section Quiz, both available at **HMHScience.com**.

Reteach Write the terms *internal stimuli* and *external stimuli* on the board. Have students name, as quickly as possible, examples of each as you write the responses under the appropriate heading.

SECTION 17.2

▼ Plan and Prepare

Activate Prior Knowledge Have students think about the behaviors they demonstrate in the course of an average day. **Ask,** What are some behaviors you have learned, and how are they adaptive? *Sample answer:* learning to read and write, which enables you to get food (read packaging at the grocery or read a menu), have a job (to obtain food and shelter), or read a medicine label (to help maintain health) Discuss whether students think they have any instinctive behaviors.

▼ Teach

Vocabulary

innate The word *innate* comes from a Latin word meaning "to be born in." Synonyms for the word include *hereditary* and *inborn*. In the text on the next page, the term *hard-wired* is used, which suggests that innate behaviors are "part of the equipment."

17.2 Instinct and Learning

KEY CONCEPT **Both genes and environment affect an animal's behavior.**

VOCABULARY

- instinct
- innate
- releaser
- habituation
- imprinting
- imitation
- classical conditioning
- operant conditioning

MAIN IDEAS

- Innate behaviors are triggered by specific internal and external stimuli.
- Many behaviors have both innate and learned components.
- Learning is adaptive.

Connect to Your World

Why are some families filled with good athletes? Is athleticism passed on from parent to child? Or are younger generations repeating behaviors they watched while they were growing up? You may have heard this "nature versus nurture" debate about many human behaviors, including musical ability, addiction, and thrill seeking. But research shows that genetic and environmental factors interact in most behaviors. "Nature versus nurture" is a false division. Most behaviors represent a mixture of both nature *and* nurture.

MAIN IDEA

Innate behaviors are triggered by specific internal and external stimuli.

Nothing teaches a spider to build a web. It builds it correctly the first time it tries. This kind of complex inborn behavior is called an **instinct.** Instinctive behavior is characterized as being innate and relatively inflexible. An **innate** behavior is performed correctly the first time an animal tries it, even when the animal has never been exposed to the stimulus that triggers the behavior. An inflexible behavior is performed in a similar way each time.

Instinctive behaviors are typically found where mistakes can have severe consequences. Baby mammals that do not suckle die of starvation. Newly hatched sea turtles, such as the one shown in **FIGURE 2.1**, that do not race to the ocean will be eaten by predators. By having set reactions to particular stimuli, animals can automatically respond correctly in a life-or-death situation.

Instinctive behavior is especially important in newborns, who have had no time to learn any behaviors. Performing certain innate behaviors is key to both the animal's survival and its ability to pass its genes on to future generations. Animals that do not perform a necessary innate behavior will likely die.

Many innate behaviors are triggered by a simple signal. The signal is called a **releaser** because it makes the animal run through a behavior. Releasers can be any kind of stimulus: a visual sign, a sound, a scent, or a touch. When a releaser signal has been detected, the animal's nervous system triggers the expression of a specific behavior. Sometimes the triggered behavior is fixed, and the animal runs through a set sequence of movements each time the behavior is performed.

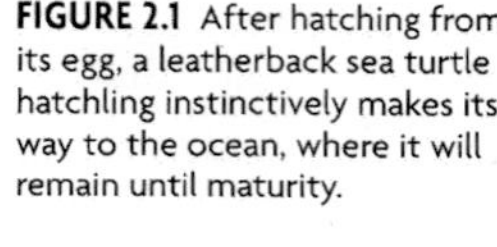
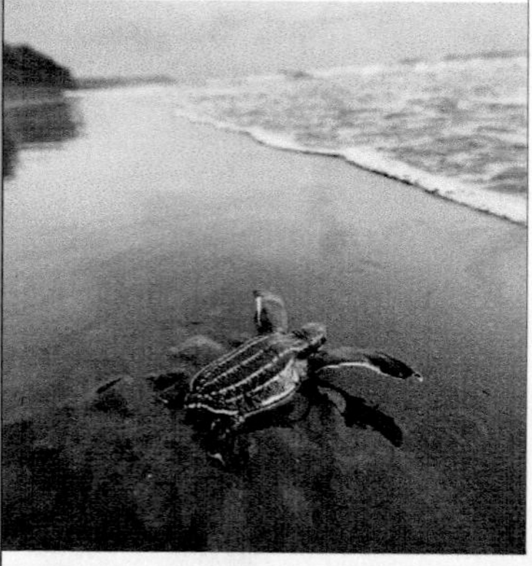

FIGURE 2.1 After hatching from its egg, a leatherback sea turtle hatchling instinctively makes its way to the ocean, where it will remain until maturity.

Differentiated Instruction

ENGLISH LEARNERS

Have small groups of students create a cause-and-effect chain showing how innate behaviors in animals are triggered by specific stimuli. It should include the following points: (1) A stimulus is presented. (2) The animal detects the releaser. (3) A sensory message is sent to the animal's brain. (4) The brain activates motor neurons that move the animal's muscles in a predictable pattern. Have students diagram three examples of cause-and-effect chains.

Teacher Toolkit, Section C, Cause-and-Effect Chain

PRE-AP

Before students read this section, have them indicate whether each of the following statements is true or false: (1) Humans do not rely on instinctive behaviors. F (2) Innate behaviors are inherited. T (3) Habituation results from imprinting. F (4) Imprinting is an instinctive behavior. T (5) Conditioning is not considered learning because an animal is forced to make an association. F Then have them reassess their responses after they read.

Teacher Toolkit, Section C, Anticipation Guide

Dutch zoologist Niko Tinbergen's experiments with herring gulls showed how simple releasers can be. Hungry herring gull chicks will peck at a red spot at the tip of a parent's bill. The parent usually responds by coughing up a bit of half-digested fish for the chick to eat. Very young chicks do not actually recognize their parent when they beg for food. Instead, the behavior is triggered simply by the sight of a long bill with a red dot near its tip. The chicks will beg from any long object with a red dot, including cardboard cutouts of a herring gull head and the end of a painted stick. Other gull species, such as the lesser black-backed gull shown in **FIGURE 2.2**, also have red-dotted bills.

FIGURE 2.2 Some gull species, such as this lesser black-backed gull, have a red-dotted bill. The red dot is the releaser that causes the gull chick to beg for food.

Biologists think that innate behaviors are hard-wired into an animal's nervous system, but they have studied the details for only a few invertebrate species. Innate behaviors are heritable and are strongly affected by gene expression. But they can also be changed by environmental factors. For example, during its lifetime, a honeybee moves through a sequence of innate behaviors that help to maintain the hive. The behaviors are regulated by different sets of genes. As a bee ages, its brain cells express different genes and its behavior changes. But gene expression is also affected by the hive's social environment. If a hive has few older foragers, some of the younger bees will mature faster. Even the bill-pecking behavior of gulls has been shown to improve with age, as young herring gulls become more accurate in their ability to aim their pecks at the red spot on their parent's bill.

A Apply **Why is behavior considered to be a mixture of both nature and nurture?**

MAIN IDEA

Many behaviors have both innate and learned components.

Animals often change their behavior as they gain real-world experience. In other words, animals learn. Learning takes many forms, ranging from simple changes in an innate behavior to problem-solving in new situations. In each case, learning involves the strengthening of nerve pathways. Most animal behaviors are not simple reactions to stimuli using preset pathways in the animal's brain. Instead, they represent a combination of innate tendencies influenced by learning and experience.

CONNECT TO

ECOLOGY

As you learned in the chapter **Interactions in Ecosystems**, organisms interact with their environment to get what they need to survive. The goal of animals' behaviors is to increase their chances of survival.

Habituation

Garden shops sell plastic owls that are supposed to frighten away birds. But a gardener who doesn't move the owls every few days may soon see birds sitting on top of them. This is an example of habituation. **Habituation** occurs when an animal's behavioral response decreases due to a repeated stimulus, even if it has features that trigger innate behaviors. The habit of seeing owls in the exact same place in the garden every day causes the birds to get used to, and basically ignore, the stimulus.

BELOW LEVEL

Write the words *instinct* and *learning* on the board. Have students call out as many of the terms that relate to these concepts as they can while you construct a cluster diagram. Have students refer to the cluster diagram as they read the section together in groups.

Teacher Toolkit, Section C, Cluster Diagram

The Inside Story

In his autobiography, zoologist **Nikolaas Tinbergen** shares the humorous story of wandering the shores of his native Holland as a child. He recounts his boyhood preference for camping and bird watching over academics. He developed a keen ability to observe detail by watching the behavior of sticklebacks in a backyard aquarium. Tinbergen scraped through school, married, and started a family. He met Konrad Lorenz at a 1936 symposium on instinct and writes, "We clicked at once." Shortly thereafter, Tinbergen became Lorenz's student.

The two men developed a lifelong friendship and collaborated on studies of animal behavior. Tinbergen published numerous books and scholarly articles on behavior, including *The Herring Gull's World* in 1953. He was awarded the Nobel Prize in 1973 along with Lorenz and colleague Karl von Frisch. The three men were acknowledged as the principal architects of a new science called **ethology,** which is the systematic study of the behavior of animals in their natural habitats.

Take It Further

Gull colonies are noisy places that can contain thousands of breeding pairs and their chicks. Nests may be only a few inches apart. It is incumbent upon the chicks to remain close to their own nest, as gulls are extremely aggressive when breeding and are known to kill chicks that wander. Chicks recognize their parents by their vocalizations, which include several kinds of calls. Parents raise the chicks together, taking turns finding fish, which they eat and then regurgitate for the chicks. As one parent lands at the nest when returning from a fishing expedition, it emits several calls. The other parent takes off, and the chicks run toward the sound of the first parent's voice for the meal they know has arrived.

Answers

A Apply Both genetic and environmental factors interact in most behaviors.

▼ Teach *continued*

QUICKLAB

Time 15 minutes TEACHER TESTED

Purpose Observe and collect data on a selected human behavior.

LAB MANAGEMENT

You may wish to give students a few minutes during class to collect data.

Answers

Analyze and Conclude

1. Answers will vary but should be quantitative. For the suggested study, people may sit in evenly spaced clumps.
2. Answers will vary, but hypotheses should be testable. Possible hypothesis: If people establish territories, they will sit a certain distance apart and in a certain place.
3. Answers will vary but should include clearly defined dependent and independent variables and a way to measure them.

The Inside Story

In his autobiography, **Konrad Lorenz** recalls a favorite childhood story about the adventures of Nils Holgersson, who traveled all over Sweden on the back of a goose. Lorenz wanted a goose of his own but instead settled for pet ducks. Lorenz writes, "I discovered imprinting and was imprinted myself." Lorenz wanted to study zoology, but his father convinced him to study medicine.

During World War II, Lorenz served as a psychiatrist in the German army. He was captured by the Russians and began writing a book on epistemology (the study of the nature of knowledge) to pass the time. After he was released, he received an unsalaried position at a research station in his native Austria. Eventually, Lorenz went to work at the Max Planck Institute in Germany, where he did ethological research until his retirement from the institute in 1973, the same year he won the Nobel Prize with colleagues Nikolaas Tinbergen and Karl von Frisch.

QUICKLAB OBSERVING

Human Behavior

Have you ever wondered what might explain a particular kind of behavior you observe in people? In this lab, you will observe some aspect of human behavior and form a hypothesis that explains the behavior.

PROBLEM What is the behavior of people in certain situations?

MATERIALS
- paper
- pencil

PROCEDURE

1. Choose a question that you have about human behavior that can be answered by observing people. For instance, you could ask, "Where do people sit in a cafeteria?"
2. Determine which behavior you will observe.
3. Determine how you will quantitatively measure the behavior. For example, you may record how many people are in the cafeteria, where people are sitting, and the number of full, partially full, and empty tables.
4. Make your observations and record your data.

ANALYZE AND CONCLUDE

1. **Analyze** Present your results in a table or graph. What can you conclude?
2. **Hypothesize** Form a hypothesis that could explain the behavior pattern you saw.
3. **Extend** Create an experiment to test your hypothesis.

Imprinting

Imprinting is a rapid and irreversible learning process that only occurs during a short time in an animal's life. During this critical period the animal may, for example, learn to identify its parents, its siblings, its offspring, characteristics of its own species, or the place it was born.

Austrian zoologist Konrad Lorenz's studies with graylag geese are among the most famous studies of imprinting. Newly hatched graylag geese normally imprint on their mother during the first two days after hatching. After this period, the goslings will follow their mother and eventually grow up to mate with other graylag geese. Lorenz divided a clutch of goose eggs in half, leaving some with the mother and raising the rest himself. The goslings that stayed with their mother behaved normally. Their siblings, which stayed with Lorenz during their critical period, did not recognize other geese as members of their own species. They followed Lorenz as goslings, and tried to mate with humans when they matured. This experiment showed that imprinting is an innate and automatic process, even though the behavior's stimulus is learned.

When working to reintroduce species into the wild, it is important to avoid having the animals imprint on their human handlers. For example, when working with endangered wattled cranes, scientists try to minimize the birds' contact with humans. When humans need to interact with the cranes, they wear costumes that cover their entire bodies. They use puppets painted to look like adult cranes to feed the young, as shown in **FIGURE 2.3**.

FIGURE 2.3 To avoid having cranes imprint on their human handlers, biologists use puppets painted to resemble the head of an adult crane to feed young birds raised in captivity.

Differentiated Instruction

PRE-AP

Have students summarize the experimental evidence for imprinting using a two-column chart labeled *Hypothesis* and *Experiment*. In the left column, have them formulate the hypothesis. In the right column, have them identify the variables and controls as well as the researcher's observations on which the conclusion was based.

Teacher Toolkit, Section C, Two-Column Notes

ENGLISH LEARNERS

Ask students to illustrate Lorenz's experiments on imprinting in a comic-strip format. Have them include several frames. For example, the first frame could show a goose sitting on a nest. The second frame could show an egg hatching. The third frame could show the gosling seeing a human, and so on.

Teacher Toolkit, Section C, Connect to Content Through Visuals

Imitation

In **imitation,** animals learn by observing the behaviors of other animals. The initial behavior becomes a model that the other animals try to copy. Young male songbirds learn to sing by listening to adult males and trying to repeat what they hear. By trial and error, over time they begin to sing the species-specific song they heard from adults. Human babies also imitate adults in a number of ways, such as when they learn to speak their native language.

Not all imitative behaviors are passed from adult to younger animals, however. For example, consider the potato washing behavior among Japanese macaques, or snow monkeys, shown in **FIGURE 2.4.** A juvenile female monkey, named Imo by researchers, discovered that it was easier to wash sand off a potato by dipping it in water rather than by brushing it off with her hands. At first, only her brothers and sisters imitated the behavior, followed by her mother. Over a period of time, a number of individuals in the troop adopted the potato washing behavior.

Infer **What would be the harm of having a captive animal intended for release imprint on its human handlers?**

FIGURE 2.4 Snow monkeys learn to wash their potatoes before eating them by imitating the behavior of other individuals.

MAIN IDEA

Learning is adaptive.

Animals that are able to learn can modify, or change, their behavior to better adapt to new situations. This ability to learn can give animals an edge in survival and reproduction, allowing them to pass their genes on to future generations.

Associative Learning

In associative learning, an animal learns to associate a specific action with its consequences. For example, an experiment with young blue jays showed that the birds do not identify prey instinctively. Instead, they ate every new insect that was offered to them. Insects that tasted good, such as grasshoppers, they ate again and again. But it only took one experience with a bad-tasting monarch butterfly to make the jays avoid them for the rest of their lives. The jays learned to associate the monarch's distinctive orange and black markings with its bad taste. Such trial-and-error learning can help animals to survive within their environments.

One type of associative learning studied by animal behavior scientists is conditioning. Conditioning is a way to modify an animal's behavior in response to certain stimuli. When teaching an animal by conditioning, two stimuli are paired together, and an animal is conditioned to give a specific response to these stimuli. The two main types of conditioning are called classical conditioning and operant conditioning.

Pavlov's Dog

History of Science

The study of **animal behavior** has a long history.

- Aristotle's anecdotal observations led him to conclude that nonhuman animals are motivated by feelings such as revenge.
- Charles Darwin in 1859 revolutionized the study of behavior when he proposed that natural selection acts on heritable behaviors; that is, animals already possessing the behavior pass along that behavior to their offspring.
- C. L. Morgan in 1903 stated that we cannot attribute higher-order thinking to a behavior if a more basic explanation will suffice.
- Ivan Pavlov in 1903 presented his paper on the conditioned response.
- Edward Thorndike in 1905 studied animal behavior by using a systematic, empirical methodology.
- Karl von Frisch is best known for his study of bees. He found that bees perform what he called "round dances" and "waggle dances" to communicate the presence, distance, and direction of food.
- B. F. Skinner in 1938 published *The Behavior of Organisms* and developed his theory of operant conditioning.

Answers

A **Infer** A captive animal would not recognize members of its same species upon release, mating would be affected, and the animal would be dependent on humans for food and other resources.

BELOW LEVEL

Have students make Venn diagrams to compare classical and operant conditioning. Their diagrams could include the following:

- classical—original stimulus, neutral stimulus, conditioned response to neutral stimulus
- operant—random behavior, positive or negative reinforcement, reinforced behavior
- area of overlap—associative learning, behavior modified by associating stimuli with response

Teacher Toolkit, Section C, Venn Diagram

HANDS-ON ACTIVITY

If you have an aquarium in your classroom, you can do a simple demonstration of classical conditioning. Before feeding the fish, ask a student to tap on the glass gently. After several trials, students should be able to tap on the glass and have the fish respond by swimming to the surface to be fed. **Ask**

- What is the neutral stimulus? tapping on the glass
- What is the conditioned response? swimming to the surface when you tap on the glass

▼ Teach continued

The Inside Story

While **Ivan Pavlov** is credited with the process of classical conditioning, it was not originally his idea. **Aristotle** came up with the idea first, except that he focused on thoughts instead of observable behaviors. Pavlov was not even the first to conduct research on classical conditioning. In 1902, **E. B. Twitmeyer,** a graduate student at the University of Pennsylvania, wrote his dissertation on the conditioning of a reflexive response. Since Twitmeyer was not yet a prominent scientist, other scientists were not interested in his research.

Answers

A Apply When the dog correctly performs the trick, a treat such as a food reward could be given to the dog so that it associates something positive with the behavior.

FIGURE 2.5 Teaching a pet a trick, such as how to shake, often involves giving it a reward after it performs the correct behavior

Classical Conditioning

Classical conditioning is a process in which an animal learns to associate a previously neutral stimulus with a behavior that was once triggered by a different stimulus. Ivan Pavlov, a Russian physiologist, was studying digestion in dogs when he realized that salivation, or drooling, is an automatic behavior. Pavlov created an experiment to determine if external stimuli are involved in this behavior.

- Normally, the presence of food makes a dog salivate.
- A bell is rung when food is presented to the dog.
- The dog salivates because of the presence of the food.
- After constantly being presented with both food and the ringing bell at the same time, when only the bell is rung, the dog salivates even though the food is not present.

In this experiment, the ringing bell is initially a neutral stimulus. The response in which the dog salivates upon hearing the ringing bell is the conditioned response. Because the dog was given food at the same time the bell rang, the dog has been conditioned to salivate when the bell is rung because it also expects to be given food.

Operant Conditioning

Operant conditioning is a process in which the likelihood of a specific behavior is increased by reinforcement. In positive reinforcement, such as a food reward as shown in **FIGURE 2.5**, a reward is given to increase a behavior. Negative reinforcement is the removal of a negative or aversive stimulus to increase a behavior.

B. F. Skinner, an American psychologist, created "Skinner boxes" to study operant conditioning. A Skinner box is a cage that has a bar or pedal on one wall. When an animal such as a rat pushes down on the bar, a food pellet pops out. The rat then associates the behavior of pressing the bar with the food reward, even if not rewarded every time. If the behavior is no longer rewarded, the rat will, over time, stop performing it.

A Apply How might you train a dog to do a trick using positive reinforcement?

▼ Assess and Reteach

Assess Use the Section Self-Check or Section Quiz, both available at **HMHScience.com**.

Reteach Write the vocabulary terms for the section on the board. Have student groups brainstorm as many examples for each term as they can in five minutes and then share their responses with the class.

17.2 Formative Assessment

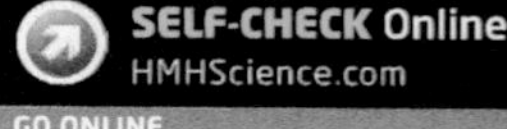

SELF-CHECK Online
HMHScience.com
GO ONLINE

REVIEWING MAIN IDEAS

1. What is the difference between an **instinct** and a learned behavior?
2. Describe a behavior that you learned by **imitation**.
3. Using either **classical** or **operant conditioning** as an example, explain how learning can be adaptive.

CRITICAL THINKING

4. **Apply** Ducklings that are shown a paper silhouette of a hawk initially freeze and cower. After repeated exposure to the silhouette they stop responding. What is this lack of response called?
5. **Summarize** What is the connection between neurons in the brain and learning?

CONNECT TO EVOLUTION

6. Monarch butterflies are toxic. Viceroy butterflies, which look like monarch butterflies, are not toxic, but birds avoid them anyway. Explain how the bird behavior described in this section could have influenced the evolution of viceroys.

17.2 FORMATIVE ASSESSMENT

1. A learned behavior is a behavior the animal must be taught how to complete. An instinct is innate. It is a behavior the animal is able to complete on its own without being taught how to do it.
2. Answers may include tying shoes, learning to speak, and learning a sport.
3. Animals that can learn are able to modify their behavior in order to adapt to new situations. In operant conditioning, the animal learns to perform a certain behavior in order to receive a reward or avoid punishment.
4. habituation
5. Research indicates that during learning, some neurons undergo structural and molecular changes that allow for the easier flow of information.
6. When a bird eats an unpalatable insect, it learns to associate the insect's appearance with the bad taste. Palatable insects that look like the bad-tasting one will also be avoided. This behavior selects for insects that mimic the appearance of the poisonous insect.

17.3 Evolution of Behavior

KEY CONCEPT **Every behavior has costs and benefits.**

MAIN IDEAS
- Even beneficial behaviors have associated costs.
- Animals perform behaviors whose benefits outweigh their costs.

OCABULARY
rvivorship
rritoriality
ɔtimal foraging

Connect to Your World

The zebra was very thirsty. It flicked his ears to and fro as it walked toward the water hole, listening carefully for any sign of a hungry lioness. Nothing looked out of the ordinary. But as it neared the edge of the water, it saw a crocodile lurking in the shallows. The zebra quickly retreated and trotted back to its herd. It needed water, but the risk to its life was too great.

MAIN IDEA

Even beneficial behaviors have associated costs.

Every behavior has benefits and costs. Shorebirds travel thousands of miles during their spring and fall migrations, burning through an enormous amount of energy in the process. But migration increases a bird's chances of survival by escaping from cold seasonal temperatures to warmer locations.

Benefits of Behavior

From an evolutionary standpoint, the most important benefits of a behavior include increased survivorship and reproduction rates. **Survivorship** refers to the number of individuals that survive from one year to the next. Certain behaviors reduce the chance that an animal will die in a given time period. Similarly, some behaviors increase the number of offspring that an animal will have during its lifetime.

Behaviors that increase an individual's survival and reproduction are behaviors that increase its fitness. These behaviors will be favored by natural selection, but they still have associated costs. For instance, when a sea star touches a sea anemone called *Stomphia*, the anemone stops feeding, wrenches free of the sea bottom, and swims away. Escape behaviors such as this are expensive in terms of energy in the short term. The animal stops eating and uses up stored energy. But dead animals cannot reproduce. The long-term benefit of the behavior is the increase in the animal's survival and reproduction rates.

GURE 3.1 These male Siberian gers are very territorial. Fights ver territory can lead to serious jury or even death.

Costs of Behavior

Behavioral costs can be broken down into three basic categories.

Energy costs Every animal behavior, such as running away from a predator, uses up ATP. When an animal uses metabolic energy for one behavior, such as searching for a mate, that energy is not available for other needs, such as searching for food.

Differentiated Instruction

ENGLISH LEARNERS

Before students read the section, have them do a think-pair-share activity. Ask a question, give individual students a chance to think about it, have student pairs compare their answers, and ask them to share a final answer with the whole class. Possible questions: What are the three categories of behavior costs? What is territoriality and what are its consequences? What is optimal foraging?

Teacher Toolkit, Section C, Think-Pair-Share

Plan and Prepare

Activate Prior Knowledge Have students participate in a cost-benefit analysis. **Ask**

- Is it worth spending $1000 for a used video game? Most students will say no.
- Is it worth spending $1000 for a used car? Many students will say yes.

Discuss the difference between the two examples. Point out that biologists consider cost-benefit analysis to be an important tool in determining why animals engage in certain behaviors.

Teach

Vocabulary

Academic Vocabulary The technique of **cost-benefit analysis** is used in business to compare the total expected costs of given activities against the total expected benefits. The goal is to choose the best or most profitable option.

▼ Teach *continued*

TEACH FROM VISUALS

FIGURE 3.2 Draw students' attention to the size disparity between the male and female spider. It is not uncommon for males and females of a species to be different sizes. **Ask,** What is an advantage of a female's being larger than a male? It allows her to produce large numbers of eggs. Other examples in which females are larger than males include many species of turtles, birds, and insects.

Take It Further

The size and distribution of **territories** vary greatly among species. For example, song sparrows have relatively small territories with no overlap. The birds have access to lookout posts and can patrol the territory by flying quickly from post to post. Mammals, on the other hand, are larger and less mobile. It is energetically more costly for them to patrol an area, so they tend to have overlapping home ranges.

In addition to benefiting the individual that controls the territory, territoriality benefits populations. When resources are scarce, individuals that are less fit, and therefore less successful at competing for resources, will die. Thus, territoriality serves to cull the population and keep it healthy.

Answers

A Analyze Answers will vary. Possible benefits: escape harsh conditions of one habitat for another more temperate location; provides access to greater genetic diversity. Possible costs: migration can lead to death due to predation along the migratory path; high energy cost in flying to another location.

ONLINE Biology
HMHScience.com

Evaluate the energy costs of certain behaviors in the Animated Biology on behavioral costs.

FIGURE 3.2 The female redback spider, shown here, eats the much smaller male as they mate.

Opportunity costs Every animal behavior takes time. When an animal spends time doing one behavior, it loses the opportunity to do a different behavior. For example, when a songbird defends its territory from rivals, it is using time that could have been spent eating or mating.

Risk costs Many behaviors expose an individual to possible injury or death. All animals have to look for food, but foraging also increases the chance that an animal will meet a predator. In many species, males risk injury by fighting for access to females during the breeding season.

Some behaviors that seem harmful may have surprising benefits for an animal. For example, while most male spiders go to great lengths to avoid getting eaten by their mates, a male Australian redback spider deliberately flips his abdomen over the female's mouth. As they mate, the female, shown in **FIGURE 3.2**, literally eats the male alive. His behavior clearly does not increase his survival. But because she lets him fertilize more of her eggs, it has the benefit of increasing his reproductive success.

A Analyze **What is the benefit of bird migration? The cost?**

MAIN IDEA

Animals perform behaviors whose benefits outweigh their costs.

It is difficult to determine if animals make conscious decisions about their actions. Whether behavioral responses are automatic or reflect more complex cognitive processes, they evolve only if they improve the fitness of those individuals that perform them. Territoriality and optimal foraging are just two examples that demonstrate how animal behaviors are expressed if their benefits outweigh their costs.

CONNECT TO

COMPETITION

Recall from **Interactions in Ecosystems** that competition occurs when two organisms fight for the same limited resources. Interspecific competition occurs when members of different species fight for access to resources. Intraspecific competition is the fight for resources between members of the same species.

Territoriality

Territoriality refers to the control of a specific area—or territory—by one or more individuals of an animal species. The benefit of territorial behavior is the ability to control the resources within the animal's territory, such as food or access to potential mates. The costs associated with territorial behavior include the energy and time that could have been used for feeding or mating. That time is instead spent protecting territory from invasion by other animals.

Consider the territorial behavior of the Hawaiian honeycreeper. This bird feeds on the nectar of flowers, and it defends a territory that has the flowers from which it feeds. The benefit of holding a territory can be measured in the amount of nectar the bird can get from the flowers located in its territory. An individual should only defend a territory if that territory holds enough flowers to provide the food it needs to at least offset the energy cost of defense. Studies of honeycreeper behavior have shown that individuals stop defending territories when the number of flowers falls below a certain minimum or exceeds a certain maximum number. Individuals only defend a territory in which there is a benefit from excluding other individuals, and in which the energy benefit from the nectar outweighs the energy cost of the defensive behavior.

Differentiated Instruction

PRE-AP

Ask students to select a behavior and do a cost-benefit analysis. For example, they could analyze the costs and benefits to a mixed flock of birds at a feeder. Possible costs include competition for the food at the feeder or being more visible to predators. Possible benefits include more eyes to search for predators or access to a concentrated food source.

Teacher Toolkit, Section C, T-Chart

TEACH WITH TECHNOLOGY

If you have GPS equipment, students can map bird territories. Select a bird that is visible, easy to follow, and has a territory on or near the school grounds. Have students follow the bird as it moves from singing post to singing post. Tell students to enter the coordinates at each post. When students are done, they can use their coordinates to estimate the size of the territory. With enough data, students may be able to compare territories of different individuals and species.

Optimal Foraging

When animals search for food, they must make decisions about what they should eat. The benefits of foraging are measured in the amount of energy gained. The costs of foraging include the energy used to search for, catch, and eat food; the risk of capture by a predator while foraging; and the loss of time to spend on other activities. The theory of **optimal foraging** states that natural selection should favor behaviors that get animals the most, or optimal amount of, calories for the cost.

The foraging methods of oystercatchers, a type of shorebird shown in **FIGURE 3.3**, have been the subject of many studies. As the birds' name suggests, they eat bivalves such as oysters and mussels. Some birds sneak up on relaxed bivalves and quickly stab out the meat. Others use their chisel-shaped beak to hammer a hole through the shells.

FIGURE 3.3 The oystercatcher uses its long, sharp beak to break open the shells of bivalves such as oysters.

Hammering oystercatchers get a benefit from eating the mollusks, but at the cost of the time and energy it takes to break open their shells. Small mussels are easy to open, but don't contain much meat. Larger mussels are meatier but harder to open. Scientists first hypothesized that oystercatchers would prefer to eat the largest mussels they could find. These mussels contained the most meat for the time the birds spent opening them.

When the biologists observed oystercatchers in the wild, they found that the birds did not eat the largest mussels they could find. Their experiment showed that there was another cost to eating mussels. Their first model assumed that the birds could open any mussel given enough time. However, their experiment showed them that the birds also faced a "handling cost" when they hunted. Birds that picked very large mussels lost time handling bivalves they could not open. They actually got less meat on average than birds that ate smaller mussels. Oystercatchers that learn to hunt medium-sized mussels get the most food for their efforts. Better-fed birds have higher survivorship so they reproduce more and their chicks, in turn, learn this behavior.

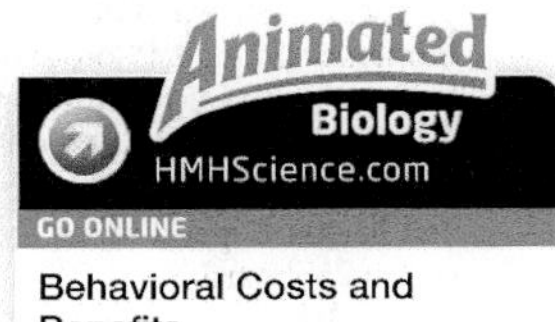

A Apply **How does optimal foraging improve an individual's overall fitness?**

17.3 Formative Assessment

REVIEWING MAIN IDEAS

1. Compare the three categories of behavior costs.
2. Any animal behavior has a cost and a benefit. Explain this statement using **optimal foraging** as an example.

CRITICAL THINKING

3. **Infer** What might be a stimulus that triggers a songbird's **territorial** behaviors?
4. **Analyze** Some species of cichlid fish hold their fertilized eggs inside their mouths until they hatch. What might be the costs and benefits of this behavior?

CONNECT TO SCIENTIFIC PROCESS

5. Some spiders build webs that include visible zigzag lines of silk. But more visible webs catch fewer insects than do less visible webs. Hypothesize what benefits the spider gets by building such a visible web.

TEACH FROM VISUALS

FIGURE 3.3 Have students examine the oystercatcher's beak. **Ask,** How is the shape of the beak adapted for opening bivalves? It is long, thin, and sharp, which allows it to break the shells and pry them open.

Vocabulary

Word Origins The Indo-European prefix *op-* is associated with wealth, as in **opulent.** In the words **optimum** and **optimal,** the meaning changes to one of favorable or most desirable outcomes.

Answers

A Apply Optimal foraging improves an individual's overall fitness by ensuring that the animal gets the most calories for the least amount of energy spent in obtaining the food item.

Assess and Reteach

Assess Use the Section Self-Check or Section Quiz, both available at **HMHScience.com**.

Reteach Have student groups each write three quiz questions for the section. Then have students switch with another group and answer the questions each has written. Continue until all groups have quizzed one another.

17.3 FORMATIVE ASSESSMENT

1. Energy costs result from behaviors that use up metabolic energy that cannot be regained. Opportunity costs refer to the time the animal loses in performing a certain behavior over another. Risk costs refer to the harm to which an animal may expose itself in conducting a certain behavior.
2. *Sample answer:* A groundhog leaves its burrow to forage. Benefit of the behavior is energy gained from food. Cost of the behavior is exposure to predators and lost opportunity to pursue other behaviors.
3. the sight of another songbird or hearing another songbird's song
4. They cannot eat while they are brooding eggs, so the behavior has an energetic cost. A benefit of the behavior is that the eggs are protected from predation, so there is a greater chance that the parent's genes will be passed on to future generations.
5. Possible hypotheses: Webs are an enormous investment in protein. The visible lines keep larger animals from crashing into the web and destroying it. The lines help hide the spider from potential predators.

Background

Drones are being used more frequently to conduct wildlife research. Drones are used to observe birds in nests and count animal populations, including birds, seals, salmon, and dugong. The data collected can be used in conservation efforts, as well as to help scientists learn more about the behavior of animals and how populations change over time.

Companies that manufacture drones are working to improve the technology, making them smaller, more maneuverable, and able to identify and move around objects. Other avenues of drone research include making drones that can perch like a bird on a tree branch and that are solar powered, which means they do not have to land to refuel or recharge batteries.

Discuss

Hold a discussion on the advantages and disadvantages of using drones to collect data on wildlife. Begin by explaining to students that even though drones are far less obtrusive than human observers to wildlife, the drones do not go unseen or unnoticed by the animals. Some animals, including birds and chimpanzees, have hit drones that have hovered too close, causing the drones to crash. In other cases, birds have run into drones while flying. A recent study found that the heart rate of black bears increased significantly when they saw or were surprised by a drone.

Drones and Wildlife Research

S.T.E.M. Interactions

Unmanned aerial vehicles (UAVs)—more familiarly known as drones—are quickly becoming a key piece of equipment for wildlife researchers. UAV technology offers safer, less costly, more efficient, and more precise data collection than traditional research methods. According to a 2003 study published in the *Wildlife Society Bulletin*, between the years 1937 and 2000, light aircraft crashes were the number-one cause of death for wildlife biologists in the field. During this time, 91 biologists and other scientists died while conducting fieldwork. Of these deaths, 60 resulted from plane or helicopter crashes. More significantly, these fatal crashes took place while the aircraft were flying at the low altitudes required to track and observe wildlife accurately.

Drones used by wildlife biologists are equipped with cameras and sensors. Digital photos taken from these drones, typically geotagged with the GPS coordinates of where they were taken, can provide a more accurate and permanent record of observations than those that rely on human eyes alone. Photos taken by the drone cameras can be fed into image-recognition programs to help improve population-count accuracy. UAVs used for wildlife research are relatively economical, typically priced between $1,000 and $2,000, depending on the number of cameras and sensors onboard.

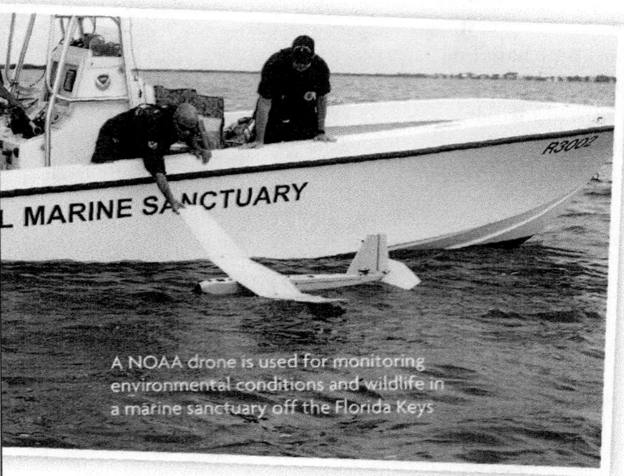

A NOAA drone is used for monitoring environmental conditions and wildlife in a marine sanctuary off the Florida Keys

Lian Pin Koh, a conservation ecologist, and Serge Wich, a primate biologist, cofounded ConservationDrones.org in 2012. The goal of their nonprofit organization is to "share knowledge of building and using low-cost unmanned aerial vehicles for conservation-related applications with conservation workers and researchers worldwide, especially those in developing countries." Koh and Wich first met in early 2011 to discuss the challenges related to wildlife conservation in Southeast Asia. They came up with the concept of using UAVs for conservation project-related research. However, they quickly determined that commercially available UAVs were far too expensive to be practical for use by conservation groups, particularly those in developing countries. So they decided to design their own low-cost UAV.

In early 2012, Koh and Wich tested their prototype UAV (which cost less than $2,000 to build) in North Sumatra, Indonesia. Over a four-day period, their prototype flew more than 30 missions and collected thousands of aerial images and many hours of video footage of the region's tropical rainforests. Following this successful test run, Koh and Wich cofounded ConservationDrones.org as a way to encourage other wildlife conservationists to build and use UAVs for conservation research.

While observation has long been an important part of wildlife research, a major downside is that watching wildlife up close can change the animals' behavior, and this is particularly true for marine animals. Research on penguins and leopard seals in Antarctica conducted by scientists with the National Oceanic and Atmospheric Administration (NOAA) showed that UAVs are less obtrusive and stressful to marine animals than boats are. The researchers noted that the UAVs were "so quiet in flight that we saw no response from the [seals] or penguins at altitudes of around 100 feet." Another project conducted by the NOAA Southwest Fisheries Center noted that marine animals showed no reaction to UAVs flown as low as 30 feet above sea level.

As UAV technology continues to improve, so too will the potential benefits to wildlife scientists in the field.

S.T.E.M. Activity

Research how animals interact with UAVs and the possible effects of these instruments on animals. Then consider ways in which drone design could be further improved to be even less obtrusive. Design a drone for wildlife research, or improve an existing design. Present your design to the class.

512 Unit 5: Ecology

17.4 Social Behavior

KEY CONCEPT **Social behaviors enhance the benefits of living in a group.**

MAIN IDEAS
- Living in groups also has benefits and costs.
- Social behaviors are interactions between members of the same or different species.
- Some behaviors benefit other group members at a cost to the individual performing them.
- Eusocial behavior is an example of extreme altruism.

VOCABULARY

pheromone
altruism
inclusive fitness
kin selection
eusocial

Connect to Your World

Many factors determine if a species lives alone or in a group. Even closely related species have different living patterns. Such is the case with marmots. Woodchucks *(Marmota monax)*, found in the eastern United States, live alone. Yellow-bellied marmots *(Marmota flaviventris)*, which live out west, live in colonies.

MAIN IDEA

Living in groups also has benefits and costs.

Some species, such as the emperor penguins shown in **FIGURE 4.1**, live together in groups. These groups may have a definite social structure or they may have a constantly changing membership. Social behaviors evolve in species in which the benefits of group living outweigh its costs.

CONNECT TO

TAKING NOTES

Use a two-column chart to take notes on the costs and benefits of social behavior.

costs	benefits

Benefits of Social Behavior

Living in a social group provides significant benefits to individuals within the group. Living in a group may lead to improved foraging, as an individual can follow other members of the group to good feeding sites. Immature or non-reproductive members of the group can provide assistance to those who do reproduce by helping to gather food for or protecting newborn members. Living in a group increases the chances of reproductive success. Having more eyes and ears in the group helps in detecting predators. Although groups of animals are easier for predators to spot, a predator can usually capture only one member of a group in any attack, letting the others escape.

FIGURE 4.1 During the breeding season, emperor penguins live in huge colonies made up of between 200 and 50,000 pairs.

Costs of Social Behavior

Living in a group also comes at some cost to an individual. Living together in large groups leads to increased visibility. A group of animals cannot hide from predators as easily as an individual can. Group living also leads to increased competition. A limited amount of resources, such as food or mates, can lead to conflicts between group members. Animals that live together in groups also have an increased chance of contracting diseases or passing parasites to each other. As group size increases, so does the risk.

(A) Connect **What is the benefit of doing group work in class? Are there any drawbacks?**

Differentiated Instruction

ENGLISH LEARNERS

Have students form small groups and number off. Ask them questions about different types of social behavior and the costs and benefits of each type. After each question, give groups time to develop their answer. Then call out a number to identify a spokesperson to answer the question for the group.

Teacher Toolkit, Section C, Numbered Heads Together

SECTION 17.4

Plan and Prepare

Activate Prior Knowledge Discuss with students how aspects of social behavior are closely associated with learning. For example, an animal's ability to identify members of its social group may be based on visual, vocal, or chemical cues. Failure to learn or respond to the appropriate cues or associate them with the appropriate individuals could mean death. **Ask,** What were the consequences of Greylag geese imprinting on a human rather than on other geese? As adults, they failed to recognize their own species, which reduced their reproductive success. Ask students to think of examples of social behavior and learning seen in high school.

Teach

Answers

(A) **Connect** Benefits include combining knowledge of the group and ability to have different people accomplish different tasks. Drawbacks include some people doing more or less than their share of the work.

▼ Teach *continued*

Science Trivia

- Auditory communication can be observed in grasshoppers when they rub their hind legs against their front wings.
- The number of call types in birds varies from about 5 to 23 depending on the species.
- The pheromone bombykol, released by the female silkworm moth, is so concentrated that it takes only one molecule to attract a male. It is theoretically estimated that 1.5 micrograms is enough to attract more than 1 billion males.
- Scents carried both externally and in the bee's stomach provide information on the type of flower available as a food source. When scouts share the scent by regurgitating their stomach contents, their hive mates will fly only to the same species of flower.

Answers

A Infer In large groups, not all individuals need to be vigilant at all times to avoid predators. Some individuals can keep watch while other individuals perform other behaviors, such as eating. The larger number also means that each individual is less likely to be killed by a predator because there are many more individuals from which to choose. Smaller groups require animals to be constantly vigilant, reducing the time for other behaviors such as eating, and also increase the risk of individuals being killed.

FIGURE 4.2 Male satin bowerbirds decorate their bowers with shiny and brightly colored objects (including human-made items) to attract a mate.

CONNECT TO

EVOLUTION

Recall from **The Evolution of Populations** that sexual selection is a factor that violates Hardy-Weinberg equilibrium. When certain traits improve mating success, alleles for these traits increase in frequency within a population, causing the population to evolve over time.

MAIN IDEA

Social behaviors are interactions between members of the same or different species.

Social behaviors are behaviors animals use when interacting with members of their own or other species. These behaviors help to make interactions such as mate selection easier, and they often involve specialized signals.

Communication

Animals use communication as a way to keep in contact with one another, raise alarm in the presence of danger, and attract a mate.

Visual Gestures or postures, such as the submissive posture of a dog with its tail between its legs, may help to identify an animal's status in the group.

Sound Animals often use calls to identify offspring, such as the specific call shared between a young penguin and its parents. Alarm calls and distress calls alert others to the presence of a threat. Mating calls are also used to advertise an animal's readiness to mate, increasing reproductive success.

Touch Bees use their antennae, for example, to interpret the waggle dance performed by a scout bee in order to locate a food source outside the hive.

Chemical Some animals communicate by using pheromones. **Pheromones** are chemicals released by an animal that affect the behavior of other individuals of the same species. Often, these chemicals announce an animal's readiness to mate. Odors are also used to identify group members and mark territory.

Mate Selection

Courtship displays are behaviors most often used by male members of a species to attract females. Scientists theorize that females use courtship displays to judge the condition of their potential mate or the quality of his genes. By being choosy about a mate, a female can help ensure that her offspring have the best chance of survival. While some behaviors may be simple in nature, such as the leg-waving dance display of the jumping spider, other behaviors are more elaborate. For example, as shown in **FIGURE 4.2**, the male satin bowerbird of Australia constructs a nest site, called a bower, that is decorated with brightly colored and shiny objects. Females inspect the bowers when choosing a mate.

Defense

Defensive behaviors include aggressive actions to protect both the individual and the group. For example, when threatened, an elephant herd will form a protective circle surrounding the younger members of the family group. Another defensive behavior is mobbing by birds. When a predator is spotted, flocks of birds, sometimes of different species, will join together to harass the intruder to force it to leave. Keeping watch is another defense tactic. For example, while foraging, one or more members of a giraffe herd will serve as a lookout for the group. While vigilant individuals forage less, they also benefit themselves and their group by keeping an eye out for predators.

A Infer How might the size of a group affect its defense?

Differentiated Instruction

BELOW LEVEL

Have students use a main idea web to take notes on the different types of social behavior. Remind them that communication supports all social behaviors, whether the behavior involves parents taking care of their young, adults mating, or a group mobbing a predator.

Teacher Toolkit, Section C, Main Idea Web

MAIN IDEA

Some behaviors benefit other group members at a cost to the individual performing them.

Individuals that live in a social group often help one another. They may share food or warmth or warn others about an approaching predator. But remember that animals typically perform behaviors that aid their own fitness. In some cases, however, social behaviors seem to reduce the fitness of the individuals that perform them. How could such behaviors evolve?

Types of Helpful Social Behavior

Most social interactions between animals improve the survival and reproduction of both individuals. The three kinds of helpful social behavior are cooperation, reciprocity, and altruism.

Cooperation involves behaviors that improve the fitness of both individuals. For example, lionesses hunt in a group and share the prey they catch, even though only one member of the pride may have made the kill.

Reciprocity involves behaviors in which individuals help other group members with the expectation that they will be helped in return. For example, vampire bats form feeding relationships with one another. Bats that have fed will regurgitate blood for other bats that are hungry. The cost to the donor bat is small. But there is a large benefit for the hungry bat, because vampire bats starve if they do not eat every few nights. By giving up some food, the donor ensures that it will be fed when it is hungry.

Altruism is a kind of behavior in which an animal reduces its own fitness to help other members of its social group. In other words, the animal appears to sacrifice itself for the good of the group. Consider the behavior of Belding's ground squirrels. A Belding's ground squirrel, shown in **FIGURE 4.3**, is a small rodent that lives in large colonies on open grasslands such as the alpine grasslands surrounding the Sierra Nevada mountains in California. When ground squirrels are active during the late spring and summer, they are hunted by predators from the air and on the ground. When an individual spots a predator, it may give an alarm call to alert the rest of the colony. But alarm calls are costly. A calling ground squirrel is twice as likely to be killed as a ground squirrel that does not call. Calling benefits other colony members because it gives them time to escape, but it is harmful to the caller.

Evolution of Altruism

How can we explain the evolution of altruism if behavior is supposed to increase fitness? British evolutionary biologist William Hamilton addressed this puzzle by asking how alleles involved in altruistic behavior could spread through a population. He realized that alleles can be transmitted and therefore spread in a population two ways, either directly from an individual to its offspring or indirectly by helping close relatives survive.

READING TOOLBOX

VOCABULARY

Reciprocity can be thought of in a "You scratch my back, I'll scratch yours" kind of way. Each animal performing the behavior will eventually benefit when another animal performs it in return.

FIGURE 4.3 An adult female Belding's ground squirrel gives an alarm call to alert her relatives to the presence of a predator.

BELOW LEVEL

Describe for students different examples of social behaviors. Ask them to characterize the behaviors in terms of costs and benefits for both individual and populations. Then have students determine the type of social behavior for each example.

Teacher Toolkit, Section D, List-Group-Label

Address Misconceptions

Common Misconception Students may think that animals that live in social groups are not territorial or are less territorial than animals who do not live in social groups.

Correcting the Misconception Although they exhibit altruism, female Belding's ground squirrels are also known to exhibit territoriality. Females share territories with closely related females but chase others away. Animals that live in other kinds of social groups also may be highly territorial. For example, gulls are not altruistic, but they nest in large colonies. Adults aggressively defend their nest and the small space surrounding it from all intruders, including unrelated chicks that may wander in.

Vocabulary

Academic Vocabulary The words **cooperation** and **reciprocity** are used in the same way in everyday language as they are in biology. However, the word **altruism** takes on a different connotation in biology. *Altruism,* in an everyday sense, is the unselfish concern for the welfare of others. In biology, altruistic behavior comes at a cost to the individual.

Take It Further

Belding's ground squirrels engage in what appears to be kissing. In reality, they are sniffing secretions from facial scent glands to identify who are family members and who are not. A Cornell University scientist conducted recognition studies by putting scent-gland samples on plastic cubes and placing the cubes at the entrances of burrows that housed previously tagged individuals. The scientist timed how long squirrels spent sniffing scents from closely related individuals and compared the results with time spent sniffing scents from distantly related and unrelated individuals. The shorter the sniff, the more related was the individual. Squirrels were able to identify individuals of varying degrees of relatedness with great precision.

▼ Teach continued

Science Trivia

Here are some unique ways to which some animal groups are referred:

- a *gang* of elk
- a *business* of ferrets
- a *prickle* of porcupines
- a *crash* of rhinoceros
- a *tribe* of goats
- a *tower* of giraffes
- a *streak* of tigers
- a *barrel* of monkeys
- a *parliament* of owls
- a *murder* of crows
- a *party* of jays
- an *army* of frogs
- an *intrusion* of cockroaches
- a *shiver* of sharks

Answers

A Infer While the group benefits, the individual who performs the altruistic behavior may be killed as a result.

Integrating Genetics

Sister wasps of the genus *Polistes* can share as much as 100 percent of their genes. A female wasp may mate with only one male and store the sperm. Because the male is haploid, the sperm are all genetically identical. The female's eggs are not genetically identical because she is diploid. Her eggs will have about 50 percent of their genes in common.

When egg and sperm unite, the resulting offspring (daughters) will have about 75 percent of their genes in common. ((100 percent from father + 50 percent from mother)/2 = 75 percent) If a mother's eggs have identical genotypes, which is possible, then sisters will share 100 percent of their genes. **Ask,** How would you expect the genotypes of sisters to compare with the genotypes of mothers and daughters? Sisters are more genetically similar (75 percent). Mothers and daughters share only about half of the same genes.

When an animal reproduces, its offspring gets half of its alleles. But its relatives also share some of the same alleles, in the following proportions:

- Parents and siblings share 50 percent of the animal's alleles.
- Nephews and nieces share 25 percent of its alleles.
- First cousins share 12.5 percent of its alleles.

The total number of genes an animal and its relatives contribute to the next generation is called its **inclusive fitness.** It includes both direct fitness from reproduction and indirect fitness from helping kin survive. When natural selection acts on alleles that favor the survival of close relatives, it is called **kin selection.**

If kin selection explains the squirrels' altruism, callers should be closely related to others in the group. Ground squirrel colonies are made up of closely related females and unrelated males. Males do not call much. Nor do adult females foraging alone. The ones that risk their lives are adult females foraging near their daughters, siblings, and nieces. They are warning their relatives.

A Infer **Why is altruistic behavior not very common?**

MAIN IDEA

Eusocial behavior is an example of extreme altruism.

Relationships within populations of some social animals are very specialized. **Eusocial** species live in large groups made up of many individuals, most of whom are members of nonreproductive castes such as workers or soldiers. All of the young in the colony are the offspring of one female, called the queen. Other adults look for food, defend the colony, care for the queen, and raise her offspring. Eusocial behaviors likely evolve by kin selection.

READING TOOLBOX

VOCABULARY

The term *eusocial* comes from the Greek prefix *eu-*, which means "good, well, or true" and the Latin word *socius*, which means "companion."

Social Insects

Many social insects, such as bees, ants, and wasps, are haplodiploid, which means their sex is determined by the number of chromosome sets in an individual. Males are haploid and females are diploid. Female social insects produce daughters through eggs fertilized by sperm. Unfertilized eggs produce sons. In these animals, daughters share half of their mother's alleles but all of their father's alleles. Sisters therefore share up to 75 percent of their alleles overall with one another, compared with 50 percent in humans and most other animals. The very close relationship between sisters in a colony may influence the evolution of eusociality in these insects.

As shown in **FIGURE 4.4**, weaver ants are one example of a eusocial insect species. The three main castes of this species are a queen, major workers, and minor workers. The worker ants work together to weave their nests from leaves that hang from branches throughout one tree or several trees located next to one another. The ants communicate by secreting pheromones. For example, the queen secretes pheromones that induce workers to groom or feed her. If threatened, major worker ants may release pheromones to call in reinforcements to help protect the nest.

Differentiated Instruction

PRE-AP

Ask students to explain how the percentages for allele sharing (at the top of the page) were derived. Assign each bulleted statement to a different group of students. Encourage students to use diagrams of meiosis to support their explanations. Invite them to present their explanations to the class. (Remind students that the percentages given are averages.)

Teacher Toolkit, Section C, Think-Pair-Share

BELOW LEVEL

Help students with the term *haplodiploid* by having them break down the word. *Haplodiploid* becomes *haplo* (haploid males) and *diploid* (females).

Teacher Toolkit, Section D, New Word Analysis

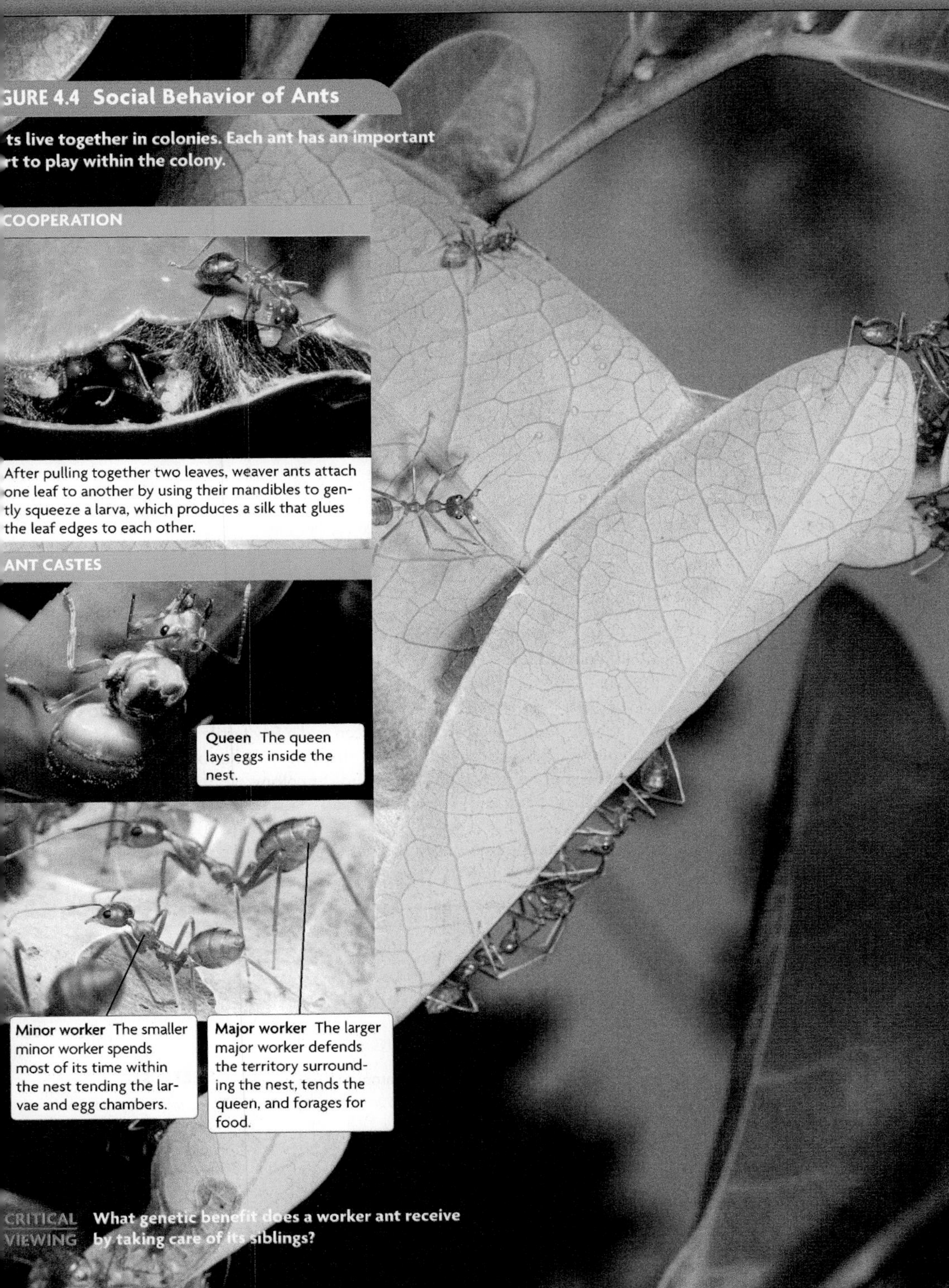

GURE 4.4 Social Behavior of Ants
ts live together in colonies. Each ant has an important
rt to play within the colony.
COOPERATION
After pulling together two leaves, weaver ants attach one leaf to another by using their mandibles to gently squeeze a larva, which produces a silk that glues the leaf edges to each other.
ANT CASTES
Queen The queen lays eggs inside the nest.
Minor worker The smaller minor worker spends most of its time within the nest tending the larvae and egg chambers.
Major worker The larger major worker defends the territory surrounding the nest, tends the queen, and forages for food.
CRITICAL VIEWING What genetic benefit does a worker ant receive by taking care of its siblings?
Chapter 17: Animal Behavior 517

HANDS-ON ACTIVITY

If you have access to an ant farm or a beehive with a glass viewing panel, let student groups take turns observing the insects and taking notes on how they behave. Students may be able to identify queens and the different kinds of workers by their activities. Students will probably be able to see the bees dance.

TEACH FROM VISUALS

FIGURE 4.4 Point out the three castes of the weaver ant shown in the figure. Tell students that after mating, the queen sheds her wings and seals herself into the nest, where she begins egg-laying. She will lay eggs for the rest of her life.

Take It Further

Army ants (*Eciton burchellii*) are found in tropical and subtropical regions of Central and South America. Colonies may contain up to two million individuals. Army ants are carnivorous swarm feeders that must migrate daily to find enough food. The lead workers leave a chemical signal on the trail for the colony to follow, because army ants are blind. They can travel at a speed of up to 20 meters per hour. On a given day, army ants can devastate an area larger than 1800 square yards (1500 m^2) and eat up to 100,000 animals. Army ants have been known to eat other ants, lizards, chickens, goats, pigs, and scorpions.

A temporary camp, called a **bivouac,** is set up each night to protect the queen. Between 150,000 and 700,000 ants work cooperatively to join their bodies together with their mandibles to make the bivouac, which can be up to a meter across. The ants also show other cooperative behaviors when crossing a stream (forming bridges by interlocking their legs and bodies) and when caught in a flood (sticking together to form a floating ball).

Answers

A Critical Viewing Because ants are haplodiploid, a worker ant is helping its close relatives when it takes care of its siblings.

▼ Teach *continued*

DATA ANALYSIS

Discuss

Have students describe the type of data given here. **Ask,** Why would you use a bar graph to depict the data shown here? The data are not continuous; each behavior is independent of the others.

Answers

1. Active perching = 41.2%; Hunting flight = 49.4%; Cruising flight = 1.1%; Other flight = 1.8%; Feeding nestlings = 6.6%. Behavior should be on the *x*-axis, and Time (%) on the *y*-axis.
2. Kites spent the most time in hunting flight in order to consume enough prey to meet their energy needs.

Ⓐ **Apply** Eusocial species are highly related to one another, which ensures that similar genetic material continues to be passed on to future generations.

Online Student Resources, Data Analysis Practice

▼ Assess and Reteach

Assess Use the Section Self-Check or Section Quiz, both available at **HMHScience.com**.

Reteach Conduct a rapid-fire question-and-answer session on the costs and benefits of different social behaviors.

DATA ANALYSIS

CONSTRUCTING BAR GRAPHS

An ethogram is a catalogue of the types of behaviors an animal may perform. A time budget shows how much time organisms spend engaged in each type of behavior. Scientists can use these time budgets to compare patterns of behavior between different species, or between different sexes or age groups of the same species.

Table 1 contains data that were recorded through observations of male and female black-shouldered kites, a type of hawk, during the summer.

1. **Graph Data** Construct a time budget that shows the percent of time (per 24-hour period) the hawks spent in each behavior. (**Hint:** Remember to convert the amount of time to a percent before graphing.)
2. **Analyze** What behavior did the hawks spend the most time engaged in? Why do you think this behavior was most common?

TABLE 1. KITE BEHAVIOR

Behavior	Time (min)
Active perching	162
Hunting flight	194
Cruising flight	4
Other flight	7
Feeding nestlings	26

Source: Jaksic et al. *The Condor* 89:4.

Other Eusocial Animals

Eusocial termites, snapping shrimp, and naked mole rats are all normal, diploid animals. But their colonies are still made up of closely related animals. These animals often live in areas where it is difficult for individuals to survive on their own. For example, naked mole rats live in colonies of 70 to 80 individuals dominated by a single queen and a few fertile male "kings." Most of the colony are the queen's siblings or offspring. Nonreproducing adults are either soldiers or workers. Soldiers defend the colony, while workers work together as a chain gang to dig through the soil to find edible tubers. This eusocial behavior may have evolved due to the amount of work needed to find food. If leaving the colony leads to starvation, kin selection may favor staying in the burrow to work together as a group instead.

Ⓐ Apply **How are eusocial behavior and a species' level of relatedness connected?**

17.4 Formative Assessment

REVIEWING ➊ MAIN IDEAS

1. Outline the costs and benefits of living in a group.
2. Use an example to explain what social behavior is.
3. What are the three types of helpful behavior?
4. What characteristic makes a social group **eusocial**?

CRITICAL THINKING

5. **Connect** Give an example of reciprocal behavior from everyday life.
6. **Analyze** Why might a juvenile scrub jay help its parents raise a new brood of chicks instead of building its own nest?

CONNECT TO GENETICS

7. How is a haplodiploid species different from a diploid species?

17.4 FORMATIVE ASSESSMENT

1. *Sample answer:* Cost—predators can spot large groups more easily; benefit—the predator is less likely to catch a particular individual.
2. Social behaviors are interactions among members of the same species. For example, giraffes often browse together, and one or more individuals may serve as lookouts for predators while other individuals feed.
3. cooperation, reciprocity, altruism
4. Most members of the group do not reproduce; only one (or a few) females in the group have offspring.
5. In the student's example, both parties must benefit, but one party receives a delayed benefit.
6. An animal shares the same number of genes with its siblings and its offspring. If young adults help raise their siblings, it gives them the same inclusive fitness by helping kin survive.
7. In haplodiploid species, males result from unfertilized eggs (haploid) and females result from fertilized eggs (diploid). In diploid species, both sexes result from fertilized eggs and have two sets of chromosomes (one from each parent).

17.5 Animal Cognition

OCABULARY
gnition
sight
ltural behavior

KEY CONCEPT **Some animals other than humans exhibit behaviors requiring complex cognitive abilities.**

MAIN IDEAS
- Animal intelligence is difficult to define.
- Some animals can solve problems.
- Cognitive ability may provide an adaptive advantage for living in social groups.

Connect to Your World

No one would deny that humans are intelligent animals. We surround ourselves with invented objects, from the clothes we wear to the buildings in which we live. But from where did human cognition come? And do other animals share aspects of this ability to think about the world?

MAIN IDEA
Animal intelligence is difficult to define.

In the first half of the 20th century, the focus of many animal intelligence studies was determining whether a certain animal was "intelligent" according to human standards. Today, learning how an animal's level of intelligence compares with a human's is no longer a focus of research. Instead, as shown in **FIGURE 5.1**, scientists study an animal's cognitive abilities. **Cognition** is the mental process of knowing through perception or reasoning. Cognitive behavior also includes awareness and the ability to judge. Animals with a higher level of cognition can solve more complex problems.

In contrast to intelligence, which is difficult to define and measure, cognitive abilities can be more objectively described and measured. However, even an animal's cognitive abilities can be difficult to distinguish from other factors that might be affecting an animal's behavior.

GURE 5.1 While considered have fewer cognitive abilities an other primates, studies ve shown that lemurs have e ability to remember long quences of images and can ace images in the correct order.

For example, in the early 1900s, a horse in Germany nicknamed Clever Hans seemed to be able to solve math questions by using its hoof to tap out the correct answer. However, upon closer inspection it was found that the horse's ability to tap out the correct answer had nothing to do with mathematical skills. Instead, it was relying on changes in the posture or facial expressions of its trainer. The horse was able to perceive the increased tension in its trainer when it neared the correct answer, and would stop tapping its hoof. This example illustrates how difficult it can be to determine the cognitive abilities of animals. While the horse was unable to solve mathematical problems, it can be argued that its ability to perceive changes in its trainer's posture is an example of cognition on a different level.

A Analyze **Why do scientists focus on an animal's cognitive abilities rather than its "intelligence" when studying animal behavior?**

Differentiated Instruction

ENGLISH LEARNERS

Have students create a two-column chart with the column headings *Main Ideas* and *Details*. In the first column, students should list main ideas, concepts, issues, and/or people. In the second column, have students give details. For the *Main Ideas* column, students may use the blue main idea headings, such as "Animal intelligence is difficult to define." Details could be "intelligence is subjective" and "cognition can be described and measured."

Teacher Toolkit, Section C, Two-Column Notes

SECTION 17.5

Plan and Prepare ▼

Activate Prior Knowledge Discuss with students how they learned to perform a task such as tying their shoe. **Ask,** How did you learn to do new things as a child? *Sample answer:* taught by an adult, imitation, trial and error Tell students that other animals think, solve problems, and learn in similar ways. Remind students that these behaviors have adaptive value, allowing the animals to survive an enormous variety of situations.

Teach ▼

Vocabulary

Academic Vocabulary When studying animal cognition, students will encounter many terms used to describe it. Have students look up the definitions of the following words.

perception	*reasoning*
comprehension	*thinking*
learning	*knowledge*

Answers

A Analyze Intelligence is subjective, while cognitive abilities can be objectively defined and measured.

Teach continued

ONLINE Biology
HMHScience.com

To learn how scientists study cognition in dolphins, birds, and chimps, have students do the WebQuest for this chapter at **HMHScience.com**.

Take It Further

Off the coast of Australia, bottlenose dolphins have been observed carrying sponges on their snouts. Scientists infer that the dolphins use the sponges as a fishing tool to probe the sea floor for fish and protect themselves from being stung by a stonefish. It appears that mothers teach this behavior to their daughters. Scientists reasoned that if the behavior were genetic, they would see males engaging in the behavior; but they do not.

Other **cultural behaviors** in cetaceans include these amazing observations:

- Bottlenose dolphins in Laguna, Brazil, herd schools of fish toward the beach and signal people fishing along the shore to cast their nets. Fish that escape the nets are then caught by the dolphins. This has been occurring since 1847.
- Female killer whales in Argentina take their young on practice seal hunts. The mothers rush toward the beach with their offspring, even if seals are not in sight, to teach them how to hunt.
- Male humpback whales that are spread out across entire oceans change their songs at almost the same time.

Answers

A Contrast Associative learning is trial-and-error learning, while insight is the ability to solve a problem mentally without repeated trial and error.

WebQuest
HMHScience.com
GO ONLINE
Animal Cognition

MAIN IDEA

Some animals can solve problems.

Scientists sometimes study how animals think by giving them problems to solve. If cognition involves the ability to invent new behaviors in new situations, then animals with cognitive abilities should be able to solve problems they have never encountered before. Different species react to new situations with varying amounts of success.

Problem-Solving Behavior

Researchers have observed extremely complex problem-solving behavior in primates, dolphins, and the corvids—a group of birds that includes crows, ravens, and jays. In one classic study, a chimpanzee was placed in a room containing boxes, sticks, and a banana hung out of reach. At first, the chimp sat around and did nothing. But after a while it suddenly piled up the boxes and climbed up to knock down the fruit with a stick. This ability to solve a problem mentally without repeated trial and error is called **insight.**

Tool Use

Tools are inanimate objects that help an animal accomplish a task, such as collecting hard-to-reach foods. A number of different animals use tools. For example, Australian bottlenose dolphins use pieces of sponge to cover their snouts when foraging. In addition to protecting their noses from stonefish stings, this method also helps to scare up fish from the ocean floor. Some primates and New Caledonian crows have been observed making tools. Chimpanzees trim sticks to make termite probes. As shown in **FIGURE 5.2,** brown capuchin monkeys use rocks to crack open palm nuts. In one experiment, crows given straight wires bent the wire to make a hook and then used it to fish food out of a tube. Tool use itself is not a sign of cognitive ability. But making tools suggests that an animal can understand cause and effect, and can make predictions about its own behavior.

FIGURE 5.2 Brown capuchin monkeys use a rock to crack open the hard shells of palm nuts.

A Contrast What is the difference between insight and associative learning?

MAIN IDEA

Cognitive ability may provide an adaptive advantage for living in social groups.

Animals we recognize as the most "intelligent" often have two things in common. They have relatively large brains for their body size, and they live in complex social groups. More neurons may mean more interconnections and greater opportunities for complex behaviors to emerge. But evidence suggests that it is just as important to live in a group with a complex social system.

Differentiated Instruction

PRE-AP

The Think Tank exhibit at the Smithsonian National Zoological Park asks visitors several questions to get them to think about the nature of tools and their use.

- Can a tool be alive?
- Can a tool be a part of the user's body?
- Must the user hold or carry the tool?
- Must the user manipulate the tool?

Have students select one of these questions and write an argument for or against it. Encourage students to give specific examples to support their position.

Teacher Toolkit, Section C, Quick-Write

FIGURE 5.3 Elephants are social animals that form close bonds within their group.

Animals that live in large groups with a definite social structure, such as the elephants shown in **FIGURE 5.3**, are surrounded by politics. Surviving and reproducing depend on remembering and being able to use a vast amount of information to the individual's advantage. These animals must be able to

- identify other individuals in the group
- remember which individuals are their allies and rivals
- keep track of the constantly changing state of affairs among individuals
- use this information to their own advantage

Cultural behavior is behavior that is spread through a population by learning, rather than by selection. The key to cultural behavior is that the behavior is taught to one generation by another. The development of cultural behavior does not require living in complex societies. For example, some scientists would argue that the transmission of birdsong is an example of cultural behavior. However, living close together in social groups may help to enhance the transmission and expression of cultural behaviors.

A Connect **What is an example of cultural behavior from your life?**

17.5 Formative Assessment

SELF-CHECK Online HMHScience.com GO ONLINE

REVIEWING MAIN IDEAS

1. Why is animal intelligence difficult to define?
2. Use an example to explain what solving a problem by using **insight** means.
3. Explain how living in a complex social group might select for increased cognitive abilities.

CRITICAL THINKING

4. **Apply** In Section 2, you learned about the potato-washing behavior of snow monkeys. Is this an example of **cultural behavior**? Explain your reasoning.
5. **Analyze** There are three keys on a table. How might you use insight to determine which key opens a nearby door?

CONNECT TO SCIENTIFIC PROCESS

6. Why are scientists so interested in studying primate behavior? What might scientists learn about human behavior?

17.5 FORMATIVE ASSESSMENT

1. Intelligence is subjective, which makes it difficult to define.
2. Insight is the ability to solve a problem mentally without repeated trial and error. For example, a crow will often choose a stick of the right length on its first try when trying to dislodge food from a tree.
3. Navigating the social hierarchy depends on remembering and manipulating a lot of information.
4. Yes; the behavior was passed between members of the group by imitation, a type of learning.
5. Insight could be used by inspecting the keyhole and comparing it with the key shape and size.
6. Primates (the mammalian order that also includes humans) are our closest relatives. Studying primate behavior might give insight into the evolution of human behavior.

History of Science

The primatologist **Jane Goodall** has been studying the chimpanzees of Gombe National Park in Tanzania since 1960. Her observations have provided invaluable information toward understanding chimpanzee behavior and culture. In 1960, Goodall observed chimpanzees using sticks as a tool to fish termites out of the ground. This observation challenged the idea that humans were the only toolmakers. She went on to document chimpanzees using various other objects such as stems, twigs, rocks, and leaves to perform tasks associated with eating, drinking, investigating, defense, and personal hygiene.

Goodall also observed similarities between chimpanzees and humans in regard to development, facial expressions, child-rearing, and diet. Goodall's observations led her to conclude that chimpanzees have distinct personalities, emotions, and family relationships, just as humans do. Goodall also documented that chimpanzee behavior for tool usage, grooming, and courtship varies between populations of chimpanzees. The only other documented animal species that has such a wide variety of cultural behaviors is humans.

Answers

A Connect *Sample answer:* learning a language or ethnic customs, such as dances or songs, from previous generations

Assess and Reteach

Assess Use the Section Self-Check or Section Quiz, both available at **HMHScience.com**.

Reteach Have students provide examples of cognition in animals as you write their responses on the board. Provide feedback for any incorrect examples that students name.

CHAPTER REVIEW

GO ONLINE

Encourage students to go to **HMHScience.com** for a detailed review of each section, including visuals and vocabulary practice.

Online Student Resources, Vocabulary Practice Worksheet

CHAPTER

17 Summary

BIG IDEA Organisms use instinctive behaviors and learned behaviors to quickly adapt to their environment.

KEY CONCEPTS

17.1 Adaptive Value of Behavior

Behavior lets organisms respond rapidly and adaptively to their environment. A stimulus is a type of information that has the potential to make an organism change its behavior. An animal's behavior can be considered as a way of maintaining homeostasis. Many animal behaviors are responses to stimuli that affect an individual's well-being. Internal and external stimuli interact to trigger specific behaviors. Some behaviors occur in cycles. Hibernation and migration are two behaviors that are controlled by an animal's biological clock.

17.2 Instinct and Learning

Both genes and environment affect an animal's behavior. Innate behaviors are inborn instinctive behaviors. Many behaviors have both innate and learned components. Animals that are able to learn can modify their behavior to adapt to new situations. Classical conditioning and operant conditioning are two examples of associative learning.

17.3 Evolution of Behavior

Every behavior has costs and benefits. Benefits of certain behaviors include increased survivorship and rates of reproduction. Three categories of behavioral costs include energy costs, opportunity costs, and risk costs. Animals perform behaviors for which the benefits outweigh the costs.

17.4 Social Behavior

Social behaviors enhance the benefits of living in a group. Social behaviors are interactions between members of the same species. Altruistic behaviors benefit other group members at the cost of the individual performing them. Eusocial behaviors are an example of extreme altruism.

17.5 Animal Cognition

Some animals other than humans exhibit behaviors requiring complex cognitive abilities. Even though animal intelligence is difficult to define, animal behavior scientists are able to study the cognitive abilities of animals. Characteristics of animal cognition include awareness, perception, reasoning, and judgment. Some animals can solve problems through the use of insight. Cultural behavior is behavior that is spread through a population by learning rather than by selection.

READING TOOLBOX SYNTHESIZE YOUR NOTES

Concept Map Use a concept map like the one below to summarize your notes on cyclical behaviors.

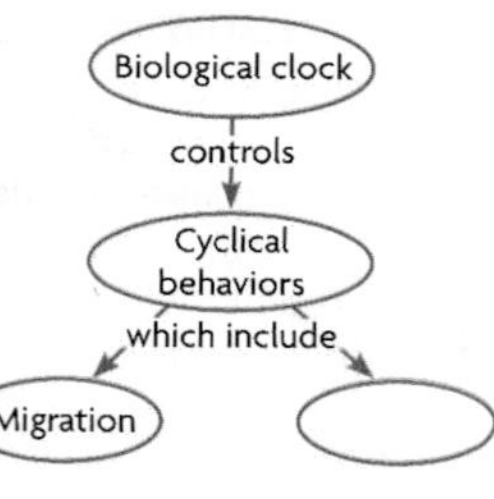

Process Diagram Use a process diagram like the one below to summarize your notes on an animal's response to a stimulus.

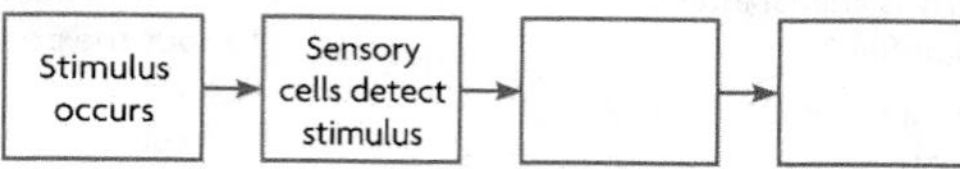

Reviewing Vocabulary

1. Both classical conditioning and operant conditioning are types of associative learning. In classical conditioning, an animal learns to associate a previously neutral stimulus with a behavior that is already being triggered by some other stimulus. In operant conditioning, an animal learns to associate an arbitrary behavior with a positive or negative outcome of performing the behavior.
2. Cultural behavior spreads through a population by learning, rather than by natural selection. Cultural behavior may be learned by imitation, in which animals learn by observing the behaviors of other animals.
3. Territoriality and optimal foraging are two behaviors in which the benefits outweigh the costs. Territoriality refers to the control of a specific area by one or more individuals of a species. Optimal foraging is a theory that states that natural selection should favor behaviors that get animals the most, or optimal, amount, of calories for the cost.
4. A taxis is a movement in a particular direction, either toward or away from a stimulus.
5. Protecting the resources within a territory through territoriality may help to increase a species' survivorship, or chance of surviving to the next year.
6. Altruism is a kind of behavior in which an animal reduces its own fitness to help other members of its social group. Eusocial behavior is an example of extreme altruism, in which a species lives in large social groups where the majority of individuals do not reproduce.
7. An instinct is a complex inborn behavior. Instinctive behavior is characterized as being innate and relatively inflexible. An innate behavior is performed correctly the first time an animal tries it, even when the animal has never been exposed to the stimulus that triggers the behavior.
8. A stimulus causes, or prods, an animal to perform a certain behavior.
9. Habituation occurs when an animal becomes used to, or conditioned, to a certain stimulus and no longer reacts to it.
10. Pheromones are chemicals that carry a signal, or an impulse, that affects the behavior of other animals.
11. An altruistic behavior is one that benefits other individuals, while putting the animal that is performing the behavior at risk.
12. Kinesis is a random movement that results from an increase in activity levels due to a stimulus.

7 Review

INTERACTIVE Review
HMHScience.com

GO ONLINE

Review Games • Concept Map • Section Self-Checks

APTER VOCABULARY

.1	stimulus kinesis taxis circadian rhythm biological clock		habituation imprinting imitation classical conditioning operant conditioning	17.4	pheromone altruism inclusive fitness kin selection eusocial
.2	instinct innate releaser	17.3	survivorship territoriality optimal foraging	17.5	cognition insight cultural behavior

eviewing Vocabulary

mpare and Contrast

scribe one similarity and one difference between e two terms in each of the following pairs.

. classical conditioning, operant conditioning
. cultural behavior, imitation
. territoriality, optimal foraging

cabulary Connections

e vocabulary terms in this chapter are related to ch other in various ways. For each group of words low, write a sentence or two to clearly explain how e terms are connected.

. stimulus, taxis
. survivorship, territoriality
. altruism, eusocial
. instinct, innate

ADING TOOLBOX GREEK AND LATIN WORD ORIGINS

. The term *stimulus* comes from a Latin word, *stimulare*, which means "to goad, prod, or urge." Explain how this meaning relates to *stimulus*.

. The term *habituation* comes from the Latin word *habitus*, which means "condition or habit." Explain how this meaning relates to *habituation*.

. The term *pheromone* comes from a combination of the Greek words *pherein*, meaning "to carry," and *horme*, meaning "impulse." How do these words relate to the meaning of *pheromone*?

. The term *altruism* comes from the Latin word *alter*, meaning "other." How is this meaning related to the definition of an altruistic individual?

. The term *kinesis* comes from the Greek word *kinein*, meaning "to move." Explain this connection.

Reviewing MAIN IDEAS

13. What is the role of the nervous system in an animal's response to a stimulus?

14. Identify the internal and external factors that are likely to lead to migration in songbirds.

15. What are some of the characteristics of innate behaviors?

16. When does habituation occur?

17. How is the ability to adapt behaviors to new situations important for an animal's survival?

18. Describe the benefits and costs of migratory behavior.

19. The territory of a pack of gray wolves can be more than 3000 square kilometers. The alpha male marks the boundaries of the territory with urine. Explain why this time-consuming behavior is important.

20. Groups of small songbirds will often mob an owl or a hawk. They fly around it and call loudly. What is the cost and benefit of this behavior to the songbirds? Explain your answer.

21. Arctic ground squirrels live in groups and forage for food during daylight. What is the cost of foraging in a group?

22. What information might be provided to potential mates by a courtship display such as the competitive performances of sage grouses?

23. In the meerkat group, one animal always stands guard and sounds an alarm call if a bird of prey is sighted. Why is this an altruistic behavior?

24. What are the characteristics of eusocial behavior?

25. What is the connection between cognitive ability and insight?

Reviewing Main Ideas

13. The nervous system generates a response to the stimulus.
14. internal: amount of fat stored in the body; external: the time of year, which brings with it certain temperatures and day lengths
15. Innate behaviors are instinctive and relatively inflexible.
16. when an animal learns to ignore a repeated stimulus, even if it may trigger an innate response
17. If an animal cannot learn from a negative experience and modify its behavior to avoid repeating that experience, it might be injured or killed.
18. The benefit is finding food. The costs are energy and putting safety at risk. It takes energy to migrate, and there are dangers along the way.
19. Territory is important to secure a food supply. Without adequate prey, it would be difficult to supply enough food for growing pups and the adults in the pack.
20. The benefit is that it alerts all the birds to the presence of a predator and makes it harder for the predator to surprise its prey. The cost would be energy involved in performing the behavior.
21. The cost is that the group of ground squirrels is more visible to predators than is a single ground squirrel.
22. Courtship displays help to determine a potential mate's condition and gene quality. A particular posture can also communicate an animal's status within the group.
23. The guard meerkat is risking its own life to save the other members of the group. The bird of prey may hear and see the guard meerkat while the others escape.
24. caste system, sterile individuals, high level of relatedness
25. Animals with increased cognitive abilities are often able to solve problems by insight, so they can solve a problem mentally without repeated trial and error.

Chapter 17: Animal Behavior 523

Critical Thinking

26. Alarm clock sound is external; the hunger that makes you take another slice of toast is internal; outside temperature is external; feeling the need for a lighter-weight jacket is internal because the heavier jacket made you feel too warm.
27. The zookeeper could provide the otter with a food reward each time it is on the scale. This would condition the otter to associate being on the scale with a positive reinforcement.
28. Chasing down prey requires energy and involves the risk of an injury. The benefits are that an older, weaker animal is easier to catch and minimizes both the energy spent on hunting and the risk of injury. A group of animals might have a better chance of catching prey than an individual, and this increases survivorship. Because all adults help feed the pups, this increases reproductive success.
29. Since the male and female perform the call together, it is important to mate selection. Because it is loud enough for other cranes to hear it, the call is also important for territorial defense.
30. This behavior was insight. The bag was opened successfully without having to try out other methods. There was no repeated trial and error.

Interpreting Visuals

31. The adults are protecting the babies.
32. The benefit for the baby is protection from predators. The cost to the adults is being more exposed to predators.
33. The benefit to the baby outweighs the cost to the adults. Protecting the baby helps ensure reproductive success for the elephant family. Adult elephants are so big and strong that the risk of being hurt by a predator is not very great.

Critical Thinking

26. Connect Your alarm clock wakes you up, and you get ready for school. You eat breakfast but then eat one more slice of toast. After stepping outside, you go back in to get a lighter jacket. Identify all the stimuli in this scene and whether they are internal or external.

27. Apply A zookeeper needs to use a scale to measure the weight of an otter. How might she use operant conditioning to get the otter onto the scale?

28. Analyze Gray wolves live in packs with about 6 to 15 members. Young pups remain behind while the older animals hunt for prey as a group. They often seek out old, sick, and slower prey animals. All of the adults regurgitate food for the pups. Suggest two costs and two benefits of gray wolf feeding behavior.

29. Infer The unison call is performed by a pair of whooping cranes. The male and female each have their own notes and perform this call often when they arrive at their nesting area. Suggest some reasons why the birds perform this call.

30. Apply You buy a bag of raisins. There are no directions on how to open it. There is no tab to pull. You do not have scissors to cut the bag open. You examine the bag for a few seconds and then pull the seams of the sealed top apart to open it. What type of problem-solving behavior did you demonstrate? Explain your answer.

Interpreting Visuals

Use the photograph to answer the next three questions.

31. Infer Why do you think the baby elephants are traveling between the adults?

32. Analyze For which elephants might there be a benefit for this type of behavior and for which elephants might there be a cost?

33. Evaluate If there is a benefit, does it outweigh the cost? Explain your answer.

Analyzing Data Construct a Bar Graph

The graph below shows a time budget for different behaviors exhibited by grizzly bears in a national park in the Yukon Territory, Canada. Use the data to answer the next three questions.

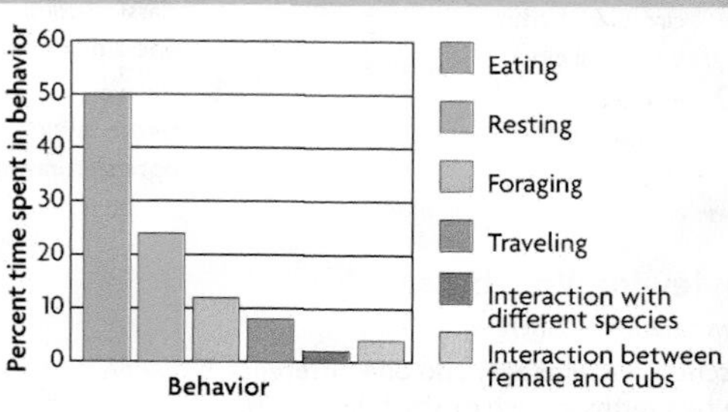

Source: MacHutchon Ursus 12:2001.

34. Analyze What behavior did the bears engage in most of the time?

35. Analyze Do the bears interact more often with other bears or with other species in this park?

36. Infer What can you infer about the habitat based on the data for foraging and eating?

Making Connections

37. Write a Fable You may remember reading Aesop's fables as a child. A fable is a story that ends with a moral, or lesson, such as "the early bird gets the worm." This chapter described reasons for animal behaviors, various types of responses, and the situations in which behaviors might occur. Write a short fable about an animal's behavior, in which the moral of the story illustrates the adaptive value of the behavior.

38. Analyze Consider again the chimpanzee shown on the chapter opener. Why might scientists be interested in studying tool use in primates such as chimpanzees?

Analyzing Data

34. eating
35. with other bears
36. Because they spend only a small amount of time looking for food compared to the time they spend eating the food, it is likely that when they do find a location with food, there is a lot of it. They do not have to spend too much time looking for food.

Standards-Based Assessment

Record your answers on a separate piece of paper.

MULTIPLE CHOICE

1 Students plan an experiment to determine whether fish exhibit different feeding behaviors when presented with food flakes of different colors. The students predict that fish will be able to see brightly colored flakes more easily and will therefore eat more of these flakes. This prediction ***most closely*** resembles a scientific —

A theory

B hypothesis

C conclusion

D law

2 A female ground squirrel may send out a call warning her offspring that a predator is near. Often, the mother sacrifices her own life since the predator can more easily locate her from the call. Even though this behavior results in death, it is beneficial to her in that —

A half of her alleles are preserved in each offspring

B all of her alleles are preserved in each offspring

C the predator may be less likely to attack the population again

D the alleles that caused her behavior will no longer be in the gene pool

3 When a frog hunts, it catches its prey with flicks of its long, sticky tongue. Energy obtained from eating the insect that is not used or stored in the body is —

A passed on to offspring

B recycled within the frog

C lost to the environment as heat

D available to organisms that eat the frog

THINK THROUGH THE QUESTION

Consider the flow of energy through an energy pyramid. In which directions does energy flow?

4

The action illustrated above will ***most likely*** result in a response produced by the —

A nervous system

B respiratory system

C endocrine system

D immune system

5

Alleles for Rabbit Fur Color and Nose Color

Allele	Trait
F	Gray Fur
f	Brown Fur
N	Pink Nose
n	Black Nose

In a hypothetical rabbit species, fur color and nose color are traits that are each controlled by one gene that can occur in a dominant form or a recessive form. Females of the species prefer to mate with gray males with pink noses over brown males with black noses. A gray female (*Ff*) with a black nose (nn) mates with a gray male (*Ff*) with a pink nose (Nn) and produces a litter of eight rabbits. Theoretically, how many of the offspring will have brown fur and black noses?

A 0

B 1

C 2

D 4

Making Connections

37. Stories should include plausible animal behaviors, and morals of stories should illustrate adaptive nature of behavior (for example, an early bird gets the worm, behavior leads to survival of bird).

38. Learning about tool use in primates may provide researchers with clues as to how tool use developed in humans.

Standards-Based Assessment

The Standards-Based Assessment questions will help students prepare for their final examination in the course. If you wish to give students practice in coding their answers, look for the Standards-Based Assessment Answer Sheet at **HMHScience.com**. To give students practice under timed testing conditions, allow them five minutes per question.

Question	Answer	Depth of Knowledge	Cognitive Complexity
1	B	I	L
2	A	II	L
3	C	I	L
4	A	II	M
5	B	IV	H

KEY

Depth of Knowledge
I Recall
II Skill/Concept
III Strategic Thinking
IV Extended Thinking

Cognitive Complexity
L Low
M Moderate
H High

UNIT

5

Introduce

Each day science information is reported in newspapers, magazines, television and radio news, and on the Internet. The scientific research that generates this information often consists of complex data, lengthy reports, and scientific jargon. The information that is of interest to the general public is typically simplified. Sometimes key information is not accurately represented. In addition, people with a certain point of view regarding a controversial issue may take the data out of context and draw conclusions that are not supported.

In 2002, a paper on the climate of Antarctica was published in the January 31 issue of the journal *Nature*. The paper included data collected on temperatures in different areas of Antarctica over a period of time. The researchers, lead by Peter Doran, concluded that the evidence showed an overwhelming warming trend. However, select areas did show a lowering of temperatures. These particular data were used as evidence that Earth's temperatures are actually cooling. This is not what Doran's team reported.

When reading about or listening to news reports about science, students should consider whether or not the scientific data involved have been simplified and possibly misinterpreted. Tell students that Peter Doran says his paper is often cited but not often read. **Ask,** What does it mean that something is taken out of context? don't have complete picture

UNIT 5: ECOLOGY

BIOZINE at HMHSCIENCE.COM

INTERNET MAGAZINE

Go online for the latest biology news and updates on all BioZine articles.

Expanding the Textbook

News Feeds

Science Daily

CNN

BBC

Careers

Bio Bytes

Opinion Poll

Strange Biology

As global temperatures rise and arctic ice melts, polar bears are losing important hunting grounds.

Climate Change—Changing the Planet

Polar bears are on the move. The area of arctic sea ice on which these carnivores hunt seals has declined 34 percent as worldwide temperatures rise. As this ice is lost, polar bears must swim as far as 100 kilometers (about 60 mi) to find their prey. Some of these polar bears cannot make it, and they drown. Now polar bears must compete with grizzly bears. If climate change is changing the shape of one of Earth's coldest regions, how will it affect the rest of our planet?

Current News

Using the Current News section of BioZine at **HMHScience.com,** have students find articles reporting on ecological or environmental issues. Have students consider these questions:

- How do the articles distinguish between short- and long-term effects?
- What data are included in the articles?
- Do you think the information was simplified or altered in such a way that making an informed decision about the issue is difficult?

Opinion Poll

Have students participate in the BioZine online poll and check the results. **Ask**

- Why do you think questions involving the relative health of ecosystems are so contentious?
- How would you describe human impact on the environment?

Ecosystems at Risk

In the 20th century, the average global temperature rose by 0.6°C (1°F). The difference may seem small, but it is an average for the entire globe. Near the poles, the effects of climate change are more dramatic. Since 1949, average annual temperatures in Alaska have risen 1.8°C (3°F)—enough to lengthen the summer melting season for sea ice and glaciers. From 1979 to 2007, Arctic sea ice retreated enough to expose an additional one million square miles of open water—the equivalent of six Californias.

Good and Bad News?

In the rest of the world, the impact of climate change on Earth's species may be mixed. Many animal species, such as birds and butterflies, can move to cooler areas as the climate warms. But insects and microorganisms that cause infectious diseases, such as malaria and yellow fever, are also spreading toward the poles. Some plant species cannot move as quickly as the climate is expected to change, and may become extinct.

Researchers are also finding that changing temperatures can affect animals in surprising ways. The sex of some reptiles, for example, is partially determined by the temperature of the developing egg. A consistent warming trend could cause some reptiles to become extinct by creating entire generations that are all the same sex. Migratory birds and marine mammals also face challenges. For example, birds that wait until their normal migration time to fly north in the spring may arrive too late, missing the best weeks for laying eggs and catching the insects they need to raise their young. In addition, some researchers have predicted that the productivity of phytoplankton, the algae on which ocean food webs are based, may decline in some areas. A change of this sort could cause a domino effect in marine food webs. If phytoplankton levels decline, fish will have less food and will be less numerous. If fish are less numerous, marine mammals and birds will have less to eat too.

In addition, studies show that this increase in global temperatures is linked to a four percent increase in ocean humidity and a six to eight percent increase in rainfall, leading to stronger hurricanes.

TECHNOLOGY STEM

Deep Sea Sediment Coring

Analyzing ocean floor sediments can provide scientists with data about how plants and animals were affected during past climate changes. The process of collecting deep sea sediments is expensive and time-consuming, but the results of this research give scientists a look at what life in the oceans was like millions of years ago.

To study these ancient organisms, scientists need sediment samples that are hundreds of meters long. To obtain these, they must use drills similar to the drills used by the oil and gas industry. Taking these samples requires many hours and can be dangerous if the seas are rough or full of ice. Once scientists have obtained the cores, they first split the core in half lengthwise. One half is sampled for fossils of ancient organisms. This is the "working half." The other half, the "archive half," is saved and stored away so that future scientists who may develop other questions can have access to this difficult-to-obtain material.

By carefully dissecting the working half of the sample, scientists discover microscopic fossils of marine animals. Scientists know that these ancient animals were very sensitive to slight changes in temperature and chemistry. These microfossils can tell scientists how Earth's climate has changed over millions of years.

Read More >> at HMHScience.com

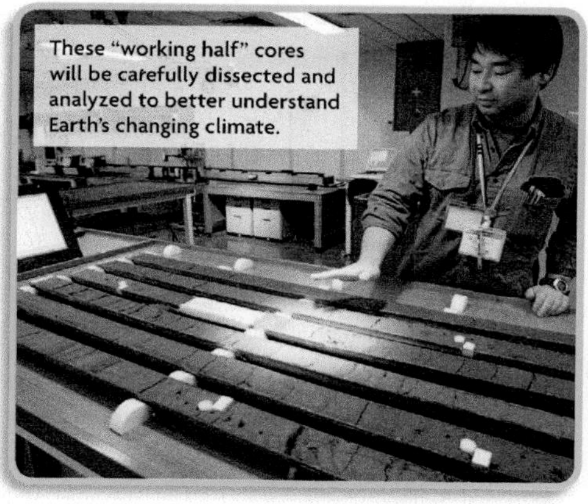
These "working half" cores will be carefully dissected and analyzed to better understand Earth's changing climate.

Expanding the Textbook

Have students go to BioZine at **HMHScience.com** to read more about plants and animals affected by climate change. Have them take notes on different organisms. Students should come to class prepared to discuss the organisms and how they are affected by climate change. Have students identify the conditions that are most often cited as sources of concern.

You could extend the discussion to include students' understanding of the factors that are causing climate change. What is the appropriate role of government in controlling climate change? What is the role of individuals? What groups, organizations, or parties might have a vested interest in the climate change debate? Students can research possible effects of climate change on ecosystems and organisms in their state.

Vocabulary of Climate Change

Students may need clarification of some of the terms used in the discussion of climate change.

global warming—an increase in the average global temperature. This temperature is calculated from data of temperatures from all over Earth. A particular area may have warmer temperatures one year and cooler temperatures the next year, but the average temperature for Earth is increasing.

greenhouse effect—the trapping of heat by Earth's atmosphere. This is a natural process without which Earth's average temperature would be around −18°C. The greenhouse effect increases as the amount of carbon dioxide in the atmosphere increases.

greenhouse gases—gases in the atmosphere that absorb infrared radiation and produce the greenhouse effect. Water vapor, carbon dioxide, and methane are three of the greenhouse gases.

climate—the average weather over a period of time. Weather is the specific conditions of the atmosphere at a particular time and place.

sea ice—ice that forms when ocean water freezes. During the coldest season, sea ice covers about 14 to 16 million square kilometers of the Arctic Ocean and 17 to 20 million square kilometers of the ocean around Antarctica. Glaciers, ice sheets, and ice caps are made up of freshwater ice and are located on land.

permafrost—a layer of permanently frozen soil or ice at or near the surface of the ground. Permafrost may be under a thin layer of soil or a body of water.

Take It Further

Another effect of climate change on ecosystems involves melting permafrost. Permafrost, as its name suggests, is soil or ice that remains frozen all year. It is located under the surface of the ground or bodies of water. More than half of Alaska's surface rests on a layer of permafrost. Most of the state's permafrost is shallow, but in northern Alaska, the permafrost is very deep. Areas farther south in the state may have little or no permafrost.

When permafrost under a body of water melts, water in the lake or pond can drain out. This has a devastating effect on aquatic ecosystems. Scientists have noticed that in many areas of Alaska, lakes and ponds are getting smaller while others have dried up and disappeared.

In areas where permafrost melts and oversaturates the ground, trees begin to die. As the trees die, the boreal forest changes into a wetland. If permafrost melts in well-drained areas, the water will move away from the area, causing the groundwater content to decrease. With less groundwater, the boreal forest changes into a grassland.

As ecosystems change, the plant and animal communities found there also change. This can affect an ecosystem's food web by disrupting feeding relationships among the different trophic levels and the flow of energy.

Computer modeling programs such as this one work to predict the effects of climate change by simulating different temperature increases.

But the news may not be all bad. Some of the same research shows that the same factors that increase the strength of a hurricane also make it less likely that the hurricane will ever make landfall. The retreat of Arctic sea ice may someday make it possible to open a shipping lane through the Arctic Ocean.

Scientists theorize that climate change has been accelerated by increased levels of carbon dioxide in the atmosphere. Many plants, including crops such as cotton, soybeans, wheat, and rice, can benefit from the increase in CO_2. They can absorb the CO_2 and yield more at harvest time as a result. On the other hand, in warmer weather crops may also be more at risk from insect pests and from severe storms or droughts.

Unanswered Questions

Scientists have little doubt that Earth's climate is changing. It is impossible to predict exactly how any ecosystem will be affected by climate change. However, biologists and climatologists are collecting data about processes, including solar radiation, precipitation, evaporation, the transfer of heat by winds and by ocean currents, and the ways in which plants affect climate. They interpret this information using computer models and try to answer questions about how climate change will affect Earth.

- Could climate change alter certain ocean currents, changing Earth's temperatures further?
- How quickly might the polar ice caps melt?
- How have global climate changes affected Earth's ecosystems in the past?
- Is there a way to preserve biodiversity on mountain tops and polar areas where animals and plants have no cooler places to migrate to?

Read More >> at HMHScience.com

CAREERS

Oceanographer in Action

RUTH CURRY

TITLE Oceanographer, Woods Hole Oceanographic Institution

EDUCATION B.S., Geology, Brown University

For Ruth Curry, spending time on the ocean waves has nothing to do with surfing or vacationing. She spends her time studying the ocean currents that affect our lives each day. Ruth Curry is an oceanographer at the Woods Hole Oceanographic Institute, an organization of scientists who research and study how the ocean affects the global environment.

Curry's research focuses on the North Atlantic circulation and the currents that carry warm waters from tropical regions northward. As these warm waters reach higher latitudes, they release heat that warms the air above them and warms the climate of western Europe. As warm water cools, its density increases and it sinks to the bottom of the ocean. There it begins a southward journey back to the tropics. This conveyor belt of water plays an important role in maintaining Earth's climate. Normally, the salinity, or saltiness, of ocean water stays about the same. But changes in global temperatures are melting large sheets of ice in Greenland, which is introducing large amounts of fresh water into the ocean. This fresh water is diluting the ocean water, making it less salty. A decrease in salinity makes ocean waters less dense and prevents them from sinking to the bottom of the ocean. Eventually, the melting of ice sheets in Greenland could cause the North Atlantic currents to slow and eventually stop, leading to dramatic changes in the Northern Hemisphere's climate.

Read More >> at HMHScience.com

BIOZINE HMHScience.com

Have students use the resources available in the BioZine for this unit at **HMHScience.com** to report about recent research on ecosystems and climate change. In addition to the resources available in BioZine, have students work with a librarian to locate the original, primary-source materials. Have students compare data in the reports. **Ask**

- How do different accounts of a research report present the findings?
- What different opinions, if any, were expressed by the researchers themselves?
- What information from the primary source could be taken out of context and used to support an alternate viewpoint?

UNIT 6

Diversity of Life

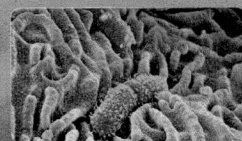

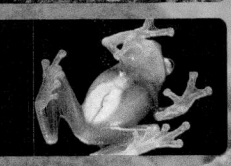

BIOZINE HMHScience.com

Pandemics—Is the Next One on the Way?

TECHNOLOGY **Dissecting a Virus**

CAREER **Epidemiologist**

Unit Project

Purpose **Investigate disease-causing organisms of the Amazon, vaccines required for travel to the area, and measures needed to prevent illness.**

Overview Students write an information packet about health precautions to take for a trip to the Amazon. Students will

- search Internet, textbook, and/or library resources about the Amazon and health concerns for travelers
- provide detailed information about the diseases, the organisms that cause the diseases, and the vaccines and behaviors that tend to prevent illness
- prepare an information packet designed to inform parents, teachers, and students about health precautions involved in traveling to the Amazon

Preparation Make a copy of the project description and rubric for each student. Tell students that their packets will be scored on organization and completeness.

Project Management Allow three weeks for the completion of the project. Have students check in weekly to monitor progress.

Online Student Resources Unit 6 Project

CHAPTER 18

Instruction and Intervention Support

The Tree of Life

① Core Instruction

The **Core Instruction** resources below can be used for all students. Core instruction should be followed by ongoing assessment to determine which students need further help.

Available in both English and Spanish

Available Online

Section	Instruction	PRINT	ONLINE	Labs
18.1	Textbook **The Linnaean System of Classification**	■	●	Creating a Dichotomous Key for Limpet Shells **Video Lab** Dichotomous Keys
	Teaching Visuals Linnaean Classification System (Fig. 1.3)		●	
	PowerPresentation and Notes 18.1		●	
18.2	Textbook **Classification Based on Evolutionary Relationships**	■	●	Constructing a Phylogenetic Tree **QuickLab** Construct a Cladogram
	That's Amazing! Video Inquiry Guitarfish		●	
	Animated Biology Build a Cladogram		●	
	Teaching Visuals Tetrapod Cladogram (Fig. 2.2)		●	
	PowerPresentation and Notes 18.2		●	
18.3	Textbook **Molecular Clocks**	■	●	Modeling DNA Hybridization Bioinformatics (Biotechnology Lab)
	Animated Biology Molecular Clock		●	
	PowerPresentation and Notes 18.3		●	
18.4	Textbook **Domains and Kingdoms**	■	●	Defining Species
	Teaching Visuals The Tree of Life (Fig. 4.3)		●	
	PowerPresentation and Notes 18.4		●	

Additional online resources available for this chapter include **Interactive Whiteboard Resources.**

GO ONLINE! for all your teacher resources at HMHScience.com

2 Support and Intervention

Support and Intervention resources are useful for students who need targeted help beyond the Core Instruction

Resources	PRINT	ONLINE
Assess and Reteach (TE wrap)	■	●
Concept Map		●
Interactive Reader	■	●
Interactive Review Games		●
Section Self-Checks		●
Study Guide B		●
Virtual Investigation Using a Key to Classify		●
Vocabulary Practice Worksheets		●

3 Specialized Support

Students who need more intensive personalized intervention benefit from **Specialized Support** resources.

Resources	PRINT	ONLINE
Chapter Audio Files		●
Differentiated Instruction Inclusion, Below Level, and English Learners (TE wrap)	■	●
ELL Strategies	■	●
Modified Lesson Plans for English Learners		●
Reinforcement Worksheets		●
Study Guide A		●

Extension and Assessment

Enrichment and Challenge

Resources	PRINT	ONLINE
Active Reading Worksheets		●
Data Analysis Practice Worksheet		●
Differentiated Instruction Pre-AP (TE wrap)	■	●
Pre-AP Activity What's in a Name?, Building a Cladogram		●
The Inside Story and **Take It** Further (TE wrap)	■	●
Unit Project		●
WebLinks		●
WebQuest Classify a Sea Cucumber (18.4)		●

Assessment

Resources	PRINT	ONLINE
Alternative Assessment		●
Chapter Tests A and B		●
Diagnostic Test		●
ExamView Banks		●
Extended Response Test		●
Online Assessment System		●
Section Quizzes		●
Standards-Based Assessment	■	●

CHAPTER 18

Chapter Overview

- **Section 1** introduces Linnaean taxonomy as a method of classifying and naming organisms based on physical and structural similarities.
- **Section 2** explains the classification of organisms based on common ancestry using evidence from living species, the fossil record, and molecular data.
- **Section 3** explains how evolutionary time can be measured by mutation rates to identify divergence between species from a common ancestor.
- **Section 4** explains the hierarchy of the classification system beginning with domains and kingdoms.

▼ Focus and Motivate

How would you classify this organism?

Help students think about how classifications are made. **Ask,** How would you classify the sport of soccer? *Sample answer:* team sport, uses a round ball, non-contact, game divided into two halves

Have students discuss different ways that living things can be classified. **Ask,** What characteristics could you use to classify the pangolin in the photograph? external physical traits, behavior, what it eats, where it lives, its genetic make-up Explain that pangolins are classified as mammals despite lacking hair because they nourish their young with milk.

BIOZINE
HMHScience.com

Students can access BioZine at **HMHScience.com** to check the daily science news feeds.

CHAPTER 18 The Tree of Life

BIG IDEA Organisms can be classified based on physical and genetic characteristics, which reveal their evolutionary relationships.

ONLINE BIOLOGY HMHScience.com

ONLINE Labs

- Creating a Dichotomous Key for Limpet Shells
- **QuickLab** Construct a Cladogram
- Modeling DNA Hybridization
- Defining Species
- Constructing a Phylogenetic Tree
- Bioinformatics
- **Video Lab** Dichotomous Keys
- **Open Inquiry Lab** The Linnaean System of Classification
- **Open Inquiry Lab** Classification Based on Evolutionary Relationships

Student Activity

Purpose **Have teams of students practice making the kinds of observations and decisions that are required to develop and use a classification system.**

Materials (per team)

Provide each group with five books of varying subjects and physical characteristics. Include one or two books from the school library, which will have already been marked by a classification method such as the Dewey decimal classification.

How would you classify this organism?

Pangolins, native to Africa and Asia, are not closely related to any other living mammals. Their backs and tails are covered with large scales similar in arrangement to dinosaur bone plates. Pangolins do not have teeth. Instead, they have an organ similar to a bird's gizzard. Due to these unique traits, pangolins are classified into their own group within class Mammalia.

READING TOOLBOX **This reading tool can help you learn the material in the following pages.**

USING LANGUAGE

Mnemonics Mnemonic devices are tools that help you remember lists or parts in their proper order. Use the first letter of every word that you want to remember as the first letter of a new word in a memorable sentence. You may be more likely to remember the sentence if the sentence is funny.

YOUR TURN

Create mnemonic devices that could help you remember all of the parts of the following groups of items.

1. the names of all of your teachers
2. the 12 months of the year

Activate Prior Knowledge

Introduce the "tree of life" as a metaphor of the relationships and evolution of all the life on Earth. **Ask**

- If we imagine a tree of life that represents the evolution of life over billions of years, what might the leaves represent? species, or different groups of closely related organisms (families)
- What might the branches, both the small and the large, represent? Large branches could represent ancestral species from which the smaller branches diverged and evolved over time.
- What might the trunk represent? the earliest life forms from which all living organisms have evolved

Preview Vocabulary

Word Origins The words *kingdom* and *domain* share the same word part *dom*. This old English root means "state" or "power." Both *kingdom* and *domain* relate to a territory that someone either controls or owns, a king, for example. In biology, the words relate to a sense of belonging by shared characteristics. Tell students they can think of a biological domain as a "superkingdom," one that encompasses smaller biological kingdoms.

Academic Vocabulary In this chapter, students will encounter the word *system* in a new way. A classification system is an organized method of grouping organisms based on similarities. *Systematics* is the science of classification.

Answers

1. Answers will vary. Accept all answers that use a mnemonic device to identify teacher names.
2. Sample answer (JFMAMJJASOND): Jimmy Finds Money and Makes Jane Jump After Sleeping Over Nine Days

Introduce Have students form small teams. Tell them to examine the books provided and develop their own book classification system that places the books into categories based on similarities.

Discuss Have students describe their classification systems. **Ask**

- What criteria did you select in setting up your system? similarities of physical attributes; subject area or genre; language
- Would these systems work if additional books were added? Answers will depend on how well the systems anticipate new additions.
- Do you think any of these books have already been classified by another system? Students may recognize the Dewey decimal classification or the Library of Congress cataloging system if books are marked in these ways.

Explain that there have been many different systems for classifying living things, and that most modern classification schemes are based on evolutionary relationships.

▼ Plan and Prepare

Activate Prior Knowledge Explain to students that while common names are how we identify species in everyday life, science requires a single scientific name for each species. **Ask,** What would be the problem with using common names? There can be many names for the same organism in one language, and the names are entirely different in another language. The large number of common names makes it difficult for scientists to communicate or share data.

▼ Teach

Vocabulary

Academic Vocabulary The terms **diverse** and **diversity** come from a Latin word meaning "in different directions." These terms appear in the context of classification because to understand and quantify the **biodiversity** of Earth, biologists need to know how two or more species are related. By analyzing evolutionary relationships, biologists can sometimes pinpoint when two species diverged from a common ancestor.

18.1 The Linnaean System of Classification

KEY CONCEPT **Organisms can be classified based on physical similarities.**

VOCABULARY

taxonomy
taxon
binomial nomenclature
genus

MAIN IDEAS

- Linnaeus developed the scientific naming system still used today.
- Linnaeus's classification system has seven levels.
- The Linnaean classification system has limitations.

Connect to Your World

The pangolin shown on the previous page may not look like any other animal that you are familiar with. However, scientists classify pangolins as mammals—the same group of animals that includes dogs, cats, mice, and humans. All female mammals have the ability to produce milk. Unlike pangolins, most mammals have hair. Scientists use key characteristics such as these to classify all living things.

READING TOOLBOX

TAKING NOTES

Use a main idea web to take notes about the Linnaean system of classification.

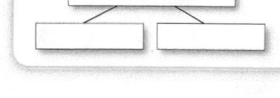

taxonomy — binomial nomenclature — Linnaeus's naming system

MAIN IDEA

Linnaeus developed the scientific naming system still used today.

Before Swedish botanist Carolus Linnaeus introduced his scientific naming system, naturalists named newly discovered organisms however they wanted. In fact, they often named organisms after themselves. Because they had no agreed-upon way to name living things, it was difficult for naturalists to talk about their findings with one another. This all changed in the 1750s, when Linnaeus devised a system that standardized the way organisms are classified and named.

Taxonomy

Taxonomy is the science of naming and classifying organisms. Taxonomy gives scientists a standard way to refer to species and organize the diversity of living things. Linnaean taxonomy classifies organisms based on their physical and structural similarities. Organisms are placed into different levels in a hierarchy—a multilevel scale in which each level is "nested" in the next-higher level. In other words, each level is included in a larger, more general level, which in turn is included in an even larger, more general level.

READING TOOLBOX

VOCABULARY

Taxonomy comes from the Greek *taxis*, which means "arrangement," and *nomie*, which means "method."

A group of organisms in a classification system is called a **taxon** (plural, *taxa*). The basic taxon in the Linnaean system is the species. In this system, species are most commonly defined as a group of organisms that can breed and produce offspring that can reproduce. Linnaeus's system gives each species a scientific name. With few changes, this method of naming is still used today.

Differentiated Instruction

BELOW LEVEL

Create an anticipation guide to evaluate students' comprehension before and after they read the section. Pose true/false statements such as the following:

Within a phylum, a class has more species than an order. T

If two species both have the word fish *in their name, they must be in the same family.* F

The best name for scientists to use for a species is its most popular common name. F

Teacher Toolkit, Section C, Anticipation

PRE-AP

To help students understand how organisms are classified in a hierarchical system, give them the analogy of the United States postal system and how it gives each home a unique address. Have students come up with a seven-step hierarchical order of geographical detail that would lead someone who is outside the continent to their front door. Remind students that the goal is to arrive at a unique place by following a universally understood convention. A good sequence would be North America, United States, state, county, city/town, street, number.

Scientific Names

Binomial nomenclature (by-NOH-mee-uhl NOH-muhn-KLAY-chuhr) is a system that gives each species a two-part scientific name using Latin roots. The first part of the name is the genus. A **genus** (plural, *genera*) includes one or more physically similar species that are thought to be closely related. For example, the genus *Quercus* includes more than 500 species of oak trees. Genus names are always capitalized. They are written in italics or underlined.

VISUAL VOCAB

Binomial nomenclature is a standard naming system that gives each species a two-part name using Latin roots.

two: bi; name: nomial; naming: nomen; system: clature

(1) Genus (2) species

The second part of the name is the species descriptor. It can refer to a trait of the species, the scientist who first described it, or its native location. Like the genus, the species descriptor is written in italics or underlined. However, it is always lowercase. The species descriptor is never written alone because, as **FIGURE 1.1** shows, the same word may be used in different genera. *Quercus alba* is the scientific name for white oak trees (*alba* means "white"), but *Tyto alba* is the scientific name for barn owls.

You may wonder why biologists use scientific names. It may seem easier to use terms such as *white oak* instead of remembering two-part Latin names, as seen in **FIGURE 1.2**. However, scientific names are helpful in many ways. First, genera such as *Quercus* contain hundreds of species. Many of these species have similar common names. Scientific names allow scientists to talk about particular species without confusion. Also, remember that biology is studied all over the world. One species may have several different common names, even within a single country. *Armadillidium vulgare* is the scientific name for pill bugs. However, this species is also called roly-poly, sow bug, and potato bug. Scientific names allow scientists around the world to communicate clearly about living things.

A Contrast **Describe the difference between a genus and a species.**

FIGURE 1.1 The white oak (*Quercus alba*) and the barn owl (*Tyto alba*) belong to different genera. The parts of their scientific names signifying species are both *alba*, meaning "white."

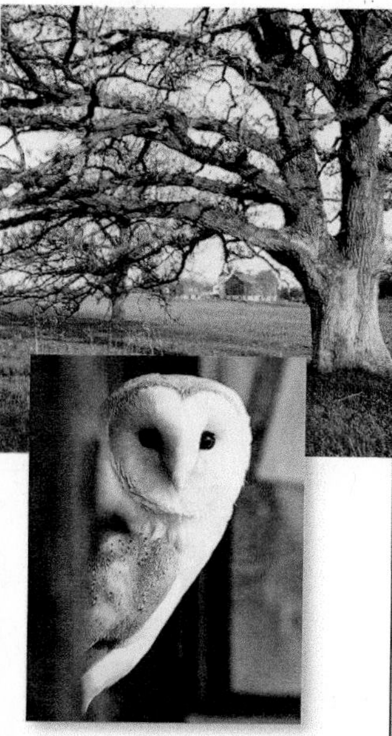

FIGURE 1.2 SCIENTIFIC AND COMMON NAMES

COMMON NAMES	SCIENTIFIC NAME	
	Genus	**species**
Roly-poly, pill bug, sow bug, potato bug	*Armadillidium*	*vulgare*
Dandelion, Irish daisy, lion's tooth	*Taraxacum*	*officinale*
House sparrow, English sparrow	*Passer*	*domesticus*
Mountain lion, cougar, puma	*Puma*	*concolor*
Red maple, scarlet maple, swamp maple	*Acer*	*rubrum*

The Inside Story

He was so serious about his classification work that **Carl Linnaeus** changed his first name to **Carolus,** a Latin transliteration. Linnaeus was compulsive about organizing life on Earth and matters in his own life. Even his private letters were classified into groups and subgroups. At first, he did not think much of his idea to give a species descriptor in addition to the genus, so he referred to them as "trivial names." In time, though, he realized how helpful descriptors were in differentiating between species.

Though his system is still the basis for classification, he classified some animals in ways that now seem odd. For example, he placed the rhinoceros among rodents. To his credit, he bravely suggested the relationship between humankind and apes—an idea that is still unsettling to many people.

Answers

A Contrast Both are groups of the biological classification system. A *species*, however, is a subset of a genus, consisting of a single type of organism. A *genus* is a group of one or more closely related and physically similar species.

TEACH WITH TECHNOLOGY

Plan an Internet activity, either in your classroom or in a computer lab. Provide students with a list of six scientific names of marine fish species that among them have several species descriptors or genus names in common. Have students organize the species into a classification scheme. Students can look up each species online at FishBase or other sites to learn common names as well as the family, class, and order of each species. English learners can use their home language's version of FishBase and share with the class the common names of the species in their language.

Students can also print out illustrations or photos of these species to illustrate their tree or classification scheme. Here is a sample list of species, representing three families, two orders, and two classes:

Makaira nigricans
Acanthurus nigricans
Naso unicornis
Naso brevirostris
Negaprion brevirostris
Negaprion acutidens
Tetrapturus audax
Makaira indica

▼ Teach *continued*

TEACH FROM VISUALS

FIGURE 1.3 Have students follow the diversity of organisms through the different levels. **Ask**

- What animals are dropped as we move from kingdom to phylum? invertebrates
- What well-known Australian animal is excluded from the Carnivora order, which includes all true bears? koala bear
- How can this be? Sharing a common name or having a similar name means very little in terms of actual relatedness. An animal called a bear may not be a true bear.
- From what you can infer from the figure, what are characteristics of animals in the order Carnivora? terrestrial, toothed, four-legged, meat-eating mammals

Vocabulary

Word Origins Students may wonder what relationship the word **tax** has to **taxonomy.** Despite the similarity, the words come from different roots. *Tax* relates to an expression in Old French that means "to touch," which developed into the idea of "touching" someone for a payment or tax. The word **taxi** has the same root, which derives from the **taximeter** that calculates the cost of a ride.

The words *taxonomy* and **taxidermy** share the same root *taxis,* meaning "arrangement." The first is a methodical arrangement of organisms; the second is the preparation and arrangement of, literally, skin—as in the stuffing of animal skin to create a lifelike form.

Answers

Ⓐ **Analyze** cats

MAIN IDEA

Linnaeus's classification system has seven levels.

CONNECT TO

DOMAINS

The tree of life has been updated since Linnaeus's time. Scientists now classify organisms into an even broader category, called the domain, above the kingdom level. You will learn more about domains and kingdoms in **Section 4.**

The Linnaean system of classification has seven levels, or taxa. From the most general to the most specific, these levels are kingdom, phylum (the term *division* is often used instead of *phylum* for plants and fungi), class, order, family, genus, and species. Each level in Linnaeus's system is nested, or included, in the level above it. A kingdom contains one or more phyla, a phylum contains one or more classes, and so forth. The classification of the gray wolf, *Canis lupus,* is shown in **FIGURE 1.3.** Moving down, the levels represent taxa that become more and more specific, until you reach the species level at the bottom.

FIGURE 1.3 The Linnaean Classification System

Linnaean taxonomy classifies living things into a hierarchy of groups called taxa. The classification of the gray wolf is illustrated here.

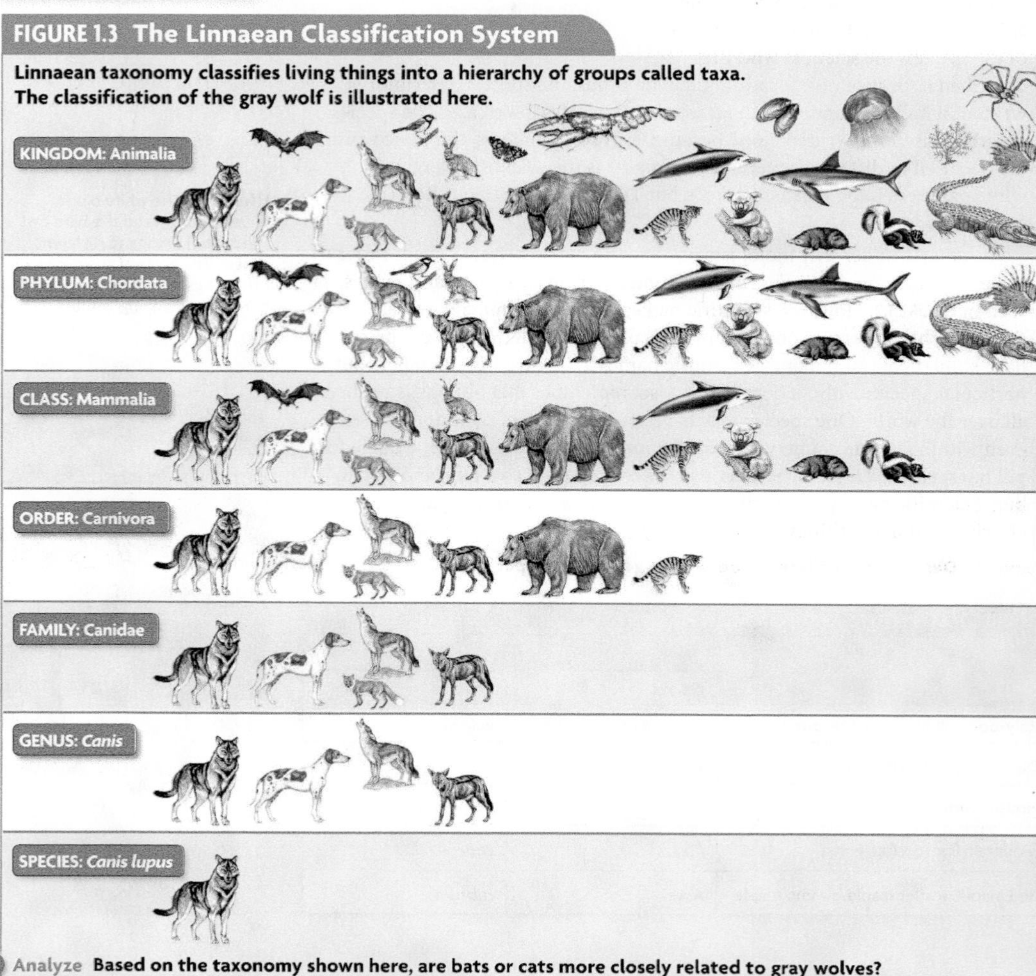

Ⓐ Analyze **Based on the taxonomy shown here, are bats or cats more closely related to gray wolves?**

Differentiated Instruction

ENGLISH LEARNERS

Mnemonics are helpful in learning the order of the nested levels of Linnaean classification. Write on the board the seven levels in order, from kingdom to species, with the first letter of each underlined. Have students think of a phrase that matches up the first letters of the Linnaean levels with the first letters of words they will remember. Example: King Philip called out for good spaghetti.

TEACH WITH TECHNOLOGY

Have students work in groups or as a class to put together a digital slide show of the classification of a species of their choice. They should prepare a visual hierarchy similar to **FIGURE 1.3** with notes on the characteristics of each level. Encourage students to select species from several different orders so that students will learn about different branches of the tree of life as they view one another's presentations.

The top level represents all of the species in kingdom Animalia. As you move down, the levels show examples of species from phylum Chordata, class Mammalia, order Carnivora, family Canidae, genus *Canis,* and the species *Canis lupis*. Each level is included in all of the more general levels above it.

Notice that gray wolves are in the same genus, *Canis,* as dogs and coyotes. Because the Linnaean system is a nested hierarchy, wolves, dogs, and coyotes also belong to the same family, order, class, phylum, and kingdom. Foxes do not belong to the *Canis* genus, but they do belong to Canidae—the same family as wolves, dogs, and coyotes. Therefore, foxes also belong to the same order, class, phylum, and kingdom as wolves, dogs, and coyotes.

A Apply If two species belong to the same order, what other levels in the Linnaean system must they have in common?

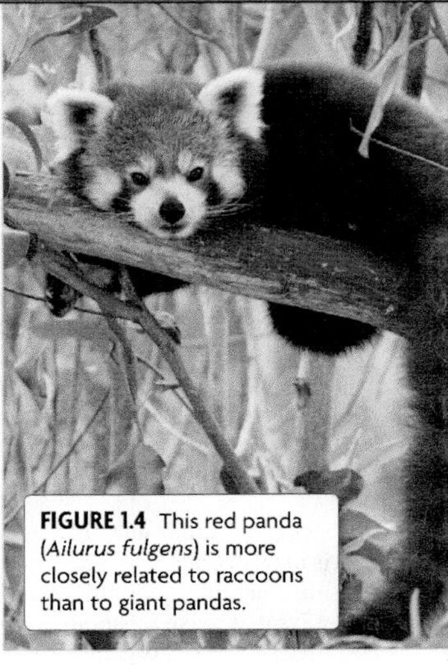

FIGURE 1.4 This red panda (*Ailurus fulgens*) is more closely related to raccoons than to giant pandas.

MAIN IDEA

The Linnaean classification system has limitations.

Linnaeus created his classification system before technology allowed us to study organisms at the molecular level. His system focuses on physical similarities alone. Remember that physical similarities between two species are not always a result of close relation between species. Unrelated species can evolve similar traits through convergent evolution. Linnaeus's system does not account for similarities that evolved this way. So today, scientists use genetic research to help classify living things. Genetic similarities between two species are more likely than physical similarities to be due to a common ancestor.

For example, the giant panda and the raccoon have similar ears and snouts. Because of these similarities, they have been placed in the same family in the Linnaean system. However, molecular biologists have found that the giant panda is more closely related to members of the bear family than it is to raccoons. Furthermore, the red panda, shown in **FIGURE 1.4**, is more closely related to the raccoon than to the giant panda.

B Infer Why is the common name *red panda* misleading in terms of classification based on relatedness?

CONNECT TO

CLASSIFICATION

Refer to **Appendix A** for a complete list of the kingdoms and their phyla.

SELF-CHECK Online
HMHScience.com
GO ONLINE

18.1 Formative Assessment

REVIEWING MAIN IDEAS

1. What is **binomial nomenclature**?
2. Name each **taxon** in the Linnaean system of classification, from most general to most specific.
3. What are some limitations of the Linnaean classification system?

CRITICAL THINKING

4. **Compare** How is a scientific name similar to an address that includes city and state?
5. **Recognize** Why is a standardized taxonomic system important to the scientific community?

CONNECT TO

HISTORY OF SCIENCE

6. During his voyages, Darwin collected thousands of organisms, which he classified using the Linnaean classification system. How did this system help him share his findings with other naturalists?

Take It Further

Our species, ***Homo sapiens,*** is in the same kingdom, phylum, and class as the dogs, cats, and bears of **FIGURE 1.3,** but we are in the order Primates and the family Hominidae, which includes our closest living relatives, the chimpanzees. Other extinct hominids have been placed in the same genus as ours. ***Homo habilis*** is believed to have lived as recently as 1.5 million years ago in what is now Java. ***Homo floresiensis,*** a hominid whose bones were recently found on the island of Flores in Indonesia, lived as recently as 18,000 years ago. It is conceivable that this hominid encountered our species as we spread out from Asia toward Australia.

Answers

A Apply class, phylum, kingdom

B Infer because red pandas are actually more closely related to raccoons than to giant pandas, which are in turn more closely related to other bears

Assess and Reteach

Assess Use the Section Self-Check or Section Quiz, both available at **HMHScience.com**.

Reteach Have students use a graphic organizer such as a cluster diagram to review the Linnaean system of classification.

18.1 FORMATIVE ASSESSMENT

1. It is a system that gives every species a unique two-part name that identifies it. The first part is the genus, and the second part is the species descriptor.
2. kingdom, phylum, class, order, family, genus, species
3. It only accounts for physical and structural similarities between organisms, which can be the result of convergent evolution and therefore not indicative of relatedness.
4. A state has many cities as a genus has many species. Like species descriptors, city names cannot be used alone because the same city names can occur in different states, as with Portland (Maine and Oregon).
5. Having a standardized way of organizing and referring to species allows scientists to communicate clearly their findings about a particular organism.
6. Others could understand the relationships between organisms, such as Darwin's finches, and there was uniformity in terms of language. Had he used common names alone, they would have required translation into many languages.

Discuss

Point out to students that about 1.8 million species have been identified, but estimates suggest there may be 8.8 million or more (some scientists speculate many more) species that have yet to be discovered. Discuss how estimates might be made, based on small plots in biodiverse areas and extrapolated to the entire range of that ecosystem. Computer modeling and complex formulas are also used. **Ask,** Why do we know more about vertebrates than about insects or bacteria? Students may recognize that the sheer physical size differences play a part; it is easier to collect and research macroscopic organisms than microscopic ones. Funding also can dictate what is researched, and there may be more interest in species that are more similar to humans than those that are not.

Explore

Encourage students to explore websites such as *Encyclopedia of Life*, an international effort to catalog all known species in an open access database. *Project Noah* encourages students, citizens, and scientists to document species in their region, gathering geographic range data for species while providing help with species identification. *Monarch Watch* counts on community observers to help document population changes of this iconic butterfly.

S.T.E.M. Interactions

Cybertaxonomy

Technology affects just about every facet of our lives, including how we do schoolwork, how we entertain ourselves, and how we communicate with friends and family. Even the centuries-old field of taxonomy, the study of biological classification, is being revolutionized by technology and emerging as the new field of cybertaxonomy.

Cybertaxonomy encompasses any way that technology is used to create, access, store, or share taxonomic information. Taxonomy strives to group living things in ways that make sense, so that we can better understand them. Early on, organisms were grouped as either plants or animals. As our understanding of the diversity of Earth's inhabitants has grown, so has the classification system. New species are being named and classified every day, requiring taxonomists to research literature to see if the organism has been previously identified elsewhere, photograph and describe specimens at museum collections around the world, and perform DNA analyses. Cybertaxonomy makes it possible for this and other information to be updated and communicated at a moment's notice.

Species collection and identification are easier than ever, with remotely operated instruments and interactive dichotomous keys and field guides. Researchers can easily share information in real time with the public. For example, they can show migration routes or geographic ranges of tracked bird, butterfly, and whale species as the tracking occurs. Experts on a particular species can be consulted via Skype™ or another video-based calling service, and high-resolution photos of a new discovery can be shared worldwide within seconds. Data collected from researchers in different fields on a single species—fragmented information that may include physical appearance, fossil findings, molecular analysis, ecological relationships and more—can all be stored in one place, in multiple, clickable layers.

Estimates indicate that millions of species remain to be discovered and named, particularly in remote areas on land and deep in the oceans, and there is a decreasing number of taxonomists to do the work. Loss of habitat and increasing pollution have made identifying and sharing species information more important than ever. By increasing access to updated information about a species' range, population size, and overall health in an area, researchers can better evaluate methods for protecting that species. Cybertaxonomy may ultimately become a vital tool not just in classifying species, but also in protecting them.

Cybertaxonomy and Butterflies

One species that may benefit from cybertaxonomy is the monarch butterfly (*Danaus plexippus*). Cybertaxonomy is used to help map the monarch's geographic ranges and ecological interactions. Although researchers have been monitoring monarchs for more than 70 years, recent technology is revealing new insights.

There are two North American populations of monarchs. One lives west of the Rocky Mountains, where the monarchs spend their winters along the California coastline near San Diego. A much larger population lives east of the Rockies and overwinters in Mexico. The eastern population migrates between Canada and Mexico, a distance of more than 3,000 miles and the longest migration of any insect. Research on monarchs is especially important now because the monarch population has drastically decreased over the last 20 years, mostly as a result of habitat loss.

Monarchs are monitored and tracked largely through the use of tagging and with the cooperation of citizens who get involved in tagging programs. A participant captures a butterfly, carefully sticks a polypropylene waterproofed tag onto the butterfly wing in a way that does not impede flight, and releases the butterfly. When citizens find a tagged butterfly, they contact the organization that provided the tag.

Participants submit a variety of observations, such as the first monarch they see of the season, the first milkweed shoot (the caterpillars' only food source and where the butterfly lays her eggs), the first monarch eggs found on the back of the milkweed leaf, and the first larva (caterpillar) they find. The submitted information is used in research and becomes data points for interactive migration maps online.

S.T.E.M. Activity

Research more about how monarch butterflies are tracked and studied. In your research, focus on the following tasks and questions.

- How do researchers track monarchs along their migration?
- How do different generations of monarchs complete different sections of the journey?
- How do you think technology available today has changed how the monarch butterfly is studied?
- Create maps showing the migration routes of the monarchs.
- Find out how you and others can participate in the tracking and monitoring of monarchs. Research Monarch Watch or another tagging organization.

Monarch migration is complex because the entire journey is not made by a single butterfly but by up to five generations of that butterfly. Biologists have learned that a monarch that begins life in the Midwest in fall does not breed right away, as do the monarchs that begin life earlier in the summer. Instead, it flies southward to mountains in Mexico, where the weather is cool and foggy (providing much-needed moisture) but not freezing. That same monarch will travel north in spring when daylight hours lengthen again. It may make it only to Texas, where it will breed, lay eggs, and die. The next generation continues on toward the Great Lakes region, the third generation toward the East Coast. The generation that begins in autumn as daylight hours shorten heads back south to the winter grounds, despite never having been there before. How the monarch performs this feat is still not entirely understood.

Chapter 18: The Tree of Life **537**

SECTION 18.2

B.5.1 Evaluate anatomical and molecular evidence to provide an explanation of how organisms are classified and named based on their evolutionary relationships into taxonomic categories.

▼ Plan and Prepare

Activate Prior Knowledge Discuss the tree of life as a symbol of evolutionary relationships. Have students compare a genealogy or family tree to the phylogeny or evolution of a group of species. **Ask,** If you think of yourself as a species, who represents the genus, family, and order? Genus would be yourself + siblings, parent, parent's siblings, and their offspring; family would be all of the above + grandparents and any siblings they had; order would be all of the above + great-grandparents and any of their siblings.

To take the analogy further, ask a student to volunteer the surnames through several generations of his or her family, which can be strung together to create names for the "taxa."

▼ Teach

Vocabulary

Greek and Latin Word Origins The word **phylogeny** comes from the following Greek words:

phylon = class or race
geneia = origin

The first root is also the origin of the words **phylogenic, phylum,** and **phylogenetic.**

18.2 Classification Based on Evolutionary Relationships

VOCABULARY

phylogeny
cladistics
cladogram
derived character

KEY CONCEPT **Modern classification is based on evolutionary relationships.**

MAIN IDEAS

- Cladistics is classification based on common ancestry.
- Molecular evidence reveals species' relatedness.

Connect to Your World

If you've ever observed bats in a zoo or in the night sky, you've likely noticed that they have several features in common with birds, such as wings. However, bats are actually more closely related to rodents and primates than they are to birds. Today, scientists agree that species should be classified based on evolutionary relationships rather than just physical similarities.

MAIN IDEA

Cladistics is classification based on common ancestry.

Similar traits between species are often the result of sharing a common ancestor, such as the ancestor shared by dogs and wolves. However, scientists now know that similar traits, such as the wings of bats and birds, can also evolve in species that are adapting to similar environmental conditions. As you have learned, this process is called convergent evolution.

To classify species according to how they are related, scientists must look at more than just physical traits. Modern classification is based on identifying evolutionary relationships using evidence from living species, the fossil record, and molecular data. The evolutionary history for a group of species is called a **phylogeny** (fy-LAHJ-uh-nee).

Phylogenies can be shown as branching tree diagrams. In a way, these diagrams are like family trees. The branches of a family tree show how family members are related to each other. The branches of an evolutionary tree show how different groups of species are related to each other.

FIGURE 2.1 The glyptodon (*Glyptotherium arizonae*), illustrated here, was the size of a small car and lived more than 10,000 years ago. It is the common ancestor to about 20 modern armadillo species, including the nine-banded armadillo (*Dasypus novemcinctus*).

Differentiated Instruction

ENGLISH LEARNERS

Have students work in small groups to preview the section, ask questions about the main ideas or unfamiliar terms, identify things that are difficult to comprehend, and then summarize the material. Students should give special attention in this section to cladograms, how they are constructed, and what each part represents in relation to evolutionary history or phylogeny.

Teacher Toolkit, Section C, Reciprocal Teaching

Cladistics

The most common method used to make evolutionary trees is called cladistics. **Cladistics** (kluh-DIHS-tihks) is classification based on common ancestry. The goal of cladistics is to place species in the order in which they descended from a common ancestor. A **cladogram** is a diagram based on patterns of shared, derived traits that shows the evolutionary relationships between groups of organisms.

At the root of the words *cladistics* and *cladogram* is the word *clade*. A clade is a group of species that shares a common ancestor. For example, the glyptodon in **FIGURE 2.1** is the common ancestor of about 20 modern species of armadillos. Together, the glyptodon and all of its descendants form a clade.

Through the course of evolution, certain traits change in some species of a clade but stay the same in other species. Therefore, each species in a clade has some traits from its ancestors that have not changed, such as the similar shells of glyptodons and modern armadillos. Organisms that do not share a common trait with the rest of the group are branched off into their own clade.

The traits that can be used to figure out evolutionary relationships among a group of species are those that are shared by some species but are not present in others. These traits are called **derived characters.** As you will soon see, cladograms are made by figuring out which derived characters are shared by which species. The more closely related species are, the more derived characters they will share. A group of species that shares no derived characters with the other groups being studied is called an outgroup.

READING TOOLBOX

VOCABULARY

The word *derived* comes from the Latin *de-*, meaning "from," and *rivus*, meaning "stream." Therefore, *derived* refers to something that has "flowed" from a source. The term *derived characters* refers to characters that have evolved in a species since sharing a common ancestor.

QUICKLAB CLASSIFYING

Construct a Cladogram

You can think of a cladogram as an evolutionary family tree in which things that are more closely related share more characteristics. As an analogy, processes that have evolved due to new technologies can be organized using cladistics. In this lab, you will fill in a cladogram for methods of transportation.

PROBLEM How can methods of transportation be organized using a cladogram?

PROCEDURE

1. Copy the cladogram axes on the right into your notebook.
2. Think about the characteristics of the following methods of transportation: bicycle, car, motorcycle, airplane, and on foot.
3. Complete your cladogram by filling in each method of transportation listed in step 2 on the appropriate line at the top.

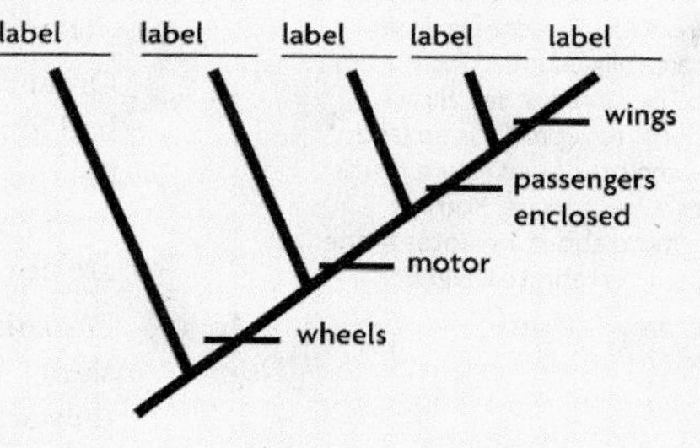

ANALYZE AND CONCLUDE

1. **Identify** What "derived characters" are used in this cladogram?
2. **Analyze** Which mode of transportation may be considered an "outgroup"—a group that has none of the characteristics labeled on the cladogram?
3. **Connect** A species that has evolved a new trait is not better than a species without that trait. Each species is just adapted to a certain way of life. When might riding a bike have an advantage over flying in an airplane?

BELOW LEVEL

To distinguish among the terms *clade, cladistics, cladogram,* and *derived characters,* have students create word squares in which they draw a cladogram, label its parts, and then define each term. They should write one or two sentences that capture the meanings of these terms. It may be helpful to use different colors of ink or pencil to distinguish one clade from another, or for the hash marks that represent derived characters.

Teacher Toolkit, Section D, Word Squares

Vocabulary

Greek and Latin Word Origins The words **clade** and **cladistics** come from the Greek *klados,* meaning "branch."

Academic Vocabulary Point out to students that the words **trait** and **character** are similar, but not synonymous. Both are heritable features, but characters relate specifically to different "states," such as "hair present" versus "hair absent," that are used for classification purposes. The word **characteristic,** meaning "a distinguishing feature," is more akin to the word *trait* in a general sense, though when referring to a phenotype, *trait* is the appropriate term.

QUICKLAB

Time 15 minutes

Purpose Learn how cladograms are constructed using shared characteristics.

Teacher Note "I've only taught cladograms in a 'traditional' sense. This lab was more meaningful, and students related to it."

Sample Data

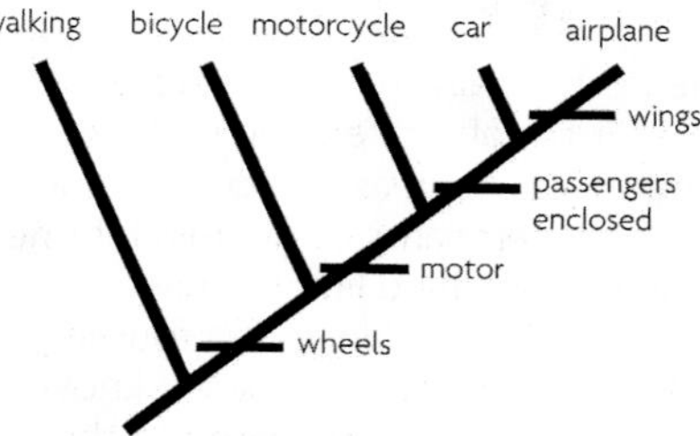

Analyze and Conclude

1. wheels, motor, passengers enclosed, wings
2. walking
3. It is not practical to board an airplane just to fly a few miles, so biking is better.

▼ Teach *continued*

Have students view the interactive animation to build a cladogram of reptiles.

Build a Cladogram

Guitarfish

Vocabulary

Academic Vocabulary The word **node** comes from a root meaning "knot." It has several applications that relate to a point of connection. In mathematics, a *node* exists where a continuous curve crosses itself. In computer science, a node is a terminal in a computer network, such as a wireless router in a series of routers. In botany, a node describes the point on a stem where a leaf is or was attached. Students can think of the node in a cladogram as the point where the rest of the branch carries on evolving, while the group that is diverging and will not have the next derived character is now off on its own.

Take It Further

One of the main characteristics of snakes is the absence of limbs. However, some snakes, such as boa constrictors, have small remnants of hind-limb bones. These vestigial hind limbs, known as **spurs,** provide evidence of a four-legged ancestor for snakes. The oldest known fossil snakes have been dated to the early Cretaceous period.

Answers

A Contrast A taxon is a group of organisms classified together in a system such as that of Linnaeus. A clade is any group of organisms that share a common ancestor, so it can contain many taxa of different levels.

CONNECT TO ANIMALS

The amniotic sac is a key characteristic of amniotes, animals that are fully adapted for life on land. The amniotic sac allows amniotes to reproduce on land; non-amniotes must return to the water to reproduce. You will learn more about amniotes in the chapter **Vertebrate Diversity.**

Interpreting a Cladogram

The main features of a cladogram are shown in **FIGURE 2.2.** Tetrapods are vertebrates that have four limbs—amphibians, reptiles, birds, and mammals. Some tetrapods, such as snakes and marine mammals, no longer have the four limbs that their known ancestors had. However, they are still members of the tetrapoda clade because they share a common ancestor.

Derived characters In a cladogram, groups of species are placed in order by the derived characters that have added up in their lineage over time. This order is hypothesized to be the order in which they descended from their common ancestor. Derived characters are shown as hash marks between the branches of the cladogram. All species above a hash mark share the derived character it represents.

Nodes Each place where a branch splits is called a node. There are five nodes on the tetrapod cladogram. The first node is where the amphibian branch splits off from the rest of the cladogram. Nodes represent the most recent common ancestor shared by a clade. Therefore, the first node of the tetrapod cladogram represents a common ancestor for the whole tetrapod clade.

Identifying clades You can identify clades by using the "snip rule." Whenever you "snip" a branch under a node, a clade falls off. In this cladogram, if you were to "snip" below the node where turtles and tortoises branch off, you would be left with the reptilia clade. This clade includes turtles and tortoises, lizards and snakes, crocodiles and alligators, and birds. As you can see, each clade is nested within the clade that forms just before it. There are five clades in the tetrapod cladogram. Crocodiles, alligators, and birds belong to all five clades.

1. All of the organisms in this cladogram belong to the tetrapoda clade (brown). They all share the derived character of four limbs.
2. An embryo protected by a fluid-filled sac is a derived character for all organisms in the amniota clade (blue). Because amphibians do not produce an amniotic sac, the amphibian branch splits off from the rest of the branches before the mark that represents this trait.
3. Organisms in the reptilia clade (yellow) have a common ancestor that had four limbs, produced protected eggs, and had a skull with openings behind the eyes. The third node in the cladogram represents this common ancestor. Because mammal skulls do not have these openings, they are not part of the reptilia clade.
4. Organisms in the diapsida clade (green) have openings in the side of the skull. The skulls of turtles and tortoises do not have these openings, so they are not part of the diapsida clade.
5. Lizards and snakes branch off of the cladogram next. Their skulls do not have certain openings in the jaw that are found in crocodiles, alligators, and birds. This is the derived character shared by all organisms in the archosauria clade (pink). Feathers and toothless beaks separate crocodiles and alligators from birds within the archosauria clade.

A Contrast What is the difference between a clade and a taxon?

Differentiated Instruction

PRE-AP

Have students take ten minutes to review **FIGURE 2.2** and write a brief essay that answers the following question: What would it mean if a new species of mammal were discovered that had skull openings behind the eyes? Students' answers should suggest that a revision to the derived character scheme of the clade might be necessary but that the new mammal's trait may be the result of convergent evolution rather than a trait shared with archosaurs, diapsids, and reptiles.

Teacher Toolkit, Section C, Quick-Write

BELOW LEVEL

Help students understand the structure and meaning of the cladogram by modeling for them how you read this page for meaning and relate your reading to **FIGURE 2.2.** Relate the branched nature of the cladogram to divergence. For example, the turtles and tortoises diverge from the other reptiles because they do not have openings in the sides of their skulls. Point out that if the cladogram went further, it would branch off into the orders, families, genera, and species within each of the clades.

FIGURE 2.2 Cladogram for Tetrapods

A cladogram presents hypothesized evolutionary relationships among a group of species based on common ancestry and derived characters.

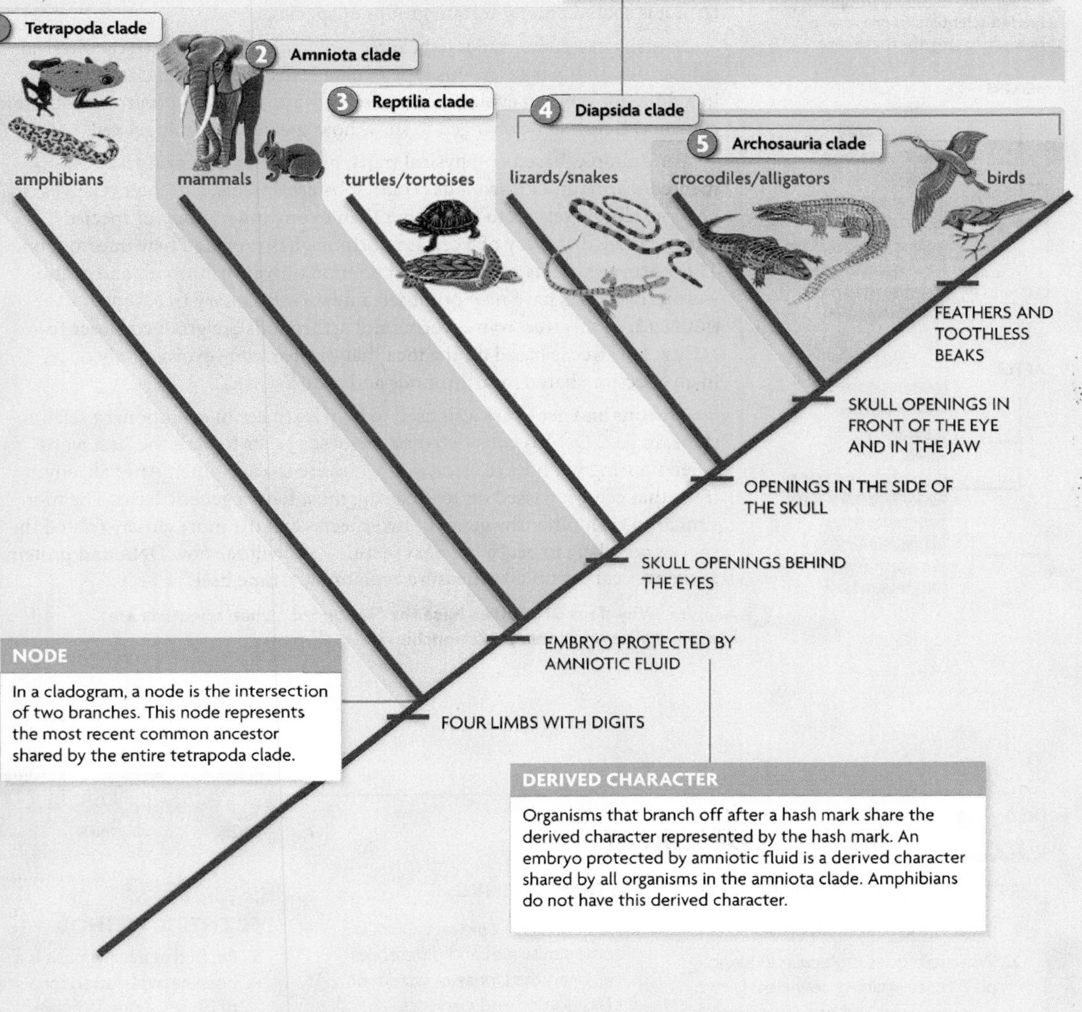

CLADE
A clade is a group of organisms that share certain traits derived from a common ancestor. In this cladogram, a clade looks like the letter V, including all the branches that extend from the right end of the V. The diapsida clade includes lizards and snakes, crocodiles and alligators, and birds.
1 Tetrapoda clade
2 Amniota clade
3 Reptilia clade
4 Diapsida clade
5 Archosauria clade
amphibians
mammals
turtles/tortoises
lizards/snakes
crocodiles/alligators
birds
FEATHERS AND TOOTHLESS BEAKS
SKULL OPENINGS IN FRONT OF THE EYE AND IN THE JAW
OPENINGS IN THE SIDE OF THE SKULL
SKULL OPENINGS BEHIND THE EYES
EMBRYO PROTECTED BY AMNIOTIC FLUID
FOUR LIMBS WITH DIGITS
NODE
In a cladogram, a node is the intersection of two branches. This node represents the most recent common ancestor shared by the entire tetrapoda clade.
DERIVED CHARACTER
Organisms that branch off after a hash mark share the derived character represented by the hash mark. An embryo protected by amniotic fluid is a derived character shared by all organisms in the amniota clade. Amphibians do not have this derived character.

A CRITICAL VIEWING **Which groups of animals belong to the amniota clade? Which belong to the archosauria clade?**

INCLUSION

Have a visually impaired student work with a classmate who will construct and describe the cladogram shown in **FIGURE 2.2.** Supply pipe cleaners and cloth or paper of varying textures, which can be used to signify derived characters. Smaller clades should be bent away from the larger ones so that the student can feel that they are distinct but also nested within other clades.

TEACH FROM VISUALS

FIGURE 2.2 Point out to students that the clades shown are nested within larger ones like the seven taxonomic levels of the Linnaean classification system. **Ask,** What types of taxonomic levels are not shown in this figure? None of the Linnaean taxa are shown in this figure. The animal kingdom has phyla that are not characterized by four limbs with digits, and we know that even the smaller groups shown, such as the crocodiles/alligators, have more than two species once we account for all the living and extinct species. **Ask**

- How could we include other taxa? We can add clades that are more general or more specific, such as the orders, families, and genera within the bird class.
- What would be some derived characters we might see if we added more general clades to this cladogram? *Sample answer:* vertebrae, bilateral symmetry, eukaryotic cells

Answers

A Critical Viewing Amniota includes everything but the amphibians; archosauria includes the crocodiles/alligators and birds.

▼ Teach *continued*

TEACH FROM VISUALS

FIGURE 2.3 This figure shows what can happen to a phylogenic tree or cladogram when scientists discover evidence of a previously unknown evolutionary relationship. **Ask**

- In the "before" diagram, which organisms are most related to mollusks? segmented worms and arthropods
- In the "after" diagram, which organisms are most closely related to mollusks? flatworms and segmented worms

Vocabulary

Remind students that the words **taxon** and **taxa** refer to any of the levels in the Linnaean classification system. This means that if two or more groups are being discussed or compared, they can be referred to as *taxa*. For example, "The bee and spider *taxa* in the phylum Arthropoda are two of the most feared groups of animals, but the spider *taxon* has only about a dozen species whose venom can hurt humans."

Answers

Ⓐ **Analyze** Shared or identical sequences of DNA give hard proof of common ancestry, whereas shared traits or similar characteristics can be the result of convergent evolution.

▼ Assess and Reteach

Assess Use the Section Self-Check or Section Quiz, both available at **HMHScience.com**.

Reteach Discuss how cladistics could be used to classify Darwin's finches or another group of organisms. Create a hypothetical cladogram by having students come up with the derived characters, branches, and clades.

FIGURE 2.3 Based on structural similarities, scientists previously classified segmented worms and arthropods as sister taxa. The discovery of a hormone found only in roundworms and arthropods has led scientists to propose a new phylogeny for these taxa.

BEFORE

flatworms
roundworms
mollusks
segmented worms
arthropods

AFTER

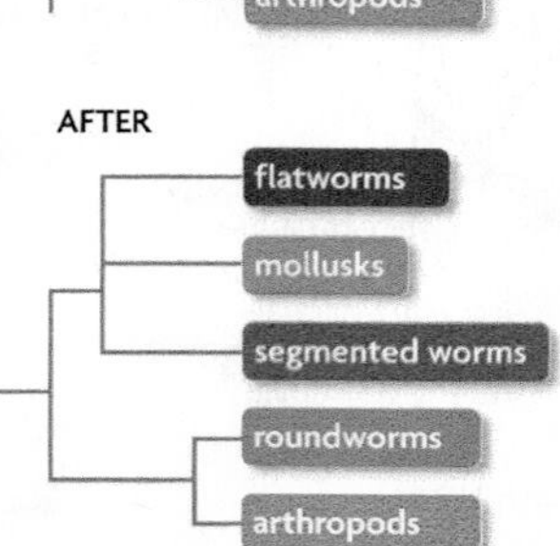

MAIN IDEA

Molecular evidence reveals species' relatedness.

You have learned how physical characteristics, such as protected eggs, can be used to build evolutionary trees. In this example, a protected egg is a derived character shared by all species in the amniota clade. Today, new technology allows biologists to compare groups of species at the molecular level. Molecular evidence, such as a certain DNA sequence, can be used as a derived character if it is shared among certain groups of species.

In many cases, molecular data agree with classification based on physical similarities. In other cases, this type of data leads scientists to classify species in a different way. An evolutionary tree is always a work in progress. With new evidence, trees can be changed to show how species are likely related.

For example, based on physical traits, most biologists considered segmented worms and arthropods (crabs, lobsters, insects, and their relatives) to be more closely related to each other than to any other group of species. However, the discovery of a certain hormone has provided new information. This hormone affects molting, and it is found only in arthropods and roundworms. Biologists have now proposed a new evolutionary tree, shown in **FIGURE 2.3**. In this tree, roundworms and arthropods are grouped closer together. This tree is based on the idea that the hormone evolved only once, in an ancestor shared by arthropods and roundworms.

Proteins and genes are also used to help learn about evolutionary relationships. In fact, DNA is considered by many scientists to have the "last word" when figuring out how related two species are to each other. After all, any traits that can get passed on to offspring must have a genetic basis. The more similar to each other the genes of two species are, the more closely related the species are likely to be. In the next section, you will see how DNA and protein sequences can be used to measure evolutionary time itself.

Ⓐ Analyze **Why does DNA often have the "last word" when scientists are constructing evolutionary relationships?**

18.2 Formative Assessment

SELF-CHECK Online
HMHScience.com
GO ONLINE

REVIEWING MAIN IDEAS

1. What is the goal of **cladistics**?
2. What role does molecular evidence play in determining how closely two species are related to each other?

CRITICAL THINKING

3. **Compare and Contrast** Discuss some similarities and differences between the Linnaean system of classification and cladistics.
4. **Analyze** Describe the relationship between clades and shared **derived characters**.

CONNECT TO
SCIENTIFIC METHOD

5. Recall that a hypothesis is a possible explanation for a set of observations. Why are **cladograms** considered to be hypotheses?

18.2 FORMATIVE ASSESSMENT

1. to arrange groups and species in the order in which they diverged from a common ancestor
2. Analysis of DNA and protein sequences can reveal differences among species. The more biomolecular similarities, the more closely related are the species.
3. Both systems attempt to classify organisms on the basis of similarities—the Linnaean by physical/structural similarities and cladistics by analyzing evolutionary relationships and species relatedness.
4. A derived character is one that emerges over time in a group of organisms and is the distinguishing trait between a diverging group, or clade, and the clades that have evolved previously. Every member of a clade can be traced back to a common ancestor that possessed and passed on that derived character.
5. Hypotheses are educated explanations that form a basis for future investigation or research. Cladistics is ongoing, and cladograms represent explanations based on the most current research.

Transforming Data

Smart Grapher
HMHScience.com
GO ONLINE
Create animated charts and graphs using Smart Grapher.

Researchers rarely publish raw data alone. Instead, data are usually analyzed in some way. This is because certain types of observations and patterns can be made clearer when data are presented in different ways. For example, data that show change or difference may be best represented as percentage difference.

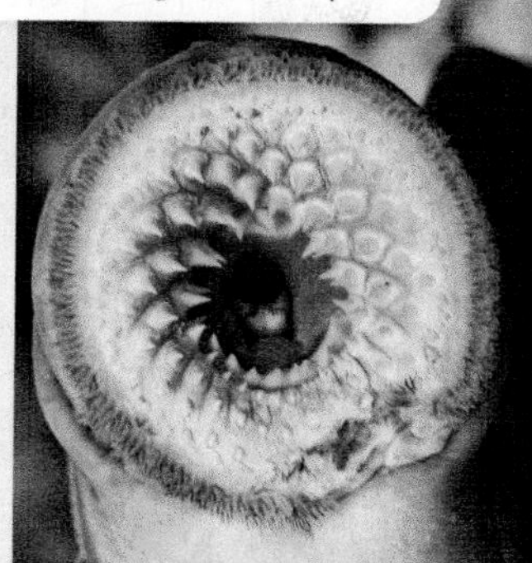
Lampreys such as this one are jawless fish with a round, sucking mouth.

Model

Cytochrome C is a protein that functions in cellular respiration. A sequence of 104 amino acids makes up the cytochrome C protein. Scientists have compared this sequence of amino acids in humans with the sequence in a variety of other species. The number of amino acid differences between cytochrome C in humans and in other species has been used to determine relatedness between species.

Look at the data table at the right. Notice that the cytochrome C of chimpanzees most closely resembles that of humans, while the cytochrome C of lampreys, a type of jawless fish, has more differences. To more clearly represent how different they are, these data can be transformed into percentage differences. To calculate the percentage difference of cytochrome C between humans and lampreys, follow this procedure.

1. First, transform the number of amino acid differences into a fraction of the total number of amino acids that make up the cytochrome C protein (104).

   $$\frac{\textbf{20 differences}}{\textbf{104 total amino acids}}$$

2. Next, perform the division.

   20 ÷ 104 = 0.1923

3. Transform this number into a percentage by multiplying by 100.

   0.1923 × 100 = 19.23% difference

TABLE 1. AMINO ACID DIFFERENCES COMPARED WITH HUMAN CYTOCHROME C

Organism	Number of Differences
Chimpanzee	0
Rhesus monkey	1
Whale	10
Turtle	15
Bullfrog	18
Lamprey	20
Tuna	21

Source: M. Dayhoff, *Atlas of Protein Sequence and Structure*

Practice Transform Data

1. **Calculate** Use the procedure outlined above to find percentage differences in cytochrome C between humans and the following animals: tunas, bullfrogs, turtles, whales, rhesus monkeys, and chimpanzees.
2. **Apply** What do the transformed data suggest about how related each type of animal is to humans?
3. **Infer** What percentage of the human cytochrome C protein is the same as that of whales? Hint: 100 percent − percentage difference = percentage similarity.

Answers

1. tuna: 20.19% difference; bullfrog: 17.31%; turtle: 14.42%; whale: 9.62%; rhesus monkey: 0.96%; chimpanzee: 0%
2. Of the animals in this data set, tuna and lamprey, which are fish, are least related to humans. Chimpanzees and rhesus monkeys, which are primate mammals, are the most related to humans.
3. 90.38%

DATA ANALYSIS

Introduce

Review with students the structure and function of amino acids. **Ask**

- What is the basic function of amino acids? They are the building blocks of proteins.
- What determines the nature and function of a protein? its sequence of amino acids
- In what ways can raw data from an investigation be analyzed and displayed? Data can be analyzed statistically or mathematically and then displayed in data tables and in different types of graphs and diagrams.

Discuss

Have students look at the types of organisms being compared in the activity. **Ask**

- Given what we know about human origins and taxonomy, should we expect humans, rhesus monkeys, and chimpanzees to have the most similar amino acid sequences? Yes, they are all members of the order Primates, so they are more closely related to each other than to any of the other organisms.
- If there are no differences between the amino acid sequences in the cytochrome C protein of humans and chimps, why aren't we the same species? Cytochrome C is just one protein that is being compared. There are many others in which we would find differences between our species and the chimpanzee.

Online Student Resources, Data Analysis Practice

SECTION 18.3

B.5.1 Evaluate anatomical and molecular evidence to provide an explanation of how organisms are classified and named based on their evolutionary relationships into taxonomic categories.

▼ Plan and Prepare

Activate Prior Knowledge Encourage students to think of different ways to estimate age. **Ask**

- How would you estimate the age of someone you do not know? height, hair color, physical maturation
- How can a botanist determine the age of a tree? count the growth rings
- How are rocks and fossils dated? radiometric dating, index fossils

Explain that just as the ages of fossils and trees can be determined through direct or relative means, scientists can use pieces of living organisms to reveal how long their species has existed.

▼ Teach

TEACH FROM VISUALS

FIGURE 3.1 Ask, What DNA base pairs change in the top lineage after 10 million years? A to T after another 10 million years? C to A

18.3 Molecular Clocks

KEY CONCEPT Molecular clocks provide clues to evolutionary history.

VOCABULARY

molecular clock
mitochondrial DNA
ribosomal RNA

MAIN IDEAS

- Molecular clocks use mutations to estimate evolutionary time.
- Mitochondrial DNA and ribosomal RNA provide two types of molecular clocks.

Connect to Your World

Have you ever played the game "Telephone?" One person whispers a message to another person, who repeats it to yet another person, and so on. By the time it reaches the final person, the message has changed. In a similar way, DNA changes slightly each time it is passed from generation to generation.

MAIN IDEA

Molecular clocks use mutations to estimate evolutionary time.

In the early 1960s, biochemists Linus Pauling and Emile Zuckerkandl proposed a new way to measure evolutionary time. They compared the amino acid sequences of hemoglobin from a wide range of species. Their findings show that the more distantly related two species are, the more amino acid differences there are in their hemoglobin. Using these data, they were able to calculate a mutation rate for part of the hemoglobin protein.

CONNECT TO

NATURAL SELECTION

In the chapter **Principles of Evolution,** you learned about the relationship between mutation and natural selection, the force behind evolution.

Molecular Evolution

Molecular clocks are models that use mutation rates to measure evolutionary time. Recall that mutations are nucleotide substitutions in DNA, some of which cause amino acid substitutions in proteins. Pauling and Zuckerkandl found that mutations tend to add up at a constant rate for a group of related species. As shown in **FIGURE 3.1,** the rate of mutations is the "ticking" that powers a molecular clock. The more time that has passed since two species have diverged from a common ancestor, the more mutations that will have built up in each lineage, and the greater the differences between the two species at the molecular level.

FIGURE 3.1 MOLECULAR EVOLUTION

Mutations add up at a fairly constant rate in the DNA of species that evolved from a common ancestor.

G A A C G T A T T C

DNA sequence from a hypothetical ancestor

Ten million years later—one mutation in each lineage

G T A C G T A T T C

The DNA sequences from two descendant species show mutations that have accumulated (black).

G A A C G T A T G C

Another ten million years later—one more mutation in each lineage

G T A A G T A T T C

The mutation rate of this sequence equals one mutation per ten million years.

G A A C C T A T G C

Differentiated Instruction

PRE-AP

Draw the following graphic on the board and have students compare it to **FIGURE 3.1.** Tell them to determine how long ago the two lineages diverged if the rate of mutation is 1 per 5 million years. For the sequences shown here, the answer is 20 million years ago.

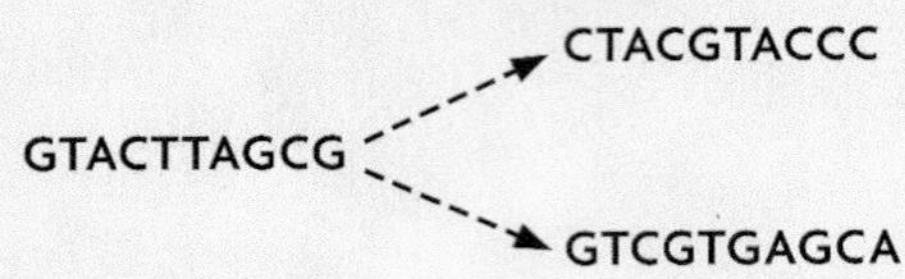

Linking Molecular Data with Real Time

To estimate mutation rates, scientists must find links between molecular data and real time. Often this link comes from the timing of a geologic event that is known to have separated the species they are studying. If scientists know when the species began to diverge from a common ancestor, they can find the mutation rate for the molecule they are studying. For example, scientists know that marsupials of Australia and those of South America diverged about 200 million years ago, when these two continents split.

A link can also come from fossil evidence. Pauling and Zuckerkandl compared their molecular data with the first appearance of each type of organism in the fossil record. Using these dates, they confirmed that the number of amino acid differences increases with the evolutionary time between each group of species. The number of amino acid differences between human hemoglobin and the hemoglobin of several other types of organisms is shown in **FIGURE 3.2.** Human hemoglobin is most different from species that diverged earliest in evolutionary time.

A Infer **Why is the hemoglobin of humans more different from that of sharks than that of birds?**

Molecular Clock

FIGURE 3.2 LINKING MOLECULAR AND FOSSIL DATA

Animal species that evolved longer ago compared with humans have more amino acid differences in the beta chain of their hemoglobin.

ANIMAL	AMINO ACID DIFFERENCES COMPARED WITH HUMANS	APPEARANCE IN FOSSIL RECORD (millions of years ago)
Mouse	16	70
Horse	18	70
Bird	35	270
Frog	62	350
Shark	79	450

B Analyze Which two animals in this table are least related to humans?

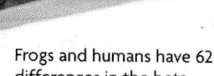

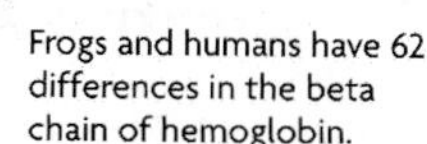
Frogs and humans have 62 differences in the beta chain of hemoglobin.

MAIN IDEA

Mitochondrial DNA and ribosomal RNA provide two types of molecular clocks.

Different molecules have different mutation rates. For example, some sequences of DNA accumulate mutations relatively quickly in a lineage, while others have very low mutation rates. Depending on how closely two species are related, scientists choose a molecule with an appropriate mutation rate to use as a molecular clock.

ENGLISH LEARNERS

Develop a list of questions to give students before they begin the sections. For example:
How can the changes that occur as species evolve be a measure of time?
What do the changes consist of?
Where do scientists look for these changes?
Remind students of these questions as you discuss the section.

Teacher Toolkit, Section C, Questions to Guide Reading

Learn how a molecular clock works. Go to Animated Biology for an interactive animation.

Take It Further

Sharks are **cartilaginous fish,** meaning their skeletal system is made of cartilage rather than bone. Because cartilage is not easily fossilized, the **fossil record** of sharks consists almost entirely of preserved teeth. A single tooth of an extinct ancestor of the great white shark can be over 6 inches (15 cm) long and weigh as much as a pound, a size that suggests that *Carcharodon megalodon,* a shark that lived between 5 and 1.6 million years ago, was over 50 feet (15 m) long. Some scientists believe that this species was so large that it could have hunted large whales.

Science Trivia

The Human Genome Project successfully listed and mapped all 3 billion base pairs in human DNA.

- Of all of those, only about 1–2 percent actually carry genetic information.
- The beta hemoglobin gene is found on the 11th chromosome, from base pairs 5,203,271 to 5,204,876.

Answers

A Infer Humans and birds diverged more recently than sharks.

B Analyze frog and shark

▼ Teach continued

The Inside Story

The Y chromosome can be used to trace descent from paternal lineages (father to son). A team of geneticists at Trinity College in Dublin, Ireland, have analyzed the Y chromosomes in almost 800 males throughout Ireland. In northwestern Ireland, 1 out of 5 men share a chromosomal marker, a sort of signature that can be traced to the 5th-century Irish king Niall. Niall, who reportedly had 12 sons, founded a dynasty that dominated Ireland for centuries. Eight percent of the males in modern Ireland—and as many as 2 to 3 million men worldwide—are thought to be descendants of Niall.

Answers

A Summarize It accumulates mutations at a relatively low rate, allowing patterns of change to remain or become clear over long periods of time.

FIGURE 3.3 INHERITANCE OF MITOCHONDRIAL DNA

grandparents
parents
child
● mitochondrial DNA
|| nuclear DNA
Mitochondrial DNA is passed down only from the mother of each generation, so it is not subject to recombination.
Nuclear DNA is inherited from both parents, making it more difficult to trace back through generations.

Mitochondrial DNA

Mitochondrial DNA (mtDNA) is DNA found only in mitochondria, the energy factories of cells. The mutation rate of mtDNA is about ten times faster than that of nuclear DNA, which makes mtDNA a good molecular clock for closely related species. Furthermore, as shown in **FIGURE 3.3**, mtDNA is always inherited from the mother because the mitochondria in a sperm cell are lost after fertilization. This type of inheritance is different from that of nuclear DNA, which is a combination of DNA from both parents. Scientists use the fact that mtDNA is passed down unshuffled to trace mutations back through many generations in a single species. In fact, mutations in mtDNA have been used to study the migration routes of humans over the past 200,000 years.

READING TOOLBOX

VOCABULARY

In this context, the word *conservative* means "resistant to change." Because ribosomes play such a crucial role in cell function, even small changes can be very disruptive and damaging to the cell. Therefore, most mutations in rRNA do not accumulate within the genome.

Ribosomal RNA

Ribosomes, the organelles that manufacture proteins in cells, contain **ribosomal RNA** (rRNA). Ribosomal RNA is useful for studying distantly related species, such as species that are in different kingdoms or phyla. When studying the relationships among species over longer time scales, it is best to use a molecule that has a lower mutation rate. Ribosomal RNA has conservative regions that accumulate mutations at a low rate relative to most DNA. Over long periods of geologic time, mutations that do build up in the rRNA of different lineages are relatively clear and can be compared. American microbiologist Carl Woese first used rRNA to establish that archaea diverged from the common ancestor they share with bacteria almost 4 billion years ago. As you will learn in the next section, these findings supported a restructuring of the tree of life at its highest level.

A Summarize **Why is rRNA useful for studying more distantly related species?**

▼ Assess and Reteach

Assess Use the Section Self-Check or Section Quiz, both available at **HMHScience.com**.

Reteach Tell students to imagine a fossil find that includes some tissue remains. Have them describe how scientists could use the fossil as a source of molecular clocks.

18.3 Formative Assessment

SELF-CHECK Online
HMHScience.com
GO ONLINE

REVIEWING MAIN IDEAS

1. How are **molecular clocks** used to measure evolutionary time?
2. What are the benefits of **mitochondrial DNA** and **ribosomal RNA** as molecular clocks?

CRITICAL THINKING

3. **Explain** How do rates of mutation "power" molecular clocks?
4. **Apply** What molecular clock might be useful to examine the evolutionary relationship between several phyla in the kingdom Plantae? Explain your answer.

CONNECT TO

HISTORY OF LIFE

5. The theory of endosymbiosis explains how eukaryotic cells may have evolved from prokaryotic cells. According to this theory, explain why mitochondria have their own DNA, separate from nuclear DNA.

18.3 FORMATIVE ASSESSMENT

1. The clocks presume that mutations occur at a constant rate for any clade or group of related taxa. Because these changes occur at a relatively constant and predictable rate, the changes can be used to measure how long ago different lineages diverged.
2. Mitochondrial DNA accumulates mutations relatively quickly, so it is most useful for analyzing relatedness within closely related species or change within a species. Ribosomal RNA has many conservative regions that accumulate mutations relatively slowly, so it is useful for studying taxa that are more distantly related.
3. Mutations tend to occur at relatively constant rates in certain proteins and DNA sequences among related taxa. Once a scale has been applied to the rate of mutation, it can function as a clock.
4. rRNA, because it accumulates mutations relatively slowly
5. Because mitochondria and chloroplasts were once free-living prokaryotes, they have their own DNA.

18.4 Domains and Kingdoms

KEY CONCEPT **The current tree of life has three domains.**

MAIN IDEAS
- Classification is always a work in progress.
- The three domains in the tree of life are Bacteria, Archaea, and Eukarya.

VOCABULARY
Bacteria
Archaea
Eukarya

Connect to Your World

Have you ever swum in a pond? Every drop of pond water is teeming with single-celled organisms. At one time, scientists classified these organisms as either plants or animals. However, classification schemes change. Single-celled eukaryotes such as these pond dwellers now have a kingdom of their own.

MAIN IDEA

Classification is always a work in progress.

The tree of life is a model that shows the most current understanding of how living things are related. Some new discoveries confirm parts of the tree that were once based on similarities in form alone. But as **FIGURE 4.1** shows, new findings can also lead scientists to change how they classify certain organisms.

- The two-kingdom system was accepted by biologists until 1866, when German biologist Ernst Haeckel proposed moving all single-celled organisms to the kingdom Protista.
- In 1938, American biologist Herbert Copeland argued that the prokaryotes deserved their own kingdom, called Monera. Prokaryotes are single-celled organisms that do not have membrane-bound nuclei or organelles.
- In 1959, American ecologist Robert Whittaker proposed that because of how they feed, fungi should be placed into their own kingdom apart from plants. The kingdom Fungi includes molds and mushrooms.
- In 1977, rRNA research by Carl Woese revealed two genetically different groups of prokaryotes. His findings led scientists to split the kingdom Monera into two kingdoms, called Bacteria and Archaea.

CONNECT TO

FUNGI

Fungi are heterotrophs that feed by absorbing dead organic materials from the environment. This is one characteristic that distinguishes fungi from plants, which are autotrophs, or organisms that make their own food. You will learn more about fungi in the chapter **Protists and Fungi.**

FIGURE 4.1 HISTORY OF THE KINGDOM SYSTEM

1753 Two kingdoms	1866 Three kingdoms	1938 Four kingdoms	1959 Five kingdoms	1977 Six kingdoms
Plantae, Animalia	Plantae, Animalia, Protista	Plantae, Animalia, Protista, Monera	Plantae, Animalia, Protista, Monera, Fungi	Plantae, Animalia, Protista, Archaea, Fungi, Bacteria

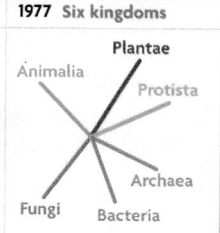

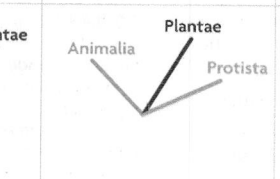

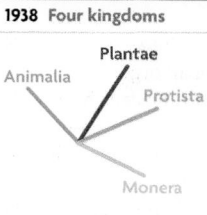

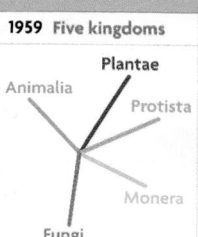

Plan and Prepare

Activate Prior Knowledge Lead a discussion about how various things in a culture are often reclassified based on new attitudes, ideas, or evidence. **Ask,** How do you classify a type of music? kinds of instruments used, beat or rhythm, region or time period it comes from The same discussion can be had about film, food, and much more. Make the point that the way science classifies Earth's biodiversity is similar to how we classify things in our culture: always changing.

Teach

CONNECT TO

Fungi Fungi differ from plants in other fundamental ways. Unlike plants, fungi lack structural specialization, and their cell walls contain chitin instead of cellulose.

Differentiated Instruction

ENGLISH LEARNERS

Have students compare and contrast the diagram of the six kingdoms shown in **FIGURE 4.1** on this page with the diagram of the three domains shown in **FIGURE 4.3**. Have students describe the reason for the change.

Teacher Toolkit, Section C, Quick-Write

TEACH WITH TECHNOLOGY

Organize students into nine groups. Six will prepare digital slide show presentations of organisms in a particular kingdom; three will do the same for the characteristics of life forms in the major domains. Have the two groups representing the Archaea and Bacteria kingdoms present in tandem with the groups representing those domains. The other four kingdom groups should follow the Eukarya domain group.

▼ Teach *continued*

Vocabulary

Greek and Latin Word Origins Tell students that **Archaea** is derived from the Greek *arkhaio*, meaning "ancient" or "primitive." The prefixes *archeo-* and *archaeo-* indicate an ancient origin. Other words in which students may recognize these roots are **archaeology** and **archaic.**

Address Misconceptions

Common Misconception Viruses and bacteria are the same thing.

Correcting the Misconception Viruses are not classified in any of the six kingdoms. Viruses cannot metabolize or reproduce independently, so many scientists do not even consider them to be living things. Because viruses have many properties that are unique and different from known life forms, they require their own classification system. Learn more in the chapter Viruses and Prokaryotes.

Science Trivia

- The total number of species on Earth is estimated to be between 10 and 100 million, with less than 2 million having been described, named, and classified by scientists.
- It's estimated that 99 percent of all plant and animal species that have ever lived are already extinct.
- Of the known animal species, 99 percent are smaller than bumblebees.

Answers

A Analyze The genetic difference between these groups of prokaryotes is greater than the genetic difference between the four eukaryotic kingdoms.

Woese's discovery did more than split the kingdom Monera. The two groups of prokaryotes that he studied have very different cell wall chemistry. In terms of genes, these two groups are more different from each other than animals are from plants, fungi, and protists. Based on these differences, Woese proposed that all life be divided into three domains. These domains are above the kingdom level.

A Analyze Why did Woese propose classifying bacteria and archaea into separate domains, rather than just separate kingdoms?

MAIN IDEA

The three domains in the tree of life are Bacteria, Archaea, and Eukarya.

Most biologists now accept Woese's domain system. This system more clearly shows the great diversity of prokaryotes in the tree of life by dividing them into two domains. These domains are called Bacteria and Archaea. All eukaryotes are placed into a third domain, called Eukarya.

READING TOOLBOX

TAKING NOTES

Use a three-column chart to take notes about the three domains and six kingdoms in the modern classification of life.

Domain Name	Characteristics	Kingdoms Included

Bacteria

The domain **Bacteria** includes single-celled prokaryotes in the kingdom Bacteria. The domain Bacteria is one of the largest groups of organisms on Earth. In fact, there are more bacteria in your mouth than there are people that have ever lived! Bacteria can be classified by many traits, such as their shape, their need for oxygen, and whether they cause disease.

Archaea

Like bacteria, organisms in the domain **Archaea** (ahr-KEE-uh) are single-celled prokaryotes. However, the cell walls of archaea and bacteria are chemically different. Archaea, like those in **FIGURE 4.2**, are known for their ability to live in extreme environments, such as deep sea vents, hot geysers, Antarctic waters, and salt lakes. All archaea are classified in the kingdom Archaea.

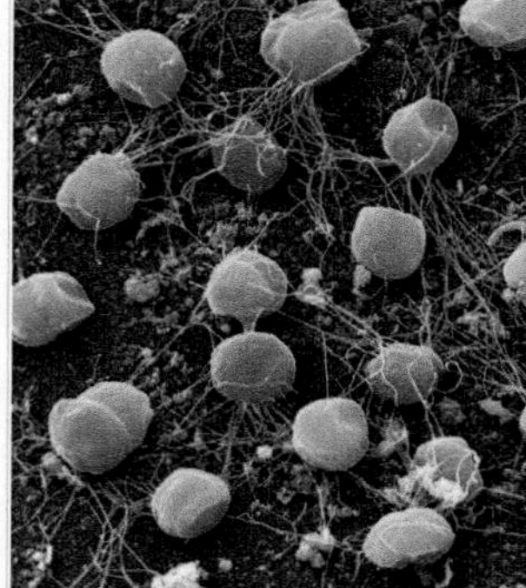

FIGURE 4.2 This archaean species, *Pyrococcus furiosus*, can be found in undersea hot vents and in the sand surrounding sulfurous volcanoes. These organisms live without oxygen and can grow in temperatures higher than the boiling point of water. (colored SEM; magnification 6500×)

Eukarya

The domain **Eukarya** (yoo-KAR-ee-uh) is made up of all organisms with eukaryotic cells. Eukaryotic cells have a distinct nucleus and membrane-bound organelles. Eukarya may be single-celled, such as most protists. They can also be colonial, such as some algae, or multicellular, like you. The domain Eukarya includes the kingdoms Protista, Plantae, Fungi, and Animalia.

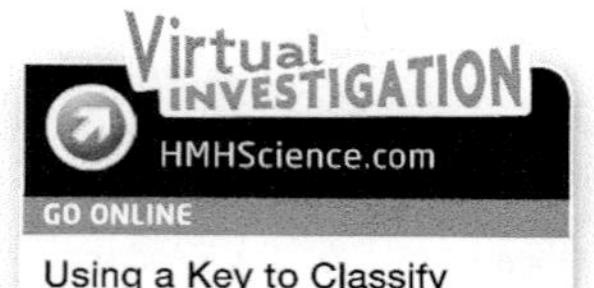

Using a Key to Classify

Differentiated Instruction

BELOW LEVEL

Have students identify the characteristics and properties of the three domains. Help them identify examples of several organisms that fit into each domain. They can use the note-taking graphic organizer shown in their textbooks to compare the relationship between domains and kingdoms.

Teacher Toolkit, Section C, Content Frame

PRE-AP

Have students think about what kingdoms might be more able to withstand the effects of climate change. Give them a scenario, such as an ice age or a major global warming, and have them discuss or write explanations for why the organisms of one kingdom might be more likely to withstand extreme climate change than another. Students should mention the Archaea prokaryotes' ability to live in hot geysers, hydrothermal vents, frigid ocean water, and other extreme environments.

Teacher Toolkit, Section C, Quick-Write

FIGURE 4.3 Tree of Life

The most recent classification system divides life into three domains, which include six kingdoms.

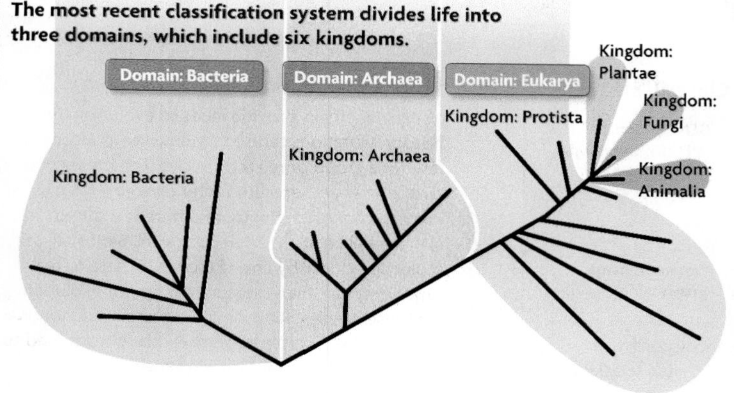

Scientists constructed this evolutionary tree by comparing rRNA sequences from species in each of the six recognized kingdoms. The distances between branches are proportional to the number of differences in rRNA sequences among these species.

Source: C. Woese, *PNAS* 97:15.

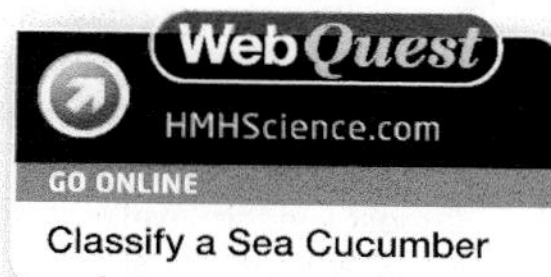

Classify a Sea Cucumber

CONNECT TO

KINGDOMS AND PHYLA

See **Appendix A** for a detailed description of each kingdom and its phyla.

Classifying Bacteria and Archaea

Some scientists think that bacteria and archaea have no true species. This is because many of these organisms transfer genes among themselves outside of typical reproduction. This sharing of genes blurs the lines between "species" as we define them in the Linnaean system. One study found that almost a quarter of the genes in the bacterium *Thermotoga maritima* are similar to archaean genes. Our understanding of how to classify prokaryotes is just beginning.

Analyze **Why are protists, plants, fungi, and animals classified into the same domain but into different kingdoms?**

18.4 Formative Assessment

SELF-CHECK Online
HMHScience.com
GO ONLINE

REVIEWING MAIN IDEAS

1. Why is the classification of life considered a work in progress?
2. What kingdoms are included in each of the three domains in the modern tree of life?

CRITICAL THINKING

3. **Apply** If you come across an unusual single-celled organism, what parts of the cell would you study in order to classify it into one of the three domains?
4. **Analyze** Why is it difficult, using the traditional definition of species, to classify some **bacteria** and **archaea** at the species level?

CONNECT TO

HISTORY OF LIFE

5. The Archaea lineage may include the first life on Earth, which began under much different environmental conditions from those present today. What characteristics of archaea help to support this statement?

ONLINE Biology

HMHScience.com

Students can go through the process of classifying a sea cucumber in the WebQuest for this chapter, available at **HMHScience.com**.

Integrating Human Biology

The human mouth is full of bacteria. Some are helpful; some are harmful. Bacteria in the ***mutans streptococci*** group are especially harmful when they are well fed. Whenever we eat simple carbohydrates, such as the sugars common in many processed foods and drinks, these bacteria are getting a meal, too. The acid produced by these bacteria when they metabolize sugar eats away at the enamel of our teeth, causing cavities and tooth loss.

Answers

A **Analyze** They all have eukaryotic cells, but are classified in different kingdoms based on differences in other characteristics.

Assess and Reteach

Assess Use the Section Self-Check or Section Quiz, both available at **HMHScience.com**.

Reteach Have students present an oral summary of the content in the section based on the section heads.

18.4 FORMATIVE ASSESSMENT

1. Scientists are always finding new information about organisms that forces a re-examination of classification schemes.
2. Bacteria—Bacteria; Archaea—Archaea; Eukarya—Protista, Fungi, Plantae, and Animalia
3. nucleus (or lack thereof) and cell wall
4. A species can be defined as an interbreeding group of organisms that produce fertile offspring. But bacteria and archaea do not breed to produce offspring; they reproduce by binary fission. In reproduction, as it is generally defined, parents also pass genetic material to their offspring. However, many bacteria and archaea can take up genetic material from their environment—a transfer of genes outside of typical reproduction that does not occur in eukaryotes.
5. Archaea can exist in extreme environments that are similar to those of early Earth.

CHAPTER REVIEW

GO ONLINE

Encourage students to go to **HMHScience.com** for a detailed review of each section, including visuals and vocabulary practice.

Online Student Resources, Vocabulary Practice Worksheet

CHAPTER 18 Summary

BIG IDEA Organisms can be classified based on physical and genetic characteristics, which reveal their evolutionary relationships.

KEY CONCEPTS

18.1 The Linnaean System of Classification

Organisms can be classified based on physical similarities. The Linnaean system of classification groups organisms based on shared physical or structural characteristics. This system is a nested hierarchy with seven taxa, or levels. The most specific level in this system is a species. Species are named according to binomial nomenclature, which gives each species a two-part scientific name using Latin roots.

GENUS: *Canis*
SPECIES: *Canis lupis*

Common name: *gray wolf*

18.2 Classification Based on Evolutionary Relationships

Modern classification is based on evolutionary relationships. Cladistics is a common method used to group species based on the order in which they diverged from a common ancestor. These evolutionary relationships can be presented in a branching diagram called a cladogram. Cladograms are constructed by identifying which derived characters are shared by which species in the group being analyzed.

Glyptodon

Armadillo

18.3 Molecular Clocks

Molecular clocks provide clues to evolutionary history. Mutations tend to accumulate at a constant rate for a group of related species. The longer that two species are separated after diverging from a common ancestor, the more different the two species will be at the molecular level. Biologists use molecular clocks by linking molecular data to real time. They can then measure the rate of evolution for these species. Ribosomal RNA and mitochondrial DNA provide two types of molecular clocks, used to measure evolution at different time scales.

18.4 Domains and Kingdoms

The current tree of life has three domains. The domains are based on fundamental differences at the cellular level. Within these domains are a total of six kingdoms. The Bacteria and Archaea domains include all organisms in the Bacteria and Archaea kingdoms, respectively. Bacteria and archaea are unicellular prokaryotes, but the genetic and cellular differences between these groups are greater than the differences between any other two kingdoms. The domain Eukarya includes all organisms with eukaryotic cells—kingdoms Protista, Fungi, Plantae, and Animalia.

Tree of life

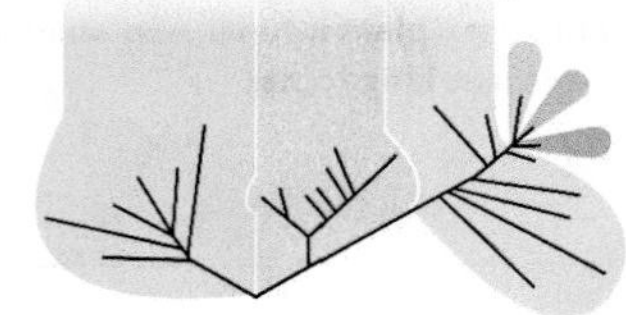

READING TOOLBOX SYNTHESIZE YOUR NOTES

Main Idea Web Use a main idea web to take notes about cladograms.

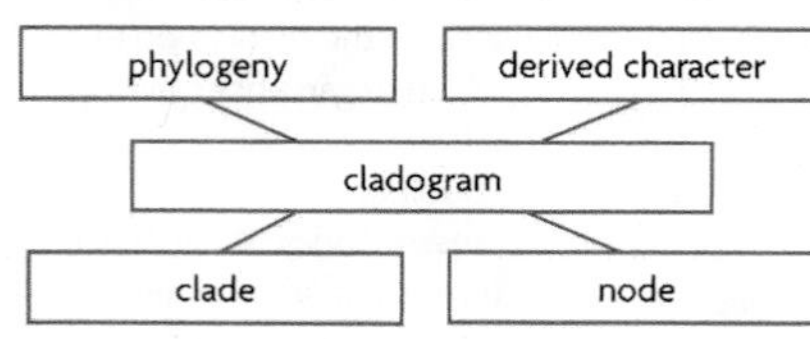

Concept Map Summarize what you know about taxonomy using a concept map.

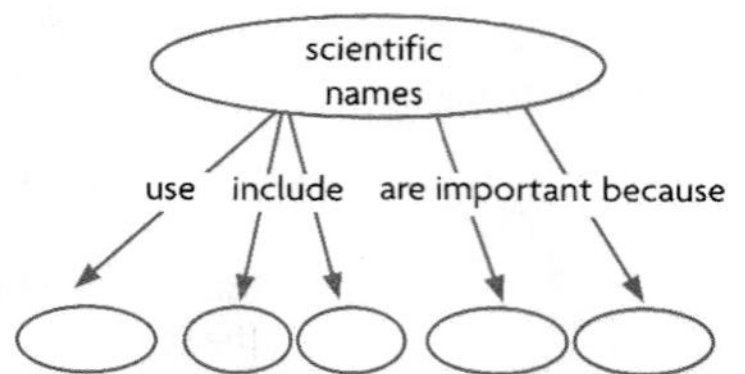

550 Unit 6: Diversity of Life

Reviewing Vocabulary

1. Binomial nomenclature is a system used to give each species a two-part scientific name, which includes a genus name and a species descriptor.
2. Life forms are currently divided into three domains: Bacteria, Archaea, and Eukarya.
3. Two molecules that are used as molecular clocks are mtDNA and rRNA.
4. *Sample question:* What method of constructing evolutionary trees makes use of the phylogeny of a species? *Answer:* cladistics
5. *Sample question:* In a cladogram, what distinguishes one clade from the next? *Answer:* derived characters
6. A cladogram is a type of chart with many branches.
7. The Archaean lineage is thought to possibly include the first, or most ancient and most primitive, life on Earth.

18 Review

INTERACTIVE Review
HMHScience.com
GO ONLINE
Review Games • Concept Map • Section Self-Checks

CHAPTER VOCABULARY

18.1 taxonomy
taxon
binomial nomenclature
genus

18.2 phylogeny
cladistics
cladogram
derived character

18.3 molecular clock
mitochondrial DNA
ribosomal RNA

18.4 Bacteria
Archaea
Eukarya

Reviewing Vocabulary

Vocabulary Connections

For each group of words below, write a sentence or two to explain clearly how the terms are connected. For example, for the terms *taxonomy* and *taxon*, you could write "In Linnaean taxonomy, each level of classification is called a taxon."

1. binomial nomenclature, genus, species
2. Bacteria, Archaea, Eukarya
3. molecular clock, mitochondrial DNA, ribosomal RNA

Write Your Own Questions

Think about the relationship between each pair of terms below. Then write a question about the first term that uses the second term as the answer. For the pair *taxonomy*, *taxon*, the question could be "In Linnaean taxonomy, what is each level of classification called?" Answer: taxon

4. phylogeny, cladistics
5. cladogram, derived characters

READING TOOLBOX GREEK AND LATIN WORD ORIGINS

6. *Klados* is Greek for "branch," and *-gram* is a suffix meaning "something written or drawn." Explain how this meaning relates to *cladogram*.

7. The prefix *archaeo-* comes from the Greek word *arkhaio*, which means "ancient" or "primitive." Explain how this meaning relates to *Archaea*.

Reviewing MAIN IDEAS

8. The scientific name for humans is *Homo sapiens*. What genus do humans belong to?

9. Why is it important for biologists to include scientific names when reporting their research to other biologists around the world?

10. Name the seven levels of organization in Linnaean taxonomy, from the most general to the most specific.

11. Current technology allows scientists to examine organisms at the molecular level. How has this technology exposed limitations in Linnaean taxonomy?

12. What basic idea does cladistics use to classify groups of organisms?

13. Two species with similar adaptations are found to have key differences at the molecular level. Scientists conclude that these species are not as closely related as previously thought. Why should the molecular evidence outweigh physical similarities that the species share?

14. A particular DNA sequence accumulated three mutations over 10,000 years. After how much time would you expect this sequence to have accumulated six more mutations? Explain.

15. Mutations accumulate more slowly in ribosomal RNA than in mitochondrial DNA. Which of these molecules would provide a better molecular clock for studying the evolution of species from different kingdoms?

16. The original Linnaean system of classification had two kingdoms. Biologists now use six kingdoms. What does this change suggest about the nature of classification?

17. What distinguishes the three domains in the tree of life from one another?

Reviewing Main Ideas

8. *Homo*
9. Scientific names are recognized by scientists around the world, no matter what languages they speak. This allows for clear communication. Also, there is only one scientific name given to each species, whereas one species may have many common names in just one language, and hundreds across multiple languages.
10. kingdom, phylum, class, order, family, genus, species
11. By studying species at the molecular level, scientists can compare the DNA of different species. Similarities in DNA are likely due to relatedness, while physical and structural similarities between species may be the result of convergent evolution and therefore not indicative of actual relatedness. Molecular evidence has led scientists to reclassify into different groups some species that were originally thought to be closely related based on physical similarities alone.

CHAPTER REVIEW

12. common ancestry, or descent from a common ancestor
13. Physical similarities may be due to convergent evolution, while similarities at the molecular level are more likely due to relatedness based on sharing a common ancestor.
14. 20,000 years. Mutations occur at a fairly constant rate, so if three mutations took place in 10,000 years, you could expect to double the number of mutations in double the amount of time.
15. rRNA. Molecules with low mutation rates accumulate fewer mutations over long periods of time. Species in different kingdoms have been diverging genetically for very long periods of time. Molecules that accumulate mutations at relatively high rates would have accumulated so many mutations that they would be almost impossible to compare between species in two different kingdoms.
16. Classification is a work in progress; it is always changing as scientists make more and more discoveries about species' relatedness.
17. The structure of cells distinguishes the three domains. Bacteria and Archaea both have prokaryotic cells, but their cell walls are chemically different. Eukarya have eukaryotic cells.

CHAPTER REVIEW

Critical Thinking

18. Organisms in the same family are more closely related than organisms in the same class. Class is a more general taxon than family in Linnaean taxonomy.
19. There are likely not enough rRNA mutations in the human lineage for comparison between different sub-groups because rRNA mutations occur very slowly.
20. birds. Crocodiles and alligators share a more recent common ancestor with birds, and both groups share the derived character of skull openings in the jaw.
21. In the Linnaean system, organisms are grouped by physical appearance and structural similarities. To classify organisms by evolutionary relationships, scientists also analyze molecular/genetic evidence, which often supports the Linnaean system but sometimes does not.
22. The three domains account for the huge genetic difference among bacteria, archaea, and eukaryotes. Eukaryotes (protists, fungi, plants, and animals) are more genetically similar to each other than bacteria are to archaea. The domain model makes this distinction more clear than the six-kingdom system alone.

Critical Thinking

18. Apply Are species in the same family more or less closely related than species in the same class? Explain your answer.

19. Evaluate Scientists have used mtDNA as a molecular clock to trace human evolution and early migration routes. Explain why mtDNA would be more useful in this research than rRNA.

20. Apply Refer to the cladogram in **FIGURE 2.2** of Section 2. Are crocodiles and alligators more closely related to snakes or to birds? Explain your answer using the terms *common ancestor* and *derived characters.*

21. Compare and Contrast What types of evidence are used for classifying organisms in the Linnaean classification system? What types of evidence are used for classifying organisms based on evolutionary relationships?

22. Evaluate What is the significance of grouping the six kingdoms into three domains? How does the domain model more clearly represent the diversity of prokaryotes than a system with the six kingdoms as its broadest divisions?

Interpreting Visuals

Use the cladogram, which classifies species A, B, C, and D, to answer the next three questions.

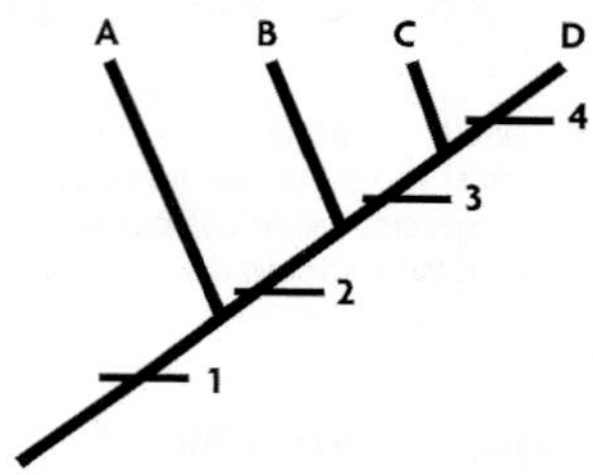

23. Apply What represents the derived characters that were used to construct this cladogram?

24. Analyze Where are the nodes in this cladogram, and what do they represent?

25. Analyze How many clades are represented in this cladogram?

Analyzing Data Transform Data

The family Ursidae contains all bear species. The data below show the number of species in each of the five genera of this family. Use these data to answer the next three questions.

GENERA OF THE FAMILY URSIDAE	
Genus Names	**Number of Species**
Ailuropoda	1
Helarctos	1
Melursus	1
Tremarctos	1
Ursus	4

Source: University of Michigan Museum of Zoology

26. Analyze How many species belong to family *Ursidae*?

27. Transform Data Transform the number of species in each genus to a percent of the total number of bear species in family Ursidae.

28. Analyze What do the transformed data show that raw data do not show?

Making Connections

29. Write a Letter Imagine that you are a modern-day molecular biologist. Write a letter to Linnaeus explaining how advances in technology have affected the way that scientists classify living organisms. Describe the parts of his classification system that are still used in the same way today. Also describe the aspects of his system that have changed over the years.

30. Compare and Contrast The pangolin on the chapter opener shares many physical traits, such as a long snout, with anteaters and aardvarks. However, these traits are known to have evolved separately in each of these groups of species. Write a paragraph that compares how Linnaeus and a modern taxonomist would likely classify pangolins. Include in your paragraph the kinds of additional information that a modern taxonomist might look for in order to classify the pangolin.

Interpreting Visuals

23. hash marks 1, 2, 3, and 4
24. Nodes are where the side branches intersect with the main branch. They represent the common ancestor of the species in each clade.
25. 3; one with A, B, C, and D; one with B, C, and D; and one with C and D

Analyzing Data

26. 8
27. *Ailuropoda, Helarctos, Melursus, Tremarctos:* 12.5 percent each; *Ursus:* 50 percent
28. Half of family Ursidae is in the genus *Ursus.*

Standards-Based Assessment

Record your answers on a separate piece of paper.

MULTIPLE CHOICE

1 Taxonomy can ***best*** be defined as a —
- A standardized means of referring to organisms using a two-part Latin name
- B means of grouping organisms based solely upon cell structure
- C hierarchal grouping of organisms based upon differences among them
- D branching classification system based on the shared characteristics of organisms

2 In the past 150 years, the classification of life has changed through the addition and restructuring of kingdoms and domains. This system is always changing because —
- A genetic research provides more accurate data
- B scientific theories never change
- C extinctions change evolutionary relationships
- D humans increase the rate of speciation

3 Birds and snakes share a common ancestor from over 250 million years ago, but now they show many physical differences. These differences are most directly the result of —
- A coevolution between species
- B molecular clocks ticking at different rates
- C the long-term accumulation of mutations
- D differences in the alleles of the ancestor

4 Scientists notice very few differences in the DNA sequences of individual cheetahs. This indicates that modern cheetahs likely descended from only a few individuals because —
- A smaller populations have less genetic variation
- B genetically different individuals are less fit
- C the mutation rate depends on population size
- D mutations do not affect small populations

5 Mammals are multicellular organisms with about 3 billion base pairs in their genome. Yeasts are single-celled organisms with about 13 million base pairs in their genome. Both of these groups are classified as eukaryotes because they —
- A have over one million base pairs
- B can reproduce sexually
- C utilize aerobic respiration
- D have a similar basic cellular structure

THINK THROUGH THE QUESTION

Do not get confused by extra information provided in this question. Focus on the definition of eukaryotes. The number of base pairs is not relevant to this question.

6

ginger	atgcgccgatccttacgtcgaatcggaac
corn	acgcaccgatacttacgtcgattcgggac
orchid	acgcgccgatacttacgtcgaatcgggac
lily	acgcgccgatacttccgtcgaatctggac

The DNA sequences above show a conserved, or essentially unchanged, gene among four related plants. The highlighted parts are ***most directly*** the result of —
- A crossing over
- B adaptation
- C mutation
- D meiosis

CHAPTER REVIEW

Standards-Based Assessment

The Standards-Based Assessment questions will help students prepare for their final examination in the course. If you wish to give students practice in coding their answers, look for the Standards-Based Assessment Answer Sheet at **HMHScience.com**. To give students practice under timed testing conditions, allow them five minutes per question.

Question	Answer	Depth of Knowledge	Cognitive Complexity
1	D	I	L
2	A	I	L
3	C	II	M
4	A	III	M
5	D	I	L
6	C	IV	H

KEY

Depth of Knowledge
- I Recall
- II Skill/Concept
- III Strategic Thinking
- IV Extended Thinking

Cognitive Complexity
- L Low
- M Moderate
- H High

Making Connections

29. Letters should include current molecular technologies and explanations of what they are, how they work, and why they are important. Linnaeus' scientific naming system and classification categories are still used today, but the way organisms are assigned to groups has changed.

30. *Sample answer:* Linnaeus would likely classify the three types of organisms very closely together since they share so many physical similarities. A modern taxonomist would realize that these similar traits may have resulted from convergent evolution. The modern taxonomist would then analyze molecular/genetic data to further investigate how closely related the three types of organisms are to each other.

THING EXPLAINER BY RANDALL MUNROE

A BOOK EXPLAINING COMPLEX IDEAS USING ONLY THE 1,000 MOST COMMON WORDS
THING EXPLAINER
COMPLICATED STUFF IN SIMPLE WORDS
RANDALL MUNROE
RANDALL MUNROE
XKCD.COM

TREE OF LIFE

All living things as part of the same family

You've learned that organisms can be classified based on physical and genetic characteristics, which reveal their evolutionary relationships. Tree diagrams are used to describe the relationships between organisms, both living and extinct. Here's one that uses easy-to-understand language.

THE STORY OF LIVING THINGS, FROM THE BEGINNING

ALL LIFE (THAT WE KNOW OF) IS PART OF A FAMILY. WE ALL COME FROM ONE LIVING THING THAT APPEARED IN THE EARLY DAYS OF THE EARTH.

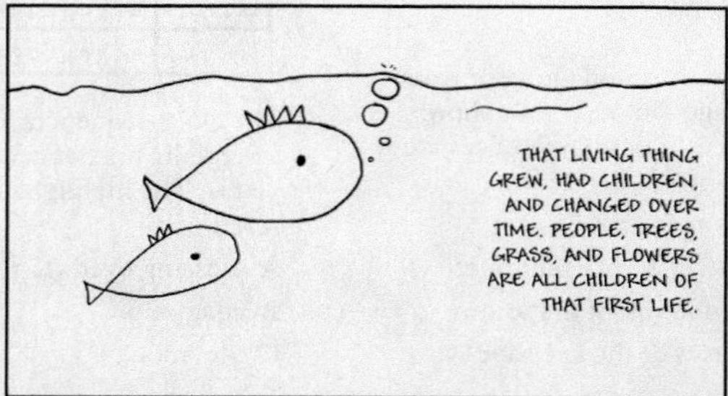

THAT LIVING THING GREW, HAD CHILDREN, AND CHANGED OVER TIME. PEOPLE, TREES, GRASS, AND FLOWERS ARE ALL CHILDREN OF THAT FIRST LIFE.

AS LIVING THINGS MAKE MORE LIVING THINGS, THE INFORMATION THEY PASS TO THEM CHANGES, MAKING THE NEW THINGS A LITTLE DIFFERENT FROM THE OLD.

OVER TIME, THESE SMALL CHANGES CAN LEAD TO VERY DIFFERENT KINDS OF LIVING THINGS GROWING FROM ONE.
FAMILY GET-TOGETHER!

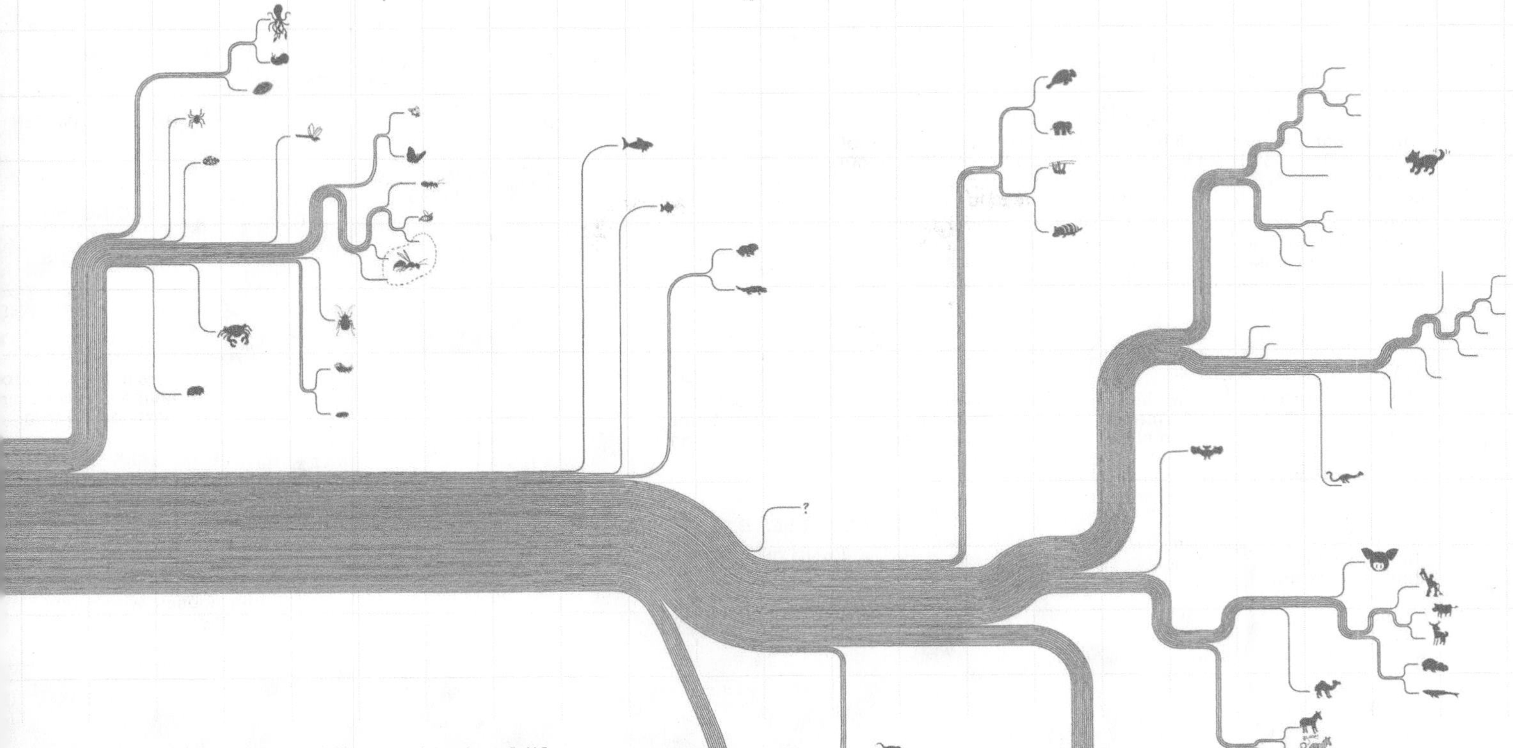

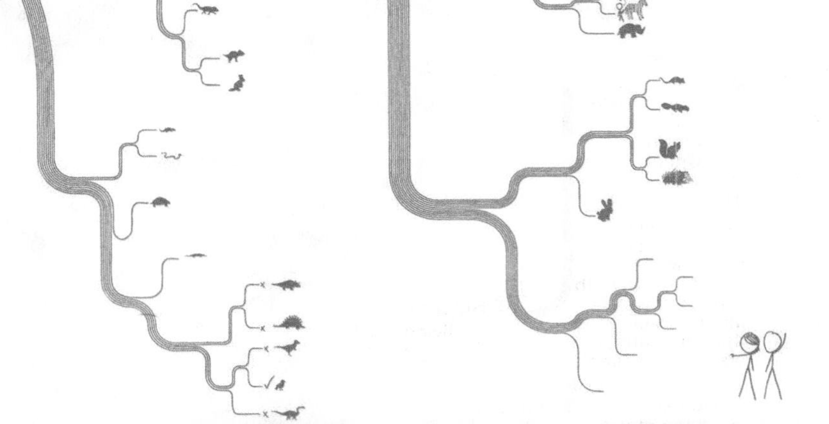

This tree shows how different kinds of life branched off from one another.

This tree doesn't show all living things, or even most of them. It just shows some of the living things you might know, along with which branch of life's family they're in.

This is just a tiny part of the tree of life. The whole tree is too big to fit in any single picture, and there are too many kinds of life for anyone to give names to all of them—no matter what kind of words they use.

And really, a true tree of life wouldn't just have a line for every *kind* of life. It would have a line for each living thing that ever was, every one of them crossing and joining and winding across the page, slowly changing from one kind of life to another, in a path that reaches all the way back, without a single break, to that very first life.

No one really knows how many living things there are in the world, but we can make some guesses, and they're big. Not only can we never find enough words to talk about all those lives, we have a hard time talking about the number itself.

Here's one way to think about how many things have lived on Earth: The world is covered in seas that are ringed with beaches of sand. One day, when you're walking on a beach, pick up some sand and look at it. Imagine that every tiny piece of sand under your feet is a whole world of its own, each one with its own seas and beaches, just like Earth.

The full tree of life has as many living things as there are bits of sand on all those beaches on all those tiny sand worlds put together.

Next to the world we're talking about, all our words are small.

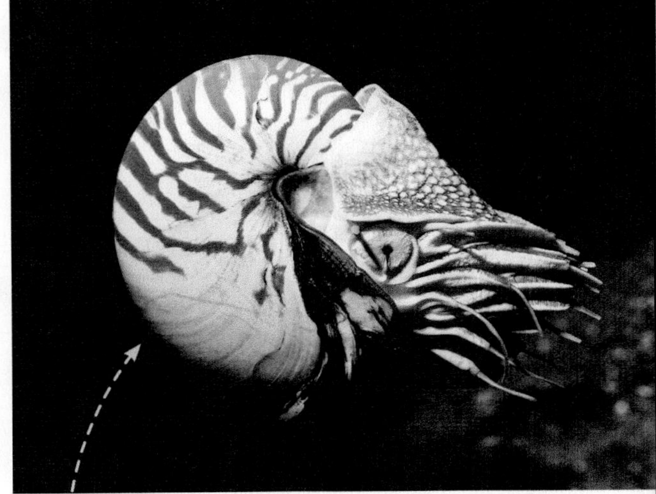

ANIMAL THAT LIVES DEEP IN THE SEA AND HAS BEEN ON EARTH FOR A VERY LONG TIME

553B

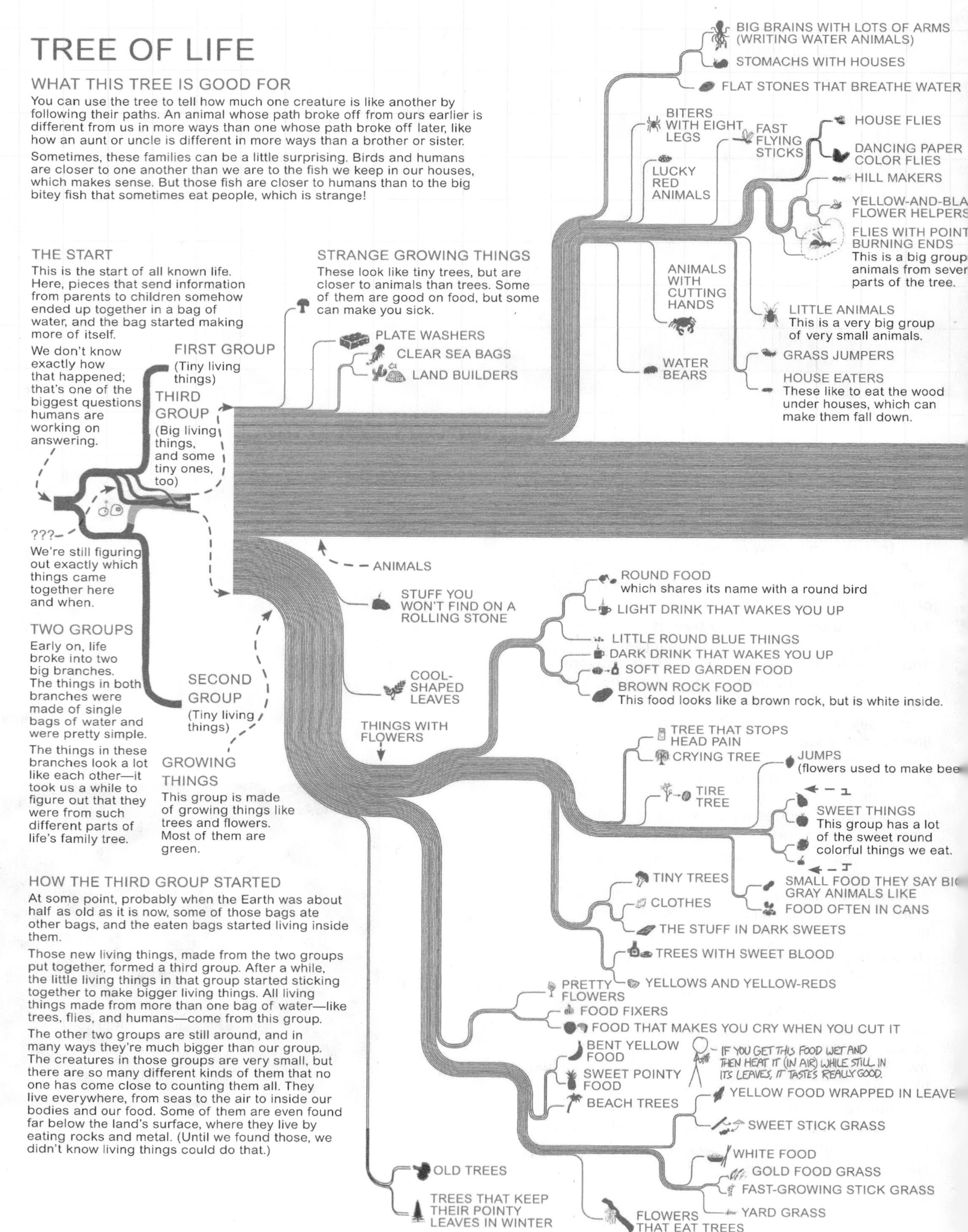
TREE OF LIFE
WHAT THIS TREE IS GOOD FOR
You can use the tree to tell how much one creature is like another by following their paths. An animal whose path broke off from ours earlier is different from us in more ways than one whose path broke off later, like how an aunt or uncle is different in more ways than a brother or sister.
Sometimes, these families can be a little surprising. Birds and humans are closer to one another than we are to the fish we keep in our houses, which makes sense. But those fish are closer to humans than to the big bitey fish that sometimes eat people, which is strange!
THE START
This is the start of all known life. Here, pieces that send information from parents to children somehow ended up together in a bag of water, and the bag started making more of itself.
We don't know exactly how that happened; that's one of the biggest questions humans are working on answering.
FIRST GROUP
(Tiny living things)
THIRD GROUP
(Big living things, and some tiny ones, too)
???
We're still figuring out exactly which things came together here and when.
TWO GROUPS
Early on, life broke into two big branches. The things in both branches were made of single bags of water and were pretty simple.
The things in these branches look a lot like each other—it took us a while to figure out that they were from such different parts of life's family tree.
SECOND GROUP
(Tiny living things)
GROWING THINGS
This group is made of growing things like trees and flowers. Most of them are green.
HOW THE THIRD GROUP STARTED
At some point, probably when the Earth was about half as old as it is now, some of those bags ate other bags, and the eaten bags started living inside them.
Those new living things, made from the two groups put together, formed a third group. After a while, the little living things in that group started sticking together to make bigger living things. All living things made from more than one bag of water—like trees, flies, and humans—come from this group.
The other two groups are still around, and in many ways they're much bigger than our group. The creatures in those groups are very small, but there are so many different kinds of them that no one has come close to counting them all. They live everywhere, from seas to the air to inside our bodies and our food. Some of them are even found far below the land's surface, where they live by eating rocks and metal. (Until we found those, we didn't know living things could do that.)
STRANGE GROWING THINGS
These look like tiny trees, but are closer to animals than trees. Some of them are good on food, but some can make you sick.
PLATE WASHERS
CLEAR SEA BAGS
LAND BUILDERS
ANIMALS
BIG BRAINS WITH LOTS OF ARMS (WRITING WATER ANIMALS)
STOMACHS WITH HOUSES
FLAT STONES THAT BREATHE WATER
BITERS WITH EIGHT LEGS
FAST FLYING STICKS
HOUSE FLIES
DANCING PAPER COLOR FLIES
LUCKY RED ANIMALS
HILL MAKERS
YELLOW-AND-BLA
FLOWER HELPERS
FLIES WITH POINT
BURNING ENDS
This is a big group
animals from sever
parts of the tree.
ANIMALS WITH CUTTING HANDS
LITTLE ANIMALS
This is a very big group of very small animals.
GRASS JUMPERS
WATER BEARS
HOUSE EATERS
These like to eat the wood under houses, which can make them fall down.
STUFF YOU WON'T FIND ON A ROLLING STONE
COOL-SHAPED LEAVES
THINGS WITH FLOWERS
ROUND FOOD
which shares its name with a round bird
LIGHT DRINK THAT WAKES YOU UP
LITTLE ROUND BLUE THINGS
DARK DRINK THAT WAKES YOU UP
SOFT RED GARDEN FOOD
BROWN ROCK FOOD
This food looks like a brown rock, but is white inside.
TREE THAT STOPS HEAD PAIN
CRYING TREE
JUMPS
(flowers used to make bee
TIRE TREE
SWEET THINGS
This group has a lot of the sweet round colorful things we eat.
TINY TREES
SMALL FOOD THEY SAY BI
GRAY ANIMALS LIKE
CLOTHES
FOOD OFTEN IN CANS
THE STUFF IN DARK SWEETS
TREES WITH SWEET BLOOD
PRETTY FLOWERS
YELLOWS AND YELLOW-REDS
FOOD FIXERS
FOOD THAT MAKES YOU CRY WHEN YOU CUT IT
BENT YELLOW FOOD
SWEET POINTY FOOD
IF YOU GET THIS FOOD WET AND THEN HEAT IT (IN AIR) WHILE STILL IN ITS LEAVES, IT TASTES REALLY GOOD.
BEACH TREES
YELLOW FOOD WRAPPED IN LEAVE
SWEET STICK GRASS
WHITE FOOD
GOLD FOOD GRASS
FAST-GROWING STICK GRASS
YARD GRASS
OLD TREES
TREES THAT KEEP THEIR POINTY LEAVES IN WINTER
FLOWERS THAT EAT TREES

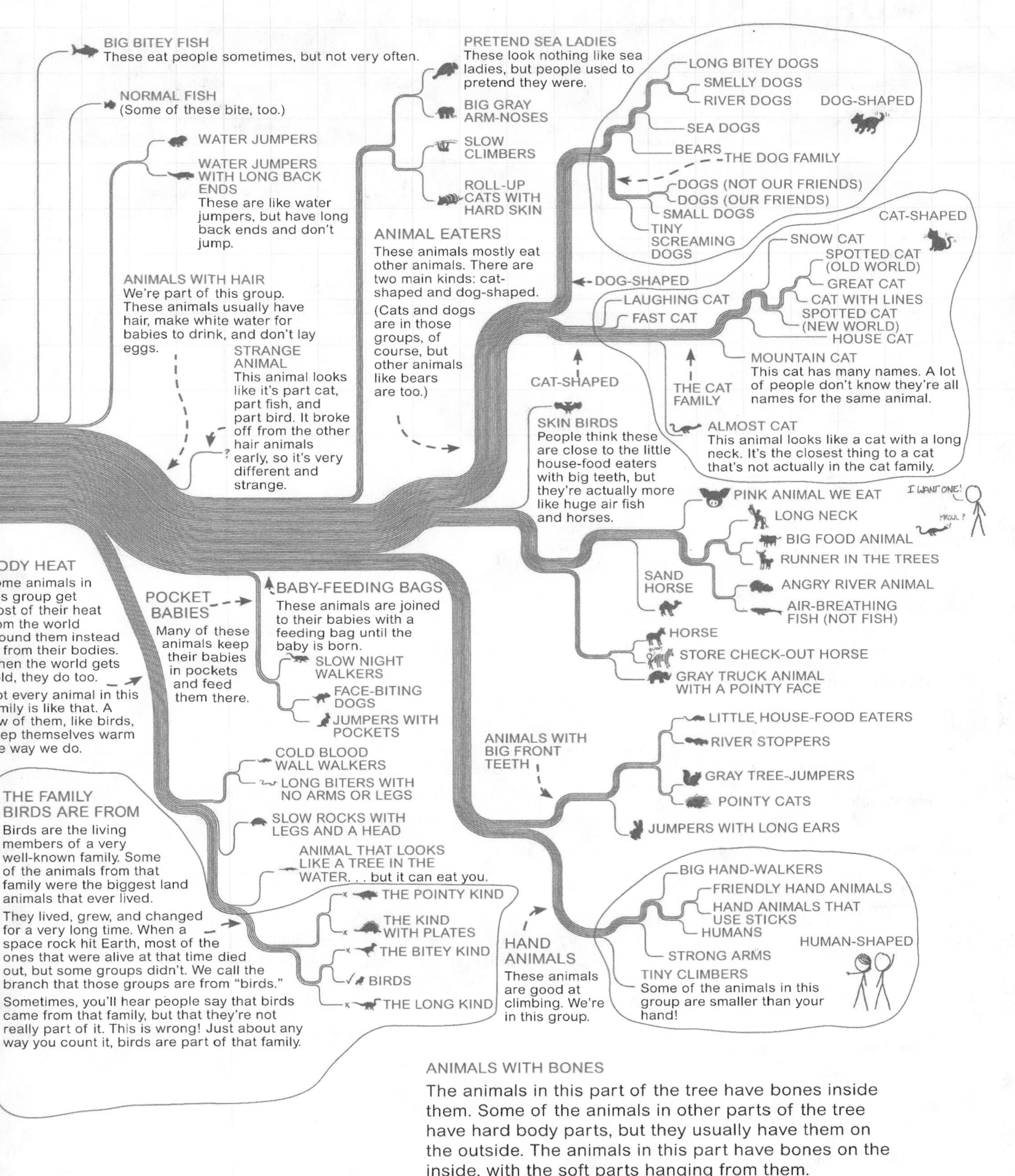
BIG BITEY FISH
These eat people sometimes, but not very often.
NORMAL FISH
(Some of these bite, too.)
WATER JUMPERS
WATER JUMPERS WITH LONG BACK ENDS
These are like water jumpers, but have long back ends and don't jump.
ANIMALS WITH HAIR
We're part of this group. These animals usually have hair, make white water for babies to drink, and don't lay eggs.
STRANGE ANIMAL
This animal looks like it's part cat, part fish, and part bird. It broke off from the other hair animals early, so it's very different and strange.
?
PRETEND SEA LADIES
These look nothing like sea ladies, but people used to pretend they were.
BIG GRAY ARM-NOSES
SLOW CLIMBERS
ROLL-UP CATS WITH HARD SKIN
ANIMAL EATERS
These animals mostly eat other animals. There are two main kinds: cat-shaped and dog-shaped.
(Cats and dogs are in those groups, of course, but other animals like bears are too.)
LONG BITEY DOGS
SMELLY DOGS
RIVER DOGS
DOG-SHAPED
SEA DOGS
BEARS
THE DOG FAMILY
DOGS (NOT OUR FRIENDS)
DOGS (OUR FRIENDS)
SMALL DOGS
TINY SCREAMING DOGS
CAT-SHAPED
SNOW CAT
SPOTTED CAT (OLD WORLD)
GREAT CAT
CAT WITH LINES
SPOTTED CAT (NEW WORLD)
HOUSE CAT
DOG-SHAPED
LAUGHING CAT
FAST CAT
MOUNTAIN CAT
This cat has many names. A lot of people don't know they're all names for the same animal.
CAT-SHAPED
THE CAT FAMILY
ALMOST CAT
This animal looks like a cat with a long neck. It's the closest thing to a cat that's not actually in the cat family.
SKIN BIRDS
People think these are close to the little house-food eaters with big teeth, but they're actually more like huge air fish and horses.
PINK ANIMAL WE EAT
I WANT ONE!
LONG NECK
MROWL?
BIG FOOD ANIMAL
RUNNER IN THE TREES
SAND HORSE
ANGRY RIVER ANIMAL
AIR-BREATHING FISH (NOT FISH)
HORSE
STORE CHECK-OUT HORSE
GRAY TRUCK ANIMAL WITH A POINTY FACE
ODY HEAT
ome animals in is group get ost of their heat om the world round them instead f from their bodies. Vhen the world gets old, they do too.
ot every animal in this amily is like that. A ew of them, like birds, eep themselves warm e way we do.
POCKET BABIES
Many of these animals keep their babies in pockets and feed them there.
BABY-FEEDING BAGS
These animals are joined to their babies with a feeding bag until the baby is born.
SLOW NIGHT WALKERS
FACE-BITING DOGS
JUMPERS WITH POCKETS
COLD BLOOD WALL WALKERS
LONG BITERS WITH NO ARMS OR LEGS
SLOW ROCKS WITH LEGS AND A HEAD
ANIMAL THAT LOOKS LIKE A TREE IN THE WATER. . . but it can eat you.
THE FAMILY BIRDS ARE FROM
Birds are the living members of a very well-known family. Some of the animals from that family were the biggest land animals that ever lived.
They lived, grew, and changed for a very long time. When a space rock hit Earth, most of the ones that were alive at that time died out, but some groups didn't. We call the branch that those groups are from "birds."
Sometimes, you'll hear people say that birds came from that family, but that they're not really part of it. This is wrong! Just about any way you count it, birds are part of that family.
THE POINTY KIND
THE KIND WITH PLATES
THE BITEY KIND
BIRDS
THE LONG KIND
ANIMALS WITH BIG FRONT TEETH
LITTLE HOUSE-FOOD EATERS
RIVER STOPPERS
GRAY TREE-JUMPERS
POINTY CATS
JUMPERS WITH LONG EARS
HAND ANIMALS
These animals are good at climbing. We're in this group.
BIG HAND-WALKERS
FRIENDLY HAND ANIMALS
HAND ANIMALS THAT USE STICKS
HUMANS
HUMAN-SHAPED
STRONG ARMS
TINY CLIMBERS
Some of the animals in this group are smaller than your hand!
ANIMALS WITH BONES
The animals in this part of the tree have bones inside them. Some of the animals in other parts of the tree have hard body parts, but they usually have them on the outside. The animals in this part have bones on the inside, with the soft parts hanging from them.

CHAPTER 19

Instruction and Intervention Support

Viruses and Prokaryotes

① Core Instruction

The **Core Instruction** resources below can be used for all students. Core instruction should be followed by ongoing assessment to determine which students need further help.

Available in both English and Spanish

Available Online

Section	Instruction	PRINT	ONLINE	Labs
19.1	Textbook **Studying Viruses and Prokaryotes**	■	●	
	PowerPresentation and Notes 19.1		●	
19.2	Textbook **Viral Structure and Reproduction**	■	●	Modeling Viruses S.T.E.M. Lab Modeling Virus Mutations
	Teaching Visuals Viral Structures (Fig. 2.2, 2.3), Lytic and Lysogenic Infections (Fig. 2.4)		●	
	PowerPresentation and Notes 19.2		●	
19.3	Textbook **Viral Diseases**	■	●	Viruses and Cancer
	PowerPresentation and Notes 19.3		●	
19.4	Textbook **Bacteria and Archaea**	■	●	**Video Lab** Bacterial Staining **Virtual Lab** Testing Antibacterial Agents
	Teaching Visuals Prokaryote Structure (Fig. 4.3)		●	
	PowerPresentation and Notes 19.4		●	
19.5	Textbook **Beneficial Roles of Prokaryotes**	■	●	Leaf Print Bacteria Using Bacteria to Break Down Oil (Design Your Own) Bacteria's Role in Wastewater Treatment (Biotechnology Lab) **QuickLab** Examining Bacteria in Yogurt
	PowerPresentation and Notes 19.5		●	
19.6	Textbook **Bacterial Diseases and Antibiotics**	■	●	
	Animated Biology What Would You Prescribe?, Koch's Postulate		●	
	PowerPresentation and Notes 19.6		●	

Additional online resources available for this chapter include **Interactive Whiteboard Resources.**

GO ONLINE! for all your teacher resources at HMHScience.com

2 Support and Intervention

Support and Intervention resources are useful for students who need targeted help beyond the Core Instruction

Resources	PRINT	ONLINE
Assess and Reteach (TE wrap)	■	●
Concept Map		●
Interactive Reader	■	●
Interactive Review Games		●
Section Self-Checks		●
Study Guide B		●
Vocabulary Practice Worksheets		●

3 Specialized Support

Students who need more intensive personalized intervention benefit from **Specialized Support** resources.

Resources	PRINT	ONLINE
Chapter Audio Files		●
Differentiated Instruction Inclusion, Below Level, and English Learners (TE wrap)	■	●
ELL Strategies	■	●
Modified Lesson Plans for English Learners		●
Reinforcement Worksheets		●
Study Guide A		●

Extension and Assessment

Enrichment and Challenge

Resources	PRINT	ONLINE
Active Reading Worksheets		●
Data Analysis Practice Worksheet		●
Differentiated Instruction Pre-AP (TE wrap)	■	●
Pre-AP Activity The Case of Typhoid Mary		●
The Inside Story and **Take It Further** (TE wrap)	■	●
Unit Project		●
WebLinks		●
WebQuest Antibiotics in Agriculture (19.6)		●

Assessment

Resources	PRINT	ONLINE
Alternative Assessment		●
Chapter Tests A and B		●
Diagnostic Test		●
ExamView Banks		●
Extended Response Test		●
Online Assessment System		●
Section Quizzes		●
Standards-Based Assessment	■	●

CHAPTER 19

Chapter Overview

- **Section 1** compares and contrasts viruses with prokaryotes.
- **Section 2** describes viral structure and reproduction.
- **Section 3** details the role of viruses in causing diseases including the common cold, influenza, SARS, and AIDS.
- **Section 4** compares characteristics of bacteria and archaea.
- **Section 5** explains the benefits of certain bacteria to organisms and the important role bacteria play in ecosystems.
- **Section 6** describes some bacterial diseases and the use of antibiotics.

Focus and Motivate

How are bacteria helpful to humans?

Tell students that intestinal bacteria break down nutrients we could not otherwise digest and keep harmful microbes at bay. For the bacteria, the intestine provides a habitat. **Ask,** What type of ecological relationship does this describe? mutualism Have students read the description of the bacterium shown in the picture. **Ask**, How might the bacteria protect humans from throat and stomach cancers? Accept all reasonable answers. Tell students that scientist think the bacteria in the esophagus produce a toxin that kills cancer cells.

BIOZINE
HMHScience.com

Students can access BioZine at **HMHScience.com** to learn about avian flu, antibiotic resistance, and viruses.

CHAPTER 19

Viruses and Prokaryotes

BIG IDEA Viruses and some bacteria can be harmful to human health or the environment, but most bacteria and archaea are an important part of every community they inhabit.

ONLINE BIOLOGY HMHScience.com

ONLINE Labs
- **QuickLab** Examining Bacteria in Yogurt
- Leaf Print Bacteria
- Using Bacteria to Break Down Oil
- Modeling Viruses
- S.T.E.M. Lab Modeling Viral Mutations
- Viruses and Cancer
- Bacteria's Role in Wastewater Treatment
- **Virtual Lab** Testing Antibacterial Agents
- **Video Lab** Bacterial Staining

Student Activity

Purpose **Have students assess the effectiveness of hand-washing for removing microbes.**

Materials (per team)
- GloGerm™ lotion
- black-light lamp
- liquid soap
- paper towels

If GloGerm™ and black lights are too expensive, use a mixture of ground cinnamon and baby oil as "germs."

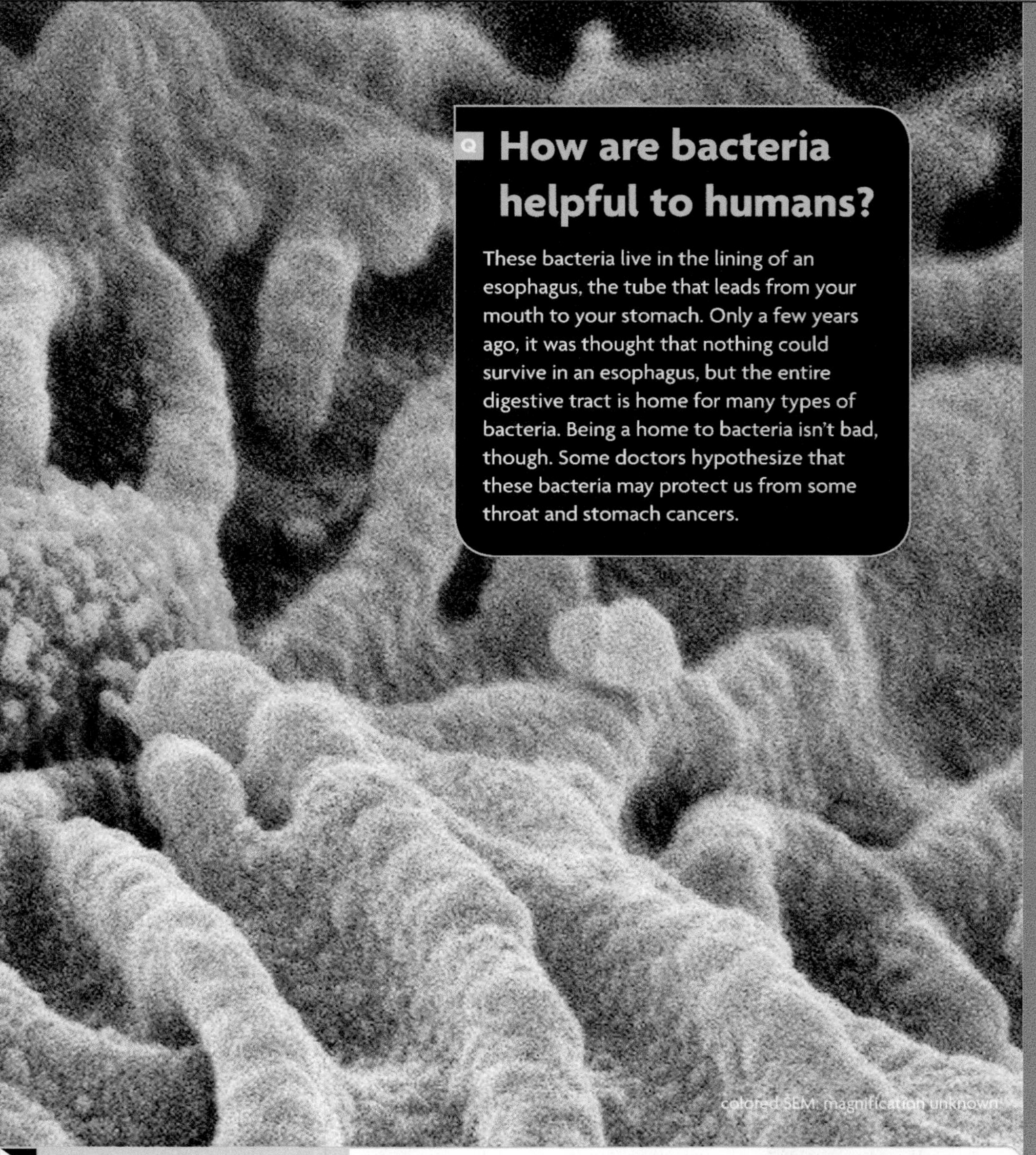

How are bacteria helpful to humans?

These bacteria live in the lining of an esophagus, the tube that leads from your mouth to your stomach. Only a few years ago, it was thought that nothing could survive in an esophagus, but the entire digestive tract is home for many types of bacteria. Being a home to bacteria isn't bad, though. Some doctors hypothesize that these bacteria may protect us from some throat and stomach cancers.

colored SEM; magnification unknown

READING TOOLBOX **This reading tool can help you learn the material in the following pages.**

USING LANGUAGE

Cause and Effect In biological processes, one step leads to another step. When reading, you can recognize cause-and-effect relationships by words that indicate a cause and result, such as *because*, *so*, *consequently*, and *as a result*.

YOUR TURN

In the following sentences, identify the cause and effect.

1. Disease spreads easily from one population to another because people travel frequently.
2. HIV infects white blood cells. Consequently, the immune system becomes vulnerable to disease.

Introduce Have students rub a small amount of GloGerm™ lotion onto their hands, making sure to rub it into the fingernails and between the fingers. Explain that GloGerm™ is meant to simulate microbes—invisible to the eye but present everywhere. Have students look at their hands under the black light. Their hands should glow. Ask students to wash their hands thoroughly for 15–20 seconds with soap and warm water, trying to remove as many of the "microbes" as possible. After rinsing and drying their hands, have students examine their hands under the black light again.

Discuss GloGerm™ is useful for those who work in industries that demand a high level of hygiene, such as medicine and food service. **Ask**

- What areas of the hand need particular attention when washing? around the nails and between the fingers
- When is it important to wash hands to minimize the spread of disease-causing microbes? before and after handling food, after using the toilet, after handling animals or their waste, after contact with someone with an infectious illness, before performing medical procedures

Activate Prior Knowledge

Students will be familiar with computer viruses. Tell them that the concept of a self-replicating agent that proliferates over the Internet has now been adapted to marketing techniques. **Ask,** Have you ever signed up for a free email account? How can such a service pay for itself? Students may recognize that the provider is supported by advertising. What students may not realize is that their emails may also pass along marketing materials to the recipient. This is called *viral marketing*. In the case of email providers, "susceptible" users sign up and then "infect" others in their social circle with promotional information from the provider. Real biological viruses are passed on in a similar way, often without the transmitter or recipient knowing they have the virus.

Preview Vocabulary

Academic Vocabulary In everyday language, we use the word *contagious* to describe the spread of laughter, fear, and other behaviors or states of mind. In biology, *contagious* describes a disease that is passed from one organism to another by direct or indirect physical contact. The term *infectious* is similar.

Both words come from the Latin:

contingere = to touch

inficere = to stain

English Learners Point out the analogy of a virus or bacterium acting like an uninvited guest. Students should look for terms in the text that relate to this analogy, such as *host, door, intruder,* and *guest*. The idea of entry is important. Students need to think about how pathogens move into hosts and how they behave once they are inside.

Answers

1. Cause: People travel frequently. Effect: Diseases spread from one population to another.
2. Cause: HIV infects white blood cells. Effect: The immune system becomes vulnerable to disease.

SECTION 19.1

▼ Plan and Prepare

Activate Prior Knowledge Many people wonder why some illnesses are easily treatable or curable, while others are not. **Ask,** Why is it that when you go to a doctor, explain your symptoms, and undergo testing, sometimes you are given an antibiotic and sometimes you are not? Antibiotics do not work on viruses. Viruses, such as those that cause the common cold, cannot be treated with antibiotics because they do not have the cellular structures that bacteria have that can be destroyed or inhibited.

▼ Teach

Vocabulary

Academic Vocabulary Tell students that the suffix *-oid* is attached to objects or beings that are similar or related to another. For example, *humanoid* describes something that has characteristics associated with humans, though it is not human. Often that which is described is *diminutive,* less substantial or smaller than the original, as is the case with **viroids** and **viruses.**

19.1 Studying Viruses and Prokaryotes

KEY CONCEPT **Infections can be caused in several ways.**

MAIN IDEAS

- Viruses, bacteria, viroids, and prions can all cause infection.

VOCABULARY

virus
pathogen
viroid
prion

Connect to Your World

Bacteria are everywhere, including in and on your own body—such as the bacteria that live in our digestive tracts. The relationship between you and the microorganisms in your body is usually mutually beneficial. Under certain conditions, however, normally harmless microorganisms can cause disease, and some types of microorganisms are particularly nasty—they always make you sick.

MAIN IDEA

Viruses, bacteria, viroids, and prions can all cause infection.

You are probably familiar with the terms *virus* and *bacteria,* but you may not know exactly what they are. A **virus** is an infectious particle made only of a strand of DNA or RNA surrounded by a protein coat. Bacteria, on the other hand, are one-celled microorganisms that can also cause infection. Any living organism or particle that can cause an infectious disease is called an infectious agent, or **pathogen.**

You have learned that all living things share certain key characteristics: the abilities to reproduce, to use nutrients and energy, to grow and develop, and to respond to their environments. They also contain genetic material that carries the code of life. Prokaryotes—such as the bacterium shown in **FIGURE 1.1**—are clearly living things, since they have each of the traits of life. But are viruses living things? Like living cells, viruses respond to their environment. Viruses have genes and can reproduce. Unlike cells, however, viruses cannot reproduce on their own. Instead, they need living cells to help them reproduce and make proteins. Viruses are also much smaller than most cells, as you can see in **FIGURE 1.2.** While viruses have key traits similar to living cells, they also have many differences. In fact, viruses are not even given a place in the Linnaean system of biological classification.

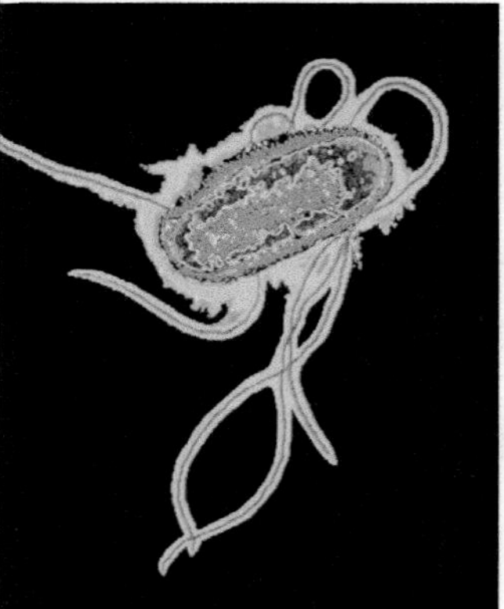

FIGURE 1.1 Prokaryotes, such as this *Escherichia coli* bacterium, are single cells that have all of the characteristics of living things. (colored TEM; magnification 6000×)

A viroid has even less in common with living things than do viruses. **Viroids** are infectious particles that cause disease in plants. Viroids are made of single-stranded RNA without a protein coat. They are passed through seeds or pollen. Viroids have had a major economic impact on agriculture because they can stunt the growth of plants.

Differentiated Instruction

ENGLISH LEARNERS

Students can use a Venn diagram to compare viruses with living things such as bacteria. In the overlapping areas, they can list the commonalities, such as "have genes," and in the other areas, they can list the differences that exclude viruses from the three domains.

Teacher Toolkit, Section C, Venn Diagram

PRE-AP

Have students create a table to organize the material of the chapter. Tell them that they will study different infectious agents, how they are structured, how they reproduce, and how they interact with other organisms, including humans, in ways that are beneficial, harmful, or benign.

Teacher Toolkit, Section C, Feature Analysis

FIGURE 1.2 Relative Sizes of Cells and Infectious Particles

Although eukaryotic and prokaryotic cells can be microscopic, they are large in comparison to viruses, viroids, and prions.

1 nanometer (nm) = one billionth of a meter

100 nm

eukaryotic cells
10,000–100,000 nm

prokaryotic cells
200–10,000 nm

viruses
50–200 nm

viroids
5–150 nm

prion
2–10 nm

A Infer Why are viroids and prions sometimes called subviral particles?

At the boundary between living and nonliving, perhaps the strangest entity of all is the prion. A **prion** (PREE-ahn) is an infectious particle made only of proteins that can cause other proteins to fold incorrectly. When proteins misfold, the protein will not work properly. Prions are unusual in that they are infectious yet have no genetic material. They play a part in certain diseases of the brain such as mad cow disease, known to scientists as bovine spongiform encephalopathy, or BSE. Humans may become infected with BSE when they eat meat from animals that are infected. Food safety laws in the United States, however, try to reduce the risk of infection. Creutzfeld-Jakob (KROYTS-fehlt YAH-kawp) disease (CJD), another brain disease that affects humans, is also associated with prions. Prion diseases can incubate for a long time with no effect on their host. However, once symptoms appear, they worsen quickly and are always fatal, because the body has no immune response against a protein.

B Synthesize Why are viruses, viroids, and prions not included in the Linnaean system of biological classification?

READING TOOLBOX

TAKING NOTES

Use a two-column chart to take notes on viruses, viroids, and prions.

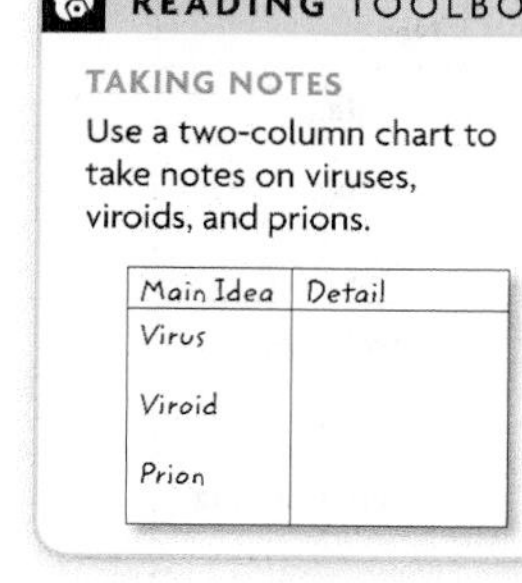

Main Idea	Detail
Virus	
Viroid	
Prion	

SELF-CHECK Online
HMHScience.com
GO ONLINE

19.1 Formative Assessment

REVIEWING MAIN IDEAS

1. What are the main differences between living cells and **viruses**?
2. Viruses, **viroids, prions,** and some bacteria can all be considered **pathogens.** What do all pathogens have in common?

CRITICAL THINKING

3. **Infer** Prions were not widely known to be infectious agents until the 1980s. Give two reasons why this might be so.
4. **Apply** An RNA-based disease spreads through pollen. Is it likely due to a virus, viroid, or prion? Explain.

CONNECT TO MEDICINE

5. To multiply, viruses must take over the functions of the cells they infect. Why does this make it difficult to make effective antiviral drugs?

19.1 FORMATIVE ASSESSMENT

1. Cells can use energy and nutrients and reproduce independently of other cells, whereas viruses rely on cells to help them reproduce and make proteins.
2. They cause infectious diseases.
3. They are very small, and prion diseases often incubate for many years before taking effect.
4. Viroids, because they are made of RNA, are passed through seeds or pollen, and infect plants.
5. Most drugs that would interfere with viral replication would also kill the host cell.

TEACH FROM VISUALS

FIGURE 1.2 Have students compare the sizes of eukaryotic cells, prokaryotic cells, viruses, viroids, and prions. **Ask,** How many times larger are the largest eukaryotic cells than the largest prions? 10,000 times larger

Integrating Epidemiology

Kuru is a **prion disease** found only among the **Fore** people of the New Guinea highlands. *Kuru* means "shiver," denoting the tremors and wobbly gait caused by the disease. Other symptoms include slurred speech and sudden maniacal laughter. The disease reached epidemic levels during the 1950s and 1960s, before scientists realized that the means of transmission was a practice known as mortuary cannibalism.

According to Fore culture, family members of a dead relative absorb that person back into the living family by cooking and eating the tissue of the deceased, including the brain. Because the incubation time of Kuru was sometimes many years, the Fore people never made the connection between their ritual and the disease. The New Guinean government's discouragement of the practice has produced a steady decline of the disease.

Answers

A Infer They are smaller than viruses.

B Synthesize They are not considered to be organisms.

Assess and Reteach

Assess Use the Section Self-Check or Section Quiz, both available at **HMHScience.com**.

Reteach Create a table on the board to compare prions, viruses, bacteria, and viroids. Have students call out the characteristics of each. Headings could include size, living or nonliving, type of genetic material (if any), and type of organisms affected.

DATA ANALYSIS

Introduce

Explain that TB is a major public health threat globally. One-third of the world's population is infected with TB, and 3 million people die from the disease each year. Worldwide, TB infection rates are increasing, and multidrug resistance is becoming more prevalent. **Ask**

- Why is it important to collect data on the spread of disease in a population? helps monitor trends, can determine what treatments are effective
- Is it better to collect discrete data, continuous data, or both? Both discrete data and continuous data are valuable for analyzing the effects of disease. Discrete data can give specifics on how many people have a disease, where they live, and how many have died. Continuous data reveals trends, such as the incidence or mortality of a disease.

Discuss

Have students consider the implications of the TB data. **Ask**

- What hypotheses might account for the decrease in TB in the United States since 1955? Answers will vary but could include increased availability of drugs, compliance in completing full drug regimens, and improved public health science.
- Do the high numbers of TB cases in California, New York, Florida, and Texas suggest that residents of these states are more likely to get TB than residents of other states? No, the numbers may be high only because they are the most populous states.
- What would be a better way to compare the incidence of TB in different states? convert the number of cases to a rate, such as cases per 100,000 people

Online Student Resources, Data Analysis Practice

DATA ANALYSIS

Choosing Data Representation

Create animated charts and graphs using SmartGrapher.

Collecting data on the spread of infectious disease in a population is an important part of monitoring trends and determining a course of treatment. Different methods of displaying data, such as bar graphs or line graphs, often convey different information. Recall from the Data Analysis activity, "Discrete and Continuous Data," the difference between these two data types.

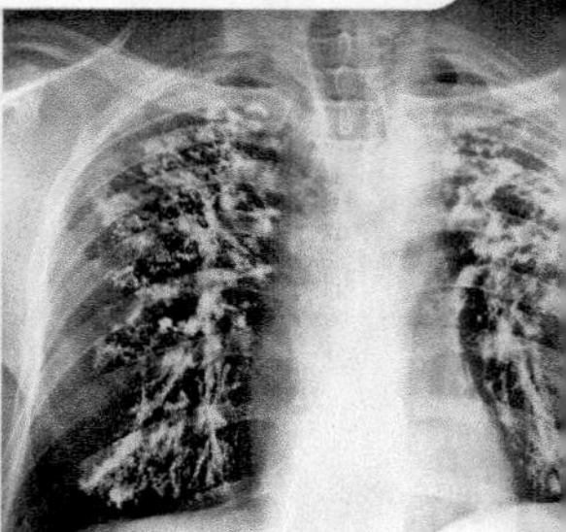

Lungs infected by tuberculosis

TABLE 1. STATES WITH MOST TB CASES IN 2005

State	Number of Cases
California	2900
Texas	1535
New York	1294
Florida	1094
Illinois	596
Georgia	510
New Jersey	485
Virginia	355
North Carolina	329
Pennsylvania	325

TABLE 2. RATE OF TB FOR U.S. RESIDENTS

Year	TB Cases per 100,000 Persons
1955	46.6
1960	30.7
1965	25.2
1970	18.1
1975	15.7
1980	12.2
1985	9.3
1990	10.3
1995	8.7
2000	5.8
2005	4.8

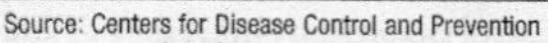

Source: Centers for Disease Control and Prevention

Practice Choose Data Representation

The tables above show two sets of data describing tuberculosis (TB) infection in the United States.

1. **Connect** For each of the tables above, identify whether the data are continuous or discrete.
2. **Graph Data** Determine which type of graph would best represent each set of data and construct the graph for each set.
3. **Analyze** What trend did your graph show in rates of tuberculosis cases in the United States between the years 1955 and 2005?
4. **Analyze** Which table gives a more complete picture of TB infection in the United States? Explain.
5. **Predict** What trend do you expect the rate of TB cases to show in 2010?

Answers

Sample Data

See sample graphs of student data in Teacher Resources at **HMHScience.com**.

Analyze and Conclude

1. Table 1: discrete; Table 2: continuous
2. Discrete data should be constructed as a bar graph. Continuous data should be constructed as a line graph.
3. The rate of TB cases declined between 1955 and 2005.
4. Table 2, because it shows how the rate of infection has declined in the United States over time, whereas Table 1 does not reveal trends and has data from only ten states in one year.
5. From the data given, one would predict a further decline in the rate of TB cases in the United States in 2010.

19.2 Viral Structure and Reproduction

KEY CONCEPT **Viruses exist in a variety of shapes and sizes.**

MAIN IDEAS
- Viruses differ in shape and in ways of entering host cells.
- Viruses cause two types of infections.

OCABULARY
apsid
acteriophage
tic infection
sogenic infection
rophage

Connect to Your World

Just like the computer viruses that you hear about in the news, viruses that affect living things pass from one host to the next. While computer viruses pass through networks from one computer to another, human viruses pass from person to person. Also like computer viruses, viruses of living things can be simple or complex in structure, and have several different ways to get into their hosts.

MAIN IDEA

Viruses differ in shape and in ways of entering host cells.

The idea that infectious agents cause certain diseases was a fairly new concept in 1892 when Russian scientist Dmitri Ivanovsky made a surprising observation. He was studying tobacco mosaic disease, named for the scar pattern left on affected leaves of tobacco or tomato plants. Mosaic disease, shown in **FIGURE 2.1**, was thought to be caused by a bacterium. But so far no one had been able to prove it. Ivanovsky passed extracts of diseased tobacco leaves through filter pores small enough to strain out bacteria and found that the extracts could still pass on the disease. Was this a new bacterium? Or was it some unknown type of organism?

In 1898, Dutch microbiologist Martinus Beijerinck built upon Ivanovsky's work. He showed that the disease agent passed through agar gel. He proposed that tiny particles within the extracts caused infection, and he called the particles *viruses,* from the Latin for "poison." The observations of Ivanovsky and Beijerinck laid the groundwork for more discoveries. Scientists began finding that many diseases of unknown causes could be explained by viruses.

Healthy leaf

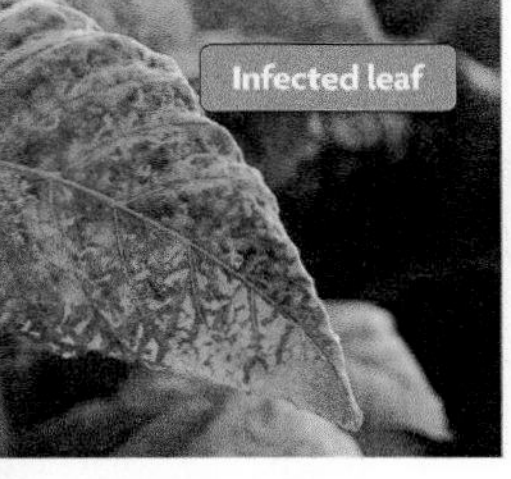

IGURE 2.1 These pictures ompare a healthy leaf and a af infected by tobacco mosaic rus (TMV). TMV was the first rus identified by scientists.

The Structure of Viruses

Viruses have an amazingly simple basic structure. A single viral particle, called a *virion,* is made up of genetic material surrounded by a protein shell called a **capsid.** Capsids can have different shapes. In some viruses, the capsid itself is surrounded by a lipid envelope. A lipid envelope is the protective outer coat of a virus, from which spiky structures of proteins and sugars may stick out.

SECTION 19.2

Plan and Prepare

Activate Prior Knowledge Have students think about a piece of computer code that makes up a computer virus. **Ask,** At what point does the virus become dangerous? when it enters into the computer's operating system and the virus's code becomes a set of instructions Discuss that any virus has to have a way inside. **Ask,** How do viruses enter into a human population? contact with infected organisms; mosquito bites; water; food; bodily fluids

Teach

History of Science

The first person to see a virus was **Wendell Stanley.** In the 1930s at the Rockefeller Institute, Stanley purified the juices of 4000 kilograms (8800 lb) of tobacco leaves to produce about one tablespoon of pure, crystallized **tobacco mosaic virus,** which scientists then examined using x-ray crystallography.

Differentiated Instruction

BELOW LEVEL

Suggest that students use a combination of diagrams and notes to summarize the content of this section. Students need to answer two basic questions:

- What are the structural parts of a virus?
- How do those different parts enable a virus to infect its host?

Teacher Toolkit, Section C, Combination Notes

Chapter 19: Viruses and Prokaryotes 559

▼ Teach *continued*

Take It Further

In addition to bearing the surface proteins that function as connecting points to host cells, the capsid offers a virus's vulnerable genetic material some basic protection from

- physical damage that can result from mechanical forces
- chemical damage, such as UV radiation from sunlight
- damage from enzymes secreted by organisms as a defense against viruses

TEACH FROM VISUALS

FIGURE 2.2 Have students look at the diagrams of the three viruses. **Ask,** What are three parts common to all viruses, and what are they used for? nucleic acid for replication, capsid for protection, surface protein for host recognition

Integrating Immunology

The structure of viral surface proteins not only helps viruses infect host cells, in some cases, it enables a virus to elude capture by the host's immune system. In humans and other animals, the immune system targets invading viruses by recognizing their surface proteins. In viruses such as **HIV** and **hepatitis C,** the genes coding for surface proteins have a high mutation rate, producing rapid changes to surface proteins that make it difficult for the immune system to detect the virus.

Answers

Ⓐ **Compare and Contrast** All the viruses have nucleic acids and surface proteins, and all three types have different shapes. Two have outer capsids, and one has capsids on its genetic material. Two have lipid envelopes, and one does not.

Some viruses attach to host cells by these spikes. The spikes are such an obvious trait of some viruses that they can be used for identification.

Viruses can only reproduce after they have infected host cells. Viruses are simply packaged sets of genes that move from one host cell to another. Unlike bacteria and other living parasites, a virus has no structures to maintain—no membranes or organelles needing ATP, oxygen, or glucose. All it carries into the cell is what it needs to reproduce—its genes.

The structure and shape of viruses play an important role in how they work. Each type of virus can infect only certain hosts. A virus identifies its host by fitting its surface proteins to receptor molecules on the surface of the host cell, like a key fitting a lock. Some viruses are able to infect several species, while other viruses can infect only a single species. Common viral shapes are shown in **FIGURE 2.2.**

FIGURE 2.2 Viral Shapes

The different proteins that make up a viral capsid give viruses a variety of shapes.

ENVELOPED

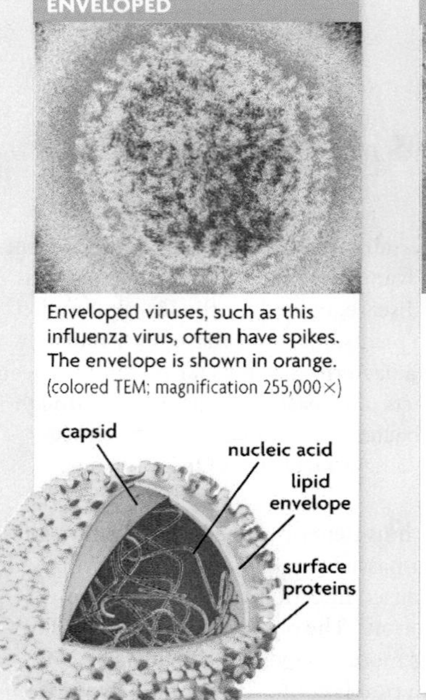

Enveloped viruses, such as this influenza virus, often have spikes. The envelope is shown in orange. (colored TEM; magnification 255,000×)

HELICAL

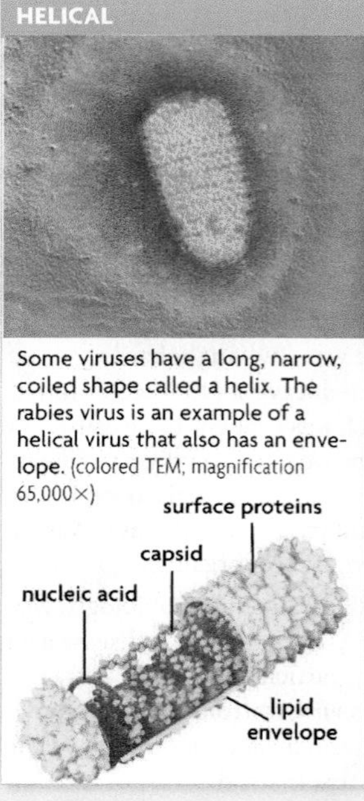

Some viruses have a long, narrow, coiled shape called a helix. The rabies virus is an example of a helical virus that also has an envelope. (colored TEM; magnification 65,000×)

POLYHEDRAL

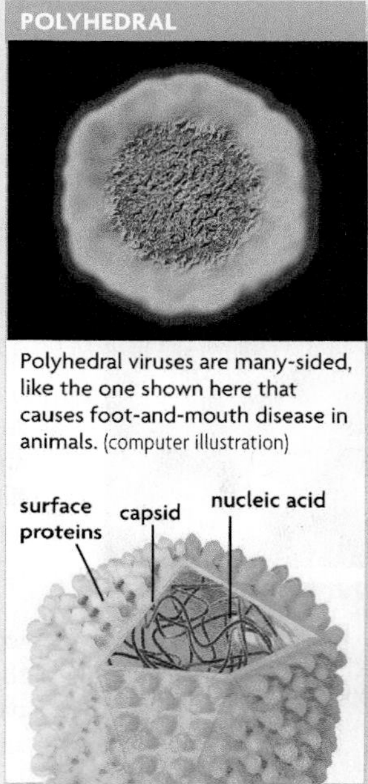

Polyhedral viruses are many-sided, like the one shown here that causes foot-and-mouth disease in animals. (computer illustration)

Ⓐ Compare and Contrast **What are the similarities and differences between the three types of viruses shown above?**

Differentiated Instruction

TEACH WITH TECHNOLOGY

Show students an animation of viral infection to help them see the role each part of the virus plays in enabling the viral DNA to take over the machinery of a cell. If possible, use the pause feature to enable students to diagram the process in their science notebooks.

In some viruses, capsids form a 20-sided polyhedral. Rod-shaped and strandlike viruses often have capsids shaped in coils, like a spring or helix.

In contrast to prokaryotes and eukaryotes, in which DNA is always the main genetic material, a virus can have either DNA or RNA but never both. The genetic material of viruses can be single-stranded or double-stranded, and linear, circular, or segmented.

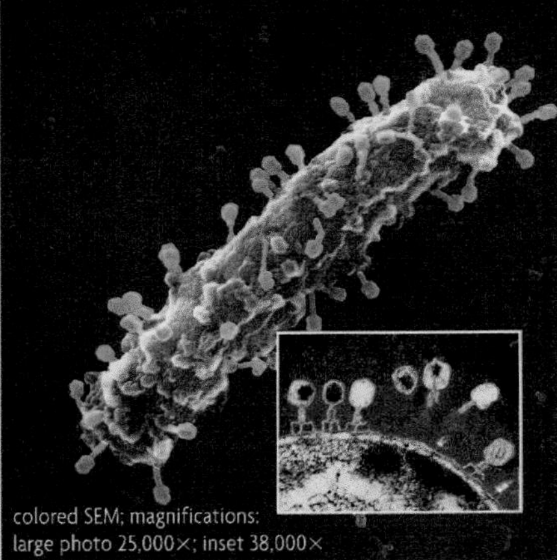

colored SEM; magnifications: large photo 25,000×; inset 38,000×

Viruses that Infect Bacteria

One group of viruses is the bacteriophages, often called simply "phages." **Bacteriophages** (bak-TEER-ee-uh-FAYJ-ihz) are viruses that infect bacteria. One example is the T-bacteriophage that infects *Escherichia coli,* the bacteria commonly found in the intestines of mammals. The T-bacteriophage shown in **FIGURE 2.3** has a 20-sided capsid connected to a long protein tail with spiky footlike fibers. The capsid contains the genetic material. The tail and its spikes help attach the virus to the host cell. After attachment, the bacteriophage's tail releases an enzyme that breaks down part of the bacterial cell wall. The tail sheath contracts, and the tail core punches through the cell wall, injecting the phage's DNA. The phage works like a syringe, injecting its genes into the host cell's cytoplasm, where its DNA is found.

FIGURE 2.3 The SEM above shows bacteriophages attacking an *E. coli* bacterium. While injecting their genetic material into the bacterium, the protein coats remain outside the cell (inset). The unique structure of a bacteriophage is shown below.

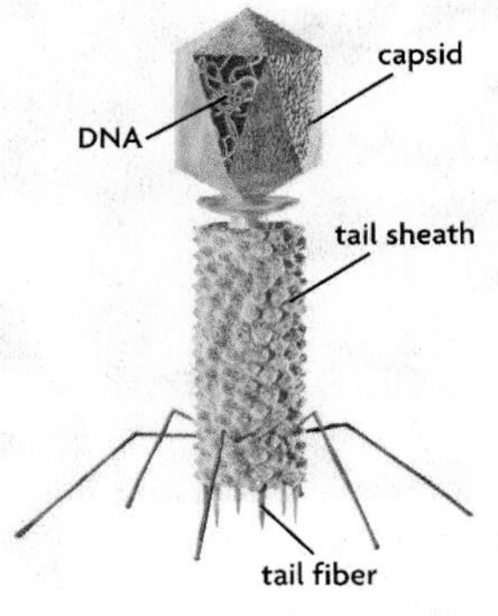

Viruses that Infect Eukaryotes

Viruses that infect eukaryotes differ from bacteriophages in their methods of entering the host cell. For example, these viruses may enter the cells by endocytosis. Recall that endocytosis is an active method of bringing molecules into a cell by forming vesicles, or membrane-bound sacs, around the molecules. If the viruses are enveloped, they can also enter a host cell by fusing with the plasma membrane of the host cell and releasing the capsid into the cell's cytoplasm. HIV is a virus that enters cells in this way. Once inside the cell, eukaryotic viruses target the nucleus of the cell.

Summarize **Describe how the structures of a bacteriophage are well-suited for their functions.**

MAIN IDEA

Viruses cause two types of infections.

The ways in which viruses enter and leave a cell may vary, but two basic pathways of infection are similar for all viruses. These pathways are shown for the most studied viruses, the bacteriophages, in **FIGURE 2.4.**

Once inside the host cell, phages follow one of two general paths in causing disease. In one path, the phage behaves like a bad houseguest. It takes over the household, eats all of the food in the refrigerator, and then blows up the house when it leaves. The other path of infection is somewhat more subtle. Instead of destroying the house, the phage becomes a permanent houseguest. Neither path is good for the host.

Vocabulary

bacteriophage Point out that word roots can sometimes be confusing. For example, a bacteriophage is a virus, not a bacterium. The root *-phage* comes from the Greek *phagein,* "to eat." *Bacteriophage* means "bacteria eater." However, a virus is smaller than a bacterium, with no mouth in sight. Suggest students think of this term functioning in the same way as *dragon-slayer.*

TEACH FROM VISUALS

FIGURE 2.3 Have students use the labeled diagram of the bacteriophage to identify phage capsids, tail sheaths, and tail fibers in the SEM image. **Ask,** How would you describe the movement of a bacteriophage's DNA during an infection? from the bacteriophage's capsid, through its tail, and into the cytoplasm of the bacterium

Vocabulary

Academic Vocabulary Point out to students that three of the structural elements associated with viruses involve a form of casing.

- **envelope,** wrapping, typically the paper wrapping for a letter
- **sheath,** close-fitting covering, as in the case for a sword or blade
- **capsid,** a protective shell, a term specifically used in biology

Answers

A Summarize The capsid houses the nucleic acids, the tail fibers help with attachment, and the tail sheath helps with injecting the genetic material of the virus.

PRE-AP

Have students draw diagrams to sequence viral infections of a bacterial cell and a eukaryotic cell. Students can review the process of endocytosis in Section 5 of the chapter Cell Structure and Function.

Teacher Toolkit, Section C, Sequence Diagram

▼ Teach *continued*

TEACH FROM VISUALS

FIGURE 2.4 Have students compare the two pathways. **Ask,** What is the difference in the way viral DNA interacts with host DNA in a lytic infection compared to a lysogenic infection? Lytic: viral DNA uses host DNA to construct new viruses but then separates from it; lysogenic: viral DNA and host DNA merge. **Ask,** If you were a researcher, which type of infection would be more obvious in a culture of bacteria? lytic: producing large number of viruses in a short period of time, and killing bacterial cells Lysogenic infections first use the host cells to produce virus-host cell DNA that is passed on to daughter cells through mitosis. Until or unless the prophage is activated, the virus is dormant.

Vocabulary

lysogenic, lytic Students can use features of the words *lysogenic* and *lytic* to remember which is which. The *-gen* root in *lysogenic* can remind them of new generations of cells that carry the viral DNA. The word *lytic* is shorter, just like the lives of the cells that are infected.

Answers

Ⓐ **Critical Viewing** The virus is not making parts; it is just replicating its DNA.

FIGURE 2.4 General Pathways of Viral Infection

A lytic infection results in the lysis, or breaking apart, of the host cell and release of new viral particles. A lysogenic infection does not destroy the host cell.

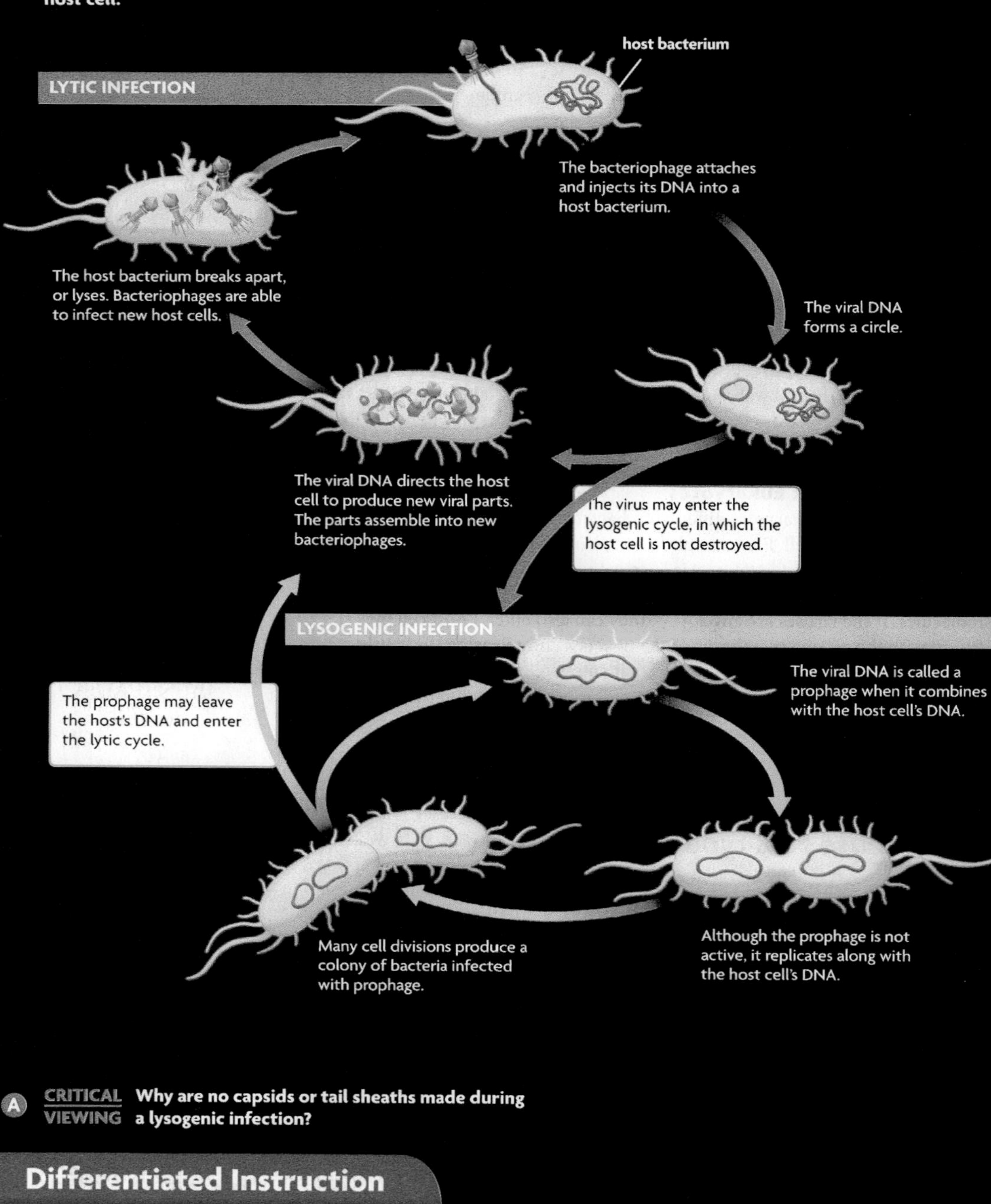

host bacterium
LYTIC INFECTION
The bacteriophage attaches and injects its DNA into a host bacterium.
The host bacterium breaks apart, or lyses. Bacteriophages are able to infect new host cells.
The viral DNA forms a circle.
The viral DNA directs the host cell to produce new viral parts. The parts assemble into new bacteriophages.
The virus may enter the lysogenic cycle, in which the host cell is not destroyed.
LYSOGENIC INFECTION
The prophage may leave the host's DNA and enter the lytic cycle.
The viral DNA is called a prophage when it combines with the host cell's DNA.
Many cell divisions produce a colony of bacteria infected with prophage.
Although the prophage is not active, it replicates along with the host cell's DNA.

Ⓐ CRITICAL VIEWING **Why are no capsids or tail sheaths made during a lysogenic infection?**

Differentiated Instruction

BELOW LEVEL

Have students make a Venn diagram to compare and contrast lytic infection and lysogenic infection. Suggest that students consider the advantages and disadvantages of each type of infection for the virus as well as the host cell. Have them include expectations of how each type of infection will affect the host organism. Ask students which infection is likely to lie dormant for a time and which is likely to create symptoms more immediately.

Teacher Toolkit, Section C, Venn Diagram

ENGLISH LEARNERS

Have students form home groups and then number off 1 and 2 for a modified jigsaw reading on lysogenic and lytic infection. The 1s go to the lytic expert group, and the 2s to the lysogenic group. Within the groups, half the students should study **FIGURE 2.4** on this page, and half should study the text on the next page. After the expert groups convene to discuss what they know, have students return to home groups to share what they have learned.

Teacher Toolkit, Section C, Jigsaw Reading

Lytic Infection

A **lytic infection** (LIHT-ihk) is an infection pathway in which the host cell bursts, releasing the new viral offspring into the host's system, where each then infects another cell.

- When the viral DNA enters the host cell, it takes over control of the host's own DNA, turning on the genes necessary to copy the viral genes.
- Under direction of the viral genes, the host's DNA undergoes transcription and translation, and produces capsids and enzymes. The enzymes then help in the copying of the virus's DNA.
- Using energy from the host cell, the capsids and viral DNA assemble into new virions. Viral enzymes dissolve the host cell membrane, releasing the new virus particles into the host's bloodstream or tissues—and destroying the host cell in the process.

READING TOOLBOX

VOCABULARY

The term *lytic* comes from the Greek word *lutikos*, meaning "able to loosen." The word *lysis* is often used in biology to describe a cell breaking apart.

Lysogenic Infection

In a **lysogenic infection** (LY-suh-JEHN-ihk), a phage combines its DNA into the host cell's DNA.

- After entering the host cell, the viral DNA combines with the host's DNA, forming a new set of genes called a prophage. A **prophage** is the phage DNA inserted into the host cell's DNA. In organisms other than bacteria, this stage is called a provirus.
- The prophage is copied and passed to daughter cells, with the host's own DNA, when the host cell undergoes mitosis. Although this process doesn't destroy the cell, it can change some of the cell's traits.
- After the cell has been copied, the prophage faces two possible paths. A trigger, such as stress, can activate the prophage, which then uses the cell to produce new viruses. Or the prophage can remain as a permanent gene.

A Connect **Using the analogy of viral infections resembling houseguests, explain which describes a lytic and which describes a lysogenic infection.**

The Inside Story

The **Ebola virus** is one of the world's deadliest pathogens. The first known outbreak occurred in 1976 in Zaire (now Republic of Congo). The virus produces a hemorrhagic fever by attacking and weakening the cells of veins and arteries. This produces severe blood loss, resulting in 50–90 percent mortality of infected people in as little as two weeks.

Of the several strains identified, all but one were restricted to Africa. In 1989, a strain was detected in a colony of macaque monkeys in a research lab in Reston, Virginia. The outbreak caused panic among government personnel, but this strain was lethal only to the monkeys. Although the outbreak was swiftly contained, the research facility was later torn down.

Answers

A Connect The house guest that takes over the household, eats all the food, and then blows up the house is similar to a lytic infection. The permanent house guest is similar to a lysogenic infection.

19.2 Formative Assessment

SELF-CHECK Online
HMHScience.com
GO ONLINE

REVIEWING MAIN IDEAS

1. Name and describe the main parts of a typical virus.
2. What are the differences between a **lytic infection** and a **lysogenic infection**? Include the effects of each type of infection on the cells of the host organism in your answer.

CRITICAL THINKING

3. **Apply** Researchers studying infection can often grow bacteria more easily than they can grow viruses. What conditions must scientists provide for viruses to multiply?
4. **Classify** A wart is caused by a virus that may lie dormant for years before any symptoms appear. Does this resemble a lytic or lysogenic infection? Explain.

CONNECT TO EVOLUTION

5. If the virus is a foreign invader, how is it possible for the proteins of its **capsid** to match the receptors on the host cell's surface? Consider natural selection in your answer.

Assess and Reteach

Assess Use the Section Self-Check or Section Quiz, both available at **HMHScience.com**.

Reteach Have students draw their own labeled diagrams that illustrate the processes of lytic infection and lysogenic infection.

19.2 FORMATIVE ASSESSMENT

1. capsid: protein shell; genetic material: single-stranded or double-stranded DNA or RNA; some viruses have a lipid envelope covering the capsid
2. lytic infection: virus replicates many times, producing many offspring; lysogenic infection: virus integrates into the host cell's DNA, with the viral genes passed to the host cell's daughter cells during mitosis. Lytic infection destroys the host cell after viral replication and release of offspring, whereas lysogenic infection generally causes no initial harm to the cell, though it can alter some of the cell's traits.
3. In order to replicate, viruses need living cells they can infect.
4. lysogenic infection; it is characterized by a virus that lies dormant.
5. Over time, viruses that happened to have the right protein "keys" would survive and pass on these traits to their offspring. Viruses without the right proteins would not be able to successfully infect the host and would probably become extinct.

SECTION 19.3

Plan and Prepare

Activate Prior Knowledge Have students think about the difference between getting a vaccination shot and taking an antibiotic. Mention that vaccines are used to prevent viral diseases. **Ask,** What vaccinations are commonly given to young children? measles, mumps, hepatitis, tetanus, polio Discuss how vaccination uses the body's own defenses to fight infection, unlike an antibiotic, which is an outside agent.

Teach

Integrating Epidemiology

Smallpox, caused by a virus, is the only infectious disease that has been globally eradicated. Highly contagious and often deadly, it originated about 10,000 BCE in Egypt or India. Smallpox epidemics throughout history claimed commoners and royalty alike. Queen Mary II of England and Louis XV of France were among its victims. In the 1950s, the annual global incidence of smallpox was 50 million. A global vaccination program began in 1967, leading to the eradication of the disease by 1980.

19.3 Viral Diseases

KEY CONCEPT **Some viral diseases can be prevented with vaccines.**

MAIN IDEAS
- Viruses cause many infectious diseases.
- Vaccines are made from weakened pathogens.

VOCABULARY
epidemic
vaccine
retrovirus

Connect to Your World

Why do we worry about catching a cold or the flu every winter? Cold weather itself does not cause us to get sick, but spending time close to other people can. For most people, winter means spending more time indoors. Cold and flu viruses then easily transfer to hands from doorknobs and other objects. That's why frequently washing your hands can help keep you healthy.

MAIN IDEA

Viruses cause many infectious diseases.

As you have read, viruses follow two pathways of infection once they encounter their target cells. But to enter the host's body in the first place, the virus must first pass a major obstacle.

First Defenses

In vertebrates, the first obstacle a virus must pass is the skin, but in other organisms it might be an outer skeleton or a tough cell wall. Viruses can penetrate the skin only through an opening such as a cut or scrape. Or they can take another route—the mucous membranes and body openings. It's no accident that some of the most common points of entry for infection are the mouth, nose, genital area, eyes, and ears.

Once inside the body, the virus finds its way to its target organ or tissue. However, the targeted cells don't just open the door to this unwanted guest. Body cells have receptors that guard against foreign intruders. These receptors act almost like locks. When the virus arrives at the host cell, it uses its own surface proteins as keys to trick the cell into allowing it to enter.

CONNECT TO

CELLS

Recall from **Cell Structure and Function** that receptors are proteins that detect chemical signals and perform an action in response. In the case of a host-specific infection, these normally helpful receptors provide little protection to the cell.

Examples of Viral Infections

Viruses can cause symptoms that range from merely bothersome to life-threatening. Below are a few of the many human illnesses caused by viruses.

The common cold The most familiar viral disease is the common cold. More than 200 viruses are known to cause this seasonal nuisance. One such cold virus is shown in **FIGURE 3.1.** With so many viruses, it's not easy to find a cure. In fact, cold viruses can mutate as they move from one person to another. Although they're unpleasant to have, colds usually last only about one week.

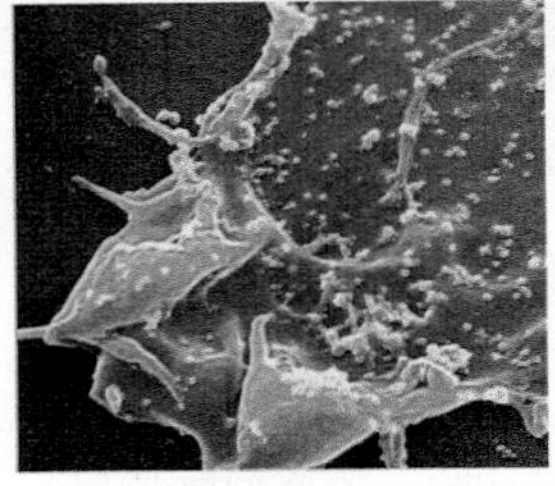

FIGURE 3.1 Cold virus particles (yellow) on the surface of a cell culture (blue). (colored SEM; magnification 10,000×)

Differentiated Instruction

BELOW LEVEL

Have students organize the material in this section, using the idea of a single infection—a flu virus. Ask students to create a sequence that describes the events involved: pathogen enters host, production of more pathogen, transmission to other hosts. Then have students repeat the sequence with the host having been immunized by a vaccine.

Teacher Toolkit, Section C, Sequence Diagram

Influenza Winter usually causes concern about the influenza, or "flu" virus—and with good reason. The flu spreads quickly and can result in frequent local epidemics. An **epidemic** is a rapid outbreak of an infection that affects many people. In the United States, up to 20 percent of the population is infected with the flu each year.

At this time, only three influenza subtypes usually infect humans; other subtypes may infect horses, pigs, whales, and seals. More than fifteen subtypes infect birds, and are all referred to as avian influenza, or bird flu. Sometimes a mutation enables a virus to jump from one species to another, making the spread of infection difficult to control. The high mutation rate of surface proteins on viral capsids makes it necessary for a new influenza vaccine to be made every year. A **vaccine** (vak-SEEN) is a substance that stimulates the body's own immune response against invasion by microbes.

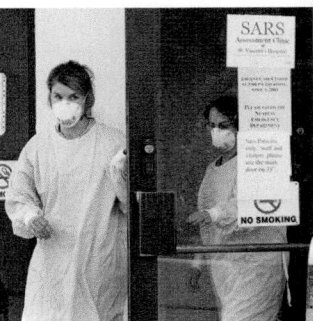

FIGURE 3.2 Nurses in Canada walk outside an emergency SARS clinic, which was opened to deal with an outbreak.

SARS Severe acute respiratory syndrome (SARS) is another viral respiratory disease. It has symptoms similar to influenza, such as fever and coughing or difficulty in breathing. SARS first appeared in Asia in late 2002. It spread throughout the world, quickly becoming pandemic. Although it seemed to disappear by the middle of 2003, SARS is still monitored globally.

HIV Human immunodeficiency virus, or HIV, is a retrovirus. *Retro-* means "backward," which describes how retroviruses work. Usually, DNA is used to make an RNA copy in a cell, but a **retrovirus** is a virus that contains RNA and uses an enzyme called *reverse transcriptase* to make a DNA copy. Double-stranded DNA then enters the nucleus and combines with the host's genes as a lysogenic infection. The viral DNA can remain dormant for years as a provirus, causing no symptoms to its human host.

When the virus becomes active, it directs the formation of new viral parts. The new viruses leave, either by budding or bursting through cell membranes, and infect new cells. This stage of the disease is a lytic infection that destroys white blood cells of the host's immune system, as shown in **FIGURE 3.3.** The loss of white blood cells ultimately causes AIDS, acquired immune deficiency syndrome. Once a person's immune system is affected, he or she may be unable to fight off even the common microorganisms that humans encounter every day. HIV's unusually high mutation rate has made it a challenge to treat. The combined use of several antiviral drugs—medications that treat viral infection—has proved somewhat effective in slowing the spread of the virus once a person is infected.

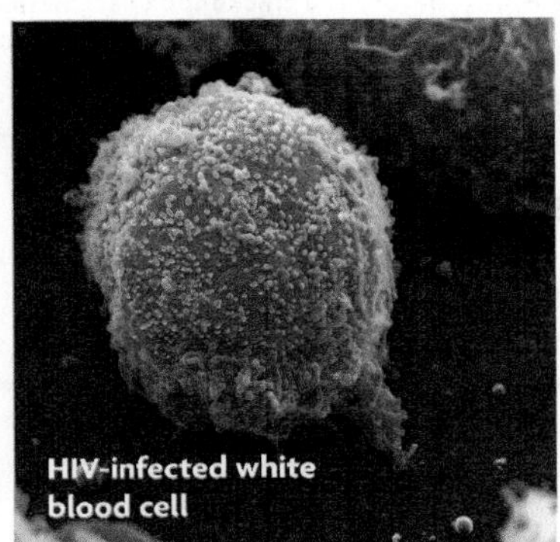

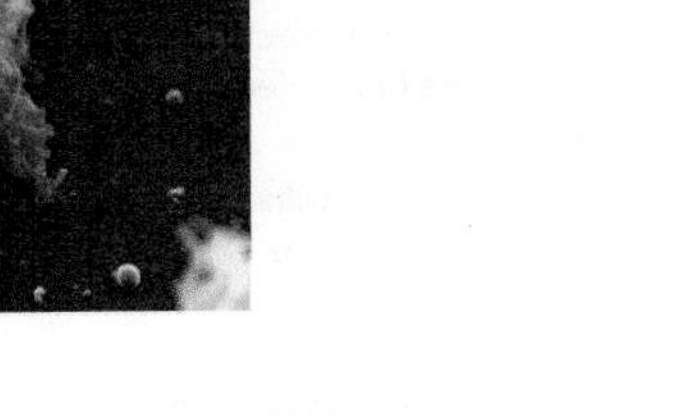

FIGURE 3.3 This scanning electron micrograph (SEM) shows the HIV virus as purple dots on an infected white blood cell. Destruction of white blood cells weakens the immune system and causes AIDS. (colored SEM; magnification: 3500×)

Analyze **How do retroviruses work differently from other viruses?**

Vocabulary

Greek and Latin Word Origins
Epidemic comes from Greek roots meaning "prevalence" and "people." **Epidemiology** is the study of diseases in populations. **Pandemic** comes from a Greek word meaning "of all the people." A pandemic is an epidemic that has spread across a very wide range and is infecting a large percentage of the population, such as the Spanish flu of 1918–1919.

Take It Further

The flu pandemic of 1918 and 1919 got the name **Spanish flu** because it was first reported in Spanish newspapers. More than 20 million Americans became sick, and an estimated 675,000 died, many within 24 hours of infection. Health departments restricted public gatherings and distributed gauze facemasks. Stores could not have sales, and funerals were limited to 15 minutes. More than 400 million people (one-fifth of the world's population) were affected, and 20 million died within one year.

Answers

Ⓐ **Analyze** A retrovirus contains RNA and uses the enzyme reverse transcriptase to make a DNA copy.

PRE-AP

Tell students that in 2003, the SARS virus spread to several continents by way of infected air travelers. Have students write a five-minute essay describing what needs to occur on both a cellular level and a population level in order for a virus to move from one person in Asia to another person in North America. They should track the virus from lysogenic infection in the carrier to a lytic infection in the recipient.

Teacher Toolkit, Section C, Quick -Write

TEACH WITH TECHNOLOGY

Show students an animation depicting how a retrovirus works. If possible, use the pause function so students can sketch the process of retroviral infection in their science notebooks.

▼ Teach *continued*

The Inside Story

In 18th-century England, more than one-third of children died of **smallpox** before the age of three. People who managed to survive the infection were immune for life, so scientists were eager to find a way to administer a strain of the virus that would be strong enough to immunize the patient from further infection yet weak enough that it would not kill the patient.

Edward Jenner, a physician, had observed that people who had contracted cowpox, a disease affecting cow udders, were immune to smallpox. For two years, he experimented with cowpox, giving it to children and then testing their immunity to smallpox a few weeks later. In 1798, he published a pamphlet describing his techniques, and **vaccination,** which comes from the Latin *vacca,* meaning "cow," was coined.

Answers

A Apply Exposing children to chickenpox once should prevent the disease from occurring again, just as a vaccine prevents the real virus from causing the viral disease.

▼ Assess and Reteach

Assess Use the Section Self-Check or Section Quiz, both available at **HMHScience.com**.

Reteach Have students make a crossword puzzle using terms and information from this section. Students can exchange puzzles and complete them, using the text for help.

FIGURE 3.4 Viral Diseases

VIRAL INFECTION	SYMPTOMS OF DISEASE	TRANSMISSION OF DISEASE	U.S. VACCINE RECOMMENDATION
Chickenpox	rash, itchy skin, fever, fatigue	contact with rash, droplet inhalation	for children between 12 and 18 months
Hepatitis A	yellow skin, fatigue, abdominal pain	contact with contaminated feces	for people traveling to infected locations and protection during outbreaks
Mumps	painful swelling in salivary glands, fever	droplet inhalation	for children between 12 and 15 months and again at 4 to 6 years
Rabies	anxiety, paralysis, fear of water	bite from infected animal	for veterinarians and biologists in contact with wildlife
West Nile	fever, headache, body ache	bite from infected mosquito	no available vaccine

MAIN IDEA

Vaccines are made from weakened pathogens.

Chances are good that you have had vaccinations. In the United States, children are vaccinated at an early age against diseases such as measles, mumps, rubella (MMR), and chickenpox. Every year, millions of people are vaccinated against influenza. How does a simple shot provide protection against disease?

A vaccine is made from the same pathogen—disease-causing agent—that it is supposed to protect against. Vaccines consist of weakened versions of the virus, or parts of the virus, that will cause the body to produce a response. The immune system is triggered by the surface proteins of a pathogen. In the host's body, the vaccine works by preparing the host's immune system for a future attack. Vaccines can prevent some bacterial and some viral infections, as shown in **FIGURE 3.4.** Whereas bacterial diseases can also be treated with medicine once they occur, viral diseases are not easily treated. Vaccination is often the only way of controlling the spread of viral disease.

Vaccines cause a mild immune response. If the body is invaded again, it will be able to start an immune defense before the virus can cause damage.

A Apply Before the chickenpox vaccination was available, children were often purposely exposed to the virus at a young age. What was the reason for doing this?

19.3 Formative Assessment

SELF-CHECK Online HMHScience.com GO ONLINE

REVIEWING MAIN IDEAS

1. Name and describe two infectious viruses and a body's first defense against infection.
2. Briefly describe how a **vaccine** can prevent some viral infections.

CRITICAL THINKING

3. **Infer** If a vaccine is in short supply, why is it often recommended that older adults and children get vaccinated first?
4. **Apply** Why might getting a flu vaccination sometimes cause you to get a mild case of the flu?

CONNECT TO

HUMAN BIOLOGY

5. People infected with HIV, the virus that causes the disease AIDS, can become unable to fight off infections by organisms that normally do not harm people. Why is this so?

19.3 FORMATIVE ASSESSMENT

1. Answers may include the common cold, flu, SARS, HIV, chickenpox, or viruses not discussed in this section. The skin is the body's first defense against infection.
2. A vaccine is made from a weakened pathogen or parts of a virus. When given, it stimulates the host's own immune system, preparing it for future infection by the real virus.
3. The immune systems of older adults and children are often weaker than those of the rest of the population, so they are more likely to become infected than a healthy person who is not very young or very old.
4. because you may be getting a weakened strain of the live virus in order to build up your immune system
5. HIV affects the immune system of an infected person, making him or her susceptible to organisms that normally are harmless.

19.4 Bacteria and Archaea

KEY CONCEPT **Bacteria and archaea are both single-celled prokaryotes.**

MAIN IDEAS
- Prokaryotes are widespread on Earth.
- Bacteria and archaea are structurally similar but have different molecular characteristics.
- Bacteria have various strategies for survival.

'OCABULARY
bligate anaerobe
bligate aerobe
acultative aerobe
lasmid
agellum
onjugation
ndospore

Connect to Your World

Humans not only share the environment with prokaryotes—for many species, we are the environment. Up to 500 types of prokaryotes can live in the human mouth. In fact, you may have as many as 25 different types in your mouth right now. One milliliter of saliva can contain up to 40 million bacterial cells.

MAIN IDEA

Prokaryotes are widespread on Earth.

Prokaryotes, which include bacteria and archaea, are the most widespread and abundant organisms on Earth. Consider that humans are one species with about 7 billion individuals. In contrast, scientists estimate there are more than 1 billion (10^9) types of bacteria and more than 10^{30} individual prokaryotic cells on, above, and under Earth's surface. Bacteria and archaea are an important part of every community they inhabit. These tiny organisms live in just about every habitat on Earth, including the air we breathe. Prokaryotes have been found living inside rocks, in deserts, and in polar ice caps. One gram of soil may contain as many as 5 billion bacterial cells from up to 10,000 types of bacteria.

Prokaryotes can be grouped based on their need for oxygen. Prokaryotes that cannot live in the presence of oxygen are called obligate anaerobes. An **obligate anaerobe** (AHB-lih-giht AN-uh-ROHB) is actually poisoned by oxygen. As you have learned, archaea are prokaryotes that can live in extreme environments. The archaea that produce methane gas are obligate anaerobes. They live in marshes, at the bottom of lakes, and in the digestive tracts of herbivores such as deer, sheep, and cows, as shown in **FIGURE 4.1.** These microorganisms release nutrients from plants that animals are unable to digest on their own.

IGURE 4.1 A "window" made ıto a cow's rumen, the first of its our stomachs, allows scientists to tudy digestion. Anaerobic bactea live mutualistically within a ow's stomach. The bacteria have helter and nutrients, and break own plant material for the cow o digest.

In contrast, some prokaryotes need the presence of oxygen in their environment. Organisms that need oxygen in their environment are called **obligate aerobes** (AHB-lih-giht AIR-OHBZ). This group includes several familiar pathogens, such as those that cause the diseases tuberculosis and leprosy. There are also prokaryotes that can survive whether oxygen is present in the environment or not. This type of prokaryote is called a **facultative aerobe** (FAK-uhl-TAY-tihv AIR-OHB).

A Evaluate **Bacteria are often associated with illness. Why is this a misconception?**

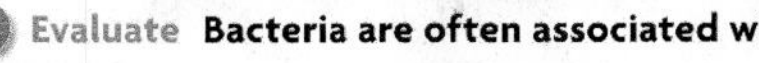

Differentiated Instruction

ENGLISH LEARNERS

Model asking key questions for before, during, and after reading. For example, before: *What do you already know about bacteria and archaea? What do you want to know?* during: *What types of shapes do we see in prokaryotes? What do you expect to learn next?* after: *What questions are still unanswered about prokaryotes?* Guide students to ask one another such questions and to listen actively to the answers.

Teacher Toolkit, Section C, Questions to Guide Reading

BELOW LEVEL

Students who are confused by the terms *obligate* and *facultative* can use contextual clues to understand what these words mean. Point out to students that they may already be familiar with the term *obligation* as something that must be done. Explain that *facultative* comes from *faculty,* meaning "an aptitude for something." Have students reread the material and then write a brief definition of each term.

Teacher Toolkit, Section D, New Word Analysis

SECTION 19.4

Plan and Prepare

Activate Prior Knowledge In general, students' ideas of bacteria are probably negative. **Ask,** What kinds of products and innovations can we use that kill bacteria or keep them away from us? various soaps and detergents, antibiotics, sewer systems, indoor plumbing, refrigeration, bleach Tell students that while there are bacteria that threaten our health, there are many types that are harmless, and others that we rely on for good health and other benefits.

Teach

Science Trivia

- It is estimated that just 1 percent of bacteria and archaea have been discovered.
- Of the more than 3000 bacteria named by science, it is estimated that fewer than 10 percent are human pathogens.

Answers

A Evaluate Only a small number of bacteria are pathogenic.

▼ Teach *continued*

CONNECT TO

Classification The domain **Archaea** is subdivided into four main groups:

- **Methanogens** produce methane gas as a waste product of making energy.
- **Psychrophiles** live at unusually low temperatures.
- **Halophiles** live in salty environments.
- **Thermophiles** live at extremely high temperatures.

Thermophiles are equipped with enzymes that help keep the shape of their proteins. Normally, high heat undoes the bonds that hold a protein in its functional shape. The **extremozymes** in thermophiles are folded up much tighter than normal proteins, and there are chemical bonds that further strengthen their shape and structure. Some thermophiles also have a protein called **chaperonin** that actually refolds other proteins back into their original shape.

Vocabulary

Academic Vocabulary The word **flagella** is the plural form of **flagellum.** Other plural/singular word pairs worth reviewing are

- *data/datum*
- *media/medium*
- *phyla/phylum*
- *bacteria/bacterium*
- *millennia/millennium*

MAIN IDEA

Bacteria and archaea are structurally similar but have different molecular characteristics.

CONNECT TO

CLASSIFICATION

Recall from the chapter **The Tree of Life** that archaea and bacteria are in separate kingdoms and in separate domains as well. Both their kingdoms and their domains have the same names, Archaea and Bacteria.

Members of domain Bacteria and domain Archaea comprise all of Earth's prokaryotes. Domain Bacteria is the more diverse and widespread of the two domains, while many archaea are found in Earth's extreme environments. Some archaea are even able to grow at temperatures greater than 100°C (212°F). Bacteria and archaea have many structural similarities but important genetic and biochemical differences.

Structural Comparisons

Even under the microscope, archaea look very similar to bacteria. For example, both archaea and bacteria are small, single-celled organisms that have cell walls and plasma membranes. Archaea come in many shapes, while the three most common forms of bacteria are shown in **FIGURE 4.2.** Bacteria are often named based upon their shapes. Rod-shaped bacteria are called *bacilli.* Spiral-shaped bacteria are called *spirilla* or *spirochetes,* and spherical bacteria are called *cocci.*

READING TOOLBOX

TAKING NOTES

Create a Venn diagram to compare bacteria and archaea using information from this section.

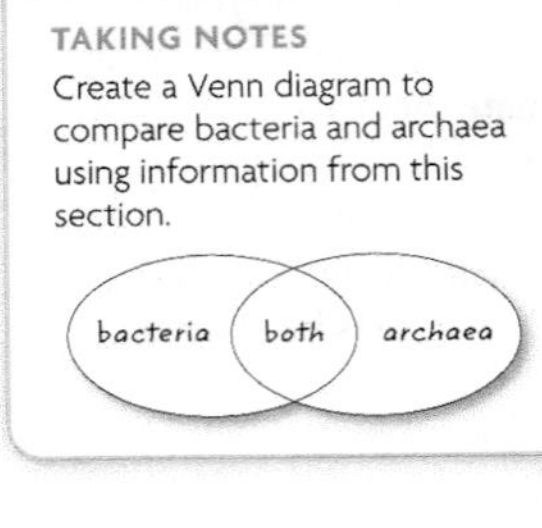

Prokaryotes do not have any membrane-bound organelles, such as a nucleus containing double-stranded DNA. Instead, their DNA is in the form of a circle and is surrounded by cytoplasm. Prokaryotes may also have plasmids. A **plasmid** is a small piece of genetic material that can replicate separately from the prokaryote's main chromosome.

Most prokaryotes can move on their own. Many bacteria and archaea move by gliding or using flagella. A **flagellum** (fluh-JEHL-uhm) is a long, whiplike structure outside of a cell that is used for movement. The flagella of prokaryotes are attached to the plasma membrane and cell wall. They may be at one end of an organism, or they may have different arrangements over the entire cell. Although similar in appearance, the flagella of bacteria and archaea are structurally different from each other. In addition, their flagella are both structurally different from the flagella of eukaryotes.

Many prokaryotes also contain structures called pili that are thinner, shorter, and often more numerous than flagella. Pili help prokaryotes stick to surfaces and to other prokaryotes. A typical prokaryote is shown in **FIGURE 4.3.**

FIGURE 4.2 The most common shapes of bacteria are rods, spirals, and spheres. Many bacteria are named after these shapes. Some examples are shown at right. (colored SEMs; magnifications: *lactobacilli* magnification unknown; *spirochaeta* 5000×; *enterococci* 7000×)

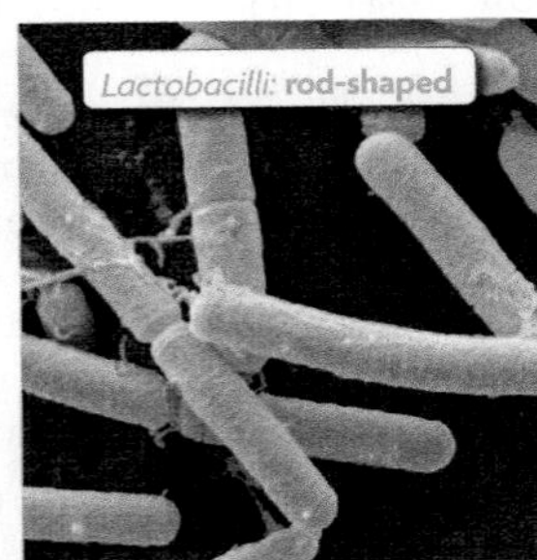

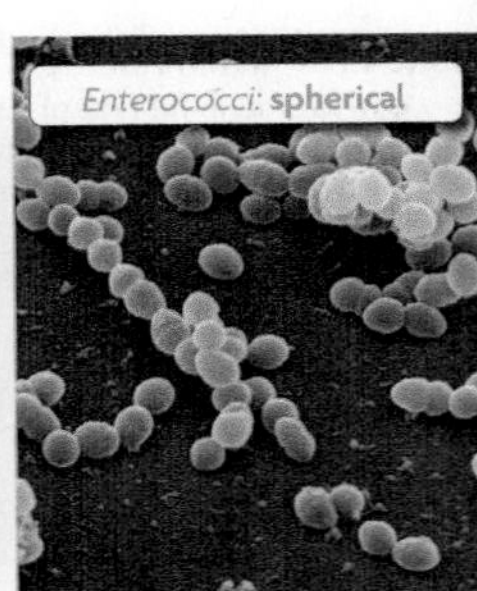

Differentiated Instruction

PRE-AP

Have students make a T-chart to compare archaea and bacteria. To get them started, have them consider these questions:

- How widespread is each group?
- What environments does each group inhabit?
- What are some differences in each group's physical traits?

Teacher Toolkit, Section C, T-Chart

FIGURE 4.3 Prokaryote Structure

This diagram shows the typical structure of a prokaryote. Archaea and bacteria look very similar, although they have important molecular differences.

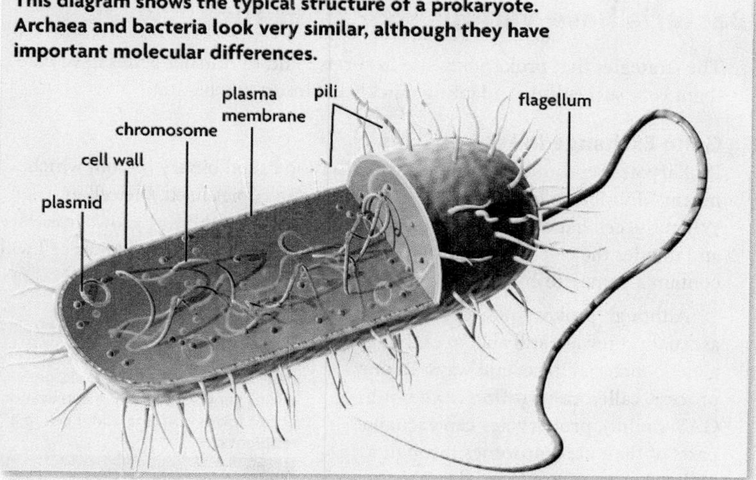

Molecular Comparisons

It was not until molecular analysis techniques were available that the many differences between bacteria and archaea became clear. Despite their similarities in function and appearance, bacteria and archaea are not closely related. Molecular evidence suggests that archaea have at least as much in common with eukaryotes as they do with bacteria. For example, archaea cell walls and membranes are chemically different from those of bacteria. The membranes of archaea contain lipids that are not found in any other type of organism on Earth, and bacteria have a polymer called peptidoglycan (pehp-tih-doh-GLY-cuhn) in their cell walls, which archaea do not.

The amount of peptidoglycan in their cell walls is an important characteristic of bacteria. Bacteria are often classified into one of two groups based on this difference, as shown in **FIGURE 4.4**. A staining method called a Gram stain is used to tell the two groups apart. The Gram stain is important for diagnosing infectious bacterial diseases, and it sometimes helps determine the type of medicine a doctor chooses to fight infection. Because of their cell wall differences, archaea are often not affected by medicine used to treat bacterial infection.

FIGURE 4.4 GRAM STAINING

A staining technique called a Gram stain is used to identify types of bacteria. This stain identifies the amount of a polymer, called peptidoglycan, that is present. The result is either gram positive or gram negative. (LMs; gram-negative 2,500×; gram-positive 550×)

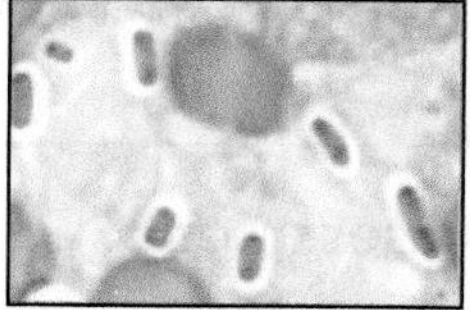

Gram-negative bacteria have a thin layer of peptidoglycan and stain red.

Gram-positive bacteria have a thicker peptidoglycan layer and stain purple.

GRAM NEGATIVE

outer membrane

cell wall

peptidoglycan

plasma membrane

GRAM POSITIVE

cell wall

A Contrast **Archaea were first named archaebacteria, a term that you may still find in some books and articles. What are two differences between archaea and bacteria?**

TEACH WITH TECHNOLOGY

Prepare a digital slide show of the process of Gram staining. Use the Internet to find images that show each step in the process, as well as photographs of slides of Gram-stained bacteria. Try to find images of bacteria with distinctive shapes or other features. Remind students that Gram staining is one of the first tests done to identify bacteria.

Integrating Microbiology

In addition to the cell wall and plasma membrane shown in **FIGURE 4.3,** some bacterial species have a thick polysaccharide or polypeptide envelope surrounding the cell. In some species, the envelope is well defined; in others, it is looser, forming a slime layer that may trail behind the bacteria as they move. Envelopes are common among pathogenic species and are thought to play a role in resisting the host's immune defenses. Among the encapsulated pathogens are types of influenza, pneumonia, and meningitis.

Answers

A Contrast Answers will vary but could include differences in their flagella, cell wall, or plasma membrane composition.

▼ Teach *continued*

Take It Further

One notable group of **endospore-forming bacteria** is the genus *Bacillus*, notably *B. anthracis*, more commonly known as anthrax—the first bacterium shown to be the cause of disease. Endospores are an evolutionary adaptation that enables the cell to lie dormant when conditions are dry or otherwise unfavorable. Endospores are covered with a tough layer of keratin and are highly resistant to heat and chemicals.

Bacillus species can be difficult to identify under the microscope. Younger bacteria stain Gram-positive, but may become Gram-negative as they age. Endospores do not respond to typical lab stains and require a special staining or other identification procedure. The location of the spore in the rod-shaped bacillus—at the cell center (central), at either end (terminal), or between the middle and end (subterminal)—offers a clue to the organism's identity.

Answers

A Connect Some form endospores, which can withstand disinfectants.

▼ Assess and Reteach

Assess Use the Section Self-Check or Section Quiz, both available at **HMHScience.com**.

Reteach Have students define or describe each of the labeled structures in **FIGURE 4.3.**

MAIN IDEA

Bacteria have various strategies for survival.

The strategies that prokaryotes use to survive and to transfer genes have made them very successful at adapting quickly to almost any habitat.

Gene Exchange in Prokaryotes

Prokaryotes reproduce by a type of cell division called binary fission, which means "division in half." While the chromosome copies itself, the cell grows. When the cell has about doubled in size, its plasma membrane grows inward and divides the cell into two equal-sized daughter cells. Each daughter cell will contain a complete copy of the parent cell's genes.

Although prokaryotes reproduce asexually, they are still able to exchange genetic material in several ways. In one process, called **conjugation** (KAHN-juh-GAY-shuhn), prokaryotes can exchange parts of their chromosomes through a hollow bridge of pili formed to connect two or more cells.

VISUAL VOCAB

In **conjugation,** genetic material transfers between prokaryotes, producing genetic variation. A conjugation bridge forms from the donor cell to a recipient cell.

conjugation bridge

TEM; magnification 6000×

VIRTUAL Lab
HMHScience.com
GO ONLINE
Testing Antibacterial Agents

Surviving Harsh Conditions

During conditions unfavorable for survival, some bacteria can produce an **endospore,** a specialized cell with a thick, protective wall. To form an endospore, the bacterium copies its chromosome and produces a wall around the copy. This thick wall around the bacterial DNA helps it survive harsh conditions such as drying out, temperature change, and disinfectants. Endospores can last for centuries. Some have even been found in Egyptian mummies!

Connect **Why are disinfectants alone not enough to kill all types of bacteria?**

19.4 Formative Assessment

SELF-CHECK Online
HMHScience.com
GO ONLINE

REVIEWING MAIN IDEAS

1. What are the three most common shapes of bacteria?
2. Why are bacteria and archaea classified into different domains?
3. Prokaryotes will take up foreign DNA. How is this characteristic used in genetic engineering?

CRITICAL THINKING

4. **Infer** Scientists estimate that only 1 percent of prokaryotes can be grown in the lab. What does this suggest about our knowledge of bacteria and archaea?
5. **Synthesize** Prokaryotes multiply by binary fission, which simply divides a cell in two. Why are mutations and conjugation important for natural selection in prokaryotes?

CONNECT TO HEALTH

6. Bacteria in your mouth convert foods containing sugar and starch into acids that can then cause cavities in your teeth. These bacteria will be present even if you brush your teeth, floss, or use mouthwash. So why are these hygiene habits so important?

19.4 FORMATIVE ASSESSMENT

1. rod, spiral, sphere
2. Archaea are biochemically and genetically different from bacteria.
3. Pieces of genes can be inserted into the genetic material of prokaryotes so that they will make the protein products encoded in the genes or copies of the genes themselves.
4. We do not know much about prokaryotes. Our understanding of prokaryotes will likely change as scientists learn more about prokaryotes that have not been able to be cultured, or grown, in the lab.
5. Binary fission produces no variation, but mutations and conjugation do. Natural selection requires variation in a population.
6. Brushing teeth is important to keep the populations of these bacteria down and to remove the food that the bacteria convert into acids.

19.5 Beneficial Roles of Prokaryotes

KEY CONCEPT **Prokaryotes perform important functions for organisms and ecosystems.**

MAIN IDEAS
- Prokaryotes provide nutrients to humans and other animals.
- Prokaryotes play important roles in ecosystems.

OCABULARY
ioremediation

Connect to Your World
People usually think bacteria in or on food are harmful, and it is true that food poisoning caused by bacteria can be a serious problem. However, some bacteria are safe in food, and actually provide a taste or texture that many people enjoy. Swiss cheese, sour cream, and butter are just a few products that are made with the help of bacteria. Eating food produced by bacteria is not dangerous, as long as they are the right kind of bacteria!

MAIN IDEA
Prokaryotes provide nutrients to humans and other animals.

Prokaryotes, such as the bacteria shown in **FIGURE 5.1**, are a key part of animal digestive systems. A balanced community of prokaryotes in our bodies is important for our health. Prokaryotes have a beneficial relationship, or mutualistic symbiosis, with the host animal and break down food while getting a place to live. They also make vitamins and other compounds, and keep away harmful microbes by filling niches that might otherwise be filled by disease-causing bacteria. In turn, the host animal provides the bacteria with food and a home with a stable pH and temperature.

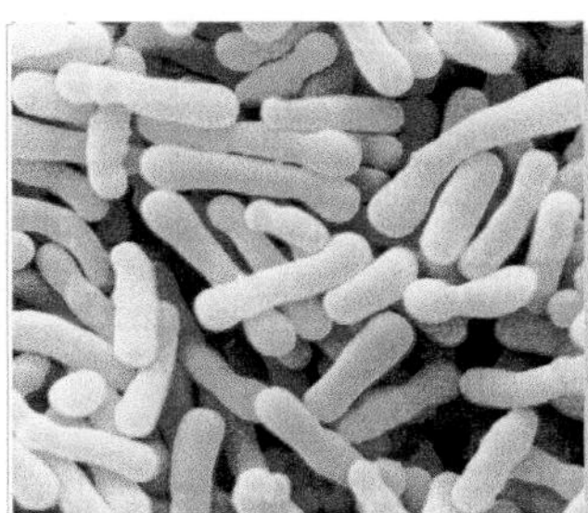

FIGURE 5.1 These bacteria, found in human intestines, are beneficial to our health. They produce B vitamins and keep out harmful microbes.

CONNECT TO
:COLOGY
ecall from the chapter **nteractions in Ecosystems** that *ymbiosis* is the close association f two or more species. A *niche* a specific role an organism lays in its environment.

Humans can get nutrients from prokaryotes in other ways as well. Many foods that humans enjoy are fermented by bacteria. Bacteria help ferment, or chemically break down, many dairy products people eat every day, such as yogurt and cheeses. Pickles, soy sauce, sauerkraut, and vinegar also depend on fermentation by prokaryotes to produce their flavors.

Ⓐ Summarize **What are two ways in which prokaryotes that live within our bodies are helpful to us?**

Differentiated Instruction

BELOW LEVEL
After reading through the section, have students write for five minutes about the ways in which prokaryotes are beneficial to humans. They should mention nitrogen fixation, oxygen production, digestion-aiding bacteria, fermentation, and bioremediation.

Teacher Toolkit, Section C, Quick-Write

PRE-AP
Have students list and then group keywords in this section, such as *photosynthesis/ cyanobacteria, biodegradable/ bioremediation,* and *nitrogen fixation/ symbiosis.* Have students differentiate between the groups by describing the subjects or phenomena that each involves.

Teacher Toolkit, Section D, List-Group-Label

SECTION 19.5

Plan and Prepare

Activate Prior Knowledge See if students are aware of the role prokaryotes play in making some of our favorite foods. **Ask**

- What kinds of foods require bacteria for their production? dairy products such as cheese and yogurt, soy products such as tofu and soy sauce, alcoholic beverages, and pickled foods
- What role do bacteria play in agriculture? nitrogen fixation

Teach

Science Trivia
- The holes in Swiss cheese are produced by carbon dioxide gas released by bacteria.
- Vitamin K, which is crucial in helping blood clot, is synthesized by bacteria living in the large intestine.

Answers
Ⓐ **Summarize** They provide nutrients, and they fill niches that might otherwise be filled by pathogenic bacteria.

▼ Teach *continued*

QUICKLAB

Time 15 minutes

TEACHER TESTED ✓

Purpose Observe bacteria on a microscope slide of yogurt.

LAB MANAGEMENT

Safety Tell students to be careful handling the sharp-edged cover slips and to carefully clean the lenses of the microscopes to avoid contamination.

Analyze and Conclude

1. Answers will vary, but students are likely to see bacilli and cocci-shaped bacteria. (This may include *Lactobacillus bulgaricus, Lactobacillus acidophilus,* and *Streptococcus thermophilus.*)
2. Many of the bacteria in yogurt produce lactase, which metabolizes the lactose in yogurt.

Take It Further

The flashlight fish (*Photoblepharon palpebratus*) gets its name from **bioluminescent bacteria,** with which it has a symbiotic relationship. The bacteria live in a sac under the fish's eyes and produce the enzyme luciferase, which glows. The glowing blue-green light helps the fish hunt for food and navigate its dark habitat. In return, the fish provides the bacteria with a safe habitat, oxygen, and nutrients. When threatened by a predator, the fish covers its light sac with a film, which effectively turns out the light, hiding the fish.

QUICKLAB OBSERVING

Examining Bacteria in Yogurt

Some types of bacteria can ferment milk, producing lactic acid in the process. Yogurt is a product of fermentation. It is acidic and stays fresh longer than milk, and it is also digested more easily. In this exercise, you will prepare a microscope slide of yogurt.

PROBLEM What types of bacteria can you observe in yogurt?

PROCEDURE

1. Using a toothpick, place a dab of yogurt on a microscope slide. **Caution:** Do not eat in the laboratory.
2. Mix the yogurt in a drop of water and carefully add a coverslip.
3. Examine the slide with a compound microscope.
4. Record your observations by drawing a picture of what you see through the microscope.

MATERIALS

- toothpick
- dab of plain yogurt
- microscope slide
- drop of water
- coverslip
- microscope

ANALYZE AND CONCLUDE

1. **Identify** Recall the terms *bacillus, coccus,* and *spirilla* from the previous section. Which type or types of bacteria did you observe in your slides?
2. **Analyze** Many people do not produce lactase, which is an enzyme that breaks down the milk sugar lactose. As a result, lactose-intolerant people have trouble digesting dairy products. Why might they have fewer problems eating yogurt?

MAIN IDEA

Prokaryotes play important roles in ecosystems.

Even though you can't easily see them, prokaryotes play important roles in every ecosystem they occupy. Some, such as cyanobacteria, produce oxygen through photosynthesis. Others help recycle carbon, nitrogen, hydrogen, and sulfur through the ecosystem. The absence of prokaryotes in the environment can disrupt an ecosystem, since other organisms rely on them for survival.

Photosynthesizing prokaryotes include purple and green photosynthetic bacteria and cyanobacteria. Whereas purple and green bacteria use light to make carbohydrates, they do not produce oxygen. Cyanobacteria, however, are similar to plants in how they produce oxygen as a byproduct of photosynthesis. Cyanobacteria are named for their greenish blue (cyan) color. Recall that cyanobacteria played an important part on early Earth, supporting the life forms we are familiar with today. Fossil evidence suggests there was very little oxygen on Earth prior to the appearance of cyanobacteria.

Some colonies of photosynthesizing cyanobacteria, as well as other bacteria, are also able to fix nitrogen. Although much of the atmosphere is made up of nitrogen gas (N_2), this is not in a form that plants or animals can use to make amino acids or proteins.

Differentiated Instruction

TEACH WITH TECHNOLOGY

Students can perform a biotechnology lab that explores the use of bacteria in bioremediation.

Online Student Resources, Labs, Bacteria's Role in Wastewater Treatment

HANDS-ON ACTIVITY

Students can see how fermentation is involved in the production of some foods and drinks by working in small groups to brew root beer, make apple cider, bake bread, or create other simple-to-make foods from basic ingredients or inexpensive kits. You can make such an activity more experimental by trying slightly different recipes or using a control group (such as no yeast).

Recall that nitrogen fixation is the process of converting atmospheric nitrogen into ammonia (NH_3) and other nitrogen compounds that plants can then use. Prokaryotes supply usable nitrogen to ecosystems ranging from grasslands and forests to the arctic tundra.

Some types of nitrogen-fixing bacteria are free-living, while others live along with other organisms. Legumes, a group of plants including peas, beans, alfalfa, and clover, have a mutualistic relationship with nitrogen-fixing bacteria. These bacteria live in the plant's nodules, small rounded lumps that form the roots, as shown in **FIGURE 5.2.** The bacteria provide usable nitrogen to the plant by capturing nitrogen gas from air trapped in the soil. They combine the nitrogen with hydrogen to produce ammonia. In return, the plant supplies food and shelter to the bacteria.

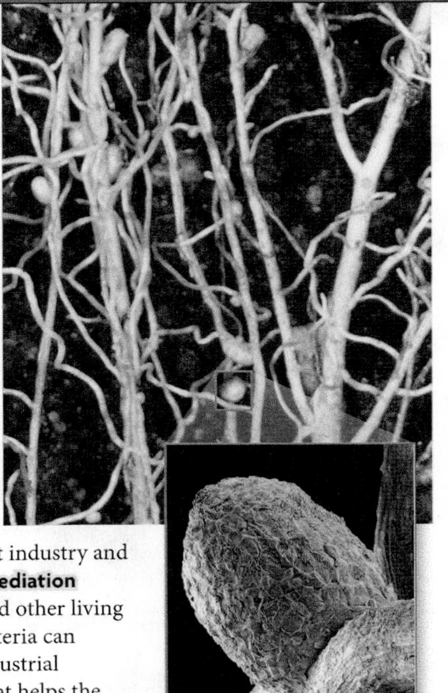

FIGURE 5.2 Root nodules of this white clover contain nitrogen-fixing bacteria. The symbiotic bacteria convert nitrogen from the atmosphere (N_2) into a form usable by the clover. In return, the plant produces carbohydrates through photosynthesis that the bacteria can consume. (inset colored SEM; magnification 90×)

Scientists have found many ways to use prokaryotes to benefit industry and the environment. One important use of prokaryotes is in **bioremediation** (BY-oh-rih-MEE-dee-AY-shuhn), a process that uses microbes and other living things to break down pollutants. For example, some types of bacteria can digest oil, which is helpful for cleaning up oil spills and other industrial accidents. Workers spray oil-polluted beaches with a fertilizer that helps the bacteria grow.

Bacteria can digest almost any product that humans can make, including poisons. Therefore, they play an important role in recycling and composting. When you hear the term *biodegradable,* it often refers to the ability of bacteria to break down a material. Some of the only materials made by humans that cannot be biodegraded are certain types of plastics.

Apply **When there is a toxic chemical spill, sometimes workers will spray bacteria over the contaminated area. Why might they do this?**

Integrating Earth Science

In 1975 in Hanahan, South Carolina, about 300,000 liters (80,000 gal) of jet fuel leaked from a nearby military fuel-storage facility. The fuel soaked into the soil and slowly spread to the groundwater. Scientists with the United States Geological Survey had discovered that certain soil micro-organisms consume fuel-derived toxic compounds, changing them into carbon dioxide, and that this process can be enhanced by adding nutrients to the soil. Using this knowledge, in 1992, scientists added nutrients to the fuel-contaminated soil around Hanahan. A year later, the contamination was reduced by more than 75 percent. The Hanahan Bioremediation Project was a success.

Answers

A **Apply** The bacteria can digest the chemicals, converting them into harmless or less-harmful compounds.

19.5 Formative Assessment

REVIEWING MAIN IDEAS

1. Describe two ways bacteria provide nutrients to humans.
2. What are two roles prokaryotes play in the cycling of elements in an ecosytem?

CRITICAL THINKING

3. **Connect** Think of an example in which the use of **bioremediation** either has improved the environment or has the potential to do so.
4. **Synthesize** How do prokaryotes lend stability to an ecosystem?

SELF-CHECK Online
HMHScience.com
GO ONLINE

CONNECT TO

ECOLOGY

5. Prokaryotes in cow intestines produce more methane if the cow is fed a diet high in grains rather than grass. Some scientists propose that overfeeding grain to cows contributes to global warming. How did these scientists arrive at this hypothesis, and how could it be tested?

Assess and Reteach

Assess Use the Section Self-Check or Section Quiz, both available at **HMHScience.com**.

Reteach Tell students that the class has been given government funding to improve the reputation of prokaryotes, which has suffered from their association with disease. Have students design posters describing the benefits of having prokaryotes in our lives.

19.5 FORMATIVE ASSESSMENT

1. Bacteria in our bodies make vitamins that we absorb, and some bacteria are needed to make foods that we eat, such as soy and dairy products.
2. *Sample answer:* producing oxygen through photosynthesis, fixing nitrogen, decomposing other organisms
3. *Sample answer:* cleaning up industrial accidents, sewage, and other waste
4. Prokaryotes lend stability to an ecosystem through their role as decomposers. Other organisms rely on prokaryotes for nitrogen and other compounds that are broken down through prokaryote metabolic activity. Some prokaryotes also help the stability of an ecosystem by releasing oxygen into the environment during photosynthesis.
5. Students can infer that the amount of methane produced by the intestines of a grain-fed cow can be compared to that produced by a grass-fed cow, perhaps by measuring concentrations of methane in closed environments after cows have fed and lived inside them for some time. The effect of methane concentration on the heat retention of the atmosphere can also presumably be tested in a small, enclosed space that is open to sunlight.

Introduce

Students have learned about the role of bacteria as pathogens that cause disease, but they may not be aware of the roles of "friendly" bacteria in their bodies. **Ask**, Why do you think some bacteria cause human diseases and others may prevent them? Explain that pathogenic bacteria cause disease by producing toxins or invading body cells, disrupting cellular functioning. The friendly bacteria discussed in this feature live among human cells but do not invade them or produce toxins. For example, *Clostridium difficile*, known as *C. diff*, causes a potentially lethal infection by producing potent toxins that attack and destroy cells in the lining of the large intestine. Although *F. prausnitzii* is distantly related to *C. diff*, it does not produce toxins, nor does it invade human cells.

Discuss

Discuss the role of dietary fiber in preventing intestinal disease. Humans cannot digest fiber, but certain bacteria, known collectively as Bacteroidetes, ferment dietary fiber and extract energy from it. If a person's diet is deficient in fiber, the starving bacteria switch to another food source—the mucous lining of the gut wall. Mucus keeps the wall intact and prevents inflammation and infection. It acts as a barrier between the bacterial community and the host tissue of the intestinal lining. When the lining thins, pathogens can enter and cause infection. In addition, the cells that make up the intestinal wall come into direct contact with the gut microbiota and become inflamed. Colitis, an intestinal disease, can result.

The interactions among Bacteroidetes, dietary fiber, and weight control are less clear. Researchers have shown that increasing the amount of fiber in the diet increases the diversity and number of Bacteroidetes in the gut. Also, lean individuals tend to have a greater diversity of these bacteria. As the bacteria ferment fiber, they produce shorter molecules that the host body uses as a source of energy. Although there seems to be a relationship among bacteria, fiber, and weight control, that relationship is not yet clear.

Human Microbiota

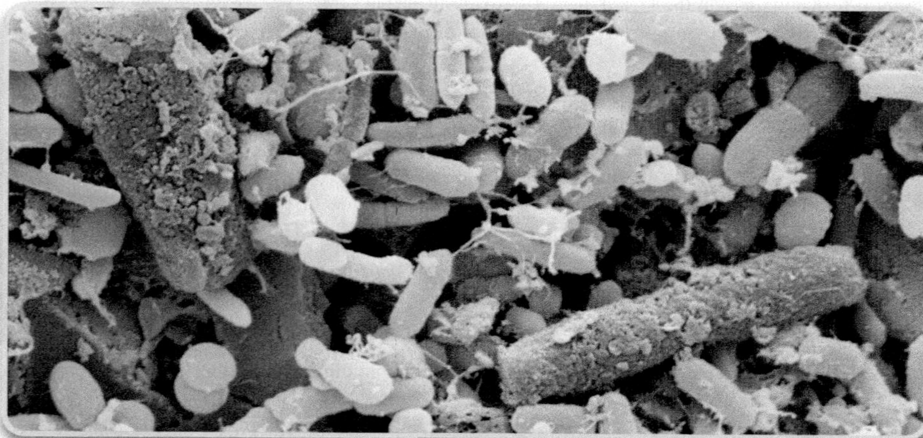

Microbiota

A healthy human has a microbial population of about 100 trillion (1×10^{14}) bacteria. To put that number in perspective, compare it with the current human world population—about 7.4 billion (7.4×10^{9}). New studies show that the *microbiota* in the digestive system, also called the gut, are much more diverse than previously thought—about 5,600 different species. But not every human has the same species of microbiota. Furthermore, the species in an individual can vary from day to day.

Most microbiota live in your gut, especially in your large intestine. These bacteria don't usually cause disease. In fact, they promote health. They eat some of your wastes, produce nutrients such as vitamin K that your body can't make, and prevent pathogens from taking over and causing disease. Scientists are finding new and unexpected functions that microbiota perform. It turns out that humans can't live without them.

Gut microbiota seem to have an anti-inflammatory function in the immune system. Several intestinal diseases, such as Crohn's disease, cause pain, swelling, and inflammation in the large intestine. Scientists have discovered that people suffering from these diseases are missing just one species of bacteria, *Faecalibacterium prausnitzii*. When doctors mixed human immune cells in a test tube with gut bacteria from people with intestinal disease, the cells became damaged. But when *F. prausnitzii* was added, inflammation was prevented.

Scientists suspect that a lack of certain gut bacteria also causes autoimmune diseases and allergies, in which the immune system overreacts and attacks the body. Current lines of research are investigating whether diet, an overly clean home, or the use of antibiotics is responsible for a loss of bacteria that keep the immune system healthy. Interestingly, researchers have found that humans who grew up in less sanitary living conditions have half the risk of developing inflammatory bowel disease as adults.

Gut microbiota seem to influence a person's weight too. Although lifestyle, diet, and exercise certainly contribute to obesity, gut microbiota also seem to play a role. Obese people have less diversity in their gut microbiota than thin people do. In an experiment, scientists removed gut bacteria from both thin and obese human twins and transferred the microbes into thin mice. Both groups of mice ate the same diet, but the mice that received bacteria from obese humans got fat, while mice that received bacteria from thin humans stayed thin.

Humans can change their microbiota. Probiotics are foods such as yogurt that contain bacterial cultures. These cultures can restore the growth and diversity of gut bacteria, especially after friendly bacteria were killed by antibiotics that were used to fight an infection. A relatively new treatment for intestinal disorders is a fecal transplant. In this treatment, fecal material is collected from a healthy donor and transferred into a person suffering from an intestinal disorder. In many cases, the technique works and a patient's health improves.

19.6 Bacterial Diseases and Antibiotics

KEY CONCEPT **Understanding bacteria is necessary to prevent and treat disease.**

VOCABULARY
oxin
ntibiotic

MAIN IDEAS
- Some bacteria cause disease.
- Antibiotics are used to fight bacterial disease.
- Bacteria can evolve resistance to antibiotics.

Connect to Your World

Check the news for the past few years. You'll likely find both local and national stories about antibiotic-resistant bacteria and the difficulty in treating the infections they cause. In learning how to deal with diseases that plagued previous generations, we accidentally created a widespread new set of problems. In addition, many diseases that were controlled are making a comeback due to antibiotic resistance.

MAIN IDEA

Some bacteria cause disease.

Some bacteria cause disease in plants and animals by disrupting the host organism's homeostasis, or the stability of its internal environment. Bacteria can cause illness to a host in two basic ways: by invading tissues and attacking cells or by making poisons, or toxins, that can be carried by blood to sites throughout the body. A **toxin** is a poison released by an organism.

The disease tuberculosis (TB) is an example of bacteria invading the host's tissues, and using the tissues for nutrients. *Mycobacterium tuberculosis* bacteria multiply in the lungs, killing white blood cells that respond to the invasion. The host's reaction to an invasion by bacteria may itself cause serious problems. In the case of TB, the host responds to the infection by releasing enzymes that cause swelling. That swelling, in turn, damages the host's lungs.

TB is a good example of the changing ecological balance between host and pathogen in an infectious disease. A host is not usually aware of pathogens that its immune system defeats. It is when the host's immune system fails that the host becomes aware of the pathogen's presence. Most healthy people can defeat a potential TB infection, especially if there are not many bacteria present.

FIGURE 6.1 *Clostridium botulinum* causes a serious illness called botulism. Food contamination by this bacterium often comes from improper home canning.

Bacteria, such as *Staphylococcus aureus* and *Clostridium botulinum,* shown in **FIGURE 6.1,** can also make their hosts sick through food poisoning. *S. aureus,* which normally lives in nasal passages, can be transferred to food when food handlers don't wash their hands after they blow their nose. This transfer can result in serious food poisoning, known as staph poisoning. Even high temperatures cannot destroy a toxin produced by *S. aureus.* The most common source of food poisoning by *S. aureus,* however, is from foods that were contaminated after they were cooked. If contaminated food is not refrigerated, bacteria can multiply and produce a large amount of toxin.

Differentiated Instruction

ENGLISH LEARNERS

Tell students that at the end of the section, they will do a five-minute quick-write on what they have learned about bacterial diseases and antibiotics. After reading the section, separate the class into two groups, one that will write on diseases and the other on antibiotics. After students have written for five minutes on their topic, have them gather in their topic groups and pool their ideas into a single essay.

Teacher Toolkit, Section C, Quick-Write; Think-Pair-Share

BELOW LEVEL

To test students' understanding, write five to ten true/false statements about the main points of the section, such as:

Bacteria can develop a resistance to an antibiotic. (T)

Have students react to the statements as being true or false both before and after reading the section. If any questions are answered incorrectly after the reading, go over the relevant material one more time and retest students for comprehension.

Teacher Toolkit, Section C, Anticipation Guide

Plan and Prepare

Activate Prior Knowledge Have students consider the language of treating infectious disease. **Ask,** If we regard ourselves as being under attack by viruses and bacteria, how do we fight back? For some viruses, we have vaccines; for bacteria, we have antibiotics. Antibiotics offer a way to win battles against bacteria, but because the life spans of bacteria are brief and ours are long, they have an advantage. **Ask,** Who can adapt faster to the tactics of the other—humans or bacteria? bacteria; because bacterial life spans are so brief, mutations accumulate much faster, allowing them to quickly adapt to the challenges we create, like antibiotics.

Teach

Take It Further

Some bacteria that are normally harmless can become pathogenic when a change in circumstances provides new opportunities. These are called **opportunistic pathogens.** For example, *E. coli,* one of the normal intestinal floras, causes illness if it invades the urinary system or contaminates a wound. Hosts whose health is compromised, such as AIDS patients, are especially vulnerable to opportunistic pathogens.

▼ Teach *continued*

History of Science

In medicine, **carriers** are people who have recovered from an infectious disease but can still infect other people, often by poor hygienic practices. One especially notorious carrier was a young cook named **Mary Mallon.** Over a 10-year period in the early 20th century, she infected with typhoid fever eight families she had worked for. Typhoid fever is a severe illness caused by the bacterium *Salmonella typhi.*

Officials investigating a typhoid outbreak in a wealthy family noted that they had become ill shortly after Mary had come to cook for them. She had since left their employ, but subsequent tracking revealed that typhoid outbreaks occurred in every family she worked for. When officials finally located Mallon, she resisted being tested and had to be forced into quarantine by several police officers.

She was released from quarantine three years later on condition that she never work again handling food. However, in 1915, she took a cooking job, infecting 25 people. Seized again by authorities, **Typhoid Mary,** as she came to be called, was again placed in quarantine, where she remained for the rest of her life.

Answers

A Apply *Staphylococcus aureus* is the most likely culprit, as the potato salad was not refrigerated.

B Infer Antibiotics act on characteristics that are unique to bacterial cells, such as their cell walls.

FIGURE 6.2 Common Bacterial Infections

INFECTION	BACTERIUM	SYMPTOMS	CAUSES
Acne	*Propionibacterium*	chronic cysts, blackheads	increased oil production in skin
Anthrax	*Bacillus anthracis*	fever, trouble breathing	inhaling endospores
Lyme disease	*Borrelia burgdorferi*	rash, aching, fever, swelling of joints	bite from infected tick
Tetanus	*Clostridium tetani*	severe muscle spasms, fever, lockjaw	wound contaminated with soil
Tooth decay	*Streptococcus mutans*	tooth cavities	large populations of bacteria in mouth

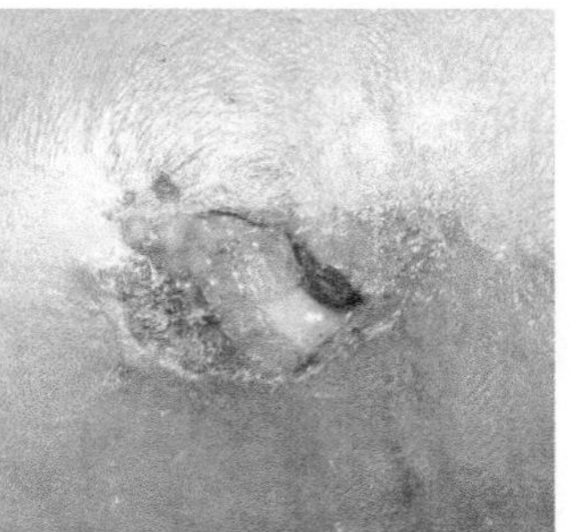

FIGURE 6.3 *Streptococcus* bacteria are commonly found on skin. They are fairly harmless unless they come in contact with tissues they do not normally colonize, such as muscle or fat. This can occur through open wounds.

Staph food poisoning can make you pretty sick, but botulism can kill you. *C. botulinum* produces a deadly toxin. Botulism poisoning is usually caused by the eating of improperly canned foods that were contaminated with endospores before being sealed. Bulging cans are a sign that *C. botulinum* may be present.

Normally harmless bacteria can be destructive when introduced to a part of the host that is not adapted to them. Disease can result if these bacteria get into tissues they do not usually colonize through a cut, scrape, or surgical incision. You can see one result of typically harmless *Streptococci*, which we have normally in our mouths and noses—and often on our skin—becoming pathogenic in **FIGURE 6.3.** These are also the bacteria that can cause what is commonly known as strep throat.

A Apply **Potato salad left out at a picnic is sometimes a source of food poisoning. Which bacterium mentioned above is the most likely culprit? Explain.**

CONNECT TO

FUNGI

Some species of fungi are used as medicine, while others can make people sick. You will learn more about fungi in the chapter **Protists and Fungi.**

MAIN IDEA

Antibiotics are used to fight bacterial disease.

If you've ever had a cold, your doctor may have told you that the only cure was to let the cold "run its course." If you had strep throat, however, the doctor would prescribe a powerful antibiotic. Why do you get antibiotics for strep throat but not for the common cold?

Colds and strep throat are treated differently because they are caused by different pathogens. Viruses cause colds, while the bacterium *Streptococcus* causes strep throat. Many types of **antibiotics**—or chemicals that kill or slow the growth of bacteria—work by stopping bacteria from making cell walls.

Antibiotics are produced naturally by some species of bacteria and fungi. They can be used as medicine for humans and other animals without damaging their cells, since animal cells do not have cell walls. Because viruses also lack cell walls, antibiotics do not work on viral infections.

Antibiotics can be effective when used properly, but they should not be the first line of defense against bacterial infection; prevention should. Overuse of antibiotics can completely wipe out the community of intestinal microbes, resulting in illness.

B Infer **Why don't antibiotics affect our bodies' own cells?**

Differentiated Instruction

PRE-AP

Have students map out a possible sequence of events predicting the spread of *pneumococcus,* a bacterium that causes pneumonia, in a crowded nursing home. Remind students that most residents in the nursing home are elderly with impaired immune systems. As they plot the movement of the bacteria, students should consider all people who pass through a nursing home each day and other people they interact with outside the home.

Teacher Toolkit, Section C, Sequence Diagram

MAIN IDEA

Bacteria can evolve resistance to antibiotics.

Although antibiotics should certainly be used when needed, the inappropriate and incomplete use of antibiotics has produced a serious public health issue—multidrug-resistant bacteria. Resistance occurs as a result of natural selection, as individuals who are more resistant are more likely to survive and reproduce. This has led to the evolution of multidrug-resistant strains of "superbugs" that are almost impossible to treat. As you can see in **FIGURE 6.4**, bacteria can acquire genes for resistance through plasmid exchange. This has happened with many bacteria treated with a wide range of commonly used antibiotics. This problem has arisen due to various factors.

Overuse The potential problem with antibiotics is that they may create a selective pressure that favors the very bacteria they are intended to destroy. Using antibiotics when bacteria are not causing an illness may make some bacteria resistant.

FIGURE 6.4 ANTIBIOTIC RESISTANCE

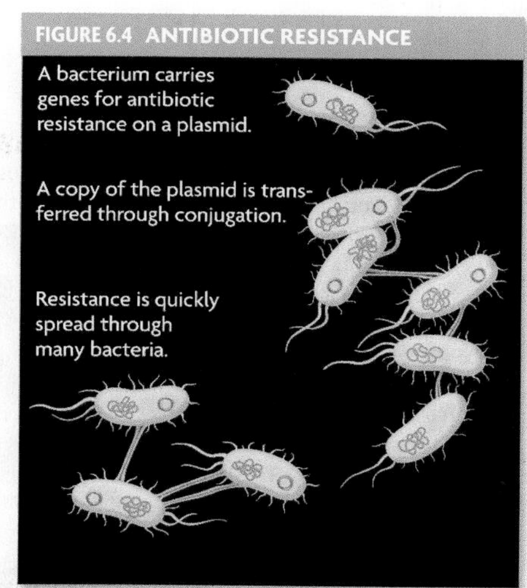

A bacterium carries genes for antibiotic resistance on a plasmid.
A copy of the plasmid is transferred through conjugation.
Resistance is quickly spread through many bacteria.

Underuse Failure to take the entire course of antibiotics prescribed for a bacterial infection is one of the main factors leading to drug resistance. If your doctor prescribed a ten-day course of an antibiotic, you must finish the entire prescription. Otherwise, you may not have destroyed all of the bacteria—only the weakest ones.

Antibiotics in Agriculture

Misuse A large portion of the antibiotics distributed in the United States are fed to livestock. Antibiotics are often misused in agriculture to increase the animals' rate of growth. However, when antibiotics are added to the food of healthy animals, bacteria within the food—including pathogens—can become resistant to multiple antibiotics.

Connect **How can you use "superbugs" as an example of natural selection?**

19.6 Formative Assessment

SELF-CHECK Online
HMHScience.com
GO ONLINE

REVIEWING MAIN IDEAS

1. What are two ways in which bacteria can cause disease?
2. How can **antibiotics** stop bacterial infections?
3. What is antibiotic resistance, and how does it occur?

CRITICAL THINKING

4. **Apply** Why are antibiotics not effective against viruses?
5. **Synthesize** Evolution is often thought of as taking thousands, or even millions, of years to occur. What are two reasons that antibiotic resistance has been able to evolve in bacteria so quickly?

CONNECT TO ECOLOGY

6. Pesticide resistance occurs in much the same way as antibiotic resistance. How could we apply what we have learned about antibiotic resistance to how pesticides are used in the environment?

19.6 FORMATIVE ASSESSMENT

1. invade tissues and attack cells directly or make a toxin that is carried by the blood
2. by disrupting cell wall synthesis in bacteria
3. Genetic mutations occur that render bacteria resistant to antibiotics. The genes are on plasmids, which are exchanged frequently between bacteria. Over time, more bacteria in the population have the antibiotic-resistant genes because these bacteria have a selective advantage.
4. Antibiotics act on parts of cells that viruses do not have, such as cell walls.
5. Bacteria can transfer genes directly to each other through conjugation, and generation times in bacteria are very brief, so mutations can occur and build up fairly quickly.
6. If pesticides are used without being needed, then pesticide resistance in organisms will build up so that when pesticides are needed, they will not work.

ONLINE Biology
HMHScience.com

To explore the role of antibiotics in agriculture and its effect, see the WebQuest for this chapter at **HMHScience.com**.

Take It Further

The resistance of certain strains of bacteria to common antibiotics is forcing pharmaceutical scientists to find new antibiotics. **Platensimycin,** a compound isolated from a soil microbe found in South Africa, was recently found to be effective in destroying *S. aureus* and *enterococci* pathogens without doing harm to the host animal's cells. When the compound was tested in mice infected with *S. aureus*, the bacteria were decreased 10,000-fold within 24 hours. If platensimycin is deemed safe enough for use in humans, it could be the most potent antibiotic to reach patients in decades.

Answers

A Connect Mutations allow bacteria to become drug resistant, and the trait is passed on to the next generation. As the drugs change, certain bacteria that are resistant to the new drug will survive, produce offspring, and through conjugation spread the resistant genes on to offspring.

Assess and Reteach

Assess Use the Section Self-Check or Section Quiz, both available at **HMHScience.com**.

Reteach As a class, make a concept map that relates to the issue of bacterial antibiotic resistance. You might begin with the following terms: *bacterial diseases, antibiotics, inappropriate uses,* and *antibiotic resistance.* Have students add terms to the map and show how to connect them.

CHAPTER REVIEW

GO ONLINE

Encourage students to go to **HMHScience.com** for a detailed review of each section, including visuals and vocabulary practice.

Online Student Resources, Vocabulary Practice Worksheet

CHAPTER

19 Summary

BIG IDEA Viruses and some bacteria can be harmful to human health or the environment, but most bacteria and archaea are an important part of every community they inhabit.

KEY CONCEPTS

19.1 Studying Viruses and Prokaryotes

Infections can be caused in several ways. Viruses, viroids, and prions have characteristics of both living and nonliving things. Unlike bacteria, viruses cannot reproduce on their own. A virus has genetic material and a protein coat. Viroids have only RNA and no protein coat. Prions are made of only protein.

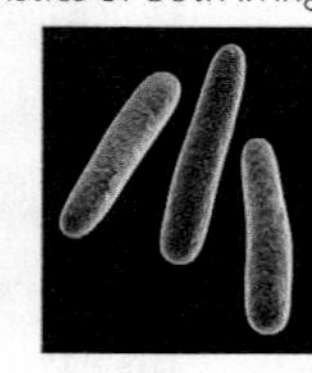

19.2 Viral Structure and Reproduction

Viruses exist in a variety of shapes and sizes. Viruses can be helical like a spring, many-sided, or enveloped. Bacteriophages, or viruses that attack bacteria, have a many-sided capsid with a long protein tail and spiky footlike fibers. There are two basic types of viral infections: lytic and lysogenic. A lytic infection results in the host cells bursting open, while the virions in a lysogenic infection do not immediately destroy the host.

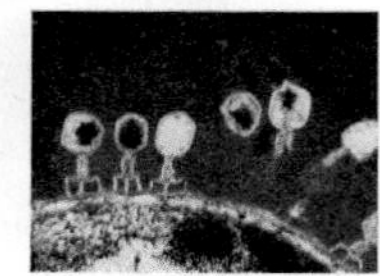

19.3 Viral Diseases

Some viral diseases can be prevented with vaccines. Viruses can enter a body through wounds or body openings such as mouths or noses. Many infectious viruses exist. Examples of illnesses caused by viruses include the common cold, influenza, SARS, and AIDS. Vaccines can prevent some, but not all, viral diseases.

19.4 Bacteria and Archaea

Bacteria and archaea are both single-celled prokaryotes. Prokaryotes are widespread on Earth. Archaea look very similar to bacteria, but many of their structures are made of different compounds. Some prokaryotes can survive harsh conditions by forming endospores. Prokaryotes can transfer genes to each other through conjugation.

19.5 Beneficial Roles of Prokaryotes

Prokaryotes perform important functions for organisms and ecosystems. Prokaryotes that live in an animal's digestive tract help the animal absorb nutrients from the food that it eats. Animals and plants also depend on prokaryotes to fix atmospheric nitrogen. Nitrogen is necessary to make amino acids and proteins. Bioremediation uses prokaryotes to help break down pollutants in the environment.

19.6 Bacterial Diseases and Antibiotics

Understanding bacteria is necessary to prevent and treat disease. Although the majority of bacteria are not pathogenic, some do cause disease. Bacteria can also cause conditions such as food poisoning, chronic acne, Lyme disease, and tooth decay. Antibiotics are used to fight bacterial infection. However, through natural selection, many bacteria have become resistant to commonly used antibiotics.

READING TOOLBOX SYNTHESIZE YOUR NOTES

Concept Map Use a concept map like the one below to summarize what you know about infectious agents. Include details about genetic material and types of hosts they infect.

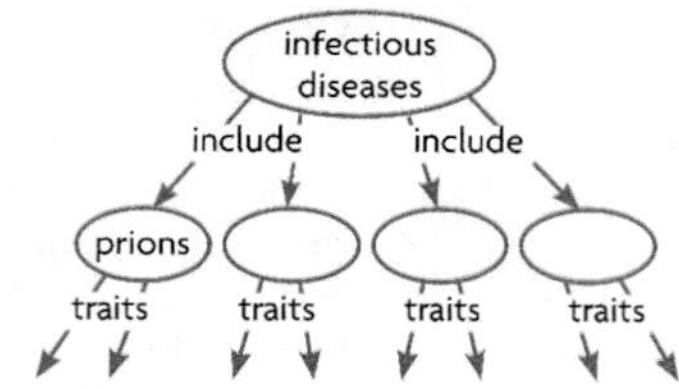

Cycle Diagram Use two cycle diagrams like the one below to summarize lytic and lysogenic infections.

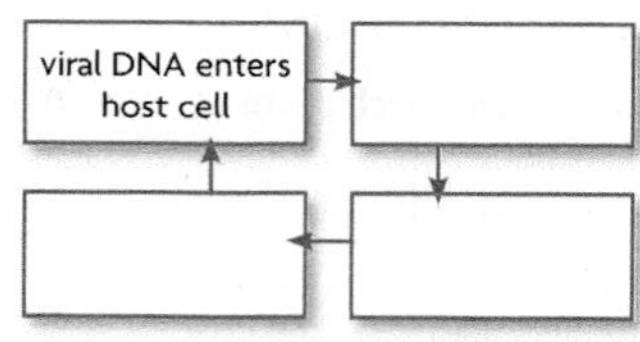

Reviewing Vocabulary

1. vaccine
2. viroid
3. prophage
4. bacteriophage
5. antibiotic
6. bioremediation
7. A flagellum is a whiplike structure of single-celled organisms.
8. Conjugation is the transfer of genetic material between prokaryotes. It occurs when two or more cells join together through a conjugation bridge of pili.
9. An epidemic is a large-scale spread of infection among a group of people or among a community.
10. An anaerobe lives without oxygen.

19 Review

INTERACTIVE Review
HMHScience.com
GO ONLINE
Review Games • Concept Map • Section Self-Checks

CHAPTER VOCABULARY

19.1 virus, pathogen, viroid, prion
19.2 capsid, bacteriophage, lytic infection, lysogenic infection, prophage
19.3 epidemic, vaccine, retrovirus
19.4 obligate anaerobe, obligate aerobe, facultative aerobe, plasmid, flagellum, conjugation, endospore
19.5 bioremediation
19.6 toxin, antibiotic

Reviewing Vocabulary

Category Clues

For each clue, list the appropriate vocabulary term from the chapter.

Category: Viral Infection

1. protects against infection
2. plant virus
3. host and viral DNA

Category: Bacteria

4. virus of bacteria
5. fights bacterial infection
6. pollution digestion

READING TOOLBOX GREEK AND LATIN WORD ORIGINS

7. The term *flagellum* comes from the Latin word *flagrum*, which means "whip." Explain how this meaning relates to flagellum.
8. The term *conjugation* comes from the Latin word *conjugare*, which means "to join together." Using this meaning, explain how it relates to what conjugation is.
9. The term *epidemic* comes from the Greek words *epi-*, which means "upon," and *demos*, which means "people." Explain how these meanings relate to an epidemic.
10. The term *aerobe* means "an organism that requires oxygen to live." The prefixes *a-* or *an-* mean "without, or not." How do these meanings relate to the term *anaerobe*?

Reviewing MAIN IDEAS

11. Viruses, viroids, and prions are not considered to be living things. Which of their traits resemble living organisms, and which traits do not?
12. The flu virus has an envelope with surface proteins that allow it to infect its host cells. What structures help viruses infect bacterial cells? Explain.
13. Explain the differences between the two ways viruses infect their host cells.
14. Children across the United States get "shots," or injections, during their physical exams. Explain what these shots are and why they are recommended for all children.
15. The success of prokaryotes is due to special characteristics they have, such as the ability to form endospores and perform conjugation. Explain how each of these abilities helps prokaryotes survive changing environments.
16. It surprises most people to learn that their lives depend on bacteria. Describe three roles bacteria play in human health and survival.
17. Due to their unique ability to break down an enormous array of substances, prokaryotes play critical roles in ecosystems. Summarize two of these roles.
18. Doctors recommend washing hands before eating to prevent the spread of disease. What is the connection between bacteria and disease?
19. Prokaryotes have the ability to carry genes other than their own. How is this trait important for genetic engineering?
20. Recently, doctors have been advised to limit the use of antibiotics whenever possible. Why is this recommendation important?

Reviewing Main Ideas

11. Viruses, viroids, and prions can multiply, and viruses and viroids have genes. None of them, however, can reproduce on their own. They all require living organisms in order to reproduce.
12. Spiky footlike fibers help attach to host cells; tails break down bacterial cell walls and then punch through, injecting the virus's genes.
13. Lytic infections cause the host cells to burst and release new virions; lysogenic infections can remain in the host cell undetected for long periods of time. In lysogenic infections, the genetic material of the virus becomes incorporated within the genetic material of the host cell.
14. Shots are usually vaccines, a preparation of weakened microbes that can prepare an individual's immune system for any future encounter with a specific virus.
15. Endospores offer protection from harsh, unfavorable conditions such as high heat or lack of water. Conjugation allows genes to quickly transfer between prokaryotes, allowing rapid adaptation to environmental conditions.
16. Bacteria break down food that we would otherwise be unable to absorb. They also make vitamins and other compounds and keep harmful microbes away by filling niches that might otherwise be filled by disease-causing bacteria.
17. Some prokaryotes can fix atmospheric nitrogen into compounds that plants and, later, animals require. Others can break down pollutants and waste products into less harmful compounds.
18. Some bacteria cause diseases in humans when they are exposed to certain types of cells or tissues.
19. Genes from other organisms can be inserted into prokaryotes that will then deliver them into other cells.
20. Many bacteria are showing resistance to multiple antibiotics. Limiting the use of antibiotics to times when they are really needed will lessen the exposure of bacteria to antibiotics and slow the rate at which they gain resistance.

Critical Thinking

21. Bacteria that consume toxic materials can clean up pollution in the environment by metabolizing the toxins and producing a less toxic or nontoxic waste product. This is the basis of bioremediation.
22. In the lysogenic infection, the virus can go undetected for a long period of time, producing copies of its genes for as long as it remains integrated with the host's genes. In the lytic cycle, the virus works quickly, and the host can release a large number of new virions at once.
23. A virus that kills the host quickly may not get the chance to infect others because the host (or its cells) are no longer interacting with others.
24. Because endospores are so resistant to harsh conditions, they give some bacteria the chance to survive freezing, canning, cooking, chemical cleaning, and other treatments designed to preserve or sterilize.

Interpreting Visuals

25. lytic infection; we see new viral parts being made and new virions leaving the host cell.
26. The viral genes direct the host to make copies of the viral parts.
27. If the host cell were eukaryotic, the virus might enter the cell by endocytosis. If the virus is enveloped, it may enter by fusing to the plasma membrane of the host cell.

Critical Thinking

21. Apply Many bacteria cause food spoilage because they have dietary needs similar to humans. However, some bacteria consume chemicals such as heavy metals, sulfur, petroleum, and mercury. How are these bacteria being used to help humans?

22. Compare and Contrast In a lysogenic infection, viral genes can become a part of the host's cell. In a lytic infection, the host cell is destroyed. What might be the benefit of each type of infection to the virus?

23. Infer New viruses may quickly kill their host after infection, but after many generations viruses tend to weaken and cause fewer deaths. Why might it be a disadvantage for a virus to quickly kill its host?

24. Synthesize Endospore-forming bacteria include those that cause the diseases tetanus, botulism, and anthrax. Endospores themselves, however, do not cause illness and cannot reproduce. Why, then, are endospores such a concern to the food and healthcare industries?

Interpreting Visuals

Use the diagram below to answer the next three questions.

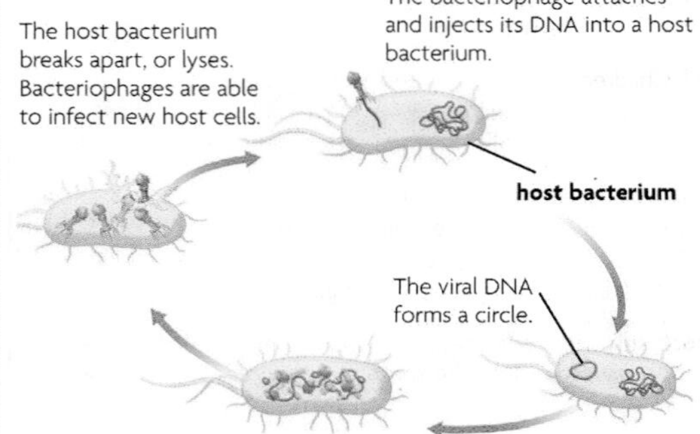
The bacteriophage attaches and injects its DNA into a host bacterium.
The host bacterium breaks apart, or lyses. Bacteriophages are able to infect new host cells.
host bacterium
The viral DNA forms a circle.
The viral DNA directs the host cell to produce new viral parts. The parts assemble into new bacteriophages.

25. Apply What type of viral infection is shown above? Explain your answer.

26. Apply Why is it necessary for the viral genes to enter the host cell?

27. Analyze How would the way that the virion enters the host cell change if the virus were a type that infected animals, and the host cell were eukaryotic rather than prokaryotic?

Analyzing Data Choose Data Representation

Use the hypothetical data below to answer the next questions.

TYPE OF BACTERIA AND LENGTH	
Type of bacteria	**Average length (nm)**
Streptococcus	500
Staphylococcus	900
Vibrio	2600
Aquaspirillum	2800

REPLICATION TIME OF STREPTOCOCCUS	
Time (min)	**Number of streptococcus cells**
0	1
28	2
56	4
84	8

28. Connect For each of the tables above, identify whether the data are continuous or discrete. Explain.

29. Calculate Assuming that nutrients are unlimited, how many *Streptococcus* cells will there be after 112 minutes? Explain.

Making Connections

30. Writing a Pamphlet Scientists agree that a form of the avian flu virus has the potential to cause a worldwide flu epidemic. This type of virus is known to mutate easily and adapt quickly to host changes. Imagine you are a representative from the Centers for Disease Control and are writing a pamphlet to educate citizens about the virus and how it actually causes infection. Using your knowledge of cells and viruses, make a detailed pamphlet that the general public could understand.

31. Synthesize The bacteria in the esophagus shown on the chapter opener are one of the many types of symbiotic prokaryotes living within our bodies. How might these types of mutualistic relationships have arisen? Consider natural selection in your answer.

Analyzing Data

28. The table of the type of bacteria displays discrete data; the other table displays continuous data. Discrete data are for specific subjects, such as the bacteria listed. Continuous data are sequential and can reveal change.
29. 16 cells; the population is doubling every 28 minutes. At 112 minutes, the population at 84 minutes (8 cells) will have doubled.

580 Unit 6: Diversity of Life

Standards-Based Assessment

Record your answers on a separate piece of paper.

MULTIPLE CHOICE

1

The Effects of Antibiotics on Infected Mice			
Antibiotic	A	B	C
Infected mice tested	30	15	15
% Effectiveness	83%	25%	100%

Scientists are testing three antibiotics—A, B, and C—on 60 mice with bacterial infections. Based on the table above, what is the *most likely* reason why the scientists concluded that they needed to do more testing on antibiotic C?

A They did not test the side effects of antibiotic C.

B Antibiotic C worked better than A and B.

C Antibiotic C had 100% effectiveness.

D The sample size was too small.

2 Impetigo is a highly contagious skin infection caused by staph or strep bacteria that are normally found on the skin, where they are harmless. This infection is *most likely* to occur when —

A the bacteria gain access to the body through scraped skin

B an uninfected person comes in contact with an infected person

C the infected person did not receive regularly scheduled vaccinations

D the bacteria release endospores on the surface of the skin

3 Hepatitis B is a viral disease that attacks cells in the liver. When should a person receive a vaccination against hepatitis B?

A before being exposed to the virus

B as soon as viral symptoms begin to appear

C after being diagnosed with the disease

D never; the overuse of vaccines has lead to viral resistance

4 Some scientists think that measures of an ecosystem's health—such as usable nitrogen levels in the soil—may become more variable as the diversity of organisms on Earth declines. This is because usable soil nitrogen depends on a variety of —

A animals that return nitrogen to the soil through respiration

B animals that return nitrogen to the soil after they die

C bacteria and other decomposers that fix nitrogen into a usable form

D plants, which produce nitrogen as a byproduct of photosynthesis

5 The main reason that viruses are not considered to be living things is because —

A they are not affected by antibiotics

B they cannot reproduce on their own

C they do not contain a nucleus

D they do not contain any nucleic acids

THINK THROUGH THE QUESTION

All of these answer choices correctly describe viruses, so do not be tricked! Look at each answer choice and try to think of a living organism that fits the characteristic described, making that answer choice wrong.

6

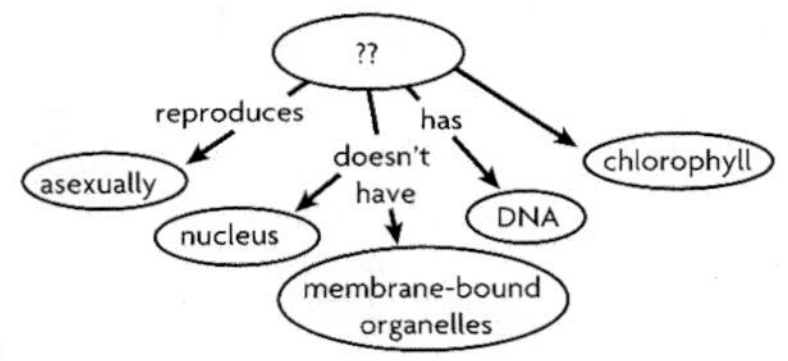

Which of the following can be described by the concept map above?

A an earthworm's muscle cell

B an oak tree's leaf cell

C a bacterium

D a human immunodeficiency virus (HIV)

Standards-Based Assessment

The Standards-Based Assessment questions will help students prepare for their final examination in the course. If you wish to give students practice in coding their answers, look for the Standards-Based Assessment Answer Sheet at **HMHScience.com**. To give students practice under timed testing conditions, allow them five minutes per question.

Question	Answer	Depth of Knowledge	Cognitive Complexity
1	D	III	M
2	A	II	M
3	A	I	L
4	C	IV	M
5	B	II	M
6	C	III	M

KEY

Depth of Knowledge		Cognitive Complexity	
I	Recall	L	Low
II	Skill/Concept	M	Moderate
III	Strategic Thinking	H	High
IV	Extended Thinking		

Making Connections

30. Students' pamphlets should explain how viruses can cause infection, mutate, and be transmitted from one organism to another.

31. *Sample answer:* These bacteria may have conferred a benefit to the animal host by protecting it from serious pathogens. The improved survivability of hosts carrying these bacteria would give a selective advantage for the bacteria because their environment would not be dying early or often.

CHAPTER 20

Instruction and Intervention Support

Protists and Fungi

① Core Instruction

The **Core Instruction** resources below can be used for all students. Core instruction should be followed by ongoing assessment to determine which students need further help.

Available in both English and Spanish

Available Online

Section	Instruction	PRINT	ONLINE	Labs
20.1	Textbook **Diversity of Protists**	■	●	Exploring Bioluminescence (Challenge Lab)
	Teaching Visuals Phylogeny of Protists (Fig. 1.3)		●	
	PowerPresentation and Notes 20.1		●	
20.2	Textbook **Animal-like Protists**	■	●	**QuickLab** Investigating Motion in Protists **Video Lab** Protistan Response to Light
	Animated Biology Malaria		●	
	Teaching Visuals Paramecium Structure (Fig. 2.4)		●	
	PowerPresentation and Notes 20.2		●	
20.3	Textbook **Plantlike Protists**	■	●	Algae in Products
	PowerPresentation and Notes 20.3		●	
20.4	Textbook **Funguslike Protists**	■	●	
	PowerPresentation and Notes 20.4		●	
20.5	Textbook **Diversity of Fungi**	■	●	Exploring Mushroom Anatomy Quantifying Mold Growth (Design Your Own) Investigating Meiosis in *Sordaria fimicola* Chemotaxis in Physarum (Challenge Lab)
	Animated Biology Protist and Fungus Life Cycle, Life Cycle of Zygote Fungi		●	
	PowerPresentation and Notes 20.5		●	
20.6	Textbook **Ecology of Fungi**	■	●	**Video Lab** Yeast and Fermentation
	That's Amazing! Video Inquiry Farmer Ants		●	
	PowerPresentation and Notes 20.6		●	

Additional online resources available for this chapter include **Interactive Whiteboard Resources.**

2 Support and Intervention

Support and Intervention resources are useful for students who need targeted help beyond the Core Instruction

Resources	PRINT	ONLINE
Assess and Reteach (TE wrap)	■	●
Concept Map		●
Interactive Reader	■	●
Interactive Review Games		●
Section Self-Checks		●
Study Guide B		●
Virtual Investigation Comparing Protists		●
Vocabulary Practice Worksheets		●

3 Specialized Support

Students who need more intensive personalized intervention benefit from **Specialized Support** resources.

Resources	PRINT	ONLINE
Chapter Audio Files		●
Differentiated Instruction Inclusion, Below Level, and English Learners (TE wrap)	■	●
ELL Strategies	■	●
Modified Lesson Plans for English Learners		●
Reinforcement Worksheets		●
Study Guide A		●

Extension and Assessment

Enrichment and Challenge

Resources	PRINT	ONLINE
Active Reading Worksheets		●
Data Analysis Practice Worksheet		●
Differentiated Instruction Pre-AP (TE wrap)	■	●
Pre-AP Activity Malaria Control: The Return of DDT		●
Smart Grapher Activity		●
The Inside Story and **Take It Further** (TE wrap)	■	●
Unit Project		●
WebLinks		●
WebQuest Sickening Protists (20.2)		●

Assessment

Resources	PRINT	ONLINE
Alternative Assessment		●
Chapter Tests A and B		●
Diagnostic Test		●
ExamView Banks		●
Extended Response Test		●
Online Assessment System		●
Section Quizzes		●
Standards-Based Assessment	■	●

CHAPTER 20

Chapter Overview

- **Section 1** describes the characteristics of protists that can be used to classify them.
- **Section 2** discusses the characteristics of animal-like protists including their role in causing certain diseases.
- **Section 3** discusses the characteristics of plantlike protists and their role in disrupting some ecosystems.
- **Section 4** discusses the characteristics of funguslike protists and their role in causing certain diseases.
- **Section 5** discusses the characteristics, diversity, and reproduction of fungi.
- **Section 6** explains the role of fungi in ecosystems and as agents of disease.

▼ Focus and Motivate

When these two protists meet, who is the prey?

Have students look at the photograph on this page. **Ask,** What do you think of when you hear the words *predator* and *prey*? Most will think of carnivorous animals hunting smaller animals. Remind students that predators come in many forms, from great white sharks to microscopic protists. Familiar fungi include yeast in bread, the fungus that causes athlete's foot, and mildew in bathrooms. We eat some protists (algae) or substances they produce in foods, such as ice cream. Many protists and fungi have applications for agriculture, industry, and health care.

BIOZINE
HMHScience.com

Students can access BioZine at **HMHScience.com** to check out articles featured in Strange Biology.

CHAPTER 20 Protists and Fungi

BIG IDEA Protists and fungi are highly diverse organisms that have both beneficial and detrimental impacts on human health and the environment.

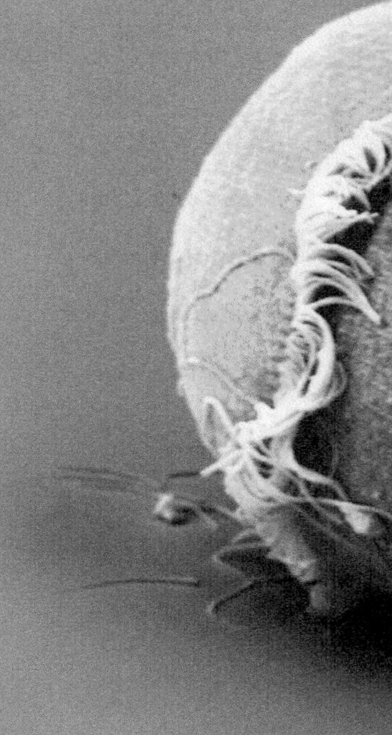

ONLINE BIOLOGY HMHScience.com

ONLINE Labs
- **QuickLab** Investigating Motion in Protists
- Exploring Mushroom Anatomy
- Quantifying Mold Growth
- Algae in Products
- Investigating Meiosis in *Sordaria fimicola*
- Chemotaxis in *Physarum*
- Exploring Bioluminescence
- **Video Lab** Protistan Response to Light
- **Video Lab** Yeast and Fermentation

Teacher Demo

Purpose **Demonstrate the production of CO_2 by yeast as a byproduct of cellular respiration and fermentation.**

Introduce Explain that yeasts are unicellular fungi and that they, like all cells, must break down glucose to get energy. Tell students that yeast is used in baking bread. The yeast cells feed on the sugars in flour and produce carbon dioxide gas, which makes the bread rise.

Materials
- packet of active dry yeast
- very warm water (105°F–115°F)
- 2 tablespoons sugar
- large rubber balloon
- small plastic water bottle
- safety goggles

Safety Wear safety goggles during the demonstration.

When these two protists meet, who is the prey?

Although they are both protists, the round *Didinium* hunts live paramecia almost exclusively. Paramecia are much longer than this predator, but that doesn't stop *Didinium*. It captures, paralyzes, and reels in paramecia like fish on a line. It then eats its prey whole, expanding its own body just so that its meal will fit.

colored SEM; magnification 2000×

READING TOOLBOX **This reading tool can help you learn the material in the following pages.**

USING LANGUAGE

General Statements A general statement summarizes the features of a group or describes an average feature of the members of the group. Some individuals in the group may not share all of the features. So, general statements may be true most of the time, but not always.

YOUR TURN

Use what you know about general statements to answer the following questions.

1. Write a general statement that summarizes the features of baseballs, basketballs, tennis balls, soccer balls, and footballs.
2. Brainstorm exceptions to the general statement "In general, dogs have four legs, fur, and a tail and can bark."

Demonstrate

1. Prepare the balloon by inflating and deflating it several times, then set it aside.
2. Add the yeast and sugar to 1 cup of warm water, and stir until they are dissolved.
3. Pour the mixture into the bottle. Bubbles should form as the yeast produces carbon dioxide. If no bubbles form, try another packet.
4. Attach the balloon to the mouth of the bottle, and set both aside.

After several minutes, the balloon will inflate and stand upright.

Discuss

Explain that when oxygen is available, cellular respiration yields carbon dioxide, water, and energy. Remind students that when oxygen is used up, cells can continue to break down glucose for energy through fermentation. Point out that in yeast, the products of fermentation are ethyl alcohol and carbon dioxide. **Ask,** What could have caused the bubbling in the bottle? production of carbon dioxide, first through cellular respiration and later by fermentation of sugar

Activate Prior Knowledge

Point out that, like bacteria, protists and fungi are living things that play a critical role in ecosystems. **Ask**

- What are some examples of fungi? mushrooms, bread mold, athlete's foot
- What is the name of the giant algae that grows in the coastal waters of California? kelp

Preview Vocabulary

Greek and Latin Roots Point out to students these important Greek prefixes that appear in different words in this chapter:

myc- = fungus
poly- = many
proto- = first
rhiz- = root
eu- = true

Academic Vocabulary In everyday life, a *strategy* is a plan of action that is consciously plotted and carried out in order to achieve a goal. In biology, a strategy is a series of activities that has evolved over time and increases evolutionary fitness. In this sense, a strategy can be anything from protective coloration to a mode of locomotion. Emphasize that a biological strategy is not consciously chosen by a species; instead, it is a trait that is adaptive given the species' environmental circumstances.

Answers

1. Accept any reasonable answers. Students should state comparisons, such as that all are round or used in sports.
2. Answers will vary. Students should be able to think of several exceptions to the statement.

SECTION 20.1

Plan and Prepare

Activate Prior Knowledge Suggest to students that in much the same way that record stores have had to completely rework their classifications of musical genres since 1977, so too have biologists been forced to rethink how life forms are classified given the discovery of archaeans in 1977. **Ask,** How would a music store your parents visited as teenagers be different from one you visit today? Students should mention new musical genres. Tell students that scientists are still trying to sort out how best to classify protists in light of all they are learning about this diverse and varied group of organisms.

Teach

Vocabulary

Greek and Latin Word Origins The word **protist** comes from the Greek *prōtistos,* which means "the very first" and comes from the simpler Greek *prōtos,* or "first." Students will recognize this root in other words, such as *prototype, proton,* and *protocol.*

20.1 Diversity of Protists

VOCABULARY
protist

KEY CONCEPT **Kingdom Protista is the most diverse of all the kingdoms.**

MAIN IDEAS
- Protists are difficult to classify.
- Protists can be informally grouped into three categories.

Connect to Your World

If you looked at a drop of water from a pond, a roadside puddle, or a bird bath, you might find specimens of both *Didinium* and *Paramecium.* Despite their unique appearances, they are single-celled. That is what makes single-celled protists so amazing—they can carry out all life functions within just one cell. As you will see, one cell can be quite complex.

MAIN IDEA

Protists are difficult to classify.

Large yellow globs of slime seemed to come out of nowhere. They were spreading across lawns and pulsing up telephone poles. Afraid that this was an alien invasion, residents of a Dallas neighborhood called police and firefighters. The firefighters turned their hoses on the blobs, but water only made the invaders grow.

Scientists came to the rescue. What the people in the Dallas neighborhood were seeing on this sunny day in 1973 wasn't an alien life form, but a slime mold. Specifically, it was *Fuligo septica,* shown in **FIGURE 1.1,** a species commonly called dog-vomit slime mold because of its resemblance to—well, dog vomit.

FIGURE 1.1 *Fuligo septica,* commonly known as the dog-vomit slime mold, is just one member of the diverse kingdom Protista.

Slime molds usually don't grow large enough to scare a neighborhood, but they are unusual. They are protists. A **protist** is a eukaryote that is not an animal, a plant, or a fungus. In the past, protists were generally grouped together because, although they share some features with animals, plants, and fungi, they also lack one or more traits that these organisms possess. Protists may be single-celled or multicellular, microscopic or very large. Some can make their own food, while others feed on other organisms. Some are parasites. Many protists have structures that allow them to move. All respond to the environment in some way. Some protists reproduce asexually, whereas others reproduce both asexually and sexually. Even among the many species of slime molds, there are significant differences.

READING TOOLBOX

VOCABULARY

The word *protist* comes from the Greek word *prōtista,* which means "the very first."

Differentiated Instruction

ENGLISH LEARNERS

After students read this short section, have them close their books and call out main ideas and details about the great diversity of protists. Record them in a concept map. Start with a central circle that contains the main concept: protist diversity. Then draw three arrows radiating out from the central circle, each one ending with a square labeled with a type of protist. Add details under or branching off from each square, such as examples of these protist types.

Teacher Toolkit, Section C, Concept Map

BELOW LEVEL

Have students preview this section and all the rest to develop a note-taking strategy for the chapter. This section gives a broad overview of protist diversity, whereas later sections go into more detail. Suggest that students use a matrix to classify different protists by their distinguishing characteristics, including examples of each, and aspects that may make them beneficial or detrimental to humans.

Teacher Toolkit, Section D, Semantic Feature Analysis

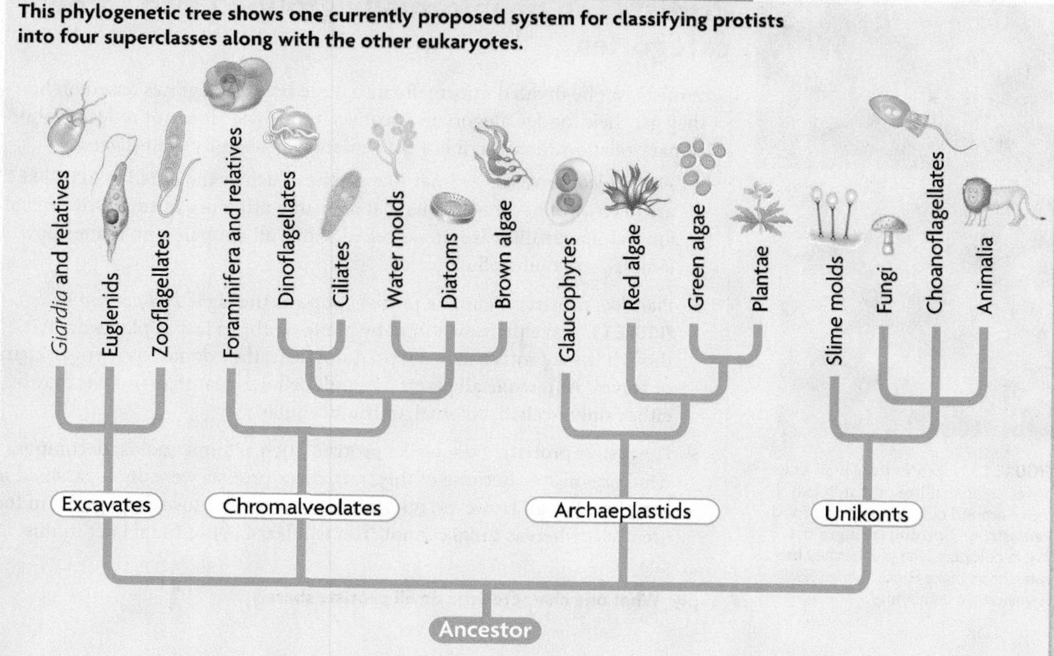

FIGURE 1.2 Relationships of Protists to Other Eukaryotes

This phylogenetic tree shows one currently proposed system for classifying protists into four superclasses along with the other eukaryotes.

In the past, scientists classified protists in kingdom Protista, a very diverse kingdom that included hundreds of phyla. Kingdom Protista could be considered the "junk drawer" for all the eukaryotes that didn't seem to fit the animal, plant, or fungi definitions. Then, research made possible by new technology revealed the sometimes surprising genetic and genomic relationships between groups of organisms. Scientists began to realize that it was not useful to try to classify all of these organisms in kingdom Protista. The word *protist* itself has been called into question, because the organisms that were once classified under this umbrella term are so diverse and are sometimes more like plants, animals, or fungi than they are like each other.

Today, scientists are rethinking the way they classify not just protists but all eukaryotes. There is an emerging consensus that a more accurate way to classify eukaryotes is in "supergroups." **FIGURE 1.2** shows a way of classifying eukaryotes into four supergroups. Two of these supergroups—Excavata and Chromalveolata—contain only protists. A third supergroup, called Archaeplastida, includes plants, and a fourth, called Unikonta, includes animals and fungi. This proposal for a new way of classifying eukaryotes is a very active field of research. As of yet, there is no one universally accepted set of supergroups.

PRE-AP

Have students speculate why single-celled organisms might be more of a challenge to classify than multicellular organisms. Suggest they organize their thoughts into a cluster diagram. They should consider the "body" that is being classified as well as how modes of reproduction might affect diversity.

Teacher Toolkit, Section C, Cluster Diagram

Science Trivia

- The largest slime mold on record was 91 centimeters (3 ft) wide and 914 centimeters (30 ft) long.
- Giant kelp, a type of alga, can grow 30 meters (100 ft) in one year and 35 centimeters (14 in.) in a single day.

Take It Further

Can **slime molds** think? Not really, but they can negotiate a maze. A team of Japanese scientists placed chunks of the slime mold *Physarum polycephalum* in a small gel maze that contained four pathways out. The mold extended its mass randomly, filling all available space in the maze. Next, the scientists placed pieces of food at two of the four exit points. The mold then changed position, extending its entirety between the two sources of nutrients, taking the shortest route possible. This suggests that the presence of food caused a chemical response in the slime mold that made it contract, extending it toward both food locations. Scientists surmise that such a cellular response is a type of primitive intelligence.

Teach continued

TEACH FROM VISUALS

FIGURE 1.2 Review the phylogenetic tree shown in the figure. **Ask**

- To which clades are the slime molds most closely related? Fungi, Choanoflagellates, and Animalia
- Which of the following are more closely related—green algae and oak trees, or green algae and red algae? green algae and oak trees

Assess and Reteach

Assess Use the Section Self-Check or Section Quiz, both available at **HMHScience.com**.

Reteach Create a three-column chart on the board and have students describe the three informal categories of protists and give some examples of each.

Answers

Ⓐ **Apply** All protists are eukaryotes.

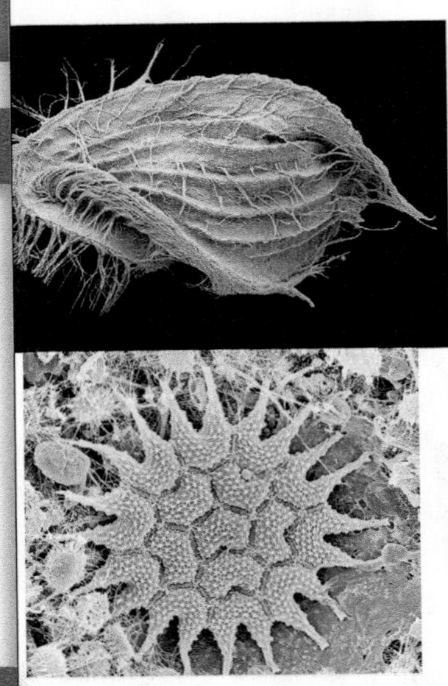

FIGURE 1.3 *Euplotes* (top) is an example of an animal-like protist. It can move around quickly to find its food. *Pediastrum* (bottom) are algae that live in colonies. Like plants, they use sunlight to make food. (colored SEMs; magnifications unknown)

MAIN IDEA

Protists can be informally grouped into three categories.

Protists can be divided informally into three broad categories based on how they get their food. Categorizing protists in this way does not reflect evolutionary relationships, but it is a convenient way to study their diversity.

- **Animal-like protists** Animal-like protists, such as the *Euplotes* in **FIGURE 1.3**, are heterotrophs—organisms that consume other organisms. However, all animal-like protists are single-celled, while all animals—no matter how simple—are multicellular.
- **Plantlike protists** Plantlike protists, such as the algae *Pediastrum* in **FIGURE 1.3**, make their own food by photosynthesis just as plants do. Although these protists may have chloroplasts, they do not have roots, stems, or leaves. And while all plants are multicellular, plantlike protists may be either single-celled, colonial, or multicellular.
- **Funguslike protists** Funguslike protists, such as slime molds, decompose dead organisms. Because of this trait, these protists were once classified in kingdom Fungi. However, funguslike protists can move during part of their life cycle, whereas fungi cannot. You will learn about fungi later in this chapter.

Ⓐpply **What one characteristic do all protists share?**

20.1 Formative Assessment

SELF-CHECK Online
HMHScience.com
GO ONLINE

REVIEWING MAIN IDEAS

1. Name the proposed supergroups for the classification of eukaryotes. Are protists classified in a supergroup or supergroups that include plants, animals, and fungi? Why or why not?
2. Give two reasons why **protists** are difficult to classify.

CRITICAL THINKING

3. **Infer** What observable traits might green algae and plants share that support the molecular evidence that these two groups are closely related?
4. **Contrast** At one time, scientists grouped all single-celled organisms together. What are the main differences between single-celled protists and bacteria or archaea?

CONNECT TO

ECOLOGY

5. Organisms that get their food by ingesting it are called heterotrophs, while those that make their own food are called autotrophs. Categorize animal-like, plantlike, and funguslike protists using these two terms.

20.1 FORMATIVE ASSESSMENT

1. Excavata, Chromalveolata, Archaeplastida, and Unikonta. Yes, protists are classified in supergroups that also include plants, animals, and fungi, because genetic and genomic evidence has shown similarities between them.
2. Some protist phyla are very distantly related, and some are more closely related to members of other kingdoms than they are to other protists. The definition of protists is based on the absence of traits that characterize the other kingdoms.
3. *Sample answer:* Both are green, have chloroplasts, are eukaryotic, and are (sometimes) multicellular.
4. Protists are eukaryotic, meaning they are made up of cells that have a nucleus and membrane-bound organelles; bacteria and archaea are prokaryotic, meaning their cells do not have a nucleus or organelles.
5. Animal-like protists and funguslike protists are heterotrophs; plantlike protists are autotrophs.

20.2 Animal-like Protists

KEY CONCEPT **Animal-like protists are single-celled heterotrophs that can move.**

MAIN IDEAS

- Animal-like protists move in various ways.
- Some animal-like protists cause disease.

VOCABULARY

protozoa
pseudopod
cilia

Connect to Your World

Think of all the ways that different animals move. Some walk on two legs, while others walk on four. Some spend most of their time flying, while others can only swim. Just like animals, animal-like protists use different ways to get around.

MAIN IDEA

Animal-like protists move in various ways.

The animal-like protists represent the largest number of protist species. In the early two-kingdom classification system, some protists were classified as animals because they had many animal-like traits. Like animals, they can move around, they consume other organisms, and their cells lack chloroplasts. The key difference between animal-like protists and animals is their body organization: all animal-like protists are unicellular, while animals are multicellular. The term **protozoa** is often used informally to describe the many phyla of animal-like protists. A few common protozoan groups are described below.

Protozoa with Flagella

The zooflagellates (zoh-uh-FLAJ-uh-lihts) are animal-like protists that have one or more flagella at some point in their life cycle. Recall that flagella are tail-like structures that help unicellular organisms swim. Although the flagella of zooflagellates look like the flagella of prokaryotes, they are structurally very different. Prokaryotic flagella attach to the surface of the cell. In contrast, eukaryotic flagella, such as those of the zooflagellate shown in **FIGURE 2.1**, are extensions of the cytoplasm. They are made of bundles of small tubes called microtubules and are enclosed by the plasma membrane. Prokaryotic flagella are also much smaller than the flagella of protists. You can easily see protist flagella with the aid of a light microscope, but prokaryotic flagella are invisible at the same magnification.

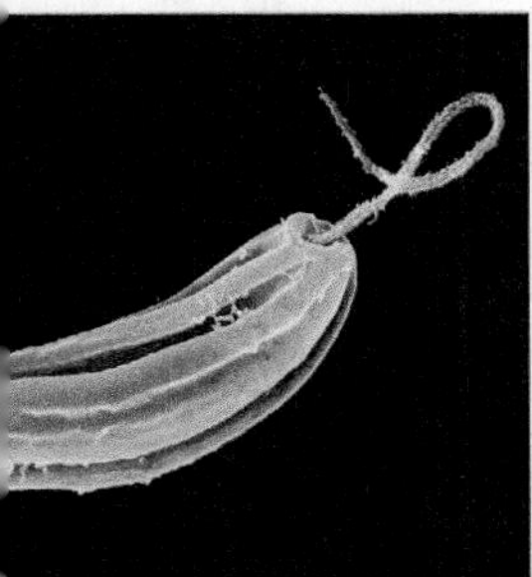

FIGURE 2.1 Zooflagellates have flagella that help them move through water. (colored SEM; magnification unknown)

More than 2000 species of zooflagellates exist. All free-living zooflagellates are heterotrophs. For example, some zooflagellates eat prokaryotes that feed on dissolved organic matter, thereby playing an important role in recycling nutrients through aquatic ecosystems. Other zooflagellates are pathogens, or disease-causing parasites of humans and other animals. Some zooflagellates live inside other organisms in mutualism—a relationship in which both organisms benefit.

Differentiated Instruction

ENGLISH LEARNERS

Have students record definitions of the words *zooflagellate, amoeba, foraminifera,* and *paramecium* in the left column of a two-column chart. In the right column, they should make a simple drawing of each, using the figures from the section as guides. Have students pair up to show each other their drawings. Tell students to use vocabulary and information from the section to describe and label the features of the four protozoa.

Teacher Toolkit, Section C, Combination Notes

Plan and Prepare

Activate Prior Knowledge Discuss the characteristics of animals. **Ask,** When you think of an animal, what are its basic characteristics? It moves, gets its nutrients from other organisms, does not have chloroplasts, and is multicellular. Tell students that animal-like protists, or protozoa, are like animals except that protozoa have only one cell.

Teach

Vocabulary

Greek and Latin Word Origins The word **protozoa** comes from the Greek *proto-,* meaning "first," and *zoion,* meaning "animal." The term *protozoa* was coined in the early 19th century when these organisms were still classified in the animal kingdom. The term was intended to distinguish the more primitive single-celled animals from the so-called true animals.

▼ Teach continued

Take It Further

Paramecium bursaria has an interesting strategy for survival. It is capable of farming *Chlorella,* a species of algae, within its own cytoplasm. The paramecium receives nutrients produced by the photosynthetic alga, and the alga receives a safe home. When other sources of nutrients are scarce, however, *P. bursaria* digests its algal symbionts as a source of nutrition.

History of Science

Dutch scientist **Antonie van Leeuwenhoek** (1632–1723) was the first person to observe protozoa under a microscope. Van Leeuwenhoek was untrained as a scientist, but he became fascinated with observing the miniscule and the invisible. He improved upon the first simple microscope that used a single small lens to produce a clear image of the specimen being observed. While examining a drop of pond water under his microscope, he observed little animal-like organisms swimming rapidly around. Van Leeuwenhoek called these organisms **animalcules,** a name that endured for almost 200 years, until it was discarded in the 1920s in favor of protozoa.

Integrating Epidemiology

Amoebic dysentery is a severe form of amoebiasis, an infection caused by a parasitic amoeba, *Entamoeba histolytica.* Usually transmitted through fecal contamination of drinking water, this amoeba causes gastrointestinal pain and diarrhea. At the 1933 World's Fair in Chicago, sewage contaminated the drinking water, causing amoebiasis in 1000 people and killing 58.

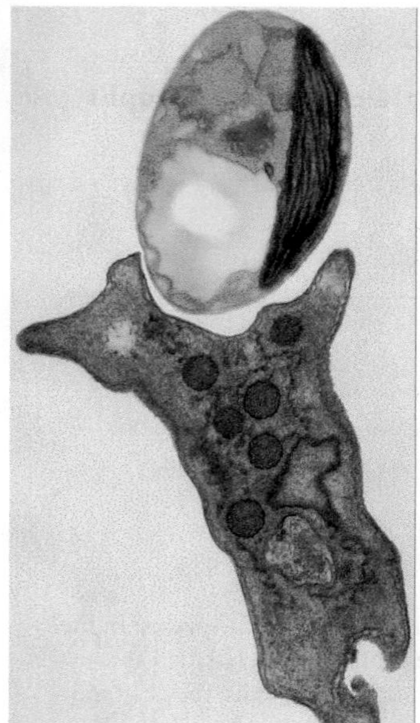

FIGURE 2.2 An amoeba extends a pseudopod to surround and ingest an algal cell. (LM; magnification 4,200×)

Sometimes zooflagellates play a crucial role in another organism's life. For example, termites cannot digest the wood they eat. Inside the gut of a termite is a complex community made of zooflagellates and bacteria that *can* digest wood. The termites get nutrition from the zooflagellate's activity, and the zooflagellates get free meals and a place to live.

Protozoa with Pseudopods

Two groups of protozoa that can easily change shape as they move are the amoebas and the foraminifera.

Amoebas The amoebas (uh-MEE-buhz) are very flexible. Amoebas form pseudopods to move. A **pseudopod** (SOO-duh-PAHD), which means "false foot," is a temporary extension of cytoplasm and plasma membrane that helps protozoa move and feed. To form a pseudopod, the cell cytoplasm flows outward, forming a bulge. This bulge spreads, anchors itself to the surface it is on, and pulls the rest of the cell toward it. Pseudopod formation uses energy. When the amoeba is not moving or feeding, it does not form pseudopods.

An amoeba's method of getting food is shown in **FIGURE 2.2.** Ingestion takes place by the process of phagocytosis. Recall that phagocytosis is the engulfing of solid material by a cell. The amoeba surrounds the food with its pseudopod, and the outer membrane of the amoeba then forms a food vacuole, or sac. Digestive enzymes enter the food vacuole from the surrounding cytoplasm, and digestion takes place.

Amoebas live in fresh water, salt water, and soil. The majority of amoebas are free-living, but some species are parasites. Most amoebas are microscopic. However, *Pelomyxa palustris* is an amoeba that can grow as large as five millimeters in diameter—a huge size for a single-celled organism—and can be seen without a microscope.

Foraminifera Another group of protozoa with pseudopods are the foraminifera (fuh-RAM-uh-NIHF-uhr-uh). Foraminifera, sometimes simply called forams, are named for their multichambered shell, shown in **FIGURE 2.3.** The Latin word *foramen* means "little hole." Their shells are made of organic matter, sand, or other materials, depending on the species. Forams make up a large group of marine protozoa that, like amoeba, use pseudopods to move.

FIGURE 2.3 Pseudopods can extend from pores in a foraminifera's multichambered shell. This shell is smaller than the head of a matchstick.

CONNECT TO

CELL ORGANELLES

Recall from the chapter **Cell Structure and Function** that a vacuole is a fluid-filled sac used for the temporary storage of materials needed by the cell.

Protozoa with Cilia

This group's name, ciliates, comes from its most obvious feature—cilia. **Cilia** are short, hairlike structures that cover some or all of the cell surface and help the organism swim and capture food. Cilia are usually much shorter than flagella and found in much greater numbers. Some ciliates have many rows of cilia all over their surface, whereas other ciliates just have clusters of cilia.

Some of the approximately 8000 species of ciliates are parasites that cause disease. However, most ciliates are free-living cells found in fresh water, such as the common pondwater protists in the genus *Paramecium*.

Structures of a paramecium are shown in **FIGURE 2.4.** Food is swept into the oral groove by the cilia, and is sent to the gullet. Eventually the food is digested in food vacuoles. Two organs that act like pumps, called contractile vacuoles, control the amount of water inside the cell. An unusual trait found in paramecia and other ciliates is the presence of two types of nuclei. Each cell has one large macronucleus, but there can be many small micronuclei. The macronucleus controls the cell's structures and activities. The micronuclei contain all of the cell's chromosomes. They function only during conjugation, a process of genetic exchange. Two paramecia unite at the oral grooves and exchange micronuclei. Some species of the genus *Paramecium* have up to 80 micronuclei. Because micronuclei can be exchanged during conjugation, having so many micronuclei allows for a huge amount of genetic variation in paramecia.

A Summarize **What functions do the two kinds of nuclei within *Paramecium* perform?**

FIGURE 2.4 PARAMECIUM

A paramecium is a single-celled protist covered with thousands of cilia. Its organelles can be identified through its transparent cell membrane.

colored SEM; magnification 400×

QUICKLAB **OBSERVING**

Investigating Motion in Protists

In this investigation you will observe the movement of one or more of the following protists: *Paramecium, Amoeba,* or *Euglena.*

PROBLEM What does a protist's movement look like?

1. Make a wet mount slide of the protist. You may need to add a drop of methylcellulose solution to the wet mount so that you can slow down the organism enough to observe. **Caution:** Do not use a cover slip on the amoeba slide, as you will crush the organism.
2. Observe how the organism moves. Make a series of three drawings that depict the movement of the organism.
3. If time allows, repeat steps 1 and 2 with the other two protists.

ANALYZE AND CONCLUDE

1. **Analyze** Describe the movement of the protist(s) you observed.
2. **Analyze** What structures did the protist that you observed use to move?
3. **Infer** Based on the structures you observed, do you think the species of protist that you observed swims in the water or crawls in the bottom sediments? Explain.

MATERIALS

- 4 eyedroppers
- 4 drops bottled spring water
- 3 microscope slides
- 2 cover slips
- culture of *Paramecium*
- 3 drops methylcellulose solution
- culture of *Amoeba*
- culture of *Euglena*
- microscope

TEACH FROM VISUALS

FIGURE 2.4 Review the labeled structures in **FIGURE 2.4.** Point out that paramecia live in a hypotonic environment. **Ask**

- What is one of the biggest challenges of living in such an environment? Water tends to flow into the cell and must be removed to maintain homeostasis.
- Which structures help the paramecium pump out water? contractile vacuoles
- What would happen if the contractile vacuoles stopped working? Water would keep moving into the cell until it burst.

Answers

A Summarize The macronucleus controls cell structures and activities. Micronuclei contain all the cell's chromosomes and function only during conjugation, a process of genetic exchange.

QUICKLAB

Time 20 minutes

Purpose Observe the movement of protozoa.

Analyze and Conclude

1. Paramecia glide, amoeba creep, and euglena swim.
2. Paramecia use cilia, amoebas use pseudopods, and euglena use flagella.
3. Euglena swim; amoebas crawl on the bottom; paramecia do both.

PRE-AP

Have students review the functions of the organelles and other structures shown in the paramecium diagram in **FIGURE 2.4.** Then ask them to write a paragraph titled "A Day in the Life of a Paramecium," describing how the organism finds food, what happens to ingested food, how it mates, and how it maintains homeostasis. The paragraph should incorporate all the structures shown in the diagram.

Teacher Toolkit, Section C, Quick-Write

BELOW LEVEL

Have students create a sequence diagram for the life cycle of the malaria parasite shown in **FIGURE 2.5** on the next page. Students should begin with a mosquito biting an infected human host. Have students compare their sequence diagrams with a partner to ensure that their diagrams begin with the mosquito's ingestion of *Plasmodium* cells from the infected human, and end with red blood cells bursting and releasing *Plasmodium* cells.

Teacher Toolkit, Section C, Sequence Diagram

▼ Teach *continued*

Learn more about disease-causing protists in this chapter's WebQuest.

History of Science

One of the great engineering feats of the 20th century was the construction of the **Panama Canal.** One of the great feats of public health was the reduced death rate among construction workers due to **malaria** and **yellow fever** during the canal's construction.

The United States began work on the canal in 1904. By late 1906, the death rate due to malaria among workers was 11.59 per 1000. Public health officials implemented a program to make the environment less mosquito-friendly by draining ponds and cutting brush. By December 1909, the death rate from malaria had dropped to 1.23 per 1000.

Answers

A Compare *Plasmodium* is transmitted by mosquito bites, whereas *Giardia* is ingested through contaminated water.

▼ Assess and Reteach

Assess Use the Section Self-Check or Section Quiz, both available at **HMHScience.com**.

Reteach Have students describe the lifestyles of the protists pictured in this chapter.

FIGURE 2.5 LIFE CYCLE OF THE MALARIA PARASITE

The life cycle of the malaria parasite *Plasmodium* requires both a mosquito and a human host.

1 When an infected mosquito bites a human, it transmits Plasmodium sporozoites that enter the liver, where they develop.
sporozoites
human liver
liver cells
developed parasites
red blood cells
2 The developed parasites leave the liver and enter red blood cells, where they reproduce asexually until the red blood cells burst.
3 Some Plasmodium cells are ingested by a mosquito biting the infected human. The cells reproduce in the mosquito's stomach and new larvae develop, which eventually release sporozoites.

MAIN IDEA

Some animal-like protists cause disease.

Protists cause some of the world's most well-known infectious diseases. The group Apicomplexa (A-pih-kuhm-PLEHK-suh) includes about 4000 species, all of which are parasites of animals. Many members of this group are known as sporozoans because they form sporozoites—infectious cells that have tough outer coats. Malaria is an example of a disease caused by sporozoans. It is caused by infection with the protozoan *Plasmodium*, shown in **FIGURE 2.5.**

Malaria is passed to humans and other animals through the bite of the *Anopheles* mosquito. Symptoms of malaria include high fever and vomiting. In some cases, the parasite can severely affect kidney and liver function, leading to coma and even death. Although the disease was once on the decline, today more than 1 million people—mostly children in developing countries—die from malaria each year. Mosquitoes have developed resistance to the insecticides that once would kill them, and *Plasmodium* species have become resistant to antimalarial drugs.

Two other parasitic protists that cause disease are *Trypanosoma* and *Giardia*. In Africa, several species of *Trypanosoma* cause the disease known as sleeping sickness in humans and other mammals. Trypanosomes are transmitted through the bite of the tsetse fly, and can cause coma and death. *Giardia* causes intestinal disease in humans. People can become infected with *Giardia* by drinking water contaminated with feces of infected animals. Campers and hikers must be careful of *Giardia*, as even streams or rivers that appear clean could be contaminated.

WebQuest HMHScience.com GO ONLINE Sickening Protists

A Compare How do the parasites *Plasmodium* and *Giardia* each infect humans?

20.2 Formative Assessment

SELF-CHECK Online HMHScience.com GO ONLINE

REVIEWING MAIN IDEAS

1. Name and describe the three basic means of movement used by animal-like protists.
2. Describe how the parasite *Plasmodium* causes disease in humans.

CRITICAL THINKING

3. **Compare and Contrast** In what ways are **cilia** and flagella similar? How are they different?
4. **Infer** Why do amoebas form **pseudopods** only when they need them?

CONNECT TO

ANALOGOUS STRUCTURES

5. The flagella of eukaryotes and prokaryotes serve the same function, but they are structurally very different. What does this suggest about the evolution of flagella?

20.2 FORMATIVE ASSESSMENT

1. flagella: tail-like extensions of cytoplasm that are used in a whiplike motion to propel the organism forward; pseudopods: the plasma membrane and cytoplasm extend to form a bulge that anchors to the surface and pulls the rest of the organism along; cilia: short hairlike structures on the surface of the organism that wave
2. The bite of a mosquito carrying *Plasmodium* transmits sporozoites into a human's bloodstream. The sporozoites enter the liver, where they develop and then move to red blood cells. They reproduce asexually until the red blood cells burst open, releasing *Plasmodium* cells that can then be ingested by mosquitoes that bite the infected host. Symptoms include severe fever, vomiting, and possibly liver and kidney problems.
3. Cilia and flagella are both used for movement in protists. Both are formed from the cell membrane and are permanent structures. However, cilia are shorter and more hairlike and can be in rows or clusters that cover parts of a cell or the entire cell. Flagella are longer, and there are usually only one or two per cell.
4. because pseudopod formation requires energy
5. The flagella of eukaryotes and prokaryotes arose separately and are an example of convergent evolution.

20.3 Plantlike Protists

KEY CONCEPT **Algae are plantlike protists.**

MAIN IDEAS
- Plantlike protists can be single-celled or multicellular.
- Many plantlike protists can reproduce both sexually and asexually.

VOCABULARY
lgae

Connect to Your World

On your birthday, do you enjoy decorations on your cake, or do you prefer it topped with ice cream? Both cake decorations and ice cream are among the many products that commonly contain substances from seaweeds, types of plantlike protists.

MAIN IDEA

Plantlike protists can be single-celled or multicellular.

Just as animal-like protists were once classified as animals, it is not surprising that many plantlike protists used to be classified as plants. Although many plantlike protists look like plants, they are different in many ways. Unlike plants, plantlike protists do not have roots, stems, leaves, specialized tissues, or the same reproductive structures that plants have. All plants are multicellular, while plantlike protists may be single-celled or multicellular.

Many single-celled plantlike protists are free-living aquatic organisms that, together with photosynthetic bacteria, are known as phytoplankton. Recall that phytoplankton form the base of aquatic food chains and provide about half of the oxygen in Earth's atmosphere. Several species of single-celled plantlike protists, such as *Volvox*, shown in **FIGURE 3.1**, live in colonies. Multicellular plantlike protists include the seaweeds or kelps. Some species eat other organisms, but most plantlike protists have chloroplasts and can produce their own food through photosynthesis. Photosynthetic plantlike protists are informally called **algae.**

colony

daughter colony

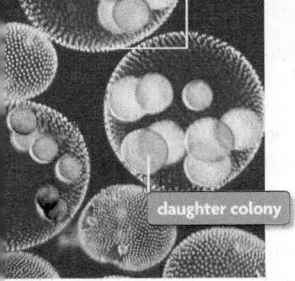

FIGURE 3.1 *Volvox* are actually hundreds of individual algae cells that join together to form a colony in the shape of a hollow ball. Offspring form smaller daughter colonies inside the parent colony. (LM; magnification 50)

From Single-Celled to Multicellular

In the distant past, single-celled organisms combined to become multicellular. It is likely that multicellular algae arose from colonies of algae such as *Volvox*. Members of the order Volvocales include three kinds of forms: single-celled forms, multicellular forms with every cell acting independently, and multicellular forms in which the cells are specialized. In the evolution from single-celled to multicellular algae, some individual cells in colonies were probably very efficient at certain tasks, such as digesting food or producing gametes. These cells and their offspring would have become more specialized over time, and eventually may have become dependent on each other. Over many generations, colonies could have led to multicellular forms.

Differentiated Instruction

ENGLISH LEARNERS

After students read the section, set up a round table by dividing them into four groups. Give each group a sheet of paper, and write this topic sentence on the board: *There are many types of single-celled and multicellular plantlike protists.* Give students three minutes to review the chapter, and then ask them to close their books. Have one student in each group write something he or she knows about the topic on the paper and pass it to the next student. That student should write something different about the topic, and so on. After a minute or two, circulate to see if students have listed the categories of euglenoids, dinoflagellates, diatoms, green algae, brown algae, and red algae. If not, write at least some of these categories on the board to start the brainstorming process. After students write for ten minutes, ask one student from each group to read the group list. Then have students compile a class list.

Teacher Toolkit, Section C, Round Table

Plan and Prepare

Activate Prior Knowledge Algae is commonly viewed as a slimy green scum that floats on ponds and covers rocks near the seashore. So it is not surprising that many people cringe at the thought of eating algae. **Ask,** Who has eaten sushi? Answers will vary. Explain that the dark green nori around maki rolls is a kind of seaweed, which is a type of algae. You may also want to mention that algae and algal products have many commercial applications such as in food processing and cosmetics manufacture.

Teach

Vocabulary

algae The plural forms of some Latin words can be confusing. Words ending in *a*, such as *alga*, are generally made plural by adding an *e*, forming *algae;* some words, such as *amoeba*, are commonly made plural by adding either an *s* or an *e*. Tell students that both *amoebas* and *amoebae* are correct plural forms.

▼ Teach *continued*

Science Trivia

- The eyespot on a euglenoid shades a light-sensitive receptor that helps orient the organism toward light.
- If kept in darkness, a euglenoid's green chloroplasts will disappear.

Integrating Ecology

The toxic dinoflagellate alga *Alexandrium fundyense* is responsible for the harmful algal blooms commonly called **red tides.** In 2005, a bloom of this alga in the marine waters of New England caused the closure of shellfish beds for much of the summer—the peak season for shellfishing and shellfish consumption. It was estimated that the bloom cost the New England shellfish industry $3 million per week. The danger of such a bloom is that filter-feeding mollusks such as soft-shell clams (steamers), quahogs, oysters, and blue mussels accumulate the toxin of the abundant algae and that this buildup of toxin can then be ingested by humans, causing an illness known as paralytic shellfish poisoning (PSP).

Scientists suspected that the high levels of precipitation in the previous winter and spring created ideal conditions for the alga by flushing more nutrients into the coastal waters. The fresh water running off from land may have also created a buoyant surface layer of water to carry the algal bloom—a natural summertime phenomenon in the colder waters of the Gulf of Maine—south towards Cape Cod and the rest of southern New England. About 15,000 square miles of ocean were closed to shellfishing as a result of the 2005 red tide.

FIGURE 3.2 EUGLENA

A euglena has both animal-like structures—such as an eyespot, contractile vacuoles, and flagella—and plantlike structures, such as chloroplasts.

contractile vacuole
pellicle
nucleus
chloroplast
flagellum
eye spot

colored SEM; magnification 1500

READING TOOLBOX

VOCABULARY

The name *dinoflagellates* comes from the Greek word *dinos*, meaning "whirling," and the Latin word *flagrum*, meaning "whip." This name describes how dinoflagellates move.

Comparing Protists

Diversity of Plantlike Protists

Plantlike protists are found in most habitats on Earth. Most are aquatic organisms that live in freshwater and marine ecosystems. Some species live in deserts, while others live in the tundra. Despite their great diversity, all plantlike protists use some form of chlorophyll for photosynthesis. Also, most plantlike protists have flagella at some point in their life cycle. Although their classification will likely change, the plantlike protists are placed into various supergroups based on their photosynthetic pigments and cell wall structure.

Euglenoids The euglenoids are a large group of single-celled organisms that swim with the aid of one or two flagella. Although most of these species are found in fresh water, some live in ocean environments. Members of this group are both animal-like and plantlike. Like animals, these protists can move around easily. Euglenoids have a pellicle, a flexible coatlike covering on their cell surface. The pellicle allows the cell to change shape. In some species, the pellicle helps the organism to creep across solid surfaces using a type of movement that resembles the inching movement of worms. Although some colorless species of euglenoids eat other organisms, most make their own food through photosynthesis.

Plantlike photosynthetic euglenoids are green, such as the euglena shown in **FIGURE 3.2.** Their bright green color comes from two different chlorophyll pigments, called chlorophyll *a* and *b*.

Dinoflagellates The dinoflagellates are single-celled. About 90 percent of dinoflagellates are marine plankton. Recall that plankton are often microscopic organisms that live suspended in the water. Some dinoflagellates are freshwater species, and a few species have even been found in snow. About half of all marine dinoflagellates photosynthesize.

Dinoflagellates have two flagella. One flagellum extends from the rear of the cell and propels it forward. The other is a ribbonlike strand that circles the cell in a groove along its body. This flagellum allows the cell to turn over and change direction. The combination of the two flagella cause this protist to turn in a spiral as it moves forward. Some species also have a covering of stiff plates that form a protective armor.

Some dinoflagellates, such as *Noctiluca*, are bioluminescent; that is, they can produce light through internal chemical reactions. The name *Noctiluca* means "night-light." If you have ever visited the ocean at night, you may have seen these tiny, blue glowing organisms along the surface of the water. They give off light when they are disturbed. The light may act as an alarm to help them avoid being eaten.

Differentiated Instruction

INCLUSION

Students who have a hard time sorting out information may need to create a table or an outline that identifies each major plantlike protist group and then gives details about that group. Students can adapt the style of the chart depending on their needs; for example, students who are visually impaired may need to use heavy markers and large lettering, while students who have learning disabilities may want to color-code each group.

Certain other photosynthetic dinoflagellates help build coral reefs through their symbiotic partnership with corals. These dinoflagellates live in the inner tissues of the corals. In return for shelter from the corals, the dinoflagellates provide the corals with nutrients in tropical waters that are usually nutrient-poor.

Some species of dinoflagellates produce toxins. A large population of these dinoflagellates can create what is known as a red tide, due to the reddish color produced by a high density of these species. Red tides, shown in **FIGURE 3.3,** occur when changes in ocean currents bring up nutrients from far below the ocean surface. The higher nutrient levels produce a rapid increase, or bloom, in the dinoflagellate population. A toxic bloom in the waters can kill large numbers of fish. The toxins can also build up in the tissues of shellfish, which then can be dangerous to humans who eat the contaminated seafood.

Diatoms Most diatoms are easy to recognize when viewed through a microscope. These tiny single-celled algae are covered with delicately patterned glasslike shells. The shells of diatoms serve almost as an external skeleton, helping the cell to hold a rigid shape. Diatom shells, such as those shown in **FIGURE 3.4,** are made of silica, the same brittle substance that is used to make glass. The silica shell is divided into two parts that overlap each other, like the lid of a box.

Like other autotrophs, all diatoms release oxygen into the environment. In fact, diatoms could be considered the world champions of photosynthesis. They play a critical role in the uptake of carbon dioxide on Earth and produce about half of the oxygen we breathe. Diatoms may be freshwater or marine. Many species are phytoplankton. Others live clinging to rocks, plants, soil, and even animals—diatoms have been found growing on crustaceans, turtles, and even whales. Because of their glassy, mineralized shells, diatoms have been well preserved in the fossil record. Some fossil rocks consist almost entirely of diatoms. These diatom skeletons have many industrial uses, such as an ingredient in scrubbing products, because of their rough texture.

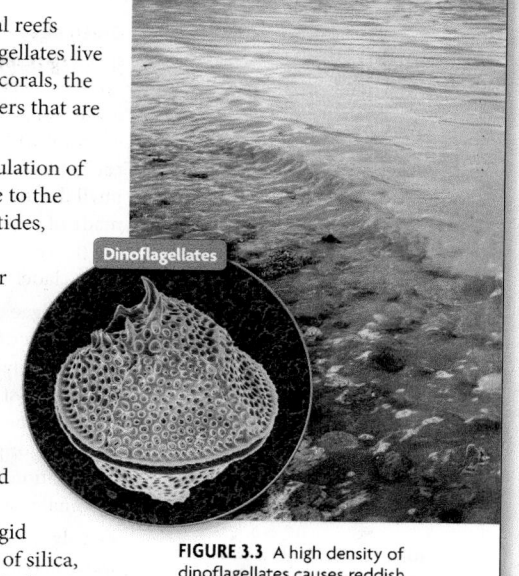

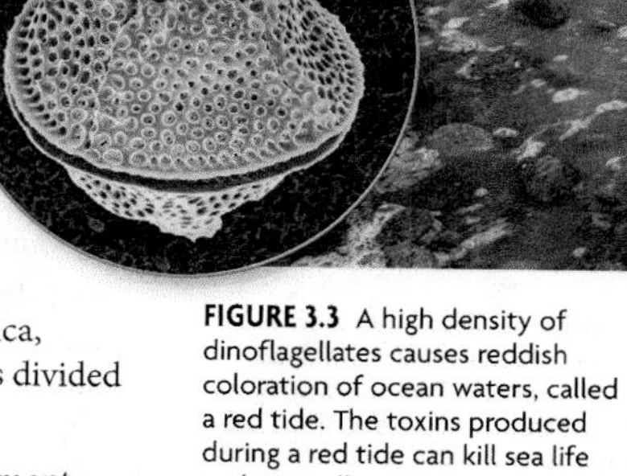
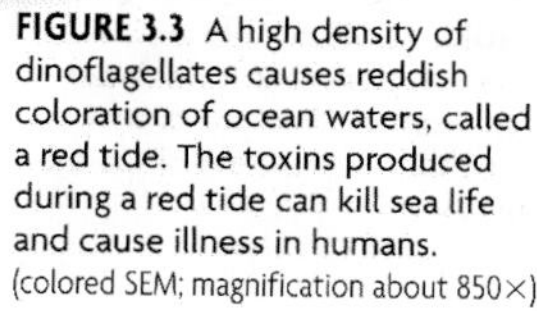

FIGURE 3.3 A high density of dinoflagellates causes reddish coloration of ocean waters, called a red tide. The toxins produced during a red tide can kill sea life and cause illness in humans. (colored SEM; magnification about 850×)

READING TOOLBOX

VOCABULARY

The name *diatom* comes from the Greek term *diatomos*, meaning "cut in half." This refers to the appearance of the diatom's overlapping shell.

FIGURE 3.4 DIATOMS

Diatoms are known for their delicate glasslike cell walls, or shells, that can have many shapes. They are common in both freshwater and marine environments.

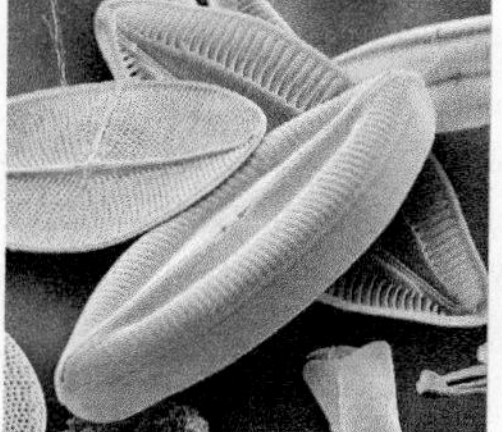
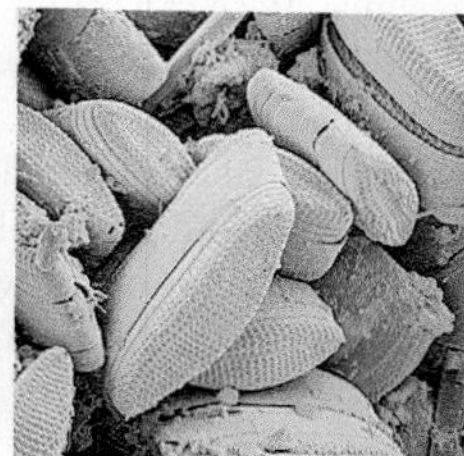
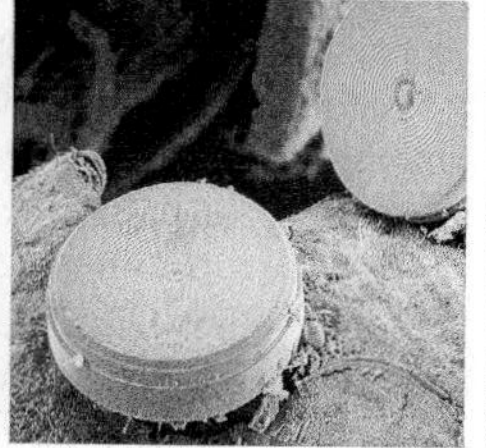

(all colored SEMs; magnification 750×; magnification 250×; magnification unknown)

Address Misconceptions

Common Misconception When the shallow coastal waters are red, it is because of a red tide.

Correcting the Misconception While some harmful algal blooms do create a reddish hue in seawater, there are others that are invisible to the human eye. A harmful red tide may not be red at all. A red color in the water may be due to a bloom or buildup of harmless red algae.

Take It Further

Phytoplankton (free-floating photosynthetic protists such as marine algae, diatoms, and dinoflagellates) play a critical role in global climate and the carbon cycle. They are responsible for roughly half of Earth's photosynthetic activity; as a result, they have a key part in regulating atmospheric CO_2 levels.

Atmospheric CO_2 not taken up by photosynthesis dissolves in oceans and lakes and is converted into carbonate, a form not usable by most plants and algae. Diatoms and other phytoplankton are able to convert carbonate back to CO_2 and use it for photosynthesis. The silica in diatom shells speeds this conversion and helps increase carbon fixation by photosynthesis. When they die, diatoms, along with the carbon they fixed, sink to the ocean floor. As the diatoms decay, the stored carbon is converted into fossil fuel.

PRE-AP

Tell students that the danger of harmful algal blooms to humans is that toxins produced by these particular algae will accumulate in shellfish and then accumulate in a person who eats clams, mussels, or oysters. Have students create a cause-and-effect chain to show how nutrient runoff from a farm upriver could result in humans getting sick from shellfish in a bay downriver.

Teacher Toolkit, Section C, Cause-and-Effect Chain

▼ Teach continued

ONLINE Biology
HMHScience.com

The tropical seaweed *Caulerpa*, accidentally introduced into the Mediterranean Sea in the 1980s, has undergone dramatic and exponential growth. Students can chart the spread of this organism using the Data Analysis Smart Grapher activity for this chapter.

Integrating Ecology

Brown kelp, sea urchins, and sea otters form a food chain in the coastal **kelp forests** of the northeastern Pacific Ocean. As primary producers, brown kelp provide food and shelter for a wide range of organisms. Sea urchins are primary consumers that graze on kelp, and sea otters are the dominant predators of sea urchins. By preying on sea urchins, sea otters keep sea urchin populations in check, so the forests are not overgrazed.

In the 1990s, the sea otter population in western Alaska began declining due to predation by killer whales. The whales normally feed on sea lions and seals; however, when these prey populations began declining, whales began hunting sea otters. Scientists attribute the decline in numbers of sea lions and seals to a decline in fish species that they feed on. Thus, the decline in the fish triggered a chain reaction that ultimately led to a population explosion of sea urchins, which are rapidly stripping the kelp forests. If the problem continues, the kelp forest ecosystem off the coast of Alaska could collapse.

Answers

A Compare and Contrast Green, red, and brown algae are photosynthetic and aquatic. They are usually all multicellular. They all have chlorophyll *a*. Green algae also have chlorophyll *b*, and brown algae also have chlorophyll *c*. Red algae can grow deeper than green and brown algae due to the blue light–absorption properties of the red pigments.

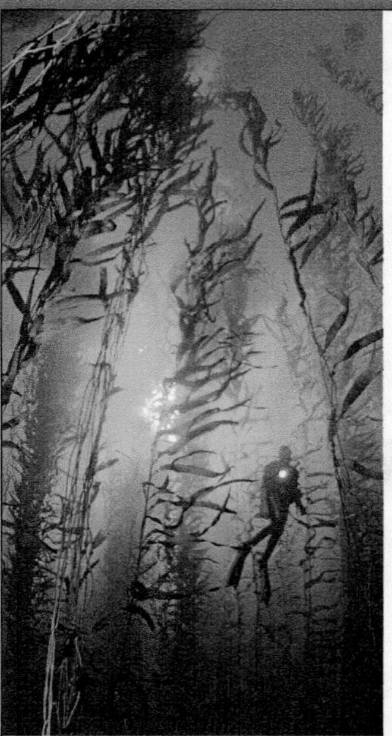

FIGURE 3.5 Giant kelp are a type of brown algae that form underwater forests. The forests are home to a large variety of marine organisms.

Green algae The green algae may be found in water or on land, although most species are aquatic. Recall that algae are not considered plants because they do not have roots, stems, or leaves. Like plants, however, green algae are multicellular and contain the photosynthetic pigments chlorophyll *a* and chlorophyll *b*. Both plants and green algae also have accessory pigments called carotenoids. Accessory pigments capture light energy and transfer it to chlorophyll during photosynthesis. Both plants and green algae also have cell walls made of cellulose and store food within their cells as starch. These similarities are the reason that current taxonomy places green algae and plants in the same clade.

Brown algae The brown algae include the giant kelp, shown in **FIGURE 3.5**, that form thick underwater forests. Brown algae are multicellular and can grow to be extremely large. Some giant kelp can grow up to 100 meters high (about 330 ft). Most brown algae live in marine environments. Brown algae are photosynthetic but have a different form of chlorophyll—chlorophyll *c*—than do plants or green algae. Brown algae share this trait with the diatoms. This observation is why brown algae and diatoms are classified together within the chromalveolates supergroup.

Red algae Most red algae are found in the ocean, though a few live in freshwater habitats. Red algae use chlorophyll *a* for photosynthesis, but they get their color from the pigment phycoerythrin. Red algae can grow at deeper depths than other algae because the red pigments allow red algae to absorb the blue light that reaches deepest into the ocean. Some species secrete calcium carbonate, forming thick crusts that look like corals and provide habitats for tiny invertebrates. Red algae provide many products for the food industry. Carrageenan and agar, thickening agents used in products such as ice cream, come from red algae. In Japan, red algae is dried to make nori, a seaweed wrap used for sushi.

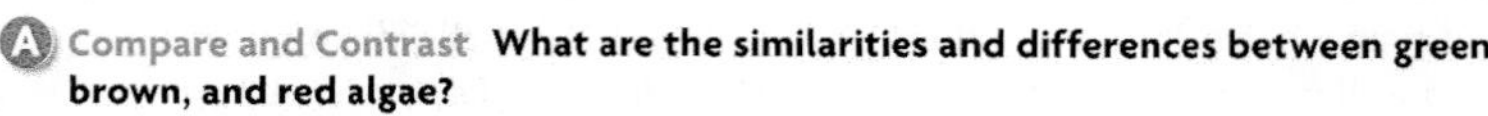

A Compare and Contrast **What are the similarities and differences between green, brown, and red algae?**

MAIN IDEA

Many plantlike protists can reproduce both sexually and asexually.

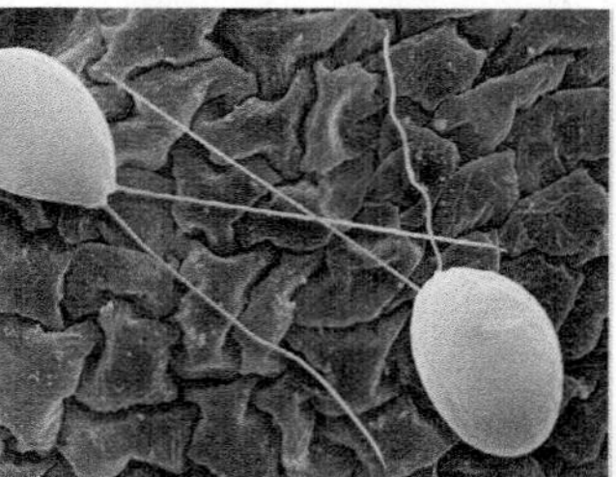

FIGURE 3.6 *Chlamydomonas* are single-celled green algae with two flagella. (colored SEM; magnification 1600×)

Most protists can undergo both sexual and asexual reproduction. All algae can reproduce asexually. Multicellular algae can fragment; each piece is capable of forming a new body. When a single-celled alga, such as the green alga *Chlamydomonas* shown in **FIGURE 3.6**, reproduces asexually, its life cycle is a bit more complex. The dominant phase of the life cycle for this species is haploid. Before reproducing asexually, the haploid parent alga absorbs its flagella and then divides by mitosis. This division may occur two or more times, producing up to eight cells. The daughter cells develop flagella and cell walls. These daughter cells, called zoospores, leave the parent cell, disperse, and grow. The zoospores then grow into mature haploid cells.

Differentiated Instruction

BELOW LEVEL

Draw a concept map to differentiate between asexual reproduction in multicellular and unicellular algae. Begin the map with the sentence "All algae can reproduce asexually" in a circle. The next two circles, branching off from the first, should be labeled "single-celled algae" and "multicellular algae." Help students complete the map.

Teacher Toolkit, Section C, Concept Map

FIGURE 3.7 Life Cycle of Single-Celled Green Algae

Some single-celled green algae, such as *Chlamydomonas*, undergo sexual as well as asexual reproduction.

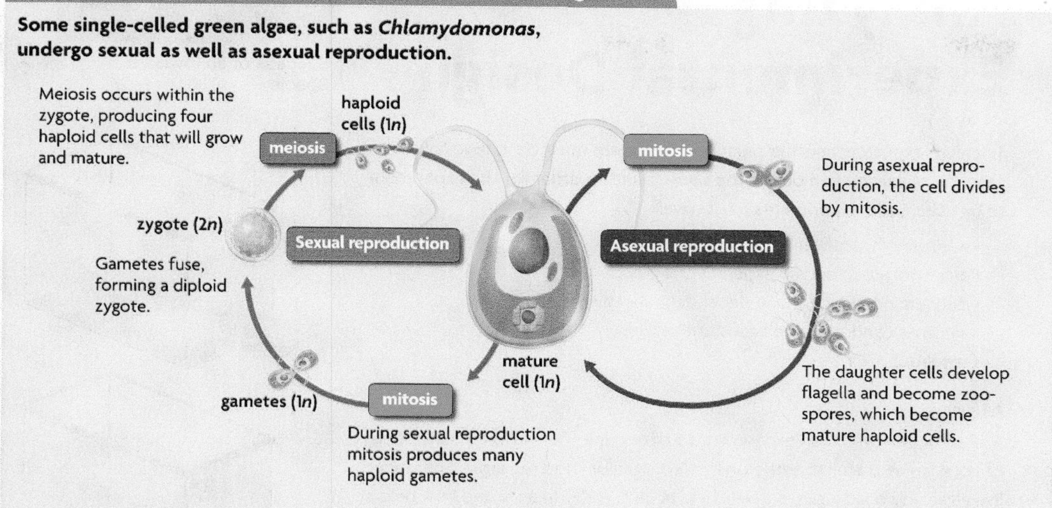

Meiosis occurs within the zygote, producing four haploid cells that will grow and mature.
haploid cells (1n)
meiosis
mitosis
During asexual reproduction, the cell divides by mitosis.
zygote (2n)
Sexual reproduction
Asexual reproduction
Gametes fuse, forming a diploid zygote.
mature cell (1n)
The daughter cells develop flagella and become zoospores, which become mature haploid cells.
gametes (1n)
mitosis
During sexual reproduction mitosis produces many haploid gametes.

Sexual reproduction occurs in algae as well. Some species alternate generations so that the offspring from sexual reproduction reproduce asexually, and the next generation then reproduces sexually. In other species, asexual reproduction occurs for several generations until conditions change. For the single-celled *Chlamydomonas,* sexual reproduction is triggered by stress such as lack of moisture or food. As shown in **FIGURE 3.7,** it begins with cells dividing by mitosis to produce one of two types of gametes. Because the gametes look identical in most species of *Chlamydomonas,* they are usually identified as different mating types, labeled + and –. When the gametes come together, they join and form a diploid zygote. The zygote may develop into a zygospore by making a thick wall that can protect it during unfavorable conditions. When favorable conditions return, meiosis occurs, producing four haploid cells.

A Apply Explain how sudden population increases, or "blooms," of algae may occur.

20.3 Formative Assessment

SELF-CHECK Online
HMHScience.com
GO ONLINE

REVIEWING MAIN IDEAS

1. Give an example of each of the following: a single-celled, a colonial, and a multicellular plantlike protist.
2. Many plantlike protists, or **algae**, reproduce sexually when conditions are harsh. Why might this be beneficial?

CRITICAL THINKING

3. **Classify** If a multicellular organism contains chlorophyll c but no silica, to which group does it likely belong?
4. **Analyze** Many biologists argue that the euglenoids should be classified as an animal-like protist rather than a plantlike protist. Explain.

CONNECT TO ECOLOGY

5. Draw a simple food web for a marine ecosystem. Include dinoflagellates, fish and shellfish, diving birds, and humans in your diagram. What might happen if nutrient levels in the water increased?

TEACH FROM VISUALS

FIGURE 3.7 Compare sexual and asexual reproduction as illustrated in the figure.
Ask

- What happens when *Chlamydomonas* undergoes mitosis during asexual reproduction? produces flagellated daughter cells that become zoospores, which become mature haploid cells
- What is the result of mitosis in sexual reproduction of *Chlamydomonas*? produces haploid gametes, which then fuse to become a diploid zygote that undergoes meiosis

Answers

A Apply Changes in conditions, such as a high level of nutrients, can trigger a change in the reproductive strategy of the algae species. For example, they may begin rapidly reproducing asexually, dramatically increasing the population in a short amount of time.

Assess and Reteach

Assess Use the Section Self-Check or Section Quiz, both available at **HMHScience.com**.

Reteach Use the PowerPresentation at **HMHScience.com** to review the material in this section.

20.3 FORMATIVE ASSESSMENT

1. *Sample answer:* single-celled plantlike protist: dinoflagellates, euglena, diatoms, *Chlamydomonas;* colonial protist: volvox; multicellular protist: green, brown, or red algae
2. Sexual reproduction will increase genetic variability within the population, improving the chances that some of the individuals will have traits that will be adaptive to harsh conditions.
3. phylum Phaeophyta, the brown algae
4. Some euglenoids lack chlorophyll and eat other organisms, while others use an animal-like creeping method of locomotion.
5. Food webs should have dinoflagellates as producers and the other organisms as consumers. If nutrient levels in the water increased, the population of dinoflagellates could drastically increase. This could harm humans if the dinoflagellates produce toxins that accumulate up the food chain.

DATA ANALYSIS

Introduce

Remind students that one of the major tenets of science is that an experiment must be repeatable by other scientists, which means that, if students follow the same protocol, they will get the same results as the original scientist. **Ask**

- What is meant by the term *experimental design*? the way that an experiment is to be carried out
- What are the characteristics of a good experiment design? All well-designed experiments have certain features in common: all are built on testable hypotheses; all contain clearly defined constants, variables, and controls; and all can be repeated.

Discuss

Work with students to write a list of the steps taken according to the flawed experimental design described. **Ask**

- What are potential problems in using different species of coral larvae for this experiment? One species may be inhibited from settling on the alga more than another species would.
- What could be the problem with releasing different numbers of larvae into each tank? A small number of larvae in any of the tanks could yield unreliable data due to small sample size. Depending on how the chemical actually inhibits the coral larvae from settling, a large number of larvae could improve the odds of at least some of them settling compared to a small number.

Online Student Resources, Data Analysis Practice

DATA ANALYSIS

Analyzing Experimental Design

Success of an Invasive Species

Scientists repeating another person's experiment must be able to follow the procedures exactly and obtain the same results in order for the experiment to be valid. Valid experiments must have:

- a testable hypothesis
- a control group and an experimental group
- defined independent and dependent variables
- all other conditions held constant
- repeated trials

Model

A student performed an experiment to determine whether a certain species of coral larvae prefer to settle on live red algae or dead red algae. She placed live algae and dead algae in a tank held at 28°C (82°F). In a second tank held at 26°C (79°F), she placed a piece of lettuce as a control because it had a texture similar to the algae. After 24 hours, she counted the number of larvae that settled on each type of algae. The following flaws exist in this experiment:

- A controlled variable—temperature—was not held constant.
- The lettuce control was separated from the algae choices.
- There were no repeated trials.

A valid experimental design would have all of the choices in a single aquarium, which makes it easier to maintain constants, and allows accurate observation of which surface types the larvae prefer. At least three aquariums should be used with the same setup so that the results could be compared.

Practice Identify Experimental Design Flaws

A student wanted to determine what concentration—low, medium, or high—of a chemical released from brown algae prevented coral larvae from settling and growing on the algae. Each concentration level of the chemical from one brown alga was added to the water of each tank. Tank size, water temperature, and algae species were held constant. A different number and species of larvae were dropped into each tank. After three days, the percent of settled larvae for each concentration of inhibiting chemical was found.

TABLE 1. RESULTS OF INHIBITING CHEMICAL ON LARVAL SETTLEMENT

Inhibiting Chemical Concentration	Low	Medium	High
Percent of Larvae Settled	85%	40%	1%

1. **Evaluate** What are the design flaws in this experiment? How would you change the experiment to make the results more valid?
2. **Analyze** The student concluded that at all levels the inhibiting chemical affected the rate of settlement of marine larvae. Is this an accurate conclusion based on the data collected? Explain.

Answers

1. There is no control group, and the numbers and species of larvae are not constant. A fourth tank with no chemical inhibitor added could be used as a control group. The same species and number of larvae should be used in each tank.
2. No, without a control group to compare, one cannot know if the chemical lowered settlement rates at all levels of concentration. If a control group was included with no chemical added and the settlement rates were also about 85 percent, it could mean that at low concentrations, the chemical does not affect settlement rates. Also, this experiment tests the effects of an inhibiting chemical on coral larvae—not all marine larvae.

20.4 Funguslike Protists

KEY CONCEPT **Funguslike protists decompose organic matter.**

MAIN IDEAS

- Slime molds and water molds are funguslike protists.

VOCABULARY

slime mold
water mold

Connect to Your World

Perhaps you have seen a funguslike protist and didn't recognize it, like the Dallas residents you read about at the start of this chapter. Most funguslike protists don't grow large enough to scare people. In fact, some you can barely see.

MAIN IDEA

Slime molds and water molds are funguslike protists.

As decomposers, funguslike protists play an important role in ecosystems by recycling nutrients such as carbon and nitrogen back into the soil. For a long time, funguslike protists were classified as fungi because they are all decomposers and have similar reproductive structures and cycles. However, funguslike protists can move during part of their life cycle, while fungi cannot.

Slime Molds

Slime molds are eukaryotic organisms that have both funguslike and animal-like traits. They can be divided into two phyla: plasmodial slime molds (phylum Myxomycota) and cellular slime molds (phylum Acrasiomycota).

Plasmodial slime molds For most of their life, plasmodial slime molds live as a single mass of cytoplasm that actually is a large single cell with many nuclei, called a plasmodium. They can grow as large as a meter or more in diameter. A plasmodium, shown in **FIGURE 4.1**, moves like a giant amoeba, creeping over the ground as it absorbs bacteria and nutrients from decaying matter. *Fuligo septica,* the dog-vomit slime mold, is typical of this group.

CONNECT TO

BIOGEOCHEMICAL CYCLES

Recall from the chapter **Principles of Ecology** that a biogeochemical cycle is the movement of a particular chemical, such as carbon or nitrogen, through the living and nonliving parts of an ecosystem.

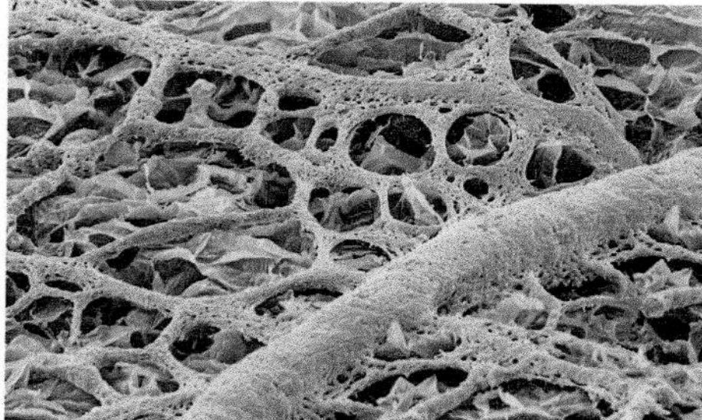

FIGURE 4.1 A plasmodial slime mold (left) in the plasmodium stage resembles a giant amoeba. A cellular slime mold (right) forms a stalk in the spore-producing stage. (colored SEM; plasmodial slime mold magnification 80×)

Differentiated Instruction

ENGLISH LEARNERS

Tell students to work in pairs to create a content frame comparing the organisms featured in this section. Students might create a chart with these column heads: Type of Funguslike Protists, Size, Number of Cells, Parasitic Appearance, Movement, Diet. Students can use these row heads: Plasmodial Slime Mold, Cellular Slime Mold, Water Mold. When all pairs are finished, have them ask each other questions based on their content frames.

Teacher Toolkit, Section C, Content Frame

BELOW LEVEL

Have students use a Venn diagram to compare slime molds and water molds. Have students consider characteristics such as habitat, type of movement, and growth patterns. Also, have students consider what roles each type of mold plays in its community.

Teacher Toolkit, Section C, Venn Diagram

SECTION 20.4

Plan and Prepare

Activate Prior Knowledge Have students imagine their room if they could not put away their clothes, even if they wanted to. Instead, they would get new clothes to wear each day. **Ask,** What would happen if the natural world had no means to "clean its room," that is remove dead or decaying organic matter? Decaying organic matter would pile up, soil would be deprived of essential nutrients, and phytoplankton would not have a source of nutrients in the oceans. Tell students that funguslike protists play the role of decomposers in the environment.

Teach

Vocabulary

plasmodium The word *plasmodium* has two distinct definitions in biology:

- a multinucleated mass of "naked" cytoplasm typical of plasmodial slime molds
- a genus of protozoan parasites, four of which cause malaria

In the first context, the word begins with a lower-case letter (plasmodium). When used to denote the protozoan genus, the word is capitalized and italicized (*Plasmodium*).

▼ Teach *continued*

Integrating Social Science

In the early 1800s, potatoes were a staple food in Ireland. Many families relied entirely on potatoes for food. The famine that followed the devastation of the potato crop by potato blight stimulated mass emigration. By 1854, almost two million Irish people had left Ireland to move abroad. One of the largest waves of immigration was to the United States. More than half a million Irish immigrants arrived in the United States in the 1840s. The **Great Potato Famine** is still remembered in Ireland, as well as in cities around the world that have large populations descended from Irish immigrants.

Answers

A Infer Having two modes of reproduction gives organisms the ability to reproduce regardless of the conditions. They can switch modes of reproduction when conditions change.

▼ Assess and Reteach

Assess Use the Section Self-Check or Section Quiz, both available at **HMHScience.com**.

Reteach Create a simple table comparing the three types of funguslike protists discussed in this chapter.

FIGURE 4.2 The water mold *Phytophthora infestans* causes disease, including potato blight in many plants. This disease was the cause of a four-year famine in Ireland in the 1800s. (colored SEM; magnification 100×)

Plasmodial slime molds are common on the underside of logs and on dead leaves. When food or moisture is in short supply, the plasmodial slime mold stops growing and develops nonmoving reproductive structures that produce spores. Such a structure is a resistant, resting form of the slime mold. When the spores are released, they are often able to move on their own. They may creep like an amoeba, or, if water is present, they can develop up to four flagella per cell. Eventually, the spores swarm together and form a new plasmodium.

Cellular slime molds The cellular slime molds are common in soil. Each spore released by a cellular slime mold becomes a single amoeba-like cell. However, when food is scarce, individual cells can release chemical signals that cause the cells to swarm together. They form a sluglike body that moves as though it were one organism. This form of a cellular slime mold is called a pseudoplasmodium, meaning "fake plasmodium," because each cell is independent—the membranes of each cell do not fuse. These slime molds are of interest to biologists who study how cells can communicate with each other.

Water Molds

Water molds are funguslike protists that are made up of branching strands of cells. They are common in freshwater habitats. Like slime molds, many water molds are decomposers. However, some water molds are parasites of plants or fish. For example, if you keep an aquarium, you may have seen a water mold that infects fish. The mold appears first as a cottony coating on the skin and gills but later causes deep wounds.

Perhaps the best known water mold is the downy mildew *Phytophthora infestans,* shown in **FIGURE 4.2**, which causes a disease called potato blight. An outbreak of this disease in Ireland from 1845 to 1849 destroyed almost all of the country's potato crops. As a result, more than 1 million people died of starvation in what became known as the Great Potato Famine.

A Infer Many protists have two modes of reproduction. How does having two modes of reproduction affect when and how they reproduce?

20.4 Formative Assessment

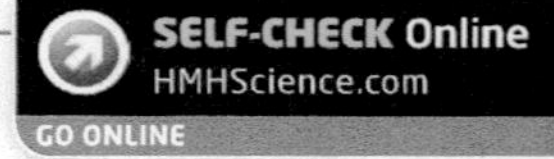

REVIEWING MAIN IDEAS

1. In what ways are **slime molds** and **water molds** similar to fungi?
2. Describe how slime molds help other organisms within an ecosystem obtain nutrients.

CRITICAL THINKING

3. **Compare** Make a three-column chart comparing plasmodial slime molds, cellular slime molds, and water molds.
4. **Analyze** Why doesn't spraying water on slime molds work to destroy them?

CONNECT TO NATURAL SELECTION

5. What might be the advantage of being able to switch from living as separate cells to become a coordinated unit acting like a single organism?

20.4 FORMATIVE ASSESSMENT

1. These funguslike protists also are decomposers that recycle nutrients back into the soil.
2. They decompose organic matter, breaking it down so that the nutrients return to the soil.
3. Charts should include all that are eukaryotic decomposers.

   Plasmodial slime molds: live as a single large cell with many nuclei (a plasmodium) that moves like a giant amoeba; are common under logs or on dead leaves; can produce spores that can have flagella or that can move like an amoeba. The spores will swarm and form a new plasmodium.

   Cellular slime molds: common in soil; their spores become amoeba-like; they swarm together to move as one organism, but each cell is independent of the others.

   Water molds: have branching strands of cells; are common in freshwater habitats; they are sometimes parasites of plants or fish.
4. Spraying water actually encourages the slime mold to grow larger, because they thrive on water and wet conditions.
5. The different body forms can be an advantage when conditions change. When there is plenty of food, the individual cells can find food easily. When food becomes scarce, they may be more likely to survive by working together to find and share food.

20.5 Diversity of Fungi

KEY CONCEPT **Fungi are heterotrophs that absorb their food.**

MAIN IDEAS
- Fungi are adapted to absorb their food from the environment.
- Fungi come in many shapes and sizes.
- Fungi reproduce sexually and asexually.

VOCABULARY
chitin
hyphae
mycelium
fruiting body
mycorrhizae
sporangia

Connect to Your World

What is the largest living thing in the world? The blue whale? A giant redwood tree? Although they are big, both species are tiny compared with a fungus growing in Oregon—a single honey mushroom, *Armillaria ostoyae*. Most of it is underground, but this mushroom could cover more than 1500 football fields. It is thought to be at least 2400 years old. As amazing as it sounds, there are other fungi throughout the world nearly as large.

MAIN IDEA

Fungi are adapted to absorb their food from the environment.

Despite how little most people know about fungi, they are all around us—in soil, water, and even in the air. Many forms live in and on plants and animals. Scientists have named about 70,000 species but estimate there may be a total of 1.5 million fungi species in the world.

Comparing Fungi and Plants

Members of the kingdom Fungi fall into one of three groups—the single-celled yeasts, the molds, and the true fungi. For many years, biologists classified fungi as plants. But there are a few traits that separate these two kingdoms.

- Plants contain chlorophyll and photosynthesize. Fungi do not have chlorophyll and get food by absorbing it from their environment.
- Plants have true roots, leaves, and stems, but fungi do not.
- Plant cell walls are made of the polysaccharide cellulose. Fungal cell walls are made of **chitin** (KYT-uhn), a tough polysaccharide that is also found in the shells of insects and their close relatives.

FIGURE 5.1 A mushroom is actually just the reproductive, or fruiting, body of a fungus. Most of the fungus grows in the ground, as a mycelium.

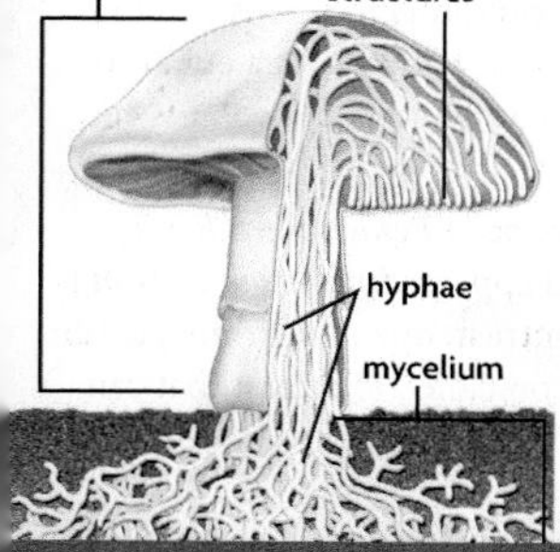

Anatomy of Fungi

With the exception of the yeasts, fungi are multicellular organisms. The bodies of multicellular fungi are made of long strands called **hyphae** (HY-fee). Hyphae (singular, *hypha*) are shown in **FIGURE 5.1**. Depending on the species, each hypha may consist of a chain of cells or may contain one large, long cell with many nuclei. In both cases, cytoplasm can flow freely throughout the hyphae, and each hypha is surrounded by a plasma membrane and a cell wall of chitin.

Differentiated Instruction

ENGLISH LEARNERS

Have individual students skim the section for the positive, negative, and neutral effects of fungi on human life and then create a semantic feature analysis of their findings. Students can choose their variables or use the following column heads: Type of Fungus, Subtype, Effect(s), + (for positive), – (for negative), 0 (for neutral); first column: primitive, sac, mold, club; second column: morels, truffles, *Penicillium*, rusts, smuts, yeast; third column: delicious to eat, prevents disease, cures disease, ruins plants, makes bread rise. Give students ten minutes to skim the section and find and record the information. If they do not find information for all cells in a row, they can use a question mark. Have students share and discuss findings by making statements about their matrices and using input from other students to revise their work.

Teacher Toolkit, Section D, Semantic Feature Analysis

Plan and Prepare

Activate Prior Knowledge Remind students that fungi, like algae, have many everyday uses. **Ask**, What are some ways that people use fungi? as food, for example, mushrooms; as leavening or fermenting agents, for example, yeast; also as antibiotics, as with penicillin

Teach

Vocabulary

polysaccharide Remind students that the prefix *poly-* means "many" and is used in science and mathematics to indicate something made up of many units. A polysaccharide is "a molecule composed of many sugars." The prefix *poly-* is found in many words:

polypeptide, a protein composed of many amino acids

polymer, a compound composed of many repeating units

polygonal, in geometry, a figure composed of many sides

polyglot, someone who speaks many languages

▼ Teach *continued*

Take It Further

Mushrooms make frequent appearances in folklore and myths. One of these is **fairy rings**—large rings of mushrooms typically found in meadows and open areas in forests. According to legend, the rings were made by fairies that gathered in the open area to dance in the moonlight. The fairies danced inside the ring and rested on the tiny stools. The actual cause of the ring pattern of these mushrooms is more down-to-earth. The rings result from the growth underground of certain fungi, such as *Marasmius oreades*. The mycelia of the fungus grow outward in a spokelike manner. The toadstools seen in a ring aboveground form at the ends of the spokes and are the fungus's fruiting bodies.

Vocabulary

Academic Vocabulary The words **primitive** and **advanced** are used differently in science than they are in everyday life. Both terms are used to describe the relative stage in the evolution of an organism or a trait. A primitive characteristic is one that developed in an ancestral species and has remained unchanged over time.

Primitive fungi are so-named because in both form and function, they more closely resemble early fungi rather than fungi that evolved more recently. Similarly, an advanced characteristic is one that developed relatively late in evolution. Because the terms *primitive* and *advanced* may imply a judgment of the sophistication of a trait or an organism, the terms *ancestral* and *derived* are frequently used in their place.

Answers

A Contrast Fungi absorb their food directly from the environment, using enzymes to digest it before it enters the fungi.

Hyphae often group together in long tangled masses to form a mycelium. A **mycelium** (my-SEE-lee-uhm) is an underground network of hyphae. Under certain conditions, such as a moist environment, a mycelium (plural, *mycelia*) can grow quickly to cover a large area. Mycelia may produce fruiting bodies. A **fruiting body** is a reproductive structure of a fungus that grows above ground. Mushrooms are one type of fruiting body.

Fungi absorb their food from their environment. The food can be from a wide variety of food sources—including tree bark, bread, cheese, and even flesh. As fungi grow, hyphae extend into the food source and release enzymes. These enzymes break down their food so that it can be absorbed across their cell walls. Fungi can take in large amounts of nutrients due to their mycelia, which in turn allows mycelia to grow very quickly.

A Contrast **How is the way that fungi get their food different from that of any other group of organisms?**

MAIN IDEA

Fungi come in many shapes and sizes.

The kingdom Fungi is diverse, and it is commonly divided into four main groups—primitive fungi (phylum Chytridiomycota), sac fungi (phylum Ascomycota), bread molds (phylum Zygomycota), and club fungi (phylum Basidiomycota).

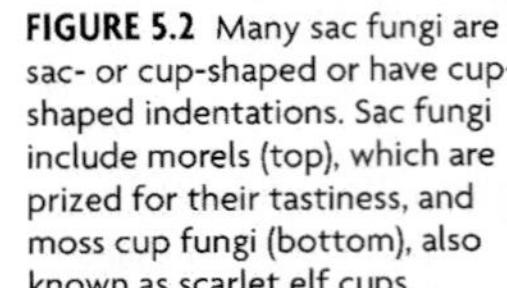

FIGURE 5.2 Many sac fungi are sac- or cup-shaped or have cup-shaped indentations. Sac fungi include morels (top), which are prized for their tastiness, and moss cup fungi (bottom), also known as scarlet elf cups.

Primitive Fungi

The primitive fungi, or chytrids, are the smallest and simplest group of fungi. They are mostly aquatic, and their spores have flagella, which help propel them through the water. They are the only fungi with flagellated spores. Some primitive fungi are decomposers, while others are parasites of protists, plants, or animals. One explanation for the global decrease of amphibians such as frogs is that a parasitic type of chytrid fungi is attacking them.

Sac Fungi

Yeasts, certain molds such as *Penicillium,* and morels and truffles—which many people consider delicious to eat—are all sac fungi. The sac fungi are a diverse group, but they have one key trait in common. They all form a sac, called an ascus, that contains spores for reproduction. Some examples of sac fungi are shown in **FIGURE 5.2**

The yeast that makes bread rise is *Saccharomyces cerevisiae*. This yeast is also an important model organism used in molecular biology. As a eukaryote, it has many of the same genes as humans. Because it is single-celled, it is easy to work with in a laboratory.

If you've ever let an orange grow moldy, you've seen *Penicillium chrysogenum*. This mold is usually a deep green color and appears fuzzy. *Penicillium* is also the source for the antibiotic penicillin. In contrast, one dangerous sac fungus is *Aspergillis flavus,* a mold that makes a poison called aflatoxin that can contaminate cereals, nuts, and milk.

Differentiated Instruction

BELOW LEVEL

Divide the class into four groups. Then have students number off into four expert groups, one for each of the four main groups of the kingdom Fungi. Have expert groups read and review the characteristics of their fungus. Then home groups reassemble so that experts can teach one another about their subject.

Teacher Toolkit, Section C, Jigsaw Reading

Bread Molds

The bread molds range from the molds you see on spoiled foods to fungi used to ferment certain foods such as soy sauce. Most members of this phylum get food by decomposing dead or decaying matter. At least one group of symbiotic fungi belongs to this group. **Mycorrhizae** (MY-kuh-RY-zuh) are mutualistic partnerships between fungi and the roots of certain plants. Mycorrhizae help these plants to fix nitrogen—that is, they take inorganic nitrogen from the soil and convert it to nitrates and ammonia, which the plants use.

Club Fungi

The club fungi get their name because their fruiting bodies are club-shaped. This phylum includes mushrooms, puffballs, and bracket, or shelf, fungi. It also includes the rusts and smuts, which are two types of fungi that cause diseases in plants. Puffballs, shown in **FIGURE 5.3**, form dry-looking structures that release their spores when someone or something strikes the mature fruiting body. Bracket fungi are a common sight in forests, where they grow outward from tree trunks, forming a little shelf.

FIGURE 5.3 Puffballs release a cloud of spores when the fruiting body matures and bursts.

A Identify **What two organisms share a mutualistic partnership in the formation of mycorrhizae?**

MAIN IDEA

Fungi reproduce sexually and asexually.

Most fungi reproduce both sexually and asexually through a wide variety of strategies.

Reproduction in Single-Celled Fungi

Yeasts are single-celled fungi. They reproduce asexually, either through simple fission or through a process called budding, shown in **FIGURE 5.4**. Fission is identical to mitosis—the cell's DNA is copied and the nucleus and cytoplasm divide, making two identical daughter cells. During budding, the parent cell forms a small bud of cytoplasm that also contains a copy of the nucleus. When these buds reach a certain size, they detach and form a cell.

Some yeasts undergo sexual reproduction. A diploid yeast cell undergoes meiosis, producing four haploid nuclei. However, the parent cell's cytoplasm does not divide. Recall that a yeast is a type of sac fungi. Instead of the cytoplasm dividing, it produces the characteristic saclike structure of this phylum called an ascus. The haploid nuclei it contains are actually a type of spore. The ascus undergoes budding, releasing each of the haploid spores. Some spores may then reproduce more haploid spores through budding. Others may fuse with other haploid spores to form diploid yeast cells.

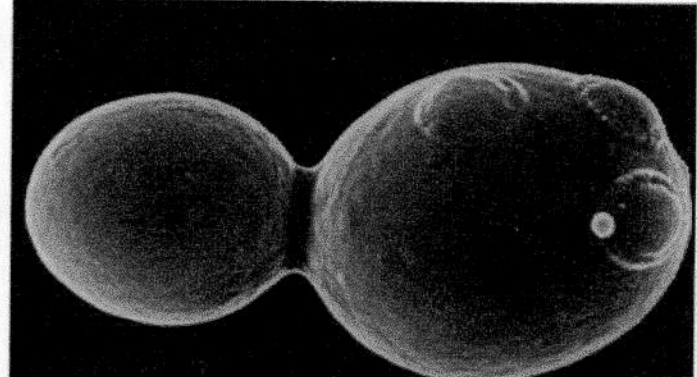

FIGURE 5.4 Yeast can reproduce by budding, the pinching of small cells off the parent cell. (colored SEM; magnification 6000×)

PRE-AP

Tell students that puffballs release their spores when an external pressure is applied to their bellowslike fruiting body. Have students write about what natural events might trigger spore dispersal (animals, raindrops) and spread spores (water, wind, animals), and how this reproductive strategy may have evolved (would confer a reproductive advantage by casting spores into a wide area).

Teacher Toolkit, Section C, Quick-Write

Integrating Agricultural Science

The **mycorrhiza** is one of the most important and common types of **symbiosis** in the natural and agricultural world. More than 90 percent of all known plant species form associations with mycorrhizal fungi. Many fruit and vegetable plants, such as corn, carrots, leeks, potatoes, legumes, tomatoes, strawberries, citrus, and apples, form mycorrhizae with soil fungi. Often, the soil in which crops are planted for the first time must be inoculated with the mycorrhizal fungi that the plants form associations with in their native environments.

Mycorrhizae greatly increase the plants' ability to absorb nutrients from the soil. Some of these fungi can be cultured and applied to soil or seedlings. The indiscriminate use of **fungicides** targeting fungi that are harmful to plants can end up killing the mycorrhizal fungi that are so beneficial.

Answers

A **Identify** a fungus and a plant

Vocabulary

Greek and Latin Word Origins The prefix *myc-* is derived from the Greek word *mykes,* meaning "fungus."

mycology, the branch of biology devoted to the study of fungi

mycologist, a scientist who studies fungi

mycorrhizae, mutualistic associations between plant roots (*rhiz-*) and fungi

Chapter 20: Protists and Fungi 601

▼ Teach continued

Have students go to Animated Biology for interactive animations on protist and fungi life cycles.

Science Trivia

- In ancient Egypt, only the pharaoh and his family could eat mushrooms. Commoners were forbidden even to touch a mushroom.
- Shiitake mushrooms have been used medicinally by the Chinese for more than 6000 years.
- Current studies of shiitake mushrooms show that they contain a compound called lentinan that strengthens the immune system and may fight cancer.

Take It Further

As with bacteria and algae, fungi are key ingredients in many processed foods, not just as mushrooms.

- Soy sauce is fermented first with the mold *Aspergillus oryz,* and then with the yeast *Saccharomyces rouxii.*
- The blue streaks and pungent flavor of blue cheeses such as Roquefort and Gorgonzola result from inoculation with *Penicillium roquefortii.*
- Chocolate is made from cacao beans, which are fermented with the yeasts *Candida krusei* and *Geotrichum.*

FIGURE 5.5 REPRODUCTIVE STRUCTURES OF FUNGI

Fungi	Reproductive feature
Club fungi (Basidiomycota)	basidia
Bread molds (Zygomycota)	zygospore
Sac fungi (Ascomycota)	asci

Reproduction in Multicellular Fungi

The multicellular fungi have complex reproductive cycles. Examples of life cycles for two phyla of fungi are shown in **FIGURE 5.6.**

Club fungi Basidiomycota are named for their club-shaped structures called basidia, where spores are produced during sexual reproduction. Basidia are found on the undersides of mushrooms. They form within the leaflike gills that you can easily see. In club fungi, unlike the other phyla, spores are most often formed by sexual reproduction.

- Nuclei within the basidia fuse to form diploid zygotes.
- The zygotes undergo meiosis to form haploid spores.
- The spores drop from the gills and are carried away by wind or by contact with animals.
- If the spores land in a favorable environment, they grow and form haploid hyphae.
- Some cells of the haploid mycelium may fuse with the cells of another haploid mycelium, producing a diploid mycelium underground.
- An environmental cue, such as rain or change in temperature, can trigger the formation of aboveground fruiting bodies such as mushrooms.

Bread molds Members of Zygomycota are also known as zygote fungi because of the structures they form during sexual reproduction. Bread molds reproduce sexually when the food supply is low but can also reproduce asexually when there is plenty of food. They reproduce asexually by producing spores in **sporangia,** spore-forming structures at the tips of their hyphae. The term *sporangium* is used to describe similar reproductive structures of a variety of organisms, including some fungi, mosses, algae, and ferns.

- As in the club fungi, sexual reproduction in zygote fungi involves hyphae that look alike but are different mating types.
- The two types of hyphae fuse their nuclei to produce a diploid zygospore that can tolerate long periods of extreme conditions.
- When the conditions become favorable, a sporangium grows and produces haploid spores.
- The spores are released and can grow into new hyphae.
- The new hyphae in turn may reproduce asexually, by forming haploid spores in sporangia. Or they may reproduce sexually, by fusing hyphae to produce more zygospores.

VISUAL VOCAB

Sporangia are structures that produce spores.

spores
sporangia

CONNECT TO

ASEXUAL REPRODUCTION

Recall from the chapter **Cell Growth and Division** that asexual reproduction is the creation of offspring from a single parent that does not involve the joining of gametes. The offspring are genetically identical to each other and to the parent.

Life Cycle of Zygote Fungus

Differentiated Instruction

BELOW LEVEL

Have students list and then group keywords in this section, such as *sporangia/basidia/asci* and *hyphae/mycelium/fruiting body.* Have students differentiate between the groups by describing the type of information each set of terms provides.

Teacher Toolkit, Section D, List-Group-Label

FIGURE 5.6 Typical Life Cycles of Fungi

Reproduction in fungi can occur in several ways. Although most club fungi reproduce sexually, bread molds can reproduce both sexually and asexually.

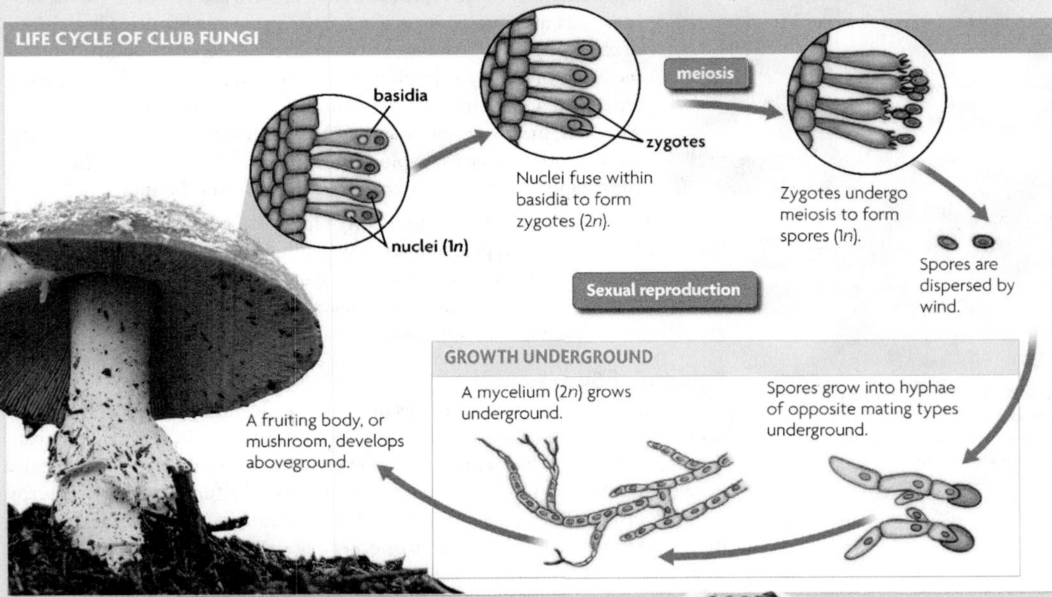
LIFE CYCLE OF CLUB FUNGI
basidia
nuclei (1n)
meiosis
zygotes
Nuclei fuse within basidia to form zygotes (2n).
Zygotes undergo meiosis to form spores (1n).
Spores are dispersed by wind.
Sexual reproduction
GROWTH UNDERGROUND
A mycelium (2n) grows underground.
Spores grow into hyphae of opposite mating types underground.
A fruiting body, or mushroom, develops aboveground.

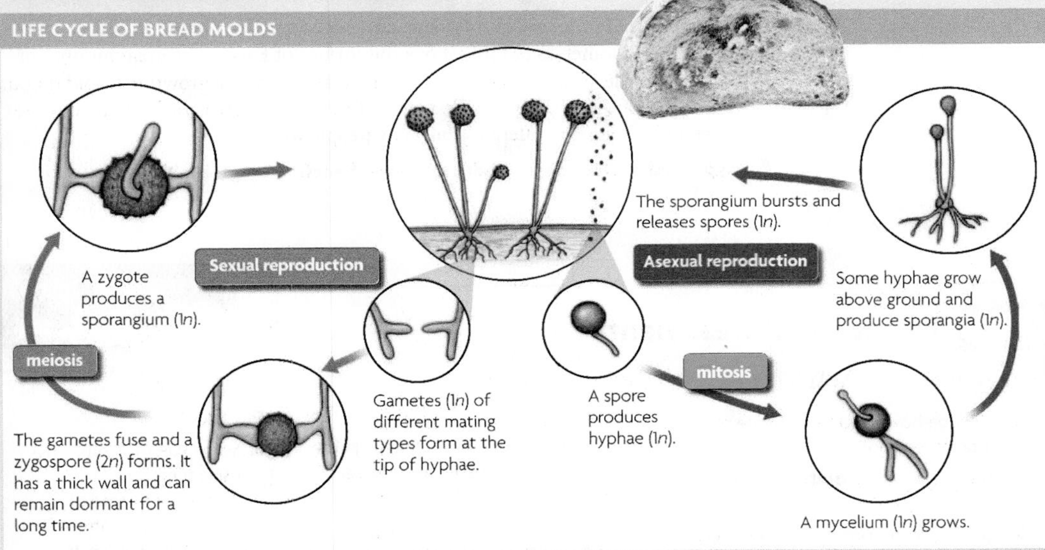
LIFE CYCLE OF BREAD MOLDS
A zygote produces a sporangium (1n).
Sexual reproduction
meiosis
The gametes fuse and a zygospore (2n) forms. It has a thick wall and can remain dormant for a long time.
Gametes (1n) of different mating types form at the tip of hyphae.
A spore produces hyphae (1n).
mitosis
The sporangium bursts and releases spores (1n).
Asexual reproduction
Some hyphae grow above ground and produce sporangia (1n).
A mycelium (1n) grows.

A CRITICAL VIEWING **How are the life cycles of club fungi and bread molds similar? How are they different?**

INCLUSION

Students who are visually impaired or who have difficulty assimilating large amounts of complex information may have difficulty interpreting **FIGURE 5.6.** Have students draw each cycle in a way that is useful to them, such as a sequence diagram. Some students may wish to color-code different stages, while other students may need to draw an enlarged chart or use mnemonics.

History of Science

Piptoporus betulinus is a bracket fungus that grows horizontally from the sides of trees. The hard, leathery upper surface of the fungus can be peeled off in strips and was used to make razor strops for sharpening straightedge razors. The fungus has numerous medicinal properties as well. It contains antibiotic substances and substances that attack intestinal whipworms, *Trichurus trichiura*. Perhaps this is why pieces of the fungus were found threaded into a necklace worn by Ötzi, a man whose 5300-year-old frozen body was found in the Alps in 1991. An autopsy revealed that he was suffering from a whipworm infestation at the time of his death.

TEACH FROM VISUALS

FIGURE 5.6 Have students review the life cycles of bread molds and club fungi. **Ask**

- Which type of fungus produces a zygospore? bread mold
- What are three characteristics of a zygospore? diploid, has a thick wall, can remain dormant for long periods
- What is a basidium, and in which type of fungus is it found? reproductive structure of a club fungus

Answers

A Critical Viewing Both club fungi and bread molds produce spores and hyphae with different mating types. They both form zygotes and undergo meiosis during sexual reproduction. A club fungus usually undergoes only sexual reproduction, whereas a bread mold may undergo both sexual and asexual reproduction. Bread mold zygotes produce sporangia, whereas club fungus zygotes produce spores directly.

▼ Teach *continued*

Address Misconceptions

Common Misconception Fungi need a warm, moist, dark environment in order to grow.

Correcting the Misconception Most fungi do grow best under such conditions; however, some fungi thrive at very high temperatures, while others exist in cold environments, including the Arctic tundra. *Aspergillus niger,* or black mold, grows on onions and garlic that grow in warm, dry areas such as the California deserts. Some fungi are very light-sensitive and require light stimulation to form spores.

Answers

A Hypothesize *Sample answer:* Spores allow offspring to grow far from the parent organism, colonize a new area, and thereby minimize competition for space in the original location. Spores allow many more offspring to be produced.

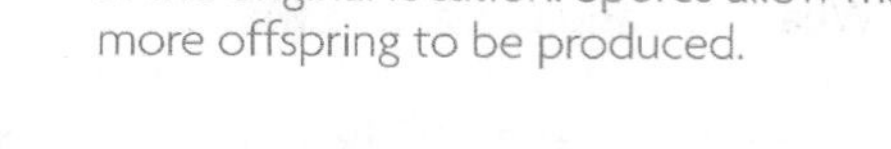

▼ Assess and Reteach

Assess Use the Section Self-Check or Section Quiz, both available at **HMHScience.com**.

Reteach Review section visuals and have students visit Animated Biology at **HMHScience.com** to view the animation of the life cycle of a cup fungus.

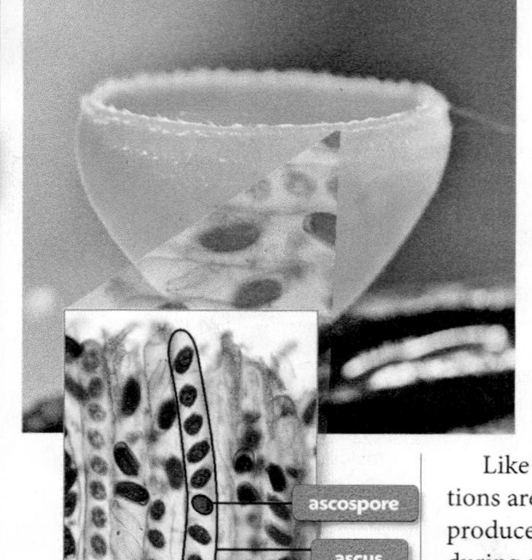

FIGURE 5.7 A cross-section of the cup-shaped fruiting body of a sac fungus shows spores encased in an ascus. (magnification 400×)

Sac fungi Members of Ascomycota are called the sac fungi due to the saclike case, or ascus (plural, *asci*), that forms during sexual reproduction. These reproductive structures are shown in **FIGURE 5.7.** Most asci are found within the fungi's cup-shaped fruiting body. As in club fungi and bread molds, sexual reproduction in multicellular sac fungi involves the joining of two mycelia that are different mating types. The joined hyphae grow into the aboveground fruiting body. An ascus, or sac, develops at the tip of each hypha within the fruiting body. Inside the ascus, haploid spores form. When mature, the cup-shaped fruiting body collapses, and releases the spores.

Like the bread molds, sac fungi usually reproduce asexually when conditions are favorable and reproduce sexually when conditions are harsh. They produce different types of spores during asexual reproduction than they do during sexual reproduction. Spores produced during asexual reproduction are called conidia, which means "dust," because they travel easily through air.

Release of Spores

Fungi release their spores at the tips of their hyphae, high above their food source. This strategy allows the small spores to be carried in air currents to a new location. Some species of fungi go even further and use unusual strategies in releasing their spores. For example, members of the fungal genus *Cordyceps* grow on insects. In some species, the fungi penetrate the insect's brain, causing the insect to climb high into a tree or other vegetation. Eventually, the insect stops climbing and remains fixed in place. The fungus then releases its spores from this greater height.

Spores of fungi are everywhere, and have even been found in the air more than 150 kilometers (93 mi) above the surface of Earth. The great number of spores in the air at any given time is the reason that the growth of mold on our leftover food cannot be avoided, even if the food is refrigerated. Fungal spores are also a source of allergies for many people worldwide.

A Hypothesize How might producing spores benefit an organism?

20.5 Formative Assessment

SELF-CHECK Online HMHScience.com GO ONLINE

REVIEWING ⊙ MAIN IDEAS

1. Describe how fungi use **hyphae** to obtain their food.
2. Describe a typical **fruiting body** of sac fungi, bread mold, and club fungi.
3. **Sporangia** are formed during the life cycle of a typical bread mold. At what stage are they formed?

CRITICAL THINKING

4. **Summarize** Draw a flowchart showing the sequence of steps in the reproduction of yeast, a single-celled fungus.
5. **Infer** The **mycelium** of a fungus grows underground. In what ways might this be helpful for the fungus?

CONNECT TO ECOLOGY

6. Some scientists support using fungi such as *Cordyceps* instead of pesticides to control insect pests in agriculture. What might be some pros and cons of such a plan?

20.5 FORMATIVE ASSESSMENT

1. The hyphae extend into the food source and release enzymes that break the food down. Nutrients are then absorbed across the cell walls.
2. The typical fruiting body of sac fungi is cup-shaped. A fruiting body of a bread mold is on a stalk as a sporangium. The typical fruiting body of club fungi is a mushroom.
3. Sporangia are formed during sexual reproduction by the zygote or during asexual reproduction after a spore produces hyphae.
4. Accept all reasonable drawings. Steps should include yeast cell undergoing meiosis, producing four haploid nuclei; production of an ascus; the ascus undergoing budding; and releasing the haploid spores. Spores may then bud, producing more haploid spores or may fuse with other spores to form diploid yeast cells.
5. It might provide protection from the environment to be underground. Even if the aboveground fruiting body is harmed, the fungus is likely to survive.
6. Using fungi rather than pesticides could help reduce the amount of toxic chemicals released into the environment. However, *Cordyceps* may affect beneficial insects or other species, not just the pests.

White-Nose Syndrome

S.T.E.M. Interactions

Bat with white-nose syndrome

A lethal visitor arrived in New York from Europe in the winter of 2006–2007, a fungus known as *Pseudogymnoascus destructans* (Pd). As the fungus spread westward through the United States and Canada, it killed millions of bats that were hibernating in caves and abandoned mines. When bats hibernate, their metabolism slows and body temperature drops. They survive on fat reserves stored in their bodies. The fungus, which grows on the noses, wings, and other hairless parts of bats' bodies, causes a disease called white-nose syndrome (WNS). Infection causes bats to come out of hibernation temporarily during the cold winter. The normal diets of these bats are insects or fruit, which are not available in winter, so the bats must deplete their fat reserves and they starve to death.

The Pd fungus thrives in cold, humid conditions. It attacks the bats while they hibernate but not during summer months, when they are active and their body temperature is warmer. Infected bats that manage to survive the winter seem to recover from the disease when their bodies warm up in the spring, creating suboptimal growing conditions for the fungus. However, these survivors are usually reinfected the following winter by fungi that live on cave or mine walls.

Scientists are searching for ways to control the fungus and fight the disease. They hope to save as many bats as possible until a long-term cure is found. One group of scientists has discovered that bacteria growing on bats' wings can kill the Pd fungus—at least in the laboratory, but they haven't tested the bacteria in the wild yet. Other scientists have discovered a soil bacterium that produces chemicals capable of killing Pd fungal spores in the lab. The scientists isolated the chemicals and applied them to hibernating bats, which emerged disease-free from their hibernation four months later. But scientists are cautious people. Instead of declaring success, they continued to analyze their data. They realized that the bats did not develop immunity to the fungus after being treated with chemicals. Surviving bats could very well become reinfected winter after winter. A vaccine would be longer lasting, if one could be developed. But how would workers vaccinate millions of bats?

Some scientists are starting to think outside the box. They hypothesize that changing the airflow in the caves where bats hibernate might make living conditions unfavorable for the fungus. By opening new routes for air to move in and out of a cave, the scientists hope to warm the air enough to drive out the fungus, which cannot grow at temperatures above 20°C. They are concerned, though, that the bats also might be driven out of their usual hibernation sites if conditions change. Still, the situation is so serious that scientists think it is worth a try. Until a breakthrough occurs, scientists and government agencies in the United States and Canada are trying to coordinate their work to save bats and permanently cure white-nose syndrome.

S.T.E.M. Activity

Choose one of the stopgap measures discussed in the article. Make a hypothesis explaining how that measure might cure WNS or increase the survival of bats during hibernation. Alternatively, suggest a different treatment that might be successful. Design an experiment that tests your hypothesis either in a lab or in a field study.

Consider the challenge of changing the airflow in a bat cave from the perspective of an engineering design problem. What would be the criteria for a successful solution? What constraints must be considered in designing a solution?

Introduce

Impress upon students that there currently is no cure for white-nose syndrome and that all "solutions" discussed in the article are only stopgap measures. **Ask** Why is it necessary to use stopgap measures if they are not permanent cures? These measures are designed to keep wild bat populations alive until a long-term cure can be discovered. If all bats died, there would be none on which to test a potential cure.

Discuss

Ask students to suggest ways the fungus might be able to break hibernation. Guide the discussion to energy use in metabolism and how metabolism changes during hibernation. Explain that studying bats' energy use during hibernation appears to be a promising line of research because energy use is very different when an animal is hibernating and when it is active. Until a cure is found, scientists have proposed two main interventions for preventing starvation in hibernating bats. Discuss the first intervention, which provides additional energy to bats in the form of food via a captive-feeding program. Have students suggest pros and cons of this method, such as the expense and time needed. Prompt students to recognize that providing food during hibernation also is not practical because hibernating bats usually do not feed during the winter. Discuss the second intervention, which reduces the amount of energy bats need during hibernation to keep from freezing. Guide students to recognize that altering airflow in caves and mines creates a microclimate of warmer air, which allows bats to use less energy in an environment that is warmer but not warm enough to break hibernation. The warmer air might also slow the growth of the fungus.

SECTION 20.6

▼ Plan and Prepare

Activate Prior Knowledge Remind students that the largest living organism on Earth is a honey mushroom thought to be at least 2400 years old, which covers more than 890 hectares (8,900,000 m^2) in eastern Oregon. **Ask,** How is it possible for a mushroom to live so long and grow so large? Traits of the fungus are adaptive to the conditions of its environment. Tell students that some scientists speculate that the dry climate of eastern Oregon is not conducive for most fungi to grow, meaning there isn't much competition for the honey mushroom. Remind them that the ability to occupy unique niches is an evolutionary advantage.

▼ Teach

Vocabulary

Academic Vocabulary The word **organic** in everyday life indicates a food or material that is made or grown naturally, without the use of pesticides, synthetic fertilizers, or hormones. In science, the word *organic* indicates matter that is derived from organisms or that contains hydrocarbons.

20.6 Ecology of Fungi

KEY CONCEPT **Fungi recycle nutrients in the environment.**

MAIN IDEAS
- Fungi may be decomposers, pathogens, or mutualists.
- Fungi are studied for many purposes.

VOCABULARY
lichen

Connect to Your World
Fungi just might be the most overlooked and unappreciated organisms on Earth. Fungi grow on shower curtains, spoil food, and cause illnesses in humans. But humans also eat some fungi and use them to make things that range from bread to antibiotics. Perhaps most importantly, these unusual organisms play a major role in every ecosystem on Earth.

MAIN IDEA
Fungi may be decomposers, pathogens, or mutualists.

Some fungi act as decomposers in the environment. Others act as either pathogens or mutualists to other organisms—including humans.

FIGURE 6.1 Fungi produce enzymes that help break down the complex molecules in wood to simpler molecules that fungi can absorb and use.

Fungi as Decomposers
Fungi and bacteria are the main decomposers in any ecosystem. Fungi, such as those shown in **FIGURE 6.1,** decompose dead and decaying organic matter such as leaves, twigs, logs, and animals. They return nutrients such as carbon, nitrogen, and minerals back into the soil. Because of the large surface area of their mycelia, fungi are well adapted for absorbing their food and can recycle nutrients quickly. This constant cycling of nutrients helps enrich soil with organic compounds. The nutrients can then be taken up by other organisms.

Plants and animals could not survive without the activity of decomposers. The ability of fungi to break down tough plant materials such as lignin and cellulose is especially important in woodland ecosystems. Fungi are the main decomposers of these hard parts of plants, which cannot be used by animals without being first broken down by decomposers.

The decomposing activity of fungi is not always helpful to humans, however. Fungi can damage fruit trees, and they can also cause damage inside wooden houses and boats. Molds and other fungi inside a house can weaken its walls, and their spores can cause respiratory illness. Homeowners should check for and remove molds that are established in their homes.

Differentiated Instruction

ENGLISH LEARNERS
Have students use a graphic organizer such as a main idea web to organize their notes for this section. Have students start by writing a main idea in a box. Lines should be angled off the box to outer boxes that contain details relating to the central concept. Another layer of boxes can be added to the second layer, and more layers added to set up a hierarchy.

Teacher Toolkit, Section C, Main Idea Web

Fungi as Pathogens

Like bacteria, some fungi can be pathogenic, or disease-causing. A few pathogenic fungi always cause disease. These fungi are called obligate pathogens—the term *obligate* means necessary or obliged. Other fungi are normally harmless, coexisting with other organisms in a delicate ecological balance. However, changes in environmental circumstances can upset this balance and lead to disease. Organisms that normally don't cause a problem until there is a change in the host's homeostasis are called opportunistic pathogens. A change in the host's body provides them an opportunity to grow unchecked and cause infection.

> CONNECT TO
> **PROKARYOTES**
> In biology, the term obligate means requiring a particular environment to survive. Recall from the chapter **Viruses and Prokaryotes** that prokaryotes can be obligate anaerobes, meaning they cannot have oxygen in their environment. Some bacteria, protists, and fungi can also be obligate pathogens or obligate parasites.

Fungi and humans The overuse and incorrect use of antibiotics is one example of how humans allow pathogens an opportunity to cause infection. Antibiotics can destroy certain beneficial bacteria in the human digestive system, allowing other organisms such as fungi to thrive. Typically harmless fungi also cause disease when the immune system is not functioning at its best. For instance, all healthy humans have populations of the yeast *Candida* that occupy certain parts of the body, such as the skin and mouth. If a human's immune system is damaged, populations may grow and cause disease.

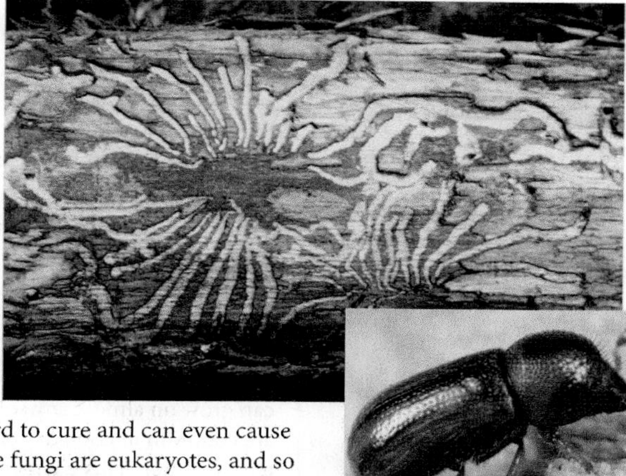

Some fungal pathogens, such as those that cause ringworm and athlete's foot, have fairly mild effects. But several fungi cause severe diseases, such as some lung illnesses, that are hard to cure and can even cause death. Fungal infections are hard to treat because fungi are eukaryotes, and so their cellular structure is very similar to ours. It is difficult to develop medicine that will harm fungal cells but not damage human cells.

Fungi and plants Fungal diseases also affect plants, and they can be especially devastating in agriculture and horticulture. Dutch elm disease is caused by a fungus that is transmitted by elm bark beetles, shown in **FIGURE 6.2.** In the United States, the first cases of Dutch elm disease were reported in Ohio in 1930. Today, the disease has destroyed more than half of the elms in the northern United States. Fungi also destroy a large portion of the world's fruit crops. A disease of peaches called peach scab is caused by a fungus and results in millions of dollars in losses to growers each year. Gray mold is a disease of produce such as strawberries. This fungus can grow even in refrigerated fruit and is a major cause of fruit spoilage during shipment and storage.

FIGURE 6.2 A fungus is responsible for Dutch elm disease. Adult elm bark beetles tunnel into the bark of elms to lay their eggs. If the trees are diseased, fungus spores stick to the adults as they visit new trees.

Fungal diseases in agriculture are often treated with chemical sprays called fungicides. Today, however, crops that are genetically engineered to resist fungi are becoming more common. Fungal diseases in animals, including those in humans, are usually treated with antifungal medications. These treatments usually come from fungi themselves, which produce them as a defense against other fungi. Like bacteria and protists, however, fungi can develop resistance to treatments if they are overused. These products should be used carefully.

BELOW LEVEL

Have students use Cornell Notes to outline this section. They can record key terms and their definitions in a left column across from the appropriate point in the outline. Then students can add a summary in the bottom section. Encourage them to be concise but still try to include all key information.

Teacher Toolkit, Section C, Cornell Notes

TEACH FROM VISUALS

FIGURE 6.2 Review the figure with students. Explain that the squiggly lines in the tree bark are made by larval bark beetles as they emerge. **Ask,** What is significant about the fungus's spores sticking to adult elm bark beetles? It explains how the fungus is transmitted between elm trees.

The Inside Story

The convulsive fits that affected several young girls in Salem, Massachusetts, in 1692 were thought at the time to be caused by **witchcraft.** Modern research by a number of scientists suggests that the symptoms displayed by the girls resulted from poisoning with a fungus, *Claviceps purpurea,* that commonly contaminates stored grains. The fungus, commonly called **ergot,** grows on stored cereal grains, notably rye. It produces a substance that has marked effects on several body systems, including the nervous system. Common symptoms include convulsions, twitching, and sometimes a feeling that the limbs are on fire.

The bizarre symptoms, coupled with certain social prejudices of the period, led to accusations that some of the people of Salem, mostly women, had put the young girls under a spell. As a result, some of the accused were executed for participating in witchcraft. Studies begun in the 1970s pointed to ergot poisoning as a possible cause of the bizarre behavior of these young women. There is some evidence that ergot was growing on stored rye in Salem homes.

Other instances of similar bizarre behavior have led scientists to suspect ergotism as a factor. Among these was the Dancing Mania that occurred across Europe during the Middle Ages. During this epidemic, groups of people would run and dance through the streets, often foaming at the mouth and screaming in an unintelligible language, until they collapsed from exhaustion or, in some cases, died.

▼ Teach *continued*

Vocabulary

saprophyte Decomposers have wrongly been tagged with the name *saprophytes,* which translates as "putrid plants." The root *sapro-* comes from the Greek word *sapros,* meaning "putrid." The term *saprophyte* was coined when fungi were still considered members of the plant kingdom. Even though incorrect, *saprophyte* is still commonly used to describe all decomposers. The more appropriate but less commonly used scientific term is *saprotroph.*

Science Trivia

- Lichens are extremely sensitive to air pollution and are used in environmental science as air-quality indicators.
- Litmus paper is made from the lichens *Ochrolechia tartarea* and *Roccella tinctoria.*
- Reindeer moss, a crusty vegetation much favored by reindeer, is actually *Cladonia rangiferina,* a lichen that grows in alpine tundra.

FIGURE 6.3 Lichens

A lichen is a symbiotic relationship between an alga and a fungus. Algae cells feed the fungus through photosynthesis, and the fungal mycelium provides habitat for the algae.

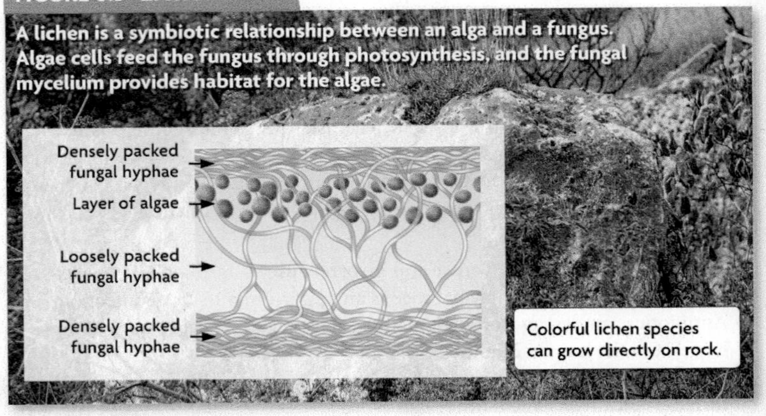

Fungi as Mutualists

Mutualism is a symbiotic relationship in which both organisms benefit. Fungi form mutualistic relationships with several types of organisms.

Lichens A **lichen** (LY-kuhn) is a mutualistic relationship between a fungus and algae or photosynthetic bacteria. Only certain fungi, algae, or cyanobacteria can combine to form a lichen body. The body itself consists mainly of fungal hyphae that surround and grow into the algal cells, as shown in **FIGURE 6.3.** The algal part of the lichen carries out photosynthesis, making sugars that feed both the alga and the fungus. Lichens (phylum Mycomycota) can grow on almost any solid surface, from tree trunks to soil to rocks. They are common in cool, dry environments. They can also withstand severe temperatures. This characteristic of lichens allows them to live in habitats such as tundra, where fungi could not survive alone.

Lichens play several roles in the environment and in the lives of humans. For example, they are extremely important during primary succession, because they can live on bare rock. Many species of lichens are sensitive to air pollution and can be used as indicators of air quality. Lichens are also important in nutrient cycling, because they function as both a decomposer and a producer. Lichens produce hundreds of unique chemicals, including pigments used as dyes in traditional cultures and compounds that have antibiotic properties.

CONNECT TO

ECOLOGY

Recall from the chapter **Interactions in Ecosystems** that primary succession occurs after disruptive events such as fires and volcanic eruptions. The first organisms to recolonize an area, such as lichens, are called pioneer species.

Mycorrhizae Mutualistic associations between plant roots and soil fungi are called mycorrhizae. More than 80 percent of the world's plants have mycorrhizae on their roots. Mycorrhizae form when the hyphae of a fungus colonize the roots of a nearby plant. The huge surface area of the fungal mycelium is much larger than the root surface area of the plants, so the mycelium can absorb soil nutrients and water faster than the plant's roots could alone. In return, the fungus benefits because it gets sugars and other nutrients from the plant. Mycorrhizae can boost plant growth and reduce the need for fertilizers, which can cause soil and water pollution. Mycorrhizae also produce chemicals with antibiotic properties that help fight harmful bacteria.

Differentiated Instruction

PRE-AP

Point out that in spite of the three fungal trophic strategies (decomposer, mutualist, and pathogen), all fungi still fall into the primary category of decomposer. Ask students to analyze the three strategies and their utility to fungi and other organisms. Then have students write a five-minute essay that identifies each trophic strategy and gives an example of a fungus that employs the strategy.

Teacher Toolkit, Section C, Quick-Write

TEACH WITH TECHNOLOGY

Use the Internet to obtain photos, video clips, and information on *Atta cephalotes,* better known as the leaf-cutter ant. Assemble a digital slide show and discuss the importance of the fungus-ant mutualism to the health of the forest ecosystem.

Fungal gardens and insects Some insects also live as partners in a mutualistic symbiosis with fungi. The leafcutter ants of Central and South America, shown in **FIGURE 6.4**, don't just use fungi—they actually grow them. These ants cut tiny pieces of leaf from plants with their jaws. They carry these leaf pieces back to an underground nest area, where they build a garden of leaf pieces. Next, the ants add pieces of the fungus. The fungus breaks down the leaf pieces and absorbs nutrients from them. The ants in turn feed on the fungal mycelium.

FIGURE 6.4 Leafcutter ants carry leaves back to their nests to provide food for fungi. The ants then eat the growing fungal mycelium.

A Summarize **Describe three ways that fungi are important to the environment.**

MAIN IDEA

Fungi are studied for many purposes.

Many species of fungi are edible, such as the mushrooms we eat on pizza and the yeast we use to bake bread. In addition, fungi make citric acid, which is used in soft drinks and some candy. Fungi are also useful in the health care industry. Since the discovery of antibiotics in the 1900s, scientists have been researching how pathogens interact with their natural environments. This knowledge is then applied to develop useful medicines. For example, in their natural habitats fungi and bacteria compete for similar resources, such as space and nutrients. This is true whether they live on a forest floor or in a human digestive tract. Over time, fungi have evolved natural defenses against bacteria.

Studies of yeast have produced equally valuable insights. These tiny single-celled organisms are among the most important model systems used in molecular biology. Most yeasts have many of the same genes and proteins found in plants and animals. Insights gained from studies of a yeast's genome can often be applied to multicellular organisms. Yeast are small, grow quickly, and are easy to culture, or raise, in the laboratory.

B Summarize **What are three ways that fungi benefit humans?**

CONNECT TO

ANTIBIOTICS

Recall from the chapter **Viruses and Prokaryotes** that an antibiotic is a chemical that kills or slows the growth of bacteria.

Take It Further

Like leaf-cutter ants, termites also cultivate **fungal gardens,** growing the fungus *Termitomyces* in giant termitaria. More than 300 termite species are completely dependent on their fungal gardens for food. *Termitomyces* is grown on termite feces inside **termitaria.** A termitarium is a large, moundlike structure that houses the fungal garden and the termites. Termitaria can be quite large. Some can house as many as several million individual termites and their crop of fungus. These structures may rise as high as nine feet into the air.

Answers

A **Summarize** Fungi are important to the environment as decomposers, as pathogens, and as mutualists that help their autotrophic partners obtain important nutrients or provide food for them.

B **Summarize** Fungi decompose dead matter and return it to the soil as nutrients; they boost plant productivity; and they are used for food and medicine.

20.6 Formative Assessment

SELF-CHECK Online
HMHScience.com
GO ONLINE

REVIEWING MAIN IDEAS

1. How do fungi contribute to the balance of an ecosystem?
2. What are three reasons **lichens** are useful to humans?

CRITICAL THINKING

3. **Compare** Draw a Venn diagram comparing lichens and mycorrhizae. Include terms such as *roots, photosynthesis,* and *mutualism.*
4. **Analyze** Some antifungal medications can damage the patient's own tissues. Why doesn't this problem occur with antibiotics?

CONNECT TO

NATURAL SELECTION

5. A peach farmer is faced every year with an outbreak of peach scab, a fungal disease of peaches. Every year he sprays his crop carefully with fungicides, but each time these seem less effective than the year before. Why might this be?

Assess and Reteach

Assess Use the Section Self-Check or Section Quiz, both available at **HMHScience.com**.

Reteach Use the PowerPresentation at **HMHScience.com** to review the material presented in this section. Have students use this review to fill in any gaps in their notes for the section.

20.6 FORMATIVE ASSESSMENT

1. Fungi contribute to the balance of an ecosystem by decomposing organic matter and recycling nutrients.
2. Answers should include three of the following: lichens produce oxygen; they grow in unfavorable environments, which then allows other organisms to grow; they are indicators of air quality; they are important decomposers that return nutrients to the soil; they can be used to produce antibiotic compounds; their pigments are used as dyes.
3. features specific to lichens: algae, photosynthesis; features specific to mycorrhizae: roots, surface area; common features: mutualism, fungus
4. Antibiotics affect prokaryotes, whereas fungi and humans are eukaryotes.
5. Fungi that survived the initial spraying may have conferred resistance to later generations. Over time, the population of fungicide-resistant fungi could increase.

GO ONLINE

Encourage students to go to **HMHScience.com** for a detailed review of each section, including visuals and vocabulary practice.

Online Student Resources, Vocabulary Practice Worksheet

CHAPTER 20 Summary

BIG IDEA Protists and fungi are highly diverse organisms that have both beneficial and detrimental impacts on human health and the environment.

KEY CONCEPTS

20.1 Diversity of Protists

Kingdom Protista is the most diverse of all the kingdoms. It includes organisms that are animal-like, plantlike, and funguslike. Protists may be single-celled or multicellular, and may be microscopic or very large. Protist classification is likely to change in the future, as some protists are more closely related to members of other kingdoms than they are to other protists.

20.2 Animal-like Protists

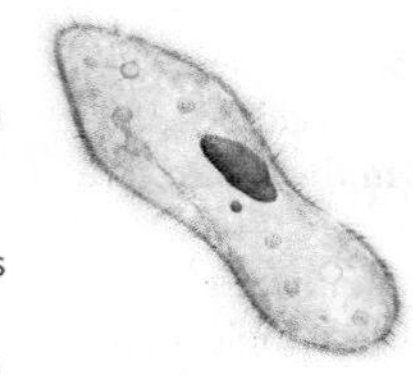

Animal-like protists are single-celled heterotrophs that can move. Commonly known as protozoa, animal-like protists have various structures that help them move, such as flagella, pseudopods, or cilia. Some animal-like protists can cause diseases such as malaria and sleeping sickness.

20.3 Plantlike Protists

Algae are plantlike protists. Unlike animal-like protists, which are all single-celled, plantlike protists can be either single-celled or multicellular. Most plantlike protists can make their own food through photosynthesis. Plantlike protists are not classified as plants because they do not have roots, stems, leaves, or the specialized tissues and reproductive structures that plants have. However, like many plants, most plantlike protists can reproduce both sexually and asexually.

20.4 Funguslike Protists

Funguslike protists decompose organic matter. These protists have an important role in recycling nutrients through ecosystems. Unlike fungi, funguslike protists can move during part of their life cycle. Funguslike protists include slime molds and water molds.

20.5 Diversity of Fungi

Fungi are heterotrophs that absorb their food. Their bodies are made of long strands, called hyphae, which grow underground in a tangled mass called a mycelium. The parts of fungi that humans normally recognize, such as mushrooms, are actually only the reproductive structures of the fungi, called fruiting bodies.

20.6 Ecology of Fungi

Fungi recycle nutrients in the environment. Some fungi cause illness in humans, such as those that cause athlete's foot and ringworm. Other fungi, such as those that cause Dutch elm disease, cause illness to plants or other organisms. Some fungi share a mutualistic relationship with organisms such as algae to form lichens, or plant roots, which form mycorrhizae. Humans use fungi for foods, medicine, and as model organisms in scientific research.

READING TOOLBOX SYNTHESIZE YOUR NOTES

Supporting Main Ideas Use a supporting main ideas diagram to summarize how the three groups of protists get their food.

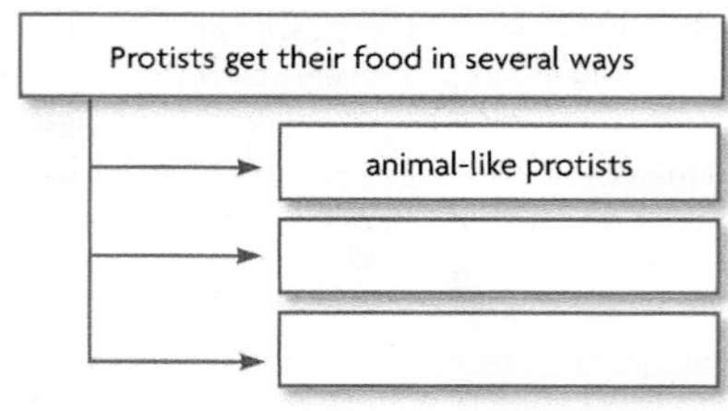

Concept Map Use a concept map like the one below to summarize what you know about the roles of fungi in the environment.

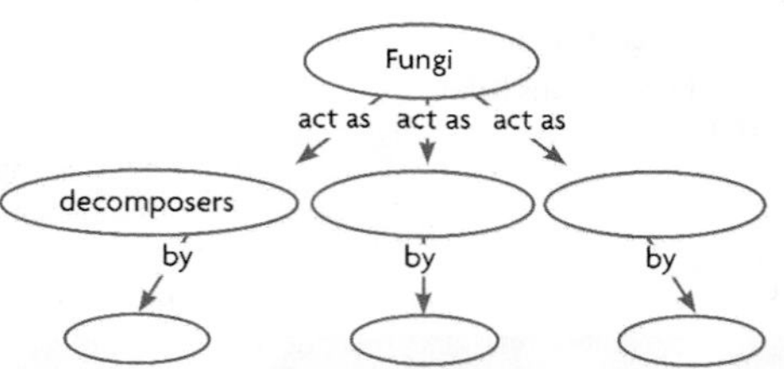

Reviewing Vocabulary

1. Both are structures that help animal-like protists move and capture food. A pseudopod is a temporary extension of the cell's cytoplasm and plasma membrane. Cilia are short, hairlike structures.
2. Both are funguslike protists and are decomposers. Slime molds can be single cells, each with many nuclei, or a single amoeba with one nucleus. Water molds are branching filaments of cells. Slime molds also have animal-like traits, and water molds do not.
3. Both are symbiotic partnerships and examples of mutualism. Mycorrhizae are symbiotic partnerships between plant roots and fungi. Lichens are composed of a fungus and an alga or a photosynthetic bacterium.
4. Both are protists. Protozoa have animal-like characteristics. Algae have plantlike characteristics.
5. Both are reproductive structures of fungi. Fruiting body refers to the reproductive structures of any fungus, whereas sporangia are fruiting bodies that form spores at the tips of hyphae.
6. Both help the fungus obtain nutrients. Hyphae are long individual filaments that excrete enzymes to digest and absorb food. Mycelia are a mass of hyphae.
7. Hyphae grow into a weblike mycelium.
8. Mycorrhizae are mutualistic relationships between a fungus mycelium and plant roots.
9. fruiting body
10. hyphae
11. mycelium

20 Review

INTERACTIVE Review
HMHScience.com
GO ONLINE
Review Games • Concept Map • Section Self-Checks

CHAPTER VOCABULARY

20.1 protist
20.2 protozoa
pseudopod
cilia
20.3 algae
20.4 slime mold
water mold
20.5 chitin
hyphae
mycelium
fruiting body
mycorrhizae
sporangia
20.6 lichen

Reviewing Vocabulary

Compare and Contrast

Describe one similarity and one difference between the two terms in each of the following pairs.

1. pseudopod, cilia
2. slime mold, water mold
3. mycorrhizae, lichen
4. protozoa, algae
5. fruiting body, sporangia
6. hyphae, mycelium

READING TOOLBOX GREEK AND LATIN WORD ORIGINS

7. The term *hyphae* comes from the Greek word *huphe*, which means "web." Explain how this meaning relates to hyphae.
8. The term *mycorrhizae* comes from the Greek words *mukes*, which means "fungus," and *rhiza*, which means "root." Explain how these meanings relate to mycorrhizae.

Labeling Diagrams

In your notebook, write the vocabulary term that matches each numbered item below.

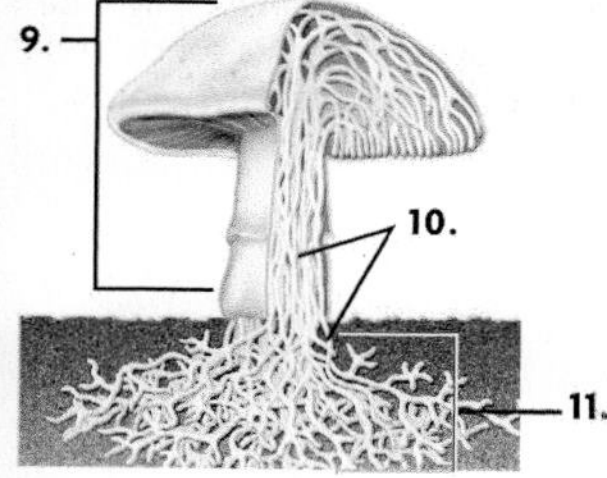

Reviewing MAIN IDEAS

12. Give one characteristic of each type of protist that explains why it is animal-like, plantlike, or funguslike.
13. Explain why the phyla of the kingdom Protista might be regrouped into several kingdoms and what would likely be the basis for this reclassification.
14. What are three types of structures that help some protists move?
15. When does an amoeba form a pseudopod?
16. Name two animal-like protists that cause disease and briefly describe the diseases they cause.
17. Are protists classified on the basis of being single-celled or multicellular? Give an example to support your answer.
18. How do multicellular algae reproduce asexually?
19. Slime molds have animal-like traits. What might be one reason they are classified with water molds as funguslike protists?
20. Explain how hyphae help a fungus absorb food.
21. The phyla Ascomycota and Basidiomycota are both in the kingdom Fungi. What structures are the basis for placing organisms in one or the other of these phyla?
22. Describe sexual reproduction in yeast, or single-celled fungi.
23. How can the hyphae of bread molds be involved in both asexual and sexual reproduction?
24. Why are yeasts useful to scientific research?
25. How is the decomposing activity of fungi both beneficial and harmful?

CHAPTER REVIEW

18. By fragmenting; each piece can then grow into another alga.
19. Slime molds are decomposers, as are water molds.
20. The hyphae extend into the food source and release enzymes that break down the food so it can be absorbed across the cell walls of the hyphae.
21. The reproductive structure that contains the spores in the Ascomycota, or sac fungi, is a sac (an ascus). The fruiting body of the Basidiomycota, or club fungi, is club-shaped (a basidium).
22. A diploid cell produces four haploid nuclei through meiosis. They are contained within a saclike structure called an ascus in the parent cell's cytoplasm. The haploid nuclei are called ascospores. These are released from the ascus through the budding process. Some of these ascospores might fuse with other haploid ascospores to form diploid cells.
23. The hyphae can form haploid spores in sporangia (asexual), or they can fuse to produce a diploid zygospore (sexual).
24. Most yeasts have many of the same genes and proteins that are found in higher eukaryotes. Therefore, studies of their genomes can be applied to multicellular organisms.
25. As decomposers, fungi help recycle nutrients such as carbon, nitrogen, and minerals back into the soil. But this same decomposing action can harm fruit trees and wooden houses and boats.

Reviewing Main Ideas

12. Animal-like protists are heterotrophic. Most plantlike protists photosynthesize their own food. Funguslike protists are decomposers.
13. Many of the phyla are distantly related to one another and are more closely related to members of other kingdoms. DNA analysis would likely provide the basis for reclassifying protists into several kingdoms.
14. flagella, pseudopods, cilia
15. when it needs to move or capture food
16. *Sample answer:* malaria from *Plasmodium;* sleeping sickness from *Trypanosoma;* intestinal diseases from *Giardia*
17. No, both unicellular and multicellular plantlike protists are classified according to their photosynthetic pigments, food storage strategies, and cell wall structure. Examples include the three phyla of green, brown, and red algae. Green algae can be multicellular or unicellular; red and brown algae are multicellular.

Critical Thinking

26. All animal-like protists, and some plantlike protists, are unicellular; all animals and plants are multicellular. Plantlike protists also do not have roots, stems, or leaves that characterize plants. Funguslike protists can move during part of their life cycle; fungi cannot.
27. Amoebas would be found on land and in water, and zooflagellates and ciliates would be found only in water environments. Flagella and cilia are structures that help protists swim. They are of no use on land or in any environment that does not include moisture. Amoebas can live in water—as long as there is a surface on which they can anchor their pseudopods—and on land in moist environments.
28. Dinoflagellata
29. The pseudoplasmodium form of a cellular slime mold moves as though it is a single individual, like a plasmodium. However, in a pseudoplasmodium, the cells remain independent, and their membranes do not fuse.
30. The broad-spectrum fungicide will also kill off beneficial fungi needed to recycle nutrients back into the soil, as well as the fungal part of the mycorrhizae on plant roots. Without proper nutrients in the soil to draw up through their roots, the crops will not grow well.

Interpreting Visuals

31. Fungi and animals are more closely related than fungi and plants.
32. Green algae are more closely related to plants than they are to red algae. The diagram shows them branching off from the common ancestor with plants at a later time than they do from the common ancestor with red algae.

Critical Thinking

26. Analyze What characteristics of protists prevent them from being classified as animals, plants, or fungi?

27. Analyze Amoebas have pseudopods, zooflagellates have flagella, and ciliates have cilia to help them move. Would you expect to find each of these types of protists on land or water? Explain your answer.

28. Classify A new plantlike protist has been discovered. It has the following characteristics: two flagella, found in a marine environment, body covering made of cellulose. What phylum would it likely be placed in?

29. Describe The prefix *pseudo-* means "false" or "fake." Why is the term *pseudoplasmodium* used to describe one form of a cellular slime mold?

30. Predict A grape crop is infected with a fungus. There is a fungicide that targets only this kind of fungus and kills it. But a broad-spectrum fungicide that kills many kinds of fungi is cheaper, and the farmer decides to use it instead. Explain why the farmer's crops may actually become less healthy.

Interpreting Visuals

Use the diagram below to answer the next two questions.

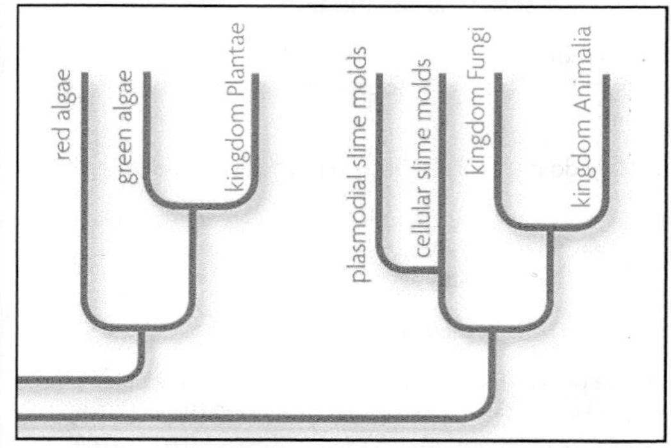

31. Analyze What does this diagram suggest about the relationship between fungi and animals, as compared with fungi and plants?

32. Interpret Are green algae more closely related to red algae or plants? Explain your answer.

Analyzing Data Analyze Experimental Design

Use the text and the data below to answer the next two questions. The following experiment was conducted by two students to determine if adding yeast to a decomposing fruit would speed up the rate of decomposition.

Two 3-cm^2 pieces of banana were cut. Each was placed in a different plastic bag and the bags were sealed. Each student took one of the banana pieces home.

- Student A placed her banana piece on a bookshelf.
- Student B put some dry yeast on his banana and resealed the bag. He also put his banana piece on a bookshelf.

Both students looked at the banana pieces every day for the next four days and recorded their observations.

PERCENT DECOMPOSITION

Organism	Day 1	Day 2	Day 3	Day 4
Student A's banana	1%	5%	7%	10%
Student B's banana	0%	4%	7%	10%

33. Experimental Design What is the main design flaw in this experiment?

34. Analyze Does the experimental design clearly support the question that the students were trying to answer? Explain.

Making Connections

35. Write an Argument Write an imaginary argument between two euglenoids in which one wants to be placed with animals and the other wants to be placed with plants. Include the decision of the referee who explains why they can be neither plants nor animals.

36. Evaluate Look again at the picture of *Didinium* eating the *Paramecium* on the chapter opener. What might be one advantage and disadvantage of having a specialist feeding strategy? a generalist feeding strategy? Explain your answer.

Analyzing Data

33. The banana without the yeast is supposed to be the control, but the two bananas are not held under the same conditions. Student B's banana piece was placed in a sealed bag; Student A's was not.
34. No, their design appears to be testing whether yeast or a closed container affects decomposition. Other conditions (temperature, light) may differ as well, meaning the purpose of the experiment is unclear.

612 Unit 6: Diversity of Life

Standards-Based Assessment

Record your answers on a separate piece of paper.

MULTIPLE CHOICE

1 When scientists first observed protists with chlorophyll, they thought the protists were actually single-celled plants. By using more recent molecular techniques, scientists have determined that these organisms are genetically different from plants. This is an example of —

A how scientific theories can change with the development of new technologies

B why scientific theories should not be influenced by new scientific evidence

C why all scientific investigations should involve genetic analysis

D why protists should be classified as plants

2

prokaryote: bacteria, archaea | eukaryote: protists, fungi, plants, animals

The grouping of kingdoms into prokaryotes and eukaryotes is shown in the Venn diagram above. One cellular characteristic that could be placed in the area that overlaps both groups is —

A nucleus

B organelles

C chloroplasts

D cell membrane

3 Diatoms carry out a large portion of the photosynthesis that occurs on Earth. In which biogeochemical cycle do diatoms probably have the greatest effect?

A phosphorus cycle

B nitrogen cycle

C carbon cycle

D water cycle

4 Most fungi are decomposers. How do their life processes affect other organisms in the community?

A Fungi keep other populations under control by preying on weak organisms.

B Fungi make stored nutrients available to other organisms.

C Fungi compete with plants for soil nutrients.

D Fungi compete with plants and animals for space.

THINK THROUGH THE QUESTION

If you are having a hard time answering this question in terms of fungi, try to consider it based on the role of decomposers in general.

5

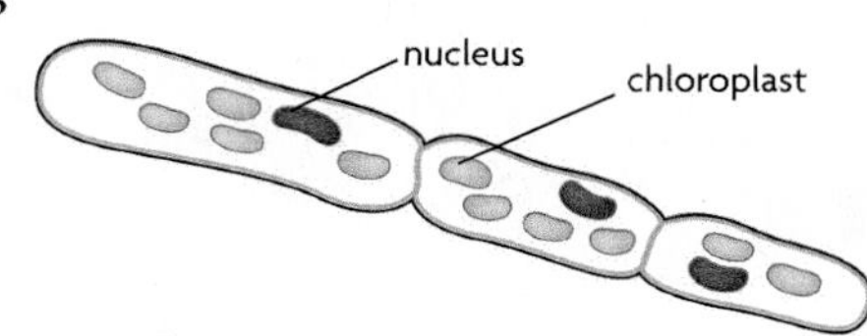

A researcher discovers a new type of organism. Only some structures, labeled above, can be seen clearly. Based on this information, the researcher is able to conclude that the organism —

A is a protist that lives in colonies

B is a multicellular protist

C can capture energy from the sun

D will not prey upon other organisms

6 Yeast is a single-celled fungus that can reproduce both asexually and sexually. How is sexual reproduction in a yeast cell different from sexual reproduction in animals?

A In a yeast cell, the DNA is not copied.

B The yeast cell does not undergo meiosis.

C During meiosis, a yeast cell produces only two haploid nuclei.

D During meiosis in a yeast cell, the cytoplasm does not divide.

Standards-Based Assessment

The Standards-Based Assessment questions will help students prepare for their final examination in the course. If you wish to give students practice in coding their answers, look for the Standards-Based Assessment Answer Sheet at **HMHScience.com**. To give students practice under timed testing conditions, allow them five minutes per question.

Question	Answer	Depth of Knowledge	Cognitive Complexity
1	A	I	L
2	D	I	L
3	C	III	M
4	B	II	M
5	C	I	M
6	D	IV	M

KEY

Depth of Knowledge
I Recall
II Skill/Concept
III Strategic Thinking
IV Extended Thinking

Cognitive Complexity
L Low
M Moderate
H High

Making Connections

35. The argument for being classified as an animal should point out that euglenoids do not have cell walls and can move easily. The argument for being classified as a plant should point out that many euglenoids are autotrophs and have chlorophyll. The referee should explain that both plants and animals are multicellular and that euglenoids are unicellular.

36. *Sample answer:* A specialist may have less competition for food but must have a way to survive during times of food shortages. A generalist has many more food choices available but might face greater competition for some or all of those food sources from many other organisms.

CHAPTER 21 Instruction and Intervention Support

Plant Diversity

1 Core Instruction

The **Core Instruction** resources below can be used for all students. Core instruction should be followed by ongoing assessment to determine which students need further help.

Available in both English and Spanish

Available Online

Section	Instruction	PRINT	ONLINE	Labs
21.1	Textbook **Origins of Plant Life**	■	●	
	Animated Biology Plant and Pollinator Matching Game		●	
	Teaching Visuals Phylogeny of Land Plants (Fig. 1.2)		●	
	PowerPresentation and Notes 21.1		●	
21.2	Textbook **Classification of Plants**	■	●	Habitat Clues Plants and Pollinators **QuickLab** Classifying Plants as Vascular or Nonvascular **Video Lab** Plant Diversity
	PowerPresentation and Notes 21.2		●	
21.3	Textbook **Diversity of Flowering Plants**	■	●	Comparing Monocots and Dicots (Design Your Own) **Video Lab** Monocot and Dicot Seeds
	Teaching Visuals Monocots and Dicots (Fig. 3.3)		●	
	PowerPresentation and Notes 21.3		●	
	That's Amazing! Video Inquiry Cotton-Ball Bats		●	
21.4	Textbook **Plants in Human Culture**	■	●	Investigating Medicinal Plants Phytoremediation (Biotechnology Lab)
	PowerPresentation and Notes 21.4		●	

Additional online resources available for this chapter include **Interactive Whiteboard Resources.**

GO ONLINE! for all your teacher resources at HMHScience.com

2 Support and Intervention

Support and Intervention resources are useful for students who need targeted help beyond the Core Instruction

Resources	PRINT	ONLINE
Assess and Reteach (TE wrap)	■	●
Concept Map		●
Interactive Reader	■	●
Interactive Review Games		●
Section Self-Checks		●
Study Guide B		●
Vocabulary Practice Worksheets		●

3 Specialized Support

Students who need more intensive personalized intervention benefit from **Specialized Support** resources.

Resources	PRINT	ONLINE
Chapter Audio Files		●
Differentiated Instruction Inclusion, Below Level, and English Learners (TE wrap)	■	●
ELL Strategies	■	●
Modified Lesson Plans for English Learners		●
Reinforcement Worksheets		●
Study Guide A		●

Extension and Assessment

Enrichment and Challenge

Resources	PRINT	ONLINE
Active Reading Worksheets		●
Data Analysis Practice Worksheet		●
Differentiated Instruction Pre-AP (TE wrap)	■	●
Pre-AP Activity Mutualism and Coevolution, Plants as Medicine in the Animal Kingdom		●
The Inside Story and **Take It Further** (TE wrap)	■	●
Unit Project		●
WebLinks		●
WebQuest Endangered Plants (21.4)		●

Assessment

Resources	PRINT	ONLINE
Alternative Assessment		●
Chapter Tests A and B		●
Diagnostic Test		●
ExamView Banks		●
Extended Response Test		●
Online Assessment System		●
Section Quizzes		●
Standards-Based Assessment	■	●

CHAPTER 21

Chapter Overview

- **Section 1** discusses the evolution and adaptions of plants over time.
- **Section 2** details the classification of plants based based on common characteristics and common ancestry.
- **Section 3** describes the characteristics of plants that can be used to classify them.
- **Section 4** covers the many uses of plants in agriculture, economics, and medicine.

Focus and Motivate

How have flowering plants come to dominate Earth's landscapes?

Have students speculate on what it means to dominate Earth's landscapes. **Ask,** What form do you think this domination takes? geographic—where flowering plants can live; numeric—number of species or individuals Discuss the large number of flowering plant species and the wide range of environments in which they live. Remind students that types of organisms that dominate in an obvious way, such as large predators, do not represent a majority in terms of numbers of organisms. Bacteria are dominant despite being relatively invisible to the eye. So are plants, which are visible but not necessarily things we notice.

Students can access BioZine at **HMHScience.com** to look for topics suitable for research reports, writing assignments, or classroom debates.

CHAPTER 21

Plant Diversity

BIG IDEA Many organisms on Earth, including humans, depend on the diversity of plants and their traits for survival.

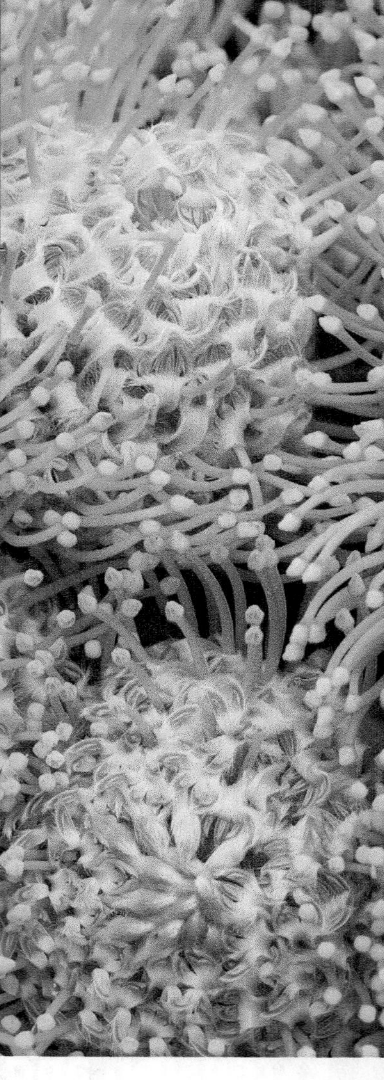

ONLINE BIOLOGY HMHScience.com

ONLINE Labs
- **QuickLab** Classifying Plants as Vascular or Nonvascular
- Habitat Clues
- Comparing Monocots and Dicots
- Investigating Medicinal Plants
- Plants and Pollinators
- Phytoremediation
- **Video Lab** Plant Diversity
- **Video Lab** Monocot and Dicot Seeds

Student Activity

Purpose **Have teams of students model plant classification. Each team classifies a variety of plants into groups based on characteristics observed in real specimens or photographs.**

Materials (per team)

Each team will need pictures or actual specimens of a variety of plants from different phyla with as many identifying characteristics as possible. Examples:

- liverworts, hornworts, and mosses
- club mosses, whisk ferns, horsetails, and ferns
- seed plants, including cone-bearing plants (cycads, ginkgo, conifers) and flowering plants

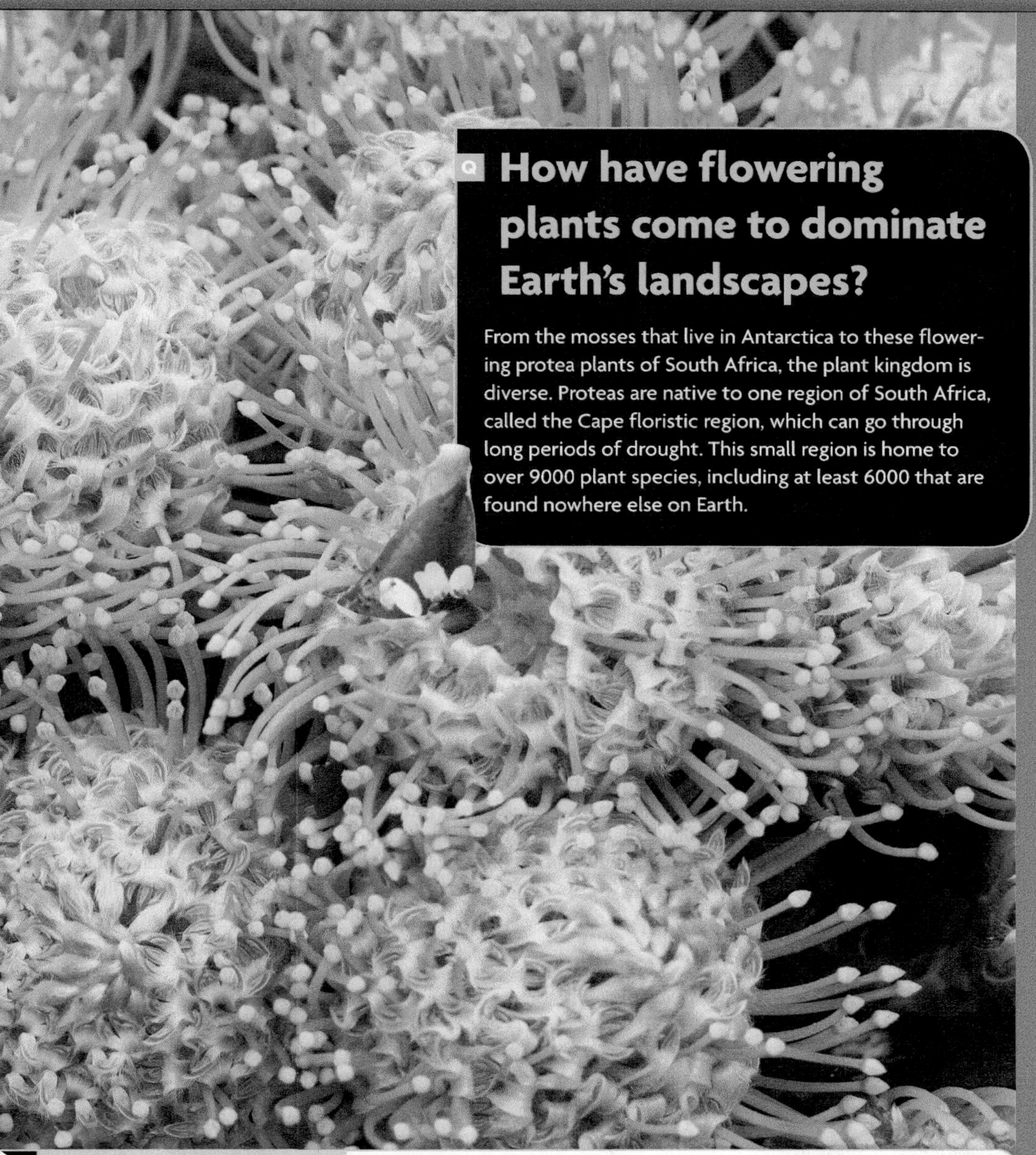

How have flowering plants come to dominate Earth's landscapes?

From the mosses that live in Antarctica to these flowering protea plants of South Africa, the plant kingdom is diverse. Proteas are native to one region of South Africa, called the Cape floristic region, which can go through long periods of drought. This small region is home to over 9000 plant species, including at least 6000 that are found nowhere else on Earth.

READING TOOLBOX **This reading tool can help you learn the material in the following pages.**

USING LANGUAGE

Classification As you read the chapter, make distinctions between general words that describe categories and specific words that describe individuals within a category. Words that name categories are more general than words that describe individuals.

YOUR TURN

Use information that you read in the chapter to answer the following questions.

1. What are two types of seedless vascular plants?
2. What is the general term identifying the category that includes mosses, liverworts, and hornworts?

Introduce Tell students that the photographs represent a variety of plants that scientists classify into different phyla based on their characteristics. Point out that students do not have to base their groups on scientific phyla, but can classify their pictures on whatever characteristics they choose. However, make sure students know that they must explain the characteristics they used for grouping the plants.

Discuss Have teams explain how they classified their plants. **Ask**

- What characteristics did you use for your groups? Accept all reasonable observable characteristics.
- What made classifying plants using pictures difficult? life cycles and some structures that cannot be observed; limited characteristics shown in photographs

Point out that scientists consider many different characteristics when classifying plants, such as internal structures, molecular data, and evolutionary relationships.

Activate Prior Knowledge

Discuss with students the wide variety of plants used by different cultures. **Ask**

- What are some of the most important plants in the United States for farming? grains, corn, vegetables, fruits, sugar cane
- What value do other plants have? lumber for construction, oxygen for our atmosphere, ecological value, medicinal value

Discuss the potential value of having high plant diversity. You may want to discuss this in terms of quality of life.

Preview Vocabulary

Academic Vocabulary

Use the context of plant classification to introduce students to these terms:

criterion = standard, rule, or test on which a judgment or decision can be based

criteria = plural of *criterion*

Like the words *datum* and *data,* students often use the plural form when they should use the singular. Encourage students to use the words in class when discussing the criteria used to classify plant groups: seed/seedless, vascular/nonvascular, flowering/cone-bearing.

Integrating Ecology

Have students recall that an ecological niche encompasses the physical, chemical, and biological factors that a species needs to survive and reproduce. The protea essentially is the Cape sugarbird's niche, because the bird depends on it for feeding, nesting, and mating.

Answers

1. Club mosses and ferns are two types of seedless vascular plants.
2. Mosses, liverworts, and hornworts are types of nonvascular plants.

SECTION 21.1

B.1.5 Develop and use a model to illustrate the hierarchical organization of interacting systems (cell, tissue, organ, organ system) that provide specific functions within multicellular organisms.

▼ Plan and Prepare

Activate Prior Knowledge Have students think about taking a hike that puts them far away from the resources they use every day. **Ask,** What do you take with you on a long hike? food, water, clothing Discuss the idea that plant ancestors are considered pioneers that moved from the shores of early Earth's lakes and oceans inland. **Ask,** What did organisms need to adapt to in order to survive the move inland? lack of moisture, fluctuations of temperature, variations in climate

▼ Teach

Take it Further

Existing species of the class Charophyceae are often called **stoneworts** because over time, calcium carbonate builds up on the plants, creating a hardened texture. Stoneworts are eaten by waterfowl and other aquatic animals, and provide shelter for fish.

21.1 Origins of Plant Life

KEY CONCEPT **Plant life began in the water and became adapted to land.**

MAIN IDEAS

- Land plants evolved from green algae.
- Plants have adaptations that allow them to live on land.
- Plants evolve with other organisms in their environment.

VOCABULARY

plant
cuticle
stomata
vascular system
lignin
pollen grain
seed

Connect to Your World

The flowering proteas shown on the previous page are not just plants with beautiful flowers. Various birds, rodents, and insects rely on protea nectar and pollen as food sources. Green protea beetles even live inside of protea flowers. Without plants, animal life as we know it would not exist on land.

MAIN IDEA

Land plants evolved from green algae.

All green algae share certain characteristics with plants. **Plants** are multicellular eukaryotes, most of which produce their own food through photosynthesis and have adapted to life on land. Like plants, green algae are photosynthetic eukaryotes. They have chlorophyll that captures energy from sunlight during photosynthesis. Chlorophyll is what makes these algae—and most of the plants that we are familiar with—green. Green algae and plants have the same types of chlorophyll. Another feature both green algae and plants share is that they use starch as a storage product. Most green algae also have cell walls that contain cellulose, a complex carbohydrate that is found in the cell walls of all plants.

Evidence from genetic analysis points to one ancient species of green algae that is the common ancestor of all plants. If it were alive today, this species would be classified as a member of the class Charophyceae, like the algae in **FIGURE 1.1.** Several other important plant characteristics likely originated in charophyceans.

- A multicellular body, which led to the specialization of cells and tissues
- A method of cell division that produces cells with small channels in their walls, which allows cells to communicate with each other chemically
- Reproduction that involves sperm traveling to and fertilizing an egg cell

Today, charophyceans are common in freshwater habitats. Scientists hypothesize that the ancestral charophycean species may have grown in areas of shallow water that dried out from time to time. Natural selection likely favored individuals that could withstand longer dry periods. Eventually, the first true plant species evolved, as shown in **FIGURE 1.2.** True plants have multicellular embryos that remain attached to the female parent as they develop.

FIGURE 1.1 Multicellular green algae of the genus *Chara* can be found in many lakes and ponds. They are called charophyceans and are thought to be the closest living relatives of the common ancestor of all plants.

Differentiated Instruction

ENGLISH LEARNERS

Suggest students use word squares as their vocabulary strategy for the section. You can review the strategy by completing one for *plant*. In the first quadrant, provide a translation of the word in several home languages, using the *Multilanguage Glossary*. Include a symbol or picture and then have students provide their own definition, in addition to one taken from the Glossary. Finally have them write a sentence that demonstrates meaning through context.

Teacher Toolkit, Section D, Word Squares

BELOW LEVEL

To test students' understanding, write five to ten true or false statements about the main points of the section. Focus on the characteristics that green algae and plants have in common, the challenges of living on land, and the adaptations that allow plants to meet these challenges. Have students react to the statements as being true or false before reading the section and then after.

Teacher Toolkit, Section C, Anticipation Guide

FIGURE 1.2 Evolution of Plants

Plants have evolved from green algae. An extinct charophycean species is the common ancestor of all plants.

charophyceans | mosses and relatives | ferns and relatives | cone-bearing plants | flowering plants

Millions of years ago: present day, 100, 200, 300, 400, 500

A Analyze What category of plants evolved most recently?

The earliest plant fossils date to more than 450 million years ago. The first true plants probably grew on the edges of lakes and streams. Like modern-day mosses, they relied on droplets of water that brought sperm to eggs to produce the next generation of plants. They also had a fairly simple structure similar to that of moss, keeping low to the ground to retain moisture. Over time, the descendants of these plants were able to live in even drier areas.

B Apply What evidence suggests that green algae are close relatives of land plants?

> CONNECT TO
>
> **ALGAE**
>
> Recall from the chapter **Protists and Fungi** that algae are plantlike protists. Photosynthetic pigments give various types of algae their distinct colors.

MAIN IDEA

Plants have adaptations that allow them to live on land.

Life on land presents different challenges than does life in the water. Unlike land plants, algae are constantly surrounded by water, which is needed for photosynthesis. The buoyancy of water supports the weight of most algae. For algae, water provides a medium through which sperm and spores can travel, allowing for reproduction and dispersal. Finally, water prevents sperm, eggs, and developing offspring from drying out.

The challenges of living on drier land have acted as selective pressures for plant life on Earth. In turn, many land plants have evolved adaptations that allow them to retain moisture, transport water and other resources between plant parts, grow upright, and reproduce without free-standing water.

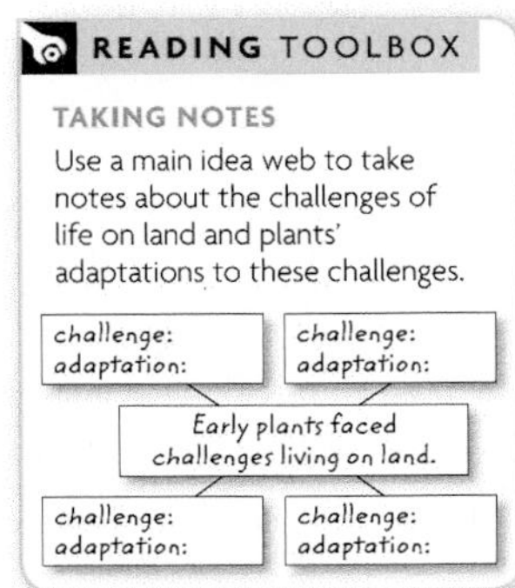

READING TOOLBOX
TAKING NOTES
Use a main idea web to take notes about the challenges of life on land and plants' adaptations to these challenges.
challenge: adaptation:
challenge: adaptation:
Early plants faced challenges living on land.
challenge: adaptation:
challenge: adaptation:

TEACH FROM VISUALS

FIGURE 1.2 Use the diagram to help students understand the evolution of plants. **Ask**

- What is the common ancestor of all plants? an extinct charophycean
- What is the first category of plants to evolve from the ancestral charophyceans? mosses and relatives
- When did the flowering plant lineage diverge from the cone-bearing plant lineage? about 150 mya

Answers

A Analyze flowering plants

B Apply Green algae have the same types of chlorophyll as plants have. Some green algae, such as charophyceans, are multicellular, and some have a method of cell division similar to that of plants that produce cells with small channels in their walls that allow for communication. Charophycean reproduction involves sperm swimming to and fertilizing an egg, which is also characteristic of plant reproduction.

INCLUSION

Help students who are literal thinkers interpret **FIGURE 1.2.** Suggest that they use their fingers to trace the lines, starting with the photograph of the charophyceans traced down to the point where it branches off. Relate that branch to the date on the left side of the diagram. Then have them trace the new line up to the photograph of mosses and their relatives. Tell students that all plants evolved from charophyceans. Each point where new branches diverge represents a common ancestor.

Teacher Toolkit, Section C, Connect to Content Through Visuals

▼ Teach continued

Integrating Ecology

The **vascular systems** of trees and other plants function not only to keep these organisms alive, but also to help mitigate the sometimes violent effects of severe rainstorms and flooding. By drawing water out of the soil, trees lessen the volume of water that would otherwise flow into a river or other low-lying area.

Trees also help to keep landforms intact by preventing erosion—lessening the impact of rainfall on the ground and holding the soil in place by the vast network of roots weaving through the ground. If trees and other plants are removed from a hillside, mudslides are far more likely, as is siltation of rivers and other bodies of water.

Vocabulary

Greek and Latin Word Origins Tell students that the term **cuticle** comes from the Latin *cuticula,* which means "little skin." In plants, the cuticle is a waxy, waterproof layer that covers the stems and leaves. In vertebrates, it is the outermost layer of skin known as the epidermis. In arthropods, such as grasshoppers, it is a tough exoskeleton. Tell students that what the cuticles of different organisms have in common is that they are outer coverings that offer protection.

Answers

A Analyze Algae are surrounded by water, so they do not have to support their own weight or cope with dry periods. Water contains dissolved minerals and nutrients, which algal cells absorb directly. Algal cells do not need to transport resources in the same way as some land plants do. Finally, water provides a medium through which sperm and spores can travel.

CONNECT TO

ECOLOGY

As you learned in the chapter **Principles of Ecology,** plants play an important role in ecosystems. They convert the sun's energy to food and produce oxygen for animals to breathe.

Retaining Moisture

Plants will die if they dry out from exposure to air and sunlight. The surfaces of plants are covered with a cuticle. A **cuticle** is a waxy, waterproof layer that helps hold in moisture. As **FIGURE 1.3** shows, there are tiny holes in the cuticle, called **stomata** (singular, *stoma*). Special cells allow stomata to close to prevent water loss, or to open to allow air to move in and out. Without stomata, the movement of air would be prevented by the cuticle.

Transporting Resources

Taller plants often have more access to sunlight than do shorter plants, but growing tall presents another challenge. While plants must get sunlight and carbon dioxide from the air, they must also get water and nutrients from the soil. A structure for moving these resources to different parts of the plant evolved in the form of a vascular system. A **vascular system** is a collection of specialized tissues that bring water and mineral nutrients up from the roots and disperse sugars down from the leaves. A vascular system allows a plant to grow higher off the ground.

VISUAL VOCAB

A **vascular system** allows water, mineral nutrients, and sugars to be transported to various parts of a plant.

water and mineral nutrients

sugars

Growing Upright

Plant height is also limited by the ability of a plant to support its own weight. Plants need structure to support their weight and provide space for vascular tissues. This support comes from a material called **lignin** (LIHG-nihn), which hardens the cell walls of some vascular tissues. Lignin is also responsible for the strength of wood and provides stiffness to the stems of other plants. As a result, plants can retain their upright structure as they grow toward the sun.

Reproducing on Land

In all plants, eggs are fertilized within the tissue of the parent plant. There, the fertilized egg develops into an embryo, the earliest stage of growth and development for a plant. Some plants reproduce with the help of rainwater or dew, while others do not need free-standing water to reproduce. Pollen and seeds are adaptations that allow seed plants to reproduce completely free of water.

A **pollen grain** is a two-celled structure that contains a cell that will divide to form sperm. Pollen can be carried by wind or animals to female reproductive structures. A **seed** is a storage device for a plant embryo. A seed has a hard coat that protects the embryo from drying wind and sunlight. Once a seed encounters the right conditions, the embryo can develop into an adult plant.

A Analyze **Discuss why the four challenges on this page do not apply to most algae.**

Differentiated Instruction

PRE-AP

Have students write a brief essay describing the selective advantages that both pollen and seeds offer to plants that reproduce this way. They should consider the effect of these adaptations on genetic diversity as well as how they might relate to seasonal changes. Also, encourage them to think about how seeds and pollen may have been advantageous for early human agriculture. Ask students what farming would be like if we did not have seeds to work with.

Teacher Toolkit, Section C, Quick-Write

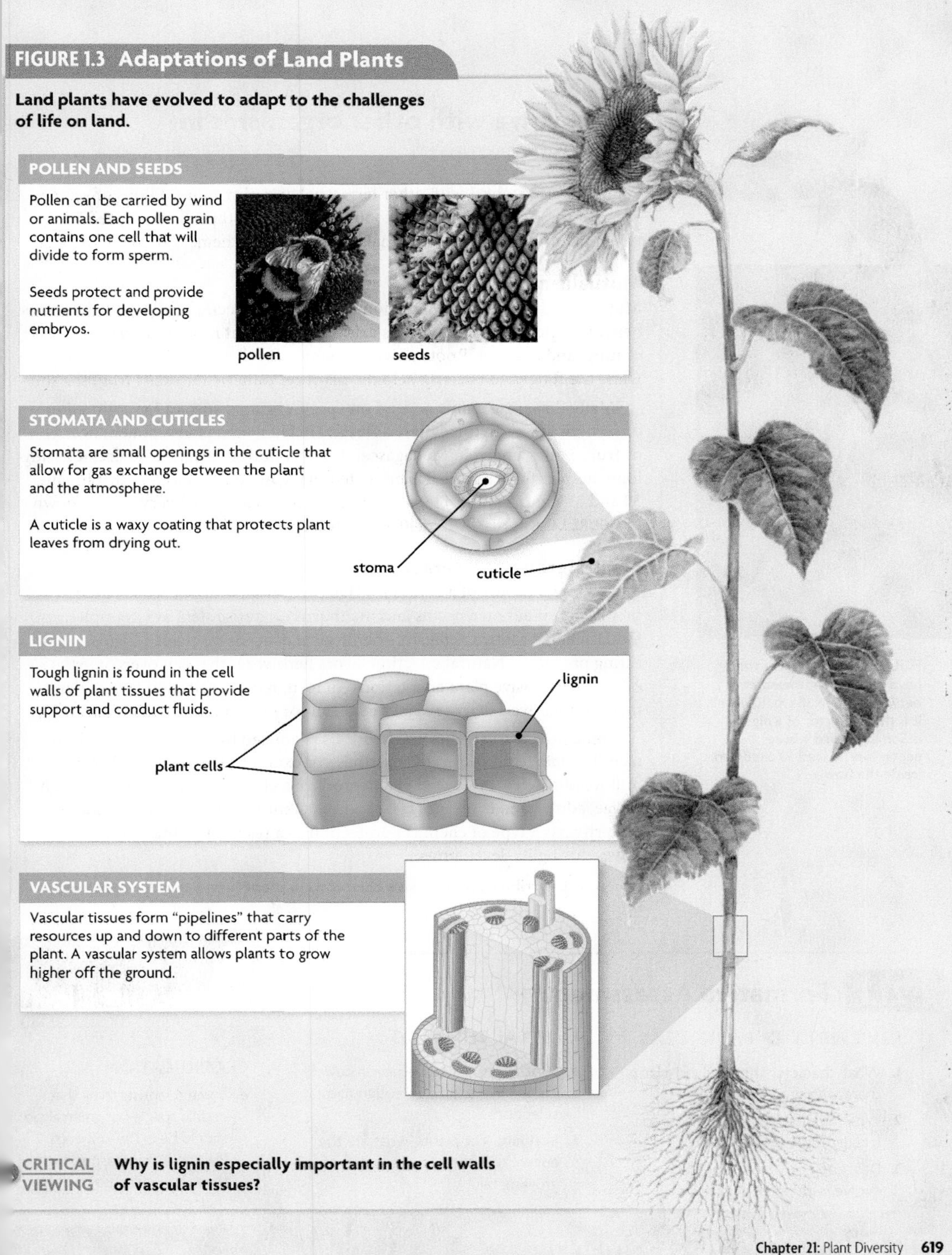

FIGURE 1.3 Adaptations of Land Plants
Land plants have evolved to adapt to the challenges of life on land.
POLLEN AND SEEDS
Pollen can be carried by wind or animals. Each pollen grain contains one cell that will divide to form sperm.
Seeds protect and provide nutrients for developing embryos.
pollen
seeds
STOMATA AND CUTICLES
Stomata are small openings in the cuticle that allow for gas exchange between the plant and the atmosphere.
A cuticle is a waxy coating that protects plant leaves from drying out.
stoma
cuticle
LIGNIN
Tough lignin is found in the cell walls of plant tissues that provide support and conduct fluids.
lignin
plant cells
VASCULAR SYSTEM
Vascular tissues form "pipelines" that carry resources up and down to different parts of the plant. A vascular system allows plants to grow higher off the ground.

CRITICAL VIEWING **Why is lignin especially important in the cell walls of vascular tissues?**

HANDS-ON ACTIVITY

To illustrate the importance of lignin in vascular tissues of plants, have students try drawing water from a cup, using both an oversized plastic straw and a piece of hard tubular plastic, such as a snorkel. Both should work well.

Try this again, only this time have another student try to squeeze each drinking tube closed. The weaker plastic straw will be compressed by the pressure, while the hard plastic tube will not.

Tell students that the hard plastic tube is analogous to the lignin-strengthened vascular system of a plant, which would be crimped closed if the plant could be bent or twisted. If vessels cannot withstand pressure, they will not be able to transport water and other resources. Discuss human-made systems or shapes that are analogous, such as underground tunnels, scuba equipment, submarines, water mains, and gas lines.

TEACH FROM VISUALS

FIGURE 1.3 Have students study the photographs and diagrams as they read the information about plant adaptations.
Ask

- What do pollen and seeds allow plants to do on land? reproduce in the absence of water
- What do stomata and cuticles allow plants to do? exchange gases while retaining moisture
- What does lignin help plants do? grow upright
- What does a vascular system allow plants to do? transport resources and grow tall

Mention that not all have the adaptations shown. For example, the presence or absence of a vascular system is one criterion used to classify plant groups.

Vocabulary

Greek and Latin Word Origins The word **vascular** comes from the Latin *vasculum,* which means "small vessel." Organisms that have vessels for transporting resources are said to have vascular systems. In plants, the fluid that flows through the vascular system is called **sap;** in most animals it is called **blood.**

Science Trivia

Lignin has been extracted and used by various industries since the 1880s, when it was used for tanning leather.

- Lignin functions as a binder in charcoal briquettes, ceramics, fiberglass insulation, dust suppressants, plywood, and animal feed pellets.
- As an emulsifier, lignin keeps products such as asphalt and pesticides from breaking down.

Answers

A Critical Viewing Lignin stiffens the cell walls in vascular tissues, allowing for the flow of water and sugars through the vessels.

Teach *continued*

ONLINE Biology
HMHScience.com

For more on the relationship between plants and their pollinators, have students play the plant and pollinator matching game at **HMHScience.com**.

TEACH FROM VISUALS

FIGURE 1.4 Discuss the relationship between the hawk moth and the orchid.
Ask

- What adaptations do the moth and the orchid have that make them dependent on each other? long tongue; nectar deep inside the flower
- How does the plant benefit from its relationship with the moth? Pollination enables fertilization of eggs.
- What is the significance of the orchid blooming at night? Moths feed at night.

Answers

A Synthesize As a result of a mutation, the leaves of a certain plant may have contained a small amount of a chemical that tasted bad to herbivores. Because the plant was not eaten, it survived longer or reproduced more than other plants in the population, and over time, the trait became more common.

Assess and Reteach

Assess Use the Section Self-Check or Section Quiz, both available at **HMHScience.com**.

Reteach Create a digital slide show of images from the Media Gallery that illustrate the parts of land plants and their functions, and also interactions between plants and other animals. Have students call out the names of the features or describe what is being shown.

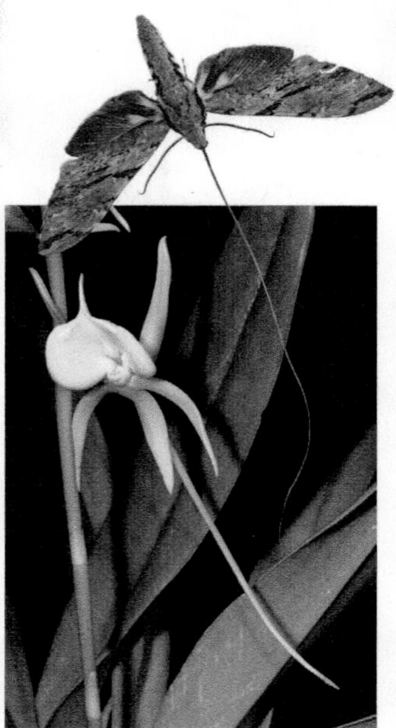

FIGURE 1.4 The hawk moth has a tongue that measures between 30 and 35 cm (10–14 in.). It is the pollinator of a night-blooming orchid whose nectar is produced 30 cm down inside the flower.

MAIN IDEA

Plants evolve with other organisms in their environment.

Plants have coevolved with other terrestrial organisms for millions of years. Some of these relationships are cooperative, while others have evolved between plant species and the animal species that eat them.

Mutualisms

Mutualism describes an interaction between two species in which both species benefit. Mutualistic relationships exist between plant roots and certain types of fungi and bacteria. Roots provide a habitat for these fungi and bacteria, while the fungi and bacteria help the plant get mineral nutrients from the soil.

Many flowering plants depend on specific animal species for pollination or seed dispersal. In turn, these animals are fed by the plant's pollen, nectar, or fruit. For example, in Madagascar, Darwin noticed a variety of orchids with long, tubular flower parts. He predicted that a nocturnal moth with a tongue 30 and 35 cm (10–14 in.) long must be the pollinator. That very moth, shown in **FIGURE 1.4**, was discovered 40 years after Darwin's prediction.

Plant-Herbivore Interactions

Plants have a variety of adaptations that discourage animals from eating them. The spines on a cactus and the thorns on a rose stem are examples. Other plants produce defensive chemicals that act as pesticides against plant-eating predators. Natural selection favors herbivores that can overcome the effects of defensive plant adaptations. In turn, natural selection favors plants that produce even sharper spines or thorns or even more toxic chemicals.

Some insects use defensive chemicals produced by plants to their advantage. The larvae of monarch butterflies, for example, feed exclusively on milkweed species. Milkweed plants produce a chemical that makes monarch larvae, adults, and even eggs taste bad to potential predators. In this way, the butterfly has a type of chemical protection as a result of eating milkweed leaves during its development.

 Synthesize **Describe how defensive chemicals in plant leaves may have evolved.**

21.1 Formative Assessment

REVIEWING MAIN IDEAS

1. What characteristics do land **plants** share with green algae?
2. What adaptations allow plants to thrive on dry land?
3. Describe two ways in which plants evolve with other organisms.

CRITICAL THINKING

4. **Synthesize** Describe how a **cuticle** could have evolved through natural selection.
5. **Evaluate** For plants, what are the advantages and disadvantages of growing tall?

SELF-CHECK Online
HMHScience.com
GO ONLINE

CONNECT TO
CLASSIFICATION

6. Some scientists think that certain species of green algae should be in the kingdom Plantae. What reasons might these scientists use to defend their position?

21.1 FORMATIVE ASSESSMENT

1. Both are eukaryotic, photosynthetic, contain the same types of chlorophyll, and use starch as a storage product.
2. cuticles and stomata, vascular systems, lignin, pollen grains, and seeds
3. Plants and other types of organisms can coevolve through mutualistic relationships and through predator-prey relationships.
4. As a result of a mutation, the leaves of a certain plant may have been covered by a waterproof layer. Through natural selection, this trait increased in frequency among the plant population.
5. Taller plants may have better access to sunlight, but they also have a longer distance to transport resources from the soil, such as water and minerals, up to the highest leaves.
6. Both green algae and plants are photosynthetic eukaryotes. Green algae have the same types of chlorophyll as plants do. Both also use starch as a storage product. Finally, plants and most green algae have cell walls that contain cellulose.

21.2 Classification of Plants

KEY CONCEPTS **Plants can be classified into nine phyla.**

MAIN IDEAS
- Mosses and their relatives are seedless nonvascular plants.
- Club mosses and ferns are seedless vascular plants.
- Seed plants include cone-bearing plants and flowering plants.

VOCABULARY
pollination
gymnosperm
angiosperm
cone
flower
fruit

Connect to Your World

How many different types of plants can you think of? You are probably familiar with the plants that grow in your neighborhood and in places you regularly visit. Scientists have described about 300,000 plant species, and many more probably remain to be found. All plants belong to the kingdom Plantae. However, DNA analysis continues to reveal new relationships that keep taxonomists updating the plant family tree.

MAIN IDEA

Mosses and their relatives are seedless nonvascular plants.

In a damp forest, mosses lend an emerald green color to the landscape. These plants do not produce seeds. They have no vascular systems. Instead, they grow close to the ground or on surfaces such as tree trunks, where they can absorb water and nutrients directly. They also rely on free-standing water to allow their sperm to swim to and fertilize eggs. Mosses belong to Bryophyta, one of the three phyla of nonvascular plants. The other phyla in this category are Hepatophyta, the liverworts, and Anthocerophyta, the hornworts.

CONNECT TO

CLASSIFICATION

Recall from the chapter **The Tree of Life** that the term *division* is sometimes used instead of the term *phylum* for the classification of plants and fungi.

Liverworts

Most liverworts live in damp environments and get moisture directly from the surface of the soil. They are often found growing on wet rocks, in greenhouse flowerpots, and in other areas with plenty of moisture. Liverworts can have one of two basic forms: thallose or leafy. The name *liverwort* refers to thallose liverworts, which look like the lobes of a liver flat on the ground. Eggs are produced on umbrella-like structures of the thallose liverwort, shown in **FIGURE 2.1**. Though thallose liverworts may be easier to recognize, leafy liverworts are much more common. Leafy liverworts have stemlike and leaflike structures. These leaflike structures are most often arranged in three rows.

FIGURE 2.1 Thallose liverworts, like the one shown here, can grow from 2 mm to 25 cm in length.

Differentiated Instruction

BELOW LEVEL

To organize notes for this section, have students identify important ideas and arrange them in a concept map. Have students start with the section's Key Concept as the central box. Have them extend it to include the three major groups at the second level—seedless vascular, seedless nonvascular, seed. Then extend to a third level to include the subgroups. Tell students to identify the characteristics of each grouping.

Teacher Toolkit, Section C, Concept Map

ENGLISH LEARNERS

Have students organize the information in this section into a chart that identifies each plant phylum by its distinguishing characteristics. Students should list characteristics as column heads, and indicate with a plus or minus sign which ones a particular phylum has.

Teacher Toolkit, Section D, Semantic Feature Analysis

SECTION 21.2

Plan and Prepare

Activate Prior Knowledge Have students think about the plants that live in the local area. **Ask,** What general categories of plants are found where you live? Answers will vary but may include pines or evergreens, deciduous, or "leafy," trees, flowers, vines, cacti, mosses, shrubs, and grasses. Discuss any plants that are distinctive to your area because of climate.

Teach

Vocabulary

Word Origins The word **wort** is often used in combination with others to form the names of plants, such as *liverworts, stoneworts* (Charophyceans), and *hornworts.* It comes from an Old English word *wyrte,* meaning "plant or root." The unrelated word **wart** is a variation on the original Old English word *wearte* and refers to a growth or lump.

▼ Teach *continued*

Vocabulary

Academic Vocabulary Point out the use of the words **colonize** and **pioneer** with reference to mosses. Their general meanings fit well with the idea of a pioneer species:

pioneer—one who ventures into unknown or unclaimed territory to settle

colonize—to migrate to and settle in a distant territory

Point out in this use that not only is the land occupied by mosses originally uninhabited, it is uninhabited because the conditions are harsh and inhospitable to other forms of life. Students may be accustomed to seeing mosses in their yards and will not necessarily make this association.

Science Trivia

- An estimated 400 billion tons of carbon are stored in peat.
- Deposits of fossilized peat—better known as coal—have been mined for centuries to produce fuel for electric plants, steam engines, and other industrial purposes.
- The Chinese used coal as long ago as 1000 B.C., to smelt copper.
- The purest form of coal is graphite, the substance that is the lead in pencils.

Answers

A Apply They have no vascular system to transport resources, so water and nutrients must be absorbed directly by the entire plant.

Hornworts

Hornworts are a widespread group of plants that are found in tropical forests and along streams around the world. Hornworts grow low to the ground, and the main plant body has a flat, lobed appearance similar to that of thallose liverworts. Little green horns rising above the flat plant body, as shown in **FIGURE 2.2**, produce spores.

FIGURE 2.2 The stalks of these hornworts are 2 to 5 cm long.

Mosses

Mosses are the most common nonvascular plants. Some look like clumps of grass, others look like tiny trees, and still others look like strands of green yarn. Mosses do not have true leaves. Instead, they have leaflike structures that are just one cell thick. While they lack vascular systems, some moss species do have cuticles, and most of them have stomata. Mosses can anchor themselves to surfaces such as soil, rocks, or tree trunks, as shown in **FIGURE 2.3**, with structures called rhizoids (RY-ZOYDZ).

Mosses are often tolerant of harsh weather conditions and nutrient-poor soils. They can grow in many places where other plants are unable to grow. Some mosses can survive in deserts and tundras by entering a stage of dormancy until water is available. In fact, mosses are often among the first plants to colonize bare land and begin the soil-making process in the early stages of primary succession.

One moss that is commonly used by humans is sphagnum (SFAG-nuhm), which grows in acidic bogs. Sphagnum does not decay when it dies, so thick deposits of this dead moss, called peat, build up over time. Peat can be cut from the ground and burned as fuel. Dried peat can absorb water, and it has antibacterial properties. In fact, dried peat has been used in products such as diapers and bandages. Peat also has an important role in the carbon cycle, as a reservoir that holds carbon in an organic form.

CONNECT TO

ECOLOGY

Recall from the chapter **Interactions in Ecosystems** that primary succession is the establishment of an ecosystem in an area that was previously uninhabited. Mosses are common pioneer species that help to break down solid rock into smaller pieces—one of the first steps in producing soil.

A Apply **Why can't nonvascular plants grow tall?**

FIGURE 2.3 Like all nonvascular plants, mosses need to live in moist environments.

Differentiated Instruction

HANDS-ON ACTIVITY

Provide pairs of students with samples of peat and a graduated cylinder, beaker, or scale. Have students predict the absorptive ability of a piece of peat. Calculations could include what percent the peat's mass increases when it is saturated or what volume of water a specific volume or mass of peat can absorb. Have students share their answers with the class and discuss the usefulness of peat in gardening as a reservoir for water available to plants.

MAIN IDEA

Club mosses and ferns are seedless vascular plants.

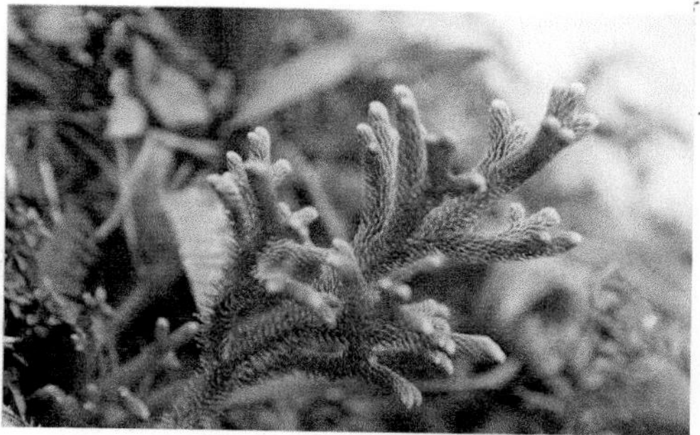

FIGURE 2.4 Club mosses, such as this *Lycopodium* species, are able to grow up off of the ground because they have vascular systems.

About 300 million years ago, during the Carboniferous period, shallow swamps were home to enormous seedless vascular plants. Over time, the dead remains of these plants were pressed and heated underground, where they gradually turned into coal. This is why we call coal a fossil fuel.

Club mosses (phylum Lycophyta) and ferns (phylum Pterophyta) are modern seedless vascular plants. Like nonvascular plants, they depend on water for reproduction. However, a vascular system allows these plants to grow higher above the ground and still get materials they need from the soil.

Club Mosses

Club mosses, which are not true mosses, belong to the oldest living group of vascular plants. Some ancient species looked like modern trees, growing more than ten stories tall. These giant plants were wiped out when the Carboniferous climate cooled, but some of the smaller species survived. One common living genus of club moss is *Lycopodium*. Some *Lycopodium* species, such as the one shown in **FIGURE 2.4**, look like tiny pine trees and are sometimes called "ground pines."

Whisk Ferns, Horsetails, and Ferns

Ferns and their relatives, whisk ferns and horsetails, can be grouped together in one phylum. Whisk ferns grow mostly in the tropics and subtropics. Although they lack true roots and leaves, DNA analysis indicates that whisk ferns are closely related to ferns.

Horsetails grow in wetland areas and along rivers and streams. They have tan, scalelike leaves that grow in whorls around a tubular stem. Like club mosses, horsetails were much larger and more common in the Carboniferous period. Because horsetails' cell walls contain a rough compound called silica, colonial settlers used the plant, also called "scouring rush," to scrub pots.

Ferns are the most successful survivors of the Carboniferous period, with about 12,000 species alive today. Most ferns grow from underground stems called rhizomes (RY-zohmz). Their large leaves, shown in **FIGURE 2.5**, are called fronds. Newly-forming fronds, called fiddleheads, uncurl as they grow. Some ferns are grown as houseplants. Others, called tree ferns, live in the tropics and can grow over three stories tall.

FIGURE 2.5 FERNS

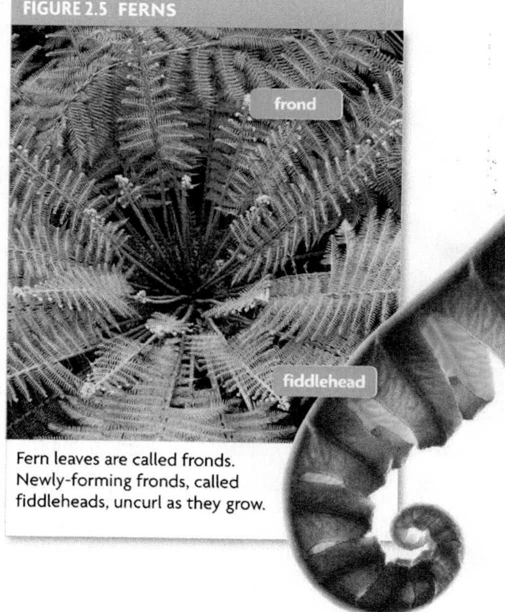

Fern leaves are called fronds. Newly-forming fronds, called fiddleheads, uncurl as they grow.

A Infer Why do most seedless vascular plants live in moist areas?

Science Trivia

One of the most dominant plant genera in the world is *Pteridium*, a fern genus that is commonly called bracken.

- Bracken is found on every continent except Antarctica, and in all regions except for arctic, alpine, and desert.
- The fiddleheads of bracken are edible and highly prized in Korea and Japan, where they are eaten fresh, cooked, and pickled.
- Bracken is highly resistant to fire. Its dead fronds can form a carpet of flammable material, which, if ignited, can burn up competing woody plants. Later, the bracken's rhizomes sprout new fronds, allowing the ferns to dominate the blackened landscape.
- The Maori, a Polynesian people that colonized New Zealand in the 13th century, ate the starchy rhizomes of bracken. By clearing and burning forest to hunt terrestrial birds and grow crops, the Maori may have provided bracken with new areas in which to grow.

Answers

A Infer They rely on water for reproduction.

BELOW LEVEL

Have students use a Y diagram to help them identify the differences and similarities between the two general categories of seedless plants, nonvascular and vascular. Students should list the characteristics of each in the "arms" of the Y, including some examples, and then identify those characteristics common to both in the "stem" of the Y.

Teacher Toolkit, Section C, Y Diagram

INCLUSION

Bring in examples of the three major groups of plants for students who are visually impaired. Have students work with a classmate who describes the distinguishing features of each group in a way that will enable the student to identify each plant.

▼ Teach *continued*

QUICKLAB

Time 15 minutes — TEACHER TESTED

Purpose Observe and compare prepared slides of vascular and nonvascular plant tissue under a microscope.

LAB MANAGEMENT

- When making comparisons, students should look for specialized cells that look like they could be "pipelines" that transport materials.

Safety Caution students to be careful in handling the slides. Remind students to wipe down the eyepieces with alcohol wipes after use.

Analyze and Conclude

1. Answers will vary depending on plants used. Both are likely green. Students should see that the tissue of vascular plants is more complex, containing "pipelines," while the tissue of nonvascular plants appears less specialized.
2. Students should have observed both types. The presence or absence of pipe-like structures should serve as evidence.
3. Nonvascular plants must absorb all water and nutrients at their surfaces (osmosis) and pass these resources from cell to cell (diffusion). This means that all cells must be relatively close to sources of water, which greatly limits their ability to grow tall.

QUICKLAB CLASSIFYING

Classifying Plants as Vascular or Nonvascular

In this lab, you will examine tissues from several plants to determine whether they are vascular or nonvascular. This is the first step in classifying plants into one of the nine phyla.

PROBLEM Are the plants vascular or nonvascular?

PROCEDURE

1. Observe each slide under the microscope.
2. Make a sketch of each plant tissue you examine.

MATERIALS

- prepared slides of plant tissue
- microscope

ANALYZE AND CONCLUDE

1. **Analyze** In what ways are the plant tissues similar? In what ways are they different?
2. **Analyze** Based on your observations, are the plants vascular or nonvascular? What evidence did you use to determine their identity?
3. **Apply** How does the absence of vascular tissue affect the size (height) of nonvascular plants?

MAIN IDEA

Seed plants include cone-bearing plants and flowering plants.

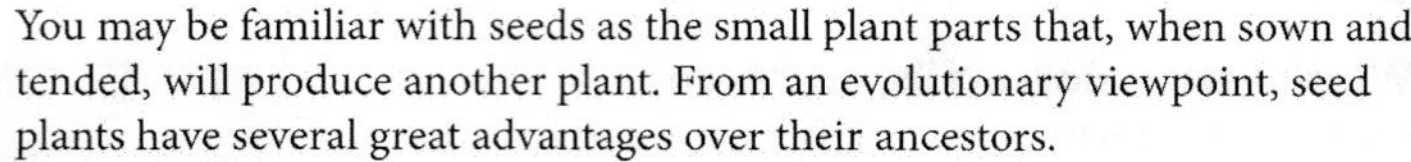

You may be familiar with seeds as the small plant parts that, when sown and tended, will produce another plant. From an evolutionary viewpoint, seed plants have several great advantages over their ancestors.

FIGURE 2.6 Seed plants produce pollen. In pine trees such as the one shown here, clouds of pollen are released from male pine cones.

- **Seed plants can reproduce without free-standing water.** Seedless plants depend on water through which sperm swim to fertilize an egg. However, seed plants do not depend on water in this way. Seed plants, such as the pine tree in **FIGURE 2.6,** produce pollen. Pollen can be carried by the wind or on the body of an animal pollinator, such as a bee. **Pollination** occurs when pollen meets female reproductive parts of the same plant species. Each pollen grain has a cell that will then divide to form sperm. Fertilization occurs when a sperm meets an egg. The ability to reproduce without free-standing water allows many seed plants to live in drier climates.
- **Seeds nourish and protect plant embryos.** A seed consists of a protective coat that contains a plant embryo and a food supply. A seed can survive for many months, or even years, in a dormant state. During this time, the seed can withstand harsh conditions, such as drought or cold, that might kill an adult plant. When conditions are right, the embryo will begin growing, using the food supply provided by the seed.
- **Seeds allow plants to disperse to new places.** Wind, water, or animals often carry seeds far from the individual plant that produced them. In fact, many seed plants have adaptations that aid in the dispersal of seeds, such as the "wings" that carry maple seeds in the wind. Because seeds can remain dormant, the embryo will not begin to develop until it reaches a suitable environment.

Differentiated Instruction

PRE-AP

Students can use a content frame to analyze and organize information about the nine plant phyla. Tell students to use the first column to list phyla, the second column to describe the main adaptations of the plants in that phylum, and any remaining columns to add more detail. Suggest that students list the phyla in the order in which they evolved, using **FIGURE 1.2** in **Section 1**, and explain how each adaptation affected their ability to live in different environments.

Teacher Toolkit, Section C, Content Frame

Scientists hypothesize that seed plants evolved as Earth's climate changed from warm and moist to hot and dry during the Devonian period, 410 to 360 million years ago. Fossil evidence suggests that seed plants evolved about 360 million years ago. Seed plants can be grouped according to whether their seeds are enclosed in fruit.

- A **gymnosperm** (JIHM-nuh-SPURM) is a seed plant whose seeds are not enclosed in fruit.
- An **angiosperm** (AN-jee-uh-SPURM) is a seed plant that has seeds enclosed in some type of fruit.

Most gymnosperms are cone-bearing and evergreen, such as pine trees. A woody **cone** is the reproductive structure of most gymnosperms. It contains hard protective scales. Pollen is produced in male cones, while eggs are produced in female cones. Seeds also develop on the scales of female cones, which protect fertilized eggs. There are three living phyla of gymnosperms: cycads (phylum Cycadophyta), *Ginkgo biloba* (phylum Ginkgophyta), and conifers (phylum Coniferophyta).

FIGURE 2.7 Cycads, such as the one shown here, produce seeds on large, protective, female cones.

READING TOOLBOX

VOCABULARY

Gymnosperm comes from the Greek words *gumnos*, which means "naked," and *sperma*, which means "seed." *Angiosperm* comes from the Greek words *angos*, which means "vessel," and *sperma*, which means "seed."

Cycads

Cycads look like palm trees with large cones, as shown in **FIGURE 2.7.** Huge forests of cycads grew during the Mesozoic era, 248 million to 65 million years ago. These plants provided food for dinosaurs. In fact, the Jurassic period of this era is commonly called the Age of the Cycads. Today, cycads grow in tropical areas in the Americas, Asia, Africa, and Australia. Many cycad species are endangered because of their slow growth and loss of habitat in these tropical areas.

Ginkgo

Like cycads, ginkgoes were abundant while the dinosaurs lived. Only one species lives today, *Ginkgo biloba*, shown in **FIGURE 2.8.** This species is native to China, and it has survived in part due to its cultivation by Buddhist monks since the year 1100. Because it so closely resembles its fossil ancestors, Darwin called this species a living fossil. In fact, the ginkgo may be the oldest living species of seed plants. Today, it is grown around the world in gardens and used in urban landscaping.

FIGURE 2.8 The name *Ginkgo biloba* refers to the two-lobed leaves of this plant. Ginkgo trees are used commonly in garden landscapes.

Science Trivia

- The female cones of gymnosperms vary in weight from less than 25 grams to more than 45 kilograms.
- Female cones vary from a few millimeters in diameter to more than a meter long.

Integrating Pharmacology

Ginkgo biloba is the oldest living tree species and one of the oldest known sources of medicine. Chinese herbal medicine has relied on the leaves and seeds of *Ginkgo biloba* for centuries, but modern medicine uses a concentrated extract made from dried leaves. Two compounds (**flavonoids** and **terpenoids**) are believed to be the most beneficial of the 40 known compounds isolated in the *Ginkgo biloba* extract. Terpenoids dilate blood vessels, allowing for improved circulation that can improve cognitive functions and memory. Flavonoids are beneficial because they destroy particles called **free radicals,** which can damage tissues and organs by attacking DNA and changing cell membranes.

HANDS-ON ACTIVITY

Have students examine a variety of seeds. For gymnosperms, students can collect pinecones and use tweezers to take apart the scales. For the seeds of angiosperms, include bare seeds and their ripened fruits, or allow students to dissect fruits to find the seeds within. Students can also go outside to gather seeds, depending on the season and the area. Students can draw detailed illustrations of the seeds and speculate on the function of any fruit that surrounds them, such as the "wings" of maple or the flesh of an apple.

▼ Teach continued

Address Misconceptions

Common Misconception Our culture tends to divide produce into fruits and vegetables, yet the distinction between the two is often artificial, based on taste or appearance more than on botanical classification. For example, students may think of tomatoes as vegetables and grapes as fruit, when in fact both are fruits.

Correcting the Misconception In botany, a fruit is simply the ripened ovary of any flowering plant. This means that peppers, tomatoes, squash, green beans, eggplant, watermelon, apples, bananas, cherries, blueberries, peaches, and cucumbers are all fruits, even though in cuisine we refer to some as vegetables. *Vegetable* really refers to the edible leaves, stalks, flower buds, or roots of a plant.

Answers

Ⓐ Apply pollen grains

FIGURE 2.9 This Ponderosa pine is a typical evergreen conifer with needlelike leaves.

Conifers

By far, the most diverse and common gymnosperms alive today are the conifers—familiar trees with needlelike leaves, such as those in FIGURE 2.9. Pines, redwood, spruce, cedar, fir, and juniper all belong to this phylum. Conifers supply most of the timber used for paper, cardboard, housing lumber, and plywood. They grow quickly, and large tree farms help produce enough wood to meet demand.

Many conifers are evergreen, or green all year-round. However, a few lose their needles in the winter. Conifers are well adapted to high altitudes, sloping hillsides, and poor soil. These characteristics allow conifers to thrive in mountainous regions.

Conifers tend to grow old and grow tall. Two known conifers hold world records. At more than 9550 years of age, one spruce tree in the Dalarna province of Sweden is the oldest known living tree. And a giant sequoia tree in Sequoia National Park in California is the world's most massive living thing. It has a mass of 1.2 million kilograms, which is about the mass of 40 buses.

Flowering Plants

Angiosperms belong to a phylum of their own (phylum Anthophyta) and are commonly called flowering plants. A **flower** is the reproductive structure of flowering plants. Flowers protect a plant's gametes and fertilized eggs, as woody cones do for most gymnosperms. A **fruit** is the mature ovary of a flower. Fruit can take the form of a juicy peach, the wings attached to a maple seed, or the fluff surrounding dandelion seeds. As you will learn in the next section, flowers and fruits have played a large role in the dominance and diversity of flowering plants today.

Ⓐ Apply **What adaptation of seed plants allows sperm to reach and fertilize an egg in the absence of water?**

▼ Assess and Reteach

Assess Use the Section Self-Check or Section Quiz, both available at **HMHScience.com**.

Reteach Draw the evolutionary tree of plants on the board, using **FIGURE 1.2** from **Section 1**. Ask students to identify plants that belong to each category and the adaptations that make them separate.

21.2 Formative Assessment

SELF-CHECK Online
HMHScience.com
GO ONLINE

REVIEWING ◐ MAIN IDEAS

1. What are the habitat requirements for seedless nonvascular plants?
2. What are the evolutionary advantages of a vascular system?
3. What are the evolutionary advantages of seeds?

CRITICAL THINKING

4. Infer In what type of environment might you find nonvascular plants, seedless vascular plants, and seed plants growing together? Explain.
5. Apply Consider the characteristics of pollen grains. Why do people with pollen allergies find it difficult to avoid exposure to pollen?

CONNECT TO HISTORY OF LIFE

6. According to the fossil record, seed plants date back to 360 million years ago, when Earth's climate was becoming hotter and drier. What role did this global climate change likely play in the evolution of seed plants?

21.2 FORMATIVE ASSESSMENT

1. environment where water and nutrients can be absorbed directly into plant body; must have free-standing water for reproduction
2. allows plants to grow taller, which can mean better access to sunlight
3. Seeds allow an embryo to remain dormant until the environmental conditions are right for growth.
4. moist environments, because all seedless plants require free-standing water for reproduction
5. Pollen grains are tiny (only two cells), and they are blown around by the wind. When pollen counts are high outdoors, it is difficult to avoid exposure unless you stay inside.
6. As the climate became drier, there was less standing water in which seedless plants could reproduce. Plants that could reproduce without free-standing water had an adaptive advantage in this situation, and they became more and more common.

Engineering the Vault: Protecting Seed Diversity

S.T.E.M. Interactions

For centuries, human beings have looked for ways to prepare for natural or human-made catastrophes. Today, people have the knowledge—and the technology—to implement plans our ancestors could only dream of. The construction of seed vaults is one of humanity's most practical precautions against disaster.

A seed vault is, quite simply, a building for storing seeds for future use. Such storage helps preserve the genetic diversity of the world's plants and protects against the extinction of plant species due to climate change, habitat destruction, disease, natural disasters, and industrial agriculture's overreliance on just a few species of plants. There are approximately 1,700 seed vaults located across the world. Some vaults store varieties of one type of staple plant, such as beans, potatoes, wheat, or rice. Others store seeds from a particular region or country.

Still other seed vaults, such as the Svalbard Global Seed Vault (SGSV), store seeds from all over the globe. The SGSV, which was established in 2008 on a Norwegian island in the Arctic Ocean, is a backup for other seed banks around the world that are in locations more susceptible to damage by climate change or war. The SGSV has room for up to 4.5 million samples of seeds. Because each sample contains 500 seeds, potentially 2.5 billion seeds can be stored there. More than 860,000 seed samples, sent from most of the world's countries, are currently stored in the SGSV.

The SGSV's location on the island of Spitsbergen is ideal for several reasons. First, Spitsbergen is very remote, far from the possibility of damage by war or civil unrest. Second, it is well above sea level, which protects against sea-level rise due to climate change. Third, the island has low humidity and is in an area not prone to earthquakes. Finally, the facility was built into the side of a mountain, and the low temperatures and thick rock keep the seeds inside frozen at −18°C.

Several natural and technological elements work in tandem to keep the seeds in the SGSV frozen. Refrigeration units in the facility keep the seeds at the required temperature. The units are powered by a local power grid, with a backup generator for extra security. But if both the local power grid and the backup generator should fail, the island's low temperatures and permafrost—and the mountain's thick rock—will keep temperatures inside the facility low.

The SGSV has been opened once already. War and civil unrest in the Syrian city of Aleppo forced scientists there to flee the violence, leaving behind the seeds at a nearby seed vault. In 2015 barley, wheat, and grass seeds were withdrawn from the SGSV to allow the relocated scientists to continue their work in safe locations in other countries.

The future is always shrouded in uncertainty, but the construction of seed vaults around the world helps ensure that humankind will be able to feed itself in the face of disaster.

S.T.E.M. Activity

Research another seed vault in a location of your choice. Learn about the vault's focus and the technology used there to store seeds safely. Then pick a location elsewhere in the world that doesn't have a seed vault. Design a seed vault that will take advantage of the area's natural and human-made characteristics. Decide what technology will be needed in the seed vault and indicate that technology in a labeled diagram.

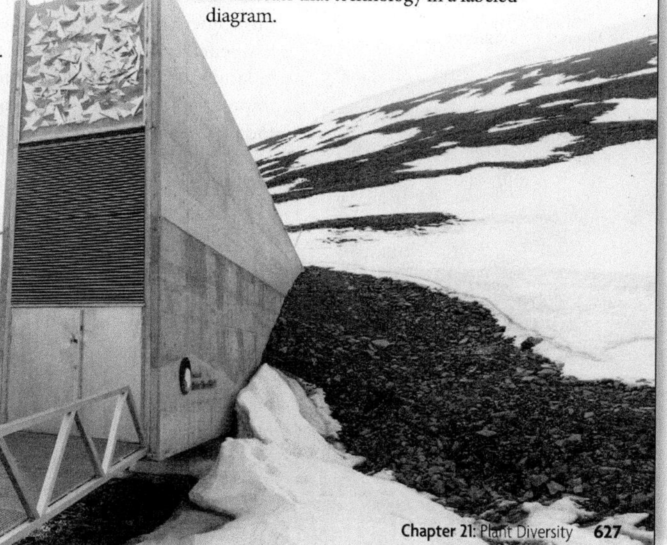

Entrance to the Svalbard Global Seed Vault

Introduce

Engage students' interest in seed vaults by explaining that different plants have, in some cases, thousands upon thousands of genetic variations. Use the apple as an example. During the 1800s, there were thousands of different varieties of apples in the United States. However, modern industrial agriculture has chosen to grow just a few of those varieties—the ones that can usually be found in grocery stores. Due to this commercial focus, many species of apples have become extinct, and many others exist only on the periphery of farms and undeveloped land. **Ask,** Why do you think modern industrial agriculture has focused on growing just a few varieties of apples? Students will most likely conclude that these varieties are desirable because of taste, juiciness, color, and other attributes.

Explain that particular apple varieties are not grown from seeds—instead, they are grown by taking a cutting from a tree with a desired apple and grafting it onto another tree. As a result, apples cannot be saved by storing their seeds in a seed bank in the way that many other plants (rice, wheat, beans, corn) can.

Students interested in ways to save apple varieties may choose to alter the focus of their STEM activity research to answer this question: How can people preserve genetic variety in plants grown by grafting or splicing?

Discuss

Ask students to present information about the seeds vaults they researched in the STEM activity. Discuss the similarities and differences between the seeds vaults. Prompt students to explain the particular problems that led to the establishment of the seed vault they researched (such as drought or war). Encourage interested students to do further research to add to the class's knowledge.

SECTION 21.3

Plan and Prepare

Activate Prior Knowledge Discuss the appeal flowers have that makes growing and selling flowering plants a multibillion dollar industry in the United States. **Ask**

- What might be the evolutionary advantage for a plant to have flowers that smell good or are bright and colorful? attracts animals that will aid in pollination or spread the seeds of the plant
- What is the evolutionary advantage of having sweet, edible fruits? Animals will eat the fruit in one location and excrete the seeds in another. The offspring can take advantage of more resources in more locations.

Teach

Vocabulary

Greek and Latin Word Origins The word **nectar** comes from the Greek *nektar,* meaning "drink of the gods." The glands that produce nectar are called **nectaries.**

21.3 Diversity of Flowering Plants

KEY CONCEPT **The largest phylum in the plant kingdom is the flowering plants.**

VOCABULARY
cotyledon
monocot
dicot
wood

MAIN IDEAS
- Flowering plants have unique adaptations that allow them to dominate in today's world.
- Flowering plants can be categorized based on seed type.
- Flowering plants are also categorized by stem type and lifespan.

Connect to Your World

Sunflower seeds in the shell aren't just a tasty snack. They are an example of one of the great adaptations of flowering plants. Like all flowering plants, sunflowers produce fruits. Technically, the fruit is the shell surrounding the sunflower seed. As you will soon learn, fruits can take many forms beyond the juicy apple or peach that may first come to mind.

MAIN IDEA

Flowering plants have unique adaptations that allow them to dominate in today's world.

CONNECT TO
EVOLUTION
Recall from the chapter **The Evolution of Populations** that mammals also went through a period of adaptive radiation after the mass extinction that killed the dinosaurs 65 million years ago.

Up until about 65 million years ago, there were far fewer flowering plants than there are today. After the mass extinction event that ended the Cretaceous period, the fossil record reveals that a major shift took place in species that dominated Earth. Dinosaurs disappeared, as did many seedless plant species. These plant extinctions left open niches into which flowering plants, such as the dogwoods in **FIGURE 3.1,** could radiate and prosper. Their diversification happened quickly in geologic terms and was closely tied to the diversification of land animals such as insects and birds. The same adaptations that were important to the success of flowering plants long ago continue to be important today.

FIGURE 3.1 Many trees, including dogwoods, are flowering plants.

Flowers and Pollination

Flowers allow for more efficient pollination than occurs in most gymnosperms, which rely on wind for pollination. You have probably observed a bee or a butterfly hovering around the center of a flower. These insects and other animals feed on pollen, which is high in protein, or on nectar, a sugary solution produced in the flowers of some plant species. As an animal feeds from a flower, it gets pollen on itself. Then, when it moves to another flower for more food, some of the pollen brushes off onto the new flower. Thus, animal pollinators transfer pollen from flower to flower in a very targeted way. For this reason, flowering plants pollinated by animals don't need to produce nearly as much pollen as do plants that rely on the wind to randomly transfer their pollen.

Differentiated Instruction

ENGLISH LEARNERS

Work with students to create a KWL chart in their science notebooks. Discuss with them what they already know, including plant names, uses, parts, and habitats. Have students list what they know in the *K* column. Under *W,* ask students to list what they would like to learn. Guide them in thinking about seed and stem types, and lifespans of various plants. Tell them to fill out the *L* column as they read the section, then compare it with what they have in the *K* column.

Teacher Toolkit, Section C, KWL Chart

BELOW LEVEL

Suggest students use a concept map to organize material for this section, as described on the first page of **Section 2.** Make sure students realize that after the division of flowering plants into monocots and dicots, the other characteristics described (stem type and lifespan) apply to both monocots and dicots.

Teacher Toolkit, Section C, Concept Map

FIGURE 3.2 Adaptations of Flowering Plants

Flowers and fruits are unique adaptations of all flowering plants.

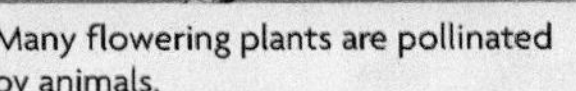

Many flowering plants are pollinated by animals.

Fruits protect the seeds of flowering plants and often play a role in seed dispersal.

Ⓐ Synthesize **How is each photograph showing a coevolutionary relationship?**

Fruits and Seed Dispersal

The many types of fruits include some very unlike the kinds you see in a grocery store. In biological terms, a fruit is a flower's ripened ovary, which surrounds and protects the seed or seeds. For example, the shells of sunflower seeds and peanuts are fruits. Fruits play an important role in seed dispersal. As shown in **FIGURE 3.2**, the more familiar fleshy fruits are tasty food sources for animals, which digest the fruit tissue but not the seeds. Seeds pass through the animal and are deposited along with a convenient supply of fecal fertilizer that is helpful during germination. Others take the form of burrs that cling to passing wildlife, or fibers that help spread seeds by wind.

Ⓑ Infer **Why is pollination by animals more efficient than wind pollination?**

MAIN IDEA

Flowering plants can be categorized based on seed type.

There are at least 300,000 identified flowering plant species. Compared with other living plant phyla—the three gymnosperm phyla have a total of 720 species—the number of flowering plants is impressive.

Botanists used to classify flowering plants into two groups based on two basic kinds of seeds: seeds with one or two cotyledons. A **cotyledon** (KAHT-uhl-EED-uhn), or seed leaf, is an embryonic leaf inside a seed. However, scientists now know that the classification of flowering plants is more complex. Based on genetic and fossil evidence, current taxonomy places plants with one cotyledon into a single group but classifies plants with two cotyledons into several diverse groups. Nevertheless, a categorization into two main groups remains useful for understanding plant structure.

HANDS-ON ACTIVITY

Have students gather samples of plants from the area outside the school or around their homes. Put students in teams and give each team several different plants to analyze. They should search for characteristics that identify the plants as either monocots or dicots. After students have successfully identified the types of plants, give them samples in which there is only one feature to analyze. For example, supply only a flower head and have students infer what type of plant the sample came from.

TEACH FROM VISUALS

FIGURE 3.2 Have students focus on the coevolution shown in the photographs. Point out the long, slender beak, the tubular red flowers, and the size correlation between the blueberry and field mouse. **Ask**

- What would happen if a bird with a short, thick beak tried to collect nectar from the flower? would not be able to reach the nectar or would destroy the flower in the process
- How would the seed dispersal of the fruit be affected if the fruit were the same size as the field mouse? The mouse may eat the fruit from around the seed instead of carrying it away or eating it whole. The seed would not be dispersed very far from the plant.

Take it Further

Fruit and seeds can be dispersed by water, as well. The **coconut,** one of the most economically important foods in the tropical Pacific, is thought to have spread to remote islands by both humans and ocean currents. On the shores of islands, many coconuts that fall to the ground from the coconut palm trees roll into the sea and get carried off by outgoing tides. The major ocean currents can then carry the coconuts, which feature a dense, fibrous husk around a hard shell, to distant shores. Many islands were probably planted with coconuts by humans, but dispersal by sea is another means of carrying some seeds.

Answers

Ⓐ **Synthesize** Because the bird has a long, slender beak, it can get food from the tubular-shaped flower. At the same time, the flower is pollinated and can reproduce. The fruit provides food for the mouse, and the mouse disperses the seeds.

Ⓑ **Infer** Wind pollination is less targeted; pollen grains land wherever the wind takes them. Animal pollinators, on the other hand, often move from flower to flower while they are feeding.

▼ Teach *continued*

The Inside Story

Carolus Linnaeus tried to classify plants by looking almost exclusively at plant reproductive organs. Any plant that lacked obvious reproductive organs was put in a class called Cryptogamia, which means "hidden marriage." This class included algae, mosses, fungi, ferns, and lichens. Meanwhile, conifers were placed in an order that included several flowering plants, as the difference between true flowers and cones was not yet understood.

Many scientists complained that Linnaeus's classification scheme for plants was artificial. **Johann Siegesbeck** criticized Linnaeus for having a scheme that was so sexually based, and called it "loathsome harlotry." Linnaeus got back at him by naming a particular weed *Siegesbeckia*.

TEACH FROM VISUALS

FIGURE 3.3 Point out the potential difficulty of determining a flowering plant's classification based solely on the number of flower parts. **Ask,** Can you think of two scenarios in which counting the number of flower parts would not tell you conclusively that a plant was a monocot or dicot? There could be 12 or 15 petals, or another number that is a multiple of both 3 and 4 or 3 and 5. Petals could be missing because the flower is damaged or dying.

Answers

A Predict No, because they are not photosynthetic. They are called "seed leaves" only because they are embryonic leaves inside of the seed.

FIGURE 3.3 Monocots and Dicots

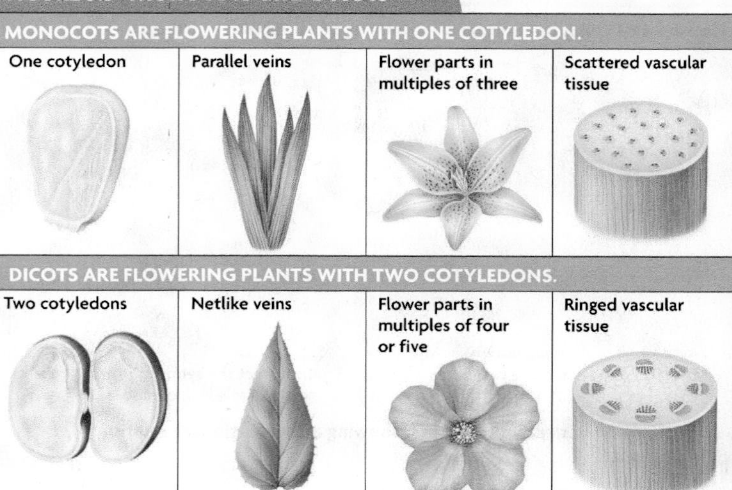

READING TOOLBOX

VOCABULARY

Mono- and *di-* are prefixes meaning "one" and "two." The word *cot* is a shortened form of the word *cotyledon*. Therefore, monocots have one cotyledon and dicots have two.

Monocots

Flowering plants whose embryos have one seed leaf are called monocotyledons, or **monocots** (MAHN-uh-KAHTS). As **FIGURE 3.3** shows, monocot plants generally have parallel veins in long, narrow leaves, such as those of an iris or lily. Their flower parts usually occur in multiples of three, and bundles of vascular tissues are scattered throughout the stem. The cereal plants we depend on—corn, wheat, rice—are monocots, as are all other grasses, irises, and lilies.

Dicots

Dicotyledons, or **dicots** (DY-KAHTS), are flowering plants whose embryos have two seed leaves. In contrast to monocots, dicots have leaves with netlike veins. Flower parts in dicots usually occur in multiples of four or five, and bundles of vascular tissue are arranged in rings. Most deciduous trees, which lose their leaves in the fall, are dicots. Peanuts are also dicots. Each "half" of a peanut that has been removed from its shell is a cotyledon.

A Predict **Would you expect that cotyledons are green inside a seed? Explain.**

MAIN IDEA

Flowering plants are also categorized by stem type and lifespan.

Flowering plants can also be categorized by stem type and lifespan, as shown in **FIGURE 3.4**. These characteristics help describe mature flowering plants and are commonly used by botanists, gardeners, landscape designers, and horticulturists.

Differentiated Instruction

PRE-AP

Students have just read about different modes of dispersal for seeds. Have them consider how the involvement of humans in the process of seed dispersal and production has altered a process that was originally driven by selective pressures. Have them write for five minutes on this question.

Teacher Toolkit, Section C, Quick-Write

Iris Monocot, herbaceous, perennial

Wheat Monocot, herbaceous, annual

Foxglove Dicot, herbaceous, biennial

Oak Dicot, woody, perennial

Big bluestem Monocot, herbaceous, perennial

FIGURE 3.4 Flowering plants are the largest and most diverse of the plant phyla. They are commonly categorized according to seed type, stem type, and lifespan.

Herbaceous or Woody Stems

Some flowering plants develop woody stems, while others do not. **Wood** is a fibrous material made up of dead cells that are part of the vascular system of some plants. High concentrations of lignin and cellulose make the cell walls of these cells thick and stiff. Woody plants therefore have stiff stems and branches. Wood also accounts for the thickness of many woody plant stems. Trees, shrubs, and most vines have woody stems. Plants that do not produce wood, such as cucumbers, cacti, and marigolds, are called herbaceous plants.

Three Types of Lifespans

It is helpful for biologists to classify plants in terms of their lifespans, since lifespan is an important life history trait.

- **Annual** Flowering plants that mature from seeds, produce flowers, and die all in one year are called annuals. Corn and lettuce are common annuals, as are some garden flowers such as zinnias.
- **Biennial** Flowering plants that take two years to complete their life cycle are called biennials. During the first year, a biennial produces a short stem, leaves that grow close to the ground, and underground food reserves. During the second year, these reserves are used to produce a taller stem, leaves, flowers, and seeds. Carrots are common biennial garden plants.
- **Perennial** Any flowering plant that lives for more than two years is a perennial. Most woody plants, including trees, are perennials. The stems and leaves of some herbaceous perennials, such as some grasses and dandelions, die at the end of the fall and grow back in the spring.

Contrast **How do the lifespans of annuals, biennials, and perennials differ?**

21.3 Formative Assessment

REVIEWING MAIN IDEAS

1. What adaptations give flowering plants a reproductive advantage over gymnosperms?
2. What are the primary differences between **monocots** and **dicots**?
3. Name three ways in which flowering plants can be categorized.

CRITICAL THINKING

4. **Contrast** In what ways does pollination in gymnosperms differ from pollination in angiosperms?
5. **Apply** How would you take plant lifespan type into account when planning a garden?

SELF-CHECK Online
HMHScience.com
GO ONLINE

CONNECT TO

MASS EXTINCTIONS

6. The fossil record reveals a mass extinction at the end of the Cretaceous period. Discuss why mass extinctions are commonly followed by a period of adaptive radiation, in this case, of flowering plants.

Vocabulary

Academic Vocabulary The word **annual** in everyday language usually is used to describe something that occurs every year, such as a holiday or the first day of school. In botany, the terms *annual*, **biennial**, and **perennial** refer to the lifespans of plants—not to how often they grow or reappear. An annual is a plant that lives for just one year—not a plant that sprouts or grows back every year. A plant that grows back every year is a perennial. In a similar way, certain sports teams are sometimes called "perennial favorites" because they perform well year after year.

Answers

A **Contrast** Annuals mature from seeds, produce flowers, and die within one year. Biennials take two years to complete their life cycle, producing a short stem, leaves, and underground food reserves in the first year and a taller stem, more leaves, flowers, and seeds during the second year. Perennials live for more than two years.

Assess and Reteach

Assess Use the Section Self-Check or Section Quiz, both available at **HMHScience.com**.

Reteach Work with students to explore the idea that special adaptations in flowering plants are associated with a plant's "lifestyle." Organize the information into a cluster diagram and ask students to identify any patterns that emerge involving these adaptations.

21.3 FORMATIVE ASSESSMENT

1. Animal pollination is more efficient than wind pollination, flower ovaries protect gametes and seeds, and fruit protects seeds and helps to disperse them.
2. monocots: one cotyledon per seed; dicots: two cotyledons per seed
3. by number of cotyledons: monocot or dicot; by stem type: woody or herbaceous; or by lifespan: annual, biennial, or perennial
4. Gymnosperms rely on wind for pollination; angiosperms are pollinated by wind or animals.
5. Annuals will need to be replanted every year. Biennial plants will not flower the first year if planted from seed, and they will need to be replanted after their second year of growth. Perennial plants will grow back every spring.
6. A mass extinction leaves open niches and unused abiotic resources. Surviving species may be able to adapt to these niches, expanding their range and possibly radiating into new species over many generations.

DATA ANALYSIS

Introduce

Scientists collect large amounts of numerical data. One way scientists make sense of this data is by using measures of central tendency to find a single number that summarizes the data. Point out that scientists usually have so much data that they use computer programs to find the mean, median, and mode. **Ask**

- Why is ordering the data points from least to greatest important when finding the median? so the point that falls in the middle can be located
- How can a data set have more than one mode? There can be several different values that occur with the same high frequency.

Inclusion Provide smaller sets of data for students who have difficulty with numbers.

Discuss

Discuss when mean, median, and mode are used when dealing with statistics. **Ask,** Which measure of central tendency is less useful if the data set contains outliers? mean

Discuss with students which measure of central tendency would be the most appropriate for determining how much money the typical worker makes in the United States. **Ask**

- Is the mean a good measure? Explain. No. The relatively few people who make millions or billions of dollars would inflate the mean far above what most people actually make.
- What measure is most appropriate, and why? median, because there would be an equal number of workers earning less and more than this value, and outliers would have no influence

Online Student Resources, Data Analysis Practice

Mean, Median, and Mode

Create animated charts and graphs with Smart Grapher.

One way to analyze data is to use measures of **central tendency,** which are measures that indicate the center of a data set. The three most common measures of central tendency are the mean, median, and mode. It is often helpful to look at all three of these measures because they may each point out different characteristics of a data set.

The **mean** is calculated by adding all of the data points together and dividing by the number of data points. The mean considers the full range of data and is therefore affected by outliers—data points that vary greatly from all of the other points in the data set.

The **median** is the data point that falls in the middle when all of the data points are ordered from least to greatest. If there is an even number of data points, the median is the average of the two middle numbers. Since outliers do not affect the median, this may be a good measure to use with a data set that includes outliers.

The **mode** is the value that occurs most frequently. It is not affected by outliers. Some data sets have more than one mode. If there are several modes that dominate the data set, it is a good idea to study these data points more closely.

Model

A class counted the number of seeds found in some common fruits. These data are shown in Table 1.

- **Oranges** The mean is an appropriate measure to use for this data set because there are no obvious outliers.
- **Watermelons** The mean is affected by an outlier, 582 seeds. The median is a good measure to represent this data set.
- **Apples** The two modes represent a trend in these results that the students may want to investigate further.

TABLE 1. NUMBER OF SEEDS IN VARIOUS FRUIT

Fruit	Number of Seeds per Fruit	Mean	Median	Mode
Apples	6, 7, 6, 4, 4, 4, 3, 6, 4, 6	5	5	4 and 6
Oranges	14, 6, 10, 8, 4, 11, 6, 3, 5, 13	8	7	6
Strawberries	171, 208, 230, 171, 159, 182, 217, 238, 165, 179	?	?	?
Watermelons	582, 133, 207, 87, 164, 290, 98, 155, 196, 278	219	180	none

Practice Choose an Appropriate Measure of Central Tendency

Use the data for the number of seeds counted in each of ten strawberries to answer the questions below.

1. **Calculate** Find the mean, median, and mode for this set of data.
2. **Evaluate** Which measure of central tendency best represents this data set? Why?

632 Unit 6: Diversity of Life

Answers

1. mean = 192, median = 180.5, mode = 171
2. The mean best represents this data set because there are no outliers.

21.4 Plants in Human Culture

VOCABULARY

botany
ethnobotany
pharmacology
alkaloid

KEY CONCEPTS **Humans rely on plants in many ways.**

MAIN IDEAS

- Agriculture provides stable food supplies for people in permanent settlements.
- Plant products are important economic resources.
- Plant compounds are essential to modern medicine.

Connect to Your World

Books are made from plants. The pages are pulverized wood from trees, the ink contains plant oil, and the glue that binds them together is made from petroleum—the ancient leftovers of algae and plants. Humans rely on plants for nearly everything in daily life. Today, crop plants are so important to our economy that their changing prices are reported in the media alongside those of stocks and bonds.

MAIN IDEA

Agriculture provides stable food supplies for people in permanent settlements.

READING TOOLBOX

VOCABULARY

The word *ethnobotany* comes from the Greek words *ethnos*, which means "people," and *botane*– which means "plants."

Some of the plants that are considered important by humans have changed over time, but plants have always been used to fill the basic needs of our species: food, shelter, clothing, and medicine. While **botany** is the study of plants, **ethnobotany** explores how people in different cultures use plants.

For most of human history, people survived by hunting and gathering. This requires a very thorough understanding of local botany—plant locations, life cycles, and characteristics. Hunting and gathering also requires people to change locations if resources are diminished by weather, disease, or overuse. People then must become familiar with the resources of the new area.

FIGURE 4.1 Agriculture has become an important part of our global economy. Many river deltas, such as the Sacramento River delta in California, are used for farmland because of their nutrient-rich soils and water.

SECTION 21.4

Plan and Prepare ▼

Activate Prior Knowledge **Ask,** What plant products have you used so far today? *Sample answer:* food, clothing, books, furniture Point out that most of the plants that people rely on are seed plants. One exception dates back to the Carboniferous period, when mosslike plants and ferns became peat and were eventually compressed and heated into coal.

Teach ▼

Vocabulary

Academic Vocabulary In biology, the word **culture** is often used as a verb that means "to grow or cultivate." To specify what is being grown, *culture* is often combined with other words or prefixes. The root *agri-* of **agriculture** comes from a Latin root meaning "field." **Aquaculture** is the cultivation of aquatic organisms such as fish and shellfish.

Differentiated Instruction

BELOW LEVEL

Have students organize the material in this section by constructing a timeline from the dates provided in the text.

Teacher Toolkit, Section C, Timeline

PRE-AP

Explain to students that cereals are grain-producing grasses. The first wild wheat had stalks that opened easily, scattering their seeds. Today, the stalks of cultivated wheat are tough and do not yield the seeds until harvested. Have students create a cause-and-effect chain to suggest how the first farmers may have affected the evolution of wheat species. Tell students to consider factors such as how easily the seeds could be dispersed.

Teacher Toolkit, Section C, Cause-and-Effect Chain

▼ Teach continued

Take It Further

One treatment for malaria is **quinine,** an alkaloid from the bark of the cinchona tree. Peruvian Indians used this bark to treat fevers before the 1600s. During the 1600s, missionaries took the bark back to Europe. Eventually, demand for the bark increased, and the number of trees began decreasing rapidly. Today, quinine is produced synthetically for use in anti-malarial medicines and as a bitter flavoring in tonic water.

Tonic water was created specifically to be taken as a preventive medicine for malaria. To make it more palatable, because tonic water was much more bitter than it is now, Englishmen in the tropics began to mix in a little gin, making the first gin and tonic. Today's tonic water has so little quinine that one would need to drink an enormous quantity to ward off malaria, which still kills about one million people every year.

Integrating Genetics

Today's crops are changing quickly as a result of **genetic engineering.** Scientists no longer rely on artificial selection. They can transfer a gene from an unrelated species into the seeds of crops. The resulting plants may be more resistant to insects and disease or may be more nutritious. Many of our crops today are grown from genetically modified seeds. However, some scientists are concerned about unknown risks to human health or to the environment. See the **BioZine** feature in the **Plants** unit for more on genetically modified foods.

Answers

A Summarize how different cultures use plants

B Connect *Sample answer:* cotton plants for t-shirts, trees for notebook paper and pencils

FIGURE 4.2 Teosinte (top) is the ancestor of modern corn. Modern corn evolved through artificial selection. Humans likely selected individual plants that had the most numerous and accessible seeds.

Archaeological evidence suggests that people started intentionally planting for harvest about 10,000 years ago. Over the centuries, ancient farmers "tamed" wild species by a process of artificial selection, as shown in **FIGURE 4.2.** They chose plants with the best traits, saved their seeds, and planted them the next year. Most of the world's staple foods—corn, rice, and wheat—were developed from wild grasses in this way. These farmers became more closely tied to particular areas.

Because farming requires people to stay in one place, agriculture gave rise to more socially complex centers of human populations. A benefit of farming was a more reliable source of food that could support a growing population. Eventually, farmers grew enough excess food to sell it to neighbors as a cash crop. In this way, farming became part of a culture's economy.

A Summarize What does an ethnobotanist study?

MAIN IDEA

Plant products are important economic resources.

Plant products have been traded among various regions for thousands of years. Spices such as pepper, cinnamon, and cloves were so valuable that they were commonly used as a form of currency during the early Middle Ages. In fact, many of the seafaring explorations to Asia and the Americas during the 1400s and 1500s were prompted by the value of spices, like those shown in **FIGURE 4.3.** Columbus, Magellan, and da Gama were all in search of a new route to the valuable commodities of the East.

Today, plants are important economic resources on a global scale. The values of rice, grains, soybeans, coffee, sugar, and cotton traded in world markets every year are each billions of dollars. Paper, textiles, and lumber are just a few of the plant-derived products that contribute to our economy.

B Connect What plants were used to make the clothes that you are wearing and the contents of your backpack?

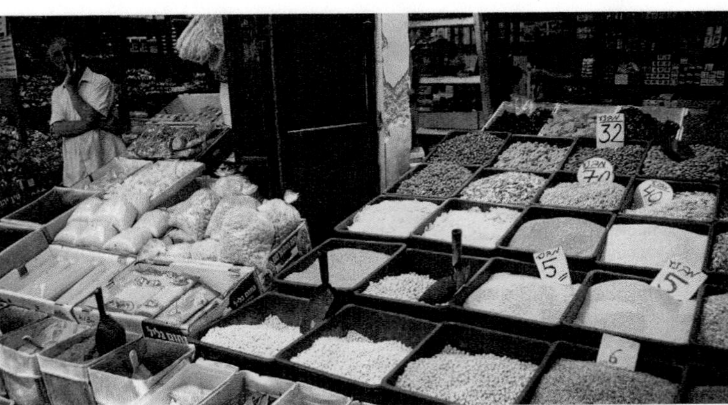

FIGURE 4.3 Spices have been an economically important resource for at least 4000 years.

Differentiated Instruction

HANDS-ON ACTIVITY

Have students work in pairs to look around the classroom and identify as many things as they can that are plant products. Give students five minutes and see which pair can come up with the longest list. When students misidentify something as a plant product when it is, in fact, synthetic, take the opportunity to discuss synthetics such as nylon and polyester. Encourage students to think of all possible plant products, including invisible things, such as oxygen.

MAIN IDEA

Plant compounds are essential to modern medicine.

The study of drugs and their effects on the body is called **pharmacology.** Many of the drugs used today are derived from plants, and much of the knowledge of these plants comes from traditional cultures. We still use some plants medicinally in the same way they have been used for thousands of years. For instance, the aloe vera gel you can buy to soothe sunburn was used for the same purpose by the Egyptians 3500 years ago.

As shown in **FIGURE 4.4**, scientists continue to look for and find new uses for plants that have been used medicinally for centuries. For example, Native Americans have long used the Pacific yew to treat a variety of conditions. In the 1960s, scientists isolated a compound called taxol from the tree, which has been used as a cancer treatment since 1993. Salicin, which comes from willow trees, is another plant compound that you are likely familiar with. It is the active ingredient in aspirin, the most widely used medicine in the world.

While plant oils and resins are common in traditional medicines, other plant compounds, including gums, steroids, and alkaloids, have found their way into modern medicines. **Alkaloids** are potent plant chemicals that contain nitrogen. In small amounts, many alkaloids are medicinal. By interfering with cell division, some alkaloids—such as taxol—have anti-cancer properties. Two alkaloids produced by the Madagascar periwinkle are used to treat childhood leukemia and Hodgkin's disease. Other alkaloids have been identified to treat conditions ranging from a nasty cough to high blood pressure.

Today, much medical research focuses on the chemical properties of various plant compounds—especially compounds from plants that have been used medicinally in traditional cultures. Chemists also work to develop synthetic drugs based on the structure of these natural compounds, often changing the structures slightly to increase effectiveness and reduce side effects.

A Infer **Why might certain plant compounds have healing effects in small quantities but be dangerous in larger doses?**

FIGURE 4.4 This scientist, standing waist-high in water, is studying a mangrove forest in Thailand. Mangrove forests grow in intertidal zones in the tropics. These diverse ecosystems may hold treatments for a variety of medical conditions.

CONNECT TO

CELLS

Some alkaloids help stop the spread of cancer by interfering with mitosis. Recall from the chapter **Cell Growth and Division** that mitosis is the phase of the cell cycle when the duplicated chromosomes separate so that two new cells form.

21.4 Formative Assessment

SELF-CHECK Online
HMHScience.com
GO ONLINE

REVIEWING MAIN IDEAS

1. How has agriculture affected the day-to-day life of humans?
2. In what ways are plants an important part of our culture today?
3. Why is a knowledge of plants so important to **pharmacology**?

CRITICAL THINKING

4. **Analyze** How did the average person's knowledge of plants change in societies that adopted agriculture? Explain your answer.
5. **Connect** Aside from food and medicine, in what ways are plants used in your life?

CONNECT TO

HUMAN IMPACT ON ECOSYSTEMS

6. Many plants harvested for medicinal purposes grow in rain forests of developing countries. How might this fact affect the ecosystems and economies of these countries?

21.4 FORMATIVE ASSESSMENT

1. Today, most humans do not rely on hunting and gathering to obtain food. Agriculture makes large quantities of food available.
2. We use plants for food, drink, medicine, construction, and numerous other products by which our cultures are largely defined.
3. Many modern medicines are derived from plants or have chemical structures based on the structures of plant chemicals.
4. In an agricultural society, the growers are the ones who know about plants; people who buy food do not need to know. In hunter-gather societies, everyone had to know where and when to find plants, and which were edible.
5. *Sample answers:* grass playing fields, cotton clothing, paper, wooden furniture, wooden pencils
6. When harvesting of a plant becomes very profitable, it can lead to overharvesting or planting of cash crops instead of food crops.

ONLINE Biology
HMHScience.com

For information on threatened or endangered plant species, see the WebQuest for this chapter at **HMHScience.com**.

Take It Further

A very small percentage of plants have been studied for potential use as medicines. The areas of Earth with the greatest potential for research are the **tropics** because of the great diversity of plants that grow there. As human demands for space and resources increase, many plant species are becoming endangered or extinct. Discuss what the extinction of plant species might mean for the discovery of new medicines.

Vocabulary

Greek and Latin Word Origins The term **pharmacology** is from the Greek word *pharmakon,* which means "drug." Other common words related to pharmacology include *pharmacist* and *pharmacy.* The word *pharmaceutical* can be used as an adjective or noun; its root is the Greek word *pharmakeutikos,* which means "preparer of drugs."

Students may have also heard of the term **apothecary,** which refers to a shop that sells or person who dispenses drugs or other medicines. It has a Greek root meaning "storehouse."

Answers

A **Infer** Large amounts of any chemical can disrupt equilibrium in body systems.

Assess and Reteach

Assess Use the Section Self-Check or Section Quiz, both available at **HMHScience.com**.

Reteach Create a cycle diagram on the board that illustrates the relationships between humans, plants, atmosphere, hydrosphere, and other systems.

CHAPTER REVIEW

INTERACTIVE Review
HMHScience.com

GO ONLINE

Encourage students to go to **HMHScience.com** for a detailed review of each section, including visuals and vocabulary practice.

Online Student Resources, Vocabulary Practice Worksheet

CHAPTER 21 **Summary**

BIG IDEA Many organisms on Earth, including humans, depend on the diversity of plants and their traits for survival.

KEY CONCEPTS

21.1 Origins of Plant Life

Plant life began in the water and became adapted to land. The common ancestor of plants is an ancient species of green algae. Green algae called charophyceans are the closest living relatives to this common ancestor. Over time, the first true plant species evolved as they adapted to life on land. Land plants have evolved mechanisms to retain moisture, transport resources, grow upright, and reproduce on land. They have also coevolved with other organisms that inhabit dry land.

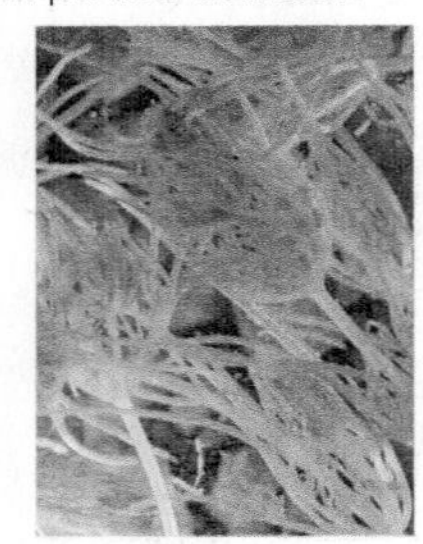

21.2 Classification of Plants

Plants can be classified into nine phyla. Mosses and their relatives make up three phyla of seedless nonvascular plants. These plants rely on water for reproduction and must grow low to the ground to absorb water and nutrients. Club mosses and ferns make up two phyla of seedless vascular plants. Vascular tissue allows these plants to grow higher above the ground. Seed plants, which include three phyla of cone-bearing plants and one phylum of flowering plants, do not rely on water for reproduction. Sperm of seed plants are produced by pollen grains. Seeds nourish and protect the embryos of these plants.

21.3 Diversity of Flowering Plants

The largest phylum in the plant kingdom is the flowering plants. Flowers and fruit are two adaptations that have allowed flowering plants to become the dominant plant group on Earth today. Flowers often allow for more efficient pollination by animals, while fruit can aid in seed dispersal. Flowering plants can be categorized into two groups based on the number of cotyledons inside the seed. Flowering plants can also be categorized based on stem type and lifespan.

21.4 Plants in Human Culture

Humans rely on plants in many ways. Plants are essential to human existence. All of the food that we eat comes either directly or indirectly from plant life. Agriculture provides stable food supplies for most people today. Many agricultural products are important economic resources on a global scale. Plants also provide us with clothing, paper, textiles, lumber, and medicines.

READING TOOLBOX SYNTHESIZE YOUR NOTES

Three-Column Chart Use a three-column chart to take notes about the nine divisions of plants. Use the columns to write the scientific names of each division, the common names, and details about the plants.

Scientific Name	Common Name	Details

Concept Map Use a concept map to review how flowering plants can be categorized.

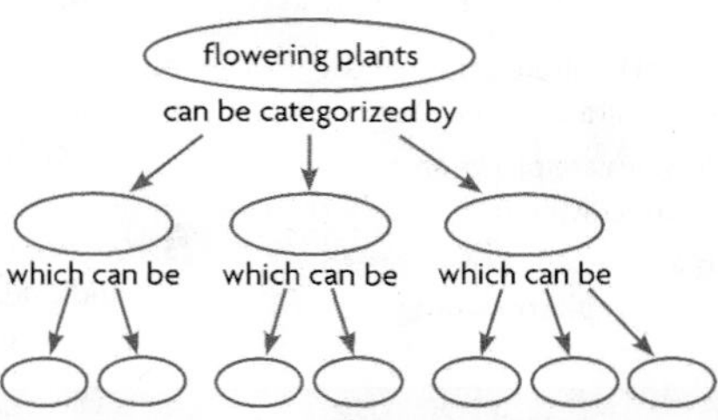

Reviewing Vocabulary

1. Wood is a fibrous material made up of dead plant cells whose cell walls contain high concentrations of lignin and cellulose.
2. Pollination occurs when a pollen grain meets the female reproductive parts of the same plant species.
3. Gymnosperms are cone-bearing seed plants.
4. Angiosperms are seed plants that produce flowers and fruit.
5. Monocots have one cotyledon, or seed leaf, whereas dicots have two.
6. Alkaloids are potent plant chemicals that are studied in pharmacology.
7. The cuticle of plants forms a protective outer layer, similar in function to the skin of animals.
8. A stoma is a hole in a leaf cuticle that allows for gas exchange; the mouth of an animal is an opening through which the animal exchanges gases by breathing.
9. Pollen grains are two-celled structures that are released in large clouds that can resemble dust or flour.
10. The scales of cones can be wedge shaped.
11. Fruits are so named because many of them are sweet or otherwise enjoyable as foods.
12. Monocots have one cotyledon, while dicots have two.

21 Review

INTERACTIVE Review
HMHScience.com

GO ONLINE

Review Games • Concept Map • Section Self-Checks

CHAPTER VOCABULARY

21.1	21.2	21.3
plant	pollination	cotyledon
cuticle	gymnosperm	monocot
stomata	angiosperm	dicot
vascular system	cone	wood
lignin	flower	**21.4** botany
pollen grain	fruit	ethnobotany
seed		pharmacology
		alkaloid

Reviewing Vocabulary

Vocabulary Connections

For each group of words below, write a sentence or two to clearly explain how the terms are connected. For example, for the terms *cuticle* and *stomata,* you could write "Together, the cuticle and stomata prevent water loss while allowing for gas exchange."

1. lignin, wood
2. pollen grain, pollination
3. gymnosperm, seed, cone
4. angiosperm, seed, flower, fruit
5. cotyledon, monocot, dicot
6. pharmacology, alkaloid

READING TOOLBOX GREEK AND LATIN WORD ORIGINS

7. *Cuticula* is the Latin word for "skin." How does this meaning relate to the definition of the word *cuticle*?

8. In Greek, the word *stoma* means "mouth." How does this meaning relate to its botanical meaning?

9. In Latin, the word *pollen* means "dust" or "fine flour." How does this meaning relate to its botanical meaning?

10. The word *conus* is a Latin word that means "wedge" or "peak." How does this meaning relate to the definition of the word *cone*?

11. *Fruī* is a Latin verb meaning "to enjoy." How does this meaning relate to the role that various fruits play in human culture?

12. The prefix *mono-* means "one" in Latin, while the prefix *di-* means "two." How do these meanings relate to the words *monocot* and *dicot*?

Reviewing MAIN IDEAS

13. Summarize the evidence supporting the statement that modern plants evolved from an ancient species of green algae.

14. Discuss four major challenges that early plants faced while adapting to life on dry land.

15. The 30-centimeter tongue of the hawk moth is long enough to reach the nectar—and reproductive organs—of the night-blooming orchid. What can be concluded about the evolution of plants from these types of relationships? Explain.

16. Describe the structural features that limit the height of mosses and their relatives.

17. Explain why most seedless vascular plants live in moist environments.

18. What is the main difference between the seeds of cone-bearing plants and the seeds of flowering plants?

19. Summarize two of the adaptations of flowering plants that allow them to flourish in today's world.

20. Describe how the number of cotyledons a plant has is useful in categorizing plants.

21. Compare and contrast annual, biennial, and perennial lifespans.

22. What role does agriculture play in the stability and survival of modern human populations?

23. How can plants play a role in developing modern medicines, even if they are not used as ingredients?

CHAPTER REVIEW

Reviewing Main Ideas

13. Green algae and plants share many characteristics. Both are able to photosynthesize; they contain the same types of chlorophyll; both use starch as a storage product; and most green algae, as well as all plants, have cell walls containing cellulose. Genetic analysis reveals that charophyceans, green algae common in shallow freshwater environments today, are the closest living relatives of plants.

14. retaining moisture, or not drying out; transporting resources that are obtained from below ground and above ground to various parts of the plant; growing upright without the support of water; reproducing without freestanding water

15. They have likely coevolved with their animal pollinators. The orchid evolved to rely on a moth with a long tongue to pollinate it, while the moth evolved to specialize in obtaining food from deep within the orchid.

16. They do not have a vascular system to carry resources to various parts of the plant. As a result, the plants' cells need to be close to water and nutrients on the ground, so height is limited.

17. They need freestanding water for reproduction; sperm must swim through water in order to reach and fertilize an egg.

18. The seeds of flowering plants are enclosed in fruit, and the seeds of cone-bearing plants are not.

19. Flowers can attract animal pollinators, and therefore allow for more efficient pollination. Fruit can protect seeds and aid in seed dispersal.

20. Plants with one cotyledon (monocots) represent one group, while plants with two cotyledons (dicots) represent several groups of plants. They are still useful categories because monocots and dicots have different plant structure.

21. Annuals mature from seed, produce flowers, and die all in one year. Biennials take two years to go through this cycle. Perennials live for more than two years.

22. Agriculture provides a more reliable source of food than hunting and gathering, and this food source can often support a growing population. Agriculture also allows for socially complex centers of human populations because people do not have to move around to find food.

23. The chemical structures of many synthetic drugs are based on the structures of plant compounds.

Critical Thinking

24. They have limited access to sunlight because some of the light is filtered out by the water. Also, gas exchange (CO_2) may be more difficult underwater, and certain minerals are much less common in aquatic soils than in terrestrial soils.
25. The sperm of seed plants are derived from pollen grains. Pollen grains are carried from the male parts of flowers to the female parts, either by wind or animals; therefore, the sperm of seed plants do not need water to "swim" through to reach an egg.
26. Seedless plants disperse by way of their spores. Seed plants disperse with their seeds.
27. Economic resources, including potential medicines, will be lost. The rain forests are some of the most biologically diverse ecosystems on Earth, so a tremendous amount of species may be lost.
28. The special markings guide animal pollinators to the pollen or nectar, and also to the plant's reproductive structures. This adaptation would be favored in order to increase the chances of pollination.
29. The fruit around dandelion seeds is a fluffy, parachute-like material that allows the seeds to be carried easily by wind. The seeds of pine trees are not enclosed in fruit and cannot be dispersed very far by wind.
30. Insecticides may cause a decline in insect populations, which means there are potentially fewer pollinators for certain plant species. If plants do not get pollinated, they cannot complete their reproductive cycle. Ultimately, this can result in declining plant populations.

Critical Thinking

24. **Analyze** Aquatic plants, which evolved from land plants, have adaptations that allow them to live in the water. Some aquatic plants grow completely submerged in water. What challenges might these plants face that do not apply to plants that live entirely on land?
25. **Analyze** The sperm of seedless plants are flagellated, while those of seed plants are not. How do the sperm of seed plants reach eggs without flagella?
26. **Compare** When a plant reproduces, it is important for its offspring to disperse so that they do not compete directly with the parent plant. Compare the structures that allow seedless plants and seed plants to disperse to new locations.
27. **Synthesize** Some experts predict that the Amazon rain forest will be completely destroyed within the next century due to human activities. What resources would potentially be lost along with this ecosystem?
28. **Infer** Some types of flowers have special markings on their petals that act as guides to the pollen or nectar for their pollinators. How could such markings have evolved through natural selection?
29. **Analyze** What evolutionary advantage do the seeds of dandelions have over the seeds of pine trees?
30. **Synthesize** How might an increase in the use of insecticides affect flowering-plant populations in the area?

Interpreting Visuals

Use the illustration below to answer the next two questions.

31. **Analyze** What parts of this plant could you examine to determine whether it is a monocot or a dicot?
32. **Apply** Is this plant likely a monocot or a dicot? Explain your reasoning.

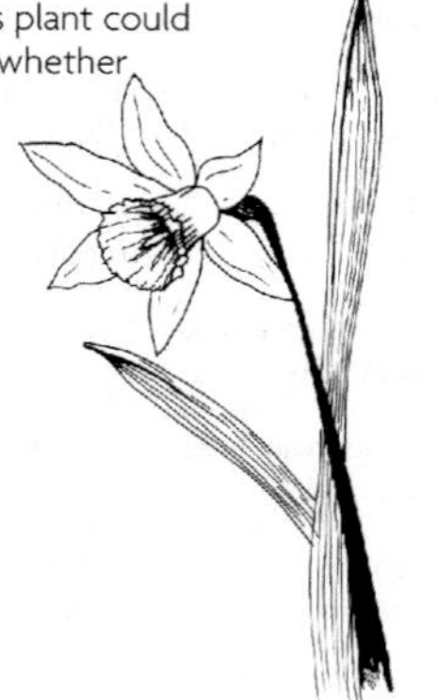

Analyzing Data Measure Central Tendency

Valencia oranges, which likely originated in Spain or Portugal, are now the most widely planted orange variety in the world. Use the data below on the number of California Valencia oranges per tree to answer the next three questions.

CALIFORNIA VALENCIA ORANGES PER TREE
596, 402, 489, 708, 374, 548, 640, 585, 518, 450

Source: *California Agricultural Statistics Service*

33. **Calculate** What are the mean, median, and mode for this data set? Round the mean to the nearest whole number.
34. **Analyze** Does this data set contain outliers? Explain your answer.
35. **Evaluate** Which measure of central tendency best represents this data set? Explain your answer.

Making Connections

36. **Write About Seeds** From the viewpoint of a plant embryo, write about the importance of a seed. What does the seed provide for you? In what ways does it help you? What advantages do you have over nonseed plants?
37. **Synthesize** The flowering proteas of South Africa are adapted to a dry climate that receives as little as 600 mm (23.6 in) of rain each year. However, plants must retain moisture in order for photosynthesis to occur. Describe the adaptations that allow these plants to retain moisture in their leaves while still allowing for air to move in and out.

Interpreting Visuals

31. From this illustration, you can examine the number of flower parts and the pattern of leaf veins to identify the plant as a monocot or a dicot.
32. It is likely a monocot because it has six petals (a multiple of 3) and parallel veins.

Analyzing Data

33. mean = 531, median = 533, mode = none
34. No outliers; the two extremes (374 and 708) do not seem different enough from the rest of the numbers to be considered outliers.
35. When there are no outliers, the mean usually best represents the data because all data points factor into it.

Standards-Based Assessment

Record your answers on a separate piece of paper.

MULTIPLE CHOICE

1 In the 1940s, Barbara McClintock observed patterns of inheritance in corn plants that could not be explained by the current gene theory. The conclusions of her work were not widely accepted for years until further supported by the work of other scientists. What does this scenario demonstrate about science?

A Data that are more than 50 years old should be discarded.

B Data that do not fit a scientific theory should be discarded.

C Theories may be modified as additional data leads to new conclusions.

D The repetition of results by many scientists is not necessary to validate a theory.

2

Tomato Plant Growth Per Week (cm)		
Plot	**Condition**	**Average Growth**
1	full sun	9 cm
2	part sun	7 cm
3	full shade	2 cm

Gardeners are testing three plots of land with similar soil to find out which is ***best*** for growing tomato plants. Which of the following conclusions is best supported by their data?

A Plot 1 received the most nutrients.

B Tomato plants grow best in full sun.

C Tomato plants cannot grow in the shade.

D The data are not reliable because there is no control.

3 The sugar in corn quickly converts to starch after the corn has been picked. After picking, corn that has the *Sh2* gene in its DNA was found to have more sugar and less starch than corn without this gene. Which of the following statements is ***most likely*** true about corn with this gene?

A Corn that expresses this gene cannot convert sugar to starch.

B This gene causes corn to convert sugar to starch when picked.

C Plants with this gene produce less sugar.

D This gene works in conjunction with other genes to convert sugar to starch.

THINK THROUGH THE QUESTION

Think about the process by which plants produce sugars. You can eliminate any answer choices that would result in plants with less sugar.

4 The beak shape shown below likely evolved as a result of the birds that could get food most efficiently with this adaptation —

A dying in the absence of long, tubular flowers

B not attracting a mate

C being able to eat a wide variety of food, such as nuts, insects, and berries

D being more likely to survive and reproduce

5 Rock from the Cretaceous period contains the fossils of a variety of dinosaurs and seedless plants. The fossil record afterwards includes the fossils of many flowering plants and smaller animals, but no dinosaurs. Which of the following statements is supported by this evidence?

A Dinosaurs had begun to die out during the Cretaceous period.

B A mass extinction at the end of the Cretaceous period made new niches available for flowering plants.

C The Cretaceous environment was less favorable to seedless plants than to flowering plants.

D Dinosaurs evolved around the end of the Cretaceous period.

Standards-Based Assessment

The Standards-Based Assessment questions will help students prepare for their final examination in the course. If you wish to give students practice in coding their answers, look for the Standards-Based Assessment Answer Sheet at **HMHScience.com**. To give students practice under timed testing conditions, allow them five minutes per question.

Question	Answer	Depth of Knowledge	Cognitive Complexity
1	C	III	M
2	B	I	L
3	A	IV	H
4	D	IV	H
5	B	III	H

KEY

Depth of Knowledge
- I Recall
- II Skill/Concept
- III Strategic Thinking
- IV Extended Thinking

Cognitive Complexity
- L Low
- M Moderate
- H High

Making Connections

36. Students should write a clear response that reflects an understanding of the adaptive advantages of seeds. A seed coat protects an embryo. A food supply within the seed coat provides nourishment. Seeds help individual plants disperse to new areas, away from the parent plant. A major advantage that seed plants have over nonseed plants is that seed plants can reproduce without freestanding water.

37. The surfaces of many plants are covered with a cuticle, which is a waxy, waterproof layer that helps hold in moisture. Tiny holes in the cuticle, called stomata, allow air to move in and out of the plant surfaces.

CHAPTER 22

Instruction and Intervention Support

Invertebrate Diversity

① Core Instruction

The **Core Instruction** resources below can be used for all students. Core instruction should be followed by ongoing assessment to determine which students need further help.

Available in both English and Spanish

Available Online

Section	Instruction	PRINT	ONLINE	Labs
22.1	Textbook **Animal Characteristics**	■	●	
	PowerPresentation and Notes 22.1		●	
22.2	Textbook **Animal Diversity**	■	●	**Video Lab** Embryonic Development
	Animated Biology Shared Body Structures, Digestive Tract Formation, Early Embryonic Development		●	
	PowerPresentation and Notes 22.2		●	
22.3	Textbook **Sponges and Cnidarians**	■	●	Feeding *Hydra* **Video Lab** Hydra Behavior
	Teaching Visuals Sponge Anatomy (Fig. 3.2), Cnidarian Anatomy (Fig. 3.4)			
	PowerPresentation and Notes 22.3		●	
22.4	Textbook **Flatworms, Mollusks, and Annelids**	■	●	Anatomy of an Annelid Cardiovascular System of Mudworms (Challenge Lab, Design Your Own) **QuickLab** Anatomy of a Clam **Video Lab** Clam Characteristics
	PowerPresentation and Notes 22.4		●	
22.5	Textbook **Roundworms**	■	●	Evolution of the Coelom
	PowerPresentation and Notes 22.5		●	
22.6	Textbook **Echinoderms**	■	●	Anatomy of a Sea Star
	PowerPresentation and Notes 22.6		●	

Additional online resources available for this chapter include **Interactive Whiteboard Resources.**

GO ONLINE! for all your teacher resources at HMHScience.com

② Support and Intervention

Support and Intervention resources are useful for students who need targeted help beyond the Core Instruction

Resources	PRINT	ONLINE
Assess and Reteach (TE wrap)	■	⊙
Concept Map		⊙
Interactive Reader	■	⊙
Interactive Review Games		⊙
Section Self-Checks		⊙
Study Guide B		⊙
Vocabulary Practice Worksheets		⊙

③ Specialized Support

Students who need more intensive personalized intervention benefit from **Specialized Support** resources.

Resources	PRINT	ONLINE
Chapter Audio Files		⊙
Differentiated Instruction Inclusion, Below Level, and English Learners (TE wrap)	■	⊙
ELL Strategies	■	⊙
Modified Lesson Plans for English Learners		⊙
Reinforcement Worksheets		⊙
Study Guide A		⊙

Extension and Assessment

Enrichment and Challenge

Resources	PRINT	ONLINE
Active Reading Worksheets		⊙
Data Analysis Practice Worksheet		⊙
Differentiated Instruction Pre-AP (TE wrap)	■	⊙
Pre-AP Activity Nematocysts in Action, Cone Snails: Nature's Drug Makers		⊙
The Inside Story and **Take It Further** (TE wrap)	■	⊙
Unit Project		⊙
WebLinks		⊙
WebQuest Parasites (22.4)		⊙

Assessment

Resources	PRINT	ONLINE
Alternative Assessment		⊙
Chapter Tests A and B		⊙
Diagnostic Test		⊙
ExamView Banks		⊙
Extended Response Test		⊙
Online Assessment System		⊙
Section Quizzes		⊙
Standards-Based Assessment	■	⊙

CHAPTER 22

Chapter Overview

- **Section 1** identifies the common characteristics shared by all animals.
- **Section 2** compares the basic characteristics of animal groups.
- **Section 3** describes the anatomy and characteristics of sponges and cnidarians.
- **Section 4** classifies flatworms, mollusks, and annelids and describes their characteristics.
- **Section 5** provides coverage of invertebrates, including the characteristics of roundworms.
- **Section 6** gives information on how echinoderms are classified and characterized.

▼ Focus and Motivate

How is this sea slug similar to a spider?

They are both invertebrates; they do not have backbones. The differences between the two animals (body make-up, habitat, diet, reproduction) are indicative of the diversity of the invertebrate group. **Ask**

- What are some invertebrates you have contact with in your daily activities? Answers may include seafoods such as shrimp, crab, lobster, and clams; natural sponges used for cleaning and bathing; spiders, mosquitoes, and houseflies.
- What are some ways that invertebrates affect human life? parasitism, disease transmission, crop pests, sources of food

BIOZINE
HMHScience.com

Students can access BioZine at **HMHScience.com** to check out articles featured in Strange Biology.

CHAPTER 22 Invertebrate Diversity

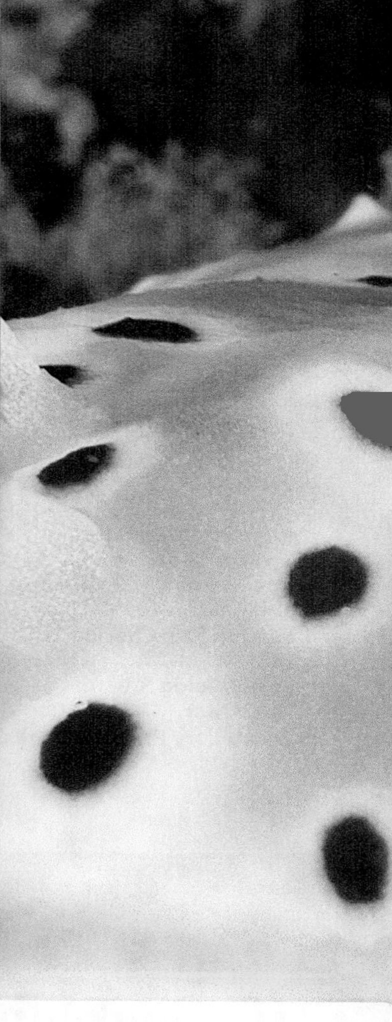

BIG IDEA Animals share many characteristics, yet have a variety of shapes, structures and sizes, and most have no backbone.

ONLINE BIOLOGY HMHScience.com

ONLINE Labs
- Feeding *Hydra*
- **QuickLab** Anatomy of a Clam
- Anatomy of a Sea Star
- Anatomy of an Annelid
- Evolution of Coelom
- Cardiovascular System of Mudworms
- **Video Lab** Embryonic Development
- **Video Lab** *Hydra* Behavior
- **Video Lab** Clam Characteristics

Teacher Demonstration

Eye Opener **Use a snail as an example of the diverse adaptations of invertebrates. Students will see that snails absorb gases through their skin and through an organ on their right side called the pneumostome.**

Materials
- snail, preferably a terrestrial species
- paper towels
- cotton swabs
- small container of white vinegar

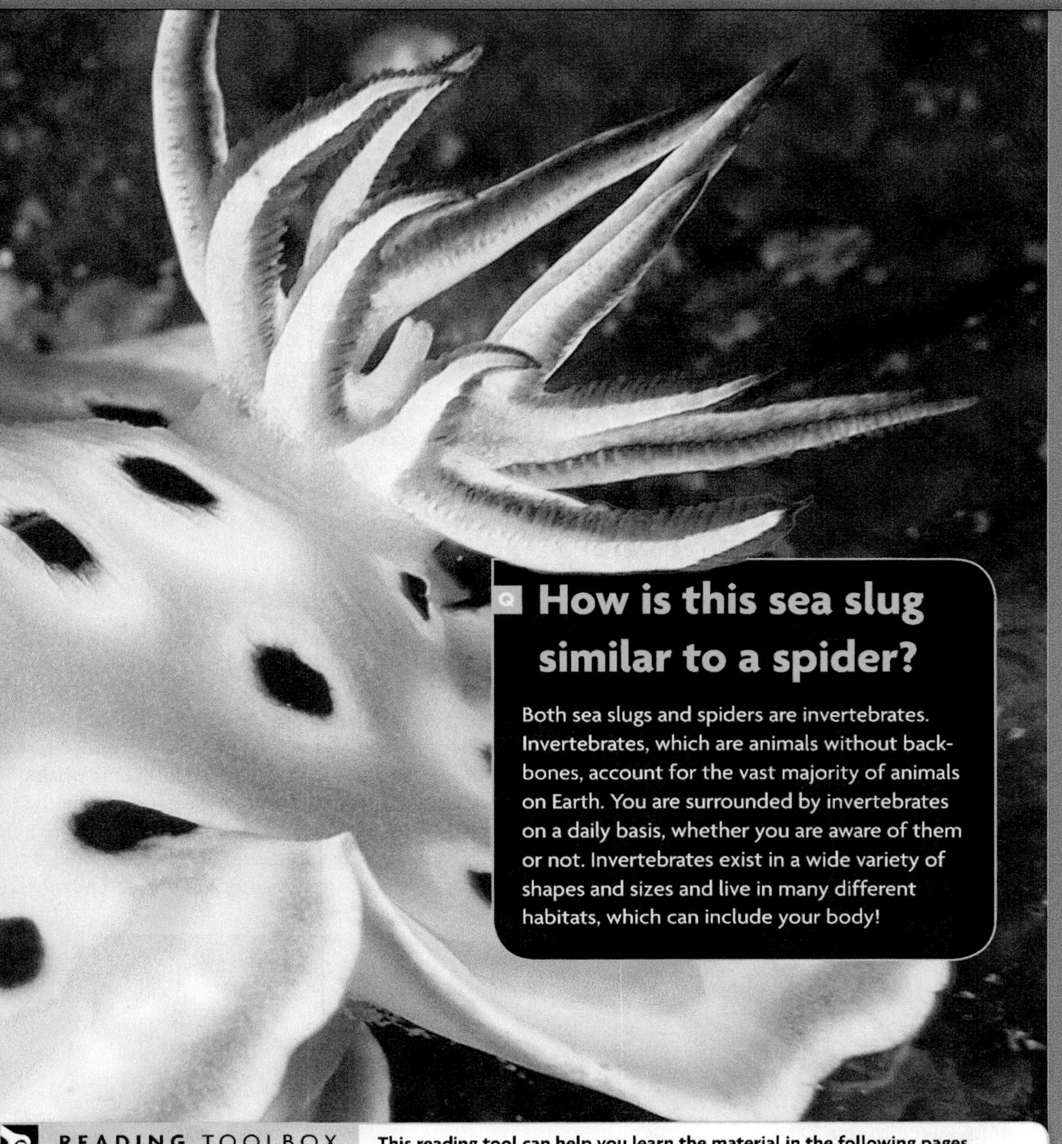

How is this sea slug similar to a spider?

Both sea slugs and spiders are invertebrates. Invertebrates, which are animals without backbones, account for the vast majority of animals on Earth. You are surrounded by invertebrates on a daily basis, whether you are aware of them or not. Invertebrates exist in a wide variety of shapes and sizes and live in many different habitats, which can include your body!

READING TOOLBOX **This reading tool can help you learn the material in the following pages.**

USING LANGUAGE

Describing Space Describing an object accurately is not as easy as it may seem. Certain words, called *spatial* words, can help you describe the shape and position of an object. Spatial words include *perpendicular, parallel, diagonal, horizontal,* and *vertical.*

YOUR TURN

Practice using spatial words by completing the activity below.

1. Look around your classroom, and choose an object to describe.
2. Without revealing what the object is, use spatial words to help a partner draw the object you have chosen.

Demonstrate

- Place a snail on a moist paper towel.
- Dip a cotton swab into vinegar, then hold the tip of the swab close to the snail's head, sides, and tail without touching it.

Discuss Have students compare how the snail reacted when the vinegar was held near different parts of its body. **Ask,** Do snails have a nose? no Point out the following:

- Snails breathe and detect smells through their skin and through a pore on their right side called the pneumostome, which connects directly to the snail's single lung.
- The layer of mucus covering the snail's skin makes it easier for the snail to exchange gases with the environment.

Activate Prior Knowledge

Direct students' attention to the chapter title. **Ask,** What is meant by the term *diversity* as it relates to organisms? number of different types of organisms or species Remind students that diversity is possible only because of natural selection and evolution. **Ask,** What allows such a wide variety of forms and organisms to exist and thrive on Earth? There are innumerable niches to be filled.

Preview Vocabulary

Greek and Latin Word Origins
Have students watch for the application of these prefixes here and in the later chapters of this unit:

meso- = middle
endo- = inner
ecto- or *exo-* = outer

Academic Vocabulary The word *hierarchy* implies a ranking based on the degree of power, ability, or status an individual has. With the great diversity and number of invertebrates, such an idea loses its power. Suggest that students think in ecological terms when learning about the different invertebrate phyla and the different niches the organisms fill.

English Learners In this chapter, students are introduced to terms that describe distinguishing characteristics of animals:

invertebrate	*vertebrate*
protostome	*deuterostome*
bilateral	*radial*

You can help students get a sense of how and when such words are used by setting up a word wall. Write the terms on individual cards and post them on the board as you introduce them. Remember to review the words periodically.

Answers

1. a bulletin board, for example
2. a large, rectangular surface of cork, whose length is perpendicular to the floor and width is parallel to the floor

SECTION 22.1

▼ Plan and Prepare

Activate Prior Knowledge Have students look at the animal diversity reflected in the photographs on the page. **Ask**

- If you were asked to classify the life forms shown on this page, where would you start? If no one had gone before you, how would you begin? Answers will vary but may be based on outward appearance, perceived size, or habitat.
- Knowing these are all animals, what can you state about these organisms with certainty? made up of eukaryotic cells, heterotrophic, consumers, require oxygen

Suggest to students that the best way to think about animal diversity is to think about all the ecological niches to be filled.

▼ Teach

TEACH FROM VISUALS

FIGURE 1.1 Have students attempt to classify the animals shown as far as they can. **Ask,** Which of the animals are vertebrates? blue whale, giraffe, Steller's jay

22.1 Animal Characteristics

KEY CONCEPT **Animals are diverse but share common characteristics.**

VOCABULARY
collagen
homeotic
homeobox

MAIN IDEAS
- Animals are the most physically diverse kingdom of organisms.
- All animals share a set of characteristics.

Connect to Your World

We are animals. So are jellyfish, squid, cockroaches, tapeworms, sea stars, and the family dog. Animals live in nearly every environment on Earth, from high in the atmosphere to the deepest sea trench. While they come in a huge variety of shapes and sizes, they all share a common ancestry and a set of common physical and genetic characteristics.

MAIN IDEA

Animals are the most physically diverse kingdom of organisms.

More than 1 million species of animals have been described so far, and scientists predict that tens of millions more have yet to be discovered. Animals are a remarkably diverse group of organisms. They range in size from blue whales twice the length of a school bus to rotifers smaller than the period at the end of this sentence. As shown in **FIGURE 1.1,** some look like soft tubes, and others have muscular bodies inside hard shells, or soft tissues over hard internal skeletons. Some animals have many specialized tissues and organs, and others have no distinct tissues at all.

FIGURE 1.1 Animal body plans vary widely in shape and size, from microscopic rotifers to blue whales 24 meters in length.

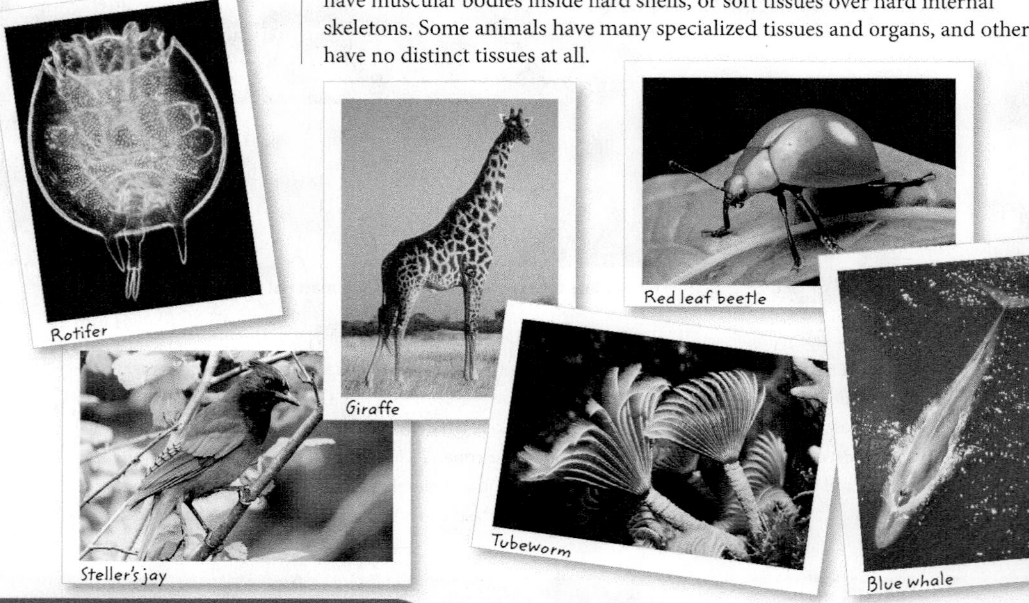

Differentiated Instruction

ENGLISH LEARNERS

Have students create a mind map to serve as a study guide for this section. They can begin with the Main Idea on the next page, "All animals share a set of characteristics." From this they can branch off to the four headings with details and notes beneath each. Have students focus on the main ideas of each paragraph and record brief definitions of key terms such as *Hox* genes, collagen, heterotroph, and diploid.

Teacher Toolkit, Section C, Mind Map

BELOW LEVEL

Prepare a list of true/false statements to test students' knowledge of animal characteristics and animal diversity. Include obvious statements, such as "All animals are multicellular." But also have students think about points of differentiation, as in "Multicellular organization means all animals have tissues, organs, and organ systems" or "All animals have blood to transport oxygen and nutrients."

Teacher Toolkit, Section C, Anticipation Guide

Animals are found nearly everywhere on Earth, including places where plants and fungi do not live. They are the dominant herbivores, predators, and detritivores in most ecosystems. Some walk, burrow, swim, fly, or slide along on mucus trails in search of food. Others spend their whole adult lives fixed to a single spot, endlessly straining water to collect microscopic particles of food.

A Connect What ecological factors determine where certain animals are found?

CONNECT TO

NICHES

Recall from **Interactions in Ecosystems** that an ecological niche includes all of the factors a species needs to survive, thrive, and reproduce.

MAIN IDEA

All animals share a set of characteristics.

Given the huge physical diversity among animals, what characteristics distinguish animals from other organisms? All animals share a set of derived characters, or heritable features, that set them apart from other eukaryotes. These characteristics suggest that all animals are the descendants of a single common ancestor.

READING TOOLBOX

TAKING NOTES

Use a diagram to take notes on the unique characteristics of animals.

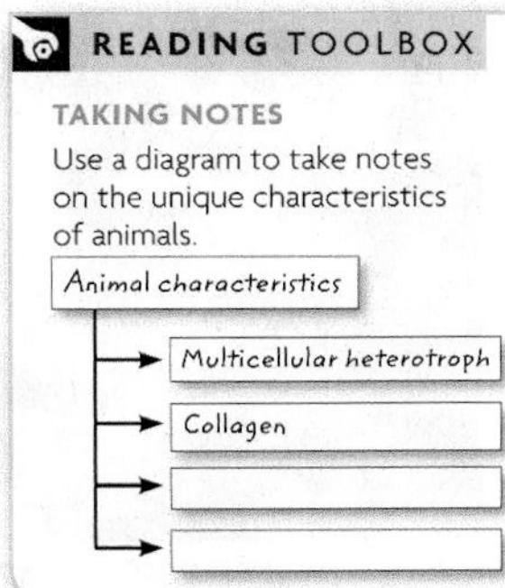

All Animals Are Multicellular Heterotrophs

Animals must eat. Their cells lack the chloroplasts that let photosynthetic organisms make their own food. All animals are heterotrophs, meaning they eat other organisms to gain the nutrients they need to survive. Any organic compound an animal uses in cellular respiration has to come from an outside source. Single-celled protists also eat other organisms. But because even the simplest animal is built of many specialized cells, all animals can ingest and process larger food particles than a single cell can engulf.

Animals are not the only eukaryotes that are both heterotrophic and multicellular. Fungi are also multicellular and use organisms for food. But cells of fungi do not have the same diversity of functions that animal cells have. Although animals and fungi share heterotrophic ancestors, it is likely that they evolved the trait of multicellularity independently.

Animal Cells Are Supported by Collagen

Unlike the cells of plants and fungi, animal cells lack rigid cell walls. Therefore, animals cannot rely on the rigidity of their cells for structural support. What component carries out these functions in animals?

Collagen (KAHL-uh-juhn), shown in **FIGURE 1.2**, is a three-stranded protein unique to animals. Animal body parts that contain collagen include skin, bone, ligaments, fingernails, and hair. Individual collagen proteins combine with one another to form ropelike fibers that are both strong and flexible. These fibers form an extracellular network that many animal cells use for support. Unlike a cell wall, the collagen network does not glue cells in place, so it is possible for cells to move within the animal's body. Collagen also forms an integral part of the jointed skeleton that many animals use to move their entire bodies.

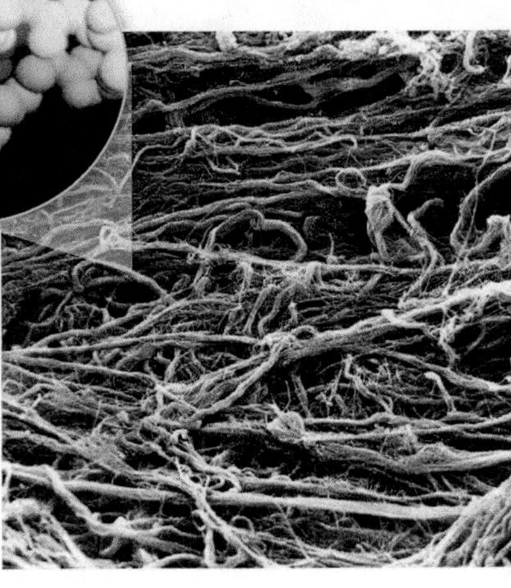

FIGURE 1.2 This molecular model and microscope image show the triple-stranded structure of collagen, a strong and flexible protein that is unique to animals.

Vocabulary

Greek and Latin Word Origins Remind students of the meanings of the roots of **heterotroph:**

hetero- = different
trophos = feeder

The opposite of a heterotroph is an **autotroph,** which produces its own food, usually through photosynthesis. Discuss with students what the implications are for an organism that gets food from its environment. Animals must have the means to do the following:

- capture and take in food
- break down food and absorb nutrients
- move nutrients throughout the body
- capture energy from nutrients
- get rid of unused materials

Science Trivia

- The word *collagen* is derived from the Greek word *colla,* meaning "glue."
- Collagen was used by ancient Egyptians to make glue.
- Gelatin is made from collagen. Gelatin is used in various foods such as gelatin desserts, marshmallows, gummy candies, soups, and cream cheese.
- The collagen used to make gelatin and glue is processed from the bones, hooves, and connective tissues of cattle, pigs, and horses.
- Collagen from cattle is also used in cosmetic surgery to make humans' lips fuller or temporarily remove the appearance of wrinkles in the skin. Because this collagen comes from a different species, allergic reactions are possible.

PRE-AP

Give students five minutes to write about these questions: What are the characteristics of all living things, and how would you expect those characteristics to be reflected in the different body systems of an animal? Remind students to keep writing for the full five minutes, even if they just list every animal they can think of and the body systems they have. Discuss what students come up with and look for commonalities as well as characteristics that would help distinguish different phyla.

Teacher Toolkit, Section C, Quick-Write

Answers

A Connect Answers may include climate and availability of food and other resources.

Chapter 22: Invertebrate Diversity 643

▼ Teach *continued*

Vocabulary

homeotic, homeobox The roots *homo-* and *homeo-* are variations of the same Greek root, meaning "like" or "similar." Students have seen these roots before in *homeostasis* and *homogeneous*. **Homeosis** refers to a situation in which one structure gets transformed into the "likeness" of another, as with the antennae that become legs in the fly shown in **FIGURE 1.3.**

Answers

Ⓐ **Analyze** *Hox* genes are one kind of homeotic gene with a sequence of 180 nucleotides that defines the head-to-tail pattern of development in animal embryos.

▼ Assess and Reteach

Assess Use the Section Self-Check or Section Quiz, both available at **HMHScience.com**.

Reteach Create a graphic organizer like the one on the previous page. Ask students to summarize the common characteristics of animals and how animals are distinguished from other living things.

FIGURE 1.3 In the wild-type fly (top), the antennae develop normally. In the mutant fly (bottom), a mutation causes legs to form in place of the antennae. (SEMs; magnification 70×)

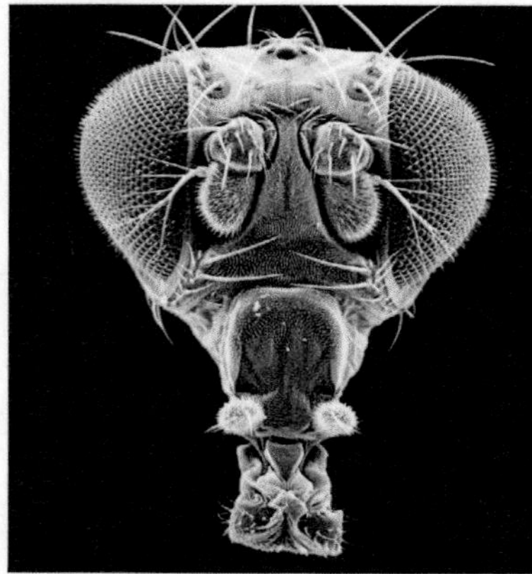

Animals Are Diploid and Usually Reproduce Sexually

Animals are the only multicellular organisms that do not alternate between free-living diploid and haploid stages. In all animal species, the individuals that reproduce are diploid and they produce offspring that are also diploid. Some kinds of animals can reproduce both asexually and sexually. For example, a *Hydra* can clone itself by budding. These species have male and female sexual organs and also reproduce sexually. A few animals have become completely asexual. All whiptail lizards, for example, are females and offspring are clones of the mother. But these animals evolved from sexual species, and their asexual habits are derived characters.

Most Animals Have *Hox* Genes

Most animals that scientists have studied so far share a group of genes called homeotic genes. **Homeotic** (HOH-mee-AH-tihk) genes are a class of genes that control early development. In animals, an important group of homeotic genes called *Hox* genes are defined by a sequence of 180 nucleotides called **homeobox** (HOH-mee-uh-BAHKS) genes. *Hox* genes define the head-to-tail pattern of development in animal embryos. Homeotic genes create segments in a larva or embryo that develop into specific organs and tissues. The *Hox* genes within these segments determine the position of cell differentiation and development by switching certain genes "on" or "off."

A mutation in a homeotic gene can lead to the development of a body structure in the wrong position. For example, the effect of a mutation in the homeotic gene *Antennapedia* determines whether an insect body segment will grow antennae or legs. As shown in **FIGURE 1.3**, in the wild-type fly (top), antennae develop normally. In a fly with a mutation in this gene (bottom), legs develop where the antennae should be, but the rest of the fly develops normally. The misplaced legs look normal in structure, but are not functional for the fly. Flies with homeotic mutations usually do not live very long.

Ⓐ Analyze **How are homeotic and *Hox* genes related?**

22.1 Formative Assessment

SELF-CHECK Online HMHScience.com GO ONLINE

REVIEWING ▶ MAIN IDEAS

1. In what ways are animals physically diverse? Give three examples.
2. List and describe the derived characters that all animals share.

CRITICAL THINKING

3. **Apply** How does the structure of animal cells allow animals to move?
4. **Hypothesize** Animals are heterotrophs. How might this have contributed to such great animal diversity?

CONNECT TO GENETICS

5. How does the genome of an offspring resulting from sexual reproduction differ from that of an offspring resulting from asexual reproduction?

22.1 FORMATIVE ASSESSMENT

1. Animals differ in size, shape, and body composition. (Some have specialized tissues and organs; others do not.)
2. All animals are multicellular heterotrophs; they need to get their nutrients from other organisms. Collagen is a strong, triple-stranded but flexible protein that supports animal cells. Animals are diploid—one set of chromosomes from each parent. Most animals reproduce sexually and have homeotic genes, which regulate embryonic development.
3. The absence of cell walls and the flexibility of collagen allows animals to move.
4. Competition for resources such as food leads to diversification. The interactions of animals with one another and with autotrophs and the environment function as selective pressure that can select for or against traits that arise naturally through genetic mutation.
5. The genome of a sexually produced offspring is diploid—contains DNA from both parents. An asexually produced offspring has DNA from just one parent.

22.2 Animal Diversity

KEY CONCEPT **More than 95 percent of all animal species are invertebrates.**

MAIN IDEAS
- Each animal phylum has a unique body plan.
- Animals are grouped using a variety of criteria.
- A comparison of structure and genetics reveals the evolutionary history of animals.

VOCABULARY
ertebrate
nvertebrate
hylum
ilateral symmetry
adial symmetry
rotostome
euterostome

Connect to Your World

When you think of an animal, something familiar such as a dog or a snake probably comes to mind. Both of these animals are vertebrates, a group that represents one small subset of animals. However, most animals are invertebrates and look nothing like your mental picture. To understand the vast diversity of animal life, biologists look for unique characteristics that help them sort animals into distinct groups and arrange those groups into a family tree.

MAIN IDEA

Each animal phylum has a unique body plan.

A **vertebrate** (VUR-tuh-briht) is an animal with an internal segmented backbone. Vertebrates are the most obvious animals around us, and we are vertebrates too. But vertebrates make up less than five percent of all known animal species. All other animals are invertebrates. **Invertebrates** (ihn-VUR-tuh-brihts) are animals without backbones. Early animal classifications divided all animals into vertebrates and invertebrates. But because invertebrates are not defined by a set of shared derived characters, the division is considered outdated. Many invertebrates are not closely related to one another.

CONNECT TO
CLASSIFICATION
ecall from the chapter **The Tree f Life** that in the Linnaean ystem of classification, phylum s the first level below kingdom. ll animals are classified in the ingdom Animalia.

FIGURE 2.1 INVERTEBRATE SPECIES BY GROUP

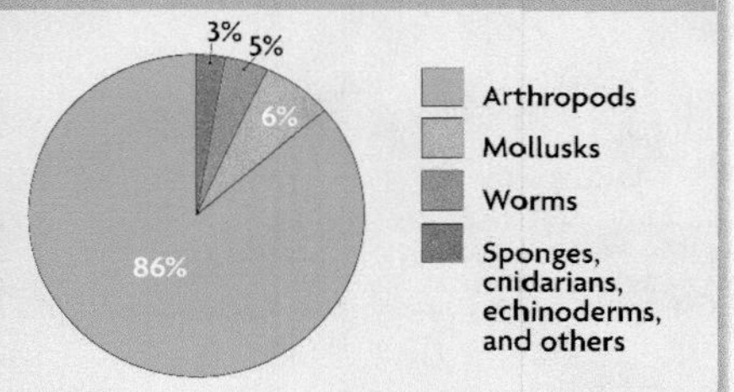

Animal Phyla

Scientists now use shared characters to divide animals into more than 30 major groups. Each group, or **phylum** (FY-luhm) (plural, *phyla*), of animals is defined by structural and functional characteristics that are different from every other animal group. Each animal phylum has a unique body plan and represents a different way that a multicellular animal is put together.

Every animal phylum has a unique set of anatomical characteristics. These unique characteristics are true of both the largest and smallest phyla. Some phyla, such as mollusks, have tens of thousands of species, ranging from land snails to marine octopuses. Others are much less diverse. Phyla such as Arthropoda contain species that look very different from one another. In other phyla, such as Nematoda, all of the species look very similar. The relative number of invertebrate species per group is shown in **FIGURE 2.1.**

SECTION 22.2

Plan and Prepare

Activate Prior Knowledge Have students consider whether symmetry in body shape is a characteristic of all animals. **Ask**

- How would you describe the symmetry of your body? bilateral symmetry
- How would you describe the symmetry of a sea star? radial symmetry
- How would you describe the symmetry of a sponge? variable

Explain that symmetry in animals relates to their development and affects the way they interact with the environment.

Teach

TEACH FROM VISUALS

FIGURE 2.1 Point out the enormousness of the arthropod group. **Ask,** Do you expect that arthropods also dominate the invertebrate group in terms of numbers of animals? Students may say yes, because many arthropods are very small and numerous. Remind students that diversity is measured in species, not in numbers of individuals.

Differentiated Instruction

BELOW LEVEL

Have students work in small groups to preview the section by looking at the different characteristics that can be used to classify groups of animals. Suggest they start with a circle containing "All Animals" and then use a cluster diagram to look for ways to organize the information. Suggest they think of the vocabulary terms as different ways to characterize body plans.

Teacher Toolkit, Section C, Think-Pair-Share; Cluster Diagram

ENGLISH LEARNERS

Have students prepare word squares to compare and contrast pairs of terms to describe different body characteristics:

invertebrate — *vertebrate*
bilateral symmetry — *radial symmetry*
anterior — *posterior*
ventral — *dorsal*
protostome — *deuterostome*

Remind students that highlighted vocabulary appears in the *Multilanguage Glossary.*

Teacher Toolkit, Section C, Word Squares

▼ **Teach** *continued*

Take It Further

The relationship between *Hox* genes and **birth defects** is an active area of research. Several studies have demonstrated a connection between **retinoic acid** (a derivative of vitamin A) and *Hox* genes controlling head and facial development. The link between retinoic acid and birth defects was first made in the 1930s, when researchers noticed that pregnant animals with either excessive or deficient levels of vitamin A produced offspring with severely malformed heads, limbs, hearts, lungs, and central nervous systems.

A spike in human birth defects in the 1980s was connected with the release of several acne and skin medications containing high levels of retinoic acid. Recent studies in mice and humans have shown that high doses of retinoic acid taken during pregnancy interfere with the expression of *Hox* genes in the embryo, leading to an increased incidence of miscarriage, cleft palate, abnormal brain development, and other anomalies.

Answers

A Analyze Because *Hox* genes regulate the formation of segments or parts of a body, a mutation of such a gene could cause dramatic variation of a body plan. Over time, these forms could be selected for, leading to diversification and speciation.

B Analyze The order of the genes corresponds to the segments or tissues in each body plan in a linear, head-to-tail way.

Homeobox Genes and Body Plans

If you take a look at the animals that you might see on a walk through a park, you may notice how different their body plans are. The fish swimming in the park's pond have sets of fins, the birds nesting in the trees have pairs of wings, and the squirrels chasing one another have four legs.

Differences in body plans result from differences in the expression of homeobox genes. As shown in **FIGURE 2.2**, homeobox genes tell embryonic cells which part of the body they are going to become, such as the head, midsection, or tail. These instructions start a chain reaction that turns on all other genes that define the adult form—where limbs go, how many eyes will develop, the location of the gut, and so on. For this reason, a mutation in a *Hox* gene can change an animal's entire body plan. Scientists think that mutations in these genes led to the vast diversity of animal species.

All the animal phyla now known first appeared during the Cambrian explosion. How did so many unique body plans appear in such a short time? The trigger may have been an increase in oxygen levels in the atmosphere that began about 700 million years ago. As oxygen levels rose, eukaryotic organisms could become more active and begin to occupy different niches within more complex ecosystems.

The Cambrian explosion was possible only because animals had already evolved *Hox* genes. These genes became a toolkit that changed animal bodies through duplication and loss. For example, a sponge is a simple animal that has at least one *Hox* gene, while an arthropod has eight. This difference suggests that over time, mutations have caused the original *Hox* gene to be copied repeatedly, forming a series of similar genes along a chromosome. Every time a gene is duplicated, one of the copies can keep doing its original job in the organism, leaving the other free to mutate and take on new roles.

A Analyze How are *Hox* genes related to the diversity of body plans?

FIGURE 2.2 *Hox* Gene Expression

The genes that determine a fruit fly's body plan are variations of the same genes that determine a human's, but they are expressed in different patterns.

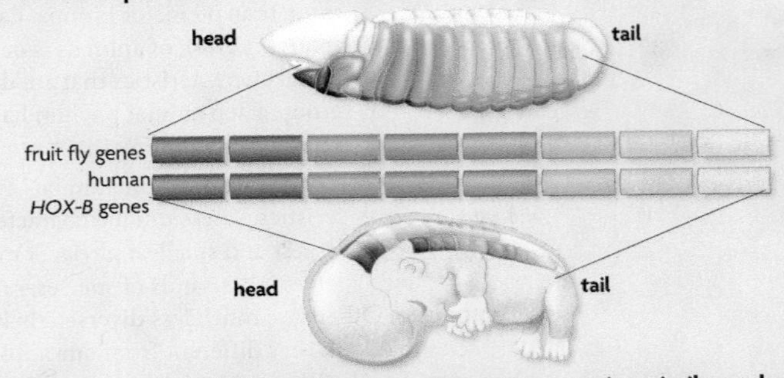

B Analyze In both fruit flies and humans, *Hox* genes occur in a similar order on chromosomes. How does the illustration emphasize this point?

Differentiated Instruction

TEACH WITH TECHNOLOGY

Collect images of closely related animals that share similar features but are phenotypically quite different. For example, compare insects such as dragonflies, butterflies, and houseflies, and point out differences in wing number and shape, eye structure and placement, antennae and mouthparts. Have students look at **FIGURE 2.2** and discuss the implications of homeobox genes that can "turn off or on" different body parts as different species evolved and occupied different niches or habitats.

MAIN IDEA

Animals are grouped using a variety of criteria.

Like other organisms, animals are placed in separate groups based on certain characteristics. Three criteria used to categorize animals are body plan symmetry, number of tissue layers, and developmental patterns.

Body Plan Symmetry

Symmetry refers to how similar an object is across a central axis. For example, if you draw a line down the middle of a square, both sides are equal in shape and size. An object is asymmetrical if the two sides are not mirror images of each other. Most animal body plans fall into one of two types of symmetry.

- Animals with **bilateral symmetry** can be divided equally along only one plane, which splits an animal into mirror-image sides.
- Animals with **radial symmetry** have body parts arranged in a circle around a central axis.

Bilateral animals have distinct heads and tails, which are called the anterior (head) and posterior (tail) ends. These animals also have distinct backs and bellies, which are called the dorsal (back) and ventral (belly) surfaces. Each of these regions can become specialized. For example, structures that an animal uses to move, such as legs, are usually found on its ventral surface. Active hunters that often travel in one direction in search of food have a head region with a concentration of nervous tissue that forms a brain and with sensory organs such as eyes.

VISUAL VOCAB

Animals with **bilateral symmetry** can be divided equally along only one plane, which splits an animal into mirror-image sides.

Animals with **radial symmetry** have body parts arranged in a circle around a central axis.

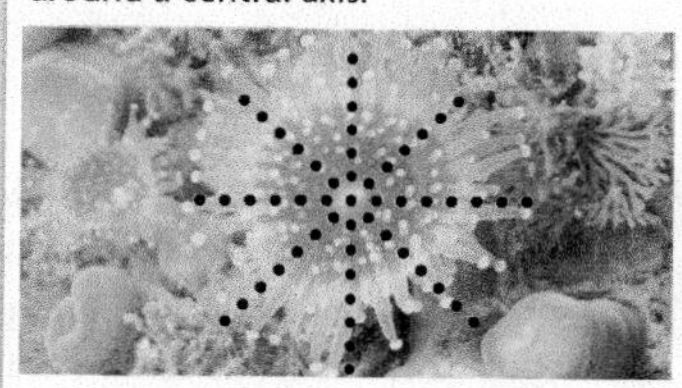

READING TOOLBOX

TAKING NOTES

Draw a simple sketch of an animal in your notes. Mark its symmetry, then label its anterior, posterior, dorsal, and ventral areas.

Tissue Layers

Bilateral animals are triploblastic, that is, they have three distinct layers of tissue. These layers are the ectoderm, endoderm, and mesoderm. The ectoderm is the outer layer that develops into the skin, the brain, and the nervous system. The endoderm is an inner layer that lines the animal's gut. The mesoderm is a middle layer that develops into internal tissues and organs. Complex organ systems resulted from the evolution of this third tissue layer.

Most radial animals have only two distinct layers of tissue. These layers are an inner endoderm and an outer ectoderm. Radial animals do not have a mesoderm layer, and therefore they lack the complex internal tissues and organs found in triploblastic animals.

READING TOOLBOX

VOCABULARY

The following Greek word parts can help you remember the names of tissue layers.

- *-derm* comes from a word meaning "skin"
- *ecto-* means "outer"
- *endo-* means "inner"
- *meso-* means "middle"

Vocabulary

Academic Vocabulary Students are probably familiar with the language of geometry used in this section.

plane, flat or level surface

axis, a straight line about which a body rotates

Point out that the term *plane* applies to both bilateral and radial symmetries. In bilateral symmetry, a plane not only divides an animal's body into two sides *(bilateral)* but also into head and tail *(anterior, posterior)* and back and belly *(dorsal, ventral)*.

In radial symmetry, any plane that passes through the central axis produces two mirror-image sides. The terms *anterior, posterior, dorsal,* and *ventral* are not used to describe radial symmetry. However, radially symmetrical animals do have two distinct ends oriented around the central axis, with one end defined by the location of the mouth.

Take It Further

An animal can be bilaterally symmetrical without its two sides displaying perfect mirror images of each other. Male **fiddler crabs,** for example, have one very large claw on one side and a much smaller one on the other. Another arthropod, the American **lobster,** *Homarus americanus,* possesses one claw that is heavy and armed with molarlike "teeth" that are good for crushing and another that is lighter and armed with smaller, sharper teeth for slicing and cutting.

INCLUSION

Use plastic models of animals to discuss body symmetry with students who are visually impaired. Discuss the implications of body shape on how animals move and how they capture food. For example, compare a jellyfish filtering food from the water with a highly maneuverable predator such as a shark.

PRE-AP

Have students take five minutes to write about how body shape affects movement and food capture for animals that are radially symmetric compared to those that are bilaterally symmetric. Also, have them consider the implications of the two dermal layers typical of radially symmetric animals compared with the three layers in bilaterally symmetric animals. Suggest that students compare a jellyfish with a shark.

Teacher Toolkit, Section C, Quick-Write

▼ Teach *continued*

Vocabulary

Greek and Latin Word Origins Students have seen the Greek root *stoma,* which is used in **protostome** and **deuterostome.** *Stoma* means "mouth"; *stomata* are the mouthlike openings in leaves that enable gases to pass in and out. *Stoma* is also the root of the word *stomach.* Add the prefix *proto-*, which means "first," or *deutero-*, which means "second," and students will see how descriptive each term is.

Integrating Embryology

The process during which embryonic cells differentiate into distinct tissue layers is called **gastrulation.** Following fertilization and cleavage, the rapidly dividing embryo is a simple ball of undifferentiated cells called a blastula. During gastrulation, the cells migrate to different parts of the embryo and begin to differentiate into the three (or two) distinct tissue types.

Answers

A Connect bilateral

B Contrast protostome: spiral cleavage pattern, and the first opening of the digestive cavity (blastopore) becomes the mouth; deuterostome: radial cleavage pattern, and the first opening in the gut becomes the anus.

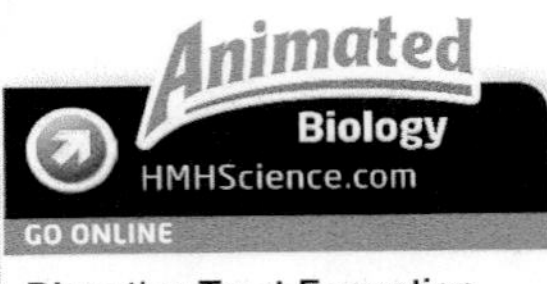

Digestive Tract Formation

FIGURE 2.3 DEVELOPMENTAL PATTERNS

PROTOSTOME	DEUTEROSTOME
2-cell	
8-cell cleavage pattern	
Blastula	
Blastula cross section	
Gut cavity formation	
ectoderm, mesoderm, endoderm, blastopore	
First opening of digestive cavity	
anus	mouth
blastopore becomes mouth	blastopore becomes anus

B Contrast How does the development of protostomes and deuterstomes differ?

Developmental Patterns

Animals are separated into two major divisions: the protostomes and the deuterostomes. As shown in **FIGURE 2.3**, protostome and deuterostome development differs in a number of ways:

- **First opening of the digestive cavity** The major difference between protostomes and deuterostomes is the structure that develops from the first opening of the digestive cavity. In **protostomes** (PROH-tuh-STOHMZ), the mouth is formed first, and the anus second. In **deuterostomes** (DOO-tuh-roh-STOHMZ), the first opening forms the anus, and the mouth is formed second.
- **Gut cavity formation** In protostomes, the gut cavity is formed from separations in the mesoderm. In deuterostomes, the gut cavity forms from pouches created by the folds in the gut tube.
- **Cleavage pattern** In most protostomes, early cell divisions lead to an eight-celled embryo in a twisted arrangement called spiral cleavage. In deuterostomes, cells divide into eight-celled embryos with cells that are lined up one atop the other in an arrangement called radial cleavage.

A Connect Is the symmetry of the human body bilateral or radial?

MAIN IDEA

A comparison of structure and genetics reveals the evolutionary history of animals.

Work by the American zoologist Libbie Hyman in the mid-1900s provided the basis for scientists' understanding of the relationships among invertebrate species. Hyman based her phylogeny, or evolutionary history, on major events in development. The ability to compare ribosomal DNA and *Hox* genes has helped to both confirm and rearrange some relationships among invertebrate animal groups.

The presence of tissues is one characteristic that separates one animal group from another. Sponges, which lack tissues, are the simplest members of the animal kingdom, followed by animals with two tissue layers, such as jellyfish and corals. Whether an animal has radial or bilateral symmetry is another defining characteristic. As shown in **FIGURE 2.4**, the two major radiations, or phylogenetic branches, are the protostomes and the deuterostomes.

Protostomes Protostomes are further divided into the Lophotrochozoa (flatworms, annelids, and mollusks) and Ecdysozoa (roundworms and arthropods). All members of the Lophotrochozoa have either a specialized feeding structure made of hollow tentacles or a free-swimming ciliated larval form. Members of the Ecdysozoa must shed their outer skin to grow.

Deuterostomes Deuterostomes include members of the Echinodermata (such as sea stars and sand dollars) and the Chordata (such as birds, mammals, and all other vertebrates). As a member of the Chordata, you are a deuterostome.

Differentiated Instruction

BELOW LEVEL

Have students consider what they learned in preceding chapters about how prokaryotes, protists, fungi, and plants get the materials they need to support life. Then ask them to write for five minutes on why, in studying animals, there is so much emphasis on the development of a digestive system.

Teacher Toolkit, Section C, Quick-Write

FIGURE 2.4 Phylogeny of Animals

Comparisons of genetic sequences were used to modify the phylogenetic tree of animals.

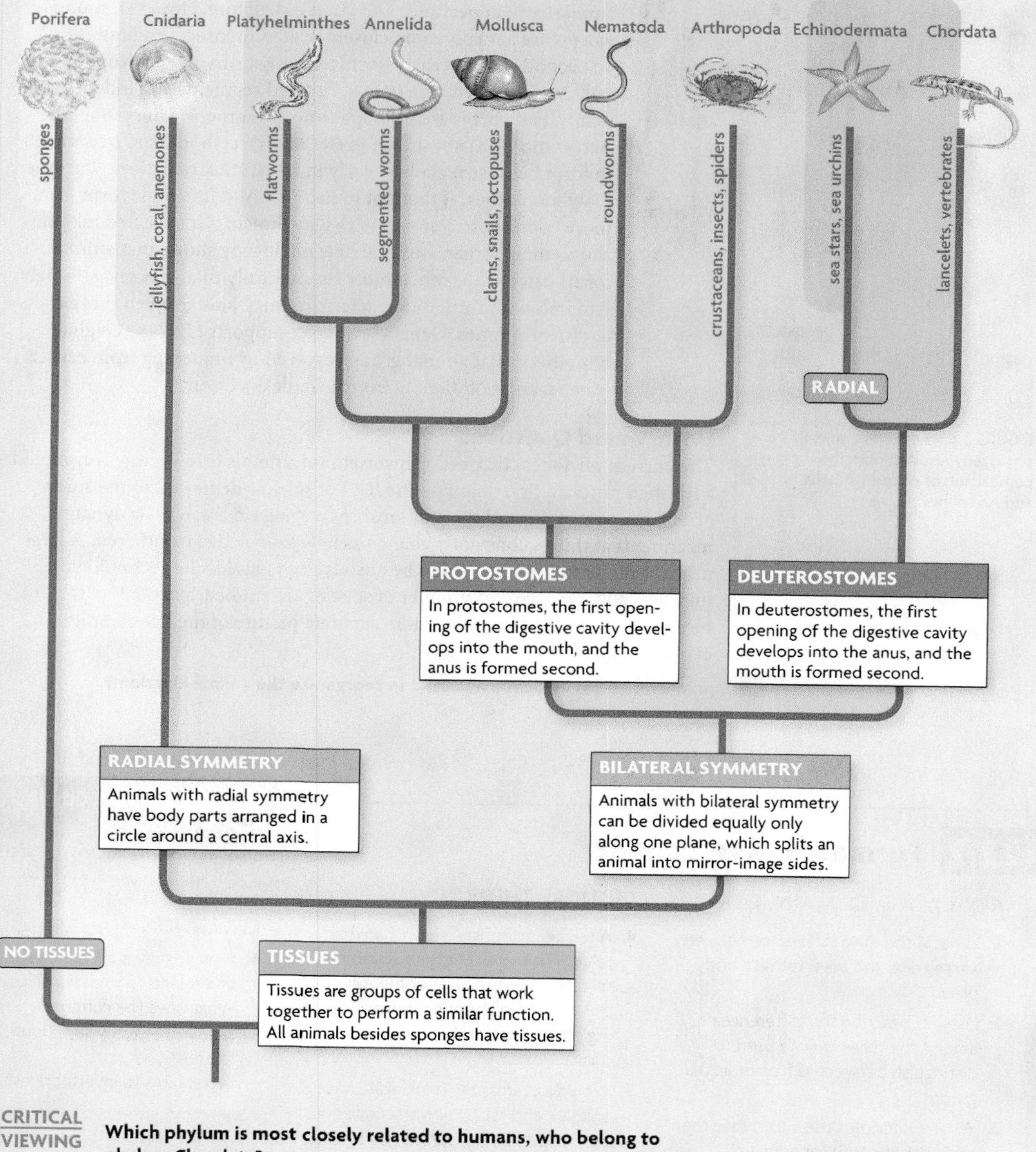

Porifera
Cnidaria
Platyhelminthes
Annelida
Mollusca
Nematoda
Arthropoda
Echinodermata
Chordata
sponges
jellyfish, coral, anemones
flatworms
segmented worms
clams, snails, octopuses
roundworms
crustaceans, insects, spiders
sea stars, sea urchins
lancelets, vertebrates
RADIAL
PROTOSTOMES
In protostomes, the first opening of the digestive cavity develops into the mouth, and the anus is formed second.
DEUTEROSTOMES
In deuterostomes, the first opening of the digestive cavity develops into the anus, and the mouth is formed second.
RADIAL SYMMETRY
Animals with radial symmetry have body parts arranged in a circle around a central axis.
BILATERAL SYMMETRY
Animals with bilateral symmetry can be divided equally only along one plane, which splits an animal into mirror-image sides.
NO TISSUES
TISSUES
Tissues are groups of cells that work together to perform a similar function. All animals besides sponges have tissues.

CRITICAL VIEWING **Which phylum is most closely related to humans, who belong to phylum Chordata?**

Take It Further

Point out that the **larvae** of many species in the invertebrate phyla have very different body plans, behaviors, means of movement, and other characteristics when compared with adults of the same species. In the case of **echinoderms,** even the symmetry is different. Adults are radial; larvae are bilateral. This is why Echinodermata appears among other bilateral phyla in **FIGURE 2.4.**

The Inside Story

In 1801, **Jean-Baptiste Lamarck** published the first authoritative book on invertebrates. Few scientists before him had studied these animals. It was Lamarck, the professor of "insects and worms" at the Muséum National d'Histoire Naturelle, who first coined the term *invertebrate*. It had been the custom to classify all animals lacking backbones as insects and worms. Or as Lamarck put it: "The celebrated Linnaeus, and almost all other naturalists up to now, have divided the entire series of invertebrate animals into only two classes: insects and worms. As a consequence, anything that could not be called an insect must belong, without exception, to the class of worms." Lamarck was the first to distinguish crustaceans, arachnids, and annelids as groups different from both insects and worms.

To appreciate the enormous task of classifying invertebrates, skip ahead to the 20th century. **Libbie Hyman** spent a good part of her life working to compile *The Invertebrates*, published in six volumes from 1940 to 1968. Hyman, who earned her living working as a writer of lab manuals, was given a laboratory to use at the American Museum of Natural History, though never a salary. She suffered from Parkinson's disease toward the end of her life, which eventually prevented her from producing volumes on arthropods and mollusks.

ENGLISH LEARNERS

Use **FIGURE 2.4** to show students how the different terms they learned for the section relate to one another. Ask questions about each branching of the diagram. Relate the information contained in the label boxes to the images of the animal phyla shown above.

Teacher Toolkit, Section C, Connect to Content Through Visuals

PRE-AP

Suggest students devise a way to remember the phyla. One mnemonic that covers them in the order shown in **FIGURE 2.4** is Proper cooks prepare a meal near an electric cooker.

Answers

A Critical Viewing Echinodermata

▼ Teach *continued*

Take It Further

In some cases, analysis of molecular and genetic evidence is the only way to classify organisms correctly and determine relationships. Two organisms may appear to be closely related—or even identical—and then DNA evidence suggests otherwise.

In 2006, a new species of hammerhead shark was discovered off the coast of South Carolina. This shark, as of yet unnamed, is visually indistinguishable from the scalloped hammerhead, *Sphyrna lewini*, but DNA analysis reveals a distinct genetic signature. It is thought that this population may breed only in certain estuaries and bays of South Carolina, and that this may have led to genetic isolation from the scalloped hammerhead over time.

Answers

A Summarize comparisons of ribosomal DNA and *Hox* genes

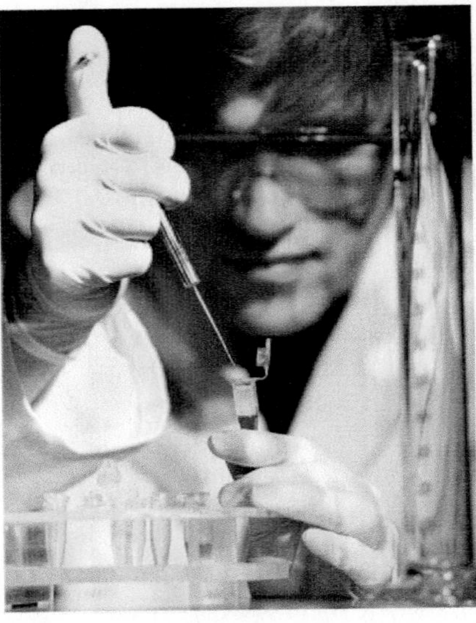

FIGURE 2.5 The current animal phylogeny resulted from the comparison of ribosomal DNA and *Hox* genes.

Unexpected Evolutionary Relationships

The new organization of the animal kingdom shows previously unexpected relationships between animals. Originally, roundworms and earthworms were grouped together because of their similarity in appearance and simple structure. However, roundworms are actually more closely related to insects and other arthropods than to earthworms. Earthworms and arthropods are not closely related and, in fact, evolved segmentation independently. Flatworms are now split into two groups. One group, the Acoelomorpha (not shown in **FIGURE 2.4**), is thought to be simple in form because it evolved early in the animal radiation. The other, Platyhelminthes, is thought to have evolved its simple form from more complex ancestors. As well as showing unexpected relationships among organisms, the new phylogeny shows that animal forms can change much more dramatically than was once thought. Animals with similar characteristics may have evolved those traits at different times. Genetic evidence supports Hyman's original hypothesis that animal groups evolved by branching from earlier groups, and not directly from a single ancestor.

Unanswered Questions

The current phylogenetic tree for invertebrate animals is in no way considered a finished product. Systematics—the field of science dedicated to the study of the diversity of life and the relationships among organisms—is dynamic, meaning that things constantly change as new knowledge is gathered. A large number of questions still need to be answered. As molecular technologies improve, and an increased number of species are studied, scientists will be able to put together an even more accurate picture of the invertebrate evolutionary tree.

A Summarize **What evidence was used to reorganize the animal kingdom?**

▼ Assess and Reteach

Assess Use the Section Self-Check or Section Quiz, both available at **HMHScience.com**.

Reteach Start a concept map on the board with the term *animal diversity*. Have students add to the map by identifying the different ways animals are distinguished from one another. Have them think about whether a certain characteristic is a subset of another.

22.2 Formative Assessment

SELF-CHECK Online HMHScience.com GO ONLINE

REVIEWING MAIN IDEAS

1. What is the main difference between **vertebrate** and **invertebrate** body plans?
2. List and describe the differences among the three criteria used to distinguish between different animal groups.
3. What evidence is used to create the phylogenetic tree for animals?

CRITICAL THINKING

4. **Analyze** Scientists' view of animal relationships has changed since the mid-1900s. What development led to this change in scientists' understanding of the relationships among animals?
5. **Provide Examples** Think again about animals, and list five invertebrates that might live in your neighborhood. To which **phylum** does each invertebrate belong?

CONNECT TO

EVOLUTION

6. A phylogeny is a hypothesis of evolutionary relationships. What does the current animal phylogeny say about the relationship of vertebrates to invertebrates?

22.2 FORMATIVE ASSESSMENT

1. Invertebrates have no backbone; vertebrates do.
2. Bilateral versus radial symmetry: body is symmetrical along the length of the animal or body plan is arranged in a circle around a central axis; two tissue layers versus three; deuterostome versus protostome development: first opening of digestive cavity becomes anus; first opening becomes mouth.
3. Evidence includes comparative anatomy, developmental patterns, and analysis of ribosomal DNA and *Hox* genes.
4. Advances in molecular studies let scientists take a closer look at the relationships among phyla by comparing ribosomal DNA and *Hox* genes.
5. Answers may include insects and spiders (Arthropoda), earthworms (Annelida), and snails and slugs (Mollusca).
6. Vertebrates evolved from invertebrate species.

22.3 Sponges and Cidarians

KEY CONCEPT **Sponges and cnidarians are the simplest animals.**

MAIN IDEAS
- Sponges have specialized cells but no tissues.
- Cnidarians are the oldest existing animals that have specialized tissues.

VOCABULARY

sessile
filter feeder
polyp
medusa
mesoglea
nematocyst
gastrovascular cavity

Connect to Your World

Imagine you are snorkeling beneath the clear blue waters surrounding Australia's Great Barrier Reef. In addition to schools of tropical fish and sharks, covering the ocean floor are brightly colored sponge and coral species. Sponges and corals are members of two of the simplest animal phyla, the Porifera and the Cnidaria.

MAIN IDEA

Sponges have specialized cells but no tissues.

READING TOOLBOX

VOCABULARY

Sessile comes from a Latin word meaning "to sit." The opposite of sessile is mobile. *Mobile* comes from a Latin word meaning "to move."

Sponges have long been considered the most primitive animals on Earth because their body plan is much like what scientists would expect for an early multicellular organism. Two lines of recent evidence have strengthened this hypothesis.

- Sponge fossils more than 570 million years old were found in Australia, making sponges one of the most ancient groups of known animals.
- Molecular evidence confirms that sponges are closely related to a group of protists called choanoflagellates. Choanoflagellates are very similar in size and shape to certain cells found within a sponge. These protists are considered the most likely ancestors of all animals.

FIGURE 3.1 Sponges are among the simplest animals that still exist today.

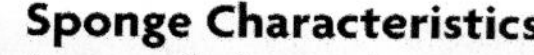

Sponge Characteristics

Sponges lack muscle and nerve cells. So, not surprisingly, they are **sessile,** meaning they are unable to move from where they are attached. As **FIGURE 3.1** shows, sponges attach to hard surfaces. They secrete toxic substances that prevent other sponges from growing into their area and also protect them from hungry predators and parasites. Some of these chemicals have been used in the development of medicines to treat forms of cancer, such as lymphoma.

Sponge Reproduction

Sponges reproduce both sexually and asexually. In sexual reproduction, some species release eggs and sperm into the water, and fertilization occurs there. In other species, sperm is released into the water, and the egg is fertilized within the female sponge. The fertilized egg develops into a free-swimming larva that attaches to a surface, where it remains and develops into its adult form.

SECTION 22.3

Plan and Prepare

Activate Prior Knowledge Sponges are so simple and vegetable-like in appearance that students may be surprised to learn that sponges are animals, not plants. **Ask,** What characteristics must sponges have to be included in the animal kingdom? multicellular, heterotrophic, have collagen, able to move, diploid Explain that sponges are free-swimming as larvae.

Teach

Vocabulary

Academic Vocabulary Two ideas are associated with the word **primitive:**

- not derived from something else, primary
- characterized by simplicity

Both meanings apply to sponges.

Take It Further

Many of the toxic substances secreted by **sponges** are being studied to determine their potential for **fighting diseases.** Extracts of the Chesapeake Bay sponge *Microciona prolifera* have been shown to inhibit the growth of tuberculosis bacteria.

Differentiated Instruction

PRE-AP

As students go through the animal phyla in this and later chapters, they will need to organize their notes in a way that will enable them to make comparisons among the phyla. You can suggest students use index cards much like baseball cards, drawing some representative examples on the front, with the pertinent statistics on the back. Remind students of the classification tables at the back of the book in **Appendix A.**

Phyla Porifera
Common Name(s) sponges
Cells pinacocytes, choanocytes, amoebocytes
Tissues none
Organ/Organ Systems none
Other Details most ancient phylum
Body Shape asymmetrical
Body Support framework of spicules, covered by two layers of cells
Life Cycle Stages (as applicable) free-swimming larvae, sessile as adult
Reproduction sexual reproduction with free-swimming sperm; asexual reproduction by budding
Food Source/Feeding filter feeding

Chapter 22: Invertebrate Diversity 651

▼ Teach *continued*

Science Trivia

- The loofa, a common bath accessory, is not a true sponge. It is derived from a gourdlike fruit that, after being dried and peeled, reveals a spongy fibrous skeleton.
- Most household sponges are synthetic and are made from rubber, cellulose, or plastic.
- The demand for natural sponges has led to sponge farming. Sponge farmers grow sponges from cuttings that are attached to growing lines suspended in the ocean.

Vocabulary

Greek and Latin Word Origins

Cytology is the study of cells, and *-cyte* is often used as a foundation for naming types of cells. The roots of the prefixes used to name the cells in this section are descriptive of each cell's function and shape:

pina- = board or plank

choanē = funnel

amoibē- = changing form, associated with movement

cnida- = sea nettle, nettles being plants with stinging hairs

Answers

A Summarize Sponges do not have tissues and lack muscle and nerve cells.

CONNECT TO

SYMBIOSIS

Recall from **Interactions in Ecosystems** that symbiosis is a close relationship between two or more species living in close contact. Sponges form symbiotic relationships with many different animals. Shrimps, crabs, and worms have been found living within the cavities of a sponge.

Some sponges reproduce asexually by budding. Buds break off from the adult sponge and float in the water until they attach to an underwater surface, where they grow into their adult form.

Sponge Anatomy

Sponges do not have mouths. As you can see in **FIGURE 3.2**, their cells are arranged around a network of channels that let water flow directly through the sponge's body. Water is pulled into the sponge through tiny pores in its body wall, and used water is ejected from a larger hole at the top of the sponge called the osculum. Of the thousands of known species of sponges, most are marine filter feeders. **Filter feeders** eat by straining particles from the water.

Sponges can be found in many colors and shapes. Some sponges are shaped like tubes, while others lie flat against the ocean floor. Regardless of their shape, all sponge bodies are made up of two layers of cells that cover a framework of collagen-like fibers, called spongin. The skeleton is usually reinforced with hard calcium- or silicon-based crystals called spicules. While sponges do not have tissues, they do have several types of specialized cells.

- **Pinacocytes** These thin and leathery cells form the sponge's outer layer.
- **Choanocytes** These cells, also called "collar cells," form the inner layer of the sponge. Each has a long flagellum surrounded by a collar of tiny hairlike structures called microvilli. These cells pull water through the sponge by beating their flagella. As the water passes the choanocytes, tiny food particles are trapped in the mucus on the microvilli.
- **Amoebocytes** These are mobile cells found in the jellylike material sandwiched between the two cell layers. Amoebocytes absorb and digest the food particles caught by the choanocytes and move the nutrients to other parts of the sponge. They also transport oxygen and wastes in the sponge. Because of their mobility, amoebocytes are important to a sponge's growth and repair of injuries.

A Summarize **What characteristics make sponges the simplest animals?**

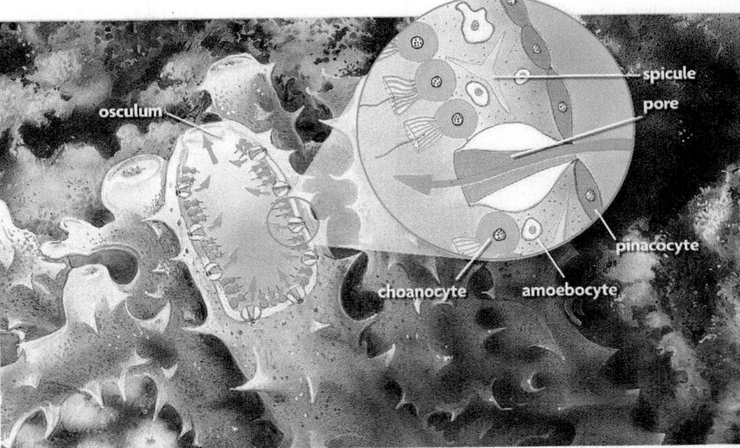

FIGURE 3.2 Sponges are animals that have specialized cells but lack tissues. This cutaway shows the internal organization of a sponge.

Differentiated Instruction

ENGLISH LEARNERS

Divide the class into two groups. Have one group review the material on sponges, and the other review cnidarians. Each group then prepares questions about their phylum, letting the vocabulary terms and heading guide them. Students then use the text to prepare answers. The two groups can then present their questions and answers to each other. This exercise could also be done with pairs of students.

Teacher Toolkit, Section C, SQ3R

PRE-AP

Have students compare and contrast the reproductive strategy of sponges to that of plants. They should consider whether sponges have the best of both worlds: the ability of a sessile organism to sexually reproduce free-swimming larvae, as well the benefits of asexual reproduction.

Teacher Toolkit, Section C, Compare/Contrast Chart

MAIN IDEA

Cnidarians are the oldest existing animals that have specialized tissues.

In contrast to sponges, cnidarians (ny-DAIR-ee-uhnz) can move. A jellyfish pulsing through the water and an anemone waving its tentacles make deliberate movements using simple nerves and muscles.

Cnidarian Characteristics

Cnidarians have two body forms: the polyp and the medusa, both of which are shown in **FIGURE 3.3. Polyps** (PAHL-ihps) are cylindrical tubes with mouth and tentacles facing upward. This form is characteristic of cnidarians such as corals. **Medusas** are umbrella-shaped, with their mouth and tentacles on the underside. This form is characteristic of free-swimming cnidarians such as jellyfish. Many cnidarian species alternate between the two forms during their life cycle. Both polyps and medusas have radial symmetry, a characteristic of all cnidarians.

FIGURE 3.3 In the polyp form of a coral (top), the tentacles and mouth face upward. In the medusa form of a jellyfish (bottom), the tentacles and mouth face downward.

Cnidarian Reproduction

A cnidarian may reproduce both asexually and sexually during its life cycle. Polyps reproduce asexually by budding. This method produces genetically identical offspring. In the medusa form, cnidarians reproduce sexually by releasing gametes into the water. The fertilized egg develops into a free-swimming larva, called a planula. The planula then develops into the polyp stage.

Cnidarian Anatomy

Cnidarian bodies have two tissue layers separated by a noncellular jellylike material called **mesoglea** (MEHZ-uh-GLEE-uh). The outer layer of tissue is made up of three types of cells.

- **Contracting cells** Contracting cells cover the surface of the cnidarian and contain muscle fibers.
- **Nerve cells** Nerve cells interconnect and form a network over the entire animal. They send sensory information around the animal and coordinate muscular contractions. Cnidarians do not have brains.
- **Cnidocytes** (NY-duh-SYTS) Cnidocytes are specialized cells that contain stinging structures used for defense and capturing prey. They are unique to cnidarians. Cnidocytes are found all over a cnidarian's body, but most of them are on the tentacles.

One type of stinging structure found in both sea anemones and jellyfish is the nematocyst. A **nematocyst** (NEHM-uh-tuh-SIHST) is a capsule containing a thin, coiled, harpoon-shaped tubule with a poisonous barb at one end.

BELOW LEVEL

Have students make a two-column chart that lists the types and functions of specialized cells found in sponges and cnidarians. They should also include other structures, such as spicules and nematocysts.

Teacher Toolkit, Section C, Two-Column Chart

TEACH FROM VISUALS

FIGURE 3.3 Have students compare the coral and jellyfish. **Ask**

- What type of symmetry is displayed by the coral and jellyfish? radial
- What is the main structural difference between the coral polyp and the jellyfish medusa? coral: tentacles and mouth face upward; jellyfish: tentacles and mouth face downward

Take It Further

Just as there are bilaterally symmetrical animals that have features that make them appear asymmetrical, there are medusas that at first glance appear to be hydras or even something entirely different. The **upside-down jellyfish,** *Cassiopea xamachana,* is a medusa that lives upside down on the sea floor in the tropics. This species uses the rhythmic pulsations of its "bell" to circulate water through its gills and trap food in its arms, which also hold photosynthetic algae. These algae use sunlight to produce food for the jellyfish. By positioning itself upside down, this species gives the algae maximum exposure to sunlight. When disturbed, this jellyfish is able to swim away.

Science Trivia

Many cnidarians are dangerous to humans. The box jellyfish, *Chironex fleckeri,* found along the northeast coast of Australia from October through April, is perhaps the worst.

- This species has tentacles up to 10 feet long, each armed with up to 5000 nematocysts.
- The venom is strong enough to kill a person within minutes, but quick treatment of the affected area with a large amount of vinegar can neutralize the venom and save a life.

▼ Teach *continued*

Science Trivia

- The Portuguese man-of-war is actually a colony of four types of polyps. The man-of-war is named after a warship because the uppermost polyp features a gas-filled bladder that floats atop the water, functioning as a sail to propel the colony through the water like a ship.
- The man-of-war has tentacles up to 50 meters (165 ft) in length, with nematocysts that deliver a neurotoxin nearly as powerful as that of the cobra.

Answers

A Contrast A polyp is a cylindrical tube topped with a mouth and tentacles. A medusa is umbrella-shaped, with the mouth and tentacles on the underside.

▼ Assess and Reteach

Assess Use the Section Self-Check or Section Quiz, both available at **HMHScience.com**.

Reteach Assemble images of cnidarians and sponges into a digital slide show to review their characteristics, diversity, habitats, and reproductive strategies.

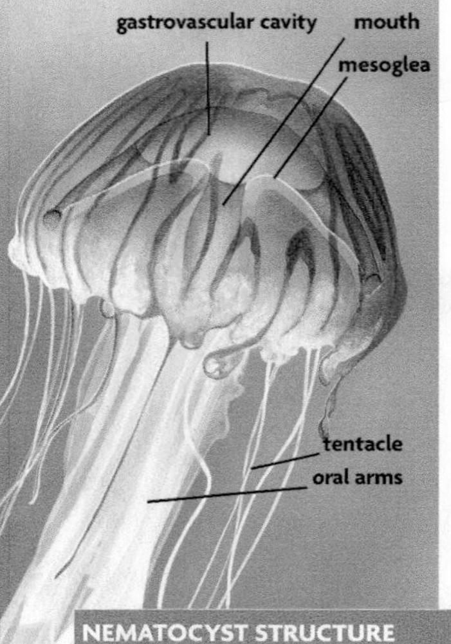

FIGURE 3.4 Cnidarians such as this jellyfish use nematocysts, a type of stinging structure found on their tentacles, to both capture prey and defend themselves against predators. (A)

Nematocysts, shown in **FIGURE 3.4**, usually do not fire on contact unless a chemical signals the presence of prey or a predator. When they fire, nemato cysts uncoil rapidly to spear and poison prey. Prey captured by nematocyst their tentacles are stuffed through the animal's mouth into a saclike digestive space called the **gastrovascular cavity.** The cavity is lined with the cnidarian's ner tissue layer, which has cells that secrete digestive enzymes and absorb nutrients. Cnidarians do not have an anus, which in other animals is a sepa rate exit for wastes. In cnidarians, wastes are pushed out through the mouth

The gastrovascular cavity also moves oxygenated water to internal cells. When the animal's mouth is closed, water in the cavity becomes pressurize and provides skeletal support to the tissue, similar to a balloon full of water Muscular contractions can work against the pressurized fluid and change th animal's shape.

Cnidarian Classes

There are four major groups, or classes, of cnidarians. Each class is defined part by which body form is dominant during the animals' lives.

- **Anthozoa** (AN-thuh-ZOH-uh) include sea anemones and corals. Th polyp form is dominant in these animals. There is no medusa stage.
- **Hydrozoa** (HY-druh-ZOH-uh) include fire corals, the Portuguese man-of-war, and hydras. These animals alternate between polyp and medusa forms. Medusas reproduce sexually, producing gametes that fuse to produce larvae. Larvae settle to the sea floor and grow into polyps. Most polyps are asexual.
- **Scyphozoa** (SY-fuh-ZOH-uh) are jellyfish. The medusa form is dom nant in these animals. Some species have either a very short polyp st or none at all.
- **Cubozoa** (KYOO-buh-ZOH-uh) include the tropical box jellyfish and sea wasps. These animals also have a dominant medusa form. Unlike Scyphozoa, they have a cube-shaped body and well-developed eyes v retinas, corneas, and lenses—though how an animal with no brain interprets visual data is still unknown.

Contrast **How do the polyp and medusa forms differ?**

SELF-CHECK Onlin HMHScience.com GO ONLINE

22.3 Formative Assessment

REVIEWING MAIN IDEAS

1. What is the main function of each of the three types of cells that make up a sponge's body?
2. What are the functions of the inner and outer tissue layers in a cnidarian?

CRITICAL THINKING

3. **Infer** What are the advantages of a **gastrovascular cavity** to the body functions of a cnidarian?
4. **Contrast** How do sponges and cnidarians defend themselves against predators? What is different about the methods used by each?

CONNECT TO **EVOLUTION**

5. Some sponges have the remarkable ability to reas semble themselves after are experimentally broke down into individual cells What might this suggest about the origin of multi lularity in animals?

22.3 FORMATIVE ASSESSMENT

1. Pinacocytes form the outer layer of the sponge; choanocytes form the inner layer and capture food particles. Amoebocytes are mobile cells between the sponge's two layers. They absorb and digest food particles, transport oxygen and wastes, and aid in growth and injury repair.
2. The inner layer of tissue is specialized for digestion, the outer layer for protection.
3. The gastrovascular cavity allows cnidarians to engulf and digest large prey and also helps transport oxygen to the inner tissue layer.
4. Sponges contain toxic substances to defend passively against predators. Cnidarians have stinging cells called cnidocytes that are used actively to strike predators and prey.
5. Multicellular animals can exist only if cells recognize each other as being the same or related. The sponges' ability to reassemble themselves suggests that early animals may have evolved from unicellular organisms that were able to recognize each other and form clumps or colonies.

Cuttlefish Camouflage

S.T.E.M. Interactions

Children playing hide-and-seek know that an effective way to hide in plain sight is simply to freeze. If one stays still, the seeker will not be able to track motion. Many animals employ this technique in a higher-stakes game—hiding from predators. The marine invertebrates called cuttlefish have taken this method and refined it; not only do they freeze when hiding from predators, but they mask their electric fields to stay out of sight.

Cuttlefish, which are related to squids and other mollusks, have soft bodies. They have eight arms and two tentacles with suction disks that they use to capture prey. Cuttlefish can defend themselves by waving their arms in an attempt to look large and intimidating and by biting with their sharp beaks. However, they also have evolved methods of camouflage that aid their survival. Scientists have known for some time that cuttlefish can change the color and even the shape of their skin to blend in with their surroundings, such as rocks or vegetation. These types of camouflage are effective defenses for the cuttlefish against predators such as sharks.

However, sharks and other predators have various ways of finding prey. Like all living organisms, cuttlefish produce an electric field generated by nerve impulses and other processes in the body. In cuttlefish, the electric field is strongest as it emanates from specific openings in the body: on the sides of the head, at the edge of the mantle, and at the rear (the rectum). At the front of their heads, sharks and some other fish have organs called ampullae of Lorenzini that can sense the electric fields generated by organisms. This "extra" sense is called electroreception. Sharks and other fish use it to locate prey. Hammerhead sharks, in particular, benefit from electroreception because the location of their eyes causes a blind spot in their vision, making it difficult for them to see anything that is right in front of them. When sharks sense the electric fields generated by other organisms, they bite, making it more likely that they will catch their prey.

What's a cuttlefish to do? Well, these organisms have a unique defense against the electroreception of predators: they simply freeze and mask their electric fields. A recent study tested the responses of cuttlefish reared in captivity to the threat of an approaching predator. During the study, cuttlefish were placed in a tank. Projected on the tank was a video that showed the approaching dark silhouettes of several marine organisms.

When the video showed the silhouettes of predators, such as sharks or groupers, the cuttlefish in the tank stopped moving, slowed their breathing, and used their arms to cover body openings from which electric currents most strongly emanate. Normally, the electric field they generate is between 10 to 30 microvolts. But when they froze and covered their openings, the electric field dropped to a mere 6 microvolts. When the video showed the silhouettes of organisms that do not prey on cuttlefish, such as crabs, the cuttlefish did not react.

The cuttlefish's unique defensive technique works about half the time, the study found. When it fails, a cuttlefish will squirt ink and propel itself away by sucking in water through an opening in its head and then expelling it through a narrow, funnel-like opening. The ink is meant to confuse predators, making them unable to see anything or tricking them into thinking that the cloud of ink is actually the cuttlefish. However, those actions generate a strong electric field that is easy for predators with electroreception to follow. Generally, it is better for the cuttlefish to hide than to run.

S.T.E.M. Activity

Imagine that you discovered a new animal species that exhibits one or more methods of camouflage. Draw and label a picture of your animal and write a short description of its camouflage abilities and the purposes for its camouflage. Include an explanation of what evolutionary pressures caused the animal to evolve in this way.

Background

Explain that cuttlefish have a high concentration of cells called chromatophores in their skin. Chromatophores contain pigment (black, red, yellow, or white) and reflect light. Male cuttlefish use their chromatophores in mating behaviors, changing the colors and patterns of their skin to attract a mate. When cuttlefish are trying to hide from predators, though, the chromatophores in their skin allow them to match the colors and patterns of whatever environment they are in. Cuttlefish also have muscles in their skin that allow them to change texture and shape to resemble plants or rocks.

Discuss

Discuss other examples of animal camouflage students may be familiar with. Encourage them to research some examples to add to the discussion. Prompt students to explain what characteristic the animal is trying to camouflage and which sense the predator uses to identify the characteristic. Discuss the effectiveness of the various methods of camouflage. Further examples of prey animals using camouflage include the chameleon's ability to change color and the zebra's ability to confuse predators with the pattern of its stripes. An example of a predator that uses camouflage to hunt its prey is the lion. The color of the lion's fur allows it to blend in with the vegetation of its habitat so it can creep up on prey undetected.

SECTION 22.4

▼ Plan and Prepare

Activate Prior Knowledge Students should already be familiar with mollusks and annelids. **Ask**

- What are some examples of mollusks? clams, mussels, squids, octopuses, snails, slugs
- What common annelid can you dig up in a yard or garden? earthworm
- What kind of symmetry do these animals exhibit? bilateral

▼ Teach

Take It Further

The ability of **planarians** to **regenerate** body tissues and structures is widely known. What often goes unrecognized is the strong sense of head and tail, or anterior and posterior polarity, in these animals. If a planarian is cut crosswise into two pieces, the head end generates a new tail, and the tail end generates a new head. If the middle is cut out, it will grow both a head and a tail.

22.4 Flatworms, Mollusks, and Annelids

KEY CONCEPT **Flatworms, mollusks, and annelids belong to closely related phyla.**

VOCABULARY

complete digestive tract
radula
hemocoel
segmentation
coelom

MAIN IDEAS

- Flatworms are simple bilateral animals.
- Mollusks are diverse animals.
- Annelids have segmented bodies.

Connect to Your World

Imagine if you had no stomach or lungs. Just like a flatworm, you would have to be rather flat and thin in order to get the oxygen and food you need to survive. While some flatworms can grow up to 20 meters long, they are never more than a few millimeters thick.

MAIN IDEA

Flatworms are simple bilateral animals.

Based on molecular studies, most flatworms, mollusks, and annelids are classified together as members of the Lophotrochozoa. These animals have either a feeding structure made of hollow tentacles called a lophophore, or a distinctive free-swimming ciliated larva called a trochophore. The name Lophotrochozoa is taken from these two anatomical features.

Flatworms have a solid body and an incomplete or absent gut. A flatworm's shape is the direct result of having no circulatory system. Flatworms can move oxygen to their cells only by diffusion, so all their cells must be close to the outside environment. Complex derived characters such as gut tubes were probably lost at a later stage of evolution, often as the flatworms became parasitic on other animals. The three classes of flatworms include planarians, flukes, and tapeworms.

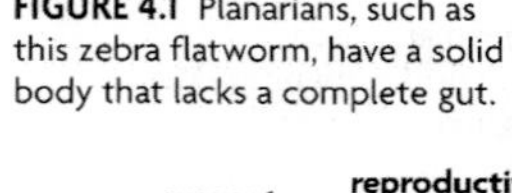

FIGURE 4.1 Planarians, such as this zebra flatworm, have a solid body that lacks a complete gut.

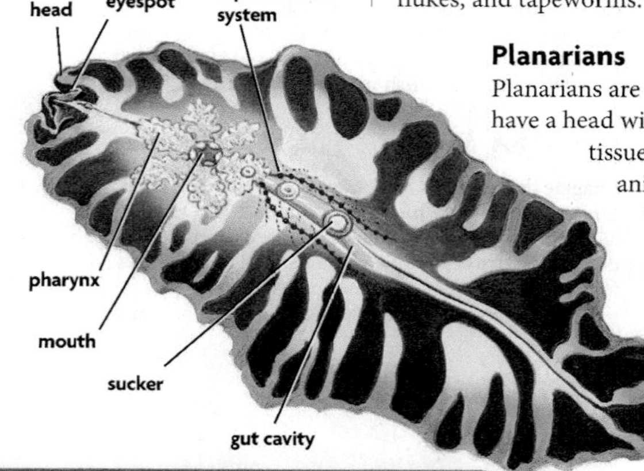

Planarians

Planarians are free-living, nonparasitic flatworms. Planarian worms have a head with eyespots and a simple brain built of a cluster of nerve tissue. As shown in **FIGURE 4.1**, the mouth is found on the animal's ventral surface rather than in its head, and it leads to a gut cavity. A muscular tube called the pharynx extends from the mouth to collect food. These worms actively hunt for food using chemoreceptors to detect odors in the water or in the air. They usually move using the cilia on their ventral surface, but they also have bands of muscle that let them twist their bodies.

Differentiated Instruction

ENGLISH LEARNERS

Before students read this section, review the four strategies for reciprocal teaching: predict, question, clarify, and summarize. Divide the class into three groups to focus on the three animal phyla in this section. Have each group divide their portion of the section so that each student has a paragraph or an idea to focus on. When all students have read their material, have the groups teach one another the material.

Teacher Toolkit, Section C, Reciprocal Teaching

PRE-AP

Have students prepare a biological profile card for each phylum introduced, as described at the beginning of this section. Remind students that flatworms belong to the phylum Platyhelminthes.

FIGURE 4.2 Life Cycle of a Parasitic Fluke

The fluke *Schistosoma* can infect humans and cause a serious disease called schistosomiasis.

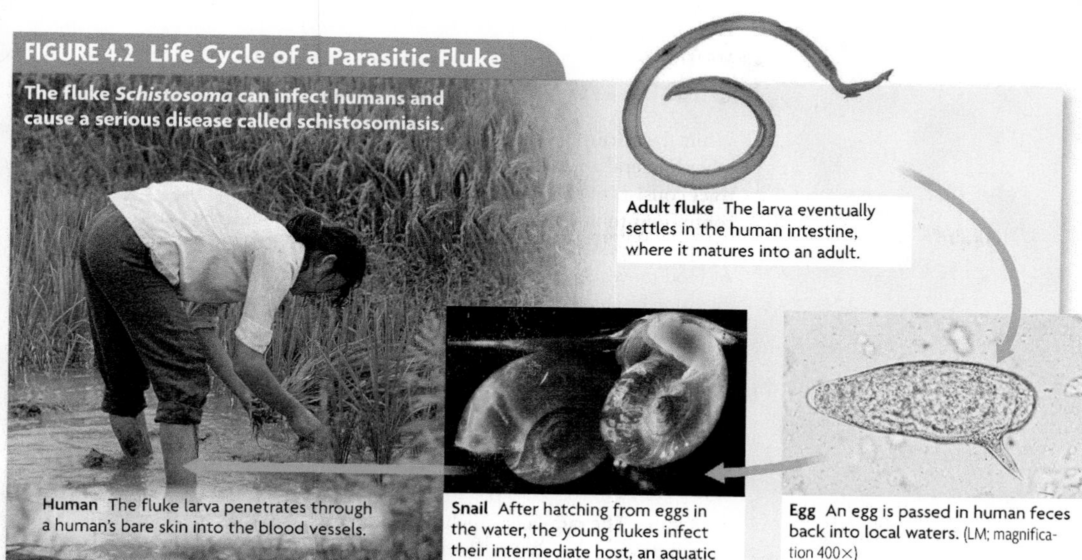

Adult fluke The larva eventually settles in the human intestine, where it matures into an adult.
Human The fluke larva penetrates through a human's bare skin into the blood vessels.
Snail After hatching from eggs in the water, the young flukes infect their intermediate host, an aquatic snail. Inside the snail, the flukes develop into tadpolelike larvae.
Egg An egg is passed in human feces back into local waters. (LM; magnification 400×)

Flukes

Flukes are parasites that feed on the body fluids of other animals. Flukes have a mouth with a pharynx that opens into a gut cavity. They are found in both invertebrate and vertebrate hosts. Many species of flukes have life cycles that involve more than one host. **FIGURE 4.2** shows the life cycle of one fluke, *Schistosoma* (SHIHS-tuh-SOHM-uh), which can infect humans and cause a serious disease called schistosomiasis. This disease affects about 200 million people in areas such as Africa and Southeast Asia. The disease is contracted by wading in or drinking fresh water contaminated with fluke larvae. Symptoms of the disease include the onset of fever and muscle pain within one to two months of infection. The disease is treated by an antiparasitic medicine.

Parasites

Tapeworms

Tapeworms are parasites that live in vertebrate guts. They have a small head with suckers or hooks used to attach to the host. Their long, ribbonlike body has no gut. Instead of swallowing food, these animals absorb nutrients from the digested food in which they live. An adult tapeworm's body is made up of segments containing both male and female sexual organs. When these segments fill with fertilized eggs, they break off and are excreted with the host's feces.

Many tapeworms have complex life cycles involving multiple hosts. The life cycle of a dog tapeworm begins when an egg is passed with a dog's feces. A flea eats the egg, and the egg develops into a larva within the flea's body. The tapeworm infects another dog when it accidentally eats the infected flea while licking its fur. The tapeworm develops into an adult within the dog's intestines, and the cycle begins again.

CONNECT TO

STRUCTURE AND FUNCTION

The simple structure of a tapeworm reflects that as an adult it does not have to move or digest food. The lack of complex internal systems allows for a simpler body plan.

A Contrast **How are planarians different from flukes and tapeworms?**

HANDS-ON ACTIVITY

The crossed "eyes" of a planarian are actually highly sensitive photoreceptors. Many organisms respond to light by moving toward it, a behavior called phototaxis. Movement away from light is called negative phototaxis. Divide students into small groups and give each a petri dish filled with fresh water, a medicine dropper, gloves, a culture of planarians, white construction paper, and a small flashlight.

Dim the classroom lights or draw the shades. Have students place the petri dish on top of the construction paper and transfer a planarian from the culture to the dish. Tell them to observe and record the planarian's movement for a moment, then shine the flashlight toward the dish from different angles and record the planarian's responses. Have students return the planarian to the culture and wash their hands. **Ask**

- How did the planarian respond to light? moved away from it
- Based on your observations, where would you expect to find these worms in nature? darker areas of aquatic habitats, such as under rocks or in muck

Students can learn about the life cycle of a tapeworm and the role humans play. Go to the WebQuest for this chapter at **HMHScience.com**.

Integrating Epidemiology

The cycle of **tapeworm infection** described is not unique to canines. Humans also are prone to parasitic infections transmitted by accidentally ingesting parasite eggs. Some infections occur through eating undercooked pork or beef infected with the eggs or cysts of a parasite. However, many infections result from contact with contaminated fecal matter. Epidemiologists have a formal name for this route of transmission: fecal-oral. Touching hands to mouth after gardening or scooping a pet's feces are common routes of fecal-oral infection. Vigorous hand-washing is the single most effective method of preventing transmission of parasites or other infectious organisms passed by this method.

Take It Further

Despite popular belief, most of the fish that is used to make **sushi** and sashimi in the United States is frozen at some point prior to consumption. This is done in large part to kill any parasites that may be living in the flesh, but also to preserve the flesh of the fish until it is ready to be consumed.

Answers

A Contrast Planarians are free-living, nonparasitic flatworms. Both flukes and tapeworms are parasites. Flukes feed on body fluids of other animals; tapeworms live in guts of invertebrates.

▼ Teach *continued*

Vocabulary

Academic Vocabulary Point out that *gut* refers to the area where food is held and digested. It is typically used for animals with simple digestive systems, ones not having separate organs for digestion. For more complex systems, the terms **digestive tract** or **alimentary canal** are used. *Gut* is not particularly useful in describing human anatomy despite slang expressions about "having the guts to act" or having a "gut feeling."

Take It Further

Snails called **naticids** are capable of boring through the hard shells of bivalves by using the **radula** in combination with a gland located at the tip of the **proboscis.** The proboscis is a long, muscular extension of the snail's mouth containing the radula and the esophagus. The gland secretes acid that dissolves the shell and then the radula drills. These two organs take turns working on the shell until it is penetrated about eight hours later. The proboscis then enters the bivalve, and the radula tears out chunks of the soft tissues within and delivers them to the esophagus for ingestion.

TEACH FROM VISUALS

FIGURE 4.3 Use the figure to review the digestive anatomy of mollusks. **Ask**

- What feature of the snail's gut distinguishes it from the flatworm's gut? an anus at the opposite end of the gut from the mouth
- What advantage does this feature provide? Food moves in one direction, allowing the animal to feed continuously.

Discuss the level of specialization shown in the snail's digestive system, including a crop for mechanical digestion and salivary and digestive glands for chemical digestion.

MAIN IDEA

Mollusks are diverse animals.

While flatworms have a digestive sac with only one opening, mollusks and all other bilateral animals have a complete digestive tract. A **complete digestive tract** consists of two openings—a mouth and an anus—at opposite ends of a continuous tube. Because food moves one way through the gut, animals with complete digestive tracts can turn their guts into disassembly lines for food. As food moves down the gut, it travels through areas that are specialized for digestion or absorption. Animals with complete digestive tracts can eat continuously. This efficient and frequent digestion allows animals to be more active.

Mollusk Anatomy

Mollusks include animals as different-looking as oysters, garden snails, and giant squid. Mollusks may be sessile filter feeders, herbivores that graze on algae, or predators. Despite this variety of form and lifestyle, all mollusks share at least one of three features, shown in **FIGURE 4.3.**

- **Radula** The **radula** is a filelike feeding organ. Mollusks eat by scraping the radula over their food. The hard teeth of the radula pick up tiny particles that the animal swallows.
- **Mantle** The mantle is an area of tissue covering the internal organs. In most mollusks, the mantle secretes a hard, calcium-based shell that protects the animal from predators.
- **Ctenidia** (tih-NIHD-ee-uh) The ctenidia are flat gills found in a pocket of the mantle tissue called the mantle cavity. The gills absorb oxygen from water that enters this cavity. In the land-dwelling snail shown below, the gills have been lost, and oxygen is absorbed from air rather than from water in the cavity.

While the gills contain blood vessels, blood is also pumped through the hemocoel. The **hemocoel** (HEE-muh-SEEL) consists of spaces between cells within the animal's tissues. This circulatory system extends into a large muscular foot. Snails and slugs crawl on the foot, while clams and scallops dig with the foot. In cephalopods, such as squids and octopuses, the foot forms a muscular siphon, parts of the tentacles, and head.

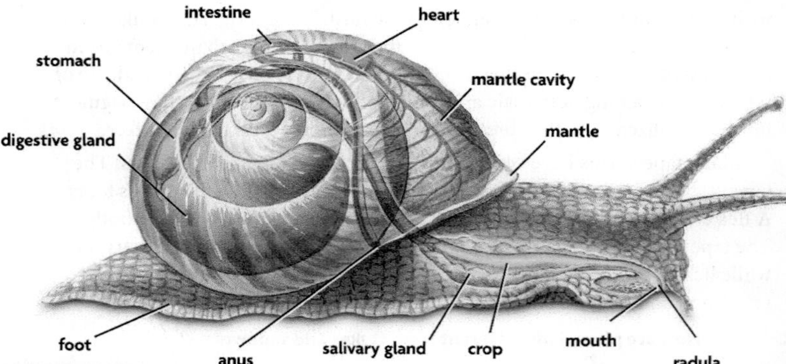

FIGURE 4.3 The anatomy of a common garden snail includes a radula and a mantle, both of which are features shared by most mollusks.

Differentiated Instruction

TEACH WITH TECHNOLOGY

Assemble a digital slide show of images that convey the wide range of form and function of the three mollusk features described in the text. For example, show photographs of the long, streamlined mantle of giant squids, the colorful, zooxanthellae-filled mantle of giant clams (genus *Tridacna*), and the edible mantles of blue mussels and quahogs. After running through a series of comparative images and pointing out these features, test students by showing new images and seeing if they can spot the radula, mantle, and ctenidia.

Classes of Mollusks

There are seven classes of mollusks. The majority of species, however, are found within three classes: the gastropods, pelecypods (bivalves), and cephalopods.

FIGURE 4.4 The Humboldt, or jumbo, squid may grow to nearly 2 meters (6 ft) in length.

- **Gastropoda** This class includes snails, nudibranchs, abalones, and limpets. Gastropods make up over half of the species found in the Mollusk phylum. They live in both land and aquatic ecosystems. This class includes species that are herbivores, carnivores, and scavengers.
- **Pelecypoda** This class includes clams, oysters, mussels, and scallops. Pelecypods, which are also called bivalves, have a soft body that is protected by two hard shells that are hinged together. Most bivalves are filter feeders that live in marine ecosystems.
- **Cephalopoda** This class includes squid, as shown in **FIGURE 4.4**, octopuses, nautiluses, and cuttlefish. Among the mollusks, the nervous system and eye of the cephalopod are the most well-developed. Cephalopods are carnivores that eat animals such as crustaceans, fish, and other mollusks.
- **Scaphopoda** This class is also called the tusk shells, so named because their shells resemble the shape of an elephant's tusks. These mollusks live at the bottom of water bodies, where they feed on detritus.
- **Polyplacophora** This class is also called the chitons, which are animals that have a shell with overlapping plates. These marine mollusks spend most of their lifetime clinging to rocks, where they feed by using their radula to scrape algae and plant matter from the rocks.
- **Aplacophora** This class includes small wormlike animals that, unlike most mollusks, do not have shells. These mollusks live in deep water. Some feed on small marine invertebrates, while others are parasites of coral.
- **Tryblidiiae** This class of mollusks was once believed to be extinct, but they were rediscovered in 1952. Little is known about these marine mollusks that live in deep water.

CONNECT TO

CONVERGENT EVOLUTION

Much like the human eye, the cephalopod eye is made up of a lens, retina, iris, and pupil. However, the evolution of cephalapod and human eyes occurred independently. Recall from **The Evolution of Populations** that convergent evolution is the evolution of similar structures in unrelated species.

Mollusk Reproduction

Mollusks use a variety of reproductive strategies. Garden snails, for example, are hermaphrodites. Hermaphrodites are organisms that have both male and female reproductive organs. Reproduction usually involves cross-fertilization. Just before mating, the impregnating snail fires a "love dart" into the other. This calcium-rich, mucus-covered dart causes the recipient snail's reproductive system to store more sperm. During mating, a packet of sperm is transferred into the recipient snail. This packet of sperm is used to fertilize the eggs. These eggs are laid in underground nests. After a period of two to four weeks, juvenile snails hatch from the eggs.

A Summarize **What common features are shared by mollusks?**

Vocabulary

Greek and Latin Word Origins Remind students that roots often contain clues about a word's meaning. For example, *gastropod* means "stomach foot," a fair description of an animal whose stomach is situated atop its muscular foot. Another example is *cephalopod*, which translates to "head foot." Cephalopods are so-named because their "feet," or tentacles, are attached to their head.

The Inside Story

In the age of wooden ships, one particular type of bivalve posed a serious threat to ocean exploration. Species of the Teredinidae family, known commonly as **shipworms**, use their specialized valves to bore into wood. The wood provided shelter and allowed the animals to strain the seawater for food. Because half of the volume of a ship's timbers could be removed by the boring bivalves before the crew even noticed the problem, numerous ships were far more vulnerable to impacts from rocks, reefs, and cannonballs.

The British navy dealt with the problem in the late 18th century by sheathing the hulls of ships in a layer of copper. This process was expensive, but it kept the bivalve out and allowed ships such as Captain James Cook's *Endeavour* and William Bligh's *Bounty* to sail for years without disintegrating.

PRE-AP

Choose a topic covered in this section, such as "Mollusk Anatomy" or "Common Characteristics of Annelids." Ask each student to state an example or known fact about the topic without repeating what has already been said. Repeat for each topic of the section. After each topic has been exhausted, you can have students spend two minutes writing down as many facts as they can recall.

Teacher Toolkit, Section C, Round Robin

Answers

A **Summarize** complete digestive tract; a radula (filelike feeding organ), mantle (area of tissue covering the internal organs), and ctenidia (flat gills found in the pocket of the mantle tissue)

Teach *continued*

QUICKLAB

Time 60 minutes — TEACHER TESTED

Purpose Observe the soft body of a clam to identify different systems.

LAB MANAGEMENT

- Make copies of the datasheet for students, available at **HMHScience.com**.
- Remind students not to touch their mouths while handling clams.

Safety Students should wash their hands thoroughly after handling the clams and before writing their analyses.

Answers

Analyze and Conclude

1. The clam draws water in through one of its siphons, passes the water over the ctenidia for gas exchange, and pumps the water out through the other siphon.
2. Water containing food particles enters the mouth from the mantle cavity. The water passes through the digestive system, where the food particles are digested and absorbed. The wastes exit through the anus into the mantle cavity and get pumped out through the siphon.
3. The clam has an open circulatory system, which pumps blood to spaces around the tissues and drains blood back to the heart. This system is a lower-pressure system than the closed system found in mammals, birds, and reptiles.

Teacher Note "I've never taught this before, and it was a lot easier than I thought it would be."

Vocabulary

Academic Vocabulary The branch of physical science or physics that studies the effects of fluids under pressure or at rest is **hydrostatics. Hydraulics** is the technology that uses liquid under pressure, typically water, to produce force or motion.

QUICKLAB OBSERVING

Anatomy of a Clam

A clam is a bivalve mollusk. In this lab, you will explore the parts and systems of a clam.

PROBLEM What are the internal organs and systems of a clam?

PROCEDURE

1. Place the clam in the dissecting tray and follow the instructions on the drawing to carefully open the shell.
2. Look for the gills, and use your probe to study them.
3. Observe and note the shape of the foot. Locate the palps.
4. Follow the instructions to peel away the muscle layer to see the internal organs.
5. Locate the reproductive organs, and then find the digestive system.
6. Dispose of your specimen as instructed by your teacher.

ANALYZE AND CONCLUDE

1. **Infer** What organ does the clam use to breathe?
2. **Infer** The clam is a filter feeder. Based on your observations of the digestive system, how does the clam eat?
3. **Infer** The arteries and veins are not attached to each other. How might the circulatory system work?

MATERIALS

- preserved clam specimen
- dissecting tray
- Anatomical Clam Drawing
- screwdriver
- scalpel
- probe
- scissors
- forceps
- 12 dissecting pins
- hand lens
- paper towels

MAIN IDEA

Annelids have segmented bodies.

All annelids share more similarities in their body plans than mollusks do. Three groups of annelids—earthworms, marine worms, and leeches—are characterized by segmentation. **Segmentation** refers to the division of an organism's body, in this case an annelid's long body, into repeated sections that contain a complex set of body structures.

Annelid Anatomy

The features of an annelid's segmented body are shown in **FIGURE 4.5.** A typical annelid segment contains part of the digestive tract, nerve cord, and blood vessels that carry blood to the worm's tissues. Annelids have a closed circulatory system, where blood travels in a closed circuit inside blood vessels. Each body segment also contains organs that collect and excrete wastes, bands of longitudinal and circular muscle, and a coelom.

The **coelom** (SEE-luhm) is a fluid-filled space that is completely surrounded by muscle. The coelom is divided by partitions called septa (singular, *septum*). The fluid inside the coelom acts as a hydrostatic skeleton. To understand how a hydrostatic skeleton works, think of a water balloon. When you squeeze one end, the water moves to the opposite end. An annelid uses its hydrostatic skeleton in a similar way to move from one place to another. When the longitudinal muscles contract, the segment shortens. When circular muscles contract, the segment lengthens. Alternating waves of contractions move from head to tail, producing the worm's characteristic crawling motion.

READING TOOLBOX

VOCABULARY

Coelom comes from a Greek word meaning "cavity." *Septum* comes from a Latin word meaning "partition."

Differentiated Instruction

HANDS-ON ACTIVITY

Provide students with a hand lens and an earthworm in a petri dish. Have them locate the earthworm's segments, mouth, and anus and observe its crawling motion. Students can use the eraser end of a pencil to prod the earthworm gently. Remind students to wash their hands after handling the earthworm.

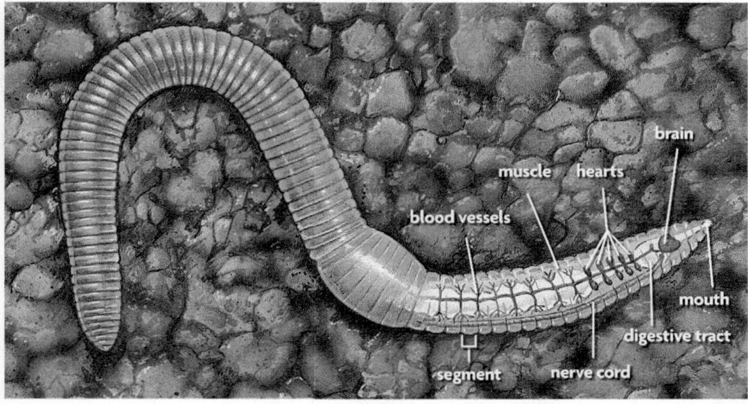

FIGURE 4.5 Annelids, such as earthworms, have similar body plans, characterized by segmentation.

Annelid Diet

Earthworms and marine worms eat organic waste material. Earthworms excrete digested material, called castings, into the soil. Castings help maintain a nutrient-rich soil. While most people think of leeches as blood-feeders, a number of leech species are actually predators that feed on invertebrates such as snails and aquatic insect larvae.

Annelid Reproduction

Annelid reproduction may be either asexual or sexual. Asexual reproduction results from fragmentation. In this method, a portion of the posterior end of the annelid breaks off and forms a new individual. Some annelids, such as earthworms, are hermaphrodites. Just as in land snails, reproduction occurs by cross-fertilization. Other annelids, such as marine worms, have separate males and females. Fertilized eggs of marine annelids initially develop into free-swimming larvae. Larvae grow in size by the formation of new segments.

Contrast **In what ways are annelids different from mollusks?**

22.4 Formative Assessment

SELF-CHECK Online
HMHScience.com
GO ONLINE

REVIEWING ◆ MAIN IDEAS

1. Describe the characteristics that separate the three groups of flatworms.
2. What is the function of a mollusk's **radula**?
3. What are the three groups of annelids? Describe their body plan, using the word **coelom.**

CRITICAL THINKING

4. **Apply** How might a community prevent *Schistosoma* infections?
5. **Infer** What adaptations might mollusks without shells use to defend against predators?

CONNECT TO EVOLUTION

6. Free-living flatworms have pairs of sensory organs in their heads. What might make two sense organs set on either side of the head more adaptive than a single central organ?

22.4 FORMATIVE ASSESSMENT

1. Flukes and tapeworms are both parasitic; planarians are not. Tapeworms feed on food within the host's digestive tract; flukes feed on the host's body fluids.
2. scrape off food particles to eat
3. Earthworms, marine worms, and leeches; all have segmented bodies with organs that collect and excrete wastes, bands of muscle, and a coelom, which is a fluid-filled space completely surrounded by muscle. The coelom helps the annelid move.
4. Sewage treatment could prevent larvae excreted by infected people from getting back into the water supply. Water treatment could kill larvae.
5. *Sample answers:* chemical defenses (inedible), camouflage, rapid escape mechanisms (jet propulsion)
6. Pairs of organs help animals determine the direction of a stimulus through comparison of the stimulus's strength from one organ to the other.

TEACH FROM VISUALS

FIGURE 4.5 Have students study the external and internal anatomy of the earthworm. Point out that the earthworm is segmented both externally and internally. **Ask**

- What organs make up the earthworm's circulatory system? hearts and blood vessels
- Is the circulatory system open or closed? closed

Take It Further

The **palolo worm,** *Palola viridis,* is a marine annelid that is considered a delicacy by the people of Samoa. This species reproduces by producing a long chain of segments at its tail end that is filled with gametes. Once a year, usually around a full moon in spring, the worms rise to the surface and release the reproductive sections, which burst open so that sperm and eggs can mix and fertilize. This **swarming** allows for a much greater chance of fertilization, but it also makes these animals vulnerable to predators, such as humans, who have learned to show up at the right place and right time for a palolo feast.

Answers

A **Contrast** Annelids have closed circulatory systems, coeloms, and segmented bodies. There is greater diversity of body plan in mollusks than in annelids.

Assess and Reteach ▼

Assess Use the Section Self-Check or Section Quiz, both available at **HMHScience.com**.

Reteach Create a crossword puzzle featuring important terms from the section.

SECTION 22.5

▼ Plan and Prepare

Activate Prior Knowledge Students with pets may be familiar with one particular type of roundworm. **Ask,** What is the common name of the parasite that can infect dogs? heartworm This roundworm species is carried by mosquitoes and infects various canines and felines.

▼ Teach

Vocabulary

Greek and Latin Word Origins The root of **cuticle** is the Latin word *cutis,* which means "skin."

The words **chiton,** a type of mollusk mentioned in **Section 4,** and **chitin** both come from the Greek *khitōn,* a name for the tunic worn by both men and women in ancient Greece. Students can describe the cuticle of roundworms or the exoskeleton of arthropods as **chitinous.**

In the phylum name Nematoda, *nema-* comes from a Greek word meaning "thread."

22.5 Roundworms

VOCABULARY

cuticle
pseudocoelom

KEY CONCEPT **Roundworms have bilateral symmetry and shed their outer skeleton to grow.**

MAIN IDEAS

- Roundworms shed their stiff outer skeleton as they grow.
- Many roundworms are parasites.

Connect to Your World

Imagine grabbing a handful of soil. In that single handful, there may be thousands of roundworms. These animals are found in nearly every ecosystem on Earth, including mountaintops and deep ocean trenches. They are also found within extreme environments such as hot springs and Arctic ice.

MAIN IDEA

Roundworms shed their stiff outer skeleton as they grow.

Roundworms, also called nematodes, are one of the most numerous kinds of animals, in terms both of numbers and of species diversity. The more than 15,000 species of roundworms vary in size from less than a millimeter to over 10 meters in length.

Roundworms are part of the group Ecdysozoa, which also includes arthropods—crustaceans, spiders, and insects. Like mollusks and annelids, members of the Ecdysozoa are protostomes and have bilateral symmetry. All Ecdysozoans have a tough exoskeleton called a cuticle. The **cuticle** (KYOO-tih-kuhl) is made of chitin, and must be shed whenever the animal grows larger. When the animal sheds its cuticle, its soft body is exposed to predators until its new skeleton hardens.

FIGURE 5.1 Roundworms have a cylindrical shape and must shed their tough outer cuticle to grow in size.

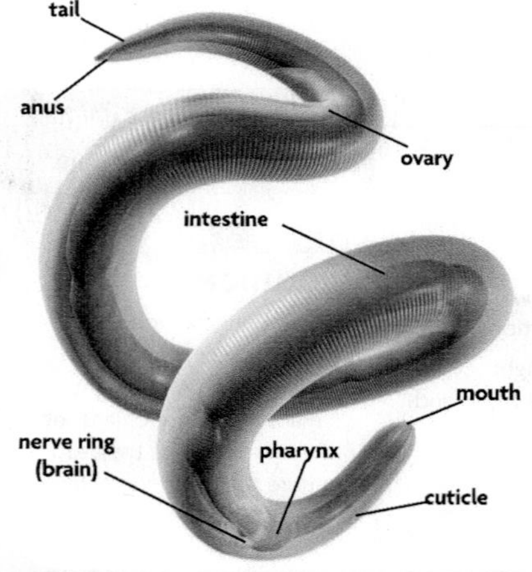

Roundworm Anatomy

As shown in **FIGURE 5.1,** a roundworm is cylindrical, with a blunt head and tapered tail. It is covered with a tough cuticle that lies over a layer of muscle. Muscle in the roundworm is laid out lengthwise. This arrangement means that a roundworm moves by bending its body side-to-side. Rather than crawling like other types of worms, a roundworm's movement is more whiplike.

Muscle within the roundworm is separated from the central gut tube by a fluid-filled space. This fluid-filled space is called a **pseudocoelom** (soo-duh-SEE-luhm) because it is not completely lined by muscle. (The prefix *pseudo-* means "false.") Roundworms do not have circulatory or respiratory systems. However, they do have a digestive system, which includes a mouth, pharynx, intestine, and anus. Food that is eaten, such as plant matter, algae, or bacteria, travels the length of the roundworm, from the mouth at one end to the anus at the other.

Differentiated Instruction

PRE-AP

Have students continue with the practice of preparing a biological profile card for each phylum, this time for the phylum Nematoda.

Roundworm Reproduction

Most roundworms reproduce sexually. In some cases, female roundworms bear live young after eggs hatch within the female's reproductive tract. In most cases, however, larvae develop from eggs laid by the female. Roundworms grow into their adult form by molting.

A Contrast How does growth differ in a roundworm and in a human?

MAIN IDEA

Many roundworms are parasites.

Roundworms are parasites of nearly every plant and animal species. These animals cause a lot of damage to the crop species they infect. Such a widespread loss of crops can seriously harm the economy of farming communities. Other roundworms infect humans. These roundworms include hookworms, pinworms, and guinea worms.

- **Hookworms** A hookworm is found within the digestive tract of its host. This parasite feeds on its host's blood. A hookworm infects its human host when a person walks barefoot over contaminated soil. Over 1 billion people are infected with hookworms. Such infections are common in the tropics and subtropics.
- **Pinworms** A pinworm is found in the gut of its host. Pinworm infections often occur when the host accidentally swallows eggs picked up from contaminated surfaces.
- **Guinea worms** Guinea worms are found in the guts and connective tissues of their hosts. Guinea worm infections occur when a person drinks contaminated water. Work by global health organizations has helped to eliminate this disease from most of the world.

"So much for being the early bird, you've got worms."

B Infer Why might most parasitic roundworms live in the gut of their host?

22.5 Formative Assessment

SELF-CHECK Online
HMHScience.com
GO ONLINE

REVIEWING MAIN IDEAS

1. Why do roundworms molt? Use the term **cuticle** in your answer.
2. What are three parasitic roundworms that infect human hosts?

CRITICAL THINKING

3. **Contrast** How are earthworm and roundworm body cavities different?
4. **Apply** How might Guinea worm infections be prevented?

CONNECT TO PARASITISM

5. Many species of roundworms are parasites of plants and animals. How is a roundworm's body plan related to its function as a parasite?

22.5 FORMATIVE ASSESSMENT

1. A roundworm's cuticle (or exoskeleton) is made of nonliving material and cannot grow as the roundworm gets bigger.
2. hookworms, pinworms, Guinea worms
3. Earthworms have coeloms; roundworms have pseudocoeloms. Functionally, the roundworm's pseudocoelom is used for circulation, whereas the earthworm's coelom is used for locomotion.
4. *Sample Answers:* avoiding contaminated water supplies and drinking only treated or filtered water
5. The roundworm's body plan is very simple, consisting of a mouth, gut tube, and anus. Because roundworms spend most of their lifetime within their host, they do not need to have a complex body plan suited for locomotion.

Integrating Epidemiology

The heartworm that affects dogs is one type of **filarial worm,** which can be very harmful to humans. The worm *Onchocerca volvulus* is transmitted to humans through black flies, and can cause a disease commonly known as **river blindness.** Flies deliver larval worms into a human's blood. These worms can grow and infest the eyes and other tissues. Nearly 18 million people have this disease, and close to one million people are blind or visually impaired as a result. This disease is especially prevalent in rural African villages near fast-moving streams, but it is also known in parts of Central and South America.

Answers

A Contrast Roundworms must shed their cuticle (exoskeleton) in order to grow. Humans have an endoskeleton that grows in size to accommodate growth of other tissues.

B Infer The gut provides a stable environment with few or no predators and plenty of available nutrients.

Assess and Reteach

Assess Use the Section Self-Check or Section Quiz, both available at **HMHScience.com**.

Reteach Set up a three-column chart on the board with the following column headings: Roundworms, Segmented Worms, Flatworms. Give students examples such as leeches, tapeworms, pinworms, and earthworms and ask them to indicate in which column each should be placed. Have students compare and contrast the phyla.

SECTION 22.6

▼ Plan and Prepare

Activate Prior Knowledge Students who have been to a beach may know at least one type of echinoderm. **Ask,** What type of animal found in tide pools is radially symmetric? sea stars, or "starfish" Introduce these as just one of five major types of echinoderms. **Ask,** What other invertebrate phylum in this chapter has radial symmetry? Cnidaria

▼ Teach

TEACH FROM VISUALS

FIGURE 6.1 Have students find the structures that make up the sea star's water vascular system. Explain that the bulblike structures extending from the radial canals are connected to the external tube feet. The tube feet extend when water from the bulbs is pushed into the tube feet. The tube feet retract when the bulbs relax.

22.6 Echinoderms

KEY CONCEPT **Echinoderms are on the same evolutionary branch as vertebrates.**

VOCABULARY
ossicle
water vascular system

MAIN IDEAS
- Echinoderms have radial symmetry.
- There are five classes of Echinoderms.

Connect to Your World

If you have ever seen a tide pool, you may have noticed several creatures clinging to the pool's rocky bottom and sides. Brightly colored sea stars and spiky sea urchins are just two of the echinoderms that are often found in these habitats.

MAIN IDEA

Echinoderms have radial symmetry.

Adult echinoderms are slow-moving marine animals that have radial symmetry. In contrast, echinoderm larvae have bilateral symmetry. This difference suggests that echinoderms had bilateral ancestors and that radial symmetry is a derived character.

Echinoderm Anatomy

The anatomy of a sea star is shown in **FIGURE 6.1.** Note that each arm of a sea star contains both digestive glands and reproductive glands. For clarity, they are shown separately in different arms in the illustration.

All echinoderms have an internal skeleton made up of many tiny interlocking calcium-based plates called **ossicles.** These ossicles are embedded within the skin. The plates are joined together by a unique catch connective tissue with adjustable stiffness. Catch connective tissue allows echinoderms to change their consistency, going from very flexible to very stiff in a matter of seconds. The combination of a firm skeleton and a surface covered with spiny projections (often poisonous) helps to fend off predators.

Echinoderms have a **water vascular system,** which is a series of water-filled radial canals that extend along each arm from the ring canal surrounding the central disk. The radial canals store water that is used for circulation and for filling tiny suckerlike appendages along the arms called tube feet. Changes in water pressure extend and retract the tube feet. On its own, a tube foot is small, but many of them working together can exert large forces. Tube feet are used to grab objects and to move around.

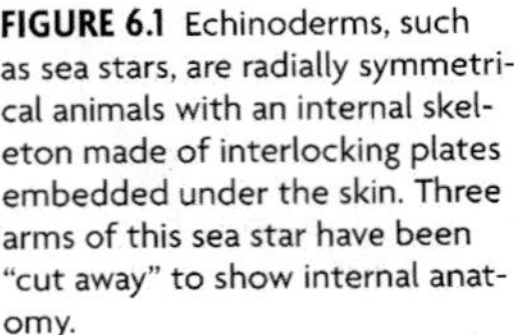

FIGURE 6.1 Echinoderms, such as sea stars, are radially symmetrical animals with an internal skeleton made of interlocking plates embedded under the skin. Three arms of this sea star have been "cut away" to show internal anatomy.

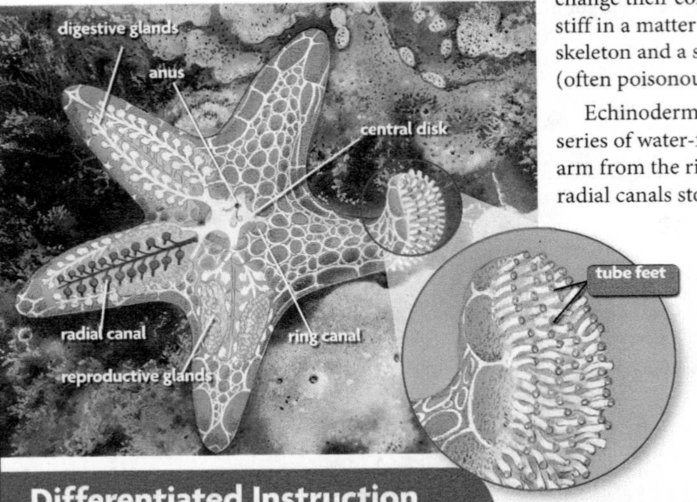

Differentiated Instruction

BELOW LEVEL

Have students consider the material in this section and previous sections. Ask them to write for five minutes on the different functions water performs in marine animals. Have them think about which of the animals they studied have blood.

Teacher Toolkit, Section C, Quick-Write

PRE-AP

Have students prepare a biological profile card for the phylum Echinodermata and its five classes.

A sea star has a complete digestive system made up of a mouth, stomach, a small length of intestine, and an anus. To eat a clam, a sea star grabs hold of the clam with its tube feet and uses pressure to pull apart the clam's shell. Sea stars are able to push their stomach out of their mouths. The stomach enters the narrow space between the two shells of a clam, and digestive juices from the digestive glands dissolve the clam's body. The clam is completely digested in the stomach. Waste material exits out the anus.

Echinoderms such as sea stars can regenerate, or regrow, their limbs, as shown in **FIGURE 6.2.** Sea cucumbers can regenerate a portion of their digestive system, which they sometimes eject when disturbed. For regeneration to occur, certain body parts, such as a portion of a sea star's central disk, must still remain.

FIGURE 6.2 Sea stars and other echinoderms are able to regenerate, or regrow, limbs.

Echinoderm Reproduction

Most echinoderms reproduce sexually. Adult sea stars, for example, release sperm and eggs from the reproductive glands in their arms into the water. The fusion of these gametes results in fertilization of the egg. The fertilized egg develops into a free-floating, planktonic larva that matures in the water. As it matures, an echinoderm undergoes a complex series of changes into its adult form. The left side of its body begins to form the tube feet, while the right side forms the ossicle plates that will protect its outer surface. Eventually, the echinoderm settles onto the ocean floor, where it develops into an adult.

A Connect **A sea star specimen has bilateral symmetry. Is it an adult or a larva? Why?**

MAIN IDEA

There are five classes of Echinoderms.

Echinoderms have a variety of body plans, ranging from the spiny round sea urchin to the oblong and the well-named sea cucumber.

Feather Stars and Sea Lilies

Feather stars and sea lilies are members of the class Crinoidea (kry-NOY-dee-uh). A feather star, shown in **FIGURE 6.3,** can move with its arms, but it is usually attached to a surface. Sea lilies are sessile. They are attached to the ocean bottom by a stalk on one side of their bodies. These animals filter feed by using the tube foot–like extensions covering their arms to collect and transfer food to the mouth.

FIGURE 6.3 Feather stars are members of the class Crinoidea. These animals are filter feeders.

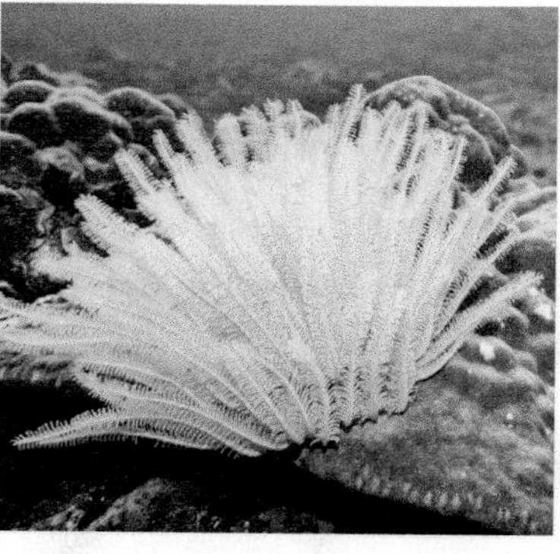

Sea Stars

Sea stars are members of the class Asteroidea (AS-tuh-ROY-dee-uh). Some sea stars are filter feeders, while others are opportunistic feeders, meaning that they will eat whatever food source they happen to come upon. Other sea stars are carnivorous predators.

Vocabulary

Greek and Latin Word Origins The word **echinoderm** comes from the Greek roots *echino-*, meaning "hedgehog" (a spiny mammal) and *-derm* meaning "skin."

Integrating Ecology

The sea star *Pisaster ochraceus* is a **keystone species** in rocky intertidal communities of the northeast Pacific Ocean. Experiments conducted in the 1960s demonstrated that if *Pisaster* individuals were removed from their communities, the community structure quickly fell into disarray, mostly through the opportunistic niche-grab of the mussel *Mytilus californicus,* a key prey of the sea star. The experimental removal of the sea star took away the predation pressure on the mussel population, which quickly multiplied, outcompeting other species for both food and space and ultimately driving down biodiversity in the community. When the sea star was reintroduced into these communities, it quickly decreased the mussel population through efficient predation.

Answers

A **Connect** The specimen is a larva. Sea stars have bilateral symmetry as larvae and radial symmetry as adults.

ENGLISH LEARNERS

Refer students to the first paragraph on this page, which describes a sea star's method of eating. Have them make a sequence diagram that summarizes the sequence of steps described in the paragraph.

Teacher Toolkit, Section C, Sequence Diagram

INCLUSION

Provide dried or live specimens of echinoderms for students who are visually impaired. Some sea urchin species have spines that are blunt and safe to touch. Sea stars will apply their tube feet to a hand, allowing students to feel how the sea star moves and attaches itself to prey and to the sea floor. Sea cucumbers can be handled as well, but be sure to tell students to handle them gently. Students should wash their hands after the activity.

Chapter 22: Invertebrate Diversity **665**

▼ Teach continued

Integrating Ecology

The **crown-of-thorns sea star,** *Acanthaster planci,* eats corals on tropical reefs throughout the South Pacific Ocean. Scientists believe that periodic surges in the populations of this species may be the result of human influences on the coral reef ecosystem. One theory suggests that the removal of the sea star's predators is to blame. The giant triton snail, humphead Maori wrasse, sweetlip emperor fish, and starry puffer fish all are known predators of the crown-of-thorns, and all have been heavily fished on various reefs in the Pacific. Another theory is that **nutrient runoff** from coastal land results in phytoplankton blooms that in turn support the larvae of the crown-of-thorns.

Answers

A Contrast Sea stars are voracious predators of clams and other organisms, while sea cucumbers are sediment-feeders.

▼ Assess and Reteach

Assess Use the Section Self-Check or Section Quiz, both available at **HMHScience.com**.

Reteach Work with students to create a compare/contrast chart that summarizes the information provided in this section about the five classes of echinoderms. The chart should address the echinoderms' mobility, methods of feeding, and body types.

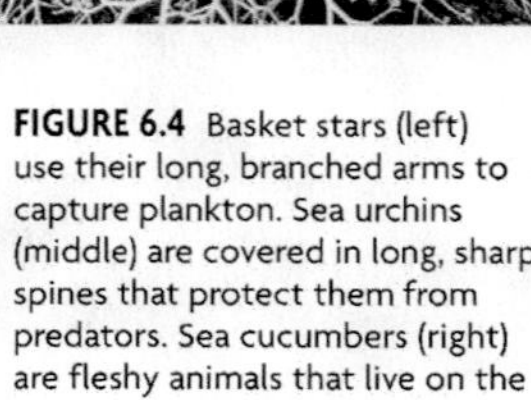

FIGURE 6.4 Basket stars (left) use their long, branched arms to capture plankton. Sea urchins (middle) are covered in long, sharp spines that protect them from predators. Sea cucumbers (right) are fleshy animals that live on the ocean floor.

Brittle Stars and Basket Stars

Brittle stars and basket stars are both members of the class Ophiuroidea (AHF-ee-yuh-ROY-dee-uh). Brittle stars have long spindly arms and are fast movers. Because their tube feet lack suckers, brittle stars use their arms to move. Some brittle stars are scavengers that feed on detritus on the ocean floor. Others are predators. Basket stars, shown in **FIGURE 6.4**, also have long arms, although with many branches. Basket stars filter feed by capturing plankton with their arms.

Sea Urchins, Sea Biscuits, and Sand Dollars

Sea urchins, sea biscuits, and sand dollars are all members of the class Echinoidea (EHK-uh-NOY-dee-uh). The bodies of sea biscuits and sand dollars are covered with tiny projections, which the animals use for movement and for burrowing on the ocean floor. Sea urchins, which do not burrow, do not have these projections. Instead, these animals are covered in long, sharp spines. Burrowing animals feed on waste matter on the ocean floor. Most sea urchins graze on algae by trapping it on sticky tentacles found on their ventral side.

Sea Cucumbers

Sea cucumbers are the only members of the class Holothuroidea (HAHL-uh-thu-ROY-dee-uh). Sea cucumbers are fleshy animals that have a long, bilateral shape. Instead of arms, sea cucumbers have thick, fleshy tentacles. These tentacles are used to capture particles of food, which the animal eats by pulling its tentacles through its mouth. Sea cucumbers, which live on the ocean floor, are also sediment feeders. These animals absorb food items in their digestive tract, and eject nonfood particles through their anus.

A Contrast How do feeding behaviors differ between sea stars and sea cucumbers?

22.6 Formative Assessment

SELF-CHECK Online HMHScience.com GO ONLINE

REVIEWING ▶ MAIN IDEAS

1. How does the **water vascular system** enable echinoderms to move?
2. Describe the differences in body plans between the five classes of echinoderms.

CRITICAL THINKING

3. **Contrast** How do the feeding habits of sessile echinoderms differ from those that are mobile?
4. **Infer** How does an echinoderm benefit from the ability to regenerate limbs?

CONNECT TO BIOINDICATORS

5. Sea urchins live on rock- and sand-covered areas of the ocean floor. What changes in an ocean ecosystem might be indicated by an increase in the sea urchin population?

Unit 6: Diversity of Life

22.6 FORMATIVE ASSESSMENT

1. The water vascular system allows echinoderms to move their tube feet by forcing water in and out of them.
2. Asteroidea: move with tube feet, regenerate limbs; Ophiuroidea: tube feet lack suckers, use long arms to move; Echinoidea: covered with spines or small projections used for movement; Holothuroidea: long bilateral shape with fleshy tentacles; Crinoidea: immobile stalk topped with feathery arms
3. Sessile echinoderms tend to be filter-feeders; mobile echinoderms tend to be active predators or sediment-feeders.
4. Echinoderms can survive extensive damage to their bodies and can regain functions.
5. decrease in marine plant life or populations of other bottom-dwelling organisms that cover sand or rock; could also indicate an abundance of the algae on which urchins feed

Analyzing Scatterplots

Smart Grapher HMHScience.com GO ONLINE

Create animated charts and graphs with Smart Grapher.

DATA ANALYSIS

A **scatterplot** is a type of graph used to identify a trend or a correlation between two variables.

- The independent variable is usually graphed on the *x*-axis.
- The dependent variable is usually graphed on the *y*-axis.
- The data points are plotted but not connected.

Three types of correlations between variables can be shown on a scatterplot.

- Positive—as one variable increases or decreases, the other variable increases or decreases respectively.
- Negative (inverse)—as one variable increases, the other decreases.
- No correlation—there is no change in one variable as the other variable either increases or decreases.

Model

Graph 1, a scatterplot of butter clam shell length and width, shows that as the width of the clam's shell increases, the length of the shell increases as well. This is a positive correlation, because as width increases, length increases. If it were an inverse correlation, one of the variables would increase as the other decreased.

Graph 2, a scatterplot of zooplankton feeding rates, shows no correlation between the feeding rates of zooplankton and the concentration of dinoflagellates. You can infer that there is no correlation from the graph, because the data are scattered across the graph and do not form a pattern.

GRAPH 1. PUGET SOUND BUTTER CLAMS

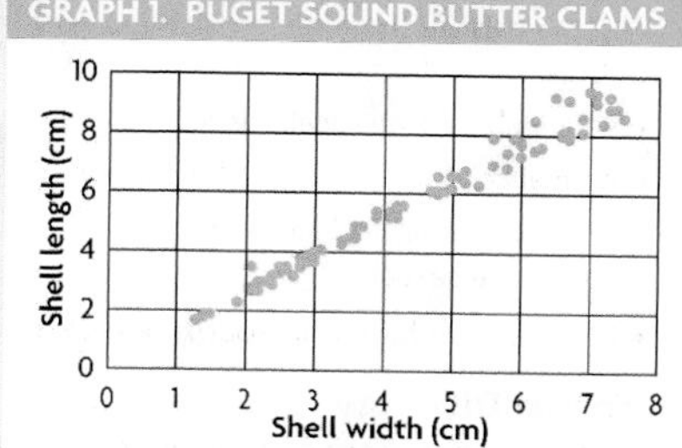

Source: Seattle Central Community College

GRAPH 2. ZOOPLANKTON FEEDING RATE

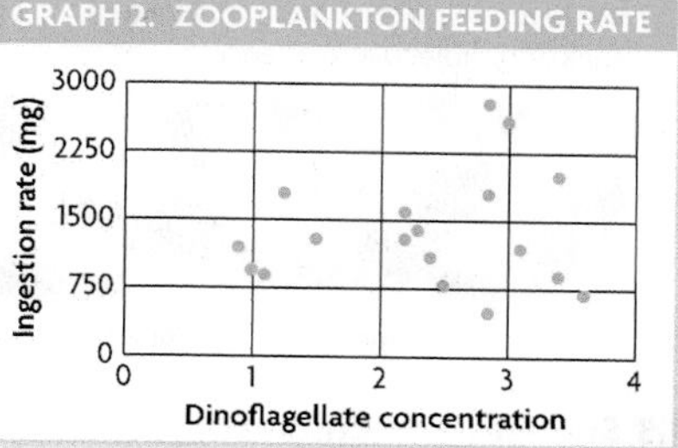

Source: Calbet, A. et al. *Journal of Aquatic Microbial Ecology, 26*

Practice Analyze a Scatterplot

Scientists measured the heart rate and shell diameter of snails. These data are shown in the graph at the right. Use the graph to answer the following three questions.

1. **Analyze** Describe the correlation between the shell diameter and the heart rate in this species of snail.
2. **Predict** If a snail shell were to grow past 14 mm, what do you think would happen to the snail's heart rate?
3. **Infer** Suggest a possible explanation for the correlation between heart rate and shell diameter.

GRAPH 3. SNAIL HEART RATE

Heart rate (beats per minute)

Shell diameter (mm)

Source: Iowa State University

Answers

1. There is a negative relationship between shell diameter and heart rate. As the shell diameter increases, the heart rate decreases.
2. The heart rate could slow a little or remain the same as the 13-mm snail.
3. A larger snail has a larger heart. A larger heart can pump a larger volume of blood than a small heart can, meaning it does not need to beat as often in order to deliver oxygen and other nutrients to the snail's tissues.

DATA ANALYSIS

Introduce

A scatterplot illustrates the relationship between two variables. This relationship may be viewed as positive, negative, or nonexistent.

Discuss

Ask students for examples of other pairs of variables that show a positive, a negative, or no relationship. Have them draw on the board what a scatterplot for each pair of variables would look like.

Discuss the gradual flattening of the slope of the plotted data on graph 3. Point out that such a trend is common when there are physiological or physical limitations at play. For example, if we plotted human population over the last thousand years, it would show remarkable growth, especially in the last century. **Ask**

- Does this mean that in another hundred years the population will have doubled again? Not necessarily; many populations reach a point or a capacity at which their rate of growth can no longer be supported by the resources. Relate this to the trend in graph 3 and to other trends in nature.
- Why might the heart rate decrease very little or not at all if a snail continues to grow beyond 14 mm in shell diameter? The heart may have a limit in terms of how much volume it can pump or how large it can grow, even if the snail continues to grow.

Online Student Resources, Data Analysis Practice

Chapter 22: Invertebrate Diversity 667

CHAPTER REVIEW

INTERACTIVE Review
HMHScience.com

GO ONLINE

Encourage students to go to **HMHScience.com** for a detailed review of each section, including visuals and vocabulary practice.

Online Student Resources, Vocabulary Practice Worksheet

CHAPTER **22** Summary

BIG IDEA Animals share many characteristics, yet have a variety of shapes, structures, and sizes, and most have no backbone.

KEY CONCEPTS

22.1 Animal Characteristics

Animals are diverse but share common characteristics. Animals are the most physically diverse kingdom of organisms. All animals share a set of characteristics.

- All animals are multicellular heterotrophs.
- Animal cells are supported by collagen.
- Animals that reproduce are diploid and usually reproduce sexually.
- Most animals have homeobox, or *Hox,* genes.

22.2 Animal Diversity

More than 95 percent of all animal species are invertebrates. Each animal phylum has a unique body plan. Scientists have constructed an invertebrate phylogenetic tree supported by anatomy comparisons and molecular evidence.

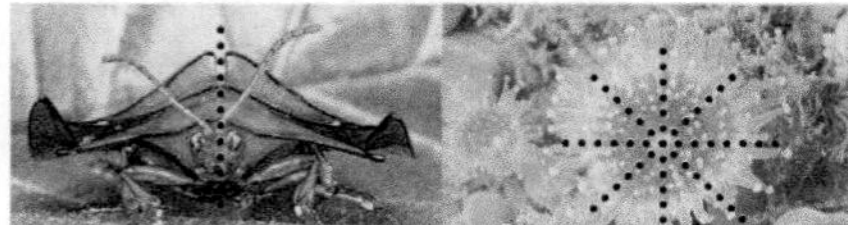

Bilateral symmetry Radial symmetry

22.3 Sponges and Cnidarians

Sponges and cnidarians are the simplest animals. Sponges are aquatic animals that have specialized cells but lack tissues. These animals were among the first to evolve during the Cambrian explosion. Cnidarians, which include jellyfish, corals, and sea anemones, are the most primitive animals with specialized tissues that are still in existence today.

22.4 Flatworms, Mollusks, and Annelids

Flatworms, mollusks, and annelids belong to closely related phyla. Flatworms are simple bilateral animals. They include planarians, flukes, and tapeworms. Mollusks share at least one feature in common: a radula, a mantle, and ctenidia. Common mollusks include snails, bivalves such as clams, and squids. Annelids have segmented bodies and include earthworms, leeches, and marine polychaete worms.

22.5 Roundworms

Roundworms have bilateral symmetry and shed their outer skeleton to grow. Roundworms are cylindrical, with a blunt head and tapered tail. They are covered with a tough cuticle that lies over a layer of muscle. Roundworms may be free-living or parasitic. Common human parasites include hookworms, pinworms, and Guinea worms.

22.6 Echinoderms

Echinoderms are on the same evolutionary branch as vertebrates. Echinoderms and vertebrates are both deuterostomes. Like cnidarians, echinoderms have radial symmetry. These animals have body parts arranged in a circle around a central axis and use a water vascular system to move and transport nutrients. Some echinoderms can regenerate portions of their body, and sometimes they use regeneration as a way to produce offspring.

READING TOOLBOX SYNTHESIZE YOUR NOTES

Concept Map Use a concept map to summarize what you know about animal phylogeny.

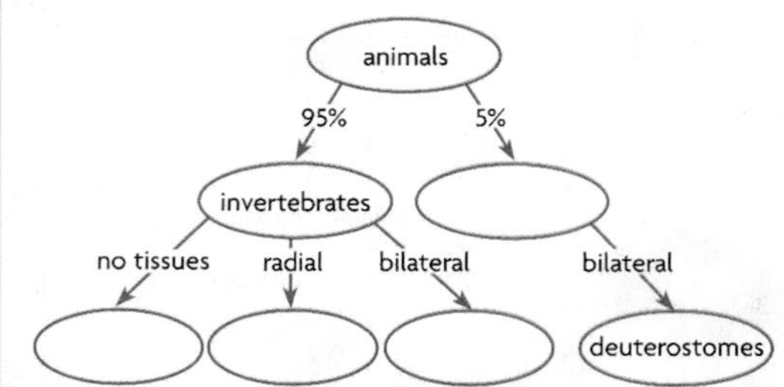

Content Frame Use a table to synthesize notes on the characteristics of the different invertebrate phyla.

Phyla	Features	Symmetry	Examples
Cnidaria	Tissues	Radial	Jellyfish, coral
Flatworms			

Reviewing Vocabulary

1. Drawing should be of three-stranded protein. Label: Collagen is a three-stranded protein.
2. Drawing should be of worm with segments. Label: Segmentation is the repetition of an annelid's body segments, each one containing a complex set of body structures.
3. Drawing should be of jellyfish with two layers separated by middle layer. Label: Mesoglea is a noncellular jellylike material that separates a cnidarian's two tissue layers.
4. Drawing should be of simple oval within a larger oval. Label: Digestive enzymes in the gastrovascular cavity absorb nutrients from food.
5. Drawing should be of umbrella-like medusa and polyp of opposite shape. Label: Polyps are cylindrical tubes with mouth and tentacles facing upward. Medusas are umbrella-shaped with downward-facing mouth and tentacles.
6. Drawing should be of radial animal such as adult echinoderm, bilateral animal such as human. Label: Radial animals have body parts arranged in a circle around a central axis. Bilateral animals can be divided equally along one plane.
7. Drawing should be of tonguelike organ. Label: The radula is a filelike feeding organ.
8. Drawing of a cavity with thick layer marked on one side. Label: The hemocoel is an open circulatory system made up of open spaces between mollusk tissue cells.
9. A phylum is a group of organisms classified by their shared characteristics and evolutionary relationships.
10. Sessile animals do not move from where they are attached, as if they are sitting in one place.
11. Segmented animals appear to be nearly cut into multiple parts.
12. Snails use their radula to scrape up food items to eat.
13. The pseudocoelom is a hollow cavity partially lined by muscle. It is a false coelom because it is only partially lined by muscle, while a true coelom is completely lined by muscle.

22 Review

INTERACTIVE Review
HMHScience.com
GO ONLINE
Review Games • Concept Map • Section Self-Checks

CHAPTER VOCABULARY

22.1 collagen
homeotic
homeobox

22.2 vertebrate
invertebrate
phylum
bilateral symmetry
radial symmetry
protostome
deuterostome

22.3 sessile
filter feeder
polyp
medusa
mesoglea
nematocyst
gastrovascular cavity

22.4 complete digestive tract
radula
hemocoel
segmentation
coelom

22.5 cuticle
pseudocoelom

22.6 ossicle
water vascular system

Reviewing Vocabulary

Visualize Vocabulary

For each word or word pair below, use simple shapes, lines, or arrows to illustrate the meaning. Label each picture, and write a short caption.

1. collagen
2. segmentation
3. mesoglea
4. gastrovascular cavity
5. polyp, medusa
6. radial symmetry, bilateral symmetry
7. radula
8. hemocoel

READING TOOLBOX GREEK AND LATIN WORD ORIGINS

Using the Greek or Latin word origins of the terms below, explain how the meaning of the root relates to the definition of the term.

9. The word *phylum* comes from the Greek word *phulon*, which means "class."

10. The word *sessile* comes from the Latin word *sedere*, which means "to sit."

11. The word *segment*, as in *segmentation*, comes from *segmentum*, from the Latin word *secare*, which means "to cut."

12. The word *radula* comes from the Latin word *radere*, which means "to scrape."

13. The word *pseudocoelom* comes from the Greek words *pseudes*, which means "false," and *koilos*, which means "hollow."

Reviewing MAIN IDEAS

14. What four characteristics are common to members of the animal kingdom?

15. What is the difference between an invertebrate and a vertebrate?

16. Describe three different criteria used to classify animals into groups.

17. What types of evidence are used to put together the evolutionary history of the animal kingdom?

18. What characteristic makes sponges the simplest animals?

19. Describe the two general body forms of cnidarians, which include jellyfish and corals.

20. What are the three types of flatworms? Describe the main features of each.

21. Mollusks have a complete digestive tract. What is one benefit of having this feature?

22. Describe what a segmented body plan looks like. Which phylum includes animals with segmented bodies?

23. Why must roundworms shed their outer skeleton?

24. Several species of roundworms are parasites with human hosts. Name one and explain how it affects human health.

25. What is the function of an echinoderm's water vascular system?

26. How does the ability to regenerate help an echinoderm escape from predators?

CHAPTER REVIEW

Reviewing Main Ideas

14. multicellular heterotrophs; cells supported by collagen; diploid and usually reproduce sexually; most have *Hox* genes
15. A vertebrate has an internal segmented backbone; an invertebrate does not.
16. body symmetry (radial or bilateral), number of tissue layers, developmental patterns
17. genetic evidence from mitochondrial DNA and *Hox* genes, along with comparisons of anatomy
18. Sponges lack tissues.
19. medusa: umbrella-shaped with mouth and tentacles pointing downward; polyp: cylindrical with mouth and tentacles pointing upward
20. planarian: free-living, nonparasitic flatworm; fluke: parasitic, feeds on body fluids; tapeworm: parasitic, feeds on food in gut of host
21. Animals with a complete digestive tract can eat continuously; food absorption is more efficient.
22. A segmented body plan has repeated sections. This is a feature of phylum Annelida.
23. In order to grow, the nongrowing cuticle must be shed.
24. *Sample answer:* Pinworms are found in the human gut. Infection occurs when a person accidentally swallows an egg from a contaminated surface.
25. The water vascular system is used in movement, to grab objects, and for circulation.
26. A part of an echinoderm, such as an arm, can be damaged or eaten without killing the animal. Later, the part can grow back.

Critical Thinking

27. Mutation or duplication of *Hox* genes led to the development of body parts in different locations than normal. Over time, this leads to a variety of different body plans and characteristics.
28. Echinoderm: deuterostome; radial cleavage; gut cavity forms from pouches created by folds in the gut tube; gut opening becomes anus.

    Mollusk: protostome; spiral cleavage; gut cavity forms from separations in the mesoderm; gut opening becomes mouth.
29. Tissues allow for the development of complex systems of organs through the specialization of different tissues.
30. Secreting toxic substances is the only method a sponge has to defend itself, because it is unable to move.
31. Molecular studies have both confirmed and rearranged relationships within and between animal phyla.
32. Each segment contains part of the central gut tube, nerve cord, and blood vessels.
33. Catch connective tissue is used to change the consistency of an echinoderm's body as a defense against predators.
34. An advantage of having a gastrovascular cavity is that digestion is a simple process compared to digestion in an animal with a complete digestive tract. A disadvantage of having a gastrovascular cavity is that the animal can digest only one thing at a time.

Interpreting Visuals

35. *Hox* genes define the head-to-tail development pattern in animal embryos and are laid out in a corresponding sequence on the chromosome.
36. The sequential layout of *Hox* genes on a chromosome and how they are expressed on the body is the same in a wide range of animals, suggesting a common origin.

Critical Thinking

27. Analyze How are the functions of *Hox* genes related to the diversity of body plans and characteristics within the animal kingdom?

28. Contrast How is development different between an echinoderm and a mollusk? Use a table to summarize their different development patterns.

29. Infer While both sponges and cnidarians are simple animals, cnidarians have specialized tissues. What might be some advantages of having specialized tissues?

30. Infer Why is the ability to secrete toxic substances important to the survival of a sponge?

31. Synthesize How has molecular biology played a critical role in our understanding of animal relationships and phylogeny?

32. Infer Even when an annelid is cut in half, it can often still survive. What anatomical feature enables an annelid to remain alive when half of its body is gone?

33. Apply What is the function of an echinoderm's catch connective tissue?

34. Compare and Contrast Animals exhibit variety in their digestive systems. What do you think are the advantages and disadvantages of having a gastrovascular cavity compared with a complete digestive tract?

Interpreting Visuals

Use the *Hox* gene diagram below to answer the next two questions.

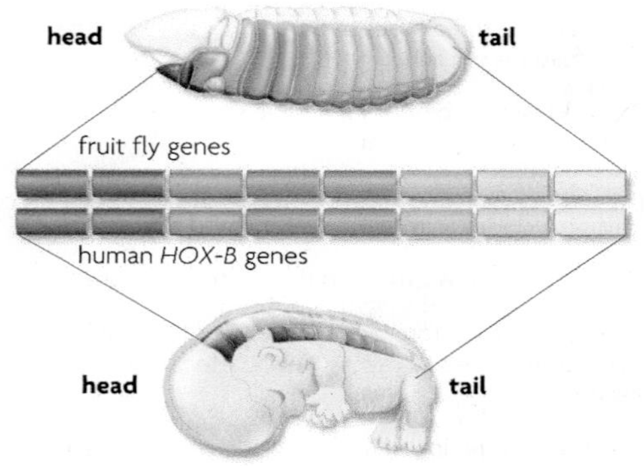

35. Apply How do the two organisms above display the pattern seen in all *Hox* genes?

36. Synthesize How does the diagram support the idea that all animals share a common ancestor?

Analyzing Data Analyze a Scatterplot

Scientists measured the depth and velocity of water in the Columbia River in Washington. These data are shown on the scatterplot graph below. Use the graph to answer the next three questions.

COLUMBIA RIVER DEPTH AND VELOCITY

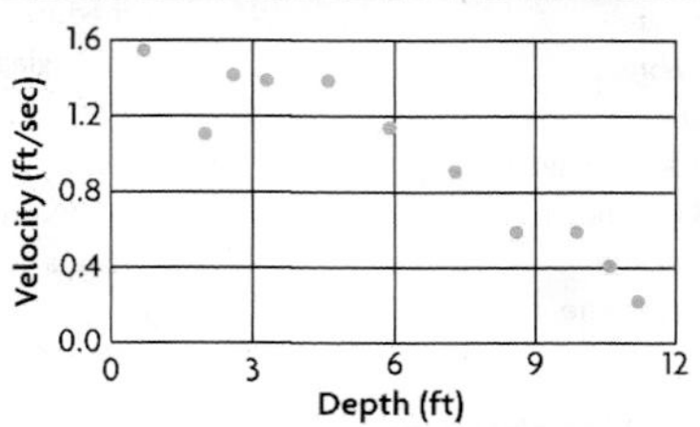

Source: *USGS*

37. Analyze What type of relationship exists between the depth and the velocity of the water? Explain your answer.

38. Predict Make a prediction about the velocity of the water if the depth were 14 feet.

39. Infer In what way might a species adapted to living at lower depths differ from a species adapted to living in shallow water?

Making Connections

40. Write a Travel Brochure Imagine you are an advertising director for a travel agency. Choose an invertebrate from this chapter, and create a brochure to entice your chosen invertebrate to visit a vacation spot. Remember that each invertebrate species has specific requirements for survival. In your brochure, include a description of the location (and why it is the perfect place for your invertebrate), the menu from a local restaurant, and other features that would make your chosen invertebrate feel at home.

41. Connect In addition to storing poisonous chemicals from their food, nudibranchs also are very colorful. In other colorful animals, such as birds, fish, and insects, colors are important for a variety of reasons. What might be the adaptive advantage of a nudibranch's bright coloration?

Analyzing Data

37. negative; as depth increases, velocity decreases
38. between 0.2 and 0.0 ft/s
39. A species living in shallow, fast-moving water might have a streamlined shape and adaptations to help it grip surfaces. A species in deeper water might be less streamlined, slower, and have adaptations for burrowing in soft sediment.

Standards-Based Assessment

Record your answers on a separate piece of paper.

MULTIPLE CHOICE

1 The earliest classification system divided all animals into two main groups. Linnaeus's original classification scheme used six major groups of animals. Now, based on hundreds of years of scientific research, over 30 animal groups, or phyla, are recognized. This progression supports the idea that scientific evidence —

A changes frequently

B should be disregarded after 100 years

C is cumulative

D is often incorrect

2

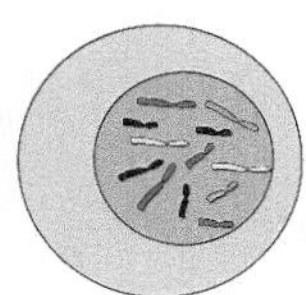

The illustration above shows the chromosomes within the egg cell of a snail. If this egg cell unites with a sperm cell of the same snail species, the offspring will have —

A 6 chromosomes from each parent

B 6 pairs of chromosomes from each parent

C 12 chromosomes from each parent

D 12 pairs of chromosomes from each parent

THINK THROUGH THE QUESTION

Recall that each egg and sperm cell has a single set of chromosomes.

3 Two roundworms mate and produce offspring. Which of the following ***most directly*** accounts for each offspring receiving half of its DNA from each parent?

A mutation

B maturation

C mitosis

D meiosis

4

Appearance of Early Animals in Fossil Record

Organism Type	Appearance in Fossil Record
Sponges	570 million years ago
Mollusks	545 million years ago
Echinoderms	500 million years ago

Choanoflagellates are animal-like protists that do not leave behind fossil evidence. They are considered the most likely ancestors to sponges and all other animals. Based on the table above, when did choanoflagellates likely evolve?

A less than 500 million years ago

B between 545 and 500 million years ago

C between 570 and 545 million years ago

D more than 570 million years ago

5 Which of the following statements ***best*** describes the impact that *Hox* genes have on animal diversity?

A Mutations in *Hox* genes lead to greater animal diversity.

B Mutations in *Hox* genes lead to decreases in animal diversity.

C Mutations in *Hox* genes lead to less variability in animal body plans.

D Mutations in *Hox* genes prevent species from occupying new niches when environmental conditions changed.

6 Which of the following provides the ***best*** evidence that animals and fungi evolved into multicellular organisms independently?

A They are both heterotrophic organisms.

B Animals have eukaryotic cells and fungi have prokaryotic cells.

C Fungal cells do not have the same functions as animal cells.

D Fungi are autotrophic organisms and animals are heterotrophic organisms.

Standards-Based Assessment

The Standards-Based Assessment questions will help students prepare for their final examination in the course. If you wish to give students practice in coding their answers, look for the Standards-Based Assessment Answer Sheet at **HMHScience.com**. To give students practice under timed testing conditions, allow them five minutes per question.

Question	Answer	Depth of Knowledge	Cognitive Complexity
1	C	I	L
2	C	I	L
3	D	II	M
4	D	I	L
5	A	IV	M
6	C	II	M

KEY

Depth of Knowledge
I Recall
II Skill/Concept
III Strategic Thinking
IV Extended Thinking

Cognitive Complexity
L Low
M Moderate
H High

Making Connections

40. Brochures should include the name of the invertebrate, features of its habitat, its prey items, and feeding habits.

41. The bright color announces to potential predators that the nudibranch is poisonous. If a predator eats a brightly colored nudibranch and gets sick, it may avoid similarly colored prey in the future. Predators also may have evolved to avoid prey of such coloration. Bright coloration may also help the nudibranch blend in with its coral reef surroundings.

Instruction and Intervention Support

Vertebrate Diversity

① Core Instruction

The **Core Instruction** resources below can be used for all students. Core instruction should be followed by ongoing assessment to determine which students need further help.

Available in both English and Spanish

Available Online

Section	Instruction	PRINT	ONLINE	Labs
23.1	Textbook **Vertebrate Origins**	■	●	Homologies in Vertebrate Skeletons
	Teaching Visuals Chordate Anatomy (Fig. 1.1), Vertebrate Phylogeny (Fig. 1.5)		●	
	PowerPresentation and Notes 23.1		●	
23.2	Textbook **Fish Diversity**	■	●	
	Animated Biology How Fish Breathe		●	
	PowerPresentation and Notes 23.2		●	
23.3	Textbook **A Closer Look at Bony Fish**	■	●	Fish Reproduction Anatomy of Bony Fish Examining Zebrafish Development (Challenge Lab)
	Animated Biology What Type of Fish Is It?		●	
	Teaching Visuals Bony Fish Anatomy (Fig. 3.3)		●	
	PowerPresentation and Notes 23.3		●	
23.4	Textbook **Amphibians**	■	●	Vanishing Amphibian—an Indicator Species **QuickLab** Frog Development **Video Lab** Live Frog Observation
	Teaching Visuals Amphibian Anatomy (Fig. 4.2)		●	
	PowerPresentation and Notes 23.4		●	
23.5	Textbook **Vertebrates on Land**	■	●	
	PowerPresentation and Notes 23.5		●	

Additional online resources available for this chapter include **Interactive Whiteboard Resources.**

GO ONLINE! for all your teacher resources at HMHScience.com

2 Support and Intervention

Support and Intervention resources are useful for students who need targeted help beyond the Core Instruction

Resources	PRINT	ONLINE
Assess and Reteach (TE wrap)	■	●
Concept Map		●
Interactive Reader	■	●
Interactive Review Games		●
Section Self-Checks		●
Study Guide B		●
Vocabulary Practice Worksheets		●

3 Specialized Support

Students who need more intensive personalized intervention benefit from **Specialized Support** resources.

Resources	PRINT	ONLINE
Chapter Audio Files		●
Differentiated Instruction Inclusion, Below Level, and English Learners (TE wrap)	■	●
ELL Strategies	■	●
Modified Lesson Plans for English Learners		●
Reinforcement Worksheets		●
Study Guide A		●

Extension and Assessment

Enrichment and Challenge

Resources	PRINT	ONLINE
Active Reading Worksheets		●
Data Analysis Practice Worksheet		●
Differentiated Instruction Pre-AP (TE wrap)	■	●
Pre-AP Activity Reproduction of Sharks, Skates, and Rays		●
Smart Grapher Activity		●
The Inside Story and **Take It Further** (TE wrap)	■	●
Unit Project		●
WebLinks		●
WebQuest Fisheries on the Brink (23.3)		●

Assessment

Resources	PRINT	ONLINE
Alternative Assessment		●
Chapter Tests A and B		●
Diagnostic Test		●
ExamView Banks		●
Extended Response Test		●
Online Assessment System		●
Section Quizzes		●
Standards-Based Assessment	■	●

CHAPTER 23

Chapter Overview

- **Section 1** describes the origins and general characteristics of vertebrates.
- **Section 2** identifies the traits that distinguish jawed fish.
- **Section 3** discusses the characteristics and anatomy of bony fish.
- **Section 4** details the characteristics of amphibians and the evolutionary adaptations that enabled them to move onto land.
- **Section 5** focuses on amniotes (reptiles, birds, and mammals) and the characteristics that allow them to live on land.

Focus and Motivate

Why is this frog see-through?

Tell students that the Fleischmann's glass frog is see-through because there is no pigment in the skin of its underbelly. **Ask,** What advantage does the frog have by being transparent when viewed from below and green when viewed from above? camouflage **Ask,** How might this camouflage be effective? Above water, the green blends in with leaves and water plants; from below, the frog's transparency reduces its silhouette against the light sky.

In this chapter, students will learn about Chordata.

Students can access BioZine at **HMHScience.com** to check out articles featured in Strange Biology.

CHAPTER 23 Vertebrate Diversity

BIG IDEA Vertebrates are a diverse group of land-based and aquatic animals that share certain characteristics.

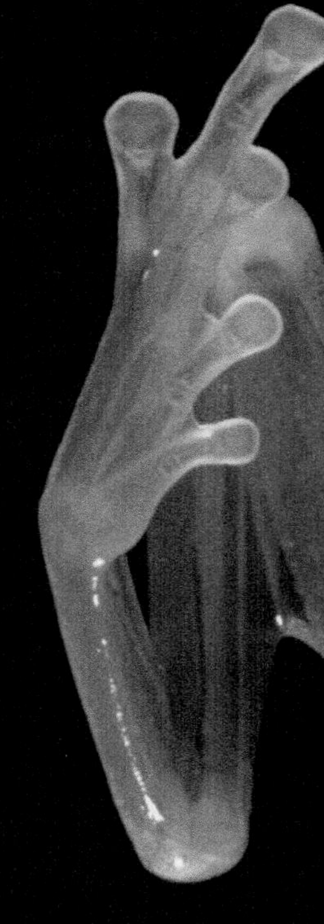

ONLINE BIOLOGY HMHScience.com

ONLINE Labs
- Fish Reproduction
- **QuickLab** Frog Development
- Anatomy of a Bony Fish
- Vanishing Amphibian—an Indicator Species
- Homologies in Vertebrate Skeletons
- Examining Zebrafish Development
- **Video Lab** Live Frog Observation

Student Activity

Purpose **Have students compare exoskeletons with external structures of animals with endoskeletons.**

Materials
- crustacean exoskeleton
- insect molt
- fish scales
- lizard or snake skin
- hand lenses or microscopes

Set up the molts and skins at viewing stations.

Why is this frog see-through?

The Fleischmann's glass frog is one of several members of the family Centrolenidae. Glass frogs lack pigment on their undersides, making their skin transparent. The skin on the top portion of their body has a pigment that reflects the same wavelength of light as plants, helping them to blend in with the green leaves on which they live.

READING TOOLBOX **This reading tool can help you learn the material in the following pages.**

USING LANGUAGE

Comparisons Comparing is a way of looking for similarities among different things. Contrasting is a way of looking for the differences. Comparison words include *like*, *similar to*, and *also*. Contrast words include *unlike*, *however*, and *although*.

YOUR TURN

In the following sentences, identify the things that are being compared or contrasted.

1. Like oranges, bananas have a thick peel. However, the seeds of bananas can be eaten easily.
2. Like fish, frogs lay eggs in water. Unlike fish, frogs do not have scales.

Introduce Tell students that for most motile animals, the outer covering of their bodies must not only protect internal structures but also provide for movement. Explain that students are to rotate through the stations in small groups and compare a selection of invertebrate exoskeletons (molts) with the skins of certain vertebrates.

Discuss Point out that the specimens are not living tissue; however, one can still make inferences about how an outer covering affects the motility—ability to move—of an organism. **Ask**

- As a body covering, how do the scales of a snake or lizard skin compare with a segmented exoskeleton? skin more flexible, surface covered by many overlapping scales, not a single unit
- What do the differences suggest about how the different animals move? exoskeleton: movement limited to joints between segments; vertebrates: whole body can flex
- What do the differences suggest about the protection offered? The exoskeleton offers more protection.

Activate Prior Knowledge

Have students call out as many aquatic animals as they can. List them on the board. *Sample answers:* whale, shark, fish, octopus, dolphin, shrimp **Ask**

- Which of these has no backbone? octopus, shrimp, and others, depending on the list Cross these off the list. The remaining organisms are vertebrates.
- How does a shark differ from a trout? It has a cartilaginous skeleton; a trout has a skeleton of bone.
- How do dolphins and whales differ from fish? They are mammals.
- How do frogs and salamanders differ from fish? They can live on land.

Preview Vocabulary

Greek and Latin Word Origins
Tell students that the animals most familiar to people belong to the phylum Chordata. The Latin word *chorda* means "cord," and one characteristic that all these animals share is a "back cord," a notochord. The Greek word *nōton* means "back."

Academic Vocabulary Tell students that they will be introduced to different classes of vertebrates in this chapter: *Agnatha, Chondrichthyes, Osteichthyes, Amphibia, Reptilia, Aves, Mammalia.* Parts of these names are found in everyday language, for example:

osteoporosis, disease characterized by fragile bones, *osteon* = bone

amphibious, able to operate on land or in water

aviator, one who operates an aircraft

reptilian, when not used to describe a reptile, means "despicable" or "treacherous"

Answers

1. The first sentence compares the peels of bananas and oranges. The second sentence contrasts the seeds of bananas and oranges.
2. The first sentence compares egg-laying behaviors of fish and frogs. The second contrasts their body coverings.

SECTION 23.1

▼ Plan and Prepare

Activate Prior Knowledge Tell students that an earthworm is an invertebrate and a snake is a vertebrate. **Ask,** In what obvious way is a snake different from a worm? A snake has a backbone; a worm does not. Have students discuss the advantages a backbone and internal skeleton provide an animal, not just in mobility but also in size. Point out that the only really large invertebrates are found in the oceans, where the water provides buoyancy.

▼ Teach

Vocabulary

Academic Vocabulary Students may wonder what the difference is between the words **cord** and **chord.** In anatomy, *chord* is a variant of *cord,* which is how it appears in *chordate* and *notochord.* When used in a musical context, the word *chord* means "a combination of three or more pitches played simultaneously" and derives from a word for the strings of a musical instrument, which produce the sound.

23.1 Vertebrate Origins

KEY CONCEPT **All vertebrates share common characteristics.**

VOCABULARY

chordate
notochord
endoskeleton

MAIN IDEAS

- The phylum Chordata contains all vertebrates and some invertebrates.
- All vertebrates share common features.
- Fossil evidence sheds light on the origins of vertebrates.

Connect to Your World

Just like the glass frog, you too are a vertebrate. So are birds, tigers, lizards, and squirrels. While the vertebrates you most often see are those that live on land like us, the group first evolved in the ocean. The first vertebrates were fish, and even today the vast majority of vertebrates are still fish.

MAIN IDEA

The phylum Chordata contains all vertebrates and some invertebrates.

The phylum Chordata is made up of three groups. One group includes all vertebrates. Vertebrates are large, active animals that have a well-developed brain encased in a hard skull. The other two groups are the tunicates and lancelets, which are both invertebrates. Tunicates, or the urochordates, include both free-swimming and sessile animals such as sea squirts. Lancelets, or the cephalochordates (SEHF-uh-luh-KAWR-DAYTS), are small eel-like animals that are commonly found in shallow, tropical oceans. Although lancelets can swim, they spend most of their lives buried in sand, filtering water for food particles.

Despite their enormous differences in body plans and ways of life, all **chordates** share the four features illustrated in **FIGURE 1.1** at some stage of their development.

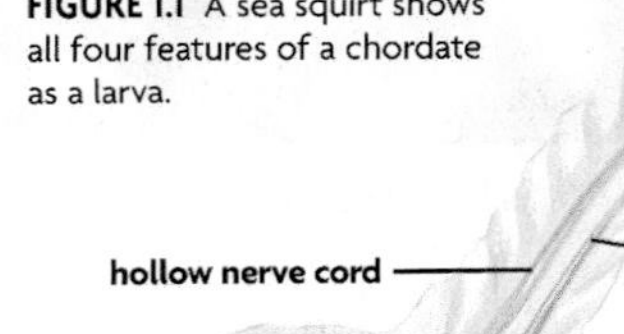

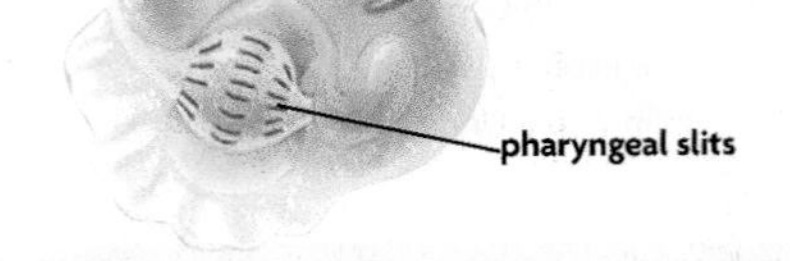

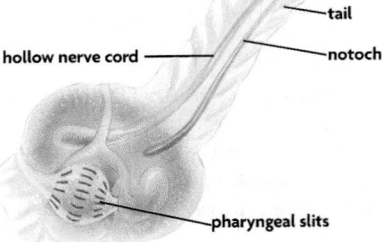

FIGURE 1.1 A sea squirt shows all four features of a chordate as a larva.

- **Notochord** A **notochord** is a flexible skeletal support rod embedded in the animal's back.
- **Hollow nerve cord** A hollow nerve cord runs along the animal's back. The nerve cord forms from a section of the ectoderm that rolls up during development.
- **Pharyngeal slits** Pharyngeal (fuh-RIHN-jee-uhl) slits are slits through the body wall in the pharynx, the part of the gut immediately beyond the mouth. Water can enter the mouth and leave the animal through these slits without passing through the entire digestive system.
- **Tail** A tail extends beyond the anal opening. The tail, as well as the rest of the animal, contains segments of muscle tissue used for movement.

Differentiated Instruction

BELOW LEVEL

Have students preview the section by preparing an outline. Tell them to look at the introductory paragraph, headings, topic sentences, and the concluding paragraph to write their outlines. Have students leave some space between entries. Then have them fill in their outline with notes as they read, focusing on the characteristics of members of the Chordata and the Vertebrata.

Teacher Toolkit, Section C, Section Preview

ENGLISH LEARNERS

To help students see how far along they are in their study of animals, have them turn back to **FIGURE 2.4** in the chapter on invertebrate diversity. Remind them that while the distinction between invertebrate and vertebrate is important, it is not a good basis for classification.

Teacher Toolkit, Section C, Connect to Content Through Visuals

Most chordate groups lose some or all of these characteristics in adulthood, but they are present in their larvae and embryos. For example, the larval form of sea squirts have all four chordate characteristics. However, an adult sea squirt, shown in **FIGURE 1.2**, retains only one chordate characteristic, the pharyngeal slits. Adult sea squirts use the pharyngeal slits for filter feeding. Similarly, vertebrate embryos have a notochord that is for the most part replaced by the vertebrae during later development. The fluid-filled disks between adjacent vertebrae are remnants of the notochord.

A Compare and Contrast How are humans similar to sea squirts? How are they different?

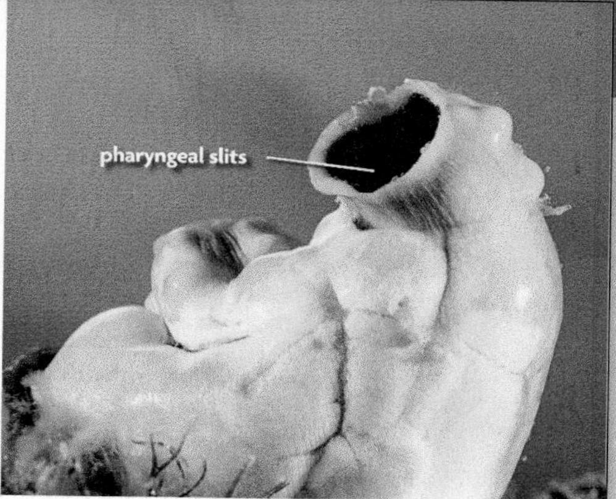

FIGURE 1.2 In its adult form, the only chordate feature a sea squirt retains is the presence of pharyngeal slits (located within the sea squirt's body).

MAIN IDEA

All vertebrates share common features.

Vertebrates tend to be large, active animals. Even the smallest living vertebrate, an Indonesian carp smaller than a fingernail, is larger than most invertebrates.

Vertebrate Endoskeleton

One characteristic that allows vertebrates to grow to large sizes is the endoskeleton. An **endoskeleton** is an internal skeleton built of bone or cartilage. Bone and cartilage are both dense connective tissues. Each tissue is made of collagen fibers that are embedded in a matrix, or combination, of harder materials.

Vertebrate endoskeletons can be divided into distinct parts. Some of these parts are shown on the ape skeleton in **FIGURE 1.3**.

- **Braincase** A braincase or cranium protects the brain.
- **Vertebrae** A series of short, stiff vertebrae are separated by joints. This internal backbone protects the spinal cord. It also replaces the notochord with harder material that can resist forces produced by large muscles. Joints between the vertebrae let the backbone bend as the animal moves.
- **Connected bone structure** Bones support and protect the body's soft tissues and provide points for muscle attachment.

The endoskeleton forms a framework that supports muscles and protects internal organs. It contains cells that can actively break down skeletal material and rebuild it. This characteristic means a vertebrate endoskeleton can slowly change size and shape. It can grow as a vertebrate changes size, unlike arthropod exoskeletons, which must be shed as the animal grows. It can also change shape in response to forces on a vertebrate's body. For example, bones subjected to large forces get thicker.

FIGURE 1.3 Every vertebrate has an endoskeleton, such as the one you see in this x-ray of a small ape.

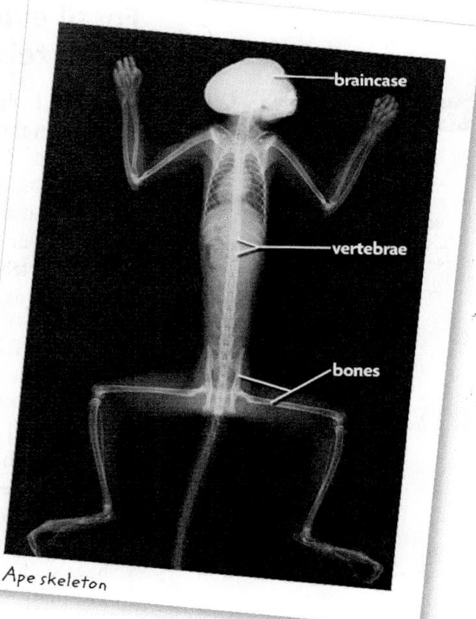

PRE-AP

Have students compare and contrast an endoskeleton with an exoskeleton. Have them include not just structural differences but also how each type of skeleton has an impact on behaviors as well as how it affects potential for ecological niches.

Teacher Toolkit, Section C, Compare/Contrast Chart

Integrating Forensic Anthropology

The branch of anatomy that deals with the study of the structure and function of bones is called **osteology.** This knowledge is applied by a **forensic anthropologist** to the study of human skeletal remains for the purpose of identification. For example, unidentified remains from a crime scene can provide information about gender, age, stature, race, and time and cause of death. The first thing a forensic anthropologist will do when only bone fragments are found is to determine if they are human. Bone density and thickness of human bone, especially of the leg and arm, can even give clues about a person's lifestyle.

Answers

A Compare and Contrast Sometime during development, humans and sea squirts have a notochord, a hollow nerve cord, pharyngeal slits, and a tail. In humans, the notochord is replaced with the vertebrae, and the pharyngeal slits and tail disappear. Sea squirts retain the pharyngeal slits but none of the other characteristics as adults.

▼ Teach *continued*

Take It Further

Some students may not be familiar with the cartilaginous fish called **chimera** (ky MEER ah). They are named after a creature from Greek mythology that was a mixture of a lion, a snake, and a goat. These fish have been described as a creature assembled by a committee that couldn't agree. They have a huge head, well-developed eyes, and an odd, rodentlike mouth with grinding teeth. The tail is very thin and streamerlike, so the chimera propels itself through the water by flapping its winglike pectoral fins. Plownose chimeras, including the elephant fish and ghost shark, can grow to about one meter in length and are commercially fished. Other types of chimera include the ratfish, rabbit fish, and spookfish.

History of Science

Fossil fish helped establish the reputation of **Jean Louis Rodolphe Agassiz.** Between the years 1833 and 1843, he published five volumes of his *Recherches sur les poissons fossiles* (Research on Fossil Fish). He became a professor of zoology at Harvard University in 1848. Eleven years later, he founded the Museum of Comparative Zoology and was a founding member of the National Academy of Sciences.

Agassiz's greatest lasting insight was the realization that paleontology, embryology, ecology, and biogeography all were necessary for any classification scheme that claimed to be based on the relationships of organisms. Yet, he was a lifelong opponent of Darwin's theory of evolution. Ironically, his greatest works have provided evolutionary biologists with tremendous insights and made lasting contributions to evolutionary biology and systematics.

Answers

A Contrast An endoskeleton grows along with the animal, while an exoskeleton must be shed in order for the animal to grow.

FIGURE 1.4 Box turtles, members of the class Reptilia, are just one of the many different animals found in the vertebrate subphylum.

Vertebrate Classes

The phylogenetic tree shown in **FIGURE 1.5** shows the probable evolutionary relationships among the seven classes of vertebrates.

Agnatha The Agnatha are the oldest class of vertebrates. These jawless animals include lampreys, a type of fish.

Chondrichthyes The Chondrichthyes, or cartilaginous fish, have skeletons made of cartilage. These animals include sharks, rays, and chimeras.

Osteichthyes The Osteichthyes, or bony fish, have skeletons made of bone. Ray-finned fish, a type of bony fish, are the most diverse group of vertebrates.

Amphibia The Amphibia were the first vertebrates adapted to live both in water and on land, although they reproduce in water or on moist land. These animals include salamanders, frogs (including toads), and caecilians.

Reptilia The Reptilia are able to retain moisture, which lets them live exclusively on land. Reptiles produce eggs that do not have to develop in water. Reptiles include snakes, lizards, crocodiles, alligators, and turtles.

Aves The Aves are birds. Aves are distinguished by the presence of feathers, along with other features.

Mammalia The Mammalia are animals that have hair, mammary glands, and three middle ear bones.

A Contrast **How does growth differ between an animal with an endoskeleton and an animal with an exoskeleton?**

MAIN IDEA

Fossil evidence sheds light on the origins of vertebrates.

READING TOOLBOX

TAKING NOTES

Use a main idea web to take notes on the origin of vertebrates.

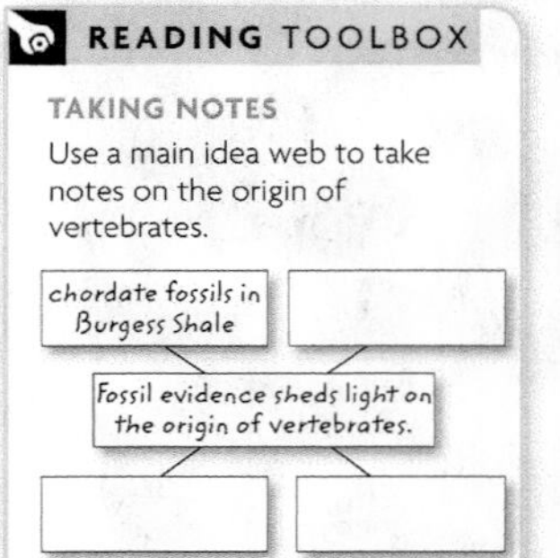
chordate fossils in Burgess Shale
Fossil evidence sheds light on the origin of vertebrates.

Much of what we know about early vertebrates comes from fossil evidence found in the Burgess Shale located in the Canadian Rocky Mountains. This fossil site, discovered in the early 1900s, was not fully explored until the late 1960s. Fossils found within the Burgess Shale date from the Cambrian explosion and include preserved exoskeletons, limbs, and in some cases, gut contents and muscles. Fossils of sponges, worms, and arthropods are among the invertebrate remains found at the quarry site. Other fossils with traces of notochords provide evidence of the earliest chordates.

Closest Relatives of Vertebrates

In the past, scientists thought that lancelets were more closely related to vertebrates than tunicates were. They based this on fossil evidence, along with anatomical comparisons and molecular evidence. However, recent research indicates that tunicates may actually be the closest relatives of vertebrates. All vertebrate embryos have strips of cells called the neural crest, which develops into parts of the nervous system, head, bone, and teeth. Scientists have found that tunicates have cells that resemble the neural crest, but lancelets do not have such cells. This evidence could indicate that either lancelets secondarily lost these cells, or tunicates are indeed the closest relatives to vertebrates.

Differentiated Instruction

ENGLISH LEARNERS

Work with students to compile cards of the seven vertebrate classes, with examples and, if available, images of each. Include cards with information on the distinguishing features of each class. Then use these cards to organize and display this information for the class.

Teacher Toolkit, Section D, Word Sort/ WordSplash

TEACH WITH TECHNOLOGY

Once students are comfortable with the seven class names and their distinguishing characteristics, assemble a digital slide show of unlabeled images of various vertebrates from all seven classes. Go through the slides, asking students to name the class to which each animal belongs and, if appropriate, the common name for that type of animal. For example, show an image of a stingray, let students call out *Chondrichthyes* and *ray*, and have them explain which characteristics identified it as such.

FIGURE 1.5 Vertebrate Phylogenetic Tree

Each vertebrate class has unique characteristics that separate one class from another.

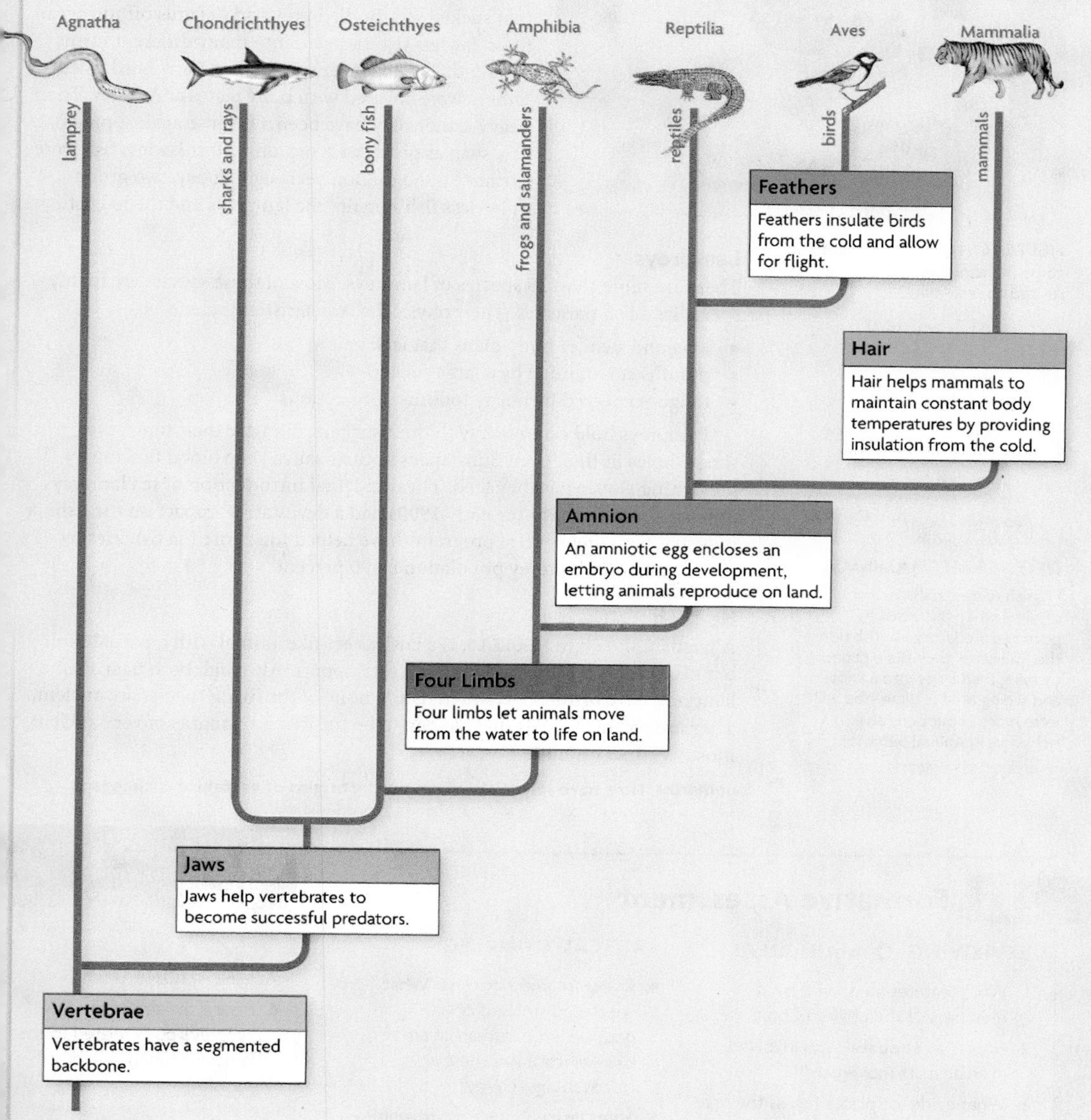

Agnatha
Chondrichthyes
Osteichthyes
Amphibia
Reptilia
Aves
Mammalia

lamprey
sharks and rays
bony fish
frogs and salamanders
reptiles
birds
mammals

Feathers
Feathers insulate birds from the cold and allow for flight.

Hair
Hair helps mammals to maintain constant body temperatures by providing insulation from the cold.

Amnion
An amniotic egg encloses an embryo during development, letting animals reproduce on land.

Four Limbs
Four limbs let animals move from the water to life on land.

Jaws
Jaws help vertebrates to become successful predators.

Vertebrae
Vertebrates have a segmented backbone.

Ⓐ CRITICAL VIEWING **What characteristic is common among reptiles, birds, and mammals?**

PRE-AP

Have students convert the phylogenetic tree in **FIGURE 1.5** into a timeline. They should do it in such a way that they can give a somewhat accurate sense of scale. For example, they might use a spiral rather than a straight line. Provide them with the following information or refer them to **FIGURE 2.2** in the chapter The History of Life.

- Jawless fish (agnathan fish) appeared and diversified during the Ordovician period (505–440 mya).
- Fossils representing most major lineages of fish and the earliest amphibians existed before the Devonian period (410–360 mya).
- Reptiles appeared during the Carboniferous period (360–286 mya).
- Mammals appeared before the end of the Triassic (248–213 mya).
- Birds appeared before the end of the Jurassic (213–145 mya).

Teacher Toolkit, Section C, Timeline

Integrating Evolutionary Biology

Students may wonder how or why vertebrates managed to make their way onto land, especially when the ocean is so vast and offers so many niches. It is likely that some ancient vertebrates were inhabitants of shallow water. These low water levels would have posed a problem for animals unable to support their own body weight or get oxygen in the absence of water.

Over time, beneficial variations among individuals led to the evolution of short, stout legs instead of fins; lungs instead of the swim bladder and gills; and tough, waterproof skin instead of soft, permeable skin. These adaptations allowed these vertebrates to survive and temporarily take advantage of an otherwise unused resource: an assortment of dry land habitats. Millions of years later, the amniotic egg evolved, enabling some vertebrates to leave the water permanently and radiate out into the biomes.

Vocabulary

amnion Tell students that the first terrestrial animals, once separated from the seas, had to have a means to protect and support an embryo as it grew. An *amnion* is a fluid-filled sac that encloses an embryo, providing it with its own self-contained aquatic environment. Tell students they will learn more about amniotes in **Section 5** and in the chapter on amniotes.

Answers

Ⓐ **Critical Viewing** All develop from an amniotic egg.

▼ Teach *continued*

Take It Further

Point out to students the very simple body plan of the **hagfish.** They have no backbone, no fins except a primitive tail fin, and reduced eyes. Newly hatched hagfish look just like the adults, except they have both male and female sex organs. They will eventually be either male or female, but retain the ability to change gender if their population structure requires it. Hagfish feed on dead animals such as whales and fish that sink to the bottom of the ocean. They will also feed on fish that have died after being caught by fishing gear set on or near the sea floor.

The hagfish's skin is processed into "eelskin" boots, wallets, and other products in South Korea. Fishers catch hagfish—which they call slime eels because of their defensive secretion of slippery slime—by sinking large barrels to the sea floor. The barrels have holes punched through their sides, allowing hagfish to swim inside to feed on bait held within.

Answers

A Summarize Evidence indicates that tunicates may be more closely related to vertebrates than to lancelets.

▼ Assess and Reteach

Assess Use the Section Self-Check or Section Quiz, both available at **HMHScience.com**.

Reteach Create a number of profiles of unknown animals that students will analyze in order to classify them. Include invertebrates so that students will distinguish between them and chordates. For each vertebrate class described in the section, offer at least one profile.

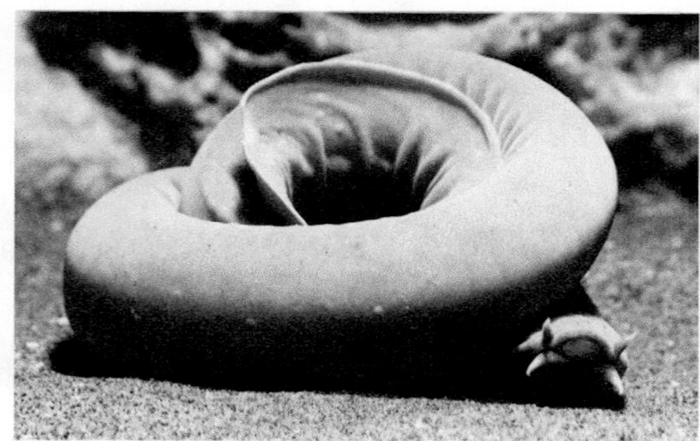

FIGURE 1.6 Hagfish are thought to be the chordates most closely related to vertebrates.

Early Vertebrates

The first recognizable vertebrates were fish. The oldest fossil fish are found in 530-million-year-old rocks from China. Early fish were small, jawless bottom-feeders that sucked soft-bodied prey and detritus off the ocean floor. Jawless fish radiated into many different forms during the Paleozoic era. Some had bony head shields. Others were covered with bony plates and scales. Their heavy armor may have been a defense against predators such as giant sea scorpions. Most jawless fish were extinct by 360 million years ago. Today, two groups of jawless fish remain: the lampreys and the hagfish.

Lampreys

There are more than 35 species of lampreys. Most of these species are highly specialized fish parasites. Their physical characteristics include

- long and slender body plans that lack paired fins
- mouths surrounded by a large sucker
- tongues covered by horny toothlike projections

Lampreys hold on to fish with their suckers, then use their tongues to scrape holes in their prey. Substances in their saliva keep blood flowing by preventing clotting as they feed. The accidental introduction of sea lampreys into the Great Lakes in the early 1900s had a devastating impact on the fishing industry. Ongoing control programs have helped to restore the fisheries by reducing the sea lamprey population by 90 percent.

CONNECT TO

DEFENSE MECHANISMS

Hagfish secrete massive amounts of slime when disturbed by potential predators. Hagfish rid themselves of their slime cocoon by tying their body into a knot and sliding off the slime. You will learn more about defensive behaviors in **Animal Behavior**.

Hagfish

A hagfish, shown in **FIGURE 1.6**, is a jawless eel-like animal with a partial skull but no vertebrae. It uses a notochord for support. Although both hagfish and lampreys have primitive characteristics, none of the living species are ancient. They are recent animals that happen to be the living remnants of very ancient, mostly extinct groups.

A Summarize **How have scientists' views on the origins of vertebrates changed?**

23.1 Formative Assessment

SELF-CHECK Online
HMHScience.com
GO ONLINE

REVIEWING ▶ MAIN IDEAS

1. What features are shared by all members of the phylum Chordata?
2. How is an **endoskeleton** involved in an animal's movement?
3. What evidence places fish as the first vertebrates?

CRITICAL THINKING

4. **Compare and Contrast** What are the advantages of having an endoskeleton instead of an exoskeleton? Are there any disadvantages? Why?
5. **Summarize** Draw a phylogenetic tree that shows the relationships between hagfish, lampreys, and all other fish.

CONNECT TO

ADAPTATIONS

6. How is the structure of a lamprey's body related to the lamprey's function as a parasite?

23.1 FORMATIVE ASSESSMENT

1. notochord, hollow nerve cord, pharyngeal slits, tail
2. The endoskeleton forms a framework that supports a vertebrate's muscles.
3. fossil evidence in 530-million-year-old rocks from China
4. Advantages: Vertebrates don't have to shed their skeleton in order to grow. An endoskeleton can change shape in response to forces on the animal's body. Disadvantages: An endoskeleton is less protective to an animal's body than is a hard exoskeleton.
5. Tree should show hagfish and lampreys diverging from a common ancestor, and jawed fishes diverging from the lamprey branch.
6. The structure of a lamprey's body is simple—long and slender, allowing its body to trail from its host like a tail on a kite. The mouth is modified as a sucker to attach to its host, with a horny tongue that scrapes a hole through which blood can be sucked out.

23.2 Fish Diversity

KEY CONCEPT **The dominant aquatic vertebrates are fish.**

MAIN IDEAS
- Fish are vertebrates with gills and paired fins.
- Jaws evolved from gill supports.
- Only two groups of jawed fish still exist.

VOCABULARY
gill
countercurrent flow
lateral line
operculum

Connect to Your World

In order to move in a swimming pool, you need to push your body through a thick, heavy blanket of water. Swimming for a long time is tiring. Long-distance swimming requires endurance and a lot of energy. Fish spend their entire lives moving through water, but adaptations to an aquatic environment make their movements through water much more energy-efficient than yours.

MAIN IDEA

Fish are vertebrates with gills and paired fins.

You get the oxygen you need by breathing in the air that surrounds you. Because fish live underwater, the way that they get oxygen is completely different from the way you breathe. Fish use specialized organs called gills to take in the oxygen dissolved in water. **Gills** are large sheets of thin frilly tissue filled with capillaries that take in dissolved oxygen from the water and release carbon dioxide. As shown in **FIGURE 2.1**, gills have a very large surface area, which increases the amount of gases they can exchange with the water. Muscles in the body wall expand and contract, creating a current of water that brings a steady supply of oxygen to the blood.

Just like you, fish have body systems that provide their cells with oxygen and nutrients and also remove waste products. Fish circulatory systems pump blood in a single circulatory loop through a heart with two main chambers. An atrium collects blood returning from the body and moves it into the ventricle. The ventricle pumps blood through the gills, where carbon dioxide is released and oxygen is picked up by the blood. The blood then carries the oxygen directly to the tissues and picks up more carbon dioxide. The blood returns to the heart, and the process begins again.

GO ONLINE
How Fish Breathe

FIGURE 2.1 Fish use the large surface area of their gills to exchange carbon dioxide and oxygen with the water in which they live.

water flow

Differentiated Instruction

HANDS-ON ACTIVITY

Bring in several whole fish from a supermarket. Lay each fish out on a dissecting tray for viewing. Have students form groups around each tray. Instruct students to look at the fish but not touch them. Pass through each station and, using a dissecting tweezers, lift the operculum to reveal the gills for students to observe. Have students sketch the fish and label the following (if present): eye, mouth, jaw, dorsal fin, caudal fin, anal fin, pectoral fin, pelvic fin, gills, operculum, lateral line, scales. **Ask**

- What is the advantage of having a gill covering? protection from injury and parasites, help in breathing
- What are the functions of fins? stability and motion in the water

If you have supplied different types of fish, have students discuss their differences and speculate on what types of habitat they live in and what they may feed on.

SECTION 23.2

Plan and Prepare

Activate Prior Knowledge Have students think about aquatic habitats and the conditions that fish must cope with. **Ask,** If you dive into a cold lake without scuba gear or a wetsuit, and you remain underwater and motionless for a few moments, what problems will you have? cannot breathe (get oxygen from your surroundings), could sink to the bottom if you do not move, lose too much heat from your body (hypothermia), cannot see very well Tell students that fish have features that allow them to cope with these and other challenging conditions of aquatic environments.

Teach

TEACH FROM VISUALS

FIGURE 2.1 Point out that oxygenated blood is shown in red and deoxygenated blood in blue. **Ask,** What is different about the flow of oxygen in a fish, compared with a human? Oxygen is dissolved in water and moves in one opening (mouth) and out another (gills); in humans oxygen is carried by air and is inhaled and exhaled through the same openings.

Chapter 23: Vertebrate Diversity 679

▼ Teach *continued*

Vocabulary

Academic Vocabulary The branch of zoology that focuses on the study of fish is **ichthyology,** and its practitioners are called *ichthyologists.*

Integrating Physics

Most bony fish depend on a swim bladder for adjusting or maintaining **buoyancy.** Freshwater fish require a larger gas bladder to keep from sinking than do marine fish, because fresh water is less dense than seawater. Most fish fill and deflate the swim bladder by diffusing gas in and out of the blood. Some deflate the bladder by pushing gas into the gullet and gills. Some simply gulp air at the surface to fill the bladder.

Answers

Ⓐ **Infer** The more a fish moves through the water, the more oxygen it needs. Because of the countercurrent flow of blood and water in the gills, faster movement through the water means that the supply of oxygen to the blood will keep up with the demand.

CONNECT TO

DIFFUSION

Recall from **Cell Structure and Function** that diffusion is the movement of dissolved molecules in a fluid from a region of higher concentration to a region of lower concentration.

Countercurrent Flow

Arteries in the gills carry blood to the exchange surfaces. The arteries are arranged so that blood flows in the opposite direction of the current of water entering the gills. **Countercurrent flow** is the opposite movement of water against the flow of blood in the fish's gills. Because oxygen dissolved in the water is at a greater concentration than the oxygen in the fish's blood, countercurrent flow maximizes the amount of oxygen the fish can pull from the water by diffusion. In countercurrent flow, blood is always passing by water that contains more oxygen than it does. Both well-aerated water entering the gills and depleted water leaving the gills pass by blood with an even lower oxygen load. Oxygen diffuses into the blood along the entire length of the gill.

VISUAL VOCAB

Countercurrent flow maximizes the amount of oxygen the fish can pull from the water.

water flow

oxygen exchange

blood flow

READING TOOLBOX

TAKING NOTES

Draw a simple picture of a fish in your notes and label the five kinds of fins found on most fish.

Swimming and Maneuvering

Most fish swim by contracting large segmented muscles on either side of their vertebral column from the head to the tail. These muscle segments power the contractions that produce a series of S-shaped waves that move down the fish's body and push it through the water. These waves also tend to nudge the fish from side to side. Such horizontal movements waste energy, so fish counteract them with their fins.

As you can see in **FIGURE 2.2,** fins are surfaces that project from a fish's body. Most fish have dorsal fins on their backs and anal fins on their bellies. Most fish also have two sets of lateral paired fins. One set, the pectoral fins, are found just behind the head. The other set, the pelvic fins, are often found near the middle of the belly. The caudal fin is another name for the tail fin. Fin tissue is supported by part of the endoskeleton, and its associated muscles let fish actively move their fins as they swim.

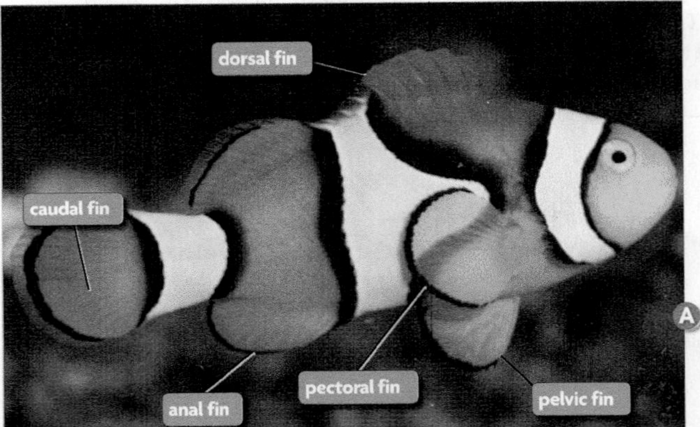

FIGURE 2.2 This clown anemone fish shows the main types of fins commonly found in fish.

Fins keep fish stable. Their movements redirect water around the fish as it swims, producing forces that keep it from rolling, pitching up and down, and moving from side to side. The dorsal and anal fins keep the fish from rolling over. The caudal fin moves the fish in a forward direction. The pectoral and pelvic paired fins help the fish to maneuver, stop, and hover in the water.

Ⓐ Infer **What is the connection between countercurrent flow and a fish's movement in the water?**

Differentiated Instruction

ENGLISH LEARNERS

Draw a cycle diagram on the board that shows how oxygen and carbon dioxide are carried through a fish's body. Have students review the last paragraph on the previous page and call out the events as you go through the diagram. Once you have gone through the cycle as a class, have students close their books and write a paragraph in their notebooks describing the circulatory cycle.

Teacher Toolkit, Section C, Cycle Diagram

TEACH WITH TECHNOLOGY

Assemble images for a digital slide show of fish. Show a variety of fin shapes and differences in the placement and number of fins. For example, show a thresher shark's long caudal fin, a spiny dogfish (no anal fin; spiny dorsal fins), a whale shark (large first dorsal fin set way back on body), an Atlantic cod (three dorsal fins), a sailfish (enormous dorsal fin), and an anglerfish (dorsal fin used as fishing pole). Have students identify each fin. Point out how the fins of some fish are movable and powerful, while in others, the same fins are immobile or not as specialized.

MAIN IDEA

Jaws evolved from gill supports.

The jaws of fish evolved from gill arches, also known as pharyngeal arches. Located on both sides of the pharynx, gill arches are structures made of bone or cartilage that function as a support for a fish's gills. As shown in **FIGURE 2.3**, jaws developed from gill arches near the mouth, which fused to the cranium. The upper section of the third gill arch attached to the cranium, forming the upper jaw. Because the gill arches are jointed, the bottom part of the gill arch could bend to open and close the mouth, forming the lower jaw.

In most fish, the fourth set of gill arches are also fused to the cranium. In these animals, the upper part of the gill arch reinforces the jaws. The gill arch's lower part supports the tissue inside the floor of the mouth. Most jawed vertebrates have teeth on their upper and lower jaws. Teeth are used to capture and process food. They evolved from the armored scales that covered early jawless fish.

As a result of natural selection, jaws gave vertebrates a huge advantage as predators and quickly pushed them to the top of the food chain. But the original function of jaws may not have been to help fish capture food. Evidence suggests that the earliest jaws prevented backflow as a fish pumped water over its gills. Clamping the front pair of arches together prevented oxygen-rich water from escaping through the mouth, ensuring that it all flowed over the gills. The fact that they also kept prey from escaping was a happy accident.

A Compare **What advantages are provided to an animal that has jaws, compared with an animal that does not have jaws?**

FIGURE 2.3 JAW EVOLUTION

Evidence from animal development studies supports the idea that jaws evolved from gill arches.

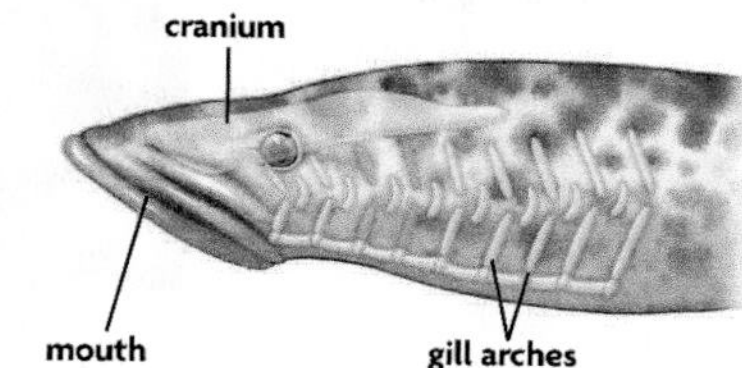

Agnatha Jawless fish such as lampreys evolved from filter-feeding ancestors. In jawless fish, the filters were modified to function as gills.

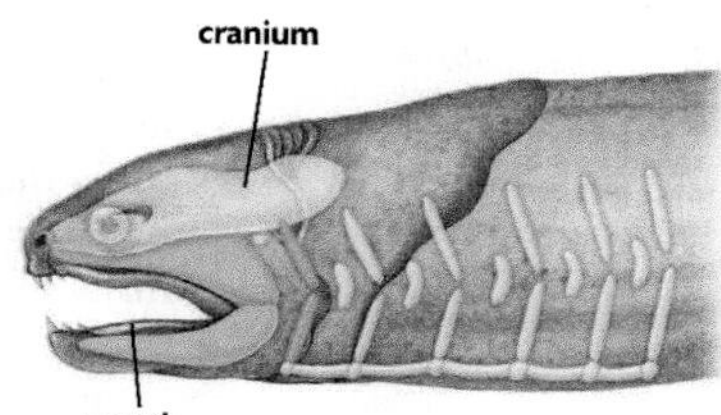

Placoderms Jaws developed from what was the third gill arch in Agnatha.

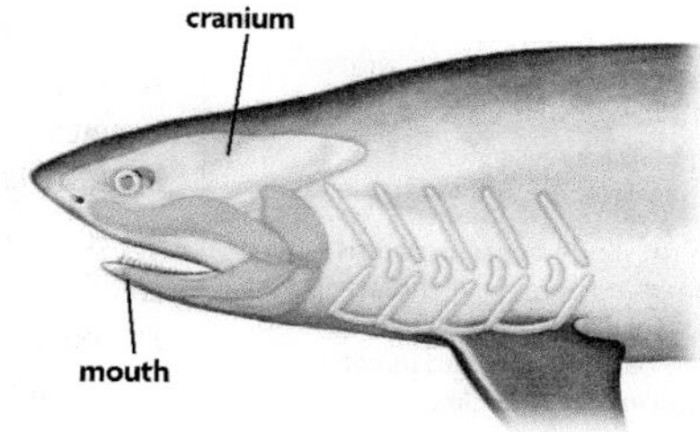

Modern fish In modern fish such as sharks, the fourth set of gill arches fused to the cranium.

MAIN IDEA

Only two groups of jawed fish still exist.

Jawed fish diversified very quickly after their first appearance about 440 million years ago. Four groups of fish appeared at this time.

- **Acanthodians** Acanthodians were fish covered with spines. They became extinct about 250 million years ago.
- **Placoderms** Placoderms were heavily armored with huge bony plates. They became extinct about 350 million years ago.
- **Cartilaginous fish** Cartilaginous fish are one of the two groups of fish that survive today. The cartilaginous fish include sharks, rays, and chimeras.
- **Bony fish** Bony fish are the group that includes all other living fish and is the other group of fish still in existence.

HANDS-ON ACTIVITY

Objects in water can be described as positively, negatively, or neutrally buoyant. For any organism that swims through the water column, the ability to achieve neutral buoyancy—whether through a physical adaptation or a behavior—is advantageous because the organism will not be expending energy trying to descend or ascend using only its muscle power. Scuba divers achieve neutral buoyancy by adjusting the amount of air in an inflatable vest worn around their torsos. Bony fish use their swim bladders to adjust their buoyancy. Cartilaginous fish get much of their buoyancy from their high-volume livers.

Demonstrate how a small volume of oil can change a negatively or neutrally buoyant object to a positively buoyant one. Fill one balloon with 1/2 L of water. Fill another with 3/4 L of water and 1/4 L of cooking oil. Place both balloons in a container of water. **Ask,** If both balloons have the same volume, why does the one with oil float more than the one filled with water? The oil is less dense than water, so as a whole, the object that contains it is more positively buoyant.

Integrating Evolutionary Biology

Scientists think that **placoderms** were the first vertebrates to live in fresh water and the open ocean. Their heavy, bony armor was usually on the head and neck, sometimes with a joint in between the head and neck plates that may have allowed the fish to open its mouth very wide.

Dunkleosteus, a marine placoderm from the Devonian period, grew to lengths of at least 6 meters (19.5 ft) and had a heavily armored skull that was 1.2 meters (4 ft) wide. The bony plates of the jaws of placoderms like *Dunkleosteus* had sharp edges that functioned like shears to slice through prey. In 1997, a placoderm fossil found in Antarctica revealed preserved pigment cells. The belly of this fish was iridescent silver; the dorsal surface was red. Placoderms became extinct at the end of the Devonian period, 360 million years ago.

Science Trivia

Over the course of hundreds of millions of years, jaws have evolved to function in a wide variety of ways.

- The Atlantic wolffish is an eel-like fish armed with large canines, heavy molars, and very powerful jaws. It eats sea urchins, mollusks, and crustaceans.
- The foremost part of the upper jaw of various billfish is like a long, sharp sword or spear that is used to slash through schools of fish.
- The jaws of the aptly named cookiecutter shark allow it to gouge out small scoops of flesh from large marine animals, such as whales, dolphins, and large bony fish. Often the victim of this shark is relatively unharmed, meaning this species is more of a parasite.

Answers

A Compare Jawed animals are able to be more effective predators, allowing them to occupy a variety of niches and move up in the food chain.

▼ Teach *continued*

Take It Further

Shark teeth are arranged in rows; when one tooth is damaged or lost, it is replaced by another that emerges from the soft gum tissue behind the visible teeth. Most sharks have about five rows of teeth, and many will go through thousands of teeth in a lifetime.

The skin of sharks is essentially a layer of tiny teeth called **dermal denticles** or placoid scales. These denticles have the same structure as a tooth: an outer layer of enamel, dentine, and a central pulp cavity. The denticles point backward toward the tail, making the shark hydrodynamic in the forward direction while offering a tough protective hide. Some cultures used sharkskin like sandpaper, and others still process shark-skin into a very durable leather used for making wallets, jackets, and other clothes or accessories.

TEACH FROM VISUALS

FIGURE 2.5 Call attention to the fin structure, body shape, and mouth and eye positions of the ray in the photograph. **Ask,** How do these adaptations help the ray live successfully in its habitat? The eyes are placed at the top of the head so it can see while flat on the ocean floor. The body is flattened, allowing it to hide on the bottom, bury itself in sand, and glide through the water. The mouth is located on the bottom, where it can grab prey from the sea floor. The bold coloration may function as a warning to potential predators.

FIGURE 2.4 The grey reef shark is found in the tropical waters surrounding coral reefs. When pursuing prey, some shark species may swim at speeds up to 48 km/h (30 mi/h).

READING TOOLBOX

VOCABULARY

In the word *Chondrichthyes*, *chondr-* comes from a Greek word meaning "cartilage," and *-ichthyes* comes from a Greek word meaning "fish."

Cartilaginous Fish

Members of the class Chondrichthyes, or cartilaginous fish, have skeletons made of cartilage, while their ancestors had skeletons made of bone. This characteristic means that their cartilaginous skeleton is not a primitive trait. These fish have lost the ability to make bone. In fact, the type of cartilage found in their skeletons is unique. It contains calcium deposits that make it stiffer than the squishy stuff found in human joints. Even though they have relatively flexible skeletons, cartilaginous fish have a strong bite, and they are major predators in every ocean. There are two groups within the Chondrichthyes—Holocephali and Elasmobranchs.

The Holocephali include chimeras, or ratfish. Chimeras are a small group of deep-sea fish with platelike grinding teeth. They feed on crustaceans and other invertebrates.

The Elasmobranchs include sharks, rays, and skates. There are more than 300 species of sharks and nearly 400 species of rays and skates. Most sharks, such as the grey reef shark shown in **FIGURE 2.4**, hunt other fish, although some species eat seals and sea lions. The biggest sharks, the whale sharks and basking sharks, are filter feeders that eat plankton.

Rays and skates have flattened bodies and large pectoral fins that they use to "fly" through the water. Most rays, such as the blue-spotted ray shown in **FIGURE 2.5**, crush invertebrates such as crustaceans for food. Others, such as the huge manta rays, are planktonic filter feeders. Most rays have poisonous venom in their barbed tails, which they use to defend themselves against predators. Skates do not have poisonous venom, but instead use thorny projections on their backs to fight off attackers.

FIGURE 2.5 The blue-spotted ray lives on sandy ocean bottoms beneath coral reefs. If threatened, the ray will use a venomous barb at the base of its tail to inject poison into its attacker.

While the cartilaginous fish as a group may be ancient, they have many advanced features. They have internal fertilization, and many species give birth to live young. They are actually denser than water, but oil stored in their livers provides buoyancy that keeps them from sinking.

Cartilaginous fish are incredibly efficient hunters. They are powerful swimmers with good eyesight and an excellent sense of smell. They can also sense their prey's movements at a distance with a sensory system called the lateral line.

Differentiated Instruction

BELOW LEVEL

Ask students to make a two-column chart titled "Characteristics of Fish." Tell them to list the following in the left column: gills, heart, movement, jaws, skeleton, and sensory organs. In the right column, have them describe each of these features in two or three sentences.

Teacher Toolkit, Section C, T-Chart

All fish have a **lateral line** system, which is a series of shallow canals on the sides of the fish made up of cells that are sensitive to small changes in water movement. The lateral line gives fish a sense of "distant touch," letting them feel the movements in the water currents created by more distant animals as they swim.

Many fish also have sensory organs that detect the electrical currents made by muscular contractions in other animals. These sensory organs are called electroreceptive cells because they receive electric signals. In cartilaginous fish, the electroreceptive cells are clustered on the snout, and they are extremely sensitive. In experiments in which all other senses are blocked, a shark can still detect the electric currents generated by the heartbeat of a hiding animal.

Bony Fish

All other living fish have skeletons made of bone. These bony fish are called the Osteichthyes (the prefix *oste-* comes from a Greek word meaning "bone"). There are more than 20,000 species of bony fish living in nearly every aquatic environment on Earth, including tropical freshwater streams, Antarctic oceans, and deep-sea trenches. Some have become parasites of other fish. One group of bony fish can even spend short periods of time on land.

The gills of all bony fish are in a chamber covered by a protective plate called the **operculum** (oh-PUR-kyuh-luhm), shown in **FIGURE 2.6.** Movements of the operculum help bony fish move water over their gills by creating a low-pressure area just outside the gills. Water flows from the high-pressure area in the mouth through the gills toward the low-pressure area by the operculum.

FIGURE 2.6 The operculum is a protective plate that covers a fish's gills, as shown on this white margate, a bony fish.

Some of these characteristics have been modified or lost in some species of bony fish. In Section 3, Osteichthyes will be examined in more detail.

Contrast **What is the difference between cartilaginous and bony fish?**

Science Trivia

While it is not unreasonable to think about whether or not you may be swimming in an area populated by sharks, we ought to be far more concerned about dogs, snakes, and lightning.

- From 2001 to 2005, there were 10 fatal shark attacks and 113 fatal dog attacks in the United States.
- In the 1990s, snakes killed an average of 15 people per year in the United States. Sharks killed 0.4 people per year.
- From 1959 to 2004, there were 22 fatal shark attacks and 1863 fatal lightning strikes in the United States.

Answers

A Contrast Cartilaginous fish have skeletons made of cartilage; bony fish have skeletons made of bone.

Assess and Reteach

Assess Use the Section Self-Check or Section Quiz, both available at **HMHScience.com**.

Reteach Display images of bony fish and cartilaginous fish. Point to their features (fins, organs, and so on) and have students identify and describe their functions. Provide simple outlines of a bony fish and a shark, and have students fill in as much detail as they can recall from the section.

23.2 Formative Assessment

REVIEWING MAIN IDEAS

1. What is the function of **countercurrent flow** in a fish's **gills**?
2. What key changes took place in the evolution of fish jaws?
3. Name the four groups of jawed fish that evolved during the Paleozoic era. Which groups are still alive today?

CRITICAL THINKING

4. **Infer** How might fin shape differ in a fish with a torpedo-shaped cylindrical body and a fish with a flattened body?
5. **Analyze** How would you expect the **lateral line** system to differ in fish that live in rivers with strong currents?

CONNECT TO

EVOLUTION

6. A shark's jaw is lined with several rows of teeth. How is this adaptation related to a shark's effectiveness as a predator?

23.2 FORMATIVE ASSESSMENT

1. Countercurrent flow is the opposite movement of water against the flow of blood in the fish's gills. This process allows blood to efficiently release carbon dioxide into the water and absorb oxygen from the water.
2. Jaws developed from gill arches near the mouth that fused to the skull. The upper section of the first gill arch attached to the skull, forming the upper jaw. The bottom part of the jointed gill arch, able to open and close the mouth, formed the lower jaw.
3. Acanthodians, placoderms, cartilaginous fish, and bony fish; cartilaginous fish and bony fish are still alive today.
4. A fish with a cylindrical body would most likely have fairly rigid fins that allow it to swim and maneuver with great speed. A fish with a flattened body is likely to have small, flexible fins that allow the fish to burrow in sediment. In some flat fish, such as rays and skates, the fins are part of the flattened shape of the body and flap like wings to propel the fish forward.
5. Fish that live in fast-moving waters may have a lateral line that is less sensitive to the movement of water.
6. Sharks can afford to be very aggressive when feeding, because broken or lost teeth will be replaced.

SECTION 23.3

▼ Plan and Prepare

Activate Prior Knowledge Have students call out the common names of various fish. Write them on the board. Remind students that some marine animals, such as jellyfish, are called "fish" even though they are invertebrates or members of other nonfish classes. **Ask,** Which of the true fish you have named are bony fish? All species that are not sharks, skates, or rays should be cited. Tell students that there are tens of thousands of bony fish known to science.

▼ Teach

TEACH FROM VISUALS

FIGURE 3.1 Point out to students that they have already encountered the torpedo-like body shape in sharks. **Ask,** What other things can you think of that are shaped similarly, and what function do they have in common? *Sample answers:* Submarines, boat hulls, bullets, airplanes, missiles; all of these are shaped in a way that allows them to move through a medium with less resistance.

23.3 A Closer Look at Bony Fish

KEY CONCEPT **Bony fish include ray-finned and lobe-finned fish.**

VOCABULARY
ray-fin
swim bladder
lobe-fin

MAIN IDEAS
- Ray-finned fish have a fan of bones in their fins.
- Lobe-finned fish have paired rounded fins supported by a single bone.

Connect to Your World

Most of the fish you are familiar with are bony fish. Perhaps you won a goldfish at a carnival or ate a tuna fish sandwich for lunch. Or maybe you fish at a local lake for trout or bass. All of these fishes are examples of bony fish.

MAIN IDEA

Ray-finned fish have a fan of bones in their fins.

All ray-finned fish, such as goldfish and tuna, have fins supported by a fan-shaped array of bones called a **ray-fin.** Ray-fins are embedded in a thin layer of skin and connective tissue. The muscles that move the bones are found in the fish's body wall. This arrangement of bones and muscles makes the fin light, collapsable, and easy to move. Ray-finned fish can quickly change a fin's shape, making the fish more maneuverable in the water. But the fins' maneuverability also means that they are thin and too weak to provide support out of water. They would buckle under the fish's weight. It would be like trying to stand on a few soda straws. Some ray-finned fish, such as mudskippers, have thickened ray-fins that let them shuffle around slowly on land.

Diversity of Body Plans

The ray-finned fish are the most diverse group of living vertebrates, making up nearly half of all vertebrate species. Most familiar species, such as tuna, have streamlined torpedo-shaped bodies that make it easier to swim through the water. But others can look quite different. As a result of natural selection, the bodies of bony fish are specialized for specific swimming and feeding strategies.

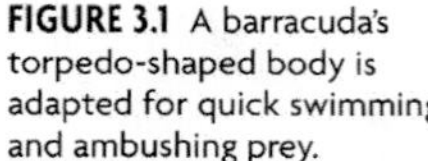

FIGURE 3.1 A barracuda's torpedo-shaped body is adapted for quick swimming and ambushing prey.

- Long, torpedo-shaped fish, such as the barracuda shown in **FIGURE 3.1,** are ambush predators that can accelerate quickly and surprise their prey.
- Fish that are flattened from side to side, such as butterfly fish, cannot swim quickly but are very maneuverable. They are usually found on coral reefs, in dense algae beds, or in large schools of their own species.
- Fish that feed on the surface of the water, such as some killifish, have flattened heads and mouths that point up. This body plan allows them to slurp up invertebrates from the surface while avoiding being seen by predators lurking above the surface.

Differentiated Instruction

ENGLISH LEARNERS

After reading the section, have small groups of students practice summarizing it by first looking at individual structural cues such as headings, boldface vocabulary, figures, and assessment questions. Students should then write down what they think are the most important concepts of the section. The groups should compare notes and come up with a list of points that they agree are the main ideas.

Teacher Toolkit, Section C, Summarizing

BELOW LEVEL

Have students prepare a Venn diagram of bony and cartilaginous fish. They can begin by filling in the characteristics of the cartilaginous fish, which they learned about in **Section 2.** As they read, they should fill in the characteristics of bony fish. When both fishes' characteristics are listed, students can merge the shared characteristics into the center field.

Teacher Toolkit, Section C, Venn Diagram

- Flatfish, such as the plaice shown in **FIGURE 3.2**, are flat-shaped and lie on the sea floor waiting for their prey to swim by. During development into its adult form, one eye migrates to the top of its head as its body flattens out.
- Some slow-swimming fish use camouflage to hide from predators or prey. For example, a leafy sea dragon has dozens of fleshy flaps on its body that make it look like the seaweed it lives in.

FIGURE 3.2 A plaice's flat-shaped body helps it to blend in with the sea floor, where it lies and waits for prey to swim by.

Staying Afloat

Most ray-finned fish have lungs modified into a buoyancy organ called a **swim bladder.** The swim bladder, shown in **FIGURE 3.3**, helps a fish float higher or lower in the water. The swim bladder lets the fish save energy because a neutrally buoyant fish does not have to swim to keep from sinking or floating toward the surface. But if the fish changes depth, it must either add or remove air from the swim bladder to maintain neutral buoyancy. Adding oxygen from the bloodstream increases buoyancy the same way inflating a life vest makes you more buoyant. Reabsorbing oxygen into the bloodstream reduces buoyancy. Some species' swim bladders are adapted for use as an amplifier, picking up sound waves and transmitting them to the inner ear through a series of bones. A few fish even use the swim bladder to make sounds by vibrating it like a loudspeaker.

Some ray-finned fish still have lungs. One example is the bichir, which lives in stagnant streams in West Africa. These fish have gills, but can also breathe air and survive out of water for several hours at a time.

CONNECT TO

BUOYANCY

You may recall from physical science that buoyancy is the upward force that a fluid exerts on an object. To rise to the surface, a fish fills its swim bladder with oxygen, increasing its volume but not its mass, causing it to float upwards.

A Explain What is a swim bladder, and how does it work?

FIGURE 3.3 Bony Fish Anatomy

The unique features of the anatomy of a bony fish include a swim bladder that maintains buoyancy and gills used to breathe.

spiny dorsal fin
soft dorsal fin
spinal cord
gallbladder
caudal fin
swim bladder
kidney
brain
lateral line
gills
heart
liver
intestine
bladder
anal fin
esophagus
pancreas
reproductive organ
anus
pelvic fin
stomach

PRE-AP

Tell students that when some bony fish are hooked and reeled to the surface, their swim bladders are so full of air that they protrude from the fish's mouth. If the fish were thrown back into the water, it would be difficult for the fish to get back down to its preferred depth. Have students write an explanation for why the fish's swim bladder would be so full of air if the fish is not trying to ascend to the surface.

Have students focus on what happened to the fish upon being hooked. They should realize that the forced and rapid ascent of the fish immediately reduces the pressure surrounding it. The gas that is in the fish's swim bladder expands much faster than it can be dissolved into the fish's bloodstream.

Teacher Toolkit, Section C, Quick-Write

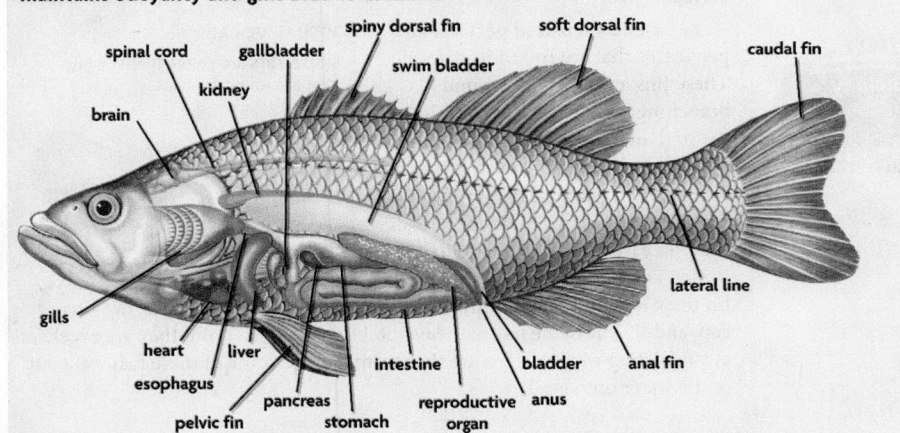

Take It Further

Most bony-fish species have a larval stage. The **winter flounder** *(Pseudopleuronectes americanus)*, a member of the same family as the plaice, starts out as a planktonic larva that swims and feeds in the water column. Once grown to 6 mm, the left eye begins to migrate toward the right side. At 8 mm, the fins are fully formed, and the left eye moves some more. At 9 mm, the pigment on the left side fades to white, both eyes are on the right side, and the fish swims to the bottom, where it will swim on its left side for the rest of its life, reaching a size of approximately 0.6 m (2 ft) and weighing 3.6 kg (8 lbs).

Science Trivia

Some species in both the cartilaginous and bony-fish classes have evolved with functional electric organs that can be used as both defensive and offensive weapons.

- The electric eel (*Electrophorus electricus*), which lives in freshwater swamps and creeks in the tropics and grows to more than 7 feet long, is able to emit an electrical charge of 300–650 volts.
- The Atlantic torpedo ray (*Torpedo nobiliana*), which grows to 6 feet long and 200 pounds, uses a charge of 220 volts to stun its prey.
- The Pacific electric ray (*Torpedo californica*), which is smaller than its Atlantic counterpart, has a charge of about 50 volts.

Answers

A Explain A swim bladder is a buoyancy organ that helps fish float higher or lower in the water. Adding or removing air from the swim bladder allows the fish to change the depth at which it swims by increasing or decreasing the fish's density relative to the surrounding water.

Chapter 23: Vertebrate Diversity 685

DATA ANALYSIS

Discuss

Scatterplots are similar to line graphs in that they use horizontal and vertical axes to plot data points. The difference is that with a scatterplot, the individual points are not connected directly together with a line, but instead express a trend. This trend can be seen by calculating and plotting a line of best fit. A line of best fit is a straight line that best represents the data on a scatter-plot. This line may pass through some of the points, none of the points, or all of the points. **Ask,** What is the general trend in these data? The larger the fish is, the older it is.

Answers

1. The plotted data should suggest a positive slope, but students should not actually draw a line of best fit.

Largemouth Bass Length and Age

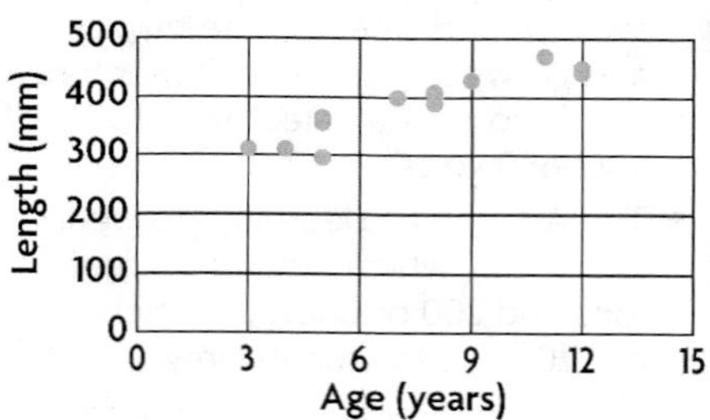

2. It is a positive correlation. As the age increases, the length increases.
3. Judging by the general trend of the data, the fish is probably less than three years old.

Online Student Resources, Data Analysis Practice

Have students complete the Data Analysis Smart Grapher activity for this chapter to look at fish diversity relative to depth. Or they can explore the current state of fisheries in the WebQuest.

DATA ANALYSIS

CONSTRUCTING SCATTERPLOTS

In order to analyze the relationship between two variables, scientists graph their data. The table below contains data about the length and age of largemouth bass in two lakes in Washington state.

1. **Graph** Construct a graph of the data in the table. Remember, for scatterplots you do not connect the data points.
2. **Analyze** What is the relationship between length and age in largemouth bass?
3. **Infer** An additional fish is measured with a length of 250 millimeters (mm). What might be the age of this fish? Explain your answer.

TABLE 1. LARGEMOUTH BASS LENGTH AND AGE

Length (mm)	295	310	310	355	365	405	390	400	410	430	470	450	442
Age (years)	5	4	3	5	5	8	8	7	8	9	11	12	12

Source: *Washington State Department of Ecology*

MAIN IDEA

Lobe-finned fish have paired rounded fins supported by a single bone.

The lobe-finned fish include the ancestors of all terrestrial vertebrates. But most species of lobe-finned fish are extinct. Only seven species remain today. These fish first appeared about 400 million years ago in the Devonian period. Despite their early presence in the fossil record, the lobe-finned fish have never been as diverse as the ray-finned fish, which first appeared in the Devonian period as well.

Lobe-fins are paired pectoral and pelvic fins that are round in shape. These fins are arranged around a branching series of bony struts, like the limb of a land vertebrate. There is always one bone at the base of the fin. It is attached to a pair of bones, which are attached to a fan of smaller bones. Muscles extend into the fin and stretch across the bones, making the fin thick and fleshy. Lobe-fins cannot change shape as quickly as ray-fins can, and they provide less maneuverability in the water. But they are excellent at supporting weight, a feature that eventually let some of these fish walk out of the water onto land.

VISUAL VOCAB

Lobe-fins are paired limblike fins that are round in shape.

lobe-fins

Animated Biology
HMHScience.com
GO ONLINE
What Type of Fish Is It?

Differentiated Instruction

BELOW LEVEL

Write the following question on the board: *Why would a fish without a swim bladder probably have to eat more than a fish that has a swim bladder?* It would use more energy swimming without the aid of buoyancy. Have students think about the question, and then form pairs to discuss and prepare their answers. Have students share their answers with the class.

Teacher Toolkit, Section C, Think-Pair-Share

PRE-AP

Have students work in pairs to design a simple dichotomous key that would enable someone to determine if a fish belongs to the cartilaginous, ray-finned, or lobe-finned class of fish. Tell students to define any key terms (such as *operculum, fin rays, swim bladder,* and *dorsal fin*) so that anyone who was fishing from the shore and caught an unfamiliar fish would be able to determine which class it belongs to.

Coelacanths

Coelacanths (SEE-luh-KANTHS) are distinctive-looking fish with thick, fleshy fins and a tail with three lobes. They breathe with gills. Their swim bladders are filled with fat and provide buoyancy. There are two species of coelacanth. Both live in deep water in the Indian Ocean.

Coelacanths were first known from fossils. They are found in freshwater and shallow marine deposits from the Devonian until the late Cretaceous periods (410 to 65 million years ago), and then completely disappear from the fossil record. Before 1938, scientists assumed that they had gone extinct at the same time as the dinosaurs. In 1938, a modern coelacanth was caught off the coast of South Africa. Another was discovered near Indonesia in 1997.

READING TOOLBOX

VOCABULARY

The name *coelacanth* comes from the combination of the Greek word *koilos*, which means "hollow," and the Greek word *akantha*, which means "spine."

Lungfish

Lungfish, such as the one shown in **FIGURE 3.4**, live in streams and swamps in Australia, South America, and Africa. They can breathe with either gills or lungs. This characteristic means that they can live in stagnant, oxygen-poor water that other fish cannot tolerate. Lungs even keep some species alive when their ponds dry up. They make burrows in the mud, which hardens as the water dries up. Then they breathe air until the next rain refills their pond.

FIGURE 3.4 Lungfish are lobe-finned fish that are able to breathe with either gills or lungs.

The relationships between lungfish, coelacanths, and the terrestrial vertebrates are controversial. Recent studies of mitochondrial DNA suggest that lungfish are the closest living relatives of terrestrial vertebrates. Anatomical evidence also supports this idea. For example, lungfish and terrestrial vertebrates are the only animals with separate blood circuits for the lungs and the rest of the body. However, this characteristic does not mean that modern lungfish are the direct ancestors of terrestrial vertebrates. Both groups are descended from ancient lungfish, and they have changed in different ways over time.

A Identify **What are two examples of living lobe-finned fish?**

23.3 Formative Assessment

SELF-CHECK Online
HMHScience.com
GO ONLINE

REVIEWING MAIN IDEAS

1. How are the bones arranged in a **ray-fin**? How is the arrangement related to the fin's function?
2. How are **lobe-finned** fish different from ray-finned fish?
3. How are lobe-fins related to vertebrate evolution?

CRITICAL THINKING

4. **Infer** You are looking at a long, torpedo-shaped fish with a flat head and a mouth that points upward. What do you predict about the hunting style of this fish?
5. **Predict** Any animal that is underwater is under pressure. Diving exposes animals to higher pressures. How would this affect a fish's **swim bladder**?

CONNECT TO GENETICS

6. Early coelacanth fossils have single dorsal and anal fins. Second sets of dorsal and anal fins appear suddenly in the fossil record and persist in modern species. Explain how *Hox* genes could be responsible for the sudden appearance of this novel feature.

23.3 FORMATIVE ASSESSMENT

1. Ray-finned fish have fins supported by a fan-shaped array of bones. The arrangement of bones and muscles makes the fin easy to maneuver.
2. Lobe-fins are paired, fleshy limblike fins that are round in shape, less maneuverable, and able to support more weight.
3. Lobe-fins are excellent at supporting weight, a feature that allowed some vertebrates to move onto land. Some lobe-fins have lungs, suggesting a possible common origin with terrestrial vertebrates.
4. The fish is probably an ambush predator that feeds at the surface.
5. The air in the swim bladder would get compressed as the fish descended, resulting in a decrease in the volume of the swim bladder.
6. *Hox* gene duplication could create a second set of instructions for fins farther down the animal's body.

The Inside Story

In 1938, the curator of the local natural history museum in East London, South Africa, received a telephone call that would change her life and rewrite some biological history. **Marjorie Courtenay-Latimer** had made it known to the local fishermen that she was interested in seeing any unusual specimens that she might add to the museum's collection. Buried in the catch of Hendrik Goosen's fishing boat was a fish that fit the bill. Courtenay-Latimer described it this way: "It was five foot long, a pale mauvy blue with faint flecks of whitish spots; it had an iridescent silver-blue-green sheen all over. It was covered in hard scales, and it had four limb-like fins and a strange puppy dog tail." She put the fish into the trunk of a taxi and took it back to the museum for examination.

It took two months and the help of taxidermists to preserve the fish to have the specimen identified. It was a **coelacanth**—a fish that was thought to have been extinct for 80 million years. In Courtenay-Latimer's honor, the fish was given the scientific name *Latimeria chalumnae*, the Chalumna River being the place where it was found.

Answers

A Infer Coelacanths and lungfish

Assess and Reteach

Assess Use the Section Self-Check or Section Quiz, both available at **HMHScience.com**.

Reteach Create a two-column chart on the board, labeled *Bony Fish Adaptations* and *Function*. One by one, fill in the function side and ask students to call out the feature or adaptation you are describing. Have students copy the chart as you complete it.

Introduce

Engage students' interest in mapping biodiversity hotspots and other ecosystem services by telling them about REDD+ (Reducing Emissions from Deforestation and Forest Degradation), a program founded by the United Nations to mitigate the effects of climate change by conserving areas of the world (mainly forests) that store carbon and keep it out of the atmosphere. The REDD+ program offers financial incentives to countries that reduce carbon emissions and develop their land in a sustainable way that keeps carbon locked up. **Ask,** How might the 2013 study done in Costa Rica on ecosystem services affect the work of REDD+? Students may conclude that the program will have to start taking into account more than just carbon storage when environmental decision-makers decide which areas of the world to protect.

Discuss

Discuss with students the concept of ecosystem services. Ask them to consider if thinking about nature in terms of its value to people is a useful way of looking at the problem of human impact on Earth. Some students might feel it is selfish to think of nature only in terms of what it can do for people. Other students might think that is a practical way to engage human interest in mitigating climate change and other problems. Tell students about the program called PES (Payments for Ecosystem Services) that has been in place in Costa Rica since 1996. The program pays land owners to use sustainable practices on their land, which results in benefits to the country's human population as well as nonhuman populations. Interested students can research the PES program and report on its successes and failures.

Biodiversity Hotspots and Other Ecosystem Services

S.T.E.M. Interactions

New ways of thinking about the benefits of ecosystems are both challenging and reinforcing a decades-old reliance on biodiversity hotspots as the gold standard of conservation efforts. Scientists and governmental regulating agencies are rethinking their previous view that biodiversity is the only important conservation consideration—while at the same time confirming that biodiversity is a good indicator of which areas of the world most need to be protected.

The concept of biodiversity hotspots emerged in 1988, championed by British ecologist Norman Myers. Biodiversity hotspots are areas of the world that contain thousands of plant and animal species that are endemic, or found only in that area, and that also have lost at least 70 percent of their original habitat to human development. Today, the number of hotspots—found on every continent except Antarctica—has grown to 35, including the island of Madagascar and a large area of Central America.

Once these areas were identified, governments and nonprofit organizations around the world began focusing their conservation efforts on the hotspots. If the endemic species of plants and animals that live in the hotspots became eradicated by development, they would become extinct, because they live nowhere else in the world.

However, today conservationists are recognizing that considerations besides biodiversity are also important in conservation and land-planning strategies. Over the past few decades, scientists have developed the concept of "ecosystem services," or benefits that people receive from ecosystems. These benefits include materials (such as food, materials for clothes and construction, and fuel), biodiversity conservation, carbon storage, water conservation, and scenic beauty. Although biodiversity is very important, these other ecosystem benefits are important as well.

A 2013 study done in Costa Rica found that conservationists must consider environmental tradeoffs carefully when deciding which areas to protect. The study's findings are good news for biodiversity hotspots, because scientists found that these areas are also high in value in other ecosystem services, such as carbon storage, water conservation, and scenic beauty. The study found that this correlation doesn't always hold true for other ecosystem services, though. If conservationists choose to preserve an area solely because it provides carbon storage, it will have lower value for other ecosystem services.

The authors of the study acknowledge that more research on ecosystem services needs to be done before scientists have a clear picture that will help governments and nonprofit organizations make decisions about conservation. However, the study's findings provide environmental decision makers with an important mission: When they map areas, they must map information on all of the area's ecosystem services. In this way, they can make informed decisions about which areas are most important to protect.

Lemurs in Madagascar

23.4 Amphibians

KEY CONCEPT **Amphibians evolved from lobe-finned fish.**

MAIN IDEAS
- Amphibians were the first animals with four limbs.
- Amphibians return to the water to reproduce.
- Modern amphibians can be divided into three groups.

VOCABULARY
tetrapod
amphibian
tadpole

Connect to Your World
What would it really be like to be a "fish out of water"? On shore, the air does not support your body. Gravity pulls on you and makes it hard to move. Your lateral line does not work. You are deaf because your body absorbs sound waves before they reach your ear. The air is too thin to let you suck food into your mouth, and it is so dry that you start losing water through your skin. These are just a few of the conditions animals faced when they first moved onto land.

MAIN IDEA
Amphibians were the first animals with four limbs.

One of the oldest known fossils of a four-limbed vertebrate was found in 360-million-year-old rocks from Greenland. We know that *Acanthostega* had lungs and eight-toed legs. But it also had gills and a lateral line system, neither of which work in air. These features suggest that the earliest animals with four limbs were aquatic and used their limbs to paddle underwater.

All of the vertebrates that live on land, as well as their descendants that have returned to aquatic environments, are tetrapods. A **tetrapod** is a vertebrate that has four limbs. Each limb evolved from a lobe-fin. Tetrapod legs contain bones arranged in the same branching pattern as lobe-fins, except that the fan of bones at the end of the fin is replaced by a set of jointed fingers, wings, or toes. Animals such as snakes, which do not have four limbs, are still considered to be tetrapods because they evolved from limbed ancestors.

Limbs and lungs were features that made these animals successful in an oxygen-poor, debris-filled underwater environment. But, over time, these adaptations let tetrapods climb out of the water to search for food or escape predators. These animals gave rise to the first amphibians. **Amphibians** are animals that can live both on land and in water. In the word *amphibian,* the root *amphi* comes from a Greek word meaning "on both sides," while the suffix *-bian* comes from a Greek word meaning "life."

A number of adaptations help amphibians to live on land. Large shoulder and hip bones help support more weight, while interlocking projections on the vertebrae help keep the backbone from twisting and sagging. A mobile, muscular tongue allows amphibians to capture and manipulate food. Development of a middle ear helps some amphibians to hear out of the water.

Differentiated Instruction

BELOW LEVEL

Before students read this section, have them prepare a three-column table with the headings *Statement, My Answer,* and *Text Answer.* Provide five to ten statements and have students answer whether they are true or false, both before and after reading the section. Examples:

1. Amphibians can breathe with skin, gills, or lungs. T
2. All amphibians lay their eggs in water. F
3. Salamanders are herbivorous. F
4. Frogs are the largest group of amphibians. T

Have students record explanatory statements or details in the Text Answer column.

Teacher Toolkit, Section C, Anticipation Guide

Plan and Prepare

Activate Prior Knowledge Students may confuse reptiles with amphibians. **Ask,** Of the following animals, which are amphibians: frog, turtle, snake, alligator, toad, salamander, iguana? frog, toad, salamander Tell students that while some reptiles and amphibians may occupy the same habitats and share some characteristics, amphibian eggs require moisture in order to develop and hatch; the other animals listed, all of which are reptiles, lay eggs that do not require moisture.

Teach

Vocabulary

tetrapod The word *tetrapod,* which comes from Greek, means "four feet." A similar word, *quadruped,* is used in zoology to describe a tetrapod that moves by using all four limbs. A *biped* moves on two feet. Bipeds and quadrupeds are tetrapods, but not all tetrapods are bipeds or quadrupeds. Snakes, for example, are tetrapods that have no feet.

▼ Teach *continued*

The Inside Story

In the mid-1700s, the Swedish botanist **Carolus Linnaeus** established the system for naming species that is still in use today. The great man had something of an attitude where amphibians were concerned. "These foul and loathsome animals are abhorrent because of their cold body, pale color, filthy skin, fierce aspect, calculating eye, offensive smell, harsh voice, squalid habitation, and terrible venom; and so their Creator has not exerted his powers to make many of them." Linnaeus was wrong: there are at least 5743 known amphibian species, and they number in the billions.

Address Misconceptions

Common Misconception Handling toads will give a person warts.

Correcting the Misconception Toads do not give people warts. Some amphibians do secrete a substance from the skin that can be very irritating if it comes into contact with the eyes, nose, or mouth, but human warts are caused by a virus, not by handling amphibians.

Vocabulary

Word Origins The word **tadpole** comes from Middle English roots:

tadde = toad
pol = head

Answers

A Analyze Large shoulder and hip bones helped to support more weight; mobile, muscular tongues let amphibians capture and manipulate food; middle-ear development let amphibians hear outside of water.

CONNECT TO

HISTORY OF LIFE

In 2006, scientists uncovered the fossil remains of a transitional species between fish and tetrapods. *Tiktaalik roseae* has fins and scales like a fish. However, it also has the beginnings of limbs, including digits, proto-wrists, elbows, and shoulders, along with a functional neck and ribs similar to a tetrapod's.

Some amphibians can hear sound due to the development of a tympanic membrane attached to a bone called the stapes. The stapes evolved from the top part of the second gill arch. Sound waves moving through the air vibrate the tympanic membrane, or eardrum, which transfers the sound waves further into the ear cavity to the middle and inner ear.

Depending on the species, amphibians breathe through their skin or with the use of gills or lungs. The balloonlike lungs of an amphibian are simple in structure. An amphibian uses its lungs to breathe by changing the amount and pressure of air in its mouth. Unlike fish, which have a two-chambered heart, amphibians have a three-chambered heart. An amphibian heart is made up of two atria and one ventricle. Oxygenated and deoxygenated blood are partially separated by the two atria. Blood is pumped through the heart on a double circuit. Blood pumped through the pulmonary circuit goes to the skin and lungs. Blood pumped through the systemic circuit brings oxygen-rich blood to the organs and returns oxygen-poor blood to the heart.

Over time, amphibian species evolved with adaptations that allowed them to live on land. But they did not evolve ways to keep themselves or their eggs from drying out in the air.

A Analyze What adaptations helped amphibians move from water to live on land?

MAIN IDEA

Amphibians return to the water to reproduce.

An amphibian's skin is thin and wet. Water constantly evaporates from it, and amphibians risk drying out if they move too far from a source of water. This need for moisture is why you rarely find an amphibian in arid habitats. A few species live in deserts, where they burrow underground, emerging only during the brief rainy season. Desert-living species can absorb large amounts of water through their skin when it is available and store it for the dry season.

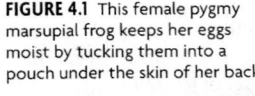

FIGURE 4.1 This female pygmy marsupial frog keeps her eggs moist by tucking them into a pouch under the skin of her back.

Reproduction Strategies

Amphibians need a source of water to reproduce. Their eggs do not have a shell, and the embryos will dry out and die without a source of moisture. Amphibians use many strategies to keep their eggs wet, including

- laying eggs directly in water
- laying eggs on moist ground
- wrapping eggs in leaves
- brooding eggs in pockets on the female's back, as shown in **FIGURE 4.1**

Some frogs start their lives as tadpoles. **Tadpoles** are aquatic larvae of frogs. Tadpoles have gills and a broad-finned tail, and they swim by wiggling their limbless bodies like fish. They typically eat algae, but some may eat small invertebrates or even other tadpoles.

Differentiated Instruction

PRE-AP

Have students write for five minutes about how amphibians are adapted to the following challenges posed by terrestrial life:

- absence of support for body weight
- inability to suck in prey from the air
- inability of vibrations to travel as well in air as in water
- scarcity of water for acquiring oxygen

Write these challenges on the board or read them aloud so students can copy them into their notebooks. Answers should include the size of the shoulder and hip bones and the interlocking projections on the vertebrae as means of supporting the body; the muscular tongue as a means of capturing food; middle ear or eardrum for hearing; specialized skin, lungs, and three-chambered heart for acquiring and distributing oxygen to the body.

Teacher Toolkit, Section C, Quick-Write

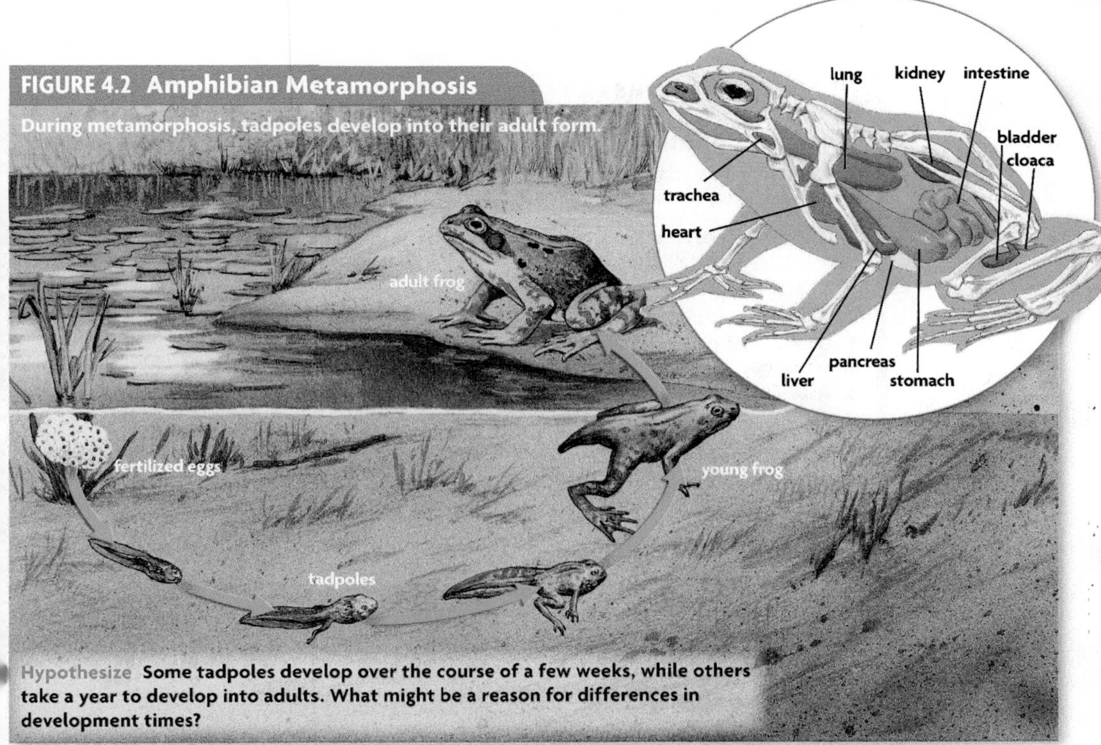

FIGURE 4.2 Amphibian Metamorphosis

During metamorphosis, tadpoles develop into their adult form.

Hypothesize Some tadpoles develop over the course of a few weeks, while others take a year to develop into adults. What might be a reason for differences in development times?

Amphibian Metamorphosis

To grow into terrestrial adults, tadpoles must undergo metamorphosis. Recall that metamorphosis is the change in form and habits of an animal. Similar to the metamorphosis of a butterfly, the metamorphosis of a tadpole into an adult frog affects nearly every organ in the tadpole's body. It produces enormous changes in the animal's body form, physiology, and behavior. The stages of amphibian metamorphosis, in which a tadpole transforms into its adult form, are shown in **FIGURE 4.2.**

During metamorphosis, the tadpole undergoes many changes. The gills are reabsorbed and lungs develop, shifting the frog from a water-breathing to an air-breathing mode of life. The circulatory system is reorganized to send blood to the lungs. The tail fin (if not the entire tail) is reabsorbed. The body grows limbs and completely reorganizes its skeleton, muscles, and parts of the nervous system. The digestive system is rebuilt to handle a carnivorous diet. In the adult amphibian, digestion occurs in the animal's stomach, and wastes are expelled through the cloaca. The cloaca is also a part of the reproductive system.

Many amphibians do not undergo metamorphosis. Adult females lay eggs on the ground or keep them in their bodies, and the young develop directly into their terrestrial forms.

Infer Describe the stages of amphibian metamorphosis.

READING TOOLBOX

TAKING NOTES

Draw a simple diagram of amphibian metamorphosis in your notes. At each step, label the changes that occur as the amphibian changes from an egg to its adult form.

TEACH FROM VISUALS

FIGURE 4.2 Go through the stages of metamorphosis with students. **Ask**

- At which stage is a frog most like a fish? freshly hatched tadpole
- How can you relate the characteristics of the tadpole and the adult frog to the meaning of the word *amphibian*, or "living on both sides"? Tadpoles have the characteristics of fish: gills and fins. Adult frogs have lungs and limbs. Tadpoles are herbivores, and frogs are carnivores.

Science Trivia

- The world's largest frog is the West African goliath frog, *Conraua goliath*. Its upper body can be more than 30 centimeters (1 ft) long; with its back legs extended, it is often more than 75 centimeters (2.5 ft) long.
- The goliath frog eats insects, crustaceans, fish, and amphibians, and may also eat aquatic birds and small mammals.

Answers

A Hypothesize Answers may include environmental differences, such as dry seasons or winter seasons causing a period of dormancy or quickening the time of development (such as in eggs that develop in short-lived puddles).

B Infer Egg—tadpole—frog; when developing into a frog, a tadpole reabsorbs its gills and develops its lungs, goes through a reorganization of its circulatory system to send blood to the lungs, absorbs its tail fin, grows limbs, and develops a digestive system suited for eating other animals.

ENGLISH LEARNERS

Have students sketch the stages of amphibian metamorphosis in a cycle diagram. Tell students to sketch all the stages in a series of boxes arranged in a circle. Tell them to label each box and explain the characteristics of each stage of development.

Teacher Toolkit, Section C, Cycle Diagram

HANDS-ON ACTIVITY

Collect tadpoles from a local source or obtain them from a biological supply company. Place them in an aquarium in the classroom. Have students observe the tadpoles daily and record any changes they see. Tell them to make sketches at regular intervals so they can see how the tadpoles are changing. Only if the tadpoles were obtained from the local environment should the adults be released into the wild.

▼ Teach *continued*

QUICKLAB

Time 30 minutes — TEACHER TESTED

Purpose Observe and describe the stages of development of a frog from embryo to adult.

LAB MANAGEMENT

As an alternative, the lab could be done with photographs of the various stages from textbooks or the Internet.

Safety Remind students to wipe down the microscopes' eyepieces with alcohol wipes after using them. Make sure they wash their hands before leaving the lab.

Answers

Analyze and Conclude

1. The embryo's tail bud stages through the latter stages of the tadpole's metamorphosis (just before legs bud) resemble a fish.
2. The tadpole has gills. During metamorphosis, gills are absorbed and lungs develop.
3. The circulatory system is reorganized to send blood to the body's lungs.
4. Students will identify various stages of frog development from embryo to adult. Answers depend on the specimens observed, but typically follow a sequence such as this: **a.** 1-cell, fertilized egg; **b.** 4-cell; **c.** 8-cell; **d.** Morula: 4 hours; **e.** Blastula: 6 to 20 hours; **f.** Mid-gastrula: 10 to 40 hours; **g.** Late gastrula; **h.** Early neurula; **i.** Neurula: 19 to 80 hours; **j.** Late neurula; **k.** Tailbud: 32 to 100 hours; **l.** Late tailbud; **m.** Tadpole: 110 to 180 hours, Gills, Rear leg buds, Rear legs (tail), Front legs (tail), Four legs (no tail); **n.** Adult: 5 weeks.

QUICKLAB OBSERVING

Frog Development

Every vertebrate starts off as a fertilized egg or zygote. In this lab, you will identify and sequence the various stages of development of a frog from embryo to adult.

PROBLEM In what order should the specimens be placed to trace the development of the frog?

PROCEDURE

1. Use a spatula to place each coded specimen in a petri dish.
2. Observe each specimen with either a hand lens or a dissecting microscope.
3. Make a drawing of each specimen.
4. When finished, return the specimens to the coded jar.
5. Label your drawings, and put them in the proper sequence.

ANALYZE AND CONCLUDE

1. **Analyze** What stage of development most resembles a fish?
2. **Analyze** Explain how the breathing mechanism changes during frog development.
3. **Identify** What change occurs in the circulatory system to accommodate the change in the breathing mechanism?
4. **Infer** What is the correct sequence of your drawings from the earliest to the latest stages of development?

MATERIALS

- preserved specimens of frog embryos and tadpoles
- petri dish
- spatula
- hand lens or dissecting microscope

MAIN IDEA

Modern amphibians can be divided into three groups.

FIGURE 4.3 The mud salamander lives in swamps, bogs, springs, and streams of the southeastern United States.

The three groups of modern amphibians are salamanders, frogs, and caecilians (suh-SIHL-yuhnz). The body plans of these amphibians are adapted to the feeding habits and requirements of the habitats in which they live.

Salamanders

There are more than 300 species of salamanders. As shown in **FIGURE 4.3**, salamanders have a long body, four walking limbs, and a tail. They walk with a side-to-side movement biologists think is similar to the way ancient tetrapods probably walked. But appearances can be deceiving. Salamanders have a number of adaptations specific to their way of life. Some salamander species, such as the axolotl (AK-suh-LAHT-uhl), retain some juvenile features as they mature, growing into aquatic adults that look like giant tadpoles with legs. Members of the largest family of salamanders do not have lungs and exchange gases through the lining of their skin and mouth.

Salamander larvae and adults are carnivorous. They eat invertebrates such as insects, worms, and snails. Large species eat smaller vertebrates such as fish and frogs. Salamander larvae and some aquatic adults suck food into their mouths as fish do. On land, a salamander hunts by flinging its sticky tongue at its prey and pulling it back into its mouth.

Differentiated Instruction

BELOW LEVEL

Have students use a combination of notes and drawings to learn the characteristics of the three groups of amphibians. In this section, with visuals available, students may wish to first re-create the salamander, frog, and caecilian shown in **FIGURES 4.3, 4.4,** and **4.5,** and then label the drawings with descriptions of external and internal characteristics.

Teacher Toolkit, Section C, Combination Notes

Frogs

Frogs make up the largest group of living amphibians, with more than 3000 species. Adult frogs are physically distinctive, with tailless bodies, long muscular hind limbs, webbed feet, exposed eardrums, and bulging eyes. Their bodies are adapted for jumping. Elongated bones in their hips, legs, and feet increase their speed and power. Their hind legs have fused bones that absorb the shock of landing.

Toads are actually one family of frogs. They have rougher and bumpier skin than do other frogs, as well as relatively shorter legs that make them poor jumpers. Glands in the bumpy skin of toads and the smooth skin of tropical frogs make toxins that protect the animals from predators. Many species of these poisonous frogs and toads have bright coloration that warns predators that they are deadly.

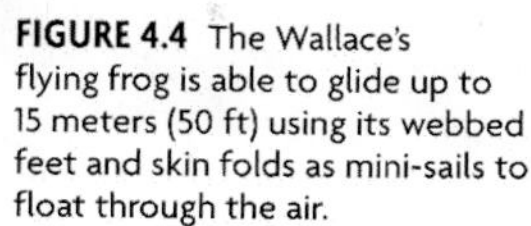

FIGURE 4.4 The Wallace's flying frog is able to glide up to 15 meters (50 ft) using its webbed feet and skin folds as mini-sails to float through the air.

Frogs live in every environment on Earth except at the poles and in the driest deserts. Although most tadpoles eat algae, adult frogs are predators and will eat any animal they can catch.

Caecilians

Caecilians (suh-SIHL-yuhnz), such as the one shown in **FIGURE 4.5**, are legless, burrowing amphibians that live in the tropics. There are 160 species, ranging in length from about 10 centimeters (4 in.) to 1.5 meters (5 ft). Caecilians have banded bodies that make them look like giant earthworms, and they are specialized for a life burrowing through the soil.

FIGURE 4.5 Caecilians, common to South America, are legless amphibians that live in underground burrows.

Like other amphibians, caecilians are predators. They burrow through the soil searching for earthworms and grubs. Because they have no legs, they cannot dig through the soil the way a mole would. Instead, like an earthworm, a caecilian uses a hydrostatic skeleton to stiffen its body and drive its head forward like a battering ram.

A Contrast **How are caecilians different from other amphibians?**

23.4 Formative Assessment

SELF-CHECK Online
HMHScience.com
GO ONLINE

REVIEWING MAIN IDEAS

1. What evidence suggests that the first **tetrapods** were **amphibians**?
2. How have amphibians adapted to living in desert environments?

CRITICAL THINKING

3. **Connect** Poison dart frogs and monarch butterflies are brightly colored. What might be the adaptive advantage of bright coloration?
4. **Apply** Amphibians are very sensitive to changes in their environment. Why might this be?

CONNECT TO EVOLUTION

5. Caecilians, snakes, and whales have no legs. Why, then, do we call them all tetrapods? (**Hint:** consider their evolutionary histories.)

23.4 FORMATIVE ASSESSMENT

1. The oldest known tetrapod fossils had lungs, legs with toes, gills, and a lateral line—characteristics shared with amphibians.
2. The desert-living species of amphibians burrow underground and emerge only during the rainy season. They can also absorb large amounts of water through their skin when it is available and store it for the dry season.
3. Bright coloration may alert potential predators that the frog is poisonous, thereby protecting the frog from predation.
4. The skin of an amphibian is very thin in order to absorb moisture (and, in some species, oxygen) from its environment. This also means that other substances, such as pollutants, may be absorbed as well.
5. Caecilians, snakes, and whales all descended from four-limbed ancestors.

Integrating Ecology

Although amphibians have radiated out into most of Earth's biomes, their populations have been declining dramatically all over the world in recent years. Habitat destruction contributes to some of the decline, but scientists infer from evidence that the thinning of the ozone layer and global climate change are playing roles too. Many amphibians lay their eggs in shallow water where they are exposed to ultraviolet radiation from the sun. Because UV rays are known to cause genetic damage, and more UV radiation is reaching Earth as a result of the thinning ozone layer, this could explain why frog eggs frequently fail to develop and hatch. Other research suggests that global climate change is making conditions ideal for a fungus that is fatal in many amphibian species.

Answers

A Contrast Caecilians are limbless and use a hydrostatic skeleton to burrow.

Assess and Reteach ▼

Assess Use the Section Self-Check or Section Quiz, both available at **HMHScience.com**.

Reteach Assemble a digital slide show of amphibians. Ask students to identify which group the animal belongs to and explain their reasoning. Include images of fish, reptiles, and worms to see if students can tell them apart from tadpoles, salamanders, and caecilians.

Chapter 23: Vertebrate Diversity 693

SECTION 23.5

Plan and Prepare

Activate Prior Knowledge Hold a chicken egg behind you. Tell students, "In my hand I'm holding an example of the adaptation that allows terrestrial vertebrates to occupy some of the most extreme biomes." **Ask,** What is this powerful adaptation? the amniotic egg Show students the chicken egg. **Ask,** Why was this so important? Because their eggs would not dry out, amniotes were able to radiate out into deserts, mountains, and other biomes where water was not always available.

Teach

Take It Further

Tell students that human embryos are encapsulated in an **amnion,** and that it is this tough, membranous sac that defines the amniotes, not the hard shell characteristic of some amniotic eggs.

Answers

A Connect Keratin; it prevents loss of water from our tissues, so we can live in drier environments.

23.5 Vertebrates on Land

KEY CONCEPT **Reptiles, birds, and mammals are adapted for life on land.**

VOCABULARY

amniote
keratin
amniotic egg
placenta

MAIN IDEAS

- Amniotes can retain moisture.
- Amniotes do not need to return to water to reproduce.

Connect to Your World

Around 350 million years ago, one group of ancient amphibians evolved traits that let them walk away from the water forever. Over time, they diversified into the types of vertebrates you are most familiar with, including reptiles, birds, and mammals—the class that includes you.

MAIN IDEA

Amniotes can retain moisture.

An **amniote** is a vertebrate that has a thin, tough, membranous sac that encloses the embryo or fetus. Amniotes first appeared as small, lizardlike creatures in the late Carboniferous period. Since that time, amniotes have evolved into thousands of different forms and have invaded nearly every ecosystem on Earth. They have become predators in the tropics, the most arid deserts, the Arctic, and in any number of freshwater and marine environments. They have become burrowers, sprinters, sit-and-wait predators, and slow trackers. Some species never leave the trees. Some specialize in eating plants and have evolved symbiotic relationships with bacteria that can break down cellulose. Some have also developed powered flight.

When you look at the phylogenetic tree of amniotes, it is clear that many of the species we see today are survivors of larger radiations that have gone extinct. Mammals are survivors of a huge line of animals that went extinct about 245 million years ago. Birds are survivors of the dinosaur radiation and extinction.

All amniotes share a set of characteristics that prevent water loss. Skin cells are waterproofed with keratin. **Keratin** is a protein that binds to lipids inside the cell, forming a hydrophobic—or water repellent—layer that keeps the water inside the animal from reaching the skin. The presence of this hydrophobic layer means that amniotes lose less water to evaporation than amphibians do. Waterproofing also means that amniotes cannot exchange gases across their skin. They rely on their lungs for respiration.

Kidneys and large intestines are bigger in amniotes than in amphibians. These organs contain tissues that reabsorb water. The increased surface area of these tissues enables amniotes to absorb more water internally, so they lose less to excretion than do amphibians.

CONNECT TO

EXTINCTION

Recall from the chapter **The Evolution of Populations** that a mass extinction is an intense period of extinction that occurs on a global scale. In the Permian-Triassic extinction, 95% of all species and over 50% of all families disappeared.

A Connect **What makes your skin cells waterproof? Why is this important?**

Differentiated Instruction

ENGLISH LEARNERS

Tell students that the key vocabulary in this section is important to the following chapter about amniotes. Have students create Frayer model charts for these terms. They should include a definition, characteristics, examples, and a drawing.

Teacher Toolkit, Section D, Frayer Model

MAIN IDEA
Amniotes do not need to return to water to reproduce.

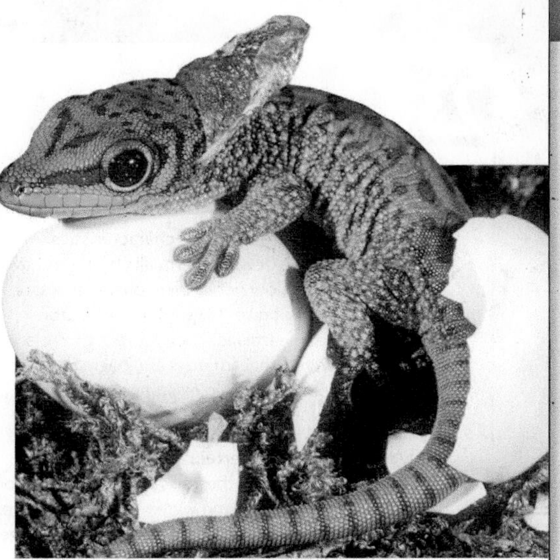

With adaptations that limit water loss, amniote adults could move into drier environments on land. But it was the evolution of the amniotic egg that let them stay there. The **amniotic egg** is an almost completely waterproof container that keeps the embryo from drying out as it develops. After it evolved, amniotes did not have to return to a wet environment to reproduce.

An amniotic egg, shown in **FIGURE 5.1**, is essentially a private pool that the mother builds for her embryo. Like any swimming pool, the egg is expensive. In egg-laying amniotes, the mother must make enough yolk and white to feed the embryo until it hatches, then build the shell around the fertilized egg. Each egg represents a large investment of energy. For example, a bird may lose 5 to 30% of its body weight as it makes an egg.

FIGURE 5.1 Amniotes, such as this gecko, develop within an amniotic egg.

Other amniotes, such as rattlesnakes and garter snakes, make eggs but do not lay them. Instead, they keep their eggs in their oviduct until they hatch. Retaining eggs protects them from predators. Some amniotes have evolved the ability to give birth to living, well-developed young.

Most mammal embryos develop inside of the mother's reproductive tract. Their eggs have no shells, but their embryos make the same series of membranes found in a typical amniotic egg. The **placenta** is a membranous organ that develops in female mammals during pregnancy. It lines the uterine wall and partially envelops the fetus. The placenta carries nutrients from the mother to the embryo and also removes metabolic wastes from the embryo.

Summarize **How is an amniotic egg protected from water loss?**

Take It Further

The **placenta** used by mammals to feed their embryonic young can be considered an example of **convergent evolution.** About 70 percent of shark species give birth to live young, and about 30 percent of these employ a placenta to nourish their young. The difference between the placenta of these sharks and that of many mammals is that it actually develops from the yolk sac and yolk stalk from which the embryo first gets its nutrients. Specifically, the stalk forms the umbilical cord, and the sac becomes the placenta. Placental sharks, including the bull shark and hammerheads, are born with the umbilical cord still attached. The cord detaches, leaving the shark pup with an umbilical scar that is analogous to the human navel, or "bellybutton."

Answers

A Summarize A tough membrane prevents water loss. In some amniotes, the eggs have a hard shell.

23.5 Formative Assessment

REVIEWING MAIN IDEAS

1. What anatomical characteristics help an **amniote** retain moisture?
2. Why don't amniotes need to return to water to reproduce?

CRITICAL THINKING

3. **Infer** If eggshells were thicker, the egg would lose even less water to the environment. Why are eggshells thin?
4. **Infer** What is an advantage of giving birth to live young, rather than having young that hatch from eggs?

SELF-CHECK Online
HMHScience.com
GO ONLINE

CONNECT TO
EVOLUTION

5. Most mammals, and at least some lizards and snakes, have evolved live birth by keeping the eggs inside the mother until they hatch. However, no bird species has ever retained its eggs. Suggest a possible explanation for this fact.

Chapter 23: Vertebrate Diversity 695

Assess and Reteach

Assess Use the Section Self-Check or Section Quiz, both available at **HMHScience.com**.

Reteach Show images of the eggs of amniotes in various environments. For example, show the eggs of a sea turtle as they are laid into a nest on a sandy tropical beach; the single eggs of king penguins in Antarctica; and the early embryo of a human. Discuss the adaptations of the amniotes (keratin in skin) and their eggs (waterproof amnion) that prevent water loss.

23.5 FORMATIVE ASSESSMENT

1. Keratin waterproofs skin cells. Larger kidneys and intestines maximize the absorption and retention of water.
2. The amniotic egg protects the embryo inside from drying out.
3. The shell must be thin enough to allow for gas exchange.
4. Live young may be better able to avoid predation. Eggs that are laid cannot defend themselves or escape predators; they depend on parental care. For the mother, carrying embryos until they are born may mean they are free to move, migrate, and find food; some species that lay eggs have to protect their eggs at all times until they hatch.
5. Birds that fly would have a difficult time doing so if they had to carry the weight of their eggs.

INTERACTIVE Review
HMHScience.com
GO ONLINE

Encourage students to go to **HMHScience.com** for a detailed review of each section, including visuals and vocabulary practice.

Online Student Resources, Vocabulary Practice Worksheet

CHAPTER 23 Summary

BIG IDEA Vertebrates are a diverse group of land-based and aquatic animals that share certain characteristics.

KEY CONCEPTS

23.1 Vertebrate Origins

All vertebrates share common characteristics. At some point during development, all chordates have a notochord, a hollow nerve cord, pharyngeal slits, and a tail. All vertebrates have an endoskeleton made of bone or cartilage. The first recognizable vertebrates were fish. Lampreys and hagfish are two primitive, jawless fish still in existence today.

23.2 Fish Diversity

The dominant aquatic vertebrates are fish. Fish use the large surface area of their gills to exchange carbon dioxide and oxygen with the water in which they live. Countercurrent flow maximizes the amount of oxygen a fish can pull from the water. Fish use their fins to move around in the water. Cartilaginous fish include sharks, rays, and chimeras. All other living fish are categorized as bony fish.

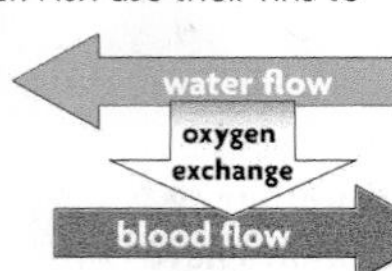

23.3 A Closer Look at Bony Fish

Bony fish include ray-finned and lobe-finned fish. Ray-finned fish have a fan of bones in their fins. Most ray-finned fish use an organ called a swim bladder to stay neutrally buoyant, which means they neither sink nor float in the water. Lobe-finned fish have a series of bones in their fins. Lobe-finned fish include the ancestors of all land vertebrates. Coelacanths and lungfish are two types of lobe-finned fish.

23.4 Amphibians

Amphibians evolved from lobe-finned fish. Amphibians were the first vertebrates with four limbs. Amphibians can live both on land and in water. However, they must live in moist environments, as they need a source of water to reproduce. Modern amphibian groups include salamanders, frogs, and caecilians.

23.5 Vertebrates on Land

Reptiles, birds, and mammals are adapted for life on land. During embryonic or fetal development, an amniote is enclosed within a thin, tough, membranous sac. This waterproof container allows amniotes to reproduce outside of water. Some amniotes give birth to live young, while others lay hard-shelled eggs.

READING TOOLBOX SYNTHESIZE YOUR NOTES

Concept Map Use a concept map like the one below to summarize what you know about fish diversity.

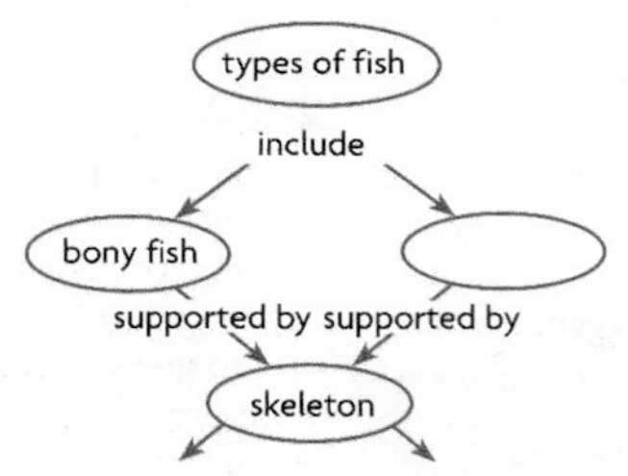

Process Diagram Use a process diagram like the one below to make a detailed summary of the steps that occur during amphibian metamorphosis.

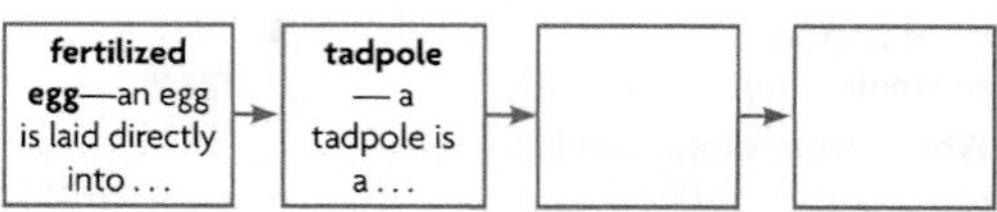

Reviewing Vocabulary

1. Both are types of animals. A vertebrate has an internal segmented backbone; an invertebrate does not.
2. Both provide support for the animals. An endoskeleton is internal; an exoskeleton is external.
3. Both are organs used for gas exchange. Gills exchange gas between an animal and water; lungs exchange gas between an animal and air.
4. Both help fish move through the water. Ray-fins are thin, have a fan-shaped array of bones, and are controlled by muscles embedded in the fish's body; lobe-fins are rounded and fleshy, have bony struts for support, and contain muscles.
5. Tetrapods are vertebrates with four limbs, such as amphibians, mammals, birds, and reptiles.
6. Both are reproductive adaptations of amniotes, but not all amniotes use a placenta. The placenta provides nutrients from the mother to the embryo; the amniotic egg is the container that protects the developing embryo.
7. The operculum covers the gills of a bony fish.
8. Caecilians live underground in the dark.
9. The notochord is a lengthy support rod (similar to a length of string) that is embedded in an animal's back.
10. Tetrapods have four limbs.
11. A shark has a skeleton made of cartilage.
12. The illustration should show two arrows pointing in opposite directions—one marked *water flow*, the other marked *blood flow*. Between the two large arrows could be smaller arrows indicating the exchange of gases. The caption could read "Countercurrent flow maximizes the amount of oxygen a fish can get from water."
13. The illustration should show a simple illustration of a fish with the lateral line marked on its body. The caption could read "The lateral line system gives fish a sense of distant touch, letting them feel the movements in the water created by animals and currents."

23 Review

INTERACTIVE Review
HMHScience.com
GO ONLINE
Review Games • Concept Map • Section Self-Checks

CHAPTER VOCABULARY

23.1 chordate
notochord
endoskeleton

23.2 gill
countercurrent flow
lateral line
operculum

23.3 ray-fin
swim bladder
lobe-fin

23.4 tetrapod
amphibian
tadpole

23.5 amniote
keratin
amniotic egg
placenta

Reviewing Vocabulary

Compare and Contrast

Describe one similarity and one difference between the two terms in each of the following pairs.

1. invertebrate, vertebrate
2. endoskeleton, exoskeleton
3. gill, lung
4. ray-fin, lobe-fin
5. tetrapod, amphibian
6. amniotic egg, placenta

READING TOOLBOX GREEK AND LATIN WORD ORIGINS

Using the Greek or Latin word origins of the terms below, explain how the meaning of the root relates to the definition of the term.

7. The word *operculum* comes from the Latin word *operire,* which means "to cover."
8. The term *caecilian* comes from the Latin word *caecus,* meaning "blind." (Hint: Consider where a caecilian lives.)
9. The word *notochord* comes from a combination of the Greek words meaning "back" and "gut or string."
10. In the term *tetrapod,* the prefix *tetra-* means "four."
11. In the term *chondrichthyes,* the word part *chondr-* comes from a Greek word meaning "cartilage." Why is a shark a member of the group Chondrichthyes?

Visualize Vocabulary

For each term below, use simple shapes, lines or arrows to illustrate their meaning. Below each picture, write a caption. Here's an example for the term *operculum.*

An operculum is a protective plate that covers the gills of a bony fish.

12. countercurrent flow
13. lateral line

Reviewing MAIN IDEAS

14. Sea squirts and dogs are both chordates, but they are very different kinds of animals. What four features do these animals share at some point in their development?
15. All vertebrates have an endoskeleton. What are the main parts of an endoskeleton?
16. Name the seven classes of living vertebrates.
17. How does countercurrent flow contribute to the function of a fish's gills?
18. What evidence indicates that the jaws of fish were once gill arches?
19. Barracuda and flatfish have very different body shapes and methods of finding food, yet both have ray-fins. How does the structure of their fins help them to survive?
20. What is the function of the swim bladder in a ray-finned fish?
21. What feature of a lobe-fin fish makes it the closest relative to terrestrial vertebrates?
22. List two adaptations of amphibians, and briefly describe why each is important for life on land.
23. Why does amphibian reproduction require a moist environment?
24. What are the three types of modern amphibians?
25. How does the presence of keratin in skin cells affect where an amniote can live?
26. Mammals and birds have very different methods of reproduction, but both are able to reproduce on land. Explain why amniotes do not need to return to water to reproduce.

CHAPTER REVIEW

Reviewing Main Ideas

14. notochord, pharyngeal arches, hollow nerve cord, tail
15. braincase, vertebrae, bones
16. Agnatha (jawless fish); Chondrichthyes (cartilaginous fish); Osteichthyes (bony fish); Amphibia (amphibians); Reptilia (reptiles); Aves (birds); Mammalia (mammals)
17. Countercurrent flow ensures that water is always flowing past blood that has a lower oxygen concentration and a higher carbon dioxide concentration than the water. This means oxygen is constantly diffusing into the bloodstream, and carbon dioxide is constantly diffusing out.
18. The third gill arch evolved into the upper and lower jaws of modern fish. The fourth arch also fused to the cranium, adding support to the jaws.
19. A ray-fin is embedded in a thin layer of skin that is light and flexible and allows the fin to change shape quickly, so the fish can maneuver in order to hunt prey or elude predators. Fins also function as stabilizers and, in some species, protection.
20. The swim bladder is a buoyancy organ that a ray-finned fish uses to adjust its depth in the water.
21. the lobe-fins themselves, which contain strutlike bones wrapped in muscle, like the limbs of a terrestrial vertebrate
22. *Sample answers:* larger shoulder and hip bones that can support more weight; interlocking projections on the vertebrae to support the backbone; ears that can detect vibrations in the air to permit hearing; a muscular tongue to catch food
23. Amphibian eggs develop outside the animal's body and do not have a waterproof shell to protect the embryo and retain nutrients.
24. salamander, frog, caecilian
25. Keratin prevents water loss, so amniotes do not have to live in moist environments.
26. Mammals retain their embryos inside their bodies, providing nutrients and water through a placenta. Birds lay waterproof eggs that keep the embryo from drying out.

Critical Thinking

27. Both the notochord and the internal backbone provide support. The notochord is flexible. The backbone is much stiffer because it is composed of short, stiff vertebrae, but it can bend because there are joints between vertebrae. The internal backbone is made of cartilage or bone.
28. *Sample answer:* At the first station, at the front of the gill, the relative concentrations of dissolved oxygen and carbon dioxide in the incoming water are 80% and 20%, respectively. The countercurrent bloodstream at this station has already been offloading carbon dioxide and taking up oxygen, but the concentrations of these gases are still such (75% O_2 and 25% CO_2) that oxygen diffuses into the blood and carbon dioxide diffuses out. At the next station, the same thing occurs, but the concentrations of the gases in the water might be more like 75% O_2 and 25% CO_2, and 70% O_2 and 30% CO_2 in the blood. This pattern of diffusion continues through the other three stations. (Concentrations of gases in blood and water are essentially changing in opposite directions.)
29. To rise, a submarine forces compressed air into a water-filled chamber. The water is forced out and replaced by the air, thereby making the submarine less dense than the water. To descend, the sub vents the air out of the chamber, allowing water to flood back in and make the sub more dense than water.
30. Webbed feet help them swim when they are in water and also help them move through soft mud. Another species' webbed feet allow it to fly.
31. The large kidneys of amniotes allow for reabsorption of water, so less is excreted.

Critical Thinking

27. Analyze Describe the structure and function of the notochord and the internal backbone of an endoskeleton.

28. Analyze Gas exchange in fish occurs in the gills using a countercurrent flow. Imagine that there are five stations in a gill at which gas exchange takes place. Describe what happens and why as the water and blood pass each other at each station.

29. Apply Submarines rise and sink using a mechanical system that works much like a swim bladder. Use your knowledge of how a swim bladder works to explain how submarines use these systems to rise and descend in the water.

30. Infer Frogs have bodies that are specialized for jumping, yet they have webbed feet. How are webbed feet beneficial for frogs?

31. Connect Why would your kidneys help you survive for a couple of days without water better than the type of kidneys that frogs have?

Interpreting Visuals

Use the image below to answer the next three questions.

32. Classify This mudskipper has climbed out of the water and is resting on a rock. Based on the physical characteristics of the mudskipper's fin shape, to which group of fish does the mudskipper belong? Explain your reasoning.

33. Analyze When it is out of the water, how might the lungless mudskipper breathe?

34. Apply If mudskippers were to evolve into a terrestrial animal, what body part might function as a limb?

Analyzing Data Construct a Scatterplot

Use the data below to answer the next three questions. The calling activity, body size, and body temperature were recorded for a population of Fowler's toads. Below is a scatterplot that shows the relationship between a male toad's body temperature and calling effort, measured as the number of seconds the male called per minute of time.

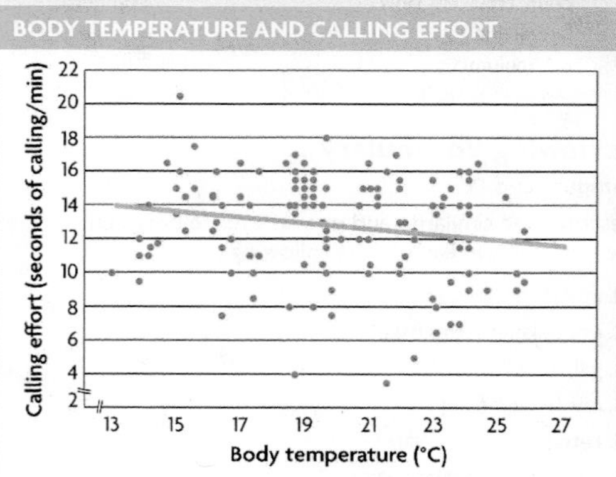

Source: *Given, M. Copeia 2002:04.*

35. Analyze What is the relationship between the body temperature of the Fowler's toad and calling efforts?

36. Analyze Is this data an example of positive correlation, negative correlation, or no relationship?

37. Predict Would you expect a toad with a body temperature of 15° Celsius to have a higher or lower calling effort than a toad with a body temperature of 21° Celsius? Explain.

Making Connections

38. Write a Letter Imagine you are a green frog, adapted to life both in water and on land, and one of your best friends is a fish that lives in a nearby lake. Write a letter to the fish, explaining what adaptations he would need to survive outside of the water on land. In the letter, be sure to compare any similar characteristics and contrast differing characteristics.

39. Connect Take another look at the glass frog on the chapter opener. Its translucent skin helps it to blend in with the green leaves on which it lives. How could natural selection have played a role in the development of this trait common among all glass frogs?

Interpreting Visuals

32. It is a bony, ray-finned fish. Mudskippers' thickened ray-fins allow them to shuffle onto land. Its fins are not fleshy or rounded like lobe-fins are.
33. The mudskipper must have some adaptation to its gills that allows it to exchange gases with the air. (Mudskippers do not have lungs. Their gill cavities are enlarged and filled with a mixture of air and water when on land. As long as the gills remain moist, they can exchange gases with air.)
34. pectoral fins or pelvic fins

Analyzing Data

35. As body temperature increases, calling effort decreases.
36. negative correlation
37. The colder toad should have a higher calling effort than the warmer toad. Judging by the line of best fit, the colder toad would call at a rate of about 14 seconds of calling per minute; the warmer toad would call at less than 13.

698 Unit 6: Diversity of Life

Standards-Based Assessment

Record your answers on a separate piece of paper.

MULTIPLE CHOICE

1 A scientist discovers a new type of organism in the deep ocean. Because this organism was found in the water, the scientist suspects it may be related to fish. This idea ***most closely*** resembles a scientific —

A theory

B hypothesis

C suggestion

D experiment

2 Fossils found in New Zealand suggest that as many as 2,000 frog species lived there in the past. Today, there are fewer than 300 frog species. What conclusion can be drawn from this information?

A The climate conditions in New Zealand have changed over time.

B The species alive today are more specialized to a particular niche than the species of the past.

C Biological diversity of frogs in New Zealand has decreased.

D There are fewer frog species today because a mass extinction occurred.

3

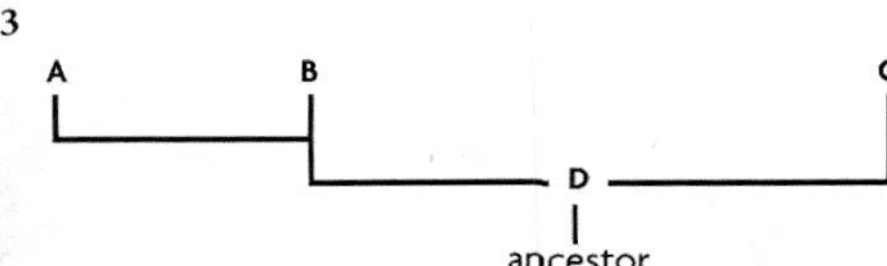

After studying fossils of prehistoric fish in one region, scientists developed this family tree to describe how the various species they found are related. Which of the following is ***true*** with regard to the diagram above?

A The Ancestor species has gone extinct.

B Species A and Species C are not related.

C Species D evolved before Species A, B, and C.

D Species C evolved before Species A and B.

4

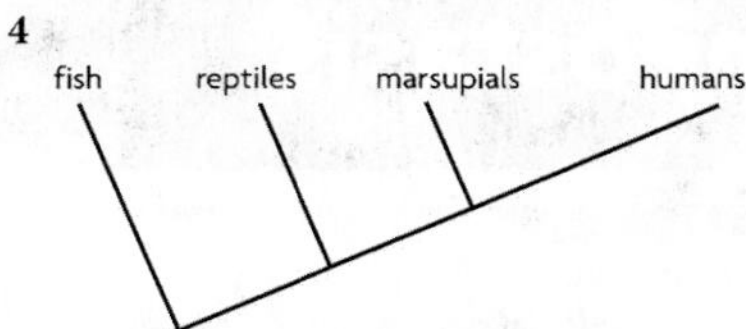

According to the cladogram above, which of the following statements is ***true***?

A Fish are more closely related to humans than reptiles.

B Reptiles are more closely related to marsupials than fish.

C Marsupials and fish do not share a common ancestor.

D Marsupials and humans share a common ancestor.

THINK THROUGH THE QUESTION

Recall that cladograms are based on common ancestry, and that they are read from left to right.

5 Countercurrent flow in a fish's gills allows blood to efficiently release carbon dioxide into the water and absorb oxygen from the water. Which of the following ***best*** describes why this process is referred to as "countercurrent flow"?

A Oxygen and carbon dioxide flow in opposite directions.

B Fish need to swim backwards in order for gas exchange to take place.

C The movement of the water flows in the opposite direction as the blood.

D Fish need to swim against the current in order for gas exchange to take place.

6 About 245 million years ago, at the boundary of the Permian and Triassic periods, 95 percent of all species died out. This event is referred to as a(n) —

A episode of speciation

B population explosion

C mass extinction

D intense adaptation

Making Connections

38. Students should mention that the fish would need large shoulder and hip bones to support more weight; mobile, muscular tongue to capture food; middle ear to hear; lungs for respiration; modified fins or true limbs to get around; three-chambered heart; way to either protect its eggs from drying out or ensure that they are in a moist environment.

39. Frogs that blend in better with their surroundings are less likely to be killed by predators, so their traits—including their coloration—are more likely to be passed on than those of frogs who do not avoid predation.

Standards-Based Assessment

The Standards-Based Assessment questions will help students prepare for their final examination in the course. If you wish to give students practice in coding their answers, look for the Standards-Based Assessment Answer Sheet at **HMHScience.com**. To give students practice under timed testing conditions, allow them five minutes per question.

Question	Answer	Depth of Knowledge	Cognitive Complexity
1	B	I	L
2	C	II	M
3	C	II	M
4	D	II	M
5	A	IV	M
6	C	II	L

KEY

Depth of Knowledge
- I Recall
- II Skill/Concept
- III Strategic Thinking
- IV Extended Thinking

Cognitive Complexity
- L Low
- M Moderate
- H High

CHAPTER 24

Instruction and Intervention Support

Human Systems and Homeostasis

① Core Instruction

The **Core Instruction** resources below can be used for all students. Core instruction should be followed by ongoing assessment to determine which students need further help.

Available in both English and Spanish

Available Online

Section	Instruction	PRINT	ONLINE	Labs
24.1	Textbook **Levels of Organization**	■	●	Homeostasis and Exercise Examining Human Cells
	Animated Biology Human Organ Systems		●	
	Teaching Visuals Organization of the Body (Fig. 1.3)		●	
	PowerPresentation and Notes 24.1		●	
24.2	Textbook **Mechanisms of Homeostasis**	■	●	Hormones and Homeostasis Negative and Positive Feedback **QuickLab** Negative Feedback Loop
	Animated Biology Keep an Athlete Running		●	
	PowerPresentation and Notes 24.2		●	
24.3	Textbook **Interactions Among Systems**	■	●	
	PowerPresentation and Notes 24.3		●	

Additional online resources available for this chapter include **Interactive Whiteboard Resources.**

GO ONLINE! for all your teacher resources at HMHScience.com

2 Support and Intervention

Support and Intervention resources are useful for students who need targeted help beyond the Core Instruction

Resources	PRINT	ONLINE
Assess and Reteach (TE wrap)	■	●
Concept Map		●
Interactive Reader	■	●
Interactive Review Games		●
Section Self-Checks		●
Study Guide B		●
Vocabulary Practice Worksheets		●

3 Specialized Support

Students who need more intensive personalized intervention benefit from **Specialized Support** resources.

Resources	PRINT	ONLINE
Chapter Audio Files		●
Differentiated Instruction Inclusion, Below Level, and English Learners (TE wrap)	■	●
ELL Strategies	■	●
Modified Lesson Plans for English Learners		●
Reinforcement Worksheets		●
Study Guide A		●

Extension and Assessment

Enrichment and Challenge

Resources	PRINT	ONLINE
Active Reading Worksheets		●
Data Analysis Practice Worksheet		●
Differentiated Instruction Pre-AP (TE wrap)	■	●
Pre-AP Activity Determination of Muscle Cells, The Dangers of Cold Exposure		●
The Inside Story and **Take It Further** (TE wrap)	■	●
Unit Project		●
WebLinks		●
WebQuest Hypothermia (24.3)		●

Assessment

Resources	PRINT	ONLINE
Alternative Assessment		●
Chapter Tests A and B		●
Diagnostic Test		●
ExamView Banks		●
Extended Response Test		●
Online Assessment System		●
Section Quizzes		●
Standards-Based Assessment	■	●

CHAPTER 24

Chapter Overview

- **Section 1** explains and relates the levels of organization in biological systems.
- **Section 2** discusses the role of internal feedback mechanisms in the maintenance of homeostasis.
- **Section 3** describes interactions among body systems to maintain homeostasis.

▼ Focus and Motivate

How does this ice climber hang on to his body temperature?

Project the Media Gallery image of the thyroxine hormone and have students read the caption. **Ask,** What cell process provides the energy and heat necessary for survival? cellular respiration

Explain to students that the body does its own balancing act. For a human body to function, body temperature cannot go much below or above the optimal temperature of 37°C (98.6°F), no matter what the outside conditions are. Maintaining body temperature depends not only on cellular activities but also on different body systems' working together. In particular, the endocrine and nervous systems interact to stabilize body temperature. Point out that the heat given off during cellular respiration helps maintain internal body temperature.

BIOZINE
HMHScience.com

Students can access BioZine at **HMHScience.com** to learn about some of the latest research in the biological sciences.

CHAPTER 24 Human Systems and Homeostasis

BIG IDEA The human body is organized into different systems that interact in a coordinated way to maintain homeostasis.

ONLINE BIOLOGY HMHScience.com

ONLINE Labs

- Homeostasis and Exercise
- **QuickLab** Negative Feedback Loop
- Examining Human Cells
- Hormones and Homeostasis
- Negative and Positive Feedback
- **Open Inquiry Lab** Interactions Among Systems

Teacher Demo

Model Demonstrate the effectiveness of water as a cooling agent, modeling the effect of sweat on cooling the body.

Materials

- 2 test tubes in test-tube rack
- hot tap water in plastic-foam cup
- dropper
- timer
- 2 thermometers
- paper towels
- 2 rubber bands

Safety Wear safety goggles and heat-resistant gloves.

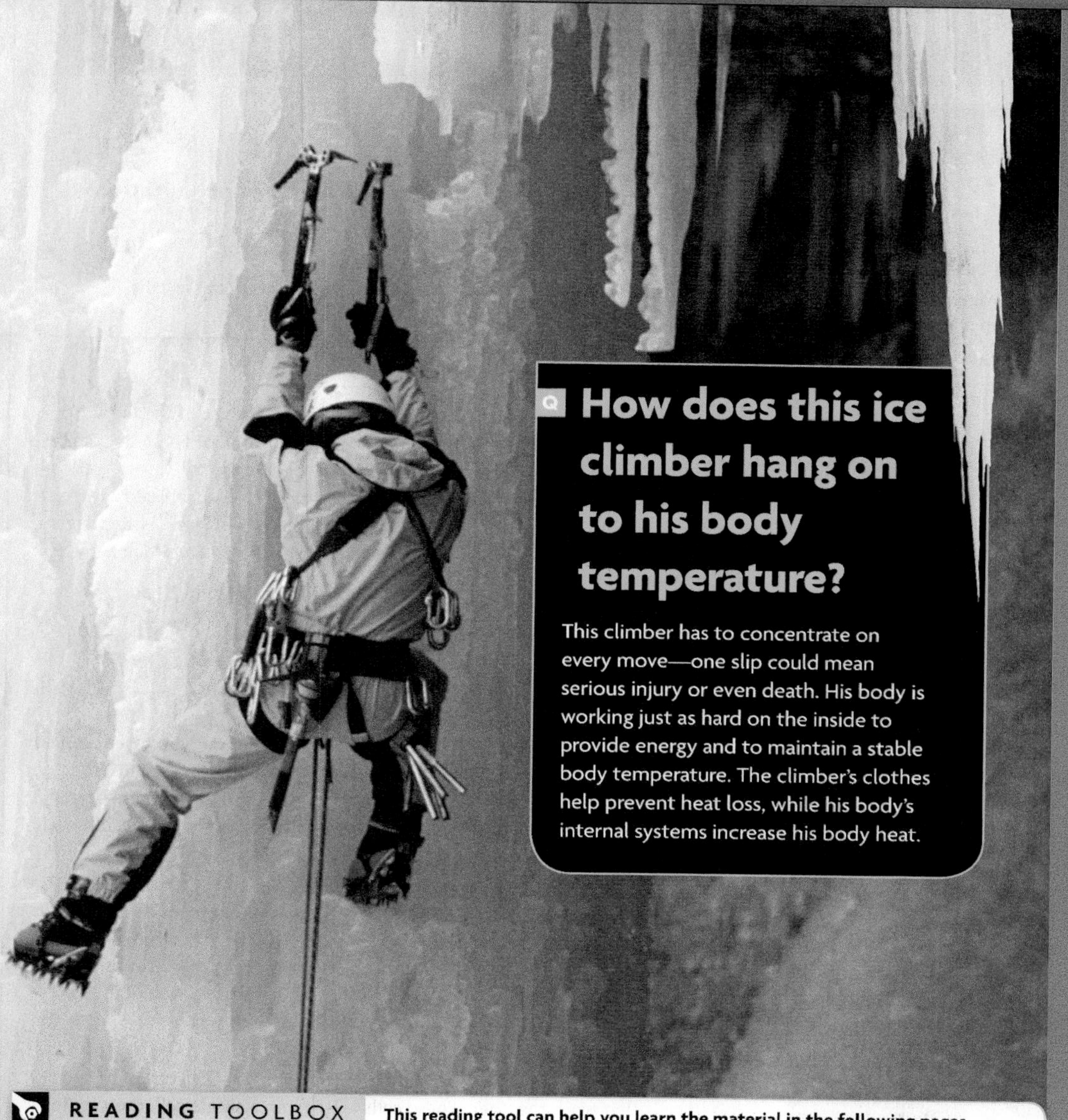

How does this ice climber hang on to his body temperature?

This climber has to concentrate on every move—one slip could mean serious injury or even death. His body is working just as hard on the inside to provide energy and to maintain a stable body temperature. The climber's clothes help prevent heat loss, while his body's internal systems increase his body heat.

READING TOOLBOX **This reading tool can help you learn the material in the following pages.**

USING LANGUAGE

Analogies Analogies compare words that have similar relationships. You can write analogies with words or with colons. For example, the analogy "up is related to down in the same way that top is related to bottom" can be written "up : down :: top : bottom." To answer an analogy problem, you must figure out how the words are related. In the example given, up is above down and top is above bottom.

YOUR TURN

Use information found in the chapter to complete the following analogies.

1. heart : pump :: kidney : _____
2. nervous system : nerves :: endocrine system : _____

Demonstrate

- Wrap a dry paper towel around one test tube and a wet paper towel around the other. Secure each towel with a rubber band.
- Use the dropper to fill the two test tubes with hot water.
- Place a thermometer into each test tube. Note the temperature of the water on the board. Then make a temperature reading of the water in each tube every minute for ten minutes.

After ten minutes, the data should show that the water in the "wet" tube has cooled at a rate faster than that in the "dry" tube.

Discuss The water in the "wet" tube returns to equilibrium (room temperature) faster than the water in the "dry" tube. When body temperature rises, the hypothalamus activates the sweat glands. **Ask**

- What effect do you think sweating has on body temperature? Sweating helps decrease body temperature through the cooling effect of evaporation.
- Why it is that on a humid day, no amount of sweating seems to help? For sweat to cool the body, it must evaporate from the skin. Moisture in the air limits evaporation.

Activate Prior Knowledge

Direct students' attention to the photograph of the ice climber. **Ask,** How quickly do you think this climber will reach the top of the ice wall? It will take a long time. For the climber to move even a short distance requires careful coordination and planning at each step.

Discuss with students their experience of activities that require a high degree of attention and coordination, for example, skateboarding or ballet. **Ask,** What would it be like for you if you had to concentrate on every step you took or every movement of your hands? It would be hard to do anything.

Discuss that the human body maintains coordination between cells, tissues, and systems that goes well beyond anything a human can experience at a conscious level. Tell students that in this chapter, they will see how body systems must work together to maintain life.

Preview Vocabulary

English Learners

Students have seen the words *structure* and *function* in their study of cells and organelles. Tell them that in this chapter, they will be looking at the levels of organization or structure in multicellular organisms starting with the cell.

cell → tissue → organ → organ system → organism

The structure of cells and the tissues and organs they form enable a certain *function,* or job, to be done. Have students watch for words in the text that are "function" words: *support, protect, transmit, receive, move, regulate, absorb, secrete.* Students should approach this chapter with these questions in mind: What job does a structure do, and how does it do it?

Reading Toolbox Answers

1. filter
2. glands

SECTION 24.1

B.4.4 Use a model to illustrate the role of cellular division (mitosis) and differentiation in producing and maintaining complex organisms.

▼ Plan and Prepare

Activate Prior Knowledge Have students think about the way employees in a large company are organized. **Ask,** How would you describe the relationships among different jobs, divisions, and levels of responsibility in a company? Every part of the company is dependent on every other part's functioning properly and efficiently. Tell students that in this section, they will learn about how the body's levels of organization work together.

▼ Teach

TEACH FROM VISUALS

FIGURE 1.1 Have students observe the differences in appearance of the cells. **Ask**

- In what way are all the cells in the body alike? have the same DNA
- What accounts for the differences in these two cells? Different genes are turned off and on depending on cell type.

Remind students of the *Hox* genes they learned about in the unit on genetics.

24.1 Levels of Organization

KEY CONCEPT **The human body has five levels of organization.**

MAIN IDEAS

- Specialized cells develop from a single zygote.
- Specialized cells function together in tissues, organs, organ systems, and the whole organism.

VOCABULARY

determination
cell differentiation
tissue
organ
organ system

Connect to Your World

Climbing a wall of ice requires careful interaction among all parts of the body. You probably know that the brain and muscles work together to coordinate the climber's movements. The heart and lungs also have to work together to help provide energy for the climb. Yet every human body starts out as a single cell, a fertilized zygote. How does a single cell give rise to all the different types of cells, tissues, and organs in the human body? Further, how do such different parts coordinate their activities to keep the body functioning?

MAIN IDEA

Specialized cells develop from a single zygote.

If you were to watch an emergency medical team in action, you would quickly notice that each person has a special job. One keeps in radio contact with the main hospital. Another monitors the patient's vital signs. Still others perform life-saving procedures. All emergency teams are made up of people, but each person within the group has a different job.

Likewise, multicellular organisms are made up of cells, but different cells in the organism have different functions. Take a moment to study the images of the blood cells and nerve cells, or neurons, in **FIGURE 1.1.** You will notice that the red blood cells are round with a concave center. This structure gives them more surface area to help deliver oxygen to all parts of the body. In contrast, neurons develop extensions that transmit and receive messages from other neurons.

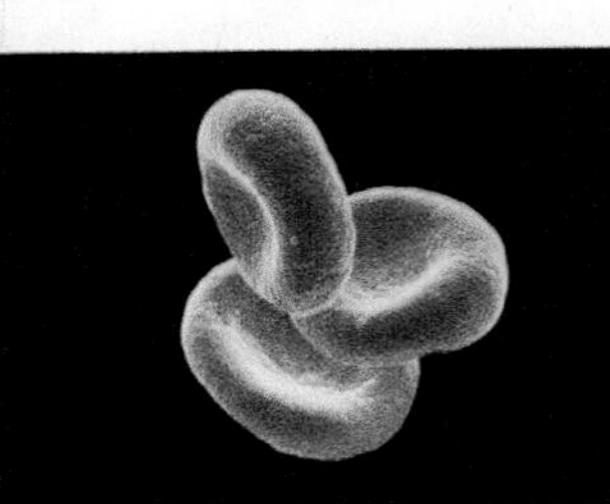

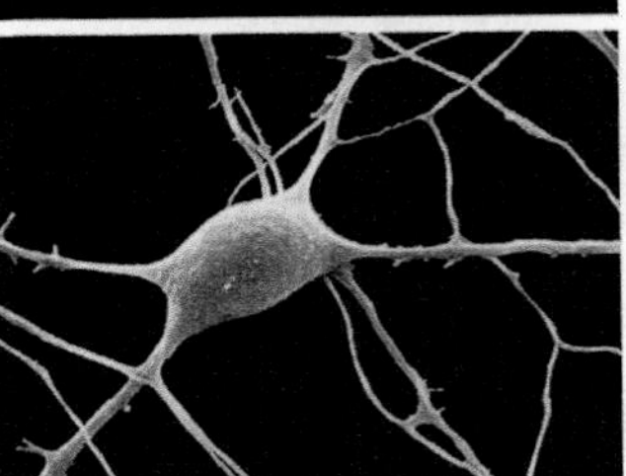

FIGURE 1.1 The disk-shaped red blood cells (top) carry oxygen to all parts of the body. The neuron (bottom), through its extensions, receives and transmits messages from and to other neurons. (colored SEMs; magnifications: blood cells 2800×; neuron about 1600×)

Humans, like almost all multicellular organisms, are collections of specialized cells that work together. These cells arise from a single cell, the zygote, which is formed by the union of an egg and sperm. The zygote divides and differentiates into more than 200 different types of human cells. These cells allow you to do everything from lifting a glass, to learning people's names, to maintaining your body temperature on a cold day. Cell specialization involves two main steps: determination and differentiation.

Determination

The cells produced during the first few divisions of the zygote are known as embryonic stem cells. These cells have the potential to become any type of specialized cell in the body. Within a few weeks, however, a process called **determination** occurs, in which most stem cells become committed to develop

Differentiated Instruction

ENGLISH LEARNERS

Have students preview the chapter by looking at headings, illustrations, and key terms. Ask them to predict what will be important and why they think so. Set up a four-column table with the headings *What I Know I Know, What I Think I Know, What I Think I'll Learn, What I Learned.* Have students fill in the first three columns, leaving the last column empty until they complete the chapter.

Teacher Toolkit, Section C, DRTA

into only one type of cell. For instance, a stem cell might become a cardiac muscle cell or a spinal neuron. These committed cells still retain all of the genetic information needed to build an entire organism. However, during determination, they lose their ability to express some of this information.

Once a cell is committed to becoming a specialized cell, it will develop into only that type of cell. For instance, a cell that will become a neuron can only be a neuron, even if it is transplanted into another part of the body. During normal development, determination cannot be reversed.

READING TOOLBOX

TAKING NOTES

Use a supporting main ideas strategy to take notes about processes such as cell specialization.

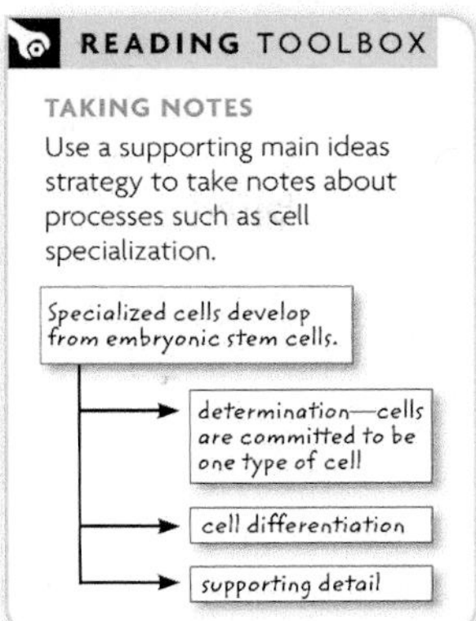

Differentiation

Cell differentiation is the process by which committed cells acquire the structures and functions of highly specialized cells. Cell differentiation occurs because specific genes in each cell are turned on and off in a complex, regulated pattern. The different structures of these specialized cells, such as those shown in **FIGURE 1.2**, allow them to perform specific functions within the body.

The specialization enabled by differentiation is what allows different types of cells to have different functions. The function of muscle cells, for example, is to produce movement by contracting and relaxing. However, skeletal muscle and smooth muscle cells have different structures. Skeletal muscle cells align in bands of orderly rows and contain many nuclei. They are responsible for nearly all voluntary muscle movements, such as lifting your foot to kick a ball. In contrast, smooth muscle cells are shorter and have only one nucleus. They perform involuntary movements, such as raising the hairs on your arm.

Other cells have even more specialized structures and functions. Sperm cells, for instance, develop whiplike tails that enable them to swim. Cells lining the gut are elongated and tightly packed to provide more surface area for the absorption of nutrients.

Not all cells continue to develop into specialized cells. The process of programmed cell death, called apoptosis (AP-uhp-TOH-sihs), is also a normal part of development. For example, when your hands first formed, your fingers resembled a mitten. The death of cells between the fingers allowed individual fingers to develop.

Analyze **Why do multicellular organisms need specialized cells?** (A)

FIGURE 1.2 Cell Differentiation

Cells develop specialized structures and functions during differentiation.

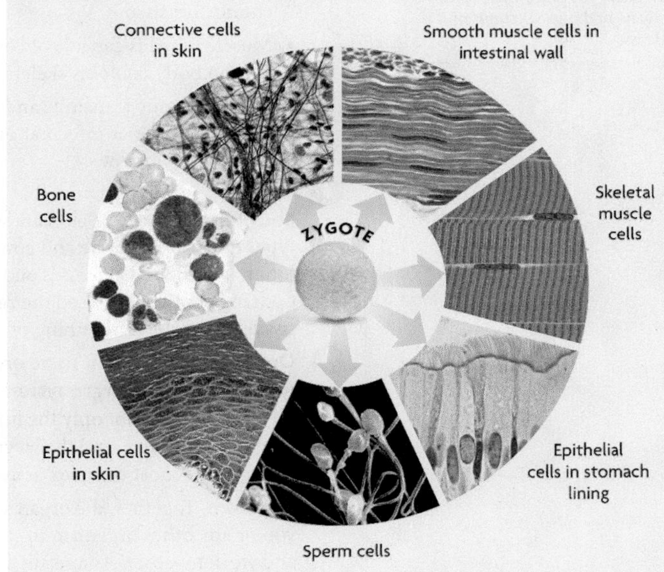

(B) Contrast **How do the structures of sperm cells and epithelial cells in the stomach differ?**

BELOW LEVEL

Have students note how key vocabulary words are used in the text. In their notebooks, have them write what each word means based on their reading of the text. Have them check the definition in the Glossary. Then have students use the word in a sentence and draw a picture that will help them remember the meaning.

Teacher Toolkit, Section D, Student Vocabulary

PRE-AP

Tell students that there are about 25 trillion red blood cells in the human body, each with a life span of about 100–120 days. Red blood cells that are worn out and die are replaced by new cells produced in the bone marrow and stored in the spleen. Have students calculate the number of blood cells the human body loses due to natural cell death each second. 25 trillion cells ÷ 10.4 million seconds = 2.4 million cells per second This is about half the number of red blood cells in one cubic millimeter of blood.

Vocabulary

Greek and Latin Word Origins Students know the word **species,** which shares the same Latin root as the word *special,* meaning "of a certain kind." Tell students that it is possible to think of **specialized** cells as belonging to a species. A "species" of muscle cell is distinct from a "species" of skin cell, in much the same way that one species of bird is different from, yet similar to, another bird species.

The Inside Story

What does it mean that you are 16 or 17 years old if your cells regularly replace themselves? **Dr. Jonas Frisén,** a stem-cell biologist at the Karolinska Institute in Stockholm, has developed a way to estimate the ages of human cells. He developed a scale for converting the carbon-14 in tissues into calendar dates. Using this dating technique, Dr. Frisén estimates that the average age of cells in an adult's body may be seven to ten years.

A hotly debated topic is whether the brain generates new neurons. Using his technique, Dr. Frisén has shown that cells from the visual cortex in the brain are the same age as the individual. These are the cells that enable you to see and interpret what you see. Still to be determined is whether the cells associated with the cerebral cortex, involved with memories and consciousness, are also as old as you are.

Answers

(A) **Analyze** Multicellular organisms need specialized cells to build specialized tissues and organs that carry out functions such as respiration, digestion, and elimination. Specialization also allows multicellular species to become much larger than unicellular species can.

(B) **Contrast** Sperm have a head and a long tail that enable them to move. Epithelial cells are elongated, are tightly packed, and have hairlike cilia at the surface to move materials.

▼ Teach *continued*

Science Trivia

- Skin is the largest organ of the human body.
- Unlike other organs that are distinct and separate structures, skin covers the entire body.
- Adults have about 1.7 square meters (20 ft^2) of skin.
- Skin makes up about 15–20 percent of a person's body weight.
- Every minute approximately 30,000–40,000 dead skin cells are removed from the body.
- In a person's lifetime, he or she will lose around 18 kilograms (40 lb) of dead skin.
- Your body will produce an entirely new layer of skin in one month's time.

CONNECT TO

PLANT BIOLOGY

Animals are not the only organisms with levels of organization that start with cells. Refer to the chapter **Plant Diversity** to review cells, tissues, organs, and organ systems of plants.

MAIN IDEA

Specialized cells function together in tissues, organs, organ systems, and the whole organism.

Specialized, or differentiated, cells are only the first level of organization in a multicellular organism. Scientists organize multicellular structures into five basic levels, beginning with cells and moving to increasingly complex levels—tissues, organs, organ systems, and the whole organism. These five levels in the human body are shown in **FIGURE 1.3**.

1. **Cells** Each type of specialized cell has a particular structure and a chemical makeup that enable it to perform a specific task. Some cells in the lungs, for instance, are involved in the exchange of gases. Others secrete mucus that helps to trap foreign particles and to protect the lungs from pathogens, such as bacteria and viruses.
2. **Tissues** A group of similar cells that work together to perform a specialized function are known as **tissue.** The human body is made up of four general types of tissues.
   - Epithelial tissue consists of protective sheets of tightly packed cells connected by special junctions. The skin and the membranes that line the stomach, the lungs, and other organs are epithelial tissues.
   - Connective tissue serves to support, bind together, and protect other tissues and organs. Tendons, ligaments, bone, and cartilage are all connective tissues.
   - Muscle tissue is capable of contracting to produce movement. The human body contains skeletal, cardiac, and smooth muscle tissues.
   - Nervous tissue transmits and receives impulses in response to stimuli, processes information, and regulates the body's response to its environment.
3. **Organs** A group of tissues that carry out a specialized function of the body form an **organ.** For example, the lungs are composed of all four types of tissues. Muscle and connective tissues expand and contract the lungs. Nervous tissue sends and receives messages that help regulate gas exchange in the lungs and the rate at which a person breathes. Epithelial tissue forms the inner lining of the lungs.
4. **Organ systems** Two or more organs that work together to perform body functions form an **organ system.** The organ system that allows you to breathe includes not only the lungs but also the sinuses, the nasal passages, the pharynx, and the larynx (the voice box). Organ systems perform the most complex activities in the body.
5. **Organism** Together, the organ systems make up the entire organism. For you or any other organism to stay alive, all of the systems must interact and work together. As a result, anything that harms one organ or organ system will affect the health of the entire body.

Differentiated Instruction

TEACH WITH TECHNOLOGY

Students might enjoy viewing a portion of the 1966 film *Fantastic Voyage*. In this science fiction film, a miniaturized medical team is inserted into the human bloodstream with the goal of removing a blood clot in the brain of an important scientist. The film was made long before the advent of computer animation yet provides an entertaining depiction of the body.

PRE-AP

The human body, with its levels of organization, can be compared to the structure of an ecosystem with its different levels of organization. Have students explore this analogy by developing a visual presentation that illustrates their interpretation of this idea. Students should provide a written explanation of the thinking behind their interpretation.

Teacher Toolkit, Section D, Analogies

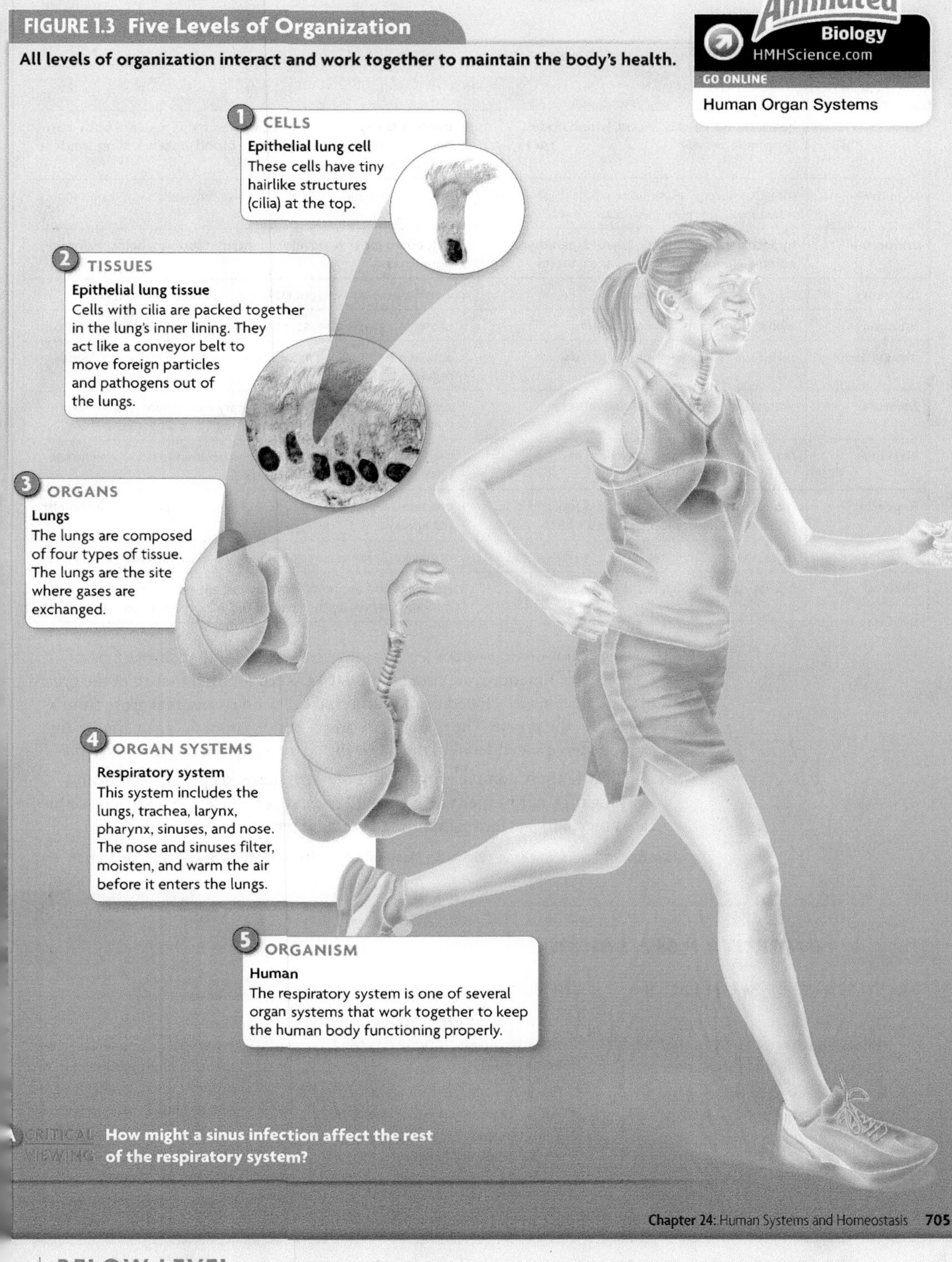
Animated Biology
HMHScience.com
GO ONLINE
Human Organ Systems
1 CELLS
Epithelial lung cell
These cells have tiny hairlike structures (cilia) at the top.
2 TISSUES
Epithelial lung tissue
Cells with cilia are packed together in the lung's inner lining. They act like a conveyor belt to move foreign particles and pathogens out of the lungs.
3 ORGANS
Lungs
The lungs are composed of four types of tissue. The lungs are the site where gases are exchanged.
4 ORGAN SYSTEMS
Respiratory system
This system includes the lungs, trachea, larynx, pharynx, sinuses, and nose. The nose and sinuses filter, moisten, and warm the air before it enters the lungs.
5 ORGANISM
Human
The respiratory system is one of several organ systems that work together to keep the human body functioning properly.

FIGURE 1.3 Five Levels of Organization

All levels of organization interact and work together to maintain the body's health.

A CRITICAL VIEWING **How might a sinus infection affect the rest of the respiratory system?**

BELOW LEVEL

Have students look at the full list of systems in **FIGURE 1.4** (next page). Point out that the first letter of each system can be used to make the words *miners* and *cider*. After reviewing the information, have students close their books. Give them five minutes to write down as many systems as they can remember and a function for each. To help them remember, remind them that *miners* like *cider*.

Teacher Toolkit, Section C, Quick-Write

TEACH FROM VISUALS

FIGURE 1.3 Point out to students that the numbers in the diagram correspond to the numbered list on the previous page. **Ask**

- What cells are featured in the figure, and what system do they belong to? epithelial cells of the lung and respiratory system
- Looking at the drawing of the girl and the organs identified in caption 4, what parts of the respiratory system lead from the nose to the lungs? nose leads to pharynx and larynx, then to trachea and into lungs
- What is the primary function of the respiratory system? exchange gases, supply oxygen needed to release energy, remove waste carbon dioxide

Science Trivia

- The size of an average human body cell is ten micrometers.
- It would take more than 39 million cells to cover the floor of a high school basketball court.
- It would take 6000 cells to cover a sheet of notebook paper.
- Roughly 1000 cells would be needed to cover a dollar bill.

Answers

A Critical Viewing Air first enters through the nose and sinuses, where it is filtered, moistened, and warmed. If the sinuses were blocked by infection, the person would have to breathe through the mouth and there would be a greater chance of harmful pathogens or foreign matter entering the lungs. Drainage from the sinuses could also spread pathogens to the airways, producing a lower respiratory infection.

▼ Teach *continued*

Take It Further

In 1989, the National Library of Medicine set out to create a digital atlas of the human body called the **Visible Human Project (VHP).** The University of Colorado Heath Sciences Center created the atlas by combining CT and MRI images of cross sections of a male cadaver and a female cadaver. Both bodies, a 39-year-old male and a 59-year-old female, had been donated to science. The VHP provides medical, research, and educational communities with the unique opportunity to see organs and systems in relation to one another, along the entire length of the human body.

Answers

Ⓐ **Compare and Contrast** Tissues are composed of one specific type of differentiated cell. Organs consist of two or more types of tissues. Organ systems are composed of two or more organs working in a coordinated fashion. Organs and organ systems perform more complex activities than tissues do.

FIGURE 1.4 Major Organ Systems

SYSTEM	MAJOR TISSUES AND ORGANS	PRIMARY FUNCTION
Circulatory	heart, blood vessels, blood, lymph nodes, lymphatic vessels	transports oxygen, nutrients, wastes; helps regulate body temperature; collects fluid lost from blood vessels and returns it to the circulatory system
Digestive	mouth, pharynx, esophagus, stomach, small/large intestines, pancreas, gallbladder, liver	breaks down and absorbs nutrients, salts, and water; eliminates some wastes
Endocrine	hypothalamus, pituitary, thyroid, parathyroid, adrenal glands, pancreas, ovaries, testes	influences growth, development, metabolism; helps maintain homeostasis
Excretory	skin, lungs, kidneys, bladder	eliminates waste products; helps maintain homeostasis
Immune	white blood cells, thymus, spleen	protects against disease; stores and generates white blood cells
Integumentary	skin, hair, nails, sweat and oil glands	acts as a barrier against infection, injury, UV radiation; helps regulate body temperature
Muscular	skeletal, smooth, and cardiac muscles	produces voluntary and involuntary movements; helps to circulate blood and move food through the digestive system
Nervous	brain, spinal cord, peripheral nerves	regulates body's response to changes in internal and external environment; processes information
Reproductive	*male:* testes, penis, associated ducts and glands *female:* ovaries, fallopian tubes, uterus, vagina	produces reproductive cells; in females, provides environment for embryo
Respiratory	nose, sinuses, pharynx, larynx, trachea, lungs	brings in O_2 for cells; expels CO_2 and water vapor
Skeletal	bones, cartilage, ligaments, tendons	supports and protects vital organs; allows movement; stores minerals; serves as the site for red blood cell production

The major organ systems in the human body, including their main parts and primary functions, are listed in **FIGURE 1.4.** Keep in mind that all of the organs in these systems developed from specialized cells and tissues that arose from a single cell, the zygote. The major parts and functions of each organ system are examined in greater detail in the following chapters on human body systems.

How do these complex organs and organ systems keep functioning and working together properly? As you will read in Section 2, the body has sophisticated mechanisms for maintaining a stable internal environment.

Ⓐ Compare and Contrast **How do tissues differ from organs and organ systems?**

▼ Assess and Reteach

Assess Use the Section Self-Check or Section Quiz, both available at **HMHScience.com**.

Reteach Have students make a graphic organizer that shows the hierarchical relationships among cells, tissues, organs, organ systems, and organism.

24.1 Formative Assessment

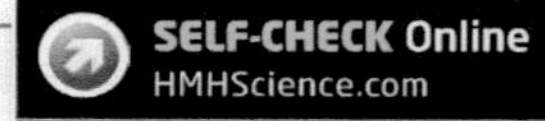

REVIEWING ➤ MAIN IDEAS

1. How does the process of cell **determination** differ from the process of cell differentiation?
2. Relate the levels of organization to each other and to the whole human body system.

CRITICAL THINKING

3. **Apply** What **organ systems** must work together to bring oxygen to the body's cells?
4. **Predict** A cell has undergone determination to become an endocrine gland cell. If it is transplanted to a leg muscle, what do you think will happen to this cell?

CONNECT TO

CELL CYCLE

5. In the spring, tadpoles lose their tails as part of their life cycle. At a certain stage in development, the human fetus acquires individual fingers and toes. What occurs in some cells of both species to explain these changes?

24.1 FORMATIVE ASSESSMENT

1. In cell determination, stem cells commit to becoming a certain type of cell, such as a muscle cell. In cell differentiation, cells develop the actual structures and functions that make them specialized cells.
2. A cell is the smallest unit of life (example: neuron). A tissue is a group of similar cells that work together to perform a specialized function (example: nerve tissue). Organs consist of two or more types of tissues that function together (example: brain). Organ systems consist of two or more organs working together (example: brain and spinal cord) which allows the human body to function as a whole system.
3. The respiratory system brings oxygen into the body. Part of the muscular system coordinates the movement of the lungs. The circulatory system picks up oxygen from the lungs and delivers it to body cells.
4. Because determination is usually not reversible, the cell and its daughter cells will continue to develop as endocrine cells.
5. Both are examples of programmed cell death, or apoptosis.

Electric Skin

The science and engineering of making prosthetic limbs has advanced greatly since the days of arms and legs molded of solid wood or metal. Today, some prostheses contain microprocessors and are connected directly to the nerves. However, there is one area in which prostheses have always been lacking: They do not have skin that can function in the same way as human skin. With the recent development of "electric skin," though, change is on its way.

In recent years, scientists have developed skinlike devices that could do one—but just one—of the things that human skin does, such as feel pressure or temperature. However, no one had been able to develop a skin that could perform more than one of these functions at the same time.

Now, scientists have finally reached that milestone with the development of "e-skin" that can feel both static and dynamic pressure, temperature, and even sound. The e-skin was modeled on the ridged skin of human fingertips, which is very sensitive to external stimuli. Mimicking the way the dermis and epidermis of human skin fit together, e-skin is made of a ridged film layered over ridged plastic and graphene sheets.

When pressure is applied to the e-skin, the ridges of the film and the ridges of the sheets are pressed together, and an electric current is generated.

The e-skin also produces an electric current when it is exposed to something hot or cold, when touching different textures causes different vibrations in the ridges, and when sound waves cause the ridges to vibrate.

So could human brain cells actually sense those electric currents? Another recently developed e-skin that senses pressure has been successful in this area. When tested, the e-skin proved capable of sending electric impulses, caused by pressure applied to the e-skin, to the brain cells of a mouse.

Scientists see multiple uses for e-skin. Because of their flexibility, e-skins could be used in hearing aids that are much more comfortable than the rigid ones available today. They also could be used as wearable medical and diagnostic devices, capable of taking temperature and measuring pulse and blood pressure. Prostheses that are covered in humanlike skin are still in the future, but recent progress in e-skin development provides hope that the technology will one day be available.

S.T.E.M. Activity

In a group, brainstorm possible uses of e-skin. Identify a need that an application of e-skin could fill. Draw a diagram of the application and write several paragraphs that explain the need, how the e-skin application could fill it, and any possible constraints on the application.

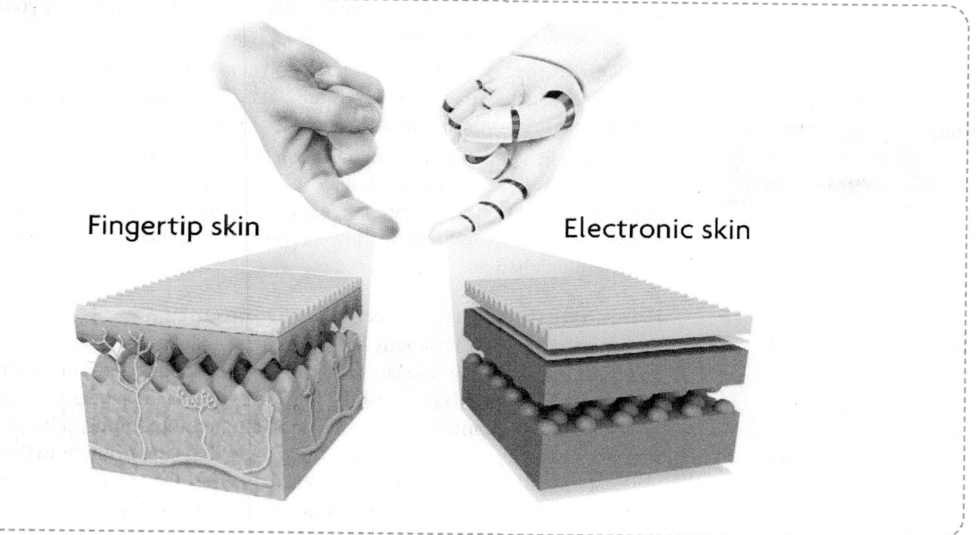

Introduce

Engage students' interest by sharing another e-skin development: the ability to self-heal, just as real human skin can do. Explain that scientists have developed sensors made of polymers that can "heal" scratches or cuts in short periods of time, some as short as a day. **Ask,** How would this be beneficial to users of prostheses that incorporate e-skin? Because people often sustain minor injuries to their arms and legs, it would be beneficial if their prostheses did not require repairs for minor damage.

Discuss

Discuss with students possible constraints that would make it difficult for applications of e-skin to reach consumers. Prompt them to point out that there must first be a need for the application, and that any application would have to be proved safe and effective. Its developers would then have to find investors willing to finance its production. In addition, the cost of the application would have to be low enough for large numbers of people to afford it, thus ensuring there would be enough demand for the supply.

SECTION 24.2

▼ Plan and Prepare

Activate Prior Knowledge Have students think about what life would be like in an environment that hovers around 38°C (100°F). **Ask,** If you had to live at one constant temperature setting, what would it be? Answers will vary; most will likely choose moderate temperatures. Discuss the normal core body temperature, 37°C (98.6°F).

▼ Teach

ONLINE Biology
HMHScience.com

Have students look at how a runner maintains homeostasis in an Animated Biology simulation.

Vocabulary

Academic Vocabulary Students may wonder if the word **homeopathy** relates to *homeostasis*. Homeopathy is a nonmedical approach to treating illness by using small amounts of the *same* substance believed to be the cause. The aim is to "cure like with like" by stimulating the body's defenses. There are no conclusive scientific studies to prove its effectiveness.

24.2 Mechanisms of Homeostasis

VOCABULARY
homeostasis
feedback
negative feedback
positive feedback

KEY CONCEPT **Homeostasis is the regulation and maintenance of the internal environment.**

MAIN IDEAS
- Conditions within the body must remain within a narrow range.
- Negative feedback loops are necessary for homeostasis.

Connect to Your World

The complex tissues, organs, and organ systems in your body must respond to a wide variety of conditions. For instance, during the summer, you might walk out of a cold, air-conditioned store into a stifling hot, summer day. Your body temperature has to remain the same under both conditions in order for you to survive. In fact, your life depends on your body's ability to maintain the delicate balance of your internal chemistry.

MAIN IDEA

Conditions within the body must remain within a narrow range.

During every moment of your life, trillions of chemical reactions are taking place in your body. The enzymes that control these reactions work best within a narrow range of conditions. One of these conditions is your internal body temperature, which should remain between 36.7°C and 37.1°C (98.2°F and 98.8°F). If it rises only a few degrees, you could easily die from overheating. At temperatures over 41°C (106°F), many enzymes stop functioning. If your internal temperature falls below 27°C (80°F), your heart may fail.

Likewise, the levels of trace minerals in your body must stay within strict limits. For instance, if calcium levels are too high, you can slip into a coma. If they are too low, your heartbeat becomes irregular.

You live in a constantly changing environment. Your body must cope not only with temperature changes but also with pollution, infection, stress, and many other conditions. Every change is a challenge to your body. What keeps the human body from breaking down every time the internal or external environment changes?

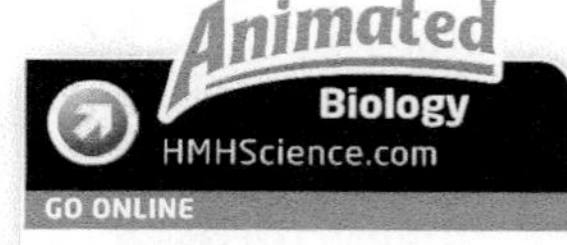

GO ONLINE
Keep an Athlete Running

READING TOOLBOX

VOCABULARY
The word *homeostasis* is formed from two Greek words: *homos*, meaning "similar," and *stasis*, meaning "standing" or "stopping."

Homeostasis and the Internal Environment

Fortunately, the body has many control systems that keep its internal environment stable. Together, these control systems are responsible for maintaining homeostasis. **Homeostasis** (HO-mee-oh-STAY-sihs) is the regulation and maintenance of the internal environment—temperature, fluids, salts, pH, nutrients, and gases—within the narrow ranges that support human life. Your internal control systems respond quickly to environmental change, whether from outside conditions or internal ones, as shown in **FIGURE 2.1.**

Differentiated Instruction

ENGLISH LEARNERS

Check on students' comprehension as you go through the material describing various control systems in the body. You can use simple signals, such as thumbs up or thumbs down for understanding. Or ask questions in which students write responses on a sheet of paper or an index card.

Teacher Toolkit, Section C, Signals; Card Responses

Control Systems in the Body

Internal control systems require sensors, a control center, communication systems, and targets.

Sensors Sensors, also called receptors, gather information about conditions inside and outside of the body. In cold or hot weather, for instance, sensors in your skin and nasal passages gather data about air temperatures. The body has thousands of internal sensors and other specialized sensors that detect changes in the outside world.

Control center A control center, often the brain, receives information from the sensors. It then compares this information to the set points, or ideal values, at which the body functions best. When conditions move above or below a set point, the control center responds by sending messages through a communication system.

Communication systems Communication is controlled by the nervous system and the endocrine system, which carry messages to all parts of the body. These messages, in the form of nerve impulses or hormones, tell targets in the body how to respond to internal or external changes.

Targets A target is any organ, tissue, or cell that changes its level of activity in response to a message. For instance, in a cold environment, a message might cause the muscles to start shivering to generate more body heat.

FIGURE 2.1 Homeostasis and Change

Control systems in the skin help reduce or conserve body heat.

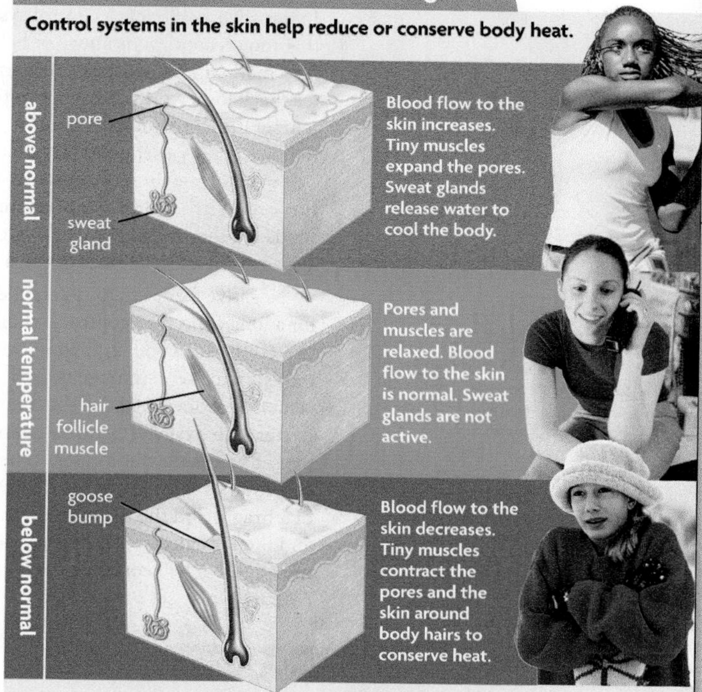

above normal
pore
sweat gland
Blood flow to the skin increases. Tiny muscles expand the pores. Sweat glands release water to cool the body.

normal temperature
hair follicle muscle
Pores and muscles are relaxed. Blood flow to the skin is normal. Sweat glands are not active.

below normal
goose bump
Blood flow to the skin decreases. Tiny muscles contract the pores and the skin around body hairs to conserve heat.

Ⓐ Apply **If the girl in cold temperature starts jogging, how would the control mechanisms in her skin respond as she runs?**

Ⓑ Explain **Why is it so important to maintain homeostasis within the body?**

MAIN IDEA

Negative feedback loops are necessary for homeostasis.

Sensors, control centers, communication systems, and targets work together in what is known as a feedback loop. **Feedback** is information from sensors that allows a control center to compare current conditions to a set of ideal values. In a feedback loop, information moves continuously among sensors, a control center, and a target. Most functions in the body are regulated by negative feedback loops.

BELOW LEVEL

Have students relate homeostasis to feedback loops by using a graphic organizer, such as a concept definition map. A concept definition map starts with a general category, in this case, how a body regulates its internal environment. A particular concept is identified, either negative or positive feedback. Then students include separate boxes to list properties and examples of each concept. Students should also compare one with the other.

Teacher Toolkit, Section D, Definition Map

TEACH FROM VISUALS

FIGURE 2.1 Explain the figure in terms of the four body-control systems. Tell students that the control center for regulating body temperature is located in the hypothalamus region of the brain.

Ask

- What sensors are involved? temperature sensors in the skin
- What are the targets? sweat glands, blood vessels, and muscles in skin
- What kinds of messages are involved in this communication system? nerve impulses and hormones

Answers

Ⓐ **Apply** Her skin would respond the way it does in hot temperatures: pores would open, and sweat glands would release water to cool the body.

Ⓑ **Explain** The processes necessary for life work best within a narrow range of conditions. To maintain these ranges, the internal environment of the body must remain stable.

Vocabulary

Academic Vocabulary Point out how the words associated with a mechanical system are applied to a living system.

mechanism a system of parts that operate or interact like those of a machine

control an instrument used to operate, regulate, or guide a machine

sensor a device that receives and responds to a signal

set point the point at which a circuit is either activated or deactivated

target something aimed or fired at

feedback return of a portion of the output of a system to the input, used to maintain performance or control

loop a closed circuit

Teach *continued*

CONNECT TO

Biochemistry Oxygen is used by the cell in the breakdown of glucose and the accompanying release of energy in the form of ATP. A lack of oxygen can lead to cell death because ATP production stops, and as a result, there is no energy for cell activities.

History of Science

The physiologist **Walter Bradford Cannon** coined the term **homeostasis,** which he described for the general public in 1932. In his book *The Wisdom of the Body,* he proposed these four general features of homeostasis:

1. The body, being an open system and subject to change, requires mechanisms to maintain constancy and a steady state.
2. Steady-state conditions require that any tendency toward change be met with resistance.
3. Homeostasis must be maintained by a regulating system that consists of a number of cooperating mechanisms acting simultaneously or in sequence.
4. Homeostasis does not occur by chance but is the result of organized self-government.

Answers

A Infer Sensors would detect too much oxygen and too little carbon dioxide in the blood. Your breathing would stop or slow down for a short time until the gases returned to their set points; then normal breathing would resume.

Negative Feedback

In **negative feedback,** a control system counteracts any change in the body that moves conditions above or below a set point. Negative feedback loops help maintain homeostasis. A thermostat is a good example of how a negative feedback loop works. A sensor in the thermostat continuously measures air temperature in a room. A control mechanism then compares the current room temperature to a set point, say 21°C (69.8°F). When the temperature falls below 21°C, the thermostat sends an electronic message that turns on the furnace. When the air temperature is at or just above 21°C, the thermostat sends another message that turns off the furnace. As a result, the room always stays within a few degrees of the desired temperature.

Negative feedback loops are the reason why you cannot hold your breath for a long time. The control systems involved in this feedback loop are shown in **FIGURE 2.2.** As you hold your breath, sensors in the circulatory and respiratory systems send information to the brain stem, the body's respiratory control center. Sensors signal a gradual increase in carbon dioxide (CO_2) and a decrease in oxygen (O_2). The control center compares this information with the set points for these gases. When the change becomes too great, the control center takes steps to counteract it. Messages are sent to the muscles of the diaphragm and the rib cage to relax and then contract, forcing you to exhale and then inhale deeply. At this point, you cannot stop these muscles from moving. You will continue to breathe rapidly and deeply until the gas levels return to their set points.

CONNECT TO

BIOCHEMISTRY

As you read in **Cells and Energy**, cells require a constant supply of oxygen to maintain cell metabolism. Oxygen is not stored in the human body in any great amounts. Once oxygen reserves have been used up, the body must have a fresh supply of oxygen to prevent cell death.

FIGURE 2.2 Negative Feedback Loop

Negative feedback counteracts any change in the body that moves conditions away from a set point.

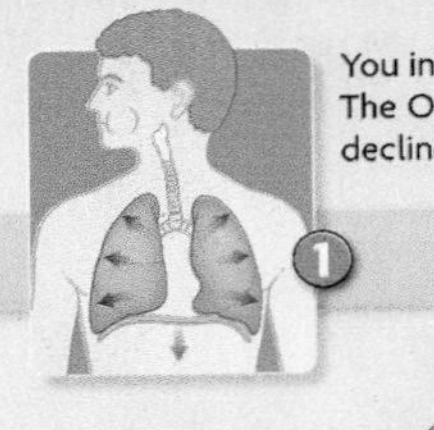

1
You inhale and hold your breath. The O_2 levels in the blood begin to decline and CO_2 levels begin to rise.

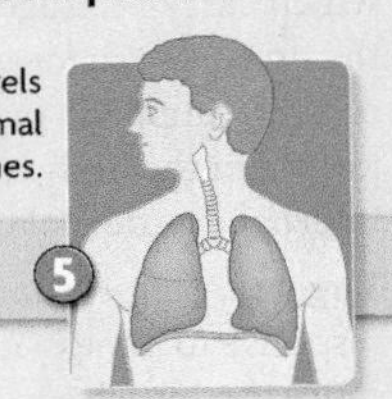

5
When O_2/CO_2 levels are restored, normal breathing resumes.

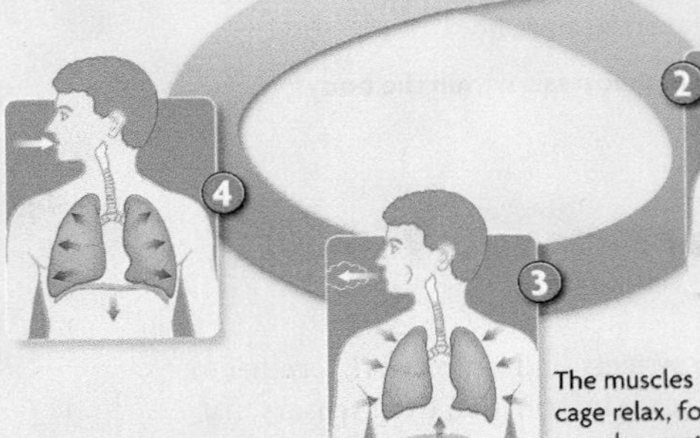

2
Sensors alert the brain stem as O_2/CO_2 levels move too far from the set points. Messages are sent through the nervous and endocrine systems to the muscles of the diaphragm and the rib cage.
3
The muscles of the diaphragm and the rib cage relax, forcing you to exhale. As the muscles contract, you inhale deeply.
4
You continue to inhale and exhale more deeply and rapidly than normal until O_2/CO_2 levels return to their set points.

A Infer **If you continued to breathe rapidly and deeply for too long in Step 4, how would this affect the negative feedback loop?**

Differentiated Instruction

ENGLISH LEARNERS

Have students work with the analogy used in the text, comparing a negative feedback system in the body to a thermostat. Have students read the text and create two cycle diagrams. The first should show how a thermostat regulates temperature. The second can detail the negative feedback loop shown in **FIGURE 2.2.** Tell students to incorporate the terms *control system, sensor, set point, target, communicate,* and *feedback.*

Teacher Toolkit, Section C, Cycle Diagram

PRE-AP

Have students set up a cycle diagram that shows a fever as a combination of positive and negative feedback mechanisms. Tell students that the body raises its temperature in response to pathogens in the body. Once the pathogens have been destroyed by heat, negative feedback brings the body temperature back down. Have students think about the experience of having a fever and relate physiological responses, such as shivering and sweating, to what is happening in the bloodstream.

Teacher Toolkit, Section C, Cycle Diagram

QUICKLAB MODELING

Negative Feedback Loop

You can experience a negative feedback loop by doing a simple demonstration.

MATERIALS
hardcover book at least 6" × 9"

PROBLEM How does a negative feedback loop work?

PROCEDURE

1. Balance the hardcover book on your head.
2. Walk 3 meters forward and backward—once with eyes open, then with eyes closed.

ANALYZE AND CONCLUDE

1. **Analyze** Summarize the negative feedback loop that helped keep the book balanced on your head. How did closing your eyes affect your ability to balance the book?
2. **Connect** Describe the role of internal feedback mechanisms in the maintenance of homeostasis.

Positive Feedback

Negative feedback loops maintain homeostasis by counteracting, or reversing, change to return conditions to their set points. In some cases, however, the body actually needs change to accomplish a specific task. In **positive feedback,** a control center uses information from sensors to increase the rate of change away from the set points. Though not as common in the body, this type of feedback is important whenever rapid change is needed.

If you cut your finger, positive feedback mechanisms increase the rate of change in clotting factors in the blood until the wound is sealed. Once the injury heals, another positive feedback loop occurs as chemicals are released to dissolve the clot. Positive feedback also occurs in the release of certain growth hormones during puberty. Your body needs higher levels of these hormones to accomplish all of the changes that take place at this time.

(A) Infer **Why are most of the functions of the body regulated by negative, rather than by positive, feedback mechanisms?**

24.2 Formative Assessment

SELF-CHECK Online
HMHScience.com
GO ONLINE

REVIEWING MAIN IDEAS

1. A system to maintain **homeostasis** must have at least four parts that function together. Name these parts, and briefly explain what each one does.
2. What is the main difference between the way **negative feedback** and **positive feedback** loops regulate change in the body?

CRITICAL THINKING

3. **Predict** When a newborn baby nurses, the mother's body is stimulated to produce milk. What would happen to the milk supply if the mother chose to bottle feed rather than breast feed? Why?
4. **Sequence** Suppose you go on a long hike in hot weather. Describe a possible negative feedback loop that would keep your body from overheating.

CONNECT TO
ZOOLOGY

5. Reptiles regulate their body temperature by changing their environment. A snake, for instance, must lie in sunlight to warm its body. Mammals can regulate their internal environment to gain or lose body heat. How might this ability give mammals an advantage over reptiles?

QUICKLAB TEACHER TESTED
Time 5 minutes

Purpose Model a negative feedback loop.

LAB MANAGEMENT

Use books that are not too heavy.

Answers

Analyze and Conclude

1. As sensors in the scalp detect changes in the book's position, they send messages to control sensors in the brain, which then send messages to the muscles. Students may have adjusted their speed, shifted their head or body, or grabbed the book with their hands. When students closed their eyes, they lost sensory information about body position relative to their surroundings, which may have made the balancing task more difficult.
2. Internal feedback mechanisms help the body respond to a constantly changing environment in order to maintain homeostasis. For example, negative feedback loops involve preset values and information about changing conditions that are relayed to control centers, which then send messages to targets to counteract changes and restore conditions to the preset values.

Answers

(A) **Infer** Negative feedback is the means by which the body maintains homeostasis. Positive feedback occurs only in situations in which a change away from set values is needed.

24.2 FORMATIVE ASSESSMENT

1. Sensors gather information. A control center analyzes and compares the information with the desired values. Communication systems send messages from the control center to regulate the change. Targets receive and respond to the messages.
2. Negative feedback loops counteract change to return to a set point, while positive feedback loops accelerate change away from a set point.
3. A nursing baby creates a positive feedback loop that causes the mother's body to lactate. Bottle feeding eliminates the stimulus.
4. Sensors would detect a rise in body temperature, increasing blood flow to the skin, activating sweat glands, and increasing heart and breathing rates.
5. Mammals can live in a wider range of habitats and tolerate rapid changes in external conditions.

Assess and Reteach

Assess Use the Section Self-Check or Section Quiz, both available at **HMHScience.com**.

Reteach Write the following headings on the board: Sensors, Control Center, Communication Systems, Targets. Have students tell you what to list beneath the headings for the respiratory control system shown in **FIGURE 2.2.**

Plan and Prepare

Activate Prior Knowledge Relate homeostasis to the idea of balance. **Ask,** What is it like to be on a balance beam or walking across a log bridge, and your weight shifts? Typically you move back and forth to reestablish balance; if you do not, you fall. Discuss how when one body system is out of balance, it affects others.

Teach

TEACH FROM VISUALS

FIGURE 3.1 Have students observe what the members of the pit crew are doing. **Ask**

- What differentiates one member of the crew from another? Each has a specific job: refuel, check tires, check engine.
- What happens if a member of the crew is missing or does not do his or her job correctly? The car will not perform as it should and could endanger the life of the driver.

Relate the makeup of the pit crew to the interaction of different systems in the body.

24.3 Interactions Among Systems

KEY CONCEPT **Systems interact to maintain homeostasis.**

MAIN IDEAS
- Each organ system affects other organ systems.
- A disruption of homeostasis can be harmful.

VOCABULARY
thermoregulation

Connect to Your World
The moment a racecar pulls in for a pit stop, the pit crew springs into action. Each person has a special role that must be coordinated with the efforts of the team. As one member jacks up the car, others are changing the tires, putting in fuel, and checking the engine. If anyone fails to do a job properly, it affects the entire team and places the driver at serious risk.

MAIN IDEA
Each organ system affects other organ systems.

At its most basic level, the body is a community of specialized cells that interact with one another. On a larger scale, all of the organ systems form a type of community regulated by feedback mechanisms. This interaction among organ systems means that what affects a single organ system affects the entire body.

Like the highly trained crew members in **FIGURE 3.1**, each organ system in your body must do its own special job. But for you to remain healthy, each system also must coordinate with other organ systems through chemical messages and nerve impulses. The relationship among your organs and organ systems is not always obvious—for example, when the body produces a substance such as vitamin D. In other cases, you are more aware that some organs are affecting others, as in the regulation of your body temperature in hot or cold weather.

FIGURE 3.1 Precision teamwork is the secret to a pit crew's success. Likewise, your life depends on every organ system doing its job at the right time and in the right order.

Vitamin D Production

You may know that sunlight plays a part in the production of vitamin D in your body. You may not know that the liver, kidneys, circulatory system, and endocrine system are necessary for this process as well. The skin contains a substance that in the presence of ultraviolet light is changed into an inactive form of vitamin D. As **FIGURE 3.2** shows, this form enters the blood and is carried to the liver. The liver changes the inactive form of vitamin D into another compound, which is then carried to the kidneys. Here, this compound is converted into active vitamin D.

The blood transports active vitamin D throughout the body, where it interacts with hormones that regulate the amount of calcium and phosphorus in the body. These two minerals are essential for building strong bones. If any organ along this path fails to do its job, the level of vitamin D in the body decreases. Without enough vitamin D, children's bones do not develop normally. Adults lose bone mass, which means their bones break more easily.

Differentiated Instruction

BELOW LEVEL

Model for students how to interpret the text describing vitamin D production on this page. Work with students to come up with a sequence diagram of the events described and the body systems involved. Students can refer to **FIGURE 1.4** in Section 1 for a summary of the body systems. Then suggest students do the same for thermoregulation on the next page.

Teacher Toolkit, Section C, Sequence Diagram

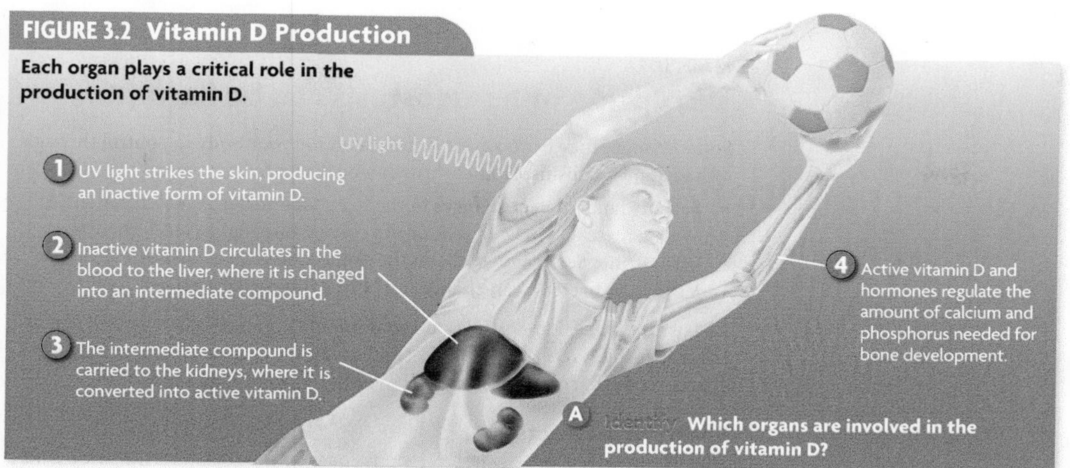

UV light
1 UV light strikes the skin, producing an inactive form of vitamin D.
2 Inactive vitamin D circulates in the blood to the liver, where it is changed into an intermediate compound.
3 The intermediate compound is carried to the kidneys, where it is converted into active vitamin D.
4 Active vitamin D and hormones regulate the amount of calcium and phosphorus needed for bone development.

FIGURE 3.2 Vitamin D Production

Each organ plays a critical role in the production of vitamin D.

A Identify **Which organs are involved in the production of vitamin D?**

Regulation of Body Temperature

The process by which the body regulates its internal temperature under a variety of conditions is known as **thermoregulation** (THUR-moh-REHG-yoo-LAY-shuhn). The most obvious organ systems involved in maintaining body temperature are the skin and muscles. You sweat in hot weather and shiver when you are cold. However, far more is going on than what you can see on the surface. Thermoregulation requires the close interaction of the respiratory, circulatory, nervous, and endocrine systems.

VISUAL VOCAB

Thermoregulation maintains a stable body temperature under a variety of conditions, just as a thermostat regulates a furnace. Both mechanisms use feedback to keep temperatures within set ranges.

control — THERMOSTAT — messages — FURNACE — target — info to control

Sensors in the skin and blood vessels provide information about body temperature to a control center in the brain called the hypothalamus. The hypothalamus protects the body's internal organs by monitoring temperature. When the hypothalamus receives information that the temperature of the blood is rising, it sends messages through the nervous and endocrine systems. These messages activate the sweat glands, dilate, or widen, blood vessels in the skin, and increase both heart and breathing rates. All of these activities carry heat away from the center of the body to the surface, where excess heat can escape.

When the temperature of the blood falls too low, the hypothalamus sends another set of signals to the skin and to the muscular, respiratory, and circulatory systems. Blood vessels in the skin constrict, reducing blood flow to prevent loss of heat. Muscles in the skin contract around the pores, reducing their size. Rapid, small contractions of skeletal muscles cause shivering. The thyroid gland releases hormones that increase metabolism. All of these activities increase body heat production and reduce the loss of heat to the environment.

B Infer **If a person's circulatory system does not function well, how might thermoregulation in his or her body be affected?**

Hypothermia

PRE-AP

Present this scenario: You and your friends have spent the day hiking on a cool fall day and are about to drive home. You see another hiker coming off the trail who is soaked and shivering. The hiker mentions having fallen into a stream. You are concerned that the hiker may be suffering from mild hypothermia, a lowered body temperature. Describe the steps you would take to assist this hiker en route to the local hospital.

Teacher Toolkit, Section C, Quick-Write

ONLINE Biology
HMHScience.com

For more on thermoregulation and hypothermia, see the WebQuest for this chapter at **HMHScience.com**.

Integrating Physics

Thermoregulation is a balancing act among systems in the body that produce heat and those that lose heat.

All body tissues produce heat as a product of **metabolism**—as bonds break and new ones form. Tissues that are the most active metabolically produce the most heat. When the body is at rest, most of its heat is produced by the liver, heart, brain, and endocrine glands. When the body is in motion, its skeletal muscles produce 30–40 times the heat generated by the rest of the body.

Most heat loss occurs in the body by four different mechanisms. Any object that is warmer than its surrounding environment radiates heat into that environment. Under normal conditions, the body loses 25–40 percent of its heat by **radiation.** Direct contact with a cool object also causes the body to lose heat by **conduction. Convection** occurs as cool air replaces the warm air released by the body, creating more opportunity for heat loss. Conduction and convection account for 15–20 percent of the body's heat loss. **Evaporation** from the lungs, mouth, and skin removes substantial amounts of body heat. Water absorbs heat and, after it has gained enough energy, vaporizes.

Answers

A Identify The organs involved in vitamin D production are the skin, liver, and kidneys.

B Infer A person with an impaired circulatory system would be less able to lose heat in hot conditions and conserve heat in cold conditions.

Teach *continued*

Integrating Medical Science

Type 2 diabetes, once thought to be an adult disease, is becoming more common in young people in the United States. The Centers for Disease Control and Prevention estimates that 206,000 people under the age of 20 have some form of diabetes.

A significant risk factor for Type 2 diabetes is being overweight or obese. The American diet has become loaded with processed foods that are high in fat and sugar. These factors, along with a lack of exercise, have put people at greater risk of increased weight and Type 2 diabetes. The percentage of children under the age of 19 who are overweight has increased from about 4.5 percent to about 15.5 percent in the 40 years after the 1960s.

Take It Further

Diabetes is a disorder linked to **diabetic retinopathy,** which causes blindness. This condition develops as a result of the reaction between excess glucose in the blood and proteins in the body. Glucose and proteins react to form a complex in which the proteins lose their flexibility. As these proteins accumulate, they cause the walls of blood vessels to thicken and lose their elasticity. The weakened blood vessels bulge and eventually leak. Any amount of blood that leaks from blood vessels in the retina can obscure vision. Laser treatments can slow the leakage of fluid and reduce the amount of retinal fluid. Similar damage occurs in other parts of the body, but it is not as readily detectable as in the eye.

Answers

A Apply Muscle cells depend on glucose for energy. The less glucose available, the more difficult it is for muscles to perform work, repair injuries, and increase mass.

MAIN IDEA

A disruption of homeostasis can be harmful.

Some changes may be too great or too rapid for your body to control through feedback mechanisms. Homeostasis can be disrupted for several reasons.

- Sensors fail to detect changes in the internal or external environment.
- Wrong messages may be sent or the correct ones fail to reach their targets.
- Serious injuries can overwhelm the homeostatic mechanisms.
- Viruses or bacteria can change the body's internal chemistry.

Disruption of homeostasis can begin in one organ or organ system and result in a chain reaction that affects other organs and organ systems. These effects can be harmful to your body over the short or long term.

Short-Term Effects

Short-term effects usually last a few days or weeks. For example, when a cold virus first enters your body, your immune system may not be able to prevent the virus from multiplying. As a result, you develop a sore throat, runny nose, and dry cough, and your muscles and joints become inflamed. However, within a few days, your body's immune system begins to kill the virus and to restore homeostasis. Usually, there is no lasting harm to your body.

FIGURE 3.3 Type 1 Diabetes

Failure to control glucose levels affects the entire body.

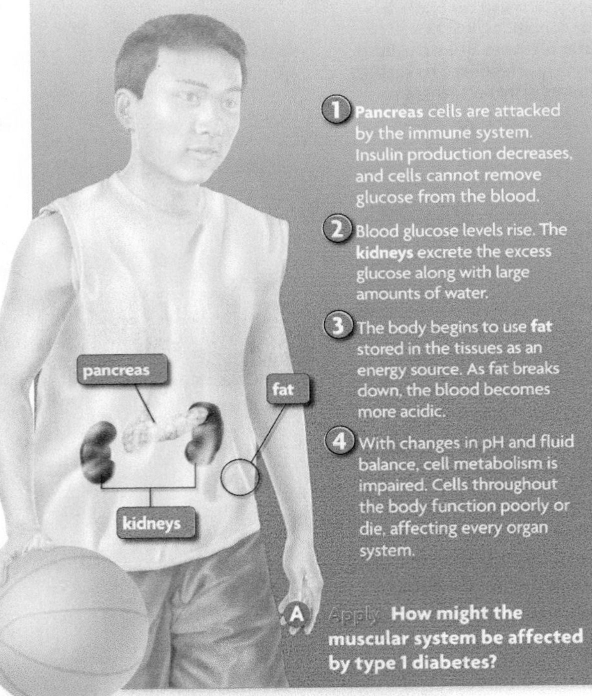

pancreas
fat
kidneys
1 Pancreas cells are attacked by the immune system. Insulin production decreases, and cells cannot remove glucose from the blood.
2 Blood glucose levels rise. The kidneys excrete the excess glucose along with large amounts of water.
3 The body begins to use fat stored in the tissues as an energy source. As fat breaks down, the blood becomes more acidic.
4 With changes in pH and fluid balance, cell metabolism is impaired. Cells throughout the body function poorly or die, affecting every organ system.

A Apply **How might the muscular system be affected by type 1 diabetes?**

Long-Term Effects

A long-term disruption of homeostasis, as in the case of diabetes, can cause more damage. Diabetes occurs when the body fails to control the amount of glucose circulating in the blood.

Normal glucose control Glucose levels are controlled by two hormones—insulin and glucagon—which are released by the pancreas. When glucose in the blood rises above a set point, beta cells in the pancreas release insulin. Insulin causes cells to take in more glucose from the blood and causes the liver to store glucose as glycogen. When blood glucose levels fall below the set point, alpha cells in the pancreas release glucagon. This hormone stimulates the liver to break down stored glycogen into glucose and release it until levels in the blood rise to the set point.

Type 1 and type 2 diabetes What if the pancreas fails to do its job? The result can be diabetes mellitus, a condition in which the body can no longer regulate glucose levels. There are two types of diabetes. Type 1 occurs when the body's immune system destroys the ability of beta cells to produce insulin. Type 2 is caused when insulin production decreases or when insulin cannot move glucose into cells.

Differentiated Instruction

ENGLISH LEARNERS

Point out the similarities in the names of one of the hormones and the sugar and fat involved in glucose regulation on this page. Have students set up a T-chart in their notes with a category for hormones (insulin, glucagon) and stimulants (glucose, glycogen). The chart should include a description of the function of each.

Teacher Toolkit, Section C, T-Chart

BELOW LEVEL

Point out the example of diabetes described in the text on this page. The text first describes the normal interaction of insulin and glucagon to control glucose levels. Have students represent this with a cycle diagram. Then, in contrast, have students create two cause-and-effect chains, one each for Type 1 and Type 2 diabetes. Have them compare this with the cycle diagram that represents normal homeostatic control of glucose.

Teacher Toolkit, Section C, Cycle Diagram; Cause-and-Effect Chain

DATA ANALYSIS

INTERPRETING INVERSE RELATIONSHIPS

Two variables are inversely related if an increase in the value of one variable is associated with a decrease in the value of the other variable. For example, the level of insulin decreases the longer a person exercises. Therefore, insulin levels have an inverse relationship with exercise time. The graphs at right show the levels of insulin, glucose, and glucagon during moderate exercise over 250 minutes. Use the graphs to answer the questions.

GRAPH 1. INSULIN LEVELS

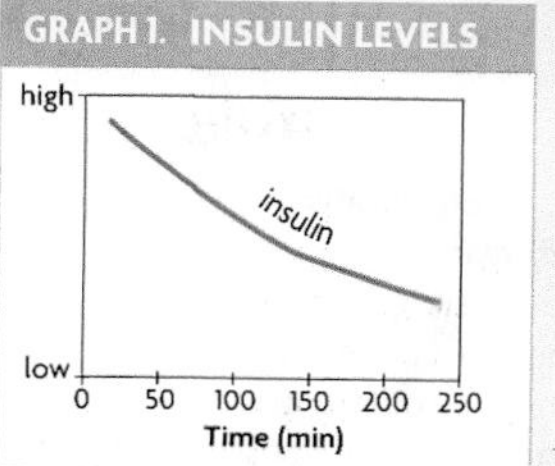

GRAPH 2. GLUCOSE LEVELS

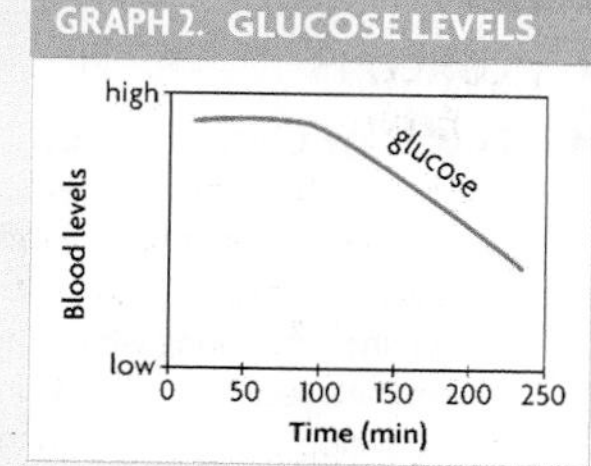

GRAPH 3. GLUCAGON LEVELS

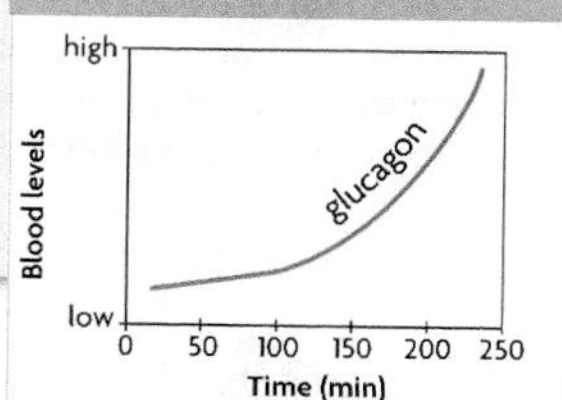

1. **Analyze** Which variable(s) has/have an inverse relationship with time?
2. **Conclude** What relationship exists between glucagon and the other two variables (insulin and glucose)? Explain.

In type 1 diabetes, the failure of the pancreas sets up a destructive chain reaction in other organ systems, as shown in **FIGURE 3.3.** As glucose builds up in the blood, the kidneys must remove it along with large amounts of water. Also, since the body is unable to use glucose as an energy source, it must use stored fat instead. As the fat breaks down, the blood becomes more acidic. This altered pH disrupts the metabolism of the cells in every organ and every system in the body. The long-term effects can result in heart disease, blindness, nerve damage, kidney damage, and even coma and death.

In type 2 diabetes, the pancreas cannot produce enough insulin, or the insulin cannot be used to move glucose into the cells. As a result, blood glucose levels rise, and the cells starve. Risk factors for developing type 2 diabetes include chronic obesity, a family history of diabetes, and aging.

A Connect Why might diabetes be a particular problem for an athlete?

DATA ANALYSIS

Discuss

Make sure students understand that the graphs relate to the same event. **Ask,** Which hormone is released when the glucose level is high? insulin When the glucose level is low? glucagon

Answers

1. Glucose and insulin levels have inverse relationships with time.
2. Inverse relationship; a high value of glucagon is associated with low values of insulin and glucose.

Online Student Resources, Data Analysis Practice

Answers

A Connect Athletes require large amounts of energy to perform. If there is not enough glucose taken into the body's cells, the athlete will not have enough energy to maintain his or her performance.

24.3 Formative Assessment

SELF-CHECK Online
HMHScience.com
GO ONLINE

REVIEWING MAIN IDEAS

1. Why do the organ systems in the body need to work so closely together?
2. Explain why a long-term disruption of homeostasis can often be more damaging to the body than a short-term disruption.

CRITICAL THINKING

3. **Analyze** Why would giving synthetic insulin to people with type 1 diabetes restore their glucose homeostasis?
4. **Predict** If you lived in Alaska for the whole year, what changes might occur in your calcium and phosphorus levels during the winter versus the summer? Explain.

CONNECT TO EVOLUTION

5. Some animals can store more glucose—in the form of glycogen—in their bodies than can other animals. What might be the evolutionary advantage of having these extra energy stores?

Assess and Reteach

Assess Use the Section Self-Check or Section Quiz, both available at **HMHScience.com.**

Reteach Use the terms from **Section 2** that describe control systems, and apply them to one of the examples in this section. Have students identify at what point homeostasis can be disrupted.

24.3 FORMATIVE ASSESSMENT

1. All body systems contribute to maintenance of homeostasis. What happens in one system may require response from another.
2. Long-term disruption can produce a type of chain reaction in which more and more organ systems are affected over time. The result can be permanent damage to organs and possibly death.
3. In Type 1 diabetes, no insulin is made. When synthetic insulin is given to people with Type 1 diabetes, glucose can enter cells, so blood glucose levels return to normal.
4. During winter months, because there is little sunlight and your skin is fully covered with clothing, you would be exposed to very little UV light. As a result, you would produce less vitamin D, and calcium and phosphorus levels in your body would decrease. In summer, your skin would be exposed to sunlight far more often. The increase in vitamin D production would result in an increase in calcium and phosphorus levels.
5. Answers may include the development of more efficient cellular metabolism, the ability to survive on an irregular food supply, or the ability to mobilize extra glucose rapidly to provide energy in fight-or-flight situations.

INTERACTIVE Review
HMHScience.com

GO ONLINE

Encourage students to go to **HMHScience.com** for a detailed review of each section, including visuals and vocabulary practice.

Online Student Resources, Vocabulary Practice Worksheet

CHAPTER 24 Summary

BIG IDEA The human body is organized into different systems that interact in a coordinated way to maintain homeostasis.

KEY CONCEPTS

24.1 Levels of Organization

The human body has five levels of organization. Specialized cells in multicellular organisms arise from the zygote. Most embryonic stem cells go through determination, during which they are committed to becoming specialized cells. During cell differentiation, cells develop specialized structures and functions.

A group of similar specialized cells form tissue. A collection of tissues with the same function form an organ, and various specialized organs together form an organ system. All of the organ systems together make up an entire organism.

Differentiated Cells

24.2 Mechanisms of Homeostasis

Homeostasis is the regulation and maintenance of the internal environment. Conditions within the body must remain within the narrow ranges that support human life. Homeostasis is maintained by internal control systems composed of sensors, a control center, communication systems, and target tissues or organs. The control centers use feedback to keep the internal environment stable. In a negative feedback loop, control systems counteract change to maintain conditions within a narrow range. In a positive feedback loop, control systems increase change away from set points.

24.3 Interactions Among Systems

Systems interact to maintain homeostasis. Each organ system affects other organ systems. For example, thermoregulation depends on the interaction of the circulatory, respiratory, endocrine, and skin systems. If one organ system fails, it can affect other systems in a chain reaction. Long-term disruptions of homeostasis, as in diabetes, are more serious than temporary, short-term disruptions because more organ systems can be damaged over time.

READING TOOLBOX SYNTHESIZE YOUR NOTES

Cycle Diagram Use this note-taking strategy to summarize what you know about how control systems work to maintain homeostasis.

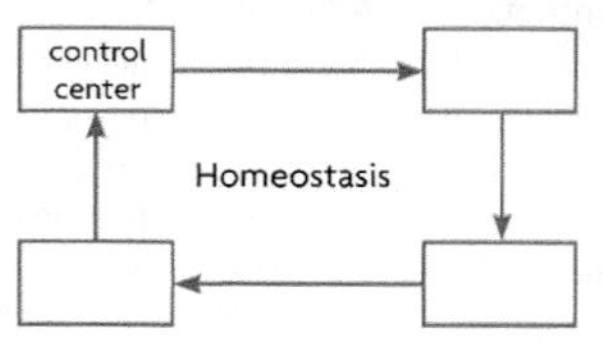

Concept Map Draw a concept map to help you remember the developmental steps of cells.

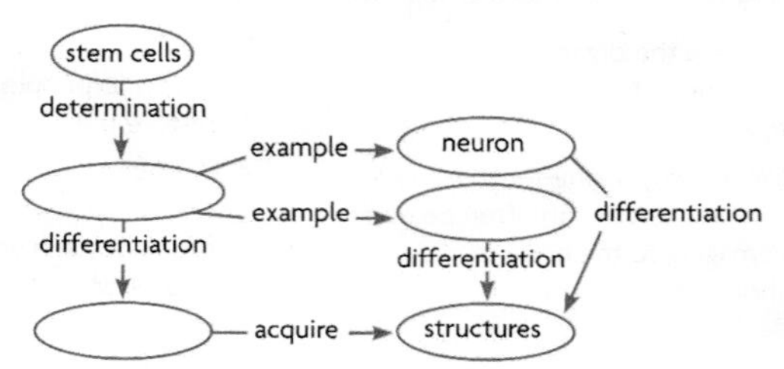

Reviewing Vocabulary

1. a group of specialized cells working together
2. different tissues working together
3. different organs working together
4. process of stem cells committing to become specific types of cells
5. process of committed cells acquiring structures and functions of specific cells
6. counteracts change away from set points
7. increases change away from set points
8. process of maintaining a stable body temperature
9. An organ is an instrument or implement that is built to carry out specific functions in the body.
10. Homeostasis means keeping or maintaining something so it remains the same.
11. Thermoregulation is the process of managing or regulating the temperature of a body or an environment to keep it within set values.
12. The electrical signal returns to its source, just as sensors in a biological source send out information to a control center that sends messages back to the biological source to make changes.

24 Review

INTERACTIVE Review
HMHScience.com
GO ONLINE
Review Games • Concept Map • Section Self-Checks

CHAPTER VOCABULARY

24.1 determination
differentiation
tissue
organ
organ system

24.2 homeostasis
feedback
negative feedback
positive feedback

24.3 thermoregulation

Reviewing Vocabulary

Keep It Short

For each vocabulary word that follows, write a short phrase that defines its meaning. For example: *cell—the basic unit of life.*

1. tissue
2. organ
3. organ system
4. determination
5. differentiation
6. negative feedback
7. positive feedback
8. thermoregulation

READING TOOLBOX GREEK AND LATIN WORD ORIGINS

9. The word *organ* comes from the Latin word *organum*, meaning "instrument" or "implement." Describe how this meaning relates to the definition of a living organ.

10. The word *homeostasis* can be broken into two parts: *homos*, meaning "similar," and *stasis*, meaning "standing" or "stopping." Write a brief definition of *homeostasis* based on the meaning of these two parts.

11. A thermos is a container for keeping liquids hot. The word comes from the Greek *thermos*, which means "hot" or "warm." How does this meaning relate to the term *thermoregulation*?

12. The word *feedback* originally comes from the field of electrical engineering. Feedback occurs when part of a signal put out by an amplifier returns to its source. It's that loud squeal you sometimes hear when someone is using a microphone. Explain how this meaning of feedback relates to what happens in a feedback loop.

Reviewing MAIN IDEAS

13. Embryonic stem cells have the potential to become any type of cell in the body. What happens to these cells during the process of determination?

14. Once a cell goes through the process of determination, what happens next as the cells develop in the embryo?

15. Briefly explain how cell differentiation and cell death are both needed to develop such structures as human hands and feet.

16. Humans are composed of five levels of organization. Name each of the levels of organization, and describe how each level relates to the next using an example.

17. Organs have many specialized cells and tissues that enable them to carry out their functions. Describe two specialized cells in the respiratory system that enable the lungs to function well.

18. Your body has control systems that keep its internal conditions within the narrow ranges that support life. On a hot day, how do your body's control center and sensors work together to help you stay cool?

19. Describe the role of internal feedback mechanisms in the maintenance of homeostasis.

20. Explain how the failure of one organ can lead to the failure of other organs or of an entire organ system.

21. When glucose levels in the blood rise above a set point, hormones are released that cause the glucose levels to decline. Is this process an example of a positive or a negative feedback loop? Explain your answer.

22. Give two examples of what can happen to a person if the body's homeostasis is not maintained.

Reviewing Main Ideas

13. During determination, committed cells acquire the unique structures and functions they need to function as specialized cells.
14. Differentiation occurs as cells acquire specialized structures and functions.
15. Differentiation creates cells that form specific structures, such as hands and feet. Cell death is needed to separate parts of the hands and feet into individual fingers and toes.
16. cells (cardiac muscle, neuron), tissues (muscle, epithelial, nervous), organs (lungs, heart, liver), organ systems (respiratory, circulatory), and the organism (human being). A multicellular organism is made up of many cells with different functions. Groups of cells with similar function make up a tissue which makes up an organ. A group of organs that work together make up an organ system. For example, cardiac muscle cells make up heart tissue and the heart is an organ that is part of the circulatory system.
17. Cilia, hairlike cells, help to move foreign particles out of the lungs. Epithelial cells line the inner surface of the lungs to keep it moist.
18. Sensors in the blood and skin relay information to the brain and endocrine systems. Messages from these centers cause blood vessels to dilate, sweat glands to release fluid, and heart and breathing rate to increase to let excess body heat escape.
19. Internal feedback mechanisms help the body to regulate its internal environment. Negative feedback loop counteracts change away from set points. Positive feedback loop increases change away from set points.
20. The organs in the body all work together, like a well-coordinated team. If one organ fails, it affects the organ that depends on it. In time, the second organ will also fail, affecting more organs in the system. The longer the problem remains, the more organs are affected.
21. Negative feedback loop; the body acts to counteract an increase away from a set point.
22. If people's fluid homeostasis is not maintained, they become dehydrated. If their glucose homeostasis is not maintained, they become diabetic. If oxygen/carbon dioxide homeostasis is not maintained, they might die within a matter of minutes.

Critical Thinking

23. A house is made up of wood, metal, plastic, glass, cloth, and other specialized materials. Each material has a particular shape and function. Likewise, different body cells have specialized structures and functions that make up the entire organism.
24. Embryonic stem cells have the potential to become any one of more than 200 different types of cells in the human body.
25. The circulatory and immune systems both contain lymph nodes and lymphatic vessels.
26. Circulatory, respiratory, integumentary, digestive, excretory, nervous, endocrine, and muscular systems would all likely be involved. Before and during the presentation, the person might be breathing faster, sweating, have an upset stomach or have to go to the bathroom more often, shiver or shake, and have a racing heart. After the presentation, all the symptoms would likely disappear and conditions return to normal.
27. Nerve cells have extensions that reach out and lie on top of muscle cells. At these points, the two different cells can exchange ions and transmit and receive information.
28. Positive feedback increases the rate of change. Therefore, only negative feedback loops could be used to counteract change and keep conditions within the ranges that support life.
29. A weak or damaged heart means that the circulatory system cannot work as well to cool or warm the blood in the body and either conserve heat or let excess heat escape.

Critical Thinking

23. Compare Explain how the cells in the human body might be similar to various building materials in a house.

24. Infer Scientists are investigating methods to use embryonic stem cells to repair any tissue in the human body. What characteristic of embryonic stem cells could make this type of treatment possible?

25. Analyze Review the chart of organ systems on the last page of Section 1. Identify some interconnections between the immune system and the circulatory system.

26. Apply Describe which organ systems you think would be involved in maintaining homeostasis when a person gives a major speech or presentation. Include what may be happening within the person just before, during, and after the speech.

27. Explain For various specialized cells to work together, they must communicate with one another. Use the information you learned in the chapter Cell Structure and Function about cell parts to describe how you think a neuron might communicate with a muscle cell.

28. Compare and Contrast Explain how the difference between negative and positive feedback makes negative feedback more effective in maintaining homeostasis in the body.

29. Describe People with weak or damaged hearts often have trouble regulating their body temperatures in a hot or a cold environment. Explain why an impaired heart might make a person less able to maintain homeostasis.

Analyzing Visuals

Use the diagram of the digestive system to answer the next three questions.

30. Analyze Why is this considered an organ system?

31. Infer How do you think the nutrients released from food leave the digestive system and travel throughout the body?

32. Relate When a person is sick and is vomiting, how does this condition affect the organ system and its ability to provide nutrients to the body?

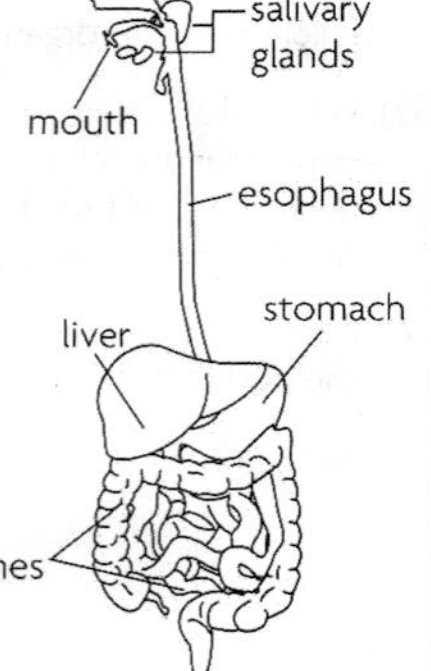

Analyzing Data Interpret an Inverse Relationship

The graph below shows the relationship between different types of energy yield during exercise. Use the graph to answer the next three questions.

EXERCISE AND ENERGY YIELD

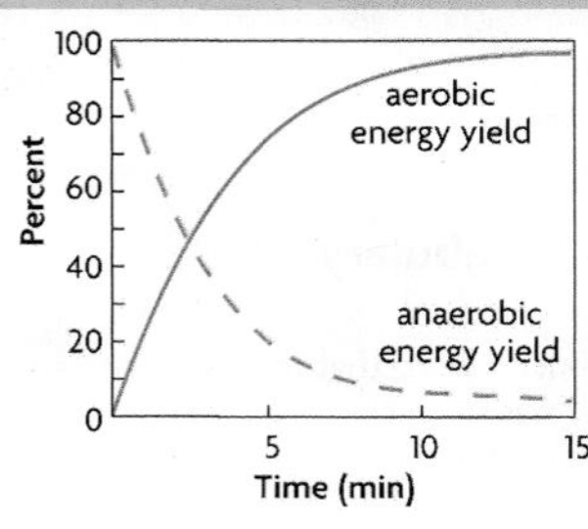

33. Compare and Contrast Within what time period does the greatest amount of change occur in both variables?

34. Analyze Which variable is inversely related to time? Explain.

35. Conclude What relationship do the two variables have to each other at the beginning and at the end of the exercise period?

Making Connections

36. Communicate Blogs have become a popular form of communicating personal experiences online. Think about the changes that occur in your body when you wake up in the morning—changes in your heart rate, in your breathing, and in the movements of your arms and legs. Describe in a blog entry some of the environmental and physical changes that you experience. Which organ systems seem to be involved? What feedback loops might be working to make sure such changes do not become too great?

37. Interpret Extreme sports test the limits of the human body. Describe one extreme condition, other than temperature, facing the ice climber in the photograph on the chapter opener. Explain how feedback mechanisms in the climber's body can maintain homeostasis under the extreme condition you choose to describe.

Analyzing Visuals

30. It consists of several organs working together.
31. Nutrients can reach other parts of the body only by traveling through the circulatory system. Therefore, there must be a connection from the digestive organs to the blood—probably through diffusion into capillaries.
32. Vomiting prevents a person from digesting food and absorbing water. Therefore, the digestive tract would be unable to provide many nutrients or fluids to the rest of the body.

Analyzing Data

33. in the first five minutes
34. Anaerobic energy yield; it declines as the length of time increases.
35. Inverse relationships at both beginning and end; one is rising while the other is falling.

Standards-Based Assessment

Record your answers on a separate piece of paper.

MULTIPLE CHOICE

1 A group of scientists investigates how the blood pressure of students changes while taking an exam. To properly control their experiment, the scientists must first select the appropriate equipment and measure the —

A number of questions on the exam
B students' grade point averages
C temperature and humidity of the exam room
D students' blood pressure before the exam

2 The hormone glucagon increases blood sugar levels while the hormone insulin reduces blood sugar levels. When blood sugar becomes too high, what is ***most likely*** to happen to insulin and glucagon levels for the body to maintain homeostasis?

A Insulin levels increase and glucagon levels decrease.
B Insulin and glucagon levels remain the same.
C Glucagon levels increase and insulin levels decrease.
D Insulin and glucagon levels decrease.

3 Why is it important that oxygen and carbon dioxide levels be closely regulated in the human body?

A Both gases are needed for the proper functioning of cell processes.
B Oxygen is needed for cell processes and carbon dioxide is a waste product.
C Both gases are waste products that need to be removed from cells.
D The carbon and oxygen from the gases are needed to build new molecules.

4 No matter what the temperature is outside, the human body temperature stays relatively constant at about 98.6°F. This is part of the body's ability to maintain —

A osmoregulation
B homeostasis
C negative feedback loops
D positive feedback loops

5 The kidneys filter wastes and excess salts from the blood. If salt concentrations are low, negative feedback mechanisms would most likely —

A decrease the amount of salts removed
B increase the amount of salts removed
C slow down overall kidney function
D increase the rate of kidney function

THINK THROUGH THE QUESTION

Think about what the body needs to do to maintain homeostasis in this situation. Remember, the feedback mechanism should affect only salt concentration.

6 Which characteristic ***best*** fits in the overlapping area of the Venn diagram below?

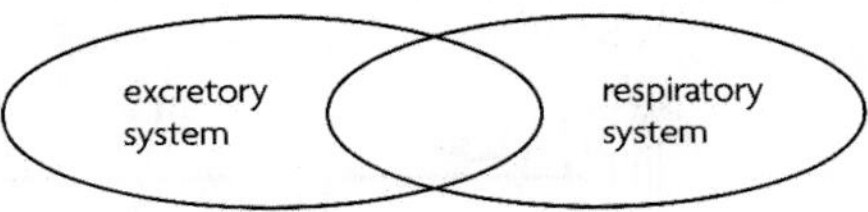

A absorbs nutrients
B brings in oxygen
C transports oxygen
D removes wastes

Standards-Based Assessment

The Standards-Based Assessment questions will help students prepare for their final examination in the course. If you wish to give students practice in coding their answers, look for the Standards-Based Assessment Answer Sheet at **HMHScience.com.** To give students practice under timed testing conditions, allow them five minutes per question.

Question	Answer	Depth of Knowledge	Cognitive Complexity
1	D	II	M
2	A	III	H
3	B	II	L
4	B	I	L
5	A	IV	H
6	D	II	L

KEY

Depth of Knowledge
I Recall
II Skill/Concept
III Strategic Thinking
IV Extended Thinking

Cognitive Complexity
L Low
M Moderate
H High

Making Connections

36. Answers will vary. Students would probably notice as they wake up that their heart beats slightly faster, their breathing rate increases, and their legs and arms move and stretch. They might sneeze or cough on waking. They might also notice the air temperature of the room is warmer or cooler than under the covers. They may notice they are hungry or need to go to the bathroom. Nearly all the organ systems would be involved. Feedback loops working to maintain homeostasis might include those in the circulatory, respiratory, endocrine, and nervous systems.

37. *Sample answer:* Conditions: extreme cold, extreme muscular exertion, extreme oxygen requirements, extreme energy (glucose) requirements. Feedback mechanisms: maintaining body temperature, blood glucose levels, oxygen levels, and activity in the brain to coordinate movements and be aware of surroundings

A BOOK EXPLAINING COMPLEX IDEAS USING ONLY THE 1,000 MOST COMMON WORDS

THING
EXPLAINER
COMPLICATED STUFF IN SIMPLE WORDS
RANDALL MUNROE

RANDALL MUNROE
XKCD.COM

BAGS OF STUFF INSIDE YOU

Parts of your body and how they work together

You know that an organ system is two or more organs working together to perform body functions. Here's a look at several organ systems in the human torso.

THE STORY OF WHAT'S INSIDE YOUR BODY
ON THE NEXT PAGES IS A MAP OF SOME OF THE DIFFERENT BAGS IN YOUR BODY AND HOW THEY JOIN TOGETHER.
BAGS INSIDE OF ME?
DO YOU KNOW YOU HAVE BAGS INSIDE OF YOU?
IT DOESN'T SHOW WHAT THEY'RE REALLY SHAPED LIKE OR HOW THEY'RE PUSHED TOGETHER INSIDE YOUR BODY.
WHO AM I? WHERE DO I COME FROM? WHY AM I HERE? WHERE AM I GOING?
HAVE YOU LOST YOUR THINKING BAG?
IN THAT WAY, IT'S KIND OF LIKE THE COLORED MAPS IN CITIES THAT TELL YOU WHERE TRAINS GO—IT SHOWS HOW THE PLACES ARE JOINED TOGETHER, BUT NOT WHAT THEY'RE SHAPED LIKE OR HOW FAR AWAY FROM EACH OTHER THEY ARE.
AIR BAG STREET
FOOD ROAD
BLOOD PUSHER DRIVE
BODY CITY
THERE ARE LOTS OF IMPORTANT PARTS OF YOUR BODY THAT AREN'T SHOWN ON THIS MAP. BUT THAT'S OKAY; A BODY HAS TOO MANY PARTS TO SHOW ON ANY MAP.
BODY CITY
YOU DID'NT MENTION ME?

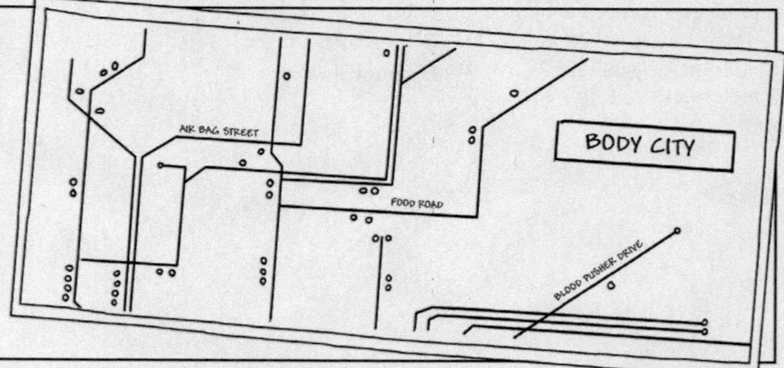

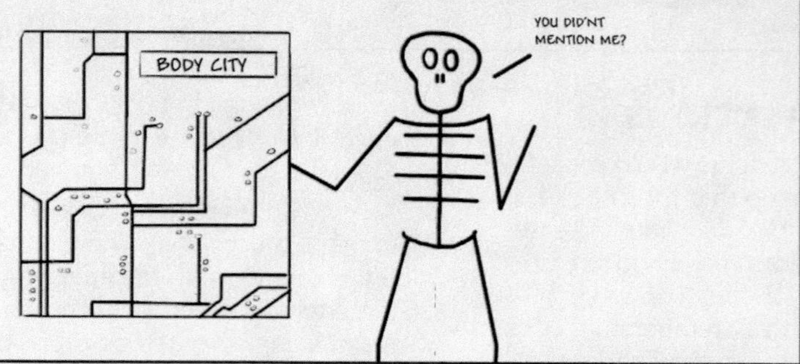

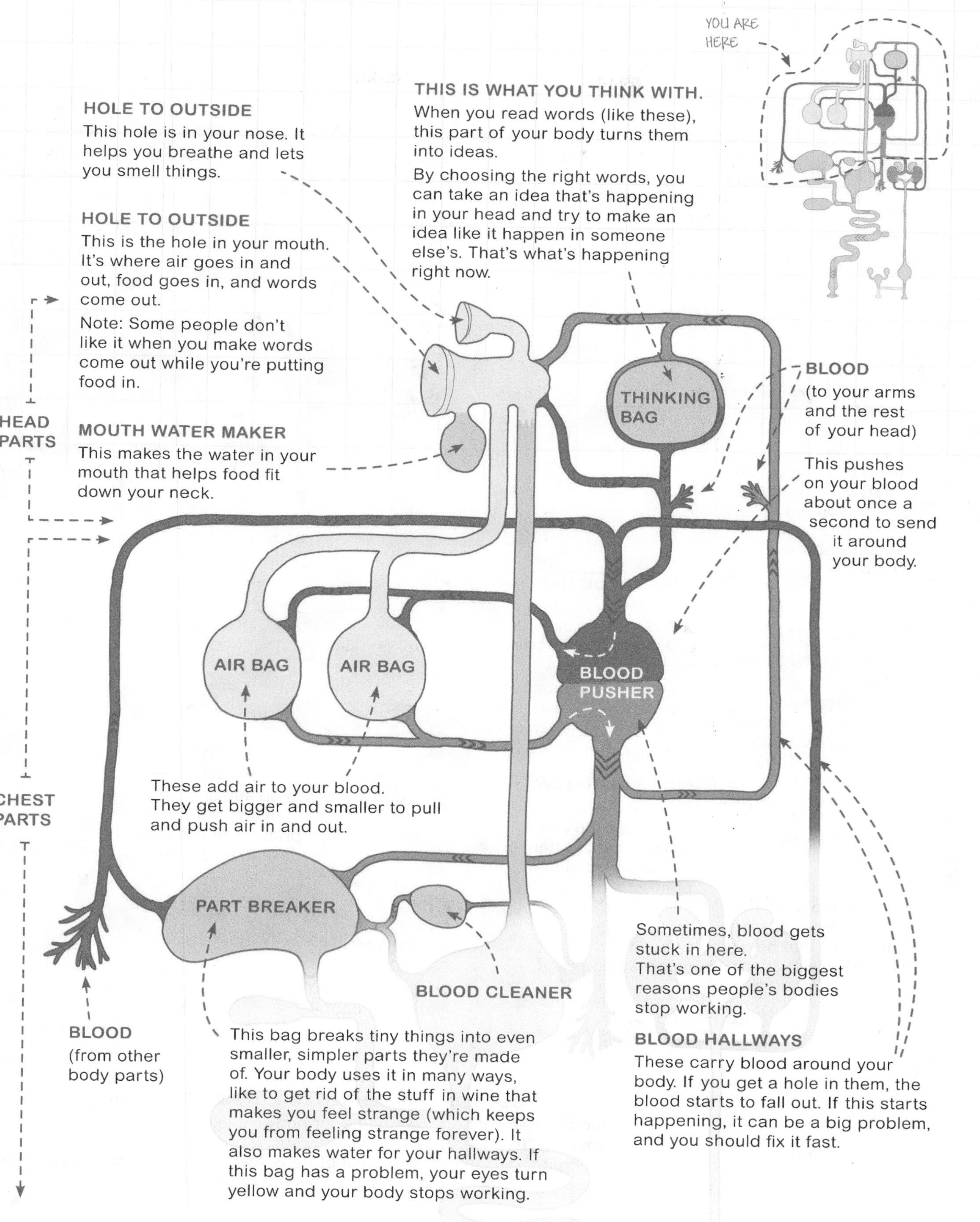
YOU ARE HERE
HOLE TO OUTSIDE
This hole is in your nose. It helps you breathe and lets you smell things.
HOLE TO OUTSIDE
This is the hole in your mouth. It's where air goes in and out, food goes in, and words come out.
Note: Some people don't like it when you make words come out while you're putting food in.
THIS IS WHAT YOU THINK WITH.
When you read words (like these), this part of your body turns them into ideas.
By choosing the right words, you can take an idea that's happening in your head and try to make an idea like it happen in someone else's. That's what's happening right now.
THINKING BAG
BLOOD
(to your arms and the rest of your head)
HEAD PARTS
MOUTH WATER MAKER
This makes the water in your mouth that helps food fit down your neck.
This pushes on your blood about once a second to send it around your body.
AIR BAG
AIR BAG
BLOOD PUSHER
These add air to your blood. They get bigger and smaller to pull and push air in and out.
CHEST PARTS
PART BREAKER
BLOOD CLEANER
Sometimes, blood gets stuck in here. That's one of the biggest reasons people's bodies stop working.
BLOOD HALLWAYS
These carry blood around your body. If you get a hole in them, the blood starts to fall out. If this starts happening, it can be a big problem, and you should fix it fast.
BLOOD
(from other body parts)
This bag breaks tiny things into even smaller, simpler parts they're made of. Your body uses it in many ways, like to get rid of the stuff in wine that makes you feel strange (which keeps you from feeling strange forever). It also makes water for your hallways. If this bag has a problem, your eyes turn yellow and your body stops working.

719B

BAGS OF STUFF INSIDE YOU

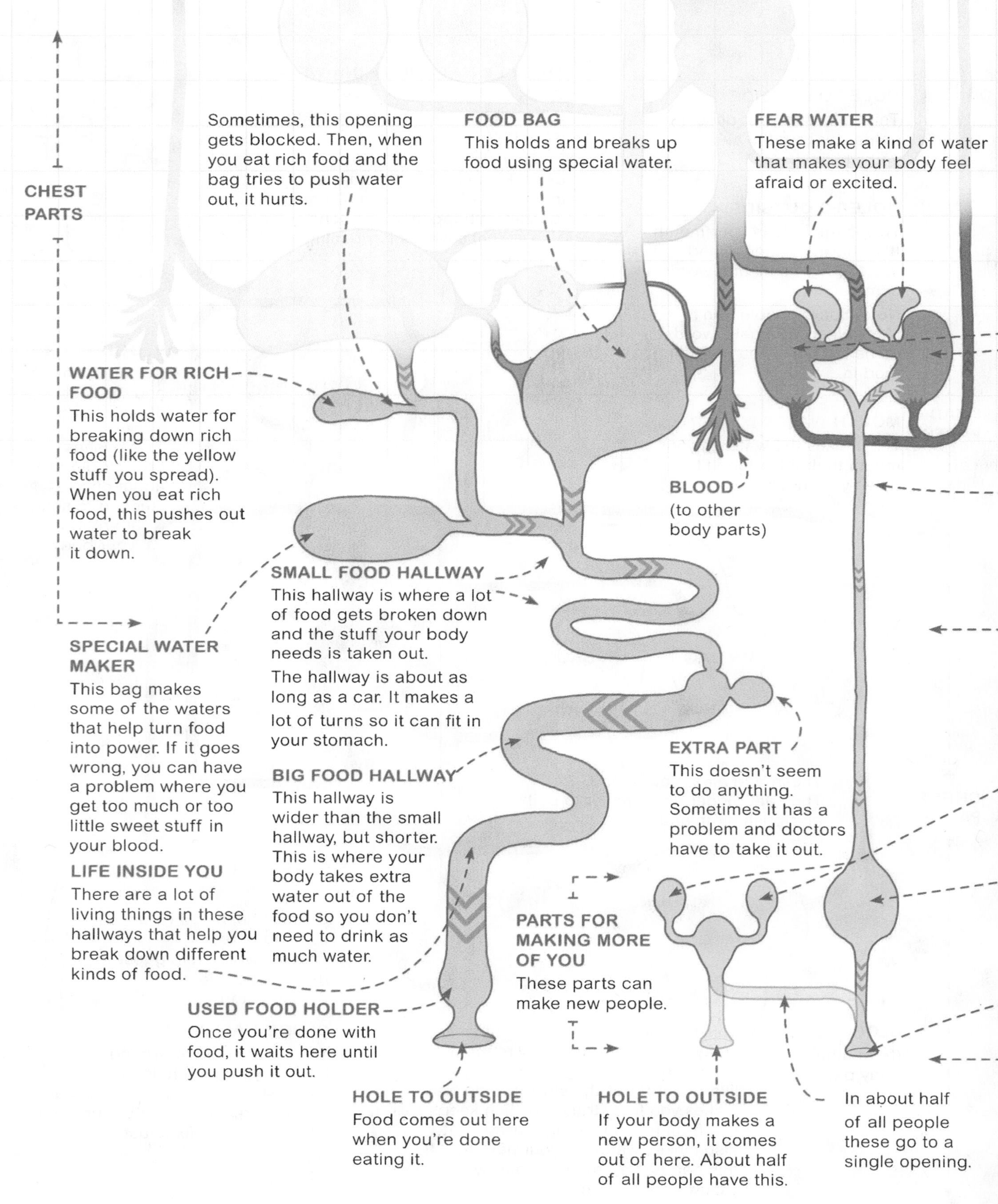

CHEST PARTS
Sometimes, this opening gets blocked. Then, when you eat rich food and the bag tries to push water out, it hurts.
FOOD BAG
This holds and breaks up food using special water.
FEAR WATER
These make a kind of water that makes your body feel afraid or excited.
WATER FOR RICH FOOD
This holds water for breaking down rich food (like the yellow stuff you spread). When you eat rich food, this pushes out water to break it down.
BLOOD
(to other body parts)
SMALL FOOD HALLWAY
This hallway is where a lot of food gets broken down and the stuff your body needs is taken out.
The hallway is about as long as a car. It makes a lot of turns so it can fit in your stomach.
SPECIAL WATER MAKER
This bag makes some of the waters that help turn food into power. If it goes wrong, you can have a problem where you get too much or too little sweet stuff in your blood.
EXTRA PART
This doesn't seem to do anything. Sometimes it has a problem and doctors have to take it out.
BIG FOOD HALLWAY
This hallway is wider than the small hallway, but shorter. This is where your body takes extra water out of the food so you don't need to drink as much water.
LIFE INSIDE YOU
There are a lot of living things in these hallways that help you break down different kinds of food.
PARTS FOR MAKING MORE OF YOU
These parts can make new people.
USED FOOD HOLDER
Once you're done with food, it waits here until you push it out.
HOLE TO OUTSIDE
Food comes out here when you're done eating it.
HOLE TO OUTSIDE
If your body makes a new person, it comes out of here. About half of all people have this.
In about half of all people these go to a single opening.

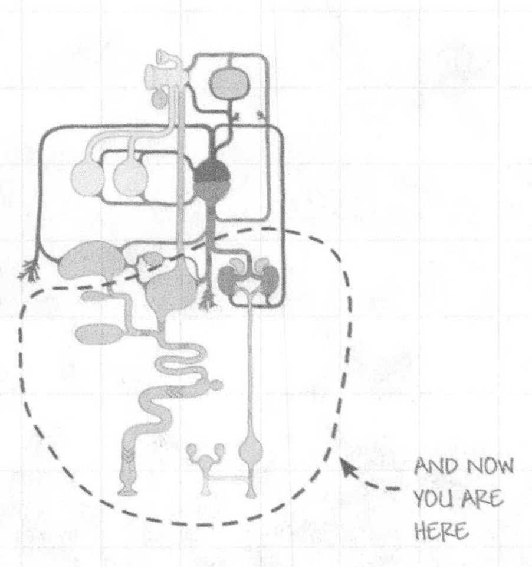

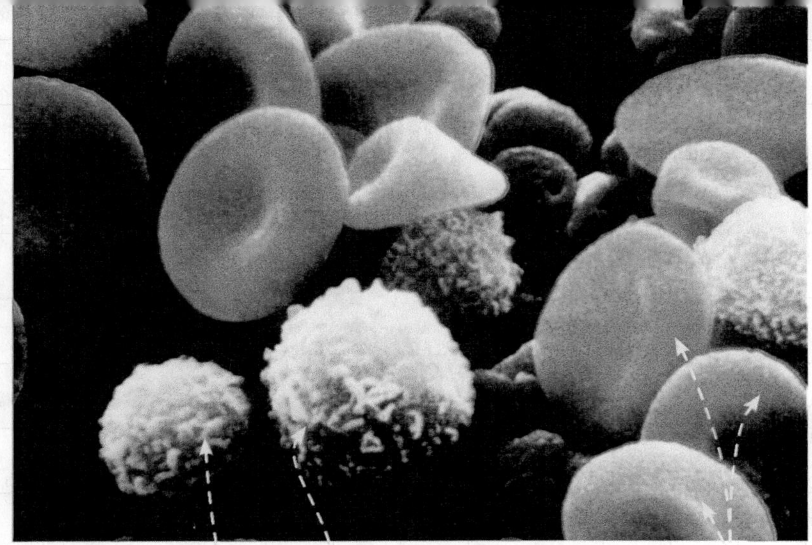

BLOOD CLEANERS
These look for stuff in your blood that you're done with or have too much of—like extra sweet stuff, or stuff from the doctor that you ate to feel better—and send it to be pushed out of your body.

YELLOW WATER HALLWAY
Most of the time, the water from your blood cleaners is yellow, but eating certain colorful foods can make it change color for a while.

(If it turns dark or red, it may mean you're sick.)

LOWER PARTS

BODY PLAN HOLDERS
These parts hold lots of plans for new people. Each plan is made from pieces of the plans used to make you.

These parts also control how your voice, hair, and body grow.

YELLOW WATER HOLDER
This holds yellow water until you push it out.

HOLE TO OUTSIDE
The yellow water from your blood comes out here.

PUSHED TOGETHER
In real life, these parts are all pushed together inside your chest like this.

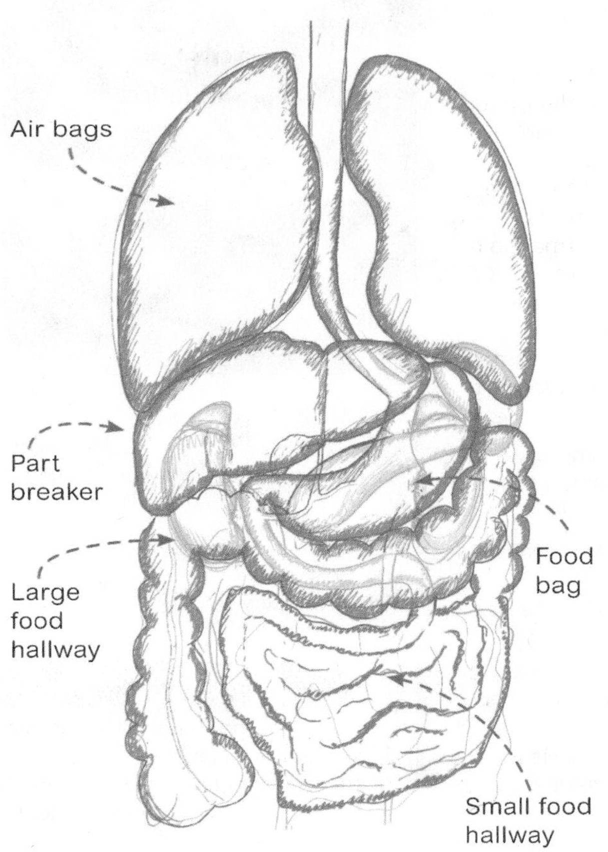

UNIT 6

Introduce

Tell students that a disease caused by an emerging virus could spread quickly around the world. Because viruses can cross continental boundaries easily, a global network of specialized agencies and their partners work together to monitor and track these viruses and have plans in place in case the viruses spread.

The World Health Organization (WHO) is the United Nations' specialized agency for health. This agency is responsible for global monitoring and the coordination of information. Global surveillance networks report suspected disease outbreaks or the presence of viruses in humans and in animals. Once the disease is detected, cases are verified, data is analyzed, and information is made available around the world. In addition, WHO coordinates a rapid response to outbreaks of diseases.

The Centers for Disease Control and Prevention (CDC) is part of the United States Department of Health and Human Services. The CDC conducts research, monitors outbreaks, develops national plans for response to disease outbreaks, and provides information to the United States government. The CDC works closely with the World Health Organization and public and private associations, organizations, departments, universities, and health professionals to try to prevent the spread of disease.

Discuss with students the importance of global monitoring and a central source for the latest information. **Ask**

- If you needed the most recent data on cases of avian flu, where would you get it? WHO or CDC Internet websites
- Why is a global network for monitoring and tracking disease important? *Sample answer:* Diseases can spread quickly around the world. Health professionals need to trade disease information to make sure preventive measures are taken and medical supplies get to where they are needed.

UNIT 6: DIVERSITY OF LIFE

BIOZINE at HMHSCIENCE.COM

INTERNET MAGAZINE

Go online for the latest biology news and updates on all BioZine articles.

Expanding the Textbook

News Feeds

Science Daily

CNN

BBC

Careers

Bio Bytes

Opinion Poll

Strange Biology

Could one of these travelers be carrying a virus that will cause the next pandemic?

Pandemics—Is the Next One on the Way?

Imagine that a new virus emerges and people have no immunity. There is no vaccine. If this were to happen, there could be mandatory travel restrictions, quarantines, and social distancing—including staying out of all crowded places. In the United States alone, such an outbreak could kill up to 2 million people. But how can such a virus emerge, and how can we prepare for it?

Current News

Using a computer and the Internet, have students look at the stories being covered in the Current News section of BioZine at **HMHScience.com**. Have students consider these questions:

- What stories deal with microbial diseases?
- How often is the word **pandemic** used? **Epidemic?** How are these terms defined?
- What local agencies track or report on disease in your area?

Careers

Have students go to BioZine to read about featured careers. Have students check the career listings in the local area. **Ask**

- What percentage of careers in your area relate to the health sciences?
- What risks do health professionals have to be aware of when working with disease-causing agents?

Pandemics

When a new virus emerges, it infects organisms that have not developed immunity, or resistance, to the virus. If a new virus infects humans, it may spread easily from person to person before a vaccine can be produced. A disease outbreak that affects large areas of the world and has a high fatality rate is called a pandemic. The disease is spread very quickly through infection—for example, by sneezing or coughing—to a great number of people.

The 1918 flu pandemic was the most devastating pandemic recorded in world history. This virus infected nearly one-fifth of the world's population, killing about 50 million people worldwide. It spread mainly along global trade routes and with the movement of soldiers during World War I.

If a new and deadly disease emerges today, a pandemic could rapidly result. A carrier could travel around the world in 24 hours. Several million people travel internationally by plane every year, easily reaching their destinations before they show any symptoms of carrying a disease.

The "Perfect" Virus

Not every virus is well suited to cause massive human casualties. For many viruses, humans represent a dead-end infection because they cannot be passed from human to human. For other viruses, victims die too quickly for the virus to reproduce. Quarantines can contain this type of virus relatively easily.

What characteristics would make an emerging virus likely to cause a pandemic? The virus would need to be adapted to humans as hosts and easily spread through casual contact. Victims would also have to survive infection long enough without symptoms to go about their daily business and infect other people. Finally, the most deadly virus would mutate rapidly, foiling the attempts of scientists to develop a vaccine or a drug that targets it.

TECHNOLOGY S.T.E.M.

Dissecting a Virus

Scientists have long debated how the genetic material of influenza A viruses, RNA, is likely arranged. In 2005 virologist Yoshihiro Kawaoka and his team of researchers at the University of Wisconsin unraveled the mystery using a technique called electron tomography.

Electron tomography is a way to construct a three-dimensional image from a series of electron microscope images taken at different angles. By making slices along flu virus particles that cut them into "top" and "bottom" halves, researchers found that all influenza A viruses have a total of eight RNA strands. Seven strands form a circle just inside the edge of the virus particle, surrounding an eighth strand in the center.

Based on this similarity in structure, the researchers concluded that all influenza A viruses must share a specific mechanism for packaging their genetic material. This knowledge may make it possible to engineer viruses that can be used to mass produce vaccines to defend against these viruses, which are responsible for regular seasonal outbreaks as well as the avian flu.

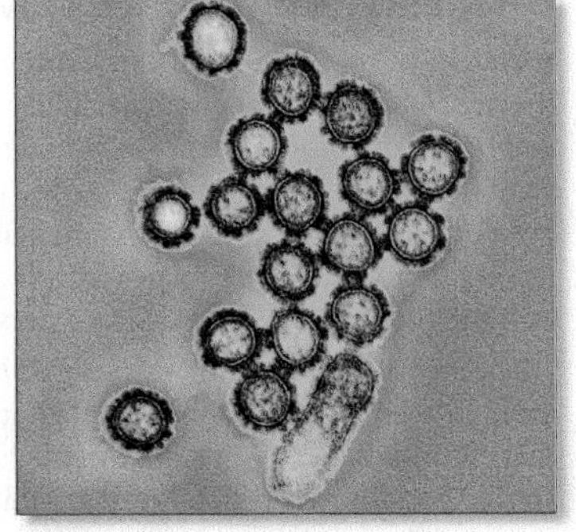

Read More >> at HMHScience.com

Strange Biology

Have students go to BioZine at **HMHScience.com** and read the information in the Strange Biology section. Have students relate that information to the key concepts in this unit. Then ask students why the information presented in the Strange Biology section could be viewed as being strange or unusual.

Vocabulary of Viruses

Students may need clarification of some of the terms relating to viruses.

emerging virus—a virus that suddenly appears or comes to the attention of medical scientists.

epidemic—an outbreak of a contagious disease that spreads rapidly in a certain area or country and occurs in a larger-than-normal number of people.

pandemic—an outbreak of a contagious disease that occurs in a large number of people. A pandemic is an epidemic that occurs over a wide geographic area.

avian flu—a highly contagious viral disease affecting birds. All birds are susceptible, but outbreaks occur most often in chickens and turkeys.

carrier—an organism that acts as host to a disease-causing bacterium or virus, transmitting the bacterium or virus to other organisms, but showing no symptoms of the disease.

mutation—any change in DNA. Specific mutations cannot be predicted. This makes it difficult or impossible to know if or when the avian flu virus could mutate and spread to people.

zoonoses—diseases that are transferable from animals to humans. The SARS virus and avian flu virus cause zoonoses.

strain—a group of organisms of the same species that have distinctive characteristics but are not different enough to be considered a separate breed.

species barrier—the limited transmission of a disease from one species to another.

UNIT 6

Take It Further

Scientists often refer to the viruses that cause influenza by their subtypes. For example, H1N1 is a virus that crossed the species barrier and moved from pigs to some humans. Similarly, H5N1 has moved from birds to some humans. The letters and numbers represent certain proteins on the surface of a virus and the way proteins combine. Scientists are concerned that the H5N1 virus could mutate and potentially cause a pandemic.

Scientists continue to track new influenza viruses that infect humans. Although other strains of influenza viruses continue to appear in small numbers of people, the H5N1 strain continues to be a concern to scientists. The virus first appeared in humans in 1997 in Hong Kong after being transmitted by poultry. Six of the eighteen people known to have had the disease died. Since then the virus has infected only small numbers of people, but the area where people have been found with the disease has expanded to other Asian countries and Africa.

CAREERS

Epidemiologist in Action

DR. BEN MUNETA

TITLE Medical Epidemiologist, Indian Health Service

EDUCATION M.D., Stanford University

In 1993, a mystery disease began to kill people in the southwestern United States. One of the experts that the Centers for Disease Control (CDC) consulted was Dr. Ben Muneta. Dr. Muneta is an epidemiologist, a scientist who studies the causes, transmission, and control of diseases within a population. He works at the Indian Health Service National Epidemiology Program in Albuquerque, New Mexico.

Dr. Muneta consulted a traditional Navajo healer. From him, Dr. Muneta learned that the disease was associated with extra rainfall, which had caused the pinon trees to produce more nuts than usual. This in turn had led to a population explosion among mice that feed on these nuts.

Using this lead, CDC researchers determined that the disease was caused by hantavirus, a virus spread through the droppings of deer mice. With further research, Dr. Muneta confirmed that some Navajo healers had even predicted the 1993 outbreak.

Read More >> at HMHScience.com

Diseases That Jump to New Species

A zoonosis is a disease that can jump between species. A virus that evolves the ability to jump from a nonhuman animal species to humans will spread very quickly in the human body, which has not yet developed defenses. If this virus exchanges genetic material with another human virus, the virus may become capable of spreading from person to person.

The swine flu pandemic was caused by the H1N1 virus that originated in pigs. In 2009, it was estimated that 22 million people were infected with the H1N1 virus! World health officials urged individuals to get vaccinated and educated people on its symptoms. A year later, the swine flu was officially contained.

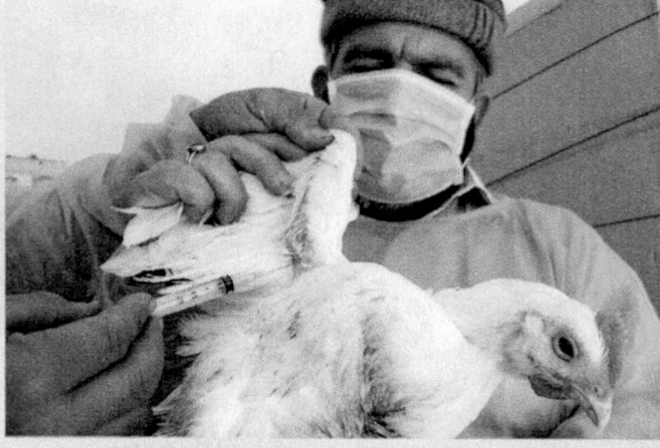

China, Thailand, Russia, Turkey, and Pakistan are among the countries that have confirmed cases of avian flu in poultry farms. Here, a Pakistani health worker vaccinates a healthy chicken.

Avian Flu H5N1

Perhaps the most familiar zoonosis is the avian flu virus. Sometimes called the bird flu, this virus normally infects wild birds such as ducks and geese as well as domestic birds such as chickens. Migrating birds can carry it to other continents.

Researchers have been tracking a form of avian flu called H5N1. Like other flu viruses, H5N1 mutates rapidly. Random mutations may or may not help the virus adapt to new host species. However, viruses can mutate in a faster, less random way. If an animal becomes infected with viruses from two different species at the same time, the viruses can exchange genetic information. If this happens, the avian flu can jump the species barrier, becoming a flu virus that can be transmitted from one human to another.

Unanswered Questions

Despite the danger that a new virus represents, no one knows how the virus may mutate or whether it will cause a pandemic. Some of the most important questions include the following:

- How can vaccines be developed quickly enough to stop a disease that can spread in hours or days?
- Can a broad-spectrum antiviral drug be developed that could target more than one flu virus?
- What specific molecular factors allow a virus to jump from one species to another?

Read More >> at HMHScience.com

BIOZINE HMHScience.com

Have students use the resources available in the BioZine for this unit at **HMHScience.com** to report on recent discoveries about viruses. In addition to sources available in BioZine, have students locate information from the World Health Organization and the Centers for Disease Control and Prevention.

Ask

- What research is being done on vaccines for viral diseases?
- How can scientists study the evolution of viruses?
- How do sources of information about viral disease get disseminated?

Student Resources

Lab Handbook

Safety

Before you work in the laboratory, read these safety rules. Ask your teacher to explain any rules that you do not completely understand. Refer to these rules later on if you have questions about safety in the science classroom.

Directions

- Know where the fire extinguisher, fire blanket, shower, and eyewash are located in your classroom.
- Read all directions and make sure that you understand them before starting an investigation or lab activity. If you do not understand how to do a procedure or how to use a piece of equipment, ask your teacher.
- Do not begin any investigation or touch any equipment until your teacher has told you to start.
- Never experiment on your own. If you want to try a procedure that the directions do not call for, ask your teacher for permission first.
- If you are hurt or injured in any way, tell your teacher immediately.

Dress Code

- Wear goggles when using glassware, sharp objects, or chemicals; heating an object; or working with anything that can easily fly up into the air and hurt someone's eye.
- Tie back long hair or hair that hangs in front of your eyes.
- Remove any article of clothing—such as a loose sweater or a scarf—that hangs down and may touch a flame, chemical, or piece of equipment.
- Observe all safety icons calling for the wearing of eye protection, gloves, and aprons.

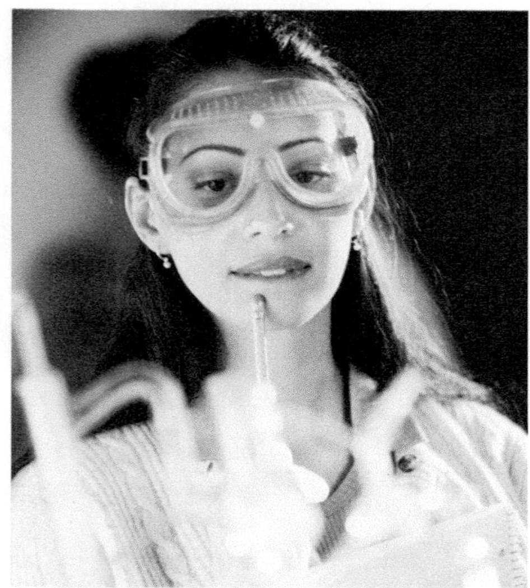

Heating and Fire Safety

- Keep your work area neat, clean, and free of extra materials.
- Use only borosilicate glass for heating substances.
- Never reach over a flame or heat source.
- Point objects being heated away from you and others.
- Never heat a substance or an object in a closed container.
- Use oven mitts, clamps, tongs, or a test tube holder to hold heated items.
- Never touch an object that has been heated. If you are unsure whether something is hot, treat it as though it is.
- After heating test tubes, place them in a test tube rack.
- Do not throw hot substances into the trash. Wait for them to cool and dispose of them in the container provided by your teacher.

Chemical Safety

- Always wear goggles when working with any type of chemical, even household items such as baking soda.
- Stand when you are working with chemicals. Pour them over a sink or your work area, not over the floor. If you spill a chemical or get it on your skin, tell your teacher right away.
- If you get a chemical in your eye, use the eyewash immediately.
- Never touch, taste, or sniff any chemicals in the lab. If you need to determine odor, waft. To waft, hold the chemical in its container 15 cm (6 in.) away from your nose, and use your fingers to bring fumes from the container to your nose.
- Keep lids on all chemicals you are not using.
- Use materials only from properly labeled containers.
- Never use more chemicals than the procedure calls for.
- When diluting acid with water, always add acid to water.
- Never put unused chemicals back into the original containers. Dispose of extra chemicals in the container provided by your teacher.
- Always wash your hands after handling chemicals.

Electrical Safety

- Never use lamps or other electrical equipment with frayed cords.
- Make sure no cord is lying on the floor where someone can trip over it.
- Do not let a cord hang over the side of a counter or table so that the equipment can easily be pulled or knocked to the floor.
- Never let cords hang into sinks or other places where water can be found.
- Turn off all power switches before plugging an appliance into an outlet.
- Never touch electrical equipment with wet hands.
- Never try to fix electrical problems. Immediately inform your teacher of any problems.
- Unplug an electrical cord by pulling on the plug, not the cord.

Glassware and Sharp-Object Safety

- Use only clean glassware that is free of chips and cracks.
- If you break glassware, tell your teacher right away.
- If you use a microscope that has a mirror, do not aim the mirror directly at the sun as you can damage your eyes.
- Use knives and other cutting instruments carefully. Always wear eye protection and cut away from yourself.
- Clean glassware according to your teacher's instructions after you use it.
- Use an appropriately sized test tube for the quantity of chemicals you are using, and store test tubes in a test tube rack.

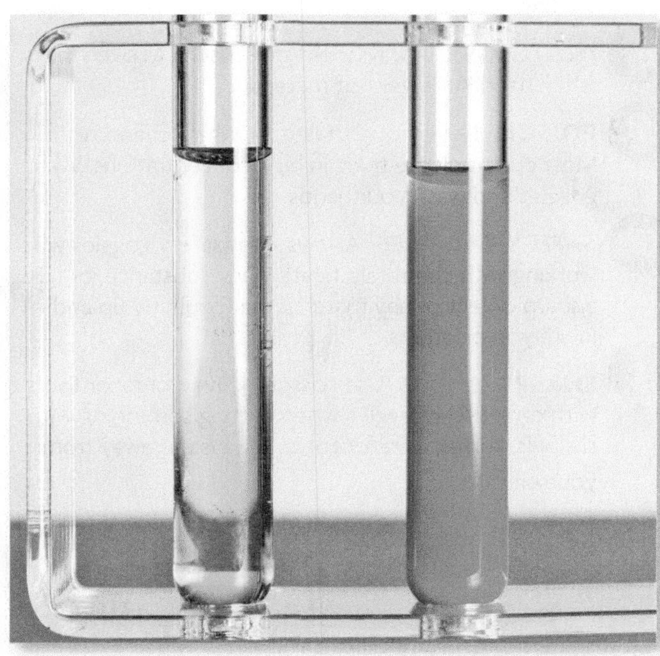

Animal Safety

- Never hurt an animal.
- Touch animals only when necessary. Follow your teacher's instructions for handling animals.
- Wear gloves when handling animals or preserved specimens.
- Specimens for dissection should be properly mounted and supported.
- Do not cut a specimen while holding it in your hands.
- Do not open containers of live microorganisms unless you are directed to do so.
- Dispose of preserved specimens as directed by your teacher.
- Always wash your hands with soap and water after working with animals or specimens.

Cleanup

- Follow your teacher's instructions for the disposal, recycling, or storage of supplies.
- Clean your work area and pick up anything that has dropped to the floor.
- Wash your hands.

R3

Lab Handbook

Safety Symbols

Safety is the priority in the science classroom. In all of the activities in this textbook, safety symbols are used to alert you to materials, procedures, or situations that could be potentially hazardous if the safety guidelines are not followed. Learn what you need to do when you see these icons, and read all lab procedures before coming to the lab so you are prepared. Always ask your teacher if you have questions.

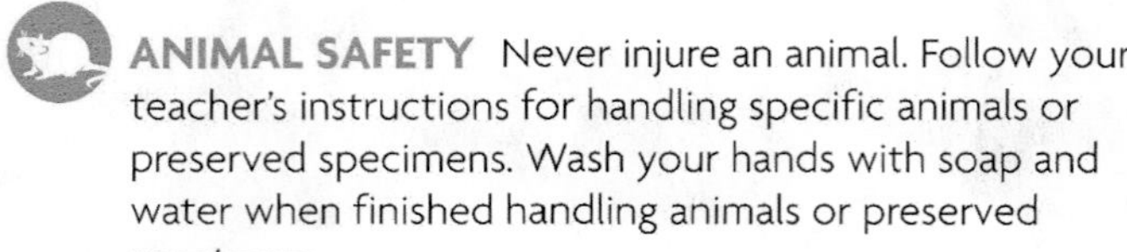

ANIMAL SAFETY Never injure an animal. Follow your teacher's instructions for handling specific animals or preserved specimens. Wash your hands with soap and water when finished handling animals or preserved specimens.

APRON Wear an apron when using any substance that could cause harm if spilled on you. Stand whenever possible to avoid spilling in your lap.

BREAKAGE Use caution when handling items that may break, such as glassware and thermometers. Always store test tubes in a test tube rack.

CHEMICAL SAFETY Always wear goggles when working with chemicals. Stand whenever possible when working with chemicals to avoid spilling on your lap. Tell your teacher immediately if you spill chemicals on yourself, the table, or floor. Never taste any substance or chemical in the lab. Always wash your hands after working with chemicals.

DISPOSAL Follow your teacher's instructions for disposing of all waste materials, including chemicals, specimens, or broken glass.

ELECTRICAL SAFETY Keep electrical cords away from water to avoid shock. Do not use cords with frayed edges. Unplug all equipment when done.

FIRE SAFETY Put on safety goggles before lighting flames. Remove loose clothing and tie back hair. Never leave a lit object unattended. Extinguish flames as soon as you finish heating.

FUMES Always work in a well-ventilated area. Bring fumes up to your nose by wafting with your fingers instead of sniffing.

GENERAL SAFETY Always follow the safety rules and ask your teacher if you are unsure about something. If you are designing your own experiment, get your teacher's approval on your plan before you start. Think about which safety rules you must follow in your experiment.

GLOVES Always wear gloves to protect your skin from possible injury when working with substances that may be harmful or when working with animals.

HAND WASHING Wash your hands with soap and water after working with soil, chemicals, animals, or preserved specimens.

HEATING SAFETY Wear goggles and never leave any substance while it is being heated. Use tongs, hot pads, or test tube holders to hold hot objects. Point any materials being heated away from you and others. Place hot objects such as test tubes in test tube racks while cooling.

HOT/GLOVE Always wear gloves such as oven mitts when handling larger hot materials.

POISON Never touch, taste, or inhale chemicals. Most chemicals are toxic in high concentrations. Wear goggles and wash your hands.

SAFETY GOGGLES Always wear safety goggles when working with chemicals, heating any substance, or using a sharp object or any material that could fly up and injure you or others.

SHARP OBJECTS Use scissors, knives, or razor tools with care. Wear goggles when cutting something with scalpels, knives, or razor tools. Always cut away from yourself.

The Metric System and SI Units

Scientists around the world use the metric system of measurement. The official name for the metric system is the International System of Units (SI). The short name SI comes from the French name, Système International d'Unitès.

SI Units

SI includes units for measuring length, mass, volume, temperature, and many other properties. The most commonly used SI units are shown in Table 1.

TABLE 1: COMMON SI UNITS	
PROPERTY	**NAME**
Length	meter (m)
Volume	liter (L)
Mass	kilogram (kg)
Temperature	Kelvin (K)

The relationships between all SI units are based on powers of 10. In most cases, an SI unit has a prefix that shows its relationship to the base unit. For example, 1 kilometer is 1000 meters, and 1 centimeter is one-hundredth of a meter. Table 2 lists the commonly used SI prefixes along with their symbols and values.

TABLE 2: SI PREFIXES		
PREFIX	**SYMBOL**	**VALUE**
giga-	G	1,000,000,000
mega-	M	1,000,000
kilo-	k	1000
hecto-	h	100
deca-	da	10
deci-	d	0.1
centi-	c	0.01
milli-	m	0.001
micro-	µ	0.000001
nano-	n	0.000000001
pico-	p	0.000000000001

For your reference, the mass of a paper clip is about 1 g. The diameter of a red blood cell is very small—about 10 µm.

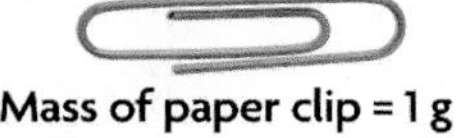

Mass of paper clip = 1 g

Diameter of a red blood cell = 10 µm

Customary to SI Conversion

Although all scientists use the metric system, in the United States the customary system of measurements is still widely used. Table 3 provides useful equivalents for making conversions between these two systems of measurement.

TABLE 3: CUSTOMARY AND SI EQUIVALENTS	
U.S. CUSTOMARY	**SI**
1 inch (in.)	2.54 centimeters (cm)
39.37 inches (in.)	1 meter (m)
0.62 miles (mi)	1 kilometer (km)
1.06 quarts (qt)	1 liter (L)
1 fluid ounce (oz)	236 milliliters (mL)
2.2 pounds (lb)	1 kilogram (kg)
1 ounce (oz)	28.3 grams (g)

Temperature

Use the formulas at right for converting between Celsius and Fahrenheit temperatures.

$$°C = \frac{5}{9} \times (°F - 32)$$

$$°F = (\frac{9}{5} \times °C) + 32$$

Measuring in the Lab

Collecting accurate and precise data in the lab requires the skillful use of some basic lab equipment. Be sure that you know how to use all equipment correctly in the lab, not only to obtain accurate results but also to ensure your safety.

Metric Rulers

- Use metric rulers or meter sticks to measure length.
- Because the end of a meter stick or ruler is often imperfect, begin the measurement from the 1 cm mark.
- Lay a ruler flat on top of the object so that the 1 cm mark lines up with one end. Make sure the ruler and the object do not move between the time you line them up and the time you take the measurement.
- Estimate the reading to one place value beyond what is marked on the ruler. The ruler is marked to the tenths place value, so estimate to the hundredths. The stem of the leaf hits the ruler about halfway between the 4.2 and 4.3 cm marks, so it is estimated at 4.25 cm. However, it is necessary to subtract 1 cm from the edge of the ruler not used in the measurement, so the leaf measures 3.25 cm.

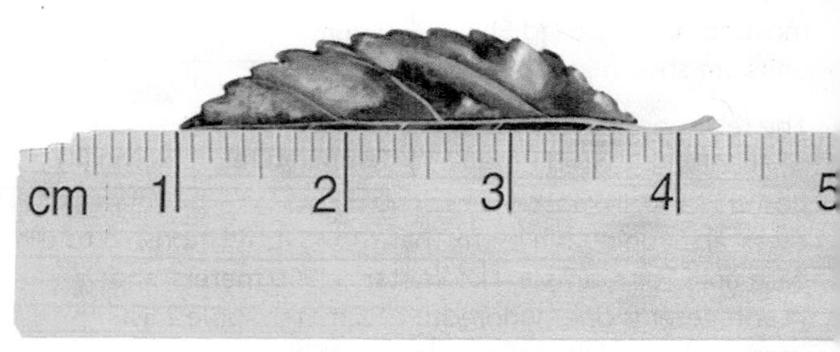

Graduated Cylinder

- Use a graduated cylinder to measure the volume of a liquid.
- You can use a graduated cylinder to find the volume of a solid object by measuring the increase in a liquid's level after you add the object to the cylinder.
- Be sure that the graduated cylinder is on a flat surface. Your eye level should be even with the surface of the liquid.
- Read the volume of the liquid at the bottom of the curve, or meniscus (muh-NIHS-kuhs).
- The volume of liquid is on the 96 mL mark. Estimate to one place value beyond what is marked on the graduated cylinder. The volume of liquid is 96.0 mL.

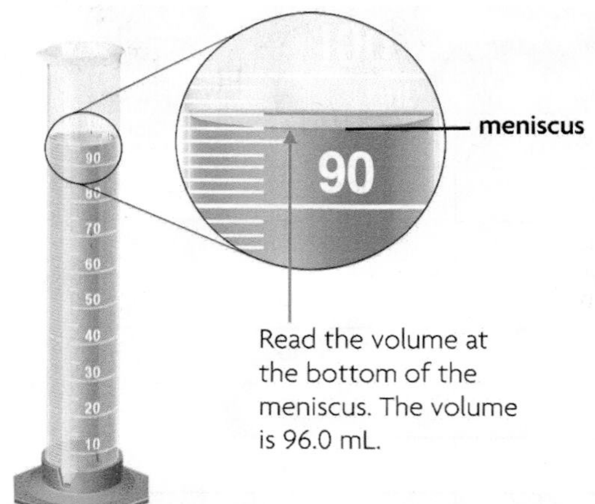

Read the volume at the bottom of the meniscus. The volume is 96.0 mL.

Thermometer

- To measure the temperature of a liquid, place a thermometer into the container without letting the thermometer touch the bottom of the container. Attach a clip to hold the thermometer in place, especially if the liquid is hot.
- As the liquid moves up or down inside the thermometer, rotate the thermometer for more accurate results.
- Record the measurement when the liquid in the thermometer stops moving. Take note of the highest point of liquid by estimating to the nearest tenth of a degree.
- The temperature on this thermometer is 24.5°C.

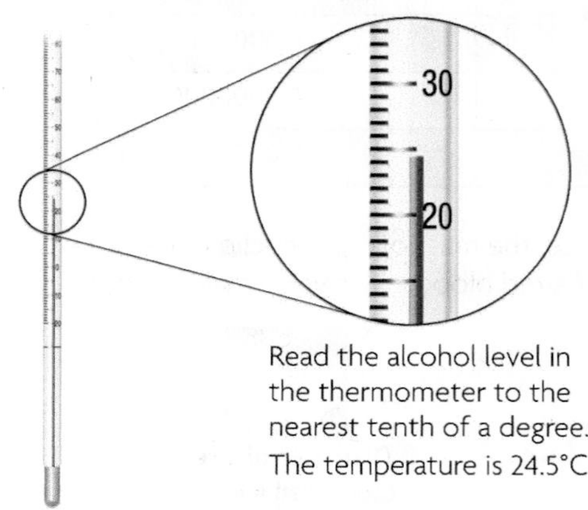

Read the alcohol level in the thermometer to the nearest tenth of a degree. The temperature is 24.5°C.

Triple-Beam Balance

This balance has a pan and three beams with sliding masses, called riders. Each beam is calibrated to a different level of mass, allowing the balance to be accurate to a tenth of a gram. At one end of the beams, a pointer indicates whether the mass on the pan is equal to the masses shown on the beams.

1. Place the balance on a stable, level surface.
2. Make sure the balance is zeroed before measuring the mass of an object. The balance is zeroed if the pointer is at zero when nothing is on the pan and the riders are at their zero points. Use the adjustment knob under the pan of the balance to zero it.
3. Place the object to be measured on the pan. Do not place a hot object or chemical on the pan. The changing temperature may have a direct impact on your measurement and can also be dangerous.
4. Move the riders one notch at a time away from the pan. Begin with the largest rider. If moving the largest rider one notch brings the pointer below zero, move the mass back and then begin measuring the mass of the object with the next smaller rider.
5. Change the positions of the riders until they balance the mass on the pan and the pointer is at zero. Then add the readings from the three beams to determine the mass of the object.
6. The balance below is being used to measure a beaker of water. To find the mass of the water inside the beaker, a student moved the riders to the positions shown. The total mass of the beaker and water is 163.0 g, but you must also subtract the mass of the empty beaker from the total.

Mass of water =	**Mass of beaker + water**	**= 163.0 g**
	– Mass of beaker =	**63.0 g**
Mass of water		**= 100.0 g**

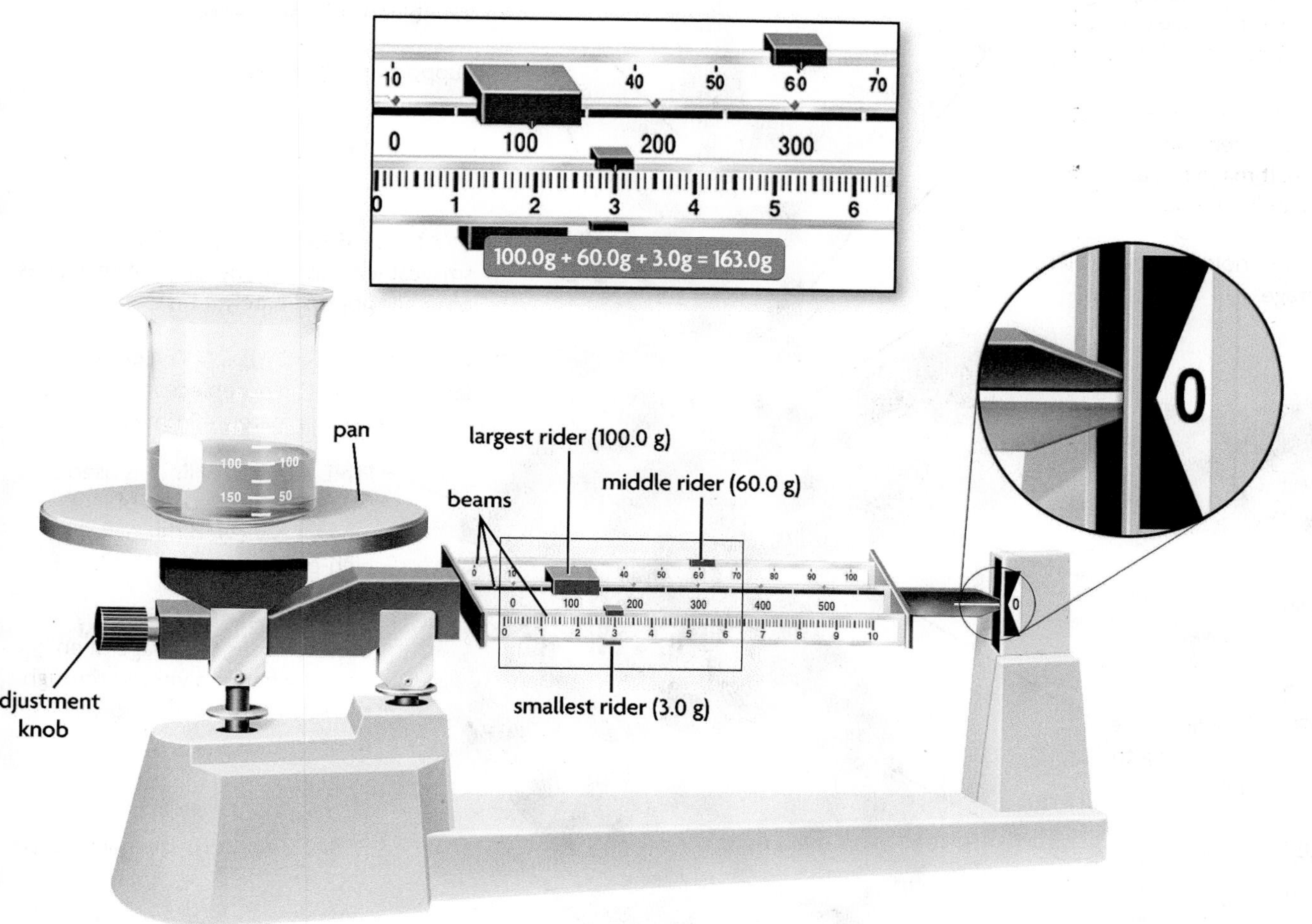

Using a Light Microscope

Microscopes are used to view objects too small to be seen with the naked eye.

Viewing an Object

Use these directions to view your specimen.

1. Use the coarse adjustment to raise the body tube.
2. Adjust the diaphragm so that you can see a bright circle of light through the eyepiece.
3. Place the slide on the stage. Be sure to center it over the hole in the stage and secure it with the stage clips.
4. Turn the nosepiece to click the scanning objective lens into place.
5. Using the coarse adjustment knob, slowly lower the lens and focus on the specimen being viewed. Be sure not to touch the slide or object with the lens.
6. When using the high power lens, use only the fine adjustment knob.
7. Move the slide on the stage with very small movements to view other parts of it. You may need to refocus using the fine adjustment.

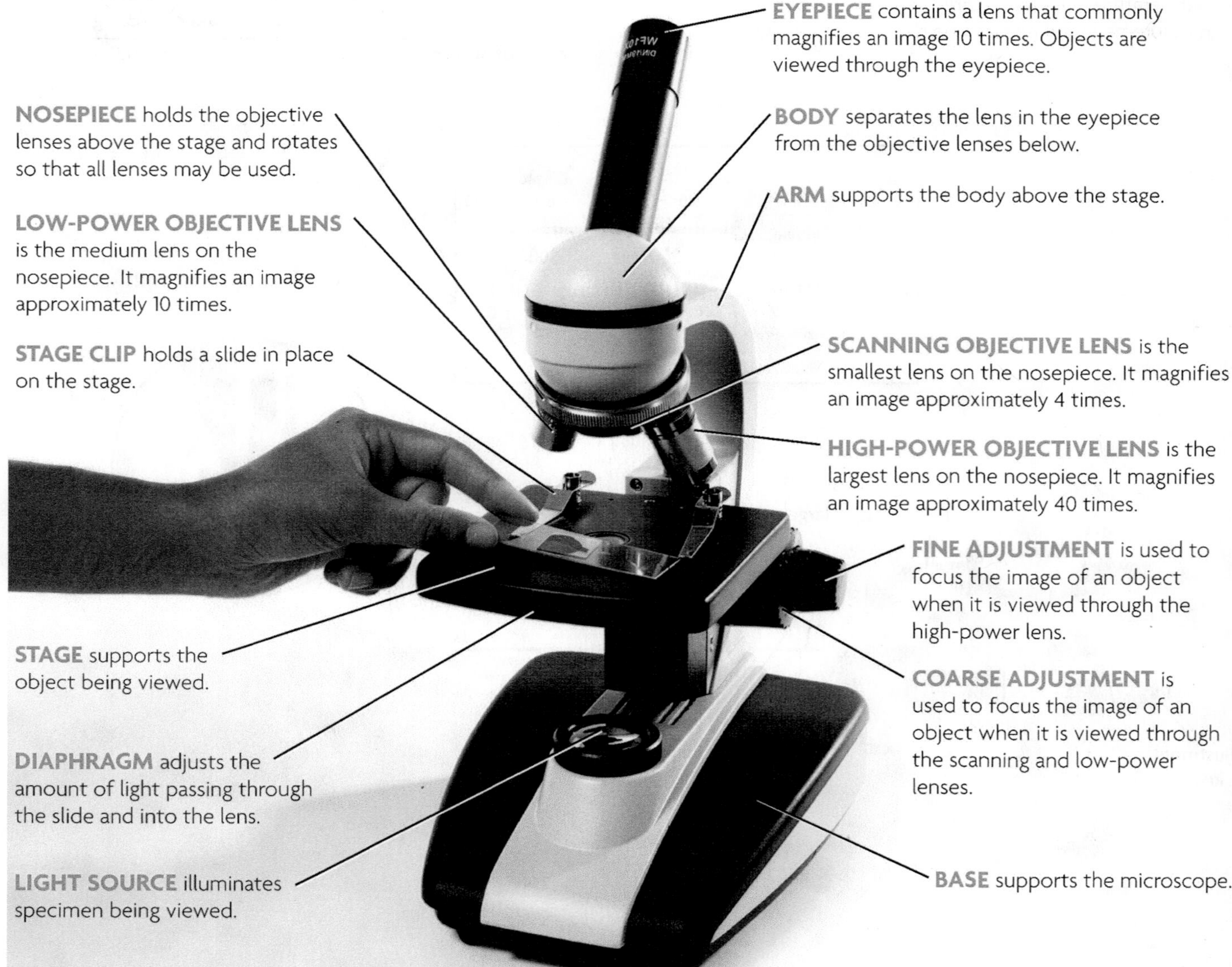
EYEPIECE contains a lens that commonly magnifies an image 10 times. Objects are viewed through the eyepiece.
NOSEPIECE holds the objective lenses above the stage and rotates so that all lenses may be used.
BODY separates the lens in the eyepiece from the objective lenses below.
ARM supports the body above the stage.
LOW-POWER OBJECTIVE LENS is the medium lens on the nosepiece. It magnifies an image approximately 10 times.
STAGE CLIP holds a slide in place on the stage.
SCANNING OBJECTIVE LENS is the smallest lens on the nosepiece. It magnifies an image approximately 4 times.
HIGH-POWER OBJECTIVE LENS is the largest lens on the nosepiece. It magnifies an image approximately 40 times.
FINE ADJUSTMENT is used to focus the image of an object when it is viewed through the high-power lens.
STAGE supports the object being viewed.
COARSE ADJUSTMENT is used to focus the image of an object when it is viewed through the scanning and low-power lenses.
DIAPHRAGM adjusts the amount of light passing through the slide and into the lens.
LIGHT SOURCE illuminates specimen being viewed.
BASE supports the microscope.

Making a Wet Mount

Use these steps to prepare a specimen to be viewed under a microscope.

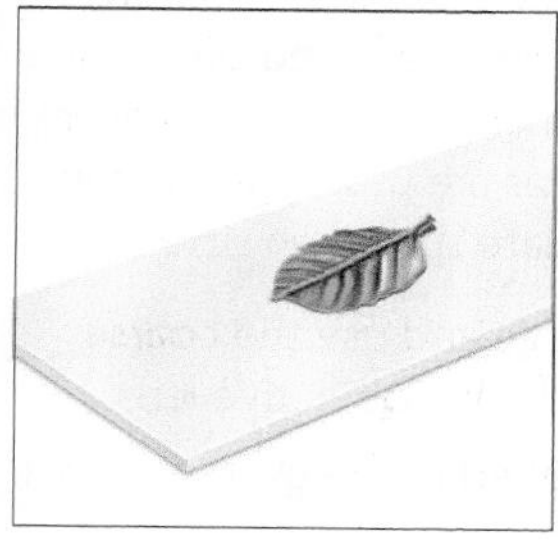

Place the specimen in the center of a clean slide.

Place a drop of water on the specimen.

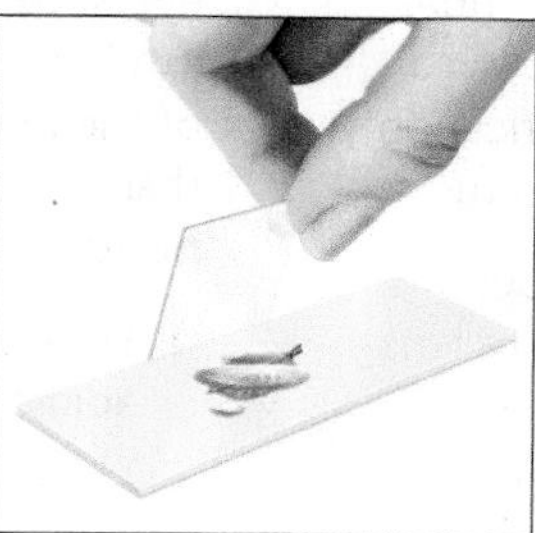

Place a cover slip on the slide. Put one edge of the cover slip into the drop of water, and slowly lower the cover slip over the specimen.

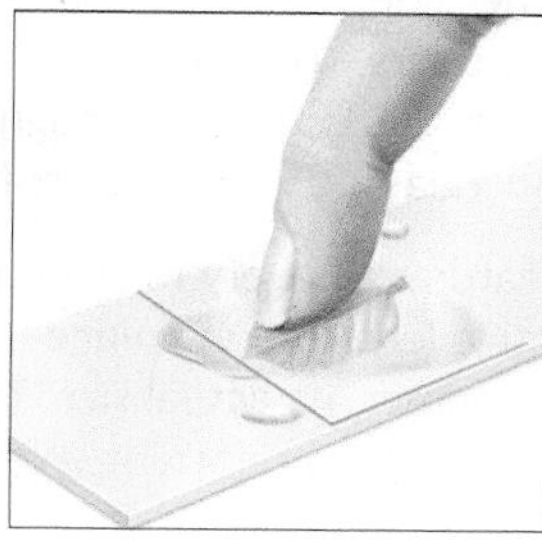

Remove any air bubbles from under the cover slip by gently tapping the cover slip.

Dry any excess water before placing the slide on the microscope stage for viewing.

Staining a Specimen

After you make a wet mount, use these steps to stain the specimen.

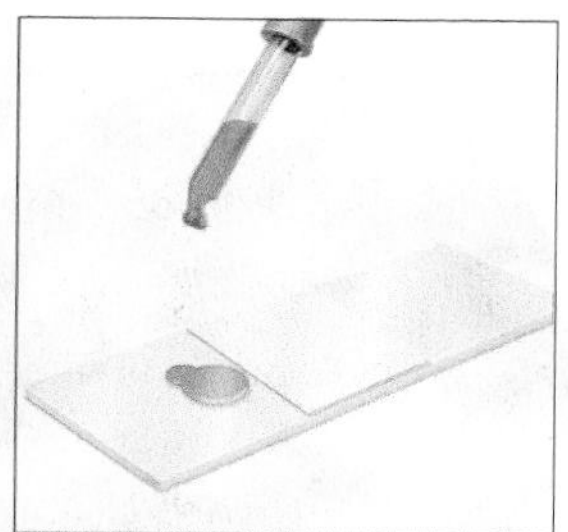

Place a drop of stain at one end of the cover slip.

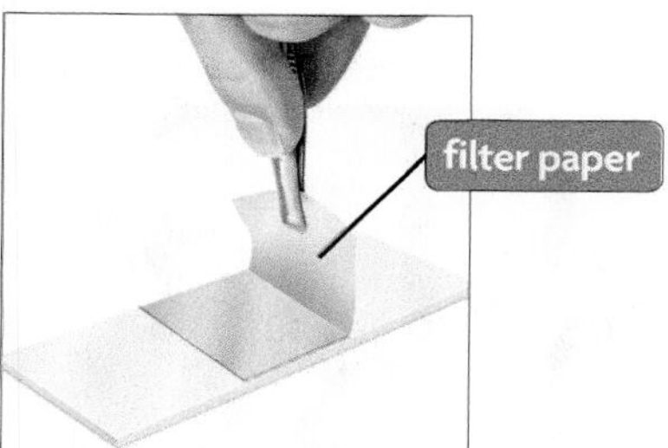

Hold a piece of filter paper with forceps at the other end of the cover slip. The stain will flow underneath the cover slip and stain the specimen.

R9

Calculating Magnification

When you look through a microscope, you see a magnified image of the specimen on the slide. Magnification describes how much larger an object appears when viewed through a microscope than its actual size. Calculating the magnification of the image will give you an idea of the sizes of its features.

There are two magnifying features of every microscope: the eyepiece and the objective lens. The **eyepiece** has a lens that magnifies the image 10× (times) its actual size. The objective lenses magnify the image by different levels.

	Scanning Objective	4×
Eyepiece 10× •	Low-Power Objective	10×
	High-Power Objective	40×

The total magnification of the image is the product of multiplying the eyepiece magnification by the objective lens magnification.

The examples below show how to calculate the total magnification of the daphnia under each lens.

EXAMPLE

Eyepiece • Scanning Objective = Total Magnification
(10×) • (4×) = 40×
This image is magnified 40× its actual size.

EXAMPLE

Eyepiece • Low-Power Objective = Total Magnification
(10×) • (10×) = 100×
The image is magnified 100× its actual size.

EXAMPLE

Eyepiece • High-Power Objective = Total Magnification
(10×) • (40×) = 400×
This image is magnified 400× its actual size.

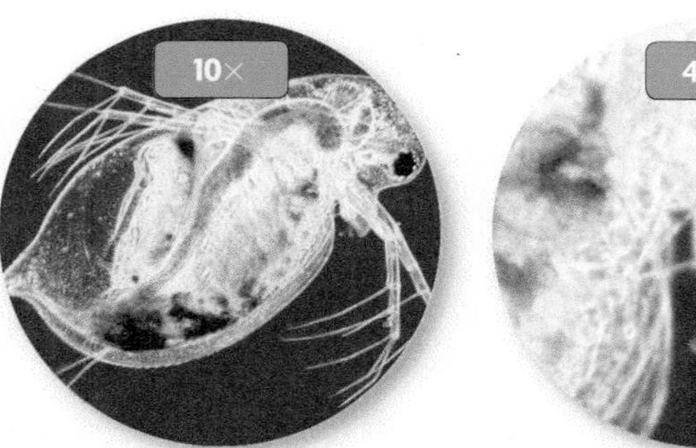

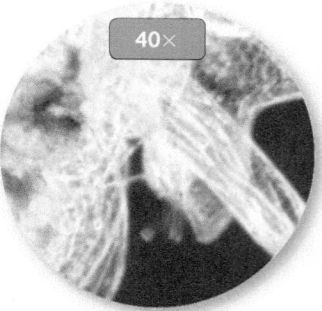

Calculating Specimen Size

The field of view is the area seen through the microscope eyepiece. You can calculate the estimated size in micrometers (μm) of a specimen or object you are viewing based on the size of the field of view. Since many specimens viewed are smaller than a millimeter, the sizes of specimens are usually written in micrometers. Use these steps to calculate specimen size.

1. Place a ruler on the microscope stage and use the coarse adjustment to focus the image in the 4× objective lens.
2. Look at the markings on a ruler viewed in the eyepiece, as shown in the image below.
3. Estimate the diameter of the field of view to the nearest millimeter, which is approximately 4 mm in this example.
4. Remove the ruler and put the slide specimen on the stage.
5. Adjust the slide so the specimen is at one side of the field of view. Estimate the size of the specimen based on the field of view. The length of the daphnia specimen viewed under the scanning objective lens is about 2 mm.
6. Convert mm to μm.

length of specimen • 1000 μm/mm = ?
2 mm • 1000 μm/mm = 2000 μm

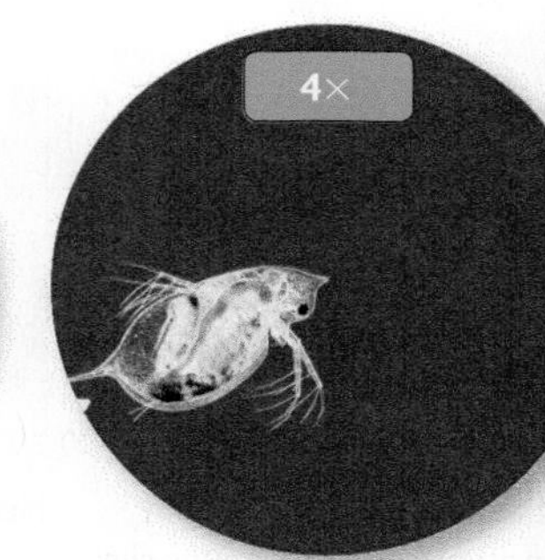

Designing Experiments

Biologists continually make observations about the natural world around them and raise questions about these observations. Designing experiments to answer these questions serves as the basis of scientific discovery.

An **experiment** is a test under controlled conditions that is made to find a cause-and-effect relationship between variables. Every well-designed experiment has a purpose and an organized, step-by-step procedure.

Determining a Purpose

A simple observation that sparks your interest can lead to a purpose for an experiment. An observation can lead to many questions, but you should choose just one question to study. From that starting point, you can do background research and examine the results of previous experiments.

- Write the purpose of your experiment as a question or problem that you want to investigate.
- Write down specific questions that you will research to find information that will help you design your experiment.

EXAMPLE

Suppose you notice that different patches of plants appear to grow better in different areas around your school. How could you use this observation to design an experiment?

Problem: How does fertilizer affect plant growth?

Research Questions
- What nutrients do plants need?
- Which fertilizers contain those nutrients?

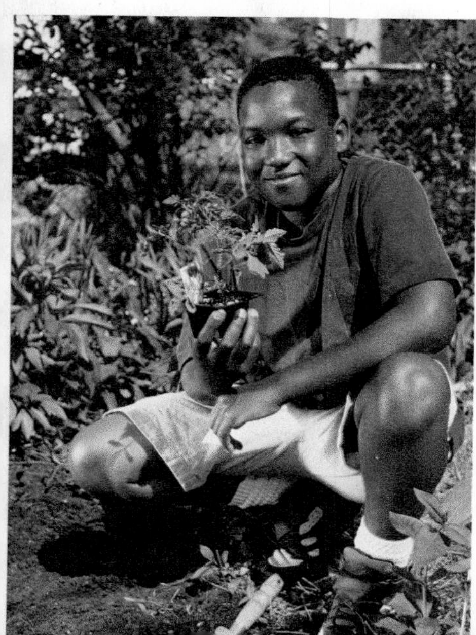

Writing a Hypothesis

A **hypothesis** is a tentative explanation for an observation. A hypothesis leads to testable predictions of what would happen if the hypothesis is valid.

An experiment is designed to test a hypothesis, not to prove that a hypothesis is correct. An experiment cannot prove a hypothesis; data from the experiment can only support it or fail to support it. Keep in mind that there are no "good-or-bad, right-or-wrong" experimental results. Even when results fail to support a hypothesis, they can lead to an idea for another experiment. Hypotheses can be written in several ways.

EXAMPLE

Hypothesis: Nitrogen is a nutrient that plants need for growth.

Testable prediction: If plants are given fertilizer that contains nitrogen, plant growth will increase.

Formalized hypothesis: If plants need the nutrient nitrogen to grow, then plants given fertilizer with nitrogen will experience an increase in growth.

Identifying Variables and Constants

All experiments include constants and variables. **Constants** are all of the factors that are kept the same—held constant—during the entire experiment. A variable is any factor that changes. The **independent variable** is the factor that you are testing and that you manipulate, or change. The **dependent variable** is the factor that you measure. The dependent variable changes, or "depends on," the independent variable. In the example below, plant growth (the dependent variable) is measured and depends on the amount of fertilizer with nitrogen (the independent variable) the plant is given.

EXAMPLE

Independent variable: amount of fertilizer with nitrogen

Dependent variable: plant growth

Constants: temperature, amount of light, intensity of light, type of plant, amount of water, frequency and time of watering, time when dependent variable is measured, amount of soil, type of soil

R11

Determining Experimental and Control Groups

An experiment to determine how two factors are related always has at least two groups—a control group and an experimental group.

- The control group is exactly the same as the experimental group—except for the factor that is being tested.
- An experiment can have one or more experimental groups. With one experimental group, you are testing whether the independent variable has an effect. With more than one experimental group, you are testing the presence of the independent variable and different amounts of it.

EXAMPLE

In our example, there are three experimental groups—each tests a different amount of fertilizer.

Experimental Groups

5 g fertilizer
10 g fertilizer
15 g fertilizer

Control Group
0 g fertilizer

Identifying Types of Data

There are two types of data: qualitative and quantitative.

- **Qualitative data** are descriptions of the dependent variable, such as color, or sound. Qualitative data can also be a simple "yes-or-no" observation about whether something happens, such as whether a plant grows.
- **Quantitative data** are numerical measurements of the dependent variable. Quantitative data include measurements of size, mass, frequency, temperature, rate, and many other factors.

Qualitative data are useful, but they cannot be statistically analyzed. No experiment is based on qualitative data alone.

Forming Operational Definitions

An **operational definition** is a description of the exact way in which you will measure the dependent variable. Your operational definition will help you determine how you will do your experiment.

EXAMPLE

Quantitative operational definition: Height of the plant's main stem (in mm) is the operational definition for the effect of fertilizer on plant growth.

Writing a Procedure

All experiments need a step-by-step written procedure. The procedure should be detailed and clear so that someone else could exactly repeat the experiment. You can think of your procedure as a cookbook recipe that has to be followed exactly. A procedure should include

- a detailed materials list
- how and when to make observations

Even if you are planning to collect only quantitative data, you can still make qualitative observations. These observations may help you to explain your data and can provide clues toward a new experiment.

If something goes wrong during your experiment, make sure you record and report it. Not following the procedure exactly can produce errors in your results that you will need to explain.

Analyzing Data

You have carried out your experiment and collected data. Do the data support your hypothesis? You cannot answer that question by looking at a list of numbers and making a guess at what they show. Without organizing and analyzing your data, it is difficult to draw conclusions from your experiment.

- Organize all of the individual measurements, or data points, in a table. Data tables provide a person evaluating your experiment with a summary of your data.
- Analyze the raw data that you organized in your table. Calculate the mean, median, mode, and range for each group in the experiment. Use whatever type of statistics are appropriate for your data.

EXAMPLE

TABLE 1. PLANT GROWTH – CONTROL GROUP

Day	Plant 1 Height (cm)	Plant 2 Height (cm)	Plant 3 Height (cm)
0	12.40	11.30	11.90
3	12.45	11.40	12.20
6	13.25	12.00	13.10
9	14.75	12.75	14.25
12	15.35	13.40	15.65
15	16.85	14.95	16.95
18	18.00	15.90	17.25
21	19.75	16.50	17.80
Total growth	7.35	5.20	5.90

Mean Growth = 6.15 cm

Presenting Results

To present your results, look at your organized and analyzed data. Look for ways to most accurately and effectively show your results. You might make a graph to show and compare the groups' means. You might make several graphs that show each group separately. When possible, use spreadsheet software to present your data.

EXAMPLE

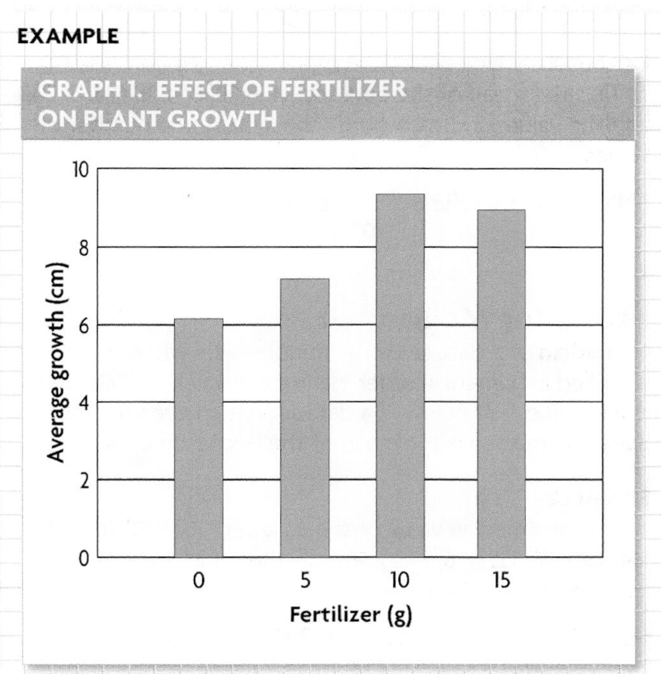

Drawing Conclusions

Compare your results with your hypothesis to determine whether your results support your hypothesis. Discuss what your results show about a relationship between the independent variable and the dependent variable. It is important to draw conclusions from your results, but do not make inferences about factors that you did not test.

EXAMPLE

Adding a fertilizer with nitrogen to soil tends to increase plant growth. Both high and moderate amounts of fertilizer tend to increase plant growth more than a low amount of fertilizer. However, high and moderate amounts of fertilizer appear to have the same effect on growth.

R13

Math and Data Analysis Handbook

Common Math Skills Used in Science

Some math skills that are often used in science are presented below.

Calculating Mean

The **mean** of a data set is the average: the sum of the values divided by the number of values.

EXAMPLE

To find the mean of the data set {14, 6, 10, 8, 4, 11, 6, 3, 5, 13}, add the values and then divide the sum by the number of values.

ANSWER $\frac{14 + 6 + 10 + 8 + 4 + 11 + 6 + 3 + 5 + 13}{10} = \frac{80}{10} = 8$

Calculating Median

The **median** of a data set is the middle value when the values are ranked in numerical order. Half of the values fall above the median value, half below. If a data set has an even number of values, the median is the mean of the two middle values.

EXAMPLE

To find the median value of the data set {582, 133, 207, 87, 164, 290, 98, 155, 196, 278 }, arrange the values in order from least to greatest. The median is the middle value.

87, 98, 133, 155, 164, 196, 207, 278, 290, 582

ANSWER The median is the mean of the two middle values, $\frac{164 + 196}{2} = 180$.

Finding Mode

The **mode** of a data set is the value that occurs most often. A data set can have more than one mode if two or more values are repeated the same number of times. A data set can have no mode if no values are repeated.

EXAMPLE

To find the mode of the data set {6, 7, 6, 4, 4, 4, 3, 6, 4, 6}, arrange the values in order from least to greatest and determine the value that occurs most often:

3, 4, 4, 4, 4, 6, 6, 6, 6, 7

ANSWER There are two modes, 4 and 6.

Using Significant Figures

The number of **significant figures** in a measurement or calculation is equal to the number of digits that are known with some degree of confidence plus the next digit, which is an estimate. When multiplying or dividing measurements, the answer should have only as many significant figures as the value with the fewest significant figures.

EXAMPLE

A density calculation is made in which 5.31 g is divided by 22 mL. The calculator output was 0.2413636 g/mL.

ANSWER There are three significant figures in the mass, but only two in the volume measurement. The density should have two significant figures: 0.24 g/mL.

Using Scientific Notation

Scientific notation is a shorthand way to write very large or very small numbers as a product of a number times a power of 10.

EXAMPLE

To convert from standard form to scientific notation:

Standard Form	Scientific Notation
720,000	7.2×10^5
5 decimal places left	Exponent is 5
0.000291	2.91×10^{-4}
4 decimal places right	Exponent is -4

To convert from scientific notation to standard form:

Scientific Notation	Standard Form
4.63×10^7	46,300,000
Exponent is 7	7 decimal places right
1.08×10^{-6}	0.00000108
Exponent is -6	6 decimal places left

Presenting Data

Scientists often communicate results of their experiments through tables and graphs. Tables and graphs organize and display information so that it can be easily interpreted.

Data Tables

A **data table** is used to organize and record data that are collected. Data tables can also help identify trends in data. Tables are organized according to the independent and dependent variables in the experiment. The **dependent variable** changes as a result of a change in the **independent variable.** The independent variable is listed in rows. The dependent variable is in columns. When repeated trials are conducted, they are recorded in subdivisions of the dependent variable column. When recording data in a table, the values of the independent variable are ordered. Most data are arranged from the smallest to largest.

The information given in each column is identified with a heading at the top of each column. When units are used, they are also included at the top of the column. Data tables should always have a title that clearly communicates what is being shown in the table. The title should make reference to the variables in the experiment.

TABLE 2. EFFECT OF HORMONES ON CELL GROWTH

Concentration of Hormone Solution (%)	Diameter of Cell Clump After 24 Hours (mm)	
	Trial 1	Trial 2
0	3	4
25	4	4
50	8	7
75	9	8

EXAMPLE

Table 2 shows data from a hypothetical experiment in which growth hormones were added to clumps of cells in a laboratory. The growth of the cell clumps was measured. In this example, the independent variable is the concentration of hormone solution. The values of the independent variable are listed in rows from lowest to highest concentration. The dependent variable, the diameter of the cell clumps after 24 hours, is in columns.

Line Graphs

A **line graph** is used to show a relationship between two variables. Line graphs are particularly useful for showing changes in variables over time. Line graphs are used when variables are continuous—that is, they can have any value including fractional values. For example, the height of a growing plant changes continuously. As a plant grows from 10 cm to 11 cm, its height can be 10.2 cm, 10.537 cm, or any other value between 10 and 11.

Line graphs are useful for representing trends. Two values are inversely related or have a **negative correlation** if an increase in the value of one variable is associated with a decrease in the value of the other variable. If an increase in one variable is associated with an increase in another variable, there is a **positive correlation** between the two variables. If there is no relationship between the two variables, they are said to have **no correlation.**

EXAMPLE

The level of the hormone insulin and length of exercise time have a negative correlation. As length of time increases, levels of insulin decrease.

GRAPH 2. BLOOD INSULIN LEVELS AND EXERCISE

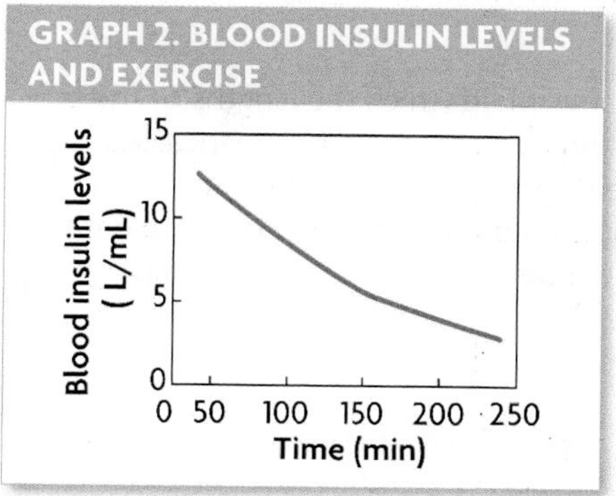

The level of the hormone glucagon and length of exercise time have a positive correlation. As length of time increases, levels of glucagon increase.

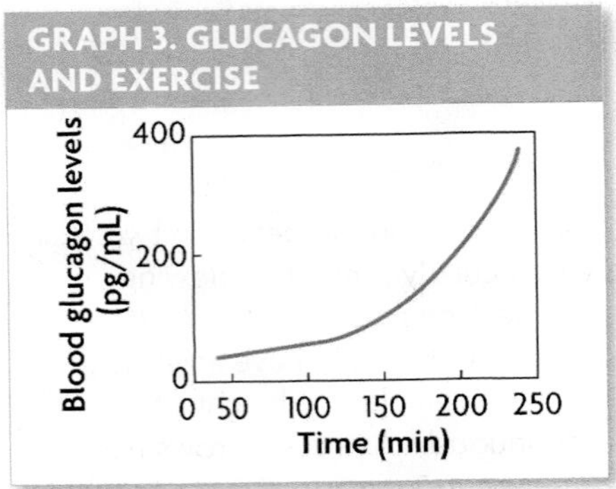

The level of the hormone ghrelin and length of exercise time have no correlation. The levels of ghrelin do not increase or decrease over time.

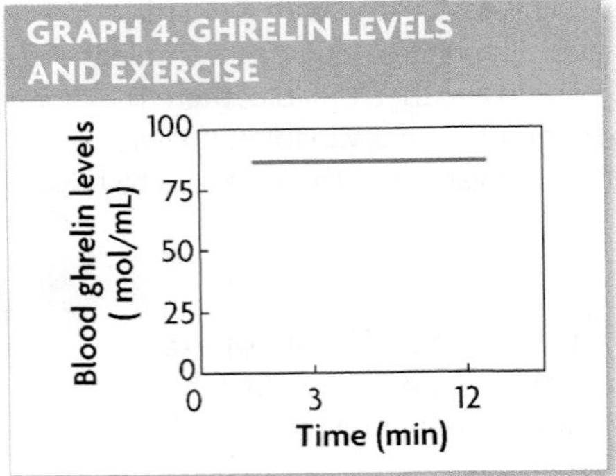

Bar Graphs

A **bar graph** is a type of graph in which the lengths of the bars are used to represent and compare data. A numerical scale is used to determine the lengths of the bars. Bar graphs can be used with either continuous or discrete data. **Discrete data** can have only whole-number values, such as the number of people or trees in a neighborhood.

EXAMPLE

The bar graph at the top of the next column contains data about the frequency of various genetic disorders in the human population. For each syndrome on the x-axis, the bar extends vertically on the y-axis to represent the incidence per 100,000 births. For example, out of 100,000 births, 111 children are born with Down syndrome.

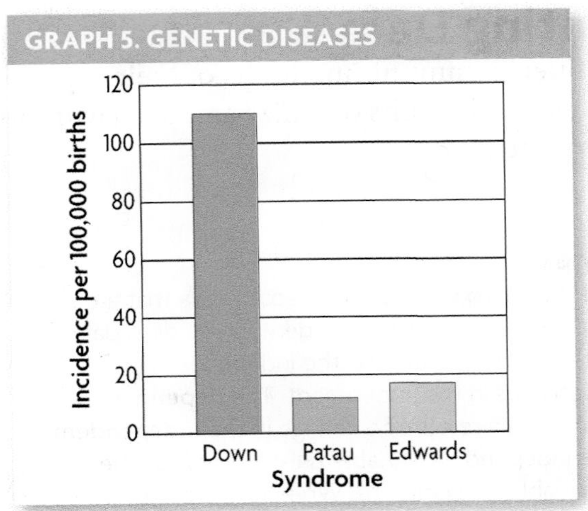

Combination Graphs

Combination graphs show two sets of data on the same graph. One set of data may be shown as a bar graph, and the other set may be shown as a line graph. The two data sets must share the same independent variable on the x-axis. Sharing the same independent variable makes it possible to determine if a relationship exists between two dependent variables.

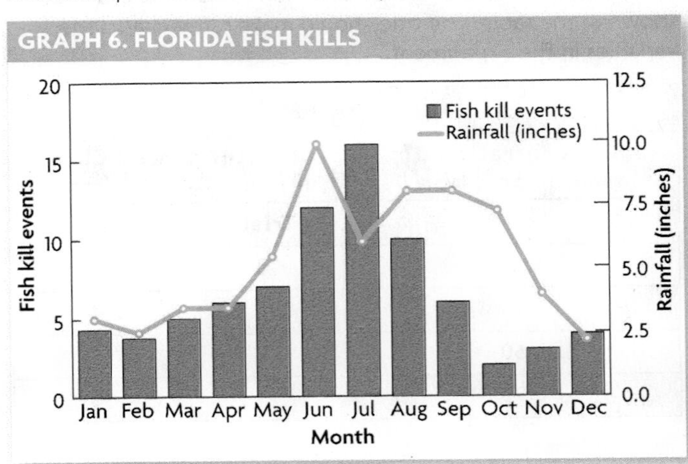

EXAMPLE

The combination graph above displays data about fish kill events and monthly rainfall in Florida.

- The y-axis on the left side of the graph represents the number of fish kill events.
- The y-axis on the right side of the graph represents rainfall amounts.
- The x-axis shows the month of data collection.

For example, the graph shows that in January there were four fish kill events and about 2.7 inches of rain.

Histograms

A **histogram** is a type of bar graph used to show the frequency distribution of data. A **frequency distribution** displays the number of cases that fit into each category of a variable.

EXAMPLE

The histogram below shows the frequency distribution of body fat in adult men. According to the histogram, the percentage body fat with the greatest frequency is 20 percent. When interpreting histograms, it is important to note that how the histogram is constructed can affect how the data are interpreted.

GRAPH 7. BODY FAT IN MEN

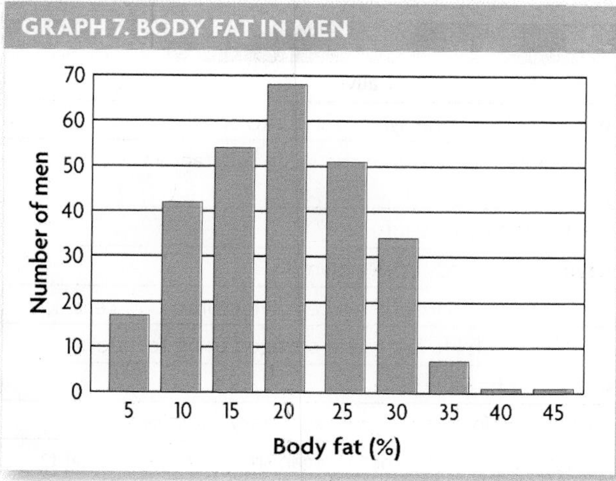

Scatterplots

A **scatterplot** is a type of graph used to identify a trend or correlation between two variables. The origin is usually at zero on both the *x*-axis and the *y*-axis. On a scatterplot, the data points are plotted but not joined together as they are on a line graph. Three types of relationships between variables that can be shown on a scatterplot are positive, negative, and no relationship. In a positive relationship, as one variable increases or decreases, the other variable increases or decreases, respectively. In a negative relationship, as one variable increases, the other variable decreases. For some variables, there is no consistent change in one variable as the other variable increases or decreases. Thus, there is no relationship between those two variables.

EXAMPLE

The scatterplot below of butter clam shell measurements shows that as the width of the clam's shell increases, its length also increases. This is a positive relationship, because as the value of one variable increases, the value of another variable increases. If it were a negative relationship, one of the variables would increase as the other decreased.

GRAPH 8. PUGET SOUND BUTTER CLAMS

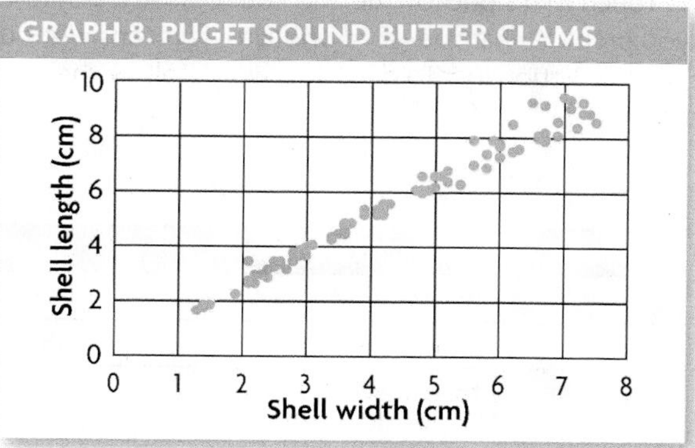

Circle Graphs

A **circle graph,** or pie chart, is a type of graph used to represent parts of a whole. It is made of a circle divided into sections that represent the frequency of each category's occurrence. To determine how much of the circle each section should cover, divide the number of occurrences for that category by the total number that the circle represents. When the result is multiplied by 100, it gives the percentage of the circle covered by the category.

EXAMPLE

In the circle graph below, the diversity of invertebrates is illustrated. Notice that all of the percentages for each category of invertebrate can be added together to equal 100. This is always the case in a circle graph, unless the values have been rounded after calculation.

GRAPH 9. INVERTEBRATE SPECIES BY GROUP

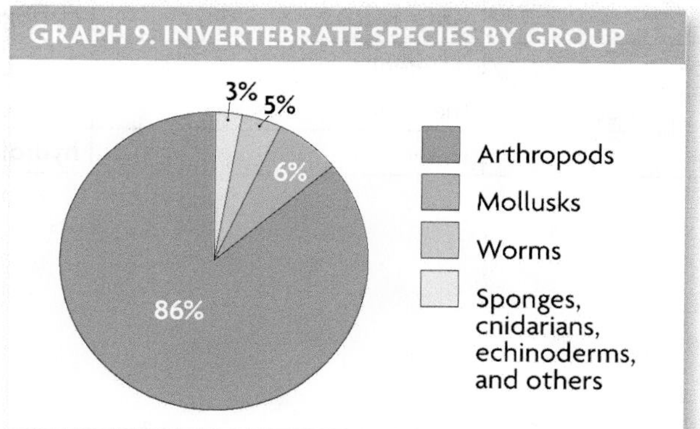

R17

Vocabulary Handbook

Greek and Latin Word Parts

Many words in the English language developed from Greek and Latin words. If you know some common Greek and Latin word parts, you can decode the meanings of other unknown words.

Suppose you read a magazine article that says, "If you see this plant, don't touch it! It's phototoxic and could cause a skin rash." How can you predict what the word *phototoxic* means without looking it up in a dictionary? To decode a word, follow the steps to the right.

Break the word into parts. Try to find the Greek or Latin word parts within the word. In the word *phototoxic*, you can find two word parts: *photo-* and *tox-*.

Look up the word parts in the table below. You will find that *photo-* means "light" and *tox-* means "poisonous."

Analyze the clues to determine a definition. In this example, your word clues are "light" and "poisonous." But there is also a clue in the sentence, "skin rash." You might guess that a phototoxic plant is one that can poison a person's skin when a chemical in the plant reacts with sunlight, and that's just what it means!

WORD PART	DEFINITION	EXAMPLE
a-	not, without	**a**biotic: factor in an ecosystem that is not alive
ab-	away, apart	**ab**sorption: movement away from one system and into another
ad-	to, toward	**ad**hesion: attraction that pulls molecules of the same substance toward one another
anti-	against	**anti**biotic: chemical that acts against bacteria
-ase	enzyme	DNA polymer**ase**: enzyme that builds DNA polymers
bi-	two	**bi**nary fission: asexual reproduction in which a cell divides into two cells
bio-	life	**bio**engineering: process by which life forms are changed using technology
cardio-	of or relating to the heart	**cardi**ac muscle: muscle in the heart
cerebr-	brain	**cerebr**al cortex: part of the brain that controls voluntary functions
chloro-	green	**chloro**phyll: green pigment in photosynthetic organisms that absorbs light
-cide	kill	insecti**cide**: chemical that kills insects
con-, co-, com-	with, together	**co**dominance: both genes expressed together
cyto-	cell	**cyto**plasm: jellylike substance within a cell
di-	two	**di**cot: plant whose seeds have two cotyledons
diplo-	double	**diplo**id: having double genetic information
ecto-	outer, outside	**ecto**therm: organism that uses the outer environment to regulate body temperature
endo-	inner, inside	**endo**skeleton: skeleton found inside of the body
-gram	write, record	clado**gram**: record of proposed evolutionary relationships
hetero-	different	**hetero**zygous: having two different alleles
homo-, homeo-	the same	**homo**zygous: having two of the same alleles
hydro-	water	**hydro**logic cycle: water cycle

WORD PART	DEFINITION	EXAMPLE
hyper-	above, over	**hyper**tonic: having a concentration above that of another solution
hypo-	below, under	**hypo**tonic: having a concentration below that of another solution
im-, in-	with, into	**im**migration: movement of individuals into a population
iso-	equal	**iso**tonic: having a concentration equal to that of another solution
-itis	inflammation	appendic**itis**: inflammation of the appendix
-lysis	decomposition, dissolving	glyco**lysis**: breakdown of glucose
meso-	middle	**meso**phyll: layer of tissue in the middle of the plant leaf
mono-	one	**mono**hybrid cross: mating that examines inheritance of one trait
-morph	form	meta**morph**osis: change in body form
neuro-	neuron	**neuro**transmitter: chemical that signals neurons
-osis	condition or process	mit**osis**: process of cell division
path-	disease	**path**ogen: disease-causing agent
peri-	around	**peri**pheral nervous system: nerves found around, or outside, the central nervous system
phago-	to eat	**phago**cytosis: engulfing, or eating, of bacteria or foreign bodies by phagocytes
-philic	having a preference for	hydro**philic**: having an attraction to water
-phobic	having an aversion for	hydro**phobic**: having an aversion to water
photo-	light	**photo**synthesis: process that uses light to make sugars
phyto-	plants	**phyto**plankton: plantlike plankton
-pod	foot	pseudo**pod**: fake foot
poly-	many	**poly**genic trait: trait resulting from the interaction or many genes
re-	again, new	**re**generation: regrowth of lost or destroyed parts or organs
sperma-	relating to sperm or seeds	**sperma**togenesis: process that forms sperm
tel-, telo-	end	**telo**phase: ending phase of mitosis
-therm	heat	endo**therm**: animal that uses its internal tissues to produce its body heat
tox-	poisonous	**tox**in: poisonous substance that can destroy cells
trans-	across	**trans**genic: an organism that contains a gene from a different species
-troph	nutrition	auto**troph**: organism that makes its own source of nutrition
-tropism	response	geo**tropism**: growth response to gravity
uni-	single, one	**uni**cellular: organism made up of one cell
zoo-	animal	**zoo**logy: study of animals

R19

Vocabulary Handbook

Academic Vocabulary

Academic vocabulary words are words that occur frequently in textbooks, instructions, and standardized tests. The words can have many meanings. Some of these words are defined below and grouped into categories. These words appear in all subject areas. The simple definitions below give only one meaning of each word, the way it might be used in this book. Learn to recognize and understand these words.

Words Used in Lab Instructions

affect to produce a change
alter to change
analyze to study the parts
assemble to put together
characteristic a distinct part or feature
component part
conduct to manage or control
confirm to use data to support a statement
consequence a result
constraint a limit
control a part of the experiment that keeps all variables constant
criteria standards for judging
demonstrate to show
dominant having the most influence or control
emerge to rise from or to come forth
extract to draw or pull out
factor an individual part of a combination, ingredient
function a job, duty, or activity
indirect not direct or to the point
method a way of doing something
model a small object made to look like the real one
modify to change
monitor to watch closely
objective a goal
obtain to get
parameter a measurable factor that can vary
potential possible but does not yet exist
process a series of actions
produce to bring forth or create
property a trait or characteristic
prove to show as true by using evidence
purpose a reason to do
represent to stand for
restrict to keep within limits
reveal to show, to make known
signal a sign for communicating
source the origin or place something began
spatial having to do with space
structure the way the parts are put together
sufficient enough, as much as needed
technique a procedure, the way something is done
trace tiny amount
trait a feature
transfer to move from one to another
variation the result of changing
vary to change or to show change

Words About Math and Measuring

approximate nearly
compile to put together into one
convert to change something to another form
cumulative increasing by adding
derive to arrive at by reasoning
dimension measurement of one part
diminish to make less or smaller
equivalent equal to
pace the rate of speed
proportion an equation stating that two ratios are equal
range the difference between the smallest and largest amounts
reduce to make smaller
solve to find the answer to a problem

Words About Importance

core the center part
crucial a must-have, extremely important
essential necessary or basic
regular usual or normal
requisite necessary, required
significance the importance
standard the usual and accepted measure for comparing

Words Found in Test Directions

analyze to study the parts
apply to put on; to be relevant
assess to figure out the value of
clarify to make clear
compose to create or write something new
critique to judge carefully
define to tell what it means
demonstrate to show
develop to add detail, to fill out
evaluate to judge or decide the value of
exhibit to show or display
indicate to point out
interpret to explain the meaning of
relate to tell; to hook to something else
revise to review and change for the better
summarize to reduce to the main points in a few words
synthesize to combine parts into a whole

Other Words Used in Tests

alternative another choice
analogy a comparison to something similar
approach to come near; the way of getting near
articulate to say or write clearly
aspect appearance from one point of view
background the knowledge behind something
concise in a few words
confirm to make sure it's true
convey to communicate or show
correspond to be similar in nature
detail an individual part
detect to discover or learn about
determine to learn the facts; to decide
emphasize to stress
establish to set up
explicit fully and clearly expressed
focus to direct to one point
general about the whole or entire thing
imply to express indirectly
optional left to a person's choice
refer to direct to a source for help
specific definite and particular
succinct in a few words
symbolize to act as a sign that stands for something else
technical used in a special job or subject
topic a subject
transition the words that link one part to the next
valid correct or well-grounded
verify to prove the truth of

Words About Organization

category a class or special division
compile to put together
consist to be made up of
correlate to put into relation to something else
differentiate to separate by differences
dominant the strongest
integrate to put together
organize to put in order
primary first or most important
sequence order
series one after another
subsequent ones coming after

Words About Ideas

abstract cannot be touched
analogy a comparison to something else
authentic real
claim a statement that says something is a fact
complex not simple
conceive to form an idea
concept an idea
concrete actual or real
credible believable
deduce to figure out by reasoning
devise to form, plan, or design
discover to notice or learn; to be the first to learn
innovation a new idea or thing
irrelevant off the point
logical reasoning in a clear manner
origin the beginning; where something began to exist
principle a basic truth, rule, or standard
relevant to the point
strategy a plan of action
subjective depends on a person's viewpoint
topic the subject of writing or speech

Words About Time

intermittent off and on
invariably always, every time
prior before
typically usually

R21

Note-taking Handbook

Graphic organizers are tools to help you take notes. Some graphic organizers are best used as you read to help you understand concepts. Others are best used to summarize or review information. Using a variety of graphic organizers will help you to understand and remember what you have learned.

During Reading

Use these graphic organizers while you are reading. They help you organize ideas in paragraphs and sections as you read them.

Process Diagrams

What is it? A process is series of steps that produces a result. Process diagrams show these steps.

How do you make it? Start with the first step, and then draw each step, one after the other, and connect them with arrows.

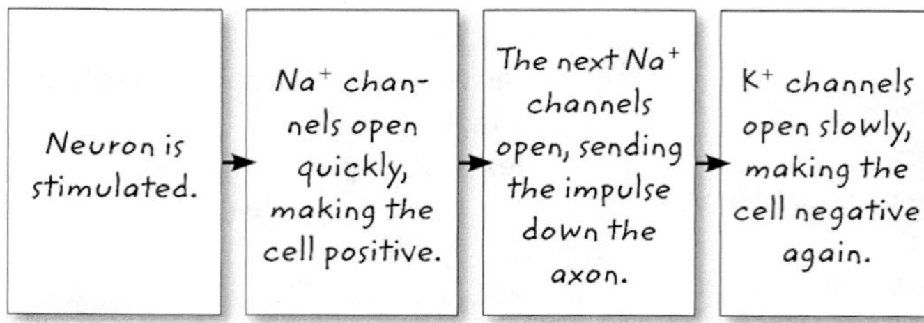

Cycle Diagrams

What is it? A cycle, such as the cell cycle, is a repeating series of events that happen one after another. Cycles do not have a beginning or an end. Cycle diagrams identify the steps in a cycle or process that repeat regularly.

How do you make it? Draw a cycle diagram to show processes that repeat without a beginning or ending. Use the arrows between the boxed steps to show the direction or order in which the cycle happens.

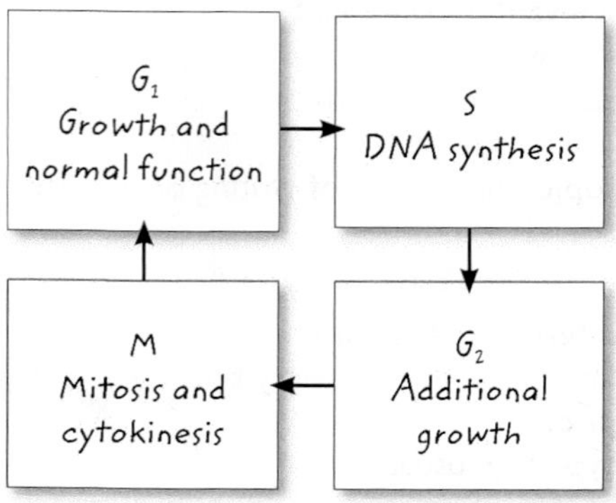

Supporting Main Ideas Notes

What is it? A main idea graphic helps separate and organize reading material into important concepts and related details of support. You can choose the main idea graphic that best fits the material. The first strategy is useful when details follow some type of order.

How do you make it? First, find the main idea. The main idea may be the title of the section, it may be labeled "main idea" or "key concept" in your book, or it may be the topic sentence in a paragraph. Write the main idea in the top box. Next, summarize or paraphrase details that help explain that idea in the boxes that follow.

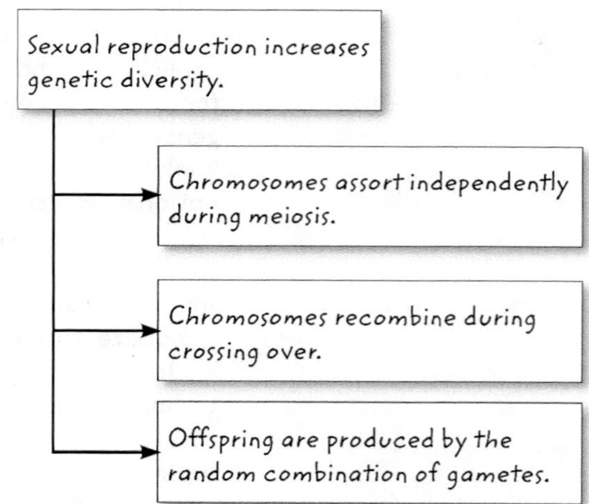

Main Idea Webs

Another way you can take notes on main ideas is to draw a web. Write the main idea in the center and the details in the web around it. This is useful when the details do not occur in any particular order.

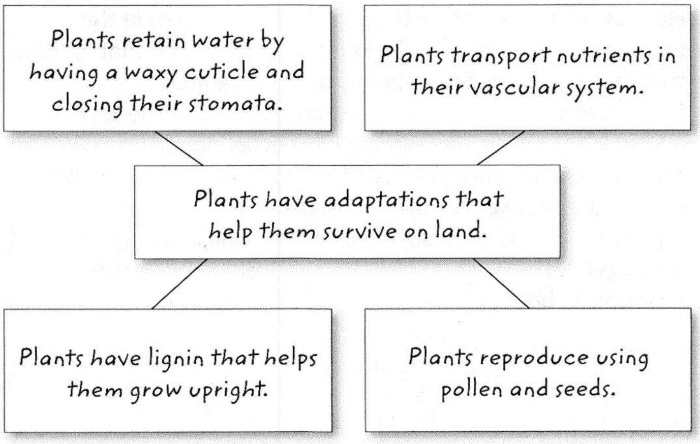

Two-Column Notes

What is it? Two-column notes is a strategy for taking notes to show

- vocabulary and their definitions
- processes or cycles and their steps
- main ideas and supporting details
- questions and possible answers
- causes and effects
- comparisons and contrasts

How do you make it? List processes, concepts, main ideas, or vocabulary in the left column of a two-column table. Write the description or explanation of the words or concepts in the right-hand column across from the words in the left column. You can also draw pictures in the right-hand column.

Leave enough space between words or concepts in the left-hand column so that you can write notes in the right column.

To study for quizzes and tests, fold your two-column notes in half vertically so you can only see the left column. Ask yourself to describe and explain the word in the left column.

Cellular Respiration	produces ATP occurs in mitochondria $C_6H_{12}O_6 + 6O_2 \rightarrow 6CO_2 + 6H_2O$
Photosynthesis	absorbs sunlight occurs in chloroplasts $6CO_2 + 6H_2O \rightarrow C_6H_{12}O_6 + 6O_2$

After Reading

Use these graphic organizers after you have read material and have taken notes on it. These organizers help you summarize the most important concepts and relate them to each other.

Cause-and-Effect Diagrams

What is it? This strategy shows cause-and-effect relationships. In the diagram below, several effects result from a single cause. Those effects can cause more effects. A cause-and-effect diagram can also be drawn to show how multiple causes can produce a single effect.

How do you make it? Write the cause in the first box, and write the effects in the boxes connected to the cause. Then think about what effects can result from the first effects, and connect them.

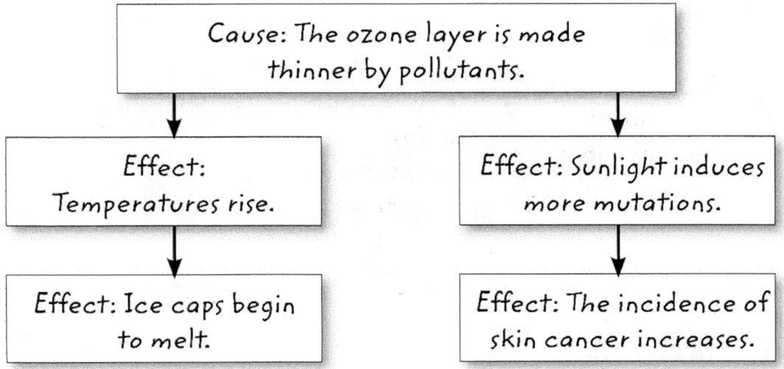

Content Frames

What is it? Content frames are tables that help you organize and condense large amounts of information.

How do you make it? To make a content frame, make a table. Label the rows along the side with characteristics. Label the columns with the topics or categories. You can also include a column for drawings or sketches.

Biome	Tropical	Temperate	Tundra
Climate	Warm and rainy	Hot summers, cold winters	Cold and dry
Vegetation	Lush, thick forests	Broadleaf forests	Mosses and similar
Example	Manaus, Brazil	Burlington, Vermont	Barrow, Alaska

Venn Diagrams

What is it? Venn diagrams help you show how two processes, ideas, or things are alike and different.

How do you make it? Draw two circles that overlap, such as the ones below. Write one of the words or processes that you are going to compare in each circle. For example, the word *arteries* is written in the left circle and the word *veins* is written in the right circle. Under *arteries,* list characteristics or traits that only arteries possess. Under *veins,* list characteristics or traits that only veins possess. In the intersection of the two circles, list the traits that both arteries and veins share.

When you finish the diagram, write a sentence to summarize the similarities and differences: "Both veins and arteries have three-tissue layers and are each part of the closed circulatory system, but arteries are thicker and more muscular, and veins are thinner and have valves."

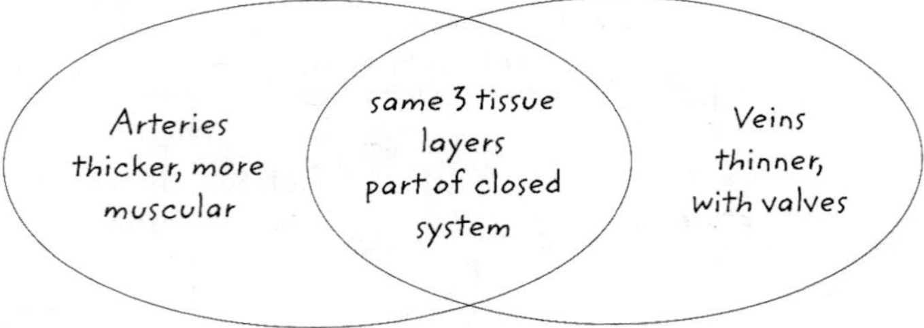

Y Diagrams

What is it? Y diagrams can be used instead of Venn diagrams to show how two processes, ideas, or things are alike and different.

How do you make it? On the top parts of the Y, list the characteristics of each topic separately. Then find the characteristics that are the same in both halves. Write them at the bottom part of the Y, and cross them out from the top half. When you finish, the top limbs of the Y show differences, and the bottom part shows similarities between the two topics.

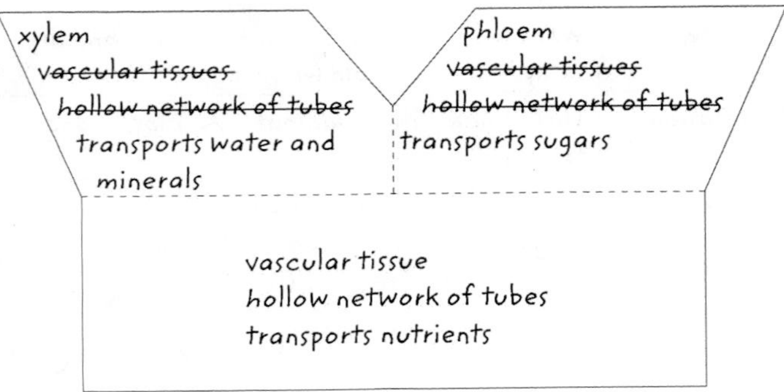

Concept Maps

What is it? A concept map is a diagram that shows the main concepts from a passage you've read as well as the relationships between those concepts. Concept maps are useful tools for organizing and reviewing information.

How do you make it? First, identify the concepts in the section you've read. A concept is a single word or short phrase that represents an idea, process, or important characteristic. Next, identify the major concept and place it at the top of your concept map. Then arrange the other concepts from the most general to the most specific. Each concept should be enclosed in an oval or box. Finally, use lines to connect concepts and write linking words on the lines. Linking words are usually verbs, verb phrases, or prepositions that show the relationship between the concepts.

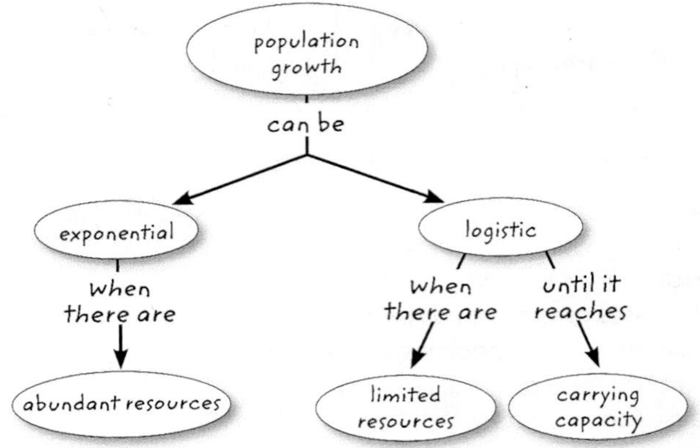

FoldNotes

FoldNotes are a useful study tool that you can use to organize concepts. One FoldNote focuses on a few main concepts. By using a FoldNote, you can learn how concepts fit together. FoldNotes are designed to make studying concepts easier, so you can remember ideas for tests.

Go to **HMDScience.com** for step-by-step illustrated instructions for how to make these FoldNotes.

Tri-Fold

A tri-fold is a useful tool that helps you track your progress. By organizing the chapter topic into what you know, what you want to know, and what you learn, you can see how much you have learned after reading a chapter.

Pyramid

A pyramid provides a unique way for taking notes. The three sides of the pyramid can summarize information into three categories. Use the pyramid as a tool for studying information in a chapter.

Booklet

A booklet is a useful tool for taking notes as you read a chapter. Each page of the booklet can contain a main topic from the chapter. Write details of each main topic on the appropriate page to create an outline of the chapter.

Layered Book

A layered book is a useful tool for taking notes as you read a chapter. The four flaps of the layered book can summarize information into four categories. Write details of each category on the appropriate flap to create a summary of the chapter.

R25

Note-taking Handbook

Double-Door Fold

A double-door fold is useful when you want to compare the characteristics of two topics. The double-door fold can organize characteristics of the two topics side by side under the flaps. Similarities and differences between the two topics can then be easily identified.

Four-Corner Fold

A four-corner fold is useful when you want to compare the characteristics of four topics. The four-corner fold can organize the characteristics of the four topics side by side under the flaps. Similarities and differences between the four topics can then be easily identified.

Table Fold

A table fold is a useful tool for comparing the characteristics of two or three topics. In a table fold, all topics are described in terms of the same characteristics so that you can easily make a thorough comparison.

Two-Panel Flip Chart

A two-panel flip chart is useful when you want to compare the characteristics of two topics. The two-panel flip chart can organize the characteristics of the two topics side by side under the flaps. Similarities and differences between the two topics can then be easily identified.

Three-Panel Flip Chart

A three-panel flip chart is useful when you want to compare the characteristics of three topics. The three-panel flip chart can organize the characteristics of the three topics side by side under the flaps. Similarities and differences between the three topics can then be easily identified.

Key-Term Fold

A key-term fold is useful for studying definitions of key terms in a chapter. Each tab can contain a key term on one side and its definition on the other. Use the key-term fold to quiz yourself on the definitions of the key terms in a chapter.

Appendix A: Classification

Living things are classified into three domains. Based on genetic evidence, systems for further classifying Domain Eukarya are changing. This chart presents an approach using four superclasses.

DOMAIN		COMMON NAME AND DESCRIPTION
DOMAIN ARCHAEA		
ARCHAEA  (Pyrococcus)		**Archaea** Single-celled prokaryotes (no nucleus or other membrane-bound organelles) with distinct rRNA sequences. Lack peptidoglycan cell walls. Reproduce asexually. Live in some of Earth's most extreme environments, including salty, hot, acidic, and the deep ocean. They are often grouped according to where they live. Examples: *Sulfolobus solfataricus, Pyrococcus.*
DOMAIN BACTERIA		
BACTERIA 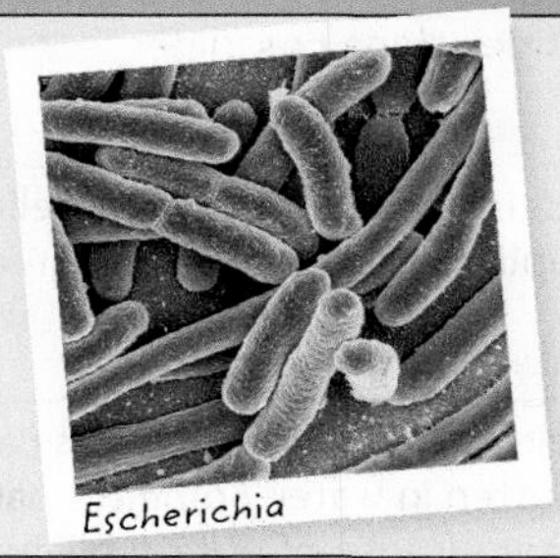 (Escherichia)		**Bacteria** Single-celled prokaryotes (no nucleus or other membrane-bound organelles), most with peptidoglycan cell walls. Live in all types of environments, including the human body. Reproduce by binary fission or budding. Examples: blue-green bacteria (cyanobacteria), *Streptococcus, Bacillus, Escherichia.*
DOMAIN EUKARYA		
EUKARYA		**Eukaryotes** Cells are larger than archaea or bacteria and are eukaryotic (have a nucleus containing DNA, as well as other membrane-bound organelles). Can be single-celled, colonial, or multicellular.
Superclass Excavata		
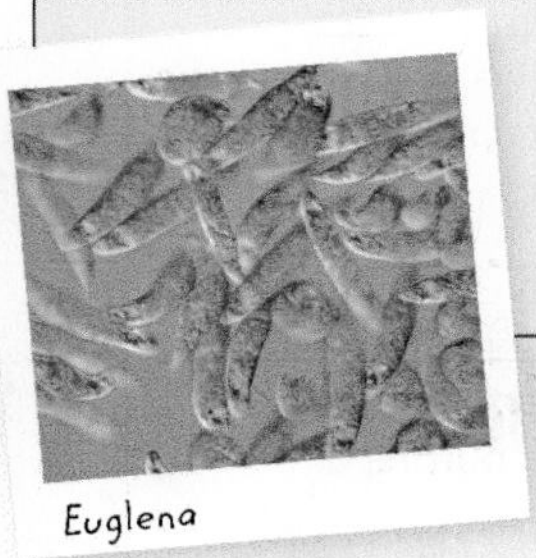 (Euglena)	Euglenozoa	**Euglenoids** Single-celled, with one or two flagella. Most live in fresh water. Some are heterotrophs, others are photosynthetic autotrophs. Examples: *Euglena, Trypanosoma.*
	Zoomastigophora	**Zooflagellates** Have usually one or two long, hairlike extensions called flagella. Sometimes called Zoomastigina. Example: *Trichomonas.*

R27

Appendix A: Classification

DOMAIN	PHYLUM	COMMON NAME AND DESCRIPTION
Superclass Chromalveolata		
	Apicomplexa	**Sporozoans** Parasites that can move by body flexion or gliding. Cause diseases in animals such as birds and humans. Example: *Plasmodium.*
	Foraminifera	**Forams** Use footlike extensions called pseudopods to move. Have multichambered shells made of organic material. Most are marine. Example: *Rosalina globularis.*
	Ciliophora	**Ciliates** Have many short, hairlike extensions called cilia, which they use for feeding and movement. Example: *Paramecium.*
	Dinoflagellata	**Dinoflagellates** Single-celled, with two flagella that allow cell to turn over and change direction. Some species are autotrophic, some are heterotrophic. In great numbers, some species can cause red tides along coastlines. Example: *Noctiluca.*
	Chrysophyta	**Chrysophytes** Also called yellow algae or golden-brown algae. Single-celled. Named for the yellow pigments in their chloroplasts (*chrysophyte,* in Greek, means "golden plant"). Example: *Thallasiosira.*
	Oomycota	**Water molds and downy mildews** Produce thin, cottonlike extensions called hyphae. Feed from dead or decaying material, often in water. Some are parasites of plants or fish. Example: *Phytophthora infestans* (cause of potato blight).
	Bacillariophyta	**Diatoms** Single-celled with glasslike shells made of silica. Shells serve as external skeleton. Example: *Amorpha ovalis.*
	Phaeophyta	**Brown algae** Multicellular, photosynthetic. Live mainly in salt water. Contain the pigment fucoxanthin, which is the source of their brown color. Includes kelp. Example: *Sargassum.*
Superclass Archaeplastida		
	Rhodophyta	**Red algae** Multicellular, photosynthetic. Most live in salt water. Contain a red pigment called phycoerythrin that makes these organisms red, purple, or reddish-black. Example: coralline algae.
	Chlorophyta	**Green algae** May be single-celled, colonial, or multicellular. Contain both chlorophyll-*a* and chlorophyll-*b*, which are the same photosynthetic pigments found in land plants. Examples: *Pediastrum, Ulva, Spirogyra.*

Paramecium

Diatom

Red Algae

KINGDOM	PHYLUM	COMMON NAME AND DESCRIPTION
Superclass Archaeplastida		
PLANTAE		**Plants** Multicellular photosynthetic autotrophs. Most have adapted to life on land. Cells have thick cell walls made of cellulose.
	Bryophyta	**Mosses** Nonvascular plants. Gametophyte generation is a grasslike plant. Most live in moist environments. Example: sphagnum (peat) moss.
	Hepatophyta	**Liverworts** Nonvascular plants named for the liver-shaped gametophyte generation. Most live in moist environments. Example: *Marchantia.*
	Anthocerotophyta	**Hornworts** Nonvascular plants named for the visible hornlike structures with which they reproduce. Live in moist, cool environments. Example: *Dendroceros.*
	Lycophyta	**Club mosses** Seedless vascular plants. Some resemble tiny pine trees. Live in wooded environments. Example: *Lycopodium* (ground pine).
	Pterophyta	**Ferns, whisk ferns, and horsetails** Seedless vascular plants. Most have fringed leaves. Whisk ferns sometimes classified in phylum Psilotophyta; horsetails sometimes classified in phylum Sphenophyta. Example: *Psilotum* (whisk fern).
	Cycadophyta	**Cycads** Gymnosperms; reproduce with seeds produced in large cones. Slow-growing, palmlike plants that grow in tropical environments. Example: sago palms
	Ginkgophyta	**Ginkgo biloba** Only species in phylum, a tree often planted in urban environments. Gymnosperm; reproduces with seeds that hang from branches.
	Coniferophyta	**Conifers** Gymnosperms; reproduce with seeds produced in cones. Usually evergreen. Examples: pines, spruces, firs, sequoias.
	Anthophyta	**Flowering plants** Also called angiosperms. Reproduce with seeds produced in flowers. Seeds are surrounded by fruit, which is the ripened plant ovary. **CLASS: Monocotyledonae** Monocots. Embryos have one cotyledon. Leaves with parallel veins, flower parts in multiples of three, and vascular bundles scattered throughout the stem. Examples: irises, tulips, grasses. **CLASS: Dicotyledonae** Dicots. Embryos have two cotyledons. Leaves with netlike veins, flower parts in multiples of four or five, and vascular bundles arranged in rings. Examples: roses, daisies, deciduous trees, foxgloves.
Superclass Unikonta		
	Acrasiomycota	**Cellular slime molds** Live partly as free-living single-celled organisms, often in the soil. When food is scarce, they can fuse together to form a many-celled mass that moves as if it's one organism. Example: *Dictyostelium.*
	Myxomycota	**Plasmodial slime molds** Live most of their lives as a mass of cytoplasm that is actually one large, slimy cell with many nuclei. Example: *Physarium* (dog-vomit slime mold).

Sago palm

Foxglove

Slime mold

R29

Appendix A: Classification

KINGDOM	PHYLUM	COMMON NAME AND DESCRIPTION
FUNGI		**Fungi** Eukaryotic, heterotrophic, usually multicellular but some are single-celled. Cells have a thick cell wall usually containing chitin. Obtain nutrients through absorption. Often function as decomposers.
	Chytridiomycota	**Chytrids** Oldest and simplest fungi, usually aquatic. Have flagellated spores. Some are decomposers, some are parasitic. Example: chytrid frog fungus.
	Ascomycota	**Sac fungi** Reproduce with spores formed in an ascus. Includes single-celled yeasts as well as morels, truffles, and molds. Example: *Penicillium.*
	Zygomycota	**Bread molds** Obtain food by decomposing dead or decaying matter. Mold hyphae grow into food source and digest it. Some are parasitic. Example: black bread molds.
	Basidiomycota	**Club fungi** Multicellular with club-shaped fruiting bodies. Examples: mushrooms, puffballs, bracket fungi, rusts, smuts.
ANIMALIA		**Animals** Multicellular, eukaryotic heterotrophs with cells supported by collagen. Cells lack cell walls. Most have cells that are organized into specialized tissues, which make up organs. Most reproduce sexually.
	Porifera	**Sponges** Spend most of their lives fixed to the ocean floor. Feed by filtering water (containing nutrients and small organisms) through their body. Reproduce sexually and asexually. Example: *Euplectella* (Venus's flower basket).
	Cnidaria	**Cnidarians** Aquatic animals with a radial (spokelike) body shape; named for their stinging cells (cnidocytes). Have two basic body forms: the polyp and the medusa. May produce sexually and asexually. **CLASS: Hydrozoa** Alternate between polyp and medusa stages. Medusas reproduce sexually, polyps reproduce asexually. Example: hydras. **CLASS: Scyphozoa** Dominant medusa form. Example: jellyfish. **CLASS: Anthozoa** Dominant polyp form; there is no medusa stage. May be colonial or solitary. Central body surrounded by tentacles. Examples: sea anemones, corals. **CLASS: Cubozoa** Dominant cube-shaped medusa form with well-developed eyes. Examples: tropical box jellyfish, sea wasps.

Sac fungus

Toad stool mushroom

Giant anemone

KINGDOM	PHYLUM	COMMON NAME AND DESCRIPTION
	Ctenophora	**Comb jellies** Resemble jellyfish; named for the comblike rows of cilia (hairlike extensions) that are used for movement. Example: *Pleurobrachia.*
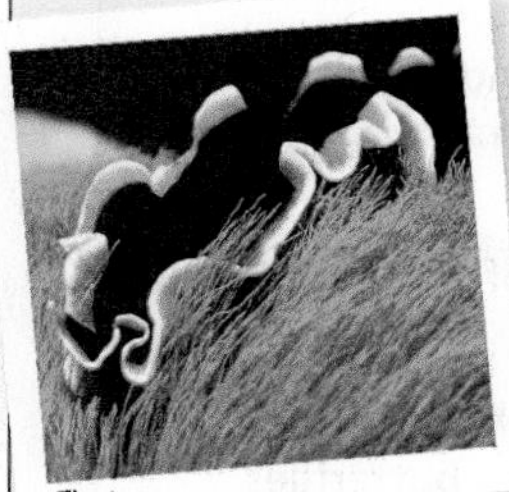 Flatworm	Platyhelminthes	**Flatworms** Thin, flattened worms with simple tissues and sensory organs. Includes planaria and tapeworms, which cause diseases in humans and other hosts. **CLASS: Turbellaria (turbellarians)** Free-living carnivores or scavengers that move with cilia. Example: planarians. **CLASS: Trematoda (flukes)** Internal parasites; life cycle often includes alternation of hosts. Example: *Schistosoma.* **CLASS: Cestoda (tapeworms)** Internal parasites; segmented body and head with suckers or hooks for attaching to host. Example: dog tapeworm.
 Nautilus	Mollusca	**Mollusks** Soft-bodied aquatic animals that usually have an outer shell. **CLASS: Gastropoda (gastropods)** Use muscular foot for movement. Have a distinct head and complete digestive tract. Most have a chambered shell. Examples: snails and slugs. **CLASS: Pelecypoda (bivalves)** Soft body protected by two hard shells that are hinged together. Most are filter feeders. Examples: clams, oysters, mussels, scallops. **CLASS: Cephalopoda (cephalopods)** Carnivores with well-developed eyes and nervous systems. Examples: squids, octopuses, nautiluses.
 Leeches	Annelida	**Segmented worms** Body is made of many similar segments. **CLASS: Polychaeta (polychaetes)** Marine worms with a pair of appendages on each segment. Have many setae. Examples: fan worms, featherduster worms. **CLASS: Oligochaeta (oligochaetes)** Earthworms; live in soil or fresh water. Have no appendages. Have few setae. Example: *Tubifex tubifex* (sludge worm). **CLASS: Hirudinea (leeches)** Most live in fresh water. Have flattened body with no appendages. Suckers at both ends; carnivores or blood-sucking parasites. Example: *Macrobdella decora* (medicinal leech).
	Nematoda	**Roundworms** Small, round worms; many species are parasites, causing diseases in humans, such as trichinosis and elephantiasis. Example: *Trichinella.*

R31

Appendix A: Classification

KINGDOM	PHYLUM	COMMON NAME AND DESCRIPTION
ANIMALIA (continued) Scorpion Dragonfly	Arthropoda	Animals with an outer skeleton called an exoskeleton, and jointed appendages such as legs or wings. **SUBPHYLUM: Trilobita (trilobites)** Includes the trilobites, which are all extinct. Important part of the Paleozoic marine ecosystems for 300 million years. Bodies divided into three lobes. Bottom feeders. **SUBPHYLUM: Crustacea (crustaceans)** Live in all of the oceans, freshwater streams, and on land. Have chewing mouthparts and two pairs of antennae. Examples: crabs, lobsters, copepods, pill bugs. **SUBPHYLUM: Chelicerata (chelicerates)** First pair of appendages specialized as daggerlike mouthparts that are used for tearing food; no antennae. Examples: horseshoe crabs, scorpions, spiders, mites, ticks. **SUBPHYLUM: Uniramia** Most live on land. Have one pair of antennae and chewing mouthparts. **CLASS: Insecta (insects)** Have three body segments with three pairs of legs attached to second segment. Examples: ants, bees, butterflies, cockroaches, flies, mosquitoes, dragonflies. **CLASS: Chilopoda (centipedes)** Body divided into many segments with one pair of legs per segment. Carnivores; first pair of legs bears fangs for capturing prey. Example: *Scutigera coleoptrata* (common house centipede). **CLASS: Diplopoda (millipedes)** Body divided into many segments with two pairs of legs per segment. Most are herbivores. Example: *Glomeris* (pill millipede).
Sea star	Echinodermata	Adults are slow-moving marine animals with radial symmetry; larvae have bilateral symmetry. Have an internal skeleton, a water vascular system, and a complete digestive system. Some can regenerate limbs. **CLASS: Crinoidea (crinoids)** Filter feeders that remain attached to a surface such as the ocean floor. Examples: feather stars, sea lilies. **CLASS: Asteroidea (sea stars)** Star-shaped bottom dwellers that may be suspension feeders, opportunistic feeders, or carnivorous predators. Example: *Acanthaster planci* (crown-of-thorns starfish). **CLASS: Ophiuroidea** Most have five long spindly arms that they use to help move and feed; tube feet lack suckers. Examples: brittle stars, basket stars. **CLASS: Echinoidea** Have a five-part body plan but no arms; body covered with projections or spines. Most graze for food on ocean floor. Examples: sea urchins, sea biscuits, sand dollars. **CLASS: Holothuroidea (sea cucumbers)** Fleshy animals with long, cylindrical shape. Tentacles are used to capture food; also feed on sediment from ocean floor. Example: *Holothuria*.

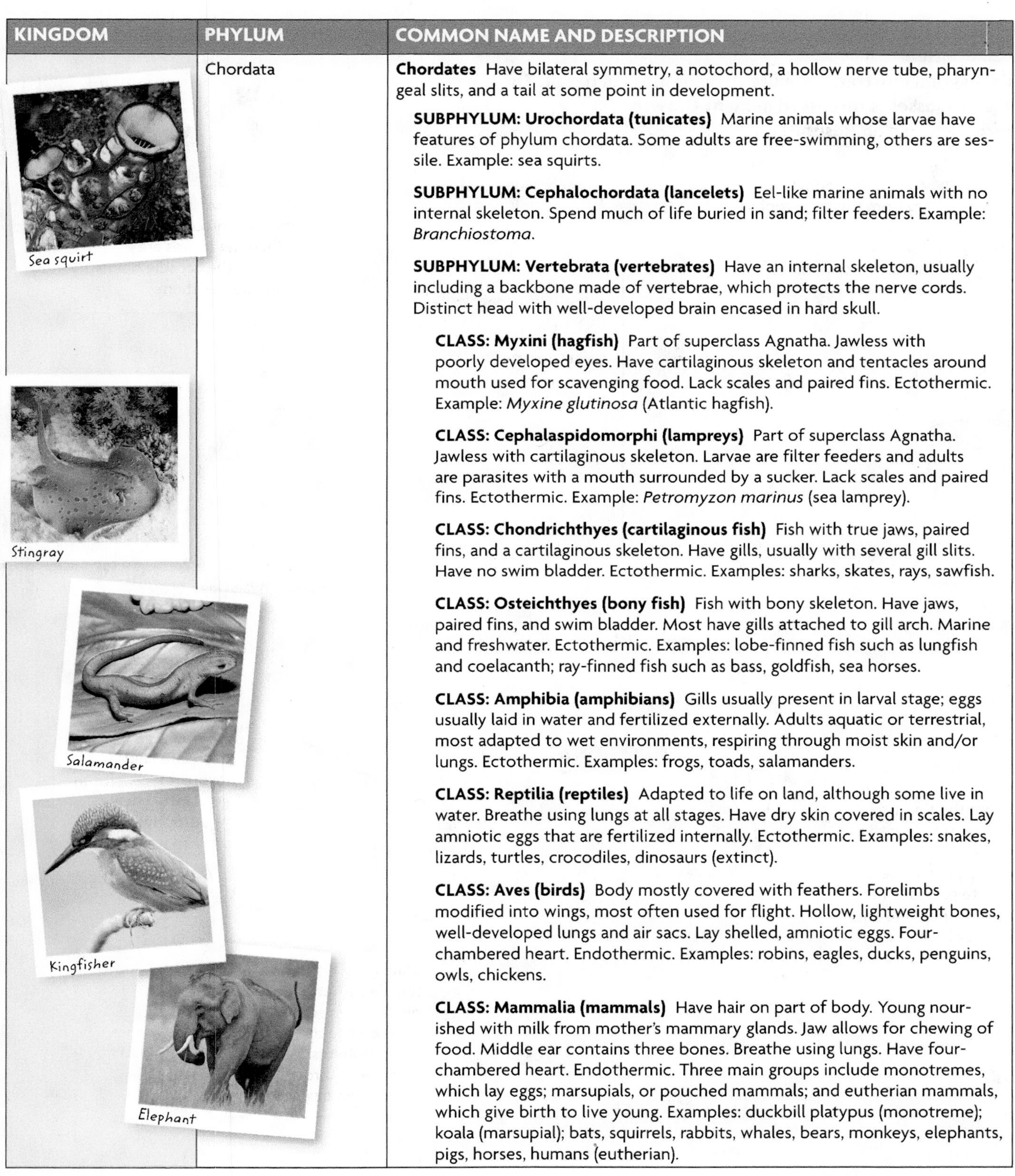

Sea squirt

Stingray

Salamander

Kingfisher

Elephant

KINGDOM	PHYLUM	COMMON NAME AND DESCRIPTION
	Chordata	**Chordates** Have bilateral symmetry, a notochord, a hollow nerve tube, pharyngeal slits, and a tail at some point in development. **SUBPHYLUM: Urochordata (tunicates)** Marine animals whose larvae have features of phylum chordata. Some adults are free-swimming, others are sessile. Example: sea squirts. **SUBPHYLUM: Cephalochordata (lancelets)** Eel-like marine animals with no internal skeleton. Spend much of life buried in sand; filter feeders. Example: *Branchiostoma*. **SUBPHYLUM: Vertebrata (vertebrates)** Have an internal skeleton, usually including a backbone made of vertebrae, which protects the nerve cords. Distinct head with well-developed brain encased in hard skull. **CLASS: Myxini (hagfish)** Part of superclass Agnatha. Jawless with poorly developed eyes. Have cartilaginous skeleton and tentacles around mouth used for scavenging food. Lack scales and paired fins. Ectothermic. Example: *Myxine glutinosa* (Atlantic hagfish). **CLASS: Cephalaspidomorphi (lampreys)** Part of superclass Agnatha. Jawless with cartilaginous skeleton. Larvae are filter feeders and adults are parasites with a mouth surrounded by a sucker. Lack scales and paired fins. Ectothermic. Example: *Petromyzon marinus* (sea lamprey). **CLASS: Chondrichthyes (cartilaginous fish)** Fish with true jaws, paired fins, and a cartilaginous skeleton. Have gills, usually with several gill slits. Have no swim bladder. Ectothermic. Examples: sharks, skates, rays, sawfish. **CLASS: Osteichthyes (bony fish)** Fish with bony skeleton. Have jaws, paired fins, and swim bladder. Most have gills attached to gill arch. Marine and freshwater. Ectothermic. Examples: lobe-finned fish such as lungfish and coelacanth; ray-finned fish such as bass, goldfish, sea horses. **CLASS: Amphibia (amphibians)** Gills usually present in larval stage; eggs usually laid in water and fertilized externally. Adults aquatic or terrestrial, most adapted to wet environments, respiring through moist skin and/or lungs. Ectothermic. Examples: frogs, toads, salamanders. **CLASS: Reptilia (reptiles)** Adapted to life on land, although some live in water. Breathe using lungs at all stages. Have dry skin covered in scales. Lay amniotic eggs that are fertilized internally. Ectothermic. Examples: snakes, lizards, turtles, crocodiles, dinosaurs (extinct). **CLASS: Aves (birds)** Body mostly covered with feathers. Forelimbs modified into wings, most often used for flight. Hollow, lightweight bones, well-developed lungs and air sacs. Lay shelled, amniotic eggs. Four-chambered heart. Endothermic. Examples: robins, eagles, ducks, penguins, owls, chickens. **CLASS: Mammalia (mammals)** Have hair on part of body. Young nourished with milk from mother's mammary glands. Jaw allows for chewing of food. Middle ear contains three bones. Breathe using lungs. Have four-chambered heart. Endothermic. Three main groups include monotremes, which lay eggs; marsupials, or pouched mammals; and eutherian mammals, which give birth to live young. Examples: duckbill platypus (monotreme); koala (marsupial); bats, squirrels, rabbits, whales, bears, monkeys, elephants, pigs, horses, humans (eutherian).

R33

Appendix B: Life Cycles

Moss Life Cycle

This diagram illustrates the life cycle of moss in detail. The life cycle of mosses is discussed in Plant Growth, Reproduction, and Response.

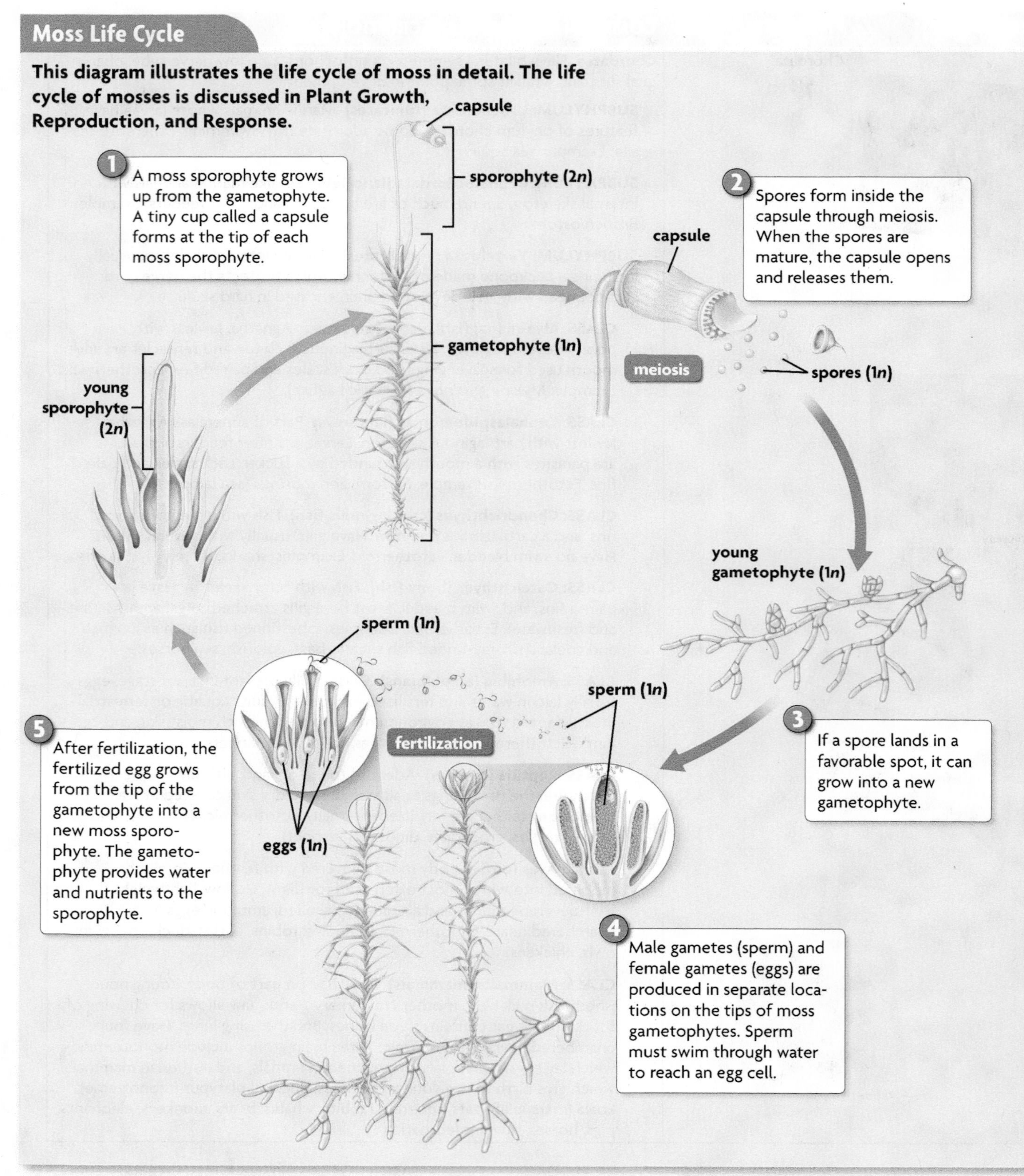

capsule
sporophyte (2n)
gametophyte (1n)
1 A moss sporophyte grows up from the gametophyte. A tiny cup called a capsule forms at the tip of each moss sporophyte.
capsule
2 Spores form inside the capsule through meiosis. When the spores are mature, the capsule opens and releases them.
meiosis
spores (1n)
young sporophyte (2n)
young gametophyte (1n)
sperm (1n)
sperm (1n)
fertilization
3 If a spore lands in a favorable spot, it can grow into a new gametophyte.
eggs (1n)
5 After fertilization, the fertilized egg grows from the tip of the gametophyte into a new moss sporophyte. The gametophyte provides water and nutrients to the sporophyte.
4 Male gametes (sperm) and female gametes (eggs) are produced in separate locations on the tips of moss gametophytes. Sperm must swim through water to reach an egg cell.

Fern Life Cycle

This diagram illustrates the life cycle of ferns in detail. The life cycle of ferns is discussed in Plant Growth, Reproduction, and Response.

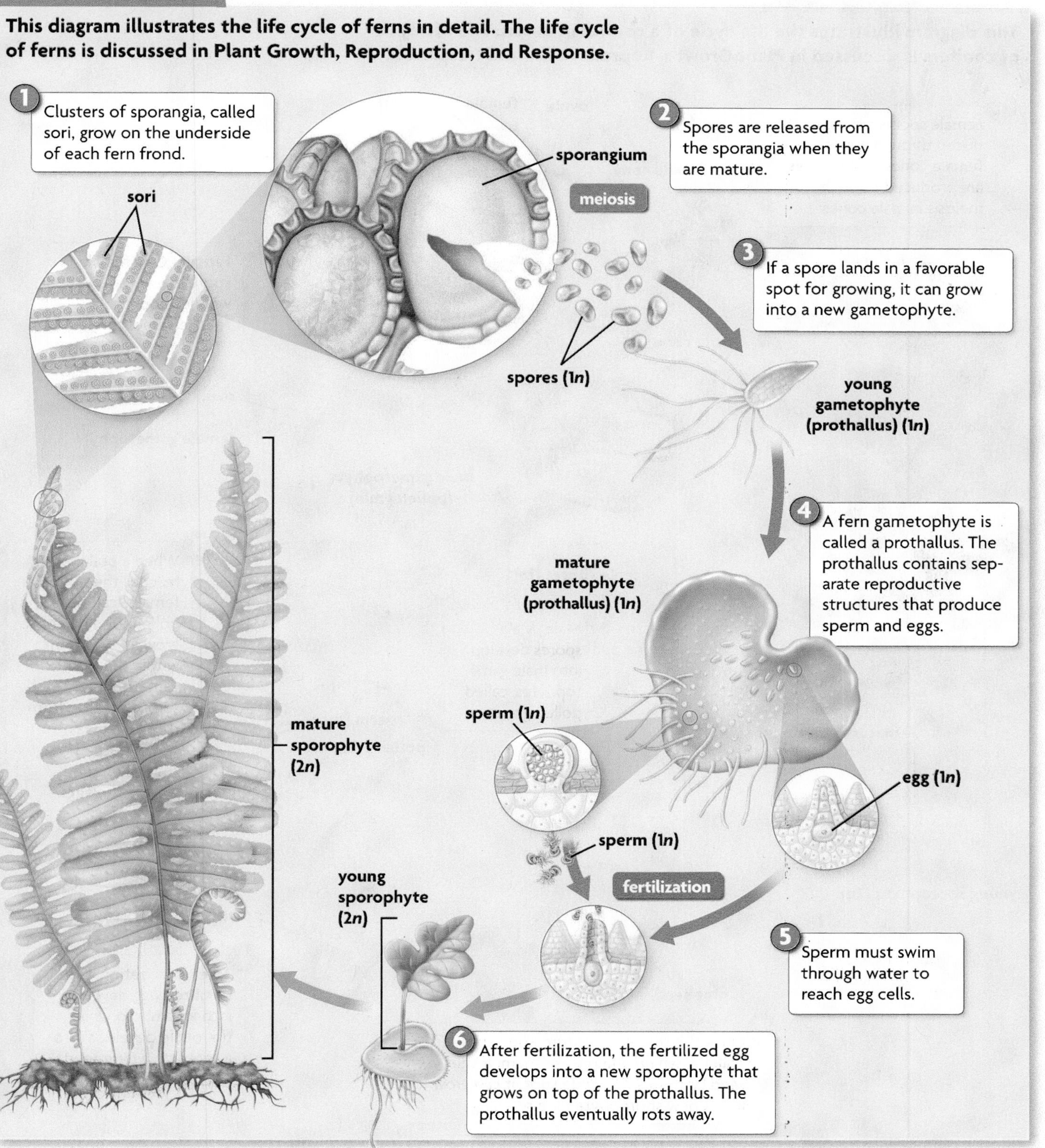
1 Clusters of sporangia, called sori, grow on the underside of each fern frond.
sori
sporangium
meiosis
2 Spores are released from the sporangia when they are mature.
3 If a spore lands in a favorable spot for growing, it can grow into a new gametophyte.
spores (1n)
young gametophyte (prothallus) (1n)
4 A fern gametophyte is called a prothallus. The prothallus contains separate reproductive structures that produce sperm and eggs.
mature gametophyte (prothallus) (1n)
mature sporophyte (2n)
sperm (1n)
egg (1n)
sperm (1n)
fertilization
young sporophyte (2n)
5 Sperm must swim through water to reach egg cells.
6 After fertilization, the fertilized egg develops into a new sporophyte that grows on top of the prothallus. The prothallus eventually rots away.

R35

Appendix B: Life Cycles

Conifer Life Cycle

This diagram illustrates the life cycle of a conifer in detail. The life cycle of conifers is discussed in Plant Growth, Reproduction, and Response.

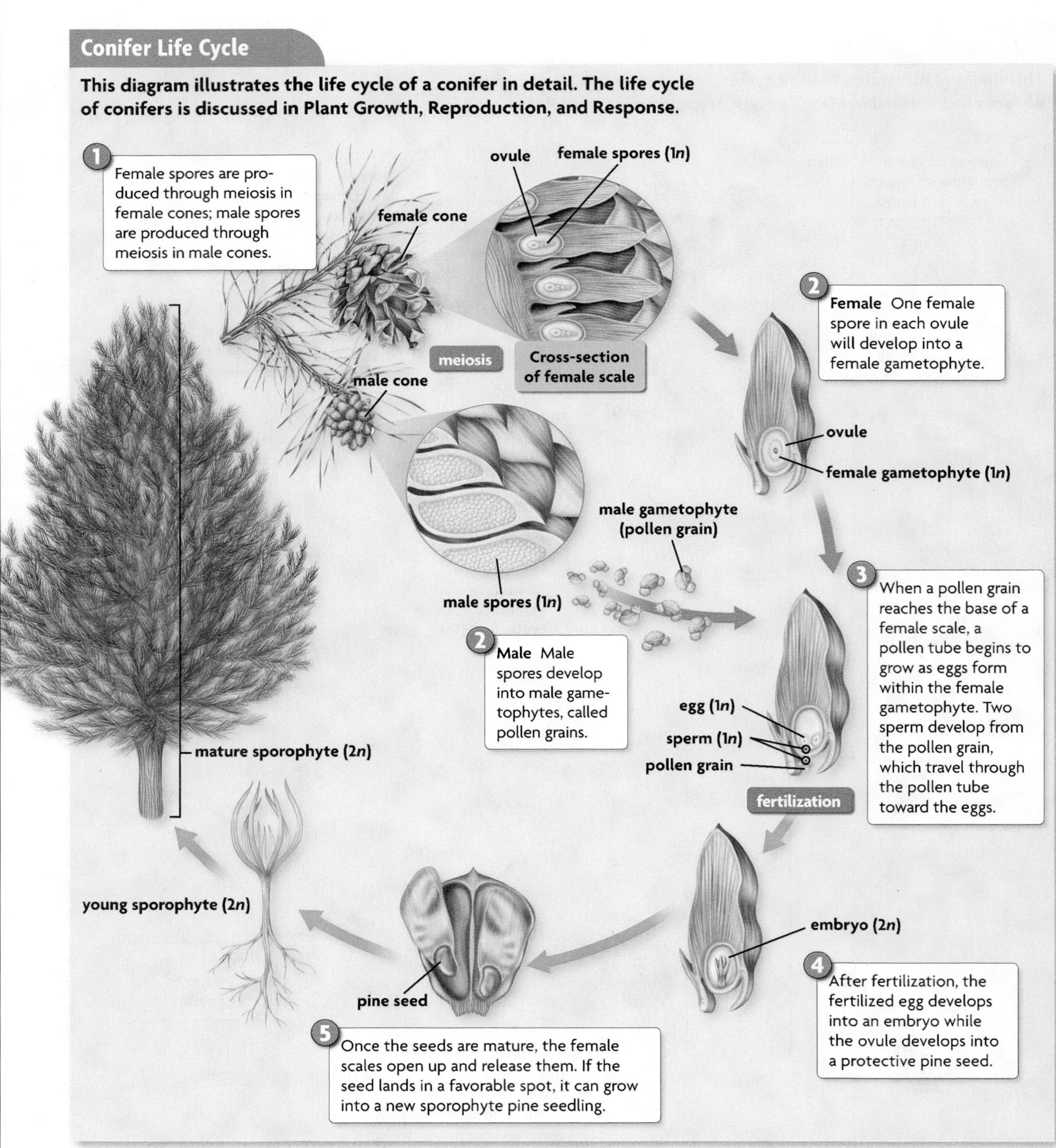

1 Female spores are produced through meiosis in female cones; male spores are produced through meiosis in male cones.
ovule
female spores (1n)
female cone
meiosis
Cross-section of female scale
male cone
2 Female One female spore in each ovule will develop into a female gametophyte.
ovule
female gametophyte (1n)
male gametophyte (pollen grain)
male spores (1n)
2 Male Male spores develop into male gametophytes, called pollen grains.
3 When a pollen grain reaches the base of a female scale, a pollen tube begins to grow as eggs form within the female gametophyte. Two sperm develop from the pollen grain, which travel through the pollen tube toward the eggs.
egg (1n)
sperm (1n)
pollen grain
fertilization
mature sporophyte (2n)
young sporophyte (2n)
embryo (2n)
4 After fertilization, the fertilized egg develops into an embryo while the ovule develops into a protective pine seed.
pine seed
5 Once the seeds are mature, the female scales open up and release them. If the seed lands in a favorable spot, it can grow into a new sporophyte pine seedling.

Flowering Plant Life Cycle

This diagram illustrates the life cycle of a flowering plant in detail. The life cycle of flowering plants is discussed in Plant Growth, Reproduction, and Response.

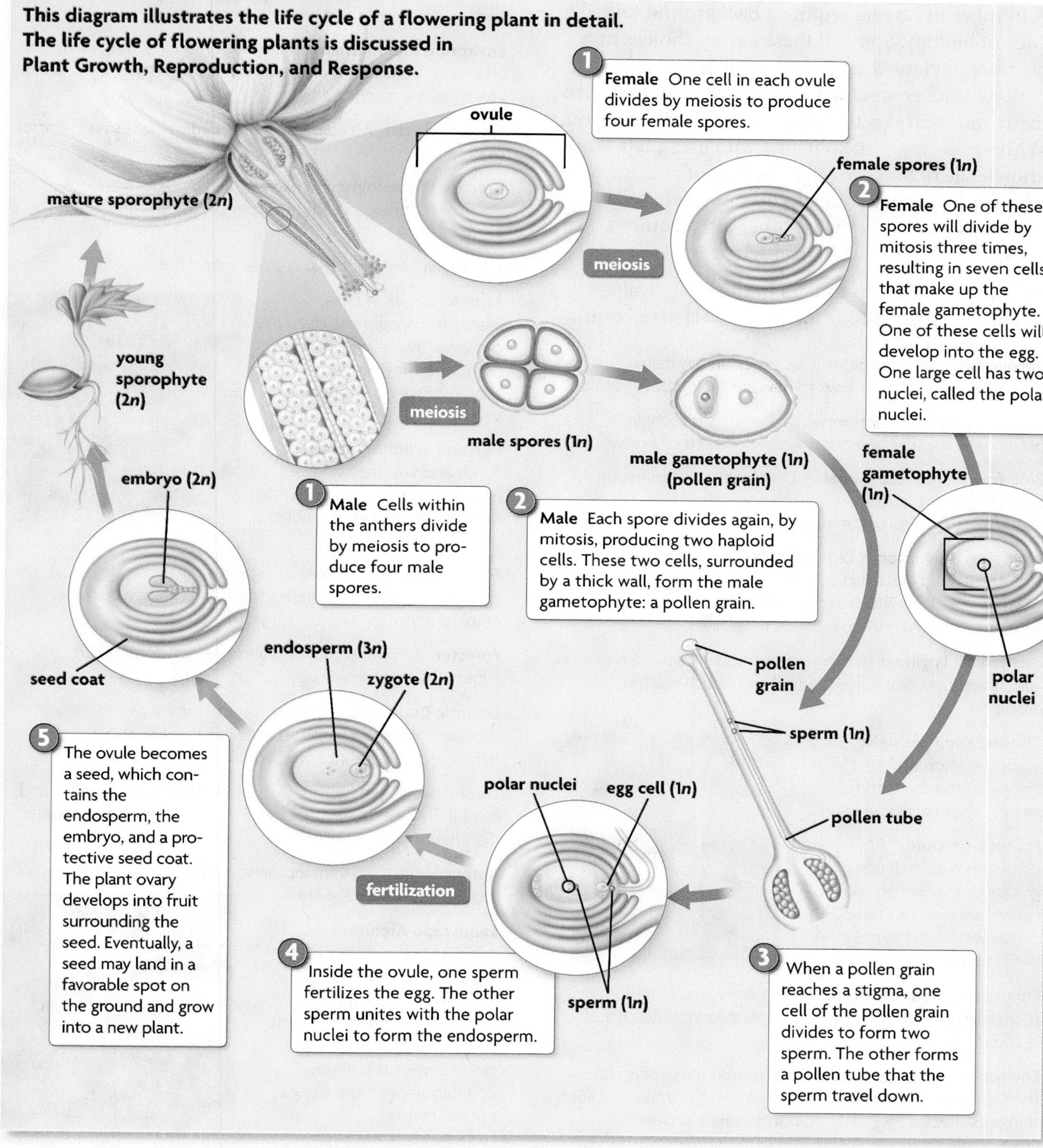

1 **Female** One cell in each ovule divides by meiosis to produce four female spores.

2 **Female** One of these spores will divide by mitosis three times, resulting in seven cells that make up the female gametophyte. One of these cells will develop into the egg. One large cell has two nuclei, called the polar nuclei.

1 **Male** Cells within the anthers divide by meiosis to produce four male spores.

2 **Male** Each spore divides again, by mitosis, producing two haploid cells. These two cells, surrounded by a thick wall, form the male gametophyte: a pollen grain.

3 When a pollen grain reaches a stigma, one cell of the pollen grain divides to form two sperm. The other forms a pollen tube that the sperm travel down.

4 Inside the ovule, one sperm fertilizes the egg. The other sperm unites with the polar nuclei to form the endosperm.

5 The ovule becomes a seed, which contains the endosperm, the embryo, and a protective seed coat. The plant ovary develops into fruit surrounding the seed. Eventually, a seed may land in a favorable spot on the ground and grow into a new plant.

mature sporophyte (2*n*)
ovule
meiosis
female spores (1*n*)
young sporophyte (2*n*)
meiosis
male spores (1*n*)
male gametophyte (1*n*) (pollen grain)
female gametophyte (1*n*)
embryo (2*n*)
polar nuclei
pollen grain
sperm (1*n*)
seed coat
endosperm (3*n*)
zygote (2*n*)
polar nuclei
egg cell (1*n*)
pollen tube
fertilization
sperm (1*n*)

Appendix C: Biology Careers

Careers in Biology

A number of careers require a background knowledge of biology. Some of these career choices may be more obvious than others, such as that of a biology teacher, doctor, or zookeeper. But there are many more careers that may be less familiar to you. While your image of someone who uses their knowledge of biology might be that of a scientist who works in a laboratory, you just might be surprised to discover what other jobs require a background in the biological sciences.

To learn more about careers in the biological sciences, go to the BioZine at **HMHScience.com**.

Agronomist An agronomist is an expert in soil management who advises farmers on how to manage their crops.

Anthropologist An anthropologist studies the origin, behavior, and social and cultural development of humans.

Bioinformatics Professional A bioinformatics professional uses computers, laboratory robots, and software to develop, manage, and interpret complex biological data.

Biological Illustrator A biological illustrator provides scientifically accurate hand-drawn or computer-aided illustrations for clients, ranging from web sites to publications such as textbooks, newspapers, or magazines.

Biomedical Engineer A biomedical engineer develops devices and procedures that solve medical and health-related problems.

Conservation Biologist A conservation biologist manages, improves, and protects natural resources.

Ecotourism Guide An ecotourism guide leads groups of tourists on trips to natural areas to promote conservation and sustain the livelihood of local people.

Emergency Medical Technician An emergency medical technician provides emergency medical services to critically ill and injured persons.

Environmental Economist An environmental economist uses the principles of economics to determine the impact of such things as species loss, pollution, and climate change.

Environmental Health Professional An environmental health professional inspects the health and safety of establishments such as restaurants and housing areas.

Environmental Journalist An environmental journalist writes articles or books on environmental topics, frequently in an investigatory manner.

Epidemiologist An epidemiologist studies causes and control of diseases.

Exercise Physiologist An exercise physiologist develops exercise routines and educates people about the benefits of exercise.

Ethologist An ethologist studies animal behavior.

Farm Manager A farm manager manages the day-to-day activities of one or more farms, focusing on the business aspects of running a farm.

Fish and Wildlife Manager A fish and wildlife manager manages the populations of fish and/or wildlife on public or private lands.

Forensic Scientist A forensic scientist analyzes biological, chemical, or physical samples taken as evidence during a criminal investigation.

Forester A forester manages and protects forests and supervises tree harvesting.

Genetic Counselor A genetic counselor is a health professional who specializes in telling families about the nature and risks of inherited conditions and syndromes.

Geneticist A geneticist specializes in the study of genes and their influence on health, as well as the treatment of genetic disorders.

Immunologist An immunologist is a medical scientist who studies the immune system.

Landscape Architect A landscape architect plans the location of buildings, roads, and walkways along with the placement of plants so that the designs are not only functional but also compatible with the natural environment.

Medical Transcriptionist A medical transcriptionist listens to dictated recordings made by doctors and other health care workers and transcribes them into medical reports.

Medical Device Sales Representative A medical device sales representative sells medical devices to health professionals.

Molecular Biologist A molecular biologist studies the structure and function of biological molecules, such as DNA and proteins.

Nature Photographer A nature photographer takes photographs of natural settings and wildlife for publication online and in print material such as books and magazines.

Neuroscientist A neuroscientist specializes in the study of the structure and function of the brain and nervous system.

Nutritionist A nutritionist plans food and nutrition programs and provides advice to those with food allergies or those seeking weight loss.

Oceanographer An oceanographer studies the world's oceans and their inhabitants.

Park Ranger A park ranger supervises, manages, and performs work in the conservation and use of resources in national, state, and city parks.

Pharmacist A pharmacist distributes drugs prescribed by doctors and other health workers and provides information to patients about medications and their use.

Phlebotomist A phlebotomist collects blood samples.

Physician Assistant A physician assistant takes medical histories, examines and treats patients, orders and interprets laboratory tests and x-rays, and makes diagnoses, all under the supervision of a doctor.

Physical Therapist A physical therapist provides services that help restore function, improve mobility, relieve pain, and prevent or limit permanent physical disabilities of patients suffering from injuries or disease.

Radiologist A radiologist is a doctor who specializes in the interpretation of x-rays and other medical images.

Respiratory Therapist A respiratory therapist evaluates, treats, and cares for patients with breathing or other cardiopulmonary disorders.

Science Editor A science editor edits scientific writing, ranging from academic journals to works meant for a general audience.

Science Museum Curator A science museum curator oversees the development and management of museum exhibits.

Science Patent Lawyer A science patent lawyer represents clients in legal proceedings, draws up legal documents, and advises clients on legal transactions.

Science Policy Analyst A science policy analyst advises lawmakers with regard to legislation focused on scientific issues such as biomedical research or environmental regulations.

Science Writer A science writer specializes in writing about scientific topics for both academic and general audiences.

Speech-Language Pathologist A speech-language pathologist tests, diagnoses, treats, and helps to prevent speech, language, and other voice-related disorders.

Sports Trainer A sports trainer helps athletes in the prevention of injury and provides initial management of a sports-related injury.

Surgical Technician A surgical technician assists in surgeries by preparing the surgical room, providing support to surgical workers, and monitoring the patient during surgery.

Ultrasound Technician An ultrasound technician operates an ultrasound machine, which collects reflected echoes and forms an image that may be videotaped, transmitted, or photographed for interpretation and diagnosis by a doctor.

X-Ray Technician An x-ray technician takes x-rays and administers nonradioactive materials into patients' bloodstreams for diagnostic purposes.

R39

Appendix D

Investigating Ecosystems

Types of Ecosystems

An ecosystem contains communities of living organisms (biotic factors) and the nonliving features (abiotic factors) characteristic of an area. Below are descriptions of ecosystems found in the United States.

Estuaries

Estuaries form when fresh water draining from rivers and streams mixes with salt water from the ocean. Microscopic plankton float in open water and form the base of many food chains. They feed small fish and crustaceans which in turn provide food for larger fin fish and marine mammals. Beds of sea grasses and other underwater plants shelter young fish, crabs, and shrimp. Estuaries provide important feeding and nesting habitats for resident and migratory birds. Many species of mammals feed in estuarine waters or along the water's edge, including muskrats, otters, and raccoons.

Riparian Woodlands

Riparian Woodlands grow in moist soil along the edges of streams. These ecosystems are also known as riparian corridors because they feature dense plant growth that provides cover for wildlife traveling from place to place. Riparian trees and shrubs often include willow, birch, and dogwood. Fallen leaves provide habitats for bacteria, fungi, worms, and insects. Animal life also includes snakes, bats, weasels, otters, deer, bobcats, and ground-dwelling birds. Roots and branches that dangle in the water provide shade and protective cover for fish, frogs, and salamanders.

Deciduous Forests

Deciduous Forests grow in drier soils at higher elevations than riparian woodlands. Deciduous hardwood trees, such as oak, walnut, birch, beech, and maple, dominate these forest ecosystems. Birds that make their homes in deciduous forests include woodpeckers, hawks, hummingbirds, songbirds, and ground-dwelling birds such as quail and wild turkey. Mammals include black bears, white-tailed deer, squirrels, coyotes, bobcats, foxes, and raccoons.

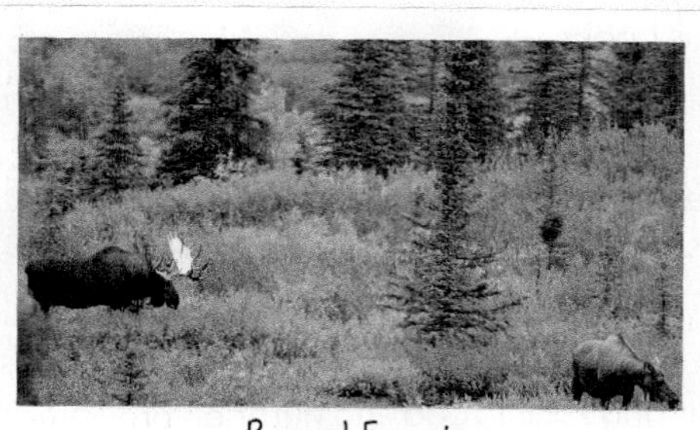

Boreal Forests

Boreal Forests grow in areas with long, cold winters and short summers. The decay of needles and leaves, slowed by cold temperatures, forms a thick layer of peat and moss on the forest floor. Among the billions of birds that nest in the boreal forest during the spring and summer months are loon, grebes, geese, hawks, owls, sandpipers, flycatchers, and sparrows. Mammal species include snowshoe hares, lynx, moose, caribou, and grizzly bears.

Desert

Desert ecosystems are characterized by dry, gravelly soils and infrequent rain. Plants adapted for desert conditions include cacti and desert wildflowers. Many desert animals, from spiders and scorpions to owls and night lizards, are nocturnal, avoiding the intense sunlight and extreme daytime temperatures. Animal life also includes kangaroo rats, jackrabbits, snakes, coyotes, woodpeckers, and roadrunners.

Analyzing a Local Ecosystem

Use the checklist below to explore and analyze an ecosystem in your area. Example answers for the pond ecosystem shown above are given for each item.

- ✓ **Define a boundary.** Locate the edges of the ecosystem you're studying. Ecosystems often blend into one another, so boundaries might not be obvious. The pond ecosystem not only includes communities of organisms that live in the pond, but also extends to the communities that live along the water's edge.
- ✓ **Identify abiotic and biotic components, including a list of species.** A list of the biotic components of this pond ecosystem would include cattails, grasses, plankton, insects, fish, frogs, birds, seeds, mice, snakes, and owls. Abiotic components include water, sunlight, oxygen, and minerals.
- ✓ **Identify abiotic factors that affect ecosystem health and analyze these factors.** In the pond ecosystem, water is the most important abiotic factor because most species could not survive if the pond dried up. Another important abiotic factor is dissolved oxygen in the water. If oxygen levels get too low, fish could not survive.
- ✓ **Model the flow of energy through the ecosystem.** Create a food web that describes as many feeding relationships as possible. A food web for the pond ecosystem would show several interrelated food chains, including fish eating plankton and insects, frogs eating insects, and herons eating fish and frogs.
- ✓ **Model the flow of matter through the ecosystem.** Create diagrams that show how water, carbon, and nitrogen move through the ecosystem. For example, a carbon cycle diagram for the pond ecosystem would show carbon entering the air through respiration, returning to the bodies of plants through photosynthesis, and moving into the bodies of animals via feeding relationships.
- ✓ **Identify symbiotic relationships among organisms in the ecosystem.** Describe any examples of mutualism, commensalism, or parasitism in the ecosystem. In the pond ecosystem, mosquitoes have a parasitic relationship with mammals and birds because they feed on the blood of these animals.

Glossary

A

abdomen part of an arthropod's body that is behind the thorax.
abdomen parte del cuerpo de un artrópodo situada detrás del tórax.

abiotic nonliving factor in an ecosystem, such as moisture, temperature, wind, sunlight, soil, and minerals.
abiótico factor inerte de un ecosistema, como la humedad, la temperatura, el viento, la luz solar, el suelo y los minerales.

ABO blood group four common blood types (A, B, AB, and O) and the protein markers that distinguish them.
grupo sanguíneo ABO sistema que contiene los cuatro tipos de sangre comunes (A, B, AB y O) y los marcadores proteicos que los distinguen.

absorption process by which nutrients move out of one system and into another.
absorción proceso mediante el cual los nutrientes pasan de un sistema del organismo a otro.

abyssal zone (uh-BIHS-uhl) depth of the ocean that lies below 2000 meters and is in complete darkness.
zona abisal región del océano por debajo de los 2000 metros de profundidad que se encuentra en total oscuridad.

accuracy a description of how close a measurement is to the true value of the quantity measured.
exactitud término que describe qué tanto se aproxima una medida al valor verdadero de la cantidad medida.

acid compound that donates a proton (H^+) when dissolved in a solution.
ácido compuesto que cede un protón (H^+) al ser disuelto en una solución.

acid rain precipitation produced when pollutants in the atmosphere cause the pH of rain to decrease.
lluvia ácida precipitación que se produce cuando los contaminantes de la atmósfera hacen que el pH de la lluvia disminuya.

acquired immune deficiency syndrome (AIDS) condition characterized by having several infections and very few T cells; caused by HIV.
síndrome de inmunodeficiencia adquirida (SIDA) enfermedad caracterizada por falta de defensa contra varias infecciones y muy pocas células T; causada por el VIH.

actin filament that is pulled by myosin filaments to cause muscle contraction.
actina filamento que al ser accionado por los filamentos de miosina provoca una contracción muscular.

action potential fast, moving change in electrical charge across a neuron's membrane; also called an impulse.
potencial de acción cambio rápido en la descarga eléctrica a lo largo de la membrana de las neuronas; también llamado impulso.

activation energy energy input necessary to initiate a chemical reaction.
energía de activación energía necesaria para iniciar una reacción química.

active immunity immunity that occurs after the body responds to an antigen.
inmunidad activa inmunidad que se produce después de que el cuerpo haya respondido a un antígeno.

active transport energy-requiring movement of molecules across a membrane from a region of lower concentration to a region of higher concentration.
transporte activo desplazamiento de moléculas a través de una membrana desde un medio de baja concentración a un medio de alta concentración.

adaptation inherited trait that is selected for over time because it allows organisms to better survive in their environment.
adaptación rasgo heredado durante un periodo de tiempo mediante selección natural, que facilita la supervivencia de los organismos en su medio ambiente.

adaptive radiation process by which one species evolves and gives rise to many descendant species that occupy different ecological niches.
radiación adaptativa proceso evolutivo mediante el cual una especie da lugar a varias nuevas especies que ocupan distintos nichos ecológicos.

addiction uncontrollable physical and mental need for something.
adicción necesidad física y mental incontrolable de alguna sustancia o actividad.

adenosine diphosphate (ADP) low-energy molecule that can be converted to ATP.
adenosín difosfato (ADP) molécula con poca energía que puede convertirse en ATP.

adenosine triphosphate (ATP) high-energy molecule that contains, within its bonds, energy that cells can use.
adenosín trifosfato (ATP) molécula de alta energía en cuyos enlaces se almacena energía para las células.

adhesion attraction between molecules of different substances.
adhesión atracción que se produce entre moléculas de diferentes sustancias.

adolescence period of life beginning at puberty and ending at adulthood.
adolescencia periodo de la vida que comienza en la pubertad y que termina en la edad adulta.

ADP *see* adenosine diphosphate.
ADP *véase* adenosín difosfato.

adulthood period of life when a person is fully developed and physical growth stops.
edad adulta período de la vida en el que un individuo alcanza su completo desarrollo y en el que cesa el crecimiento.

aerobic (ay-ROH-bihk) process that requires oxygen to occur.
aeróbico proceso que requiere la presencia de oxígeno para ocurrir.

airfoil surface, such as a bird's wing, whose shape moves air faster over the top than underneath it, allowing for flight.
superficie aerodinámica superficie de ala cuya forma, como en el caso de las aves, permite que el aire se mueva más rápido por arriba que por abajo, facilitando así el vuelo.

air sac air-filled space that connects to a bird's lungs, aiding in breathing.
sacos aéreos órganos llenos de aire conectados a los pulmones de las aves para facilitar la respiración.

algae (singular: *alga*) photosynthetic plantlike protists.
alga protista fotosintética de aspecto vegetal.

alkaloid chemical produced by plants that contains nitrogen, many of which are used in medicines.
alcaloide compuesto químico, producido por las plantas, que contiene nitrógeno y es usado en muchos medicamentos.

allele (uh-LEEL) any of the alternative forms of a gene that occurs at a specific place on a chromosome.
alelo cualquier variante de un gen que ocupa la misma posición en un cromosoma.

allele frequency proportion of one allele, compared with all the alleles for that trait, in the gene pool.
frecuencia alélica proporción de un alelo determinado con respecto a los demás alelos del mismo rasgo en una misma población.

allergen antigen that does not cause disease but still produces an immune response.
alérgeno antígeno que, si bien no causa una enfermedad, produce una respuesta inmune.

allergy immune response that occurs when the body responds to a nondisease-causing antigen, such as pollen or animal dander.
alergia respuesta inmune producida cuando el organismo responde a aquellos antígenos que no causan enfermedades, como el polen o la caspa de ciertos animales.

alternation of generations plant life cycle in which the plant alternates between haploid and diploid phases.
alternancia generacional ciclo de vida de las plantas en el que la planta alterna fases haploides y diploides.

altruism behavior in which an animal reduces its own fitness to help the other members of its social group.
altruismo patrón de comportamiento animal, en el cual un individuo sacrifica su integridad para beneficiar a otros miembros de su grupo social.

alveolus (al-VEE-uh-luhs) (plural: *alveoli*) tiny, thin-walled structure across which oxygen gas is absorbed and carbon dioxide is released in the lungs.
alvéolo pequeña estructura de paredes delgadas a través de la cual se absorbe oxígeno gaseoso y se libera dióxido de carbono en los pulmones.

amino acid molecule that makes up proteins; composed of carbon, hydrogen, oxygen, nitrogen, and sometimes sulfur.
aminoácido molécula que forma las proteínas; está compuesta de carbono, hidrógeno, oxígeno, nitrógeno y, a veces, de azufre.

amniote vertebrate whose embryo or fetus is enclosed by a thin, tough membranous sac.
amniota vertebrado cuyo embrión o feto está envuelto en un saco membranoso delgado y resistente.

amniotic egg waterproof container that allows an embryo to develop out of water and externally from the mother without drying out.
huevo amniótico envoltura impermeable que permite el desarrollo del embrión fuera del agua y de la propia madre sin que éste se deshidrate.

amniotic sac fluid-filled organ that cushions and protects the developing embryo of some vertebrates.
saco amniótico membrana que contiene líquido y que amortigua y protege el embrión de ciertos vertebrados.

amphibian vertebrate that can live on land and in water.
anfibio vertebrado que puede vivir en el agua y en tierra firme.

anaerobic process that does not require oxygen to occur.
anaeróbico proceso que no requiere oxígeno para ocurrir.

analogous structure body part that is similar in function as a body part of another organism but is structurally different.
estructura análoga parte del cuerpo que cumple una función similar a la parte del cuerpo de un organismo diferente, pero que tiene una estructura diferente.

anaphase third phase of mitosis during which chromatids separate and are pulled to opposite sides of the cell.
anafase tercera fase de la mitosis, en la cual las cromátidas se separan y se dirigen hacia los polos opuestos de la célula.

anaphylaxis (an-uh-fuh-LAK-sihs) severe allergic reaction that causes airways to tighten and blood vessels to leak.
anafilaxis reacción alérgica grave que produce rigidez de las vías aéreas y el drenaje de líquido de los vasos sanguíneos.

angiosperm (AN-jee-uh-SPURM) seed plant whose embryos are enclosed by fruit.
angiosperma planta cuyos embriones se encuentran encerrados en el fruto.

anthropoid humanlike primate.
antropoide primate semejante al ser humano.

antibiotic chemical that kills or slows the growth of bacteria.
antibiótico compuesto químico que mata o inhibe el desarrollo de las bacterias.

antibiotic resistance process by which bacteria mutate so that they are no longer affected by an antibiotic.
resistencia antibiótica proceso mediante el cual una bacteria sufre mutaciones y para hacerse resistente a los antibióticos.

R43

Glossary

antibody protein produced by B cells that aids in the destruction of pathogens.
anticuerpo proteína producida por las células B que contribuye a la destrucción de los patógenos.

anticodon set of three nucleotides in a tRNA molecule that binds to a complementary mRNA codon during translation.
anticodón grupo de tres nucleótidos de la molécula de ARNt que se acopla a un codón complementario de ARNm durante la traslación.

antigen (AN-tih-juhn) protein marker that helps the immune system identify foreign particles.
antígeno marcador proteico que ayuda al sistema immune a identificar sustancias extrañas tales como los virus.

antiseptic (AN-tih-SEHP-tihk) chemical, such as soap, vinegar, or rubbing alcohol, that destroys pathogens outside of the body.
antiséptico compuesto químico, como el jabón, el vinagre o el alcohol, que destruyen los patógenos fuera del cuerpo.

apoptosis (AP-uhp-TOH-sihs) programmed cell death.
apoptosis muerte celular programada.

appendage extension, such as an antenna or arm, that is attached to the body.
apéndice prolongación del cuerpo, como una antena o un brazo, unida o contigua al mismo.

appendicular skeleton part of the skeletal system that allows for most of the body's movements; includes bones of the arms, shoulders, legs, and pelvis.
esqueleto apendicular parte del sistema esquelético que permite la mayor parte de los movimientos del cuerpo; consta, entre otros, de los huesos de los brazos, hombros, piernas y la pelvis.

arachnid terrestrial chelicerate, such as a spider.
arácnido quelicerado terrestre, como la araña.

Archaea one of the three domains of life, containing single-celled prokaryotes in the kingdom Archaea.
Arqueas uno de los tres dominios de la vida, compuesto de procariontes unicelulares del reino Archaea.

artery large blood vessel that carries blood away from the heart.
arteria gran vaso sanguíneo que transporta la sangre desde el corazón.

arthropod invertebrate with an exoskeleton, jointed appendages, and a segmented body.
artrópodo invertebrado con exoesqueleto, apéndices articulados y cuerpo segmentado.

artificial selection process by which humans modify a species by breeding it for certain traits
selección artificial proceso mediante el cual los seres humanos modifican una especie al criarla para obtener ciertos rasgos.

asexual reproduction process by which offspring are produced from a single parent; does not involve the joining of gametes.
reproducción asexual proceso mediante el cual se producen descendientes de un solo progenitor, sin necesidad de la unión de gametos.

asthma (AZ-muh) condition in which air pathways in the lungs constrict, making breathing difficult.
asma enfermedad que, al estrechar las vías aéreas de los pulmones, dificulta la respiración.

atmosphere air blanketing Earth's solid surface.
atmósfera envoltura de aire que rodea la superficie sólida de la Tierra.

atom smallest basic unit of matter.
átomo unidad básica más pequeña de la materia.

ATP *see* adenosine triphosphate.
ATP *véase* adenosín trifosfato.

ATP synthase enzyme that catalyzes the reaction that adds a high-energy phosphate group to ADP to form ATP.
ATP sintetasa enzima que cataliza la reacción para enlazar un grupo fosfato de alta energía al ADP y formar así el ATP.

atrium (plural: *atria*) small chamber in the human heart that receives blood from the veins.
aurícula pequeña cavidad del corazón humano que recibe sangre de las venas.

autonomic nervous system division of the peripheral nervous system that controls involuntary functions.
sistema nervioso autónomo parte del sistema nervioso periférico que controla las funciones involuntarias.

autosome chromosome that contains genes for characteristics not directly related to the sex of the organism.
autosoma cromosoma cuyos genes no rigen los rasgos relacionados directamente con el sexo del organismo.

autotroph organism that obtains its energy from abiotic sources, such as sunlight or inorganic chemicals.
autótrofo organismo que obtiene su energía a partir de fuentes abióticas como, por ejemplo, la luz solar o sustancias inorgánicas.

auxin (AWK-sihn) plant hormone that stimulates the lengthening of cells in the growing tip.
auxina hormona vegetal que estimula la elongación de las células y regula el crecimiento de las plantas.

axial skeleton part of the skeletal system that supports the body's weight and protects the body's internal tissues; includes the bones of the skull, spinal column, and rib cage.
esqueleto axial parte del sistema esquelético que da soporte al peso corporal y que protege los tejidos internos del organismo; consta de los huesos del cráneo, la columna vertebral y la caja torácica.

axon long extension of the neuron membrane that carries impulses from one neuron to another.
axón prolongación de la membrana de la neurona que transmite impulsos eléctricos de una neurona a otra.

B

Bacteria one of the three domains of life, containing single-celled prokaryotes in the kingdom Bacteria.
Bacteria uno de los tres dominios en los que se dividen los seres vivos, que consta de procariontes unicelulares del reino Bacteria.

bacteriophage virus that infects bacteria.
bacteriófago virus que infecta a las bacterias.

bacterium (plural: *bacteria*) organism that is within the kingdom Bacteria.
bacteria organismo perteneciento al reino Bacteria.

base compound that accepts a proton (H^+) when dissolved in solution.
base compuesto que al disolverlo en una solución acepta un protón (H^+).

base pairing rules rule that describes how nucleotides form bonds in DNA; adenine (A) always bonds with thymine (T), and guanine (G) always bonds with cytosine (C).
reglas de apareamiento de bases regla que describe cómo se enlazan los nucleótidos en el ADN; la adenina (A) siempre se enlaza con la timina (T), y la guanina (G) siempre se enlaza con la citosina (C).

bathyal zone (BATH-ee-uhl) zone of the ocean that extends from the edge of the neritic zone to the base of the continental shelf.
zona batial region océanica que se extiende desde el límite de la zona nerítica hasta la base de la plataforma continental.

B cell white blood cell that matures in the bone marrow and produces antibodies that fight off infection; also called a B-lymphocyte.
célula B glóbulo blanco que madura en la médula osea y que produce los anticuerpos que combaten las infecciones; también se conoce como linfocito B.

behavioral isolation isolation between populations due to differences in courtship or mating behavior.
aislamiento etológico aislamiento entre poblaciones debido a diferencias en los rituales de cortejo o apareamiento.

benign having no dangerous effect on health, especially referring to an abnormal growth of cells that are not cancerous.
benigno que no tiene efectos graves sobre la salud; se refiere particularmente al crecimiento anormal de células que no son cancerosas.

benthic zone lake or pond bottom, where little to no sunlight can reach.
zona béntica fondo de un lago o estanque, adonde llega poca o ninguna luz.

bilateral symmetry body plan of some organisms in which the body can be divided equally along only one plane.
simetría bilateral se observa en los organismos que pueden dividirse en partes iguales a lo largo de un plano único.

bile fluid released by the liver and gallbladder into the small intestine that aids in the digestion and absorption of fats.
bilis fluido segregado por el hígado y almacenado en la vesícula biliar, y que es liberado al intestino delgado para facilitar la digestión y la absorción de las grasas.

binary fission (BY-nuh-ree FIHSH-uhn) asexual reproduction in which a cell divides into two equal parts.
fisión binaria reproducción asexual en la que una célula se divide en dos partes iguales.

binomial nomenclature naming system in which each species is given a two-part scientific name (genus and species) using Latin words.
nomenclatura binomial sistema de denominación de especies mediante el cual se les otorga un nombre científico que consta de dos palabras en latín (género y especie).

biodiversity variety of life within an area.
biodiversidad variedad de las formas de vida en una zona determinada.

biogeochemical cycle movement of a chemical through the biological and geological, or living and nonliving, parts of an ecosystem.
ciclo biogeoquímico movimiento de una sustancia química a través de los componentes biológicos y geológicos, o vivos e inertes, de un ecosistema.

biogeography study of the distribution of organisms around the world.
biogeografía estudio de la distribución de los organismos en el mundo.

bioinformatics use of computer databases to organize and analyze biological data.
bioinformática utilización de bases de datos de computación para organizar y analizar datos biológicos.

biological clock internal mechanism that controls an animal's activity patterns.
reloj biológico mecanismo interno que controla el ritmo de actividad de un animal.

biology scientific study of all forms of life.
biología estudio científico de todas las formas de vida.

biomagnification condition of toxic substances being more concentrated in tissues of organisms higher on the food chain than ones lower in the food chain.
biomagnificación condición en la cual la concentración de sustancias tóxicas en los tejidos de los organismos que pertenecen a eslabones más altos de la cadena alimentaria es mayor que la concentración en los organismos de los eslabones más bajos.

biomass total dry mass of all organisms in a given area.
biomasa masa deshidratada total de todos los organismos de un área determinada.

Glossary

biome regional or global community of organisms characterized by the climate conditions and plant communities that thrive there.
bioma comunidad regional o global de organismos caracterizada por las condiciones climáticas y el tipo de vegetación del área.

bioremediation process by which humans use living things to break down pollutants.
biorremediación proceso mediante el cual los seres humanos emplean organismos vivos para descomponer sustancias contaminantes.

biosphere all organisms and the part of Earth where they exist.
biosfera todos los seres vivos y las partes de la Tierra en las que existen.

biota collection of living things.
biota conjunto de seres vivos.

biotechnology use and application of living things and biological processes.
biotecnología aprovechamiento y aplicación de los seres vivos y de sus procesos biológicos.

biotic living things, such as plants, animals, fungi, and bacteria.
biótico referente a los seres vivos, tales como las plantas, los animales, los hongos y las bacterias.

bipedal animal that walks on two legs.
bípedo animal que camina sobre dos patas.

blade broad part of a leaf where most of the photosynthesis of a plant takes place.
lámina parte ancha de la hoja donde ocurre la mayor parte de la fotosíntesis de una planta.

blastocyst stage of development during which the zygote consists of a ball of cells.
blastocisto fase de desarrollo en la que el cigoto consta de células apelotonadas.

blood pressure force with which blood pushes against the wall of an artery.
presión sanguínea fuerza que ejerce la sangre contra las paredes de las arterias.

bond energy amount of energy needed to break a bond between two particular atoms; or the amount of energy released when a bond forms between two particular atoms.
energía de enlace energía necesaria para romper un enlace entre dos partículas atómicas; energía liberada al formarse un enlace entre dos átomos determinados.

book lung respiratory organ that has several membranes that are arranged like the pages in a book.
pulmón en libro órgano respiratorio compuesto por una serie de membranas dispuestas como las páginas de un libro.

botany study of plants.
botánica estudio de las plantas.

bottleneck effect genetic drift that results from an event that drastically reduces the size of a population.
efecto de cuello de botella deriva genética resultante de un acontecimiento que reduce drásticamente el tamaño de una población.

brain stem structure that connects the brain to the spinal cord and controls breathing and heartbeat.
tronco del encéfalo estructura que conecta el cerebro con la médula espinal y que controla la respiración y los latidos del corazón.

C

calcification process that hardens bones by adding calcium phosphate and collagen.
calcificación proceso que endurece los huesos mediante depósitos de fosfato cálcico y colágeno.

Calorie measure of energy released from digesting food; one Calorie equals one kilocalorie of heat.
caloría medida de energía liberada al digerir la comida; una caloría equivale a una kilocaloría de calor.

Calvin cycle process by which a photosynthetic organism uses energy to synthesize simple sugars from CO_2.
ciclo de Calvin proceso mediante el cual un organismo fotosintético usa energía para sintetizar monosacáridos a partir del CO_2.

Cambrian explosion earliest part of the Paleozoic era, when a huge diversity of animal species evolved.
explosión Cámbrica periodo inicial de la era paleozoica, en la que surgió una enorme diversidad de especies animales.

cancer common name for a class of diseases characterized by uncontrolled cell division.
cáncer nombre común de una clase de enfermedades caracterizadas por una división descontrolada de las células.

canopy dense covering formed by the uppermost branches of trees.
cobertura arbórea tupido entramado formado por las ramas más altas de los árboles.

capillary tiny blood vessel that transports blood between larger blood vessels and other tissues in the body.
capilar diminuto vaso sanguíneo que transporta la sangre entre vasos sanguíneos más grandes y otros tejidos del cuerpo.

capsid protein shell that surrounds a virus.
cápsida cubierta proteica que envuelve al virus.

carapace (KAR-uh-PAYS) plate of exoskeleton that covers the head and thorax of a crustacean.
caparazón parte del exoesqueleto de los crustáceos que cubre la cabeza y el tórax.

carbohydrate molecule composed of carbon, hydrogen, and oxygen; includes sugars and starches.
carbohidrato molécula compuesta de carbono, hidrógeno y oxígeno; incluye los azúcares y los almidones.

carcinogen substance that produces or promotes the development of cancer.
carcinógeno sustancia que estimula o contribuye a inducir el cáncer.

cardiac muscle muscle tissue that is only found in the heart.
músculo cardíaco tejido muscular, también conocido como miocardio, que sólo se halla en el corazón.

carnivore organism that obtains energy by eating only animals.
carnívoro organismo que obtiene energía al alimentarse únicamente de otros animales.

carpel female structure of flowering plants; made of the ovary, style, and stigma.
carpelo estructura reproductora femenina de las plantas con flor; consta de ovario, estilo y stigma.

carrier organism whose genome contains a gene for a certain trait or disease that is not expressed in the organism's phenotype.
portador organismo cuyo genoma contiene un gen de cierto rasgo o enfermedad que no se encuentra expresado en el fenotipo de dicho organismo.

carrying capacity number of individuals that the resources of an environment can normally and persistently support.
capacidad de carga de población número de individuos que los recursos de un ambiente pueden sustentar normalmente de manera continua.

cartilage tough, elastic, and fibrous connective tissue found between bones.
cartílago tejido conectivo resistente, fibroso y elástico que se encuentra entre los huesos.

catalyst (KAT-uhl-ihst) substance that decreases activation energy and increases reaction rate in a chemical reaction.
catalizador sustancia que disminuye la energía de activación y aumenta la tasa de reacción de una reacción química determinada.

catastrophism theory that states that natural disasters such as floods and volcanic eruptions shaped Earth's landforms and caused extinction of some species.
catastrofismo teoría según la cual la configuración actual de los accidentes geográficos de la Tierra y la extinción de algunas especies se debió a inundaciones, erupciones volcánicas y otras catástrofes naturales.

cell basic unit of life.
célula unidad básica de la vida.

cell cycle pattern of growth, DNA replication, and cell division that occurs in a eukaryotic cell.
ciclo celular proceso de crecimiento, replicación de ADN y división celular que ocurre en las células eucarióticas.

cell differentiation processes by which unspecialized cells develop into their mature form and function.
diferenciación celular proceso mediante el cual las células no especializadas adquieren una forma y una función determinada.

cell membrane double-layer of phospholipids that forms a boundary between a cell and the surrounding environment and controls the passage of materials into and out of a cell.
membrana celular capa doble de fosfolípidos que forma una barrera entre la célula y el medio que la rodea, y que controla el flujo de materiales hacia dentro y hacia fuera de la célula.

cell theory theory that states that all organisms are made of cells, all cells are produced by other living cells, and the cell is the most basic unit of life.
teoría celular establece que todos los organismos están formados por células, que todas las células proceden de otras células vivas y que la célula es la unidad básica de la vida.

cellular immunity immune response that relies on T cells to destroy infected body cells.
inmunidad celular respuesta inmune que depende de las células T para atacar las células infectadas del cuerpo.

cellular respiration process of producing ATP by breaking down carbon-based molecules when oxygen is present.
respiración celular proceso de producción de ATP mediante la descomposición de moléculas de carbono en presencia de oxígeno.

cell wall rigid structure that gives protection, support, and shape to cells in plants, algae, fungi, and bacteria.
pared celular estructura rígida que proteje, sustenta y da forma a las células de las plantas, algas, hongos y bacterias.

Cenozoic geologic time period that began 65 million years ago and continues today.
Cenozoico período geológico que empezó hace 65 millones de años y que se extiende hasta la actualidad.

central dogma theory that states that, in cells, information only flows from DNA to RNA to proteins.
dogma central teoría que formula que la información en las células siempre fluye del ADN al ARN y luego a las proteínas.

central nervous system (CNS) part of the nervous system that interprets messages from other nerves in the body; includes the brain and spinal cord.
sistema nervioso central parte del sistema nervioso encargada de interpretar los mensajes recibidos de otros nervios del cuerpo; consta del cerebro y de la médula espinal.

centriole (SEHN-tree-OHL) small cylinder-shaped organelle made of protein tubes arranged in a circle; aids mitosis.
centriolo orgánulo celular con forma de pequeño cilindro formado por una serie de tubos de proteínas en disposición circular; participa en la reproducción celular.

centromere (SEHN-truh-MEER) region of condensed chromosome that looks pinched; where spindle fibers attach during meiosis and mitosis.
centrómero región de condensación del cromosoma donde se une el huso durante la meiosis y la mitosis.

R47

Glossary

cephalothorax (SEHF-uh-luh-THAWR-AKS) region of a crustacean body where the head and thorax meet.
cefalotórax región del cuerpo de los crustáceos donde se unen la cabeza y el tórax.

cerebellum (SEHR-uh-BEHL-uhm) part of the brain that coordinates and regulates all voluntary muscle movement and maintains posture and balance.
cerebelo parte del encéfalo que coordina y regula todos los movimientos musculares voluntarios, y que permite mantener la postura y el equilibrio.

cerebral cortex layer of gray matter on the surface of the cerebrum that receives information and generates responses.
corteza cerebral capa de material gris situada en la superficie del cerebro que se encarga de recibir información y de generar respuestas.

cerebrum (SEHR-uh-bruhm) largest part of the brain, coordinating movement, thought, reasoning, and memory; includes the cerebral cortex and the white matter beneath it.
cerebro la parte más grande del encéfalo que se encarga de coordinar el movimiento, el pensamiento, el razonamiento y la memoria; incluye la corteza cerebral y la materia blanca que se encuentra debajo de ésta.

chaparral (SHAP-uh-RAL) biome characterized by hot, dry summers and cool, moist winters; also called Mediterranean shrubland.
chaparral bioma caracterizado por veranos secos y calurosos e inviernos frescos y húmedos; también se conoce como matorral mediterráneo.

chelicerate arthropod that lacks antennae and has four pairs of walking legs and a pair of fanglike mouth parts.
quelicerado artrópodo sin antenas con cuatro pares de patas y una boca de dos piezas en forma de colmillos.

chemical reaction process by which substances change into different substances through the breaking and forming of chemical bonds.
reacción química proceso mediante el cual una sustancia se transforma en otra sustancia diferente al romperse sus enlaces químicos y formarse otros nuevos.

chemosynthesis (KEE-mo-SIHN-thih-sihs) process by which ATP is synthesized by using chemicals as an energy source instead of light.
quimiosíntesis proceso de síntesis del ATP cuya fuente de energía no es la luz, sino determinadas sustancias químicas.

childhood period of life from age two until puberty.
infancia periodo de la vida comprendido entre los dos años y la pubertad.

chitin tough, protective polysaccharide that makes up arthropod skeletons and the cell walls of some fungi.
quitina polisacárido duro que forma los exoesqueletos de los artrópodos y las paredes celulares de algunos hongos.

chlorophyll (KLAWR-uh-fihl) light-absorbing pigment molecule in photosynthetic organisms.
clorofila molécula pigmentaria de los organismos fotosintéticos que absorbe la luz.

chloroplast (KLAWR-uh-PLAST) organelle composed of numerous membranes that are used to convert solar energy into chemical energy; contains chlorophyll.
colorplasto orgánulo compuesto de numerosas membranes cuya funcción es transformer la energía solar en energía química; contiene clorofila.

chordate any animal having, at some stage in development, a hollow nerve cord, pharyngeal slits, and tail.
cordado todo tipo de animal que en alguna fase de su desarrollo tiene un cordón nervioso dorsal, hendiduras faríngeas y cola.

chromatid (KROH-muh-tihd) one half of a duplicated chromosome.
cromátida mitad de un cromosoma duplicado.

chromatin loose combination of DNA and proteins that is present during interphase.
cromatina conjunto de ADN y proteínas que se manifiesta durante la interfase.

chromosome long, continuous thread of DNA that consists of numerous genes and regulatory information.
cromosoma un largo y continuo filamento de ADN formado por numerosos genes y que almacena información genética.

chyme (kym) partially digested, semi-liquid mixture that passes from the stomach to the small intestine.
quimo mezcla semi líquida parcialmente digerida que pasa del estómago al intestino delgado.

cilia (singular: *cilium*) short hairlike structures that cover some or all of the cell surface and help the organism swim and capture food.
cilios estructuras en forma de pelillos cortos que cubren total o parcialmente la superficie de determinadas células y que ayuda a los organismos a nadar y capturar alimentos.

circadian rhythm daily cycle of activity that occurs over a 24-hour period of time.
ritmo circadiano ciclo diario de actividad que abarca 24 horas.

circulatory system body system that transports nutrients and wastes between various body tissues; includes heart, blood, and blood vessels.
sistema circulatorio sistema corporal encargado de transportar nutrientes y desechos entre diversos tejidos corporales; consta del corazón, la sangre y los vasos sanguíneos.

citric acid cycle *see* Krebs cycle.
ciclo del ácido cítrico *véase* ciclo de Krebs.

R48

cladistics method of organizing species by evolutionary relationships in which species are grouped according to the order that they diverged from their ancestral line.
cladismo método de clasificación de las especies según su parentesco evolutivo en el que las especies son agrupadas en el orden en que se separaron de su linaje ancestral.

cladogram diagram that displays proposed evolutionary relationships among a group of species.
cladograma diagrama en el que se presentan los parentescos evolutivos propuestos de un grupo determinado de especies.

classical conditioning process by which an organism learns to associate a previously neutral stimulus with a reward or punishment.
condicionamiento clásico proceso mediante el cual un organismo aprende a asociar un estímulo, que previamente había sido neutro, con un premio o castigo.

climate average long-term weather pattern of a region.
clima promedio de valores del tiempo en una región a largo plazo.

clone genetically identical copy of a single gene or an entire organism.
clon copia genéticamente exacta de un gen o de un organismo completo.

codominance heterozygous genotype that equally expresses the traits from both alleles.
codominancia genotipo heterocigoto que expresa equitativamente los rasgos de ambos alelos.

codon sequence of three nucleotides that codes for one amino acid.
codón secuencia de tres nucleotides que codifica un aminoácido.

coelom fluid-filled space that is completely covered by muscle.
celoma cavidad llena de líquido cubierta enteramente por el músculo.

coevolution process in which two or more species evolve in response to changes in each other.
coevolución proceso mediante el cual dos o más especies evolucionan a consecuencia de cambios producidos en cada uno de ellas.

cognition mental process of knowing, including aspects such as awareness, perception, reasoning, and judgment.
cognición conjunto de procesos mentales cuya función es el conocimiento y que incluyen la conciencia, la percepción, el razonamiento y el juicio.

cohesion attraction between molecules of the same substance.
cohesión atracción entre moléculas de una misma sustancia.

cohesion tension theory theory that explains how the physical properties of water allow it to move through the xylem of plants.
teoría de la tensión-cohesión teoría que explica el modo en que las propiedades físicas del agua permiten que ésta fluya a través del xilema de las plantas.

collagen three-stranded protein, unique to animals, that combines to form strong, flexible fibers.
colágeno proteína animal compuesta por tres cadenas que se enlazan para formar fibras resistentes y flexibles.

collenchyma cell elongated cells with unevenly thick walls that form a supportive tissue of plants.
célula del colénquima célula alargada con paredes de grosor irregular que forma el tejido de sostén de las plantas.

commensalism ecological relationship in which one species receives a benefit but the other species is not affected one way or another.
comensalismo relación ecológica entre dos especies en la que una se beneficia sin perjudicar ni beneficiar a la otra.

community collection of all of the different populations that live in one area.
comunidad conjunto de todas las poblaciones que viven en un área determinada.

competition ecological relationship in which two organisms attempt to obtain the same resource.
competencia relación ecológica en la que dos organismos tratan de obtener el mismo recurso.

competitive exclusion theory that states that no two species can occupy the same niche at the same time.
exclusión competitiva teoría según la cual dos especies distintas no pueden ocupar el mismo nicho al mismo tiempo.

complete digestive tract digestive system that has two openings, a mouth and an anus, that are at opposite ends of a continuous tube.
tubo digestivo completo sistema digestivo con dos aperturas, la boca y el ano, situadas en los extremos opuestos de un tubo continuo.

complete metamorphosis process by which immature organisms change their body form before becoming an adult.
metamorfosis completa proceso mediante el cual se van produciendo cambios en los organismos inmaduros antes de llegar a adultos.

compound substance made of atoms of different elements that are bonded together in a particular ratio.
compuesto sustancia formada por átomos de diversos elementos combinados en una proporción determinada.

concentration gradient difference in the concentration of a substance from one location to another.
gradiente de concentración diferencia en la concentración de una sustancia entre un lugar y otro.

cone reproductive structure of gymnosperms inside of which the female gamete is fertilized and seeds are produced.
cono estructura reproductora de las gimnospermas en cuyo interior se fertiliza el gameto femenino y se producen semillas.

cone cell sensory neuron in the eye that detects color.
cono (célula) neurona sensorial del ojo que detecta el color.

R49

Glossary

coniferous tree that retains its needles year-round and reproduces with cones.
conífera árbol que mantiene sus hojas durante todo el año y que se reproduce mediante conos.

conjugation process by which a prokaryote transfers part of its chromosome to another prokaryote.
conjugación proceso mediante el cual un procarionte transfiere parte de su cromosoma a otro procarionte.

constant condition that is controlled so that it does not change during an experiment.
constante condición controlada de un experimento que no varía en el transcurso del mismo.

consumer organism that obtains its energy and nutrients by eating other organisms.
consumidor organismo que obtiene su energía y nutrientes mediante la ingestión de otros organismos.

convergent evolution evolution toward similar characteristics in unrelated species, resulting from adaptations to similar environmental conditions.
evolución convergente evolución hacia características similares en especies no relacionadas, que resulta de adaptaciones a condiciones ambientales similares.

coral reef ocean habitat found in the shallow coastal waters in a tropical climate.
arrecife de coral hábitat oceánico que se encuentra en aguas costeras poco profundas de climas tropicales.

corpus luteum (KAWR-puhs LOO-tee-uhm) follicle after ovulation; also called a yellow body because of its yellow color.
cuerpo lúteo folículo que aparece después de la ovulación; se conoce también como cuerpo amarillo a causa de su color.

cotyledon (KAHT-uhl-EED-uhn) embryonic leaf inside of a seed.
cotiledón hoja embriónica que se forma en el interior de la semilla.

countercurrent flow flow of water opposite that of the flow of blood in a fish's gills.
flujo contracorriente flujo de agua en sentido opuesto al flujo de la sangre en las branquias de los peces.

covalent bond chemical bond formed when two atoms share one or more pairs of electrons.
enlace covalente enlace químico que se forma cuando dos átomos comparten uno o más pares de electrones.

cross mating of two organisms.
cruzamiento apareamiento de dos organismos.

crossing over exchange of chromosome segments between homologous chromosomes during meiosis I.
entrecruzamiento intercambio de segmentos de cromosomas entre cromosomas homólogos durante la meiosis I.

crustacean any of the aquatic arthropods, such as lobsters, crabs, and shrimps, that has a segmented body, an exoskeleton, and paired, jointed limbs.
crustáceo artrópodo acuático, como las langostas, los cangrejos y los camarones, que se caracteriza por tener un cuerpo segmentado, un exoesqueleto y pares de extremidades articuladas.

cultural behavior behavior that is passed between members of the same population by learning and not natural selection.
comportamiento cultural comportamiento que se transmite entre los miembros de una misma población, no por selección natural, sino mediante un proceso de aprendizaje.

cuticle in plants, a waxy layer that holds in moisture; in insects, a tough exoskeleton made of nonliving material.
cutícula en las plantas, es una capa de cera que mantiene la humedad; en los insectos, exoesqueleto duro de material inerte.

cyanobacteria (singular: *cyanobaterium*) bacteria that can carry out photosynthesis.
cianobacteria bacteria capaz de realizar la fotosíntesis.

cytokinesis (SY-toh-kuh-NEE-sihs) process by which the cell cytoplasm divides.
citocinesis proceso mediante el cual el citoplasma celular se divide.

cytokinin (SY-tuh-KY-nihn) plant hormone that stimulates the final stage of cell division, cytokinesis; also involved in the growth of side branches.
citoquinina hormona vegetal que estimula la última fase de la división celular: la citocinesis; también participa en el crecimiento de las ramas laterales.

cytoplasm jellylike substance inside cells that contains molecules and in some cells organelles.
citoplasma sustancia gelatinosa del interior de las células que contiene diversos tipos de moléculas y, en algunas células, orgánulos.

cytoskeleton network of proteins, such as microtubules and microfilaments, inside a eukaryotic cell that supports and shapes the cell.
citoesqueleto red proteica, como los microtúbulos y los microfilamentos, dentro de una célula eucariótica que da soporte y define la forma de la célula.

D

data (singular: *datum*) observations and measurements recorded during an experiment.
datos observaciones y medidas registrados en el transcurso de un experimento.

deciduous tree that has adapted to winter temperatures by dropping its leaves and going dormant during the cold season.
caducifolio árbol que pierde su foliaje y entra en un período de letargo para adaptarse a las temperaturas invernales.

decomposer detritivore that breaks down organic matter into simpler compounds, returning nutrients back into an ecosystem.
descomponedor detritívoro que, al descomponer la materia orgánica en compuestos más sencillos, devuelve al ecosistema sus nutrientes básicos.

dendrite branchlike extension of a neuron that receives impulses from neighboring neurons.
dendrita prolongación ramificada de la neurona que recibe impulsos eléctricos de las neuronas adyacentes.

density-dependent limiting factor environmental resistance that affects a population that has become overly crowded.
factor limitativo dependiente de la densidad resistencia ambiental que afecta a una población sometida a una densidad demográfica excesiva.

density-independent limiting factor environmental resistance that affects a population regardless of population density.
factor limitativo independiente de la densidad resistencia ambiental que afecta a una población sin importar su densidad demográfica.

dependent variable experimental data collected through observation and measurement.
variable dependiente datos de una investigación recolectados por medio de la observación y de la medición.

depressant drug that causes fewer signals to be transmitted between neurons.
depresor medicamento que reduce la transmisión de señales entre las neuronas.

derived characteristic trait that differs in structure or function from that found in the ancestral line for a group of species; used in constructing cladograms.
caracter derivado rasgo que difiere, en su estructura o función, del hallado en un linaje ancestral de un grupo de especies; se usa para crear cladogramas.

dermal tissue tissue system that covers the outside of plants and animals.
tejido dérmico sistema de tejidos que cubre la superficie de los animales y las plantas.

dermis second layer of skin that includes structural proteins, blood vessels, glands, and hair follicles.
dermis segunda capa de piel formada por proteínas estructurales, vasos sanguíneos y folículos capilares.

desensitization process by which neurons in the brain break down neurotransmitter receptors in response to a larger amount of neurotransmitter in the synapse than usual.
desensibilización proceso mediante el cual las neuronas del cerebro inactivan los receptores de los neurotransmisores como respuesta a una cantidad de neurotransmisores mayor de lo habitual en la sinapsis.

desert biome characterized by a very dry climate.
desierto bioma caracterizado por un clima muy seco.

determination process by which stem cells become committed to develop into only one type of cell.
determinación celular proceso mediante el cual las células madre se desarrollan en un tipo específico de célula.

detritivore organism that eats dead organic matter.
detritívoro organismo que se alimenta de materia orgánica muerta.

deuterostome animal development in which the animal's anus develops before the mouth.
deuterostomia desarrollo animal en el que el ano del animal se desarrolla antes que la boca.

dialysis treatment in which a patient's blood is filtered through a machine, the waste is removed, and the cleaned blood is returned to the patient's body.
diálisis tratamiento médico que consiste en filtrar la sangre del paciente mediante una máquina que elimina los desechos y devuelve la sangre purificada al cuerpo del paciente.

diaphragm thin muscle below the rib cage that controls the flow of air into and out of the lungs.
diafragma músculo delgado situado debajo de la caja torácica que controla el flujo de aire hacia el interior y el exterior de los pulmones.

diastolic pressure (DY-uh-STAHL-ihk) pressure in an artery when the left ventricle relaxes.
presión diastólica presión en la arteria en el momento en que se relaja el ventrículo izquierdo.

dicot (DY-KAHT) flowering plant whose embryos have two cotyledons.
dicotiledónea planta con flor cuyos embriones tienen dos cotiledones.

differentiation process by which committed cells acquire the structures and functions of highly specialized cells.
diferenciación celular proceso mediante el cual ciertas células adquieren estructuras y funciones altamente especializadas.

diffusion movement of dissolved molecules in a fluid or gas from a region of higher concentration to a region of lower concentration.
difusión movimiento de las moléculas disueltas en un líquido o gas desde una región de alta concentración a otra región de menor concentración.

digestion process by which large, complex molecules are broken down into smaller molecules that can be used by cells.
digestión proceso mediante el cual grandes y complejas moléculas se descomponen en moléculas más pequeñas que pueden ser absorbidas por las células.

Glossary

digestive system body system that digests food; includes mouth, esophagus, stomach, pancreas, intestines, liver, gallbladder, rectum, and anus.
sistema digestivo sistema corporal encargado de la digestión de los alimentos; consta de la boca, el esófago, el estómago, el páncreas, los intestinos, el hígado, la vesícula biliar, el recto y el ano.

dihybrid cross cross, or mating, between organisms involving two pairs of contrasting traits.
cruzamiento dihíbrido cruzamiento o apareamiento entre organismos que tienen dos pares de rasgos opuestos.

diploid (DIHP-LOYD) cell that has two copies of each chromosome, one from an egg and one from a sperm.
diploide celula que tiene dos copias de cada cromosoma, una proveniente de un óvulo y la otra de un espermatozoide.

directional selection pathway of natural selection in which one uncommon phenotype is selected over a more common phenotype.
selección direccional proceso de selección natural en el que se favorece un fenotipo menos común sobre un fenotipo más común.

disruptive selection pathway of natural selection in which two opposite, but equally uncommon, phenotypes are selected over the most common phenotype.
selección disruptiva proceso de selección natural en el que se favorece a dos fenotipos opuestos, pero igualmente poco comunes, sobre el fenotipo común.

divergent evolution evolution of one or more closely related species into different species; resulting from adaptations to different environmental conditions.
evolución divergente evolución de una o más especies afines que lleva a la formación de especies diferentes como resultado de adaptaciones a diversas condiciones ambientales.

DNA; deoxyribonucleic acid (dee-AHK-see-RY-boh-noo-KLEE-ihk) molecule that stores genetic information in all organisms.
ADN (ácido desoxirribonucleico) molécula que almacena la información genética de todos los organismos.

DNA fingerprint unique sequence of DNA base pairs that can be used to identify a person at the molecular level.
identificación por ADN secuencia única de pares de bases de ADN que permite la identificación de una persona a nivel molecular.

DNA microarray research tool used to study gene expression.
micromatriz de material genético (biochip) instrumento de investigación usado para estudiar la expresión de los genes.

DNA polymerase (puh-LIM-muh-rays) enzyme that makes bonds between nucleotides, forming an identical strand of DNA during replication.
ADN polimerasa enzima que establece enlaces entre los nucleótidos y que permite la formación de cadenas idénticas de ADN durante el proceso de replicación.

dominant allele that is expressed when two different alleles are present in an organism's genotype.
dominante el alelo que se expresa de entre dos alelos diferentes que integran el genotipo de un organismo determinado.

dormancy state of inactivity during which an organism or embryo is not growing.
letargo periodo de inactividad durante el cual un organismo o embrión no crece.

double fertilization process by which two sperm of a flowering plant join with an egg and a polar body, forming an embryo and endosperm.
fertilización doble proceso mediante el cual dos gametos masculinos de una planta angiosperma se combinan con un óvulo y un núcleo polar para dar lugar al embrión y al endosperma.

double helix model that compares the structure of a DNA molecule, in which two strands wind around one another, to that of a twisted ladder.
doble hélice modelo mediante el cual se representa la estructura molecular del ADN como dos cadenas que giran sobre sí mismas, como una escalera espiroidal.

E

ecological equivalents organisms that share a similar niche but live in different geographical regions.
equivalentes ecológicos organismos que tienen nichos ecológicos similares, pero que viven en diferentes zonas geográficas.

ecological footprint amount of land necessary to produce and maintain enough food, water, shelter, energy, and waste.
huella ecológica espacio que requiere una población humana para producir y mantener suficiente alimento, agua, alojamiento y energía, y para contener sus desperdicios.

ecological niche all of the physical, chemical, and biological factors that a species needs to survive, stay healthy, and reproduce in an ecosystem.
nicho ecológico conjunto de factores físicos, químicos y biológicos que una especie requiere para sobrevivir de manera saludable y reproducirse en un ecosistema determinado.

ecology study of the interactions among living things and their surroundings.
ecología estudio de las interacciones entre los seres vivos y su entorno.

ecosystem collection of organisms and nonliving things, such as climate, soil, water, and rocks, in an area.
ecosistema conjunto de organismos y factores físicos, como el clima, el suelo, el agua y las rocas, que caracterizan una zona determinada.

ectotherm organism that regulates its body temperature by exchanging heat with its environment.
poiquilotermo organismo que regula su temperatura corporal mediante el intercambio de calor con el ambiente.

egg female gamete.
óvulo gameto femenino.

electron transport chain series of proteins in the thylakoid and mitochondrial membranes that aid in converting ADP to ATP by transferring electrons.
cadena de transporte de electrones serie de proteínas de las membranas de las mitocondrias y los tilacoides que contribuyen a transformar ADP en ATP mediante la transferencia de electrones.

element substance made of only one type of atom that cannot be broken down by chemical means.
elemento sustancia formada por un solo tipo de átomo que no se puede descomponer por medios químicos.

embryo stage of development after the fertilized cell implants into the uterus but before the cells take on a recognizable shape.
embrión fase de desarrollo a partir de la implantación del óvulo fertilizado en el útero, anterior a la etapa en que las células adquieren una forma reconocible.

emigration movement of individuals out of a population.
emigración flujo de individuos que abandonan una población.

emphysema (EHM-fih-SEE-muh) condition of the lungs in which the surface area of alveoli decreases, making breathing difficult.
enfisema enfermedad de los pulmones que causa una reducción en la superficie de los alvéolos y, en consecuencia, dificulta la respiración.

endocrine system (EHN-duh-krihn) body system that controls growth, development, and responses to the environment by releasing chemical signals into the bloodstream.
sistema endocrino sistema corporal que controla el crecimiento, el desarrollo y las respuestas al entorno, mediante la liberación de señales químicas al torrente sanguíneo.

endocytosis (EHN-doh-sy-TOH-sihs) uptake of liquids or large molecules into a cell by inward folding of the cell membrane.
endocitosis captación celular de líquidos o de grandes moléculas mediante una invaginación de la membrana hacia el interior de la célula.

endometrium (EHN-doh-MEE-tree-uhm) lining of the uterus.
endometrio recubrimiento interior del útero.

endoplasmic reticulum (EHN-duh-PLAZ-mihk rih-TIHK-yuh-luhm) interconnected network of thin, folded membranes that produce, process, and distribute proteins.
retículo endoplasmático red de finas membranas interconectadas y plegadas que producen, procesan y distribuyen proteínas.

endoskeleton internal skeleton built of bone or cartilage.
endoesqueleto esqueleto interno formado por huesos y cartílagos.

endosperm tissue within seeds of flowering plants that nourishes an embryo.
endosperma tejido de reserva dentro de las semillas de las plantas con flor que abastece el embrión.

endospore prokaryotic cell with a thick, protective wall surrounding its DNA.
endospora célula procariótica cuyo ADN está protegido por una gruesa pared.

endosymbiosis ecological relationship in which one organism lives within the body of another.
endosimbiosis relación ecológica en la que un organismo vive en el interior de otro.

endotherm organism that produces its own heat through metabolic processes.
endotermo organismo que regula la temperatura de su cuerpo mediante sus propios procesos metabólicos.

endothermic chemical reaction that requires a net input of energy.
endotérmica reacción química que requiere un aporte neto de energía.

energy pyramid diagram that compares energy used by producers, primary consumers, and other trophic levels.
pirámide de energía diagrama mediante el cual se compara la energía usada por los productores, los consumidores primarios y otros niveles tróficos.

enzyme protein that catalyzes chemical reactions for organisms.
enzima proteína que cataliza reacciones químicas para los organismos.

epidemic rapid outbreak of a disease that affects many people.
epidemia aparición repentina de una enfermedad que afecta a muchas personas.

epidermis outermost layer of skin that consists mainly of dead skin cells, and provides a barrier to pathogens.
epidermis primera capa de piel, que consta principalmente de células epiteliales muertas y que constituye una barrera para los patógenos.

epididymis coiled tube through which sperm leave the testes and enter the vas deferens.
epidídimo tubo enrollado a través del cuál los espermatozoides salen de los testículos y pasan al conducto deferente.

epoch smallest unit of geologic time, lasting several million years.
época unidad más pequeña de tiempo geológico, que dura varios millones de años.

equilibrium (EE-kwuh-LIHB-ree-uhm) condition in which reactants and products of a chemical reaction are formed at the same rate.
equilibrio químico estado en el que los reactivos y los productos de una reacción química se forman a la misma velocidad.

R53

Glossary

era second largest unit of geologic time, lasting tens to hundreds of millions of years and consisting of two or more periods.
era segunda unidad más amplia de tiempo geológico; que abarca entre decenas y cientos de millones de años y consta de dos o más períodos.

esophagus (ih-SAHF-uh-guhs) tube-shaped tissue of the digestive system that connects the mouth to the stomach.
esófago tejido en forma de tubo del sistema digestivo que conecta la boca con el estómago.

estrogen steroid hormone that is found in greater quantities in women than men and contributes to female sexual characteristics and development.
estrógeno hormona esteroide que abunda más en las mujeres que en los hombres, y que contribuye al desarrollo de las características sexuales femeninas.

estuary partially enclosed body of water found where a river flows into the ocean.
estuario masa de agua parcialmente cerrada donde un río desemboca en el océano.

ethnobotany study of how various cultures use plants.
etnobotánica estudio del conocimiento que tienen las culturas sobre el uso de las plantas.

ethylene (EHTH-uh-LEEN) plant hormone that is produced in fruits and causes them to ripen.
etileno hormona vegetal que se produce en las frutas y que las hace madurar.

Eukarya one of the three domains of life, contains all eukaryotes in kingdoms Protista, Plantae, Fungi, and Animalia.
Eukarya uno de los tres dominios de la vida; consta de todos los eucariotas de los reinos protistas, plantashongos y animales.

eukaryotic cell (yoo-KAR-ee-AHT-ihk) cell that has a nucleus and other membrane-bound organelles.
célula eucariota célula que consta de un núcleo y de otros orgánulos limitados por una membrana.

eusocial organism population in which the role of each organism is specialized and not all of the organisms will reproduce.
eusocial población de organismos en la que todos tienen una función especializada y en la que algunos de ellos no se reproducen.

eutherian mammal that gives birth to live young that have completed fetal development.
euterio mamífero cuyas crías nacen tras un desarrollo fetal completo.

evolution change in a species over time; process of biological change by which descendents come to differ from their ancestors.
evolución proceso de cambio de las especies a través del tiempo; proceso de cambios biológicos a través del cual los descendientes se diferencian de sus ancestros.

excretory system body system that collects and eliminates wastes from the body; includes the kidneys and bladder.
sistema excretor sistema corporal que recoge y elimina los desechos del organismo; consta de los riñones y la vejiga urinaria.

exocytosis (EHK-soh-sy-TOH-sihs) release of substances out of a cell by the fusion of a vesicle with the membrane.
exocitosis expulsión de sustancias de una célula mediante la fusión de una vesícula citoplasmática con la membrana celular.

exon sequence of DNA that codes information for protein synthesis.
exón secuencia de ADN que codifica la información para la síntesis de las proteínas.

exoskeleton hard outer structure, such as the shell of an insect or crustacean, that provides protection and support for the organism.
exoesqueleto estructura exterior dura como, por ejemplo, el caparazón de un crustáceo, que protege y sustenta al organismo.

exothermic chemical reaction that yields a net release of energy in the form of heat.
exotérmica reacción química que, al producirse, libera energía en forma calor.

experiment process that tests a hypothesis by collecting information under controlled conditions.
experimento procedimiento mediante el cual se trata de comprobar una hipótesis mediante la recolección de datos bajo condiciones controladas.

exponential growth dramatic increase in population over a short period of time.
crecimiento exponencial intenso incremento de población en un breve espacio de tiempo.

extinction elimination of a species from Earth.
extinción desaparición de una especie o grupo de especies de la Tierra.

F

facilitated diffusion diffusion of molecules assisted by protein channels that pierce a cell membrane.
difusión facilitada difusión de moléculas asistida mediante canales de proteínas que perforan la membrana celular.

facultative aerobe organism that can live with or without oxygen.
aerobio facultativo organismo capaz de vivir con o sin oxígeno.

fallopian tube tube of connective tissue that attaches the ovary to the uterus in the female reproductive system and in which fertilization occurs.
trompa de Falopio conducto de tejido conjuntivo que conecta el ovario con el útero en el sistema reproductor femenino, y donde se produce la fertilización.

fatty acid hydrocarbon chain often bonded to glycerol in a lipid.
ácido graso cadena de hidrocarbono que suele enlazarce con los glicéridos de un lípido.

feedback information that is compared with a set of ideal values and aids in maintaining homeostasis.
retroalimentación información que se compara con un grupo de valores ideales y que contribuye al mantenimiento de la homeóstasis.

fermentation anaerobic process by which ATP is produced by glycolysis.
fermentación proceso anaeróbico que da lugar al ATP mediante la glicólisis.

fertilization fusion of an egg and sperm cell.
fertilización fusión de un gameto masculino y uno femenino.

fetus unborn offspring from the end of the eighth week after conception to the moment of birth.
feto cría no nacida desde el final de la octava semana después de la concepción hasta el momento del nacimiento.

fibrous root root system made up of many threadlike members of more or less equal length.
raíces fibrosas sistema radical compuesto de una multitud de filamentos que tienen una longitud aproximadamente igual.

filter feeder animal that eats by straining particles from water.
organismo filtrador animal que se alimenta mediante la filtración de partículas del agua.

fitness measure of an organism's ability to survive and produce offspring relative to other members of a population.
aptitud biológica capacidad de un organismo determinado para sobrevivir y producir descendencia en relación con los demás miembros de una población.

flagellum (plural: *flagella*) whiplike structure outside of a cell that is used for movement.
flagelo estructura en forma de látigo del exterior de determinadas células que les permite moverse en su medio.

flower reproductive structure of an angiosperm.
flor sistema reproductor de una angiosperma.

fluid mosaic model model that describes the arrangement and movement of the molecules that make up a cell membrane.
modelo de mosaico fluido modelo que describe la disposición y movimiento de las moléculas que conforman la membrana celular.

follicle collection of cells that surrounds and nourishes an egg while it is in the ovary.
folículo conjunto de células que rodean y nutren al óvulo mientras éste permanece en el ovario.

food chain model that links organisms by their feeding relationships.
cadena alimentaria modelo que relaciona los organismos según sus interacciones alimentarias.

food web model that shows the complex network of feeding relationships within an ecosystem.
red alimentaria modelo que representa una red compleja de relaciones alimentarias en un ecosistema determinado.

fossil trace of an organism from the past.
fósil huella de un organismo del pasado.

founder effect genetic drift that occurs after a small number of individuals colonize a new area.
efecto fundador deriva genética que se produce cuando un pequeño número de individuos coloniza una nueva región.

frameshift mutation mutation that involves the insertion or deletion of a nucleotide in the DNA sequence.
mutación del marco de lectura mutación que implica la incorporación o la eliminación de un nucleótido en una secuencia de ADN.

fruit fertilized and mature ovary of a flower.
fruto ovario fertilizado y maduro de una flor.

fruiting body spore-producing structure of a fungus that grows above ground.
esporocarpo estructura productora de esporas de un hongo que crece sobre la tierra.

G

gamete sex cell; an egg or a sperm cell.
gameto célula sexual; óvulo o espermatozoide.

gametogenesis (guh-MEE-tuh-JEHN-ih-sihs) process by which gametes are produced through the combination of meiosis and other maturational changes.
gametogénesis proceso de producción de gametos mediante una combinación de meiosis y otros cambios de maduración.

gametophyte (guh-MEE-tuh-FYT) haploid, gamete-producing phase in a plant life cycle.
gametofito fase de producción de gametos o células sexuales haploides en el ciclo de vida de las plantas.

gastrovascular cavity saclike digestive space.
cavidad gastrovascular espacio digestivo en forma de bolsa.

gel electrophoresis (ih-LEHK-troh-fuh-REE-sihs) method of separating various lengths of DNA strands by applying an electrical current to a gel.
electroforesis en gel método de separación de fragmentos de ADN mediante la aplicación de una corriente eléctrica a un gel.

gene specific region of DNA that codes for a particular protein.
gen parte específica del ADN con información codificada para sintetizar una proteína.

gene flow physical movement of alleles from one population to another.
flujo génico desplazamiento físico de alelos de una población a otra.

Glossary

gene knockout genetic manipulation in which one or more of an organism's genes are prevented from being expressed.
supresión génica manipulación genética mediante la cual se anula la capacidad de expresarse de uno o más genes de un organismo determinado.

gene pool collection of alleles found in all of the individuals of a population.
acervo genético colección de alelos de todos los individuos de una población determinada.

generalist species that does not rely on a single source of prey.
generalista especie que no depende de un solo tipo de presa.

gene sequencing process of determining the order of DNA nucleotides in genes and genomes.
secuenciación génica proceso de determinación del orden de los nucleótidos de ADN en los genes y en los genomas.

gene therapy procedure to treat a disease in which a defective or missing gene is replaced or a new gene is inserted into a patient's genome.
terapia génica procedimiento para el tratamiento de una enfermedad en el que un gen defectuoso o ausente se reemplaza por uno sano que se inserta en el genoma del paciente.

genetic drift change in allele frequencies due to chance alone, occurring most commonly in small populations.
deriva genética cambio en las frecuencias de alelos que se produce, sobre todo, en poblaciones pequeñas.

genetic engineering process of changing an organism's DNA to give the organism new traits.
ingeniería genética proceso de modifación del ADN de un organismo con el fin de dotarlo de nuevos rasgos.

genetic linkage tendency for genes located close together on the same chromosome to be inherited together.
ligamiento genético tendencia de los genes que se encuentran muy próximos en un cromosoma a ser transmitidos juntos a la descendencia.

genetics study of the heredity patterns and variation of organisms.
genética estudio de los patrones hereditarios y de la variación de los organismos.

genetic screening process of testing DNA to determine the chance a person has, or might pass on, a genetic disorder.
análisis genético proceso de análisis de ADN para determinar las probabilidades que tiene una persona de contraer o transmitir una enfermedad genética.

genome all of an organism's genetic material.
genoma todo el material genético de un organismo determinado.

genomics (juh-NOH-mihks) study and comparison of genomes within a single species or among different species.
genómica estudio comparativo de los genomas de una misma especie y de especies diferentes.

genotype (JEHN-uh-TYP) collection of all of an organism's genetic information that codes for traits.
genotipo conjunto de todos los rasgos codificados en la información genética de un organismo.

genus first name in binomial nomenclature; the second-most specific taxon in the Linnaean classification system that includes one or more physically similar species, which are thought to be closely related.
género primera palabra de la nomenclatura binomial; segundo taxón más específico del sistema de clasificación de las especies de Linneo, que consta de dos o más especies físicamente semejantes consideradas muy próximas.

geographic isolation isolation between populations due to physical barriers.
aislamiento geográfico separación entre poblaciones debido a barreras físicas.

geologic time scale time scale representing the history of Earth.
escala de tiempo geológico escala de tiempo para representar la historia de la Tierra.

geosphere features of Earth's surface—such as continents and the sea floor—and everything below Earth's surface.
geosfera componentes de la superficie de la Tierra, es decir, los continentes, el suelo oceánico y el interior mismo de la Tierra.

germination process by which seeds or spores sprout and begin to grow.
germinación proceso mediante el cual las semillas o esporas brotan y empiezan a crecer.

germ theory theory that states that diseases are caused by microscopic particles called pathogens.
teoría de los gérmenes teoría según la cual las enfermedades son causadas por unas partículas microscópicas llamadas patógenos.

gibberellin (JIHB-uh-REHL-ihn) plant hormone that stimulates cell growth.
giberelina hormona vegetal que estimula el crecimiento celular.

gill respiratory organ of aquatic animals that allows breathing underwater.
branquia órgano respiratorio de numerosos animales acuáticos que permite respirar bajo el agua.

gland organ that produces and releases chemicals that affect the activities of other tissues.
glándula órgano que produce y secreta compuestos químicos que afectan el funcionamiento de otros tejidos.

global warming worldwide trend of increasing average temperatures.
calentamiento global incremento del promedio de la temperatura en toda la Tierra.

glomerulus (gloh-MEHR-yuh-luhs) tangled ball of capillaries that circulates blood in the kidneys.
glomérulos ovillo de vasos capilares por los que circula la sangre en los riñones.

glycolysis (gly-KAHL-uh-sihs) anaerobic process in which glucose is broken down into two molecules of pyruvate and two net ATP are produced.
glicólisis proceso anaeróbico en el que la glucosa se descompone en dos moléculas de piruvato y se producen dos moléculas de ATP.

Golgi apparatus (GOHL-jee) stack of flat, membrane-enclosed spaces containing enzymes that process, sort, and deliver proteins.
aparato de Golgi conjunto de sacos apilados y aplanados rodeados de una membrana que contienen enzimas que procesan, clasifican y distribuyen proteínas.

gradualism principle that states that the changes in landforms result from slow changes over a long period of time.
gradualismo principio que postula que los cambios en los accidentes geográficos resultan de pequeños cambios graduales durante extensos períodos de tiempo.

grassland biome in which the primary plant life is grass.
pradera bioma en la que las forma de vida vegetal predominante son las hierbas y los pastos.

gravitropism growth of plants in response to gravity; plant stems grow upward, against gravity, and roots grow toward the gravitational pull.
gravitropismo crecimiento de las plantas condicionado por la gravedad; el tallo crece hacia arriba, en sentido inverso a la fuerza de gravedad, y las raíces crecen hacia abajo, en el mismo sentido que la gravedad.

greenhouse effect normal warming effect produced when gases, such as carbon dioxide and methane, trap heat in Earth's atmosphere.
efecto invernadero calentamiento producido cuando ciertos gases, como el dióxido de carbono y el metano, atrapan el calor en la atmósfera terrestre.

ground tissue tissue system that makes up the majority of a plant.
tejido fundamental sistema de tejidos que comprende la parte principal del cuerpo de la planta.

growth factor broad group of proteins that stimulate cell division.
factor de crecimiento grupo numeroso de proteínas que estimulan la división celular.

guard cell one of a pair of cells that controls the opening and closing of a stoma in plant tissue.
células oclusivas las dos células que controlan la apertura y cierre de los estomas en el tejido vegetal.

gymnosperm (JIHM-nuh-SPURM) seed plant whose seeds are not enclosed by fruit.
gimnosperma planta productora de semillas que no están encerradas en una fruta.

H

habitat combined biotic and abiotic factors found in the area where an organism lives.
hábitat conjunto de factores bióticos y abióticos de la zona donde vive un organismo determinado.

habitat fragmentation process by which part of an organism's preferred habitat range becomes inaccessible.
fragmentación del hábitat proceso mediante el cual una parte del hábitat de un organismo se hace inaccesible.

habituation process of eventually ignoring a repeated stimulus.
habituación proceso que eventualmente conduce a ignorar un estímulo que se repite.

hair cell mechanoreceptor in the inner ear that detects sound waves when bent.
célula ciliada mecanoreceptor del oído interno que detecta las ondas sonoras que lo accionan.

hair follicle pit in the dermis of the skin that contains cells that produce hair.
folículo piloso estrecha cavidad de la piel que contiene células que forman el cabello.

half-life amount of time it takes for half of the isotope in a sample to decay into its product isotope.
vida mitad intervalo de tiempo necesario para que la mitad de los átomos de una muestra de isótopos se desintegren.

haploid (HAP-LOYD) cell that has only one copy of each chromosome.
haploide célula que sólo tiene una copia de cada cromosoma.

Hardy-Weinberg equilibrium condition in which a population's allele frequencies for a given trait do not change from generation to generation.
equilibrio de Hardy-Weinberg condición en la que las frecuencias alélicas de un rasgo determinado en una población determinada se mantienen constantes de una generación a otra.

heart muscle in the chest that moves blood throughout the body.
corazón músculo situado en el pecho que hace circular la sangre por el cuerpo.

hemocoel open space between cells in animal tissues.
hemocele cavidad intracelular de los tejidos animales.

hemoglobin (HEE-muh-GLOH-bihn) iron-rich protein in red blood cells that allows the cells to absorb oxygen gas.
hemoglobina proteína rica en hierro de los glóbulos rojos que permite a las células absorber oxígeno gaseoso.

herbivore organism that eats only plants.
herbívoro organismo que sólo se alimenta de plantas.

heritability ability of a trait to be passed from one generation to the next.
heredabilidad propiedad de un rasgo determinado de ser transmitido de una generación a la siguiente.

heterotroph organism that obtains its energy and nutrients by consuming other organisms.
heterótrofo organismo que obtiene su energía y sus nutrientes alimentándose de otros organismos.

heterozygous characteristic of having two different alleles that appear at the same locus of sister chromatids.
heterocigoto característica que consiste en tener dos alelos diferentes en el mismo locus de cromátidas hermanas.

histone protein that organizes chromosomes and around which DNA wraps.
histona proteína que ordena los cromosomas y alrededor de la cual se enrolla el ADN.

homeobox (HOH-mee-uh-BAHKS) genes that define the head-to-tail pattern of development in animal embryos; also called *Hox* genes.
homeobox genes que definen el desarrollo de los embriones animales organizado de cabeza a cola; también se conocen como genes *Hox*.

homeostasis (HOH-mee-oh-STAY-sihs) regulation and maintenance of constant internal conditions in an organism.
homeostasis regulación y mantenimiento de condiciones internas constantes en un organismo determinado.

homeotic (hoh-mee-AH-tihk) genes that control early development in animals.
homeóticos genes que controlan la primera fase del desarrollo de los animales.

hominid primate group that includes orangutans, chimpanzees, gorillas, and humans, as well as their immediate ancestors.
homínido grupo de primates que incluye orangutanes, chimpancés, gorilas, así como humanos y los antepasados inmediatos de éstos.

homologous chromosomes chromosomes that have the same length, appearance, and copies of genes, although the alleles may differ.
cromosomas homólogos cromosomas de la misma longitud, aspecto y secuencia de genes, aunque los alelos de uno y otro cromosoma pueden ser distintos.

homologous structure body part that is similar in structure on different organisms but performs different functions.
estructura homóloga estructura anatómica similar de organismos diferentes pero que cumplen funciones diferentes.

homozygous characteristic of having two of the same alleles at the same locus of sister chromatids.
homocigoto característica que consiste en tener los mismos alelos en el mismo locus de cromátidas hermanas.

hormone chemical signal that is produced in one part of an organism and affects cell activity in another part.
hormona señal química producida en una parte del organismo que afecta a la actividad celular en otra parte del cuerpo.

Human Genome Project project whose goal is to map, sequence, and identify all of the genes in the human genome.
Proyecto Genoma Humano proyecto cuya meta consiste en cartografiar un mapa, identificar y hallar la secuencia de todos los genes del genoma humano.

human immunodeficiency virus (HIV) virus that weakens the immune system by reproducing in and destroying T cells; causes AIDS.
virus de inmunodeficiencia humana (VIH) virus que debilita el sistema inmune al reproducirse en las células T y destruirlas; causa el SIDA.

humoral immunity immune response that relies on B cells to produce antibodies to help fight infection.
inmunidad humoral respuesta inmune basada en los anticuerpos producidos por las células B para combatir las infecciones.

hydrogen bond attraction between a slightly positive hydrogen atom and a slightly negative atom.
enlace de hidrógeno atracción entre un átomo de hidrógeno con una carga parcial positiva y otro con una carga parcial negativa.

hydrologic cycle pathway of water from the atmosphere to Earth's surface, below ground, and back.
ciclo hidrológico movimiento del agua desde la atmósfera hasta la superficie de la Tierra, al subsuelo y de vuelta a la atmósfera.

hydrosphere collection of Earth's water bodies, ice, and water vapor.
hidrosfera conjunto de las masas de agua líquida, sólida y gaseosa de la Tierra.

hypertonic solution that has a higher concentration of dissolved particles compared with another solution.
hipertónica solución con una concentración mayor de partículas disueltas que otra solución.

hypha (plural: *hyphae*) threadlike filament forming the body and mycelium of a fungus.
hifa filamento que forman el cuerpo y el micelio de los hongos.

hypothalamus small area of the midbrain that plays a role in the nervous and endocrine systems.
hipotálamo área reducida del cerebro medio que participa en las funciones de los sistemas nervioso y endocrino.

hypothesis (plural: *hypotheses*) proposed explanation or answer to a scientific question.
hipótesis proceso de explicación o respuesta a una pregunta científica.

hypotonic solution that has a lower concentration of dissolved particles compared with another solution.
hipotónica solución con una concentración menor de partículas disueltas que otra solución.

I

imitation process by which an organism learns a behavior by observing other individuals.
imitación proceso mediante el cual un organismo aprende un determinado comportamiento mediante la observación de otros individuos.

immigration movement of individuals into a population.
inmigración desplazamiento de individuos hacia una población establecida.

immune system body system that fights off infections.
sistema inmune sistema encargado de combatir las infecciones.

imprinting process by which a newborn animal quickly learns to recognize another animal, such as a parent.
impronta filial proceso mediante el cual un animal recién nacido aprende rápidamente a reconocer a otro como, por ejemplo, su progenitor.

inclusive fitness total number of genes an animal contributes to the next generation.
aptitud inclusiva número total de genes que un animal transmite a la siguiente generación.

incomplete dominance heterozygous phenotype that is a blend of the two homozygous phenotypes.
dominancia incompleta fenotipo heterocigoto que resulta de la mezcla de dos fenotipos homocigotos.

incomplete metamorphosis process by which immature arthropods look similar to their adult form.
metamorfosis incompleta proceso mediante el cual los especímenes jóvenes de los artrópodos son muy similares en forma a los adultos.

independent variable condition or factor that is manipulated by a scientist during an experiment.
variable independiente condición o factor que es manipulado en el transcurso de un experimento científico.

index fossil fossil of an organism that existed during only specific spans of geologic time across large geographic areas.
fósil índice fósil de un organismo que existió en el pasado geológico durante un intervalo corto con una amplia distribución geográfica.

indicator species species whose presence in an ecosystem gives clues about the condition of that ecosystem.
especies indicadoras especies cuya presencia en un ecosistema proporcionan claves sobre el estado en que se encuentra dicho ecosistema.

infancy period of life from birth until the ability to walk has been acquired.
infancia periodo de vida comprendido entre el nacimiento y los primeros pasos.

infertility persistent condition in which offspring cannot be produced.
esterilidad incapacidad recurrente de un individuo para reproducirse.

inflammation immune response that is characterized by swelling, redness, pain, and itching.
inflamación respuesta inmune caracterizada por hinchazón, rubor, dolor y picazón.

innate behavior that is not learned through experience.
innato comportamiento que no se aprende a través de la experiencia.

insecticide chemical that is used to kill insects.
insecticida compuesto químico usado para matar insectos.

insight ability to solve a problem without repeated trial and error.
perspicacia capacidad para resolver un problema sin necesidad de pasar por procesos reiterados de prueba y error.

instinct inborn pattern of behavior that is characteristic of a species.
instinto patrón innato de comportamiento característico de cada especie.

integumentary system body system that separates the other body systems from the external environment; includes the skin and the tissues found within it.
sistema tegumentario sistema que delimita los sistemas corporales del medio exterior; consta de la piel y de los tejidos que la conforman.

interferon type of protein, produced by body cells, that prevents viruses from replicating in infected cells.
interferón tipo de proteína generada por las células corporales que impide la replicación de los virus en el interior de las células infectadas.

intertidal zone strip of land between the high and low tide lines.
zona intermareal banda de tierra comprendida entra las líneas de pleamar y de bajamar.

introduced species species that is not native and was brought to an area as a result of human activities.
especie introducida especie no autóctona que llega a otras regiones como resultado de actividades humanas.

intron segment of a gene that does not code for an amino acid.
intrón región de un gen que no participa en la codificación de amino ácidos.

invertebrate animal without a backbone.
invertebrado animal sin columna vertebral.

ion atom that has gained or lost one or more electrons.
ión átomo que ha ganado o perdido uno o más electrones.

R59

Glossary

ionic bond chemical bond formed through the electrical force between oppositely charged ions.
enlace iónico enlace químico que se establece mediante la fuerza eléctrica ejercida entre dos iones de cargas opuestas.

isotonic solution that has an equal concentration of dissolved particles compared with another solution.
isotónica solución que tiene la misma concentración de partículas disueltas que otra solución.

isotope form of an element that has the same number of protons but a different number of neutrons as another element.
isótopo átomo de un elemento químico que tiene el mismo número de protones, pero una cantidad diferente de neutrones que otro átomo del mismo elemento.

J

joint location in the body where two bones meet.
articulación área del cuerpo en la que se unen dos huesos.

K

karyotype (KAR-ee-uh-TYP) image of all of the chromosomes in a cell.
cariotipo imagen de todos los cromosomas de una célula.

kelp forest ocean habitat that exists in cold, nutrient-rich, shallow coastal waters, composed of large communities of kelp, a seaweed.
bosques de quelpo hábitat oceánico de frías aguas costeras de poca profundidad que son ricas en nutrientes y en las que abundan grandes comunidades de algas pardas llamadas quelpos.

keratin protein that binds to lipids inside a skin cell, forming a waterproof layer within the skin.
queratina proteína que se enlaza con los lípidos dentro de las células epiteliales creando una capa impermeable en el interior de la piel.

keystone species organism that has an unusually large effect on its ecosystem.
especie clave organismo que tiene una rol dominante en su ecosistema.

kidney organ of the excretory system that removes waste from the blood and helps to maintain stable water levels in the body.
riñón órgano del sistema excretor que elimina los desechos de la sangre y contribuye a mantener niveles estables de agua en el organismo.

kinesis random movement that results from an increase in activity levels due to a stimulus.
quinesia movimiento aleatorio que resulta de un incremento en los niveles de actividad producidos por un estímulo.

kin selection when natural selection acts on alleles that favor the survival of close relatives.
nepotismo selección natural de los alelos que favorece la supervivencia de los familiares más próximos.

Krebs cycle process during cellular respiration that breaks down a carbon molecule to produce molecules that are used in the electron transport chain.
ciclo de Krebs proceso de respiración celular en el que se desintegra una molécula de carbono para generar moléculas que intervienen en la cadena de transporte de electrones.

L

lactic acid product of fermentation in many types of cells, including human muscle cells.
ácido láctico producto de fermentación de muchos tipos de células como, por ejemplo, las células musculares humanas.

lateral line sensory system in fish that allows them to sense distant movements in the water.
línea lateral sistema sensorial de los peces que les permite captar movimientos lejanos en el agua.

law of independent assortment Mendel's second law, stating that allele pairs separate from one another during gamete formation.
ley de transmisión independiente segunda ley de Mendel, según la cual los pares de alelos se separan durante la formación de los gametos.

law of segregation Mendel's first law, stating that (1) organisms inherit two copies of genes, one from each parent, and (2) organisms donate only one copy of each gene in their gametes because the genes separate during gamete formation.
ley de la segregación primera ley de Mendel, según la cual (1) los organismos heredan dos copias de cada gen, una de cada progenitor, y (2) que los organismos sólo reciben una copia de cada gen de los gametos de sus progenitores ya que los genes se separan durante la formación de gametos.

leukemia cancer of the bone marrow that weakens the immune system by preventing white blood cells from maturing.
leucemia cáncer de la medula ósea que debilita el sistema inmune al impedir que maduren los glóbulos blancos.

lichen fungus that grows symbiotically with algae, resulting in a composite organism that grows on rocks or tree trunks.
liquen organismo compuesto por un hongo y una alga que viven en y que crece sobre las rocas y los troncos de los árboles.

ligament long, flexible band of connective tissue that joins two bones across a joint.
ligamento tira alargada y flexible de tejido conjuntivo que une dos huesos a través de una articulación.

light-dependent reactions part of photosynthesis that absorbs energy from sunlight and transfers energy to the light-independent reactions.
reacciones lumínicas etapa de la fotosíntesis en la que se absorbe energía solar para luego usarse en las reacciones oscuras.

light-independent reactions part of photosynthesis that uses energy absorbed during the light-dependent reactions to synthesize carbohydrates.
reacciones oscuras etapa de la fotosíntesis en que se aplica la energía absorbida durante las reacciones lumínicas para la síntesis de carbohidratos.

lignin (LIHG-nihn) complex polymer that hardens cell walls of some vascular tissues in plants.
lignina polímero complejo que endurece las paredes celulares de determinados tejidos vasculares de las plantas.

limiting factor environmental factor that limits the growth and size of a population.
factor limitante factor ambiental que limita el crecimiento y tamaño de una población determinada.

limnetic zone open water of a lake or pond that is located away from shore.
zona limnética aguas abiertas de un lago o estanque alejadas de las orillas.

linkage map diagram that shows the relative locations of genes on a chromosome.
mapa de ligamiento diagrama que representa la situación relativa de los genes en un cromosoma determinado.

lipid nonpolar molecule composed of carbon, hydrogen, and oxygen; includes fats and oils.
lípido molécula apolar compuesta de carbono, hidrógeno y oxígeno; las grasas y los aceites son lípidos.

littoral zone area between the high and low water marks along the shoreline of a lake or pond.
zona litoral área de aguas de profundidad intermedia a lo largo de la orilla de un lago o estanque.

lobe-fin paired limblike fin that is round in shape.
aleta lobulada tipo de aleta de forma redondeada que se presenta en pares y que se asemeja a una extremidad.

logistic growth population growth that is characterized by a period of slow growth, followed by a period of exponential growth, followed by another period of almost no growth.
crecimiento logístico crecimiento de población que se caracteriza por un período de crecimiento lento, seguido por un período de crecimiento exponencial al que le sigue un período de crecimiento insignificante.

lung organ that absorbs oxygen gas from air that an organism inhales.
pulmón órgano que absorbe el oxígeno gaseoso que inhala un organismo.

lymph collection of interstitial fluid and white blood cells that flows through the lymphatic system.
linfa conjunto de los fluidos intersticiales y de glóbulos blancos que circulan por el sistema linfático.

lymphatic system (lihm-FAT-ihk) body system that consists of organs, vessels, and nodes through which lymph circulates.
sistema linfático sistema corporal que consta de órganos, vasos y nódulos a través de los cuales circula la linfa.

lymphocyte (LIHM-fuh-SYT) white blood cell that plays a role in an immune response; *see* B cell and T cell.
linfocito glóbulo blanco que participa en la respuesta inmune; *véanse* célula B y célula T.

lysogenic infection infectious pathway of a virus in which host cells are not immediately destroyed.
infección lisogénica infección vírica en la que las células huésped no son destruidas de inmediato.

lysosome (LY-suh-SOHM) organelle that contains enzymes.
lisosoma orgánulo que contiene enzimas.

lytic infection infectious pathway of a virus in which host cells are destroyed.
infección lítica infección vírica en la que se destruyen las células huésped.

M

malignant cancerous tumor in which cells break away and spread to other parts of the body, causing harm to the organism's health.
maligno tumor canceroso en el que las células se desprenden y se diseminan a otras partes del cuerpo provocando daños a la salud del organismo.

mammal endothermic organism that has hair, mammary glands, bones in the ear that allow for hearing, and a jaw for chewing food.
mamífero organismo endotérmico que tiene pelo y glándulas mamarias, además de huesos en el oído que le permiten oír y una mandíbula para masticar.

mammary gland gland that produces milk.
glándula mamaria glándula productora de leche.

mandible appendage that is used to crush and bite food.
mandíbula apéndice empleado para triturar y morder la comida.

marsupial mammal whose young complete fetal development in the mother's external pouch.
marsupial mamífero cuyas crías terminan su desarrollo fetal en una bolsa exterior de la madre.

measurement a determination of the dimensions of something using a standard unit.
medida una determinación de las dimensiones de algo por medio del uso de una unidad estándar.

Glossary

medusa umbrella-shaped body form of a cnidarian in which the mouth and tentacles are on the underside.
medusa organismo cnidario en forma de paraguas que tiene la boca y los tentáculos en la superficie cóncava.

meiosis (my-OH-sihs) form of nuclear division that divides a diploid cell into haploid cells; important in forming gametes for sexual reproduction.
meiosis forma de división nuclear en la que una célula diploide se divide en células haploides; importante en la formación de gametos para la reproducción sexual.

memory cell specialized white blood cell that contributes to acquired immunity by acting quickly to a foreign substance that infected the body previously.
célula de memoria glóbulo blanco que participa en el proceso de inmunización mediante una respuesta rápida ante una sustancia extraña que ya había infectado el organismo anteriormente.

menopause period of life when the female reproductive system permanently stops the menstrual cycle.
menopausia período de la vida en que el sistema reproductor femenino deja de producir el ciclo menstrual.

menstrual cycle series of changes in the female reproductive system that takes place over the course of one month.
ciclo menstrual sucesión de cambios en el sistema reproductor femenino que ocurre en el plazo de un mes.

meristem undifferentiated plant tissue from which new cells are formed.
meristemo tejido indiferenciado de las plantas en el que se forman nuevas células.

mesoglea jellylike material that separates the two tissue layers of a cnidarian.
mesoglea matriz gelatinosa que separa las dos capas de tejidos de un cnidario.

mesophyll photosynthetic tissue of a leaf, located between the upper and lower epidermis.
mesófilo tejido fotosintético de la hoja, situado entre la epidermis superior y la epidermis inferior de la hoja.

Mesozoic era during which dinosaurs roamed Earth (from 248 million years ago to 65 million years ago).
Mesozoico era de la Tierra que se inició hace unos 248 millones de años y que finalizó hace 65 millones de años en la que abundaron los dinosaurios.

messenger RNA (mRNA) form of RNA that carries genetic information from the nucleus to the cytoplasm, where it serves as a template for protein synthesis.
ARN mensajero (ARNm) forma de ARN que transporta la información genética del núcleo al citoplasma, donde sirve de patrón para la síntesis de las proteínas.

metabolism all chemical processes that synthesize or break down materials within an organism.
metabolismo conjunto de procesos químicos que sintetizan o descomponen sustancias en el interior de los organismos.

metaphase second phase of mitosis when spindle fibers align the chromosomes along the cell equator.
metafase segunda fase de la mitosis en la que las fibras de los husos alinean los cromosomas en el plano ecuatorial de la célula.

metastasize (mih-TAS-tuh-SYZ) to spread by transferring a disease-causing agent from the site of the disease to other parts of the body.
metástasis diseminación de una enfermedad causada por un agente patógeno del foco en que se origina a otras partes del cuerpo.

microclimate climate of a specific location within a larger area.
microclima clima de un lugar específico enclavado en un área más extensa.

microevolution observable change in the allele frequencies of a population over a few generations.
microevolución cambio observable en las frecuencias alélicas de una población en el transcurso de unas pocas generaciones.

microscope tool that provides an enlarged image of an object.
microscopio instrumento que permite ver una imagen amplificada de un objeto.

microvillus (plural: *microvilli*) small hairlike projection on the surface of a villus in the small intestine.
microvellosidad proyección pilosa muy pequeña que recubre las vellosidades del intestino delgado.

mineral inorganic material, such as calcium, iron, potassium, sodium, or zinc, that is essential to the nutrition of an organism.
mineral material inorgánico, como el calcio, el hierro, el potasio, el sodio o el zinc, que resulta esencial en la nutrición de los organismos.

mitochondrial DNA DNA found only in mitochondria, often used as a molecular clock.
ADN mitocondrial ADN propio de las mitocondrias que suele actuar a modo de reloj molecular.

mitochondrion (MY-tuh-KAHN-dree-uhn) (plural: *mitochondria*) bean-shaped organelle that supplies energy to the cell and has its own ribosomes and DNA.
mitocondria orgánulo en forma de fríjol que suministra energía a la célula y que tiene sus propios ribosomas y ADN.

mitosis (my-TOH-sihs) process by which a cell divides its nucleus and contents.
mitosis proceso en el cual tanto el núcleo como los demás elementos de la célula se duplican.

molecular clock theoretical clock that uses the rate of mutation to measure evolutionary time.
reloj molecular reloj teórico que emplea la tasa de mutación para medir el tiempo evolutivo.

molecular genetics study of DNA structure and function on the molecular level.
genética molecular estudio de la estructura y función del ADN a nivel molecular.

molecule two or more atoms held together by covalent bonds; not necessarily a compound.
molécula dos o más átomos unidos mediante enlaces covalentes; no forman necesariamente un compuesto.

monocot (MAHN-uh-KAHT) flowering plant whose embryos have one cotyledon.
monocotiledónea planta angiosperma cuyos embriones tienen un solo cotiledón.

monohybrid cross cross, or mating, between organisms that involves only one pair of contrasting traits.
cruzamiento monohíbrido cruzamiento o apareamiento entre dos organismos que sólo involucra un par de rasgos diferentes.

monomer molecular subunit of a polymer.
monómero subunidad molecular del polímero.

monotreme mammal whose offspring complete fetal development in laid eggs.
monotrema mamífero que pone huevos donde sus crías completan su desarrollo fetal.

muscle fiber cell of the muscular system that shortens when it is stimulated by the nervous system.
fibra muscular célula del sistema muscular que se contrae al ser estimulada por el sistema nervioso.

muscular system body system that moves bones within and substances throughout the body.
sistema muscular sistema corporal que mueve los huesos y que hace circular sustancias a través del cuerpo.

mutagen agent that can induce or increase the frequency of mutation in organisms.
mutágeno agente que puede inducir mutaciones en un organismo o incrementar la frecuencia de éstas.

mutation change in the DNA sequence.
mutación cambio en la secuencia de ADN.

mutualism ecological relationship between two species in which each species gets a benefit from the interaction.
mutualismo relación ecológica entre dos especies que resulta beneficiosa para ambas.

mycelium vegetative part of a fungus, consisting of a mass of branching, threadlike hyphae that grows underground.
micelio parte vegetativa del hongo compuesta de un entramado de filamentos ramificados, llamados hifas, que crece bajo tierra.

mycorrhizae ecological relationship between the mycelium of a fungus and the roots of certain plants.
micorriza relación ecológica entre el micelio de un hongo y las raíces de determinadas plantas.

myofibril long strand of protein within a muscle fiber.
miofibrilla larga cadena proteica dentro de una fibra muscular.

myosin filament that pulls actin filaments to cause muscle contraction.
miosina filamento que al tensar los filamentos de actina causa la contracción muscular.

N

natural selection mechanism by which individuals that have inherited beneficial adaptations produce more offspring on average than do other individuals.
selección natural mecanismo mediante el cual los organismos que han heredado adaptaciones beneficiosas producen un promedio más alto de descendientes que los demás individuos.

nebula rotating cloud of gas and dust.
nebulosa nube giratoria de polvo y gases.

negative feedback control system for homeostasis that adjusts the body's conditions when the conditions vary from the ideal.
retroalimentación negativa sistema de control de la homeostasis que regula las condiciones del cuerpo cuando éstas no son óptimas.

nematocyst capsule containing a thin, coiled tubule with a poisonous barb at one end.
nematocisto cápsula que contiene un fino túbulo enrollado con un aguijón venenoso en la punta.

nephron (NEHF-rahn) individual filtering unit of the kidney that removes waste from the blood.
nefrona unidad de filtración del riñón que retira los desechos de la sangre.

neritic zone zone of the ocean that extends from the intertidal zone out to the edge of the continental shelf.
zona nerítica zona del océano que se extiende desde la zona intermareal hasta el límite de la plataforma continental.

nervous system body system that controls sensation, interpretation, and response; includes the brain, spinal cord, and nerves.
sistema nervioso sistema corporal que controla las sensaciones, las interpretaciones y las respuestas; incluye el encéfalo, la médula espinal y los nervios.

neuron cell of the nervous system that transmits impulses between the body systems as well as interprets and stores some messages in the brain.
neurona célula del sistema nervioso que transmite impulsos entre los diversos sistemas del organismo y que, además, interpreta y almacena información en el cerebro.

neurotransmitter (NUR-oh-TRANS-miht-uhr) chemical that transmits a nervous system's signal across a synapse.
neurotransmisor compuesto químico que transmite una señal del sistema nervioso a través de la sinapsis.

R63

nitrogen fixation process by which certain types of bacteria convert gaseous nitrogen into nitrogen compounds.
fijación del nitrógeno proceso mediante el cual ciertos tipos de bacterias transforman el nitrógeno gaseoso en compuestos nitrogenados.

node organ located along the lymphatic vessels that filters bacteria and foreign particles from lymph.
ganglio linfático órgano situado a lo largo de los vasos linfáticos encargado de filtrar bacterias y sustancias extrañas de la linfa.

nonrenewable resource natural resource that is used more quickly than it can be formed.
recurso no renovable recurso natural que se consume con más rapidez de la que se puede reponer.

normal distribution distribution in a population in which allele frequency is highest near the mean range value and decreases progressively toward each extreme end.
distribución normal distribución de la población en la que la frecuencia alélica es mayor en la zona de valor medio y disminuye progresivamente hacia ambos extremos.

notochord flexible skeletal support rod embedded in an animal's back.
notocordio bastón esqueletal flexible que proporciona sostén y que está situado en el dorso de los animales.

nucleic acid polymer of nucleotides; the genetic material of organisms.
ácido nucleico polímero de nucleótidos; material genético de los organismos.

nucleotide (NOO-klee-uh-TYD) monomer that forms DNA and has a phosphate group, a sugar, and a nitrogen-containing base.
nucleótido monómero que forma el ADN y que tiene un grupo fosfato, un azúcar y una base nitrogenada.

nucleus (NOO-klee-uhs) (plural: *nuclei*) organelle composed of a double membrane that acts as the storehouse for most of a cell's DNA.
núcleo orgánulo compuesto de una doble membrana que almacena la mayor parte del ADN de la célula.

O

obligate aerobe prokaryote that cannot survive without the presence of oxygen.
aerobio obligado procariota que no puede sobrevivir en un entorno sin oxígeno.

obligate anaerobe prokaryote that cannot survive in the presence of oxygen.
anaerobio obligado procariota que no puede sobrevivir en un entorno oxigenado.

observation using the senses to study the world; using tools to collect measurements; examining previous research results.
observación utilización de los sentidos para estudiar el mundo; uso de instrumentos de medición; análisis de resultados de investigación.

omnivore organism that eats both plants and animals.
omnívoro organismo que se alimenta tanto de animales como de plantas.

operant conditioning process by which a behavior increases or decreases as the result of a reward or punishment.
condicionamiento operante proceso mediante el cual varía la frecuencia de un comportamiento como resultado de un premio o un castigo.

operculum protective bony plate that covers a fish's gills.
opérculo placa protectora ósea que recubre las branquias de los peces.

operon section of DNA that contains all of the code to begin transcription, regulate transcription, and build a protein; includes a promotor, regulatory gene, and structural gene
operon sección de ADN que contiene todos los códigos necesarios para iniciar y regular el proceso de transcripción y para sintetizar una proteína: consta de un promotor, de un gen regulador y de un gen estuctural.

opportunistic infection infection caused by a pathogen that a healthy immune system would normally be able to fight off.
infección oportunista infección causada por un patógeno que un sistema inmune saludable podría combatir con eficacia.

optimal foraging theory that states that natural selection will favor organisms that have behaviors that can gather the best food sources.
abastecimiento óptimo teoría según la cual la selección natural favorece a aquellos organismos cuyos comportamientos les permiten acceder a las mejores fuentes de alimento.

organ group of different types of tissues that work together to perform a specific function or related functions.
órgano grupo de diversos tipos de tejidos que funcionan de manera coordinada para desarrollar una función específica o funciones relacionadas.

organelle membrane-bound structure that is specialized to perform a distinct process within a cell.
orgánulo estructura intracelular que se especializa en una función específica.

organism any individual living thing.
organismo cualquier ser vivo.

organ system two or more organs that work in a coordinated way to carry out similar functions.
sistema de órganos dos o más órganos que funcionan de manera coordinada para realizar funciones similares.

osmosis diffusion of water molecules across a semipermeable membrane from an area of higher water concentration to an area of lower water concentration.
ósmosis difusión de moléculas de agua a través de una membrana semipermeable, desde un área de mayor concentración de agua a otra de menor concentración de agua.

ossicle small bone, especially one of the three found in the middle ear of mammals.
huesecillo en los mamíferos, cada uno de los tres huesos pequeños que se encuentran en el oído medio.

ovary organ in which female gametes develop prior to fertilization.
ovario órgano en el que se desarrollan los gametos femeninos antes de la fertilización.

oviparous reproductive strategy in which the embryos develop outside of the mother's body.
ovíparo organismo que se reproduce mediante un sistema en el que los embriones se desarrollan fuera del cuerpo materno.

ovulation process by which an egg is released from the ovary and becomes available for fertilization.
ovulación proceso mediante el cual se libera un óvulo del ovario, quedando susceptible a ser fertilizado.

ovum (plural: *ova*) egg cell that is produced by the female reproductive system.
óvulo ovocito producido en el sistema reproductor femenino.

P

pacemaker collection of cells that stimulates the pumping action of the heart.
nódulo sinusal conjunto de células que estimula los latidos del corazón; también conocido como marcapaso natural.

paleontology study of fossils or extinct organisms.
paleontología estudio de los fósiles o de los organismos extinctos.

Paleozoic era of geologic time (from 544 to 248 million years ago) during which members of every major animal group alive today evolved.
Paleozoico era geológica (desde hace 544 a 248 millones de años) durante la cual evolucionaron especies de los principales grupos de animales de la actualidad.

parasitism ecological relationship in which one organism benefits by harming another organism.
parasitismo relación ecológica en la que un organismo se beneficia perjudicando al otro organismo.

parasympathetic nervous system division of the peripheral nervous system that calms the body and helps the body to conserve energy.
sistema nervioso parasimpático parte del sistema nervioso periférico encargado de mantener un estado corporal de descanso y ayudar al cuerpo a conservar energía.

parenchyma cell cell with thin walls that forms tissues within leaves, roots, stems, and fruit of plants.
célula del parénquima célula de paredes delgadas que forma tejidos en el interior de las hojas, raíces, tallos y frutas de las plantas.

particulate microscopic bits of dust, metal, and unburned fuel produced by industrial processes.
materia particulada partículas microscópicas de polvo, metal y combustibles sin quemar, que se generan en los procesos industriales.

passive immunity immunity that occurs without the body undergoing an immune response.
inmunidad pasiva inmunidad que tiene lugar sin que el cuerpo experimente una reacción inmune.

passive transport movement of molecules across the cell membrane without energy input from the cell.
transporte pasivo movimiento de moléculas a través de la membrana celular, que se produce sin aporte de energía celular.

pathogen agent that causes disease.
patógeno agente que causa una enfermedad.

pedigree chart of the phenotypes and genotypes in a family that is used to determine whether an individual is a carrier of a recessive allele.
pedigrí diagrama de los fenotipos y genotipos de una familia que se emplea para determinar si un individuo es portador de un alelo recesivo.

period unit of geologic time that lasts tens of millions of years and is associated with a particular type of rock system.
periodo unidad de tiempo geológico que abarca decenas de millones de años y que suele asociarse a tipos determinados de formaciones rocosas.

peripheral nervous system (PNS) division of the nervous system that transmits impulses between the central nervous system and other organs in the body.
sistema nervioso periférico (SNP) división del sistema nervioso que transmite impulsos entre el sistema nervioso central y otros órganos del cuerpo.

peristalsis (PEHR-ih-STAWL-sihs) wavelike involuntary muscle contractions that push food through the organs of the digestive system.
peristaltismo contracciones involuntarias en forma de ondas que impulsan los alimentos a través de los órganos del sistema digestivo.

petal modified leaf that surrounds a flower's reproductive structures.
pétalo hoja modificada que rodea las estructuras reproductivas de la flor.

petiole stalk that attaches a leaf blade to a stem.
peciolo rabillo que une la lámina de la hoja al tallo.

Glossary

pH measurement of acidity; related to free hydrogen ion concentration in solution.
pH medida de acidez; relacionada con la concentración de los iones libres de hidrógeno en una solución.

phagocyte cell that destroys other cells by surrounding and engulfing them.
fagocito célula que destruye a otras células rodeándolas y engulléndolas.

phagocytosis (FAG-uh-sy-TOH-sihs) uptake of a solid particle into a cell by engulfing the particle; *see* endocytosis.
fagocitosis absorción de una partícula sólida por parte de una célula que la envuelve: *véase* endocitosis.

pharmacology study of drugs and their effects on the body.
farmacología estudio de los medicamentos y de los efectos que causan en el cuerpo.

phenotype collection of all of an organism's physical characteristics.
fenotipo conjunto de todas las características físicas de un organismo determinado.

pheromone chemical released by an organism that stimulates a behavior in other organisms of the same species.
feromona compuesto químico liberado por un organismo que estimula ciertos comportamientos en otros organismos de la misma especie.

phloem tissue that transports sugars in vascular plants.
floema tejido transportador de azúcares en las plantas vasculares.

phospholipid molecule that forms a double-layered cell membrane; consists of a glycerol, a phosphate group, and two fatty acids.
fosfolípido molécula que forma una membrana de capa doble; consta de glicerol, un grupo fosfato y dos ácidos grasos.

photoperiodism response of an organism to changes in the length of the day.
fotoperiodismo respuesta de un organismo a las variaciones de luz en un período de 24 horas.

photosynthesis process by which light energy is converted to chemical energy; produces sugar and oxygen from carbon dioxide and water.
fotosíntesis proceso mediante el cual la energía del sol se convierte en energía química; produce azúcar y oxígeno a partir de dióxido de carbono y agua.

photosystem series of light-absorbing pigments and proteins that capture and transfer energy in the thylakoid membrane.
fotosistema conjunto de pigmentos y proteínas que capturan y transfieren energía en la membrana tilacoide.

phototropism growth of a plant toward a light source.
fototropismo crecimiento de la planta hacia la luz.

phylogeny evolutionary history of a group of related species.
filogenia historia evolutiva de un grupo de especies relacionadas.

phylum group of animals defined by structural and functional characteristics that are different from every other animal phylum.
división grupo de animales definidos por una serie de características estructurales y funcionales que se diferencian de cualquier otra división; también se conoce como filum.

phytoplankton photosynthetic microscopic protists, such as algae.
fitoplancton colonia de protistas microscópicas fotosintéticas, como las algas.

pioneer species organism that is the first to live in a previously uninhabited area.
especie pionera primer organismo que vive en una zona hasta entonces deshabitada.

pituitary gland area in the middle of the brain that makes and releases hormones that control cell growth and osmoregulation, water levels in the blood.
glándula pituitaria zona en el centro del cerebro que produce y segrega hormonas que controlan el crecimiento celular y la osmorregulación, es decir, la regulación de los niveles de líquidos en la sangre.

placenta (pluh-SEHN-tuh) organ that develops in female mammals during pregnancy and carries nutrients from the mother to the embryo.
placenta órgano que se desarrolla en las hembras de los mamíferos durante la gestación y que lleva nutrientes de la madre al embrión.

plankton microscopic, free-floating organisms, which may be animals or protists, that live in the water.
plancton organismos microscópicos, animales o protistas, que flotan libremente en el agua.

plant multicellular eukaryote that produces its own food through photosynthesis.
planta organismo eucariota multicelular que produce su propio alimento mediante la fotosíntesis.

plasma clear yellowish fluid, about 90 percent water, that suspends cells in the blood.
plasma líquido de color amarillento pálido que consisten en un 90 por ciento deagua en el que están suspendidas las células sanguíneas.

plasmid circular piece of genetic material found in bacteria that can replicate separately from the DNA of the main chromosome.
plásmido cadena de material genético en forma circular que se encuentra en las bacterias y que se replica independientemente del ADN cromosómico.

R66

platelet cell fragment that is produced in the bone marrow and is important for blood clotting.
plaqueta fragmento celular que se produce en la médula ósea y que cumple una función importante en la coagulación de la sangre.

point mutation mutation that involves a substitution of only one nucleotide.
mutación puntual mutación que involucra la sustitución de un solo nucleótido.

polar body haploid cell produced during meiosis in the female of many species; these cells have little more than DNA and eventually disintegrate.
cuerpo polar célula haploide producida durante la meiosis en las hembras de muchas especies; esta célula tiene poco más que ADN y termina por desintegrarse.

pollen grain two-celled structure that contains the male form of the plant's gamete.
grano de polen estructura formada por dos células que contiene el gameto masculino de la planta.

pollination process by which seed plants become fertilized without the need for free-standing water.
polinización proceso mediante el cual las plantas con semillas se fertilizan sin depender del agua del suelo.

pollution anything that is added to the environment and has a negative affect on the environment or its organisms.
contaminación cualquier sustancia que se libera en el medio ambiente con efectos negativos para los organismos que lo habitan y su entorno.

polygenic trait trait that is produced by two or more genes.
rasgo poligénico rasgo producido por dos o más genes.

polymer large, carbon-based molecule formed by monomers.
polímero gran molécula de carbono formada por monómeros.

polymerase chain reaction (PCR) method for increasing the quantity of DNA by separating it into two strands and adding primers and enzymes.
reacción en cadena de la polimerasa (RCP) método para obtener un gran número de copias de ADN separándolo en dos hebras y añadiendo cebadores y enzimas.

polyp tube-shaped body form of a cnidarian in which the mouth and tentacles face upward.
pólipo cuerpo de forma tubular de un cnidario con la boca y los tentáculos orientados hacia arriba.

population all of the individuals of a species that live in the same area.
población conjunto de individuos de la misma especie que viven en la misma zona.

population crash dramatic decline in the size of a population over a short period of time.
colapso poblacional reducción drástica del tamaño de una población en un breve período de tiempo.

population density measure of individuals living in a defined area.
densidad de población cantidad de habitantes que viven en un área determinada.

population dispersion way in which individuals of a population are spread out over an area or volume.
dispersión de población manera en la que los individuos de una población determinada se han distribuido en una área o en un volumen.

positive feedback control system in which sensory information causes the body to increase the rate of change away from homeostasis.
retroalimentación positiva sistema de control mediante el cual la información sensorial estimula el cuerpo a incrementar la tasa de cambio, alejándola de valores homeostáticos.

precision the exactness of a measurement.
precisión la exactitud de una medición.

predation process by which one organism hunts and kills another organism for food.
predación proceso mediante el cual un organismo acecha, mata y se come a otro organismo.

pressure-flow model model for predicting how sugars are transported from photosynthetic tissue to the rest of a plant.
modelo de flujo de presión modelo para predecir la forma en que los azúcares son transportados del tejido fotosintético al resto de una planta.

primary growth growth in vascular plants resulting in elongation of the plant body.
crecimiento primario crecimiento de las plantas vasculares que resulta de la elongación del cuerpo de la planta.

primary succession establishment and development of an ecosystem in an area that was previously uninhabited.
sucesión primaria establecimiento y desarrollo de un ecosistema en una zona hasta entonces deshabitada.

primate mammal with flexible hands and feet, forward-looking eyes, and enlarged brains relative to body size.
primate mamífero de manos y pies flexibles, mirada frontal y un cerebro grande en relación con el tamaño del cuerpo.

primer short segment of DNA that initiates replication by DNA polymerase.
cebador pequeño segmento de ADN que inicia la replicación mediante ADN polimerasa.

prion infectious agent that consists of a protein fragment that can cause other proteins to fold incorrectly.
prión agente infeccioso que consta de una partícula proteica que induce a otras proteínas a plegarse de forma incorrecta.

probability likelihood that a particular event will happen.
probabilidad posibilidad de que ocurra un suceso en particular.

Glossary

producer organism that obtains its energy from abiotic sources, such as sunlight or inorganic chemicals.
productor organismo que obtiene su alimento de fuentes abióticas, como la luz solar o compuestos inorgánicos.

product substance formed by a chemical reaction.
producto sustancia formada por una reacción química.

prokaryotic cell (proh-KAR-ee-AHT-ihk) cell that does not have a nucleus or other membrane-bound organelles.
célula procarionta célula que no tiene núcleo ni orgánulos limitados por membranas.

promoter section of DNA to which RNA polymerase binds, starting the transcription of mRNA.
promotor sección de ADN a la que se enlaza el ARN polimerasa al inicio del proceso de transcripción de ARNm.

prophage DNA of a bacteriophage inserted into a host cell's DNA.
profago ADN de un bacteriófago insertado en el ADN de la célula huésped.

prophase first phase of mitosis when chromatin condenses, the nuclear envelope breaks down, the nucleolus disappears, and the centrosomes and centrioles migrate to opposite sides of the cell.
profase primera fase de la mitosis, en la que la cromatina se condensa, la membrana nuclear se desintegra, el nucleolo desaparece y los centrosomas y los centriolos migran a lados opuestos de la célula.

prosimian oldest primate group that includes mostly small, nocturnal primates such as lemurs.
prosimio grupo de primates más antiguo que consta, principalmente, de pequeños primates nocturnos, como los lemures.

protein polymer composed of amino acids linked by peptide bonds; folds into a particular structure depending on bonds between amino acids.
proteína polímero compuesto de aminoácidos unidos por enlaces peptídicos; se pliega formando una estructura determinada según sean los enlaces que hay entre los aminoácidos.

proteomics (PROH-tee-AH-mihks) study and comparison of all the proteins produced by an organism's genome.
proteómica estudio y comparación de todas las proteínas producidas por el genoma de un organismo determinado.

protist eukaryote that is not an animal, plant, or fungus.
protista organismo eucariota que no es un animal, una planta, ni un hongo.

protostome animal development in which the animal's mouth develops before the anus.
protóstomo animal en el que la boca se desarrolla antes que el ano.

protozoa animal-like protist.
protozoo protista con características animales.

pseudocoelom fluid-filled space with mesoderm only on one side of the space.
pseudoceloma cavidad llena de fluido que tiene mesodermo en un solo lado de la cavidad.

pseudopod temporary extension of cytoplasm and plasma membrane that helps protozoa move and feed.
pseudópodo extensión temporal del citoplasma y de la membrana plasmática que permite a los protozoos moverse y alimentarse.

puberty stage of adolescence that is marked by the production of hormones involved in reproduction.
pubertad fase de la adolescencia marcada por la producción de hormonas involucradas en la reproducción.

pulmonary circuit (PUL-muh-NEHR-ee) collection of blood vessels that carries blood between the lungs and heart.
circuito pulmonar conjunto de vasos sanguíneos que transporta sangre entre los pulmones y el corazón.

pulmonary circulation *see* pulmonary circuit.
circulación pulmonar *véanse* circuito pulmonar.

punctuated equilibrium theory that states that speciation occurs suddenly and rapidly followed by long periods of little evolutionary change.
equilibrio puntuado teoría según la cual la especiación se produce repentinamente y va seguida de largos períodos de escasa actividad evolutiva.

Punnett square model for predicting all possible genotypes resulting from a cross, or mating.
cuadrado de Punnet modelo de predicción de todos los genotipos posibles que se pueden obtener a partir de un determinado cruzamiento o apareamiento.

pupa stage of metamorphosis in which the organism reorganizes into a completely new body form.
pupa fase de la metamorfosis en la que el organismo adopta una nueva forma corporal.

purebred type of organism whose ancestors are genetically uniform.
pura raza organismo de ancestros con uniformidad genética.

R

radial symmetry arrangement of body parts in a circle around a central axis.
simetría radial disposición de las partes del cuerpo en un círculo que rodea un eje central.

radiometric dating technique that uses the natural decay rate of isotopes to calculate the age of material.
fechado radiométrico técnica para medir la tasa natural de decaimiento de los isótopos para calcular la edad de los materiales.

radula filelike feeding organ found in mollusks.
rádula órgano raspador con el que se alimentan los moluscos.

ray-fin fan-shaped arrangement of bones in a fish's fin.
aleta radial disposición en abanico de las espinas de una aleta de pez.

reactant substance that is changed by a chemical reaction.
reactante sustancia que cambia a consecuencia de una reacción química.

receptor protein that detects a signal molecule and performs an action in response.
receptor proteína que detecta la señal de una molécula y responde con una acción concreta.

recessive allele that is not expressed unless two copies are present in an organism's genotype.
recesivo alelo que no se expresa, a menos que en el genotipo del organismo en cuestión estén presenten dos copias de dicho gen.

recombinant DNA (ree-KAHM-buh-nuhnt) genetically engineered DNA that contains genes from more than one organism or species.
ADN recombinante ADN manipulado geneticamente que contiene genes de más de un organismo o especie.

red blood cell cell that carries oxygen gas from the lungs to the rest of the body.
glóbulo rojo célula encargada de transportar oxígeno gaseoso de los pulmones al resto del cuerpo.

reflex arc nerve pathway in which an impulse crosses only two synapses before producing a response
arco reflejo circuito nervioso en el que un impulso sólo atraviesa dos simpasis antes de producir una respuesta.

regeneration process by which a new plant can grow from a fragment of a nonreproductive structure, such as a root, stem, or leaf.
regeneración proceso mediante el cual una nueva planta puede desarrollarse a partir de un fragmento de una estructura no reproductora, como una raíz, un tallo o una hoja.

relative dating estimate of the age of a fossil based on the location of fossils in strata.
datación relativa estimación de la edad de un fósil según la ubicación de los fósiles en los estratos.

releaser stimulus that triggers a specific behavior.
estímulo liberador que suscita un comportamiento específico.

releasing hormone chemical that stimulates other glands to release their hormones.
hormona liberadora sustancia química que estimula otras glándulas para que secreten hormonas.

renewable resource resource that replenishes itself quickly enough so that it will not be used faster than it can be produced.
recurso renovable recurso natural que se restablece a un ritmo superior del ritmo al que se consume.

replication process by which DNA is copied.
replicación proceso mediante el cual se copian las moléculas de ADN.

reproductive isolation final stage in speciation, in which members of isolated populations are either no longer able to mate or no longer able to produce viable offspring.
aislamiento reproductor fase final de la especiación en la que los miembros de poblaciones aisladas pierden la capacidad de aparearse o no pueden producir crías viables.

reproductive system body system that allows for sexual reproduction; includes testes, ovaries, uterus, and other male and female sex organs.
sistema reproductor sistema corporal que permite la reproducción sexual; consta de testículos, ovarios, útero y otros órganos sexuales masculinos y femeninos.

reptile ectotherm that is covered with dry scales, breathes with lungs, and reproduces by laying eggs.
reptil vertebrado ectotermo con la piel cubierta de escamas, que respira con pulmones y que pone huevos para reproducirse.

respiratory system body system that brings oxygen into the body and removes carbon dioxide; includes the nose, trachea, and lungs.
sistema respiratorio sistema corporal que lleva oxígeno al cuerpo y elimina el dióxido de carbono; consta de nariz, tráquea y pulmones.

resting potential difference in electrical charge between the inside and outside of a neuron; contains the potential energy needed to transmit the impulse.
potencial de reposo diferencia de carga eléctrica entre el interior y el exterior de una neurona; energía potencial necesaria para transmitir un impulso.

restriction enzyme enzyme that cuts DNA molecules at specific nucleotide sequences.
enzima de restricción enzima que fragmenta moléculas de ADN en secuencias específicas de nucleótidos.

restriction map diagram that shows the lengths of fragments between restriction sites in the strand of DNA.
mapa de restricción diagrama que representa las longitudes de los fragmentos entre los sitios de corte de una hebra de ADN.

retrovirus virus that contains RNA and uses the enzyme called reverse transcriptase to make a DNA copy.
retrovirus virus que contiene ARN y que usa una enzima llamada transcriptasa para hacer una copia del ADN.

Rh factor surface protein on red blood cells in the ABO blood group; people can be Rh^+ or Rh^-.
factor Rh proteína de la superficie de los glóbulos rojos de los grupos sanguíneos ABO; el factor Rh de las personas puede ser Rh^+ o Rh^-.

Glossary

ribosomal RNA (rRNA) RNA that is in the ribosome and guides the translation of mRNA into a protein; also used as a molecular clock.
ARN ribosómico (ARNr) ARN presente en los ribosomas que guía el proceso de síntesis de las proteínas a partir del ARNm; también denominado reloj molecular.

ribosome (RY-buh-SOHM) organelle that links amino acids together to form proteins.
ribosoma orgánulo que enlaza las moléculas de aminoácidos para formar proteínas.

ribozyme RNA molecule that can catalyze specific chemical reactions.
Ribozima molécula de ARN que tiene la capacidad de catalizar determinadas reacciones químicas.

RNA nucleic acid molecule that allows for the transmission of genetic information and protein synthesis.
ARN molécula de ácido nucleico encargada de la transmisión de información genética y de la síntesis de las proteínas.

RNA polymerase enzyme that catalyzes the synthesis of a complementary strand of RNA from a DNA template.
ARN polimerasa enzima que cataliza la síntesis de una hebra complementaria de ARN a partir de un patrón de ADN.

rod cell photoreceptor in the eye that detects light intensity and contributes to black and white vision.
bastoncillo célula fotosensible del ojo que detecta la intensidad de la luz y contribuye a la visión en blanco y negro.

root cap mass of cells that covers and protects the tips of plant roots.
ápice de la raíz masa de células que cubre y protege las puntas de las raíces de las plantas.

root hair thin hairlike outgrowth of an epidermal cell of a plant root that absorbs water and minerals from the soil.
pelos radicales finas extensiones de la célula epidérmica en las raíces de una planta encargada de absorber agua y minerales del suelo.

S

sarcomere section of a muscle fiber that contains all of the filaments necessary to cause muscle contraction.
sarcómero sección de fibra muscular con todos los filamentos necesarios para generar una contracción muscular.

science the knowledge obtained by observing natural events and conditions in order to discover facts and formulate laws or principles that can be verified or tested.
ciencia el conocimiento que se obtiene por medio de la observación natural de acontecimientos y condiciones con el fin de descubrir hechos y formular leyes o principios que puedan ser verificados o probados.

sclerenchyma cell thick-walled, lignin-rich cell that forms a supportive plant tissue.
esclereida célula rica en lignina que constituye el esclerénquima, un tejido de sostén de las plantas.

scrotum skin that encloses the testes outside of the male body.
escroto piel que envuelve las gónadas masculinas en el exterior del cuerpo.

secondary growth growth in woody plants resulting in wider roots, branches, and stems.
crecimiento secundario crecimiento de las plantas que produce un engrosamiento de las raíces, de las ramas y de los tallos.

secondary succession reestablishment of a damaged ecosystem in an area where the soil was left intact.
sucesión secundaria desarrollo de un ecosistema dañado en una zona donde el suelo permanece inalterado.

seed structure used by some land plants to store and protect the embryo.
semilla estructura empleada por algunas plantas para almacenar y proteger al embrión.

segmentation repeated sections of an annelid's long body that contain the same set of body structures, apart from its distinct head and tail region.
segmentación secciones repetidas del cuerpo alargado de un anélido, cada una de las cueles contiene el mismo conjunto de estructuras corporales, con excepción de la cabeza y de la cola.

selective permeability condition or quality of allowing some, but not all, materials to cross a barrier or membrane.
permeabilidad selectiva condición o cualidad que permite discriminar el flujo de determinados materiales a través de una membrana o barrera.

semen white substance that contains sperm and fluids produced by sex glands of the male reproductive system.
semen sustancia blanca que contiene espermatozoides y fluidos generados por las glándulas sexuales del sistema reproductor masculino.

sepal modified leaf that covers and protects the flower while it develops.
sépalo hoja modificada que cubre la flor durante su desarrollo.

sensitization process by which a neuron adds more receptors to its surface in response to consistently lower amounts of a neurotransmitter in the synapse.
sensibilización proceso mediante el cual una neurona incorpora a su superficie más receptores en respuesta a una insuficiencia sostenida de neurotransmisores en el espacio sináptico.

sessile unable to move from a fixed point.
sésil fijo a un punto, que no se mueve.

sex chromosome chromosome that directly controls the development of sexual characteristics.
cromosoma sexual cromosoma que controla directamente el desarrollo de las características sexuales.

sex-linked gene gene that is located on a sex chromosome.
gen ligado al sexo gen ubicado en un cromosoma sexual.

sexually transmitted disease (STD) disease that is passed from one person to another during sexual contact.
enfermedad de transmisión sexual (ETS) enfermedad que se transmite de una persona a otra durante el contacto sexual.

sexual reproduction process by which two gametes fuse and offspring that are a genetic mixture of both parents are produced.
reproducción sexual proceso mediante el cual se unen dos gametos que dan lugar a crías cuyo genoma es una mezcla del de los dos progenitores.

sexual selection selection in which certain traits enhance mating success; traits are, therefore, passed on to offspring.
selección sexual selección en la que determinados rasgos incrementan el éxito del apareamiento; en consecuencia, tales rasgos se transmiten a las crías.

skeletal muscle muscle tissue that is attached to the skeletal system and, when contracted, moves bones.
músculo esquelético tejido muscular adherido al sistema esquelético que, al contraerse, mueve los músculos.

skeletal system body system that includes bones and the connective tissues that hold the bones together in the body.
sistema esquelético sistema que consta de los huesos y de los tejidos conjuntivos que mantienen unidos a los huesos.

slime mold protist with a slimelike amoeboid stage that grows on decaying vegetation and in moist soil.
moho mucoso protista de aspecto gelatinoso con una fase ameboide, que crece en material vegetal en descomposición y en la tierra húmeda.

small intestine organ of the digestive system that connects the stomach to the large intestine and in which chemical digestion takes place.
intestino delgado órgano del sistema digestivo que conecta el estómago al intestino grueso y en el que se produce la digestión química.

smog air pollution in which gases released from burning fossil fuels form a fog when they react with sunlight.
smog contaminación atmosférica en la que los gases liberados por la combustión de hidrocarburos reaccionan con la luz creando una niebla.

smooth muscle muscle tissue that moves substances, such as food and blood, through organs and tissues, such as the digestive system organs and blood vessels.
músculo liso tejido muscular que mueve los alimentos y la sangre por los órganos y los tejidos como, por ejemplo, los órganos del sistema digestivo y los vasos sanguíneos.

sodium potassium pump active transport protein in neurons that carries sodium (Na^+) ions out of the cell and bring potassium (K^+) ions into the cell.
bomba sodio-potasio transporte activo de proteínas en las neuronas, en el que se extrae de la célula iones de sodio (Na^+) y se mete iones de potasio (K^+).

solute substance that dissolves in a solvent and is present at a lower concentration than the solvent.
soluto sustancia que se disuelve en un solvente y que aparece en menor concentración que éste.

solution mixture that is consistent throughout; also called a homogeneous mixture.
solución mezcla uniforme en toda su extensión; también se conoce como mezcla homogénea.

solvent substance in which solutes dissolve and that is present in greatest concentration in a solution.
solvente sustancia en la que se disuelve un soluto y que se presenta en mayor concentración que éste.

somatic cell (soh-MAT-ihk) cell that makes up all of the body tissues and organs, except gametes.
célula somática célula que conforma todos los tejidos y órganos del organismo, excepto los gametos.

somatic nervous system division of the peripheral nervous system that transports signals from the brain to the muscles that produce voluntary movements.
sistema nervioso somático parte del sistema nervioso periférico que transporta señales del encéfalo a los músculos para producir los movimientos voluntarios.

specialist consumer that eats only one type of organism.
especialista consumidor que se alimenta de un solo tipo de organismo.

speciation evolution of two or more species from one ancestral species.
especiación evolución de dos o más especies a partir de una sola especie ancestral.

species group of organisms so similar to one another that they can breed and produce fertile offspring.
especie grupo de organismos tan semejantes entre sí que pueden reproducirse y tener descendencia fértil.

sperm male gamete.
espermatozoide gameto masculino.

sphincter (SFIHNGK-tuhr) ring of muscle that separates the different organs of the digestive system.
esfínter músculo en forma de anillo que separa a los diversos órganos del sistema digestivo.

spiracle (SPIHR-uh-kuhl) hole on the body of an insect's exoskeleton through which air can be taken in or released.
espiráculo orificio en el cuerpo del exoesqueleto de los insectos a través del cual entra y sale aire.

sporangia spore-forming structures found in fungi, algae, and some plants.
esporangio estructura que produce esporas y que se encuentra en los hongos, las algas y algunas plantas.

sporophyte (SPAWR-uh-FYT) diploid, spore-producing phase of a plant life cycle.
esporofita fase diploide de producción de esporas en el ciclo de vida de una planta.

Glossary

stabilizing selection pathway of natural selection in which intermediate phenotypes are selected over phenotypes at both extremes.
selección estabilizadora proceso de selección natural en el que se da preferencia a los fenotipos intermedios sobre los fenotipos de ambos extremos.

stamen male structure of flowering plants; includes the stalk and anther, which produces pollen.
estambre estructura floral masculina de las gimnospermas; consiste de una antera productora de polen unida a un pedicelo.

start codon codon that signals to ribosomes to begin translation; codes for the first amino acid in a protein.
codón de iniciación codón que da la señal a los ribosomas para que inicien el proceso de traducción; codifica el primer aminoácido de la proteína.

stem cell cell that can divide for long periods of time while remaining undifferentiated.
célula madre célula capaz de dividirse durante largos periodos de tiempo sin diferenciarse.

sternum long, flat bone that connects the ribs in front of the chest and to which the chest muscle attaches.
esternón hueso plano y alargado que conecta las costillas a la altura del pecho y al que van adheridos los músculos pectorales.

stimulant drug that increases the number of impulses that neurons generate.
estimulante droga que incrementa el número de impulsos que generan las neuronas.

stimulus (STIHM-yuh-luhs) (plural: *stimuli*) something that causes a physiological response.
estímulo cualquier cosa capaz de provocar una respuesta fisiológica.

stomach muscular sac in the digestive system that breaks down food into a liquidlike mixture.
estómago saco muscular del sistema digestivo donde se descompone la comida en una mezcla líquida.

stomata (singular: *stoma*) pores in the cuticle of a plant through which gas exchange occurs.
estoma poro en la cutícula de una planta a través del cual se produce el intercambio gaseoso.

stop codon codon that signals to ribosomes to stop translation.
codón de terminación codón que indica a los ribosomas que detengan el proceso de traducción.

substrate reactant in a chemical reaction upon which an enzyme acts.
sustrato reactivo de una reacción química sobre el que actúa un enzima.

succession sequence of biotic changes that regenerate a damaged community or start a community in a previously uninhabited area.
sucesión secuencia de cambios bióticos que regeneran una comunidad dañada o que crean una nueva comunidad en una zona hasta entonces deshabitada.

survivorship probability of surviving to a particular age.
supervivencia probabilidad de sobrevivir hasta una edad determinada.

survivorship curve graph showing the surviving members of each age group of a population over time.
curva de sobrevivencia gráfica que representa los sobrevivientes de una población por grupos de edad durante un periodo determinado.

sustainable development practice of not using natural resources more quickly than they can be replenished.
desarrollo sostenible práctica que consiste en no utilizar los recursos naturales más rápidamente de lo que pueden ser generarlos.

swim bladder buoyancy organ that helps fish to swim at different depths in the water.
vejiga natatoria órgano de flotación que permite a los peces nadar a diferentes profundidades.

symbiosis ecological relationship between members of at least two different species that live in direct contact with one another.
simbiosis relación ecológica en la que los miembros de al menos dos especies diferentes viven en contacto directo.

sympathetic nervous system part of the autonomic nervous system that prepares the body for action and stress.
sistema nervioso simpático sistema que forma parte del sistema nervioso autónomo y que se encarga de preparar el cuerpo para situaciones de acción y de estrés.

synapse tiny gap between neurons through which chemical signals are sent.
sinapsis pequeño espacio entre las neuronas a través del cual se envían señales químicas.

system changing, organized group of related parts that interact to form a whole.
sistema conjunto organizado y dinámico de partes que interactúan entre sí para formar un todo.

systemic circuit (sihs-STEHM-ihk) collection of blood vessels that carries blood between the heart and the rest of the body, except for the lungs.
circuito sistémico conjunto de vasos sanguíneos que transporta la sangre entre el corazón y el resto del cuerpo, excepto los pulmones.

systemic circulation *see* systemic circuit.
circulación sistémica *véanse* circuito sistémico.

systolic pressure (sih-STAHL-ihk) measure of pressure on the walls of an artery when the left ventricle contracts to pump blood through the body.
presión sistólica medida de la presión de las paredes arteriales cuando el ventrículo izquierdo se contrae para bombear sangre a través del cuerpo.

T

tadpole aquatic larva of frogs or toads.
renacuajo larva acuática de las ranas y los sapos.

taiga (TY-guh) biome with long and cold winters, lasting up to six months; also called a boreal forest.
taiga bioma propio de zonas de largos y fríos inviernos de hasta seis meses de duración; también se conoce como bosque boreal.

taproot main root of some plants, usually larger than other roots and growing straight down from a stem.
raíz pivotante raíz principal de determinadas plantas, normalmente más grande que las demás raíces y que crece en en lína recta hacia abajo a partir del tallo.

taxis movement in a particular direction, either toward or away from a stimulus.
taxismo movimiento en una dirección determinada, ya sea hacia un estímulo o en sentido opuesto a éste; conocido también como taxis.

taxon (plural: *taxa*) level within the Linnaean system of classification (kingdom, phylum, class, order, family, genus, or species) that is organized into a nested hierarchy.
taxón cualquiera de los niveles del sistema de clasificación jerárquico de Linneo, (reino, división, clase, orden, familia, género o especie).

taxonomy science of classifying and naming organisms.
taxonomía ciencia dedicada a la clasificación y nomenclatura de los organismos.

T cell white blood cell that matures in the thymus and destroys infected body cells by causing them to burst; also called a T-lymphocyte.
célula T glóbulo blanco que madura en el timo y que destruye las células infectadas haciéndolas reventar; también se conoce como linfocito T.

telomere (TEHL-uh-MEER) repeating nucleotide at the ends of DNA molecules that do not form genes and help prevent the loss of genes.
telómero extremo de la molécula de ADN compuesto de nucleótidos repetidos que no producen genes pero que ayudan a prevenir la pérdida de éstos.

telophase last phase of mitosis when a complete set of identical chromosomes is positioned at each pole of the cell, the nuclear membranes start to form, the chromosomes begin to uncoil, and the spindle fibers disassemble.
telofase última fase de la mitosis en que un conjunto completo de cromosomas idénticos se sitúa en los polos opuestos de la célula; empiezan a formarse las membranas nucleares; los cromosomas empiezan a desenrollarse y el huso mitótico se desintegra.

temporal isolation isolation between populations due to barriers related to time, such as differences in mating periods or differences in the time of day that individuals are most active.
aislamiento temporal aislamiento entre poblaciones que se produce por motivos de índole temporal como, por ejemplo, diferencias en los períodos de apareamiento o de las horas del día en que los individuos son más activos.

tendon band of connective tissue that joins a muscle to the bone that it moves.
tendón banda de tejido conjuntivo que conecta cada músculo con el hueso que mueve.

terminal end of the neuron's axon from which neurotransmitters are released to stimulate an adjacent cell.
terminal extremo del axón de la neurona desde el cual se segregan neurotransmisores para estimular a la célula adyacente.

territoriality behavior pattern in which an organism controls and defends a specific area.
territorialidad patrón de comportamiento mediante el cual un organismo determinado controla y defiende un área específica.

testcross cross between an organism with an unknown genotype and an organism with a recessive phenotype.
cruzamiento de prueba cruzamiento entre un organismo de genotipo desconocido y un organismo de fenotipo recesivo.

testis (plural: *testes*) organ of the male reproductive system that produces sperm.
testículo órgano del sistema reproductor masculino encargado de la producción de espermatozoides.

testosterone (tehs-TAHS-tuh-ROHN) steroid hormone that is found in greater quantities in men than women and contributes to male sexual characteristics and development.
testosterona hormona esteroide que se encuentra en mayor cantidad en el hombre que en la mujer y que contribuye al desarrollo de las características sexuales masculinas.

tetrapod vertebrate with four limbs.
tetrápodo vertebrado con cuatro extremidades.

theory proposed explanation for a wide variety of observations and experimental results.
teoría explicación de un fenómeno a partir de una amplia gama de observaciones y resultados experimentales.

Glossary

thermoregulation (THUR-moh-REHG-yoo-LAY-shuhn) process of the body maintaining a stable internal temperature under various conditions.
termorregulación proceso que permite mantener una temperatura interna constante bajo diferentes condiciones.

thigmotropism turning or bending of a plant in response to contact with an object.
tigmotropismo giro o flexión de una planta como respuesta al contacto con un objeto.

thylakoid (THY-luh-KOYD) membrane-bound structure within chloroplasts that contains chlorophyll and other light-absorbing pigments used in the light-dependent reactions of photosynthesis.
tilacoide estructura de la membrana interna de los cloroplastos que contiene clorofila y otros pigmentos fotoabsorbentes que intervienen en las reacciones captadoras de luz de la fotosíntesis.

tissue group of cells that work together to perform a similar function.
tejido grupo de células similares que trabajan juntas para desempeñar la misma función.

tissue rejection process by which a transplant recipient's immune system makes antibodies against the protein markers on the donor's tissue; could result in the destruction of the donor tissue.
rechazo de tejidos proceso mediante el cual el sistema inmune de un individuo receptor de un transplante genera anticuerpos contra los marcadores proteicos del tejido donante; puede producir la destrucción del tejido donante.

tolerance drug resistance that occurs when cells adapt, requiring larger doses of the drug to produce the same effect.
tolerancia resistencia a una droga producida cuando las células se adaptan a ella, lo cual requiere un aumento de la dosis para producir el mismo efecto.

toxin poison released by an organism.
toxina sustancia tóxica producida por un organismo.

trachea (TRAY-kee-uh) (plural: *tracheae*) long structure made of soft tissue that connects the mouth and nose to the lungs in human; a system of thin branching tubes in the bodies of insects that allow for breathing.
tráquea tubo alargado de tejido blando que conecta la boca y la nariz con los pulmones de los humanos; sistema de finos tubos ramificados en el cuerpo de los insectos que les permite respirar.

trait characteristic that is inherited.
rasgo característica heredada.

transcription process of copying a nucleotide sequence of DNA to form a complementary strand of mRNA.
transcripción proceso donde se copia una secuencia de ADN para formar una cadena complementaria de ARNm.

transfer RNA (tRNA) form of RNA that brings amino acids to ribosomes during protein synthesis.
ARN de transferencia (ARNt) tipo de ARN que transporta aminoácidos a los ribosomas durante el proceso de síntesis proteica.

transgenic organism whose genome has been altered to contain one or more genes from another organism or species.
transgénico organismo cuyo genoma ha sido alterado mediante la incorporación de uno o más genes de otro organismo o especie.

translation process by which mRNA is decoded and a protein is produced.
traducción proceso mediante el cual se decodifica el ARNm y se produce una proteína.

transpiration release of vapor through the pores of the skin or the stomata of plant tissue.
transpiración liberación de vapor a través de los poros de la piel o, en los tejidos vegetales, de los estomas.

trimester one of three periods of approximately three months each into which a human pregnancy is divided.
trimestre uno de los períodos de aproximadamente tres meses en que se divide la gestación humana.

trophic level level of nourishment in a food chain.
nivel trófico nivel de alimentación de la cadena trófica.

tropism movement or growth of a plant in response to an environmental stimulus.
tropismo movimiento o crecimiento determinado por un estímulo ambiental.

tundra biome found at far northern latitudes where winters last as long as ten months per year.
tundra bioma de latitudes septentrionales extremas donde los inviernos duran hasta diez meses.

U

umbilical cord structure that connects an embryo to its mother and provides the embryo with nourishment and waste removal.
cordón umbilical estructura que conecta el embrión con su madre y que le suministra alimento y un sistema de eliminación de residuos.

umbrella species species whose being protected under the Endangered Species Act leads to the preservation of its habitat and all of the other organisms in its community.
especie paraguas especie protegida por la Ley de Especies en Peligro de Extinción cuya salvaguarda conlleva la protección de su hábitat y la de todos los otros organismos que viven en él.

uniformitarianism theory that states that the geologic processes that shape Earth are uniform through time.
uniformitarismo teoría según la cual los procesos geológicos que dan forma a la Tierra se producen de manera uniforme a lo largo del tiempo.

ureter (yu-REE-tuhr) tube of connective tissue that carries urine from each of the kidneys to the bladder.
uréter tubo de tejido conjuntivo que transporta la orina desde los riñones hasta la vejiga.

urinary bladder saclike organ that collects and stores urine before it is excreted from the body.
vejiga urinaria órgano en forma de bolsa donde se recoge y se almacena la orina antes de ser excretada del cuerpo.

uterus organ of the female reproductive system in which a fertilized egg attaches and a fetus develops.
útero órgano del sistema reproductor femenino al que se adhiere el huevo fertilizado y dónde se desarrolla el feto.

V

vaccine substance that stimulates an immune response, producing acquired immunity without illness or infection.
vacuna sustancia que estimula una respuesta inmune y que proporciona inmunidad ante una enfermedad o infección determinada sin provocarla.

vacuole (VAK-yoo-OHL) organelle that is used to store materials, such as water, food, or enzymes, that are needed by the cell.
vacuola orgánulo encargado de almacenar diversos materiales necesarios para la célula, como el agua, nutrientes o enzimas.

valve flap of tissue that prevents blood from flowing backward into a blood vessel or heart chamber.
válvula tejido membranoso encargado de evitar que la sangre refluya por el vaso sanguíneo en que circula o hacia una cavidad del corazón.

variation differences in physical traits of an individual from the group to which it belongs.
variación diferencia en rasgos físicos que presenta un individuo con respecto al grupo al que pertenece.

vascular cylinder center of a root or stem that contains phloem and xylem.
cilindro vascular cilindro en el centro de una raíz o tallo que contiene el floema y el xilema.

vascular system collection of specialized tissues in some plants that transports mineral nutrients up from the roots and brings sugars down from the leaves.
sistema vascular conjunto de tejidos especializados de determinadas plantas que transportan nutrientes minerales desde las raíces hacia arriba y que conducen el azúcar de las hojas hacia abajo.

vascular tissue supportive and conductive tissue in plants, consisting of xylem and phloem.
tejido vascular tejido conductor y de sostén de las plantas que consta de xilema y de floema.

vas deferens duct in which sperm mixes with other fluids before reaching the urethra.
conducto deferente conducto en el que el esperma se mezcla con otros fluidos antes de alcanzar la uretra.

vector organism, such as a mosquito or tick, that transfers pathogens from one host to another.
vector organismo, como o el mosquito o la garrapatas que puede transferir patógenos de un huésped a otro.

vegetative reproduction asexual reproduction in which a stem, leaf, or root will produce a new individual when detached from a parent plant.
reproducción vegetativa reproducción asexual en la que un tallo, una hoja o una raíz producen un nuevo individuo cuando se separan de la planta de la cual forman parte.

vein large blood vessel that carries blood from the rest of the body to the heart.
vena vaso sanguíneo de gran caudal que transporta la sangre desde todas las partes del cuerpo hasta el corazón.

ventricle large chamber in the heart that receives blood from an atrium and pumps blood to the rest of the body.
ventrículo amplia cámara del corazón que recibe sangre de la aurícula y la impulsa al resto del cuerpo.

vertebra (plural: *vertebrae*) bone that makes up the spinal column.
vértebra hueso que compone la columna vertebral.

vertebrate animal with an internal segmented backbone.
vertebrado animal con una columna vertebral interna y segmentada.

vesicle (VEHS-ih-kuhl) small organelle that contains and transports materials within the cytoplasm.
vesícula pequeño orgánulo que contiene y transporta materiales en el interior del citoplasma.

vestigial structure remnants of an organ or structure that functioned in an earlier ancestor.
estructura vestigial restos de algún órgano o estructura en una especie determinada que cumplieron alguna función en un ancestrode ésta.

villus (VIHL-uhs) (plural: *villi*) small fingerlike projection in the small intestine that absorbs nutrients.
vellosidades pequeñas proyecciones en forma de dedo del intestino delgado encargadas de absorber los nutrientes.

viroid infectious particle made of single-stranded RNA without a protein coat, that almost always uses plants as its host.
viroide partícula infecciosa que consta de un solo filamento de ARN sin envoltura de proteínas, que casi siempre se hospeda como parásito en las plantas.

virus infectious particle made only of a strand of either DNA or RNA surrounded by a protein coat.
virus partícula infecciosa que consta de un sólo filamento de ADN o ARN y rodeado por una envuelta de proteína.

vitamin organic molecule that works with enzymes to regulate cell function, growth, and development.
vitamina molécula orgánica que funciona con enzimas para regular el funcionamiento, el crecimiento y el desarrollo de las células.

R7

viviparous reproductive strategy in which the embryo develops within the mother's body.
vivíparo modalidad de reproducción en la que los embriones se desarrollan en el interior de la madre.

W

water mold fungus that is either a parasite or decomposer and lives in fresh water or moist soil.
moho acuático hongo acuático o de suelos húmedos que actúa como parásito o descomponedor de materia orgánica.

watershed region of land that drains into a river, river system, or other body of water.
cuenca hidrográfica área terrestre que vierte sus aguas hacia un río, una red fluvial o cualquier otra masa acuática.

water vascular system system of water-filled canals that extend down each arm of a echinoderm, such as a sea star.
sistema ambulacral sistema formado por una serie de tubos llenos de agua que se prolongan por los brazos de los equinodermos como, por ejemplo, la estrella de mar.

white blood cell cell that attacks pathogens.
glóbulo blanco célula cuya funcíon es atacar a los patógenos.

wood fibrous material made of dead cells that are part of the vascular system in some plants.
madera material fibroso formado por células muertas que forman parte del sistema vascular de algunas plantas.

X

X chromosome inactivation process that occurs in female mammals in which one of the X chromosomes is randomly turned off in each cell.
inactivación X proceso en los mamíferos del sexo femenino en que uno de los cromosomas X de cada célula se desactiva aleatoriamente.

xylem tissue that transports water and dissolved minerals in vascular plants.
xilema tejido de las plantas vasculares que transporta agua y sales minerales disueltas.

Z

zooplankton animal plankton.
zooplancton plancton animal.

zygote cell that forms when a male gamete fertilizes a female gamete.
cigoto célula formada cuando un gameto masculino fertiliza un gameto femenino.

Index

Page numbers for illustrations, maps, and charts are printed in *italics*. Page numbers for definitions are printed in **boldface** type.

Index

Index

C

Index

Index

E

Index

F

G

Index

H

Index

L

M

Index

N

Index

O

Index

Index

Index

T

Index

Index

Periodic Table

HYDROGEN
Hydrogen is found in all organic compounds. Hydrogen ions (H^+) are needed for the production of ATP.

SODIUM, POTASSIUM, CALCIUM
In their elemental forms, sodium, potassium, and calcium are soft, explosive metals. In their ionic forms (Na^+, K^+, and Ca^{2+}) in animals, they are all necessary for the proper functioning of the nervous system.

CHROMIUM
Chromium is needed for glucose metabolism and may have a role in the regulation of the activity of insulin. Above trace amounts, chromium is highly toxic.

IRON
The iron found in the center of hemoglobin molecules transports oxygen in the blood of vertebrates.

BARIUM
Barium and most of its compounds are highly toxic. In one of its nontoxic compounds, barium is used in medical imaging.

	1	2	3	4	5	6	7	8	9
1	1 H Hydrogen 1.008								
2	3 Li Lithium 6.94	4 Be Beryllium 9.012							
3	11 Na Sodium 22.990	12 Mg Magnesium 24.305							
4	19 K Potassium 39.098	20 Ca Calcium 40.078	21 Sc Scandium 44.956	22 Ti Titanium 47.87	23 V Vanadium 50.942	24 Cr Chromium 51.996	25 Mn Manganese 54.938	26 Fe Iron 55.845	27 Co Cobalt 58.933
5	37 Rb Rubidium 85.468	38 Sr Strontium 87.62	39 Y Yttrium 88.906	40 Zr Zirconium 91.224	41 Nb Niobium 92.906	42 Mo Molybdenum 95.94	43 Tc Technetium (98)	44 Ru Ruthenium 101.07	45 Rh Rhodium 102.906
6	55 Cs Cesium 132.905	56 Ba Barium 137.327	57 La Lanthanum 138.906	72 Hf Hafnium 178.49	73 Ta Tantalum 180.95	74 W Tungsten 183.84	75 Re Rhenium 186.207	76 Os Osmium 190.23	77 Ir Iridium 192.217
7	87 Fr Francium (223)	88 Ra Radium (226)	89 Ac Actinium (227)	104 Rf Rutherfordium (261)	105 Db Dubnium (262)	106 Sg Seaborgium (266)	107 Bh Bohrium (264)	108 Hs Hassium (277)	109 Mt Meitnerium (268)

58 Ce Cerium 140.116	59 Pr Praseodymium 140.908	60 Nd Neodymium 144.24	61 Pm Promethium (145)	62 Sm Samarium 150.36
90 Th Thorium 232.038	91 Pa Protactinium 231.036	92 U Uranium 238.029	93 Np Neptunium (237)	94 Pu Plutonium (244)

Metal  Metalloid  Nonmetal **Fe** Solid  Liquid Ⓞ Gas

OXYGEN
Oxygen is found in many organic molecules and is needed for the aerobic stages of cellular respiration. Oxygen also is a waste product of photosynthesis and is in some cases toxic to cells.

NITROGEN
Proteins and nucleic acids both contain nitrogen. Although nitrogen makes up almost 80 percent of Earth's atmosphere, plants and animals cannot directly use nitrogen gas.

CARBON
All organic molecules, which are the basic building blocks of life, contain carbon.

ZINC
Zinc is found in many enzymes. Zinc is also important for maturation of human reproductive systems.

10	11	12	13	14	15	16	17	18
								2 He Helium 4.003
			5 B Boron ***10.81***	6 C Carbon ***12.01***	7 N Nitrogen ***14.007***	8 O Oxygen ***15.999***	9 F Fluorine 18.998	10 Ne Neon 20.180
			13 Al Aluminum 26.982	14 Si Silicon ***28.085***	15 P Phosphorus 30.974	16 S Sulfur ***32.06***	17 Cl Chlorine ***35.45***	18 Ar Argon 39.948
28 Ni Nickel 58.69	29 Cu Copper 63.546	30 Zn Zinc 65.39	31 Ga Gallium 69.723	32 Ge Germanium 72.63	33 As Arsenic 74.922	34 Se Selenium 78.96	35 Br Bromine 79.904	36 Kr Krypton 83.80
46 Pd Palladium 106.42	47 Ag Silver 107.868	48 Cd Cadmium 112.4	49 In Indium 114.818	50 Sn Tin 118.710	51 Sb Antimony 121.760	52 Te Tellurium 127.60	53 I Iodine 126.904	54 Xe Xenon 131.29
78 Pt Platinum 195.078	79 Au Gold 196.967	80 Hg Mercury 200.59	81 Tl Thallium ***204.38***	82 Pb Lead 207.2	83 Bi Bismuth 208.980	84 Po Polonium (209)	85 At Astatine (210)	86 Rn Radon (222)
110 Ds Darmstadtium (281)	111 Rg Roentgenium (272)	112 Cn Copernicium (285)	113 Uut Ununtrium (284)	114 Fl Flerovium (289)	115 Uup Ununpentium (288)	116 Lv Livermorium (292)	117 Uus Ununseptium (294)	118 Uuo Ununoctium (294)

CHLORINE
Chlorine gas is a deadly poison. Chloride ions (Cl^-) are necessary for the transmission of certain types of signals in the nervous system.

PHOSPHORUS
Phosphorus is found in the lipids that make up all cell membranes. It is a part of the "backbone" of both DNA and RNA molecules. On a larger scale, both bones and teeth contain phosphorus.

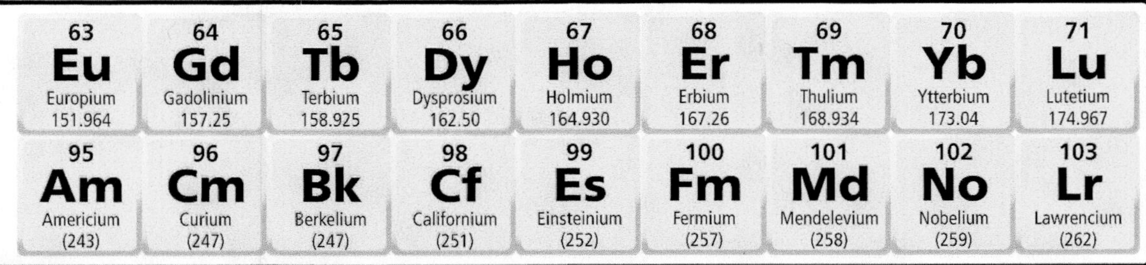

63 Eu Europium 151.964	64 Gd Gadolinium 157.25	65 Tb Terbium 158.925	66 Dy Dysprosium 162.50	67 Ho Holmium 164.930	68 Er Erbium 167.26	69 Tm Thulium 168.934	70 Yb Ytterbium 173.04	71 Lu Lutetium 174.967
95 Am Americium (243)	96 Cm Curium (247)	97 Bk Berkelium (247)	98 Cf Californium (251)	99 Es Einsteinium (252)	100 Fm Fermium (257)	101 Md Mendelevium (258)	102 No Nobelium (259)	103 Lr Lawrencium (262)

Atomic number Number of protons in the nucleus of the element

Name

1 H Hydrogen *1.008*

Symbol Each element has a symbol. The symbol's color represents the element's state at room temperature.

Atomic mass This value is the average atomic mass of isotopes of this element. Each element for which this value is bolded and italicized has an atomic mass that is officially expressed as a range of values. In nature, the average atomic mass often varies depending on the properties of the material in which the element is found. Values in parentheses indicate the atomic mass of the most stable isotope.